WIN the complete library of RSMeans Online data!

Register your book below to receive your FREE quarterly updates, PLUS you will be entered into a quarterly drawing to win the COMPLETE RSMeans Online library of 2015 data!

Be sure to keep up-to-date in 2015!

Fill out the card below for RSMeans' free quarterly updates,
as well as a chance to win the complete RSMeans Online library.
Please provide your name, address, and email below and return
this card by mail, or to register online:

http://info.thegordiangroup.com/RSMeans.html

Name _____

email_____ Title_____

Company _____

Street _____

City/Town _____ State/Prov. _____ Zip/Postal Code _____

RSMeans

WIN the complete library of RSMeans Online 2015 data!

See other side for details.

RSMeans Site Work & Landscape Cost Data

2015 34th annual edition

Robert Fortier, PE, Senior Editor

Engineering Director
Bob Mewis, CCC (*1, 14, 41*)

Contributing Editors
Christopher Babbitt
Adrian C. Charest, PE
(*26, 27, 28, 48*)
Cheryl Elsmore
Robert Fortier, PE
(*2, 31, 32, 33, 34, 35, 44, 46*)
Robert J. Kuchta (*8*)
Thomas Lane (*6, 7*)
Robert C. McNichols

Numbers in italics are the divisional responsibilities for each editor. Please contact the designated editor directly with any questions.

Genevieve Medeiros
Melville J. Mossman, PE
(*21, 22, 23*)
Jeannene D. Murphy
Marilyn Phelan, AIA
(*9, 10, 11, 12*)
Stephen C. Plotner (*3, 5*)
Siobhan Soucie (*4, 13*)

Vice President Data & Engineering
Chris Anderson

Cover Design
Sara Rutan

Product Manager
Andrea Sillah

Production Manager
Debbie Panarelli

Production
Jill Goodman
Jonathan Forgit
Sara Rutan
Mary Lou Geary

Technical Support
Gary L. Hoitt
Kathryn S. Rodriguez

RSMeans
Construction Publishers & Consultants
700 Longwater Drive
Norwell, MA 02061
United States of America
1-877-737-1594
www.rsmeans.com

Copyright 2014 by RSMeans
All rights reserved.
Cover photo ©
Samuel Borges/iStock/Thinkstock

Printed in the United States of America
ISSN 1520-5320
ISBN 978-1-940238-66-1

0285 $199.95 per copy (in United States)
Price is subject to change without prior notice.

Related RSMeans Products and Services

This book is focused primarily on commercial and industrial projects or large multi-family housing projects costing $3,500,000 and up. For civil engineering structures such as bridges, dams, highways, or the like, please refer to *RSMeans Heavy Construction Cost Data.*

The engineers at RSMeans suggest the following products and services as companion information resources to *RSMeans Site Work & Landscape Cost Data:*

Construction Cost Data Books
Building Construction Cost Data 2015
Heavy Construction Costs 2015

Reference Books
Landscape Estimating Methods
Estimating Building Costs
RSMeans Estimating Handbook
Green Building: Project Planning & Estimating
How to Estimate with Means Data and CostWorks
Plan Reading & Material Takeoff
Project Scheduling and Management for Construction

Seminars and In-House Training
Site Work & Heavy Construction Estimating
RSMeans Online® Training
Plan Reading & Material Takeoff
Scheduling with MSProject for Construction Professionals
Unit Price Estimating

RSMeans Online Bookstore
Visit RSMeans at **www.rsmeans.com** for a one-stop portal for the most reliable and current resources available on the market. Here you can learn about our more than 20 annual cost data books and eBooks, also available on CD and online versions, as well as our libary of reference books and RSMeans seminars.

RSMeans Electronic Data
Get the information found in RSMeans cost books electronically at **RSMeansOnline.com**.

RSMeans Business Solutions
Cost engineers and analysts conduct facility life cycle and benchmark research studies and predictive cost modeling, as well as offer consultation services for conceptual estimating and real property management. Research studies are designed with the application of proprietary cost and project data from RSMeans' extensive North American databases. Analysts offer building product manufacturers qualitative and quantitative market research, as well as time/motion studies for new products, and Web-based dashboards for market opportunity analysis. Clients are from both the public and private sectors, including federal, state, and municipal agencies; corporations; institutions; construction management firms; hospitals; and associations.

Construction Costs for Software Applications
More than 25 unit price and assemblies cost databases are available through a number of leading estimating and facilities management software partners. For more information see the "Other RSMeans Products and Services" pages at the back of this publication.

RSMeans data is also available to federal, state, and local government agencies as multi-year, multi-seat licenses.

For information on our current partners, visit: **www.rsmeans.com/partners** or call 1-877-737-1594.

ii

Table of Contents

Foreword

Our Mission

Since 1942, RSMeans has been actively engaged in construction cost publishing and consulting throughout North America.

Today, more than 70 years after RSMeans began, our primary objective remains the same: to provide you, the construction and facilities professional, with the most current and comprehensive construction cost data possible.

Whether you are a contractor, owner, architect, engineer, facilities manager, or anyone else who needs a reliable construction cost estimate, you'll find this publication to be a highly useful and necessary tool.

With the constant flow of new construction methods and materials today, it's difficult to find the time to look at and evaluate all the different construction cost possibilities. In addition, because labor and material costs keep changing, last year's cost information is not a reliable basis for today's estimate or budget.

That's why so many construction professionals turn to RSMeans. We keep track of the costs for you, along with a wide range of other key information, from city cost indexes . . . to productivity rates . . . to crew composition . . . to contractor's overhead and profit rates.

RSMeans performs these functions by collecting data from all facets of the industry and organizing it in a format that is instantly accessible to you. From the preliminary budget to the detailed unit price estimate, you'll find the data in this book useful for all phases of construction cost determination.

The Staff, the Organization, and Our Services

When you purchase one of RSMeans' publications, you are, in effect, hiring the services of a full-time staff of construction and engineering professionals.

Our thoroughly experienced and highly qualified staff works daily at collecting, analyzing, and disseminating comprehensive cost information for your needs. These staff members have years of practical construction experience and engineering training prior to joining the firm. As a result, you can count on them not only for accurate cost figures, but also for additional background reference information that will help you create a realistic estimate.

The RSMeans organization is always prepared to help you solve construction problems through its variety of data solutions, including online, CD, and print book formats, as well as cost estimating expertise available via our business solutions, training, and seminars.

Besides a full array of construction cost estimating books, RSMeans also publishes a number of other reference works for the construction industry. Subjects include construction estimating and project and business management, green building, and a library of facility management references.

In addition, you can access all of our construction cost data electronically in convenient CD format or on the web. Visit **RSMeansOnline.com** for more information on our 24/7 online cost data.

What's more, you can increase your knowledge and improve your construction estimating and management performance with an RSMeans construction seminar or in-house training program. These two-day seminar programs offer unparalleled opportunities for everyone in your organization to become updated on a wide variety of construction-related issues.

RSMeans is also a worldwide provider of construction cost management and analysis services for commercial and government owners.

In short, RSMeans can provide you with the tools and expertise for constructing accurate and dependable construction estimates and budgets in a variety of ways.

Robert Snow Means Established a Tradition of Quality That Continues Today

Robert Snow Means spent years building RSMeans, making certain he always delivered a quality product.

Today, at RSMeans, we do more than talk about the quality of our data and the usefulness of our books. We stand behind all of our data, from historical cost indexes to construction materials and techniques to current costs.

If you have any questions about our products or services, please call us toll-free at 1-877-737-1594. Our customer service representatives will be happy to assist you. You can also visit our website at **www.rsmeans.com**

How the Book Is Built: An Overview

The Construction Specifications Institute (CSI) and Construction Specifications Canada (CSC) have produced the 2014 edition of MasterFormat®, a system of titles and numbers used extensively to organize construction information.

All unit price data in the RSMeans cost data books is now arranged in the 50-division MasterFormat® 2014 system.

A Powerful Construction Tool

You have in your hands one of the most powerful construction tools available today. A successful project is built on the foundation of an accurate and dependable estimate. This book will enable you to construct just such an estimate.

For the casual user the book is designed to be:

- quickly and easily understood so you can get right to your estimate.
- filled with valuable information so you can understand the necessary factors that go into the cost estimate.

For the regular user, the book is designed to be:

- a handy desk reference that can be quickly referred to for key costs.
- a comprehensive, fully reliable source of current construction costs and productivity rates so you'll be prepared to estimate any project.
- a source book for preliminary project cost, product selections, and alternate materials and methods.

To meet all of these requirements, we have organized the book into the following clearly defined sections.

Quick Start

See our "Quick Start" instructions on the following page to get started right away.

Estimating with RSMeans Unit Price Cost Data

Please refer to these steps for guidance on completing an estimate using RSMeans unit price cost data.

How to Use the Book:
The Details

This section contains an in-depth explanation of how the book is arranged . . . and how you can use it to determine a reliable construction cost estimate. It includes information about how we develop our cost figures and how to completely prepare your estimate.

Unit Price Section

All cost data has been divided into the 50 divisions according to the MasterFormat system of classification and numbering. For a listing of these divisions and an outline of their subdivisions, see the Unit Price Section Table of Contents.
Estimating tips are included at the beginning of each division.

Assemblies Section

The cost data in this section has been organized in an "Assemblies" format. These assemblies are the functional elements of a building and are arranged according to the 7 elements of the UNIFORMAT II classification system. For a complete explanation of a typical "Assemblies" page, see "How RSMeans Assemblies Data Works."

Reference Section

This section includes information on Equipment Rental Costs, Crew Listings, Historical Cost Indexes, City Cost Indexes, Location Factors, Reference Tables, Change Orders, Square Foot Costs, and a listing of Abbreviations.

Equipment Rental Costs: This section contains the average costs to rent and operate hundreds of pieces of construction equipment.

Crew Listings: This section lists all of the crews referenced in the book. For the purposes of this book, a crew is composed of more than one trade classification and/or the addition of power equipment to any trade classification. Power equipment is included in the cost of the crew. Costs are shown both with bare labor rates and with the installing contractor's overhead and profit added. For each, the total crew cost per eight-hour day and the composite cost per labor-hour are listed.

Historical Cost Indexes: These indexes provide you with data to adjust construction costs over time.

City Cost Indexes: All costs in this book are U.S. national averages. Costs vary because of the regional economy. You can adjust costs by CSI Division to over 700 locations throughout the U.S. and Canada by using the data in this section.

Location Factors: You can adjust total project costs to over 900 locations throughout the U.S. and Canada by using the data in this section.

Reference Tables: At the beginning of selected major classifications in the Unit Price Section are reference numbers shown in a shaded box. These numbers refer you to related information in the Reference Section. In this section, you'll find reference tables, explanations, estimating information that support how we develop the unit price data, technical data, and estimating procedures.

Change Orders: This section includes information on the factors that influence the pricing of change orders.

Square Foot Costs: This section contains costs for 59 different building types that allow you to make a rough estimate for the overall cost of a project or its major components.

Abbreviations: A listing of abbreviations used throughout this book, along with the terms they represent, is included in this section.

Index

A comprehensive listing of all terms and subjects in this book will help you quickly find what you need when you are not sure where it occurs in MasterFormat.

The Scope of This Book

This book is designed to be as comprehensive and as easy to use as possible. To that end we have made certain assumptions and limited its scope in two key ways:

1. We have established material prices based on a national average.
2. We have computed labor costs based on a 30-city national average of union wage rates.

For a more detailed explanation of how the cost data is developed, see "How To Use the Book: The Details."

Project Size/Type

The material prices in RSMeans cost data books are "contractor's prices." They are the prices that contractors can expect to pay at the lumberyards, suppliers'/distributors warehouses, etc. Small orders of speciality items would be higher than the costs shown, while very large orders, such as truckload lots, would be less. The variation would depend on the size, timing, and negotiating power of the contractor. The labor costs are primarily for new construction or major renovation rather than repairs or minor alterations.
With reasonable exercise of judgment, the figures can be used for any building work.

Absolute Essentials for a Quick Start

If you feel you are ready to use this book and don't think you will need the detailed instructions that begin on the following page, this Absolute Essentials for a Quick Start page is for you. These steps will allow you to get started estimating in a matter of minutes.

1 Scope

Think through the project that you will be estimating, and identify the many individual work tasks that will need to be covered in your estimate.

2 Quantify

Determine the number of units that will be required for each work task that you identified.

3 Pricing

Locate individual Unit Price line items that match the work tasks you identified. The Unit Price Section Table of Contents that begins on page 1 and the Index in the back of the book will help you find these line items.

4 Multiply

Multiply the Total Incl O&P cost for a Unit Price line item in the book by your quantity for that item. The price you calculate will be an estimate for a completed item of work performed by a subcontractor. Keep adding line items in this manner to build your estimate.

5 Project Overhead

Include project overhead items in your estimate. These items are needed to make the job run and are typically, but not always, provided by the General Contractor. They can be found in Division 1. An alternate method of estimating project overhead costs is to apply a percentage of the total project cost.

Include rented tools not included in crews, waste, rubbish handling, and cleanup.

6 Estimate Summary

Include General Contractor's markup on subcontractors, General Contractor's office overhead and profit, and sales tax on materials and equipment.

Adjust your estimate to the project's location by using the City Cost Indexes or Location Factors found in the Reference Section.

Editors' Note: We urge you to spend time reading and understanding the supporting material in the front of this book. An accurate estimate requires experience, knowledge, and careful calculation. The more you know about how we at RSMeans developed the data, the more accurate your estimate will be. In addition, it is important to take into consideration the reference material in the back of the book such as Equipment Listings, Crew Listings, City Cost Indexes, Location Factors, and Reference Tables.

Estimating with RSMeans Unit Price Cost Data

Following these steps will allow you to complete an accurate estimate using RSMeans Unit Price cost data.

1 Scope Out the Project

- Think through the project and identify those CSI Divisions needed in your estimate.
- Identify the individual work tasks that will need to be covered in your estimate.
- The Unit Price data in this book has been divided into 50 Divisions according to the CSI MasterFormat® 2014—their titles are listed on the back cover of your book.
- The Unit Price Section Table of Contents on page 1 may also be helpful when scoping out your project.
- Experienced estimators find it helpful to begin with Division 2 and continue through completion. Division 1 can be estimated after the full project scope is known.

2 Quantify

- Determine the number of units required for each work task that you identified.
- Experienced estimators include an allowance for waste in their quantities. (Waste is not included in RSMeans Unit Price line items unless so stated.)

3 Price the Quantities

- Use the Unit Price Table of Contents, and the Index, to locate individual Unit Price line items for your estimate.
- Reference Numbers indicated within a Unit Price section refer to additional information that you may find useful.
- The crew indicates who is performing the work for that task. Crew codes are expanded in the Crew Listings in the Reference Section to include all trades and equipment that comprise the crew.
- The Daily Output is the amount of work the crew is expected to do in one day.
- The Labor-Hours value is the amount of time it will take for the crew to install one unit of work.
- The abbreviated Unit designation indicates the unit of measure upon which the crew, productivity, and prices are based.
- Bare Costs are shown for materials, labor, and equipment needed to complete the Unit Price line item. Bare costs do not include waste, project overhead, payroll insurance, payroll taxes, main office overhead, or profit.
- The Total Incl O&P cost is the billing rate or invoice amount of the installing contractor or subcontractor who performs the work for the Unit Price line item.

4 Multiply

- Multiply the total number of units needed for your project by the Total Incl O&P cost for each Unit Price line item.
- Be careful that your take off unit of measure matches the unit of measure in the Unit column.
- The price you calculate is an estimate for a completed item of work.
- Keep scoping individual tasks, determining the number of units required for those tasks, matching each task with individual Unit Price line items in the book, and multiply quantities by Total Incl O&P costs.
- An estimate completed in this manner is priced as if a subcontractor, or set of subcontractors, is performing the work. The estimate does not yet include Project Overhead or Estimate Summary components such as General Contractor markups on subcontracted work, General Contractor office overhead and profit, contingency, and location factor.

5 Project Overhead

- Include project overhead items from Division 1 – General Requirements.
- These items are needed to make the job run. They are typically, but not always, provided by the General Contractor. Items include, but are not limited to, field personnel, insurance, performance bond, permits, testing, temporary utilities, field office and storage facilities, temporary scaffolding and platforms, equipment mobilization and demobilization, temporary roads and sidewalks, winter protection, temporary barricades and fencing, temporary security, temporary signs, field engineering and layout, final cleaning and commissioning.
- Each item should be quantified, and matched to individual Unit Price line items in Division 1, and then priced and added to your estimate.
- An alternate method of estimating project overhead costs is to apply a percentage of the total project cost, usually 5% to 15% with an average of 10% (see General Conditions, page ix).
- Include other project related expenses in your estimate such as:
  - Rented equipment not itemized in the Crew Listings
  - Rubbish handling throughout the project (see 02 41 19.19)

6 Estimate Summary

- Include sales tax as required by laws of your state or county.
- Include the General Contractor's markup on self-performed work, usually 5% to 15% with an average of 10%.
- Include the General Contractor's markup on subcontracted work, usually 5% to 15% with an average of 10%.
- Include General Contractor's main office overhead and profit:
  - ☐ RSMeans gives general guidelines on the General Contractor's main office overhead (see section 01 31 13.60 and Reference Number R013113-50).
  - ☐ RSMeans gives no guidance on the General Contractor's profit.

  - ☐ Markups will depend on the size of the General Contractor's operations, his projected annual revenue, the level of risk he is taking on, and on the level of competition in the local area and for this project in particular.
- Include a contingency, usually 3% to 5%, if appropriate.
- Adjust your estimate to the project's location by using the City Cost Indexes or the Location Factors in the Reference Section:
  - ☐ Look at the rules on the pages for "How to Use the City Cost Indexes" to see how to apply the Indexes for your location.
  - ☐ When the proper Index or Factor has been identified for the project's location, convert it to a multiplier by dividing it by 100, and then multiply that multiplier by your estimated total cost. The original estimated total cost will now be adjusted up or down from the national average to a total that is appropriate for your location.

Editors' Notes:
We urge you to spend time reading and understanding the supporting material in the front of this book. An accurate estimate requires experience, knowledge, and careful calculation. The more you know about how we at RSMeans developed the data, the more accurate your estimate will be. In addition, it is important to take into consideration the reference material in the back of the book such as Equipment Listings, Crew Listings, City Cost Indexes, Location Factors, and Reference Tables.

How to Use the Book: The Details

What's Behind the Numbers? The Development of Cost Data

The staff at RSMeans continually monitors developments in the construction industry in order to ensure reliable, thorough, and up-to-date cost information. While overall construction costs may vary relative to general economic conditions, price fluctuations within the industry are dependent upon many factors. Individual price variations may, in fact, be opposite to overall economic trends. Therefore, costs are constantly tracked and complete updates are published yearly. Also, new items are frequently added in response to changes in materials and methods.

Costs—$ (U.S.)

All costs represent U.S. national averages and are given in U.S. dollars. The RSMeans City Cost Indexes can be used to adjust costs to a particular location. The City Cost Indexes for Canada can be used to adjust U.S. national averages to local costs in Canadian dollars. No exchange rate conversion is necessary.

G The processes or products identified by the green symbol in our publications have been determined to be environmentally responsible and/or resource-efficient solely by the RSMeans engineering staff. The inclusion of the green symbol does not represent compliance with any specific industry association or standard.

Material Costs

The RSMeans staff contacts manufacturers, dealers, distributors, and contractors all across the U.S. and Canada to determine national average material costs. If you have access to current material costs for your specific location, you may wish to make adjustments to reflect differences from the national average. Included within material costs are fasteners for a normal installation. RSMeans engineers use manufacturers' recommendations, written specifications, and/ or standard construction practice for size and spacing of fasteners. Adjustments to material costs may be required for your specific application or location. The manufacturer's warranty is assumed. Extended warranties are

not included in the material costs. Material costs do not include sales tax.

Labor Costs

Labor costs are based on the average of wage rates from 30 major U.S. cities. Rates are determined from labor union agreements or prevailing wages for construction trades for the current year. Rates, along with overhead and profit markups, are listed on the inside back cover of this book.

- If wage rates in your area vary from those used in this book, or if rate increases are expected within a given year, labor costs should be adjusted accordingly.

Labor costs reflect productivity based on actual working conditions. In addition to actual installation, these figures include time spent during a normal weekday on tasks such as, material receiving and handling, mobilization at site, site movement, breaks, and cleanup.

Productivity data is developed over an extended period so as not to be influenced by abnormal variations and reflects a typical average.

Equipment Costs

Equipment costs include not only rental, but also operating costs for equipment under normal use. The operating costs include parts and labor for routine servicing such as repair and replacement of pumps, filters, and worn lines. Normal operating expendables, such as fuel, lubricants, tires, and electricity (where applicable), are also included. Extraordinary operating expendables with highly variable wear patterns, such as diamond bits and blades, are excluded. These costs are included under materials. Equipment rental rates are obtained from industry sources throughout North America—contractors, suppliers, dealers, manufacturers, and distributors.

Equipment costs do not include operators' wages; nor do they include the cost to move equipment to a job site (mobilization) or from a job site (demobilization).

Equipment Cost/Day——The cost of power equipment required for each crew is included in the Crew Listings in the Reference Section (small tools that are considered as essential everyday tools are not listed out separately). The

Crew Listings itemize specialized tools and heavy equipment along with labor trades. The daily cost of itemized equipment included in a crew is based on dividing the weekly bare rental rate by 5 (number of working days per week) and then adding the hourly operating cost times 8 (the number of hours per day). This Equipment Cost/ Day is shown in the last column of the Equipment Rental Cost pages in the Reference Section.

Mobilization/Demobilization——The cost to move construction equipment from an equipment yard or rental company to the job site and back again is not included in equipment costs. Mobilization (to the site) and demobilization (from the site) costs can be found in the Unit Price Section. If a piece of equipment is already at the job site, it is not appropriate to utilize mob./demob. costs again in an estimate.

General Conditions

Cost data in this book is presented in two ways: Bare Costs and Total Cost including O&P (Overhead and Profit). General Conditions, when applicable, should also be added to the Total Cost including O&P. The costs for General Conditions are listed in Division 1 of the Unit Price Section and the Reference Section of this book. General Conditions for the *Installing Contractor* may range from 0% to 10% of the Total Cost including O&P. For the *General* or *Prime Contractor*, costs for General Conditions may range from 5% to 15% of the Total Cost including O&P, with a figure of 10% as the most typical allowance. If applicable, the Assemblies and Models sections of this book use costs that include the installing contractor's overhead and profit (O&P).

Overhead and Profit

Total Cost including O&P for the *Installing Contractor* is shown in the last column on both the Unit Price and the Assemblies pages of this book. This figure is the sum of the bare material cost plus 10% for profit, the bare labor cost plus total overhead and profit, and the bare equipment cost plus 10% for profit. Details for the calculation of Overhead and Profit on labor are shown on the inside back cover and in the Reference Section of this book. (See the "How RSMeans Data Works" for an example of this calculation.)

Factors Affecting Costs

Costs can vary depending upon a number of variables. Here's how we have handled the main factors affecting costs.

Quality——The prices for materials and the workmanship upon which productivity is based represent sound construction work. They are also in line with U.S. government specifications.

Overtime——We have made no allowance for overtime. If you anticipate premium time or work beyond normal working hours, be sure to make an appropriate adjustment to your labor costs.

Productivity——The productivity, daily output, and labor-hour figures for each line item are based on working an eight-hour day in daylight hours in moderate temperatures. For work that extends beyond normal work hours or is performed under adverse conditions, productivity may decrease. (See "How RSMeans Unit Price Data Works" for more on productivity.)

Size of Project——The size, scope of work, and type of construction project will have a significant impact on cost. Economies of scale can reduce costs for large projects. Unit costs can often run higher for small projects.

Location——Material prices in this book are for metropolitan areas. However, in dense urban areas, traffic and site storage limitations may increase costs. Beyond a 20-mile radius of large cities, extra trucking or transportation charges may also increase the material costs slightly. On the other hand, lower wage rates may be in effect. Be sure to consider both of these factors when preparing an estimate, particularly if the job site is located in a central city or remote rural location. In addition, highly specialized subcontract items may require travel and per-diem expenses for mechanics.

Other Factors

- contractor management
- weather conditions
- local union conditions
- building code requirements
- availability of:
  - adequate energy
  - skilled labor
  - building materials
- owner's special requirements/restrictions
- safety requirements
- environmental considerations
- traffic control

Unpredictable Factors——General business conditions influence "in-place" costs of all items. Substitute materials and construction methods may have to be employed. These may affect the installed cost and/or life cycle costs. Such factors may be difficult to evaluate and cannot necessarily be predicted on the basis of the job's location in a particular section of the country. Thus, where these factors apply, you may find significant but unavoidable cost variations for which you will have to apply a measure of judgment to your estimate.

Rounding of Costs

In general, all unit prices in excess of $5.00 have been rounded to make them easier to use and still maintain adequate precision of the results. The rounding rules we have chosen are in the following table.

Prices from . . .	Rounded to the nearest . . .
$.01 to $5.00	$.01
$5.01 to $20.00	$.05
$20.01 to $100.00	$.50
$100.01 to $300.00	$1.00
$300.01 to $1,000.00	$5.00
$1,000.01 to $10,000.00	$25.00
$10,000.01 to $50,000.00	$100.00
$50,000.01 and above	$500.00

How Subcontracted Items Affect Costs

A considerable portion of all large construction jobs is usually subcontracted. In fact, the percentage done by subcontractors is constantly increasing and may run over 90%. Since the workers employed by these companies do nothing else but install their particular product, they soon become expert in that line. The result is, installation by these firms is accomplished so efficiently that the total in-place cost, even adding the general contractor's overhead and profit, is no more, and often less, than if the principal contractor had handled the installation himself/herself. There is, moreover, the big advantage of having the work done correctly. Companies that deal with construction specialties are anxious to have their product perform well, and, consequently, the installation will be the best possible.

Contingencies

The contractor should consider inflationary price trends and possible material shortages during the course of the job. These escalation factors are dependent upon both economic conditions and the anticipated time between the estimate and actual construction. If drawings are not complete or approved, or a budget cost is wanted, it is wise to add 5% to 10%. Contingencies, then, are a matter of judgment. Additional allowances for contingencies are shown in Division 1.

Estimating Precision

When making a construction cost estimate, ignore the cents column. Use only the total per-unit cost to the nearest dollar. The cents will average in a column of figures. A construction cost estimate of $257,323.37 is cumbersome. A figure of $257,325 is certainly more sensible, and $257,000 is better and just as likely to be correct.

If you follow this simple instruction, the time saved is tremendous, with an added important advantage. Using round figures leaves the professional estimator free to exercise judgment and common sense rather than being overwhelmed by a mass of computations.

Final Checklist

Estimating can be a straightforward process provided you remember the basics. Here's a checklist of some of the steps you should remember to complete before finalizing your estimate.

Did you remember to . . .

- factor in the City Cost Index for your locale?

- take into consideration which items have been marked up and by how much?
- mark up the entire estimate sufficiently for your purposes?
- read the background information on techniques and technical matters that could impact your project time span and cost?
- include all components of your project in the final estimate?
- double check your figures for accuracy?
- call RSMeans if you have any questions about your estimate or the data you've found in our publications? Remember, RSMeans stands behind its publications. If you have any questions about your estimate . . . about the costs you've used

from our books . . . or even about the technical aspects of the job that may affect your estimate, feel free to call the RSMeans editors at 1-877-737-1594.

Free Quarterly Updates

Stay up-to-date throughout 2015 with RSMeans' free cost data updates four times a year. Sign up online to make sure you have access to the newest data. Every quarter we provide the city cost adjustment factors for hundreds of cities and key materials. Register at:
http://info.thegordiangroup.com/RSMeans.html.

Unit Price Section

Table of Contents

1

Table of Contents (cont.)

How RSMeans Unit Price Data Works

All RSMeans unit price data is organized in the same way.

It is important to understand the structure, so that you can find information easily and use it correctly.

RSMeans **Line Numbers** consist of 12 characters, which identify a unique location in the database for each task. The first 6 or 8 digits conform to the Construction Specifications Institute MasterFormat® 2014. The remainder of the digits are a further breakdown by RSMeans in order to arrange items in understandable groups of similar tasks. Line numbers are consistent across all RSMeans publications, so a line number in any RSMeans product will always refer to the same unit of work.

RSMeans engineers have created **reference** information to assist you in your estimate. If there is information that applies to a section, it will be indicated at the start of the section. In this case, R033105-10 provides information on the proportionate quantities of formwork, reinforcing, and concrete used in cast-in-place concrete items such as footings, slabs, beams, and columns. The Reference Section is located in the back of the book on the pages with a gray edge.

RSMeans **Descriptions** are shown in a hierarchical structure to make them readable. In order to read a complete description, read up through the indents to the top of the section. Include everything that is above and to the left that is not contradicted by information below. For instance, the complete description for line 03 30 53.40 3550 is "Concrete in place, including forms (4 uses), Grade 60 rebar, concrete (Portland cement Type 1), placement and finishing unless otherwise indicated; Equipment pad (3000 psi), 4' x 4' x 6" thick."

When using **RSMeans data**, it is important to read through an entire section to ensure that you use the data that most closely matches your work. Note that sometimes there is additional information shown in the section that may improve your price. There are frequently lines that further describe, add to, or adjust data for specific situations.

03 30 Cast-In-Place Concrete

03 30 53 – Miscellaneous Cast-In-Place Concrete

03 30 53.40 Concrete In Place

0010	**CONCRETE IN PLACE**	R033105-10
0020	Including forms (4 uses), Grade 60 rebar, concrete (Portland cement	R033105-20
0050	Type I), placement and finishing unless otherwise indicated	R033105-50
0300	Beams (3500 psi), 5 kip per L.F., 10' span	R033105-65
0350	25' span	R033105-70
0500	Chimney foundations (5000 psi), over 5 C.Y.	R033105-85
0510	(3500 psi), under 5 C.Y.	
0700	Columns, square (4000 psi), 12" x 12", less than 2% reinforcing	
3450	Over 10,000 S.F.	
3500	Add per floor for 3 to 6 stories high	
3520	For 7 to 20 stories high	
3540	Equipment pad (3000 psi), 3' x 3' x 6" thick	
3550	4' x 4' x 6" thick	
3560	5' x 5' x 8" thick	
3570	6' x 6' x 8" thick	

The data published in RSMeans print books represents a "national average" cost. This data should be modified to the project location using the **City Cost Indexes** or **Location Factors** tables found in the Reference Section (see pages 748–796). Use the location factors to adjust estimate totals if the project covers multiple trades. Use the city cost indexes (CCI) for single trade projects or projects where a more detailed analysis is required. All figures in the two tables are derived from the same research. The last row of data in the CCI, the weighted average, is the same as the numbers reported for each location in the location factor table.

4

Crews include labor or labor and equipment necessary to accomplish each task. In this case, Crew C-14H is used. RSMeans selects a crew to represent the workers and equipment that are typically used for that task. In this case, Crew C-14H consists of one carpenter foreman (outside), two carpenters, one rodman, one laborer, one cement finisher, and one gas engine vibrator. Details of all crews can be found in the reference section.

Crews

Crew No.	Bare Costs		Incl. Subs O&P		Cost Per Labor-Hour	
Crew C-14H	**Hr.**	**Daily**	**Hr.**	**Daily**	Bare Costs	Incl. O&P
1 Carpenter Foreman (outside)	$48.95	$391.60	$75.35	$602.80	$46.33	$71.08
2 Carpenters	46.95	751.20	72.25	1156.00		
1 Rodman (reinf.)	52.55	420.40	82.10	656.80		
1 Laborer	37.60	300.80	57.85	462.80		
1 Cement Finisher	45.00	360.00	66.65	533.20		
1 Gas Engine Vibrator		31.20		34.32	.65	.71
48 L.H., Daily Totals		$2255.20		$3445.92	$46.98	$71.79

The **Daily Output** is the amount of work that the crew can do in a normal 8-hour workday, including mobilization, layout, movement of materials, and cleanup. In this case, crew C-14H can install thirty 4' x 4' x 6" thick concrete pads in a day. Daily output is variable, based on many factors, including the size of the job, location, and environmental conditions. RSMeans data represents work done in daylight (or adequate lighting) and temperate conditions.

Bare Costs are the costs of materials, labor, and equipment that the installing contractor pays. They represent the cost, in U.S. dollars, for one unit of work. They do not include any markups for profit or labor burden.

Crew	Daily Output	Labor-Hours	Unit	Material	2015 Bare Costs Labor	Equipment	Total	Total Incl O&P
C-14A	15.62	12.804	C.Y.	320	605	48	973	1,325
"	18.55	10.782		335	510	40.50	885.50	1,200
C-14C	32.22	3.476		150	157	.97	307.97	405
"	23.71	4.724		177	213	1.32	391.32	525
C-14A	11.96	16.722		365	790	63	1,218	1,700
	2200	.025		.94	1.07	.33	2.34	3.02
	31800	.002			.07	.02	.09	.13
	21200	.003			.11	.03	.14	.21
C-14H	45	1.067	Ea.	47	49.50	.69	97.19	128
	30	1.600		69.50	74	1.04	144.54	191
	18	2.667		122	124	1.73	247.73	325
	14	3.429		164	159	2.23	325.23	425

The **Total Incl O&P column** is the total cost, including overhead and profit, that the installing contractor will charge the customer. This represents the cost of materials plus 10% profit, the cost of labor plus labor burden and 10% profit, and the cost of equipment plus 10% profit. It does not include the general contractor's overhead and profit. Note: See the inside back cover for details of how RSMeans calculates labor burden.

The **Total column** represents the total bare cost for the installing contractor, in U.S. dollars. In this case, the sum of $69.50 for material + $74.00 for labor + $1.04 for equipment is $144.54.

The figure in the **Labor Hours** column is the amount of labor required to perform one unit of work—in this case the amount of labor required to construct one 4' x 4' equipment pad. This figure is calculated by dividing the number of hours of labor in the crew by the daily output (48 labor hours divided by 30 pads = 1.6 hours of labor per pad). Multiply 1.600 times 60 to see the value in minutes: 60 x 1.6 = 96 minutes. Note: the labor hour figure is not dependent on the crew size. A change in crew size will result in a corresponding change in daily output, but the labor hours per unit of work will not change.

All RSMeans unit cost data includes the typical **Unit of Measure** used for estimating that item. For concrete-in-place the typical unit is cubic yards (C.Y.) or each (Ea.). For installing broadloom carpet it is square yard, and for gypsum board it is square foot. The estimator needs to take special care that the unit in the data matches the unit in the take-off. Unit conversions may be found in the Reference Section.

How RSMeans Unit Price Data Works (Continued)

Sample Estimate

This sample demonstrates the elements of an estimate, including a tally of the RSMeans data lines, and a summary of the markups on a contractor's work to arrive at a total cost to the owner. The RSMeans Location Factor is added at the bottom of the estimate to adjust the cost of the work to a specific location.

Work Performed: The body of the estimate shows the RSMeans data selected, including line number, a brief description of each item, its take-off unit and quantity, and the bare costs of materials, labor, and equipment. This estimate also includes a column titled "SubContract." This data is taken from the RSMeans column "Total Incl O&P," and represents the total that a subcontractor would charge a general contractor for the work, including the sub's markup for overhead and profit.

Division 1, General Requirements: This is the first division numerically, but the last division estimated. Division 1 includes project-wide needs provided by the general contractor. These requirements vary by project, but may include temporary facilities and utilities, security, testing, project cleanup, etc. For small projects a percentage can be used, typically between 5% and 15% of project cost. For large projects the costs may be itemized and priced individually.

Bonds: Bond costs should be added to the estimate. The figures here represent a typical performance bond, ensuring the owner that if the general contractor does not complete the obligations in the construction contract the bonding company will pay the cost for completion of the work.

Location Adjustment: RSMeans published data is based on national average costs. If necessary, adjust the total cost of the project using a location factor from the "Location Factor" table or the "City Cost Index" table. Use location factors if the work is general, covering multiple trades. If the work is by a single trade (e.g., masonry) use the more specific data found in the "City Cost Indexes."

This estimate is based on an interactive spreadsheet. A copy of this spreadsheet is located on the RSMeans website at **http://www.reedconstructiondata.com/rsmeans/extras/546011.** You are free to download it and adjust it to your methodology.

Project Name: Pre-Engineered Steel Building			Architect: As Shown	
Location:	**Anywhere, USA**			
Line Number	**Description**	**Qty**	**Unit**	**Material**
03 30 53.40 3940	Strip footing, 12" x 24", reinforced	34	C.Y.	$4,726.00
03 30 53.40 3950	Strip footing, 12" x 36", reinforced	15	C.Y.	$1,995.00
03 11 13.65 3000	Concrete slab edge forms	500	L.F.	$175.00
03 22 11.10 0200	Welded wire fabric reinforcing	150	C.S.F.	$2,580.00
03 31 13.35 0300	Ready mix concrete, 4000 psi for slab on grade	278	C.Y.	$29,746.00
03 31 13.70 4300	Place, strike off & consolidate concrete slab	278	C.Y.	$0.00
03 35 13.30 0250	Machine float & trowel concrete slab	15,000	S.F.	$0.00
03 15 16.20 0140	Cut control joints in concrete slab	950	L.F.	$57.00
03 39 23.13 0300	Sprayed concrete curing membrane	150	C.S.F.	$1,657.50
Division 03	**Subtotal**			**$40,936.50**
08 36 13.10 2650	Manual 10' x 10' steel sectional overhead door	8	Ea.	$8,800.00
08 36 13.10 2860	Insulation and steel back panel for OH door	800	S.F.	$3,800.00
Division 08	**Subtotal**			**$12,600.00**
13 34 19.50 1100	Pre-Engineered Steel Building, 100' x 150' x 24'	15,000	SF Flr.	$0.00
13 34 19.50 6050	Framing for PESB door opening, 3' x 7'	4	Opng.	$0.00
13 34 19.50 6100	Framing for PESB door opening, 10' x 10'	8	Opng.	$0.00
13 34 19.50 6200	Framing for PESB window opening, 4' x 3'	6	Opng.	$0.00
13 34 19.50 5750	PESB door, 3' x 7', single leaf	4	Opng.	$2,340.00
13 34 19.50 7750	PESB sliding window, 4' x 3' with screen	6	Opng.	$2,280.00
13 34 19.50 6550	PESB gutter, eave type, 26 ga., painted	300	L.F.	$2,085.00
13 34 19.50 8650	PESB roof vent, 12" wide x 10' long	15	Ea.	$540.00
13 34 19.50 6900	PESB insulation, vinyl faced, 4" thick	27,400	S.F.	$11,508.00
Division 13	**Subtotal**			**$18,753.00**
			Subtotal	$72,289.50
Division 01	**General Requirements @ 7%**			**5,060.27**
			Estimate Subtotal	$77,349.77
			Sales Tax @ 5%	3,867.49
			Subtotal A	81,217.25
			GC O & P	8,121.73
			Subtotal B	89,338.98
			Contingency @ 5%	
			Subtotal C	
			Bond @ $12/1000 +10% O&P	
			Subtotal D	
			Location Adjustment Factor	
			Grand Total	

This example shows the cost to construct a pre-engineered steel building. The foundation, doors, windows, and insulation will be installed by the general contractor. A subcontractor will install the structural steel, roofing, and siding.

Labor	Equipment	SubContract	01/01/15 Estimate Total	STD
$3,570.00	$22.10	$0.00		
$1,260.00	$7.80	$0.00		
$1,190.00	$0.00	$0.00		
$4,050.00	$0.00	$0.00		
$0.00	$0.00	$0.00		
$4,753.80	$158.46	$0.00		
$9,000.00	$450.00	$0.00		
$380.00	$85.50	$0.00		
$952.50	$0.00	$0.00		
$25,156.30	$723.86	$0.00	$66,816.66	Division 03
$3,320.00	$0.00	$0.00		
$0.00	$0.00	$0.00		
$3,320.00	$0.00	$0.00	$15,920.00	Division 08
$0.00	$0.00	$352,500.00		
$0.00	$0.00	$2,280.00		
$0.00	$0.00	$9,200.00		
$0.00	$0.00	$3,330.00		
$672.00	$0.00	$0.00		
$576.00	$67.20	$0.00		
$789.00	$0.00	$0.00		
$3,165.00	$0.00	$0.00		
$9,042.00	$0.00	$0.00		
$14,244.00	$67.20	$367,310.00	$400,374.20	Division 13
$42,720.30	$791.06	$367,310.00	$483,110.86	Subtotal
2,990.42	55.37	25,711.70		Gen. Requirements
$45,710.72	$846.43	$393,021.70	$483,110.86	Estimate Subtotal
	42.32	9,825.54		Sales tax
45,710.72	888.76	402,847.24		Subtotal
24,912.34	88.88	40,284.72		GC O&P
70,623.06	977.63	443,131.97	$604,071.64	Subtotal
			30,203.58	Contingency
			$634,275.22	Subtotal
			8,372.43	Bond
			$642,647.66	Subtotal
102.30			14,780.90	Location Adjustment
			$657,428.55	Grand Total

Sales Tax: If the work is subject to state or local sales taxes, the amount must be added to the estimate. Sales tax may be added to material costs, equipment costs, and subcontracted work. In this case, sales tax was added in all three categories. It was assumed that approximately half the subcontracted work would be material cost, so the tax was applied to 50% of the subcontract total.

GC O&P: This entry represents the general contractor's markup on material, labor, equipment, and subcontractor costs. RSMeans' standard markup on materials, equipment, and subcontracted work is 10%. In this estimate, the markup on the labor performed by the GC's workers uses "Skilled Workers Average" shown in Column F on the table "Installing Contractor's Overhead & Profit," which can be found on the inside-back cover of the book.

Contingency: A factor for contingency may be added to any estimate to represent the cost of unknowns that may occur between the time that the estimate is performed and the time the project is constructed. The amount of the allowance will depend on the stage of design at which the estimate is done, and the contractor's assessment of the risk involved. Refer to section 01 21 16.50 for contigency allowances.

Estimating Tips

01 20 00 Price and Payment Procedures

- Allowances that should be added to estimates to cover contingencies and job conditions that are not included in the national average material and labor costs are shown in section 01 21.

- When estimating historic preservation projects (depending on the condition of the existing structure and the owner's requirements), a 15%–20% contingency or allowance is recommended, regardless of the stage of the drawings.

01 30 00 Administrative Requirements

- Before determining a final cost estimate, it is a good practice to review all the items listed in Subdivisions 01 31 and 01 32 to make final adjustments for items that may need customizing to specific job conditions.

- Requirements for initial and periodic submittals can represent a significant cost to the General Requirements of a job. Thoroughly check the submittal specifications when estimating a project to determine any costs that should be included.

01 40 00 Quality Requirements

- All projects will require some degree of Quality Control. This cost is not included in the unit cost of construction listed in each division. Depending upon the terms of the contract, the various costs of inspection and testing can be the responsibility of either the owner or the contractor. Be sure to include the required costs in your estimate.

01 50 00 Temporary Facilities and Controls

- Barricades, access roads, safety nets, scaffolding, security, and many more requirements for the execution of a safe project are elements of direct cost. These costs can easily be overlooked when preparing an estimate. When looking through the major classifications of this subdivision, determine which items apply to each division in your estimate.

- Construction Equipment Rental Costs can be found in the Reference Section in section 01 54 33. Operators' wages are not included in equipment rental costs.

- Equipment mobilization and demobilization costs are not included in equipment rental costs and must be considered separately in section 01 54 36.50.

- The cost of small tools provided by the installing contractor for his workers is covered in the "Overhead" column on the "Installing Contractor's Overhead and Profit" table that lists labor trades, base rates and markups and, therefore, is included in the "Total Incl. O&P" cost of any Unit Price line item.

01 70 00 Execution and Closeout Requirements

- When preparing an estimate, thoroughly read the specifications to determine the requirements for Contract Closeout. Final cleaning, record documentation, operation and maintenance data, warranties and bonds, and spare parts and maintenance materials can all be elements of cost for the completion of a contract. Do not overlook these in your estimate.

Reference Numbers

Reference numbers are shown in shaded boxes at the beginning of some major classifications. These numbers refer to related items in the Reference Section. The reference information may be an estimating procedure, an alternate pricing method, or technical information.

Note: Not all subdivisions listed here necessarily appear in this publication. ■

Division 1 – General Requirements

01 11 Summary of Work

01 11 31 – Professional Consultants

01 11 31.10 Architectural Fees

		Crew	Daily Output	Labor-Hours	Unit	Material	2015 Bare Costs Labor	Equipment	Total	Total Incl O&P
0010	**ARCHITECTURAL FEES** R011110-10									
0020	For new construction									
0060	Minimum				Project				4.90%	4.90%
0090	Maximum				"				16%	16%

01 11 31.20 Construction Management Fees

		Crew	Daily Output	Labor-Hours	Unit	Material	Labor	Equipment	Total	Total Incl O&P
0010	**CONSTRUCTION MANAGEMENT FEES**									
0020	$1,000,000 job, minimum				Project				4.50%	4.50%
0050	Maximum								7.50%	7.50%
0300	$50,000,000 job, minimum								2.50%	2.50%
0350	Maximum				↓				4%	4%

01 11 31.30 Engineering Fees

		Crew	Daily Output	Labor-Hours	Unit	Material	Labor	Equipment	Total	Total Incl O&P
0010	**ENGINEERING FEES** R011110-30									
0800	Landscaping & site development, minimum				Contrct				2.50%	2.50%
0900	Maximum				"				6%	6%

01 11 31.50 Models

		Crew	Daily Output	Labor-Hours	Unit	Material	Labor	Equipment	Total	Total Incl O&P
0010	**MODELS**									
0500	2 story building, scaled 100' x 200', simple materials and details				Ea.	5,000			5,000	5,500
0510	Elaborate materials and details				"	30,000			30,000	33,000

01 11 31.75 Renderings

		Crew	Daily Output	Labor-Hours	Unit	Material	Labor	Equipment	Total	Total Incl O&P
0010	**RENDERINGS** Color, matted, 20" x 30", eye level,									
0020	1 building, minimum				Ea.	2,050			2,050	2,275
0050	Average					2,875			2,875	3,175
0100	Maximum					4,625			4,625	5,100
1000	5 buildings, minimum					4,125			4,125	4,525
1100	Maximum					8,250			8,250	9,075
2000	Aerial perspective, color, 1 building, minimum					3,000			3,000	3,275
2100	Maximum					8,150			8,150	8,950
3000	5 buildings, minimum					5,875			5,875	6,450
3100	Maximum				↓	11,700			11,700	12,900

01 21 Allowances

01 21 16 – Contingency Allowances

01 21 16.50 Contingencies

		Crew	Daily Output	Labor-Hours	Unit	Material	Labor	Equipment	Total	Total Incl O&P
0010	**CONTINGENCIES**, Add to estimate									
0020	Conceptual stage				Project				20%	20%
0050	Schematic stage								15%	15%
0100	Preliminary working drawing stage (Design Dev.)								10%	10%
0150	Final working drawing stage				↓				3%	3%

01 21 53 – Factors Allowance

01 21 53.50 Factors

		Crew	Daily Output	Labor-Hours	Unit	Material	Labor	Equipment	Total	Total Incl O&P
0010	**FACTORS** Cost adjustments									
0100	Add to construction costs for particular job requirements									
1100	Equipment usage curtailment, add, minimum				Costs	1%	1%			
1150	Maximum					3%	10%			
1400	Material handling & storage limitation, add, minimum					1%	1%			
1450	Maximum					6%	7%			
2300	Temporary shoring and bracing, add, minimum					2%	5%			
2350	Maximum					5%	12%			
2400	Work inside prisons and high security areas, add, minimum				↓		30%			

01 21 Allowances

01 21 53 – Factors Allowance

01 21 53.50 Factors	Crew	Daily Output	Labor-Hours	Unit	Material	2015 Bare Costs Labor	Equipment	Total	Total Incl O&P
2450 Maximum				Costs		50%			

01 21 57 – Overtime Allowance

01 21 57.50 Overtime

0010 **OVERTIME** for early completion of projects or where R012909-90									
0020 labor shortages exist, add to usual labor, up to				Costs		100%			

01 21 61 – Cost Indexes

01 21 61.10 Construction Cost Index

0010 **CONSTRUCTION COST INDEX** (Reference) over 930 zip code locations in									
0020 the U.S. and Canada, total bldg. cost, min. (Fayetteville, AR)				%				75.40%	75.40%
0050 Average								100%	100%
0100 Maximum (New York, NY)								131.80%	131.80%

01 21 61.30 Labor Index

0010 **LABOR INDEX** (Reference) For over 930 zip code locations in									
0020 the U.S. and Canada, minimum (Beaufort, SC)				%		44.90%			
0050 Average						100%			
0100 Maximum (New York, NY)						168.90%			

01 21 61.50 Material Index

0010 **MATERIAL INDEX** (Reference) For over 930 zip code locations in									
0020 the U.S. and Canada, minimum (Oil City, PA)				%	92.40%				
0040 Average					100%				
0060 Maximum (Ketchikan, AK)					132%				

01 21 63 – Taxes

01 21 63.10 Taxes

0010 **TAXES** R012909-80									
0020 Sales tax, State, average				%	5.04%				
0050 Maximum R012909-85					7.50%				
0200 Social Security, on first $117,000 of wages						7.65%			
0300 Unemployment, combined Federal and State, minimum						.60%			
0350 Average						7.80%			
0400 Maximum						12.87%			

01 31 Project Management and Coordination

01 31 13 – Project Coordination

01 31 13.20 Field Personnel

0010 **FIELD PERSONNEL**									
0020 Clerk, average				Week		450		450	695
0100 Field engineer, minimum						1,075		1,075	1,650
0120 Average						1,400		1,400	2,150
0140 Maximum						1,575		1,575	2,450
0160 General purpose laborer, average						1,500		1,500	2,325
0180 Project manager, minimum						1,975		1,975	3,075
0200 Average						2,275		2,275	3,525
0220 Maximum						2,600		2,600	4,025
0240 Superintendent, minimum						1,925		1,925	2,975
0260 Average						2,125		2,125	3,275
0280 Maximum						2,400		2,400	3,725
0290 Timekeeper, average						1,225		1,225	1,900

For customer support on your Site Work & Landscape Cost Data, call 877.737.1594.

11

01 31 Project Management and Coordination

01 31 13 – Project Coordination

01 31 13.30 Insurance		Crew	Daily Output	Labor-Hours	Unit	Material	2015 Bare Costs Labor	Equipment	Total	Total Incl O&P
0010	**INSURANCE** R013113-40									
0020	Builders risk, standard, minimum				Job				.24%	.24%
0050	Maximum R013113-60								.64%	.64%
0200	All-risk type, minimum								.25%	.25%
0250	Maximum								.62%	.62%
0400	Contractor's equipment floater, minimum				Value				.50%	.50%
0450	Maximum				"				1.50%	1.50%
0600	Public liability, average				Job				2.02%	2.02%
0800	Workers' compensation & employer's liability, average									
0850	by trade, carpentry, general				Payroll		14.93%			
0900	Clerical						.50%			
0950	Concrete						12.93%			
1000	Electrical						5.76%			
1050	Excavation						9.70%			
1250	Masonry						13.68%			
1300	Painting & decorating						11.72%			
1350	Pile driving						14.31%			
1450	Plumbing						6.98%			
1600	Steel erection, structural						31.68%			
1650	Tile work, interior ceramic						8.86%			
1700	Waterproofing, brush or hand caulking						6.56%			
1800	Wrecking						26.14%			
2000	Range of 35 trades in 50 states, excl. wrecking, min.						1.31%			
2100	Average						13.50%			
2200	Maximum						132%			

01 31 13.40 Main Office Expense

01 31 13.40 Main Office Expense		Crew	Daily Output	Labor-Hours	Unit	Material	Labor	Equipment	Total	Total Incl O&P
0010	**MAIN OFFICE EXPENSE** Average for General Contractors R013113-50									
0020	As a percentage of their annual volume									
0125	Annual volume under 1 million dollars				% Vol.				17.50%	
0145	Up to 2.5 million dollars								8%	
0150	Up to 4.0 million dollars								6.80%	
0200	Up to 7.0 million dollars								5.60%	
0250	Up to 10 million dollars								5.10%	
0300	Over 10 million dollars								3.90%	

01 31 13.50 General Contractor's Mark-Up

01 31 13.50 General Contractor's Mark-Up		Crew	Daily Output	Labor-Hours	Unit	Material	Labor	Equipment	Total	Total Incl O&P
0010	**GENERAL CONTRACTOR'S MARK-UP** on Change Orders									
0200	Extra work, by subcontractors, add				%				10%	10%
0250	By General Contractor, add								15%	15%
0400	Omitted work, by subcontractors, deduct all but								5%	5%
0450	By General Contractor, deduct all but								7.50%	7.50%
0600	Overtime work, by subcontractors, add								15%	15%
0650	By General Contractor, add								10%	10%

01 31 13.60 Installing Contractor's Main Office Overhead

01 31 13.60 Installing Contractor's Main Office Overhead		Crew	Daily Output	Labor-Hours	Unit	Material	Labor	Equipment	Total	Total Incl O&P
0010	**INSTALLING CONTRACTOR'S MAIN OFFICE OVERHEAD** R013113-50									
0020	As percent of direct costs, minimum				%				5%	
0050	Average								13%	
0100	Maximum								30%	

01 31 Project Management and Coordination

01 31 13 – Project Coordination

01 31 13.80 Overhead and Profit

		Crew	Daily Output	Labor-Hours	Unit	Material	2015 Bare Costs Labor	Equipment	Total	Total Incl O&P
0010	**OVERHEAD & PROFIT** Allowance to add to items in this									
0020	book that do not include Subs O&P, average				%				25%	
0100	Allowance to add to items in this book that									
0110	do include Subs O&P, minimum				%				5%	5%
0150	Average								10%	10%
0200	Maximum								15%	15%
0300	Typical, by size of project, under $100,000								30%	
0350	$500,000 project								25%	
0400	$2,000,000 project								20%	
0450	Over $10,000,000 project								15%	

01 31 13.90 Performance Bond

		Crew	Daily Output	Labor-Hours	Unit	Material	2015 Bare Costs Labor	Equipment	Total	Total Incl O&P
0010	**PERFORMANCE BOND**									
0020	For buildings, minimum				Job				.60%	.60%
0100	Maximum								2.50%	2.50%
0190	Highways & Bridges, new construction, minimum								1%	1%
0200	Maximum								1.50%	1.50%
0300	Highways & Bridges, resurfacing, minimum								.40%	.40%
0350	Maximum								.94%	.94%

01 32 Construction Progress Documentation

01 32 13 – Scheduling of work

01 32 13.50 Scheduling

		Crew	Daily Output	Labor-Hours	Unit	Material	2015 Bare Costs Labor	Equipment	Total	Total Incl O&P
0010	**SCHEDULING**									
0020	Critical path, as % of architectural fee, minimum				%				.50%	.50%
0100	Maximum				"				1%	1%
0300	Computer-update, micro, no plots, minimum				Ea.				455	500
0400	Including plots, maximum				"				1,450	1,600
0600	Rule of thumb, CPM scheduling, small job ($10 Million)				Job				.05%	.05%
0650	Large job ($50 Million +)								.03%	.03%
0700	Including cost control, small job								.08%	.08%
0750	Large job								.04%	.04%

01 32 33 – Photographic Documentation

01 32 33.50 Photographs

		Crew	Daily Output	Labor-Hours	Unit	Material	2015 Bare Costs Labor	Equipment	Total	Total Incl O&P
0010	**PHOTOGRAPHS**									
0020	8" x 10", 4 shots, 2 prints ea., std. mounting				Set	475			475	525
0100	Hinged linen mounts					530			530	580
0200	8" x 10", 4 shots, 2 prints each, in color					425			425	470
0300	For I.D. slugs, add to all above					5.30			5.30	5.85
0500	Aerial photos, initial fly-over, 5 shots, digital images					400			400	440
0550	10 shots, digital images, 1 print					450			450	495
0600	For each addtional print from fly-over					200			200	220
0700	For full color prints, add					40%				
0750	Add for traffic control area				Ea.	305			305	335
0900	For over 30 miles from airport, add per				Mile	6			6	6.60
1500	Time lapse equipment, camera and projector, buy				Ea.	2,650			2,650	2,925
1550	Rent per month				"	1,600			1,600	1,750
1700	Cameraman and film, including processing, B.&W.				Day	1,225			1,225	1,350
1720	Color				"	1,425			1,425	1,550

R013113-50

For customer support on your Site Work & Landscape Cost Data, call 877.737.1594.

13

01 41 Regulatory Requirements

01 41 26 – Permit Requirements

01 41 26.50 Permits		Crew	Daily Output	Labor-Hours	Unit	Material	2015 Bare Costs Labor	Equipment	Total	Total Incl O&P
0010	**PERMITS**									
0020	Rule of thumb, most cities, minimum				Job				.50%	.50%
0100	Maximum				"				2%	2%

01 45 Quality Control

01 45 23 – Testing and Inspecting Services

01 45 23.50 Testing

01 45 23.50 Testing		Crew	Daily Output	Labor-Hours	Unit	Material	2015 Bare Costs Labor	Equipment	Total	Total Incl O&P
0010	**TESTING** and Inspecting Services									
0080	Supervision of Earthwork per day	1 Skwk	1	8	Day		390		390	600
0082	Quality Control of Earthwork per day	1 Clab	1	8	"		300		300	465
0200	Asphalt testing, compressive strength Marshall stability, set of 3				Ea.				145	165
0220	Density, set of 3 R312323-30								86	95
0250	Extraction, individual tests on sample								136	150
0300	Penetration								41	45
0350	Mix design, 5 specimens								182	200
0360	Additional specimen								36	40
0400	Specific gravity								41	45
0420	Swell test								64	70
0450	Water effect and cohesion, set of 6								182	200
0470	Water effect and plastic flow								64	70
0600	Concrete testing, aggregates, abrasion, ASTM C 131								136	150
0650	Absorption, ASTM C 127								42	46
0800	Petrographic analysis, ASTM C 295								775	850
0900	Specific gravity, ASTM C 127								50	55
1000	Sieve analysis, washed, ASTM C 136								59	65
1050	Unwashed								59	65
1200	Sulfate soundness								114	125
1300	Weight per cubic foot								36	40
1500	Cement, physical tests, ASTM C 150								320	350
1600	Chemical tests, ASTM C 150								245	270
1800	Compressive test, cylinder, delivered to lab, ASTM C 39								12	13
1900	Picked up by lab, minimum								14	15
1950	Average								18	20
2000	Maximum								27	30
2200	Compressive strength, cores (not incl. drilling), ASTM C 42								36	40
2250	Core drilling, 4" diameter (plus technician)				Inch				23	25
2260	Technician for core drilling				Hr.				45	50
2300	Patching core holes				Ea.				22	24
2400	Drying shrinkage at 28 days								236	260
2500	Flexural test beams, ASTM C 78								59	65
2600	Mix design, one batch mix								259	285
2650	Added trial batches								120	132
2800	Modulus of elasticity, ASTM C 469								164	180
2900	Tensile test, cylinders, ASTM C 496								45	50
3000	Water-Cement ratio curve, 3 batches								141	155
3100	4 batches								186	205
3300	Masonry testing, absorption, per 5 brick, ASTM C 67								45	50
3350	Chemical resistance, per 2 brick								50	55
3400	Compressive strength, per 5 brick, ASTM C 67								68	75
3420	Efflorescence, per 5 brick, ASTM C 67								68	75
3440	Imperviousness, per 5 brick								87	96

01 45 23.50 Testing		Crew	Daily Output	Labor-Hours	Unit	Material	2015 Bare Costs Labor	Equipment	Total	Total Incl O&P
3470	Modulus of rupture, per 5 brick				Ea.				86	95
3500	Moisture, block only								32	35
3550	Mortar, compressive strength, set of 3								23	25
4100	Reinforcing steel, bend test								55	61
4200	Tensile test, up to #8 bar								36	40
4220	#9 to #11 bar								41	45
4240	#14 bar and larger								64	70
4300	Seed testing, complete test								45	50
4310	Purity, noxious and germination								32	35
4320	Purity and noxious								18	20
4330	Germination								23	25
4340	Tetrazolium								23	25
4350	Vigor test								9	10
4360	Electrophoresis, purity analysis								136	150
4365	Genetic variation								320	350
4370	Breeder evaluation								375	410
4375	Self counts								118	130
4380	Offtype counts								118	130
4385	Seed type analysis								91	100
4400	Soil testing, Atterberg limits, liquid and plastic limits								59	65
4510	Hydrometer analysis								109	120
4530	Specific gravity, ASTM D 354								44	48
4600	Sieve analysis, washed, ASTM D 422								55	60
4700	Unwashed, ASTM D 422								59	65
4710	Consolidation test (ASTM D2435), minimum								250	275
4715	Maximum								430	475
4720	Density and classification of undisturbed sample								73	80
4735	Soil density, nuclear method, ASTM D2922								35	38.50
4740	Sand cone method ASTM D1556								27	30
4750	Moisture content, ASTM D 2216								9	10
4780	Permeability test, double ring infiltrometer								500	550
4800	Permeability, var. or constant head, undist., ASTM D 2434								227	250
4850	Recompacted								250	275
4900	Proctor compaction, 4" standard mold, ASTM D 698								123	135
4950	6" modified mold								68	75
5100	Shear tests, triaxial, minimum								410	450
5150	Maximum								545	600
5300	Direct shear, minimum, ASTM D 3080								320	350
5350	Maximum								410	450
5550	Technician for inspection, per day, earthwork								320	350
5570	Concrete								280	310
5650	Bolting								400	440
5750	Roofing								480	530
5790	Welding				▼				480	530
5820	Non-destructive metal testing, dye penetrant				Day				310	340
5840	Magnetic particle								310	340
5860	Radiography								450	495
5880	Ultrasonic				▼				310	340
6000	Welding certification, minimum				Ea.				91	100
6100	Maximum				"				250	275
7000	Underground storage tank									
7500	Volumetric tightness test ,<=12,000 gal.				Ea.				435	480
7510	<=30,000 gal.				"				615	675

01 45 Quality Control

01 45 23 – Testing and Inspecting Services

01 45 23.50 Testing		Crew	Daily Output	Labor-Hours	Unit	Material	2015 Bare Costs Labor	Equipment	Total	Total Incl O&P
7600	Vadose zone (soil gas) sampling, 10-40 samples, min.				Day				1,375	1,500
7610	Maximum				"				2,275	2,500
7700	Ground water monitoring incl. drilling 3 wells, min.				Total				4,550	5,000
7710	Maximum				"				6,375	7,000
8000	X-ray concrete slabs				Ea.				182	200

01 51 Temporary Utilities

01 51 13 – Temporary Electricity

01 51 13.50 Temporary Power Equip (Pro-Rated Per Job)

		Crew	Daily Output	Labor-Hours	Unit	Material	2015 Bare Costs Labor	Equipment	Total	Total Incl O&P
0010	**TEMPORARY POWER EQUIP (PRO-RATED PER JOB)**									
0020	Service, overhead feed, 3 use									
0030	100 Amp	1 Elec	1.25	6.400	Ea.	735	350		1,085	1,325
0040	200 Amp		1	8		960	440		1,400	1,700
0050	400 Amp		.75	10.667		1,775	585		2,360	2,825
0060	600 Amp		.50	16		2,600	875		3,475	4,150
0100	Underground feed, 3 use									
0110	100 Amp	1 Elec	2	4	Ea.	700	219		919	1,100
0120	200 Amp		1.15	6.957		955	380		1,335	1,625
0130	400 Amp		1	8		1,775	440		2,215	2,600
0140	600 Amp		.75	10.667		2,225	585		2,810	3,300
0150	800 Amp		.50	16		3,375	875		4,250	5,025
0160	1000 Amp		.35	22.857		3,750	1,250		5,000	6,000
0170	1200 Amp		.25	32		4,225	1,750		5,975	7,275
0180	2000 Amp		.20	40		5,125	2,200		7,325	8,900
0200	Transformers, 3 use									
0210	30 kVA	1 Elec	1	8	Ea.	1,650	440		2,090	2,475
0220	45 kVA		.75	10.667		1,975	585		2,560	3,050
0230	75 kVA		.50	16		3,325	875		4,200	4,950
0240	112.5 kVA		.40	20		3,600	1,100		4,700	5,625
0250	Feeder, PVC, CU wire in trench									
0260	60 Amp	1 Elec	96	.083	L.F.	3.76	4.56		8.32	11
0270	100 Amp		85	.094		6.85	5.15		12	15.20
0280	200 Amp		59	.136		16.35	7.40		23.75	29
0290	400 Amp		42	.190	"	40.50	10.40		50.90	60
0300	Feeder, PVC, aluminum wire in trench									
0310	60 Amp	1 Elec	96	.083	L.F.	4.70	4.56		9.26	12
0320	100 Amp		85	.094		5.30	5.15		10.45	13.55
0330	200 Amp		59	.136		11.65	7.40		19.05	24
0340	400 Amp		42	.190		24	10.40		34.40	42
0350	Feeder, EMT, CU wire									
0360	60 Amp	1 Elec	90	.089	L.F.	3.30	4.86		8.16	10.95
0370	100 Amp		80	.100		6.90	5.45		12.35	15.80
0380	200 Amp		60	.133		15.35	7.30		22.65	28
0390	400 Amp		35	.229		44.50	12.50		57	68
0400	Feeder, EMT, alum. wire									
0410	60 Amp	1 Elec	90	.089	L.F.	5.30	4.86		10.16	13.10
0420	100 Amp		80	.100		6.60	5.45		12.05	15.45
0430	200 Amp		60	.133		16.90	7.30		24.20	29.50
0440	400 Amp		35	.229		30.50	12.50		43	52.50
0500	Equipment, 3 use									
0510	Spider box 50 Amp	1 Elec	8	1	Ea.	950	54.50		1,004.50	1,125

01 51 Temporary Utilities

01 51 13 – Temporary Electricity

01 51 13.50 Temporary Power Equip (Pro-Rated Per Job)

	Crew	Daily Output	Labor-Hours	Unit	Material	2015 Bare Costs Labor	2015 Bare Costs Equipment	Total	Total Incl O&P
0520	Lighting cord 100'	1 Elec	8	1	Ea.	118	54.50		172.50	212
0530	Light stanchion		8	1		72	54.50		126.50	161
0540	Temporary cords, 100', 3 use									
0550	Feeder cord, 50 Amp	1 Elec	16	.500	Ea.	445	27.50		472.50	530
0560	Feeder cord, 100 Amp		12	.667		1,175	36.50		1,211.50	1,350
0570	Tap cord, 50 Amp		12	.667		232	36.50		268.50	310
0580	Tap cord, 100 Amp		6	1.333		1,175	73		1,248	1,400
0590	Temporary cords, 50', 3 use									
0600	Feeder cord, 50 Amp	1 Elec	16	.500	Ea.	210	27.50		237.50	272
0610	Feeder cord, 100 Amp		12	.667		680	36.50		716.50	805
0620	Tap cord, 50 Amp		12	.667		122	36.50		158.50	190
0630	Tap cord, 100 Amp		6	1.333		680	73		753	860
0700	Connections									
0710	Compressor or pump									
0720	30 Amp	1 Elec	7	1.143	Ea.	21	62.50		83.50	117
0730	60 Amp		5.30	1.509		37.50	82.50		120	166
0740	100 Amp		4	2		85.50	109		194.50	258
0860	Office trailer									
0870	60 Amp	1 Elec	4.50	1.778	Ea.	115	97		212	273
0880	100 Amp		3	2.667		224	146		370	465
0890	200 Amp		2	4		755	219		974	1,150
0900	Lamping, add per floor				Total				625	690
0910	Maintenance, total temp. power cost				Job				5%	5%

01 51 13.80 Temporary Utilities

	Crew	Daily Output	Labor-Hours	Unit	Material	2015 Bare Costs Labor	2015 Bare Costs Equipment	Total	Total Incl O&P
0010	**TEMPORARY UTILITIES**									
0350	Lighting, lamps, wiring, outlets, 40,000 SF building, 8 strings	1 Elec	34	.235	CSF Flr	4.91	12.85		17.76	24.50
0360	16 strings	"	17	.471		9.80	25.50		35.30	49.50
0400	Power for temp lighting only, 6.6 KWH, per month								.92	1.01
0430	11.8 KWH, per month								1.65	1.82
0450	23.6 KWH, per month								3.30	3.63
0600	Power for job duration incl. elevator, etc., minimum								47	51.50
0650	Maximum								110	121
0700	Temporary construction water bill per mo. average				Month	68			68	75

01 52 Construction Facilities

01 52 13 – Field Offices and Sheds

01 52 13.20 Office and Storage Space

	Crew	Daily Output	Labor-Hours	Unit	Material	2015 Bare Costs Labor	2015 Bare Costs Equipment	Total	Total Incl O&P
0010	**OFFICE AND STORAGE SPACE**									
0020	Office trailer, furnished, no hookups, 20' x 8', buy	2 Skwk	1	16	Ea.	10,400	780		11,180	12,600
0250	Rent per month					188			188	206
0300	32' x 8', buy	2 Skwk	.70	22.857		15,500	1,100		16,600	18,800
0350	Rent per month					239			239	262
0400	50' x 10', buy	2 Skwk	.60	26.667		24,100	1,300		25,400	28,500
0450	Rent per month					340			340	375
0500	50' x 12', buy	2 Skwk	.50	32		29,400	1,550		30,950	34,700
0550	Rent per month					410			410	455
0700	For air conditioning, rent per month, add					48.50			48.50	53.50
0800	For delivery, add per mile				Mile	11			11	12.10
0890	Delivery each way				Ea.	200			200	220
0900	Bunk house trailer, 8' x 40' duplex dorm with kitchen, no hookups, buy	2 Carp	1	16		37,300	750		38,050	42,200
0910	9 man with kitchen and bath, no hookups, buy		1	16		38,000	750		38,750	43,000

For customer support on your Site Work & Landscape Cost Data, call 877.737.1594.

17

01 52 Construction Facilities

01 52 13 – Field Offices and Sheds

01 52 13.20 Office and Storage Space	Crew	Daily Output	Labor-Hours	Unit	Material	2015 Bare Costs Labor	Equipment	Total	Total Incl O&P
0920 18 man sleeper with bath, no hookups, buy	2 Carp	1	16	Ea.	49,000	750		49,750	55,000
1000 Portable buildings, prefab, on skids, economy, 8' x 8'		265	.060	S.F.	25	2.83		27.83	32
1100 Deluxe, 8' x 12'		150	.107	"	20	5		25	29.50
1200 Storage boxes, 20' x 8', buy	2 Skwk	1.80	8.889	Ea.	2,775	430		3,205	3,725
1250 Rent per month					82.50			82.50	91
1300 40' x 8', buy	2 Skwk	1.40	11.429		3,850	555		4,405	5,075
1350 Rent per month					101			101	111

01 52 13.40 Field Office Expense

	Crew	Daily Output	Labor-Hours	Unit	Material	2015 Bare Costs Labor	Equipment	Total	Total Incl O&P
0010 **FIELD OFFICE EXPENSE**									
0100 Office equipment rental average				Month	200			200	220
0120 Office supplies, average				"	80			80	88
0125 Office trailer rental, see Section 01 52 13.20									
0140 Telephone bill; avg. bill/month incl. long dist.				Month	85			85	93.50
0160 Lights & HVAC				"	160			160	176

01 54 Construction Aids

01 54 09 – Protection Equipment

01 54 09.60 Safety Nets

	Crew	Daily Output	Labor-Hours	Unit	Material	2015 Bare Costs Labor	Equipment	Total	Total Incl O&P
0010 **SAFETY NETS**									
0020 No supports, stock sizes, nylon, 3 1/2" mesh				S.F.	2.91			2.91	3.20
0100 Polypropylene, 6" mesh					1.59			1.59	1.75
0200 Small mesh debris nets, 1/4" mesh, stock sizes					.67			.67	.74
0220 Combined 3 1/2" mesh and 1/4" mesh, stock sizes					4.65			4.65	5.10
0300 Monthly rental, 4" mesh, stock sizes, 1st month					.50			.50	.55
0320 2nd month rental					.25			.25	.28
0340 Maximum rental/year					1.15			1.15	1.27
6220 Safety supplies and first aid kits				Month	24.50			24.50	27

01 54 16 – Temporary Hoists

01 54 16.50 Weekly Forklift Crew

	Crew	Daily Output	Labor-Hours	Unit	Material	2015 Bare Costs Labor	Equipment	Total	Total Incl O&P
0010 **WEEKLY FORKLIFT CREW**									
0100 All-terrain forklift, 45' lift, 35' reach, 9000 lb. capacity	A-3P	.20	40	Week		1,950	2,625	4,575	5,850

01 54 19 – Temporary Cranes

01 54 19.50 Daily Crane Crews

	Crew	Daily Output	Labor-Hours	Unit	Material	2015 Bare Costs Labor	Equipment	Total	Total Incl O&P
0010 **DAILY CRANE CREWS** for small jobs, portal to portal									
0100 12-ton truck-mounted hydraulic crane	A-3H	1	8	Day		415	860	1,275	1,575
0200 25-ton	A-3I	1	8			415	990	1,405	1,725
0300 40-ton	A-3J	1	8			415	1,225	1,640	1,975
0400 55-ton	A-3K	1	16			775	1,625	2,400	2,975
0500 80-ton	A-3L	1	16			775	2,350	3,125	3,750
0600 100-ton	A-3M	1	16			775	2,325	3,100	3,750
0900 If crane is needed on a Saturday, Sunday or Holiday									
0910 At time-and-a-half, add				Day		50%			
0920 At double time, add				"		100%			

01 54 19.60 Monthly Tower Crane Crew

	Crew	Daily Output	Labor-Hours	Unit	Material	2015 Bare Costs Labor	Equipment	Total	Total Incl O&P
0010 **MONTHLY TOWER CRANE CREW**, excludes concrete footing									
0100 Static tower crane, 130' high, 106' jib, 6200 lb. capacity	A-3N	.05	176	Month		9,100	24,800	33,900	41,100

01 54 Construction Aids

01 54 23 – Temporary Scaffolding and Platforms

01 54 23.70 Scaffolding	Crew	Daily Output	Labor-Hours	Unit	Material	2015 Bare Costs Labor	Equipment	Total	Total Incl O&P
0010 **SCAFFOLDING** R015423-10									
0015 Steel tube, regular, no plank, labor only to erect & dismantle									
0090 Building exterior, wall face, 1 to 5 stories, 6'-4" x 5' frames	3 Carp	8	3	C.S.F.		141		141	217
0460 Building interior, wall face area, up to 16' high	"	12	2			94		94	145
0906 Complete system for face of walls, no plank, material only rent/mo					35.50			35.50	39.50
0908 Interior spaces, no plank, material only rent/mo				C.C.F.	4.33			4.33	4.76
0910 Steel tubular, heavy duty shoring, buy									
0920 Frames 5' high 2' wide				Ea.	81.50			81.50	90
0925 5' high 4' wide					93			93	102
0930 6' high 2' wide					93.50			93.50	103
0935 6' high 4' wide					109			109	120
0940 Accessories									
0945 Cross braces				Ea.	15.50			15.50	17.05
0950 U-head, 8" x 8"					19.10			19.10	21
0955 J-head, 4" x 8"					13.90			13.90	15.30
0960 Base plate, 8" x 8"					15.50			15.50	17.05
0965 Leveling jack					33.50			33.50	36.50
1000 Steel tubular, regular, buy									
1100 Frames 3' high 5' wide				Ea.	75			75	82.50
1150 5' high 5' wide					86.50			86.50	95
1200 6'-4" high 5' wide					118			118	129
1350 7'-6" high 6' wide					158			158	173
1500 Accessories cross braces					15.50			15.50	17.05
1550 Guardrail post					16.40			16.40	18.05
1600 Guardrail 7' section					8.70			8.70	9.60
1650 Screw jacks & plates					21.50			21.50	24
1700 Sidearm brackets					30.50			30.50	33.50
1750 8" casters					31			31	34
1800 Plank 2" x 10" x 16'-0"					57.50			57.50	63.50
1900 Stairway section					286			286	315
1910 Stairway starter bar					32			32	35
1920 Stairway inside handrail					58.50			58.50	64
1930 Stairway outside handrail					86.50			86.50	95
1940 Walk-thru frame guardrail					41.50			41.50	46
2000 Steel tubular, regular, rent/mo.									
2100 Frames 3' high 5' wide				Ea.	5			5	5.50
2150 5' high 5' wide					5			5	5.50
2200 6'-4" high 5' wide					5.50			5.50	6.05
2250 7'-6" high 6' wide					10			10	11
2500 Accessories, cross braces					1			1	1.10
2550 Guardrail post					1			1	1.10
2600 Guardrail 7' section					1			1	1.10
2650 Screw jacks & plates					2			2	2.20
2700 Sidearm brackets					2			2	2.20
2750 8" casters					8			8	8.80
2800 Outrigger for rolling tower					3			3	3.30
2850 Plank 2" x 10" x 16'-0"					10			10	11
2900 Stairway section					35			35	38.50
2940 Walk-thru frame guardrail					2.50			2.50	2.75
3000 Steel tubular, heavy duty shoring, rent/mo.									
3250 5' high 2' & 4' wide				Ea.	8.50			8.50	9.35
3300 6' high 2' & 4' wide					8.50			8.50	9.35

For customer support on your Site Work & Landscape Cost Data, call 877.737.1594.

19

01 54 23 – Temporary Scaffolding and Platforms

01 54 23.70 Scaffolding

01 54 23.70 Scaffolding		Crew	Daily Output	Labor-Hours	Unit	Material	2015 Bare Costs Labor	Equipment	Total	Total Incl O&P
3500	Accessories, cross braces				Ea.	1			1	1.10
3600	U - head, 8" x 8"					2.50			2.50	2.75
3650	J - head, 4" x 8"					2.50			2.50	2.75
3700	Base plate, 8" x 8"					1			1	1.10
3750	Leveling jack					2.50			2.50	2.75
5700	Planks, 2" x 10" x 16'-0", labor only to erect & remove to 50' H	3 Carp	72	.333			15.65		15.65	24
5800	Over 50' high	4 Carp	80	.400			18.80		18.80	29
6000	Heavy duty shoring for elevated slab forms to 8'-2" high, floor area									
6100	Labor only to erect & dismantle	4 Carp	16	2	C.S.F.		94		94	145
6110	Materials only, rent.mo				"	44.50			44.50	49
6500	To 14'-8" high									
6600	Labor only to erect & dismantle	4 Carp	10	3.200	C.S.F.		150		150	231
6610	Materials only, rent/mo				"	65			65	71.50

01 54 23.75 Scaffolding Specialties

	01 54 23.75 Scaffolding Specialties	Crew	Daily Output	Labor-Hours	Unit	Material	2015 Bare Costs Labor	Equipment	Total	Total Incl O&P
0010	**SCAFFOLDING SPECIALTIES**									
1200	Sidewalk bridge, heavy duty steel posts & beams, including									
1210	parapet protection & waterproofing (material cost is rent/month)									
1220	8' to 10' wide, 2 posts	3 Carp	15	1.600	L.F.	45	75		120	166
1230	3 posts	"	10	2.400	"	69.50	113		182.50	250
1500	Sidewalk bridge using tubular steel scaffold frames including									
1510	planking (material cost is rent/month)	3 Carp	45	.533	L.F.	8.55	25		33.55	48
1600	For 2 uses per month, deduct from all above					50%				
1700	For 1 use every 2 months, add to all above					100%				
1900	Catwalks, 20" wide, no guardrails, 7' span, buy				Ea.	166			166	183
2000	10' span, buy					233			233	256
3800	Rolling ladders with handrails, 30" wide, buy, 2 step					267			267	294
4000	7 step					760			760	835
4050	10 step					1,075			1,075	1,175
4100	Rolling towers, buy, 5' wide, 7' long, 10' high					1,200			1,200	1,325
4200	For 5' high added sections, to buy, add					204			204	224
4300	Complete incl. wheels, railings, outriggers,									
4350	21' high, to buy				Ea.	2,025			2,025	2,225
4400	Rent/month = 5% of purchase cost				"	200			200	220

01 54 36 – Equipment Mobilization

01 54 36.50 Mobilization

	01 54 36.50 Mobilization	Crew	Daily Output	Labor-Hours	Unit	Material	2015 Bare Costs Labor	Equipment	Total	Total Incl O&P
0010	**MOBILIZATION** (Use line item again for demobilization) R015436-50									
0015	Up to 25 mi. haul dist. (50 mi. RT for mob/demob crew)									
1200	Small equipment, placed in rear of, or towed by pickup truck	A-3A	4	2	Ea.		97	39	136	191
1300	Equipment hauled on 3-ton capacity towed trailer	A-3Q	2.67	3			146	67	213	295
1400	20-ton capacity	B-34U	2	8			355	237	592	795
1500	40-ton capacity	B-34N	2	8			365	375	740	965
1600	50-ton capacity	B-34V	1	24			1,125	1,050	2,175	2,850
1700	Crane, truck-mounted, up to 75 ton (driver only)	1 Eqhv	4	2			103		103	157
1800	Over 75 ton (with chase vehicle)	A-3E	2.50	6.400			294	62.50	356.50	515
2400	Crane, large lattice boom, requiring assembly	B-34W	.50	144			6,275	7,500	13,775	17,800
2500	For each additional 5 miles haul distance, add						10%	10%		
3000	For large pieces of equipment, allow for assembly/knockdown									
3001	For mob/demob of vibrofloatation equip, see Section 31 45 13.10									
3100	For mob/demob of micro-tunneling equip, see Section 33 05 23.19									
3200	For mob/demob of pile driving equip, see Section 31 62 19.10									
3300	For mob/demob of caisson drilling equip, see Section 31 63 26.13									

01 55 Vehicular Access and Parking

01 55 23 – Temporary Roads

01 55 23.50 Roads and Sidewalks	Crew	Daily Output	Labor-Hours	Unit	Material	2015 Bare Costs Labor	Equipment	Total	Total Incl O&P
0010 **ROADS AND SIDEWALKS** Temporary									
0050 Roads, gravel fill, no surfacing, 4" gravel depth	B-14	715	.067	S.Y.	4.04	2.67	.51	7.22	9.10
0100 8" gravel depth	"	615	.078	"	8.10	3.10	.59	11.79	14.30
1000 Ramp, 3/4" plywood on 2" x 6" joists, 16" O.C.	2 Carp	300	.053	S.F.	1.58	2.50		4.08	5.60
1100 On 2" x 10" joists, 16" O.C.	"	275	.058	"	2.24	2.73		4.97	6.65

01 56 Temporary Barriers and Enclosures

01 56 13 – Temporary Air Barriers

01 56 13.60 Tarpaulins

	Crew	Daily Output	Labor-Hours	Unit	Material	2015 Bare Costs Labor	Equipment	Total	Total Incl O&P
0010 **TARPAULINS**									
0020 Cotton duck, 10 oz. to 13.13 oz. per S.Y., 6'x8'				S.F.	.83			.83	.91
0050 30'x30'					.59			.59	.65
0100 Polyvinyl coated nylon, 14 oz. to 18 oz., minimum					1.36			1.36	1.50
0150 Maximum					1.36			1.36	1.50
0200 Reinforced polyethylene 3 mils thick, white					.04			.04	.04
0300 4 mils thick, white, clear or black					.09			.09	.10
0400 5.5 mils thick, clear					.18			.18	.20
0500 White, fire retardant					.44			.44	.48
0600 12 mils, oil resistant, fire retardant					.39			.39	.43
0700 8.5 mils, black					.57			.57	.63
0710 Woven polyethylene, 6 mils thick					.18			.18	.20
0730 Polyester reinforced w/integral fastening system 11 mils thick					.21			.21	.23
0740 Mylar polyester, non-reinforced, 7 mils thick					1.17			1.17	1.29

01 56 13.90 Winter Protection

	Crew	Daily Output	Labor-Hours	Unit	Material	2015 Bare Costs Labor	Equipment	Total	Total Incl O&P
0010 **WINTER PROTECTION**									
0100 Framing to close openings	2 Clab	500	.032	S.F.	.46	1.20		1.66	2.35
0200 Tarpaulins hung over scaffolding, 8 uses, not incl. scaffolding		1500	.011		.24	.40		.64	.88
0250 Tarpaulin polyester reinf. w/integral fastening system 11 mils thick		1600	.010		.21	.38		.59	.81
0300 Prefab fiberglass panels, steel frame, 8 uses		1200	.013		2.40	.50		2.90	3.41

01 56 16 – Temporary Dust Barriers

01 56 16.10 Dust Barriers, Temporary

	Crew	Daily Output	Labor-Hours	Unit	Material	2015 Bare Costs Labor	Equipment	Total	Total Incl O&P
0010 **DUST BARRIERS, TEMPORARY**									
0020 Spring loaded telescoping pole & head, to 12', erect and dismantle	1 Clab	240	.033	Ea.		1.25		1.25	1.93
0025 Cost per day (based upon 250 days)				Day	.26			.26	.29
0030 To 21', erect and dismantle	1 Clab	240	.033	Ea.		1.25		1.25	1.93
0035 Cost per day (based upon 250 days)				Day	.44			.44	.48
0040 Accessories, caution tape reel, erect and dismantle	1 Clab	480	.017	Ea.		.63		.63	.96
0045 Cost per day (based upon 250 days)				Day	.36			.36	.40
0060 Foam rail and connector, erect and dismantle	1 Clab	240	.033	Ea.		1.25		1.25	1.93
0065 Cost per day (based upon 250 days)				Day	.10			.10	.11
0070 Caution tape	1 Clab	384	.021	C.L.F.	2.70	.78		3.48	4.18
0080 Zipper, standard duty		60	.133	Ea.	8	5		13	16.50
0090 Heavy duty		48	.167	"	9.50	6.25		15.75	20
0100 Polyethylene sheet, 4 mil		37	.216	Sq.	2.90	8.15		11.05	15.70
0110 6 mil		37	.216	"	4.02	8.15		12.17	16.90
1000 Dust partition, 6 mil polyethylene, 1" x 3" frame	2 Carp	2000	.008	S.F.	.30	.38		.68	.90
1080 2" x 4" frame	"	2000	.008	"	.35	.38		.73	.97

For customer support on your Site Work & Landscape Cost Data, call 877.737.1594.

21

01 56 Temporary Barriers and Enclosures

01 56 23 – Temporary Barricades

01 56 23.10 Barricades	Crew	Daily Output	Labor-Hours	Unit	Material	2015 Bare Costs Labor	Equipment	Total	Total Incl O&P
0010 **BARRICADES**									
0020 5' high, 3 rail @ 2" x 8", fixed	2 Carp	20	.800	L.F.	6	37.50		43.50	64.50
0150 Movable	"	30	.533	"	5	25		30	44
0300 Stock units, 6' high, 8' wide, plain, buy				Ea.	390			390	430
0350 With reflective tape, buy				"	405			405	445
0400 Break-a-way 3" PVC pipe barricade									
0410 with 3 ea. 1' x 4' reflectorized panels, buy				Ea.	106			106	117
0500 Plywood with steel legs, 24" wide					59			59	65
0600 Warning signal flag tree, 11' high, 2 flags, buy					257			257	283
0800 Traffic cones, PVC, 18" high					12.50			12.50	13.75
0850 28" high					19.50			19.50	21.50
1000 Guardrail, wooden, 3' high, 1" x 6", on 2" x 4" posts	2 Carp	200	.080	L.F.	1.27	3.76		5.03	7.20
1100 2" x 6", on 4" x 4" posts	"	165	.097		2.46	4.55		7.01	9.70
1200 Portable metal with base pads, buy					15.55			15.55	17.10
1250 Typical installation, assume 10 reuses	2 Carp	600	.027		2.55	1.25		3.80	4.74
1300 Barricade tape, polyethylene, 7 mil, 3" wide x 500' long roll				Ea.	25			25	27.50
3000 Detour signs, set up and remove									
3010 Reflective aluminum, MUTCD, 24" x 24", post mounted	1 Clab	20	.400	Ea.	2.46	15.05		17.51	25.50

01 56 26 – Temporary Fencing

01 56 26.50 Temporary Fencing	Crew	Daily Output	Labor-Hours	Unit	Material	2015 Bare Costs Labor	Equipment	Total	Total Incl O&P
0010 **TEMPORARY FENCING**									
0020 Chain link, 11 ga., 4' high	2 Clab	400	.040	L.F.	2.95	1.50		4.45	5.55
0100 6' high		300	.053		2.95	2.01		4.96	6.35
0200 Rented chain link, 6' high, to 1000' (up to 12 mo.)		400	.040		4.29	1.50		5.79	7.05
0250 Over 1000' (up to 12 mo.)		300	.053		4.29	2.01		6.30	7.80
0350 Plywood, painted, 2" x 4" frame, 4' high	A-4	135	.178		6.20	7.95		14.15	19
0400 4" x 4" frame, 8' high	"	110	.218		12	9.75		21.75	28
0500 Wire mesh on 4" x 4" posts, 4' high	2 Carp	100	.160		9.85	7.50		17.35	22.50
0550 8' high	"	80	.200		14.90	9.40		24.30	31
0600 Plastic safety fence, light duty, 4' high, posts at 10'	B-1	500	.048		1.17	1.84		3.01	4.11
0610 Medium duty, 4' high, posts at 10'		500	.048		1.58	1.84		3.42	4.57
0620 Heavy duty, 4' high, posts at 10'		500	.048		2.19	1.84		4.03	5.25
0630 Reflective heavy duty, 4' high, posts at 10'		500	.048		4.24	1.84		6.08	7.50

01 56 29 – Temporary Protective Walkways

01 56 29.50 Protection	Crew	Daily Output	Labor-Hours	Unit	Material	2015 Bare Costs Labor	Equipment	Total	Total Incl O&P
0010 **PROTECTION**									
0020 Stair tread, 2" x 12" planks, 1 use	1 Carp	75	.107	Tread	5.10	5		10.10	13.30
0100 Exterior plywood, 1/2" thick, 1 use		65	.123		1.97	5.80		7.77	11.05
0200 3/4" thick, 1 use		60	.133		2.78	6.25		9.03	12.70
2200 Sidewalks, 2" x 12" planks, 2 uses		350	.023	S.F.	.85	1.07		1.92	2.59
2300 Exterior plywood, 2 uses, 1/2" thick		750	.011		.33	.50		.83	1.13
2400 5/8" thick		650	.012		.39	.58		.97	1.32
2500 3/4" thick		600	.013		.46	.63		1.09	1.47

01 56 32 – Temporary Security

01 56 32.50 Watchman	Crew	Daily Output	Labor-Hours	Unit	Material	2015 Bare Costs Labor	Equipment	Total	Total Incl O&P
0010 **WATCHMAN**									
0020 Service, monthly basis, uniformed person, minimum				Hr.				25	27.50
0100 Maximum								45.50	50
0200 Person and command dog, minimum								31	34
0300 Maximum								54.50	60

01 56 Temporary Barriers and Enclosures

01 56 32 – Temporary Security

01 56 32.50 Watchman	Crew	Daily Output	Labor-Hours	Unit	Material	2015 Bare Costs Labor	Equipment	Total	Total Incl O&P
0500	Sentry dog, leased, with job patrol (yard dog), 1 dog				Week				290	320
0600	2 dogs				"				390	430
0800	Purchase, trained sentry dog, minimum				Ea.				1,375	1,500
0900	Maximum				"				2,725	3,000

01 58 Project Identification

01 58 13 – Temporary Project Signage

01 58 13.50 Signs	Crew	Daily Output	Labor-Hours	Unit	Material	2015 Bare Costs Labor	Equipment	Total	Total Incl O&P
0010	**SIGNS**									
0020	High intensity reflectorized, no posts, buy				Ea.	25			25	27.50

01 71 Examination and Preparation

01 71 23 – Field Engineering

01 71 23.13 Construction Layout	Crew	Daily Output	Labor-Hours	Unit	Material	2015 Bare Costs Labor	Equipment	Total	Total Incl O&P
0010	**CONSTRUCTION LAYOUT**									
1100	Crew for layout of building, trenching or pipe laying, 2 person crew	A-6	1	16	Day		750	55	805	1,200
1200	3 person crew	A-7	1	24			1,225	54.50	1,279.50	1,950
1400	Crew for roadway layout, 4 person crew	A-8	1	32			1,600	54.50	1,654.50	2,500

01 71 23.19 Surveyor Stakes	Crew	Daily Output	Labor-Hours	Unit	Material	2015 Bare Costs Labor	Equipment	Total	Total Incl O&P
0010	**SURVEYOR STAKES**									
0020	Hardwood, 1" x 1" x 48" long				C	70			70	77
0100	2" x 2" x 18" long					78			78	86
0150	2" x 2" x 24" long					140			140	154

01 74 Cleaning and Waste Management

01 74 13 – Progress Cleaning

01 74 13.20 Cleaning Up	Crew	Daily Output	Labor-Hours	Unit	Material	2015 Bare Costs Labor	Equipment	Total	Total Incl O&P
0010	**CLEANING UP**									
0020	After job completion, allow, minimum				Job				.30%	.30%
0040	Maximum				"				1%	1%
0200	Rubbish removal, see Section 02 41 19.19									

01 76 Protecting Installed Construction

01 76 13 – Temporary Protection of Installed Construction

01 76 13.20 Temporary Protection	Crew	Daily Output	Labor-Hours	Unit	Material	2015 Bare Costs Labor	Equipment	Total	Total Incl O&P
0010	**TEMPORARY PROTECTION**									
0020	Flooring, 1/8" tempered hardboard, taped seams	2 Carp	1500	.011	S.F.	.41	.50		.91	1.22
0030	Peel away carpet protection	1 Clab	3200	.003	"	.11	.09		.20	.26

For customer support on your Site Work & Landscape Cost Data, call 877.737.1594.

23

01 91 Commissioning

01 91 13 – General Commissioning Requirements

01 91 13.50 Building Commissioning	Crew	Daily Output	Labor-Hours	Unit	Material	2015 Bare Costs Labor	Equipment	Total	Total Incl O&P
0010 **BUILDING COMMISSIONING**									
0100 Basic building commissioning, minimum				%				.25%	.25%
0150 Maximum								.50%	.50%
0200 Enhanced building commissioning, minimum								.50%	.50%
0250 Maximum				▼				1%	1%

Estimating Tips

02 30 00 Subsurface Investigation

In preparing estimates on structures involving earthwork or foundations, all information concerning soil characteristics should be obtained. Look particularly for hazardous waste, evidence of prior dumping of debris, and previous stream beds.

02 40 00 Demolition and Structure Moving

The costs shown for selective demolition do not include rubbish handling or disposal. These items should be estimated separately using RSMeans data or other sources.

- Historic preservation often requires that the contractor remove materials from the existing structure, rehab them, and replace them. The estimator must be aware of any related measures and precautions that must be

taken when doing selective demolition and cutting and patching. Requirements may include special handling and storage, as well as security.

- In addition to Subdivision 02 41 00, you can find selective demolition items in each division. Example: Roofing demolition is in Division 7.

02 40 00 Building Deconstruction

This section provides costs for the careful dismantling and recycling of most of low-rise building materials.

02 50 00 Containment of Hazardous Waste

This section addresses on-site hazardous waste disposal costs.

02 80 00 Hazardous Material Disposal/ Remediation

This subdivision includes information on hazardous waste handling, asbestos remediation,

lead remediation, and mold remediation. See reference R028213-20 and R028319-60 for further guidance in using these unit price lines.

02 90 00 Monitoring Chemical Sampling, Testing Analysis

This section provides costs for on-site sampling and testing hazardous waste.

Reference Numbers

Reference numbers are shown in shaded boxes at the beginning of some major classifications. These numbers refer to related items in the Reference Section. The reference information may be an estimating procedure, an alternate pricing method, or technical information.

Note: Not all subdivisions listed here necessarily appear in this publication. ■

02 21 Surveys

02 21 13 – Site Surveys

02 21 13.09 Topographical Surveys

	02 21 13.09 Topographical Surveys	Crew	Daily Output	Labor-Hours	Unit	Material	2015 Bare Costs Labor	Equipment	Total	Total Incl O&P
0010	**TOPOGRAPHICAL SURVEYS**									
0020	Topographical surveying, conventional, minimum	A-7	3.30	7.273	Acre	20	375	16.60	411.60	615
0100	Maximum	A-8	.60	53.333	"	60	2,675	91	2,826	4,250

02 21 13.13 Boundary and Survey Markers

		Crew	Daily Output	Labor-Hours	Unit	Material	2015 Bare Costs Labor	Equipment	Total	Total Incl O&P
0010	**BOUNDARY AND SURVEY MARKERS**									
0300	Lot location and lines, large quantities, minimum	A-7	2	12	Acre	35	620	27.50	682.50	1,025
0320	Average	"	1.25	19.200		55	990	44	1,089	1,625
0400	Small quantities, maximum	A-8	1	32		75	1,600	54.50	1,729.50	2,600
0600	Monuments, 3' long	A-7	10	2.400	Ea.	40	124	5.45	169.45	240
0800	Property lines, perimeter, cleared land	"	1000	.024	L.F.	.05	1.24	.05	1.34	2.02
0900	Wooded land	A-8	875	.037	"	.07	1.83	.06	1.96	2.95

02 21 13.16 Aerial Surveys

		Crew	Daily Output	Labor-Hours	Unit	Material	2015 Bare Costs Labor	Equipment	Total	Total Incl O&P
0010	**AERIAL SURVEYS**									
1500	Aerial surveying, including ground control, minimum fee, 10 acres				Total				4,700	4,700
1510	100 acres								9,400	9,400
1550	From existing photography, deduct								1,625	1,625
1600	2' contours, 10 acres				Acre				470	470
1850	100 acres								94	94
2000	1000 acres								90	90
2050	10,000 acres								85	85

02 32 Geotechnical Investigations

02 32 13 – Subsurface Drilling and Sampling

02 32 13.10 Boring and Exploratory Drilling

		Crew	Daily Output	Labor-Hours	Unit	Material	2015 Bare Costs Labor	Equipment	Total	Total Incl O&P
0010	**BORING AND EXPLORATORY DRILLING**									
0020	Borings, initial field stake out & determination of elevations	A-6	1	16	Day		750	55	805	1,200
0100	Drawings showing boring details				Total		335		335	425
0200	Report and recommendations from P.E.						775		775	970
0300	Mobilization and demobilization	B-55	4	6			229	271	500	650
0350	For over 100 miles, per added mile		450	.053	Mile		2.03	2.41	4.44	5.75
0600	Auger holes in earth, no samples, 2-1/2" diameter		78.60	.305	L.F.		11.65	13.75	25.40	33
0650	4" diameter		67.50	.356			13.55	16.05	29.60	38
0800	Cased borings in earth, with samples, 2-1/2" diameter		55.50	.432		14	16.50	19.50	50	62
0850	4" diameter		32.60	.736		18	28	33	79	99.50
1000	Drilling in rock, "BX" core, no sampling	B-56	34.90	.458			19.75	45.50	65.25	80
1050	With casing & sampling		31.70	.505		14	22	50.50	86.50	104
1200	"NX" core, no sampling		25.92	.617			26.50	61.50	88	108
1250	With casing and sampling		25	.640		15	27.50	63.50	106	129
1400	Borings, earth, drill rig and crew with truck mounted auger	B-55	1	24	Day		915	1,075	1,990	2,600
1450	Rock using crawler type drill	B-56	1	16	"		690	1,600	2,290	2,800
1500	For inner city borings add, minimum								10%	10%
1510	Maximum								20%	20%

02 32 19 – Exploratory Excavations

02 32 19.10 Test Pits

		Crew	Daily Output	Labor-Hours	Unit	Material	2015 Bare Costs Labor	Equipment	Total	Total Incl O&P
0010	**TEST PITS**									
0020	Hand digging, light soil	1 Clab	4.50	1.778	C.Y.		67		67	103
0100	Heavy soil	"	2.50	3.200			120		120	185
0120	Loader-backhoe, light soil	B-11M	28	.571			25	14	39	54
0130	Heavy soil	"	20	.800			35.50	19.60	55.10	75.50
1000	Subsurface exploration, mobilization				Mile				6.75	8.40

02 32 Geotechnical Investigations

02 32 19 – Exploratory Excavations

02 32 19.10 Test Pits	Crew	Daily Output	Labor-Hours	Unit	Material	2015 Bare Costs Labor	Equipment	Total	Total Incl O&P
1010	Difficult access for rig, add				Hr.				260	320
1020	Auger borings, drill rig, incl. samples				L.F.				26.50	33
1030	Hand auger								31.50	40
1050	Drill and sample every 5', split spoon				▼				31.50	40
1060	Extra samples				Ea.				36	45.50

02 41 Demolition

02 41 13 – Selective Site Demolition

02 41 13.15 Hydrodemolition

		Crew	Daily Output	Labor-Hours	Unit	Material	Labor	Equipment	Total	Total Incl O&P
0010	**HYDRODEMOLITION** R024119-10									
0015	Hydrodemolition, concrete pavement									
0120	20,000 PSI, Crew to include loader / vacuum truck as required									
0130	2" depth	B-5	1000	.056	S.F.		2.33	1.42	3.75	5.15
0410	4" depth		800	.070			2.91	1.78	4.69	6.40
0420	6" depth	▼	600	.093	▼		3.88	2.37	6.25	8.55

02 41 13.17 Demolish, Remove Pavement and Curb

		Crew	Daily Output	Labor-Hours	Unit	Material	Labor	Equipment	Total	Total Incl O&P
0010	**DEMOLISH, REMOVE PAVEMENT AND CURB** R024119-10									
5010	Pavement removal, bituminous roads, up to 3" thick	B-38	690	.058	S.Y.		2.48	1.85	4.33	5.80
5050	4" to 6" thick		420	.095			4.08	3.04	7.12	9.60
5100	Bituminous driveways		640	.063			2.68	1.99	4.67	6.30
5200	Concrete to 6" thick, hydraulic hammer, mesh reinforced		255	.157			6.70	5	11.70	15.75
5300	Rod reinforced		200	.200	▼		8.55	6.40	14.95	20
5400	Concrete, 7" to 24" thick, plain		33	1.212	C.Y.		52	38.50	90.50	122
5500	Reinforced	▼	24	1.667	"		71.50	53	124.50	168
5600	With hand held air equipment, bituminous, to 6" thick	B-39	1900	.025	S.F.		1	.12	1.12	1.67
5700	Concrete to 6" thick, no reinforcing		1600	.030			1.19	.15	1.34	1.99
5800	Mesh reinforced		1400	.034			1.36	.17	1.53	2.27
5900	Rod reinforced	▼	765	.063	▼		2.50	.30	2.80	4.16
6000	Curbs, concrete, plain	B-6	360	.067	L.F.		2.75	1.01	3.76	5.30
6100	Reinforced		275	.087			3.60	1.32	4.92	6.95
6200	Granite		360	.067			2.75	1.01	3.76	5.30
6300	Bituminous		528	.045			1.88	.69	2.57	3.63
6400	Wood		570	.042			1.74	.64	2.38	3.36
6500	Site demo, berms under 4" in height, bituminous		528	.045			1.88	.69	2.57	3.63
6600	4" or over in height	▼	300	.080	▼		3.30	1.21	4.51	6.40

02 41 13.20 Selective Demo, Highway Guard Rails & Barriers

		Crew	Daily Output	Labor-Hours	Unit	Material	Labor	Equipment	Total	Total Incl O&P
0010	**SELECTIVE DEMOLITION, HIGHWAY GUARD RAILS & BARRIERS**									
0100	Guard rail, corrugated steel	B-6	600	.040	L.F.		1.65	.61	2.26	3.20
0200	End sections		40	.600	Ea.		25	9.10	34.10	48
0300	Wrap around		40	.600	"		25	9.10	34.10	48
0400	Timber 4" x 8"		600	.040	L.F.		1.65	.61	2.26	3.20
0500	Three 3/4" cables		600	.040	"		1.65	.61	2.26	3.20
0600	Wood posts	▼	240	.100	Ea.		4.13	1.52	5.65	7.95
0700	Guide rail, 6" x 6" box beam	B-80B	120	.267	L.F.		10.75	2.03	12.78	18.75
0800	Median barrier, 6" x 8" box beam		240	.133			5.40	1.02	6.42	9.35
0850	Precast concrete 3'-6" high x 2' wide	▼	300	.107	▼		4.30	.81	5.11	7.50
0900	Impact barrier, UTMCD, barrel type	B-16	60	.533	Ea.		20.50	11.50	32	44
1000	Resilient guide fence and light shield 6' high	"	120	.267	L.F.		10.30	5.75	16.05	22
1100	Concrete posts, 6'-5" triangular	B-6	200	.120	Ea.		4.95	1.82	6.77	9.60
1200	Speed bumps 10-1/2" x 2-1/4" x 48"	▼	300	.080	L.F.		3.30	1.21	4.51	6.40

For customer support on your Site Work & Landscape Cost Data, call 877.737.1594.

27

02 41 13 – Selective Site Demolition

02 41 13.20 Selective Demo, Highway Guard Rails & Barriers	Crew	Daily Output	Labor-Hours	Unit	Material	2015 Bare Costs Labor	Equipment	Total	Total Incl O&P
1300	Pavement marking channelizing	B-6	200	.120	Ea.		4.95	1.82	6.77	9.60
1400	Barrier and curb delineators		300	.080			3.30	1.21	4.51	6.40
1500	Rumble strips 24" x 3-1/2" x 1/2"	↓	150	.160	↓		6.60	2.43	9.03	12.75

02 41 13.23 Utility Line Removal

		Crew	Daily Output	Labor-Hours	Unit	Material	Labor	Equipment	Total	Total Incl O&P
0010	**UTILITY LINE REMOVAL**									
0015	No hauling, abandon catch basin or manhole	B-6	7	3.429	Ea.		142	52	194	274
0020	Remove existing catch basin or manhole, masonry		4	6			248	91	339	480
0030	Catch basin or manhole frames and covers, stored		13	1.846			76	28	104	148
0040	Remove and reset	↓	7	3.429			142	52	194	274
0900	Hydrants, fire, remove only	B-21A	5	8			375	94.50	469.50	675
0950	Remove and reset	"	2	20	↓		940	237	1,177	1,675
2900	Pipe removal, sewer/water, no excavation, 12" diameter	B-6	175	.137	L.F.		5.65	2.08	7.73	10.95
2930	15"-18" diameter	B-12Z	150	.160			6.75	10.70	17.45	22
2960	21"-24" diameter		120	.200			8.45	13.40	21.85	27.50
3000	27"-36" diameter	↓	90	.267			11.30	17.85	29.15	37
3200	Steel, welded connections, 4" diameter	B-6	160	.150			6.20	2.28	8.48	11.95
3300	10" diameter	"	80	.300	↓		12.40	4.55	16.95	24

02 41 13.30 Minor Site Demolition

		Crew	Daily Output	Labor-Hours	Unit	Material	Labor	Equipment	Total	Total Incl O&P
0010	**MINOR SITE DEMOLITION** R024119-10									
0100	Roadside delineators, remove only	B-80	175	.183	Ea.		7.55	4.12	11.67	16.05
0110	Remove and reset	"	100	.320	"		13.20	7.20	20.40	28
0800	Guiderail, corrugated steel, remove only	B-80A	100	.240	L.F.		9	3.03	12.03	17.25
0850	Remove and reset	"	40	.600	"		22.50	7.60	30.10	43
0860	Guide posts, remove only	B-80B	120	.267	Ea.		10.75	2.03	12.78	18.75
0870	Remove and reset	B-55	50	.480	"		18.30	21.50	39.80	52
1000	Masonry walls, block, solid	B-5	1800	.031	C.F.		1.29	.79	2.08	2.85
1200	Brick, solid		900	.062			2.59	1.58	4.17	5.70
1400	Stone, with mortar		900	.062			2.59	1.58	4.17	5.70
1500	Dry set	↓	1500	.037	↓		1.55	.95	2.50	3.42
1600	Median barrier, precast concrete, remove and store	B-3	430	.112	L.F.		4.57	6	10.57	13.55
1610	Remove and reset	"	390	.123	"		5.05	6.60	11.65	14.95
4000	Sidewalk removal, bituminous, 2" thick	B-6	350	.069	S.Y.		2.83	1.04	3.87	5.45
4010	2-1/2" thick		325	.074			3.05	1.12	4.17	5.90
4050	Brick, set in mortar		185	.130			5.35	1.97	7.32	10.35
4060	Dry set		270	.089			3.67	1.35	5.02	7.10
4100	Concrete, plain, 4"		160	.150			6.20	2.28	8.48	11.95
4110	Plain, 5"		140	.171			7.05	2.60	9.65	13.70
4120	Plain, 6"		120	.200			8.25	3.04	11.29	16
4200	Mesh reinforced, concrete, 4"		150	.160			6.60	2.43	9.03	12.75
4210	5" thick		131	.183			7.55	2.78	10.33	14.60
4220	6" thick	↓	112	.214	↓		8.85	3.25	12.10	17.15
4300	Slab on grade removal, plain	B-5	45	1.244	C.Y.		52	31.50	83.50	114
4310	Mesh reinforced		33	1.697			70.50	43	113.50	156
4320	Rod reinforced	↓	25	2.240			93	57	150	206
4400	For congested sites or small quantities, add up to								200%	200%
4450	For disposal on site, add	B-11A	232	.069			3.04	6	9.04	11.25
4500	To 5 miles, add	B-34D	76	.105	↓		4.22	9.75	13.97	17.05

02 41 13.33 Railtrack Removal

		Crew	Daily Output	Labor-Hours	Unit	Material	Labor	Equipment	Total	Total Incl O&P
0010	**RAILTRACK REMOVAL**									
3500	Railroad track removal, ties and track	B-13	330	.170	L.F.		6.95	2.23	9.18	13.10
3600	Ballast	B-14	500	.096	C.Y.		3.82	.73	4.55	6.65
3700	Remove and re-install, ties & track using new bolts & spikes	↓	50	.960	L.F.		38	7.30	45.30	66.50

For customer support on your Site Work & Landscape Cost Data, call 877.737.1594.

02 41 Demolition

02 41 13 – Selective Site Demolition

02 41 13.33 Railtrack Removal

		Crew	Daily Output	Labor-Hours	Unit	Material	2015 Bare Costs Labor	2015 Bare Costs Equipment	Total	Total Incl O&P
3800	Turnouts using new bolts and spikes	B-14	1	48	Ea.		1,900	365	2,265	3,325

02 41 13.34 Selective Demolition, Utility Materials

		Crew	Daily Output	Labor-Hours	Unit	Material	Labor	Equipment	Total	Total Incl O&P
0010	**SELECTIVE DEMOLITION, UTILITY MATERIALS** R024119-10									
0015	Excludes excavation									
0020	See other utility items in Section 02 41 13.33									
0100	Fire Hydrant extensions	B-20	14	1.714	Ea.		72		72	111
0200	Precast Utility boxes up to 8' x 14' x 7'	B-13	2	28			1,150	370	1,520	2,150
0300	Handholes and meter pits	B-6	2	12			495	182	677	960
0400	Utility valves 4"-12"	B-20	4	6			252		252	390
0500	14"-24"	B-21	2	14			605	69	674	1,000

02 41 13.36 Selective Demolition, Utility Valves and Accessories

		Crew	Daily Output	Labor-Hours	Unit	Material	Labor	Equipment	Total	Total Incl O&P
0010	**SELECTIVE DEMOLITION, UTILITY VALVES & ACCESSORIES**									
0015	Excludes excavation									
0100	Utility valves 4"-12" diam.	B-20	4	6	Ea.		252		252	390
0200	14"-24" diam.	B-21	2	14			605	69	674	1,000
0300	Crosses 4"-12"	B-20	8	3			126		126	194
0400	14"-24"	B-21	4	7			305	34.50	339.50	505
0500	Utility cut-in valves 4"-12" diam.	B-20	20	1.200			50.50		50.50	77.50
0600	Curb boxes	"	20	1.200			50.50		50.50	77.50

02 41 13.38 Selective Demo., Water & Sewer Piping & Fittings

		Crew	Daily Output	Labor-Hours	Unit	Material	Labor	Equipment	Total	Total Incl O&P
0010	**SELECTIVE DEMOLITION, WATER & SEWER PIPING AND FITTINGS**									
0015	Excludes excavation									
0090	Concrete pipe 4"-10" dia	B-6	250	.096	L.F.		3.96	1.46	5.42	7.65
0100	42"-48" diameter	B-13B	96	.583			24	11.75	35.75	49.50
0200	60"-84" diameter	"	80	.700			28.50	14.10	42.60	59.50
0300	96" diameter	B-13C	80	.700			28.50	21	49.50	67
0400	108"-144" diameter	"	64	.875			36	26	62	83.50
0450	Concrete fittings 12" diameter	B-6	24	1	Ea.		41.50	15.20	56.70	79.50
0480	Concrete end pieces 12" diameter		200	.120	L.F.		4.95	1.82	6.77	9.60
0485	15" diameter		150	.160			6.60	2.43	9.03	12.75
0490	18" diameter		150	.160			6.60	2.43	9.03	12.75
0500	24"-36" diameter		100	.240			9.90	3.64	13.54	19.15
0600	Concrete fittings 24"-36" diameter		12	2	Ea.		82.50	30.50	113	160
0700	48"-84" diameter	B-13B	12	4.667			191	94	285	395
0800	96" diameter	"	8	7			287	141	428	595
0900	108"-144" diameter	B-13C	4	14			575	415	990	1,350
1000	Ductile iron pipe 4" diameter	B-21B	200	.200	L.F.		8.15	3.27	11.42	16.10
1100	6"-12" diameter		175	.229			9.35	3.74	13.09	18.40
1200	14"-24" diameter		120	.333			13.60	5.45	19.05	27
1300	Ductile iron fittings 4"-12" diameter		24	1.667	Ea.		68	27.50	95.50	134
1400	14"-16" diameter		18	2.222			90.50	36.50	127	179
1500	18"-24" diameter		12	3.333			136	54.50	190.50	269
1600	Plastic pipe 3/4"-4" diameter	B-6	700	.034	L.F.		1.42	.52	1.94	2.74
1700	6"-8" diameter		500	.048			1.98	.73	2.71	3.83
1800	10"-18" diameter		300	.080			3.30	1.21	4.51	6.40
1900	20"-36" diameter		200	.120			4.95	1.82	6.77	9.60
1910	42"-48" diameter		180	.133			5.50	2.02	7.52	10.65
1920	54"-60" diameter		160	.150			6.20	2.28	8.48	11.95
2000	Plastic fittings 4"-8" diameter		75	.320	Ea.		13.20	4.86	18.06	25.50
2100	10"-14" diameter		50	.480			19.80	7.30	27.10	38.50
2200	16"-24" diameter		20	1.200			49.50	18.20	67.70	96
2210	30"-36" diameter		15	1.600			66	24.50	90.50	128

For customer support on your Site Work & Landscape Cost Data, call 877.737.1594.

29

02 41 13.38 Selective Demo., Water & Sewer Piping & Fittings	Crew	Daily Output	Labor-Hours	Unit	Material	2015 Bare Costs Labor	Equipment	Total	Total Incl O&P
2220 42"- 48" diameter	B-6	12	2	Ea.		82.50	30.50	113	160
2300 Copper pipe 3/4"-2" diameter	Q-1	500	.032	L.F.		1.69		1.69	2.55
2400 2 1/2" - 3" diameter		300	.053			2.82		2.82	4.25
2500 4"- 6" diameter		200	.080			4.23		4.23	6.40
2600 Copper fittings 3/4"- 2" diameter		15	1.067	Ea.		56.50		56.50	85
2700 Cast iron pipe 4" diameter		200	.080	L.F.		4.23		4.23	6.40
2800 5"- 6" diameter	Q-2	200	.120			6.55		6.55	9.95
2900 8"- 12" diameter	Q-3	200	.160			8.95		8.95	13.50
3000 Cast iron fittings 4" diameter	Q-1	30	.533	Ea.		28		28	42.50
3100 5"- 6" diameter	Q-2	30	.800			44		44	66
3200 8"- 15" diameter	Q-3	30	1.067			59.50		59.50	90
3300 Vent cast iron pipe 4"- 8" diameter	Q-1	200	.080	L.F.		4.23		4.23	6.40
3400 10"- 15" diameter	Q-3	200	.160	"		8.95		8.95	13.50
3500 Vent cast iron fittings 4"- 8" diameter	Q-2	30	.800	Ea.		44		44	66
3600 10"- 15" diameter	"	20	1.200	"		65.50		65.50	99.50

02 41 13.40 Selective Demolition, Metal Drainage Piping

	Crew	Daily Output	Labor-Hours	Unit	Material	Labor	Equipment	Total	Total Incl O&P
0010 **SELECTIVE DEMOLITION, METAL DRAINAGE PIPING**									
0015 Excludes excavation									
0100 CMP pipe, aluminum, 6"-10" dia	B-21	800	.035	L.F.		1.52	.17	1.69	2.52
0110 12" dia		600	.047			2.02	.23	2.25	3.36
0120 18" dia		600	.047			2.02	.23	2.25	3.36
0140 Steel, 6"-10" dia		800	.035			1.52	.17	1.69	2.52
0150 12" dia		600	.047			2.02	.23	2.25	3.36
0160 18" dia		400	.070			3.03	.34	3.37	5.05
0170 24" dia	B-13	300	.187			7.65	2.45	10.10	14.40
0180 30" - 36" dia		250	.224			9.20	2.95	12.15	17.30
0190 48" - 60" dia		200	.280			11.50	3.68	15.18	21.50
0200 72" dia	B-13B	100	.560			23	11.30	34.30	47.50
0210 CMP end sections, steel, 10"-18" dia	B-21	40	.700	Ea.		30.50	3.44	33.94	50.50
0220 24"-36" dia	B-13	30	1.867			76.50	24.50	101	144
0230 48" dia		20	2.800			115	37	152	217
0240 60" dia		10	5.600			230	73.50	303.50	430
0250 72" dia	B-13B	10	5.600			230	113	343	475
0260 CMP fittings, 8"-12" dia	B-21	60	.467			20	2.30	22.30	33.50
0270 18" dia	"	40	.700			30.50	3.44	33.94	50.50
0280 24"-48" dia	B-13	30	1.867			76.50	24.50	101	144
0290 60" dia	"	20	2.800			115	37	152	217
0300 72" dia	B-13B	10	5.600			230	113	343	475
0310 Oval arch 17" x 13", 21" x 15", 15-18" equivalent	B-21	400	.070	L.F.		3.03	.34	3.37	5.05
0320 28" x 20", 24" equivalent	B-13	300	.187			7.65	2.45	10.10	14.40
0330 35" x 24", 42" x 29", 30-36" equivalent		250	.224			9.20	2.95	12.15	17.30
0340 49" x 33", 57" x 38", 42-48" equivalent		200	.280			11.50	3.68	15.18	21.50
0350 Oval arch 17" x 13" end piece, 15" equivalent	B-21	40	.700	Ea.		30.50	3.44	33.94	50.50
0360 42" x 29" end piece, 36" equivalent	B-13	30	1.867	"		76.50	24.50	101	144

02 41 13.42 Selective Demolition, Manholes and Catch Basins

	Crew	Daily Output	Labor-Hours	Unit	Material	Labor	Equipment	Total	Total Incl O&P
0010 **SELECTIVE DEMOLITION, MANHOLES & CATCH BASINS**									
0015 Excludes excavation									
0100 Manholes, precast or brick over 8' deep	B-6	8	3	V.L.F.		124	45.50	169.50	239
0200 Cast in place 4'-8' deep	B-9	127	.315	SF Face		11.95	1.83	13.78	20.50
0300 Over 8' deep	"	100	.400	"		15.20	2.33	17.53	26
0400 Top, precast, 8" thick, 4'-6' dia	B-6	8	3	Ea.		124	45.50	169.50	239
0500 Steps	1 Clab	60	.133	"		5		5	7.70

02 41 Demolition

02 41 13 – Selective Site Demolition

02 41 13.43 Selective Demolition, Box Culvert	Crew	Daily Output	Labor-Hours	Unit	Material	2015 Bare Costs Labor	Equipment	Total	Total Incl O&P
0010 **SELECTIVE DEMOLITION, BOX CULVERT**									
0015 Excludes excavation									
0100 Box culvert 8' x 6' x 3' to 8' x 8' x 8'	B-69	300	.160	L.F.		6.65	5.40	12.05	16.10
0200 8' x 10' x 3' to 8' x 12' x 8'	"	200	.240	"		9.95	8.10	18.05	24

02 41 13.44 Selective Demolition, Septic Tanks and Related Components

	Crew	Daily Output	Labor-Hours	Unit	Material	2015 Bare Costs Labor	Equipment	Total	Total Incl O&P
0010 **SELECTIVE DEMOLITION, SEPTIC TANKS & RELATED COMPONENTS**									
0020 Excludes excavation									
0100 Septic tanks, precast, 1000-1250 gal.	B-21	8	3.500	Ea.		152	17.20	169.20	252
0200 1500 gal.		7	4			173	19.70	192.70	288
0300 2000-2500 gal.		5	5.600			243	27.50	270.50	405
0400 4000 gal.		4	7			305	34.50	339.50	505
0500 Precast, 5000 gal., 4 piece	B-13	3	18.667			765	245	1,010	1,450
0600 15,000 gal.	B-13B	1.70	32.941			1,350	665	2,015	2,800
0700 25,000 gal.		1.10	50.909			2,075	1,025	3,100	4,325
0800 40,000 gal.		.80	70			2,875	1,400	4,275	5,950
0900 Precast, 50,000 gal., 5 piece	B-13C	.60	93.333			3,825	2,775	6,600	8,900
1000 Cast-in-place, 75,000 gal.	B-9	.06	666			25,300	3,875	29,175	43,300
1100 100,000 gal.	"	.05	800			30,400	4,650	35,050	52,000
1200 HDPE, 1000 gal.	B-21	9	3.111			135	15.30	150.30	224
1300 1500 gal.		8	3.500			152	17.20	169.20	252
1400 Galley, 4' x 4' x 4'		16	1.750			76	8.60	84.60	126
1500 Distribution boxes, concrete, 7 outlets	2 Clab	16	1			37.50		37.50	58
1600 9 outlets	"	8	2			75		75	116
1700 Leaching chambers 13' x 3'-7" x 1'-4", standard	B-13	16	3.500			143	46	189	271
1800 8' x 4' x 1'-6", heavy duty		14	4			164	52.50	216.50	310
1900 13' x 3'-9" x 1'-6"		12	4.667			191	61.50	252.50	360
2100 20' x 4' x 1'-6"		5	11.200			460	147	607	865
2200 Leaching pit 6'-6" x 6' deep	B-21	5	5.600			243	27.50	270.50	405
2300 6'-6" x 8' deep		4	7			305	34.50	339.50	505
2400 8' x 6' deep H20		4	7			305	34.50	339.50	505
2500 8' x 8' deep H20		3	9.333			405	46	451	670
2600 Velocity reducing pit, precast 6' x 3' deep		4.70	5.957			258	29.50	287.50	425

02 41 13.46 Selective Demolition, Steel Pipe With Insulation

	Crew	Daily Output	Labor-Hours	Unit	Material	2015 Bare Costs Labor	Equipment	Total	Total Incl O&P
0010 **SELECTIVE DEMOLITION, STEEL PIPE WITH INSULATION**									
0020 Excludes excavation									
0100 Steel pipe, with insulation, 3/4"-4"	B-1A	400	.060	L.F.		2.30	.82	3.12	4.43
0200 5"-10"	B-1B	360	.089			3.70	2.72	6.42	8.65
0300 12"-16"		240	.133			5.55	4.09	9.64	13
0400 18"-24"		160	.200			8.35	6.15	14.50	19.50
0450 26"-36"		100	.320			13.30	9.80	23.10	31.50
0500 Steel gland seal, with insulation, 3/4"-4"	B-1A	100	.240	Ea.		9.20	3.27	12.47	17.75
0600 5"-10"	B-1B	75	.427			17.75	13.05	30.80	41.50
0700 12"-16"		60	.533			22	16.35	38.35	52
0800 18"-24"		50	.640			26.50	19.60	46.10	62.50
0850 26"-36"		40	.800			33.50	24.50	58	78
0900 Demo steel fittings with insulation 3/4"-4"	B-1A	60	.400			15.30	5.45	20.75	29.50
1000 5"-10"	B-1B	40	.800			33.50	24.50	58	78
1100 12"-16"		30	1.067			44.50	32.50	77	104
1200 18"-24"		20	1.600			66.50	49	115.50	156
1300 26"-36"		15	2.133			89	65.50	154.50	208
1400 Steel pipe anchors, 5"-10"		40	.800			33.50	24.50	58	78
1500 12"-16"		30	1.067			44.50	32.50	77	104

For customer support on your Site Work & Landscape Cost Data, call 877.737.1594.

31

02 41 Demolition

02 41 13 – Selective Site Demolition

02 41 13.46 Selective Demolition, Steel Pipe With Insulation

		Crew	Daily Output	Labor-Hours	Unit	Material	2015 Bare Costs Labor	Equipment	Total	Total Incl O&P
1600	18"-24"	B-1B	20	1.600	Ea.		66.50	49	115.50	156
1700	26"-36"	↓	15	2.133	↓		89	65.50	154.50	208

02 41 13.48 Selective Demolition, Gasoline Containment Piping

		Crew	Daily Output	Labor-Hours	Unit	Material	Labor	Equipment	Total	Total Incl O&P
0010	**SELECTIVE DEMOLITION, GASOLINE CONTAINMENT PIPING**									
0020	Excludes excavation									
0030	Excludes environmental site remediation									
0100	Gasoline plastic primary containment piping 2" to 4"	Q-6	800	.030	L.F.		1.67		1.67	2.53
0200	Fittings 2" to 4"		40	.600	Ea.		33.50		33.50	50.50
0300	Gasoline plastic secondary containment piping 3" to 6"		800	.030	L.F.		1.67		1.67	2.53
0400	Fittings 3" to 6"	↓	40	.600	Ea.		33.50		33.50	50.50

02 41 13.50 Selective Demolition, Natural Gas, PE Pipe

		Crew	Daily Output	Labor-Hours	Unit	Material	Labor	Equipment	Total	Total Incl O&P
0010	**SELECTIVE DEMOLITION, NATURAL GAS, PE PIPE**									
0020	Excludes excavation									
0100	Natural gas coils, PE, 1 1/4" to 3"	Q-6	800	.030	L.F.		1.67		1.67	2.53
0200	Joints, 40', PE, 3" - 4"		800	.030			1.67		1.67	2.53
0300	6" - 8"	↓	600	.040	↓		2.23		2.23	3.37

02 41 13.51 Selective Demolition, Natural Gas, Steel Pipe

		Crew	Daily Output	Labor-Hours	Unit	Material	Labor	Equipment	Total	Total Incl O&P
0010	**SELECTIVE DEMOLITION, NATURAL GAS, STEEL PIPE**									
0020	Excludes excavation									
0100	Natural gas steel pipe 1" - 4"	B-1A	800	.030	L.F.		1.15	.41	1.56	2.22
0200	5" - 10"	B-1B	360	.089			3.70	2.72	6.42	8.65
0300	12" - 16"		240	.133			5.55	4.09	9.64	13
0400	18" - 24"	↓	160	.200	↓		8.35	6.15	14.50	19.50
0500	Natural gas steel fittings 1" - 4"	B-1A	160	.150	Ea.		5.75	2.04	7.79	11.10
0600	5" - 10"	B-1B	160	.200			8.35	6.15	14.50	19.50
0700	12" - 16"		108	.296			12.35	9.10	21.45	29
0800	18" - 24"	↓	70	.457	↓		19.05	14	33.05	44.50

02 41 13.52 Selective Demo, Natural Gas, Valves, Fittings, Regulators

		Crew	Daily Output	Labor-Hours	Unit	Material	Labor	Equipment	Total	Total Incl O&P
0010	**SELECTIVE DEMO, NATURAL GAS, VALVES, FITTINGS, REGULATORS**									
0100	Gas stops 1 1/4" - 2"	1 Plum	22	.364	Ea.		21.50		21.50	32
0200	Gas regulator 1 1/2" - 2"	"	22	.364			21.50		21.50	32
0300	3" - 4"	Q-1	22	.727			38.50		38.50	58
0400	Gas plug valve, 3/4" - 2"	1 Plum	22	.364			21.50		21.50	32
0500	2 1/2" - 3"	Q-1	10	1.600	↓		84.50		84.50	128

02 41 13.54 Selective Demolition, Electric Ducts and Fittings

		Crew	Daily Output	Labor-Hours	Unit	Material	Labor	Equipment	Total	Total Incl O&P
0010	**SELECTIVE DEMOLITION, ELECTRIC DUCTS & FITTINGS**									
0020	Excludes excavation									
0100	Plastic conduit, 1/2" - 2"	1 Elec	600	.013	L.F.		.73		.73	1.09
0200	3" - 6"	2 Elec	400	.040	"		2.19		2.19	3.28
0300	Fittings, 1/2" - 2"	1 Elec	50	.160	Ea.		8.75		8.75	13.10
0400	3" - 6"	"	40	.200	"		10.95		10.95	16.40

02 41 13.56 Selective Demolition, Electric Duct Banks

		Crew	Daily Output	Labor-Hours	Unit	Material	Labor	Equipment	Total	Total Incl O&P
0010	**SELECTIVE DEMOLITION, ELECTRIC DUCT BANKS**									
0020	Excludes excavation									
0100	Hand holes sized to 4' x 4' x 4'	R-3	7	2.857	Ea.		155	19.70	174.70	255
0200	Manholes sized to 6' x 10' x 7'	B-13	6	9.333	"		385	123	508	720
0300	Conduit 1 @ 2" diameter, EB plastic, no concrete	2 Elec	1000	.016	L.F.		.88		.88	1.31
0400	2 @ 2" diameter		500	.032			1.75		1.75	2.62
0500	4 @ 2" diameter		250	.064			3.50		3.50	5.25
0600	1 @ 3" diameter		800	.020			1.09		1.09	1.64
0700	2 @ 3" diameter	↓	400	.040			2.19		2.19	3.28

For customer support on your Site Work & Landscape Cost Data, call 877.737.1594.

02 41 Demolition

02 41 13 – Selective Site Demolition

02 41 13.56 Selective Demolition, Electric Duct Banks

		Crew	Daily Output	Labor-Hours	Unit	Material	2015 Bare Costs Labor	Equipment	Total	Total Incl O&P
0800	4 @ 3" diameter	2 Elec	200	.080	L.F.		4.38		4.38	6.55
0900	1 @ 4" diameter		800	.020			1.09		1.09	1.64
1000	2 @ 4" diameter		400	.040			2.19		2.19	3.28
1100	4 @ 4" diameter		200	.080			4.38		4.38	6.55
1200	6 @ 4" diameter		100	.160			8.75		8.75	13.10
1300	1 @ 5" diameter		500	.032			1.75		1.75	2.62
1400	2 @ 5" diameter		250	.064			3.50		3.50	5.25
1500	4 @ 5" diameter		160	.100			5.45		5.45	8.20
1600	6 @ 5" diameter		100	.160			8.75		8.75	13.10
1700	1 @ 6" diameter		500	.032			1.75		1.75	2.62
1800	2 @ 6" diameter		250	.064			3.50		3.50	5.25
1900	4 @ 6" diameter		160	.100			5.45		5.45	8.20
2000	6 @ 6" diameter	↓	100	.160			8.75		8.75	13.10
2100	Conduit 1 EB plastic, with concrete, 0.92 C.F./L.F.	B-9	150	.267			10.15	1.55	11.70	17.30
2200	2 EB plastic 1.52 C.F./L.F.		100	.400			15.20	2.33	17.53	26
2300	2 x 2 EB plastic 2.51 C.F./L.F.		80	.500			19	2.91	21.91	32
2400	2 x 3 EB plastic 3.56 C.F./L.F.	↓	60	.667			25.50	3.88	29.38	43.50
2500	Conduit 2 @ 2" diameter, steel, no concrete	2 Elec	400	.040			2.19		2.19	3.28
2600	4 @ 2" diameter		200	.080			4.38		4.38	6.55
2700	2 @ 3" diameter		200	.080			4.38		4.38	6.55
2800	4 @ 3" diameter		100	.160			8.75		8.75	13.10
2900	2 @ 4" diameter		200	.080			4.38		4.38	6.55
3000	4 @ 4" diameter		100	.160			8.75		8.75	13.10
3100	6 @ 4" diameter		50	.320			17.50		17.50	26
3200	2 @ 5" diameter		120	.133			7.30		7.30	10.95
3300	4 @ 5" diameter		60	.267			14.60		14.60	22
3400	6 @ 5" diameter		40	.400			22		22	33
3500	2 @ 6" diameter		120	.133			7.30		7.30	10.95
3600	4 @ 6" diameter		60	.267			14.60		14.60	22
3700	6 @ 6" diameter	↓	40	.400			22		22	33
3800	Conduit 2 steel, with concrete, 1.52 C.F./L.F.	B-9	80	.500			19	2.91	21.91	32
3900	2 x 2 EB steel 2.51 C.F./L.F.		60	.667			25.50	3.88	29.38	43.50
4000	2 x 3 steel 3.56 C.F./L.F.	↓	50	.800	↓		30.50	4.66	35.16	52
4100	Conduit fittings, PVC type EB, 2" - 3"	1 Elec	30	.267	Ea.		14.60		14.60	22
4200	4" - 6"	"	20	.400	"		22		22	33

02 41 13.60 Selective Demolition Fencing

		Crew	Daily Output	Labor-Hours	Unit	Material	2015 Bare Costs Labor	Equipment	Total	Total Incl O&P
0010	**SELECTIVE DEMOLITION FENCING** R024119-10									
0700	Snow fence, 4' high	B-6	1000	.024	L.F.		.99	.36	1.35	1.92
1600	Fencing, barbed wire, 3 strand	2 Clab	430	.037			1.40		1.40	2.15
1650	5 strand	"	280	.057			2.15		2.15	3.31
1700	Chain link, posts & fabric, 8' to 10' high, remove only	B-6	445	.054			2.23	.82	3.05	4.31
1750	Remove and reset		70	.343			14.15	5.20	19.35	27
1755	6' high, remove only		520	.046			1.90	.70	2.60	3.68
1756	Remove and reset	↓	84	.286			11.80	4.34	16.14	23
1760	Wood fence to 6', remove only, minimum	2 Clab	500	.032			1.20		1.20	1.85
1770	Maximum		250	.064			2.41		2.41	3.70
1775	Fencing, wood, average all types, 4' to 6' high		432	.037	↓		1.39		1.39	2.14
1780	Fence post, wood, 4" x 4", 6' to 8' high		96	.167	Ea.		6.25		6.25	9.65
1785	Fence rail, 2" x 4", 8' long, remove only	↓	7680	.002	L.F.		.08		.08	.12
1790	Remove and store	B-80	235	.136	"		5.60	3.07	8.67	11.90

For customer support on your Site Work & Landscape Cost Data, call 877.737.1594.

33

02 41 Demolition

02 41 13 – Selective Site Demolition

02 41 13.62 Selective Demo., Chain Link Fences & Gates

		Crew	Daily Output	Labor-Hours	Unit	Material	2015 Bare Costs Labor	2015 Bare Costs Equipment	Total	Total Incl O&P
0010	**SELECTIVE DEMOLITION, CHAIN LINK FENCES & GATES**									
0100	Chain link, gates, 3' - 4' width	B-6	30	.800	Ea.		33	12.15	45.15	64
0200	10-12' width		16	1.500			62	23	85	120
0300	14' width		15	1.600			66	24.50	90.50	128
0400	20' width		10	2.400			99	36.50	135.50	192
0500	18' width with overhead & cantilever		80	.300	L.F.		12.40	4.55	16.95	24
0510	Sliding		80	.300			12.40	4.55	16.95	24
0520	Cantilever to 40' wide		80	.300			12.40	4.55	16.95	24
0530	Motor operators	2 Skwk	1	16	Ea.		780		780	1,200
0540	Transmitter systems	"	15	1.067	"		52		52	80
0600	Chain link, fence, 5' high	B-6	890	.027	L.F.		1.11	.41	1.52	2.15
0650	3' - 4' high		1000	.024			.99	.36	1.35	1.92
0675	12' high		400	.060			2.48	.91	3.39	4.79
0800	Chain link, fence, braces	B-1	2000	.012	Ea.		.46		.46	.71
0900	Privacy slats	"	2000	.012			.46		.46	.71
1000	Fence posts, steel, in concrete	B-6	80	.300			12.40	4.55	16.95	24
1100	Fence fabric & accessories, fabric to 8' high		800	.030	L.F.		1.24	.46	1.70	2.39
1200	Barbed wire		5000	.005	"		.20	.07	.27	.38
1300	Extension arms & eye tops		300	.080	Ea.		3.30	1.21	4.51	6.40
1400	Fence rails		2000	.012	L.F.		.50	.18	.68	.96
1500	Reinforcing wire		5000	.005	"		.20	.07	.27	.38

02 41 13.64 Selective Demolition, Vinyl Fences and Gates

		Crew	Daily Output	Labor-Hours	Unit	Material	2015 Bare Costs Labor	2015 Bare Costs Equipment	Total	Total Incl O&P
0010	**SELECTIVE DEMOLITION, VINYL FENCES & GATES**									
0100	Vinyl fence up to 6' high	B-6	1000	.024	L.F.		.99	.36	1.35	1.92
0200	Gates, up to 6' high	"	40	.600	Ea.		25	9.10	34.10	48

02 41 13.66 Selective Demolition, Misc Metal Fences and Gates

		Crew	Daily Output	Labor-Hours	Unit	Material	2015 Bare Costs Labor	2015 Bare Costs Equipment	Total	Total Incl O&P
0010	**SELECTIVE DEMOLITION, MISC METAL FENCES & GATES**									
0100	Misc steel mesh fences, 4' - 6' high	B-6	600	.040	L.F.		1.65	.61	2.26	3.20
0200	Kennels, 6' - 12' long	2 Clab	8	2	Ea.		75		75	116
0300	Tops, 6' - 12' long	"	30	.533	"		20		20	31
0400	Security fences, 12' - 16' high	B-6	100	.240	L.F.		9.90	3.64	13.54	19.15
0500	Metal tubular picket fences 4' - 6' high		500	.048	"		1.98	.73	2.71	3.83
0600	Gates 3' - 4' wide		20	1.200	Ea.		49.50	18.20	67.70	96

02 41 13.68 Selective Demolition, Wood Fences and Gates

		Crew	Daily Output	Labor-Hours	Unit	Material	2015 Bare Costs Labor	2015 Bare Costs Equipment	Total	Total Incl O&P
0010	**SELECTIVE DEMOLITION, WOOD FENCES & GATES**									
0100	Wood fence gates 3' - 4' wide	2 Clab	20	.800	Ea.		30		30	46.50
0200	Wood fence, open rail, to 4' high		2560	.006	L.F.		.24		.24	.36
0300	to 8' high		368	.043	"		1.63		1.63	2.52
0400	Post, in concrete		50	.320	Ea.		12.05		12.05	18.50

02 41 13.70 Selective Demolition, Rip-Rap and Rock Lining

		Crew	Daily Output	Labor-Hours	Unit	Material	2015 Bare Costs Labor	2015 Bare Costs Equipment	Total	Total Incl O&P
0010	**SELECTIVE DEMOLITION, RIP-RAP & ROCK LINING** R024119-10									
0100	Slope protection, broken stone	B-13	62	.903	C.Y.		37	11.90	48.90	69.50
0200	3/8 to 1/4 C.Y. pieces		60	.933	S.Y.		38.50	12.25	50.75	72
0300	18 inch depth		60	.933	"		38.50	12.25	50.75	72
0400	Dumped stone		93	.602	Ton		24.50	7.90	32.40	46.50
0500	Gabions, 6 – 12 inches deep		60	.933	S.Y.		38.50	12.25	50.75	72
0600	18 – 36 inches deep		30	1.867	"		76.50	24.50	101	144

02 41 13.72 Selective Demo., Shore Protect/Mooring Struct.

		Crew	Daily Output	Labor-Hours	Unit	Material	2015 Bare Costs Labor	2015 Bare Costs Equipment	Total	Total Incl O&P
0010	**SELECTIVE DEMOLITION, SHORE PROTECT/MOORING STRUCTURES**									
0100	Breakwaters, bulkheads, concrete, maximum R024119-10	B-9	12	3.333	L.F.		127	19.40	146.40	217
0200	Breakwaters, bulkheads, concrete, 12', minimum		10	4			152	23.50	175.50	260

02 41 Demolition

02 41 13 – Selective Site Demolition

02 41 13.72 Selective Demo., Shore Protect/Mooring Struct.		Crew	Daily Output	Labor-Hours	Unit	Material	2015 Bare Costs Labor	Equipment	Total	Total Incl O&P
0300	Maximum	B-9	9	4.444	L.F.		169	26	195	289
0400	Steel, from shore	B-40B	54	.889			37	21.50	58.50	80
0500	from barge	B-76A	30	2.133			86.50	69	155.50	209
0600	Jetties, docks, floating	B-21B	600	.067	S.F.		2.72	1.09	3.81	5.35
0700	Pier supported, 3" - 4" decking		300	.133			5.45	2.18	7.63	10.75
0800	Floating, prefab, small boat, minimum		600	.067			2.72	1.09	3.81	5.35
0900	Maximum		300	.133			5.45	2.18	7.63	10.75
1000	Floating, prefab, per slip, minimum		3.20	12.500	Ea.		510	204	714	1,000
1010	Maximum		2.80	14.286	"		585	234	819	1,150

02 41 13.74 Selective Demolition, Piles

		Crew	Daily Output	Labor-Hours	Unit	Material	2015 Bare Costs Labor	Equipment	Total	Total Incl O&P
0010	**SELECTIVE DEMOLITION, PILES**									
0100	Cast in place piles, corrugated, 8" - 10"	B-19	600	.107	V.L.F.		5.10	2.90	8	11.10
0200	12"-14"		500	.128			6.10	3.47	9.57	13.30
0300	16"		400	.160			7.60	4.34	11.94	16.65
0400	fluted, 12"		600	.107			5.10	2.90	8	11.10
0500	14"-18"		500	.128			6.10	3.47	9.57	13.30
0600	end bearing, 12"		600	.107			5.10	2.90	8	11.10
0700	14"-18"		500	.128			6.10	3.47	9.57	13.30
0800	Precast prestressed piles, 12"-14" dia		700	.091			4.36	2.48	6.84	9.55
0900	16"-24" dia		600	.107			5.10	2.90	8	11.10
1000	36"-66" dia		300	.213			10.15	5.80	15.95	22
1100	10"-14" thick		600	.107			5.10	2.90	8	11.10
1200	16"-24" thick		500	.128			6.10	3.47	9.57	13.30
1300	Pressure grouted pile, 5"		150	.427			20.50	11.60	32.10	44.50
1400	Steel piles, 8"-12" tip		600	.107			5.10	2.90	8	11.10
1500	H sections HP8 to HP12		600	.107			5.10	2.90	8	11.10
1600	HP14	B-19A	600	.107			5.10	3.61	8.71	11.85
1700	Steel pipe piles, 8"-12"	B-19	600	.107			5.10	2.90	8	11.10
1800	14"-18" plain		500	.128			6.10	3.47	9.57	13.30
1900	concrete filled, 14"-18"		400	.160			7.60	4.34	11.94	16.65
2000	Timber piles to 14" dia		600	.107			5.10	2.90	8	11.10

02 41 13.76 Selective Demolition, Water Wells

		Crew	Daily Output	Labor-Hours	Unit	Material	2015 Bare Costs Labor	Equipment	Total	Total Incl O&P
0010	**SELECTIVE DEMOLITION, WATER WELLS**									
0100	Well, 40' deep with casing & gravel pack, 24"-36" dia	B-23	.25	160	Ea.		6,075	11,400	17,475	21,900
0200	Riser pipe, 1-1/4", for observation well	"	300	.133	L.F.		5.05	9.50	14.55	18.25
0300	Pump, 1/2 to 5 HP up to 100' depth	Q-1	3	5.333	Ea.		282		282	425
0400	Up to 150' well 25 HP pump	Q-22	1.50	10.667			565	435	1,000	1,325
0500	Up to 500' well 30 HP pump	"	1	16			845	655	1,500	2,000
0600	Well screen 2" to 8"	B-23	300	.133	V.L.F.		5.05	9.50	14.55	18.25
0700	10" to 16"		200	.200			7.60	14.25	21.85	27.50
0800	18" to 26"		150	.267			10.15	18.95	29.10	36.50
0900	Slotted PVC for wells 1-1/4"-8"		600	.067			2.53	4.74	7.27	9.10
1000	Well screen and casing 6" to 16"		300	.133			5.05	9.50	14.55	18.25
1100	18" to 26"		150	.267			10.15	18.95	29.10	36.50
1200	30" to 36"		100	.400			15.20	28.50	43.70	55

02 41 13.78 Selective Demolition, Radio Towers

		Crew	Daily Output	Labor-Hours	Unit	Material	2015 Bare Costs Labor	Equipment	Total	Total Incl O&P
0010	**SELECTIVE DEMOLITION, RADIO TOWERS**									
0100	Radio tower, guyed, 50'	2 Skwk	16	1	Ea.		48.50		48.50	75
0200	190', 40 lb. section	K-2	.70	34.286			1,675	435	2,110	3,275
0300	200', 70 lb. section		.70	34.286			1,675	435	2,110	3,275
0400	300', 70 lb. section		.40	60			2,925	760	3,685	5,725
0500	270', 90 lb. section		.40	60			2,925	760	3,685	5,725

For customer support on your Site Work & Landscape Cost Data, call 877.737.1594.

35

02 41 13.78 Selective Demolition, Radio Towers		Crew	Daily Output	Labor-Hours	Unit	Material	2015 Bare Costs Labor	Equipment	Total	Total Incl O&P
0600	400'	K-2	.30	80	Ea.		3,900	1,000	4,900	7,650
0700	Self supported, 60'		.90	26.667			1,300	335	1,635	2,550
0800	120'		.80	30			1,475	380	1,855	2,875
0900	190'		.40	60			2,925	760	3,685	5,725

02 41 13.80 Selective Demo., Utility Poles and Cross Arms

		Crew	Daily Output	Labor-Hours	Unit	Material	Labor	Equipment	Total	Total Incl O&P
0010	SELECTIVE DEMOLITION, UTILITY POLES & CROSS ARMS									
0100	Utility poles, wood, 20' - 30' high	R-3	6	3.333	Ea.		181	23	204	297
0200	35' - 45' high	"	5	4			217	27.50	244.50	355
0300	Cross arms, wood, 4' - 6' long	1 Elec	5	1.600			87.50		87.50	131

02 41 13.82 Selective Removal, Pavement Lines and Markings

		Crew	Daily Output	Labor-Hours	Unit	Material	Labor	Equipment	Total	Total Incl O&P
0010	SELECTIVE REMOVAL, PAVEMENT LINES & MARKINGS									
0015	Does not include traffic control costs									
0020	See other items in Section 32 17 23.13									
0100	Remove permanent painted traffic lines and markings	B-78A	500	.016	C.L.F.		.78	1.64	2.42	2.99
0200	Temporary traffic line tape	2 Clab	1500	.011	L.F.		.40		.40	.62
0300	Thermoplastic traffic lines and markings	B-79A	500	.024	C.L.F.		1.17	2.56	3.73	4.58
0400	Painted pavement markings	B-78B	500	.036	S.F.		1.40	.75	2.15	2.98

02 41 13.84 Selective Demolition, Walks, Steps and Pavers

		Crew	Daily Output	Labor-Hours	Unit	Material	Labor	Equipment	Total	Total Incl O&P
0010	SELECTIVE DEMOLITION, WALKS, STEPS AND PAVERS									
0100	Splash blocks	1 Clab	300	.027	S.F.		1		1	1.54
0200	Tree grates	"	50	.160	Ea.		6		6	9.25
0300	Walks, limestone pavers	2 Clab	150	.107	S.F.		4.01		4.01	6.15
0400	Redwood sections		600	.027			1		1	1.54
0500	Redwood planks		480	.033			1.25		1.25	1.93
0600	Shale paver		300	.053			2.01		2.01	3.09
0700	Tile thinset paver		675	.024			.89		.89	1.37
0800	Wood round	B-1	350	.069	Ea.		2.62		2.62	4.04
0900	Asphalt block	2 Clab	450	.036	S.F.		1.34		1.34	2.06
1000	Bluestone		450	.036			1.34		1.34	2.06
1100	Slate, 1" or thinner		675	.024			.89		.89	1.37
1200	Granite blocks		300	.053			2.01		2.01	3.09
1300	Precast patio blocks		450	.036			1.34		1.34	2.06
1400	Planter blocks		600	.027			1		1	1.54
1500	Brick paving, dry set		300	.053			2.01		2.01	3.09
1600	Mortar set		180	.089			3.34		3.34	5.15
1700	Dry set on edge		240	.067			2.51		2.51	3.86
1800	Steps, brick		200	.080	L.F.		3.01		3.01	4.63
1900	Railroad tie		150	.107			4.01		4.01	6.15
2000	Bluestone		180	.089			3.34		3.34	5.15
2100	Wood/steel edging for steps		1000	.016			.60		.60	.93
2200	Timber or railroad tie edging for steps		400	.040			1.50		1.50	2.31

02 41 13.86 Selective Demolition, Athletic Surfaces

		Crew	Daily Output	Labor-Hours	Unit	Material	Labor	Equipment	Total	Total Incl O&P
0010	SELECTIVE DEMOLITION, ATHLETIC SURFACES									
0100	Synthetic grass	2 Clab	2000	.008	S.F.		.30		.30	.46
0200	Surface coat latex rubber	"	2000	.008	"		.30		.30	.46
0300	Tennis court posts	B-11C	16	1	Ea.		44	23	67	92.50

02 41 13.88 Selective Demolition, Lawn Sprinkler Systems

		Crew	Daily Output	Labor-Hours	Unit	Material	Labor	Equipment	Total	Total Incl O&P
0010	SELECTIVE DEMOLITION, LAWN SPRINKLER SYSTEMS									
0100	Golf course sprinkler system, 9 hole	4 Skwk	.10	320	Ea.		15,600		15,600	24,000
0200	Sprinkler system, 24' diam. @ 15' O.C., per head	B-20	110	.218	Head		9.15		9.15	14.10
0300	60' diam. @ 24' O.C., per head	"	52	.462	"		19.35		19.35	30

02 41 Demolition

02 41 13 – Selective Site Demolition

02 41 13.88 Selective Demolition, Lawn Sprinkler Systems

		Crew	Daily Output	Labor-Hours	Unit	Material	2015 Bare Costs Labor	Equipment	Total	Total Incl O&P
0400	Sprinkler heads, plastic	2 Skwk	150	.107	Ea.		5.20		5.20	8
0500	Impact circle pattern, 28' - 76' diam.		75	.213			10.40		10.40	16.05
0600	Pop-up, 42' - 76' diam.		50	.320			15.55		15.55	24
0700	39' - 99' diameter		50	.320			15.55		15.55	24
0800	Sprinkler valves		40	.400			19.45		19.45	30
0900	Valve boxes		40	.400			19.45		19.45	30
1000	Controls		2	8			390		390	600
1100	Backflow preventer		4	4			195		195	300
1200	Vacuum breaker		4	4			195		195	300

02 41 13.90 Selective Demolition, Retaining Walls

		Crew	Daily Output	Labor-Hours	Unit	Material	2015 Bare Costs Labor	Equipment	Total	Total Incl O&P
0010	**SELECTIVE DEMOLITION, RETAINING WALLS**									
0020	See other retaining wall items in Section 02 41 13.33									
0100	Concrete retaining wall, 6' high, no reinforcing	B-13K	200	.080	L.F.		4.14	8.10	12.24	15.20
0200	8' high		150	.107			5.50	10.80	16.30	20
0300	10' high		150	.107			5.50	10.80	16.30	20
0400	With reinforcing, 6' high		200	.080			4.14	8.10	12.24	15.20
0500	8' high		150	.107			5.50	10.80	16.30	20
0600	10' high		120	.133			6.90	13.50	20.40	25.50
0700	20' high		60	.267			13.80	27	40.80	50.50
0800	Concrete cribbing, 12' high, open/closed face		150	.107	S.F.		5.50	10.80	16.30	20
0900	Interlocking segmental retaining wall	B-62	800	.030			1.24	.22	1.46	2.13
1000	Wall caps	"	600	.040			1.65	.29	1.94	2.85
1100	Metal bin retaining wall, 10' wide, 4-12' high	B-13	1200	.047			1.91	.61	2.52	3.61
1200	10' wide, 16-28' high		1000	.056			2.30	.74	3.04	4.32
1300	Stone filled gabions, 6' x 3' x 1'		170	.329	Ea.		13.50	4.33	17.83	25.50
1400	6' x 3' x 1'-6"		75	.747			30.50	9.80	40.30	58
1500	6' x 3' x 3'		25	2.240			92	29.50	121.50	174
1600	9' x 3' x 1'		75	.747			30.50	9.80	40.30	58
1700	9' x 3' x 1'-6"		33	1.697			69.50	22.50	92	132
1800	9' x 3' x 3'		12	4.667			191	61.50	252.50	360
1900	12' x 3' x 1'		42	1.333			54.50	17.55	72.05	103
2000	12' x 3' x 1'-6"		20	2.800			115	37	152	217
2100	12' x 3' x 3'		6	9.333			385	123	508	720

02 41 13.92 Selective Demolition, Parking Appurtenances

		Crew	Daily Output	Labor-Hours	Unit	Material	2015 Bare Costs Labor	Equipment	Total	Total Incl O&P
0010	**SELECTIVE DEMOLITION, PARKING APPURTENANCES**									
0100	Bumper rails, garage, 6" wide	B-6	300	.080	L.F.		3.30	1.21	4.51	6.40
0200	12" channel rail		300	.080			3.30	1.21	4.51	6.40
0300	Parking bumper, timber		1000	.024			.99	.36	1.35	1.92
0400	Folding, with locks	B-1	100	.240	Ea.		9.20		9.20	14.15
0500	Flexible fixed garage stanchion	B-6	150	.160			6.60	2.43	9.03	12.75
0600	Wheel stops, precast concrete		120	.200			8.25	3.04	11.29	16
0700	Thermoplastic		120	.200			8.25	3.04	11.29	16
0800	Pipe bollards, 6" - 12" dia		80	.300			12.40	4.55	16.95	24

02 41 13.93 Selective Demolition, Site Furnishings

		Crew	Daily Output	Labor-Hours	Unit	Material	2015 Bare Costs Labor	Equipment	Total	Total Incl O&P
0010	**SELECTIVE DEMOLITION, SITE FURNISHINGS**									
0100	Benches, all types	2 Clab	10	1.600	Ea.		60		60	92.50
0200	Trash receptacles, all types		80	.200			7.50		7.50	11.55
0300	Trash enclosures, steel or wood		10	1.600			60		60	92.50

For customer support on your Site Work & Landscape Cost Data, call 877.737.1594.

37

02 41 Demolition

02 41 13 – Selective Site Demolition

02 41 13.94 Selective Demolition, Athletic Screening

		Crew	Daily Output	Labor-Hours	Unit	Material	2015 Bare Costs Labor	Equipment	Total	Total Incl O&P
0010	**SELECTIVE DEMOLITION, ATHLETIC SCREENING**									
0020	See other items in Section 02 41 13.60 & 02 41 13.62									
0100	Baseball backstops	B-6	2	12	Ea.		495	182	677	960
0200	Basketball goal, single		6	4			165	60.50	225.50	320
0300	Double		4	6			248	91	339	480
0400	Tennis wire mesh, pair ends		5	4.800	Set		198	73	271	385
0500	Enclosed court		3	8	Ea.		330	121	451	640
0600	Wood or masonry handball court		1	24	"		990	365	1,355	1,925

02 41 13.95 Selective Demo., Athletic/Playground Equipment

		Crew	Daily Output	Labor-Hours	Unit	Material	2015 Bare Costs Labor	Equipment	Total	Total Incl O&P
0010	**SELECTIVE DEMO., ATHLETIC/PLAYGROUND EQUIPMENT**									
0020	See other items in Section 02 41 13.96									
0100	Bike rack	B-6	32	.750	Ea.		31	11.40	42.40	60
0200	Climber arch		16	1.500			62	23	85	120
0300	Fitness trail, 9 to 10 stations wood or metal		.50	48			1,975	730	2,705	3,825
0400	16 to 20 stations wood or metal		.25	96			3,950	1,450	5,400	7,650
0500	Monkey bars 14' long		8	3			124	45.50	169.50	239
0600	Parallel bars 10' long		8	3			124	45.50	169.50	239
0700	Post tether ball		32	.750			31	11.40	42.40	60
0800	Poles 10'-6" long		32	.750			31	11.40	42.40	60
0900	Pole ground sockets		80	.300			12.40	4.55	16.95	24
1000	See-saw, 2 units		12	2			82.50	30.50	113	160
1100	4 units		10	2.400			99	36.50	135.50	192
1200	6 units		8	3			124	45.50	169.50	239
1300	Shelter, fiberglass, 3 person		10	2.400			99	36.50	135.50	192
1400	Slides, 12' long		8	3			124	45.50	169.50	239
1500	20' long		6	4			165	60.50	225.50	320
1600	Swings, 4 seats		6	4			165	60.50	225.50	320
1700	8 seats		4	6			248	91	339	480
1800	Whirlers, 8 – 10' diameter		6	4			165	60.50	225.50	320
1900	Football or football/soccer goal posts		3	8	Pair		330	121	451	640
2000	Soccer goal posts		4	6	"		248	91	339	480
2100	Playground surfacing, 4" depth	2 Clab	900	.018	S.F.		.67		.67	1.03
2200	2" topping	"	1800	.009	"		.33		.33	.51
2300	Platform/paddle tennis court, alum. deck & frame	B-1	.20	120	Court		4,600		4,600	7,075
2400	Aluminum deck and wood frame		.25	96	"		3,675		3,675	5,650
2500	Heater		2	12	Ea.		460		460	705
2600	Wood deck & frame		.25	96	Court		3,675		3,675	5,650
2700	Wood deck & steel frame		.25	96			3,675		3,675	5,650
2800	Steel deck & wood frame		.25	96			3,675		3,675	5,650

02 41 13.96 Selective Demo., Modular Playground Equipment

		Crew	Daily Output	Labor-Hours	Unit	Material	2015 Bare Costs Labor	Equipment	Total	Total Incl O&P
0010	**SELECTIVE DEMOLITION, MODULAR PLAYGROUND EQUIPMENT**									
0100	Modular playground, 48" deck, square or triangle shape	B-1	2	12	Ea.		460		460	705
0200	Various posts		18	1.333			51		51	78.50
0300	Roof 54" x 54"		18	1.333			51		51	78.50
0400	Wheel chair transfer module		6	4			153		153	236
0500	Guardrail pipe		90	.267	L.F.		10.20		10.20	15.70
0600	Steps, 3 risers		16	1.500	Ea.		57.50		57.50	88.50
0700	Activity panel crawl through		8	3			115		115	177
0800	Alphabet/spelling panel		8	3			115		115	177
0900	Crawl tunnel, each 4' section		8	3			115		115	177
1000	Slide tunnel		16	1.500			57.50		57.50	88.50
1100	Spiral slide tunnel		12	2			76.50		76.50	118

38

02 41 Demolition

02 41 13 – Selective Site Demolition

02 41 13.96 Selective Demo., Modular Playground Equipment

		Crew	Daily Output	Labor-Hours	Unit	Material	2015 Bare Costs Labor	Equipment	Total	Total Incl O&P
1200	Ladder, horizontal or vertical	B-1	10	2.400	Ea.		92		92	141
1300	Corkscrew climber		6	4			153		153	236
1400	Fire pole		12	2			76.50		76.50	118
1500	Bridge, ring chamber		8	3			115		115	177
1600	Bridge, suspension		8	3			115		115	177

02 41 13.97 Selective Demolition, Traffic Light Systems

		Crew	Daily Output	Labor-Hours	Unit	Material	2015 Bare Costs Labor	Equipment	Total	Total Incl O&P
0010	**SELECTIVE DEMOLITION, TRAFFIC LIGHT SYSTEMS**									
0100	Traffic signal, pedestrian cross walk	R-2	.50	112	Total		5,475	550	6,025	8,875
0200	8 signal intersection, 2 each direction	"	.25	224			10,900	1,100	12,000	17,700
0300	Each traffic phase controller	L-9	3	12			515		515	820
0400	Each semi-actuated detector		1.50	24			1,025		1,025	1,625
0500	Each fully-actuated detector		1.50	24			1,025		1,025	1,625
0600	Pedestrian push button system		2	18			775		775	1,225
0650	Each optically programmed head		3	12			515		515	820
0700	School signal flashing system		1	36	Signal		1,550		1,550	2,450
0800	Complete traffic light intersection system, without lane control	R-2	.25	224	Ea.		10,900	1,100	12,000	17,700
0900	With lane control		.20	280			13,700	1,375	15,075	22,200
1000	Traffic light, each left turn protection system		.66	84.848			4,150	415	4,565	6,725

02 41 13.98 Select. Demo., Sod, Edging, Planters & Tree Guying

		Crew	Daily Output	Labor-Hours	Unit	Material	2015 Bare Costs Labor	Equipment	Total	Total Incl O&P
0010	**SELECTIVE DEMOLITION, SOD, EDGING, PLANTERS & TREE GUYING**									
0100	Remove sod 1" deep, 3 M.S.F. or greater, level ground	B-63	40	1	M.S.F.		40	4.34	44.34	66
0200	Less than 3 M.S.F., level ground		27	1.481			59	6.45	65.45	97.50
0300	3 M.S.F. or greater, sloped ground		12	3.333			133	14.45	147.45	219
0400	Less than 3 M.S.F., sloped ground		8	5			199	21.50	220.50	330
0500	Edging, aluminum	B-1	800	.030	L.F.		1.15		1.15	1.77
0600	Brick horizontal		400	.060			2.30		2.30	3.53
0700	Brick vertical		200	.120			4.59		4.59	7.05
0800	Corrugated aluminum		1200	.020			.77		.77	1.18
0900	Granite 5" x 16"		600	.040			1.53		1.53	2.36
1000	Polyethylene grass barrier		1200	.020			.77		.77	1.18
1100	Precast 2" x 8" x 16"		800	.030			1.15		1.15	1.77
1200	Railroad ties		200	.120			4.59		4.59	7.05
1300	Wood		400	.060			2.30		2.30	3.53
1400	Steel strips including stakes		600	.040			1.53		1.53	2.36
1500	Planters, concrete, 48" dia	2 Clab	30	.533	Ea.		20		20	31
1600	Concrete 7' dia		20	.800			30		30	46.50
1700	Fiberglass 36" dia		30	.533			20		20	31
1800	60" dia		20	.800			30		30	46.50
1900	24" square		30	.533			20		20	31
2000	48" square		30	.533			20		20	31
2100	Wood 48" square		30	.533			20		20	31
2200	48" dia		20	.800			30		30	46.50
2300	72" dia		20	.800			30		30	46.50
2400	Planter/bench, fiberglass 72" - 96" square		10	1.600			60		60	92.50
2500	Wood, 72" square		10	1.600			60		60	92.50
2600	Tree guying, stakes, 3" - 4" caliper		40	.400			15.05		15.05	23
2700	anchors, 3" caliper		40	.400			15.05		15.05	23
2800	3" - 6" caliper		30	.533			20		20	31
2900	6" caliper		20	.800			30		30	46.50
3000	8" caliper		15	1.067			40		40	61.50

For customer support on your Site Work & Landscape Cost Data, call 877.737.1594.

39

02 41 Demolition

02 41 16 – Structure Demolition

02 41 16.13 Building Demolition

		Crew	Daily Output	Labor-Hours	Unit	Material	2015 Bare Costs Labor	2015 Bare Costs Equipment	Total	Total Incl O&P
0010	**BUILDING DEMOLITION** Large urban projects, incl. 20 mi. haul R024119-10									
0011	No foundation or dump fees, C.F. is vol. of building standing									
0020	Steel	B-8	21500	.003	C.F.		.13	.15	.28	.36
0050	Concrete		15300	.004			.18	.22	.40	.51
0080	Masonry		20100	.003			.14	.16	.30	.39
0100	Mixture of types		20100	.003			.14	.16	.30	.39
0500	Small bldgs, or single bldgs, no salvage included, steel	B-3	14800	.003			.13	.17	.30	.39
0600	Concrete		11300	.004			.17	.23	.40	.52
0650	Masonry		14800	.003			.13	.17	.30	.39
0700	Wood		14800	.003			.13	.17	.30	.39
0750	For buildings with no interior walls, deduct								50%	50%
1000	Demoliton single family house, one story, wood 1600 S.F.	B-3	1	48	Ea.		1,975	2,575	4,550	5,825
1020	3200 S.F.		.50	96			3,925	5,150	9,075	11,700
1200	Demoliton two family house, two story, wood 2400 S.F.		.67	71.964			2,950	3,850	6,800	8,750
1220	4200 S.F.		.38	128			5,250	6,850	12,100	15,600
1300	Demoliton three family house, three story, wood 3200 S.F.		.50	96			3,925	5,150	9,075	11,700
1320	5400 S.F.		.30	160			6,550	8,575	15,125	19,400
5000	For buildings with no interior walls, deduct								50%	50%

02 41 16.15 Explosive/Implosive Demolition

		Crew	Daily Output	Labor-Hours	Unit	Material	2015 Bare Costs Labor	2015 Bare Costs Equipment	Total	Total Incl O&P
0010	**EXPLOSIVE/IMPLOSIVE DEMOLITION** R024119-10									
0011	Large projects,									
0020	No disposal fee based on building volume, steel building	B-5B	16900	.003	C.F.		.13	.17	.30	.38
0100	Concrete building		16900	.003			.13	.17	.30	.38
0200	Masonry building		16900	.003			.13	.17	.30	.38
0400	Disposal of material, minimum	B-3	445	.108	C.Y.		4.41	5.80	10.21	13.10
0500	Maximum	"	365	.132	"		5.40	7.05	12.45	15.95

02 41 16.17 Building Demolition Footings and Foundations

		Crew	Daily Output	Labor-Hours	Unit	Material	2015 Bare Costs Labor	2015 Bare Costs Equipment	Total	Total Incl O&P
0010	**BUILDING DEMOLITION FOOTINGS AND FOUNDATIONS** R024119-10									
0200	Floors, concrete slab on grade,									
0240	4" thick, plain concrete	B-13L	5000	.003	S.F.		.17	.41	.58	.70
0280	Reinforced, wire mesh		4000	.004			.21	.51	.72	.88
0300	Rods		4500	.004			.18	.46	.64	.78
0400	6" thick, plain concrete		4000	.004			.21	.51	.72	.88
0420	Reinforced, wire mesh		3200	.005			.26	.64	.90	1.10
0440	Rods		3600	.004			.23	.57	.80	.98
1000	Footings, concrete, 1' thick, 2' wide	B-5	300	.187	L.F.		7.75	4.74	12.49	17.10
1080	1'-6" thick, 2' wide		250	.224			9.30	5.70	15	20.50
1120	3' wide		200	.280			11.65	7.10	18.75	25.50
1140	2' thick, 3' wide		175	.320			13.30	8.10	21.40	29.50
1200	Average reinforcing, add								10%	10%
1220	Heavy reinforcing, add								20%	20%
2000	Walls, block, 4" thick	B-13L	8000	.002	S.F.		.10	.26	.36	.44
2040	6" thick		6000	.003			.14	.34	.48	.59
2080	8" thick		4000	.004			.21	.51	.72	.88
2100	12" thick		3000	.005			.28	.68	.96	1.17
2200	For horizontal reinforcing, add								10%	10%
2220	For vertical reinforcing, add								20%	20%
2400	Concrete, plain concrete, 6" thick	B-13L	4000	.004			.21	.51	.72	.88
2420	8" thick		3500	.005			.24	.59	.83	1.01
2440	10" thick		3000	.005			.28	.68	.96	1.17
2500	12" thick		2500	.006			.33	.82	1.15	1.40
2600	For average reinforcing, add								10%	10%

40

02 41 Demolition

02 41 16 – Structure Demolition

02 41 16.17 Building Demolition Footings and Foundations	Crew	Daily Output	Labor-Hours	Unit	Material	2015 Bare Costs Labor	Equipment	Total	Total Incl O&P
2620 For heavy reinforcing, add				S.F.				20%	20%
4000 For congested sites or small quantities, add up to				↓				200%	200%
4200 Add for disposal, on site	B-11A	232	.069	C.Y.		3.04	6	9.04	11.25
4250 To five miles	B-30	220	.109	"		4.75	10.95	15.70	19.25

02 41 16.33 Bridge Demolition

	Crew	Daily Output	Labor-Hours	Unit	Material	2015 Bare Costs Labor	Equipment	Total	Total Incl O&P
0010 **BRIDGE DEMOLITION**									
0100 Bridges, pedestrian, precast, 60' to 150' long	B-21C	250	.224	S.F.		9.20	7.35	16.55	22
0200 Steel, 50' to 160' long, 8' to 10' wide	"	500	.112			4.59	3.68	8.27	11.10
0300 Laminated wood, 80' to 130' long	C-12	300	.160	↓		7.45	2.18	9.63	13.80

02 41 19 – Selective Demolition

02 41 19.13 Selective Building Demolition

	Crew	Daily Output	Labor-Hours	Unit	Material	2015 Bare Costs Labor	Equipment	Total	Total Incl O&P
0010 **SELECTIVE BUILDING DEMOLITION**									
0020 Costs related to selective demolition of specific building components									
0025 are included under Common Work Results (XX 05)									
0030 in the component's appropriate division.									

02 41 19.16 Selective Demolition, Cutout

	Crew	Daily Output	Labor-Hours	Unit	Material	2015 Bare Costs Labor	Equipment	Total	Total Incl O&P
0010 **SELECTIVE DEMOLITION, CUTOUT** R024119-10									
0020 Concrete, elev. slab, light reinforcement, under 6 C.F.	B-9	65	.615	C.F.		23.50	3.58	27.08	40
0050 Light reinforcing, over 6 C.F.		75	.533	"		20.50	3.10	23.60	34.50
0200 Slab on grade to 6" thick, not reinforced, under 8 S.F.		85	.471	S.F.		17.90	2.74	20.64	30.50
0250 8 – 16 S.F.	↓	175	.229	"		8.70	1.33	10.03	14.80
0255 For over 16 S.F. see Line 02 41 16.17 0400									
0600 Walls, not reinforced, under 6 C.F.	B-9	60	.667	C.F.		25.50	3.88	29.38	43.50
0650 6 – 12 C.F.	"	80	.500	"		19	2.91	21.91	32
0655 For over 12 C.F. see Line 02 41 16.17 2500									
1000 Concrete, elevated slab, bar reinforced, under 6 C.F.	B-9	45	.889	C.F.		34	5.15	39.15	57.50
1050 Bar reinforced, over 6 C.F.		50	.800	"		30.50	4.66	35.16	52
1200 Slab on grade to 6" thick, bar reinforced, under 8 S.F.		75	.533	S.F.		20.50	3.10	23.60	34.50
1250 8 – 16 S.F.	↓	150	.267	"		10.15	1.55	11.70	17.30
1255 For over 16 S.F. see Line 02 41 16.17 0440									
1400 Walls, bar reinforced, under 6 C.F.	B-9	50	.800	C.F.		30.50	4.66	35.16	52
1450 6 – 12 C.F.	"	70	.571	"		21.50	3.33	24.83	37
1455 For over 12 C.F. see Lines 02 41 16.17 2500 and 2600									
2000 Brick, to 4 S.F. opening, not including toothing									
2040 4" thick	B-9	30	1.333	Ea.		50.50	7.75	58.25	86.50
2060 8" thick		18	2.222			84.50	12.95	97.45	144
2080 12" thick		10	4			152	23.50	175.50	260
2400 Concrete block, to 4 S.F. opening, 2" thick		35	1.143			43.50	6.65	50.15	74.50
2420 4" thick		30	1.333			50.50	7.75	58.25	86.50
2440 8" thick		27	1.481			56.50	8.60	65.10	96
2460 12" thick		24	1.667			63.50	9.70	73.20	108
2600 Gypsum block, to 4 S.F. opening, 2" thick		80	.500			19	2.91	21.91	32
2620 4" thick		70	.571			21.50	3.33	24.83	37
2640 8" thick		55	.727			27.50	4.23	31.73	47
2800 Terra cotta, to 4 S.F. opening, 4" thick		70	.571			21.50	3.33	24.83	37
2840 8" thick		65	.615			23.50	3.58	27.08	40
2880 12" thick	↓	50	.800	↓		30.50	4.66	35.16	52
3000 Toothing masonry cutouts, brick, soft old mortar	1 Brhe	40	.200	V.L.F.		7.60		7.60	11.60
3100 Hard mortar		30	.267			10.15		10.15	15.50
3200 Block, soft old mortar		70	.114			4.35		4.35	6.65
3400 Hard mortar	↓	50	.160	↓		6.10		6.10	9.30
6000 Walls, interior, not including re-framing,									

For customer support on your Site Work & Landscape Cost Data, call 877.737.1594.

41

02 41 Demolition

02 41 19 – Selective Demolition

02 41 19.16 Selective Demolition, Cutout

		Crew	Daily Output	Labor-Hours	Unit	Material	2015 Bare Costs Labor	2015 Bare Costs Equipment	Total	Total Incl O&P
6010	openings to 5 S.F.									
6100	Drywall to 5/8" thick	1 Clab	24	.333	Ea.		12.55		12.55	19.30
6200	Paneling to 3/4" thick		20	.400			15.05		15.05	23
6300	Plaster, on gypsum lath		20	.400			15.05		15.05	23
6340	On wire lath		14	.571			21.50		21.50	33
7000	Wood frame, not including re-framing, openings to 5 S.F.									
7200	Floors, sheathing and flooring to 2" thick	1 Clab	5	1.600	Ea.		60		60	92.50
7310	Roofs, sheathing to 1" thick, not including roofing		6	1.333			50		50	77
7410	Walls, sheathing to 1" thick, not including siding		7	1.143			43		43	66

02 41 19.18 Selective Demolition, Disposal Only

			Crew	Daily Output	Labor-Hours	Unit	Material	2015 Bare Costs Labor	2015 Bare Costs Equipment	Total	Total Incl O&P
0010	**SELECTIVE DEMOLITION, DISPOSAL ONLY**	R024119-10									
0015	Urban bldg w/salvage value allowed										
0020	Including loading and 5 mile haul to dump										
0200	Steel frame		B-3	430	.112	C.Y.		4.57	6	10.57	13.55
0300	Concrete frame			365	.132			5.40	7.05	12.45	15.95
0400	Masonry construction			445	.108			4.41	5.80	10.21	13.10
0500	Wood frame			247	.194			7.95	10.40	18.35	23.50

02 41 19.19 Selective Demolition

			Crew	Daily Output	Labor-Hours	Unit	Material	2015 Bare Costs Labor	2015 Bare Costs Equipment	Total	Total Incl O&P
0010	**SELECTIVE DEMOLITION,** Rubbish Handling	R024119-10									
0020	The following are to be added to the demolition prices										
0050	The following are components for a complete chute system										
0100	Top chute circular steel, 4' long, 18" diameter	R024119-30	B-1C	15	1.600	Ea.	266	61	29	356	420
0102	23" diameter			15	1.600		288	61	29	378	440
0104	27" diameter			15	1.600		310	61	29	400	465
0106	30" diameter			15	1.600		330	61	29	420	490
0108	33" diameter			15	1.600		355	61	29	445	515
0110	36" diameter			15	1.600		375	61	29	465	540
0112	Regular chute, 18" diameter			15	1.600		199	61	29	289	345
0114	23" diameter			15	1.600		222	61	29	312	370
0116	27" diameter			15	1.600		243	61	29	333	395
0118	30" diameter			15	1.600		266	61	29	356	420
0120	33" diameter			15	1.600		288	61	29	378	440
0122	36" diameter			15	1.600		310	61	29	400	465
0124	Control door chute, 18" diameter			15	1.600		375	61	29	465	540
0126	23" diameter			15	1.600		400	61	29	490	565
0128	27" diameter			15	1.600		420	61	29	510	590
0130	30" diameter			15	1.600		445	61	29	535	615
0132	33" diameter			15	1.600		465	61	29	555	635
0134	36" diameter			15	1.600		490	61	29	580	660
0136	Chute liners, 14 ga., 18-30" diameter			15	1.600		223	61	29	313	370
0138	33-36" diameter			15	1.600		280	61	29	370	435
0140	17% thinner chute, 30" diameter			15	1.600		222	61	29	312	370
0142	33% thinner chute, 30" diameter			15	1.600		167	61	29	257	310
0144	Top chute cover		1 Clab	24	.333		153	12.55		165.55	187
0146	Door chute cover		"	24	.333		153	12.55		165.55	187
0148	Top chute trough		2 Clab	12	1.333		510	50		560	635
0150	Bolt down frame & counter weights, 250 lb.		B-1	4	6		4,250	230		4,480	5,000
0152	500 lb.			4	6		6,200	230		6,430	7,175
0154	750 lb.			4	6		9,100	230		9,330	10,400
0156	1000 lb.			2.67	8.989		10,200	345		10,545	11,700
0158	1500 lb.			2.67	8.989		13,000	345		13,345	14,800
0160	Chute warning light system, 5 stories		B-1C	4	6		8,975	230	109	9,314	10,400

02 41 19.19 Selective Demolition		Crew	Daily Output	Labor-Hours	Unit	Material	2015 Bare Costs Labor	Equipment	Total	Total Incl O&P
0162	10 stories	B-1C	2	12	Ea.	14,300	460	218	14,978	16,600
0164	Dust control device for dumpsters	1 Clab	8	1		102	37.50		139.50	170
0166	Install or replace breakaway cord		8	1		27	37.50		64.50	87.50
0168	Install or replace warning sign		16	.500		11.45	18.80		30.25	41.50
0600	Dumpster, weekly rental, 1 dump/week, 6 C.Y. capacity (2 Tons)				Week	415			415	455
0700	10 C.Y. capacity (3 Tons)					480			480	530
0725	20 C.Y. capacity (5 Tons)	R024119-20				565			565	625
0800	30 C.Y. capacity (7 Tons)					730			730	800
0840	40 C.Y. capacity (10 Tons)					775			775	850
0900	Alternate pricing for dumpsters									
0910	Delivery, average for all sizes				Ea.	75			75	82.50
0920	Haul, average for all sizes					235			235	259
0930	Rent per day, average for all sizes					20			20	22
0940	Rent per month, average for all sizes					80			80	88
0950	Disposal fee per ton, average for all sizes				Ton	88			88	97
2000	Load, haul, dump and return, 0 – 50' haul, hand carried	2 Clab	24	.667	C.Y.		25		25	38.50
2005	Wheeled		37	.432			16.25		16.25	25
2040	0 – 100' haul, hand carried		16.50	.970			36.50		36.50	56
2045	Wheeled		25	.640			24		24	37
2080	Haul and return, add per each extra 100' haul, hand carried		35.50	.451			16.95		16.95	26
2085	Wheeled		54	.296			11.15		11.15	17.15
2120	For travel in elevators, up to 10 floors, add		140	.114			4.30		4.30	6.60
2130	0 – 50' haul, incl. up to 5 riser stair, hand carried		23	.696			26		26	40
2135	Wheeled		35	.457			17.20		17.20	26.50
2140	6 – 10 riser stairs, hand carried		22	.727			27.50		27.50	42
2145	Wheeled		34	.471			17.70		17.70	27
2150	11 – 20 riser stairs, hand carried		20	.800			30		30	46.50
2155	Wheeled		31	.516			19.40		19.40	30
2160	21 – 40 riser stairs, hand carried		16	1			37.50		37.50	58
2165	Wheeled		24	.667			25		25	38.50
2170	0 – 100' haul, incl. 5 riser stair, hand carried		15	1.067			40		40	61.50
2175	Wheeled		23	.696			26		26	40
2180	6 – 10 riser stair, hand carried		14	1.143			43		43	66
2185	Wheeled		21	.762			28.50		28.50	44
2190	11 – 20 riser stair, hand carried		12	1.333			50		50	77
2195	Wheeled		18	.889			33.50		33.50	51.50
2200	21 – 40 riser stair, hand carried		8	2			75		75	116
2205	Wheeled		12	1.333			50		50	77
2210	Haul and return, add per each extra 100' haul, hand carried		35.50	.451			16.95		16.95	26
2215	Wheeled		54	.296			11.15		11.15	17.15
2220	For each additional flight of stairs, up to 5 risers, add		550	.029	Flight		1.09		1.09	1.68
2225	6 – 10 risers, add		275	.058			2.19		2.19	3.37
2230	11 – 20 risers, add		138	.116			4.36		4.36	6.70
2235	21 – 40 risers, add		69	.232			8.70		8.70	13.40
3000	Loading & trucking, including 2 mile haul, chute loaded	B-16	45	.711	C.Y.		27.50	15.35	42.85	59
3040	Hand loading truck, 50' haul	"	48	.667			26	14.40	40.40	55.50
3080	Machine loading truck	B-17	120	.267			10.90	6.45	17.35	24
5000	Haul, per mile, up to 8 C.Y. truck	B-34B	1165	.007			.28	.59	.87	1.07
5100	Over 8 C.Y. truck	"	1550	.005			.21	.45	.66	.80

For customer support on your Site Work & Landscape Cost Data, call 877.737.1594.

43

02 41 Demolition

02 41 19 – Selective Demolition

02 41 19.20 Selective Demolition, Dump Charges		Crew	Daily Output	Labor-Hours	Unit	Material	2015 Bare Costs Labor	Equipment	Total	Total Incl O&P
0010	**SELECTIVE DEMOLITION, DUMP CHARGES** R024119-10									
0020	Dump charges, typical urban city, tipping fees only									
0100	Building construction materials				Ton	74			74	81
0200	Trees, brush, lumber					63			63	69.50
0300	Rubbish only					63			63	69.50
0500	Reclamation station, usual charge					74			74	81

02 41 19.21 Selective Demolition, Gutting

		Crew	Daily Output	Labor-Hours	Unit	Material	Labor	Equipment	Total	Total Incl O&P
0010	**SELECTIVE DEMOLITION, GUTTING** R024119-10									
0020	Building interior, including disposal, dumpster fees not included									
0500	Residential building									
0560	Minimum	B-16	400	.080	SF Flr.		3.10	1.73	4.83	6.65
0580	Maximum	"	360	.089	"		3.44	1.92	5.36	7.35
0900	Commercial building									
1000	Minimum	B-16	350	.091	SF Flr.		3.54	1.97	5.51	7.55
1020	Maximum	"	250	.128	"		4.95	2.76	7.71	10.65

02 41 19.25 Selective Demolition, Saw Cutting

		Crew	Daily Output	Labor-Hours	Unit	Material	Labor	Equipment	Total	Total Incl O&P
0010	**SELECTIVE DEMOLITION, SAW CUTTING** R024119-10									
0015	Asphalt, up to 3" deep	B-89	1050	.015	L.F.	.12	.67	.46	1.25	1.65
0020	Each additional inch of depth	"	1800	.009		.04	.39	.27	.70	.93
1200	Masonry walls, hydraulic saw, brick, per inch of depth	B-89B	300	.053		.04	2.34	2.86	5.24	6.75
1220	Block walls, solid, per inch of depth	"	250	.064		.04	2.81	3.43	6.28	8.05
2000	Brick or masonry w/hand held saw, per inch of depth	A-1	125	.064		.05	2.41	.65	3.11	4.46
5000	Wood sheathing to 1" thick, on walls	1 Carp	200	.040			1.88		1.88	2.89
5020	On roof	"	250	.032			1.50		1.50	2.31

02 41 19.27 Selective Demolition, Torch Cutting

		Crew	Daily Output	Labor-Hours	Unit	Material	Labor	Equipment	Total	Total Incl O&P
0010	**SELECTIVE DEMOLITION, TORCH CUTTING** R024119-10									
0020	Steel, 1" thick plate	E-25	333	.024	L.F.	.84	1.31	.03	2.18	3.24
0040	1" diameter bar	"	600	.013	Ea.	.14	.73	.02	.89	1.44
1000	Oxygen lance cutting, reinforced concrete walls									
1040	12" to 16" thick walls	1 Clab	10	.800	L.F.		30		30	46.50
1080	24" thick walls	"	6	1.333	"		50		50	77

02 42 Removal and Salvage of Construction Materials

02 42 10 – Building Deconstruction

02 42 10.10 Estimated Salvage Value or Savings

		Crew	Daily Output	Labor-Hours	Unit	Material	Labor	Equipment	Total	Total Incl O&P
0010	**ESTIMATED SALVAGE VALUE OR SAVINGS**									
0015	Excludes material handling, packaging, container costs and									
0020	transportation for salvage or disposal									
0050	All Items in Section 02 42 10.10 are credit deducts and not costs									
0100	Copper Wire Salvage Value G				Lb.				1.60	1.60
0110	Disposal Savings G								.04	.04
0200	Copper Pipe Salvage Value G								2.50	2.50
0210	Disposal Savings G								.05	.05
0300	Steel Pipe Salvage Value G								.06	.06
0310	Disposal Savings G								.03	.03
0400	Cast Iron Pipe Salvage Value G								.03	.03
0410	Disposal Savings G								.01	.01
0500	Steel Doors or Windows Salvage Value G								.06	.06
0510	Aluminum G								.55	.55
0520	Disposal Savings G								.03	.03

02 42 Removal and Salvage of Construction Materials

02 42 10 – Building Deconstruction

	02 42 10.10 Estimated Salvage Value or Savings		Crew	Daily Output	Labor-Hours	Unit	Material	2015 Bare Costs Labor	Equipment	Total	Total Incl O&P
0600	Aluminum Siding Salvage Value	G				Lb.				.49	.49
0630	Disposal Savings	G				▼				.03	.03
0640	Wood Siding (no lead or asbestos)	G				C.Y.				12	12
0800	Clean Concrete Disposal Savings	G				Ton				62	62
0850	Asphalt Shingles Disposal Savings	G				"				60	60
1000	Wood wall framing clean salvage value	G				M.B.F.				55	55
1010	Painted	G								44	44
1020	Floor framing	G								55	55
1030	Painted	G								44	44
1050	Roof framing	G								55	55
1060	Painted	G								44	44
1100	Wood beams salvage value	G				▼				55	55
1200	Wood framing and beams disposal savings	G				Ton				66	66
1220	Wood sheating and sub-base flooring	G								72.50	72.50
1230	Wood wall paneling (1/4 inch thick)	G				▼				66	66
1300	Wood panel 3/4-1 inch thick low salvage value	G				S.F.				.55	.55
1350	high salvage value	G				"				2.20	2.20
1400	Disposal savings	G				Ton				66	66
1500	Flooring tongue and groove 25/32 inch thick low salvage value	G				S.F.				.55	.55
1530	High salvage value	G				"				1.10	1.10
1560	Disposal savings	G				Ton				66	66
1600	Drywall or sheet rock salvage value	G				▼				22	22
1650	Disposal savings	G				▼				66	66

02 42 10.20 Deconstruction of Building Components

			Crew	Daily Output	Labor-Hours	Unit	Material	2015 Bare Costs Labor	Equipment	Total	Total Incl O&P
0010	**DECONSTRUCTION OF BUILDING COMPONENTS**										
0012	Buildings one or two stories only										
0015	Excludes material handling, packaging, container costs and										
0020	transportation for salvage or disposal										
0050	Deconstruction of Plumbing Fixtures										
0100	Wall hung or countertop lavatory	G	2 Clab	16	1	Ea.		37.50		37.50	58
0110	Single or double compartment kitchen sink	G		14	1.143			43		43	66
0120	Wall hung urinal	G		14	1.143			43		43	66
0130	Floor mounted	G		8	2			75		75	116
0140	Floor mounted water closet	G		16	1			37.50		37.50	58
0150	Wall hung	G		14	1.143			43		43	66
0160	Water fountain, free standing	G		16	1			37.50		37.50	58
0170	Wall hung or deck mounted	G		12	1.333			50		50	77
0180	Bathtub, steel or fiberglass	G		10	1.600			60		60	92.50
0190	Cast iron	G		8	2			75		75	116
0200	Shower, single	G		6	2.667			100		100	154
0210	Group	G	▼	7	2.286	▼		86		86	132
0300	Deconstruction of Electrical Fixtures										
0310	Surface mount incandescent fixtures	G	2 Clab	48	.333	Ea.		12.55		12.55	19.30
0320	Fluorescent, 2 lamp	G		32	.500			18.80		18.80	29
0330	4 lamp	G		24	.667			25		25	38.50
0340	Strip Fluorescent, 1 lamp	G		40	.400			15.05		15.05	23
0350	2 lamp	G		32	.500			18.80		18.80	29
0400	Recessed drop-in fluorescent fixture, 2 lamp	G		27	.593			22.50		22.50	34.50
0410	4 lamp	G	▼	18	.889	▼		33.50		33.50	51.50
0500	Deconstruction of appliances										
0510	Cooking stoves	G	2 Clab	26	.615	Ea.		23		23	35.50
0520	Dishwashers	G	"	26	.615	"		23		23	35.50

For customer support on your Site Work & Landscape Cost Data, call 877.737.1594.

45

02 42 10.20 Deconstruction of Building Components		Crew	Daily Output	Labor-Hours	Unit	Material	2015 Bare Costs Labor	Equipment	Total	Total Incl O&P
0600	Deconstruction of millwork and trim									
0610	Cabinets, wood	G	2 Carp	40	.400	L.F.		18.80		18.80	29
0620	Countertops	G		100	.160	"		7.50		7.50	11.55
0630	Wall paneling, 1 inch thick	G		500	.032	S.F.		1.50		1.50	2.31
0640	Ceiling trim	G		500	.032	L.F.		1.50		1.50	2.31
0650	Wainscoting	G		500	.032	S.F.		1.50		1.50	2.31
0660	Base, 3/4" to 1" thick	G		600	.027	L.F.		1.25		1.25	1.93
0700	Deconstruction of doors and windows										
0710	Doors, wrap, interior, wood, single, no closers	G	2 Carp	21	.762	Ea.	4.50	36		40.50	60
0720	Double	G		13	1.231		9	58		67	99
0730	Solid core, single, exterior or interior	G		10	1.600		4.50	75		79.50	121
0740	Double	G		8	2		9	94		103	155
0810	Windows, wrap, wood, single										
0812	with no casement or cladding	G	2 Carp	21	.762	Ea.	4.50	36		40.50	60
0820	with casement and/or cladding	G	"	18	.889	"	4.50	41.50		46	69
0900	Deconstruction of interior finishes										
0910	Drywall for recycling	G	2 Clab	1775	.009	S.F.		.34		.34	.52
0920	Plaster wall, first floor	G		1775	.009			.34		.34	.52
0930	Second floor	G		1330	.012			.45		.45	.70
1000	Deconstruction of roofing and accessories										
1010	Built-up roofs	G	2 Clab	570	.028	S.F.		1.06		1.06	1.62
1020	Gutters, facia and rakes	G	"	1140	.014	L.F.		.53		.53	.81
2000	Deconstruction of wood components										
2010	Roof sheeting	G	2 Clab	570	.028	S.F.		1.06		1.06	1.62
2020	Main roof framing	G		760	.021	L.F.		.79		.79	1.22
2030	Porch roof framing	G		445	.036			1.35		1.35	2.08
2040	Beams 4" x 8"	G	B-1	375	.064			2.45		2.45	3.77
2050	4" x 10"	G		300	.080			3.06		3.06	4.71
2055	4" x 12"	G		250	.096			3.67		3.67	5.65
2060	6" x 8"	G		250	.096			3.67		3.67	5.65
2065	6" x 10"	G		200	.120			4.59		4.59	7.05
2070	6" x 12"	G		170	.141			5.40		5.40	8.30
2075	8" x 12"	G		126	.190			7.30		7.30	11.20
2080	10" x 12"	G		100	.240			9.20		9.20	14.15
2100	Ceiling joists	G	2 Clab	800	.020			.75		.75	1.16
2150	Wall framing, interior	G		1230	.013			.49		.49	.75
2160	Sub-floor	G		2000	.008	S.F.		.30		.30	.46
2170	Floor joists	G		2000	.008	L.F.		.30		.30	.46
2200	Wood siding (no lead or asbestos)	G		1300	.012	S.F.		.46		.46	.71
2300	Wall framing, exterior	G		1600	.010	L.F.		.38		.38	.58
2400	Stair risers	G		53	.302	Ea.		11.35		11.35	17.45
2500	Posts	G		800	.020	L.F.		.75		.75	1.16
3000	Deconstruction of exterior brick walls										
3010	Exterior brick walls, first floor	G	2 Clab	200	.080	S.F.		3.01		3.01	4.63
3020	Second floor	G		64	.250	"		9.40		9.40	14.45
3030	Brick chimney	G		100	.160	C.F.		6		6	9.25
4000	Deconstruction of concrete										
4010	Slab on grade, 4" thick, plain concrete	G	B-9	500	.080	S.F.		3.04	.47	3.51	5.20
4020	Wire mesh reinforced	G		470	.085			3.23	.50	3.73	5.50
4030	Rod reinforced	G		400	.100			3.80	.58	4.38	6.50
4110	Foundation wall, 6" thick, plain concrete	G		160	.250			9.50	1.46	10.96	16.20
4120	8" thick	G		140	.286			10.85	1.66	12.51	18.55
4130	10" thick	G		120	.333			12.65	1.94	14.59	21.50

02 42 Removal and Salvage of Construction Materials

02 42 10 – Building Deconstruction

02 42 10.20 Deconstruction of Building Components

		Crew	Daily Output	Labor-Hours	Unit	Material	2015 Bare Costs Labor	Equipment	Total	Total Incl O&P
9000	Deconstruction process, support equipment as needed									
9010	Daily use, portal to portal, 12-ton truck-mounted hydraulic crane crew	G A-3H	1	8	Day		415	860	1,275	1,575
9020	Daily use, skid steer and operator	G A-3C	1	8			390	320	710	940
9030	Daily use, backhoe 48 H.P., operator and labor	G "	1	8	↓		390	320	710	940

02 42 10.30 Deconstruction Material Handling

		Crew	Daily Output	Labor-Hours	Unit	Material	2015 Bare Costs Labor	Equipment	Total	Total Incl O&P
0010	**DECONSTRUCTION MATERIAL HANDLING**									
0012	Buildings one or two stories only									
0100	Clean and stack brick on pallet	G 2 Clab	1200	.013	Ea.		.50		.50	.77
0200	Haul 50' and load rough lumber up to 2" x 8" size	G	2000	.008	"		.30		.30	.46
0210	Lumber larger than 2" x 8"	G	3200	.005	B.F.		.19		.19	.29
0300	Finish wood for recycling stack and wrap per pallet	G	8	2	Ea.	36	75		111	156
0350	Light fixtures		6	2.667		65	100		165	226
0375	Windows		6	2.667		61	100		161	222
0400	Miscellaneous materials	↓	8	2	↓	18	75		93	136
1000	See Section 02 41 19.19 for bulk material handling									

02 43 Structure Moving

02 43 13 – Structure Relocation

02 43 13.13 Building Relocation

		Crew	Daily Output	Labor-Hours	Unit	Material	2015 Bare Costs Labor	Equipment	Total	Total Incl O&P
0010	**BUILDING RELOCATION**									
0011	One day move, up to 24' wide									
0020	Reset on existing foundation				Total				11,500	11,500
0040	Wood or steel frame bldg., based on ground floor area	G B-4	185	.259	S.F.		9.95	2.78	12.73	18.30
0060	Masonry bldg., based on ground floor area	G "	137	.350			13.45	3.75	17.20	24.50
0200	For 24' to 42' wide, add				↓				15%	15%

02 56 Site containment

02 56 13 – Waste containment

02 56 13.10 Containment of Hazardous Waste

		Crew	Daily Output	Labor-Hours	Unit	Material	2015 Bare Costs Labor	Equipment	Total	Total Incl O&P
0010	**CONTAINMENT OF HAZARDOUS WASTE**									
0020	OSHA hazard level C									
0030	OSHA Hazard level D decrease labor and equipment, deduct						-45%	-45%		
0035	OSHA Hazard level B increase labor and equipment, add						22%	22%		
0040	OSHA Hazard level A increase labor and equipment, add						71%	71%		
0100	Excavation of contaminated soil & waste									
0105	Includes one respirator filter and two disposable suits per work day									
0110	3/4 C.Y. excavator to 10 feet deep	B-12F	51	.314	B.C.Y.	1.59	14	12.85	28.44	37.50
0120	Labor crew to 6' deep	B-2	19	2.105		10.65	80		90.65	135
0130	6' - 12' deep	"	12	3.333	↓	16.85	127		143.85	214
0200	Move contaminated soil/waste upto 150' on-site with 2.5 C.Y. loader	B-10T	300	.040	L.C.Y.	.27	1.85	1.73	3.85	5.05
0210	300'	"	186	.065	"	.43	2.99	2.80	6.22	8.10
0300	Secure burial cell construction									
0310	Various liner and cover materials									
0400	Very low density polyethylene (VLDPE)									
0410	50 mil top cover	B-47H	4000	.008	S.F.	.42	.39	.08	.89	1.15
0420	80 mil liner	"	4000	.008	"	.52	.39	.08	.99	1.26
0500	Chlorosulfunated polyethylene									
0510	36 mil hypalon top cover	B-47H	4000	.008	S.F.	1.57	.39	.08	2.04	2.42
0520	45 mil hypalon liner	"	4000	.008	"	1.71	.39	.08	2.18	2.57

For customer support on your Site Work & Landscape Cost Data, call 877.737.1594.

47

02 56 Site containment

02 56 13 – Waste containment

02 56 13.10 Containment of Hazardous Waste

		Crew	Daily Output	Labor-Hours	Unit	Material	2015 Bare Costs Labor	Equipment	Total	Total Incl O&P
0600	Polyvinyl chloride (PVC)									
0610	60 mil top cover	B-47H	4000	.008	S.F.	.81	.39	.08	1.28	1.58
0620	80 mil liner	"	4000	.008	"	.97	.39	.08	1.44	1.76
0700	Rough textured H.D. polyethylene (HDPE)									
0710	40 mil top cover	B-47H	4000	.008	S.F.	.40	.39	.08	.87	1.13
0720	60 mil top cover		4000	.008		.46	.39	.08	.93	1.20
0722	60 mil liner		4000	.008		.42	.39	.08	.89	1.15
0730	80 mil liner		3800	.008		.53	.41	.08	1.02	1.31
1000	3/4" crushed stone, 6" deep ballast around liner	B-6	30	.800	L.C.Y.	23.50	33	12.15	68.65	90
1100	Hazardous waste, ballast cover with common borrow material	B-63	56	.714		12.40	28.50	3.10	44	60.50
1110	Mixture of common borrow & topsoil		56	.714		18.45	28.50	3.10	50.05	67.50
1120	Bank sand		56	.714		17.85	28.50	3.10	49.45	66.50
1130	Medium priced clay		44	.909		24	36	3.95	63.95	86.50
1140	Mixture of common borrow & medium priced clay		56	.714		18.20	28.50	3.10	49.80	67

02 58 Snow Control

02 58 13 – Snow Fencing

02 58 13.10 Snow Fencing System

		Crew	Daily Output	Labor-Hours	Unit	Material	2015 Bare Costs Labor	Equipment	Total	Total Incl O&P
0010	**SNOW FENCING SYSTEM**									
7001	Snow fence on steel posts 10' O.C., 4' high	B-1	500	.048	L.F.	.93	1.84		2.77	3.85

02 65 Underground Storage Tank Removal

02 65 10 – Underground Tank and Contaminated Soil Removal

02 65 10.30 Removal of Underground Storage Tanks

			Crew	Daily Output	Labor-Hours	Unit	Material	2015 Bare Costs Labor	Equipment	Total	Total Incl O&P
0010	**REMOVAL OF UNDERGROUND STORAGE TANKS**	R026510-20									
0011	Petroleum storage tanks, non-leaking										
0100	Excavate & load onto trailer										
0110	3000 gal. to 5000 gal. tank	G	B-14	4	12	Ea.		475	91	566	830
0120	6000 gal. to 8000 gal. tank	G	B-3A	3	13.333			535	345	880	1,200
0130	9000 gal. to 12000 gal. tank	G	"	2	20			805	515	1,320	1,800
0190	Known leaking tank, add					%				100%	100%
0200	Remove sludge, water and remaining product from tank bottom										
0201	of tank with vacuum truck										
0300	3000 gal. to 5000 gal. tank	G	A-13	5	1.600	Ea.		78	153	231	286
0310	6000 gal. to 8000 gal. tank	G		4	2			97	191	288	360
0320	9000 gal. to 12000 gal. tank	G		3	2.667			130	254	384	475
0390	Dispose of sludge off-site, average					Gal.				6.25	6.80
0400	Insert inert solid CO_2 "dry ice" into tank										
0401	For cleaning/transporting tanks (1.5 lb./100 gal. cap)	G	1 Clab	500	.016	Lb.	1.17	.60		1.77	2.22
0403	Insert solid carbon dioxide, 1.5 lb./100 gal.	G	"	400	.020	"	1.17	.75		1.92	2.45
0503	Disconnect and remove piping	G	1 Plum	160	.050	L.F.		2.94		2.94	4.43
0603	Transfer liquids, 10% of volume	G	"	1600	.005	Gal.		.29		.29	.44
0703	Cut accessway into underground storage tank	G	1 Clab	5.33	1.501	Ea.		56.50		56.50	87
0813	Remove sludge, wash and wipe tank, 500 gal.	G	1 Plum	8	1			58.50		58.50	88.50
0823	3,000 gal.	G		6.67	1.199			70.50		70.50	106
0833	5,000 gal.	G		6.15	1.301			76.50		76.50	115
0843	8,000 gal.	G		5.33	1.501			88		88	133
0853	10,000 gal.	G		4.57	1.751			103		103	155
0863	12,000 gal.	G		4.21	1.900			112		112	168

02 65 Underground Storage Tank Removal

02 65 10 – Underground Tank and Contaminated Soil Removal

02 65 10.30 Removal of Underground Storage Tanks		Crew	Daily Output	Labor-Hours	Unit	Material	2015 Bare Costs Labor	Equipment	Total	Total Incl O&P
1020	Haul tank to certified salvage dump, 100 miles round trip									
1023	3000 gal. to 5000 gal. tank				Ea.				760	830
1026	6000 gal. to 8000 gal. tank								880	960
1029	9,000 gal. to 12,000 gal. tank				▼				1,050	1,150
1100	Disposal of contaminated soil to landfill									
1110	Minimum				C.Y.				145	160
1111	Maximum				"				400	440
1120	Disposal of contaminated soil to									
1121	bituminous concrete batch plant									
1130	Minimum				C.Y.				80	88
1131	Maximum				"				115	125
1203	Excavate, pull, & load tank, backfill hole, 8,000 gal. +	G	B-12C	.50	32	Ea.		1,425	2,350	3,775	4,750
1213	Haul tank to certified dump, 100 miles rt, 8,000 gal. +	G	B-34K	1	8			320	950	1,270	1,525
1223	Excavate, pull, & load tank, backfill hole, 500 gal.	G	B-11C	1	16			705	365	1,070	1,475
1233	Excavate, pull, & load tank, backfill hole, 3,000 – 5,000 gal.	G	B-11M	.50	32			1,400	785	2,185	3,000
1243	Haul tank to certified dump, 100 miles rt, 500 gal.	G	B-34L	1	8			390	245	635	860
1253	Haul tank to certified dump, 100 miles rt, 3,000 – 5,000 gal.	G	B-34M	1	8	▼		390	305	695	925
2010	Decontamination of soil on site incl poly tarp on top/bottom									
2011	Soil containment berm, and chemical treatment									
2020	Minimum	G	B-11C	100	.160	C.Y.	7.80	7.05	3.64	18.49	23.50
2021	Maximum	G	"	100	.160	▼	10.10	7.05	3.64	20.79	26
2050	Disposal of decontaminated soil, minimum									135	150
2055	Maximum				▼				400	440

02 81 Transportation and Disposal of Hazardous Materials

02 81 20 – Hazardous Waste Handling

02 81 20.10 Hazardous Waste Cleanup/Pickup/Disposal

		Crew	Daily Output	Labor-Hours	Unit	Material	2015 Bare Costs Labor	Equipment	Total	Total Incl O&P
0010	**HAZARDOUS WASTE CLEANUP/PICKUP/DISPOSAL**									
0100	For contractor rental equipment, i.e., Dozer,									
0110	Front end loader, Dump truck, etc., see 01 54 33 Reference Section									
1000	Solid pickup									
1100	55 gal. drums				Ea.				240	265
1120	Bulk material, minimum				Ton				190	210
1130	Maximum				"				595	655
1200	Transportation to disposal site									
1220	Truckload = 80 drums or 25 C.Y. or 18 tons									
1260	Minimum				Mile				3.95	4.45
1270	Maximum				"				7.25	7.35
3000	Liquid pickup, vacuum truck, stainless steel tank									
3100	Minimum charge, 4 hours									
3110	1 compartment, 2200 gallon				Hr.				140	155
3120	2 compartment, 5000 gallon				"				200	225
3400	Transportation in 6900 gallon bulk truck				Mile				7.95	8.75
3410	In teflon lined truck				"				10.20	11.25
5000	Heavy sludge or dry vacuumable material				Hr.				140	160
6000	Dumpsite disposal charge, minimum				Ton				140	155
6020	Maximum				"				415	455

For customer support on your Site Work & Landscape Cost Data, call 877.737.1594.

49

02 91 Chemical Sampling, Testing and Analysis

02 91 10 – Monitoring, Sampling, Testing and Analysis

02 91 10.10 Monitoring, Chemical Sampling, Testing and Analysis	Crew	Daily Output	Labor-Hours	Unit	Material	2015 Bare Costs Labor	2015 Bare Costs Equipment	Total	Total Incl O&P
0010 **MONITORING, CHEMICAL SAMPLING, TESTING AND ANALYSIS**									
0015 Field Sampling of waste									
0100 Field samples, sample collection, sludge	1 Skwk	32	.250	Ea.		12.15		12.15	18.80
0110 Contaminated soils	"	32	.250	"		12.15		12.15	18.80
0200 Vials and bottles									
0210 32 oz. clear wide mouth jar (case of 12)				Ea.	43.50			43.50	48
0220 32 oz. Boston round bottle (case of 12)					38			38	42
0230 32 oz. HDPE bottle (case of 12)				↓	36			36	39.50
0300 Laboratory analytical services									
0310 Laboratory testing 13 metals				Ea.	187			187	205
0312 13 metals + mercury					220			220	242
0314 8 metals					160			160	176
0316 Mercury only					42			42	46
0318 Single metal (only Cs, Li, Sr, Ta)					43			43	47.50
0320 Single metal (excludes Hg, Cs, Li, Sr, Ta)					43			43	47.50
0400 Hydrocarbons standard					89			89	98
0410 Hydrocarbons fingerprint					161			161	177
0500 Radioactivity gross alpha					154			154	169
0510 Gross alpha & beta					154			154	169
0520 Radium 226					87			87	96
0530 Radium 228					128			128	141
0540 Radon					148			148	162
0550 Uranium					90			90	99
0600 Volatile organics without GC/MS					156			156	172
0610 Volatile organics including GC/MS					179			179	197
0630 Synthetic organic compounds					1,025			1,025	1,125
0640 Herbicides					215			215	237
0650 Pesticides					151			151	166
0660 PCB's				↓	138			138	152

For customer support on your Site Work & Landscape Cost Data, call 877.737.1594.

Estimating Tips
General

- Carefully check all the plans and specifications. Concrete often appears on drawings other than structural drawings, including mechanical and electrical drawings for equipment pads. The cost of cutting and patching is often difficult to estimate. See Subdivision 03 81 for Concrete Cutting, Subdivision 02 41 19.16 for Cutout Demolition, Subdivision 03 05 05.10 for Concrete Demolition, and Subdivision 02 41 19.19 for Rubbish Handling (handling, loading and hauling of debris).

- Always obtain concrete prices from suppliers near the job site. A volume discount can often be negotiated, depending upon competition in the area. Remember to add for waste, particularly for slabs and footings on grade.

03 10 00 Concrete Forming and Accessories

- A primary cost for concrete construction is forming. Most jobs today are constructed with prefabricated forms. The selection of the forms best suited for the job and the total square feet of forms required for efficient concrete forming and placing are key elements in estimating concrete construction. Enough forms must be available for erection to make efficient use of the concrete placing equipment and crew.

- Concrete accessories for forming and placing depend upon the systems used. Study the plans and specifications to ensure that all special accessory requirements have been included in the cost estimate, such as anchor bolts, inserts, and hangers.

- Included within costs for forms-in-place are all necessary bracing and shoring.

03 20 00 Concrete Reinforcing

- Ascertain that the reinforcing steel supplier has included all accessories, cutting, bending, and an allowance for lapping, splicing, and waste. A good rule of thumb is 10% for lapping, splicing, and waste. Also, 10% waste should be allowed for welded wire fabric.

- The unit price items in the subdivisions for Reinforcing In Place, Glass Fiber Reinforcing, and Welded Wire Fabric include the labor to install accessories such as beam and slab bolsters, high chairs, and bar ties and tie wire. The material cost for these accessories is not included; they may be obtained from the Accessories Division.

03 30 00 Cast-In-Place Concrete

- When estimating structural concrete, pay particular attention to requirements for concrete additives, curing methods, and surface treatments. Special consideration for climate, hot or cold, must be included in your estimate. Be sure to include requirements for concrete placing equipment, and concrete finishing.

- For accurate concrete estimating, the estimator must consider each of the following major components individually: forms, reinforcing steel, ready-mix concrete, placement of the concrete, and finishing of the top surface. For faster estimating, Subdivision 03 30 53.40 for Concrete-In-Place can be used; here, various items of concrete work are presented that include the costs of all five major components (unless specifically stated otherwise).

03 40 00 Precast Concrete
03 50 00 Cast Decks and Underlayment

- The cost of hauling precast concrete structural members is often an important factor. For this reason, it is important to get a quote from the nearest supplier. It may become economically feasible to set up precasting beds on the site if the hauling costs are prohibitive.

Reference Numbers
Reference numbers are shown in shaded boxes at the beginning of some major classifications. These numbers refer to related items in the Reference Section. The reference information may be an estimating procedure, an alternate pricing method, or technical information.

Note: Not all subdivisions listed here necessarily appear in this publication. ∎

03 01 Maintenance of Concrete

03 01 30 – Maintenance of Cast-In-Place Concrete

03 01 30.62 Concrete Patching	Crew	Daily Output	Labor-Hours	Unit	Material	2015 Bare Costs Labor	2015 Bare Costs Equipment	Total	Total Incl O&P
0010 **CONCRETE PATCHING**									
0100 Floors, 1/4" thick, small areas, regular grout	1 Cefi	170	.047	S.F.	1.46	2.12		3.58	4.74
0150 Epoxy grout	"	100	.080	"	8.05	3.60		11.65	14.25
2000 Walls, including chipping, cleaning and epoxy grout									
2100 1/4" deep	1 Cefi	65	.123	S.F.	7.65	5.55		13.20	16.65
2150 1/2" deep	↓	50	.160		15.35	7.20		22.55	27.50
2200 3/4" deep	↓	40	.200	↓	23	9		32	39
2400 Walls, including chipping or sand blasting,									
2410 Priming, and two part polymer mix, 1/4" deep	1 Cefi	80	.100	S.F.	2.25	4.50		6.75	9.10
2420 1/2" deep		60	.133		4.50	6		10.50	13.85
2430 3/4" deep	↓	40	.200	↓	6.75	9		15.75	21

03 05 Common Work Results for Concrete

03 05 05 – Selective Demolition for Concrete

03 05 05.10 Selective Demolition, Concrete

03 05 05.10 Selective Demolition, Concrete	Crew	Daily Output	Labor-Hours	Unit	Material	2015 Bare Costs Labor	2015 Bare Costs Equipment	Total	Total Incl O&P
0010 **SELECTIVE DEMOLITION, CONCRETE** R024119-10									
0012 Excludes saw cutting, torch cutting, loading or hauling									
0050 Break into small pieces, reinf. less than 1% of cross-sectional area	B-9	24	1.667	C.Y.		63.50	9.70	73.20	108
0060 Reinforcing 1% to 2% of cross-sectional area	↓	16	2.500			95	14.55	109.55	162
0070 Reinforcing more than 2% of cross-sectional area	↓	8	5	↓		190	29	219	325
0150 Remove whole pieces, up to 2 tons per piece	E-18	36	1.111	Ea.		58.50	26.50	85	128
0160 2 – 5 tons per piece		30	1.333			70	31.50	101.50	154
0170 5 – 10 tons per piece		24	1.667			87.50	39.50	127	193
0180 10 – 15 tons per piece	↓	18	2.222			117	52.50	169.50	256
0250 Precast unit embedded in masonry, up to 1 C.F.	D-1	16	1			42		42	64.50
0260 1 – 2 C.F.		12	1.333			56		56	85.50
0270 2 – 5 C.F.		10	1.600			67.50		67.50	103
0280 5 – 10 C.F.	↓	8	2	↓		84		84	129
0990 For hydrodemolition see Section 02 41 13.15									

03 05 13 – Basic Concrete Materials

03 05 13.20 Concrete Admixtures and Surface Treatments

03 05 13.20 Concrete Admixtures and Surface Treatments	Crew	Daily Output	Labor-Hours	Unit	Material	2015 Bare Costs Labor	2015 Bare Costs Equipment	Total	Total Incl O&P
0010 **CONCRETE ADMIXTURES AND SURFACE TREATMENTS**									
0040 Abrasives, aluminum oxide, over 20 tons				Lb.	1.88			1.88	2.07
0050 1 to 20 tons					2.02			2.02	2.22
0070 Under 1 ton					2.10			2.10	2.31
0100 Silicon carbide, black, over 20 tons					2.87			2.87	3.16
0110 1 to 20 tons					3.04			3.04	3.35
0120 Under 1 ton				↓	3.17			3.17	3.49
0200 Air entraining agent, .7 to 1.5 oz. per bag, 55 gallon drum				Gal.	14			14	15.40
0220 5 gallon pail					19.25			19.25	21
0300 Bonding agent, acrylic latex, 250 S.F. per gallon, 5 gallon pail					22.50			22.50	25
0320 Epoxy resin, 80 S.F. per gallon, 4 gallon case				↓	61			61	67
0400 Calcium chloride, 50 lb. bags, TL lots				Ton	810			810	890
0420 Less than truckload lots				Bag	24			24	26.50
0500 Carbon black, liquid, 2 to 8 lb. per bag of cement				Lb.	9.10			9.10	10
0600 Colored pigments, integral, 2 to 10 lb. per bag of cement, subtle colors					2.40			2.40	2.64
0610 Standard colors					3.26			3.26	3.59
0620 Premium colors				↓	5.40			5.40	5.95
0920 Dustproofing compound, 250 S.F./gal., 5 gallon pail				Gal.	6.65			6.65	7.30
1010 Epoxy based, 125 S.F./gal., 5 gallon pail				"	55.50			55.50	61

03 05 Common Work Results for Concrete

03 05 13 – Basic Concrete Materials

03 05 13.20 Concrete Admixtures and Surface Treatments	Crew	Daily Output	Labor-Hours	Unit	Material	2015 Bare Costs Labor	Equipment	Total	Total Incl O&P
1100 Hardeners, metallic, 55 lb. bags, natural (grey)				Lb.	.70			.70	.76
1200 Colors					2.27			2.27	2.50
1300 Non-metallic, 55 lb. bags, natural grey					.43			.43	.47
1320 Colors					.94			.94	1.04
1550 Release agent, for tilt slabs, 5 gallon pail				Gal.	17.60			17.60	19.40
1570 For forms, 5 gallon pail					12.50			12.50	13.75
1590 Concrete release agent for forms, 100% biodegradeable, zero VOC, 5 gal pail G					19.95			19.95	22
1595 55 gallon drum G					16.80			16.80	18.50
1600 Sealer, hardener and dustproofer, epoxy-based, 125 S.F./gal., 5 gallon unit					55.50			55.50	61
1620 3 gallon unit					61			61	67.50
1630 Sealer, solvent-based, 250 S.F./gal., 55 gallon drum					24.50			24.50	27
1640 5 gallon pail					30.50			30.50	34
1650 Sealer, water based, 350 S.F., 55 gallon drum					22.50			22.50	25
1660 5 gallon pail					25.50			25.50	28.50
1900 Set retarder, 100 S.F./gal., 1 gallon pail					22.50			22.50	24.50
2000 Waterproofing, integral 1 lb. per bag of cement				Lb.	2.12			2.12	2.33
2100 Powdered metallic, 40 lb. per 100 S.F., standard colors					2.52			2.52	2.77
2120 Premium colors					3.53			3.53	3.88
3000 For integral colored pigments, 2500 psi (5 bag mix)									
3100 Standard colors, 1.8 lb. per bag, add				C.Y.	21.50			21.50	24
3200 9.4 lb. per bag, add					113			113	124
3400 Premium colors, 1.8 lb. per bag, add					29.50			29.50	32.50
3500 7.5 lb. per bag, add					122			122	134
3700 Ultra premium colors, 1.8 lb. per bag, add					49			49	53.50
3800 7.5 lb. per bag, add					203			203	224
6000 Concrete ready mix additives, recycled coal fly ash, mixed at plant G				Ton	58.50			58.50	64
6010 Recycled blast furnace slag, mixed at plant G				"	91			91	100

03 05 13.25 Aggregate

03 05 13.25 Aggregate	Crew	Daily Output	Labor-Hours	Unit	Material	2015 Bare Costs Labor	Equipment	Total	Total Incl O&P
0010 **AGGREGATE** R033105-20									
0100 Lightweight vermiculite or perlite, 4 C.F. bag, C.L. lots G				Bag	23.50			23.50	26
0150 L.C.L. lots G				"	26.50			26.50	29
0250 Sand & stone, loaded at pit, crushed bank gravel				Ton	21.50			21.50	23.50
0350 Sand, washed, for concrete					19.35			19.35	21.50
0400 For plaster or brick					19.35			19.35	21.50
0450 Stone, 3/4" to 1-1/2"					17.80			17.80	19.60
0470 Round, river stone					26.50			26.50	29
0500 3/8" roofing stone & 1/2" pea stone					26			26	28.50
0550 For trucking 10-mile round trip, add to the above	B-34B	117	.068			2.74	5.90	8.64	10.65
0600 For trucking 30-mile round trip, add to the above	"	72	.111			4.45	9.60	14.05	17.30
0850 Sand & stone, loaded at pit, crushed bank gravel				C.Y.	30			30	33
0950 Sand, washed, for concrete					27			27	29.50
1000 For plaster or brick					27			27	29.50
1050 Stone, 3/4" to 1-1/2"					34			34	37.50
1055 Round, river stone					36			36	39.50
1100 3/8" roofing stone & 1/2" pea stone					25.50			25.50	28
1150 For trucking 10-mile round trip, add to the above	B-34B	78	.103			4.11	8.85	12.96	15.95
1200 For trucking 30-mile round trip, add to the above	"	48	.167			6.70	14.40	21.10	26
1310 Onyx chips, 50 lb. bags				Cwt.	34			34	37
1330 Quartz chips, 50 lb. bags					33.50			33.50	37
1410 White marble, 3/8" to 1/2", 50 lb. bags					7.50			7.50	8.25
1430 3/4", bulk				Ton	117			117	129

For customer support on your Site Work & Landscape Cost Data, call 877.737.1594.

53

03 05 Common Work Results for Concrete

03 05 13 – Basic Concrete Materials

03 05 13.30 Cement

		Crew	Daily Output	Labor-Hours	Unit	Material	2015 Bare Costs Labor	Equipment	Total	Total Incl O&P
0010	**CEMENT** R033105-20									
0240	Portland, Type I/II, TL lots, 94 lb. bags				Bag	9.90			9.90	10.90
0250	LTL/LCL lots				"	11			11	12.10
0300	Trucked in bulk, per Cwt.				Cwt.	7.10			7.10	7.85
0400	Type III, high early strength, TL lots, 94 lb. bags				Bag	11.80			11.80	13
0420	L.T.L. or L.C.L. lots					12.10			12.10	13.30
0500	White, type III, high early strength, T.L. or C.L. lots, bags					23.50			23.50	26
0520	L.T.L. or L.C.L. lots					24			24	26.50
0600	White, type I, T.L. or C.L. lots, bags					25			25	27.50
0620	L.T.L. or L.C.L. lots					26.50			26.50	29

03 05 13.80 Waterproofing and Dampproofing

		Crew	Daily Output	Labor-Hours	Unit	Material	2015 Bare Costs Labor	Equipment	Total	Total Incl O&P
0010	**WATERPROOFING AND DAMPPROOFING**									
0050	Integral waterproofing, add to cost of regular concrete				C.Y.	12.70			12.70	14

03 05 13.85 Winter Protection

		Crew	Daily Output	Labor-Hours	Unit	Material	2015 Bare Costs Labor	Equipment	Total	Total Incl O&P
0010	**WINTER PROTECTION**									
0012	For heated ready mix, add				C.Y.	4.05			4.05	4.46
0100	Temporary heat to protect concrete, 24 hours	2 Clab	50	.320	M.S.F.	535	12.05		547.05	605
0200	Temporary shelter for slab on grade, wood frame/polyethylene sheeting									
0201	Build or remove, light framing for short spans	2 Carp	10	1.600	M.S.F.	310	75		385	460
0210	Large framing for long spans	"	3	5.333	"	415	250		665	840
0500	Electrically heated pads, 110 volts, 15 watts per S.F., buy				S.F.	10.35			10.35	11.40
0600	20 watts per S.F., buy					13.80			13.80	15.15
0710	Electrically, heated pads, 15 watts/S.F., 20 uses					.52			.52	.57

03 11 Concrete Forming

03 11 13 – Structural Cast-In-Place Concrete Forming

03 11 13.20 Forms In Place, Beams and Girders

		Crew	Daily Output	Labor-Hours	Unit	Material	2015 Bare Costs Labor	Equipment	Total	Total Incl O&P
0010	**FORMS IN PLACE, BEAMS AND GIRDERS** R031113-40									
3500	Bottoms only, to 30" wide, job-built plywood, 1 use R031113-60	C-2	230	.209	SFCA	4.27	9.55		13.82	19.40
3550	2 use		265	.181		2.39	8.30		10.69	15.40
3600	3 use		280	.171		1.71	7.85		9.56	13.95
3650	4 use		290	.166		1.39	7.55		8.94	13.20
4000	Sides only, vertical, 36" high, job-built plywood, 1 use		335	.143		5.20	6.55		11.75	15.80
4050	2 use		405	.119		2.86	5.40		8.26	11.50
4100	3 use		430	.112		2.08	5.10		7.18	10.15
4150	4 use		445	.108		1.69	4.93		6.62	9.45
4500	Sloped sides, 36" high, 1 use		305	.157		5	7.20		12.20	16.55
4550	2 use		370	.130		2.80	5.95		8.75	12.25
4600	3 use		405	.119		2.01	5.40		7.41	10.55
4650	4 use		425	.113		1.63	5.15		6.78	9.75
5000	Upstanding beams, 36" high, 1 use		225	.213		6.35	9.75		16.10	22
5050	2 use		255	.188		3.53	8.60		12.13	17.15
5100	3 use		275	.175		2.56	8		10.56	15.10
5150	4 use		280	.171		2.08	7.85		9.93	14.35

03 11 13.25 Forms In Place, Columns

		Crew	Daily Output	Labor-Hours	Unit	Material	2015 Bare Costs Labor	Equipment	Total	Total Incl O&P
0010	**FORMS IN PLACE, COLUMNS** R031113-40									
0500	Round fiberglass, 4 use per mo., rent, 12" diameter	C-1	160	.200	L.F.	8.95	8.90		17.85	23.50
0550	16" diameter R031113-60		150	.213		10.65	9.50		20.15	26.50
0600	18" diameter		140	.229		11.95	10.20		22.15	29
0650	24" diameter		135	.237		14.85	10.55		25.40	32.50

54

03 11 Concrete Forming

03 11 13 – Structural Cast-In-Place Concrete Forming

03 11 13.25 Forms In Place, Columns

		Crew	Daily Output	Labor-Hours	Unit	Material	2015 Bare Costs Labor	Equipment	Total	Total Incl O&P
0700	28" diameter	C-1	130	.246	L.F.	16.60	11		27.60	35
0800	30" diameter		125	.256		17.35	11.40		28.75	36.50
0850	36" diameter		120	.267		23	11.90		34.90	44
1500	Round fiber tube, recycled paper, 1 use, 8" diameter [G]		155	.206		1.77	9.20		10.97	16.10
1550	10" diameter [G]		155	.206		2.40	9.20		11.60	16.80
1600	12" diameter [G]		150	.213		2.83	9.50		12.33	17.75
1650	14" diameter [G]		145	.221		3.91	9.85		13.76	19.45
1700	16" diameter [G]		140	.229		4.88	10.20		15.08	21
1720	18" diameter [G]		140	.229		5.70	10.20		15.90	22
1750	20" diameter [G]		135	.237		7.60	10.55		18.15	24.50
1800	24" diameter [G]		130	.246		9.70	11		20.70	27.50
1850	30" diameter [G]		125	.256		14.50	11.40		25.90	33.50
1900	36" diameter [G]		115	.278		17.10	12.40		29.50	38
1950	42" diameter [G]		100	.320		44.50	14.30		58.80	71
2000	48" diameter [G]		85	.376		51.50	16.80		68.30	83
2200	For seamless type, add					15%				
5000	Job-built plywood, 8" x 8" columns, 1 use	C-1	165	.194	SFCA	2.73	8.65		11.38	16.30
5050	2 use		195	.164		1.56	7.30		8.86	12.95
5100	3 use		210	.152		1.09	6.80		7.89	11.65
5150	4 use		215	.149		.90	6.65		7.55	11.20
5500	12" x 12" columns, 1 use		180	.178		2.62	7.95		10.57	15.10
5550	2 use		210	.152		1.44	6.80		8.24	12.05
5600	3 use		220	.145		1.05	6.50		7.55	11.15
5650	4 use		225	.142		.85	6.35		7.20	10.70
6000	16" x 16" columns, 1 use		185	.173		2.62	7.70		10.32	14.75
6050	2 use		215	.149		1.41	6.65		8.06	11.75
6100	3 use		230	.139		1.05	6.20		7.25	10.70
6150	4 use		235	.136		.86	6.05		6.91	10.30
6500	24" x 24" columns, 1 use		190	.168		2.97	7.50		10.47	14.80
6550	2 use		216	.148		1.63	6.60		8.23	11.95
6600	3 use		230	.139		1.19	6.20		7.39	10.85
6650	4 use		238	.134		.96	6		6.96	10.30
7000	36" x 36" columns, 1 use		200	.160		2.31	7.15		9.46	13.55
7050	2 use		230	.139		1.31	6.20		7.51	11
7100	3 use		245	.131		.92	5.85		6.77	9.95
7150	4 use		250	.128		.75	5.70		6.45	9.65
7400	Steel framed plywood, based on 50 uses of purchased									
7420	forms, and 4 uses of bracing lumber									
7500	8" x 8" column	C-1	340	.094	SFCA	2.14	4.20		6.34	8.80
7550	10" x 10"		350	.091		1.87	4.08		5.95	8.35
7600	12" x 12"		370	.086		1.59	3.86		5.45	7.70
7650	16" x 16"		400	.080		1.23	3.57		4.80	6.85
7700	20" x 20"		420	.076		1.09	3.40		4.49	6.45
7750	24" x 24"		440	.073		.79	3.24		4.03	5.85
7755	30" x 30"		440	.073		1	3.24		4.24	6.10
7760	36" x 36"		460	.070		.88	3.10		3.98	5.75

03 11 13.30 Forms In Place, Culvert

		Crew	Daily Output	Labor-Hours	Unit	Material	2015 Bare Costs Labor	Equipment	Total	Total Incl O&P
0010	**FORMS IN PLACE, CULVERT** R031113-40									
0015	5' to 8' square or rectangular, 1 use	C-1	170	.188	SFCA	4.03	8.40		12.43	17.35
0050	2 use R031113-60		180	.178		2.42	7.95		10.37	14.85
0100	3 use		190	.168		1.89	7.50		9.39	13.65
0150	4 use		200	.160		1.62	7.15		8.77	12.80

03 11 Concrete Forming

03 11 13 – Structural Cast-In-Place Concrete Forming

03 11 13.35 Forms In Place, Elevated Slabs

		Crew	Daily Output	Labor-Hours	Unit	Material	2015 Bare Costs Labor	2015 Bare Costs Equipment	Total	Total Incl O&P
0010	**FORMS IN PLACE, ELEVATED SLABS** R031113-40									
1000	Flat plate, job-built plywood, to 15' high, 1 use R031113-60	C-2	470	.102	S.F.	3.86	4.67		8.53	11.45
1050	2 use		520	.092		2.13	4.22		6.35	8.85
1100	3 use		545	.088		1.55	4.03		5.58	7.90
1150	4 use		560	.086		1.26	3.92		5.18	7.45
1500	15' to 20' high ceilings, 4 use		495	.097		1.30	4.43		5.73	8.25
1600	21' to 35' high ceilings, 4 use		450	.107		1.60	4.88		6.48	9.25
2000	Flat slab, drop panels, job-built plywood, to 15' high, 1 use		449	.107		4.42	4.89		9.31	12.35
2050	2 use		509	.094		2.43	4.31		6.74	9.30
2100	3 use		532	.090		1.77	4.13		5.90	8.30
2150	4 use		544	.088		1.43	4.04		5.47	7.80
2250	15' to 20' high ceilings, 4 use		480	.100		2.47	4.57		7.04	9.75
2350	20' to 35' high ceilings, 4 use		435	.110		2.77	5.05		7.82	10.80
3000	Floor slab, hung from steel beams, 1 use		485	.099		2.73	4.53		7.26	9.95
3050	2 use		535	.090		2.12	4.10		6.22	8.65
3100	3 use		550	.087		1.92	3.99		5.91	8.25
3150	4 use		565	.085	▼	1.81	3.89		5.70	8
5000	Box out for slab openings, over 16" deep, 1 use		190	.253	SFCA	4.57	11.55		16.12	23
5050	2 use		240	.200	"	2.51	9.15		11.66	16.80
5500	Shallow slab box outs, to 10 S.F.		42	1.143	Ea.	12.10	52.50		64.60	94
5550	Over 10 S.F. (use perimeter)		600	.080	L.F.	1.61	3.66		5.27	7.45
6000	Bulkhead forms for slab, with keyway, 1 use, 2 piece		500	.096		2.14	4.39		6.53	9.10
6100	3 piece (see also edge forms)	▼	460	.104		2.31	4.77		7.08	9.90
6200	Slab bulkhead form, 4-1/2" high, exp metal, w/keyway & stakes **G**	C-1	1200	.027		.92	1.19		2.11	2.84
6210	5-1/2" high **G**		1100	.029		1.12	1.30		2.42	3.23
6215	7-1/2" high **G**		960	.033		1.31	1.49		2.80	3.73
6220	9-1/2" high **G**		840	.038		1.43	1.70		3.13	4.19
6500	Curb forms, wood, 6" to 12" high, on elevated slabs, 1 use		180	.178	SFCA	1.68	7.95		9.63	14.05
6550	2 use		205	.156		.93	6.95		7.88	11.70
6600	3 use		220	.145		.67	6.50		7.17	10.75
6650	4 use		225	.142	▼	.55	6.35		6.90	10.35
7000	Edge forms to 6" high, on elevated slab, 4 use		500	.064	L.F.	.21	2.86		3.07	4.62
7070	7" to 12" high, 1 use		162	.198	SFCA	1.27	8.80		10.07	14.95
7080	2 use		198	.162		.70	7.20		7.90	11.85
7090	3 use		222	.144		.51	6.45		6.96	10.45
7101	4 use		350	.091	▼	.21	4.08		4.29	6.55
7500	Depressed area forms to 12" high, 4 use		300	.107	L.F.	1.02	4.76		5.78	8.40
7550	12" to 24" high, 4 use		175	.183		1.38	8.15		9.53	14.05
8000	Perimeter deck and rail for elevated slabs, straight		90	.356		12.45	15.85		28.30	38
8050	Curved		65	.492	▼	17.05	22		39.05	53
8500	Void forms, round plastic, 8" high x 3" diameter **G**		450	.071	Ea.	.71	3.17		3.88	5.65
8550	4" diameter **G**		425	.075		1.06	3.36		4.42	6.30
8600	6" diameter **G**		400	.080		1.75	3.57		5.32	7.45
8650	8" diameter **G**	▼	375	.085	▼	3.13	3.81		6.94	9.30

03 11 13.40 Forms In Place, Equipment Foundations

		Crew	Daily Output	Labor-Hours	Unit	Material	2015 Bare Costs Labor	2015 Bare Costs Equipment	Total	Total Incl O&P
0010	**FORMS IN PLACE, EQUIPMENT FOUNDATIONS** R031113-40									
0020	1 use	C-2	160	.300	SFCA	3.45	13.70		17.15	25
0050	2 use R031113-60		190	.253		1.90	11.55		13.45	19.90
0100	3 use		200	.240		1.38	11		12.38	18.40
0150	4 use	▼	205	.234	▼	1.12	10.70		11.82	17.75

03 11 Concrete Forming

03 11 13 - Structural Cast-In-Place Concrete Forming

03 11 13.45 Forms In Place, Footings

		Crew	Daily Output	Labor-Hours	Unit	Material	2015 Bare Costs Labor	Equipment	Total	Total Incl O&P
0010	**FORMS IN PLACE, FOOTINGS** R031113-40									
0020	Continuous wall, plywood, 1 use	C-1	375	.085	SFCA	6.80	3.81		10.61	13.35
0050	2 use	R031113-60	440	.073		3.74	3.24		6.98	9.10
0100	3 use		470	.068		2.72	3.04		5.76	7.65
0150	4 use		485	.066		2.22	2.94		5.16	6.95
0500	Dowel supports for footings or beams, 1 use		500	.064	L.F.	.94	2.86		3.80	5.40
1000	Integral starter wall, to 4" high, 1 use		400	.080		.98	3.57		4.55	6.60
1500	Keyway, 4 use, tapered wood, 2" x 4"	1 Carp	530	.015		.22	.71		.93	1.34
1550	2" x 6"		500	.016		.33	.75		1.08	1.52
2000	Tapered plastic		530	.015		1.31	.71		2.02	2.53
2250	For keyway hung from supports, add		150	.053		.94	2.50		3.44	4.88
3000	Pile cap, square or rectangular, job-built plywood, 1 use	C-1	290	.110	SFCA	2.91	4.92		7.83	10.75
3050	2 use		346	.092		1.60	4.13		5.73	8.10
3100	3 use		371	.086		1.16	3.85		5.01	7.20
3150	4 use		383	.084		.95	3.73		4.68	6.80
4000	Triangular or hexagonal, 1 use		225	.142		3.40	6.35		9.75	13.50
4050	2 use		280	.114		1.87	5.10		6.97	9.90
4100	3 use		305	.105		1.36	4.68		6.04	8.70
4150	4 use		315	.102		1.11	4.53		5.64	8.15
5000	Spread footings, job-built lumber, 1 use		305	.105		2.28	4.68		6.96	9.70
5050	2 use		371	.086		1.27	3.85		5.12	7.30
5100	3 use		401	.080		.91	3.56		4.47	6.50
5150	4 use		414	.077		.74	3.45		4.19	6.10
6000	Supports for dowels, plinths or templates, 2' x 2' footing		25	1.280	Ea.	6.05	57		63.05	94.50
6050	4' x 4' footing		22	1.455		12.10	65		77.10	113
6100	8' x 8' footing		20	1.600		24	71.50		95.50	137
6150	12' x 12' footing		17	1.882		32.50	84		116.50	165
7000	Plinths, job-built plywood, 1 use		250	.128	SFCA	3.38	5.70		9.08	12.50
7100	4 use		270	.119	"	1.11	5.30		6.41	9.35

03 11 13.47 Forms In Place, Gas Station Forms

			Crew	Daily Output	Labor-Hours	Unit	Material	2015 Bare Costs Labor	Equipment	Total	Total Incl O&P
0010	**FORMS IN PLACE, GAS STATION FORMS**										
0050	Curb fascia, with template, 12 ga. steel, left in place, 9" high	G	1 Carp	50	.160	L.F.	13.90	7.50		21.40	27
1000	Sign or light bases, 18" diameter, 9" high	G		9	.889	Ea.	87.50	41.50		129	160
1050	30" diameter, 13" high	G		8	1		139	47		186	226
2000	Island forms, 10' long, 9" high, 3'- 6" wide	G	C-1	10	3.200		390	143		533	645
2050	4' wide	G		9	3.556		400	159		559	685
2500	20' long, 9" high, 4' wide	G		6	5.333		645	238		883	1,075
2550	5' wide	G		5	6.400		670	286		956	1,175

03 11 13.50 Forms In Place, Grade Beam

		Crew	Daily Output	Labor-Hours	Unit	Material	2015 Bare Costs Labor	Equipment	Total	Total Incl O&P
0010	**FORMS IN PLACE, GRADE BEAM** R031113-40									
0020	Job-built plywood, 1 use	C-2	530	.091	SFCA	3.14	4.14		7.28	9.80
0050	2 use	R031113-60	580	.083		1.73	3.78		5.51	7.70
0100	3 use		600	.080		1.25	3.66		4.91	7.05
0150	4 use		605	.079		1.02	3.63		4.65	6.70

03 11 13.55 Forms In Place, Mat Foundation

		Crew	Daily Output	Labor-Hours	Unit	Material	2015 Bare Costs Labor	Equipment	Total	Total Incl O&P
0010	**FORMS IN PLACE, MAT FOUNDATION** R031113-40									
0020	Job-built plywood, 1 use	C-2	290	.166	SFCA	3.08	7.55		10.63	15.05
0050	2 use	R031113-60	310	.155		1.26	7.10		8.36	12.30
0100	3 use		330	.145		.81	6.65		7.46	11.15
0120	4 use		350	.137		.74	6.25		6.99	10.45

For customer support on your Site Work & Landscape Cost Data, call 877.737.1594.

57

03 11 13 – Structural Cast-In-Place Concrete Forming

03 11 13.65 Forms In Place, Slab On Grade

		Crew	Daily Output	Labor-Hours	Unit	Material	2015 Bare Costs Labor	Equipment	Total	Total Incl O&P
0010	**FORMS IN PLACE, SLAB ON GRADE** R031113-40									
1000	Bulkhead forms w/keyway, wood, 6" high, 1 use	C-1	510	.063	L.F.	1.04	2.80		3.84	5.45
1050	2 uses R031113-60		400	.080		.57	3.57		4.14	6.15
1100	4 uses		350	.091		.34	4.08		4.42	6.65
1400	Bulkhead form for slab, 4-1/2" high, exp metal, incl keyway & stakes G		1200	.027		.92	1.19		2.11	2.84
1410	5-1/2" high G		1100	.029		1.12	1.30		2.42	3.23
1420	7-1/2" high G		960	.033		1.31	1.49		2.80	3.73
1430	9-1/2" high G		840	.038		1.43	1.70		3.13	4.19
2000	Curb forms, wood, 6" to 12" high, on grade, 1 use		215	.149	SFCA	2.44	6.65		9.09	12.90
2050	2 use		250	.128		1.35	5.70		7.05	10.30
2100	3 use		265	.121		.98	5.40		6.38	9.35
2150	4 use		275	.116		.79	5.20		5.99	8.85
3000	Edge forms, wood, 4 use, on grade, to 6" high		600	.053	L.F.	.35	2.38		2.73	4.04
3050	7" to 12" high		435	.074	SFCA	.79	3.28		4.07	5.90
3060	Over 12"		350	.091	"	.91	4.08		4.99	7.30
3500	For depressed slabs, 4 use, to 12" high		300	.107	L.F.	.75	4.76		5.51	8.15
3550	To 24" high		175	.183		.99	8.15		9.14	13.65
4000	For slab blockouts, to 12" high, 1 use		200	.160		.80	7.15		7.95	11.85
4050	To 24" high, 1 use		120	.267		1.01	11.90		12.91	19.40
4100	Plastic (extruded), to 6" high, multiple use, on grade		800	.040		8.20	1.78		9.98	11.75
5020	Wood, incl. wood stakes, 1" x 3"		900	.036		.77	1.59		2.36	3.28
5050	2" x 4"		900	.036		.80	1.59		2.39	3.32
6000	Trench forms in floor, wood, 1 use		160	.200	SFCA	1.94	8.90		10.84	15.90
6050	2 use		175	.183		1.06	8.15		9.21	13.70
6100	3 use		180	.178		.77	7.95		8.72	13.05
6150	4 use		185	.173		.63	7.70		8.33	12.55
8760	Void form, corrugated fiberboard, 4" x 12", 4' long G		3000	.011	S.F.	2.87	.48		3.35	3.88
8770	6" x 12", 4' long		3000	.011		3.42	.48		3.90	4.49
8780	1/4" thick hardboard protective cover for void form	2 Carp	1500	.011		.58	.50		1.08	1.41

03 11 13.85 Forms In Place, Walls

		Crew	Daily Output	Labor-Hours	Unit	Material	2015 Bare Costs Labor	Equipment	Total	Total Incl O&P
0010	**FORMS IN PLACE, WALLS** R031113-10									
0100	Box out for wall openings, to 16" thick, to 10 S.F.	C-2	24	2	Ea.	27	91.50		118.50	171
0150	Over 10 S.F. (use perimeter) R031113-40	"	280	.171	L.F.	2.31	7.85		10.16	14.60
0250	Brick shelf, 4" w, add to wall forms, use wall area above shelf									
0260	1 use R031113-60	C-2	240	.200	SFCA	2.50	9.15		11.65	16.80
0300	2 use		275	.175		1.37	8		9.37	13.80
0350	4 use		300	.160		1	7.30		8.30	12.35
0500	Bulkhead, wood with keyway, 1 use, 2 piece		265	.181	L.F.	2.12	8.30		10.42	15.10
0600	Bulkhead forms with keyway, 1 piece expanded metal, 8" wall G	C-1	1000	.032		1.31	1.43		2.74	3.64
0610	10" wall G		800	.040		1.43	1.78		3.21	4.32
0620	12" wall G		525	.061	SFCA	1.72	2.72		4.44	6.05
0700	Buttress, to 8' high, 1 use	C-2	350	.137	SFCA	4.28	6.25		10.53	14.35
0750	2 use		430	.112		2.35	5.10		7.45	10.45
0800	3 use		460	.104		1.72	4.77		6.49	9.25
0850	4 use		480	.100		1.41	4.57		5.98	8.60
1100	3 use		175	.274	L.F.	.95	12.55		13.50	20.50
1150	4 use		180	.267	"	.77	12.20		12.97	19.60
2000	Wall, job-built plywood, to 8' high, 1 use		370	.130	SFCA	2.74	5.95		8.69	12.15
2050	2 use		435	.110		1.75	5.05		6.80	9.65
2100	3 use		495	.097		1.27	4.43		5.70	8.20
2150	4 use		505	.095		1.03	4.35		5.38	7.85
2400	Over 8' to 16' high, 1 use		280	.171		3.03	7.85		10.88	15.40

For customer support on your Site Work & Landscape Cost Data, call 877.737.1594.

03 11 Concrete Forming

03 11 13 – Structural Cast-In-Place Concrete Forming

	03 11 13.85 Forms In Place, Walls	Crew	Daily Output	Labor-Hours	Unit	Material	2015 Bare Costs Labor	Equipment	Total	Total Incl O&P
2450	2 use	C-2	345	.139	SFCA	1.34	6.35		7.69	11.25
2500	3 use		375	.128		.95	5.85		6.80	10.05
2550	4 use		395	.122		.78	5.55		6.33	9.40
2700	Over 16' high, 1 use		235	.204		2.71	9.35		12.06	17.35
2750	2 use		290	.166		1.49	7.55		9.04	13.30
2800	3 use		315	.152		1.09	6.95		8.04	11.90
2850	4 use		330	.145		.88	6.65		7.53	11.20
4000	Radial, smooth curved, job-built plywood, 1 use		245	.196		2.55	8.95		11.50	16.60
4050	2 use		300	.160		1.40	7.30		8.70	12.80
4100	3 use		325	.148		1.02	6.75		7.77	11.50
4150	4 use		335	.143		.83	6.55		7.38	11
4200	Below grade, job-built plywood, 1 use		225	.213		2.77	9.75		12.52	18.05
4210	2 use		225	.213		1.53	9.75		11.28	16.70
4220	3 use		225	.213		1.27	9.75		11.02	16.40
4230	4 use		225	.213		.90	9.75		10.65	16
4300	Curved, 2' chords, job-built plywood, to 8' high, 1 use		290	.166		2.16	7.55		9.71	14
4350	2 use		355	.135		1.19	6.20		7.39	10.80
4400	3 use		385	.125		.86	5.70		6.56	9.70
4450	4 use		400	.120		.70	5.50		6.20	9.20
4500	Over 8' to 16' high, 1 use		290	.166		.93	7.55		8.48	12.65
4525	2 use		355	.135		.51	6.20		6.71	10.05
4550	3 use		385	.125		.37	5.70		6.07	9.15
4575	4 use		400	.120		.31	5.50		5.81	8.80
4600	Retaining wall, battered, job-built plyw'd, to 8' high, 1 use		300	.160		2.03	7.30		9.33	13.50
4650	2 use		355	.135		1.12	6.20		7.32	10.75
4700	3 use		375	.128		.81	5.85		6.66	9.90
4750	4 use		390	.123		.66	5.65		6.31	9.40
4900	Over 8' to 16' high, 1 use		240	.200		2.22	9.15		11.37	16.50
4950	2 use		295	.163		1.22	7.45		8.67	12.80
5000	3 use		305	.157		.89	7.20		8.09	12.05
5050	4 use		320	.150		.72	6.85		7.57	11.35
5100	Retaining wall form, plywood, smooth curve, 1 use		200	.240		3.29	11		14.29	20.50
5120	2 use		235	.204		1.81	9.35		11.16	16.35
5130	3 use		250	.192		1.32	8.80		10.12	14.95
5140	4 use	▼	260	.185		1.08	8.45		9.53	14.20
5500	For gang wall forming, 192 S.F. sections, deduct					10%	10%			
5550	384 S.F. sections, deduct					20%	20%			
7500	Lintel or sill forms, 1 use	1 Carp	30	.267		3.26	12.50		15.76	23
7520	2 use		34	.235		1.79	11.05		12.84	18.95
7540	3 use		36	.222		1.30	10.45		11.75	17.50
7560	4 use	▼	37	.216	▼	1.06	10.15		11.21	16.75
7800	Modular prefabricated plywood, based on 20 uses of purchased									
7820	forms, and 4 uses of bracing lumber									
7860	To 8' high	C-2	800	.060	SFCA	.94	2.74		3.68	5.25
8060	Over 8' to 16' high		600	.080		.99	3.66		4.65	6.75
8600	Pilasters, 1 use		270	.178		3.19	8.15		11.34	16
8620	2 use		330	.145		1.75	6.65		8.40	12.20
8640	3 use		370	.130		1.27	5.95		7.22	10.55
8660	4 use	▼	385	.125	▼	1.04	5.70		6.74	9.90
9010	Steel framed plywood, based on 50 uses of purchased									
9020	forms, and 4 uses of bracing lumber									
9060	To 8' high	C-2	600	.080	SFCA	.74	3.66		4.40	6.45
9260	Over 8' to 16' high	▼	450	.107	▼	.74	4.88		5.62	8.30

For customer support on your Site Work & Landscape Cost Data, call 877.737.1594.

59

03 11 Concrete Forming

03 11 13 – Structural Cast-In-Place Concrete Forming

03 11 13.85 Forms In Place, Walls		Crew	Daily Output	Labor-Hours	Unit	Material	2015 Bare Costs Labor	Equipment	Total	Total Incl O&P
9460	Over 16' to 20' high	C-2	400	.120	SFCA	.74	5.50		6.24	9.25
9480	For battered walls, 1 side battered, add					10%	10%			
9485	For battered walls, 2 sides battered, add					15%	15%			

03 11 16 – Architectural Cast-in Place Concrete Forming

03 11 16.13 Concrete Form Liners

		Crew	Daily Output	Labor-Hours	Unit	Material	2015 Bare Costs Labor	Equipment	Total	Total Incl O&P
0010	**CONCRETE FORM LINERS**									
5750	Liners for forms (add to wall forms), ABS plastic									
5800	Aged wood, 4" wide, 1 use	1 Carp	256	.031	SFCA	3.30	1.47		4.77	5.90
5820	2 use		256	.031		1.82	1.47		3.29	4.26
5830	3 use		256	.031		1.32	1.47		2.79	3.71
5840	4 use		256	.031		1.07	1.47		2.54	3.44
5900	Fractured rope rib, 1 use		192	.042		4.79	1.96		6.75	8.25
5925	2 use		192	.042		2.63	1.96		4.59	5.90
5950	3 use		192	.042		1.92	1.96		3.88	5.10
6000	4 use		192	.042		1.56	1.96		3.52	4.72
6100	Ribbed, 3/4" deep x 1-1/2" O.C., 1 use		224	.036		4.79	1.68		6.47	7.85
6125	2 use		224	.036		2.63	1.68		4.31	5.50
6150	3 use		224	.036		1.92	1.68		3.60	4.69
6200	4 use		224	.036		1.56	1.68		3.24	4.29
6300	Rustic brick pattern, 1 use		224	.036		3.30	1.68		4.98	6.20
6325	2 use		224	.036		1.82	1.68		3.50	4.58
6350	3 use		224	.036		1.32	1.68		3	4.03
6400	4 use		224	.036		1.07	1.68		2.75	3.76
6500	3/8" striated, random, 1 use		224	.036		3.30	1.68		4.98	6.20
6525	2 use		224	.036		1.82	1.68		3.50	4.58
6550	3 use		224	.036		1.32	1.68		3	4.03
6600	4 use		224	.036		1.07	1.68		2.75	3.76
6850	Random vertical rustication, 1 use		384	.021		6.25	.98		7.23	8.40
6900	2 use		384	.021		3.45	.98		4.43	5.30
6925	3 use		384	.021		2.51	.98		3.49	4.27
6950	4 use		384	.021		2.04	.98		3.02	3.75
7050	Wood, beveled edge, 3/4" deep, 1 use		384	.021	L.F.	.16	.98		1.14	1.69
7100	1" deep, 1 use		384	.021	"	.33	.98		1.31	1.87
7200	4" wide aged cedar, 1 use		256	.031	SFCA	3.30	1.47		4.77	5.90
7300	4" variable depth rough cedar		224	.036	"	4.79	1.68		6.47	7.85

03 11 19 – Insulating Concrete Forming

03 11 19.10 Insulating Forms, Left In Place

			Crew	Daily Output	Labor-Hours	Unit	Material	2015 Bare Costs Labor	Equipment	Total	Total Incl O&P
0010	**INSULATING FORMS, LEFT IN PLACE**										
0020	S.F. is for exterior face, but includes forms for both faces (total R22)										
2000	4" wall, straight block, 16" x 48" (5.33 S.F.)	G	2 Carp	90	.178	Ea.	19.60	8.35		27.95	34.50
2010	90 corner block, exterior 16" x 38" x 22" (6.67 S.F.)	G		75	.213		23	10		33	41
2020	45 corner block, exterior 16" x 34" x 18" (5.78 S.F.)	G		75	.213		23	10		33	41
2100	6" wall, straight block, 16" x 48" (5.33 S.F.)	G		90	.178		20	8.35		28.35	35
2110	90 corner block, exterior 16" x 32" x 24" (6.22 S.F.)	G		75	.213		25	10		35	43
2120	45 corner block, exterior 16" x 26" x 18" (4.89 S.F.)	G		75	.213		22.50	10		32.50	40
2130	Brick ledge block, 16" x 48" (5.33 S.F.)	G		80	.200		25	9.40		34.40	42
2140	Taper top block, 16" x 48" (5.33 S.F.)	G		80	.200		23.50	9.40		32.90	40.50
2200	8" wall, straight block, 16" x 48" (5.33 S.F.)	G		90	.178		21.50	8.35		29.85	36.50
2210	90 corner block, exterior 16" x 34" x 26" (6.67 S.F.)	G		75	.213		27.50	10		37.50	46
2220	45 corner block, exterior 16" x 28" x 20" (5.33 S.F.)	G		75	.213		23.50	10		33.50	41.50
2230	Brick ledge block, 16" x 48" (5.33 S.F.)	G		80	.200		26.50	9.40		35.90	43.50
2240	Taper top block, 16" x 48" (5.33 S.F.)	G		80	.200		24.50	9.40		33.90	41.50

03 11 Concrete Forming

03 11 23 – Permanent Stair Forming

03 11 23.75 Forms In Place, Stairs		Crew	Daily Output	Labor-Hours	Unit	Material	2015 Bare Costs Labor	Equipment	Total	Total Incl O&P
0010	**FORMS IN PLACE, STAIRS** R031113-40									
0015	(Slant length x width), 1 use	C-2	165	.291	S.F.	5.90	13.30		19.20	27
0050	2 use R031113-60		170	.282		3.35	12.90		16.25	23.50
0100	3 use		180	.267		2.50	12.20		14.70	21.50
0150	4 use		190	.253	↓	2.08	11.55		13.63	20
1000	Alternate pricing method (1.0 L.F./S.F.), 1 use		100	.480	LF Rsr	5.90	22		27.90	40.50
1050	2 use		105	.457		3.35	21		24.35	35.50
1100	3 use		110	.436		2.50	19.95		22.45	33.50
1150	4 use		115	.417	↓	2.08	19.10		21.18	32
2000	Stairs, cast on sloping ground (length x width), 1 use		220	.218	S.F.	2.36	10		12.36	17.95
2025	2 use		232	.207		1.30	9.45		10.75	15.95
2050	3 use		244	.197		.94	9		9.94	14.90
2100	4 use	↓	256	.188	↓	.77	8.55		9.32	14.05

03 15 Concrete Accessories

03 15 05 – Concrete Forming Accessories

03 15 05.12 Chamfer Strips

		Crew	Daily Output	Labor-Hours	Unit	Material	Labor	Equipment	Total	Total Incl O&P
0010	**CHAMFER STRIPS**									
2000	Polyvinyl chloride, 1/2" wide with leg	1 Carp	535	.015	L.F.	.57	.70		1.27	1.71
2200	3/4" wide with leg		525	.015		.68	.72		1.40	1.85
2400	1" radius with leg		515	.016		.64	.73		1.37	1.82
2800	2" radius with leg		500	.016		1.22	.75		1.97	2.50
5000	Wood, 1/2" wide		535	.015		.15	.70		.85	1.25
5200	3/4" wide		525	.015		.16	.72		.88	1.28
5400	1" wide	↓	515	.016	↓	.33	.73		1.06	1.48

03 15 05.30 Hangers

					Unit	Material	Labor	Equipment	Total	Total Incl O&P
0010	**HANGERS**									
8500	Wire, black annealed, 15 gage	G			Cwt.	151			151	167
8600	16 ga				"	203			203	223

03 15 05.70 Shores

		Crew	Daily Output	Labor-Hours	Unit	Material	Labor	Equipment	Total	Total Incl O&P
0010	**SHORES**									
0020	Erect and strip, by hand, horizontal members									
0500	Aluminum joists and stringers	G	2 Carp	60	.267	Ea.		12.50		12.50	19.25
0600	Steel, adjustable beams	G		45	.356			16.70		16.70	25.50
0700	Wood joists			50	.320			15		15	23
0800	Wood stringers			30	.533			25		25	38.50
1000	Vertical members to 10' high	G		55	.291			13.65		13.65	21
1050	To 13' high	G		50	.320			15		15	23
1100	To 16' high	G		45	.356	↓		16.70		16.70	25.50
1500	Reshoring	G		1400	.011	S.F.	.58	.54		1.12	1.47
1600	Flying truss system	G	C-17D	9600	.009	SFCA		.43	.08	.51	.75
1760	Horizontal, aluminum joists, 6-1/4" high x 5' to 21' span, buy	G				L.F.	15.45			15.45	17
1770	Beams, 7-1/4" high x 4' to 30' span	G				"	18.10			18.10	19.90
1810	Horizontal, steel beam, W8x10, 7' span, buy	G				Ea.	57			57	63
1830	10' span	G					67.50			67.50	74.50
1920	15' span	G					117			117	128
1940	20' span	G			↓	164			164	180
1970	Steel stringer, W8x10, 4' to 16' span, buy	G				L.F.	6.80			6.80	7.45
3000	Rent for job duration, aluminum joist @ 2' O.C., per mo.	G				SF Flr.	.39			.39	.43
3050	Steel W8x10	G				↓	.17			.17	.19

For customer support on your Site Work & Landscape Cost Data, call 877.737.1594.

61

03 15 Concrete Accessories

03 15 05 – Concrete Forming Accessories

03 15 05.70 Shores

		Crew	Daily Output	Labor-Hours	Unit	Material	2015 Bare Costs Labor	Equipment	Total	Total Incl O&P
3060	Steel adjustable	G			SF Flr.	.17			.17	.19
3500	#1 post shore, steel, 5'-7" to 9'-6" high, 10000# cap., buy	G			Ea.	148			148	163
3550	#2 post shore, 7'-3" to 12'-10" high, 7800# capacity	G				171			171	188
3600	#3 post shore, 8'-10" to 16'-1" high, 3800# capacity	G				187			187	206
5010	Frame shoring systems, steel, 12000#/leg, buy									
5040	Frame, 2' wide x 6' high	G			Ea.	93.50			93.50	103
5250	X-brace	G				15.50			15.50	17.05
5550	Base plate	G				15.50			15.50	17.05
5600	Screw jack	G				33.50			33.50	36.50
5650	U-head, 8" x 8"	G				19.10			19.10	21

03 15 05.75 Sleeves and Chases

		Crew	Daily Output	Labor-Hours	Unit	Material	2015 Bare Costs Labor	Equipment	Total	Total Incl O&P
0010	**SLEEVES AND CHASES**									
0100	Plastic, 1 use, 12" long, 2" diameter	1 Carp	100	.080	Ea.	2.15	3.76		5.91	8.15
0150	4" diameter		90	.089		6.05	4.17		10.22	13.05
0200	6" diameter		75	.107		10.65	5		15.65	19.40
0250	12" diameter		60	.133		31.50	6.25		37.75	44
5000	Sheet metal, 2" diameter	G	100	.080		1.36	3.76		5.12	7.30
5100	4" diameter	G	90	.089		1.70	4.17		5.87	8.25
5150	6" diameter	G	75	.107		1.82	5		6.82	9.70
5200	12" diameter	G	60	.133		3.63	6.25		9.88	13.65
6000	Steel pipe, 2" diameter	G	100	.080		4.55	3.76		8.31	10.80
6100	4" diameter	G	90	.089		16.30	4.17		20.47	24.50
6150	6" diameter	G	75	.107		36.50	5		41.50	47.50
6200	12" diameter	G	60	.133		86.50	6.25		92.75	105

03 15 05.80 Snap Ties

		Crew	Daily Output	Labor-Hours	Unit	Material	2015 Bare Costs Labor	Equipment	Total	Total Incl O&P
0010	**SNAP TIES**, 8-1/4" L&W (Lumber and wedge)									
0100	2250 lb., w/flat washer, 8" wall	G			C	90			90	99
0150	10" wall	G				131			131	144
0200	12" wall	G				136			136	150
0250	16" wall	G				150			150	165
0300	18" wall	G				156			156	172
0500	With plastic cone, 8" wall	G				80			80	88
0550	10" wall	G				83			83	91.50
0600	12" wall	G				89			89	98
0650	16" wall	G				98			98	108
0700	18" wall	G				101			101	111
1000	3350 lb., w/flat washer, 8" wall	G				163			163	179
1100	10" wall	G				179			179	197
1150	12" wall	G				183			183	201
1200	16" wall	G				210			210	231
1250	18" wall	G				218			218	240
1500	With plastic cone, 8" wall	G				132			132	145
1550	10" wall	G				145			145	160
1600	12" wall	G				149			149	164
1650	16" wall	G				170			170	187
1700	18" wall	G				176			176	194

03 15 05.85 Stair Tread Inserts

		Crew	Daily Output	Labor-Hours	Unit	Material	2015 Bare Costs Labor	Equipment	Total	Total Incl O&P
0010	**STAIR TREAD INSERTS**									
0105	Cast nosing insert, abrasive surface, pre-drilled, includes screws									
0110	Aluminum, 3" wide x 3' long	1 Cefi	32	.250	Ea.	55	11.25		66.25	77
0120	4' long		31	.258		70	11.60		81.60	94
0130	5' long		30	.267		87	12		99	113

03 15 Concrete Accessories

03 15 05 – Concrete Forming Accessories

03 15 05.85 Stair Tread Inserts

		Crew	Daily Output	Labor-Hours	Unit	Material	2015 Bare Costs Labor	Equipment	Total	Total Incl O&P
0135	Extruded nosing insert, black abrasive strips, continuous anchor									
0140	Aluminum, 3" wide x 3' long	1 Cefi	64	.125	Ea.	35.50	5.65		41.15	47.50
0150	4' long		60	.133		55	6		61	69.50
0160	5' long		56	.143		62	6.45		68.45	77.50
0165	Extruded nosing insert, black abrasive strips, pre-drilled, incl. screws									
0170	Aluminum, 3" wide x 3' long	1 Cefi	32	.250	Ea.	49	11.25		60.25	70.50
0180	4' long		31	.258		63.50	11.60		75.10	87
0190	5' long		30	.267		74.50	12		86.50	100

03 15 05.95 Wall and Foundation Form Accessories

							Unit	Material	Labor	Equipment	Total	Total Incl O&P
0010	**WALL AND FOUNDATION FORM ACCESSORIES**											
0020	Coil tie system											
0050	Coil ties 1/2", 6000 lb., to 8"	G					C	245			245	270
0150	24"	G						415			415	455
0300	3/4", 12,000 lb., to 8"	G						475			475	520
0400	24"	G						700			700	770
0900	Coil bolts, 1/2" diameter x 3" long	G						138			138	152
0940	12" long	G						395			395	435
1000	3/4" diameter x 3" long	G						300			300	330
1040	12" long	G						830			830	915
1300	Adjustable coil tie, 3/4" diameter, 20" long	G						1,150			1,150	1,275
1350	3/4" diameter, 36" long	G						1,400			1,400	1,550
1400	Tie cones, plastic, 1" setback length, 1/2" bolt diameter							84			84	92.50
1420	3/4" bolt diameter							164			164	180
1500	Welding coil tie, 1/2" diameter x 4" long	G						226			226	249
1550	3/4" diameter x 6" long	G						300			300	330
1700	Waler holders, 1/2" diameter	G						237			237	261
1750	3/4" diameter	G						265			265	292
1900	Flat washers, 4" x 5" x 1/4" for 3/4" diameter	G						950			950	1,050
2000	Footings, turnbuckle form aligner	G					Ea.	16.20			16.20	17.85
2050	Spreaders for footer, adjustable	G					"	25			25	27.50
2100	Lagstud, threaded, 1/2" diameter	G					C.L.F.	136			136	150
2200	1" diameter	G					"	495			495	545
2300	Lagnuts, 1/2" diameter	G					C	33			33	36.50
2400	1" diameter	G						228			228	251
2600	Lagnuts with handle, 1/2" diameter	G						299			299	330
2700	1" diameter	G						840			840	920
2750	Plastic set back plugs for 3/4" diameter							95			95	105
2800	Rock anchors, 1/2" diameter	G						1,150			1,150	1,250
2900	1" diameter	G						1,600			1,600	1,775
2950	Batter washer, 1/2" diameter	G						640			640	705
3000	Form oil, up to 1200 S.F. per gallon coverage						Gal.	13.55			13.55	14.90
3050	Up to 800 S.F. per gallon						"	20.50			20.50	22.50
3500	Form patches, 1-3/4" diameter						C	27			27	29.50
3550	2-3/4" diameter						"	47			47	51.50
4000	Nail stakes, 3/4" diameter, 18" long	G					Ea.	3.30			3.30	3.63
4050	24" long	G						4.26			4.26	4.69
4200	30" long	G						5.45			5.45	6
4250	36" long	G						6.60			6.60	7.25
5000	Pencil rods, 1/4" diameter	G					C.L.F.	48			48	53
5200	Clamps for 1/4" pencil rods	G					Ea.	5.80			5.80	6.40
5300	Clamping jacks for 1/4" pencil rod clamp	G					"	76			76	83.50
6000	She-bolts, 7/8" x 20"	G					C	4,500			4,500	4,950

For customer support on your Site Work & Landscape Cost Data, call 877.737.1594.

63

03 15 Concrete Accessories

03 15 05 – Concrete Forming Accessories

03 15 05.95 Wall and Foundation Form Accessories

		Crew	Daily Output	Labor-Hours	Unit	Material	2015 Bare Costs Labor	Equipment	Total	Total Incl O&P
6150	1-1/4" x 20"	G			C	6,025			6,025	6,625
6300	Inside rods, threaded, 1/2" diameter x 6"	G				183			183	201
6350	1/2" diameter x 12"	G				265			265	292
6500	3/4" diameter x 6"	G				390			390	430
6550	3/4" diameter x 12"	G				550			550	605
6700	For wing nuts, see taper ties									
7000	Taper tie system									
7100	Taper ties, 3/4" to 1/2" diameter x 30"	G			Ea.	62.50			62.50	69
7200	1-1/4" to 1" diameter x 30"	G			"	73.50			73.50	81
7300	Wing nuts, 1/2" diameter	G			C	670			670	735
7550	1-1/4" diameter	G				1,000			1,000	1,100
7700	Flat washers, 1/4" x 3" x 4", for 1/2" diam. bolt	G				271			271	298
7800	7/16" x 5" x 5", for 1" diam. bolt	G				1,275			1,275	1,400
9000	Wood form accessories									
9100	Tie plate	G			C	610			610	670
9200	Corner washer	G				1,200			1,200	1,325
9300	Panel bolt	G				900			900	990
9400	Panel wedge	G				159			159	175
9500	Stud clamp	G				680			680	745

03 15 13 – Waterstops

03 15 13.50 Waterstops

		Crew	Daily Output	Labor-Hours	Unit	Material	2015 Bare Costs Labor	Equipment	Total	Total Incl O&P
0010	**WATERSTOPS**, PVC and Rubber									
0020	PVC, ribbed 3/16" thick, 4" wide	1 Carp	155	.052	L.F.	1.35	2.42		3.77	5.20
0050	6" wide		145	.055		2.27	2.59		4.86	6.50
0500	With center bulb, 6" wide, 3/16" thick		135	.059		1.99	2.78		4.77	6.45
0550	3/8" thick		130	.062		3.67	2.89		6.56	8.50
0600	9" wide x 3/8" thick		125	.064		6.05	3		9.05	11.25
0800	Dumbbell type, 6" wide, 3/16" thick		150	.053		2.02	2.50		4.52	6.05
0850	3/8" thick		145	.055		3.79	2.59		6.38	8.15
1000	9" wide, 3/8" thick, plain		130	.062		5.65	2.89		8.54	10.65
1050	Center bulb		130	.062		9.15	2.89		12.04	14.55
1250	Ribbed type, split, 3/16" thick, 6" wide		145	.055		1.92	2.59		4.51	6.10
1300	3/8" thick		130	.062		4.38	2.89		7.27	9.25
2000	Rubber, flat dumbbell, 3/8" thick, 6" wide		145	.055		10.60	2.59		13.19	15.65
2050	9" wide		135	.059		16.15	2.78		18.93	22
2500	Flat dumbbell split, 3/8" thick, 6" wide		145	.055		1.92	2.59		4.51	6.10
2550	9" wide		135	.059		4.38	2.78		7.16	9.10
3000	Center bulb, 1/4" thick, 6" wide		145	.055		10.45	2.59		13.04	15.50
3050	9" wide		135	.059		23	2.78		25.78	30
3500	Center bulb split, 3/8" thick, 6" wide		145	.055		14.80	2.59		17.39	20.50
3550	9" wide		135	.059		25.50	2.78		28.28	32.50
5000	Waterstop fittings, rubber, flat									
5010	Dumbbell or center bulb, 3/8" thick,									
5200	Field union, 6" wide	1 Carp	50	.160	Ea.	35.50	7.50		43	51
5250	9" wide		50	.160		47.50	7.50		55	64
5500	Flat cross, 6" wide		30	.267		45	12.50		57.50	69
5550	9" wide		30	.267		64.50	12.50		77	90.50
6000	Flat tee, 6" wide		30	.267		43.50	12.50		56	67.50
6050	9" wide		30	.267		59	12.50		71.50	84.50
6500	Flat ell, 6" wide		40	.200		42.50	9.40		51.90	61
6550	9" wide		40	.200		54.50	9.40		63.90	74.50
7000	Vertical tee, 6" wide		25	.320		31.50	15		46.50	58

03 15 Concrete Accessories

03 15 13 – Waterstops

03 15 13.50 Waterstops		Crew	Daily Output	Labor-Hours	Unit	Material	2015 Bare Costs Labor	Equipment	Total	Total Incl O&P
7050	9" wide	1 Carp	25	.320	Ea.	45	15		60	72.50
7500	Vertical ell, 6" wide		35	.229		29.50	10.75		40.25	49
7550	9" wide		35	.229		38	10.75		48.75	58

03 15 16 – Concrete Construction Joints

03 15 16.20 Control Joints, Saw Cut

		Crew	Daily Output	Labor-Hours	Unit	Material	Labor	Equipment	Total	Total Incl O&P
0010	**CONTROL JOINTS, SAW CUT**									
0100	Sawcut control joints in green concrete									
0120	1" depth	C-27	2000	.008	L.F.	.04	.36	.08	.48	.66
0140	1-1/2" depth		1800	.009		.06	.40	.09	.55	.75
0160	2" depth		1600	.010		.08	.45	.10	.63	.88
0180	Sawcut joint reservoir in cured concrete									
0182	3/8" wide x 3/4" deep, with single saw blade	C-27	1000	.016	L.F.	.06	.72	.17	.95	1.31
0184	1/2" wide x 1" deep, with double saw blades		900	.018		.11	.80	.19	1.10	1.52
0186	3/4" wide x 1-1/2" deep, with double saw blades		800	.020		.23	.90	.21	1.34	1.82
0190	Water blast joint to wash away laitance, 2 passes	C-29	2500	.003			.12	.03	.15	.22
0200	Air blast joint to blow out debris and air dry, 2 passes	C-28	2000	.004			.18	.01	.19	.28
0300	For backer rod, see Section 07 91 23.10									
0340	For joint sealant, see Sections 03 15 16.30 or 07 92 13.20									
0900	For replacement of joint sealant, see Section 07 01 90.81									

03 15 16.30 Expansion Joints

			Crew	Daily Output	Labor-Hours	Unit	Material	Labor	Equipment	Total	Total Incl O&P
0010	**EXPANSION JOINTS**										
0020	Keyed, cold, 24 ga., incl. stakes, 3-1/2" high	G	1 Carp	200	.040	L.F.	.81	1.88		2.69	3.78
0050	4-1/2" high	G		200	.040		.92	1.88		2.80	3.90
0100	5-1/2" high	G		195	.041		1.12	1.93		3.05	4.19
0150	7-1/2" high	G		190	.042		1.31	1.98		3.29	4.48
0160	9-1/2" high	G		185	.043		1.43	2.03		3.46	4.69
0300	Poured asphalt, plain, 1/2" x 1"		1 Clab	450	.018		.69	.67		1.36	1.79
0350	1" x 2"			400	.020		2.76	.75		3.51	4.20
0500	Neoprene, liquid, cold applied, 1/2" x 1"			450	.018		2.88	.67		3.55	4.20
0550	1" x 2"			400	.020		11.50	.75		12.25	13.80
0700	Polyurethane, poured, 2 part, 1/2" x 1"			400	.020		1.28	.75		2.03	2.57
0750	1" x 2"			350	.023		5.10	.86		5.96	6.95
0900	Rubberized asphalt, hot or cold applied, 1/2" x 1"			450	.018		.40	.67		1.07	1.47
0950	1" x 2"			400	.020		1.60	.75		2.35	2.92
1100	Hot applied, fuel resistant, 1/2" x 1"			450	.018		.60	.67		1.27	1.69
1150	1" x 2"			400	.020		2.40	.75		3.15	3.80
2000	Premolded, bituminous fiber, 1/2" x 6"		1 Carp	375	.021		.44	1		1.44	2.02
2050	1" x 12"			300	.027		1.99	1.25		3.24	4.12
2140	Concrete expansion joint, recycled paper and fiber, 1/2" x 6"	G		390	.021		.42	.96		1.38	1.94
2150	1/2" x 12"	G		360	.022		.83	1.04		1.87	2.53
2250	Cork with resin binder, 1/2" x 6"			375	.021		1.11	1		2.11	2.76
2300	1" x 12"			300	.027		3.11	1.25		4.36	5.35
2500	Neoprene sponge, closed cell, 1/2" x 6"			375	.021		2.37	1		3.37	4.15
2550	1" x 12"			300	.027		8.25	1.25		9.50	11.05
2750	Polyethylene foam, 1/2" x 6"			375	.021		.68	1		1.68	2.29
2800	1" x 12"			300	.027		2.19	1.25		3.44	4.34
3000	Polyethylene backer rod, 3/8" diameter			460	.017		.03	.82		.85	1.29
3050	3/4" diameter			460	.017		.06	.82		.88	1.32
3100	1" diameter			460	.017		.09	.82		.91	1.36
3500	Polyurethane foam, with polybutylene, 1/2" x 1/2"			475	.017		1.14	.79		1.93	2.47
3550	1" x 1"			450	.018		2.88	.83		3.71	4.45
3750	Polyurethane foam, regular, closed cell, 1/2" x 6"			375	.021		.84	1		1.84	2.46

For customer support on your Site Work & Landscape Cost Data, call 877.737.1594.

65

03 15 Concrete Accessories

03 15 16 – Concrete Construction Joints

03 15 16.30 Expansion Joints		Crew	Daily Output	Labor-Hours	Unit	Material	2015 Bare Costs Labor	Equipment	Total	Total Incl O&P
3800	1" x 12"	1 Carp	300	.027	L.F.	3	1.25		4.25	5.25
4000	Polyvinyl chloride foam, closed cell, 1/2" x 6"		375	.021		2.28	1		3.28	4.05
4050	1" x 12"		300	.027		7.85	1.25		9.10	10.60
4100	Rod, 3/8" polyethylene/rubberized asphalt sealer, 1/4" x 3/4"	2 Clab	600	.027		.23	1		1.23	1.79
4250	Rubber, gray sponge, 1/2" x 6"	1 Carp	375	.021		1.92	1		2.92	3.65
4300	1" x 12"		300	.027		6.90	1.25		8.15	9.55
4400	Redwood heartwood, 1" x 4"		400	.020		1.16	.94		2.10	2.73
4450	1" x 6"		375	.021		1.75	1		2.75	3.47
5000	For installation in walls, add						75%			
5250	For installation in boxouts, add						25%			

03 15 19 – Cast-In Concrete Anchors

03 15 19.05 Anchor Bolt Accessories

			Crew	Daily Output	Labor-Hours	Unit	Material	2015 Bare Costs Labor	Equipment	Total	Total Incl O&P
0010	**ANCHOR BOLT ACCESSORIES**										
0015	For anchor bolts set in fresh concrete, see Section 03 15 19.10										
8150	Anchor bolt sleeve, plastic, 1" diam. bolts		1 Carp	60	.133	Ea.	8.20	6.25		14.45	18.70
8500	1-1/2" diameter			28	.286		14.60	13.40		28	36.50
8600	2" diameter			24	.333		18.60	15.65		34.25	44.50
8650	3" diameter			20	.400		34	18.80		52.80	66.50
8800	Templates, steel, 8" bolt spacing	G	2 Carp	16	1		10.80	47		57.80	84.50
8850	12" bolt spacing	G		15	1.067		11.25	50		61.25	89.50
8900	16" bolt spacing	G		14	1.143		13.50	53.50		67	97.50
8950	24" bolt spacing	G		12	1.333		18	62.50		80.50	116
9100	Wood, 8" bolt spacing			16	1		.87	47		47.87	73.50
9150	12" bolt spacing			15	1.067		1.15	50		51.15	78.50
9200	16" bolt spacing			14	1.143		1.44	53.50		54.94	84
9250	24" bolt spacing			16	1		2.01	47		49.01	74.50

03 15 19.10 Anchor Bolts

			Crew	Daily Output	Labor-Hours	Unit	Material	2015 Bare Costs Labor	Equipment	Total	Total Incl O&P
0010	**ANCHOR BOLTS**										
0015	Made from recycled materials										
0025	Single bolts installed in fresh concrete, no templates										
0030	Hooked w/nut and washer, 1/2" diameter, 8" long	G	1 Carp	132	.061	Ea.	1.33	2.85		4.18	5.85
0040	12" long	G		131	.061		1.48	2.87		4.35	6.05
0050	5/8" diameter, 8" long	G		129	.062		2.98	2.91		5.89	7.75
0060	12" long	G		127	.063		3.67	2.96		6.63	8.60
0070	3/4" diameter, 8" long	G		127	.063		3.67	2.96		6.63	8.60
0080	12" long	G		125	.064		4.59	3		7.59	9.65
0090	2-bolt pattern, including job-built 2-hole template, per set										
0100	J-type, incl. hex nut & washer, 1/2" diameter x 6" long	G	1 Carp	21	.381	Set	5.20	17.90		23.10	33.50
0110	12" long	G		21	.381		5.80	17.90		23.70	34
0120	18" long	G		21	.381		6.70	17.90		24.60	35
0130	3/4" diameter x 8" long	G		20	.400		10.20	18.80		29	40
0140	12" long	G		20	.400		12	18.80		30.80	42
0150	18" long	G		20	.400		14.75	18.80		33.55	45.50
0160	1" diameter x 12" long	G		19	.421		20.50	19.75		40.25	53
0170	18" long	G		19	.421		24	19.75		43.75	57
0180	24" long	G		19	.421		28.50	19.75		48.25	62
0190	36" long	G		18	.444		38	21		59	74
0200	1-1/2" diameter x 18" long	G		17	.471		37.50	22		59.50	75.50
0210	24" long	G		16	.500		44	23.50		67.50	84.50
0300	L-type, incl. hex nut & washer, 3/4" diameter x 12" long	G		20	.400		12.90	18.80		31.70	43
0310	18" long	G		20	.400		15.75	18.80		34.55	46.50
0320	24" long	G		20	.400		18.60	18.80		37.40	49.50

03 15 Concrete Accessories

03 15 19 – Cast-In Concrete Anchors

03 15 19.10 Anchor Bolts

			Crew	Daily Output	Labor-Hours	Unit	Material	2015 Bare Costs Labor	Equipment	Total	Total Incl O&P
0330	30" long	G	1 Carp	20	.400	Set	23	18.80		41.80	54
0340	36" long	G		20	.400		25.50	18.80		44.30	57.50
0350	1" diameter x 12" long	G		19	.421		19.55	19.75		39.30	52
0360	18" long	G		19	.421		23.50	19.75		43.25	56.50
0370	24" long	G		19	.421		28.50	19.75		48.25	62
0380	30" long	G		19	.421		33	19.75		52.75	67
0390	36" long	G		18	.444		37.50	21		58.50	73.50
0400	42" long	G		18	.444		45	21		66	81.50
0410	48" long	G		18	.444		50	21		71	87
0420	1-1/4" diameter x 18" long	G		18	.444		30	21		51	65
0430	24" long	G		18	.444		35	21		56	70.50
0440	30" long	G		17	.471		40	22		62	78
0450	36" long	G		17	.471		45	22		67	83.50
0460	42" long	G	2 Carp	32	.500		50.50	23.50		74	91.50
0470	48" long	G		32	.500		57	23.50		80.50	99
0480	54" long	G		31	.516		67	24		91	111
0490	60" long	G		31	.516		73	24		97	118
0500	1-1/2" diameter x 18" long	G		33	.485		51	23		74	91
0510	24" long	G		32	.500		59	23.50		82.50	101
0520	30" long	G		31	.516		66	24		90	110
0530	36" long	G		30	.533		75.50	25		100.50	122
0540	42" long	G		30	.533		85.50	25		110.50	133
0550	48" long	G		29	.552		96	26		122	145
0560	54" long	G		28	.571		116	27		143	170
0570	60" long	G		28	.571		127	27		154	182
0580	1-3/4" diameter x 18" long	G		31	.516		74.50	24		98.50	120
0590	24" long	G		30	.533		87	25		112	134
0600	30" long	G		29	.552		101	26		127	151
0610	36" long	G		28	.571		114	27		141	168
0620	42" long	G		27	.593		128	28		156	184
0630	48" long	G		26	.615		141	29		170	200
0640	54" long	G		26	.615		174	29		203	236
0650	60" long	G		25	.640		187	30		217	252
0660	2" diameter x 24" long	G		27	.593		111	28		139	166
0670	30" long	G		27	.593		125	28		153	181
0680	36" long	G		26	.615		137	29		166	196
0690	42" long	G		25	.640		153	30		183	214
0700	48" long	G		24	.667		175	31.50		206.50	241
0710	54" long	G		23	.696		208	32.50		240.50	280
0720	60" long	G		23	.696		223	32.50		255.50	297
0730	66" long	G		22	.727		239	34		273	315
0740	72" long	G		21	.762		261	36		297	340
1000	4-bolt pattern, including job-built 4-hole template, per set										
1100	J-type, incl. hex nut & washer, 1/2" diameter x 6" long	G	1 Carp	19	.421	Set	7.55	19.75		27.30	39
1110	12" long	G		19	.421		8.75	19.75		28.50	40
1120	18" long	G		18	.444		10.55	21		31.55	43.50
1130	3/4" diameter x 8" long	G		17	.471		17.55	22		39.55	53.50
1140	12" long	G		17	.471		21	22		43	57.50
1150	18" long	G		17	.471		26.50	22		48.50	63.50
1160	1" diameter x 12" long	G		16	.500		38	23.50		61.50	77.50
1170	18" long	G		15	.533		45	25		70	88
1180	24" long	G		15	.533		54	25		79	98
1190	36" long	G		15	.533		73	25		98	119

03 15 19 – Cast-In Concrete Anchors

03 15 19.10 Anchor Bolts		Crew	Daily Output	Labor-Hours	Unit	Material	2015 Bare Costs Labor	2015 Bare Costs Equipment	Total	Total Incl O&P
1200	1-1/2" diameter x 18" long	G 1 Carp	13	.615	Set	72	29		101	124
1210	24" long	G	12	.667		85.50	31.50		117	142
1300	L-type, incl. hex nut & washer, 3/4" diameter x 12" long	G	17	.471		23	22		45	59.50
1310	18" long	G	17	.471		28.50	22		50.50	65.50
1320	24" long	G	17	.471		34.50	22		56.50	72
1330	30" long	G	16	.500		43	23.50		66.50	83
1340	36" long	G	16	.500		48.50	23.50		72	89.50
1350	1" diameter x 12" long	G	16	.500		36	23.50		59.50	76
1360	18" long	G	15	.533		44.50	25		69.50	87.50
1370	24" long	G	15	.533		54	25		79	98
1380	30" long	G	15	.533		63.50	25		88.50	109
1390	36" long	G	15	.533		72	25		97	118
1400	42" long	G	14	.571		87	27		114	138
1410	48" long	G	14	.571		97.50	27		124.50	149
1420	1-1/4" diameter x 18" long	G	14	.571		57	27		84	104
1430	24" long	G	14	.571		67	27		94	115
1440	30" long	G	13	.615		77	29		106	129
1450	36" long	G	13	.615		87	29		116	141
1460	42" long	G 2 Carp	25	.640		98	30		128	154
1470	48" long	G	24	.667		112	31.50		143.50	171
1480	54" long	G	23	.696		131	32.50		163.50	195
1490	60" long	G	23	.696		144	32.50		176.50	209
1500	1-1/2" diameter x 18" long	G	25	.640		99	30		129	155
1510	24" long	G	24	.667		115	31.50		146.50	174
1520	30" long	G	23	.696		129	32.50		161.50	193
1530	36" long	G	22	.727		148	34		182	216
1540	42" long	G	22	.727		169	34		203	238
1550	48" long	G	21	.762		189	36		225	263
1560	54" long	G	20	.800		230	37.50		267.50	310
1570	60" long	G	20	.800		251	37.50		288.50	335
1580	1-3/4" diameter x 18" long	G	22	.727		146	34		180	214
1590	24" long	G	21	.762		171	36		207	243
1600	30" long	G	21	.762		199	36		235	273
1610	36" long	G	20	.800		226	37.50		263.50	305
1620	42" long	G	19	.842		254	39.50		293.50	340
1630	48" long	G	18	.889		278	41.50		319.50	370
1640	54" long	G	18	.889		345	41.50		386.50	445
1650	60" long	G	17	.941		370	44		414	480
1660	2" diameter x 24" long	G	19	.842		220	39.50		259.50	305
1670	30" long	G	18	.889		247	41.50		288.50	335
1680	36" long	G	18	.889		272	41.50		313.50	365
1690	42" long	G	17	.941		305	44		349	405
1700	48" long	G	16	1		345	47		392	455
1710	54" long	G	15	1.067		415	50		465	530
1720	60" long	G	15	1.067		445	50		495	565
1730	66" long	G	14	1.143		475	53.50		528.50	605
1740	72" long	G	14	1.143		520	53.50		573.50	655
1990	For galvanized, add				Ea.	75%				

03 15 19.20 Dovetail Anchor System

0010	DOVETAIL ANCHOR SYSTEM									
0500	Dovetail anchor slot, galvanized, foam-filled, 26 ga.	G 1 Carp	425	.019	L.F.	.88	.88		1.76	2.33
0600	24 ga.	G	400	.020		1.64	.94		2.58	3.25

03 15 Concrete Accessories

03 15 19 – Cast-In Concrete Anchors

03 15 19.20 Dovetail Anchor System

		Crew	Daily Output	Labor-Hours	Unit	Material	2015 Bare Costs Labor	2015 Bare Costs Equipment	Total	Total Incl O&P
0625	22 ga.	G 1 Carp	400	.020	L.F.	1.92	.94		2.86	3.56
0900	Stainless steel, foam-filled, 26 ga.	G	375	.021		1.41	1		2.41	3.09
1200	Dovetail brick anchor, corrugated, galvanized, 3-1/2" long, 16 ga.	G 1 Bric	10.50	.762	C	30.50	35		65.50	87
1300	12 ga.	G	10.50	.762		43.50	35		78.50	101
1500	Seismic, galvanized, 3-1/2" long, 16 ga.	G	10.50	.762		44.50	35		79.50	102
1600	12 ga.	G	10.50	.762		41.50	35		76.50	99
6000	Dovetail stone panel anchors, galvanized, 1/8" x 1" wide, 3-1/2" long	G	10.50	.762		99	35		134	163
6100	1/4" x 1" wide	G	10.50	.762		112	35		147	177

03 15 19.30 Inserts

		Crew	Daily Output	Labor-Hours	Unit	Material	2015 Bare Costs Labor	2015 Bare Costs Equipment	Total	Total Incl O&P
0010	**INSERTS**									
6000	Thin slab, ferrule type									
6100	1/2" diameter bolt	G 1 Carp	60	.133	Ea.	4.06	6.25		10.31	14.10
6150	5/8" diameter bolt	G	60	.133		5	6.25		11.25	15.15
6200	3/4" diameter bolt	G	60	.133		5.80	6.25		12.05	16.05
6250	1" diameter bolt	G	60	.133		9.35	6.25		15.60	19.95

03 15 19.45 Machinery Anchors

		Crew	Daily Output	Labor-Hours	Unit	Material	2015 Bare Costs Labor	2015 Bare Costs Equipment	Total	Total Incl O&P
0010	**MACHINERY ANCHORS**, heavy duty, incl. sleeve, floating base nut,									
0020	lower stud & coupling nut, fiber plug, connecting stud, washer & nut.									
0030	For flush mounted embedment in poured concrete heavy equip. pads.									
0200	Stud & bolt, 1/2" diameter	G E-16	40	.400	Ea.	72.50	21.50	3.65	97.65	122
0300	5/8" diameter	G	35	.457		80.50	24.50	4.17	109.17	136
0500	3/4" diameter	G	30	.533		93	28.50	4.86	126.36	157
0600	7/8" diameter	G	25	.640		101	34.50	5.85	141.35	177
0800	1" diameter	G	20	.800		117	43	7.30	167.30	212
0900	1-1/4" diameter	G	15	1.067		141	57	9.75	207.75	265

03 21 Reinforcement Bars

03 21 05 – Reinforcing Steel Accessories

03 21 05.10 Rebar Accessories

		Crew	Daily Output	Labor-Hours	Unit	Material	2015 Bare Costs Labor	2015 Bare Costs Equipment	Total	Total Incl O&P
0010	**REBAR ACCESSORIES**	R032110-70								
0030	Steel & plastic made from recycled materials									
0700	Bag ties, 16 ga., plain, 4" long	G			C	4			4	4.40
0710	5" long	G				5			5	5.50
0720	6" long	G				4			4	4.40
0730	7" long	G				5			5	5.50
1200	High chairs, individual (HC), 3" high, plain steel	G				59			59	65
1202	Galvanized	G				71			71	78
1204	Stainless tipped legs	G				485			485	530
1206	Plastic tipped legs	G				64			64	70.50
1210	5" high, plain	G				86			86	94.50
1212	Galvanized	G				103			103	114
1214	Stainless tipped legs	G				510			510	560
1216	Plastic tipped legs	G				94			94	103
1220	8" high, plain	G				126			126	139
1222	Galvanized	G				151			151	166
1224	Stainless tipped legs	G				550			550	605
1226	Plastic tipped legs	G				139			139	153
1230	12" high, plain	G				300			300	330
1232	Galvanized	G				360			360	395
1234	Stainless tipped legs	G				725			725	800

For customer support on your Site Work & Landscape Cost Data, call 877.737.1594.

69

03 21 05 – Reinforcing Steel Accessories

03 21 05.10 Rebar Accessories		Crew	Daily Output	Labor-Hours	Unit	Material	2015 Bare Costs Labor	Equipment	Total	Total Incl O&P
1236	Plastic tipped legs	G				C	330			330	360
1400	Individual high chairs, with plate (HCP), 5" high	G					179			179	197
1410	8" high	G					248			248	273
1500	Bar chair (BC), 1-1/2" high, plain steel	G					38			38	42
1520	Galvanized	G					43			43	47.50
1530	Stainless tipped legs	G					470			470	515
1540	Plastic tipped legs	G					41			41	45
1700	Continuous high chairs (CHC), legs 8" O.C., 4" high, plain steel	G				C.L.F.	51			51	56
1705	Galvanized	G					61			61	67.50
1710	Stainless tipped legs	G					475			475	525
1715	Plastic tipped legs	G					69			69	76
1718	Epoxy dipped	G					89			89	98
1720	6" high, plain	G					70			70	77
1725	Galvanized	G					84			84	92.50
1730	Stainless tipped legs	G					495			495	545
1735	Plastic tipped legs	G					94			94	103
1738	Epoxy dipped	G					121			121	133
1740	8" high, plain	G					100			100	110
1745	Galvanized	G					120			120	132
1750	Stainless tipped legs	G					525			525	580
1755	Plastic tipped legs	G					119			119	131
1758	Epoxy dipped	G					153			153	169
1900	For continuous bottom wire runners, add	G					52			52	57
1940	For continuous bottom plate, add	G					214			214	235
2200	Screed chair base, 1/2" coil thread diam., 2-1/2" high, plain steel	G				C	325			325	360
2210	Galvanized	G					390			390	430
2220	5-1/2" high, plain	G					395			395	430
2250	Galvanized	G					470			470	520
2300	3/4" coil thread diam., 2-1/2" high, plain steel	G					410			410	450
2310	Galvanized	G					490			490	540
2320	5-1/2" high, plain steel	G					505			505	555
2350	Galvanized	G					605			605	665
2400	Screed holder, 1/2" coil thread diam. for pipe screed, plain steel, 6" long	G					395			395	435
2420	12" long	G					605			605	665
2500	3/4" coil thread diam. for pipe screed, plain steel, 6" long	G					565			565	625
2520	12" long	G					905			905	995
2700	Screw anchor for bolts, plain steel, 3/4" diameter x 4" long	G					540			540	595
2720	1" diameter x 6" long	G					890			890	975
2740	1-1/2" diameter x 8" long	G					1,125			1,125	1,250
2800	Screw anchor eye bolts, 3/4" x 3" long	G					2,825			2,825	3,125
2820	1" x 3-1/2" long	G					3,800			3,800	4,175
2840	1-1/2" x 6" long	G					11,600			11,600	12,800
2900	Screw anchor bolts, 3/4" x 9" long	G					1,625			1,625	1,775
2920	1" x 12" long	G					3,125			3,125	3,425
3800	Subgrade chairs, #4 bar head, 3-1/2" high	G					38			38	42
3850	12" high	G					45			45	49.50
3900	#6 bar head, 3-1/2" high	G					38			38	42
3950	12" high	G					45			45	49.50
4200	Subgrade stakes, no nail holes, 3/4" diameter, 12" long	G					294			294	325
4250	24" long	G					360			360	395
4300	7/8" diameter, 12" long	G					375			375	410
4350	24" long	G					625			625	690
4500	Tie wire, 16 ga. annealed steel	G				Cwt.	203			203	223

For customer support on your Site Work & Landscape Cost Data, call 877.737.1594.

03 21 Reinforcement Bars

03 21 11 – Plain Steel Reinforcement Bars

03 21 11.50 Reinforcing Steel, Mill Base Plus Extras		Crew	Daily Output	Labor-Hours	Unit	Material	2015 Bare Costs Labor	Equipment	Total	Total Incl O&P
0010	**REINFORCING STEEL, MILL BASE PLUS EXTRAS** R032110-10									
0150	Reinforcing, A615 grade 40, mill base G				Ton	725			725	800
0200	Detailed, cut, bent, and delivered G					1,000			1,000	1,100
0650	Reinforcing steel, A615 grade 60, mill base G					725			725	800
0700	Detailed, cut, bent, and delivered G					1,000			1,000	1,100
1000	Reinforcing steel, extras, included in delivered price									
1005	Mill extra, added for delivery to shop				Ton	34			34	37.50
1010	Shop extra, added for for handling & storage					43			43	47.50
1020	Shop extra, added for bending, limited percent of bars					32.50			32.50	36
1030	Average percent of bars					65			65	71.50
1050	Large percent of bars R032110-70					130			130	143
1200	Shop extra, added for detailing, under 50 tons					50.50			50.50	55.50
1250	50 to 150 tons R032110-80					38			38	42
1300	150 to 500 tons					36			36	39.50
1350	Over 500 tons					34			34	37.50
1700	Shop extra, added for listing					5			5	5.50
2000	Mill extra, added for quantity, under 20 tons					22			22	24
2100	Shop extra, added for quantity, under 20 tons					32			32	35
2200	20 to 49 tons					24			24	26.50
2250	50 to 99 tons					16			16	17.60
2300	100 to 300 tons					9.60			9.60	10.55
2500	Shop extra, added for size, #3					152			152	167
2550	#4					76			76	83.50
2600	#5					38			38	42
2650	#6					34			34	37.50
2700	#7 to #11					45.50			45.50	50
2750	#14					57			57	62.50
2800	#18					64.50			64.50	71
2900	Shop extra, added for delivery to job					17			17	18.70

03 21 11.60 Reinforcing In Place

		Crew	Daily Output	Labor-Hours	Unit	Material	2015 Bare Costs Labor	Equipment	Total	Total Incl O&P
0010	**REINFORCING IN PLACE**, 50-60 ton lots, A615 Grade 60 R032110-10									
0020	Includes labor, but not material cost, to install accessories									
0030	Made from recycled materials									
0100	Beams & Girders, #3 to #7 G	4 Rodm	1.60	20	Ton	970	1,050		2,020	2,725
0150	#8 to #18 G		2.70	11.852		970	625		1,595	2,050
0200	Columns, #3 to #7 G		1.50	21.333		970	1,125		2,095	2,825
0250	#8 to #18 G		2.30	13.913		970	730		1,700	2,225
0300	Spirals, hot rolled, 8" to 15" diameter G		2.20	14.545		1,575	765		2,340	2,925
0320	15" to 24" diameter G		2.20	14.545		1,500	765		2,265	2,850
0330	24" to 36" diameter G		2.30	13.913		1,425	730		2,155	2,725
0340	36" to 48" diameter G		2.40	13.333		1,350	700		2,050	2,600
0360	48" to 64" diameter G		2.50	12.800		1,500	675		2,175	2,700
0380	64" to 84" diameter R032110-70 G		2.60	12.308		1,575	645		2,220	2,725
0390	84" to 96" diameter G		2.70	11.852		1,650	625		2,275	2,800
0400	Elevated slabs, #4 to #7 R032110-80 G		2.90	11.034		970	580		1,550	1,975
0500	Footings, #4 to #7 G		2.10	15.238		970	800		1,770	2,325
0550	#8 to #18 G		3.60	8.889		970	465		1,435	1,800
0600	Slab on grade, #3 to #7 G		2.30	13.913		970	730		1,700	2,225
0700	Walls, #3 to #7 G		3	10.667		970	560		1,530	1,950
0750	#8 to #18 G		4	8		970	420		1,390	1,725
0900	For other than 50 – 60 ton lots									
1000	Under 10 ton job, #3 to #7, add					25%	10%			

For customer support on your Site Work & Landscape Cost Data, call 877.737.1594.

71

03 21 Reinforcement Bars

03 21 11 – Plain Steel Reinforcement Bars

03 21 11.60 Reinforcing In Place		Crew	Daily Output	Labor-Hours	Unit	Material	2015 Bare Costs Labor	Equipment	Total	Total Incl O&P
1010	#8 to #18, add					20%	10%			
1050	10 – 50 ton job, #3 to #7, add					10%				
1060	#8 to #18, add					5%				
1100	60 – 100 ton job, #3 to #7, deduct					5%				
1110	#8 to #18, deduct					10%				
1150	Over 100 ton job, #3 to #7, deduct					10%				
1160	#8 to #18, deduct					15%				
1200	Reinforcing in place, A615 Grade 75, add G				Ton	92.50			92.50	102
1220	Grade 90, add					125			125	138
2000	Unloading & sorting, add to above	C-5	100	.560			29	7.35	36.35	53
2200	Crane cost for handling, 90 picks/day, up to 1.5 Tons/bundle, add to above		135	.415			21.50	5.45	26.95	39
2210	1.0 Ton/bundle		92	.609			31.50	8	39.50	58
2220	0.5 Ton/bundle		35	1.600			82.50	21	103.50	151
2400	Dowels, 2 feet long, deformed, #3 G	2 Rodm	520	.031	Ea.	.40	1.62		2.02	2.97
2410	#4 G		480	.033		.71	1.75		2.46	3.52
2420	#5 G		435	.037		1.11	1.93		3.04	4.24
2430	#6 G		360	.044		1.60	2.34		3.94	5.40
2450	Longer and heavier dowels, add G		725	.022	Lb.	.53	1.16		1.69	2.40
2500	Smooth dowels, 12" long, 1/4" or 3/8" diameter G		140	.114	Ea.	.72	6		6.72	10.20
2520	5/8" diameter G		125	.128		1.26	6.75		8.01	11.90
2530	3/4" diameter G		110	.145		1.57	7.65		9.22	13.65
2600	Dowel sleeves for CIP concrete, 2-part system									
2610	Sleeve base, plastic, for 5/8" smooth dowel sleeve, fasten to edge form	1 Rodm	200	.040	Ea.	.53	2.10		2.63	3.86
2615	Sleeve, plastic, 12" long, for 5/8" smooth dowel, snap onto base		400	.020		1.18	1.05		2.23	2.94
2620	Sleeve base, for 3/4" smooth dowel sleeve		175	.046		.53	2.40		2.93	4.33
2625	Sleeve, 12" long, for 3/4" smooth dowel		350	.023		1.33	1.20		2.53	3.34
2630	Sleeve base, for 1" smooth dowel sleeve		150	.053		.67	2.80		3.47	5.10
2635	Sleeve, 12" long, for 1" smooth dowel		300	.027		1.40	1.40		2.80	3.73
2700	Dowel caps, visual warning only, plastic, #3 to #8	2 Rodm	800	.020		.26	1.05		1.31	1.93
2720	#8 to #18		750	.021		.63	1.12		1.75	2.44
2750	Impalement protective, plastic, #4 to #9		800	.020		1.22	1.05		2.27	2.98

03 21 13 – Galvanized Reinforcement Steel Bars

03 21 13.10 Galvanized Reinforcing

0010	**GALVANIZED REINFORCING**									
0150	Add to plain steel rebar pricing for galvanized rebar				Ton	460			460	505

03 21 16 – Epoxy-Coated Reinforcement Steel Bars

03 21 16.10 Epoxy-Coated Reinforcing

0010	**EPOXY-COATED REINFORCING**									
0100	Add to plain steel rebar pricing for epoxy-coated rebar				Ton	420			420	465

03 21 21 – Composite Reinforcement Bars

03 21 21.11 Glass Fiber-Reinf. Polymer Reinforcement Bars

0010	**GLASS FIBER-REINFORCED POLYMER REINFORCEMENT BARS**									
0020	Includes labor, but not material cost, to install accessories									
0050	#2 bar, .043 lb./L.F.	4 Rodm	9500	.003	L.F.	.40	.18		.58	.72
0100	#3 bar, .092 lb./L.F.		9300	.003		.49	.18		.67	.82
0150	#4 bar, .160 lb./L.F.		9100	.004		.71	.19		.90	1.07
0200	#5 bar, .258 lb./L.F.		8700	.004		1.09	.19		1.28	1.50
0250	#6 bar, .372 lb./L.F.		8300	.004		1.41	.20		1.61	1.87
0300	#7 bar, .497 lb./L.F.		7900	.004		1.84	.21		2.05	2.35
0350	#8 bar, .620 lb./L.F.		7400	.004		2.38	.23		2.61	2.97
0400	#9 bar, .800 lb./L.F.		6800	.005		3.10	.25		3.35	3.80

03 21 Reinforcement Bars

03 21 21 – Composite Reinforcement Bars

03 21 21.11 Glass Fiber-Reinf. Polymer Reinforcement Bars	Crew	Daily Output	Labor-Hours	Unit	Material	2015 Bare Costs Labor	Equipment	Total	Total Incl O&P
0450	#10 bar, 1.08 lb./L.F.	4 Rodm	5800	.006	L.F.	3.75	.29		4.04	4.58
0500	For Bends, add per bend				Ea.	1.48			1.48	1.63

03 22 Fabric and Grid Reinforcing

03 22 11 – Plain Welded Wire Fabric Reinforcing

03 22 11.10 Plain Welded Wire Fabric

			Crew	Daily Output	Labor-Hours	Unit	Material	2015 Bare Costs Labor	Equipment	Total	Total Incl O&P
0010	**PLAIN WELDED WIRE FABRIC** ASTM A185	R032205-30									
0020	Includes labor, but not material cost, to install accessories										
0030	Made from recycled materials										
0050	Sheets										
0100	6 x 6 - W1.4 x W1.4 (10 x 10) 21 lb. per C.S.F.	G	2 Rodm	35	.457	C.S.F.	14.50	24		38.50	53.50
0200	6 x 6 - W2.1 x W2.1 (8 x 8) 30 lb. per C.S.F.	G		31	.516		17.20	27		44.20	61.50
0300	6 x 6 - W2.9 x W2.9 (6 x 6) 42 lb. per C.S.F.	G		29	.552		22.50	29		51.50	70
0400	6 x 6 - W4 x W4 (4 x 4) 58 lb. per C.S.F.	G		27	.593		31.50	31		62.50	83
0500	4 x 4 - W1.4 x W1.4 (10 x 10) 31 lb. per C.S.F.	G		31	.516		20	27		47	64.50
0600	4 x 4 - W2.1 x W2.1 (8 x 8) 44 lb. per C.S.F.	G		29	.552		25	29		54	73
0650	4 x 4 - W2.9 x W2.9 (6 x 6) 61 lb. per C.S.F.	G		27	.593		40.50	31		71.50	93
0700	4 x 4 - W4 x W4 (4 x 4) 85 lb. per C.S.F.	G		25	.640		50.50	33.50		84	108
0750	Rolls										
0800	2 x 2 - #14 galv., 21 lb./C.S.F., beam & column wrap	G	2 Rodm	6.50	2.462	C.S.F.	41.50	129		170.50	248
0900	2 x 2 - #12 galv. for gunite reinforcing	G	"	6.50	2.462	"	62.50	129		191.50	271

03 22 13 – Galvanized Welded Wire Fabric Reinforcing

03 22 13.10 Galvanized Welded Wire Fabric

						Unit	Material			Total	Total Incl O&P
0010	**GALVANIZED WELDED WIRE FABRIC**										
0100	Add to plain welded wire pricing for galvanized welded wire					Lb.	.23			.23	.25

03 22 16 – Epoxy-Coated Welded Wire Fabric Reinforcing

03 22 16.10 Epoxy-Coated Welded Wire Fabric

						Unit	Material			Total	Total Incl O&P
0010	**EPOXY-COATED WELDED WIRE FABRIC**										
0100	Add to plain welded wire pricing for epoxy-coated welded wire					Lb.	.21			.21	.23

03 23 Stressed Tendon Reinforcing

03 23 05 – Prestressing Tendons

03 23 05.50 Prestressing Steel

		Crew	Daily Output	Labor-Hours	Unit	Material	2015 Bare Costs Labor	Equipment	Total	Total Incl O&P
0010	**PRESTRESSING STEEL**									
3000	Slabs on grade, 0.5-inch diam. non-bonded strands, HDPE sheathed,									
3050	attached dead-end anchors, loose stressing-end anchors									
3100	25' x 30' slab, strands @ 36" O.C., placing	2 Rodm	2940	.005	S.F.	.60	.29		.89	1.11
3105	Stressing	C-4A	3750	.004			.22	.01	.23	.36
3110	42" O.C., placing	2 Rodm	3200	.005		.53	.26		.79	1
3115	Stressing	C-4A	4040	.004			.21	.01	.22	.34
3120	48" O.C., placing	2 Rodm	3510	.005		.47	.24		.71	.88
3125	Stressing	C-4A	4390	.004			.19	.01	.20	.31
3150	25' x 40' slab, strands @ 36" O.C., placing	2 Rodm	3370	.005		.58	.25		.83	1.03
3155	Stressing	C-4A	4360	.004			.19	.01	.20	.31
3160	42" O.C., placing	2 Rodm	3760	.004		.50	.22		.72	.90
3165	Stressing	C-4A	4820	.003			.17	.01	.18	.28
3170	48" O.C., placing	2 Rodm	4090	.004		.45	.21		.66	.81
3175	Stressing	C-4A	5190	.003			.16	.01	.17	.26

For customer support on your Site Work & Landscape Cost Data, call 877.737.1594.

73

03 23 Stressed Tendon Reinforcing

03 23 05 – Prestressing Tendons

03 23 05.50 Prestressing Steel

		Crew	Daily Output	Labor-Hours	Unit	Material	2015 Bare Costs Labor	Equipment	Total	Total Incl O&P
3200	30' x 30' slab, strands @ 36" O.C., placing	2 Rodm	3260	.005	S.F.	.58	.26		.84	1.04
3205	Stressing	C-4A	4190	.004			.20	.01	.21	.32
3210	42" O.C., placing	2 Rodm	3530	.005		.52	.24		.76	.95
3215	Stressing	C-4A	4500	.004			.19	.01	.20	.30
3220	48" O.C., placing	2 Rodm	3840	.004		.47	.22		.69	.85
3225	Stressing	C-4A	4850	.003			.17	.01	.18	.28
3230	30' x 40' slab, strands @ 36" O.C., placing	2 Rodm	3780	.004		.56	.22		.78	.97
3235	Stressing	C-4A	4920	.003			.17	.01	.18	.28
3240	42" O.C., placing	2 Rodm	4190	.004		.49	.20		.69	.85
3245	Stressing	C-4A	5410	.003			.16	.01	.17	.25
3250	48" O.C., placing	2 Rodm	4520	.004		.45	.19		.64	.78
3255	Stressing	C-4A	5790	.003			.15	.01	.16	.24
3260	30' x 50' slab, strands @ 36" O.C., placing	2 Rodm	4300	.004		.53	.20		.73	.90
3265	Stressing	C-4A	5650	.003			.15	.01	.16	.24
3270	42" O.C., placing	2 Rodm	4720	.003		.47	.18		.65	.80
3275	Stressing	C-4A	6150	.003			.14	.01	.15	.22
3280	48" O.C., placing	2 Rodm	5240	.003		.42	.16		.58	.71
3285	Stressing	C-4A	6760	.002	▼		.12	.01	.13	.20

03 24 Fibrous Reinforcing

03 24 05 – Reinforcing Fibers

03 24 05.30 Synthetic Fibers

					Unit	Material	Labor	Equipment	Total	Total Incl O&P
0010	**SYNTHETIC FIBERS**									
0100	Synthetic fibers, add to concrete				Lb.	4.40			4.40	4.84
0110	1-1/2 lb. per C.Y.				C.Y.	6.80			6.80	7.50

03 24 05.70 Steel Fibers

						Unit	Material	Labor	Equipment	Total	Total Incl O&P
0010	**STEEL FIBERS**										
0140	ASTM A850, Type V, continuously deformed, 1-1/2" long x 0.045" diam.										
0150	Add to price of ready mix concrete	G				Lb.	1.13			1.13	1.24
0205	Alternate pricing, dosing at 5 lb. per C.Y., add to price of RMC	G				C.Y.	5.65			5.65	6.20
0210	10 lb. per C.Y.	G					11.30			11.30	12.45
0215	15 lb. per C.Y.	G					16.95			16.95	18.65
0220	20 lb. per C.Y.	G					22.50			22.50	25
0225	25 lb. per C.Y.	G					28.50			28.50	31
0230	30 lb. per C.Y.	G					34			34	37.50
0235	35 lb. per C.Y.	G					39.50			39.50	43.50
0240	40 lb. per C.Y.	G					45			45	49.50
0250	50 lb. per C.Y.	G					56.50			56.50	62
0275	75 lb. per C.Y.	G					85			85	93
0300	100 lb. per C.Y.	G			▼		113			113	124

03 30 53 – Miscellaneous Cast-In-Place Concrete

03 30 53.40 Concrete In Place		Crew	Daily Output	Labor-Hours	Unit	Material	2015 Bare Costs Labor	Equipment	Total	Total Incl O&P
0010	**CONCRETE IN PLACE** R033053-60									
0020	Including forms (4 uses), Grade 60 rebar, concrete (Portland cement									
0050	Type I), placement and finishing unless otherwise indicated R033105-20									
0300	Beams (3500 psi), 5 kip per L.F., 10' span R033105-70	C-14A	15.62	12.804	C.Y.	320	605	48	973	1,325
0350	25' span	"	18.55	10.782		335	510	40.50	885.50	1,200
0500	Chimney foundations (5000 psi), over 5 C.Y.	C-14C	32.22	3.476		150	157	.97	307.97	405
0510	(3500 psi), under 5 C.Y.	"	23.71	4.724		177	213	1.32	391.32	525
0700	Columns, square (4000 psi), 12" x 12", less than 2% reinforcing	C-14A	11.96	16.722		365	790	63	1,218	1,700
0800	16" x 16", less than 2% reinforcing		16.22	12.330		286	585	46.50	917.50	1,250
0900	24" x 24", less than 2% reinforcing		23.66	8.453		241	400	32	673	915
1000	36" x 36", less than 2% reinforcing		33.69	5.936		212	281	22.50	515.50	690
1100	Columns, round (4000 psi), tied, 12" diameter, less than 2% reinforcing		20.97	9.537		315	450	36	801	1,075
1200	16" diameter, less than 2% reinforcing		31.49	6.351		289	300	24	613	800
1300	20" diameter, less than 2% reinforcing		41.04	4.873		289	230	18.30	537.30	690
1400	24" diameter, less than 2% reinforcing		51.85	3.857		269	182	14.50	465.50	595
1500	36" diameter, less than 2% reinforcing		75.04	2.665		266	126	10	402	500
3100	Elevated slabs, flat plate, including finish, not									
3110	including forms or reinforcing									
3150	Regular concrete (4000 psi), 4" slab	C-8	2613	.021	S.F.	1.43	.90	.28	2.61	3.24
3200	6" slab		2585	.022		2.09	.91	.28	3.28	3.99
3250	2-1/2" thick floor fill		2685	.021		.94	.87	.27	2.08	2.65
3300	Lightweight, 110# per C.F., 2-1/2" thick floor fill		2585	.022		1.46	.91	.28	2.65	3.30
3400	Cellular concrete, 1-5/8" fill, under 5000 S.F.		2000	.028		.99	1.17	.36	2.52	3.27
3450	Over 10,000 S.F.		2200	.025		.94	1.07	.33	2.34	3.02
3540	Equipment pad (3000 psi), 3' x 3' x 6" thick	C-14H	45	1.067	Ea.	47	49.50	.69	97.19	128
3550	4' x 4' x 6" thick		30	1.600		69.50	74	1.04	144.54	191
3560	5' x 5' x 8" thick		18	2.667		122	124	1.73	247.73	325
3570	6' x 6' x 8" thick		14	3.429		164	159	2.23	325.23	425
3580	8' x 8' x 10" thick		8	6		350	278	3.90	631.90	815
3590	10' x 10' x 12" thick		5	9.600		595	445	6.25	1,046.25	1,350
3600	Flexural concrete on grade, direct chute, 500 psi, no forms, reinf, finish	C-8A	150	.320	C.Y.	102	12.95		114.95	132
3610	650 psi		150	.320		113	12.95		125.95	145
3620	750 psi		150	.320		170	12.95		182.95	207
3650	Pumped, 500 psi	C-8	70	.800		102	33.50	10.30	145.80	174
3660	650 psi		70	.800		113	33.50	10.30	156.80	187
3670	750 psi		70	.800		170	33.50	10.30	213.80	249
3800	Footings (3000 psi), spread under 1 C.Y.	C-14C	28	4		166	180	1.12	347.12	460
3825	1 C.Y. to 5 C.Y.		43	2.605		201	117	.73	318.73	405
3850	Over 5 C.Y.		75	1.493		185	67.50	.42	252.92	310
3900	Footings, strip (3000 psi), 18" x 9", unreinforced	C-14L	40	2.400		125	105	.79	230.79	300
3920	18" x 9", reinforced	C-14C	35	3.200		148	144	.90	292.90	385
3925	20" x 10", unreinforced	C-14L	45	2.133		122	93.50	.70	216.20	278
3930	20" x 10", reinforced	C-14C	40	2.800		140	126	.78	266.78	350
3935	24" x 12", unreinforced	C-14L	55	1.745		120	76.50	.58	197.08	250
3940	24" x 12", reinforced	C-14C	48	2.333		139	105	.65	244.65	315
3945	36" x 12", unreinforced	C-14L	70	1.371		116	60	.45	176.45	219
3950	36" x 12", reinforced	C-14C	60	1.867		133	84	.52	217.52	276
4000	Foundation mat (3000 psi), under 10 C.Y.		38.67	2.896		204	131	.81	335.81	425
4050	Over 20 C.Y.		56.40	1.986		178	89.50	.56	268.06	335
4200	Wall, free-standing (3000 psi), 8" thick, 8' high	C-14D	45.83	4.364		160	204	16.40	380.40	510
4250	14' high		27.26	7.337		190	345	27.50	562.50	770
4260	12" thick, 8' high		64.32	3.109		145	146	11.70	302.70	395
4270	14' high		40.01	4.999		154	234	18.80	406.80	550

For customer support on your Site Work & Landscape Cost Data, call 877.737.1594.

75

03 30 53.40 Concrete In Place		Crew	Daily Output	Labor-Hours	Unit	Material	2015 Bare Costs Labor	Equipment	Total	Total Incl O&P
4300	15" thick, 8' high	C-14D	80.02	2.499	C.Y.	139	117	9.40	265.40	345
4350	12' high		51.26	3.902		139	183	14.65	336.65	450
4500	18' high	↓	48.85	4.094	↓	157	192	15.40	364.40	485
4520	Handicap access ramp (4000 psi), railing both sides, 3' wide	C-14H	14.58	3.292	L.F.	320	153	2.14	475.14	585
4525	5' wide		12.22	3.928		330	182	2.55	514.55	645
4530	With 6" curb and rails both sides, 3' wide		8.55	5.614		330	260	3.65	593.65	765
4535	5' wide	↓	7.31	6.566	↓	335	305	4.27	644.27	840
4650	Slab on grade (3500 psi), not including finish, 4" thick	C-14E	60.75	1.449	C.Y.	124	67.50	.51	192.01	242
4700	6" thick	"	92	.957	"	119	44.50	.33	163.83	200
4701	Thickened slab edge (3500 psi), for slab on grade poured									
4702	monolithically with slab; depth is in addition to slab thickness;									
4703	formed vertical outside edge, earthen bottom and inside slope									
4705	8" deep x 8" wide bottom, unreinforced	C-14L	2190	.044	L.F.	3.47	1.92	.01	5.40	6.80
4710	8" x 8", reinforced	C-14C	1670	.067		5.75	3.02	.02	8.79	10.95
4715	12" deep x 12" wide bottom, unreinforced	C-14L	1800	.053		7.05	2.34	.02	9.41	11.35
4720	12" x 12", reinforced	C-14C	1310	.086		11.20	3.85	.02	15.07	18.30
4725	16" deep x 16" wide bottom, unreinforced	C-14L	1440	.067		11.85	2.92	.02	14.79	17.50
4730	16" x 16", reinforced	C-14C	1120	.100		16.80	4.51	.03	21.34	25.50
4735	20" deep x 20" wide bottom, unreinforced	C-14L	1150	.083		17.90	3.66	.03	21.59	25.50
4740	20" x 20", reinforced	C-14C	920	.122		24	5.50	.03	29.53	35
4745	24" deep x 24" wide bottom, unreinforced	C-14L	930	.103		25	4.53	.03	29.56	35
4750	24" x 24", reinforced	C-14C	740	.151	↓	33.50	6.80	.04	40.34	47
4751	Slab on grade (3500 psi), incl. troweled finish, not incl. forms									
4760	or reinforcing, over 10,000 S.F., 4" thick	C-14F	3425	.021	S.F.	1.35	.90	.01	2.26	2.85
4820	6" thick		3350	.021		1.98	.92	.01	2.91	3.57
4840	8" thick		3184	.023		2.71	.97	.01	3.69	4.44
4900	12" thick		2734	.026		4.06	1.13	.01	5.20	6.15
4950	15" thick	↓	2505	.029	↓	5.10	1.23	.01	6.34	7.45
5000	Slab on grade (3000 psi), incl. broom finish, not incl. forms									
5001	or reinforcing, 4" thick	C-14G	2873	.019	S.F.	1.32	.82	.01	2.15	2.69
5010	6" thick		2590	.022		2.07	.91	.01	2.99	3.65
5020	8" thick	↓	2320	.024	↓	2.70	1.02	.01	3.73	4.50
5200	Lift slab in place above the foundation, incl. forms, reinforcing,									
5210	concrete (4000 psi) and columns, over 20,000 S.F. per floor	C-14B	2113	.098	S.F.	6.90	4.64	.36	11.90	15.15
5900	Pile caps (3000 psi), incl. forms and reinf., sq. or rect., under 10 C.Y.	C-14C	54.14	2.069	C.Y.	168	93.50	.58	262.08	330
5950	Over 10 C.Y.		75	1.493		157	67.50	.42	224.92	277
6000	Triangular or hexagonal, under 10 C.Y.		53	2.113		123	95.50	.59	219.09	283
6050	Over 10 C.Y.	↓	85	1.318		138	59.50	.37	197.87	244
6200	Retaining walls (3000 psi), gravity, 4' high see Section 32 32	C-14D	66.20	3.021		140	141	11.35	292.35	385
6250	10' high		125	1.600		134	75	6	215	269
6300	Cantilever, level backfill loading, 8' high		70	2.857		150	134	10.75	294.75	385
6350	16' high	↓	91	2.198	↓	145	103	8.25	256.25	325
6800	Stairs (3500 psi), not including safety treads, free standing, 3'-6" wide	C-14H	83	.578	LF Nose	5.60	27	.38	32.98	47.50
6850	Cast on ground		125	.384	"	4.63	17.80	.25	22.68	33
7000	Stair landings, free standing		200	.240	S.F.	4.52	11.10	.16	15.78	22
7050	Cast on ground	↓	475	.101	"	3.52	4.68	.07	8.27	11.15

03 31 Structural Concrete

03 31 13 – Heavyweight Structural Concrete

03 31 13.25 Concrete, Hand Mix

		Crew	Daily Output	Labor-Hours	Unit	Material	2015 Bare Costs Labor	2015 Bare Costs Equipment	Total	Total Incl O&P
0010	**CONCRETE, HAND MIX** for small quantities or remote areas									
0050	Includes bulk local aggregate, bulk sand, bagged Portland									
0060	cement (Type I) and water, using gas powered cement mixer									
0125	2500 psi	C-30	135	.059	C.F.	3.29	2.23	1.28	6.80	8.45
0130	3000 psi		135	.059		3.52	2.23	1.28	7.03	8.70
0135	3500 psi		135	.059		3.66	2.23	1.28	7.17	8.85
0140	4000 psi		135	.059		3.82	2.23	1.28	7.33	9.05
0145	4500 psi		135	.059		4	2.23	1.28	7.51	9.25
0150	5000 psi	↓	135	.059	↓	4.26	2.23	1.28	7.77	9.50
0300	Using pre-bagged dry mix and wheelbarrow (80-lb. bag = 0.6 C.F.)									
0340	4000 psi	1 Clab	48	.167	C.F.	6.25	6.25		12.50	16.55

03 31 13.30 Concrete, Volumetric Site-Mixed

		Crew	Daily Output	Labor-Hours	Unit	Material	2015 Bare Costs Labor	2015 Bare Costs Equipment	Total	Total Incl O&P
0010	**CONCRETE, VOLUMETRIC SITE-MIXED**									
0015	Mixed on-site in volumetric truck									
0020	Includes local aggregate, sand, Portland cement (Type I) and water									
0025	Excludes all additives and treatments									
0100	3000 psi, 1 C.Y. mixed and discharged				C.Y.	177			177	194
0110	2 C.Y.					138			138	151
0120	3 C.Y.					124			124	136
0130	4 C.Y.					113			113	124
0140	5 C.Y.				↓	106			106	117
0200	For truck holding/waiting time past first 2 on-site hours, add				Hr.	78			78	86
0210	For trip charge beyond first 20 miles, each way, add				Mile	3.50			3.50	3.85
0220	For each additional increase of 500 psi, add				Ea.	4.17			4.17	4.59

03 31 13.35 Heavyweight Concrete, Ready Mix

		Crew	Daily Output	Labor-Hours	Unit	Material	2015 Bare Costs Labor	2015 Bare Costs Equipment	Total	Total Incl O&P
0010	**HEAVYWEIGHT CONCRETE, READY MIX**, delivered									
0012	Includes local aggregate, sand, Portland cement (Type I) and water									
0015	Excludes all additives and treatments R033105-20									
0020	2000 psi				C.Y.	97			97	107
0100	2500 psi					99.50			99.50	109
0150	3000 psi					102			102	112
0200	3500 psi					104			104	115
0300	4000 psi					107			107	118
0350	4500 psi					110			110	121
0400	5000 psi					113			113	125
0411	6000 psi					116			116	128
0412	8000 psi					123			123	135
0413	10,000 psi					129			129	142
0414	12,000 psi					135			135	149
1000	For high early strength (Portland cement Type III), add					10%				
1010	For structural lightweight with regular sand, add					25%				
1300	For winter concrete (hot water), add					4.05			4.05	4.46
1410	For mid-range water reducer, add					3.31			3.31	3.64
1420	For high-range water reducer/superplasticizer, add					5.65			5.65	6.20
1430	For retarder, add					3.23			3.23	3.55
1440	For non-Chloride accelerator, add					5.50			5.50	6.05
1450	For Chloride accelerator, per 1%, add					2.90			2.90	3.19
1460	For fiber reinforcing, synthetic (1 lb./C.Y.), add					6.65			6.65	7.30
1500	For Saturday delivery, add				↓	10.80			10.80	11.90
1510	For truck holding/waiting time past 1st hour per load, add				Hr.	94			94	103
1520	For short load (less than 4 C.Y.), add per load				Ea.	60.50			60.50	66.50
2000	For all lightweight aggregate, add				C.Y.	45%				

03 31 Structural Concrete

03 31 13 – Heavyweight Structural Concrete

03 31 13.35 Heavyweight Concrete, Ready Mix

	03 31 13.35 Heavyweight Concrete, Ready Mix	Crew	Daily Output	Labor-Hours	Unit	Material	2015 Bare Costs Labor	Equipment	Total	Total Incl O&P
4000	Flowable fill: ash, cement, aggregate, water									
4100	40 – 80 psi				C.Y.	77			77	85
4150	Structural: ash, cement, aggregate, water & sand									
4200	50 psi				C.Y.	77			77	85
4250	140 psi					78			78	85.50
4300	500 psi					80			80	88
4350	1000 psi					83.50			83.50	91.50

03 31 13.70 Placing Concrete

	03 31 13.70 Placing Concrete	Crew	Daily Output	Labor-Hours	Unit	Material	2015 Bare Costs Labor	Equipment	Total	Total Incl O&P
0010	**PLACING CONCRETE** R033105-70									
0020	Includes labor and equipment to place, level (strike off) and consolidate									
0050	Beams, elevated, small beams, pumped	C-20	60	1.067	C.Y.		43	13.05	56.05	80.50
0100	With crane and bucket	C-7	45	1.600			65.50	27	92.50	130
0200	Large beams, pumped	C-20	90	.711			28.50	8.70	37.20	53.50
0250	With crane and bucket	C-7	65	1.108			45.50	18.70	64.20	89.50
0400	Columns, square or round, 12" thick, pumped	C-20	60	1.067			43	13.05	56.05	80.50
0450	With crane and bucket	C-7	40	1.800			73.50	30.50	104	146
0600	18" thick, pumped	C-20	90	.711			28.50	8.70	37.20	53.50
0650	With crane and bucket	C-7	55	1.309			53.50	22	75.50	107
0800	24" thick, pumped	C-20	92	.696			28	8.50	36.50	52.50
0850	With crane and bucket	C-7	70	1.029			42	17.35	59.35	83
1000	36" thick, pumped	C-20	140	.457			18.45	5.60	24.05	34
1050	With crane and bucket	C-7	100	.720			29.50	12.15	41.65	58.50
1400	Elevated slabs, less than 6" thick, pumped	C-20	140	.457			18.45	5.60	24.05	34
1450	With crane and bucket	C-7	95	.758			31	12.80	43.80	61.50
1500	6" to 10" thick, pumped	C-20	160	.400			16.15	4.89	21.04	30
1550	With crane and bucket	C-7	110	.655			27	11.05	38.05	53
1600	Slabs over 10" thick, pumped	C-20	180	.356			14.35	4.35	18.70	27
1650	With crane and bucket	C-7	130	.554			22.50	9.35	31.85	45
1900	Footings, continuous, shallow, direct chute	C-6	120	.400			15.65	.52	16.17	24.50
1950	Pumped	C-20	150	.427			17.25	5.20	22.45	32.50
2000	With crane and bucket	C-7	90	.800			32.50	13.50	46	65
2100	Footings, continuous, deep, direct chute	C-6	140	.343			13.45	.45	13.90	21
2150	Pumped	C-20	160	.400			16.15	4.89	21.04	30
2200	With crane and bucket	C-7	110	.655			27	11.05	38.05	53
2400	Footings, spread, under 1 C.Y., direct chute	C-6	55	.873			34	1.13	35.13	53.50
2450	Pumped	C-20	65	.985			40	12.05	52.05	74.50
2500	With crane and bucket	C-7	45	1.600			65.50	27	92.50	130
2600	Over 5 C.Y., direct chute	C-6	120	.400			15.65	.52	16.17	24.50
2650	Pumped	C-20	150	.427			17.25	5.20	22.45	32.50
2700	With crane and bucket	C-7	100	.720			29.50	12.15	41.65	58.50
2900	Foundation mats, over 20 C.Y., direct chute	C-6	350	.137			5.35	.18	5.53	8.40
2950	Pumped	C-20	400	.160			6.45	1.96	8.41	12
3000	With crane and bucket	C-7	300	.240			9.80	4.05	13.85	19.45
3200	Grade beams, direct chute	C-6	150	.320			12.55	.42	12.97	19.60
3250	Pumped	C-20	180	.356			14.35	4.35	18.70	27
3300	With crane and bucket	C-7	120	.600			24.50	10.10	34.60	48.50
3700	Pile caps, under 5 C.Y., direct chute	C-6	90	.533			21	.69	21.69	33
3750	Pumped	C-20	110	.582			23.50	7.10	30.60	44
3800	With crane and bucket	C-7	80	.900			37	15.15	52.15	72.50
4000	Over 10 C.Y., direct chute	C-6	215	.223			8.75	.29	9.04	13.65
4050	Pumped	C-20	240	.267			10.75	3.26	14.01	20
4100	With crane and bucket	C-7	185	.389			15.95	6.55	22.50	31.50

03 31 Structural Concrete

03 31 13 – Heavyweight Structural Concrete

03 31 13.70 Placing Concrete

		Crew	Daily Output	Labor-Hours	Unit	Material	2015 Bare Costs Labor	Equipment	Total	Total Incl O&P
4300	Slab on grade, up to 6" thick, direct chute R033105-70	C-6	110	.436	C.Y.		17.10	.57	17.67	26.50
4350	Pumped	C-20	130	.492			19.90	6	25.90	37
4400	With crane and bucket	C-7	110	.655			27	11.05	38.05	53
4600	Over 6" thick, direct chute	C-6	165	.291			11.40	.38	11.78	17.80
4650	Pumped	C-20	185	.346			14	4.23	18.23	26
4700	With crane and bucket	C-7	145	.497			20.50	8.35	28.85	40
4900	Walls, 8" thick, direct chute	C-6	90	.533			21	.69	21.69	33
4950	Pumped	C-20	100	.640			26	7.85	33.85	48
5000	With crane and bucket	C-7	80	.900			37	15.15	52.15	72.50
5050	12" thick, direct chute	C-6	100	.480			18.80	.62	19.42	29
5100	Pumped	C-20	110	.582			23.50	7.10	30.60	44
5200	With crane and bucket	C-7	90	.800			32.50	13.50	46	65
5300	15" thick, direct chute	C-6	105	.457			17.90	.59	18.49	28
5350	Pumped	C-20	120	.533			21.50	6.50	28	40
5400	With crane and bucket	C-7	95	.758			31	12.80	43.80	61.50
5600	Wheeled concrete dumping, add to placing costs above									
5610	Walking cart, 50' haul, add	C-18	32	.281	C.Y.		10.65	1.88	12.53	18.40
5620	150' haul, add		24	.375			14.20	2.50	16.70	25
5700	250' haul, add		18	.500			18.90	3.34	22.24	32.50
5800	Riding cart, 50' haul, add	C-19	80	.113			4.25	1.25	5.50	7.90
5810	150' haul, add		60	.150			5.65	1.66	7.31	10.60
5900	250' haul, add		45	.200			7.55	2.22	9.77	14.10
6000	Concrete in-fill for pan-type metal stairs and landings. Manual placement									
6010	includes up to 50' horizontal haul from point of concrete discharge.									
6100	Stair pan treads, 2" deep									
6110	Flights in 1st floor level up/down from discharge point	C-8A	3200	.015	S.F.		.61		.61	.92
6120	2nd floor level		2500	.019			.78		.78	1.18
6130	3rd floor level		2000	.024			.97		.97	1.47
6140	4th floor level		1800	.027			1.08		1.08	1.63
6200	Intermediate stair landings, pan-type 4" deep									
6210	Flights in 1st floor level up/down from discharge point	C-8A	2000	.024	S.F.		.97		.97	1.47
6220	2nd floor level		1500	.032			1.29		1.29	1.96
6230	3rd floor level		1200	.040			1.62		1.62	2.45
6240	4th floor level		1000	.048			1.94		1.94	2.94

03 35 Concrete Finishing

03 35 13 – High-Tolerance Concrete Floor Finishing

03 35 13.30 Finishing Floors, High Tolerance

		Crew	Daily Output	Labor-Hours	Unit	Material	2015 Bare Costs Labor	Equipment	Total	Total Incl O&P
0010	**FINISHING FLOORS, HIGH TOLERANCE**									
0012	Finishing of fresh concrete flatwork requires that concrete									
0013	first be placed, struck off & consolidated									
0015	Basic finishing for various unspecified flatwork									
0100	Bull float only	C-10	4000	.006	S.F.		.26		.26	.38
0125	Bull float & manual float		2000	.012			.51		.51	.76
0150	Bull float, manual float, & broom finish, w/edging & joints		1850	.013			.55		.55	.83
0200	Bull float, manual float & manual steel trowel		1265	.019			.81		.81	1.21
0210	For specified Random Access Floors in ACI Classes 1, 2, 3 and 4 to achieve									
0215	Composite Overall Floor Flatness and Levelness values up to FF35/FL25									
0250	Bull float, machine float & machine trowel (walk-behind)	C-10C	1715	.014	S.F.		.60	.03	.63	.92
0300	Power screed, bull float, machine float & trowel (walk-behind)	C-10D	2400	.010			.43	.05	.48	.69
0350	Power screed, bull float, machine float & trowel (ride-on)	C-10E	4000	.006			.26	.06	.32	.45

03 35 Concrete Finishing

03 35 13 – High-Tolerance Concrete Floor Finishing

03 35 13.30 Finishing Floors, High Tolerance	Crew	Daily Output	Labor-Hours	Unit	Material	2015 Bare Costs Labor	Equipment	Total	Total Incl O&P
0352	For specified Random Access Floors in ACI Classes 5, 6, 7 and 8 to achieve								
0354	Composite Overall Floor Flatness and Levelness values up to FF50/FL50								
0356	Add for two-dimensional restraightening after power float	C-10	6000	.004	S.F.		.17		.17	.25
0358	For specified Random or Defined Access Floors in ACI Class 9 to achieve								
0360	Composite Overall Floor Flatness and Levelness values up to FF100/FL100								
0362	Add for two-dimensional restraightening after bull float & power float	C-10	3000	.008	S.F.		.34		.34	.51
0364	For specified Superflat Defined Access Floors in ACI Class 9 to achieve								
0366	Minimum Floor Flatness and Levelness values of FF100/FL100								
0368	Add for 2-dim'l restraightening after bull float, power float, power trowel	C-10	2000	.012	S.F.		.51		.51	.76

03 35 16 – Heavy-Duty Concrete Floor Finishing

03 35 16.30 Finishing Floors, Heavy-Duty

		Crew	Daily Output	Labor-Hours	Unit	Material	Labor	Equipment	Total	Total Incl O&P
0010	**FINISHING FLOORS, HEAVY-DUTY**									
1800	Floor abrasives, dry shake on fresh concrete, .25 psf, aluminum oxide	1 Cefi	850	.009	S.F.	.53	.42		.95	1.21
1850	Silicon carbide		850	.009		.79	.42		1.21	1.50
2000	Floor hardeners, dry shake, metallic, light service, .50 psf		850	.009		.54	.42		.96	1.22
2050	Medium service, .75 psf		750	.011		.80	.48		1.28	1.59
2100	Heavy service, 1.0 psf		650	.012		1.07	.55		1.62	2
2150	Extra heavy, 1.5 psf		575	.014		1.61	.63		2.24	2.70
2300	Non-metallic, light service, .50 psf		850	.009		.21	.42		.63	.87
2350	Medium service, .75 psf		750	.011		.32	.48		.80	1.06
2400	Heavy service, 1.00 psf		650	.012		.43	.55		.98	1.29
2450	Extra heavy, 1.50 psf		575	.014		.64	.63		1.27	1.64
2800	Trap rock wearing surface, dry shake, for monolithic floors									
2810	2.0 psf	C-10B	1250	.032	S.F.	.02	1.30	.22	1.54	2.22
3800	Dustproofing, liquid, for cured concrete, solvent-based, 1 coat	1 Cefi	1900	.004		.18	.19		.37	.47
3850	2 coats		1300	.006		.63	.28		.91	1.11
4000	Epoxy-based, 1 coat		1500	.005		.14	.24		.38	.51
4050	2 coats		1500	.005		.28	.24		.52	.67

03 35 19 – Colored Concrete Finishing

03 35 19.30 Finishing Floors, Colored

		Crew	Daily Output	Labor-Hours	Unit	Material	Labor	Equipment	Total	Total Incl O&P
0010	**FINISHING FLOORS, COLORED**									
3000	Floor coloring, dry shake on fresh concrete (0.6 psf)	1 Cefi	1300	.006	S.F.	.44	.28		.72	.89
3050	(1.0 psf)	"	625	.013	"	.73	.58		1.31	1.66
3100	Colored dry shake powder only				Lb.	.73			.73	.81
3600	1/2" topping using 0.6 psf dry shake powdered color	C-10B	590	.068	S.F.	4.96	2.75	.46	8.17	10.10
3650	1.0 psf dry shake powdered color	"	590	.068	"	5.25	2.75	.46	8.46	10.45

03 35 23 – Exposed Aggregate Concrete Finishing

03 35 23.30 Finishing Floors, Exposed Aggregate

		Crew	Daily Output	Labor-Hours	Unit	Material	Labor	Equipment	Total	Total Incl O&P
0010	**FINISHING FLOORS, EXPOSED AGGREGATE**									
1600	Exposed local aggregate finish, seeded on fresh concrete, 3 lb. per S.F.	1 Cefi	625	.013	S.F.	.47	.58		1.05	1.36
1650	4 lb. per S.F.	"	465	.017	"	.87	.77		1.64	2.11

03 35 29 – Tooled Concrete Finishing

03 35 29.30 Finishing Floors, Tooled

		Crew	Daily Output	Labor-Hours	Unit	Material	Labor	Equipment	Total	Total Incl O&P
0010	**FINISHING FLOORS, TOOLED**									
4400	Stair finish, fresh concrete, float finish	1 Cefi	275	.029	S.F.		1.31		1.31	1.94
4500	Steel trowel finish		200	.040			1.80		1.80	2.67
4600	Silicon carbide finish, dry shake on fresh concrete, .25 psf		150	.053		.53	2.40		2.93	4.13

03 35 Concrete Finishing

03 35 29 – Tooled Concrete Finishing

03 35 29.60 Finishing Walls

		Crew	Daily Output	Labor-Hours	Unit	Material	2015 Bare Costs Labor	2015 Bare Costs Equipment	Total	Total Incl O&P
0010	**FINISHING WALLS**									
0020	Break ties and patch voids	1 Cefi	540	.015	S.F.	.04	.67		.71	1.03
0050	Burlap rub with grout		450	.018		.04	.80		.84	1.23
0100	Carborundum rub, dry		270	.030			1.33		1.33	1.97
0150	Wet rub	↓	175	.046			2.06		2.06	3.05
0300	Bush hammer, green concrete	B-39	1000	.048			1.91	.23	2.14	3.19
0350	Cured concrete	"	650	.074			2.94	.36	3.30	4.90
0500	Acid etch	1 Cefi	575	.014		.14	.63		.77	1.08
0600	Float finish, 1/16" thick	"	300	.027		.36	1.20		1.56	2.18
0700	Sandblast, light penetration	E-11	1100	.029		.46	1.23	.21	1.90	2.77
0750	Heavy penetration	"	375	.085	↓	.92	3.61	.63	5.16	7.60
0850	Grind form fins flush	1 Clab	700	.011	L.F.		.43		.43	.66

03 35 33 – Stamped Concrete Finishing

03 35 33.50 Slab Texture Stamping

		Crew	Daily Output	Labor-Hours	Unit	Material	2015 Bare Costs Labor	2015 Bare Costs Equipment	Total	Total Incl O&P
0010	**SLAB TEXTURE STAMPING**									
0050	Stamping requires that concrete first be placed, struck off, consolidated,									
0060	bull floated and free of bleed water. Decorative stamping tasks include:									
0100	Step 1 - first application of dry shake colored hardener	1 Cefi	6400	.001	S.F.	.43	.06		.49	.55
0110	Step 2 - bull float		6400	.001			.06		.06	.08
0130	Step 3 - second application of dry shake colored hardener	↓	6400	.001		.21	.06		.27	.31
0140	Step 4 - bull float, manual float & steel trowel	3 Cefi	1280	.019			.84		.84	1.25
0150	Step 5 - application of dry shake colored release agent	1 Cefi	6400	.001		.10	.06		.16	.19
0160	Step 6 - place, tamp & remove mats	3 Cefi	2400	.010		1.43	.45		1.88	2.25
0170	Step 7 - touch up edges, mat joints & simulated grout lines	1 Cefi	1280	.006			.28		.28	.42
0300	Alternate stamping estimating method includes all tasks above	4 Cefi	800	.040		2.17	1.80		3.97	5.05
0400	Step 8 - pressure wash @ 3000 psi after 24 hours	1 Cefi	1600	.005			.23		.23	.33
0500	Step 9 - roll 2 coats cure/seal compound when dry	"	800	.010	↓	.62	.45		1.07	1.35

03 37 Specialty Placed Concrete

03 37 13 – Shotcrete

03 37 13.30 Gunite (Dry-Mix)

		Crew	Daily Output	Labor-Hours	Unit	Material	2015 Bare Costs Labor	2015 Bare Costs Equipment	Total	Total Incl O&P
0010	**GUNITE (DRY-MIX)**									
0020	Typical in place, 1" layers, no mesh included	C-16	2000	.028	S.F.	.35	1.17	.20	1.72	2.38
0100	Mesh for gunite 2 x 2, #12	2 Rodm	800	.020		.63	1.05		1.68	2.33
0150	#4 reinforcing bars @ 6" each way	"	500	.032		1.61	1.68		3.29	4.41
0300	Typical in place, including mesh, 2" thick, flat surfaces	C-16	1000	.056		1.32	2.34	.39	4.05	5.45
0350	Curved surfaces		500	.112		1.32	4.69	.79	6.80	9.40
0500	4" thick, flat surfaces		750	.075		2.02	3.13	.52	5.67	7.55
0550	Curved surfaces	↓	350	.160		2.02	6.70	1.12	9.84	13.60
0900	Prepare old walls, no scaffolding, good condition	C-10	1000	.024			1.02		1.02	1.53
0950	Poor condition	"	275	.087			3.71		3.71	5.55
1100	For high finish requirement or close tolerance, add						50%			
1150	Very high				↓		110%			

03 37 13.60 Shotcrete (Wet-Mix)

		Crew	Daily Output	Labor-Hours	Unit	Material	2015 Bare Costs Labor	2015 Bare Costs Equipment	Total	Total Incl O&P
0010	**SHOTCRETE (WET-MIX)**									
0020	Wet mix, placed @ up to 12 C.Y. per hour, 3000 psi	C-8C	80	.600	C.Y.	113	25	5.70	143.70	168
0100	Up to 35 C.Y. per hour	C-8E	240	.200	"	101	8.20	2.21	111.41	127
1010	Fiber reinforced, 1" thick	C-8C	1740	.028	S.F.	.83	1.14	.26	2.23	2.94
1020	2" thick		900	.053		1.66	2.20	.51	4.37	5.75
1030	3" thick	↓	825	.058	↓	2.48	2.40	.55	5.43	7

03 37 Specialty Placed Concrete

03 37 13 – Shotcrete

03 37 13.60 Shotcrete (Wet-Mix)	Crew	Daily Output	Labor-Hours	Unit	Material	2015 Bare Costs Labor	Equipment	Total	Total Incl O&P
1040 4" thick	C-8C	750	.064	S.F.	3.31	2.65	.61	6.57	8.35

03 37 23 – Roller-Compacted Concrete

03 37 23.50 Concrete, Roller-Compacted

	Crew	Daily Output	Labor-Hours	Unit	Material	2015 Bare Costs Labor	Equipment	Total	Total Incl O&P
0010 **CONCRETE, ROLLER-COMPACTED**									
0100 Mass placement, 1' lift, 1' layer	B-10C	1280	.009	C.Y.		.43	1.39	1.82	2.19
0200 2' lift, 6" layer	"	1600	.008			.35	1.11	1.46	1.76
0210 Vertical face, formed, 1' lift	B-11V	400	.060			2.26	.45	2.71	3.97
0220 6" lift	"	200	.120			4.51	.90	5.41	7.95
0300 Sloped face, nonformed, 1' lift	B-11L	384	.042			1.84	1.92	3.76	4.91
0360 6" lift	"	192	.083			3.67	3.83	7.50	9.80
0400 Surface preparation, vacuum truck	B-6A	3280	.006	S.Y.		.26	.11	.37	.52
0450 Water clean	B-9A	3000	.008			.31	.17	.48	.65
0460 Water blast	B-9B	800	.030			1.15	.72	1.87	2.55
0500 Joint bedding placement, 1" thick	B-11C	975	.016			.72	.37	1.09	1.51
0510 Conveyance of materials, 18 C.Y. truck, 5 min. cycle	B-34F	2048	.004	C.Y.		.16	.74	.90	1.05
0520 10 min. cycle		1024	.008			.31	1.48	1.79	2.09
0540 15 min. cycle		680	.012			.47	2.22	2.69	3.15
0550 With crane and bucket	C-23A	1600	.025			1.06	1.42	2.48	3.18
0560 With 4 C.Y. loader, 4 min. cycle	B-10U	480	.025			1.16	2.25	3.41	4.24
0570 8 min. cycle		240	.050			2.31	4.51	6.82	8.50
0580 12 min. cycle		160	.075			3.47	6.75	10.22	12.75
0590 With belt conveyor	C-7D	600	.093			3.71	.33	4.04	6.05
0600 With 17 C.Y. scraper, 5 min. cycle	B-33J	1440	.006			.28	1.31	1.59	1.87
0610 10 min. cycle		720	.011			.56	2.62	3.18	3.73
0620 15 min. cycle		480	.017			.84	3.93	4.77	5.60
0630 20 min. cycle		360	.022			1.12	5.25	6.37	7.45
0640 Water cure, small job, < 500 C.Y.	B-94C	8	1	Hr.		37.50	10.50	48	69.50
0650 Large job, over 500 C.Y.	B-59A	8	3	"		115	62.50	177.50	245
0660 RCC paving, with asphalt paver including material	B-25C	1000	.048	C.Y.	75	2.03	2.37	79.40	88
0670 8" thick layers		4200	.011	S.Y.	19.55	.48	.56	20.59	23
0680 12" thick layers		2800	.017	"	29	.72	.85	30.57	34

03 39 Concrete Curing

03 39 13 – Water Concrete Curing

03 39 13.50 Water Curing

	Crew	Daily Output	Labor-Hours	Unit	Material	2015 Bare Costs Labor	Equipment	Total	Total Incl O&P
0010 **WATER CURING**									
0015 With burlap, 4 uses assumed, 7.5 oz.	2 Clab	55	.291	C.S.F.	13.05	10.95		24	31
0100 10 oz.	"	55	.291	"	23.50	10.95		34.45	43
0400 Curing blankets, 1" to 2" thick, buy				S.F.	.19			.19	.21

03 39 23 – Membrane Concrete Curing

03 39 23.13 Chemical Compound Membrane Concrete Curing

	Crew	Daily Output	Labor-Hours	Unit	Material	2015 Bare Costs Labor	Equipment	Total	Total Incl O&P
0010 **CHEMICAL COMPOUND MEMBRANE CONCRETE CURING**									
0300 Sprayed membrane curing compound	2 Clab	95	.168	C.S.F.	11.05	6.35		17.40	22
0700 Curing compound, solvent based, 400 S.F./gal., 55 gallon lots				Gal.	24.50			24.50	27
0720 5 gallon lots					30.50			30.50	34
0800 Curing compound, water based, 250 S.F./gal., 55 gallon lots					22.50			22.50	25
0820 5 gallon lots					25.50			25.50	28.50

03 39 23.23 Sheet Membrane Concrete Curing

	Crew	Daily Output	Labor-Hours	Unit	Material	2015 Bare Costs Labor	Equipment	Total	Total Incl O&P
0010 **SHEET MEMBRANE CONCRETE CURING**									
0200 Curing blanket, burlap/poly, 2-ply	2 Clab	70	.229	C.S.F.	23	8.60		31.60	38.50

03 41 Precast Structural Concrete

03 41 13 – Precast Concrete Hollow Core Planks

03 41 13.50 Precast Slab Planks	Crew	Daily Output	Labor-Hours	Unit	Material	2015 Bare Costs Labor	Equipment	Total	Total Incl O&P
0010 **PRECAST SLAB PLANKS**									
0020 Prestressed roof/floor members, grouted, solid, 4" thick	C-11	2400	.030	S.F.	5.85	1.56	.76	8.17	9.90
0050 6" thick		2800	.026		6.65	1.34	.65	8.64	10.30
0100 Hollow, 8" thick		3200	.023		7.10	1.17	.57	8.84	10.40
0150 10" thick		3600	.020		7.75	1.04	.50	9.29	10.80
0200 12" thick		4000	.018		7.90	.93	.45	9.28	10.75

03 41 23 – Precast Concrete Stairs

03 41 23.50 Precast Stairs	Crew	Daily Output	Labor-Hours	Unit	Material	2015 Bare Costs Labor	Equipment	Total	Total Incl O&P
0010 **PRECAST STAIRS**									
0020 Precast concrete treads on steel stringers, 3' wide	C-12	75	.640	Riser	135	30	8.70	173.70	203
0200 Front entrance 4' wide with 48" platform, 2 risers		17	2.824	Flight	425	131	38.50	594.50	715
0250 5 risers		13	3.692		655	172	50.50	877.50	1,050
0300 Front entrance, 5' wide with 48" platform, 2 risers		16	3		485	140	41	666	790
1200 Basement entrance stairwell, 6 steps, incl. steel bulkhead door	B-51	22	2.182		1,450	83.50	11.15	1,544.65	1,725
1250 14 steps	"	11	4.364		2,400	167	22.50	2,589.50	2,900

03 41 33 – Precast Structural Pretensioned Concrete

03 41 33.10 Precast Beams	Crew	Daily Output	Labor-Hours	Unit	Material	2015 Bare Costs Labor	Equipment	Total	Total Incl O&P
0010 **PRECAST BEAMS**									
0011 L-shaped, 20' span, 12" x 20"	C-11	32	2.250	Ea.	3,000	117	56.50	3,173.50	3,550
1200 Rectangular, 20' span, 12" x 20"		32	2.250		2,925	117	56.50	3,098.50	3,450
1250 18" x 36"		24	3		3,600	156	75.50	3,831.50	4,325
1300 24" x 44"		22	3.273		4,325	170	82.50	4,577.50	5,125
1400 30' span, 12" x 36"		24	3		4,875	156	75.50	5,106.50	5,700
1450 18" x 44"		20	3.600		5,850	187	90.50	6,127.50	6,875
1500 24" x 52"		16	4.500		7,075	234	113	7,422	8,300
1600 40' span, 12" x 52"		20	3.600		7,225	187	90.50	7,502.50	8,375
1650 18" x 52"		16	4.500		8,225	234	113	8,572	9,575
1700 24" x 52"		12	6		9,425	310	151	9,886	11,100
2000 "T" shaped, 20' span, 12" x 20"		32	2.250		3,425	117	56.50	3,598.50	4,025
2050 18" x 36"		24	3		4,600	156	75.50	4,831.50	5,425
2100 24" x 44"		22	3.273		5,525	170	82.50	5,777.50	6,450
2200 30' span, 12" x 36"		24	3		6,325	156	75.50	6,556.50	7,300
2250 18" x 44"		20	3.600		7,675	187	90.50	7,952.50	8,850
2300 24" x 52"		16	4.500		9,175	234	113	9,522	10,600
2500 40' span, 12" x 52"		20	3.600		10,400	187	90.50	10,677.50	11,900
2550 18" x 52"		16	4.500		11,000	234	113	11,347	12,700
2600 24" x 52"		12	6		12,200	310	151	12,661	14,200

03 45 Precast Architectural Concrete

03 45 13 – Faced Architectural Precast Concrete

03 45 13.50 Precast Wall Panels	Crew	Daily Output	Labor-Hours	Unit	Material	2015 Bare Costs Labor	Equipment	Total	Total Incl O&P
0010 **PRECAST WALL PANELS**									
0050 Uninsulated, smooth gray									
0150 Low rise, 4' x 8' x 4" thick	C-11	320	.225	S.F.	20.50	11.70	5.65	37.85	49
0210 8' x 8', 4" thick		576	.125		20.50	6.50	3.15	30.15	37
0250 8' x 16' x 4" thick		1024	.070		20.50	3.65	1.77	25.92	30.50
0600 High rise, 4' x 8' x 4" thick		288	.250		20.50	13	6.30	39.80	52
0650 8' x 8' x 4" thick		512	.141		20.50	7.30	3.54	31.34	39
0700 8' x 16' x 4" thick		768	.094		20.50	4.87	2.36	27.73	33.50
0750 10' x 20', 6" thick		1400	.051		34.50	2.67	1.30	38.47	44

03 45 Precast Architectural Concrete

03 45 13 – Faced Architectural Precast Concrete

03 45 13.50 Precast Wall Panels	Crew	Daily Output	Labor-Hours	Unit	Material	2015 Bare Costs Labor	Equipment	Total	Total Incl O&P
0800	Insulated panel, 2" polystyrene, add				S.F.	1.04			1.04	1.14
0850	2" urethane, add					.80			.80	.88
1200	Finishes, white, add					2.93			2.93	3.22
1250	Exposed aggregate, add					2.17			2.17	2.39
1300	Granite faced, domestic, add					29.50			29.50	32.50
1350	Brick faced, modular, red, add					9			9	9.90
2200	Fiberglass reinforced cement with urethane core									
2210	R20, 8' x 8', 5" plain finish	E-2	750	.075	S.F.	21	3.86	2.01	26.87	32
2220	Exposed aggregate or brick finish	"	600	.093	"	32	4.83	2.52	39.35	46

03 47 Site-Cast Concrete

03 47 13 – Tilt-Up Concrete

03 47 13.50 Tilt-Up Wall Panels

		Crew	Daily Output	Labor-Hours	Unit	Material	2015 Bare Costs Labor	Equipment	Total	Total Incl O&P
0010	TILT-UP WALL PANELS									
0015	Wall panel construction, walls only, 5-1/2" thick	C-14	1600	.090	S.F.	5.55	4.16	1.02	10.73	13.60
0100	7-1/2" thick	"	1550	.093	"	6.90	4.29	1.05	12.24	15.30

03 48 Precast Concrete Specialties

03 48 43 – Precast Concrete Trim

03 48 43.40 Precast Lintels

		Crew	Daily Output	Labor-Hours	Unit	Material	2015 Bare Costs Labor	Equipment	Total	Total Incl O&P
0010	PRECAST LINTELS, smooth gray, prestressed, stock units only									
0800	4" wide, 8" high, x 4' long	D-10	28	1.143	Ea.	25	52.50	16.90	94.40	126
0850	8' long		24	1.333		60.50	61.50	19.70	141.70	182
1000	6" wide, 8" high, x 4' long		26	1.231		35.50	56.50	18.20	110.20	146
1050	10' long		22	1.455		91	67	21.50	179.50	226
1200	8" wide, 8" high, x 4' long		24	1.333		45	61.50	19.70	126.20	165
1250	12' long		20	1.600		146	73.50	23.50	243	299
1275	For custom sizes, types, colors, or finishes of precast lintels, add					150%				

03 53 Concrete Topping

03 53 16 – Iron-Aggregate Concrete Topping

03 53 16.50 Floor Topping

		Crew	Daily Output	Labor-Hours	Unit	Material	2015 Bare Costs Labor	Equipment	Total	Total Incl O&P
0010	FLOOR TOPPING									
0400	Integral topping/finish, on fresh concrete, using 1:1:2 mix, 3/16" thick	C-10B	1000	.040	S.F.	.10	1.62	.27	1.99	2.86
0450	1/2" thick		950	.042		.28	1.71	.29	2.28	3.21
0500	3/4" thick		850	.047		.42	1.91	.32	2.65	3.70
0600	1" thick		750	.053		.56	2.16	.36	3.08	4.28
0800	Granolithic topping, on fresh or cured concrete, 1:1:1-1/2 mix, 1/2" thick		590	.068		.31	2.75	.46	3.52	5
0820	3/4" thick		580	.069		.46	2.80	.47	3.73	5.25
0850	1" thick		575	.070		.62	2.82	.47	3.91	5.45
0950	2" thick		500	.080		1.23	3.24	.55	5.02	6.85
1200	Heavy duty, 1:1:2, 3/4" thick, preshrunk, gray, 20 M.S.F.		320	.125		.80	5.05	.85	6.70	9.45
1300	100 M.S.F.		380	.105		.42	4.27	.72	5.41	7.70

03 54 Cast Underlayment

03 54 16 – Hydraulic Cement Underlayment

03 54 16.50 Cement Underlayment	Crew	Daily Output	Labor-Hours	Unit	Material	2015 Bare Costs Labor	Equipment	Total	Total Incl O&P
0010 **CEMENT UNDERLAYMENT**									
2510 Underlayment, P.C based, self-leveling, 4100 psi, pumped, 1/4" thick	C-8	20000	.003	S.F.	1.55	.12	.04	1.71	1.92
2520 1/2" thick		19000	.003		3.09	.12	.04	3.25	3.63
2530 3/4" thick		18000	.003		4.64	.13	.04	4.81	5.35
2540 1" thick		17000	.003		6.20	.14	.04	6.38	7.05
2550 1-1/2" thick		15000	.004		9.30	.16	.05	9.51	10.50
2560 Hand placed, 1/2" thick	C-18	450	.020		3.09	.76	.13	3.98	4.71
2610 Topping, P.C based, self-leveling, 6100 psi, pumped, 1/4" thick	C-8	20000	.003		2.26	.12	.04	2.42	2.71
2620 1/2" thick		19000	.003		4.52	.12	.04	4.68	5.20
2630 3/4" thick		18000	.003		6.80	.13	.04	6.97	7.70
2660 1" thick		17000	.003		9.05	.14	.04	9.23	10.20
2670 1-1/2" thick		15000	.004		13.55	.16	.05	13.76	15.20
2680 Hand placed, 1/2" thick	C-18	450	.020		4.52	.76	.13	5.41	6.30

03 62 Non-Shrink Grouting

03 62 13 – Non-Metallic Non-Shrink Grouting

03 62 13.50 Grout, Non-Metallic Non-shrink

	Crew	Daily Output	Labor-Hours	Unit	Material	2015 Bare Costs Labor	Equipment	Total	Total Incl O&P
0010 **GROUT, NON-METALLIC NON-SHRINK**									
0300 Non-shrink, non-metallic, 1" deep	1 Cefi	35	.229	S.F.	6.50	10.30		16.80	22.50
0350 2" deep	"	25	.320	"	13	14.40		27.40	36

03 62 16 – Metallic Non-Shrink Grouting

03 62 16.50 Grout, Metallic Non-Shrink

	Crew	Daily Output	Labor-Hours	Unit	Material	2015 Bare Costs Labor	Equipment	Total	Total Incl O&P
0010 **GROUT, METALLIC NON-SHRINK**									
0020 Column & machine bases, non-shrink, metallic, 1" deep	1 Cefi	35	.229	S.F.	10.25	10.30		20.55	26.50
0050 2" deep	"	25	.320	"	20.50	14.40		34.90	44

03 63 Epoxy Grouting

03 63 05 – Grouting of Dowels and Fasteners

03 63 05.10 Epoxy Only

	Crew	Daily Output	Labor-Hours	Unit	Material	2015 Bare Costs Labor	Equipment	Total	Total Incl O&P
0010 **EPOXY ONLY**									
1500 Chemical anchoring, epoxy cartridge, excludes layout, drilling, fastener									
1530 For fastener 3/4" diam. x 6" embedment	2 Skwk	72	.222	Ea.	5.65	10.80		16.45	23
1535 1" diam. x 8" embedment		66	.242		8.45	11.80		20.25	27.50
1540 1-1/4" diam. x 10" embedment		60	.267		16.90	12.95		29.85	38.50
1545 1-3/4" diam. x 12" embedment		54	.296		28	14.40		42.40	53.50
1550 14" embedment		48	.333		34	16.20		50.20	62
1555 2" diam. x 12" embedment		42	.381		45	18.55		63.55	78
1560 18" embedment		32	.500		56.50	24.50		81	99.50

03 81 Concrete Cutting

03 81 13 – Flat Concrete Sawing

03 81 13.50 Concrete Floor/Slab Cutting

		Crew	Daily Output	Labor-Hours	Unit	Material	2015 Bare Costs Labor	Equipment	Total	Total Incl O&P
0010	**CONCRETE FLOOR/SLAB CUTTING**									
0050	Includes blade cost, layout and set-up time									
0300	Saw cut concrete slabs, plain, up to 3" deep	B-89	1060	.015	L.F.	.14	.66	.46	1.26	1.66
0320	Each additional inch of depth		3180	.005		.05	.22	.15	.42	.55
0400	Mesh reinforced, up to 3" deep		980	.016		.16	.72	.50	1.38	1.80
0420	Each additional inch of depth		2940	.005		.05	.24	.17	.46	.60
0500	Rod reinforced, up to 3" deep		800	.020		.19	.88	.61	1.68	2.21
0520	Each additional inch of depth		2400	.007		.06	.29	.20	.55	.73

03 81 13.75 Concrete Saw Blades

		Crew	Daily Output	Labor-Hours	Unit	Material	2015 Bare Costs Labor	Equipment	Total	Total Incl O&P
0010	**CONCRETE SAW BLADES**									
3000	Blades for saw cutting, included in cutting line items									
3020	Diamond, 12" diameter				Ea.	241			241	265
3040	18" diameter					465			465	510
3080	24" diameter					770			770	845
3120	30" diameter					1,100			1,100	1,200
3160	36" diameter					1,425			1,425	1,550
3200	42" diameter					2,625			2,625	2,875

03 81 16 – Track Mounted Concrete Wall Sawing

03 81 16.50 Concrete Wall Cutting

		Crew	Daily Output	Labor-Hours	Unit	Material	2015 Bare Costs Labor	Equipment	Total	Total Incl O&P
0010	**CONCRETE WALL CUTTING**									
0750	Includes blade cost, layout and set-up time									
0800	Concrete walls, hydraulic saw, plain, per inch of depth	B-89B	250	.064	L.F.	.05	2.81	3.43	6.29	8.10
0820	Rod reinforcing, per inch of depth	"	150	.107	"	.06	4.68	5.70	10.44	13.45

03 82 Concrete Boring

03 82 13 – Concrete Core Drilling

03 82 13.10 Core Drilling

		Crew	Daily Output	Labor-Hours	Unit	Material	2015 Bare Costs Labor	Equipment	Total	Total Incl O&P
0010	**CORE DRILLING**									
0015	Includes bit cost, layout and set-up time									
0020	Reinforced concrete slab, up to 6" thick									
0100	1" diameter core	B-89A	17	.941	Ea.	.18	40.50	6.80	47.48	70
0150	For each additional inch of slab thickness in same hole, add		1440	.011		.03	.48	.08	.59	.86
0200	2" diameter core		16.50	.970		.28	42	7	49.28	72.50
0250	For each additional inch of slab thickness in same hole, add		1080	.015		.05	.64	.11	.80	1.15
0300	3" diameter core		16	1		.38	43	7.25	50.63	75
0350	For each additional inch of slab thickness in same hole, add		720	.022		.06	.96	.16	1.18	1.73
0500	4" diameter core		15	1.067		.49	46	7.70	54.19	80
0550	For each additional inch of slab thickness in same hole, add		480	.033		.08	1.44	.24	1.76	2.58
0700	6" diameter core		14	1.143		.76	49.50	8.25	58.51	86
0750	For each additional inch of slab thickness in same hole, add		360	.044		.13	1.92	.32	2.37	3.45
0900	8" diameter core		13	1.231		1.05	53	8.90	62.95	93
0950	For each additional inch of slab thickness in same hole, add		288	.056		.17	2.40	.40	2.97	4.32
1100	10" diameter core		12	1.333		1.48	57.50	9.65	68.63	101
1150	For each additional inch of slab thickness in same hole, add		240	.067		.25	2.88	.48	3.61	5.25
1300	12" diameter core		11	1.455		1.78	62.50	10.50	74.78	110
1350	For each additional inch of slab thickness in same hole, add		206	.078		.30	3.35	.56	4.21	6.10
1500	14" diameter core		10	1.600		2.08	69	11.55	82.63	121
1550	For each additional inch of slab thickness in same hole, add		180	.089		.35	3.83	.64	4.82	7
1700	18" diameter core		9	1.778		2.82	76.50	12.85	92.17	135
1750	For each additional inch of slab thickness in same hole, add		144	.111		.47	4.79	.80	6.06	8.80

03 82 Concrete Boring

03 82 13 – Concrete Core Drilling

03 82 13.10 Core Drilling

		Crew	Daily Output	Labor-Hours	Unit	Material	2015 Bare Costs Labor	Equipment	Total	Total Incl O&P
1754	24" diameter core	B-89A	8	2	Ea.	4.02	86.50	14.45	104.97	153
1756	For each additional inch of slab thickness in same hole, add		120	.133		.67	5.75	.96	7.38	10.65
1760	For horizontal holes, add to above						20%	20%		
1770	Prestressed hollow core plank, 8" thick									
1780	1" diameter core	B-89A	17.50	.914	Ea.	.24	39.50	6.60	46.34	68.50
1790	For each additional inch of plank thickness in same hole, add		3840	.004		.03	.18	.03	.24	.34
1794	2" diameter core		17.25	.928		.38	40	6.70	47.08	69.50
1796	For each additional inch of plank thickness in same hole, add		2880	.006		.05	.24	.04	.33	.46
1800	3" diameter core		17	.941		.51	40.50	6.80	47.81	70.50
1810	For each additional inch of plank thickness in same hole, add		1920	.008		.06	.36	.06	.48	.69
1820	4" diameter core		16.50	.970		.66	42	7	49.66	73
1830	For each additional inch of plank thickness in same hole, add		1280	.013		.08	.54	.09	.71	1.02
1840	6" diameter core		15.50	1.032		1.01	44.50	7.45	52.96	78
1850	For each additional inch of plank thickness in same hole, add		960	.017		.13	.72	.12	.97	1.38
1860	8" diameter core		15	1.067		1.40	46	7.70	55.10	81
1870	For each additional inch of plank thickness in same hole, add		768	.021		.17	.90	.15	1.22	1.75
1880	10" diameter core		14	1.143		1.98	49.50	8.25	59.73	87.50
1890	For each additional inch of plank thickness in same hole, add		640	.025		.25	1.08	.18	1.51	2.13
1900	12" diameter core		13.50	1.185		2.37	51	8.55	61.92	91
1910	For each additional inch of plank thickness in same hole, add		548	.029		.30	1.26	.21	1.77	2.50
3000	Bits for core drilling, included in drilling line items									
3010	Diamond, premium, 1" diameter				Ea.	70.50			70.50	78
3020	2" diameter					113			113	124
3030	3" diameter					152			152	168
3040	4" diameter					197			197	217
3060	6" diameter					305			305	335
3080	8" diameter					420			420	460
3110	10" diameter					595			595	650
3120	12" diameter					710			710	780
3140	14" diameter					835			835	915
3180	18" diameter					1,125			1,125	1,250
3240	24" diameter					1,600			1,600	1,775

03 82 16 – Concrete Drilling

03 82 16.10 Concrete Impact Drilling

		Crew	Daily Output	Labor-Hours	Unit	Material	2015 Bare Costs Labor	Equipment	Total	Total Incl O&P
0010	**CONCRETE IMPACT DRILLING**									
0020	Includes bit cost, layout and set-up time, no anchors									
0050	Up to 4" deep in concrete/brick floors/walls									
0100	Holes, 1/4" diameter	1 Carp	75	.107	Ea.	.07	5		5.07	7.75
0150	For each additional inch of depth in same hole, add		430	.019		.02	.87		.89	1.36
0200	3/8" diameter		63	.127		.06	5.95		6.01	9.20
0250	For each additional inch of depth in same hole, add		340	.024		.01	1.10		1.11	1.72
0300	1/2" diameter		50	.160		.06	7.50		7.56	11.60
0350	For each additional inch of depth in same hole, add		250	.032		.01	1.50		1.51	2.33
0400	5/8" diameter		48	.167		.09	7.85		7.94	12.15
0450	For each additional inch of depth in same hole, add		240	.033		.02	1.56		1.58	2.43
0500	3/4" diameter		45	.178		.12	8.35		8.47	13
0550	For each additional inch of depth in same hole, add		220	.036		.03	1.71		1.74	2.66
0600	7/8" diameter		43	.186		.16	8.75		8.91	13.60
0650	For each additional inch of depth in same hole, add		210	.038		.04	1.79		1.83	2.79
0700	1" diameter		40	.200		.17	9.40		9.57	14.65
0750	For each additional inch of depth in same hole, add		190	.042		.04	1.98		2.02	3.09
0800	1-1/4" diameter		38	.211		.26	9.90		10.16	15.50

For customer support on your Site Work & Landscape Cost Data, call 877.737.1594.

87

03 82 Concrete Boring

03 82 16 – Concrete Drilling

03 82 16.10 Concrete Impact Drilling	Crew	Daily Output	Labor-Hours	Unit	Material	2015 Bare Costs Labor	Equipment	Total	Total Incl O&P
0850	For each additional inch of depth in same hole, add	1 Carp	180	.044	Ea.	.06	2.09		2.15	3.28
0900	1-1/2" diameter		35	.229		.39	10.75		11.14	16.95
0950	For each additional inch of depth in same hole, add	↓	165	.048	↓	.10	2.28		2.38	3.61
1000	For ceiling installations, add						40%			

Estimating Tips
04 05 00 Common Work Results for Masonry

- The terms mortar and grout are often used interchangeably, and incorrectly. Mortar is used to bed masonry units, seal the entry of air and moisture, provide architectural appearance, and allow for size variations in the units. Grout is used primarily in reinforced masonry construction and is used to bond the masonry to the reinforcing steel. Common mortar types are M(2500 psi), S(1800 psi), N(750 psi), and O(350 psi), and conform to ASTM C270. Grout is either fine or coarse and conforms to ASTM C476, and in-place strengths generally exceed 2500 psi. Mortar and grout are different components of masonry construction and are placed by entirely different methods. An estimator should be aware of their unique uses and costs.

- Mortar is included in all assembled masonry line items. The mortar cost, part of the assembled masonry material cost, includes all ingredients, all labor, and all equipment required. Please see reference number R040513-10.

- Waste, specifically the loss/droppings of mortar and the breakage of brick and block, is included in all masonry assemblies in this division. A factor of 25% is added for mortar and 3% for brick and concrete masonry units.

- Scaffolding or staging is not included in any of the Division 4 costs. Refer to Subdivision 01 54 23 for scaffolding and staging costs.

04 20 00 Unit Masonry

- The most common types of unit masonry are brick and concrete masonry. The major classifications of brick are building brick (ASTM C62), facing brick (ASTM C216), glazed brick, fire brick, and pavers. Many varieties of texture and appearance can exist within these classifications, and the estimator would be wise to check local custom and availability within the project area. For repair and remodeling jobs, matching the existing brick may be the most important criteria.

- Brick and concrete block are priced by the piece and then converted into a price per square foot of wall. Openings less than two square feet are generally ignored by the estimator because any savings in units used is offset by the cutting and trimming required.

- It is often difficult and expensive to find and purchase small lots of historic brick. Costs can vary widely. Many design issues affect costs, selection of mortar mix, and repairs or replacement of masonry materials. Cleaning techniques must be reflected in the estimate.

- All masonry walls, whether interior or exterior, require bracing. The cost of bracing walls during construction should be included by the estimator, and this bracing must remain in place until permanent bracing is complete. Permanent bracing of masonry walls is accomplished by masonry itself, in the form of pilasters or abutting wall corners, or by anchoring the walls to the structural frame. Accessories in the form of anchors, anchor slots, and ties are used, but their supply and installation can be by different trades. For instance, anchor slots on spandrel beams and columns are supplied and welded in place by the steel fabricator, but the ties from the slots into the masonry are installed by the bricklayer. Regardless of the installation method, the estimator must be certain that these accessories are accounted for in pricing.

Reference Numbers
Reference numbers are shown in shaded boxes at the beginning of some major classifications. These numbers refer to related items in the Reference Section. The reference information may be an estimating procedure, an alternate pricing method, or technical information.

Note: Not all subdivisions listed here necessarily appear in this publication. ∎

04 01 20 – Maintenance of Unit Masonry

04 01 20.10 Patching Masonry

		Crew	Daily Output	Labor-Hours	Unit	Material	2015 Bare Costs Labor	Equipment	Total	Total Incl O&P
0010	**PATCHING MASONRY**									
0500	CMU patching, includes chipping, cleaning and epoxy									
0520	1/4" deep	1 Cefi	65	.123	S.F.	7.45	5.55		13	16.40
0540	3/8" deep		50	.160		11.15	7.20		18.35	23
0580	1/2" deep		40	.200		14.90	9		23.90	30

04 01 20.20 Pointing Masonry

		Crew	Daily Output	Labor-Hours	Unit	Material	2015 Bare Costs Labor	Equipment	Total	Total Incl O&P
0010	**POINTING MASONRY**									
0300	Cut and repoint brick, hard mortar, running bond	1 Bric	80	.100	S.F.	.56	4.62		5.18	7.65
0320	Common bond		77	.104		.56	4.80		5.36	7.90
0360	Flemish bond		70	.114		.59	5.25		5.84	8.70
0400	English bond		65	.123		.59	5.70		6.29	9.30
0600	Soft old mortar, running bond		100	.080		.56	3.69		4.25	6.25
0620	Common bond		96	.083		.56	3.85		4.41	6.45
0640	Flemish bond		90	.089		.59	4.10		4.69	6.90
0680	English bond		82	.098		.59	4.50		5.09	7.50
0700	Stonework, hard mortar		140	.057	L.F.	.74	2.64		3.38	4.85
0720	Soft old mortar		160	.050	"	.74	2.31		3.05	4.34
1000	Repoint, mask and grout method, running bond		95	.084	S.F.	.74	3.89		4.63	6.75
1020	Common bond		90	.089		.74	4.10		4.84	7.05
1040	Flemish bond		86	.093		.78	4.29		5.07	7.40
1060	English bond		77	.104		.78	4.80		5.58	8.15
2000	Scrub coat, sand grout on walls, thin mix, brushed		120	.067		2.96	3.08		6.04	7.95
2020	Troweled		98	.082		4.12	3.77		7.89	10.30

04 05 05 – Selective Demolition for Masonry

04 05 05.10 Selective Demolition

		Crew	Daily Output	Labor-Hours	Unit	Material	2015 Bare Costs Labor	Equipment	Total	Total Incl O&P
0010	**SELECTIVE DEMOLITION** R024119-10									
1000	Chimney, 16" x 16", soft old mortar	1 Clab	55	.145	C.F.		5.45		5.45	8.40
1020	Hard mortar		40	.200			7.50		7.50	11.55
1030	16" x 20", soft old mortar		55	.145			5.45		5.45	8.40
1040	Hard mortar		40	.200			7.50		7.50	11.55
1050	16" x 24", soft old mortar		55	.145			5.45		5.45	8.40
1060	Hard mortar		40	.200			7.50		7.50	11.55
1080	20" x 20", soft old mortar		55	.145			5.45		5.45	8.40
1100	Hard mortar		40	.200			7.50		7.50	11.55
1110	20" x 24", soft old mortar		55	.145			5.45		5.45	8.40
1120	Hard mortar		40	.200			7.50		7.50	11.55
1140	20" x 32", soft old mortar		55	.145			5.45		5.45	8.40
1160	Hard mortar		40	.200			7.50		7.50	11.55
1200	48" x 48", soft old mortar		55	.145			5.45		5.45	8.40
1220	Hard mortar		40	.200			• 7.50		7.50	11.55
1250	Metal, high temp steel jacket, 24" diameter	E-2	130	.431	V.L.F.		22.50	11.60	34.10	50.50
1260	60" diameter	"	60	.933			48.50	25	73.50	109
1280	Flue lining, up to 12" x 12"	1 Clab	200	.040			1.50		1.50	2.31
1282	Up to 24" x 24"	"	150	.053			2.01		2.01	3.09
4000	Fireplace, brick, 30" x 24" opening									
4020	Soft old mortar	1 Clab	2	4	Ea.		150		150	231
4040	Hard mortar		1.25	6.400			241		241	370
4100	Stone, soft old mortar		1.50	5.333			201		201	310
4120	Hard mortar		1	8			300		300	465

04 05 Common Work Results for Masonry

04 05 13 – Masonry Mortaring

04 05 13.10 Cement		Crew	Daily Output	Labor-Hours	Unit	Material	2015 Bare Costs Labor	Equipment	Total	Total Incl O&P
0010	**CEMENT**									
0100	Masonry, 70 lb. bag, T.L. lots				Bag	12.15			12.15	13.35
0150	L.T.L. lots					12.85			12.85	14.15
0200	White, 70 lb. bag, T.L. lots					15.85			15.85	17.45
0250	L.T.L. lots					16.70			16.70	18.40

04 05 13.20 Lime										
0010	**LIME**									
0020	Masons, hydrated, 50 lb. bag, T.L. lots				Bag	10.10			10.10	11.10
0050	L.T.L. lots					11.10			11.10	12.20
0200	Finish, double hydrated, 50 lb. bag, T.L. lots					8.65			8.65	9.55
0250	L.T.L. lots					9.55			9.55	10.50

04 05 13.23 Surface Bonding Masonry Mortaring

0010	**SURFACE BONDING MASONRY MORTARING**									
0020	Gray or white colors, not incl. block work	1 Bric	540	.015	S.F.	.13	.68		.81	1.19

04 05 13.30 Mortar

0010	**MORTAR** R040513-10									
0020	With masonry cement									
0100	Type M, 1:1:6 mix	1 Brhe	143	.056	C.F.	5.25	2.13		7.38	9
0200	Type N, 1:3 mix		143	.056		5.40	2.13		7.53	9.20
0300	Type O, 1:3 mix		143	.056		4.18	2.13		6.31	7.85
0400	Type PM, 1:1:6 mix, 2500 psi		143	.056		6	2.13		8.13	9.85
0500	Type S, 1/2:1:4 mix		143	.056		5.25	2.13		7.38	9.05
2000	With portland cement and lime									
2100	Type M, 1:1/4:3 mix	1 Brhe	143	.056	C.F.	8.95	2.13		11.08	13.05
2200	Type N, 1:1:6 mix, 750 psi		143	.056		7.15	2.13		9.28	11.15
2300	Type O, 1:2:9 mix (Pointing Mortar)		143	.056		8.35	2.13		10.48	12.40
2400	Type PL, 1:1/2:4 mix, 2500 psi		143	.056		6	2.13		8.13	9.85
2600	Type S, 1:1/2:4 mix, 1800 psi		143	.056		8.20	2.13		10.33	12.30
2650	Pre-mixed, type S or N					5.05			5.05	5.55
2700	Mortar for glass block	1 Brhe	143	.056		11.05	2.13		13.18	15.40
2900	Mortar for fire brick, dry mix, 10 lb. pail				Ea.	27			27	29.50

04 05 13.91 Masonry Restoration Mortaring

0010	**MASONRY RESTORATION MORTARING**									
0020	Masonry restoration mix				Lb.	.29			.29	.32
0050	White				"	.29			.29	.32

04 05 13.93 Mortar Pigments

0010	**MORTAR PIGMENTS**, 50 lb. bags (2 bags per M bricks) R040513-10									
0020	Color admixture, range 2 to 10 lb. per bag of cement, light colors				Lb.	4.37			4.37	4.81
0050	Medium colors					6.40			6.40	7
0100	Dark colors					13.25			13.25	14.60

04 05 13.95 Sand

0010	**SAND**, screened and washed at pit									
0020	For mortar, per ton				Ton	19.35			19.35	21.50
0050	With 10 mile haul					33.50			33.50	37
0100	With 30 mile haul					65.50			65.50	72
0200	Screened and washed, at the pit				C.Y.	27			27	29.50
0250	With 10 mile haul					47			47	51.50
0300	With 30 mile haul					91			91	100

For customer support on your Site Work & Landscape Cost Data, call 877.737.1594.

91

04 05 Common Work Results for Masonry

04 05 13 – Masonry Mortaring

04 05 13.98 Mortar Admixtures

		Crew	Daily Output	Labor-Hours	Unit	Material	2015 Bare Costs Labor	Equipment	Total	Total Incl O&P
0010	**MORTAR ADMIXTURES**									
0020	Waterproofing admixture, per quart (1 qt. to 2 bags of masonry cement)				Qt.	3.22			3.22	3.54

04 05 16 – Masonry Grouting

04 05 16.30 Grouting

			Crew	Daily Output	Labor-Hours	Unit	Material	Labor	Equipment	Total	Total Incl O&P
0010	**GROUTING**	R040513-10									
0011	Bond beams & lintels, 8" deep, 6" thick, 0.15 C.F. per L.F.		D-4	1480	.022	L.F.	.66	.92	.09	1.67	2.24
0020	8" thick, 0.2 C.F. per L.F.			1400	.023		1.06	.98	.10	2.14	2.75
0050	10" thick, 0.25 C.F. per L.F.			1200	.027		1.11	1.14	.11	2.36	3.08
0060	12" thick, 0.3 C.F. per L.F.			1040	.031		1.33	1.31	.13	2.77	3.60
0200	Concrete block cores, solid, 4" thk., by hand, 0.067 C.F./S.F. of wall		D-8	1100	.036	S.F.	.30	1.56		1.86	2.71
0210	6" thick, pumped, 0.175 C.F. per S.F.		D-4	720	.044		.77	1.90	.19	2.86	3.94
0250	8" thick, pumped, 0.258 C.F. per S.F.			680	.047		1.14	2.01	.20	3.35	4.53
0300	10" thick, pumped, 0.340 C.F. per S.F.			660	.048		1.50	2.07	.20	3.77	5.05
0350	12" thick, pumped, 0.422 C.F. per S.F.			640	.050		1.87	2.14	.21	4.22	5.55
0500	Cavity walls, 2" space, pumped, 0.167 C.F./S.F. of wall			1700	.019		.74	.80	.08	1.62	2.13
0550	3" space, 0.250 C.F./S.F.			1200	.027		1.11	1.14	.11	2.36	3.08
0600	4" space, 0.333 C.F. per S.F.			1150	.028		1.47	1.19	.12	2.78	3.56
0700	6" space, 0.500 C.F. per S.F.			800	.040		2.21	1.71	.17	4.09	5.20
0800	Door frames, 3' x 7' opening, 2.5 C.F. per opening			60	.533	Opng.	11.05	23	2.22	36.27	49
0850	6' x 7' opening, 3.5 C.F. per opening			45	.711	"	15.45	30.50	2.97	48.92	67
2000	Grout, C476, for bond beams, lintels and CMU cores			350	.091	C.F.	4.42	3.91	.38	8.71	11.25

04 05 19 – Masonry Anchorage and Reinforcing

04 05 19.05 Anchor Bolts

		Crew	Daily Output	Labor-Hours	Unit	Material	Labor	Equipment	Total	Total Incl O&P
0010	**ANCHOR BOLTS**									
0015	Installed in fresh grout in CMU bond beams or filled cores, no templates									
0020	Hooked, with nut and washer, 1/2" diam., 8" long	1 Bric	132	.061	Ea.	1.33	2.80		4.13	5.75
0030	12" long		131	.061		1.48	2.82		4.30	5.95
0040	5/8" diameter, 8" long		129	.062		2.98	2.86		5.84	7.65
0050	12" long		127	.063		3.67	2.91		6.58	8.50
0060	3/4" diameter, 8" long		127	.063		3.67	2.91		6.58	8.50
0070	12" long		125	.064		4.59	2.95		7.54	9.55

04 05 19.16 Masonry Anchors

		Crew	Daily Output	Labor-Hours	Unit	Material	Labor	Equipment	Total	Total Incl O&P
0010	**MASONRY ANCHORS**									
0020	For brick veneer, galv., corrugated, 7/8" x 7", 22 Ga.	1 Bric	10.50	.762	C	14.35	35		49.35	69.50
0100	24 Ga.		10.50	.762		9.85	35		44.85	64.50
0150	16 Ga.		10.50	.762		28	35		63	84
0200	Buck anchors, galv., corrugated, 16 ga., 2" bend, 8" x 2"		10.50	.762		56.50	35		91.50	116
0250	8" x 3"		10.50	.762		58.50	35		93.50	118
0300	Adjustable, rectangular, 4-1/8" wide									
0350	Anchor and tie, 3/16" wire, mill galv.									
0400	2-3/4" eye, 3-1/4" tie	1 Bric	1.05	7.619	M	450	350		800	1,025
0500	4-3/4" tie		1.05	7.619		485	350		835	1,075
0520	5-1/2" tie		1.05	7.619		525	350		875	1,125
0550	4-3/4" eye, 3-1/4" tie		1.05	7.619		495	350		845	1,075
0570	4-3/4" tie		1.05	7.619		535	350		885	1,125
0580	5-1/2" tie		1.05	7.619		585	350		935	1,175
0660	Cavity wall, Z-type, galvanized, 6" long, 1/8" diam.		10.50	.762	C	25	35		60	81
0670	3/16" diameter		10.50	.762		29	35		64	85.50
0680	1/4" diameter		10.50	.762		40.50	35		75.50	98
0850	8" long, 3/16" diameter		10.50	.762		25	35		60	81
0855	1/4" diameter		10.50	.762		49	35		84	108

For customer support on your Site Work & Landscape Cost Data, call 877.737.1594.

04 05 19.16 Masonry Anchors	Crew	Daily Output	Labor-Hours	Unit	Material	2015 Bare Costs Labor	Equipment	Total	Total Incl O&P
1000	Rectangular type, galvanized, 1/4" diameter, 2" x 6"	1 Bric	10.50	.762	C	72.50	35		107.50	134
1050	4" x 6"		10.50	.762		87.50	35		122.50	150
1100	3/16" diameter, 2" x 6"		10.50	.762		45	35		80	103
1150	4" x 6"		10.50	.762		51.50	35		86.50	110
1200	Mesh wall tie, 1/2" mesh, hot dip galvanized									
1400	16 ga., 12" long, 3" wide	1 Bric	9	.889	C	88.50	41		129.50	160
1420	6" wide		9	.889		130	41		171	206
1440	12" wide		8.50	.941		208	43.50		251.50	296
1500	Rigid partition anchors, plain, 8" long, 1" x 1/8"		10.50	.762		235	35		270	315
1550	1" x 1/4"		10.50	.762		277	35		312	360
1580	1-1/2" x 1/8"		10.50	.762		259	35		294	340
1600	1-1/2" x 1/4"		10.50	.762		325	35		360	410
1650	2" x 1/8"		10.50	.762		305	35		340	390
1700	2" x 1/4"		10.50	.762		405	35		440	500
2000	Column flange ties, wire, galvanized									
2300	3/16" diameter, up to 3" wide	1 Bric	10.50	.762	C	87.50	35		122.50	150
2350	To 5" wide		10.50	.762		95	35		130	158
2400	To 7" wide		10.50	.762		102	35		137	167
2600	To 9" wide		10.50	.762		109	35		144	174
2650	1/4" diameter, up to 3" wide		10.50	.762		110	35		145	175
2700	To 5" wide		10.50	.762		119	35		154	185
2800	To 7" wide		10.50	.762		133	35		168	201
2850	To 9" wide		10.50	.762		144	35		179	212
2900	For hot dip galvanized, add					35%				
4000	Channel slots, 1-3/8" x 1/2" x 8"									
4100	12 ga., plain	1 Bric	10.50	.762	C	213	35		248	288
4150	16 ga., galvanized	"	10.50	.762	"	146	35		181	214
4200	Channel slot anchors									
4300	16 ga., galvanized, 1-1/4" x 3-1/2"				C	56.50			56.50	62.50
4350	1-1/4" x 5-1/2"					66			66	73
4400	1-1/4" x 7-1/2"					75			75	82.50
4500	1/8" plain, 1-1/4" x 3-1/2"					143			143	157
4550	1-1/4" x 5-1/2"					152			152	167
4600	1-1/4" x 7-1/2"					166			166	183
4700	For corrugation, add					76.50			76.50	84.50
4750	For hot dip galvanized, add					35%				
5000	Dowels									
5100	Plain, 1/4" diameter, 3" long				C	55.50			55.50	61
5150	4" long					61.50			61.50	67.50
5200	6" long					75			75	82.50
5300	3/8" diameter, 3" long					73			73	80.50
5350	4" long					91			91	100
5400	6" long					105			105	115
5500	1/2" diameter, 3" long					107			107	117
5550	4" long					127			127	139
5600	6" long					164			164	180
5700	5/8" diameter, 3" long					146			146	161
5750	4" long					180			180	198
5800	6" long					247			247	272
6000	3/4" diameter, 3" long					182			182	200
6100	4" long					231			231	254
6150	6" long					330			330	365
6300	For hot dip galvanized, add					35%				

04 05 Common Work Results for Masonry

04 05 19 – Masonry Anchorage and Reinforcing

04 05 19.26 Masonry Reinforcing Bars

	04 05 19.26 Masonry Reinforcing Bars	Crew	Daily Output	Labor-Hours	Unit	Material	Labor	Equipment	Total	Total Incl O&P
0010	**MASONRY REINFORCING BARS** R040519-50									
0015	Steel bars A615, placed horiz., #3 & #4 bars	1 Bric	450	.018	Lb.	.48	.82		1.30	1.78
0020	#5 & #6 bars		800	.010		.48	.46		.94	1.23
0050	Placed vertical, #3 & #4 bars		350	.023		.48	1.06		1.54	2.14
0060	#5 & #6 bars		650	.012		.48	.57		1.05	1.40
0200	Joint reinforcing, regular truss, to 6" wide, mill std galvanized		30	.267	C.L.F.	22.50	12.30		34.80	43.50
0250	12" wide		20	.400		26	18.45		44.45	56.50
0400	Cavity truss with drip section, to 6" wide		30	.267		22.50	12.30		34.80	43.50
0450	12" wide		20	.400		26	18.45		44.45	56.50
0500	Joint reinforcing, ladder type, mill std galvanized									
0600	9 ga. sides, 9 ga. ties, 4" wall	1 Bric	30	.267	C.L.F.	19.85	12.30		32.15	41
0650	6" wall		30	.267		18.40	12.30		30.70	39.50
0700	8" wall		25	.320		19.70	14.75		34.45	44
0750	10" wall		20	.400		22	18.45		40.45	52
0800	12" wall		20	.400		23	18.45		41.45	53.50
1000	Truss type									
1100	9 ga. sides, 9 ga. ties, 4" wall	1 Bric	30	.267	C.L.F.	21.50	12.30		33.80	42.50
1150	6" wall		30	.267		22	12.30		34.30	43
1200	8" wall		25	.320		26	14.75		40.75	51.50
1250	10" wall		20	.400		21.50	18.45		39.95	51.50
1300	12" wall		20	.400		22.50	18.45		40.95	52.50
1500	3/16" sides, 9 ga. ties, 4" wall		30	.267		25	12.30		37.30	46.50
1550	6" wall		30	.267		31.50	12.30		43.80	53.50
1600	8" wall		25	.320		33	14.75		47.75	58.50
1650	10" wall		20	.400		33.50	18.45		51.95	65
1700	12" wall		20	.400		33.50	18.45		51.95	65
2000	3/16" sides, 3/16" ties, 4" wall		30	.267		35.50	12.30		47.80	58
2050	6" wall		30	.267		36.50	12.30		48.80	59
2100	8" wall		25	.320		37.50	14.75		52.25	64
2150	10" wall		20	.400		39.50	18.45		57.95	71.50
2200	12" wall		20	.400		41.50	18.45		59.95	74
2500	Cavity truss type, galvanized									
2600	9 ga. sides, 9 ga. ties, 4" wall	1 Bric	25	.320	C.L.F.	37	14.75		51.75	63.50
2650	6" wall		25	.320		35	14.75		49.75	61
2700	8" wall		20	.400		39	18.45		57.45	71
2750	10" wall		15	.533		41	24.50		65.50	82.50
2800	12" wall		15	.533		37.50	24.50		62	79
3000	3/16" sides, 9 ga. ties, 4" wall		25	.320		35.50	14.75		50.25	61.50
3050	6" wall		25	.320		32.50	14.75		47.25	58.50
3100	8" wall		20	.400		47	18.45		65.45	79.50
3150	10" wall		15	.533		33.50	24.50		58	74.50
3200	12" wall		15	.533		37.50	24.50		62	78.50
3500	For hot dip galvanizing, add				Ton	460			460	505

04 05 23 – Masonry Accessories

04 05 23.13 Masonry Control and Expansion Joints

	04 05 23.13 Masonry Control and Expansion Joints	Crew	Daily Output	Labor-Hours	Unit	Material	Labor	Equipment	Total	Total Incl O&P
0010	**MASONRY CONTROL AND EXPANSION JOINTS**									
0020	Rubber, for double wythe 8" minimum wall (Brick/CMU)	1 Bric	400	.020	L.F.	2.07	.92		2.99	3.69
0025	"T" shaped		320	.025		1.23	1.15		2.38	3.11
0030	Cross-shaped for CMU units		280	.029		1.45	1.32		2.77	3.61
0050	PVC, for double wythe 8" minimum wall (Brick/CMU)		400	.020		1.47	.92		2.39	3.03
0120	"T" shaped		320	.025		.75	1.15		1.90	2.59
0160	Cross-shaped for CMU units		280	.029		.92	1.32		2.24	3.02

94

For customer support on your Site Work & Landscape Cost Data, call 877.737.1594.

04 05 Common Work Results for Masonry

04 05 23 – Masonry Accessories

04 05 23.95 Wall Plugs		Crew	Daily Output	Labor- Hours	Unit	Material	2015 Bare Costs Labor	Equipment	Total	Total Incl O&P
0010	**WALL PLUGS** (for nailing to brickwork)									
0020	25 ga., galvanized, plain	1 Bric	10.50	.762	C	26.50	35		61.50	82.50
0050	Wood filled	"	10.50	.762	"	68	35		103	128

04 21 Clay Unit Masonry

04 21 13 – Brick Masonry

04 21 13.13 Brick Veneer Masonry

		Crew	Daily Output	Labor- Hours	Unit	Material	2015 Bare Costs Labor	Equipment	Total	Total Incl O&P
0010	**BRICK VENEER MASONRY**, T.L. lots, excl. scaff., grout & reinforcing R042110-20									
0015	Material costs incl. 3% brick and 25% mortar waste									
0020	Standard, select common, 4" x 2-2/3" x 8" (6.75/S.F.)	D-8	1.50	26.667	M	615	1,150		1,765	2,425
0050	Red, 4" x 2-2/3" x 8", running bond		1.50	26.667		550	1,150		1,700	2,350
0100	Full header every 6th course (7.88/S.F.) R042110-50		1.45	27.586		550	1,175		1,725	2,400
0150	English, full header every 2nd course (10.13/S.F.)		1.40	28.571		550	1,225		1,775	2,475
0200	Flemish, alternate header every course (9.00/S.F.)		1.40	28.571		550	1,225		1,775	2,475
0250	Flemish, alt. header every 6th course (7.13/S.F.)		1.45	27.586		550	1,175		1,725	2,400
0300	Full headers throughout (13.50/S.F.)		1.40	28.571		545	1,225		1,770	2,475
0350	Rowlock course (13.50/S.F.)		1.35	29.630		545	1,275		1,820	2,550
0400	Rowlock stretcher (4.50/S.F.)		1.40	28.571		555	1,225		1,780	2,500
0450	Soldier course (6.75/S.F.)		1.40	28.571		550	1,225		1,775	2,475
0500	Sailor course (4.50/S.F.)		1.30	30.769		555	1,325		1,880	2,650
0601	Buff or gray face, running bond, (6.75/S.F.)		1.50	26.667		550	1,150		1,700	2,350
0700	Glazed face, 4" x 2-2/3" x 8", running bond		1.40	28.571		1,825	1,225		3,050	3,900
0750	Full header every 6th course (7.88/S.F.)		1.35	29.630		1,750	1,275		3,025	3,875
1000	Jumbo, 6" x 4" x 12", (3.00/S.F.)		1.30	30.769		1,725	1,325		3,050	3,925
1051	Norman, 4" x 2-2/3" x 12" (4.50/S.F.)		1.45	27.586		1,175	1,175		2,350	3,100
1100	Norwegian, 4" x 3-1/5" x 12" (3.75/S.F.)		1.40	28.571		1,400	1,225		2,625	3,425
1150	Economy, 4" x 4" x 8" (4.50 per S.F.)		1.40	28.571		915	1,225		2,140	2,875
1201	Engineer, 4" x 3-1/5" x 8", (5.63/S.F.)		1.45	27.586		645	1,175		1,820	2,500
1251	Roman, 4" x 2" x 12", (6.00/S.F.)		1.50	26.667		1,175	1,150		2,325	3,050
1300	S.C.R. 6" x 2-2/3" x 12" (4.50/S.F.)		1.40	28.571		1,350	1,225		2,575	3,375
1350	Utility, 4" x 4" x 12" (3.00/S.F.)		1.08	37.037		1,600	1,600		3,200	4,175
1360	For less than truck load lots, add					15%				
1400	For battered walls, add						30%			
1450	For corbels, add						75%			
1500	For curved walls, add						30%			
1550	For pits and trenches, deduct						20%			
1999	Alternate method of figuring by square foot									
2000	Standard, sel. common, 4" x 2-2/3" x 8", (6.75/S.F.)	D-8	230	.174	S.F.	4.16	7.45		11.61	16
2020	Red, 4" x 2-2/3" x 8", running bond		220	.182		3.72	7.80		11.52	16
2050	Full header every 6th course (7.88/S.F.)		185	.216		4.34	9.30		13.64	18.90
2100	English, full header every 2nd course (10.13/S.F.)		140	.286		5.55	12.25		17.80	25
2150	Flemish, alternate header every course (9.00/S.F.)		150	.267		4.94	11.45		16.39	23
2200	Flemish, alt. header every 6th course (7.13/S.F.)		205	.195		3.93	8.35		12.28	17.10
2250	Full headers throughout (13.50/S.F.)		105	.381		7.40	16.35		23.75	33
2300	Rowlock course (13.50/S.F.)		100	.400		7.40	17.15		24.55	34
2350	Rowlock stretcher (4.50/S.F.)		310	.129		2.51	5.55		8.06	11.20
2400	Soldier course (6.75/S.F.)		200	.200		3.72	8.60		12.32	17.20
2450	Sailor course (4.50/S.F.)		290	.138		2.51	5.90		8.41	11.80
2600	Buff or gray face, running bond, (6.75/S.F.)		220	.182		3.93	7.80		11.73	16.20
2700	Glazed face brick, running bond		210	.190		11.75	8.15		19.90	25.50

04 21 13.13 Brick Veneer Masonry

		Crew	Daily Output	Labor-Hours	Unit	Material	2015 Bare Costs Labor	Equipment	Total	Total Incl O&P
2750	Full header every 6th course (7.88/S.F.)	D-8	170	.235	S.F.	13.70	10.10		23.80	30.50
3000	Jumbo, 6" x 4" x 12" running bond (3.00/S.F.)		435	.092		4.67	3.95		8.62	11.15
3050	Norman, 4" x 2-2/3" x 12" running bond, (4.5/S.F.)		320	.125		5.95	5.35		11.30	14.70
3100	Norwegian, 4" x 3-1/5" x 12" (3.75/S.F.)		375	.107		5.15	4.58		9.73	12.65
3150	Economy, 4" x 4" x 8" (4.50/S.F.)		310	.129		4.08	5.55		9.63	12.95
3200	Engineer, 4" x 3-1/5" x 8" (5.63/S.F.)		260	.154		3.61	6.60		10.21	14.05
3250	Roman, 4" x 2" x 12" (6.00/S.F.)		250	.160		6.95	6.85		13.80	18.10
3300	SCR, 6" x 2-2/3" x 12" (4.50/S.F.)		310	.129		6	5.55		11.55	15.05
3350	Utility, 4" x 4" x 12" (3.00/S.F.)		360	.111		4.65	4.77		9.42	12.40
3360	For less than truck load lots, add				M	15%				
3400	For cavity wall construction, add						15%			
3450	For stacked bond, add						10%			
3500	For interior veneer construction, add						15%			
3550	For curved walls, add						30%			

04 21 13.14 Thin Brick Veneer

		Crew	Daily Output	Labor-Hours	Unit	Material	2015 Bare Costs Labor	Equipment	Total	Total Incl O&P
0010	**THIN BRICK VENEER**									
0015	Material costs incl. 3% brick and 25% mortar waste									
0020	On & incl. metal panel support sys, modular, 2-2/3" x 5/8" x 8", red	D-7	92	.174	S.F.	9	6.65		15.65	19.70
0100	Closure, 4" x 5/8" x 8"		110	.145		8.80	5.55		14.35	17.85
0110	Norman, 2-2/3" x 5/8" x 12"		110	.145		8.85	5.55		14.40	17.90
0120	Utility, 4" x 5/8" x 12"		125	.128		8.55	4.89		13.44	16.65
0130	Emperor, 4" x 3/4" x 16"		175	.091		9.65	3.49		13.14	15.80
0140	Super emperor, 8" x 3/4" x 16"		195	.082		9.95	3.13		13.08	15.60
0150	For L shaped corners with 4" return, add				L.F.	9.25			9.25	10.20
0200	On masonry/plaster back-up, modular, 2-2/3" x 5/8" x 8", red	D-7	137	.117	S.F.	4.21	4.46		8.67	11.25
0210	Closure, 4" x 5/8" x 8"		165	.097		3.98	3.70		7.68	9.85
0220	Norman, 2-2/3" x 5/8" x 12"		165	.097		4.02	3.70		7.72	9.85
0230	Utility, 4" x 5/8" x 12"		185	.086		3.75	3.30		7.05	9
0240	Emperor, 4" x 3/4" x 16"		260	.062		4.85	2.35		7.20	8.80
0250	Super emperor, 8" x 3/4" x 16"		285	.056		5.15	2.14		7.29	8.80
0260	For L shaped corners with 4" return, add				L.F.	9.25			9.25	10.20
0270	For embedment into pre-cast concrete panels, add				S.F.	14.40			14.40	15.85

04 21 13.18 Columns

		Crew	Daily Output	Labor-Hours	Unit	Material	2015 Bare Costs Labor	Equipment	Total	Total Incl O&P
0010	**COLUMNS**, solid, excludes scaffolding, grout and reinforcing									
0050	Brick, 8" x 8", 9 brick per V.L.F.	D-1	56	.286	V.L.F.	4.76	12.05		16.81	23.50
0100	12" x 8", 13.5 brick per V.L.F.		37	.432		7.15	18.20		25.35	36
0200	12" x 12", 20 brick per V.L.F.		25	.640		10.60	27		37.60	52.50
0300	16" x 12", 27 brick per V.L.F.		19	.842		14.30	35.50		49.80	69.50
0400	16" x 16", 36 brick per V.L.F.		14	1.143		19.05	48		67.05	94.50
0500	20" x 16", 45 brick per V.L.F.		11	1.455		24	61		85	120
0600	20" x 20", 56 brick per V.L.F.		9	1.778		29.50	75		104.50	147
0700	24" x 20", 68 brick per V.L.F.		7	2.286		36	96		132	187
0800	24" x 24", 81 brick per V.L.F.		6	2.667		43	112		155	218
1000	36" x 36", 182 brick per V.L.F.		3	5.333		96.50	225		321.50	450

04 21 13.35 Common Building Brick

		Crew	Daily Output	Labor-Hours	Unit	Material	2015 Bare Costs Labor	Equipment	Total	Total Incl O&P
0010	**COMMON BUILDING BRICK**, C62, TL lots, material only									
0020	Standard				M	490			490	540
0050	Select				"	500			500	550

04 21 13.45 Face Brick

		Crew	Daily Output	Labor-Hours	Unit	Material	2015 Bare Costs Labor	Equipment	Total	Total Incl O&P
0010	**FACE BRICK** Material Only, C216, TL lots									
0300	Standard modular, 4" x 2-2/3" x 8"				M	435			435	480
0450	Economy, 4" x 4" x 8"					775			775	855

04 21 Clay Unit Masonry

04 21 13 – Brick Masonry

04 21 13.45 Face Brick

		Crew	Daily Output	Labor-Hours	Unit	Material	2015 Bare Costs Labor	Equipment	Total	Total Incl O&P
0510	Economy, 4" x 4" x 12"				M	1,225			1,225	1,350
0550	Jumbo, 6" x 4" x 12"					1,400			1,400	1,550
0610	Jumbo, 8" x 4" x 12"					1,400			1,400	1,550
0650	Norwegian, 4" x 3-1/5" x 12"					1,225			1,225	1,350
0710	Norwegian, 6" x 3-1/5" x 12"					1,525			1,525	1,675
0850	Standard glazed, plain colors, 4" x 2-2/3" x 8"					1,600			1,600	1,750
1000	Deep trim shades, 4" x 2-2/3" x 8"					2,025			2,025	2,225
1080	Jumbo utility, 4" x 4" x 12"					1,400			1,400	1,525
1120	4" x 8" x 8"					1,775			1,775	1,950
1140	4" x 8" x 16"					5,225			5,225	5,750
1260	Engineer, 4" x 3-1/5" x 8"					525			525	575
1350	King, 4" x 2-3/4" x 10"					485			485	530
1770	Standard modular, double glazed, 4" x 2-2/3" x 8"					2,400			2,400	2,650
1850	Jumbo, colored glazed ceramic, 6" x 4" x 12"					2,525			2,525	2,775
2050	Jumbo utility, glazed, 4" x 4" x 12"					4,750			4,750	5,225
2100	4" x 8" x 8"					5,600			5,600	6,150
2150	4" x 16" x 8"					6,550			6,550	7,200
2170	For less than truck load lots, add					15			15	16.50
2180	For buff or gray brick, add					16			16	17.60
3050	Used brick					405			405	445
3150	Add for brick to match existing work, minimum					5%				
3200	Maximum					50%				

04 22 Concrete Unit Masonry

04 22 10 – Concrete Masonry Units

04 22 10.10 Concrete Block

		Crew	Daily Output	Labor-Hours	Unit	Material	2015 Bare Costs Labor	Equipment	Total	Total Incl O&P
0010	**CONCRETE BLOCK** Material Only R042210-20									
0020	2" x 8" x 16" solid, normal-weight, 2,000 psi				Ea.	1.04			1.04	1.14
0050	3,500 psi					1.11			1.11	1.22
0100	5,000 psi					1.27			1.27	1.40
0150	Lightweight, std.					1.22			1.22	1.34
0300	3" x 8" x 16" solid, normal-weight, 2000 psi					.92			.92	1.01
0350	3,500 psi					1.27			1.27	1.40
0400	5,000 psi					1.44			1.44	1.58
0450	Lightweight, std.					1.18			1.18	1.30
0600	4" x 8" x 16" hollow, normal-weight, 2000 psi					1.19			1.19	1.31
0650	3,500 psi					1.31			1.31	1.44
0700	5000 psi					1.54			1.54	1.69
0750	Lightweight, std.					1.28			1.28	1.41
1300	Solid, normal-weight, 2,000 psi					1.42			1.42	1.56
1350	3,500 psi					1.58			1.58	1.74
1400	5,000 psi					1.34			1.34	1.47
1450	Lightweight, std.					1.13			1.13	1.24
1600	6" x 8" x 16" hollow, normal-weight, 2,000 psi					1.54			1.54	1.69
1650	3,500 psi					1.76			1.76	1.94
1700	5,000 psi					1.89			1.89	2.08
1750	Lightweight, std.					1.84			1.84	2.02
2300	Solid, normal-weight, 2,000 psi					1.69			1.69	1.86
2350	3,500 psi					1.50			1.50	1.65
2400	5,000 psi					2			2	2.20
2450	Lightweight, std.					2.19			2.19	2.41

For customer support on your Site Work & Landscape Cost Data, call 877.737.1594.

97

04 22 10.10 Concrete Block	Crew	Daily Output	Labor-Hours	Unit	Material	2015 Bare Costs Labor	Equipment	Total	Total Incl O&P
2600	8" x 8" x 16" hollow, normal-weight, 2000 psi				Ea.	1.88			1.88	2.07
2650	3500 psi					1.68			1.68	1.85
2700	5,000 psi					2.30			2.30	2.53
2750	Lightweight, std.					2.22			2.22	2.44
3200	Solid, normal-weight, 2,000 psi					2.50			2.50	2.75
3250	3,500 psi					2.86			2.86	3.15
3300	5,000 psi					2.94			2.94	3.23
3350	Lightweight, std.					2.81			2.81	3.09
3400	10" x 8" x 16" hollow, normal-weight, 2000 psi					1.88			1.88	2.07
3410	3500 psi					1.68			1.68	1.85
3420	5,000 psi					2.30			2.30	2.53
3430	Lightweight, std.					2.22			2.22	2.44
3480	Solid, normal-weight, 2,000 psi					2.50			2.50	2.75
3490	3,500 psi					2.86			2.86	3.15
3500	5,000 psi					2.94			2.94	3.23
3510	Lightweight, std.					2.81			2.81	3.09
3600	12" x 8" x 16" hollow, normal-weight, 2000 psi					2.72			2.72	2.99
3650	3,500 psi					2.76			2.76	3.04
3700	5,000 psi					3.08			3.08	3.39
3750	Lightweight, std.					2.77			2.77	3.05
4300	Solid, normal-weight, 2,000 psi					3.85			3.85	4.24
4350	3,500 psi					3.35			3.35	3.69
4400	5,000 psi					3.25			3.25	3.58
4500	Lightweight, std.					2.71			2.71	2.98

04 22 10.14 Concrete Block, Back-Up

		Crew	Daily Output	Labor-Hours	Unit	Material	Labor	Equipment	Total	Total Incl O&P
0010	**CONCRETE BLOCK, BACK-UP**, C90, 2000 psi									
0020	Normal weight, 8" x 16" units, tooled joint 1 side									
0050	Not-reinforced, 2000 psi, 2" thick	D-8	475	.084	S.F.	1.50	3.61		5.11	7.15
0200	4" thick		460	.087		1.79	3.73		5.52	7.65
0300	6" thick		440	.091		2.31	3.90		6.21	8.50
0350	8" thick		400	.100		2.84	4.29		7.13	9.65
0400	10" thick		330	.121		2.96	5.20		8.16	11.20
0450	12" thick	D-9	310	.155		4.05	6.50		10.55	14.40

04 22 10.16 Concrete Block, Bond Beam

		Crew	Daily Output	Labor-Hours	Unit	Material	Labor	Equipment	Total	Total Incl O&P
0010	**CONCRETE BLOCK, BOND BEAM**, C90, 2000 psi									
0020	Not including grout or reinforcing									
0125	Regular block, 6" thick	D-8	584	.068	L.F.	2.65	2.94		5.59	7.40
0130	8" high, 8" thick	"	565	.071		2.71	3.04		5.75	7.60
0150	12" thick	D-9	510	.094		4.02	3.96		7.98	10.45
0525	Lightweight, 6" thick	D-8	592	.068		2.73	2.90		5.63	7.45
0530	8" high, 8" thick	"	575	.070		3.29	2.99		6.28	8.20
0550	12" thick	D-9	520	.092		4.43	3.89		8.32	10.80
2000	Including grout and 2 #5 bars									
2100	Regular block, 8" high, 8" thick	D-8	300	.133	L.F.	4.78	5.70		10.48	14
2150	12" thick	D-9	250	.192		6.65	8.10		14.75	19.70
2500	Lightweight, 8" high, 8" thick	D-8	305	.131		5.35	5.65		11	14.50
2550	12" thick	D-9	255	.188		7.05	7.90		14.95	19.90

04 22 10.19 Concrete Block, Insulation Inserts

		Crew	Daily Output	Labor-Hours	Unit	Material	Labor	Equipment	Total	Total Incl O&P
0010	**CONCRETE BLOCK, INSULATION INSERTS**									
0100	Styrofoam, plant installed, add to block prices									
0200	8" x 16" units, 6" thick				S.F.	1.20			1.20	1.32
0250	8" thick					1.35			1.35	1.49

For customer support on your Site Work & Landscape Cost Data, call 877.737.1594.

04 22 Concrete Unit Masonry

04 22 10 – Concrete Masonry Units

04 22 10.19 Concrete Block, Insulation Inserts	Crew	Daily Output	Labor-Hours	Unit	Material	2015 Bare Costs Labor	Equipment	Total	Total Incl O&P
0300 10" thick				S.F.	1.40			1.40	1.54
0350 12" thick					1.55			1.55	1.71
0500 8" x 8" units, 8" thick					1.20			1.20	1.32
0550 12" thick					1.40			1.40	1.54

04 22 10.23 Concrete Block, Decorative

	Crew	Daily Output	Labor-Hours	Unit	Material	Labor	Equipment	Total	Total Incl O&P
0010 **CONCRETE BLOCK, DECORATIVE**, C90, 2000 psi									
0020 Embossed, simulated brick face									
0100 8" x 16" units, 4" thick	D-8	400	.100	S.F.	2.70	4.29		6.99	9.50
0200 8" thick		340	.118		2.95	5.05		8	10.95
0250 12" thick		300	.133		4.98	5.70		10.68	14.20
0400 Embossed both sides									
0500 8" thick	D-8	300	.133	S.F.	3.97	5.70		9.67	13.10
0550 12" thick	"	275	.145	"	5.20	6.25		11.45	15.30
1000 Fluted high strength									
1100 8" x 16" x 4" thick, flutes 1 side,	D-8	345	.116	S.F.	3.83	4.98		8.81	11.80
1150 Flutes 2 sides		335	.119		4.40	5.10		9.50	12.65
1200 8" thick		300	.133		5.15	5.70		10.85	14.45
1250 For special colors, add					.62			.62	.68
1400 Deep grooved, smooth face									
1450 8" x 16" x 4" thick	D-8	345	.116	S.F.	2.46	4.98		7.44	10.30
1500 8" thick	"	300	.133	"	3.89	5.70		9.59	13.05
2000 Formblock, incl. inserts & reinforcing									
2100 8" x 16" x 8" thick	D-8	345	.116	S.F.	3.44	4.98		8.42	11.40
2150 12" thick	"	310	.129	"	4.55	5.55		10.10	13.45
2500 Ground face									
2600 8" x 16" x 4" thick	D-8	345	.116	S.F.	3.58	4.98		8.56	11.55
2650 6" thick		325	.123		3.98	5.30		9.28	12.45
2700 8" thick		300	.133		4.39	5.70		10.09	13.55
2750 12" thick	D-9	265	.181		5.60	7.65		13.25	17.80
2900 For special colors, add, minimum					15%				
2950 For special colors, add, maximum					45%				
4000 Slump block									
4100 4" face height x 16" x 4" thick	D-1	165	.097	S.F.	3.89	4.08		7.97	10.55
4150 6" thick		160	.100		5.65	4.21		9.86	12.70
4200 8" thick		155	.103		5.60	4.35		9.95	12.80
4250 10" thick		140	.114		10.95	4.81		15.76	19.40
4300 12" thick		130	.123		11.85	5.20		17.05	21
4400 6" face height x 16" x 6" thick		155	.103		5.25	4.35		9.60	12.45
4450 8" thick		150	.107		7.95	4.49		12.44	15.60
4500 10" thick		130	.123		12.80	5.20		18	22
4550 12" thick		120	.133		13.15	5.60		18.75	23
5000 Split rib profile units, 1" deep ribs, 8 ribs									
5100 8" x 16" x 4" thick	D-8	345	.116	S.F.	3.84	4.98		8.82	11.85
5150 6" thick		325	.123		4.37	5.30		9.67	12.85
5200 8" thick		300	.133		4.94	5.70		10.64	14.20
5250 12" thick	D-9	275	.175		5.80	7.35		13.15	17.55
5400 For special deeper colors, 4" thick, add					1.24			1.24	1.37
5450 12" thick, add					1.28			1.28	1.40
5600 For white, 4" thick, add					1.24			1.24	1.37
5650 6" thick, add					1.27			1.27	1.39
5700 8" thick, add					1.29			1.29	1.42
5750 12" thick, add					1.33			1.33	1.47

For customer support on your Site Work & Landscape Cost Data, call 877.737.1594.

99

04 22 Concrete Unit Masonry

04 22 10 – Concrete Masonry Units

04 22 10.23 Concrete Block, Decorative		Crew	Daily Output	Labor-Hours	Unit	Material	2015 Bare Costs Labor	Equipment	Total	Total Incl O&P
6000	Split face									
6100	8" x 16" x 4" thick	D-8	350	.114	S.F.	3.48	4.90		8.38	11.35
6150	6" thick		325	.123		3.98	5.30		9.28	12.40
6200	8" thick		300	.133		4.47	5.70		10.17	13.65
6250	12" thick	D-9	270	.178		5.40	7.50		12.90	17.40
6300	For scored, add					.37			.37	.41
6400	For special deeper colors, 4" thick, add					.60			.60	.66
6450	6" thick, add					.71			.71	.78
6500	8" thick, add					.73			.73	.81
6550	12" thick, add					.76			.76	.83
6650	For white, 4" thick, add					1.23			1.23	1.35
6700	6" thick, add					1.24			1.24	1.37
6750	8" thick, add					1.25			1.25	1.38
6800	12" thick, add					1.28			1.28	1.40
7000	Scored ground face, 2 to 5 scores									
7100	8" x 16" x 4" thick	D-8	340	.118	S.F.	7.55	5.05		12.60	16
7150	6" thick		310	.129		8.40	5.55		13.95	17.65
7200	8" thick		290	.138		9.45	5.90		15.35	19.45
7250	12" thick	D-9	265	.181		12.70	7.65		20.35	25.50
8000	Hexagonal face profile units, 8" x 16" units									
8100	4" thick, hollow	D-8	340	.118	S.F.	3.63	5.05		8.68	11.70
8200	Solid		340	.118		4.65	5.05		9.70	12.80
8300	6" thick, hollow		310	.129		3.82	5.55		9.37	12.65
8350	8" thick, hollow		290	.138		4.36	5.90		10.26	13.85
8500	For stacked bond, add						26%			
8550	For high rise construction, add per story	D-8	67.80	.590	M.S.F.		25.50		25.50	38.50
8600	For scored block, add					10%				
8650	For honed or ground face, per face, add				Ea.	1.13			1.13	1.24
8700	For honed or ground end, per end, add				"	1.13			1.13	1.24
8750	For bullnose block, add					10%				
8800	For special color, add					13%				

04 22 10.24 Concrete Block, Exterior

		Crew	Daily Output	Labor-Hours	Unit	Material	Labor	Equipment	Total	Total Incl O&P
0010	**CONCRETE BLOCK, EXTERIOR**, C90, 2000 psi R042210-20									
0020	Reinforced alt courses, tooled joints 2 sides									
0100	Normal weight, 8" x 16" x 6" thick	D-8	395	.101	S.F.	2.32	4.35		6.67	9.20
0200	8" thick		360	.111		4	4.77		8.77	11.70
0250	10" thick		290	.138		4.24	5.90		10.14	13.70
0300	12" thick	D-9	250	.192		4.84	8.10		12.94	17.65
0500	Lightweight, 8" x 16" x 6" thick	D-8	450	.089		3.10	3.81		6.91	9.20
0600	8" thick		430	.093		3.94	3.99		7.93	10.45
0650	10" thick		395	.101		4.08	4.35		8.43	11.15
0700	12" thick	D-9	350	.137		4.12	5.75		9.87	13.35

04 22 10.26 Concrete Block Foundation Wall

		Crew	Daily Output	Labor-Hours	Unit	Material	Labor	Equipment	Total	Total Incl O&P
0010	**CONCRETE BLOCK FOUNDATION WALL**, C90/C145									
0050	Normal-weight, cut joints, horiz joint reinf, no vert reinf.									
0200	Hollow, 8" x 16" x 6" thick	D-8	455	.088	S.F.	2.89	3.77		6.66	8.90
0250	8" thick		425	.094		3.45	4.04		7.49	9.95
0300	10" thick		350	.114		3.57	4.90		8.47	11.40
0350	12" thick	D-9	300	.160		4.68	6.75		11.43	15.45
0500	Solid, 8" x 16" block, 6" thick	D-8	440	.091		3.05	3.90		6.95	9.30
0550	8" thick	"	415	.096		4.15	4.14		8.29	10.85
0600	12" thick	D-9	350	.137		5.95	5.75		11.70	15.35

04 22 Concrete Unit Masonry

04 22 10 – Concrete Masonry Units

04 22 10.26 Concrete Block Foundation Wall

		Crew	Daily Output	Labor-Hours	Unit	Material	2015 Bare Costs Labor	Equipment	Total	Total Incl O&P
1000	Reinforced, #4 vert @ 48"									
1100	Hollow, 8" x 16" block, 4" thick	D-8	455	.088	S.F.	2.88	3.77		6.65	8.90
1125	6" thick		445	.090		3.76	3.86		7.62	10.05
1150	8" thick		415	.096		4.69	4.14		8.83	11.45
1200	10" thick		340	.118		5.15	5.05		10.20	13.40
1250	12" thick	D-9	290	.166		6.65	6.95		13.60	17.95
1500	Solid, 8" x 16" block, 6" thick	D-8	430	.093		3.08	3.99		7.07	9.50
1600	8" thick	"	405	.099		4.15	4.24		8.39	11
1650	12" thick	D-9	340	.141		5.95	5.95		11.90	15.65

04 22 10.32 Concrete Block, Lintels

		Crew	Daily Output	Labor-Hours	Unit	Material	2015 Bare Costs Labor	Equipment	Total	Total Incl O&P
0010	**CONCRETE BLOCK, LINTELS**, C90, normal weight									
0100	Including grout and horizontal reinforcing									
0200	8" x 8" x 8", 1 #4 bar	D-4	300	.107	L.F.	3.74	4.56	.44	8.74	11.55
0250	2 #4 bars		295	.108		3.96	4.63	.45	9.04	11.90
0400	8" x 16" x 8", 1 #4 bar		275	.116		3.83	4.97	.49	9.29	12.35
0450	2 #4 bars		270	.119		4.05	5.05	.49	9.59	12.70
1000	12" x 8" x 8", 1 #4 bar		275	.116		5.20	4.97	.49	10.66	13.85
1100	2 #4 bars		270	.119		5.40	5.05	.49	10.94	14.20
1150	2 #5 bars		270	.119		5.65	5.05	.49	11.19	14.45
1200	2 #6 bars		265	.121		5.95	5.15	.50	11.60	14.95
1500	12" x 16" x 8", 1 #4 bar		250	.128		5.80	5.45	.53	11.78	15.35
1600	2 #3 bars		245	.131		5.80	5.60	.54	11.94	15.50
1650	2 #4 bars		245	.131		6	5.60	.54	12.14	15.70
1700	2 #5 bars		240	.133		6.25	5.70	.56	12.51	16.20

04 22 10.34 Concrete Block, Partitions

		Crew	Daily Output	Labor-Hours	Unit	Material	2015 Bare Costs Labor	Equipment	Total	Total Incl O&P
0010	**CONCRETE BLOCK, PARTITIONS**, excludes scaffolding R042210-20									
1000	Lightweight block, tooled joints, 2 sides, hollow									
1100	Not reinforced, 8" x 16" x 4" thick	D-8	440	.091	S.F.	1.80	3.90		5.70	7.95
1150	6" thick		410	.098		2.56	4.19		6.75	9.20
1200	8" thick		385	.104		3.13	4.46		7.59	10.25
1250	10" thick		370	.108		3.79	4.64		8.43	11.25
1300	12" thick	D-9	350	.137		4.01	5.75		9.76	13.20
1500	Reinforced alternate courses, 4" thick	D-8	435	.092		1.95	3.95		5.90	8.15
1600	6" thick		405	.099		2.70	4.24		6.94	9.40
1650	8" thick		380	.105		3.28	4.52		7.80	10.50
1700	10" thick		365	.110		3.95	4.70		8.65	11.55
1750	12" thick	D-9	345	.139		4.18	5.85		10.03	13.55
4000	Regular block, tooled joints, 2 sides, hollow									
4100	Not reinforced, 8" x 16" x 4" thick	D-8	430	.093	S.F.	1.70	3.99		5.69	7.95
4150	6" thick		400	.100		2.22	4.29		6.51	9
4200	8" thick		375	.107		2.74	4.58		7.32	10
4250	10" thick		360	.111		2.86	4.77		7.63	10.45
4300	12" thick	D-9	340	.141		3.95	5.95		9.90	13.45
4500	Reinforced alternate courses, 8" x 16" x 4" thick	D-8	425	.094		1.86	4.04		5.90	8.20
4550	6" thick		395	.101		2.39	4.35		6.74	9.30
4600	8" thick		370	.108		2.94	4.64		7.58	10.35
4650	10" thick		355	.113		3.98	4.84		8.82	11.80
4700	12" thick	D-9	335	.143		4.12	6.05		10.17	13.75

For customer support on your Site Work & Landscape Cost Data, call 877.737.1594.

101

04 27 Multiple-Wythe Unit Masonry

04 27 10 – Multiple-Wythe Masonry

04 27 10.30 Brick Walls

04 27 10.30 Brick Walls	Crew	Daily Output	Labor-Hours	Unit	Material	2015 Bare Costs Labor	Equipment	Total	Total Incl O&P
0010 **BRICK WALLS**, including mortar, excludes scaffolding R042110-20									
0020 Estimating by number of brick									
0140 Face brick, 4" thick wall, 6.75 brick/S.F.	D-8	1.45	27.586	M	540	1,175		1,715	2,400
0150 Common brick, 4" thick wall, 6.75 brick/S.F. R042110-50		1.60	25		595	1,075		1,670	2,300
0204 8" thick, 13.50 bricks per S.F.		1.80	22.222		615	955		1,570	2,125
0250 12" thick, 20.25 bricks per S.F.		1.90	21.053		620	905		1,525	2,050
0304 16" thick, 27.00 bricks per S.F.		2	20		630	860		1,490	2,000
0500 Reinforced, face brick, 4" thick wall, 6.75 brick/S.F.		1.40	28.571		565	1,225		1,790	2,500
0520 Common brick, 4" thick wall, 6.75 brick/S.F.		1.55	25.806		620	1,100		1,720	2,375
0550 8" thick, 13.50 bricks per S.F.		1.75	22.857		640	980		1,620	2,200
0600 12" thick, 20.25 bricks per S.F.		1.85	21.622		645	930		1,575	2,125
0650 16" thick, 27.00 bricks per S.F.		1.95	20.513		655	880		1,535	2,075
0790 Alternate method of figuring by square foot									
0800 Face brick, 4" thick wall, 6.75 brick/S.F.	D-8	215	.186	S.F.	3.65	8		11.65	16.20
0850 Common brick, 4" thick wall, 6.75 brick/S.F.		240	.167		4.03	7.15		11.18	15.35
0900 8" thick, 13.50 bricks per S.F.		135	.296		8.30	12.70		21	28.50
1000 12" thick, 20.25 bricks per S.F.		95	.421		12.55	18.05		30.60	41.50
1050 16" thick, 27.00 bricks per S.F.		75	.533		17	23		40	53.50
1200 Reinforced, face brick, 4" thick wall, 6.75 brick/S.F.		210	.190		3.82	8.15		11.97	16.70
1220 Common brick, 4" thick wall, 6.75 brick/S.F.		235	.170		4.20	7.30		11.50	15.75
1250 8" thick, 13.50 bricks per S.F.		130	.308		8.65	13.20		21.85	29.50
1300 12" thick, 20.25 bricks per S.F.		90	.444		13.05	19.05		32.10	43.50
1350 16" thick, 27.00 bricks per S.F.		70	.571		17.65	24.50		42.15	57

04 27 10.40 Steps

	Crew	Daily Output	Labor-Hours	Unit	Material	2015 Bare Costs Labor	Equipment	Total	Total Incl O&P
0010 **STEPS**									
0012 Entry steps, select common brick	D-1	.30	53.333	M	500	2,250		2,750	3,975

04 41 Dry-Placed Stone

04 41 10 – Dry Placed Stone

04 41 10.10 Rough Stone Wall

		Crew	Daily Output	Labor-Hours	Unit	Material	2015 Bare Costs Labor	Equipment	Total	Total Incl O&P
0011 **ROUGH STONE WALL**, Dry										
0012 Dry laid (no mortar), under 18" thick	G	D-1	60	.267	C.F.	12.90	11.25		24.15	31.50
0100 Random fieldstone, under 18" thick	G	D-12	60	.533		12.90	22.50		35.40	48.50
0150 Over 18" thick	G	"	63	.508		15.50	21.50		37	50
0500 Field stone veneer	G	D-8	120	.333	S.F.	12.20	14.30		26.50	35.50

04 43 Stone Masonry

04 43 10 – Masonry with Natural and Processed Stone

04 43 10.05 Ashlar Veneer

	Crew	Daily Output	Labor-Hours	Unit	Material	2015 Bare Costs Labor	Equipment	Total	Total Incl O&P
0011 **ASHLAR VENEER** 4" + or - thk, random or random rectangular									
0150 Sawn face, split joints, low priced stone	D-8	140	.286	S.F.	11.60	12.25		23.85	31.50
0200 Medium priced stone		130	.308		13.35	13.20		26.55	34.50
0300 High priced stone		120	.333		17.90	14.30		32.20	41.50
0600 Seam face, split joints, medium price stone		125	.320		19	13.75		32.75	42
0700 High price stone		120	.333		18.75	14.30		33.05	42.50
1000 Split or rock face, split joints, medium price stone		125	.320		11.40	13.75		25.15	33.50
1100 High price stone		120	.333		17.25	14.30		31.55	41

04 43 Stone Masonry

04 43 10 – Masonry with Natural and Processed Stone

04 43 10.10 Bluestone

		Crew	Daily Output	Labor-Hours	Unit	Material	2015 Bare Costs Labor	Equipment	Total	Total Incl O&P
0010	**BLUESTONE**, cut to size									
0100	Paving, natural cleft, to 4', 1" thick	D-8	150	.267	S.F.	6.50	11.45		17.95	24.50
0150	1-1/2" thick		145	.276		6.50	11.85		18.35	25
0200	Smooth finish, 1" thick		150	.267		7	11.45		18.45	25
0250	1-1/2" thick		145	.276		7.50	11.85		19.35	26.50
0300	Thermal finish, 1" thick		150	.267		7	11.45		18.45	25
0350	1-1/2" thick	▼	145	.276	▼	7.50	11.85		19.35	26.50
0500	Sills, natural cleft, 10" wide to 6' long, 1-1/2" thick	D-11	70	.343	L.F.	13.35	15.15		28.50	37.50
0550	2" thick		63	.381		14.60	16.80		31.40	41.50
0600	Smooth finish, 1-1/2" thick		70	.343		12	15.15		27.15	36
0650	2" thick		63	.381		13	16.80		29.80	40
0800	Thermal finish, 1-1/2" thick		70	.343		12	15.15		27.15	36
0850	2" thick	▼	63	.381		13	16.80		29.80	40
1000	Stair treads, natural cleft, 12" wide, 6' long, 1-1/2" thick	D-10	115	.278		12	12.80	4.12	28.92	37
1050	2" thick		105	.305		13	14	4.51	31.51	41
1100	Smooth finish, 1-1/2" thick		115	.278		12	12.80	4.12	28.92	37
1150	2" thick		105	.305		13	14	4.51	31.51	41
1300	Thermal finish, 1-1/2" thick		115	.278		12	12.80	4.12	28.92	37
1350	2" thick	▼	105	.305	▼	13	14	4.51	31.51	41
2000	Coping, finished top & 2 sides, 12" to 6'									
2100	Natural cleft, 1-1/2" thick	D-10	115	.278	L.F.	12.50	12.80	4.12	29.42	38
2150	2" thick		105	.305		13.50	14	4.51	32.01	41.50
2200	Smooth finish, 1-1/2" thick		115	.278		12.50	12.80	4.12	29.42	38
2250	2" thick		105	.305		13.50	14	4.51	32.01	41.50
2300	Thermal finish, 1-1/2" thick		115	.278		12.50	12.80	4.12	29.42	38
2350	2" thick	▼	105	.305	▼	13.50	14	4.51	32.01	41.50

04 43 10.45 Granite

		Crew	Daily Output	Labor-Hours	Unit	Material	2015 Bare Costs Labor	Equipment	Total	Total Incl O&P
0010	**GRANITE**, cut to size									
0050	Veneer, polished face, 3/4" to 1-1/2" thick									
0150	Low price, gray, light gray, etc.	D-10	130	.246	S.F.	26.50	11.35	3.64	41.49	51
0180	Medium price, pink, brown, etc.		130	.246		29.50	11.35	3.64	44.49	54
0220	High price, red, black, etc.	▼	130	.246	▼	42	11.35	3.64	56.99	68
0300	1-1/2" to 2-1/2" thick, veneer									
0350	Low price, gray, light gray, etc.	D-10	130	.246	S.F.	28.50	11.35	3.64	43.49	53
0500	Medium price, pink, brown, etc.		130	.246		33.50	11.35	3.64	48.49	58.50
0550	High price, red, black, etc.	▼	130	.246	▼	52.50	11.35	3.64	67.49	79
0700	2-1/2" to 4" thick, veneer									
0750	Low price, gray, light gray, etc.	D-10	110	.291	S.F.	38.50	13.40	4.30	56.20	67.50
0850	Medium price, pink, brown, etc.		110	.291		44	13.40	4.30	61.70	73.50
0950	High price, red, black, etc.	▼	110	.291		63	13.40	4.30	80.70	94.50
1000	For bush hammered finish, deduct					5%				
1050	Coarse rubbed finish, deduct					10%				
1100	Honed finish, deduct					5%				
1150	Thermal finish, deduct				▼	18%				
1800	Carving or bas-relief, from templates or plaster molds									
1850	Low price, gray, light gray, etc.	D-10	80	.400	C.F.	178	18.40	5.90	202.30	231
1875	Medium price, pink, brown, etc.		80	.400		350	18.40	5.90	374.30	420
1900	High price, red, black, etc.	▼	80	.400	▼	520	18.40	5.90	544.30	605
2000	Intricate or hand finished pieces									
2010	Mouldings, radius cuts, bullnose edges, etc.									
2050	Add for low price gray, light gray, etc.					30%				
2075	Add for medium price, pink, brown, etc.					165%				

For customer support on your Site Work & Landscape Cost Data, call 877.737.1594.

103

04 43 Stone Masonry

04 43 10 – Masonry with Natural and Processed Stone

04 43 10.45 Granite

		Crew	Daily Output	Labor-Hours	Unit	Material	2015 Bare Costs Labor	Equipment	Total	Total Incl O&P
2100	Add for high price red, black, etc.					300%				
2450	For radius under 5', add				L.F.	100%				
2500	Steps, copings, etc., finished on more than one surface									
2550	Low price, gray, light gray, etc.	D-10	50	.640	C.F.	91	29.50	9.45	129.95	155
2575	Medium price, pink, brown, etc.		50	.640		118	29.50	9.45	156.95	185
2600	High price, red, black, etc.		50	.640		146	29.50	9.45	184.95	215
2700	Pavers, Belgian block, 8"-13" long, 4"-6" wide, 4"-6" deep	D-11	120	.200	S.F.	27	8.80		35.80	43
2800	Pavers, 4" x 4" x 4" blocks, split face and joints									
2850	Low price, gray, light gray, etc.	D-11	80	.300	S.F.	13.10	13.25		26.35	34.50
2875	Medium price, pinks, browns, etc.		80	.300		21	13.25		34.25	43
2900	High price, red, black, etc.		80	.300		29	13.25		42.25	52
3000	Pavers, 4" x 4" x 4", thermal face, sawn joints									
3050	Low price, gray, light gray, etc.	D-11	65	.369	S.F.	24.50	16.30		40.80	51.50
3075	Medium price, pink, brown, etc.		65	.369		28	16.30		44.30	56
3100	High price, red, black, etc.		65	.369		32	16.30		48.30	60.50
4000	Soffits, 2" thick, low price, gray, light gray	D-13	35	1.371		37.50	61.50	13.50	112.50	150
4050	Medium price, pink, brown, etc.		35	1.371		64.50	61.50	13.50	139.50	180
4100	High price, red, black, etc.		35	1.371		91.50	61.50	13.50	166.50	209
4200	Low price, gray, light gray, etc.		35	1.371		63	61.50	13.50	138	178
4250	Medium price, pink, brown, etc.		35	1.371		91	61.50	13.50	166	209
4300	High price, red, black, etc.		35	1.371		119	61.50	13.50	194	240

04 43 10.50 Lightweight Natural Stone

		Crew	Daily Output	Labor-Hours	Unit	Material	2015 Bare Costs Labor	Equipment	Total	Total Incl O&P
0011	**LIGHTWEIGHT NATURAL STONE** Lava type									
0100	Veneer, rubble face, sawed back, irregular shapes	G D-10	130	.246	S.F.	8.50	11.35	3.64	23.49	30.50
0200	Sawed face and back, irregular shapes	G "	130	.246	"	8.50	11.35	3.64	23.49	30.50

04 43 10.55 Limestone

		Crew	Daily Output	Labor-Hours	Unit	Material	2015 Bare Costs Labor	Equipment	Total	Total Incl O&P
0010	**LIMESTONE**, cut to size									
0020	Veneer facing panels									
0500	Texture finish, light stick, 4-1/2" thick, 5' x 12'	D-4	300	.107	S.F.	19.50	4.56	.44	24.50	29
1400	Sugarcube, textured finish, 4-1/2" thick, 5' x 12'	D-10	275	.116		31	5.35	1.72	38.07	44
1450	5" thick, 5' x 14' panels		275	.116		32	5.35	1.72	39.07	45.50
2000	Coping, sugarcube finish, top & 2 sides		30	1.067	C.F.	67.50	49	15.80	132.30	166
2100	Sills, lintels, jambs, trim, stops, sugarcube finish, simple		20	1.600		67.50	73.50	23.50	164.50	212
2150	Detailed		20	1.600		67.50	73.50	23.50	164.50	212
2300	Steps, extra hard, 14" wide, 6" rise		50	.640	L.F.	25	29.50	9.45	63.95	83
3000	Quoins, plain finish, 6" x 12" x 12"	D-12	25	1.280	Ea.	37.50	54.50		92	125
3050	6" x 16" x 24"	"	25	1.280	"	50	54.50		104.50	139

04 43 10.60 Marble

		Crew	Daily Output	Labor-Hours	Unit	Material	2015 Bare Costs Labor	Equipment	Total	Total Incl O&P
0011	**MARBLE**, ashlar, split face, 4" + or - thick, random									
0040	Lengths 1' to 4' & heights 2" to 7-1/2", average	D-8	175	.229	S.F.	17.45	9.80		27.25	34
1000	Facing, polished finish, cut to size, 3/4" to 7/8" thick									
1050	Carrara or equal	D-10	130	.246	S.F.	19	11.35	3.64	33.99	42.50
1100	Arabescato or equal		130	.246		39	11.35	3.64	53.99	64.50
1300	1-1/4" thick, Botticino Classico or equal		125	.256		24	11.80	3.79	39.59	48.50
1350	Statuarietto or equal		125	.256		41.50	11.80	3.79	57.09	67.50
1500	2" thick, Crema Marfil or equal		120	.267		42.50	12.25	3.94	58.69	70
1550	Cafe Pinta or equal		120	.267		70	12.25	3.94	86.19	100
1700	Rubbed finish, cut to size, 4" thick									
1740	Average	D-10	100	.320	S.F.	40	14.70	4.73	59.43	71.50
1780	Maximum	"	100	.320	"	69	14.70	4.73	88.43	104
2500	Flooring, polished tiles, 12" x 12" x 3/8" thick									
2510	Thin set, Giallo Solare or equal	D-11	90	.267	S.F.	14.75	11.75		26.50	34

For customer support on your Site Work & Landscape Cost Data, call 877.737.1594.

04 43 Stone Masonry

04 43 10 – Masonry with Natural and Processed Stone

04 43 10.60 Marble	Crew	Daily Output	Labor-Hours	Unit	Material	2015 Bare Costs Labor	2015 Bare Costs Equipment	Total	Total Incl O&P
2600	Sky Blue or equal	D-11	90	.267	S.F.	16	11.75		27.75	35.50
2700	Mortar bed, Giallo Solare or equal		65	.369		14.75	16.30		31.05	41.50
2740	Sky Blue or equal	↓	65	.369	↓	16	16.30	·	32.30	42.50
3210	Stairs, risers, 7/8" thick x 6" high	D-10	115	.278	L.F.	15.25	12.80	4.12	32.17	41
3360	Treads, 12" wide x 1-1/4" thick	"	115	.278	"	43.50	12.80	· 4.12	60.42	72
3500	Thresholds, 3' long, 7/8" thick, 4" to 5" wide, plain	D-12	24	1.333	Ea.	35.50	57		92.50	126
3550	Beveled	"	24	1.333	"	70.50	57		127.50	164

04 43 10.75 Sandstone or Brownstone	Crew	Daily Output	Labor-Hours	Unit	Material	2015 Bare Costs Labor	2015 Bare Costs Equipment	Total	Total Incl O&P
0011	**SANDSTONE OR BROWNSTONE**									
0100	Sawed face veneer, 2-1/2" thick, to 2' x 4' panels	D-10	130	.246	S.F.	19	11.35	3.64	33.99	42.50
0150	4" thick, to 3'-6" x 8' panels		100	.320		19	14.70	4.73	38.43	48.50
0300	Split face, random sizes	↓	100	.320	↓	13.65	14.70	4.73	33.08	42.50

04 43 10.80 Slate	Crew	Daily Output	Labor-Hours	Unit	Material	2015 Bare Costs Labor	2015 Bare Costs Equipment	Total	Total Incl O&P
0010	**SLATE**									
0040	Pennsylvania - blue gray to black									
0050	Vermont - unfading green, mottled green & purple, gray & purple									
0100	Virginia - blue black									
0200	Exterior paving, natural cleft, 1" thick									
0250	6" x 6" Pennsylvania	D-12	100	.320	S.F.	7.15	13.65		20.80	29
0300	Vermont		100	.320		11.25	13.65		24.90	33.50
0350	Virginia		100	.320		14.95	13.65		28.60	37.50
0500	24" x 24", Pennsylvania		120	.267		13.80	11.35		25.15	32.50
0550	Vermont		120	.267		28	11.35		39.35	48
0600	Virginia		120	.267		21.50	11.35		32.85	41.50
0700	18" x 30" Pennsylvania		120	.267		15.65	11.35		27	34.50
0750	Vermont		120	.267		28	11.35		39.35	48
0800	Virginia	↓	120	.267	↓	19.30	11.35		30.65	38.50
1000	Interior flooring, natural cleft, 1/2" thick									
1100	6" x 6" Pennsylvania	D-12	100	.320	S.F.	4.24	13.65		17.89	25.50
1150	Vermont		100	.320		9.90	13.65		23.55	32
1200	Virginia		100	.320		11.80	13.65		25.45	34
1300	24" x 24" Pennsylvania		120	.267		8.20	11.35		19.55	26.50
1350	Vermont		120	.267		22.50	11.35		33.85	42.50
1400	Virginia		120	.267		15.60	11.35		26.95	34.50
1500	18" x 24" Pennsylvania		120	.267		8.20	11.35		19.55	26.50
1550	Vermont		120	.267		18	11.35		29.35	37
1600	Virginia	↓	120	.267	↓	15.85	11.35		27.20	35
2000	Facing panels, 1-1/4" thick, to 4' x 4' panels									
2100	Natural cleft finish, Pennsylvania	D-10	180	.178	S.F.	36	8.20	2.63	46.83	55
2110	Vermont		180	.178		29	8.20	2.63	39.83	47
2120	Virginia	↓	180	.178		35	8.20	2.63	45.83	54.50
2150	Sand rubbed finish, surface, add					10.80			10.80	11.85
2200	Honed finish, add					7.80			7.80	8.55
2500	Ribbon, natural cleft finish, 1" thick, to 9 S.F.	D-10	80	.400		13.90	18.40	5.90	38.20	50
2550	Sand rubbed finish		80	.400		18.80	18.40	5.90	43.10	55
2600	Honed finish		80	.400		17.50	18.40	5.90	41.80	54
2700	1-1/2" thick		78	.410		18.05	18.90	6.05	43	55.50
2750	Sand rubbed finish		78	.410		24	18.90	6.05	48.95	61.50
2800	Honed finish		78	.410		22.50	18.90	6.05	47.45	60.50
2850	2" thick		76	.421		21.50	19.35	6.25	47.10	60.50
2900	Sand rubbed finish		76	.421		30	19.35	6.25	55.60	69.50
2950	Honed finish	↓	76	.421	↓	27.50	19.35	6.25	53.10	67

04 43 Stone Masonry

04 43 10 – Masonry with Natural and Processed Stone

04 43 10.80 Slate

		Crew	Daily Output	Labor-Hours	Unit	Material	2015 Bare Costs Labor	Equipment	Total	Total Incl O&P
3100	Stair landings, 1" thick, black, clear	D-1	65	.246	S.F.	21	10.35		31.35	39.50
3200	Ribbon	"	65	.246	▼	23.50	10.35		33.85	41.50
3500	Stair treads, sand finish, 1" thick x 12" wide									
3550	Under 3 L.F.	D-10	85	.376	L.F.	23.50	17.30	5.55	46.35	58
3600	3 L.F. to 6 L.F.	"	120	.267	"	25	12.25	3.94	41.19	50.50
3700	Ribbon, sand finish, 1" thick x 12" wide									
3750	To 6 L.F.	D-10	120	.267	L.F.	21	12.25	3.94	37.19	46.50
4000	Stools or sills, sand finish, 1" thick, 6" wide	D-12	160	.200		12.20	8.50		20.70	26.50
4100	Honed finish		160	.200		11.65	8.50		20.15	26
4200	10" wide		90	.356		18.80	15.15		33.95	43.50
4250	Honed finish		90	.356		17.50	15.15		32.65	42.50
4400	2" thick, 6" wide		140	.229		19.60	9.75		29.35	36.50
4450	Honed finish		140	.229		18.65	9.75		28.40	35.50
4600	10" wide		90	.356		30.50	15.15		45.65	57
4650	Honed finish	▼	90	.356		29	15.15		44.15	55
4800	For lengths over 3', add				▼	25%				

04 54 Refractory Brick Masonry

04 54 10 – Refractory Brick Work

04 54 10.10 Fire Brick

		Crew	Daily Output	Labor-Hours	Unit	Material	2015 Bare Costs Labor	Equipment	Total	Total Incl O&P
0010	**FIRE BRICK**									
0012	Low duty, 2000°F, 9" x 2-1/2" x 4-1/2"	D-1	.60	26.667	M	1,425	1,125		2,550	3,300
0050	High duty, 3000°F	"	.60	26.667	"	2,600	1,125		3,725	4,575

04 54 10.20 Fire Clay

		Crew	Daily Output	Labor-Hours	Unit	Material	2015 Bare Costs Labor	Equipment	Total	Total Incl O&P
0010	**FIRE CLAY**									
0020	Gray, high duty, 100 lb. bag				Bag	33			33	36.50
0050	100 lb. drum, premixed (400 brick per drum)				Drum	41			41	45

04 57 Masonry Fireplaces

04 57 10 – Brick or Stone Fireplaces

04 57 10.10 Fireplace

		Crew	Daily Output	Labor-Hours	Unit	Material	2015 Bare Costs Labor	Equipment	Total	Total Incl O&P
0010	**FIREPLACE**									
0100	Brick fireplace, not incl. foundations or chimneys									
0110	30" x 29" opening, incl. chamber, plain brickwork	D-1	.40	40	Ea.	550	1,675		2,225	3,175
0200	Fireplace box only (110 brick)	"	2	8	"	157	335		492	685
0300	For elaborate brickwork and details, add					35%	35%			
0400	For hearth, brick & stone, add	D-1	2	8	Ea.	205	335		540	740

04 72 Cast Stone Masonry

04 72 10 – Cast Stone Masonry Features

04 72 10.10 Coping		Crew	Daily Output	Labor-Hours	Unit	Material	2015 Bare Costs Labor	2015 Bare Costs Equipment	Total	Total Incl O&P
0010	**COPING**, stock units									
0050	Precast concrete, 10" wide, 4" tapers to 3-1/2", 8" wall	D-1	75	.213	L.F.	17.10	9		26.10	32.50
0100	12" wide, 3-1/2" tapers to 3", 10" wall		70	.229		18.45	9.60		28.05	35
0110	14" wide, 4" tapers to 3-1/2", 12" wall		65	.246		20.50	10.35		30.85	38.50
0150	16" wide, 4" tapers to 3-1/2", 14" wall		60	.267	▼	22	11.25		33.25	41.50
0250	Precast concrete corners		40	.400	Ea.	29	16.85		45.85	57
0300	Limestone for 12" wall, 4" thick		90	.178	L.F.	14.70	7.50		22.20	27.50
0350	6" thick		80	.200		22	8.40		30.40	37.50
0500	Marble, to 4" thick, no wash, 9" wide		90	.178		12.05	7.50		19.55	24.50
0550	12" wide		80	.200		16.15	8.40		24.55	30.50
0700	Terra cotta, 9" wide		90	.178		6.35	7.50		13.85	18.40
0750	12" wide		80	.200		8.65	8.40		17.05	22.50
0800	Aluminum, for 12" wall	▼	80	.200	▼	8.90	8.40		17.30	22.50

04 72 20 – Cultured Stone Veneer

04 72 20.10 Cultured Stone Veneer Components

		Crew	Daily Output	Labor-Hours	Unit	Material	2015 Bare Costs Labor	2015 Bare Costs Equipment	Total	Total Incl O&P
0010	**CULTURED STONE VENEER COMPONENTS**									
0110	On wood frame and sheathing substrate, random sized cobbles, corner stones	D-8	70	.571	V.L.F.	10.15	24.50		34.65	48.50
0120	Field stones		140	.286	S.F.	7.40	12.25		19.65	27
0130	Random sized flats, corner stones		70	.571	V.L.F.	10.05	24.50		34.55	48.50
0140	Field stones		140	.286	S.F.	8.70	12.25		20.95	28.50
0150	Horizontal lined ledgestones, corner stones		75	.533	V.L.F.	10.15	23		33.15	46
0160	Field stones		150	.267	S.F.	7.40	11.45		18.85	25.50
0170	Random shaped flats, corner stones		65	.615	V.L.F.	10.15	26.50		36.65	51.50
0180	Field stones		150	.267	S.F.	7.40	11.45		18.85	25.50
0190	Random shaped/textured face, corner stones		65	.615	V.L.F.	10.15	26.50		36.65	51.50
0200	Field stones		130	.308	S.F.	7.40	13.20		20.60	28
0210	Random shaped river rock, corner stones		65	.615	V.L.F.	10.15	26.50		36.65	51.50
0220	Field stones		130	.308	S.F.	7.40	13.20		20.60	28
0240	On concrete or CMU substrate, random sized cobbles, corner stones		70	.571	V.L.F.	9.55	24.50		34.05	48
0250	Field stones		140	.286	S.F.	7.10	12.25		19.35	26.50
0260	Random sized flats, corner stones		70	.571	V.L.F.	9.45	24.50		33.95	48
0270	Field stones		140	.286	S.F.	8.40	12.25		20.65	28
0280	Horizontal lined ledgestones, corner stones		75	.533	V.L.F.	9.55	23		32.55	45.50
0290	Field stones		150	.267	S.F.	7.10	11.45		18.55	25.50
0300	Random shaped flats, corner stones		70	.571	V.L.F.	9.55	24.50		34.05	48
0310	Field stones		140	.286	S.F.	7.10	12.25		19.35	26.50
0320	Random shaped/textured face, corner stones		65	.615	V.L.F.	9.55	26.50		36.05	51
0330	Field stones		130	.308	S.F.	7.10	13.20		20.30	28
0340	Random shaped river rock, corner stones		65	.615	V.L.F.	9.55	26.50		36.05	51
0350	Field stones	▼	130	.308	S.F.	7.10	13.20		20.30	28
0360	Cultured stone veneer, #15 felt weather resistant barrier	1 Clab	3700	.002	Sq.	5.40	.08		5.48	6.10
0370	Expanded metal lath, diamond, 2.5 lb./S.Y., galvanized	1 Lath	85	.094	S.Y.	2.72	4.05		6.77	8.95
0390	Water table or window sill, 18" long	1 Bric	80	.100	Ea.	10.30	4.62		14.92	18.40

For customer support on your Site Work & Landscape Cost Data, call 877.737.1594.

107

Division Notes

	CREW	DAILY OUTPUT	LABOR-HOURS	UNIT	BARE COSTS				TOTAL INCL O&P
					MAT.	LABOR	EQUIP.	TOTAL	

Estimating Tips
05 05 00 Common Work Results for Metals

- Nuts, bolts, washers, connection angles, and plates can add a significant amount to both the tonnage of a structural steel job and the estimated cost. As a rule of thumb, add 10% to the total weight to account for these accessories.
- Type 2 steel construction, commonly referred to as "simple construction," consists generally of field-bolted connections with lateral bracing supplied by other elements of the building, such as masonry walls or x-bracing. The estimator should be aware, however, that shop connections may be accomplished by welding or bolting. The method may be particular to the fabrication shop and may have an impact on the estimated cost.

05 10 00 Structural Steel

- Steel items can be obtained from two sources: a fabrication shop or a metals service center. Fabrication shops can fabricate items under more controlled conditions than can crews in the field. They are also more efficient and can produce items more economically. Metal service centers serve as a source of long mill shapes to both fabrication shops and contractors.
- Most line items in this structural steel subdivision, and most items in 05 50 00 Metal Fabrications, are indicated as being shop fabricated. The bare material cost for these shop fabricated items is the "Invoice Cost" from the shop and includes the mill base price of steel plus mill extras, transportation to the shop, shop drawings and detailing where warranted, shop fabrication and handling, sandblasting and a shop coat of primer paint, all necessary structural bolts, and delivery to the job site. The bare labor cost and bare equipment cost for these shop fabricated items is for field installation or erection.
- Line items in Subdivision 05 12 23.40 Lightweight Framing, and other items scattered in Division 5, are indicated as being field fabricated. The bare material cost for these field fabricated items is the "Invoice Cost" from the metals service center and includes the mill base price of steel plus mill extras, transportation to the metals service center, material handling, and delivery of long lengths of mill shapes to the job site. Material costs for structural bolts and welding rods should be added to the estimate. The bare labor cost and bare equipment cost for these items is for both field fabrication and field installation or erection, and include time for cutting, welding and drilling in the fabricated metal items. Drilling into concrete and fasteners to fasten field fabricated items to other work are not included and should be added to the estimate.

05 20 00 Steel Joist Framing

- In any given project the total weight of open web steel joists is determined by the loads to be supported and the design. However, economies can be realized in minimizing the amount of labor used to place the joists. This is done by maximizing the joist spacing, and therefore minimizing the number of joists required to be installed on the job. Certain spacings and locations may be required by the design, but in other cases maximizing the spacing and keeping it as uniform as possible will keep the costs down.

05 30 00 Steel Decking

- The takeoff and estimating of metal deck involves more than simply the area of the floor or roof and the type of deck specified or shown on the drawings. Many different sizes and types of openings may exist. Small openings for individual pipes or conduits may be drilled after the floor/roof is installed, but larger openings may require special deck lengths as well as reinforcing or structural support. The estimator should determine who will be supplying this reinforcing. Additionally, some deck terminations are part of the deck package, such as screed angles and pour stops, and others will be part of the steel contract, such as angles attached to structural members and cast-in-place angles and plates. The estimator must ensure that all pieces are accounted for in the complete estimate.

05 50 00 Metal Fabrications

- The most economical steel stairs are those that use common materials, standard details, and most importantly, a uniform and relatively simple method of field assembly. Commonly available A36 channels and plates are very good choices for the main stringers of the stairs, as are angles and tees for the carrier members. Risers and treads are usually made by specialty shops, and it is most economical to use a typical detail in as many places as possible. The stairs should be pre-assembled and shipped directly to the site. The field connections should be simple and straightforward to be accomplished efficiently, and with minimum equipment and labor.

Reference Numbers
Reference numbers are shown in shaded boxes at the beginning of some major classifications. These numbers refer to related items in the Reference Section. The reference information may be an estimating procedure, an alternate pricing method, or technical information.

Note: Not all subdivisions listed here necessarily appear in this publication. ■

05 01 Maintenance of Metals

05 01 10 – Maintenance of Structural Metal Framing

05 01 10.51 Cleaning of Structural Metal Framing

		Crew	Daily Output	Labor-Hours	Unit	Material	2015 Bare Costs Labor	2015 Bare Costs Equipment	Total	Total Incl O&P
0010	**CLEANING OF STRUCTURAL METAL FRAMING**									
6125	Steel surface treatments, PDCA guidelines									
6170	Wire brush, hand (SSPC-SP2)	1 Psst	400	.020	S.F.	.02	.83		.85	1.49
6180	Power tool (SSPC-SP3)	"	700	.011		.09	.47		.56	.92
6215	Pressure washing, up to 5000 psi, 5000-15,000 S.F./day	1 Pord	10000	.001			.03		.03	.05
6220	Steam cleaning, 600 psi @ 300 F, 1250 – 2500 S.F./day		2000	.004			.16		.16	.24
6225	Water blasting, up to 25,000 psi, 1750 – 3500 S.F./day		2500	.003			.13		.13	.19
6230	Brush-off blast (SSPC-SP7)	E-11	1750	.018		.15	.77	.13	1.05	1.59
6235	Com'l blast (SSPC-SP6), loose scale, fine pwder rust, 2.0#/S.F. sand		1200	.027		.31	1.13	.20	1.64	2.41
6240	Tight mill scale, little/no rust, 3.0#/S.F. sand		1000	.032		.46	1.35	.24	2.05	2.99
6245	Exist coat blistered/pitted, 4.0#/S.F. sand		875	.037		.62	1.55	.27	2.44	3.52
6250	Exist coat badly pitted/nodules, 6.7#/S.F. sand		825	.039		1.03	1.64	.29	2.96	4.14
6255	Near white blast (SSPC-SP10), loose scale, fine rust, 5.6#/S.F. sand		450	.071		.86	3.01	.52	4.39	6.45
6260	Tight mill scale, little/no rust, 6.9#/S.F. sand		325	.098		1.06	4.16	.73	5.95	8.80
6265	Exist coat blistered/pitted, 9.0#/S.F. sand		225	.142		1.39	6	1.05	8.44	12.55
6270	Exist coat badly pitted/nodules, 11.3#/S.F. sand		150	.213		1.74	9	1.57	12.31	18.45

05 05 Common Work Results for Metals

05 05 05 – Selective Demolition for Metals

05 05 05.10 Selective Demolition, Metals

		Crew	Daily Output	Labor-Hours	Unit	Material	2015 Bare Costs Labor	2015 Bare Costs Equipment	Total	Total Incl O&P
0010	**SELECTIVE DEMOLITION, METALS** R024119-10									
0015	Excludes shores, bracing, cutting, loading, hauling, dumping									
0020	Remove nuts only up to 3/4" diameter	1 Sswk	480	.017	Ea.		.88		.88	1.52
0030	7/8" to 1-1/4" diameter		240	.033			1.75		1.75	3.05
0040	1-3/8" to 2" diameter		160	.050			2.63		2.63	4.57
0060	Unbolt and remove structural bolts up to 3/4" diameter		240	.033			1.75		1.75	3.05
0070	7/8" to 2" diameter		160	.050			2.63		2.63	4.57
0140	Light weight framing members, remove whole or cut up, up to 20 lb.		240	.033			1.75		1.75	3.05
0150	21 – 40 lb.	2 Sswk	210	.076			4.01		4.01	6.95
0160	41 – 80 lb.	3 Sswk	180	.133			7		7	12.20
0170	81 – 120 lb.	4 Sswk	150	.213			11.25		11.25	19.50
0230	Structural members, remove whole or cut up, up to 500 lb.	E-19	48	.500			26	19.75	45.75	65.50
0240	1/4 – 2 tons	E-18	36	1.111			58.50	26.50	85	128
0250	2 – 5 tons	E-24	30	1.067			55.50	24.50	80	121
0260	5 – 10 tons	E-20	24	2.667			138	48.50	186.50	287
0270	10 – 15 tons	E-2	18	3.111			161	84	245	365
0340	Fabricated item, remove whole or cut up, up to 20 lb.	1 Sswk	96	.083			4.39		4.39	7.60
0350	21 – 40 lb.	2 Sswk	84	.190			10.05		10.05	17.40
0360	41 – 80 lb.	3 Sswk	72	.333			17.55		17.55	30.50
0370	81 – 120 lb.	4 Sswk	60	.533			28		28	49
0380	121 – 500 lb.	E-19	48	.500			26	19.75	45.75	65.50
0390	501 – 1000 lb.	"	36	.667			34.50	26.50	61	87
0500	Steel roof decking, uncovered, bare	B-2	5000	.008	S.F.		.30		.30	.47

05 05 13 – Shop-Applied Coatings for Metal

05 05 13.50 Paints and Protective Coatings

		Crew	Daily Output	Labor-Hours	Unit	Material	2015 Bare Costs Labor	2015 Bare Costs Equipment	Total	Total Incl O&P
0010	**PAINTS AND PROTECTIVE COATINGS**									
5900	Galvanizing structural steel in shop, under 1 ton				Ton	550			550	605
5950	1 ton to 20 tons					505			505	555
6000	Over 20 tons					460			460	505

05 05 19 – Post-Installed Concrete Anchors

05 05 19.10 Chemical Anchors

		Crew	Daily Output	Labor-Hours	Unit	Material	2015 Bare Costs Labor	2015 Bare Costs Equipment	Total	Total Incl O&P
0010	**CHEMICAL ANCHORS**									
0020	Includes layout & drilling									
1430	Chemical anchor, w/rod & epoxy cartridge, 3/4" diam. x 9-1/2" long	B-89A	27	.593	Ea.	9.80	25.50	4.28	39.58	55
1435	1" diameter x 11-3/4" long		24	.667		17.55	29	4.82	51.37	69
1440	1-1/4" diameter x 14" long		21	.762		36.50	33	5.50	75	96.50
1445	1-3/4" diameter x 15" long		20	.800		65	34.50	5.80	105.30	131
1450	18" long		17	.941		78	40.50	6.80	125.30	156
1455	2" diameter x 18" long		16	1		103	43	7.25	153.25	187
1460	24" long	▼	15	1.067	▼	134	46	7.70	187.70	227

05 05 19.20 Expansion Anchors

			Crew	Daily Output	Labor-Hours	Unit	Material	2015 Bare Costs Labor	2015 Bare Costs Equipment	Total	Total Incl O&P
0010	**EXPANSION ANCHORS**										
0100	Anchors for concrete, brick or stone, no layout and drilling										
0200	Expansion shields, zinc, 1/4" diameter, 1-5/16" long, single	G	1 Carp	90	.089	Ea.	.43	4.17		4.60	6.85
0300	1-3/8" long, double	G		85	.094		.54	4.42		4.96	7.40
0600	1/2" diameter, 2-1/16" long, single	G		80	.100		1.18	4.70		5.88	8.55
1000	3/4" diameter, 2-3/4" long, single	G		70	.114		3.09	5.35		8.44	11.65
1100	3-15/16" long, double	G		65	.123		5	5.80		10.80	14.40
3400	1/4" diameter, 3" long	G		75	.107		.34	5		5.34	8.05
3600	3/8" diameter, 3" long	G	▼	70	.114	▼	.84	5.35		6.19	9.15
5000	Screw anchors for concrete, masonry,										
5100	stone & tile, no layout or drilling included										
6600	Lead, #6 & #8, 3/4" long	G	1 Carp	260	.031	Ea.	.18	1.44		1.62	2.42
6700	#10 - #14, 1-1/2" long	G		200	.040		.37	1.88		2.25	3.30
6800	#16 & #18, 1-1/2" long	G		160	.050		.41	2.35		2.76	4.06
6900	Plastic, #6 & #8, 3/4" long		▼	260	.031	▼	.04	1.44		1.48	2.26
8000	Wedge anchors, not including layout or drilling										
8050	Carbon steel, 1/4" diameter, 1-3/4" long	G	1 Carp	150	.053	Ea.	.41	2.50		2.91	4.30
8100	3-1/4" long	G		140	.057		.54	2.68		3.22	4.72
8150	3/8" diameter, 2-1/4" long	G		145	.055		.50	2.59		3.09	4.54
8200	5" long	G		140	.057		.88	2.68		3.56	5.10
8250	1/2" diameter, 2-3/4" long	G		140	.057		.99	2.68		3.67	5.20
8300	7" long	G		125	.064		1.70	3		4.70	6.50
8350	5/8" diameter, 3-1/2" long	G		130	.062		1.86	2.89		4.75	6.50
8400	8-1/2" long	G		115	.070		3.95	3.27		7.22	9.40
8450	3/4" diameter, 4-1/4" long	G		115	.070		2.90	3.27		6.17	8.25
8500	10" long	G		95	.084		6.60	3.95		10.55	13.35
8550	1" diameter, 6" long	G		100	.080		9.30	3.76		13.06	16.05
8575	9" long	G		85	.094		12.10	4.42		16.52	20
8600	12" long	G		75	.107		13.10	5		18.10	22
8650	1-1/4" diameter, 9" long	G		70	.114		24.50	5.35		29.85	35.50
8700	12" long	G	▼	60	.133	▼	31.50	6.25		37.75	44
8750	For type 303 stainless steel, add						350%				
8800	For type 316 stainless steel, add						450%				
8950	Self-drilling concrete screw, hex washer head, 3/16" diam. x 1-3/4" long	G	1 Carp	300	.027	Ea.	.20	1.25		1.45	2.15
8960	2-1/4" long	G		250	.032		.24	1.50		1.74	2.57
8970	Phillips flat head, 3/16" diam. x 1-3/4" long	G		300	.027		.21	1.25		1.46	2.16
8980	2-1/4" long	G	▼	250	.032	▼	.23	1.50		1.73	2.56

For customer support on your Site Work & Landscape Cost Data, call 877.737.1594.

111

05 05 21.10 Cutting Steel

		Crew	Daily Output	Labor-Hours	Unit	Material	2015 Bare Costs Labor	Equipment	Total	Total Incl O&P
0010	**CUTTING STEEL**									
0020	Hand burning, incl. preparation, torch cutting & grinding, no staging									
0050	Steel to 1/4" thick	E-25	400	.020	L.F.	.19	1.09	.03	1.31	2.13
0100	1/2" thick		320	.025		.35	1.37	.04	1.76	2.80
0150	3/4" thick		260	.031		.58	1.68	.04	2.30	3.61
0200	1" thick		200	.040		.84	2.19	.06	3.09	4.78

05 05 21.15 Drilling Steel

		Crew	Daily Output	Labor-Hours	Unit	Material	2015 Bare Costs Labor	Equipment	Total	Total Incl O&P
0010	**DRILLING STEEL**									
1910	Drilling & layout for steel, up to 1/4" deep, no anchor									
1920	Holes, 1/4" diameter	1 Sswk	112	.071	Ea.	.09	3.76		3.85	6.65
1925	For each additional 1/4" depth, add		336	.024		.09	1.25		1.34	2.28
1930	3/8" diameter		104	.077		.09	4.05		4.14	7.15
1935	For each additional 1/4" depth, add		312	.026		.09	1.35		1.44	2.44
1940	1/2" diameter		96	.083		.10	4.39		4.49	7.70
1945	For each additional 1/4" depth, add		288	.028		.10	1.46		1.56	2.65
1950	5/8" diameter		88	.091		.14	4.79		4.93	8.45
1955	For each additional 1/4" depth, add		264	.030		.14	1.60		1.74	2.93
1960	3/4" diameter		80	.100		.18	5.25		5.43	9.35
1965	For each additional 1/4" depth, add		240	.033		.18	1.75		1.93	3.25
1970	7/8" diameter		72	.111		.23	5.85		6.08	10.40
1975	For each additional 1/4" depth, add		216	.037		.23	1.95		2.18	3.65
1980	1" diameter		64	.125		.24	6.60		6.84	11.70
1985	For each additional 1/4" depth, add		192	.042		.24	2.19		2.43	4.07
1990	For drilling up, add						40%			

05 05 21.90 Welding Steel

		Crew	Daily Output	Labor-Hours	Unit	Material	2015 Bare Costs Labor	Equipment	Total	Total Incl O&P
0010	**WELDING STEEL**, Structural R050521-20									
0020	Field welding, 1/8" E6011, cost per welder, no operating engineer	E-14	8	1	Hr.	4.33	54.50	18.25	77.08	120
0200	With 1/2 operating engineer	E-13	8	1.500		4.33	79	18.25	101.58	157
0300	With 1 operating engineer	E-12	8	2		4.33	103	18.25	125.58	194
0500	With no operating engineer, 2# weld rod per ton	E-14	8	1	Ton	4.33	54.50	18.25	77.08	120
0600	8# E6011 per ton	"	2	4		17.30	219	73	309.30	480
0800	With one operating engineer per welder, 2# E6011 per ton	E-12	8	2		4.33	103	18.25	125.58	194
0900	8# E6011 per ton	"	2	8		17.30	415	73	505.30	775
1200	Continuous fillet, down welding									
1300	Single pass, 1/8" thick, 0.1#/L.F.	E-14	150	.053	L.F.	.22	2.91	.97	4.10	6.35
1400	3/16" thick, 0.2#/L.F.		75	.107		.43	5.85	1.94	8.22	12.75
1500	1/4" thick, 0.3#/L.F.		50	.160		.65	8.75	2.92	12.32	19.10
1800	3 passes, 3/8" thick, 0.5#/L.F.		30	.267		1.08	14.55	4.86	20.49	32
2010	4 passes, 1/2" thick, 0.7#/L.F.		22	.364		1.52	19.85	6.65	28.02	43.50
2600	For vertical joint welding, add						20%			
2700	Overhead joint welding, add						300%			
2900	For semi-automatic welding, obstructed joints, deduct						5%			
3000	Exposed joints, deduct						15%			
4000	Cleaning and welding plates, bars, or rods									
4010	to existing beams, columns, or trusses	E-14	12	.667	L.F.	1.08	36.50	12.15	49.73	78

05 05 23 – Metal Fastenings

05 05 23.10 Bolts and Hex Nuts

			Crew	Daily Output	Labor-Hours	Unit	Material	2015 Bare Costs Labor	Equipment	Total	Total Incl O&P
0010	**BOLTS & HEX NUTS**, Steel, A307										
0100	1/4" diameter, 1/2" long	G	1 Sswk	140	.057	Ea.	.06	3.01		3.07	5.30
0200	1" long	G		140	.057		.07	3.01		3.08	5.35
0400	3" long	G		130	.062		.15	3.24		3.39	5.80

05 05 23 – Metal Fastenings

05 05 23.10 Bolts and Hex Nuts		Crew	Daily Output	Labor-Hours	Unit	Material	2015 Bare Costs Labor	Equipment	Total	Total Incl O&P
0600	3/8" diameter, 1" long	G	1 Sswk	130	.062	Ea.	.14	3.24		3.38	5.80
0800	3" long	G		120	.067		.24	3.51		3.75	6.35
1100	1/2" diameter, 1-1/2" long	G		120	.067		.40	3.51		3.91	6.55
1400	6" long	G		110	.073		1.05	3.83		4.88	7.80
1600	5/8" diameter, 1-1/2" long	G		120	.067		.98	3.51		4.49	7.20
2000	8" long	G		105	.076		3.06	4.01		7.07	10.30
2200	3/4" diameter, 2" long	G		120	.067		1.15	3.51		4.66	7.35
2600	10" long	G		85	.094		4.20	4.96		9.16	13.20
2800	1" diameter, 3" long	G		105	.076		2.69	4.01		6.70	9.90
3000	12" long	G		75	.107		7.10	5.60		12.70	17.55
3100	For galvanized, add						75%				
3200	For stainless, add						350%				

05 05 23.30 Lag Screws

0010	**LAG SCREWS**										
0020	Steel, 1/4" diameter, 2" long	G	1 Carp	200	.040	Ea.	.09	1.88		1.97	2.99
0100	3/8" diameter, 3" long	G		150	.053		.30	2.50		2.80	4.18
0200	1/2" diameter, 3" long	G		130	.062		.64	2.89		3.53	5.15
0300	5/8" diameter, 3" long	G		120	.067		1.15	3.13		4.28	6.10

05 05 23.35 Machine Screws

0010	**MACHINE SCREWS**										
0020	Steel, round head, #8 x 1" long	G	1 Carp	4.80	1.667	C	3.93	78.50		82.43	124
0110	#8 x 2" long	G		2.40	3.333		6.20	157		163.20	248
0200	#10 x 1" long	G		4	2		5.20	94		99.20	151
0300	#10 x 2" long	G		2	4		8.65	188		196.65	299

05 05 23.50 Powder Actuated Tools and Fasteners

0010	**POWDER ACTUATED TOOLS & FASTENERS**										
0020	Stud driver, .22 caliber, single shot					Ea.	148			148	163
0100	.27 caliber, semi automatic, strip					"	440			440	485
0300	Powder load, single shot, .22 cal, power level 2, brown					C	5.35			5.35	5.90
0400	Strip, .27 cal, power level 4, red						7.70			7.70	8.50
0600	Drive pin, .300 x 3/4" long	G	1 Carp	4.80	1.667		4.11	78.50		82.61	125
0700	.300 x 3" long with washer	G	"	4	2		12.65	94		106.65	159

05 05 23.80 Vibration and Bearing Pads

0010	**VIBRATION & BEARING PADS**										
0300	Laminated synthetic rubber impregnated cotton duck, 1/2" thick		2 Sswk	24	.667	S.F.	69	35		104	137
0400	1" thick			20	.800		135	42		177	222
0600	Neoprene bearing pads, 1/2" thick			24	.667		26.50	35		61.50	90
0700	1" thick			20	.800		52.50	42		94.50	131
0900	Fabric reinforced neoprene, 5000 psi, 1/2" thick			24	.667		11.50	35		46.50	73.50
1000	1" thick			20	.800		23	42		65	98.50
1200	Felt surfaced vinyl pads, cork and sisal, 5/8" thick			24	.667		29	35		64	93
1300	1" thick			20	.800		52.50	42		94.50	131
1500	Teflon bonded to 10 ga. carbon steel, 1/32" layer			24	.667		51.50	35		86.50	118
1600	3/32" layer			24	.667		77	35		112	146
1800	Bonded to 10 ga. stainless steel, 1/32" layer			24	.667		91	35		126	161
1900	3/32" layer			24	.667		120	35		155	193
2100	Circular machine leveling pad & stud					Kip	6.45			6.45	7.10

05 05 23.90 Welding Rod

0010	**WELDING ROD**										
0020	Steel, type 6011, 1/8" diam., less than 500#					Lb.	2.16			2.16	2.38
0100	500# to 2,000#						1.95			1.95	2.15

For customer support on your Site Work & Landscape Cost Data, call 877.737.1594.

113

05 05 Common Work Results for Metals

05 05 23 – Metal Fastenings

05 05 23.90 Welding Rod		Crew	Daily Output	Labor-Hours	Unit	Material	2015 Bare Costs Labor	Equipment	Total	Total Incl O&P
0200	2,000# to 5,000#				Lb.	1.83			1.83	2.02
0300	5/32" diameter, less than 500#					2.20			2.20	2.42
0310	500# to 2,000#					1.98			1.98	2.18
0320	2,000# to 5,000#					1.86			1.86	2.05
0400	3/16" diam., less than 500#					2.46			2.46	2.71
0500	500# to 2,000#					2.22			2.22	2.44
0600	2,000# to 5,000#					2.09			2.09	2.30
0620	Steel, type 6010, 1/8" diam., less than 500#					2.23			2.23	2.45
0630	500# to 2,000#					2.01			2.01	2.21
0640	2,000# to 5,000#					1.89			1.89	2.08
0650	Steel, type 7018 Low Hydrogen, 1/8" diam., less than 500#					2.16			2.16	2.38
0660	500# to 2,000#					1.95			1.95	2.15
0670	2,000# to 5,000#					1.83			1.83	2.02
0700	Steel, type 7024 Jet Weld, 1/8" diam., less than 500#					2.50			2.50	2.75
0710	500# to 2,000#					2.25			2.25	2.48
0720	2,000# to 5,000#					2.12			2.12	2.33
1550	Aluminum, type 4043 TIG, 1/8" diam., less than 10#					5.10			5.10	5.65
1560	10# to 60#					4.61			4.61	5.05
1570	Over 60#					4.33			4.33	4.77
1600	Aluminum, type 5356 TIG, 1/8" diam., less than 10#					5.45			5.45	6
1610	10# to 60#					4.90			4.90	5.40
1620	Over 60#					4.61			4.61	5.05
1900	Cast iron, type 8 Nickel, 1/8" diam., less than 500#					22			22	24
1910	500# to 1,000#					19.75			19.75	21.50
1920	Over 1,000#					18.55			18.55	20.50
2000	Stainless steel, type 316/316L, 1/8" diam., less than 500#					7.10			7.10	7.85
2100	500# to 1000#					6.40			6.40	7.05
2220	Over 1000#					6.05			6.05	6.65

05 12 Structural Steel Framing

05 12 23 – Structural Steel for Buildings

05 12 23.15 Columns, Lightweight

			Crew	Daily Output	Labor-Hours	Unit	Material	Labor	Equipment	Total	Total Incl O&P
0010	**COLUMNS, LIGHTWEIGHT**										
1000	Lightweight units (lally), 3-1/2" diameter		E-2	780	.072	L.F.	8.25	3.71	1.94	13.90	17.50
5800	Adjustable jack post, 8' maximum height, 2-3/4" diameter	G				Ea.	52.50			52.50	58
5850	4" diameter	G				"	84			84	92.50

05 12 23.17 Columns, Structural

			Crew	Daily Output	Labor-Hours	Unit	Material	Labor	Equipment	Total	Total Incl O&P
0010	**COLUMNS, STRUCTURAL**	R051223-10									
0015	Made from recycled materials										
0020	Shop fab'd for 100-ton, 1-2 story project, bolted connections										
0800	Steel, concrete filled, extra strong pipe, 3-1/2" diameter		E-2	660	.085	L.F.	43.50	4.39	2.29	50.18	58
0830	4" diameter			780	.072		48.50	3.71	1.94	54.15	62
0890	5" diameter			1020	.055		58	2.84	1.48	62.32	70.50
0930	6" diameter			1200	.047		77	2.41	1.26	80.67	90
0940	8" diameter			1100	.051		77	2.63	1.37	81	90.50
1100	For galvanizing, add					Lb.	.25			.25	.28
1500	Steel pipe, extra strong, no concrete, 3" to 5" diameter	G	E-2	16000	.004		1.33	.18	.09	1.60	1.86
1600	6" to 12" diameter	G		14000	.004		1.33	.21	.11	1.65	1.93
3300	Structural tubing, square, A500GrB, 4" to 6" square, light section	G		11270	.005		1.33	.26	.13	1.72	2.04
3600	Heavy section	G		32000	.002		1.33	.09	.05	1.47	1.66
5100	Structural tubing, rect., 5" to 6" wide, light section	G		8000	.007		1.33	.36	.19	1.88	2.28

05 12 Structural Steel Framing

05 12 23 – Structural Steel for Buildings

05 12 23.17 Columns, Structural

			Crew	Daily Output	Labor-Hours	Unit	Material	2015 Bare Costs Labor	2015 Bare Costs Equipment	Total	Total Incl O&P
5200	Heavy section	G	E-2	12000	.005	Lb.	1.33	.24	.13	1.70	2.01
5300	7" to 10" wide, light section	G		15000	.004		1.33	.19	.10	1.62	1.89
5400	Heavy section	G		18000	.003	↓	1.33	.16	.08	1.57	1.82
6800	W Shape, A992 steel, 2 tier, W8 x 24	G		1080	.052	L.F.	35	2.68	1.40	39.08	44.50
6900	W8 x 48	G		1032	.054		70	2.81	1.46	74.27	83.50
7050	W10 x 68	G		984	.057		99	2.94	1.54	103.48	116
7100	W10 x 112	G		960	.058		163	3.02	1.57	167.59	187
7200	W12 x 87	G		984	.057		127	2.94	1.54	131.48	146
7250	W12 x 120	G		960	.058		175	3.02	1.57	179.59	199
7350	W14 x 74	G		984	.057		108	2.94	1.54	112.48	126
7450	W14 x 176	G	↓	912	.061	↓	257	3.18	1.66	261.84	289
8090	For projects 75 to 99 tons, add					All	10%				
8092	50 to 74 tons, add						20%				
8094	25 to 49 tons, add						30%	10%			
8096	10 to 24 tons, add						50%	25%			
8098	2 to 9 tons, add						75%	50%			
8099	Less than 2 tons, add					↓	100%	100%			

05 12 23.20 Curb Edging

			Crew	Daily Output	Labor-Hours	Unit	Material	2015 Bare Costs Labor	2015 Bare Costs Equipment	Total	Total Incl O&P
0010	**CURB EDGING**										
0020	Steel angle w/anchors, shop fabricated, on forms, 1" x 1", 0.8#/L.F.	G	E-4	350	.091	L.F.	1.67	4.86	.42	6.95	10.75
0100	2" x 2" angles, 3.92#/L.F.	G		330	.097		6.65	5.15	.44	12.24	16.75
0200	3" x 3" angles, 6.1#/L.F.	G		300	.107		10.50	5.65	.49	16.64	22
0300	4" x 4" angles, 8.2#/L.F.	G		275	.116		13.85	6.20	.53	20.58	26.50
1000	6" x 4" angles, 12.3#/L.F.	G		250	.128		20.50	6.80	.58	27.88	35
1050	Steel channels with anchors, on forms, 3" channel, 5#/L.F.	G		290	.110		8.35	5.85	.50	14.70	19.95
1100	4" channel, 5.4#/L.F.	G		270	.119		9	6.30	.54	15.84	21.50
1200	6" channel, 8.2#/L.F.	G		255	.125		13.85	6.65	.57	21.07	27.50
1300	8" channel, 11.5#/L.F.	G		225	.142		19.10	7.55	.65	27.30	35
1400	10" channel, 15.3#/L.F.	G		180	.178		25	9.45	.81	35.26	45
1500	12" channel, 20.7#/L.F.	G	↓	140	.229		33.50	12.15	1.04	46.69	59
2000	For curved edging, add					↓	35%	10%			

05 12 23.40 Lightweight Framing

			Crew	Daily Output	Labor-Hours	Unit	Material	2015 Bare Costs Labor	2015 Bare Costs Equipment	Total	Total Incl O&P
0010	**LIGHTWEIGHT FRAMING**	R051223-35									
0015	Made from recycled materials										
0400	Angle framing, field fabricated, 4" and larger	G	E-3	440	.055	Lb.	.77	2.91	.33	4.01	6.25
0450	Less than 4" angles	R051223-45 G		265	.091		.80	4.83	.55	6.18	9.90
0600	Channel framing, field fabricated, 8" and larger	G		500	.048		.80	2.56	.29	3.65	5.65
0650	Less than 8" channels	G		335	.072		.80	3.82	.44	5.06	8
1000	Continuous slotted channel framing system, shop fab, simple framing	G	2 Sswk	2400	.007		4.11	.35		4.46	5.15
1200	Complex framing	G	"	1600	.010		4.64	.53		5.17	6
1300	Cross bracing, rods, shop fabricated, 3/4" diameter	G	E-3	700	.034		1.59	1.83	.21	3.63	5.15
1310	7/8" diameter	G		850	.028		1.59	1.51	.17	3.27	4.56
1320	1" diameter	G		1000	.024		1.59	1.28	.15	3.02	4.13
1330	Angle, 5" x 5" x 3/8"	G		2800	.009		1.59	.46	.05	2.10	2.60
1350	Hanging lintels, shop fabricated	G	↓	850	.028		1.59	1.51	.17	3.27	4.56
1380	Roof frames, shop fabricated, 3'-0" square, 5' span	G	E-2	4200	.013		1.59	.69	.36	2.64	3.31
1400	Tie rod, not upset, 1-1/2" to 4" diameter, with turnbuckle	G	2 Sswk	800	.020		1.72	1.05		2.77	3.72
1420	No turnbuckle	G		700	.023		1.66	1.20		2.86	3.91
1500	Upset, 1-3/4" to 4" diameter, with turnbuckle	G		800	.020		1.72	1.05		2.77	3.72
1520	No turnbuckle	G	↓	700	.023	↓	1.66	1.20		2.86	3.91

For customer support on your Site Work & Landscape Cost Data, call 877.737.1594.

115

05 12 Structural Steel Framing

05 12 23 – Structural Steel for Buildings

05 12 23.45 Lintels

		Crew	Daily Output	Labor-Hours	Unit	Material	2015 Bare Costs Labor	Equipment	Total	Total Incl O&P
0010	**LINTELS**									
0015	Made from recycled materials									
0020	Plain steel angles, shop fabricated, under 500 lb.	G 1 Bric	550	.015	Lb.	1.02	.67		1.69	2.15
0100	500 to 1000 lb.	G	640	.013		.99	.58		1.57	1.97
0200	1,000 to 2,000 lb.	G	640	.013		.97	.58		1.55	1.94
0300	2,000 to 4,000 lb.	G	640	.013		.94	.58		1.52	1.91
0500	For built-up angles and plates, add to above	G				1.33			1.33	1.46
0700	For engineering, add to above					.13			.13	.15
0900	For galvanizing, add to above, under 500 lb.					.30			.30	.33
0950	500 to 2,000 lb.					.28			.28	.30
1000	Over 2,000 lb.					.25			.25	.28
2000	Steel angles, 3-1/2" x 3", 1/4" thick, 2'-6" long	G 1 Bric	47	.170	Ea.	14.30	7.85		22.15	28
2100	4'-6" long	G	26	.308		26	14.20		40.20	50
2600	4" x 3-1/2", 1/4" thick, 5'-0" long	G	21	.381		33	17.60		50.60	63
2700	9'-0" long	G	12	.667		59	31		90	112

05 12 23.60 Pipe Support Framing

		Crew	Daily Output	Labor-Hours	Unit	Material	2015 Bare Costs Labor	Equipment	Total	Total Incl O&P
0010	**PIPE SUPPORT FRAMING**									
0020	Under 10#/L.F., shop fabricated	G E-4	3900	.008	Lb.	1.78	.44	.04	2.26	2.75
0200	10.1 to 15#/L.F.	G	4300	.007		1.75	.40	.03	2.18	2.65
0400	15.1 to 20#/L.F.	G	4800	.007		1.72	.35	.03	2.10	2.54
0600	Over 20#/L.F.	G	5400	.006		1.70	.32	.03	2.05	2.45

05 12 23.65 Plates

			Crew	Daily Output	Labor-Hours	Unit	Material	2015 Bare Costs Labor	Equipment	Total	Total Incl O&P
0010	**PLATES**	R051223-80									
0015	Made from recycled materials										
0020	For connections & stiffener plates, shop fabricated										
0050	1/8" thick (5.1 lb./S.F.)	G				S.F.	6.75			6.75	7.45
0100	1/4" thick (10.2 lb./S.F.)	G					13.50			13.50	14.85
0300	3/8" thick (15.3 lb./S.F.)	G					20.50			20.50	22.50
0400	1/2" thick (20.4 lb./S.F.)	G					27			27	29.50
0450	3/4" thick (30.6 lb./S.F.)	G					40.50			40.50	44.50
0500	1" thick (40.8 lb./S.F.)	G					54			54	59.50
2000	Steel plate, warehouse prices, no shop fabrication										
2100	1/4" thick (10.2 lb./S.F.)	G				S.F.	7.30			7.30	8

05 12 23.75 Structural Steel Members

			Crew	Daily Output	Labor-Hours	Unit	Material	2015 Bare Costs Labor	Equipment	Total	Total Incl O&P
0010	**STRUCTURAL STEEL MEMBERS**	R051223-10									
0015	Made from recycled materials										
0020	Shop fab'd for 100-ton, 1-2 story project, bolted connections										
0300	W 8 x 10	G	E-2	600	.093	L.F.	14.60	4.83	2.52	21.95	27
0500	x 31	G		550	.102		45	5.25	2.75	53	61.50
0600	W 10 x 12	G		600	.093		17.50	4.83	2.52	24.85	30
0700	x 22	G		600	.093		32	4.83	2.52	39.35	46.50
0900	x 49	G		550	.102		71.50	5.25	2.75	79.50	90.50
1100	W 12 x 16	G		880	.064		23.50	3.29	1.72	28.51	33
1700	x 72	G		640	.088		105	4.53	2.36	111.89	125
1900	W 14 x 26	G		990	.057		38	2.93	1.53	42.46	48
2500	x 120	G		720	.078		175	4.02	2.10	181.12	201
3300	W 18 x 35	G	E-5	960	.083		51	4.35	1.73	57.08	65.50
4100	W 21 x 44	G		1064	.075		64	3.93	1.56	69.49	79
4900	W 24 x 55	G		1110	.072		80	3.76	1.49	85.25	96
5900	x 94	G		1190	.067		137	3.51	1.39	141.90	158
6100	W 30 x 99	G		1200	.067		144	3.48	1.38	148.86	166

05 12 23.75 Structural Steel Members

		Crew	Daily Output	Labor-Hours	Unit	Material	2015 Bare Costs Labor	Equipment	Total	Total Incl O&P
6700	W 33 x 118 [G]	E-5	1176	.068	L.F.	172	3.55	1.41	176.96	197
7300	W 36 x 135 [G]	↓	1170	.068		197	3.57	1.42	201.99	224
8490	For projects 75 to 99 tons, add					10%				
8492	50 to 74 tons, add					20%				
8494	25 to 49 tons, add					30%	10%			
8496	10 to 24 tons, add					50%	25%			
8498	2 to 9 tons, add					75%	50%			
8499	Less than 2 tons, add				↓	100%	100%			

05 12 23.77 Structural Steel Projects

			Crew	Daily Output	Labor-Hours	Unit	Material	2015 Bare Costs Labor	Equipment	Total	Total Incl O&P
0010	**STRUCTURAL STEEL PROJECTS**	R050516-30									
0015	Made from recycled materials										
0020	Shop fab'd for 100-ton, 1-2 story project, bolted connections										
0200	Apartments, nursing homes, etc., 1 to 2 stories	R050523-10 [G]	E-5	10.30	7.767	Ton	2,650	405	161	3,216	3,800
1300	Industrial bldgs., 1 story, beams & girders, steel bearing	[G]	↓	12.90	6.202		2,650	325	128	3,103	3,625
1400	Masonry bearing	R051223-10 [G]	↓	10	8		2,650	420	166	3,236	3,825
2800	Power stations, fossil fuels, simple connections	[G]	E-6	11	11.636		2,650	610	168	3,428	4,125
2900	Moment/composite connections	R051223-20 [G]	"	5.70	22.456		3,975	1,175	325	5,475	6,725
5390	For projects 75 to 99 tons, add						10%				
5392	50 to 74 tons, add	R051223-25					20%				
5394	25 to 49 tons, add						30%	10%			
5396	10 to 24 tons, add	R051223-30					50%	25%			
5398	2 to 9 tons, add						75%	50%			
5399	Less than 2 tons, add					↓	100%	100%			

05 12 23.78 Structural Steel Secondary Members

		Crew	Daily Output	Labor-Hours	Unit	Material	2015 Bare Costs Labor	Equipment	Total	Total Incl O&P
0010	**STRUCTURAL STEEL SECONDARY MEMBERS**									
0015	Made from recycled materials									
0020	Shop fabricated for 20-ton girt/purlin framing package, materials only									
0100	Girts/purlins, C/Z-shapes, includes clips and bolts									
0110	6" x 2-1/2" x 2-1/2", 16 ga., 3.0 lb./L.F.				L.F.	3.58			3.58	3.94
0115	14 ga., 3.5 lb./L.F.					4.17			4.17	4.59
0120	8" x 2-3/4" x 2-3/4", 16 ga., 3.4 lb./L.F.					4.05			4.05	4.46
0125	14 ga., 4.1 lb./L.F.					4.89			4.89	5.40
0130	12 ga., 5.6 lb./L.F.					6.70			6.70	7.35
0135	10" x 3-1/2" x 3-1/2", 14 ga., 4.7 lb./L.F.					5.60			5.60	6.15
0140	12 ga., 6.7 lb./L.F.					8			8	8.80
0145	12" x 3-1/2" x 3-1/2", 14 ga., 5.3 lb./L.F.					6.30			6.30	6.95
0150	12 ga., 7.4 lb./L.F.				↓	8.80			8.80	9.70
0200	Eave struts, C-shape, includes clips and bolts									
0210	6" x 4" x 3", 16 ga., 3.1 lb./L.F.				L.F.	3.70			3.70	4.07
0215	14 ga., 3.9 lb./L.F.					4.65			4.65	5.10
0220	8" x 4" x 3", 16 ga., 3.5 lb./L.F.					4.17			4.17	4.59
0225	14 ga., 4.4 lb./L.F.					5.25			5.25	5.75
0230	12 ga., 6.2 lb./L.F.					7.40			7.40	8.15
0235	10" x 5" x 3", 14 ga., 5.2 lb./L.F.					6.20			6.20	6.80
0240	12 ga., 7.3 lb./L.F.					8.70			8.70	9.60
0245	12" x 5" x 4", 14 ga., 6.0 lb./L.F.					7.15			7.15	7.85
0250	12 ga., 8.4 lb./L.F.				↓	10			10	11
0300	Rake/base angle, excludes concrete drilling and expansion anchors									
0310	2" x 2", 14 ga., 1.0 lb./L.F.	2 Sswk	640	.025	L.F.	1.19	1.32		2.51	3.60
0315	3" x 2", 14 ga., 1.3 lb./L.F.		535	.030		1.55	1.57		3.12	4.45
0320	3" x 3", 14 ga., 1.6 lb./L.F.		500	.032		1.91	1.68		3.59	5.05
0325	4" x 3", 14 ga., 1.8 lb./L.F.	↓	480	.033	↓	2.15	1.75		3.90	5.40

For customer support on your Site Work & Landscape Cost Data, call 877.737.1594.

117

05 12 Structural Steel Framing

05 12 23 – Structural Steel for Buildings

05 12 23.78 Structural Steel Secondary Members

	05 12 23.78 Structural Steel Secondary Members	Crew	Daily Output	Labor-Hours	Unit	Material	2015 Bare Costs Labor	Equipment	Total	Total Incl O&P
0600	Installation of secondary members, erection only									
0610	Girts, purlins, eave struts, 16 ga., 6" deep	E-18	100	.400	Ea.		21	9.50	30.50	46
0615	8" deep		80	.500			26.50	11.85	38.35	57.50
0620	14 ga., 6" deep		80	.500			26.50	11.85	38.35	57.50
0625	8" deep		65	.615			32.50	14.60	47.10	71
0630	10" deep		55	.727			38.50	17.25	55.75	84
0635	12" deep		50	.800			42	19	61	92.50
0640	12 ga., 8" deep		50	.800			42	19	61	92.50
0645	10" deep		45	.889			47	21	68	103
0650	12" deep		40	1			52.50	23.50	76	115
0900	For less than 20-ton job lots									
0905	For 15 to 19 tons, add					10%				
0910	For 10 to 14 tons, add					25%				
0915	For 5 to 9 tons, add					50%	50%	50%		
0920	For 1 to 4 tons, add					75%	75%	75%		
0925	For less than 1 ton, add					100%	100%	100%		

05 15 Wire Rope Assemblies

05 15 16 – Steel Wire Rope Assemblies

05 15 16.05 Accessories for Steel Wire Rope

	05 15 16.05 Accessories for Steel Wire Rope		Crew	Daily Output	Labor-Hours	Unit	Material	2015 Bare Costs Labor	Equipment	Total	Total Incl O&P
0010	**ACCESSORIES FOR STEEL WIRE ROPE**										
0015	Made from recycled materials										
1500	Thimbles, heavy duty, 1/4"	G	E-17	160	.100	Ea.	.52	5.35		5.87	9.85
1510	1/2"	G		160	.100		2.29	5.35		7.64	11.80
1520	3/4"	G		105	.152		5.20	8.20		13.40	19.90
1530	1"	G		52	.308		10.40	16.50		26.90	40
1540	1-1/4"	G		38	.421		16	22.50		38.50	56.50
1550	1-1/2"	G		13	1.231		45	66		111	165
1560	1-3/4"	G		8	2		93	107		200	288
1570	2"	G		6	2.667		135	143		278	400
1580	2-1/4"	G		4	4		183	215		398	575
1600	Clips, 1/4" diameter	G		160	.100		2.74	5.35		8.09	12.30
1610	3/8" diameter	G		160	.100		3.01	5.35		8.36	12.60
1620	1/2" diameter	G		160	.100		4.84	5.35		10.19	14.60
1630	3/4" diameter	G		102	.157		7.85	8.40		16.25	23.50
1640	1" diameter	G		64	.250		13.05	13.40		26.45	38
1650	1-1/4" diameter	G		35	.457		21.50	24.50		46	66
1670	1-1/2" diameter	G		26	.615		29	33		62	89.50
1680	1-3/4" diameter	G		16	1		67.50	53.50		121	167
1690	2" diameter	G		12	1.333		75	71.50		146.50	207
1700	2-1/4" diameter	G		10	1.600		110	86		196	270
1800	Sockets, open swage, 1/4" diameter	G		160	.100		47	5.35		52.35	61.50
1810	1/2" diameter	G		77	.208		68	11.15		79.15	94
1820	3/4" diameter	G		19	.842		105	45		150	195
1830	1" diameter	G		9	1.778		188	95.50		283.50	375
1840	1-1/4" diameter	G		5	3.200		262	172		434	585
1850	1-1/2" diameter	G		3	5.333		575	286		861	1,125
1860	1-3/4" diameter	G		3	5.333		1,025	286		1,311	1,625
1870	2" diameter	G		1.50	10.667		1,550	570		2,120	2,700
1900	Closed swage, 1/4" diameter	G		160	.100		28	5.35		33.35	40
1910	1/2" diameter	G		104	.154		48	8.25		56.25	67.50

05 15 Wire Rope Assemblies

05 15 16 – Steel Wire Rope Assemblies

05 15 16.05 Accessories for Steel Wire Rope		Crew	Daily Output	Labor-Hours	Unit	Material	2015 Bare Costs Labor	Equipment	Total	Total Incl O&P
1920	3/4" diameter	G	E-17	32	.500	Ea.	72	27		99	126
1930	1" diameter	G		15	1.067		126	57		183	239
1940	1-1/4" diameter	G		7	2.286		189	123		312	420
1950	1-1/2" diameter	G		4	4		345	215		560	755
1960	1-3/4" diameter	G		3	5.333		505	286		791	1,050
1970	2" diameter	G		2	8		985	430		1,415	1,825
2000	Open spelter, galv., 1/4" diameter	G		160	.100		59.50	5.35		64.85	75
2010	1/2" diameter	G		70	.229		62	12.25		74.25	89.50
2020	3/4" diameter	G		26	.615		93	33		126	160
2030	1" diameter	G		10	1.600		258	86		344	435
2040	1-1/4" diameter	G		5	3.200		370	172		542	705
2050	1-1/2" diameter	G		4	4		785	215		1,000	1,225
2060	1-3/4" diameter	G		2	8		1,375	430		1,805	2,250
2070	2" diameter	G		1.20	13.333		1,575	715		2,290	2,975
2080	2-1/2" diameter	G		1	16		2,900	860		3,760	4,675
2100	Closed spelter, galv., 1/4" diameter	G		160	.100		49.50	5.35		54.85	64
2110	1/2" diameter	G		88	.182		53	9.75		62.75	75.50
2120	3/4" diameter	G		30	.533		80.50	28.50		109	138
2130	1" diameter	G		13	1.231		171	66		237	305
2140	1-1/4" diameter	G		7	2.286		274	123		397	515
2150	1-1/2" diameter	G		6	2.667		590	143		733	900
2160	1-3/4" diameter	G		2.80	5.714		785	305		1,090	1,400
2170	2" diameter	G		2	8		970	430		1,400	1,825
2200	Jaw & jaw turnbuckles, 1/4" x 4"	G		160	.100		16.25	5.35		21.60	27
2250	1/2" x 6"	G		96	.167		20.50	8.95		29.45	38
2260	1/2" x 9"	G		77	.208		27.50	11.15		38.65	49.50
2270	1/2" x 12"	G		66	.242		31	13		44	56.50
2300	3/4" x 6"	G		38	.421		40	22.50		62.50	83.50
2310	3/4" x 9"	G		30	.533		44.50	28.50		73	98.50
2320	3/4" x 12"	G		28	.571		57.50	30.50		88	117
2330	3/4" x 18"	G		23	.696		68.50	37.50		106	141
2350	1" x 6"	G		17	.941		78	50.50		128.50	173
2360	1" x 12"	G		13	1.231		85.50	66		151.50	209
2370	1" x 18"	G		10	1.600		128	86		214	290
2380	1" x 24"	G		9	1.778		141	95.50		236.50	320
2400	1-1/4" x 12"	G		7	2.286		144	123		267	370
2410	1-1/4" x 18"	G		6.50	2.462		178	132		310	425
2420	1-1/4" x 24"	G		5.60	2.857		240	153		393	530
2450	1-1/2" x 12"	G		5.20	3.077		465	165		630	795
2460	1-1/2" x 18"	G		4	4		495	215		710	920
2470	1-1/2" x 24"	G		3.20	5		665	268		933	1,200
2500	1-3/4" x 18"	G		3.20	5		1,000	268		1,268	1,575
2510	1-3/4" x 24"	G		2.80	5.714		1,150	305		1,455	1,775
2550	2" x 24"	G		1.60	10		1,550	535		2,085	2,625

05 15 16.50 Steel Wire Rope

0010	**STEEL WIRE ROPE**										
0015	Made from recycled materials										
0020	6 x 19, bright, fiber core, 5000' rolls, 1/2" diameter	G				L.F.	.85			.85	.93
0050	Steel core	G					1.12			1.12	1.23
0100	Fiber core, 1" diameter	G					2.86			2.86	3.15
0150	Steel core	G					3.26			3.26	3.59
0300	6 x 19, galvanized, fiber core, 1/2" diameter	G					1.25			1.25	1.38

05 15 Wire Rope Assemblies

05 15 16 - Steel Wire Rope Assemblies

05 15 16.50 Steel Wire Rope		Crew	Daily Output	Labor-Hours	Unit	Material	2015 Bare Costs Labor	Equipment	Total	Total Incl O&P
0350	Steel core	G			L.F.	1.43			1.43	1.57
0400	Fiber core, 1" diameter	G				3.67			3.67	4.03
0450	Steel core	G				3.84			3.84	4.23
0500	6 x 7, bright, IPS, fiber core, <500 L.F. w/acc., 1/4" diameter	G	E-17	6400	.003		1.51	.13		1.64	1.89
0510	1/2" diameter	G		2100	.008		3.68	.41		4.09	4.76
0520	3/4" diameter	G		960	.017		6.65	.89		7.54	8.90
0550	6 x 19, bright, IPS, IWRC, <500 L.F. w/acc., 1/4" diameter	G		5760	.003		.94	.15		1.09	1.29
0560	1/2" diameter	G		1730	.009		1.52	.50		2.02	2.53
0570	3/4" diameter	G		770	.021		2.64	1.11		3.75	4.84
0580	1" diameter	G		420	.038		4.47	2.04		6.51	8.45
0590	1-1/4" diameter	G		290	.055		7.40	2.96		10.36	13.30
0600	1-1/2" diameter	G		192	.083		9.10	4.47		13.57	17.80
0610	1-3/4" diameter	G	E-18	240	.167		14.55	8.75	3.95	27.25	35
0620	2" diameter	G		160	.250		18.65	13.15	5.95	37.75	49.50
0630	2-1/4" diameter	G		160	.250		25	13.15	5.95	44.10	56.50
0650	6 x 37, bright, IPS, IWRC, <500 L.F. w/acc., 1/4" diameter	G	E-17	6400	.003		1.11	.13		1.24	1.45
0660	1/2" diameter	G		1730	.009		1.88	.50		2.38	2.93
0670	3/4" diameter	G		770	.021		3.04	1.11		4.15	5.30
0680	1" diameter	G		430	.037		4.83	2		6.83	8.75
0690	1-1/4" diameter	G		290	.055		7.30	2.96		10.26	13.15
0700	1-1/2" diameter	G		190	.084		10.45	4.52		14.97	19.35
0710	1-3/4" diameter	G	E-18	260	.154		16.55	8.10	3.65	28.30	36
0720	2" diameter	G		200	.200		21.50	10.55	4.74	36.79	46.50
0730	2-1/4" diameter	G		160	.250		28.50	13.15	5.95	47.60	60
0800	6 x 19 & 6 x 37, swaged, 1/2" diameter	G	E-17	1220	.013		2.47	.70		3.17	3.94
0810	9/16" diameter	G		1120	.014		2.87	.77		3.64	4.49
0820	5/8" diameter	G		930	.017		3.41	.92		4.33	5.35
0830	3/4" diameter	G		640	.025		4.34	1.34		5.68	7.10
0840	7/8" diameter	G		480	.033		5.50	1.79		7.29	9.15
0850	1" diameter	G		350	.046		6.70	2.45		9.15	11.60
0860	1-1/8" diameter	G		288	.056		8.20	2.98		11.18	14.25
0870	1-1/4" diameter	G		230	.070		9.95	3.73		13.68	17.45
0880	1-3/8" diameter	G		192	.083		11.50	4.47		15.97	20.50
0890	1-1/2" diameter	G	E-18	300	.133		13.95	7	3.16	24.11	30.50

05 15 16.60 Galvanized Steel Wire Rope and Accessories

		Crew	Daily Output	Labor-Hours	Unit	Material	Labor	Equipment	Total	Total Incl O&P
0010	**GALVANIZED STEEL WIRE ROPE & ACCESSORIES**									
0015	Made from recycled materials									
3000	Aircraft cable, galvanized, 7 x 7 x 1/8"	G	E-17	5000	.003	L.F.	.20	.17		.37	.52
3100	Clamps, 1/8"	G	"	125	.128	Ea.	1.96	6.85		8.81	14.10

05 15 16.70 Temporary Cable Safety Railing

		Crew	Daily Output	Labor-Hours	Unit	Material	Labor	Equipment	Total	Total Incl O&P
0010	**TEMPORARY CABLE SAFETY RAILING**, Each 100' strand incl.									
0020	2 eyebolts, 1 turnbuckle, 100' cable, 2 thimbles, 6 clips									
0025	Made from recycled materials									
0100	One strand using 1/4" cable & accessories	G	2 Sswk	4	4	C.L.F.	209	211		420	595
0200	1/2" cable & accessories	G	"	2	8	"	440	420		860	1,225

05 21 Steel Joist Framing

05 21 13 – Deep Longspan Steel Joist Framing

05 21 13.50 Deep Longspan Joists		Crew	Daily Output	Labor-Hours	Unit	Material	2015 Bare Costs Labor	Equipment	Total	Total Incl O&P
0010	**DEEP LONGSPAN JOISTS**									
3015	Made from recycled materials									
3500	For less than 40-ton job lots									
3502	For 30 to 39 tons, add					10%				
3504	20 to 29 tons, add					20%				
3506	10 to 19 tons, add					30%				
3507	5 to 9 tons, add					50%	25%			
3508	1 to 4 tons, add					75%	50%			
3509	Less than 1 ton, add					100%	100%			
4010	SLH series, 40-ton job lots, bolted cross bridging, shop primer									
4040	Spans to 200' (shipped in 3 pieces) **G**	E-7	13	6.154	Ton	1,975	320	139	2,434	2,875
6100	For less than 40-ton job lots									
6102	For 30 to 39 tons, add					10%				
6104	20 to 29 tons, add					20%				
6106	10 to 19 tons, add					30%				
6107	5 to 9 tons, add					50%	25%			
6108	1 to 4 tons, add					75%	50%			
6109	Less than 1 ton, add					100%	100%			

05 21 16 – Longspan Steel Joist Framing

05 21 16.50 Longspan Joists		Crew	Daily Output	Labor-Hours	Unit	Material	2015 Bare Costs Labor	Equipment	Total	Total Incl O&P
0010	**LONGSPAN JOISTS**									
2000	LH series, 40-ton job lots, bolted cross bridging, shop primer									
2015	Made from recycled materials									
2600	For less than 40-ton job lots									
2602	For 30 to 39 tons, add					10%				
2604	20 to 29 tons, add					20%				
2606	10 to 19 tons, add					30%				
2607	5 to 9 tons, add					50%	25%			
2608	1 to 4 tons, add					75%	50%			
2609	Less than 1 ton, add					100%	100%			

05 21 19 – Open Web Steel Joist Framing

05 21 19.10 Open Web Joists		Crew	Daily Output	Labor-Hours	Unit	Material	2015 Bare Costs Labor	Equipment	Total	Total Incl O&P
0010	**OPEN WEB JOISTS**									
0015	Made from recycled materials									
0440	K series, 30' to 50' spans **G**	E-7	17	4.706	Ton	1,625	246	106	1,977	2,325
0800	For less than 40-ton job lots									
0802	For 30 to 39 tons, add					10%				
0804	20 to 29 tons, add					20%				
0806	10 to 19 tons, add					30%				
0807	5 to 9 tons, add					50%	25%			
0808	1 to 4 tons, add					75%	50%			
0809	Less than 1 ton, add					100%	100%			
1010	CS series, 40-ton job lots, horizontal bridging, shop primer									
1040	Spans to 30' **G**	E-7	12	6.667	Ton	1,700	350	150	2,200	2,625
1500	For less than 40-ton job lots									
1502	For 30 to 39 tons, add					10%				
1504	20 to 29 tons, add					20%				
1506	10 to 19 tons, add					30%				
1507	5 to 9 tons, add					50%	25%			
1508	1 to 4 tons, add					75%	50%			
1509	Less than 1 ton, add					100%	100%			

For customer support on your Site Work & Landscape Cost Data, call 877.737.1594.

121

05 31 Steel Decking

05 31 13 – Steel Floor Decking

05 31 13.50 Floor Decking

		Crew	Daily Output	Labor-Hours	Unit	Material	2015 Bare Costs Labor	Equipment	Total	Total Incl O&P
0010	**FLOOR DECKING** R053100-10									
0015	Made from recycled materials									
5100	Non-cellular composite decking, galvanized, 1-1/2" deep, 16 ga.	G	E-4	3500	.009	S.F.	3.44	.49	.04	3.97	4.68
5120	18 ga.	G		3650	.009		2.78	.47	.04	3.29	3.91
5140	20 ga.	G		3800	.008		2.22	.45	.04	2.71	3.26
5200	2" deep, 22 ga.	G		3860	.008		1.93	.44	.04	2.41	2.93
5300	20 ga.	G		3600	.009		2.13	.47	.04	2.64	3.20
5400	18 ga.	G		3380	.009		2.73	.50	.04	3.27	3.92
5500	16 ga.	G		3200	.010		3.41	.53	.05	3.99	4.72
5700	3" deep, 22 ga.	G		3200	.010		2.10	.53	.05	2.68	3.28
5800	20 ga.	G		3000	.011		2.34	.57	.05	2.96	3.62
5900	18 ga.	G		2850	.011		2.90	.60	.05	3.55	4.29
6000	16 ga.	G		2700	.012		3.87	.63	.05	4.55	5.40

05 31 23 – Steel Roof Decking

05 31 23.50 Roof Decking

		Crew	Daily Output	Labor-Hours	Unit	Material	2015 Bare Costs Labor	Equipment	Total	Total Incl O&P
0010	**ROOF DECKING**									
0015	Made from recycled materials									
2100	Open type, 1-1/2" deep, Type B, wide rib, galv., 22 ga., under 50 sq.	G	E-4	4500	.007	S.F.	2.05	.38	.03	2.46	2.95
2400	Over 500 squares	G		5100	.006		1.47	.33	.03	1.83	2.23
2600	20 ga., under 50 squares	G		3865	.008		2.39	.44	.04	2.87	3.43
2700	Over 500 squares	G		4300	.007		1.72	.40	.03	2.15	2.63
2900	18 ga., under 50 squares	G		3800	.008		3.09	.45	.04	3.58	4.22
3000	Over 500 squares	G		4300	.007		2.22	.40	.03	2.65	3.18
3050	16 ga., under 50 squares	G		3700	.009		4.17	.46	.04	4.67	5.45
3100	Over 500 squares	G		4200	.008		3	.41	.03	3.44	4.04
3200	3" deep, Type N, 22 ga., under 50 squares	G		3600	.009		3.01	.47	.04	3.52	4.17
3260	over 500 squares	G		4000	.008		2.17	.43	.04	2.64	3.17
3300	20 ga., under 50 squares	G		3400	.009		3.26	.50	.04	3.80	4.50
3360	over 500 squares	G		3800	.008		2.35	.45	.04	2.84	3.40
3400	18 ga., under 50 squares	G		3200	.010		4.21	.53	.05	4.79	5.60
3460	over 500 squares	G		3600	.009		3.03	.47	.04	3.54	4.19
3500	16 ga., under 50 squares	G		3000	.011		5.55	.57	.05	6.17	7.15
3560	over 500 squares	G		3400	.009		4	.50	.04	4.54	5.35
3700	4-1/2" deep, Type J, 20 ga., over 50 squares	G		2700	.012		3.64	.63	.05	4.32	5.15
4100	6" deep, Type H, 18 ga., over 50 squares	G		2000	.016		5.75	.85	.07	6.67	7.90
4500	7-1/2" deep, Type H, 18 ga., over 50 squares	G		1690	.019		6.85	1.01	.09	7.95	9.35

05 31 33 – Steel Form Decking

05 31 33.50 Form Decking

		Crew	Daily Output	Labor-Hours	Unit	Material	2015 Bare Costs Labor	Equipment	Total	Total Incl O&P
0010	**FORM DECKING**									
0015	Made from recycled materials									
6100	Slab form, steel, 28 ga., 9/16" deep, Type UFS, uncoated	G	E-4	4000	.008	S.F.	1.55	.43	.04	2.02	2.48
6200	Galvanized	G	"	4000	.008	"	1.37	.43	.04	1.84	2.29

05 35 Raceway Decking Assemblies

05 35 13 – Steel Cellular Decking

05 35 13.50 Cellular Decking

		Crew	Daily Output	Labor-Hours	Unit	Material	2015 Bare Costs Labor	Equipment	Total	Total Incl O&P
0010	**CELLULAR DECKING**									
0015	Made from recycled materials									
0200	Cellular units, galv, 1-1/2" deep, Type BC, 20-20 ga., over 15 squares	G	E-4	1460	.022	S.F.	8.10	1.17	.10	9.37	11.05
0250	18-20 ga.	G		1420	.023		9.20	1.20	.10	10.50	12.30
0300	18-18 ga.	G		1390	.023		9.40	1.22	.11	10.73	12.60
0320	16-18 ga.	G		1360	.024		11.25	1.25	.11	12.61	14.65
0340	16-16 ga.	G		1330	.024		12.50	1.28	.11	13.89	16.10
0400	3" deep, Type NC, galvanized, 20-20 ga.	G		1375	.023		8.90	1.24	.11	10.25	12.05

05 51 Metal Stairs

05 51 13 – Metal Pan Stairs

05 51 13.50 Pan Stairs

		Crew	Daily Output	Labor-Hours	Unit	Material	2015 Bare Costs Labor	Equipment	Total	Total Incl O&P
0010	**PAN STAIRS**, shop fabricated, steel stringers									
0015	Made from recycled materials									
0200	Cement fill metal pan, picket rail, 3'-6" wide	G	E-4	35	.914	Riser	500	48.50	4.17	552.67	640
0300	4'-0" wide	G		30	1.067		560	56.50	4.86	621.36	720
0350	Wall rail, both sides, 3'-6" wide	G		53	.604		380	32	2.75	414.75	480
1500	Landing, steel pan, conventional	G		160	.200	S.F.	66	10.65	.91	77.56	92.50
1600	Pre-erected	G		255	.125	"	118	6.65	.57	125.22	142
1700	Pre-erected, steel pan tread, 3'-6" wide, 2 line pipe rail	G	E-2	87	.644	Riser	550	33.50	17.35	600.85	680

05 51 16 – Metal Floor Plate Stairs

05 51 16.50 Floor Plate Stairs

		Crew	Daily Output	Labor-Hours	Unit	Material	2015 Bare Costs Labor	Equipment	Total	Total Incl O&P
0010	**FLOOR PLATE STAIRS**, shop fabricated, steel stringers									
0015	Made from recycled materials									
0400	Cast iron tread and pipe rail, 3'-6" wide	G	E-4	35	.914	Riser	535	48.50	4.17	587.67	675
0500	Checkered plate tread, industrial, 3'-6" wide	G		28	1.143		330	60.50	5.20	395.70	470
0550	Circular, for tanks, 3'-0" wide	G		33	.970		370	51.50	4.42	425.92	500
0600	For isolated stairs, add							100%		
0800	Custom steel stairs, 3'-6" wide, economy	G	E-4	35	.914		500	48.50	4.17	552.67	640
0810	Medium priced	G		30	1.067		660	56.50	4.86	721.36	835
0900	Deluxe	G		20	1.600		825	85	7.30	917.30	1,075
1100	For 4' wide stairs, add							5%	5%		
1300	For 5' wide stairs, add							10%	10%		

05 51 19 – Metal Grating Stairs

05 51 19.50 Grating Stairs

		Crew	Daily Output	Labor-Hours	Unit	Material	2015 Bare Costs Labor	Equipment	Total	Total Incl O&P
0010	**GRATING STAIRS**, shop fabricated, steel stringers, safety nosing on treads									
0015	Made from recycled materials									
0020	Grating tread and pipe railing, 3'-6" wide	G	E-4	35	.914	Riser	330	48.50	4.17	382.67	450
0100	4'-0" wide	G	"	30	1.067	"	430	56.50	4.86	491.36	580

05 51 33 – Metal Ladders

05 51 33.13 Vertical Metal Ladders

		Crew	Daily Output	Labor-Hours	Unit	Material	2015 Bare Costs Labor	Equipment	Total	Total Incl O&P
0010	**VERTICAL METAL LADDERS**, shop fabricated									
0015	Made from recycled materials									
0020	Steel, 20" wide, bolted to concrete, with cage	G	E-4	50	.640	V.L.F.	64	34	2.92	100.92	133
0100	Without cage	G		85	.376		38	20	1.72	59.72	79
0300	Aluminum, bolted to concrete, with cage	G		50	.640		120	34	2.92	156.92	194
0400	Without cage	G		85	.376		51	20	1.72	72.72	93

05 51 Metal Stairs

05 51 33 – Metal Ladders

05 51 33.16 Inclined Metal Ladders		Crew	Daily Output	Labor-Hours	Unit	Material	2015 Bare Costs Labor	Equipment	Total	Total Incl O&P
0010	**INCLINED METAL LADDERS**, shop fabricated									
0015	Made from recycled materials									
3900	Industrial ships ladder, steel, 24" W, grating treads, 2 line pipe rail	G	E-4	30	1.067	Riser	193	56.50	4.86	254.36	315
4000	Aluminum	G	"	30	1.067	"	270	56.50	4.86	331.36	400

05 52 Metal Railings

05 52 13 – Pipe and Tube Railings

05 52 13.50 Railings, Pipe		Crew	Daily Output	Labor-Hours	Unit	Material	2015 Bare Costs Labor	Equipment	Total	Total Incl O&P
0010	**RAILINGS, PIPE**, shop fab'd, 3'-6" high, posts @ 5' O.C.									
0015	Made from recycled materials									
0020	Aluminum, 2 rail, satin finish, 1-1/4" diameter	G	E-4	160	.200	L.F.	36	10.65	.91	47.56	59
0030	Clear anodized	G		160	.200		44	10.65	.91	55.56	68
0040	Dark anodized	G		160	.200		49	10.65	.91	60.56	73.50
0080	1-1/2" diameter, satin finish	G		160	.200		42.50	10.65	.91	54.06	66
0090	Clear anodized	G		160	.200		47.50	10.65	.91	59.06	71.50
0100	Dark anodized	G		160	.200		52.50	10.65	.91	64.06	77
0140	Aluminum, 3 rail, 1-1/4" diam., satin finish	G		137	.234		54.50	12.40	1.07	67.97	82
0150	Clear anodized	G		137	.234		67.50	12.40	1.07	80.97	97
0160	Dark anodized	G		137	.234		75	12.40	1.07	88.47	105
0200	1-1/2" diameter, satin finish	G		137	.234		64.50	12.40	1.07	77.97	93.50
0210	Clear anodized	G		137	.234		74	12.40	1.07	87.47	104
0220	Dark anodized	G		137	.234		80.50	12.40	1.07	93.97	111
0500	Steel, 2 rail, on stairs, primed, 1-1/4" diameter	G		160	.200		25	10.65	.91	36.56	47
0520	1-1/2" diameter	G		160	.200		27	10.65	.91	38.56	49.50
0540	Galvanized, 1-1/4" diameter	G		160	.200		34	10.65	.91	45.56	57
0560	1-1/2" diameter	G		160	.200		38.50	10.65	.91	50.06	61.50
0580	Steel, 3 rail, primed, 1-1/4" diameter	G		137	.234		37.50	12.40	1.07	50.97	63.50
0600	1-1/2" diameter	G		137	.234		39	12.40	1.07	52.47	65.50
0620	Galvanized, 1-1/4" diameter	G		137	.234		52.50	12.40	1.07	65.97	80
0640	1-1/2" diameter	G		137	.234		60.50	12.40	1.07	73.97	89
0700	Stainless steel, 2 rail, 1-1/4" diam. #4 finish	G		137	.234		110	12.40	1.07	123.47	144
0720	High polish	G		137	.234		178	12.40	1.07	191.47	219
0740	Mirror polish	G		137	.234		223	12.40	1.07	236.47	268
0760	Stainless steel, 3 rail, 1-1/2" diam., #4 finish	G		120	.267		166	14.15	1.22	181.37	209
0770	High polish	G		120	.267		275	14.15	1.22	290.37	330
0780	Mirror finish	G		120	.267		335	14.15	1.22	350.37	395
0900	Wall rail, alum. pipe, 1-1/4" diam., satin finish	G		213	.150		20	8	.69	28.69	36.50
0905	Clear anodized	G		213	.150		25	8	.69	33.69	42
0910	Dark anodized	G		213	.150		29.50	8	.69	38.19	47
0915	1-1/2" diameter, satin finish	G		213	.150		22.50	8	.69	31.19	39.50
0920	Clear anodized	G		213	.150		28	8	.69	36.69	45.50
0925	Dark anodized	G		213	.150		35	8	.69	43.69	53
0930	Steel pipe, 1-1/4" diameter, primed	G		213	.150		15	8	.69	23.69	31
0935	Galvanized	G		213	.150		22	8	.69	30.69	38.50
0940	1-1/2" diameter	G		176	.182		15.50	9.65	.83	25.98	35
0945	Galvanized	G		213	.150		22	8	.69	30.69	38.50
0955	Stainless steel pipe, 1-1/2" diam., #4 finish	G		107	.299		88	15.90	1.36	105.26	126
0960	High polish	G		107	.299		179	15.90	1.36	196.26	226
0965	Mirror polish	G		107	.299		212	15.90	1.36	229.26	262
2000	2-line pipe rail (1-1/2" T&B) with 1/2" pickets @ 4-1/2" O.C.,									

05 52 Metal Railings

05 52 13 – Pipe and Tube Railings

05 52 13.50 Railings, Pipe

		Crew	Daily Output	Labor-Hours	Unit	Material	2015 Bare Costs Labor	Equipment	Total	Total Incl O&P
2005	attached handrail on brackets									
2010	42" high aluminum, satin finish, straight & level	G E-4	120	.267	L.F.	198	14.15	1.22	213.37	244
2050	42" high steel, primed, straight & level	G "	120	.267		127	14.15	1.22	142.37	166
4000	For curved and level rails, add					10%	10%			
4100	For sloped rails for stairs, add					30%	30%			

05 52 16 – Industrial Railings

05 52 16.50 Railings, Industrial

		Crew	Daily Output	Labor-Hours	Unit	Material	2015 Bare Costs Labor	Equipment	Total	Total Incl O&P
0010	**RAILINGS, INDUSTRIAL**, shop fab'd, 3'-6" high, posts @ 5' O.C.									
0020	2 rail, 3'-6" high, 1-1/2" pipe	G E-4	255	.125	L.F.	27	6.65	.57	34.22	42
0100	2" angle rail	G "	255	.125		25	6.65	.57	32.22	39.50
0200	For 4" high kick plate, 10 ga., add	G				5.65			5.65	6.20
0300	1/4" thick, add	G				7.40			7.40	8.15
0500	For curved level rails, add					10%	10%			
0550	For sloped rails for stairs, add					30%	30%			

05 53 Metal Gratings

05 53 13 – Bar Gratings

05 53 13.10 Floor Grating, Aluminum

		Crew	Daily Output	Labor-Hours	Unit	Material	2015 Bare Costs Labor	Equipment	Total	Total Incl O&P
0010	**FLOOR GRATING, ALUMINUM**, field fabricated from panels									
0015	Made from recycled materials									
0110	Bearing bars @ 1-3/16" O.C., cross bars @ 4" O.C.,									
0111	Up to 300 S.F., 1" x 1/8" bar	G E-4	900	.036	S.F.	17.35	1.89	.16	19.40	22.50
0112	Over 300 S.F.	G	850	.038		15.80	2	.17	17.97	21
0113	1-1/4" x 1/8" bar, up to 300 S.F.	G	800	.040		18.05	2.13	.18	20.36	23.50
0114	Over 300 S.F.	G	1000	.032		16.40	1.70	.15	18.25	21
0122	1-1/4" x 3/16" bar, up to 300 S.F.	G	750	.043		27.50	2.27	.19	29.96	34.50
0124	Over 300 S.F.	G	1000	.032		25	1.70	.15	26.85	30.50
0132	1-1/2" x 3/16" bar, up to 300 S.F.	G	700	.046		32	2.43	.21	34.64	39.50
0134	Over 300 S.F.	G	1000	.032		29	1.70	.15	30.85	35
0136	1-3/4" x 3/16" bar, up to 300 S.F.	G	500	.064		35.50	3.40	.29	39.19	45
0138	Over 300 S.F.	G	1000	.032		32.50	1.70	.15	34.35	38.50
0146	2-1/4" x 3/16" bar, up to 300 S.F.	G	600	.053		45	2.83	.24	48.07	54.50
0148	Over 300 S.F.	G	1000	.032		41	1.70	.15	42.85	48
0162	Cross bars @ 2" O.C., 1" x 1/8", up to 300 S.F.	G	600	.053		30.50	2.83	.24	33.57	38.50
0164	Over 300 S.F.	G	1000	.032		27.50	1.70	.15	29.35	33.50
0172	1-1/4" x 3/16" bar, up to 300 S.F.	G	600	.053		49.50	2.83	.24	52.57	59.50
0174	Over 300 S.F.	G	1000	.032		45	1.70	.15	46.85	52.50
0182	1-1/2" x 3/16" bar, up to 300 S.F.	G	600	.053		57	2.83	.24	60.07	68
0184	Over 300 S.F.	G	1000	.032		52	1.70	.15	53.85	60
0186	1-3/4" x 3/16" bar, up to 300 S.F.	G	600	.053		62	2.83	.24	65.07	73
0188	Over 300 S.F.	G	1000	.032		56	1.70	.15	57.85	65
0200	For straight cuts, add				L.F.	4.30			4.30	4.73
0212	Bearing bars @ 15/16" O.C., 1" x 1/8", up to 300 S.F.	G E-4	520	.062	S.F.	29.50	3.27	.28	33.05	38.50
0214	Over 300 S.F.	G	920	.035		27	1.85	.16	29.01	33
0222	1-1/4" x 3/16", up to 300 S.F.	G	520	.062		49	3.27	.28	52.55	59.50
0224	Over 300 S.F.	G	920	.035		44.50	1.85	.16	46.51	52.50
0232	1-1/2" x 3/16", up to 300 S.F.	G	520	.062		56.50	3.27	.28	60.05	68
0234	Over 300 S.F.	G	920	.035		51	1.85	.16	53.01	60
0300	For curved cuts, add				L.F.	5.30			5.30	5.85
0400	For straight banding, add	G				5.50			5.50	6.05

05 53 Metal Gratings

05 53 13 – Bar Gratings

05 53 13.10 Floor Grating, Aluminum

		Crew	Daily Output	Labor-Hours	Unit	Material	2015 Bare Costs Labor	Equipment	Total	Total Incl O&P
0500	For curved banding, add	G			L.F.	6.60			6.60	7.25
0600	For aluminum checkered plate nosings, add	G				7.15			7.15	7.85
0700	For straight toe plate, add	G				10.80			10.80	11.90
0800	For curved toe plate, add	G				12.60			12.60	13.85
1000	For cast aluminum abrasive nosings, add	G				10.50			10.50	11.55
1200	Expanded aluminum, .65# per S.F.	G	E-4	1050	.030	S.F.	12.45	1.62	.14	14.21	16.65
1400	Extruded I bars are 10% less than 3/16" bars										
1600	Heavy duty, all extruded plank, 3/4" deep, 1.8# per S.F.	G	E-4	1100	.029	S.F.	26.50	1.55	.13	28.18	32
1700	1-1/4" deep, 2.9# per S.F.	G		1000	.032		29	1.70	.15	30.85	35
1800	1-3/4" deep, 4.2# per S.F.	G		925	.035		40.50	1.84	.16	42.50	48
1900	2-1/4" deep, 5.0# per S.F.	G		875	.037		60.50	1.94	.17	62.61	70
2100	For safety serrated surface, add						15%				

05 53 13.70 Floor Grating, Steel

		Crew	Daily Output	Labor-Hours	Unit	Material	2015 Bare Costs Labor	Equipment	Total	Total Incl O&P
0010	**FLOOR GRATING, STEEL**, field fabricated from panels										
0015	Made from recycled materials										
0300	Platforms, to 12' high, rectangular	G	E-4	3150	.010	Lb.	3.21	.54	.05	3.80	4.52
0400	Circular	G	"	2300	.014	"	4.01	.74	.06	4.81	5.75
0410	Painted bearing bars @ 1-3/16"										
0412	Cross bars @ 4" O.C., 3/4" x 1/8" bar, up to 300 S.F.	G	E-2	500	.112	S.F.	8.25	5.80	3.02	17.07	22
0414	Over 300 S.F.	G		750	.075		7.50	3.86	2.01	13.37	16.95
0422	1-1/4" x 3/16", up to 300 S.F.	G		400	.140		12.75	7.25	3.78	23.78	30.50
0424	Over 300 S.F.	G		600	.093		11.60	4.83	2.52	18.95	23.50
0432	1-1/2" x 3/16", up to 300 S.F.	G		400	.140		14.85	7.25	3.78	25.88	32.50
0434	Over 300 S.F.	G		600	.093		13.50	4.83	2.52	20.85	25.50
0436	1-3/4" x 3/16", up to 300 S.F.	G		400	.140		18.50	7.25	3.78	29.53	37
0438	Over 300 S.F.	G		600	.093		16.80	4.83	2.52	24.15	29.50
0452	2-1/4" x 3/16", up to 300 S.F.	G		300	.187		23	9.65	5.05	37.70	47.50
0454	Over 300 S.F.	G		450	.124		21	6.45	3.36	30.81	37.50
0462	Cross bars @ 2" O.C., 3/4" x 1/8", up to 300 S.F.	G		500	.112		15.15	5.80	3.02	23.97	29.50
0464	Over 300 S.F.	G		750	.075		12.60	3.86	2.01	18.47	22.50
0472	1-1/4" x 3/16", up to 300 S.F.	G		400	.140		19.80	7.25	3.78	30.83	38.50
0474	Over 300 S.F.	G		600	.093		16.50	4.83	2.52	23.85	29
0482	1-1/2" x 3/16", up to 300 S.F.	G		400	.140		22.50	7.25	3.78	33.53	41
0484	Over 300 S.F.	G		600	.093		18.60	4.83	2.52	25.95	31.50
0486	1-3/4" x 3/16", up to 300 S.F.	G		400	.140		33.50	7.25	3.78	44.53	53.50
0488	Over 300 S.F.	G		600	.093		28	4.83	2.52	35.35	42
0502	2-1/4" x 3/16", up to 300 S.F.	G		300	.187		33	9.65	5.05	47.70	58
0504	Over 300 S.F.	G		450	.124		27.50	6.45	3.36	37.31	44.50
0601	Painted bearing bars @ 15/16" O.C., cross bars @ 4" O.C.,										
0612	Up to 300 S.F., 3/4" x 3/16" bars	G	E-4	850	.038	S.F.	12.20	2	.17	14.37	17.05
0622	1-1/4" x 3/16" bars	G		600	.053		16	2.83	.24	19.07	23
0632	1-1/2" x 3/16" bars	G		550	.058		17.95	3.09	.27	21.31	25.50
0636	1-3/4" x 3/16" bars	G		450	.071		24.50	3.78	.32	28.60	34
0652	2-1/4" x 3/16" bars	G	E-2	300	.187		27.50	9.65	5.05	42.20	52
0662	Cross bars @ 2" O.C., up to 300 S.F., 3/4" x 3/16"	G		500	.112		15.80	5.80	3.02	24.62	30.50
0672	1-1/4" x 3/16" bars	G		400	.140		20	7.25	3.78	31.03	38.50
0682	1-1/2" x 3/16" bars	G		400	.140		23	7.25	3.78	34.03	41.50
0686	1-3/4" x 3/16" bars	G		300	.187		29	9.65	5.05	43.70	53.50
0690	For galvanized grating, add						25%				
0800	For straight cuts, add					L.F.	6.15			6.15	6.75
0900	For curved cuts, add						7.80			7.80	8.60
1000	For straight banding, add	G					6.60			6.60	7.25

126

05 53 Metal Gratings

05 53 13 – Bar Gratings

05 53 13.70 Floor Grating, Steel

		Crew	Daily Output	Labor-Hours	Unit	Material	2015 Bare Costs Labor	Equipment	Total	Total Incl O&P
1100	For curved banding, add	G			L.F.	8.70			8.70	9.55
1200	For checkered plate nosings, add	G				7.65			7.65	8.40
1300	For straight toe or kick plate, add	G				13.70			13.70	15.05
1400	For curved toe or kick plate, add	G				15.50			15.50	17.05
1500	For abrasive nosings, add	G				10.15			10.15	11.15
1600	For safety serrated surface, bearing bars @ 1-3/16" O.C., add					15%				
1700	Bearing bars @ 15/16" O.C., add					25%				
2000	Stainless steel gratings, close spaced, 1" x 1/8" bars, up to 300 S.F.	G	E-4	450	.071	S.F.	73	3.78	.32	77.10	87.50
2100	Standard spacing, 3/4" x 1/8" bars	G		500	.064		84	3.40	.29	87.69	98
2200	1-1/4" x 3/16" bars	G		400	.080		80	4.25	.36	84.61	96
2400	Expanded steel grating, at ground, 3.0# per S.F.	G		900	.036		8.05	1.89	.16	10.10	12.35
2500	3.14# per S.F.	G		900	.036		7.15	1.89	.16	9.20	11.35
2600	4.0# per S.F.	G		850	.038		8.60	2	.17	10.77	13.15
2650	4.27# per S.F.	G		850	.038		9.30	2	.17	11.47	13.90
2700	5.0# per S.F.	G		800	.040		13.80	2.13	.18	16.11	19.05
2800	6.25# per S.F.	G		750	.043		17.80	2.27	.19	20.26	24
2900	7.0# per S.F.	G		700	.046		19.65	2.43	.21	22.29	26
3100	For flattened expanded steel grating, add						8%				
3300	For elevated installation above 15', add						15%				

05 53 16 – Plank Gratings

05 53 16.50 Grating Planks

		Crew	Daily Output	Labor-Hours	Unit	Material	2015 Bare Costs Labor	Equipment	Total	Total Incl O&P
0010	**GRATING PLANKS**, field fabricated from planks									
0020	Aluminum, 9-1/2" wide, 14 ga., 2" rib	G	E-4	950	.034	L.F.	25.50	1.79	.15	27.44	31.50
0200	Galvanized steel, 9-1/2" wide, 14 ga., 2-1/2" rib	G		950	.034		16.80	1.79	.15	18.74	22
0300	4" rib	G		950	.034		18.50	1.79	.15	20.44	24
0500	12 ga., 2-1/2" rib	G		950	.034		16.90	1.79	.15	18.84	22
0600	3" rib	G		950	.034		22.50	1.79	.15	24.44	28
0800	Stainless steel, type 304, 16 ga., 2" rib	G		950	.034		37	1.79	.15	38.94	44
0900	Type 316	G		950	.034		57	1.79	.15	58.94	66.50

05 53 19 – Floor Grating Frame

05 53 19.30 Grating Frame

		Crew	Daily Output	Labor-Hours	Unit	Material	2015 Bare Costs Labor	Equipment	Total	Total Incl O&P
0010	**GRATING FRAME**, field fabricated									
0020	Aluminum, for gratings 1" to 1-1/2" deep	G	1 Sswk	70	.114	L.F.	3.78	6		9.78	14.60
0100	For each corner, add	G				Ea.	5.65			5.65	6.25

05 54 Metal Floor Plates

05 54 13 – Floor Plates

05 54 13.20 Checkered Plates

		Crew	Daily Output	Labor-Hours	Unit	Material	2015 Bare Costs Labor	Equipment	Total	Total Incl O&P
0010	**CHECKERED PLATES**, steel, field fabricated									
0015	Made from recycled materials									
0020	1/4" & 3/8", 2000 to 5000 S.F., bolted	G	E-4	2900	.011	Lb.	.88	.59	.05	1.52	2.05
0100	Welded	G		4400	.007	"	.84	.39	.03	1.26	1.63
0300	Pit or trench cover and frame, 1/4" plate, 2' to 3' wide	G		100	.320	S.F.	11.35	17	1.46	29.81	43.50
0400	For galvanizing, add	G				Lb.	.29			.29	.32
0500	Platforms, 1/4" plate, no handrails included, rectangular	G	E-4	4200	.008		3.21	.41	.03	3.65	4.27
0600	Circular	G	"	2500	.013		4.01	.68	.06	4.75	5.65

05 54 13.70 Trench Covers

		Crew	Daily Output	Labor-Hours	Unit	Material	2015 Bare Costs Labor	Equipment	Total	Total Incl O&P
0010	**TRENCH COVERS**, field fabricated									
0020	Cast iron grating with bar stops and angle frame, to 18" wide	G	1 Sswk	20	.400	L.F.	213	21		234	271
0100	Frame only (both sides of trench), 1" grating	G		45	.178		1.37	9.35		10.72	17.75

For customer support on your Site Work & Landscape Cost Data, call 877.737.1594.

127

05 54 Metal Floor Plates

05 54 13 – Floor Plates

05 54 13.70 Trench Covers

		Crew	Daily Output	Labor-Hours	Unit	Material	2015 Bare Costs Labor	Equipment	Total	Total Incl O&P
0150	2" grating	G 1 Sswk	35	.229	L.F.	3.23	12.05		15.28	24.50
0200	Aluminum, stock units, including frames and									
0210	3/8" plain cover plate, 4" opening	G E-4	205	.156	L.F.	21	8.30	.71	30.01	38
0300	6" opening	G	185	.173		25.50	9.20	.79	35.49	45
0400	10" opening	G	170	.188		34.50	10	.86	45.36	56.50
0500	16" opening	G	155	.206		48	10.95	.94	59.89	73
0700	Add per inch for additional widths to 24"	G				2			2	2.20
0900	For custom fabrication, add					50%				
1100	For 1/4" plain cover plate, deduct					12%				
1500	For cover recessed for tile, 1/4" thick, deduct					12%				
1600	3/8" thick, add					5%				
1800	For checkered plate cover, 1/4" thick, deduct					12%				
1900	3/8" thick, add					2%				
2100	For slotted or round holes in cover, 1/4" thick, add					3%				
2200	3/8" thick, add					4%				
2300	For abrasive cover, add					12%				

05 55 Metal Stair Treads and Nosings

05 55 13 – Metal Stair Treads

05 55 13.50 Stair Treads

		Crew	Daily Output	Labor-Hours	Unit	Material	2015 Bare Costs Labor	Equipment	Total	Total Incl O&P
0010	**STAIR TREADS**, stringers and bolts not included									
3000	Diamond plate treads, steel, 1/8" thick									
3005	Open riser, black enamel									
3010	9" deep x 36" long	G 2 Sswk	48	.333	Ea.	91.50	17.55		109.05	131
3020	42" long	G	48	.333		96.50	17.55		114.05	137
3030	48" long	G	48	.333		101	17.55		118.55	142
3040	11" deep x 36" long	G	44	.364		96.50	19.15		115.65	140
3050	42" long	G	44	.364		102	19.15		121.15	146
3060	48" long	G	44	.364		108	19.15		127.15	153
3110	Galvanized, 9" deep x 36" long	G	48	.333		144	17.55		161.55	190
3120	42" long	G	48	.333		154	17.55		171.55	200
3130	48" long	G	48	.333		163	17.55		180.55	210
3140	11" deep x 36" long	G	44	.364		149	19.15		168.15	198
3150	42" long	G	44	.364		163	19.15		182.15	213
3160	48" long	G	44	.364		169	19.15		188.15	220
3200	Closed riser, black enamel									
3210	12" deep x 36" long	G 2 Sswk	40	.400	Ea.	110	21		131	158
3220	42" long	G	40	.400		119	21		140	168
3230	48" long	G	40	.400		126	21		147	175
3240	Galvanized, 12" deep x 36" long	G	40	.400		173	21		194	228
3250	42" long	G	40	.400		189	21		210	245
3260	48" long	G	40	.400		198	21		219	255
4000	Bar grating treads									
4005	Steel, 1-1/4" x 3/16" bars, anti-skid nosing, black enamel									
4010	8-5/8" deep x 30" long	G 2 Sswk	48	.333	Ea.	54	17.55		71.55	90
4020	36" long	G	48	.333		63.50	17.55		81.05	100
4030	48" long	G	48	.333		97.50	17.55		115.05	138
4040	10-15/16" deep x 36" long	G	44	.364		70	19.15		89.15	111
4050	48" long	G	44	.364		100	19.15		119.15	144
4060	Galvanized, 8-5/8" deep x 30" long	G	48	.333		62	17.55		79.55	99
4070	36" long	G	48	.333		73.50	17.55		91.05	112

05 55 Metal Stair Treads and Nosings

05 55 13 – Metal Stair Treads

05 55 13.50 Stair Treads

		Crew	Daily Output	Labor-Hours	Unit	Material	2015 Bare Costs Labor	2015 Bare Costs Equipment	Total	Total Incl O&P
4080	48" long	G	2 Sswk	48	.333	Ea.	108	17.55		125.55	150
4090	10-15/16" deep x 36" long	G		44	.364		86.50	19.15		105.65	129
4100	48" long	G	↓	44	.364	↓	112	19.15		131.15	157
4200	Aluminum, 1-1/4" x 3/16" bars, serrated, with nosing										
4210	7-5/8" deep x 18" long	G	2 Sswk	52	.308	Ea.	50	16.20		66.20	83
4220	24" long	G		52	.308		59	16.20		75.20	93
4230	30" long	G		52	.308		68.50	16.20		84.70	103
4240	36" long	G		52	.308		177	16.20		193.20	223
4250	8-13/16" deep x 18" long	G		48	.333		67	17.55		84.55	105
4260	24" long	G		48	.333		99.50	17.55		117.05	140
4270	30" long	G		48	.333		115	17.55		132.55	157
4280	36" long	G		48	.333		194	17.55		211.55	245
4290	10" deep x 18" long	G		44	.364		130	19.15		149.15	177
4300	30" long	G	↓	44	.364		173	19.15		192.15	224
4310	36" long	G	↓	44	.364	↓	210	19.15		229.15	265
5000	Channel grating treads										
5005	Steel, 14 ga., 2-12" thick, galvanized										
5010	9" deep x 36" long	G	2 Sswk	48	.333	Ea.	103	17.55		120.55	144
5020	48" long	G	"	48	.333	"	139	17.55		156.55	183

05 55 19 – Metal Stair Tread Covers

05 55 19.50 Stair Tread Covers for Renovation

		Crew	Daily Output	Labor-Hours	Unit	Material	2015 Bare Costs Labor	2015 Bare Costs Equipment	Total	Total Incl O&P
0010	**STAIR TREAD COVERS FOR RENOVATION**										
0205	Extruded tread cover with nosing, pre-drilled, includes screws										
0210	Aluminum with black abrasive strips, 9" wide x 3' long	1 Carp	24	.333	Ea.	107	15.65		122.65	142
0220	4' long		22	.364		142	17.05		159.05	183
0230	5' long		20	.400		177	18.80		195.80	223
0240	11" wide x 3' long		24	.333		139	15.65		154.65	177
0250	4' long		22	.364		179	17.05		196.05	223
0260	5' long	↓	20	.400	↓	230	18.80		248.80	281
0305	Black abrasive strips with yellow front strips										
0310	Aluminum, 9" wide x 3' long	1 Carp	24	.333	Ea.	116	15.65		131.65	151
0320	4' long		22	.364		154	17.05		171.05	197
0330	5' long		20	.400		196	18.80		214.80	245
0340	11" wide x 3' long		24	.333		149	15.65		164.65	188
0350	4' long		22	.364		192	17.05		209.05	238
0360	5' long	↓	20	.400	↓	247	18.80		265.80	300
0405	Black abrasive strips with photoluminescent front strips										
0410	Aluminum, 9" wide x 3' long	1 Carp	24	.333	Ea.	156	15.65		171.65	195
0420	4' long		22	.364		172	17.05		189.05	216
0430	5' long		20	.400		215	18.80		233.80	265
0440	11" wide x 3' long		24	.333		153	15.65		168.65	192
0450	4' long		22	.364		204	17.05		221.05	251
0460	5' long	↓	20	.400	↓	255	18.80		273.80	310

05 56 Metal Castings

05 56 13 – Metal Construction Castings

05 56 13.50 Construction Castings		Crew	Daily Output	Labor-Hours	Unit	Material	2015 Bare Costs Labor	2015 Bare Costs Equipment	Total	Total Incl O&P
0010	**CONSTRUCTION CASTINGS**									
0020	Manhole covers and frames, see Section 33 44 13.13									
0100	Column bases, cast iron, 16" x 16", approx. 65 lb.	G	E-4	46	.696	Ea.	142	37	3.17	182.17	223
0200	32" x 32", approx. 256 lb.	G		23	1.391	"	520	74	6.35	600.35	710
0600	Miscellaneous C.I. castings, light sections, less than 150 lb.	G		3200	.010	Lb.	8.95	.53	.05	9.53	10.80
1100	Heavy sections, more than 150 lb.	G		4200	.008		4.66	.41	.03	5.10	5.90
1300	Special low volume items	G		3200	.010		11.25	.53	.05	11.83	13.30
1500	For ductile iron, add						100%				

05 58 Formed Metal Fabrications

05 58 21 – Formed Chain

05 58 21.05 Alloy Steel Chain

		Crew	Daily Output	Labor-Hours	Unit	Material	2015 Bare Costs Labor	2015 Bare Costs Equipment	Total	Total Incl O&P
0010	**ALLOY STEEL CHAIN**, Grade 80, for lifting										
0015	Self-colored, cut lengths, 1/4"	G	E-17	4	4	C.L.F.	765	215		980	1,225
0020	3/8"	G		2	8		980	430		1,410	1,825
0030	1/2"	G		1.20	13.333		1,550	715		2,265	2,975
0040	5/8"	G		.72	22.222		2,450	1,200		3,650	4,750
0050	3/4"	G	E-18	.48	83.333		3,300	4,375	1,975	9,650	13,300
0060	7/8"	G		.40	100		5,725	5,275	2,375	13,375	17,800
0070	1"	G		.35	114		7,975	6,025	2,700	16,700	22,000
0080	1-1/4"	G		.24	166		13,400	8,775	3,950	26,125	34,000
0110	Hook, Grade 80, Clevis slip, 1/4"	G				Ea.	26			26	28.50
0120	3/8"	G					30.50			30.50	33.50
0130	1/2"	G					49.50			49.50	54.50
0140	5/8"	G					73			73	80
0150	3/4"	G					101			101	111
0160	Hook, Grade 80, eye/sling w/hammerlock coupling, 15 Ton	G					340			340	375
0170	22 Ton	G					925			925	1,025
0180	37 Ton	G					2,825			2,825	3,100

05 58 25 – Formed Lamp Posts

05 58 25.40 Lamp Posts

		Crew	Daily Output	Labor-Hours	Unit	Material	2015 Bare Costs Labor	2015 Bare Costs Equipment	Total	Total Incl O&P
0010	**LAMP POSTS**										
0020	Aluminum, 7' high, stock units, post only	G	1 Carp	16	.500	Ea.	82	23.50		105.50	126
0100	Mild steel, plain	G	"	16	.500	"	73	23.50		96.50	116

05 71 Decorative Metal Stairs

05 71 13 – Fabricated Metal Spiral Stairs

05 71 13.50 Spiral Stairs

		Crew	Daily Output	Labor-Hours	Unit	Material	2015 Bare Costs Labor	2015 Bare Costs Equipment	Total	Total Incl O&P
0010	**SPIRAL STAIRS**										
1805	Shop fabricated, custom ordered										
1810	Aluminum, 5'-0" diameter, plain units	G	E-4	45	.711	Riser	575	38	3.24	616.24	705
1900	Cast iron, 4'-0" diameter, plain units	G		45	.711		540	38	3.24	581.24	665
1920	Fancy Units	G		25	1.280		735	68	5.85	808.85	935
2000	Steel, industrial checkered plate, 4' diameter	G		45	.711		540	38	3.24	581.24	665
2200	6' diameter	G		40	.800		650	42.50	3.65	696.15	795
3100	Spiral stair kits, 12 stacking risers to fit exact floor height										
3110	Steel, flat metal treads, primed, 3'-6" diameter	G	2 Carp	1.60	10	Flight	1,275	470		1,745	2,125
3120	4'-0" diameter	G		1.45	11.034		1,450	520		1,970	2,400
3130	4'-6" diameter	G		1.35	11.852		1,600	555		2,155	2,625

05 71 Decorative Metal Stairs

05 71 13 – Fabricated Metal Spiral Stairs

05 71 13.50 Spiral Stairs		Crew	Daily Output	Labor-Hours	Unit	Material	2015 Bare Costs Labor	Equipment	Total	Total Incl O&P
3140	5'-0" diameter	G	2 Carp	1.25	12.800	Flight	1,750	600		2,350	2,850
3210	Galvanized, 3'-6" diameter	G		1.60	10		1,525	470		1,995	2,400
3220	4'-0" diameter	G		1.45	11.034		1,750	520		2,270	2,725
3230	4'-6" diameter	G		1.35	11.852		1,925	555		2,480	2,975
3240	5'-0" diameter	G		1.25	12.800		2,100	600		2,700	3,225
3310	Checkered plate tread, primed, 3'-6" diameter	G		1.45	11.034		1,500	520		2,020	2,450
3320	4'-0" diameter	G		1.35	11.852		1,700	555		2,255	2,725
3330	4'-6" diameter	G		1.25	12.800		1,850	600		2,450	2,975
3340	5'-0" diameter	G		1.15	13.913		2,025	655		2,680	3,225
3410	Galvanized, 3'-6" diameter	G		1.45	11.034		1,800	520		2,320	2,800
3420	4'-0" diameter	G		1.35	11.852		2,050	555		2,605	3,100
3430	4'-6" diameter	G		1.25	12.800		2,225	600		2,825	3,375
3440	5'-0" diameter	G		1.15	13.913		2,425	655		3,080	3,675
3510	Red oak covers on flat metal treads, 3'-6" diameter			1.35	11.852		2,600	555		3,155	3,725
3520	4'-0" diameter			1.25	12.800		2,875	600		3,475	4,100
3530	4'-6" diameter			1.15	13.913		3,100	655		3,755	4,400
3540	5'-0" diameter			1.05	15.238		3,375	715		4,090	4,825

05 73 Decorative Metal Railings

05 73 16 – Wire Rope Decorative Metal Railings

05 73 16.10 Cable Railings

05 73 16.10 Cable Railings		Crew	Daily Output	Labor-Hours	Unit	Material	2015 Bare Costs Labor	Equipment	Total	Total Incl O&P
0010	**CABLE RAILINGS**, with 316 stainless steel 1 x 19 cable, 3/16" diameter									
0015	Made from recycled materials									
0100	1-3/4" diameter stainless steel posts x 42" high, cables 4" OC	G	2 Sswk	25	.640	L.F.	33	33.50		66.50	95

05 73 23 – Ornamental Railings

05 73 23.50 Railings, Ornamental

05 73 23.50 Railings, Ornamental		Crew	Daily Output	Labor-Hours	Unit	Material	2015 Bare Costs Labor	Equipment	Total	Total Incl O&P
0010	**RAILINGS, ORNAMENTAL**, 3'-6" high, posts @ 6' O.C.									
0020	Bronze or stainless, hand forged, plain	G	2 Sswk	24	.667	L.F.	122	35		157	195
0100	Fancy	G		18	.889		223	47		270	325
0200	Aluminum, panelized, plain	G		24	.667		13.60	35		48.60	76
0300	Fancy	G		18	.889		30	47		77	115
0400	Wrought iron, hand forged, plain	G		24	.667		81	35		116	150
0500	Fancy	G		18	.889		159	47		206	257
0550	Steel, panelized, plain	G		24	.667		20.50	35		55.50	83.50
0560	Fancy	G		18	.889		32	47		79	117
0600	Composite metal/wood/glass, plain			18	.889		119	47		166	213
0700	Fancy			12	1.333		238	70		308	385

For customer support on your Site Work & Landscape Cost Data, call 877.737.1594.

131

Division Notes

	CREW	DAILY OUTPUT	LABOR-HOURS	UNIT	BARE COSTS				TOTAL INCL O&P
					MAT.	LABOR	EQUIP.	TOTAL	

Estimating Tips
06 05 00 Common Work Results for Wood, Plastics, and Composites

- Common to any wood-framed structure are the accessory connector items such as screws, nails, adhesives, hangers, connector plates, straps, angles, and hold-downs. For typical wood-framed buildings, such as residential projects, the aggregate total for these items can be significant, especially in areas where seismic loading is a concern. For floor and wall framing, the material cost is based on 10 to 25 lbs. per MBF. Hold-downs, hangers, and other connectors should be taken off by the piece.

  Included with material costs are fasteners for a normal installation. RSMeans engineers use manufacturer's recommendations, written specifications, and/or standard construction practice for size and spacing of fasteners. Prices for various fasteners are shown for informational purposes only. Adjustments should be made if unusual fastening conditions exist.

06 10 00 Carpentry

- Lumber is a traded commodity and therefore sensitive to supply and demand in the marketplace. Even in "budgetary" estimating of wood-framed projects, it is advisable to call local suppliers for the latest market pricing.

- Common quantity units for wood-framed projects are "thousand board feet" (MBF). A board foot is a volume of wood, 1" x 1' x 1', or 144 cubic inches. Board-foot quantities are generally calculated using nominal material dimensions— dressed sizes are ignored. Board foot per lineal foot of any stick of lumber can be calculated by dividing the nominal cross-sectional area by 12. As an example, 2,000 lineal feet of 2 x 12 equates to 4 MBF by dividing the nominal area, 2 x 12, by 12, which equals 2, and multiplying by 2,000 to give 4,000 board feet. This simple rule applies to all nominal dimensioned lumber.

- Waste is an issue of concern at the quantity takeoff for any area of construction. Framing lumber is sold in even foot lengths, i.e., 10', 12', 14', 16' and, depending on spans, wall heights, and the grade of lumber, waste is inevitable. A rule of thumb for lumber waste is 5%–10% depending on material quality and the complexity of the framing.

- Wood in various forms and shapes is used in many projects, even where the main structural framing is steel, concrete, or masonry.

Plywood as a back-up partition material and 2x boards used as blocking and cant strips around roof edges are two common examples. The estimator should ensure that the costs of all wood materials are included in the final estimate.

06 20 00 Finish Carpentry

- It is necessary to consider the grade of workmanship when estimating labor costs for erecting millwork and interior finish. In practice, there are three grades: premium, custom, and economy. The RSMeans daily output for base and case moldings is in the range of 200 to 250 L.F. per carpenter per day. This is appropriate for most average custom-grade projects. For premium projects, an adjustment to productivity of 25%–50% should be made, depending on the complexity of the job.

Reference Numbers
Reference numbers are shown in shaded boxes at the beginning of some major classifications. These numbers refer to related items in the Reference Section. The reference information may be an estimating procedure, an alternate pricing method, or technical information.

Note: Not all subdivisions listed here necessarily appear in this publication. ∎

06 05 05 – Selective Demolition for Wood, Plastics, and Composites

06 05 05.10 Selective Demolition Wood Framing

		Crew	Daily Output	Labor-Hours	Unit	Material	2015 Bare Costs Labor	Equipment	Total	Total Incl O&P
0010	**SELECTIVE DEMOLITION WOOD FRAMING** R024119-10									
0100	Timber connector, nailed, small	1 Clab	96	.083	Ea.		3.13		3.13	4.82
0110	Medium		60	.133			5		5	7.70
0120	Large		48	.167			6.25		6.25	9.65
0130	Bolted, small		48	.167			6.25		6.25	9.65
0140	Medium		32	.250			9.40		9.40	14.45
0150	Large		24	.333			12.55		12.55	19.30
3162	Alternate pricing method	B-1	1.10	21.818	M.B.F.		835		835	1,275

06 05 23 – Wood, Plastic, and Composite Fastenings

06 05 23.60 Timber Connectors

		Crew	Daily Output	Labor-Hours	Unit	Material	2015 Bare Costs Labor	Equipment	Total	Total Incl O&P
0010	**TIMBER CONNECTORS**									
0020	Add up cost of each part for total cost of connection									
0100	Connector plates, steel, with bolts, straight	2 Carp	75	.213	Ea.	30.50	10		40.50	49
0110	Tee, 7 ga.		50	.320		35	15		50	61.50
0120	T- Strap, 14 ga., 12" x 8" x 2"		50	.320		35	15		50	61.50
0150	Anchor plates, 7 ga., 9" x 7"		75	.213		30.50	10		40.50	49
0200	Bolts, machine, sq. hd. with nut & washer, 1/2" diameter, 4" long	1 Carp	140	.057		.75	2.68		3.43	4.96
0300	7-1/2" long		130	.062		1.37	2.89		4.26	5.95
0500	3/4" diameter, 7-1/2" long		130	.062		3.20	2.89		6.09	7.95
0610	Machine bolts, w/nut, washer, 3/4" diam., 15" L, HD's & beam hangers		95	.084		5.95	3.95		9.90	12.65
0800	Drilling bolt holes in timber, 1/2" diameter		450	.018	Inch		.83		.83	1.28
0900	1" diameter		350	.023	"		1.07		1.07	1.65

06 11 Wood Framing

06 11 10 – Framing with Dimensional, Engineered or Composite Lumber

06 11 10.14 Posts and Columns

		Crew	Daily Output	Labor-Hours	Unit	Material	2015 Bare Costs Labor	Equipment	Total	Total Incl O&P
0010	**POSTS AND COLUMNS**									
0100	4" x 4"	2 Carp	390	.041	L.F.	1.73	1.93		3.66	4.86
0150	4" x 6"		275	.058		2.84	2.73		5.57	7.30
0200	4" x 8"		220	.073		2.89	3.41		6.30	8.45
0250	6" x 6"		215	.074		5.05	3.49		8.54	10.95
0300	6" x 8"		175	.091		7.40	4.29		11.69	14.75
0350	6" x 10"		150	.107		6.45	5		11.45	14.80

06 11 10.20 Framing, Light

		Crew	Daily Output	Labor-Hours	Unit	Material	2015 Bare Costs Labor	Equipment	Total	Total Incl O&P
0010	**FRAMING, LIGHT**									
0020	Average cost for all light framing	2 Carp	1.05	15.238	M.B.F.	730	715		1,445	1,900
2870	Redwood joists, 2" x 6"		1.50	10.667		3,425	500		3,925	4,525
2880	2" x 8"		1.75	9.143		3,425	430		3,855	4,400
2890	2" x 10"		1.75	9.143		4,525	430		4,955	5,625
4000	Platform framing, 2" x 4"		.70	22.857		635	1,075		1,710	2,350
4100	2" x 6"		.76	21.053		665	990		1,655	2,250
4200	Pressure treated 6" x 6"		.80	20		1,400	940		2,340	2,975
4220	8" x 8"		.60	26.667		1,675	1,250		2,925	3,750
4500	Cedar post, columns & girts, 4" x 4"		.52	30.769		2,925	1,450		4,375	5,450
4510	4" x 6"		.55	29.091		3,675	1,375		5,050	6,125
4520	6" x 6"		.65	24.615		4,175	1,150		5,325	6,375
4530	8" x 8"		.70	22.857		3,725	1,075		4,800	5,750
4540	Redwood post, columns & girts, 4" x 4"		.52	30.769		4,800	1,450		6,250	7,525
4550	4" x 6"		.55	29.091		6,275	1,375		7,650	9,000
4560	6" x 6"		.65	24.615		8,225	1,150		9,375	10,800

06 11 Wood Framing

06 11 10 – Framing with Dimensional, Engineered or Composite Lumber

06 11 10.20 Framing, Light	Crew	Daily Output	Labor-Hours	Unit	Material	2015 Bare Costs Labor	2015 Bare Costs Equipment	Total	Total Incl O&P
4570 8" x 8"	2 Carp	.70	22.857	M.B.F.	8,875	1,075		9,950	11,400

06 11 10.34 Sleepers

		Crew	Daily Output	Labor-Hours	Unit	Material	Labor	Equipment	Total	Total Incl O&P
0010	**SLEEPERS**									
0100	On concrete, treated, 1" x 2"	2 Carp	2350	.007	L.F.	.27	.32		.59	.79
0150	1" x 3"		2000	.008		.45	.38		.83	1.08
0200	2" x 4"		1500	.011		.55	.50		1.05	1.37
0250	2" x 6"		1300	.012		.86	.58		1.44	1.84

06 11 10.38 Treated Lumber Framing Material

		Crew	Daily Output	Labor-Hours	Unit	Material	Labor	Equipment	Total	Total Incl O&P
0010	**TREATED LUMBER FRAMING MATERIAL**									
0100	2" x 4"				M.B.F.	755			755	830
0110	2" x 6"					770			770	845
0120	2" x 8"					780			780	855
0130	2" x 10"					830			830	910
0140	2" x 12"					960			960	1,050
0200	4" x 4"					975			975	1,075
0210	4" x 6"					925			925	1,025
0220	4" x 8"					1,400			1,400	1,550

06 11 10.42 Furring

		Crew	Daily Output	Labor-Hours	Unit	Material	Labor	Equipment	Total	Total Incl O&P
0010	**FURRING**									
0012	Wood strips, 1" x 2", on walls, on wood	1 Carp	550	.015	L.F.	.24	.68		.92	1.31
0015	On wood, pneumatic nailed		710	.011		.24	.53		.77	1.07
0300	On masonry		495	.016		.26	.76		1.02	1.46
0400	On concrete		260	.031		.26	1.44		1.70	2.51
0600	1" x 3", on walls, on wood		550	.015		.39	.68		1.07	1.47
0605	On wood, pneumatic nailed		710	.011		.39	.53		.92	1.23
0700	On masonry		495	.016		.42	.76		1.18	1.63
0800	On concrete		260	.031		.42	1.44		1.86	2.68

06 13 Heavy Timber Construction

06 13 33 – Heavy Timber Pier Construction

06 13 33.50 Jetties, Docks, Fixed

		Crew	Daily Output	Labor-Hours	Unit	Material	Labor	Equipment	Total	Total Incl O&P
0010	**JETTIES, DOCKS, FIXED**									
0020	Pile supported, treated wood,									
0030	5' x 20' platform, freshwater	F-3	115	.348	S.F.	18.50	16.65	5.70	40.85	52.50
0060	Saltwater		115	.348		39	16.65	5.70	61.35	74.50
0100	6' x 20' platform, freshwater		110	.364		16.15	17.40	5.95	39.50	51
0160	Saltwater		110	.364		34.50	17.40	5.95	57.85	71
0200	8' x 20' platform, freshwater		105	.381		13.35	18.25	6.25	37.85	49.50
0260	Saltwater		105	.381		29.50	18.25	6.25	54	67.50
0420	5' x 30' platform, freshwater		100	.400		17.90	19.15	6.55	43.60	56.50
0460	Saltwater		100	.400		54	19.15	6.55	79.70	95.50
0500	For Greenhart lumber, add					40%				
0550	Diagonal planking, add								25%	25%

06 13 33.52 Jetties, Piers

		Crew	Daily Output	Labor-Hours	Unit	Material	Labor	Equipment	Total	Total Incl O&P
0010	**JETTIES, PIERS**, Municipal with 3" x 12" framing and 3" decking,									
0020	wood piles and cross bracing, alternate bents battered	B-76	60	1.200	S.F.	76	57	55	188	233
0200	Treated piles, not including mobilization									
0210	50' long, 20 lb. creosote, shore driven	B-19	540	.119	V.L.F.	19.35	5.65	3.22	28.22	34
0220	Barge driven	B-76	320	.225		19.35	10.70	10.35	40.40	49.50
0230	2.5 lb. treatment, shore driven	B-19	540	.119		18.40	5.65	3.22	27.27	32.50

06 13 Heavy Timber Construction

06 13 33 – Heavy Timber Pier Construction

06 13 33.52 Jetties, Piers

		Crew	Daily Output	Labor-Hours	Unit	Material	2015 Bare Costs Labor	Equipment	Total	Total Incl O&P
0240	Barge driven	B-76	320	.225	V.L.F.	18.40	10.70	10.35	39.45	48
0250	30' long, 20 lb. creosote, shore driven	B-19	540	.119		17.80	5.65	3.22	26.67	32
0260	Barge driven	B-76	320	.225		17.80	10.70	10.35	38.85	47.50
0270	2.5 lb. treatment, shore driven	B-19	540	.119		18.40	5.65	3.22	27.27	32.50
0280	Barge driven	B-76	320	.225		18.40	10.70	10.35	39.45	48
0300	Mobilization, barge, by tug boat	B-83	25	.640	Mile		28	35	63	81.50
0350	Standby time for shore pile driving crew				Hr.				600	750
0360	Standby time for barge driving rig				"				840	1,050

06 18 Glued-Laminated Construction

06 18 13 – Glued-Laminated Beams

06 18 13.20 Laminated Framing

		Crew	Daily Output	Labor-Hours	Unit	Material	2015 Bare Costs Labor	Equipment	Total	Total Incl O&P
0010	**LAMINATED FRAMING**									
0200	Straight roof beams, 20' clear span, beams 8' O.C.	F-3	2560	.016	SF Flr.	2.04	.75	.26	3.05	3.67
0500	40' clear span, beams 8' O.C.	"	3200	.013		3.90	.60	.20	4.70	5.45
0800	60' clear span, beams 8' O.C.	F-4	2880	.017		6.70	.79	.39	7.88	9.05
1700	Radial arches, 60' clear span, frames 8' O.C.		1920	.025		8.85	1.19	.59	10.63	12.15
2000	100' clear span, frames 8' O.C.		1600	.030		9.15	1.42	.71	11.28	13
2300	120' clear span, frames 8' O.C.		1440	.033		12.15	1.58	.78	14.51	16.65
2600	Bowstring trusses, 20' O.C., 40' clear span	F-3	2400	.017		5.50	.80	.27	6.57	7.60
2700	60' clear span	F-4	3600	.013		4.92	.63	.31	5.86	6.70
2800	100' clear span	"	4000	.012		6.95	.57	.28	7.80	8.85
4300	Alternate pricing method: (use nominal footage of									
4310	components). Straight beams, camber less than 6"	F-3	3.50	11.429	M.B.F.	2,925	545	187	3,657	4,250
4600	Curved members, radius over 32'		2.50	16		3,200	765	262	4,227	5,000
4700	Radius 10' to 32'		3	13.333		3,175	640	218	4,033	4,725
6000	Laminated veneer members, southern pine or western species									
6050	1-3/4" wide x 5-1/2" deep	2 Carp	480	.033	L.F.	3.44	1.56		5	6.20
6100	9-1/2" deep		480	.033		4.74	1.56		6.30	7.60
6150	14" deep		450	.036		7.85	1.67		9.52	11.20
6200	18" deep		450	.036		10.65	1.67		12.32	14.30
6300	Parallel strand members, southern pine or western species									
6350	1-3/4" wide x 9-1/4" deep	2 Carp	480	.033	L.F.	5.10	1.56		6.66	8
6400	11-1/4" deep		450	.036		5.75	1.67		7.42	8.90
6450	14" deep		400	.040		7.85	1.88		9.73	11.55
6500	3-1/2" wide x 9-1/4" deep		480	.033		16.30	1.56		17.86	20.50
6550	11-1/4" deep		450	.036		20.50	1.67		22.17	25
6600	14" deep		400	.040		24	1.88		25.88	29.50
6650	7" wide x 9-1/4" deep		450	.036		34.50	1.67		36.17	40.50
6700	11-1/4" deep		420	.038		43.50	1.79		45.29	50.50
6750	14" deep		400	.040		52	1.88		53.88	60

06 44 Ornamental Woodwork

06 44 39 – Wood Posts and Columns

06 44 39.20 Columns		Crew	Daily Output	Labor-Hours	Unit	Material	2015 Bare Costs Labor	Equipment	Total	Total Incl O&P
0010	**COLUMNS**									
4000	Rough sawn cedar posts, 4" x 4"	2 Carp	250	.064	V.L.F.	3.90	3		6.90	8.90
4100	4" x 6"		235	.068		6.80	3.20		10	12.40
4200	6" x 6"		220	.073		9.90	3.41		13.31	16.15
4300	8" x 8"		200	.080		19.20	3.76		22.96	27

For customer support on your Site Work & Landscape Cost Data, call 877.737.1594.

137

Division Notes

	CREW	DAILY OUTPUT	LABOR-HOURS	UNIT	BARE COSTS				TOTAL INCL O&P
					MAT.	LABOR	EQUIP.	TOTAL	

Estimating Tips
07 10 00 Dampproofing and Waterproofing

- Be sure of the job specifications before pricing this subdivision. The difference in cost between waterproofing and dampproofing can be great. Waterproofing will hold back standing water. Dampproofing prevents the transmission of water vapor. Also included in this section are vapor retarding membranes.

07 20 00 Thermal Protection

- Insulation and fireproofing products are measured by area, thickness, volume or R-value. Specifications may give only what the specific R-value should be in a certain situation. The estimator may need to choose the type of insulation to meet that R-value.

07 30 00 Steep Slope Roofing
07 40 00 Roofing and Siding Panels

- Many roofing and siding products are bought and sold by the square. One square is equal to an area that measures 100 square feet.

  This simple change in unit of measure could create a large error if the estimator is not observant. Accessories necessary for a complete installation must be figured into any calculations for both material and labor.

07 50 00 Membrane Roofing
07 60 00 Flashing and Sheet Metal
07 70 00 Roofing and Wall Specialties and Accessories

- The items in these subdivisions compose a roofing system. No one component completes the installation, and all must be estimated. Built-up or single-ply membrane roofing systems are made up of many products and installation trades. Wood blocking at roof perimeters or penetrations, parapet coverings, reglets, roof drains, gutters, downspouts, sheet metal flashing, skylights, smoke vents, and roof hatches all need to be considered along with the roofing material. Several different installation trades will need to work together on the roofing system. Inherent difficulties in the scheduling and coordination of various trades must be accounted for when estimating labor costs.

07 90 00 Joint Protection

- To complete the weather-tight shell, the sealants and caulkings must be estimated. Where different materials meet—at expansion joints, at flashing penetrations, and at hundreds of other locations throughout a construction project—they provide another line of defense against water penetration. Often, an entire system is based on the proper location and placement of caulking or sealants. The detailed drawings that are included as part of a set of architectural plans show typical locations for these materials. When caulking or sealants are shown at typical locations, this means the estimator must include them for all the locations where this detail is applicable. Be careful to keep different types of sealants separate, and remember to consider backer rods and primers if necessary.

Reference Numbers

Reference numbers are shown in shaded boxes at the beginning of some major classifications. These numbers refer to related items in the Reference Section. The reference information may be an estimating procedure, an alternate pricing method, or technical information.

Note: Not all subdivisions listed here necessarily appear in this publication. ∎

07 01 90 – Maintenance of Joint Protection

07 01 90.81 Joint Sealant Replacement

		Crew	Daily Output	Labor-Hours	Unit	Material	2015 Bare Costs Labor	2015 Bare Costs Equipment	Total	Total Incl O&P
0010	**JOINT SEALANT REPLACEMENT**									
0050	Control joints in concrete floors/slabs									
0100	Option 1 for joints with hard dry sealant									
0110	Step 1: Sawcut to remove 95% of old sealant									
0112	1/4" wide x 1/2" deep, with single saw blade	C-27	4800	.003	L.F.	.02	.15	.03	.20	.28
0114	3/8" wide x 3/4" deep, with single saw blade		4000	.004		.03	.18	.04	.25	.36
0116	1/2" wide x 1" deep, with double saw blades		3600	.004		.06	.20	.05	.31	.42
0118	3/4" wide x 1-1/2" deep, with double saw blades		3200	.005		.13	.23	.05	.41	.53
0120	Step 2: Water blast joint faces and edges	C-29	2500	.003			.12	.03	.15	.22
0130	Step 3: Air blast joint faces and edges	C-28	2000	.004			.18	.01	.19	.28
0140	Step 4: Sand blast joint faces and edges	E-11	2000	.016			.68	.12	.80	1.24
0150	Step 5: Air blast joint faces and edges	C-28	2000	.004			.18	.01	.19	.28
0200	Option 2 for joints with soft pliable sealant									
0210	Step 1: Plow joint with rectangular blade	B-62	2600	.009	L.F.		.38	.07	.45	.65
0220	Step 2: Sawcut to re-face joint faces									
0222	1/4" wide x 1/2" deep, with single saw blade	C-27	2400	.007	L.F.	.02	.30	.07	.39	.55
0224	3/8" wide x 3/4" deep, with single saw blade		2000	.008		.04	.36	.08	.48	.67
0226	1/2" wide x 1" deep, with double saw blades		1800	.009		.09	.40	.09	.58	.78
0228	3/4" wide x 1-1/2" deep, with double saw blades		1600	.010		.17	.45	.10	.72	.98
0230	Step 3: Water blast joint faces and edges	C-29	2500	.003			.12	.03	.15	.22
0240	Step 4: Air blast joint faces and edges	C-28	2000	.004			.18	.01	.19	.28
0250	Step 5: Sand blast joint faces and edges	E-11	2000	.016			.68	.12	.80	1.24
0260	Step 6: Air blast joint faces and edges	C-28	2000	.004			.18	.01	.19	.28
0290	For saw cutting new control joints, see Section 03 15 16.20									
8910	For backer rod, see Section 07 91 23.10									
8920	For joint sealant, see Sections 03 15 16.30 or 07 92 13.20									

07 11 Dampproofing

07 11 13 – Bituminous Dampproofing

07 11 13.10 Bituminous Asphalt Coating

		Crew	Daily Output	Labor-Hours	Unit	Material	2015 Bare Costs Labor	2015 Bare Costs Equipment	Total	Total Incl O&P
0010	**BITUMINOUS ASPHALT COATING**									
0030	Brushed on, below grade, 1 coat	1 Rofc	665	.012	S.F.	.22	.48		.70	1.07
0100	2 coat		500	.016		.45	.64		1.09	1.59
0300	Sprayed on, below grade, 1 coat		830	.010		.22	.39		.61	.91
0400	2 coat		500	.016		.44	.64		1.08	1.58
0500	Asphalt coating, with fibers				Gal.	8.25			8.25	9.10
0600	Troweled on, asphalt with fibers, 1/16" thick	1 Rofc	500	.016	S.F.	.36	.64		1	1.50
0700	1/8" thick		400	.020		.64	.80		1.44	2.07
1000	1/2" thick		350	.023		2.07	.92		2.99	3.83

07 11 16 – Cementitious Dampproofing

07 11 16.20 Cementitious Parging

		Crew	Daily Output	Labor-Hours	Unit	Material	2015 Bare Costs Labor	2015 Bare Costs Equipment	Total	Total Incl O&P
0010	**CEMENTITIOUS PARGING**									
0020	Portland cement, 2 coats, 1/2" thick	D-1	250	.064	S.F.	.33	2.69		3.02	4.47
0100	Waterproofed Portland cement, 1/2" thick, 2 coats	"	250	.064	"	3.93	2.69		6.62	8.45

07 12 Built-up Bituminous Waterproofing

07 12 13 – Built-Up Asphalt Waterproofing

07 12 13.20 Membrane Waterproofing	Crew	Daily Output	Labor-Hours	Unit	Material	2015 Bare Costs Labor	Equipment	Total	Total Incl O&P
0010 **MEMBRANE WATERPROOFING**									
0012 On slabs, 1 ply, felt, mopped	G-1	3000	.019	S.F.	.42	.70	.19	1.31	1.87
0015 On walls, 1 ply, felt, mopped		3000	.019		.42	.70	.19	1.31	1.87
0100 On slabs, 1 ply, glass fiber fabric, mopped		2100	.027		.46	1	.27	1.73	2.51
0105 On walls, 1 ply, glass fiber fabric, mopped		2100	.027		.46	1	.27	1.73	2.51
0300 On slabs, 2 ply, felt, mopped		2500	.022		.83	.84	.23	1.90	2.59
0305 On walls, 2 ply, felt, mopped		2500	.022		.83	.84	.23	1.90	2.59
0400 On slabs, 2 ply, glass fiber fabric, mopped		1650	.034		1.01	1.27	.34	2.62	3.66
0405 On walls, 2 ply, glass fiber fabric, mopped		1650	.034		1.01	1.27	.34	2.62	3.66
0600 On slabs, 3 ply, felt, mopped		2100	.027		1.25	1	.27	2.52	3.38
0605 On walls, 3 ply, felt, mopped		2100	.027		1.25	1	.27	2.52	3.38
0700 On slabs, 3 ply, glass fiber fabric, mopped		1550	.036		1.37	1.36	.37	3.10	4.22
0705 On walls, 3 ply, glass fiber fabric, mopped	▼	1550	.036		1.37	1.36	.37	3.10	4.22
0710 Asphaltic hardboard protection board, 1/8" thick	2 Rofc	500	.032		.61	1.28		1.89	2.86
0715 1/4" thick		450	.036		1.70	1.43		3.13	4.30
1000 EPS membrane protection board, 1/4"		3500	.005		.33	.18		.51	.68
1050 3/8" thick		3500	.005		.36	.18		.54	.71
1060 1/2" thick		3500	.005		.40	.18		.58	.74
1070 Fiberglass fabric, black, 20/10 mesh	▼	116	.138	Sq.	15.40	5.55		20.95	26.50

07 13 Sheet Waterproofing

07 13 53 – Elastomeric Sheet Waterproofing

07 13 53.10 Elastomeric Sheet Waterproofing and Access.

	Crew	Daily Output	Labor-Hours	Unit	Material	2015 Bare Costs Labor	Equipment	Total	Total Incl O&P
0010 **ELASTOMERIC SHEET WATERPROOFING AND ACCESS.**									
0090 EPDM, plain, 45 mils thick	2 Rofc	580	.028	S.F.	1.41	1.11		2.52	3.44
0100 60 mils thick		570	.028		1.47	1.13		2.60	3.54
0300 Nylon reinforced sheets, 45 mils thick		580	.028		1.55	1.11		2.66	3.59
0400 60 mils thick	▼	570	.028	▼	1.64	1.13		2.77	3.73
0600 Vulcanizing splicing tape for above, 2" wide				C.L.F.	60.50			60.50	66.50
0700 4" wide				"	121			121	133
0900 Adhesive, bonding, 60 S.F. per gal.				Gal.	27			27	29.50
1000 Splicing, 75 S.F. per gal.				"	41			41	45
1200 Neoprene sheets, plain, 45 mils thick	2 Rofc	580	.028	S.F.	1.70	1.11		2.81	3.76
1300 60 mils thick		570	.028		2.17	1.13		3.30	4.31
1500 Nylon reinforced, 45 mils thick		580	.028		1.96	1.11		3.07	4.05
1600 60 mils thick		570	.028		3.05	1.13		4.18	5.30
1800 120 mils thick	▼	500	.032	▼	6.05	1.28		7.33	8.85
1900 Adhesive, splicing, 150 S.F. per gal. per coat				Gal.	41			41	45
2100 Fiberglass reinforced, fluid applied, 1/8" thick	2 Rofc	500	.032	S.F.	1.63	1.28		2.91	3.98
2200 Polyethylene and rubberized asphalt sheets, 60 mils thick		550	.029		.92	1.17		2.09	3
2400 Polyvinyl chloride sheets, plain, 10 mils thick		580	.028		.15	1.11		1.26	2.06
2500 20 mils thick		570	.028		.19	1.13		1.32	2.13
2700 30 mils thick	▼	560	.029	▼	.24	1.15		1.39	2.22
3000 Adhesives, trowel grade, 40-100 S.F. per gal.				Gal.	24			24	26.50
3100 Brush grade, 100-250 S.F. per gal.				"	21.50			21.50	24
3300 Bitumen modified polyurethane, fluid applied, 55 mils thick	2 Rofc	665	.024	S.F.	.93	.96		1.89	2.67

For customer support on your Site Work & Landscape Cost Data, call 877.737.1594.

141

07 16 Cementitious and Reactive Waterproofing

07 16 16 – Crystalline Waterproofing

07 16 16.20 Cementitious Waterproofing		Crew	Daily Output	Labor-Hours	Unit	Material	2015 Bare Costs Labor	Equipment	Total	Total Incl O&P
0010	**CEMENTITIOUS WATERPROOFING**									
0020	1/8" application, sprayed on	G-2A	1000	.024	S.F.	.73	.86	.72	2.31	3.01
0050	4 coat cementitious metallic slurry	1 Cefi	1.20	6.667	C.S.F.	32	300		332	480

07 17 Bentonite Waterproofing

07 17 13 – Bentonite Panel Waterproofing

07 17 13.10 Bentonite

		Crew	Daily Output	Labor-Hours	Unit	Material	2015 Bare Costs Labor	Equipment	Total	Total Incl O&P
0010	**BENTONITE**									
0020	Panels, 4' x 4', 3/16" thick	1 Rofc	625	.013	S.F.	1.57	.51		2.08	2.61
0100	Rolls, 3/8" thick, with geotextile fabric both sides	"	550	.015	"	1.47	.58		2.05	2.62
0300	Granular bentonite, 50 lb. bags (.625 C.F.)				Bag	20.50			20.50	22.50
0400	3/8" thick, troweled on	1 Rofc	475	.017	S.F.	1.02	.68		1.70	2.27
0500	Drain board, expanded polystyrene, 1-1/2" thick	1 Rohe	1600	.005		.38	.15		.53	.67
0510	2" thick		1600	.005		.50	.15		.65	.81
0520	3" thick		1600	.005		.75	.15		.90	1.09
0530	4" thick		1600	.005		1	.15		1.15	1.36
0600	With filter fabric, 1-1/2" thick		1600	.005		.44	.15		.59	.74
0625	2" thick		1600	.005		.56	.15		.71	.88
0650	3" thick		1600	.005		.81	.15		.96	1.16
0675	4" thick		1600	.005		1.06	.15		1.21	1.43

07 19 Water Repellents

07 19 19 – Silicone Water Repellents

07 19 19.10 Silicone Based Water Repellents

		Crew	Daily Output	Labor-Hours	Unit	Material	2015 Bare Costs Labor	Equipment	Total	Total Incl O&P
0010	**SILICONE BASED WATER REPELLENTS**									
0020	Water base liquid, roller applied	2 Rofc	7000	.002	S.F.	.53	.09		.62	.74
0200	Silicone or stearate, sprayed on CMU, 1 coat	1 Rofc	4000	.002		.34	.08		.42	.51
0300	2 coats	"	3000	.003		.68	.11		.79	.93

07 21 Thermal Insulation

07 21 13 – Board Insulation

07 21 13.10 Rigid Insulation

			Crew	Daily Output	Labor-Hours	Unit	Material	2015 Bare Costs Labor	Equipment	Total	Total Incl O&P
0010	**RIGID INSULATION**, for walls										
0040	Fiberglass, 1.5#/C.F., unfaced, 1" thick, R4.1	G	1 Carp	1000	.008	S.F.	.27	.38		.65	.88
0060	1-1/2" thick, R6.2	G		1000	.008		.40	.38		.78	1.02
0080	2" thick, R8.3	G		1000	.008		.45	.38		.83	1.08
0120	3" thick, R12.4	G		800	.010		.56	.47		1.03	1.34
0370	3#/C.F., unfaced, 1" thick, R4.3	G		1000	.008		.52	.38		.90	1.15
0390	1-1/2" thick, R6.5	G		1000	.008		.78	.38		1.16	1.44
0400	2" thick, R8.7	G		890	.009		1.05	.42		1.47	1.81
0420	2-1/2" thick, R10.9	G		800	.010		1.10	.47		1.57	1.93
0440	3" thick, R13	G		800	.010		1.59	.47		2.06	2.47
0520	Foil faced, 1" thick, R4.3	G		1000	.008		.90	.38		1.28	1.57
0540	1-1/2" thick, R6.5	G		1000	.008		1.35	.38		1.73	2.07
0560	2" thick, R8.7	G		890	.009		1.69	.42		2.11	2.51
0580	2-1/2" thick, R10.9	G		800	.010		1.98	.47		2.45	2.90
0600	3" thick, R13	G		800	.010		2.18	.47		2.65	3.12

07 21 Thermal Insulation

07 21 13 – Board Insulation

07 21 13.10 Rigid Insulation

			Crew	Daily Output	Labor-Hours	Unit	Material	2015 Bare Costs Labor	Equipment	Total	Total Incl O&P
1600	Isocyanurate, 4' x 8' sheet, foil faced, both sides										
1610	1/2" thick	G	1 Carp	800	.010	S.F.	.31	.47		.78	1.06
1620	5/8" thick	G		800	.010		.33	.47		.80	1.08
1630	3/4" thick	G		800	.010		.36	.47		.83	1.12
1640	1" thick	G		800	.010		.52	.47		.99	1.29
1650	1-1/2" thick	G		730	.011		.63	.51		1.14	1.48
1660	2" thick	G		730	.011		.80	.51		1.31	1.67
1670	3" thick	G		730	.011		1.80	.51		2.31	2.77
1680	4" thick	G		730	.011		2.05	.51		2.56	3.05
1700	Perlite, 1" thick, R2.77	G		800	.010		.42	.47		.89	1.18
1750	2" thick, R5.55	G		730	.011		.75	.51		1.26	1.62
1900	Extruded polystyrene, 25 PSI compressive strength, 1" thick, R5	G		800	.010		.53	.47		1	1.30
1940	2" thick R10	G		730	.011		1.04	.51		1.55	1.93
1960	3" thick, R15	G		730	.011		1.50	.51		2.01	2.44
2100	Expanded polystyrene, 1" thick, R3.85	G		800	.010		.25	.47		.72	1
2120	2" thick, R7.69	G		730	.011		.50	.51		1.01	1.34
2140	3" thick, R11.49	G		730	.011		.75	.51		1.26	1.62

07 21 13.13 Foam Board Insulation

			Crew	Daily Output	Labor-Hours	Unit	Material	2015 Bare Costs Labor	Equipment	Total	Total Incl O&P
0010	**FOAM BOARD INSULATION**										
0600	Polystyrene, expanded, 1" thick, R4	G	1 Carp	680	.012	S.F.	.25	.55		.80	1.13
0700	2" thick, R8	G	"	675	.012	"	.50	.56		1.06	1.41

07 21 23 – Loose-Fill Insulation

07 21 23.20 Masonry Loose-Fill Insulation

			Crew	Daily Output	Labor-Hours	Unit	Material	2015 Bare Costs Labor	Equipment	Total	Total Incl O&P
0010	**MASONRY LOOSE-FILL INSULATION**, vermiculite or perlite										
0100	In cores of concrete block, 4" thick wall, .115 C.F./S.F.	G	D-1	4800	.003	S.F.	.60	.14		.74	.87
0200	6" thick wall, .175 C.F./S.F.	G		3000	.005		.91	.22		1.13	1.34
0300	8" thick wall, .258 C.F./S.F.	G		2400	.007		1.34	.28		1.62	1.91
0400	10" thick wall, .340 C.F./S.F.	G		1850	.009		1.77	.36		2.13	2.51
0500	12" thick wall, .422 C.F./S.F.	G		1200	.013		2.20	.56		2.76	3.28
0600	Poured cavity wall, vermiculite or perlite, water repellant	G		250	.064	C.F.	5.20	2.69		7.89	9.85
0700	Foamed in place, urethane in 2-5/8" cavity	G	G-2A	1035	.023	S.F.	1.38	.83	.69	2.90	3.65
0800	For each 1" added thickness, add	G	"	2372	.010	"	.53	.36	.30	1.19	1.51

07 25 Weather Barriers

07 25 10 – Weather Barriers or Wraps

07 25 10.10 Weather Barriers

		Crew	Daily Output	Labor-Hours	Unit	Material	2015 Bare Costs Labor	Equipment	Total	Total Incl O&P
0010	**WEATHER BARRIERS**									
0400	Asphalt felt paper, 15#	1 Carp	37	.216	Sq.	5.40	10.15		15.55	21.50
0401	Per square foot	"	3700	.002	S.F.	.05	.10		.15	.22
0450	Housewrap, exterior, spun bonded polypropylene									
0470	Small roll	1 Carp	3800	.002	S.F.	.15	.10		.25	.31
0480	Large roll	"	4000	.002	"	.14	.09		.23	.29
2100	Asphalt felt roof deck vapor barrier, class 1 metal decks	1 Rofc	37	.216	Sq.	22	8.65		30.65	39
2200	For all other decks	"	37	.216		16.50	8.65		25.15	33
2800	Asphalt felt, 50% recycled content, 15 lb., 4 sq. per roll	1 Carp	36	.222		5.40	10.45		15.85	22
2810	30 lb., 2 sq. per roll	"	36	.222		10.80	10.45		21.25	28
3000	Building wrap, spunbonded polyethylene	2 Carp	8000	.002	S.F.	.15	.09		.24	.31

07 26 Vapor Retarders

07 26 10 – Above-Grade Vapor Retarders

07 26 10.10 Vapor Retarders

	07 26 10.10 Vapor Retarders		Crew	Daily Output	Labor-Hours	Unit	Material	2015 Bare Costs Labor	Equipment	Total	Total Incl O&P
0010	**VAPOR RETARDERS**										
0020	Aluminum and kraft laminated, foil 1 side	G	1 Carp	37	.216	Sq.	12.50	10.15		22.65	29.50
0100	Foil 2 sides	G		37	.216		14	10.15		24.15	31
0600	Polyethylene vapor barrier, standard, 2 mil	G		37	.216		1.50	10.15		11.65	17.25
0700	4 mil	G		37	.216		2.90	10.15		13.05	18.80
0900	6 mil	G		37	.216		4.02	10.15		14.17	20
1200	10 mil	G		37	.216		8.85	10.15		19	25.50
1300	Clear reinforced, fire retardant, 8 mil	G		37	.216		10.85	10.15		21	27.50
1350	Cross laminated type, 3 mil	G		37	.216		7.60	10.15		17.75	24
1400	4 mil	G		37	.216		7.95	10.15		18.10	24.50
1800	Reinf. waterproof, 2 mil polyethylene backing, 1 side			37	.216		6.05	10.15		16.20	22.50
1900	2 sides			37	.216		7.95	10.15		18.10	24.50
2400	Waterproofed kraft with sisal or fiberglass fibers		▼	37	.216	▼	12.75	10.15		22.90	29.50

07 31 Shingles and Shakes

07 31 13 – Asphalt Shingles

07 31 13.10 Asphalt Roof Shingles

	07 31 13.10 Asphalt Roof Shingles		Crew	Daily Output	Labor-Hours	Unit	Material	2015 Bare Costs Labor	Equipment	Total	Total Incl O&P
0010	**ASPHALT ROOF SHINGLES**										
0100	Standard strip shingles										
0150	Inorganic, class A, 25 year		1 Rofc	5.50	1.455	Sq.	79.50	58.50		138	187
0155	Pneumatic nailed			7	1.143		79.50	46		125.50	166
0200	30 year			5	1.600		94	64		158	213
0205	Pneumatic nailed		▼	6.25	1.280	▼	94	51.50		145.50	191
0250	Standard laminated multi-layered shingles										
0300	Class A, 240-260 lb./square		1 Rofc	4.50	1.778	Sq.	110	71.50		181.50	243
0305	Pneumatic nailed			5.63	1.422		110	57		167	219
0350	Class A, 250-270 lb./square			4	2		110	80		190	258
0355	Pneumatic nailed		▼	5	1.600	▼	110	64		174	231
0400	Premium, laminated multi-layered shingles										
0450	Class A, 260-300 lb./square		1 Rofc	3.50	2.286	Sq.	153	91.50		244.50	325
0455	Pneumatic nailed			4.37	1.831		153	73.50		226.50	293
0500	Class A, 300-385 lb./square			3	2.667		230	107		337	435
0505	Pneumatic nailed			3.75	2.133		230	85.50		315.50	400
0800	#15 felt underlayment			64	.125		5.40	5		10.40	14.50
0825	#30 felt underlayment			58	.138		10.60	5.55		16.15	21
0850	Self adhering polyethylene and rubberized asphalt underlayment			22	.364	▼	75	14.60		89.60	108
0900	Ridge shingles			330	.024	L.F.	2.10	.97		3.07	3.97
0905	Pneumatic nailed		▼	412.50	.019	"	2.10	.78		2.88	3.64
1000	For steep roofs (7 to 12 pitch or greater), add							50%			

07 31 26 – Slate Shingles

07 31 26.10 Slate Roof Shingles

	07 31 26.10 Slate Roof Shingles		Crew	Daily Output	Labor-Hours	Unit	Material	2015 Bare Costs Labor	Equipment	Total	Total Incl O&P
0010	**SLATE ROOF SHINGLES**										
0100	Buckingham Virginia black, 3/16" - 1/4" thick	G	1 Rots	1.75	4.571	Sq.	470	183		653	830

144

07 32 Roof Tiles

07 32 13 – Clay Roof Tiles

07 32 13.10 Clay Tiles

	07 32 13.10 Clay Tiles	Crew	Daily Output	Labor-Hours	Unit	Material	2015 Bare Costs Labor	Equipment	Total	Total Incl O&P
0010	**CLAY TILES**, including accessories									
0300	Flat shingle, interlocking, 15", 166 pcs/sq, fireflashed blend	3 Rots	6	4	Sq.	505	160		665	830
0500	Terra cotta red		6	4		510	160		670	835
0600	Roman pan and top, 18", 102 pcs/sq, fireflashed blend		5.50	4.364		555	175		730	910
0640	Terra cotta red	1 Rots	2.40	3.333		555	134		689	840
1100	Barrel mission tile, 18", 166 pcs/sq, fireflashed blend	3 Rots	5.50	4.364		410	175		585	750
1140	Terra cotta red		5.50	4.364		410	175		585	750
1700	Scalloped edge flat shingle, 14", 145 pcs/sq, fireflashed blend		6	4		1,125	160		1,285	1,525
1800	Terra cotta red		6	4		1,100	160		1,260	1,500
3010	#15 felt underlayment	1 Rofc	64	.125		5.40	5		10.40	14.50
3020	#30 felt underlayment		58	.138		10.60	5.55		16.15	21
3040	Polyethylene and rubberized asph. underlayment		22	.364		75	14.60		89.60	108

07 32 16 – Concrete Roof Tiles

07 32 16.10 Concrete Tiles

	07 32 16.10 Concrete Tiles	Crew	Daily Output	Labor-Hours	Unit	Material	2015 Bare Costs Labor	Equipment	Total	Total Incl O&P
0010	**CONCRETE TILES**									
0020	Corrugated, 13" x 16-1/2", 90 per sq., 950 lb. per sq.									
0050	Earthtone colors, nailed to wood deck	1 Rots	1.35	5.926	Sq.	106	238		344	520
0150	Blues		1.35	5.926		106	238		344	520
0200	Greens		1.35	5.926		106	238		344	520
0250	Premium colors		1.35	5.926		106	238		344	520
0500	Shakes, 13" x 16-1/2", 90 per sq., 950 lb. per sq.									
0600	All colors, nailed to wood deck	1 Rots	1.50	5.333	Sq.	108	214		322	485
1500	Accessory pieces, ridge & hip, 10" x 16-1/2", 8 lb. each	"	120	.067	Ea.	3.20	2.67		5.87	8.10
1700	Rake, 6-1/2" x 16-3/4", 9 lb. each					3.20			3.20	3.52
1800	Mansard hip, 10" x 16-1/2", 9.2 lb. each					3.20			3.20	3.52
1900	Hip starter, 10" x 16-1/2", 10.5 lb. each					9.90			9.90	10.90
2000	3 or 4 way apex, 10" each side, 11.5 lb. each					11.40			11.40	12.55

07 32 19 – Metal Roof Tiles

07 32 19.10 Metal Roof Tiles

	07 32 19.10 Metal Roof Tiles	Crew	Daily Output	Labor-Hours	Unit	Material	2015 Bare Costs Labor	Equipment	Total	Total Incl O&P
0010	**METAL ROOF TILES**									
0020	Accessories included, .032" thick aluminum, mission tile	1 Carp	2.50	3.200	Sq.	825	150		975	1,150
0200	Spanish tiles	"	3	2.667	"	570	125		695	820

07 41 Roof Panels

07 41 13 – Metal Roof Panels

07 41 13.10 Aluminum Roof Panels

	07 41 13.10 Aluminum Roof Panels	Crew	Daily Output	Labor-Hours	Unit	Material	2015 Bare Costs Labor	Equipment	Total	Total Incl O&P
0010	**ALUMINUM ROOF PANELS**									
0020	Corrugated or ribbed, .0155" thick, natural	G-3	1200	.027	S.F.	.99	1.25		2.24	3
0300	Painted		1200	.027		1.44	1.25		2.69	3.49
0400	Corrugated, .018" thick, on steel frame, natural finish		1200	.027		1.30	1.25		2.55	3.34
0600	Painted		1200	.027		1.60	1.25		2.85	3.67
0700	Corrugated, on steel frame, natural, .024" thick		1200	.027		1.85	1.25		3.10	3.95
0800	Painted		1200	.027		2.25	1.25		3.50	4.39
0900	.032" thick, natural		1200	.027		2.39	1.25		3.64	4.54
1200	Painted		1200	.027		3.06	1.25		4.31	5.30
1300	V-Beam, on steel frame construction, .032" thick, natural		1200	.027		2.53	1.25		3.78	4.69
1500	Painted		1200	.027		3.10	1.25		4.35	5.30
1600	.040" thick, natural		1200	.027		3.07	1.25		4.32	5.30
1800	Painted		1200	.027		3.70	1.25		4.95	6
1900	.050" thick, natural		1200	.027		3.69	1.25		4.94	5.95

For customer support on your Site Work & Landscape Cost Data, call 877.737.1594.

145

07 41 Roof Panels

07 41 13 – Metal Roof Panels

07 41 13.10 Aluminum Roof Panels

		Crew	Daily Output	Labor-Hours	Unit	Material	2015 Bare Costs Labor	Equipment	Total	Total Incl O&P
2100	Painted	G-3	1200	.027	S.F.	4.45	1.25		5.70	6.80
2200	For roofing on wood frame, deduct		4600	.007	↓	.08	.33		.41	.59
2400	Ridge cap, .032" thick, natural	↓	800	.040	L.F.	2.91	1.87		4.78	6.05

07 41 13.20 Steel Roofing Panels

		Crew	Daily Output	Labor-Hours	Unit	Material	2015 Bare Costs Labor	Equipment	Total	Total Incl O&P
0010	**STEEL ROOFING PANELS**									
0012	Corrugated or ribbed, on steel framing, 30 ga. galv	G-3	1100	.029	S.F.	1.60	1.36		2.96	3.85
0100	28 ga.		1050	.030		1.65	1.43		3.08	4
0300	26 ga.		1000	.032		1.68	1.50		3.18	4.14
0400	24 ga.		950	.034		2.90	1.58		4.48	5.60
0600	Colored, 28 ga.		1050	.030		1.67	1.43		3.10	4.02
0700	26 ga.	↓	1000	.032	↓	1.98	1.50		3.48	4.47

07 41 33 – Plastic Roof Panels

07 41 33.10 Fiberglass Panels

		Crew	Daily Output	Labor-Hours	Unit	Material	2015 Bare Costs Labor	Equipment	Total	Total Incl O&P
0010	**FIBERGLASS PANELS**									
0012	Corrugated panels, roofing, 8 oz. per S.F.	G-3	1000	.032	S.F.	2.10	1.50		3.60	4.60
0100	12 oz. per S.F.		1000	.032		4.18	1.50		5.68	6.90
0300	Corrugated siding, 6 oz. per S.F.		880	.036		2.10	1.70		3.80	4.92
0400	8 oz. per S.F.		880	.036		2.10	1.70		3.80	4.92
0500	Fire retardant		880	.036		3.80	1.70		5.50	6.80
0600	12 oz. siding, textured		880	.036		3.75	1.70		5.45	6.75
0700	Fire retardant		880	.036		4.35	1.70		6.05	7.40
0900	Flat panels, 6 oz. per S.F., clear or colors		880	.036		2.40	1.70		4.10	5.25
1100	Fire retardant, class A		880	.036		3.45	1.70		5.15	6.40
1300	8 oz. per S.F., clear or colors		880	.036		2.52	1.70		4.22	5.40
1700	Sandwich panels, fiberglass, 1-9/16" thick, panels to 20 S.F.		180	.178		36	8.30		44.30	52.50
1900	As above, but 2-3/4" thick, panels to 100 S.F.	↓	265	.121	↓	26	5.65		31.65	37

07 42 Wall Panels

07 42 13 – Metal Wall Panels

07 42 13.20 Aluminum Siding Panels

		Crew	Daily Output	Labor-Hours	Unit	Material	2015 Bare Costs Labor	Equipment	Total	Total Incl O&P
0010	**ALUMINUM SIDING PANELS**									
0012	Corrugated, on steel framing, .019 thick, natural finish	G-3	775	.041	S.F.	1.52	1.93		3.45	4.63
0100	Painted		775	.041		1.66	1.93		3.59	4.79
0400	Farm type, .021" thick on steel frame, natural		775	.041		1.55	1.93		3.48	4.67
0600	Painted		775	.041		1.65	1.93		3.58	4.78
0700	Industrial type, corrugated, on steel, .024" thick, mill		775	.041		2.15	1.93		4.08	5.35
0900	Painted		775	.041		2.31	1.93		4.24	5.50
1000	.032" thick, mill		775	.041		2.45	1.93		4.38	5.65
1200	Painted		775	.041		3	1.93		4.93	6.25
2750	.050" thick, natural		775	.041		3.15	1.93		5.08	6.45
2760	Painted		775	.041		3.63	1.93		5.56	6.95
3300	For siding on wood frame, deduct from above	↓	2800	.011	↓	.09	.53		.62	.92
3400	Screw fasteners, aluminum, self tapping, neoprene washer, 1"				M	210			210	231
3600	Stitch screws, self tapping, with neoprene washer, 5/8"				"	158			158	174
3630	Flashing, sidewall, .032" thick	G-3	800	.040	L.F.	2.96	1.87		4.83	6.15
3650	End wall, .040" thick		800	.040		3.46	1.87		5.33	6.70
3670	Closure strips, corrugated, .032" thick		800	.040		.88	1.87		2.75	3.84
3680	Ribbed, 4" or 8", .032" thick		800	.040		.88	1.87		2.75	3.84
3690	V-beam, .040" thick	↓	800	.040	↓	1.18	1.87		3.05	4.17
3800	Horizontal, colored clapboard, 8" wide, plain	2 Carp	515	.031	S.F.	2.45	1.46		3.91	4.94

07 42 Wall Panels

07 42 13 – Metal Wall Panels

07 42 13.20 Aluminum Siding Panels	Crew	Daily Output	Labor-Hours	Unit	Material	2015 Bare Costs Labor	Equipment	Total	Total Incl O&P
3810 Insulated	2 Carp	515	.031	S.F.	2.67	1.46		4.13	5.20

07 42 13.30 Steel Siding

0010 **STEEL SIDING**									
0020 Beveled, vinyl coated, 8" wide	1 Carp	265	.030	S.F.	1.85	1.42		3.27	4.22
0050 10" wide	"	275	.029		1.88	1.37		3.25	4.17
0080 Galv, corrugated or ribbed, on steel frame, 30 ga.	G-3	800	.040		1.20	1.87		3.07	4.19
0100 28 ga.		795	.040		1.28	1.88		3.16	4.30
0300 26 ga.		790	.041		1.80	1.90		3.70	4.88
0400 24 ga.		785	.041		1.85	1.91		3.76	4.96
0600 22 ga.		770	.042		2.15	1.94		4.09	5.35
0700 Colored, corrugated/ribbed, on steel frame, 10 yr. finish, 28 ga.		800	.040		1.95	1.87		3.82	5
0900 26 ga.		795	.040		2.09	1.88		3.97	5.20
1000 24 ga.		790	.041		2.37	1.90		4.27	5.50
1020 20 ga.		785	.041		3	1.91		4.91	6.20

07 46 Siding

07 46 23 – Wood Siding

07 46 23.10 Wood Board Siding

0010 **WOOD BOARD SIDING**									
3200 Wood, cedar bevel, A grade, 1/2" x 6"	1 Carp	295	.027	S.F.	4.14	1.27		5.41	6.50
3300 1/2" x 8"		330	.024		5.90	1.14		7.04	8.25
3500 3/4" x 10", clear grade		375	.021		6.30	1		7.30	8.45
3600 "B" grade		375	.021		3.79	1		4.79	5.70
3800 Cedar, rough sawn, 1" x 4", A grade, natural		220	.036		6.55	1.71		8.26	9.90
3900 Stained		220	.036		6.70	1.71		8.41	10
4100 1" x 12", board & batten, #3 & Btr., natural		420	.019		4.48	.89		5.37	6.30
4200 Stained		420	.019		4.81	.89		5.70	6.70
4400 1" x 8" channel siding, #3 & Btr., natural		330	.024		4.57	1.14		5.71	6.75
4500 Stained		330	.024		4.92	1.14		6.06	7.15
4700 Redwood, clear, beveled, vertical grain, 1/2" x 4"		220	.036		4.11	1.71		5.82	7.15
4750 1/2" x 6"		295	.027		4.49	1.27		5.76	6.90
4800 1/2" x 8"		330	.024		4.89	1.14		6.03	7.15
5000 3/4" x 10"		375	.021		4.50	1		5.50	6.50
5400 White pine, rough sawn, 1" x 8", natural		330	.024		2.19	1.14		3.33	4.16

07 46 29 – Plywood Siding

07 46 29.10 Plywood Siding Options

0010 **PLYWOOD SIDING OPTIONS**									
0900 Plywood, medium density overlaid, 3/8" thick	2 Carp	750	.021	S.F.	1.25	1		2.25	2.92
1000 1/2" thick		700	.023		1.44	1.07		2.51	3.23
1100 3/4" thick		650	.025		1.85	1.16		3.01	3.82
1600 Texture 1-11, cedar, 5/8" thick, natural		675	.024		2.57	1.11		3.68	4.54
1900 Texture 1-11, fir, 5/8" thick, natural		675	.024		1.57	1.11		2.68	3.44
2050 Texture 1-11, S.Y.P., 5/8" thick, natural		675	.024		1.37	1.11		2.48	3.22
2200 Rough sawn cedar, 3/8" thick, natural		675	.024		1.25	1.11		2.36	3.09
2500 Rough sawn fir, 3/8" thick, natural		675	.024		.84	1.11		1.95	2.63

07 46 33 – Plastic Siding

07 46 33.10 Vinyl Siding

0010 **VINYL SIDING**									
3995 Clapboard profile, woodgrain texture, .048 thick, double 4	2 Carp	495	.032	S.F.	1.04	1.52		2.56	3.49
4000 Double 5		550	.029		1.04	1.37		2.41	3.25

For customer support on your Site Work & Landscape Cost Data, call 877.737.1594.

147

07 46 33.10 Vinyl Siding	Crew	Daily Output	Labor-Hours	Unit	Material	2015 Bare Costs Labor	Equipment	Total	Total Incl O&P
4005	Single 8	2 Carp	495	.032	S.F.	1.26	1.52		2.78	3.73
4010	Single 10		550	.029		1.51	1.37		2.88	3.77
4015	.044 thick, double 4		495	.032		.99	1.52		2.51	3.43
4020	Double 5		550	.029		.99	1.37		2.36	3.19
4025	.042 thick, double 4		495	.032		.92	1.52		2.44	3.36
4030	Double 5		550	.029		.92	1.37		2.29	3.12
4035	Cross sawn texture, .040 thick, double 4		495	.032		.67	1.52		2.19	3.08
4040	Double 5		550	.029		.67	1.37		2.04	2.84
4045	Smooth texture, .042 thick, double 4		495	.032		.75	1.52		2.27	3.17
4050	Double 5		550	.029		.75	1.37		2.12	2.93
4055	Single 8		495	.032		.75	1.52		2.27	3.17
4060	Cedar texture, .044 thick, double 4		495	.032		1.01	1.52		2.53	3.46
4065	Double 6		600	.027		1.01	1.25		2.26	3.05
4070	Dutch lap profile, woodgrain texture, .048 thick, double 5		550	.029		1.04	1.37		2.41	3.25
4075	.044 thick, double 4.5		525	.030		1.01	1.43		2.44	3.32
4080	.042 thick, double 4.5		525	.030		.84	1.43		2.27	3.13
4085	.040 thick, double 4.5		525	.030		.67	1.43		2.10	2.94
4100	Shake profile, 10" wide		400	.040		3.45	1.88		5.33	6.70
4105	Vertical pattern, .046 thick, double 5		550	.029		1.42	1.37		2.79	3.67
4110	.044 thick, triple 3		550	.029		1.56	1.37		2.93	3.82
4115	.040 thick, triple 4		550	.029		1.50	1.37		2.87	3.76
4120	.040 thick, triple 2.66		550	.029		1.81	1.37		3.18	4.10
4125	Insulation, fan folded extruded polystyrene, 1/4"		2000	.008		.28	.38		.66	.89
4130	3/8"		2000	.008	▼	.31	.38		.69	.92
4135	Accessories, J channel, 5/8" pocket		700	.023	L.F.	.46	1.07		1.53	2.15
4140	3/4" pocket		695	.023		.50	1.08		1.58	2.21
4145	1-1/4" pocket		680	.024		.77	1.10		1.87	2.54
4150	Flexible, 3/4" pocket		600	.027		2.33	1.25		3.58	4.49
4155	Under sill finish trim		500	.032		.50	1.50		2	2.86
4160	Vinyl starter strip		700	.023		.58	1.07		1.65	2.29
4165	Aluminum starter strip		700	.023		.28	1.07		1.35	1.96
4170	Window casing, 2-1/2" wide, 3/4" pocket		510	.031		1.57	1.47		3.04	3.99
4175	Outside corner, woodgrain finish, 4" face, 3/4" pocket		700	.023		1.92	1.07		2.99	3.77
4180	5/8" pocket		700	.023		1.92	1.07		2.99	3.77
4185	Smooth finish, 4" face, 3/4" pocket		700	.023		1.92	1.07		2.99	3.77
4190	7/8" pocket		690	.023		1.89	1.09		2.98	3.76
4195	1-1/4" pocket		700	.023		1.33	1.07		2.40	3.12
4200	Soffit and fascia, 1' overhang, solid		120	.133		4.29	6.25		10.54	14.35
4205	Vented		120	.133		4.29	6.25		10.54	14.35
4207	18" overhang, solid		110	.145		5	6.85		11.85	16
4208	Vented		110	.145		5	6.85		11.85	16
4210	2' overhang, solid		100	.160		5.70	7.50		13.20	17.85
4215	Vented		100	.160		5.70	7.50		13.20	17.85
4217	3' overhang, solid		100	.160		7.10	7.50		14.60	19.40
4218	Vented	▼	100	.160	▼	7.10	7.50		14.60	19.40
4220	Colors for siding and soffits, add				S.F.	.14			.14	.15
4225	Colors for accessories and trim, add				L.F.	.30			.30	.33

07 46 33.20 Polypropylene Siding

0010	POLYPROPYLENE SIDING									
4090	Shingle profile, random grooves, double 7	2 Carp	400	.040	S.F.	2.99	1.88		4.87	6.20
4092	Cornerpost for above	1 Carp	365	.022	L.F.	12	1.03		13.03	14.80
4095	Triple 5	2 Carp	400	.040	S.F.	2.99	1.88		4.87	6.20

07 46 Siding

07 46 33 – Plastic Siding

07 46 33.20 Polypropylene Siding

		Crew	Daily Output	Labor-Hours	Unit	Material	2015 Bare Costs Labor	Equipment	Total	Total Incl O&P
4097	Cornerpost for above	1 Carp	365	.022	L.F.	11.05	1.03		12.08	13.75
5000	Staggered butt, double 7"	2 Carp	400	.040	S.F.	3.45	1.88		5.33	6.70
5002	Cornerpost for above	1 Carp	365	.022	L.F.	12	1.03		13.03	14.80
5010	Half round, double 6-1/4"	2 Carp	360	.044	S.F.	3.40	2.09		5.49	6.95
5020	Shake profile, staggered butt, double 9"	"	510	.031	"	3.45	1.47		4.92	6.05
5022	Cornerpost for above	1 Carp	365	.022	L.F.	9	1.03		10.03	11.50
5030	Straight butt, double 7"	2 Carp	400	.040	S.F.	3.40	1.88		5.28	6.65
5032	Cornerpost for above	1 Carp	365	.022	L.F.	11.90	1.03		12.93	14.65
6000	Accessories, J channel, 5/8" pocket	2 Carp	700	.023		.46	1.07		1.53	2.15
6010	3/4" pocket		695	.023		.50	1.08		1.58	2.21
6020	1-1/4" pocket		680	.024		.77	1.10		1.87	2.54
6030	Aluminum starter strip		700	.023		.28	1.07		1.35	1.96

07 51 Built-Up Bituminous Roofing

07 51 13 – Built-Up Asphalt Roofing

07 51 13.10 Built-Up Roofing Components

		Crew	Daily Output	Labor-Hours	Unit	Material	2015 Bare Costs Labor	Equipment	Total	Total Incl O&P
0010	**BUILT-UP ROOFING COMPONENTS**									
0012	Asphalt saturated felt, #30, 2 square per roll	1 Rofc	58	.138	Sq.	10.60	5.55		16.15	21
0200	#15, 4 sq. per roll, plain or perforated, not mopped		58	.138		5.40	5.55		10.95	15.40
0300	Roll roofing, smooth, #65		15	.533		9.65	21.50		31.15	47
0500	#90		12	.667		37	26.50		63.50	86
0520	Mineralized		12	.667		35	26.50		61.50	84
0540	D.C. (Double coverage), 19" selvage edge		10	.800		52.50	32		84.50	113
0580	Adhesive (lap cement)				Gal.	8.85			8.85	9.75
0800	Steep, flat or dead level asphalt, 10 ton lots, packaged				Ton	925			925	1,025

07 51 13.20 Built-Up Roofing Systems

		Crew	Daily Output	Labor-Hours	Unit	Material	2015 Bare Costs Labor	Equipment	Total	Total Incl O&P
0010	**BUILT-UP ROOFING SYSTEMS**									
0120	Asphalt flood coat with gravel/slag surfacing, not including									
0140	Insulation, flashing or wood nailers									
0200	Asphalt base sheet, 3 plies #15 asphalt felt, mopped	G-1	22	2.545	Sq.	100	95.50	26	221.50	300
0350	On nailable decks		21	2.667		102	100	27	229	315
0500	4 plies #15 asphalt felt, mopped		20	2.800		136	105	28.50	269.50	360
0550	On nailable decks		19	2.947		120	111	30	261	355
0700	Coated glass base sheet, 2 plies glass (type IV), mopped		22	2.545		107	95.50	26	228.50	310
0850	3 plies glass, mopped		20	2.800		130	105	28.50	263.50	355
0950	On nailable decks		19	2.947		122	111	30	263	355

07 51 13.30 Cants

		Crew	Daily Output	Labor-Hours	Unit	Material	2015 Bare Costs Labor	Equipment	Total	Total Incl O&P
0010	**CANTS**									
0012	Lumber, treated, 4" x 4" cut diagonally	1 Rofc	325	.025	L.F.	1.75	.99		2.74	3.62
0300	Mineral or fiber, trapezoidal, 1" x 4" x 48"		325	.025		.25	.99		1.24	1.97
0400	1-1/2" x 5-5/8" x 48"		325	.025		.44	.99		1.43	2.17

For customer support on your Site Work & Landscape Cost Data, call 877.737.1594.

149

07 65 Flexible Flashing

07 65 10 – Sheet Metal Flashing

07 65 10.10 Sheet Metal Flashing and Counter Flashing	Crew	Daily Output	Labor-Hours	Unit	Material	2015 Bare Costs Labor	Equipment	Total	Total Incl O&P
0010 **SHEET METAL FLASHING AND COUNTER FLASHING**									
0011 Including up to 4 bends									
0020 Aluminum, mill finish, .013" thick	1 Rofc	145	.055	S.F.	.79	2.21		3	4.65
0030 .016" thick		145	.055		.91	2.21		3.12	4.78
0060 .019" thick		145	.055		1.15	2.21		3.36	5.05
0100 .032" thick		145	.055		1.35	2.21		3.56	5.25
0200 .040" thick		145	.055		2.31	2.21		4.52	6.30
0300 .050" thick	↓	145	.055		2.43	2.21		4.64	6.45
0400 Painted finish, add				↓	.29			.29	.32

07 65 12 – Fabric and Mastic Flashings

07 65 12.10 Fabric and Mastic Flashing and Counter Flashing

	Crew	Daily Output	Labor-Hours	Unit	Material	2015 Bare Costs Labor	Equipment	Total	Total Incl O&P
0010 **FABRIC AND MASTIC FLASHING AND COUNTER FLASHING**									
1300 Asphalt flashing cement, 5 gallon				Gal.	9.20			9.20	10.10
4900 Fabric, asphalt-saturated cotton, specification grade	1 Rofc	35	.229	S.Y.	2.96	9.15		12.11	18.90
5000 Utility grade		35	.229		1.42	9.15		10.57	17.20
5300 Close-mesh fabric, saturated, 17 oz. per S.Y.		35	.229		2.15	9.15		11.30	18
5500 Fiberglass, resin-coated	↓	35	.229	↓	.97	9.15		10.12	16.70

07 71 Roof Specialties

07 71 19 – Manufactured Gravel Stops and Fasciae

07 71 19.10 Gravel Stop

	Crew	Daily Output	Labor-Hours	Unit	Material	2015 Bare Costs Labor	Equipment	Total	Total Incl O&P
0010 **GRAVEL STOP**									
0020 Aluminum, .050" thick, 4" face height, mill finish	1 Shee	145	.055	L.F.	6.30	3.09		9.39	11.60
0080 Duranodic finish	"	145	.055	"	6.75	3.09		9.84	12.15

07 71 23 – Manufactured Gutters and Downspouts

07 71 23.10 Downspouts

	Crew	Daily Output	Labor-Hours	Unit	Material	2015 Bare Costs Labor	Equipment	Total	Total Incl O&P
0010 **DOWNSPOUTS**									
0020 Aluminum, embossed, .020" thick, 2" x 3"	1 Shee	190	.042	L.F.	.98	2.36		3.34	4.68
0100 Enameled		190	.042		1.37	2.36		3.73	5.10
0300 .024" thick, 2' x 3"		180	.044		2.05	2.49		4.54	6.05
0400 3" x 4"		140	.057		2.33	3.20		5.53	7.45
0600 Round, corrugated aluminum, 3" diameter, .020" thick		190	.042		1.95	2.36		4.31	5.75
0700 4" diameter, .025" thick		140	.057		2.53	3.20		5.73	7.65
4800 Steel, galvanized, round, corrugated, 2" or 3" diameter, 28 ga.		190	.042		2.08	2.36		4.44	5.90
4900 4" diameter, 28 ga.		145	.055		2.52	3.09		5.61	7.50
5100 5" diameter, 26 ga.		130	.062		4	3.44		7.44	9.65
5400 6" diameter, 28 ga.		105	.076		4.20	4.26		8.46	11.10
5700 Rectangular, corrugated, 28 ga., 2" x 3"		190	.042		1.94	2.36		4.30	5.75
5800 3" x 4"		145	.055		1.82	3.09		4.91	6.70
6000 Rectangular, plain, 28 ga., galvanized, 2" x 3"		190	.042		3.65	2.36		6.01	7.60
6100 3" x 4"	↓	145	.055	↓	4.06	3.09		7.15	9.20

07 71 23.30 Gutters

	Crew	Daily Output	Labor-Hours	Unit	Material	2015 Bare Costs Labor	Equipment	Total	Total Incl O&P
0010 **GUTTERS**									
0012 Aluminum, stock units, 5" K type, .027" thick, plain	1 Shee	125	.064	L.F.	2.72	3.58		6.30	8.45
0100 Enameled		125	.064		2.66	3.58		6.24	8.35
0300 5" K type type, .032" thick, plain		125	.064		3.23	3.58		6.81	9
0400 Enameled		125	.064		3.02	3.58		6.60	8.75
0700 Copper, half round, 16 oz., stock units, 4" wide		125	.064		8.90	3.58		12.48	15.25
0900 5" wide		125	.064		7.25	3.58		10.83	13.40
1000 6" wide	↓	118	.068	↓	11.85	3.79		15.64	18.80

150

07 71 Roof Specialties

07 71 23 – Manufactured Gutters and Downspouts

07 71 23.30 Gutters		Crew	Daily Output	Labor-Hours	Unit	Material	2015 Bare Costs Labor	Equipment	Total	Total Incl O&P
1200	K type, 16 oz., stock, 5" wide	1 Shee	125	.064	L.F.	8.05	3.58		11.63	14.30
1300	6" wide		125	.064		8.50	3.58		12.08	14.80
1500	Lead coated copper, 16 oz., half round, stock, 4" wide		125	.064		13.80	3.58		17.38	20.50
1600	6" wide		118	.068		21.50	3.79		25.29	30
1800	K type, stock, 5" wide		125	.064		18.35	3.58		21.93	25.50
1900	6" wide		125	.064		17.90	3.58		21.48	25
2100	Copper clad stainless steel, K type, 5" wide		125	.064		7.50	3.58		11.08	13.70
2200	6" wide		125	.064		9.45	3.58		13.03	15.85
2400	Steel, galv, half round or box, 28 ga., 5" wide, plain		125	.064		2.10	3.58		5.68	7.75
2500	Enameled		125	.064		2.10	3.58		5.68	7.75
2700	26 ga., stock, 5" wide		125	.064		2.18	3.58		5.76	7.85
2800	6" wide		125	.064		2.71	3.58		6.29	8.45
3000	Vinyl, O.G., 4" wide	1 Carp	115	.070		1.25	3.27		4.52	6.45
3100	5" wide		115	.070		1.55	3.27		4.82	6.75
3200	4" half round, stock units		115	.070		1.30	3.27		4.57	6.50
3250	Joint connectors				Ea.	2.90			2.90	3.19
3300	Wood, clear treated cedar, fir or hemlock, 3" x 4"	1 Carp	100	.080	L.F.	10	3.76		13.76	16.80
3400	4" x 5"	"	100	.080	"	16.75	3.76		20.51	24.50
5000	Accessories, end cap, K type, aluminum 5"	1 Shee	625	.013	Ea.	.66	.72		1.38	1.82
5010	6"		625	.013		1.44	.72		2.16	2.67
5020	Copper, 5"		625	.013		3.22	.72		3.94	4.63
5030	6"		625	.013		3.54	.72		4.26	4.98
5040	Lead coated copper, 5"		625	.013		12.50	.72		13.22	14.85
5050	6"		625	.013		13.35	.72		14.07	15.80
5060	Copper clad stainless steel, 5"		625	.013		3	.72		3.72	4.39
5070	6"		625	.013		3.60	.72		4.32	5.05
5080	Galvanized steel, 5"		625	.013		1.28	.72		2	2.50
5090	6"		625	.013		2.18	.72		2.90	3.49
5100	Vinyl, 4"	1 Carp	625	.013		13.15	.60		13.75	15.40
5110	5"	"	625	.013		13.15	.60		13.75	15.40
5120	Half round, copper, 4"	1 Shee	625	.013		4.53	.72		5.25	6.05
5130	5"		625	.013		4.53	.72		5.25	6.05
5140	6"		625	.013		7.65	.72		8.37	9.55
5150	Lead coated copper, 5"		625	.013		14.15	.72		14.87	16.65
5160	6"		625	.013		21	.72		21.72	24.50
5170	Copper clad stainless steel, 5"		625	.013		4.50	.72		5.22	6.05
5180	6"		625	.013		4.50	.72		5.22	6.05
5190	Galvanized steel, 5"		625	.013		2.25	.72		2.97	3.57
5200	6"		625	.013		2.80	.72		3.52	4.17
5210	Outlet, aluminum, 2" x 3"		420	.019		.62	1.07		1.69	2.31
5220	3" x 4"		420	.019		1.05	1.07		2.12	2.79
5230	2-3/8" round		420	.019		.56	1.07		1.63	2.25
5240	Copper, 2" x 3"		420	.019		6.50	1.07		7.57	8.80
5250	3" x 4"		420	.019		7.85	1.07		8.92	10.30
5260	2-3/8" round		420	.019		4.55	1.07		5.62	6.65
5270	Lead coated copper, 2" x 3"		420	.019		25.50	1.07		26.57	29.50
5280	3" x 4"		420	.019		28.50	1.07		29.57	33
5290	2-3/8" round		420	.019		25.50	1.07		26.57	29.50
5300	Copper clad stainless steel, 2" x 3"		420	.019		6.50	1.07		7.57	8.80
5310	3" x 4"		420	.019		7.85	1.07		8.92	10.30
5320	2-3/8" round		420	.019		4.55	1.07		5.62	6.65
5330	Galvanized steel, 2" x 3"		420	.019		3.18	1.07		4.25	5.15
5340	3" x 4"		420	.019		4.90	1.07		5.97	7.05

07 71 Roof Specialties

07 71 23 – Manufactured Gutters and Downspouts

07 71 23.30 Gutters		Crew	Daily Output	Labor-Hours	Unit	Material	2015 Bare Costs Labor	Equipment	Total	Total Incl O&P
5350	2-3/8" round	1 Shee	420	.019	Ea.	3.98	1.07		5.05	6
5360	K type mitres, aluminum		65	.123		3	6.90		9.90	13.80
5370	Copper		65	.123		17.40	6.90		24.30	29.50
5380	Lead coated copper		65	.123		54.50	6.90		61.40	70.50
5390	Copper clad stainless steel		65	.123		27.50	6.90		34.40	41
5400	Galvanized steel		65	.123		22.50	6.90		29.40	35.50
5420	Half round mitres, copper		65	.123		63.50	6.90		70.40	80.50
5430	Lead coated copper		65	.123		89.50	6.90		96.40	109
5440	Copper clad stainless steel		65	.123		56	6.90		62.90	72.50
5450	Galvanized steel		65	.123		25.50	6.90		32.40	38.50
5460	Vinyl mitres and outlets		65	.123		9.75	6.90		16.65	21.50
5470	Sealant		940	.009	L.F.	.01	.48		.49	.74
5480	Soldering		96	.083	"	.19	4.66		4.85	7.30

07 71 29 – Manufactured Roof Expansion Joints

07 71 29.10 Expansion Joints

		Crew	Daily Output	Labor-Hours	Unit	Material	2015 Bare Costs Labor	Equipment	Total	Total Incl O&P
0010	**EXPANSION JOINTS**									
0300	Butyl or neoprene center with foam insulation, metal flanges									
0400	Aluminum, .032" thick for openings to 2-1/2"	1 Rofc	165	.048	L.F.	11.30	1.94		13.24	15.75
0600	For joint openings to 3-1/2"		165	.048		11.30	1.94		13.24	15.75
0610	For joint openings to 5"		165	.048		13.10	1.94		15.04	17.70
0620	For joint openings to 8"		165	.048		15.80	1.94		17.74	20.50
0700	Copper, 16 oz. for openings to 2-1/2"		165	.048		16.70	1.94		18.64	21.50
0900	For joint openings to 3-1/2"		165	.048		16.70	1.94		18.64	21.50
0910	For joint openings to 5"		165	.048		18.90	1.94		20.84	24.50
0920	For joint openings to 8"		165	.048		22	1.94		23.94	27.50
1000	Galvanized steel, 26 ga. for openings to 2-1/2"		165	.048		9.80	1.94		11.74	14.10
1200	For joint openings to 3-1/2"		165	.048		9.80	1.94		11.74	14.10
1210	For joint openings to 5"		165	.048		11.30	1.94		13.24	15.75
1220	For joint openings to 8"		165	.048		14.80	1.94		16.74	19.60
1810	For joint openings to 5"		165	.048		17.20	1.94		19.14	22
1820	For joint openings to 8"		165	.048		21	1.94		22.94	26.50
1900	Neoprene, double-seal type with thick center, 4-1/2" wide		125	.064		14.50	2.57		17.07	20.50
1950	Polyethylene bellows, with galv steel flat flanges		100	.080		6.20	3.21		9.41	12.30
1960	With galvanized angle flanges		100	.080		6.40	3.21		9.61	12.55
2000	Roof joint with extruded aluminum cover, 2"	1 Shee	115	.070		28	3.89		31.89	37
2700	Wall joint, closed cell foam on PVC cover, 9" wide	1 Rofc	125	.064		5	2.57		7.57	9.90
2800	12" wide	"	115	.070		6	2.79		8.79	11.35

07 71 43 – Drip Edge

07 71 43.10 Drip Edge, Rake Edge, Ice Belts

		Crew	Daily Output	Labor-Hours	Unit	Material	2015 Bare Costs Labor	Equipment	Total	Total Incl O&P
0010	**DRIP EDGE, RAKE EDGE, ICE BELTS**									
0020	Aluminum, .016" thick, 5" wide, mill finish	1 Carp	400	.020	L.F.	.55	.94		1.49	2.06
0100	White finish		400	.020		.63	.94		1.57	2.14
0200	8" wide, mill finish		400	.020		1.45	.94		2.39	3.05
0300	Ice belt, 28" wide, mill finish		100	.080		7.65	3.76		11.41	14.25
0400	Galvanized, 5" wide		400	.020		.53	.94		1.47	2.03
0500	8" wide, mill finish		400	.020		.80	.94		1.74	2.33

07 72 Roof Accessories

07 72 53 – Snow Guards

07 72 53.10 Snow Guard Options	Crew	Daily Output	Labor-Hours	Unit	Material	2015 Bare Costs Labor	Equipment	Total	Total Incl O&P
0010 **SNOW GUARD OPTIONS**									
0100 Slate & asphalt shingle roofs, fastened with nails	1 Rofc	160	.050	Ea.	12.55	2.01		14.56	17.20
0200 Standing seam metal roofs, fastened with set screws		48	.167		16.95	6.70		23.65	30
0300 Surface mount for metal roofs, fastened with solder		48	.167		6.05	6.70		12.75	18.05
0400 Double rail pipe type, including pipe		130	.062	L.F.	32	2.47		34.47	39

07 76 Roof Pavers

07 76 16 – Roof Decking Pavers

07 76 16.10 Roof Pavers and Supports	Crew	Daily Output	Labor-Hours	Unit	Material	2015 Bare Costs Labor	Equipment	Total	Total Incl O&P
0010 **ROOF PAVERS AND SUPPORTS**									
1000 Roof decking pavers, concrete blocks, 2" thick, natural	1 Clab	115	.070	S.F.	3.37	2.62		5.99	7.75
1100 Colors		115	.070	"	3.73	2.62		6.35	8.10
1200 Support pedestal, bottom cap		960	.008	Ea.	3	.31		3.31	3.78
1300 Top cap		960	.008		4.80	.31		5.11	5.80
1400 Leveling shims, 1/16"		1920	.004		1.20	.16		1.36	1.56
1500 1/8"		1920	.004		1.20	.16		1.36	1.56
1600 Buffer pad		960	.008		2.50	.31		2.81	3.23
1700 PVC legs (4" SDR 35)		2880	.003	Inch	.12	.10		.22	.29
2000 Alternate pricing method, system in place		101	.079	S.F.	7	2.98		9.98	12.30

07 81 Applied Fireproofing

07 81 16 – Cementitious Fireproofing

07 81 16.10 Sprayed Cementitious Fireproofing	Crew	Daily Output	Labor-Hours	Unit	Material	2015 Bare Costs Labor	Equipment	Total	Total Incl O&P
0010 **SPRAYED CEMENTITIOUS FIREPROOFING**									
0050 Not including canvas protection, normal density									
0100 Per 1" thick, on flat plate steel	G-2	3000	.008	S.F.	.53	.32	.04	.89	1.11
0200 Flat decking		2400	.010		.53	.40	.06	.99	1.24
0400 Beams		1500	.016		.53	.63	.09	1.25	1.64
0500 Corrugated or fluted decks		1250	.019		.79	.76	.11	1.66	2.14
0700 Columns, 1-1/8" thick		1100	.022		.59	.86	.12	1.57	2.08

07 91 Preformed Joint Seals

07 91 23 – Backer Rods

07 91 23.10 Backer Rods	Crew	Daily Output	Labor-Hours	Unit	Material	2015 Bare Costs Labor	Equipment	Total	Total Incl O&P
0010 **BACKER RODS**									
0030 Backer rod, polyethylene, 1/4" diameter	1 Bric	4.60	1.739	C.L.F.	2.13	80.50		82.63	125
0050 1/2" diameter		4.60	1.739		3.40	80.50		83.90	127
0070 3/4" diameter		4.60	1.739		5.55	80.50		86.05	129
0090 1" diameter		4.60	1.739		8.85	80.50		89.35	133

07 91 26 – Joint Fillers

07 91 26.10 Joint Fillers	Crew	Daily Output	Labor-Hours	Unit	Material	2015 Bare Costs Labor	Equipment	Total	Total Incl O&P
0010 **JOINT FILLERS**									
4360 Butyl rubber filler, 1/4" x 1/4"	1 Bric	290	.028	L.F.	.22	1.27		1.49	2.19
4365 1/2" x 1/2"		250	.032		.89	1.48		2.37	3.23
4370 1/2" x 3/4"		210	.038		1.34	1.76		3.10	4.15
4375 3/4" x 3/4"		230	.035		2.01	1.61		3.62	4.66
4380 1" x 1"		180	.044		2.68	2.05		4.73	6.05

For customer support on your Site Work & Landscape Cost Data, call 877.737.1594.

153

07 91 26 – Joint Fillers

07 91 26.10 Joint Fillers	Crew	Daily Output	Labor-Hours	Unit	Material	2015 Bare Costs Labor	Equipment	Total	Total Incl O&P
4390	For coloring, add					12%				
4980	Polyethylene joint backing, 1/4" x 2"	1 Bric	2.08	3.846	C.L.F.	12	178		190	284
4990	1/4" x 6"		1.28	6.250	"	28	288		316	470
5600	Silicone, room temp vulcanizing foam seal, 1/4" x 1/2"		1312	.006	L.F.	.33	.28		.61	.80
5610	1/2" x 1/2"		656	.012		.67	.56		1.23	1.59
5620	1/2" x 3/4"		442	.018		1	.84		1.84	2.38
5630	3/4" x 3/4"		328	.024		1.50	1.13		2.63	3.37
5640	1/8" x 1"		1312	.006		.33	.28		.61	.80
5650	1/8" x 3"		442	.018		1	.84		1.84	2.38
5670	1/4" x 3"		295	.027		2	1.25		3.25	4.11
5680	1/4" x 6"		148	.054		3.99	2.49		6.48	8.20
5690	1/2" x 6"		82	.098		8	4.50		12.50	15.65
5700	1/2" x 9"		52.50	.152		12	7.05		19.05	24
5710	1/2" x 12"		33	.242		15.95	11.20		27.15	34.50

07 92 13 – Elastomeric Joint Sealants

07 92 13.20 Caulking and Sealant Options

		Crew	Daily Output	Labor-Hours	Unit	Material	2015 Bare Costs Labor	Equipment	Total	Total Incl O&P
0010	**CAULKING AND SEALANT OPTIONS**									
0050	Latex acrylic based, bulk				Gal.	26.50			26.50	29.50
0055	Bulk in place 1/4" x 1/4" bead	1 Bric	300	.027	L.F.	.08	1.23		1.31	1.97
0060	1/4" x 3/8"		294	.027		.14	1.26		1.40	2.07
0065	1/4" x 1/2"		288	.028		.19	1.28		1.47	2.17
0075	3/8" x 3/8"		284	.028		.21	1.30		1.51	2.21
0080	3/8" x 1/2"		280	.029		.28	1.32		1.60	2.32
0085	3/8" x 5/8"		276	.029		.35	1.34		1.69	2.43
0095	3/8" x 3/4"		272	.029		.42	1.36		1.78	2.53
0100	1/2" x 1/2"		275	.029		.37	1.34		1.71	2.46
0105	1/2" x 5/8"		269	.030		.47	1.37		1.84	2.61
0110	1/2" x 3/4"		263	.030		.56	1.40		1.96	2.76
0115	1/2" x 7/8"		256	.031		.65	1.44		2.09	2.92
0120	1/2" x 1"		250	.032		.75	1.48		2.23	3.07
0125	3/4" x 3/4"		244	.033		.84	1.51		2.35	3.24
0130	3/4" x 1"		225	.036		1.12	1.64		2.76	3.74
0135	1" x 1"		200	.040		1.50	1.85		3.35	4.47
0190	Cartridges				Gal.	32			32	35.50
0200	11 fl. oz. cartridge				Ea.	2.76			2.76	3.04
0400	1/4" x 1/4"	1 Bric	300	.027	L.F.	.11	1.23		1.34	2
0410	1/4" x 3/8"		294	.027		.17	1.26		1.43	2.11
0500	1/4" x 1/2"		288	.028		.23	1.28		1.51	2.21
0510	3/8" x 3/8"		284	.028		.25	1.30		1.55	2.26
0520	3/8" x 1/2"		280	.029		.34	1.32		1.66	2.38
0530	3/8" x 5/8"		276	.029		.42	1.34		1.76	2.50
0540	3/8" x 3/4"		272	.029		.50	1.36		1.86	2.63
0600	1/2" x 1/2"		275	.029		.45	1.34		1.79	2.55
0610	1/2" x 5/8"		269	.030		.56	1.37		1.93	2.72
0620	1/2" x 3/4"		263	.030		.68	1.40		2.08	2.88
0630	1/2" x 7/8"		256	.031		.79	1.44		2.23	3.07
0640	1/2" x 1"		250	.032		.90	1.48		2.38	3.24
0800	3/4" x 3/4"		244	.033		1.01	1.51		2.52	3.43
0900	3/4" x 1"		225	.036		1.35	1.64		2.99	4

154

For customer support on your Site Work & Landscape Cost Data, call 877.737.1594.

07 92 Joint Sealants

07 92 13 – Elastomeric Joint Sealants

07 92 13.20 Caulking and Sealant Options	Crew	Daily Output	Labor-Hours	Unit	Material	2015 Bare Costs Labor	Equipment	Total	Total Incl O&P
1000	1" x 1"	1 Bric	200	.040	L.F.	1.69	1.85		3.54	4.68
3200	Polyurethane, 1 or 2 component				Gal.	49			49	54
3300	Cartridges				"	64			64	70.50
3500	Bulk, in place, 1/4" x 1/4"	1 Bric	300	.027	L.F.	.16	1.23		1.39	2.06
3510	1/4" x 3/8"		294	.027		.24	1.26		1.50	2.18
3520	3/8" x 3/8"		284	.028		.36	1.30		1.66	2.38
3530	3/8" x 1/2"		280	.029		.48	1.32		1.80	2.54
3540	3/8" x 5/8"		276	.029		.60	1.34		1.94	2.70
3550	3/8" x 3/4"		272	.029		.72	1.36		2.08	2.87
3560	1/2" x 1/2"		275	.029		.64	1.34		1.98	2.75
3570	1/2" x 5/8"		269	.030		.79	1.37		2.16	2.97
3580	1/2" x 3/4"		263	.030		.97	1.40		2.37	3.20
3590	1/2" x 7/8"		256	.031		1.12	1.44		2.56	3.43
3655	1/2" x 1/4"		288	.028		.32	1.28		1.60	2.31
3800	3/4" x 3/8"		272	.029		.72	1.36		2.08	2.87
3850	3/4" x 3/4"		244	.033		1.45	1.51		2.96	3.90
3875	3/4" x 1"		225	.036		1.89	1.64		3.53	4.59
3900	1" x 1/2"		250	.032		1.28	1.48		2.76	3.66
4000	For coloring, add					15%				

07 95 Expansion Control

07 95 13 – Expansion Joint Cover Assemblies

07 95 13.50 Expansion Joint Assemblies

		Crew	Daily Output	Labor-Hours	Unit	Material	2015 Bare Costs Labor	Equipment	Total	Total Incl O&P
0010	**EXPANSION JOINT ASSEMBLIES**									
0200	Floor cover assemblies, 1" space, aluminum	1 Sswk	38	.211	L.F.	16.85	11.10		27.95	38
0300	Bronze		38	.211		54.50	11.10		65.60	79.50
2000	Roof closures, aluminum, flat roof, low profile, 1" space		57	.140		22.50	7.40		29.90	38
2300	Roof to wall, low profile, 1" space		57	.140		21.50	7.40		28.90	36.50

Division Notes

	CREW	DAILY OUTPUT	LABOR-HOURS	UNIT	BARE COSTS				TOTAL INCL O&P
					MAT.	LABOR	EQUIP.	TOTAL	

Estimating Tips
08 10 00 Doors and Frames

All exterior doors should be addressed for their energy conservation (insulation and seals).

- Most metal doors and frames look alike, but there may be significant differences among them. When estimating these items, be sure to choose the line item that most closely compares to the specification or door schedule requirements regarding:
  - type of metal
  - metal gauge
  - door core material
  - fire rating
  - finish

- Wood and plastic doors vary considerably in price. The primary determinant is the veneer material. Lauan, birch, and oak are the most common veneers. Other variables include the following:
  - hollow or solid core
  - fire rating
  - flush or raised panel
  - finish

- Door pricing includes bore for cylindrical lockset and mortise for hinges.

08 30 00 Specialty Doors and Frames

- There are many varieties of special doors, and they are usually priced per each. Add frames, hardware, or operators required for a complete installation.

08 40 00 Entrances, Storefronts, and Curtain Walls

- Glazed curtain walls consist of the metal tube framing and the glazing material. The cost data in this subdivision is presented for the metal tube framing alone or the composite wall. If your estimate requires a detailed takeoff of the framing, be sure to add the glazing cost and any tints.

08 50 00 Windows

- Most metal windows are delivered preglazed. However, some metal windows are priced without glass. Refer to 08 80 00 Glazing for glass pricing. The grade C indicates commercial grade windows, usually ASTM C-35.

- All wood windows and vinyl are priced preglazed. The glazing is insulating glass. Add the cost of screens and grills if required, and not already included.

08 70 00 Hardware

- Hardware costs add considerably to the cost of a door. The most efficient method to determine the hardware requirements for a project is to review the door and hardware schedule together. One type of door may have different hardware, depending on the door usage.

- Door hinges are priced by the pair, with most doors requiring 1-1/2 pairs per door. The hinge prices do not include installation labor, because it is included in door installation.

Hinges are classified according to the frequency of use, base material, and finish.

08 80 00 Glazing

- Different openings require different types of glass. The most common types are:
  - float
  - tempered
  - insulating
  - impact-resistant
  - ballistic-resistant

- Most exterior windows are glazed with insulating glass. Entrance doors and window walls, where the glass is less than 18" from the floor, are generally glazed with tempered glass. Interior windows and some residential windows are glazed with float glass.

- Coastal communities require the use of impact-resistant glass, dependant on wind speed.

- The insulation or 'u' value is a strong consideration, along with solar heat gain, to determine total energy efficiency.

Reference Numbers

Reference numbers are shown in shaded boxes at the beginning of some major classifications. These numbers refer to related items in the Reference Section. The reference information may be an estimating procedure, an alternate pricing method, or technical information.

Note: Not all subdivisions listed here necessarily appear in this publication. ■

Division 8 – Openings

08 05 Common Work Results for Openings

08 05 05 – Selective Demolition for Openings

08 05 05.10 Selective Demolition Doors

		Crew	Daily Output	Labor-Hours	Unit	Material	2015 Bare Costs Labor	Equipment	Total	Total Incl O&P
0010	**SELECTIVE DEMOLITION DOORS** R024119-10									
0200	Doors, exterior, 1-3/4" thick, single, 3' x 7' high	1 Clab	16	.500	Ea.		18.80		18.80	29
0220	Double, 6' x 7' high		12	.667			25		25	38.50
0500	Interior, 1-3/8" thick, single, 3' x 7' high		20	.400			15.05		15.05	23
0520	Double, 6' x 7' high		16	.500			18.80		18.80	29
0700	Bi-folding, 3' x 6'-8" high		20	.400			15.05		15.05	23
0720	6' x 6'-8" high		18	.444			16.70		16.70	25.50
0900	Bi-passing, 3' x 6'-8" high		16	.500			18.80		18.80	29
0940	6' x 6'-8" high	▼	14	.571			21.50		21.50	33
1500	Remove and reset, hollow core	1 Carp	8	1			47		47	72.50
1520	Solid		6	1.333			62.50		62.50	96.50
2000	Frames, including trim, metal	▼	8	1			47		47	72.50
2200	Wood	2 Carp	32	.500			23.50		23.50	36
3000	Special doors, counter doors		6	2.667			125		125	193
3100	Double acting		10	1.600			75		75	116
3200	Floor door (trap type), or access type		8	2			94		94	145
3300	Glass, sliding, including frames		12	1.333			62.50		62.50	96.50
3400	Overhead, commercial, 12' x 12' high		4	4			188		188	289
3440	up to 20' x 16' high		3	5.333			250		250	385
3445	up to 35' x 30' high		1	16			750		750	1,150
3500	Residential, 9' x 7' high		8	2			94		94	145
3540	16' x 7' high		7	2.286			107		107	165
3620	Large		2.50	6.400			300		300	460
3700	Roll-up grille		5	3.200			150		150	231
3800	Revolving door		2	8			375		375	580
3900	Storefront swing door	▼	3	5.333	▼		250		250	385
7550	Hangar door demo	2 Sswk	330	.048	S.F.		2.55		2.55	4.43

08 05 05.20 Selective Demolition of Windows

		Crew	Daily Output	Labor-Hours	Unit	Material	2015 Bare Costs Labor	Equipment	Total	Total Incl O&P
0010	**SELECTIVE DEMOLITION OF WINDOWS** R024119-10									
0200	Aluminum, including trim, to 12 S.F.	1 Clab	16	.500	Ea.		18.80		18.80	29
0240	To 25 S.F.		11	.727			27.50		27.50	42
0280	To 50 S.F.		5	1.600	▼		60		60	92.50
0600	Glass, up to 10 SF per window		200	.040	S.F.		1.50		1.50	2.31
0620	Over 10 SF per window		150	.053	"		2.01		2.01	3.09
1000	Steel, including trim, to 12 S.F.		13	.615	Ea.		23		23	35.50
1020	To 25 S.F.		9	.889			33.50		33.50	51.50
1040	To 50 S.F.		4	2			75		75	116
2000	Wood, including trim, to 12 S.F.		22	.364			13.65		13.65	21
2020	To 25 S.F.		18	.444			16.70		16.70	25.50
2060	To 50 S.F.		13	.615			23		23	35.50
2065	To 180 S.F.	▼	8	1			37.50		37.50	58
5083	Remove unit skylight	1 Carp	1.54	5.202	▼		244		244	375

08 12 Metal Frames

08 12 13 – Hollow Metal Frames

08 12 13.13 Standard Hollow Metal Frames		Crew	Daily Output	Labor-Hours	Unit	Material	2015 Bare Costs		Total	Total Incl O&P
							Labor	Equipment		
0010	**STANDARD HOLLOW METAL FRAMES**									
0020	16 ga., up to 5-3/4" jamb depth									
0025	3'-0" x 6'-8" single	G	2 Carp	16	1	Ea.	146	47		193	233
0028	3'-6" wide, single	G		16	1		153	47		200	242
0030	4'-0" wide, single	G		16	1		152	47		199	240
0040	6'-0" wide, double	G		14	1.143		204	53.50		257.50	305
0045	8'-0" wide, double	G		14	1.143		213	53.50		266.50	315
3600	up to 5-3/4" jamb depth, 4'-0" x 7'-0" single			15	1.067		185	50		235	280
3620	6'-0" wide, double			12	1.333		235	62.50		297.50	355
3640	8'-0" wide, double			12	1.333		246	62.50		308.50	370
4400	8-3/4" deep, 4'-0" x 7'-0", single			15	1.067		252	50		302	355
4440	8'-0" wide, double			12	1.333		315	62.50		377.50	440
4900	For welded frames, add						63			63	69.50
6200	8-3/4" deep, 4'-0" x 7'-0" single		2 Carp	15	1.067		291	50		341	395
6300	For "A" label use same price as "B" label										

08 13 Metal Doors

08 13 13 – Hollow Metal Doors

08 13 13.13 Standard Hollow Metal Doors

08 13 13.13 Standard Hollow Metal Doors		Crew	Daily Output	Labor-Hours	Unit	Material	2015 Bare Costs		Total	Total Incl O&P
							Labor	Equipment		
0010	**STANDARD HOLLOW METAL DOORS** R081313-20									
0015	Flush, full panel, hollow core									
0017	When noted doors are prepared but do not include glass or louvers									
0020	1-3/8" thick, 20 ga., 2'-0" x 6'-8"	G	2 Carp	20	.800	Ea.	335	37.50		372.50	430
0060	3'-0" x 6'-8"	G		17	.941		350	44		394	455
0100	3'-0" x 7'-0"	G		17	.941		360	44		404	465
0120	For vision lite, add						94.50			94.50	104
0140	For narrow lite, add						102			102	113
0320	Half glass, 20 ga., 2'-0" x 6'-8"	G	2 Carp	20	.800		490	37.50		527.50	600
0360	3'-0" x 6'-8"	G		17	.941		510	44		554	630
0400	3'-0" x 7'-0"	G		17	.941		625	44		669	760
0410	1-3/8" thick, 18 ga., 2'-0" x 6'-8"	G		20	.800		400	37.50		437.50	500
0420	3'-0" x 6'-8"	G		17	.941		405	44		449	515
0425	3'-0" x 7'-0"	G		17	.941		415	44		459	530
0450	For vision lite, add						94.50			94.50	104
0452	For narrow lite, add						102			102	113
0460	Half glass, 18 ga., 2'-0" x 6'-8"	G	2 Carp	20	.800		555	37.50		592.50	675
0470	3'-0" x 6'-8"	G		17	.941		565	44		609	690
0475	3'-0" x 7'-0"	G		17	.941		565	44		609	695
0500	Hollow core, 1-3/4" thick, full panel, 20 ga., 2'-8" x 6'-8"	G		18	.889		420	41.50		461.50	525
0520	3'-0" x 6'-8"	G		17	.941		420	44		464	530
0640	3'-0" x 7'-0"	G		17	.941		435	44		479	550
1000	18 ga., 2'-8" x 6'-8"	G		17	.941		490	44		534	610
1020	3'-0" x 6'-8"	G		16	1		475	47		522	600
1120	3'-0" x 7'-0"	G		17	.941		515	44		559	635
1212	For vision lite, add						94.50			94.50	104
1214	For narrow lite, add						102			102	113
1230	Half glass, 20 ga., 2'-8" x 6'-8"	G	2 Carp	20	.800		575	37.50		612.50	695
1240	3'-0" x 6'-8"	G		18	.889		575	41.50		616.50	700
1280	Embossed panel, 1-3/4" thick, poly core, 20 ga., 3'-0" x 7'-0"	G		18	.889		415	41.50		456.50	520
1290	Half glass, 1-3/4" thick, poly core, 20 ga., 3'-0" x 7'-0"	G		18	.889		610	41.50		651.50	735
1320	18 ga., 2'-8" x 6'-8"	G		18	.889		640	41.50		681.50	770

For customer support on your Site Work & Landscape Cost Data, call 877.737.1594.

159

08 13 Metal Doors

08 13 13 – Hollow Metal Doors

08 13 13.13 Standard Hollow Metal Doors

		Crew	Daily Output	Labor-Hours	Unit	Material	2015 Bare Costs Labor	2015 Bare Costs Equipment	Total	Total Incl O&P
1340	3'-0" x 6'-8" [G]	2 Carp	17	.941	Ea.	635	44		679	765
1720	Insulated, 1-3/4" thick, full panel, 18 ga., 3'-0" x 6'-8" [G]		15	1.067		475	50		525	600
1760	3'-0" x 7'-0" [G]		15	1.067		490	50		540	615
1820	Half glass, 18 ga., 3'-0" x 6'-8" [G]		16	1		635	47		682	770
1860	3'-0" x 7'-0" [G]	↓	16	1		685	47		732	830
2000	For vision lite, add					94.50			94.50	104
2010	For narrow lite, add					102			102	113
8100	For bottom louver, add				↓	282			282	310

08 13 13.15 Metal Fire Doors

		Crew	Daily Output	Labor-Hours	Unit	Material	2015 Bare Costs Labor	2015 Bare Costs Equipment	Total	Total Incl O&P
0010	**METAL FIRE DOORS**									
0015	Steel, flush, "B" label, 90 minute									
0020	Full panel, 20 ga., 2'-0" x 6'-8"	2 Carp	20	.800	Ea.	420	37.50		457.50	520
0060	3'-0" x 6'-8"		17	.941		435	44		479	550
0080	3'-0" x 7'-0"		17	.941		455	44		499	570
0140	18 ga., 3'-0" x 6'-8"	↓	16	1	↓	495	47		542	620
0220	For "A" label, 3 hour, 18 ga., use same price as "B" label									
0240	For vision lite, add				Ea.	156			156	172
0520	Flush, "B" label 90 min., egress core, 20 ga., 2'-0" x 6'-8"	2 Carp	18	.889		655	41.50		696.50	785
0580	3'-0" x 7'-0"		16	1		685	47		732	825
0640	Flush, "A" label 3 hour, egress core, 18 ga., 3'-0" x 6'-8"		15	1.067		720	50		770	870
0680	3'-0" x 7'-0"	↓	15	1.067	↓	740	50		790	890

08 14 Wood Doors

08 14 16 – Flush Wood Doors

08 14 16.09 Smooth Wood Doors

		Crew	Daily Output	Labor-Hours	Unit	Material	2015 Bare Costs Labor	2015 Bare Costs Equipment	Total	Total Incl O&P
0010	**SMOOTH WOOD DOORS**									
0015	Flush, interior, hollow core									
0180	3'-0" x 6'-8"	2 Carp	17	.941	Ea.	95.50	44		139.50	173
0202	1-3/4", 2'-0" x 6'-8"	"	17	.941		50.50	44		94.50	124
0430	For 7'-0" high, add					26			26	28.50
0480	For prefinishing, clear, add					46			46	50.50
1720	H.P. plastic laminate, 1-3/8", 2'-0" x 6'-8"	2 Carp	16	1		260	47		307	360
1780	3'-0" x 6'-8"		15	1.067		290	50		340	395
2020	Particle core, lauan face, 1-3/8", 2'-6" x 6'-8"		15	1.067		92	50		142	178
2080	3'-0" x 7'-0"		13	1.231		101	58		159	200
2110	1-3/4", 3'-0" x 7'-0"	↓	13	1.231	↓	145	58		203	249

08 14 16.20 Wood Fire Doors

		Crew	Daily Output	Labor-Hours	Unit	Material	2015 Bare Costs Labor	2015 Bare Costs Equipment	Total	Total Incl O&P
0010	**WOOD FIRE DOORS**									
0020	Particle core, 7 face plys, "B" label,									
0040	1 hour, birch face, 1-3/4" x 2'-6" x 6'-8"	2 Carp	14	1.143	Ea.	420	53.50		473.50	545
0080	3'-0" x 6'-8"		13	1.231		400	58		458	530
0090	3'-0" x 7'-0"		12	1.333		435	62.50		497.50	575
0440	M.D. overlay on hardboard, 2'-6" x 6'-8"		15	1.067		315	50		365	420
0480	3'-0" x 6'-8"		14	1.143		375	53.50		428.50	500
0740	90 minutes, birch face, 1-3/4" x 2'-6" x 6'-8"		14	1.143		325	53.50		378.50	440
0780	3'-0" x 6'-8"		13	1.231		320	58		378	440
0790	3'-0" x 7'-0"	↓	12	1.333	↓	390	62.50		452.50	525
2200	Custom architectural "B" label, flush, 1-3/4" thick, birch,									
2260	3'-0" x 7'-0"	2 Carp	14	1.143	Ea.	315	53.50		368.50	430

08 14 Wood Doors

08 14 33 – Stile and Rail Wood Doors

08 14 33.20 Wood Doors Residential		Crew	Daily Output	Labor-Hours	Unit	Material	2015 Bare Costs Labor	Equipment	Total	Total Incl O&P
0010	**WOOD DOORS RESIDENTIAL**									
1000	Entrance door, colonial, 1-3/4" x 6'-8" x 2'-8" wide	2 Carp	16	1	Ea.	500	47		547	625
1300	Flush, birch, solid core, 1-3/4" x 6'-8" x 2'-8" wide	"	16	1	"	113	47		160	198
7310	Passage doors, flush, no frame included									
7700	Birch, hollow core, 1-3/8" x 6'-8" x 1'-6" wide	2 Carp	18	.889	Ea.	41	41.50		82.50	109
7740	2'-6" wide	"	18	.889	"	50	41.50		91.50	119

08 31 Access Doors and Panels

08 31 13 – Access Doors and Frames

08 31 13.20 Bulkhead/Cellar Doors

		Crew	Daily Output	Labor-Hours	Unit	Material	2015 Bare Costs Labor	Equipment	Total	Total Incl O&P
0010	**BULKHEAD/CELLAR DOORS**									
0020	Steel, not incl. sides, 44" x 62"	1 Carp	5.50	1.455	Ea.	560	68.50		628.50	720
0100	52" x 73"		5.10	1.569		790	73.50		863.50	985
0500	With sides and foundation plates, 57" x 45" x 24"		4.70	1.702		845	80		925	1,050
0600	42" x 49" x 51"	↓	4.30	1.860	↓	915	87.50		1,002.50	1,125

08 31 13.30 Commercial Floor Doors

		Crew	Daily Output	Labor-Hours	Unit	Material	2015 Bare Costs Labor	Equipment	Total	Total Incl O&P
0010	**COMMERCIAL FLOOR DOORS**									
0020	Aluminum tile, steel frame, one leaf, 2' x 2' opng.	2 Sswk	3.50	4.571	Opng.	880	241		1,121	1,400
0050	3'-6" x 3'-6" opening	"	3.50	4.571	"	1,600	241		1,841	2,175

08 32 Sliding Glass Doors

08 32 19 – Sliding Wood-Framed Glass Doors

08 32 19.10 Sliding Wood Doors

		Crew	Daily Output	Labor-Hours	Unit	Material	2015 Bare Costs Labor	Equipment	Total	Total Incl O&P
0010	**SLIDING WOOD DOORS**									
0020	Wood, tempered insul. glass, 6' wide, premium	2 Carp	4	4	Ea.	1,425	188		1,613	1,875
0100	Economy		4	4		1,175	188		1,363	1,575
0150	8' wide, wood, premium		3	5.333		1,825	250		2,075	2,375
0200	Economy		3	5.333		1,500	250		1,750	2,025
0235	10' wide, wood, premium		2.50	6.400		2,600	300		2,900	3,300
0240	Economy		2.50	6.400		2,200	300		2,500	2,875
0250	12' wide, wood, premium		2.50	6.400		3,000	300		3,300	3,750
0300	Economy	↓	2.50	6.400	↓	2,450	300		2,750	3,150

08 32 19.15 Sliding Glass Vinyl-Clad Wood Doors

			Crew	Daily Output	Labor-Hours	Unit	Material	2015 Bare Costs Labor	Equipment	Total	Total Incl O&P
0010	**SLIDING GLASS VINYL-CLAD WOOD DOORS**										
0020	Glass, sliding vinyl clad, insul. glass, 6'-0" x 6'-8"	G	2 Carp	4	4	Opng.	1,500	188		1,688	1,975
0025	6'-0" x 6'-10" high	G		4	4		1,650	188		1,838	2,125
0030	6'-0" x 8'-0" high	G		4	4		1,975	188		2,163	2,475
0100	8'-0" x 6'-10" high	G		4	4		2,025	188		2,213	2,525
0500	4 leaf, 9'-0" x 6'-10" high	G		3	5.333		3,250	250		3,500	3,950
0600	12'-0" x 6'-10" high	G	↓	3	5.333	↓	3,875	250		4,125	4,650

For customer support on your Site Work & Landscape Cost Data, call 877.737.1594.

161

08 34 Special Function Doors

08 34 16 – Hangar Doors

08 34 16.10 Aircraft Hangar Doors

		Crew	Daily Output	Labor-Hours	Unit	Material	2015 Bare Costs Labor	Equipment	Total	Total Incl O&P
0010	**AIRCRAFT HANGAR DOORS**									
0020	Bi-fold, ovhd., 20 psf wind load, incl. elec. oper.									
0100	12' high x 40'	2 Sswk	240	.067	S.F.	16.45	3.51		19.96	24
0200	16' high x 60'		230	.070		19.80	3.66		23.46	28.50
0300	20' high x 80'	↓	220	.073	↓	21.50	3.83		25.33	30

08 36 Panel Doors

08 36 13 – Sectional Doors

08 36 13.10 Overhead Commercial Doors

		Crew	Daily Output	Labor-Hours	Unit	Material	2015 Bare Costs Labor	Equipment	Total	Total Incl O&P
0010	**OVERHEAD COMMERCIAL DOORS**									
1000	Stock, sectional, heavy duty, wood, 1-3/4" thick, 8' x 8' high	2 Carp	2	8	Ea.	1,050	375		1,425	1,725
1200	12' x 12' high		1.50	10.667		2,050	500		2,550	3,025
1300	Chain hoist, 14' x 14' high		1.30	12.308		3,300	580		3,880	4,525
1500	20' x 8' high		1.30	12.270		2,675	575		3,250	3,825
2300	Fiberglass and aluminum, heavy duty, sectional, 12' x 12' high		1.50	10.667		2,700	500		3,200	3,750
2600	Steel, 24 ga. sectional, manual, 8' x 8' high		2	8		820	375		1,195	1,475
2800	Chain hoist, 20' x 14' high	↓	.70	22.857	↓	3,725	1,075		4,800	5,750
2850	For 1-1/4" rigid insulation and 26 ga. galv.									
2860	back panel, add				S.F.	4.75			4.75	5.25
2900	For electric trolley operator, 1/3 H.P., to 12' x 12', add	1 Carp	2	4	Ea.	950	188		1,138	1,350
2950	Over 12' x 12', 1/2 H.P., add	"	1	8	"	1,125	375		1,500	1,825

08 41 Entrances and Storefronts

08 41 13 – Aluminum-Framed Entrances and Storefronts

08 41 13.20 Tube Framing

		Crew	Daily Output	Labor-Hours	Unit	Material	2015 Bare Costs Labor	Equipment	Total	Total Incl O&P
0010	**TUBE FRAMING**, For window walls and store fronts, aluminum stock									
1000	Flush tube frame, mill finish, 1/4" glass, 1-3/4" x 4", open header	2 Glaz	80	.200	L.F.	13.25	9		22.25	28.50
1050	Open sill		82	.195		10.85	8.80		19.65	25.50
1100	Closed back header		83	.193		19	8.70		27.70	34.50
1200	Vertical mullion, one piece		75	.213		19.90	9.60		29.50	36.50
1300	90° or 180° vertical corner post		75	.213		32.50	9.60		42.10	50
5000	Flush tube frame, mill fin., thermal brk., 2-1/4" x 4-1/2", open header		74	.216		17.15	9.75		26.90	33.50
5050	Open sill		75	.213		15.10	9.60		24.70	31.50
5100	Vertical mullion, one piece		69	.232		17.75	10.45		28.20	35.50
5200	90° or 180° vertical corner post	↓	69	.232	↓	19.10	10.45		29.55	37

08 41 26 – All-Glass Entrances and Storefronts

08 41 26.10 Window Walls Aluminum, Stock

		Crew	Daily Output	Labor-Hours	Unit	Material	2015 Bare Costs Labor	Equipment	Total	Total Incl O&P
0010	**WINDOW WALLS ALUMINUM, STOCK**, including glazing									
0020	Minimum	H-2	160	.150	S.F.	46.50	6.40		52.90	61.50
0050	Average		140	.171		64	7.30		71.30	81.50
0100	Maximum	↓	110	.218	↓	172	9.30		181.30	203

08 42 Entrances

08 42 26 – All-Glass Entrances

08 42 26.10 Swinging Glass Doors	Crew	Daily Output	Labor-Hours	Unit	Material	2015 Bare Costs Labor	Equipment	Total	Total Incl O&P
0010 **SWINGING GLASS DOORS**									
0020 Including hardware, 1/2" thick, tempered, 3' x 7' opening	2 Glaz	2	8	Opng.	2,200	360		2,560	2,975
0100 6' x 7' opening	"	1.40	11.429	"	4,400	515		4,915	5,600

08 43 Storefronts

08 43 13 – Aluminum-Framed Storefronts

08 43 13.20 Storefront Systems

	Crew	Daily Output	Labor-Hours	Unit	Material	2015 Bare Costs Labor	Equipment	Total	Total Incl O&P
0010 **STOREFRONT SYSTEMS**, aluminum frame clear 3/8" plate glass									
0020 incl. 3' x 7' door with hardware (400 sq. ft. max. wall)									
0500 Wall height to 12' high, commercial grade	2 Glaz	150	.107	S.F.	22.50	4.81		27.31	32.50
0700 Monumental grade		115	.139		40.50	6.25		46.75	54
1000 6' x 7' door with hardware, commercial grade		135	.119		30	5.35		35.35	41
1200 Monumental grade	↓	100	.160	↓	54.50	7.20		61.70	71

08 44 Curtain Wall and Glazed Assemblies

08 44 13 – Glazed Aluminum Curtain Walls

08 44 13.10 Glazed Curtain Walls

	Crew	Daily Output	Labor-Hours	Unit	Material	2015 Bare Costs Labor	Equipment	Total	Total Incl O&P
0010 **GLAZED CURTAIN WALLS**, aluminum, stock, including glazing									
0020 Minimum	H-1	205	.156	S.F.	37.50	7.65		45.15	54
0150 Average, double glazed	"	180	.178	"	69	8.70		77.70	90.50

08 51 Metal Windows

08 51 13 – Aluminum Windows

08 51 13.10 Aluminum Sash

	Crew	Daily Output	Labor-Hours	Unit	Material	2015 Bare Costs Labor	Equipment	Total	Total Incl O&P
0010 **ALUMINUM SASH**									
0020 Stock, grade C, glaze & trim not incl., casement	2 Sswk	200	.080	S.F.	39	4.21		43.21	50.50
0100 Fixed casement	"	200	.080	"	17.35	4.21		21.56	26.50

08 51 13.20 Aluminum Windows

	Crew	Daily Output	Labor-Hours	Unit	Material	2015 Bare Costs Labor	Equipment	Total	Total Incl O&P
0010 **ALUMINUM WINDOWS**, incl. frame and glazing, commercial grade									
1000 Stock units, casement, 3'-1" x 3'-2" opening	2 Sswk	10	1.600	Ea.	375	84		459	555
3000 Single hung, 2' x 3' opening, enameled, standard glazed		10	1.600		208	84		292	375
3100 Insulating glass		10	1.600		252	84		336	425
3890 Awning type, 3' x 3' opening standard glass		14	1.143		425	60		485	575
4000 Sliding aluminum, 3' x 2' opening, standard glazed		10	1.600		217	84		301	385
5500 Sliding, with thermal barrier and screen, 6' x 4', 2 track		8	2		725	105		830	980
5700 4 track	↓	8	2	↓	910	105		1,015	1,175

08 51 23 – Steel Windows

08 51 23.10 Steel Sash

	Crew	Daily Output	Labor-Hours	Unit	Material	2015 Bare Costs Labor	Equipment	Total	Total Incl O&P
0010 **STEEL SASH** Custom units, glazing and trim not included									
0100 Casement, 100% vented	2 Sswk	200	.080	S.F.	66.50	4.21		70.71	80.50
0200 50% vented		200	.080		54.50	4.21		58.71	67
0300 Fixed		200	.080		29	4.21		33.21	39.50
2000 Industrial security sash, 50% vented		200	.080		57.50	4.21		61.71	70.50
2100 Fixed	↓	200	.080	↓	47	4.21		51.21	59

08 51 Metal Windows

08 51 66 – Metal Window Screens

08 51 66.10 Screens		Crew	Daily Output	Labor-Hours	Unit	Material	2015 Bare Costs Labor	Equipment	Total	Total Incl O&P
0010	**SCREENS**									
0020	For metal sash, aluminum or bronze mesh, flat screen	2 Sswk	1200	.013	S.F.	4.30	.70		5	5.95
0800	Security screen, aluminum frame with stainless steel cloth	"	1200	.013	"	24	.70		24.70	27

08 52 Wood Windows

08 52 10 – Plain Wood Windows

08 52 10.40 Casement Window

			Crew	Daily Output	Labor-Hours	Unit	Material	Labor	Equipment	Total	Total Incl O&P
0010	**CASEMENT WINDOW**, including frame, screen and grilles										
0100	2'-0" x 3'-0" H, dbl. insulated glass	G	1 Carp	10	.800	Ea.	268	37.50		305.50	355
0200	2'-0" x 4'-6" high, double insulated glass	G		9	.889		360	41.50		401.50	460
0522	Vinyl clad, premium, double insulated glass, 2'-0" x 3'-0"	G		10	.800		271	37.50		308.50	355
0525	2'-0" x 5'-0"	G		8	1		360	47		407	475

08 52 10.50 Double Hung

			Crew	Daily Output	Labor-Hours	Unit	Material	Labor	Equipment	Total	Total Incl O&P
0010	**DOUBLE HUNG**, Including frame, screens and grilles										
0100	2'-0" x 3'-0" high, low E insul. glass	G	1 Carp	10	.800	Ea.	210	37.50		247.50	289
0300	4'-0" x 4'-6" high, low E insulated glass	G	"	8	1	"	320	47		367	430

08 52 10.70 Sliding Windows

			Crew	Daily Output	Labor-Hours	Unit	Material	Labor	Equipment	Total	Total Incl O&P
0010	**SLIDING WINDOWS**										
0100	3'-0" x 3'-0" high, double insulated	G	1 Carp	10	.800	Ea.	284	37.50		321.50	370
0200	4'-0" x 3'-6" high, double insulated	G	"	9	.889	"	355	41.50		396.50	455

08 52 13 – Metal-Clad Wood Windows

08 52 13.10 Awning Windows, Metal-Clad

			Crew	Daily Output	Labor-Hours	Unit	Material	Labor	Equipment	Total	Total Incl O&P
0010	**AWNING WINDOWS, METAL-CLAD**										
2000	Metal clad, awning deluxe, double insulated glass, 34" x 22"		1 Carp	9	.889	Ea.	247	41.50		288.50	335
2100	40" x 22"		"	9	.889	"	291	41.50		332.50	385

08 52 13.20 Casement Windows, Metal-Clad

			Crew	Daily Output	Labor-Hours	Unit	Material	Labor	Equipment	Total	Total Incl O&P
0010	**CASEMENT WINDOWS, METAL-CLAD**										
0100	Metal clad, deluxe, dbl. insul. glass, 2'-0" x 3'-0" high	G	1 Carp	10	.800	Ea.	279	37.50		316.50	365
0130	2'-0" x 5'-0" high	G	"	8	1	"	325	47		372	435

08 52 13.30 Double-Hung Windows, Metal-clad

			Crew	Daily Output	Labor-Hours	Unit	Material	Labor	Equipment	Total	Total Incl O&P
0010	**DOUBLE-HUNG WINDOWS, METAL-CLAD**										
0100	Metal clad, deluxe, dbl. insul. glass, 2'-6" x 3'-0" high	G	1 Carp	10	.800	Ea.	272	37.50		309.50	355
0160	3'-0" x 4'-6" high	G	"	9	.889	"	345	41.50		386.50	445

08 52 13.35 Picture and Sliding Windows Metal-Clad

			Crew	Daily Output	Labor-Hours	Unit	Material	Labor	Equipment	Total	Total Incl O&P
0010	**PICTURE AND SLIDING WINDOWS METAL-CLAD**										
2400	Metal clad, dlx sliding, double insulated glass, 3'-0" x 3'-0" high	G	1 Carp	10	.800	Ea.	330	37.50		367.50	420
2420	4'-0" x 3'-6" high	G	"	9	.889	"	400	41.50		441.50	505

08 52 16 – Plastic-Clad Wood Windows

08 52 16.70 Vinyl Clad, Premium, Dbl. Insulated Glass

			Crew	Daily Output	Labor-Hours	Unit	Material	Labor	Equipment	Total	Total Incl O&P
0010	**VINYL CLAD, PREMIUM, DBL. INSULATED GLASS**										
1000	Sliding, 3'-0" x 3'-0"	G	1 Carp	10	.800	Ea.	605	37.50		642.50	725
1100	5'-0" x 4'-0"	G	"	9	.889	"	900	41.50		941.50	1,050

08 71 20 – Hardware

08 71 20.35 Panic Devices

		Crew	Daily Output	Labor-Hours	Unit	Material	2015 Bare Costs Labor	Equipment	Total	Total Incl O&P
0010	**PANIC DEVICES**									
0015	For rim locks, single door exit only	1 Carp	6	1.333	Ea.	460	62.50		522.50	600
0020	Outside key and pull		5	1.600		570	75		645	745
0200	Bar and vertical rod, exit only		5	1.600		865	75		940	1,075
0600	Touch bar, exit only		6	1.333		555	62.50		617.50	705
1000	Mortise, bar, exit only		4	2		725	94		819	945
1600	Touch bar, exit only		4	2		760	94		854	980
2000	Narrow stile, rim mounted, bar, exit only		6	1.333		610	62.50		672.50	765
2010	Outside key and pull		5	1.600		890	75		965	1,100

08 71 20.40 Lockset

		Crew	Daily Output	Labor-Hours	Unit	Material	2015 Bare Costs Labor	Equipment	Total	Total Incl O&P
0010	**LOCKSET**, Standard duty									
0020	Non-keyed, passage, w/sect.trim	1 Carp	12	.667	Ea.	70	31.50		101.50	125
0100	Privacy		12	.667		75	31.50		106.50	131
0400	Keyed, single cylinder function		10	.800		108	37.50		145.50	176
0500	Lever handled, keyed, single cylinder function		10	.800		128	37.50		165.50	199

08 71 20.41 Dead Locks

		Crew	Daily Output	Labor-Hours	Unit	Material	2015 Bare Costs Labor	Equipment	Total	Total Incl O&P
0010	**DEAD LOCKS**									
0011	Mortise heavy duty outside key (security item)	1 Carp	9	.889	Ea.	175	41.50		216.50	257
0020	Double cylinder		9	.889		175	41.50		216.50	257
1000	Tubular, standard duty, outside key		10	.800		45	37.50		82.50	108
1010	Double cylinder		10	.800		60	37.50		97.50	124

08 71 20.50 Door Stops

		Crew	Daily Output	Labor-Hours	Unit	Material	2015 Bare Costs Labor	Equipment	Total	Total Incl O&P
0010	**DOOR STOPS**									
0020	Holder & bumper, floor or wall	1 Carp	32	.250	Ea.	34.50	11.75		46.25	55.50
1300	Wall bumper, 4" diameter, with rubber pad, aluminum		32	.250		11.70	11.75		23.45	31
1600	Door bumper, floor type, aluminum		32	.250		8.10	11.75		19.85	27
1900	Plunger type, door mounted		32	.250		28	11.75		39.75	48.50

08 71 20.65 Thresholds

		Crew	Daily Output	Labor-Hours	Unit	Material	2015 Bare Costs Labor	Equipment	Total	Total Incl O&P
0010	**THRESHOLDS**									
0011	Threshold 3' long saddles aluminum	1 Carp	48	.167	L.F.	9.40	7.85		17.25	22.50
0100	Aluminum, 8" wide, 1/2" thick		12	.667	Ea.	49	31.50		80.50	102
0700	Rubber, 1/2" thick, 5-1/2" wide		20	.400		40	18.80		58.80	73
0800	2-3/4" wide		20	.400		45	18.80		63.80	78.50

08 71 20.90 Hinges

		Crew	Daily Output	Labor-Hours	Unit	Material	2015 Bare Costs Labor	Equipment	Total	Total Incl O&P
0010	**HINGES**									
0012	Full mortise, avg. freq., steel base, USP, 4-1/2" x 4-1/2"				Pr.	36			36	40
0080	US10A					49.50			49.50	54.50
0400	Brass base, 4-1/2" x 4-1/2", US10					58.50			58.50	64.50
0480	US10B					63			63	69.50
0950	Full mortise, high frequency, steel base, 3-1/2" x 3-1/2", US26D					30			30	33
1000	4-1/2" x 4-1/2", USP					63			63	69
1400	Brass base, 3-1/2" x 3-1/2", US4					51			51	56
1430	4-1/2" x 4-1/2", US10					73.50			73.50	81
3000	Half surface, half mortise, or full surface, average frequency									
3010	Steel base, 4-1/2" x 4-1/2", USP				Pr.	44.50			44.50	49
3400	Brass base, 4-1/2" x 4-1/2", US10				"	164			164	181

08 71 20.91 Special Hinges

		Crew	Daily Output	Labor-Hours	Unit	Material	2015 Bare Costs Labor	Equipment	Total	Total Incl O&P
0010	**SPECIAL HINGES**									
1500	Non template, full mortise, average frequency									
1510	Steel base, 4" x 4", USP				Pr.	36			36	39.50
4600	Spring hinge, single acting, 6" flange, steel				Ea.	50			50	55

08 71 Door Hardware

08 71 20 – Hardware

08 71 20.91 Special Hinges	Crew	Daily Output	Labor-Hours	Unit	Material	2015 Bare Costs Labor	Equipment	Total	Total Incl O&P
4700　Brass				Ea.	94.50			94.50	104

08 71 21 – Astragals

08 71 21.10 Exterior Mouldings, Astragals

	Crew	Daily Output	Labor-Hours	Unit	Material	2015 Bare Costs Labor	Equipment	Total	Total Incl O&P
0010　**EXTERIOR MOULDINGS, ASTRAGALS**									
2000　"L" extrusion, neoprene bulbs	1 Carp	75	.107	L.F.	4.10	5		9.10	12.20
2400　Spring hinged security seal, with cam	"	75	.107	"	6.80	5		11.80	15.20
3000　One piece stile protection									
3020　Neoprene fabric loop, nail on aluminum strips	1 Carp	60	.133	L.F.	1.10	6.25		7.35	10.85
3600　Spring bronze strip, nail on type		105	.076		1.85	3.58		5.43	7.55
4000　Extruded aluminum retainer, flush mount, pile insert	↓	105	.076	↓	2.25	3.58		5.83	8
5000　Two piece overlapping astragal, extruded aluminum retainer									
5010　Pile insert	1 Carp	60	.133	L.F.	3.35	6.25		9.60	13.35
5500　Interlocking aluminum, 5/8" x 1" neoprene bulb insert	"	45	.178	"	5.70	8.35		14.05	19.10

08 71 25 – Weatherstripping

08 71 25.10 Mechanical Seals, Weatherstripping

	Crew	Daily Output	Labor-Hours	Unit	Material	2015 Bare Costs Labor	Equipment	Total	Total Incl O&P
0010　**MECHANICAL SEALS, WEATHERSTRIPPING**									
1000　Doors, wood frame, interlocking, for 3' x 7' door, zinc	1 Carp	3	2.667	Opng.	44	125		169	242
1300　6' x 7' opening, zinc	"	2	4	"	54	188		242	350
1700　Wood frame, spring type, bronze									
1800　3' x 7' door	1 Carp	7.60	1.053	Opng.	23	49.50		72.50	102

08 75 Window Hardware

08 75 30 – Weatherstripping

08 75 30.10 Mechanical Weather Seals

	Crew	Daily Output	Labor-Hours	Unit	Material	2015 Bare Costs Labor	Equipment	Total	Total Incl O&P
0010　**MECHANICAL WEATHER SEALS**, Window, double hung, 3' X 5'									
0020　Zinc	1 Carp	7.20	1.111	Opng.	20	52		72	103
0500　As above but heavy duty, zinc	"	4.60	1.739	"	20	81.50		101.50	148

08 81 Glass Glazing

08 81 10 – Float Glass

08 81 10.10 Various Types and Thickness of Float Glass

	Crew	Daily Output	Labor-Hours	Unit	Material	2015 Bare Costs Labor	Equipment	Total	Total Incl O&P
0010　**VARIOUS TYPES AND THICKNESS OF FLOAT GLASS**									
0020　3/16" Plain	2 Glaz	130	.123	S.F.	5.05	5.55		10.60	14
0200　Tempered, clear	"	130	.123	"	6.95	5.55		12.50	16.10

08 81 30 – Insulating Glass

08 81 30.10 Reduce Heat Transfer Glass

		Crew	Daily Output	Labor-Hours	Unit	Material	2015 Bare Costs Labor	Equipment	Total	Total Incl O&P
0010　**REDUCE HEAT TRANSFER GLASS**										
0015　2 lites 1/8" float, 1/2" thk under 15 S.F.										
0020　Clear	G	2 Glaz	95	.168	S.F.	10.05	7.60		17.65	22.50
0200　2 lites 3/16" float, for 5/8" thk unit, 15 to 30 S.F., clear	G		90	.178		13.70	8		21.70	27.50
0400　1" thk, dbl. glazed, 1/4" float, 30-70 S.F., clear	G	↓	75	.213	↓	16.80	9.60		26.40	33

08 83 Mirrors

08 83 13 – Mirrored Glass Glazing

08 83 13.10 Mirrors		Crew	Daily Output	Labor-Hours	Unit	Material	2015 Bare Costs Labor	Equipment	Total	Total Incl O&P
0010	**MIRRORS**, No frames, wall type, 1/4" plate glass, polished edge									
0100	Up to 5 S.F.	2 Glaz	125	.128	S.F.	9.50	5.75		15.25	19.25
1000	Float glass, up to 10 S.F., 1/8" thick		160	.100		5.90	4.51		10.41	13.35
1100	3/16" thick		150	.107		7.30	4.81		12.11	15.40

08 88 Special Function Glazing

08 88 56 – Ballistics-Resistant Glazing

08 88 56.10 Laminated Glass		Crew	Daily Output	Labor-Hours	Unit	Material	2015 Bare Costs Labor	Equipment	Total	Total Incl O&P
0010	**LAMINATED GLASS**									
0020	Clear float .03" vinyl 1/4"	2 Glaz	90	.178	S.F.	12.40	8		20.40	26
0200	.06" vinyl, 1/2" thick	"	65	.246	"	25.50	11.10		36.60	45

For customer support on your Site Work & Landscape Cost Data, call 877.737.1594.

167

Division Notes

	CREW	DAILY OUTPUT	LABOR-HOURS	UNIT	BARE COSTS				TOTAL INCL O&P
					MAT.	LABOR	EQUIP.	TOTAL	

Estimating Tips
General
- Room Finish Schedule: A complete set of plans should contain a room finish schedule. If one is not available, it would be well worth the time and effort to obtain one.

09 20 00 Plaster and Gypsum Board
- Lath is estimated by the square yard plus a 5% allowance for waste. Furring, channels, and accessories are measured by the linear foot. An extra foot should be allowed for each accessory miter or stop.
- Plaster is also estimated by the square yard. Deductions for openings vary by preference, from zero deduction to 50% of all openings over 2 feet in width. The estimator should allow one extra square foot for each linear foot of horizontal interior or exterior angle located below the ceiling level. Also, double the areas of small radius work.
- Drywall accessories, studs, track, and acoustical caulking are all measured by the linear foot. Drywall taping is figured by the square foot. Gypsum wallboard is estimated by the square foot. No material deductions should be made for door or window openings under 32 S.F.

09 60 00 Flooring
- Tile and terrazzo areas are taken off on a square foot basis. Trim and base materials are measured by the linear foot. Accent tiles are listed per each. Two basic methods of installation are used. Mud set is approximately 30% more expensive than thin set. In terrazzo work, be sure to include the linear footage of embedded decorative strips, grounds, machine rubbing, and power cleanup.
- Wood flooring is available in strip, parquet, or block configuration. The latter two types are set in adhesives with quantities estimated by the square foot. The laying pattern will influence labor costs and material waste. In addition to the material and labor for laying wood floors, the estimator must make allowances for sanding and finishing these areas, unless the flooring is prefinished.
- Sheet flooring is measured by the square yard. Roll widths vary, so consideration should be given to use the most economical width, as waste must be figured into the total quantity. Consider also the installation methods available, direct glue down or stretched.

09 70 00 Wall Finishes
- Wall coverings are estimated by the square foot. The area to be covered is measured, length by height of wall above baseboards, to calculate the square footage of each wall. This figure is divided by the number of square feet in the single roll which is being used. Deduct, in full, the areas of openings such as doors and windows. Where a pattern match is required allow 25%–30% waste.

09 80 00 Acoustic Treatment
- Acoustical systems fall into several categories. The takeoff of these materials should be by the square foot of area with a 5% allowance for waste. Do not forget about scaffolding, if applicable, when estimating these systems.

09 90 00 Painting and Coating
- A major portion of the work in painting involves surface preparation. Be sure to include cleaning, sanding, filling, and masking costs in the estimate.
- Protection of adjacent surfaces is not included in painting costs. When considering the method of paint application, an important factor is the amount of protection and masking required. These must be estimated separately and may be the determining factor in choosing the method of application.

Reference Numbers
Reference numbers are shown in shaded boxes at the beginning of some major classifications. These numbers refer to related items in the Reference Section. The reference information may be an estimating procedure, an alternate pricing method, or technical information.

Note: Not all subdivisions listed here necessarily appear in this publication. ∎

09 05 05 – Selective Demolition for Finishes

09 05 05.10 Selective Demolition, Ceilings	Crew	Daily Output	Labor-Hours	Unit	Material	2015 Bare Costs Labor	Equipment	Total	Total Incl O&P
0010 **SELECTIVE DEMOLITION, CEILINGS** R024119-10									
0200 Ceiling, drywall, furred and nailed or screwed	2 Clab	800	.020	S.F.		.75		.75	1.16
0220 On metal frame		760	.021			.79		.79	1.22
0240 On suspension system, including system		720	.022			.84		.84	1.29
1000 Plaster, lime and horse hair, on wood lath, incl. lath		700	.023			.86		.86	1.32
1020 On metal lath		570	.028			1.06		1.06	1.62
1100 Gypsum, on gypsum lath		720	.022			.84		.84	1.29
1120 On metal lath		500	.032			1.20		1.20	1.85
1200 Suspended ceiling, mineral fiber, 2' x 2' or 2' x 4'		1500	.011			.40		.40	.62
1250 On suspension system, incl. system		1200	.013			.50		.50	.77
1500 Tile, wood fiber, 12" x 12", glued		900	.018			.67		.67	1.03
1540 Stapled		1500	.011			.40		.40	.62
1580 On suspension system, incl. system		760	.021			.79		.79	1.22
2000 Wood, tongue and groove, 1" x 4"		1000	.016			.60		.60	.93
2040 1" x 8"		1100	.015			.55		.55	.84
2400 Plywood or wood fiberboard, 4' x 8' sheets		1200	.013			.50		.50	.77

09 05 05.20 Selective Demolition, Flooring

09 05 05.20 Selective Demolition, Flooring	Crew	Daily Output	Labor-Hours	Unit	Material	2015 Bare Costs Labor	Equipment	Total	Total Incl O&P
0010 **SELECTIVE DEMOLITION, FLOORING** R024119-10									
0200 Brick with mortar	2 Clab	475	.034	S.F.		1.27		1.27	1.95
0400 Carpet, bonded, including surface scraping		2000	.008			.30		.30	.46
0440 Scrim applied		8000	.002			.08		.08	.12
0480 Tackless		9000	.002			.07		.07	.10
0500 Carpet pad		3500	.005	S.Y.		.17		.17	.26
0550 Carpet tile, releasable adhesive		5000	.003	S.F.		.12		.12	.19
0560 Permanent adhesive		1850	.009			.33		.33	.50
0600 Composition, acrylic or epoxy		400	.040			1.50		1.50	2.31
0700 Concrete, scarify skin	A-1A	225	.036			1.73	.95	2.68	3.72
0800 Resilient, sheet goods	2 Clab	1400	.011			.43		.43	.66
0820 For gym floors	"	900	.018			.67		.67	1.03
0850 Vinyl or rubber cove base	1 Clab	1000	.008	L.F.		.30		.30	.46
0860 Vinyl or rubber cove base, molded corner	"	1000	.008	Ea.		.30		.30	.46
0870 For glued and caulked installation, add to labor						50%			
0900 Vinyl composition tile, 12" x 12"	2 Clab	1000	.016	S.F.		.60		.60	.93
2000 Tile, ceramic, thin set		675	.024			.89		.89	1.37
2020 Mud set		625	.026			.96		.96	1.48
2200 Marble, slate, thin set		675	.024			.89		.89	1.37
2220 Mud set		625	.026			.96		.96	1.48
2600 Terrazzo, thin set		450	.036			1.34		1.34	2.06
2620 Mud set		425	.038			1.42		1.42	2.18
2640 Terrazzo, cast in place		300	.053			2.01		2.01	3.09
8000 Remove flooring, bead blast, simple floor plan	A-1A	1000	.008			.39	.21	.60	.84
8100 complex floor plan		400	.020			.97	.54	1.51	2.09
8150 Mastic only		1500	.005			.26	.14	.40	.56

09 05 05.30 Selective Demolition, Walls and Partitions

09 05 05.30 Selective Demolition, Walls and Partitions	Crew	Daily Output	Labor-Hours	Unit	Material	2015 Bare Costs Labor	Equipment	Total	Total Incl O&P
0010 **SELECTIVE DEMOLITION, WALLS AND PARTITIONS** R024119-10									
0100 Brick, 4" to 12" thick	B-9	220	.182	C.F.		6.90	1.06	7.96	11.80
0200 Concrete block, 4" thick		1150	.035	S.F.		1.32	.20	1.52	2.25
0280 8" thick		1050	.038			1.45	.22	1.67	2.47
1000 Drywall, nailed or screwed	1 Clab	1000	.008			.30		.30	.46
1010 2 layers		400	.020			.75		.75	1.16
1020 Glued and nailed		900	.009			.33		.33	.51
1540 Insulation, fiberglass batts or blankets, 15" wide		3200	.003			.09		.09	.14

09 05 Common Work Results for Finishes

09 05 05 – Selective Demolition for Finishes

09 05 05.30 Selective Demolition, Walls and Partitions	Crew	Daily Output	Labor-Hours	Unit	Material	2015 Bare Costs Labor	Equipment	Total	Total Incl O&P
1550	Rigid insulation, 1" thick	1 Clab	2000	.004	S.F.		.15		.15	.23
2200	Metal or wood studs, finish 2 sides, fiberboard	B-1	520	.046			1.77		1.77	2.72
2250	Lath and plaster		260	.092			3.53		3.53	5.45
2300	Plasterboard (drywall)		520	.046			1.77		1.77	2.72
2350	Plywood	↓	450	.053			2.04		2.04	3.14
3760	Tile, ceramic, on walls, thin set	1 Clab	300	.027	↓		1		1	1.54
3800	Toilet partitions, slate or marble		5	1.600	Ea.		60		60	92.50
3820	Metal or plastic		8	1	"		37.50		37.50	58
4060	Vapor barrier, polyethylene		7400	.001	S.F.		.04		.04	.06
5000	Wallcovering, vinyl	1 Pape	700	.011			.47		.47	.70
5010	With release agent		1500	.005			.22		.22	.33
5025	Wallpaper, 2 layers or less, by hand		250	.032			1.31		1.31	1.97
5035	3 layers or more		165	.048			1.98		1.98	2.99
5040	Designer	↓	480	.017	↓		.68		.68	1.03

09 21 Plaster and Gypsum Board Assemblies

09 21 13 – Plaster Assemblies

09 21 13.10 Plaster Partition Wall

		Crew	Daily Output	Labor-Hours	Unit	Material	2015 Bare Costs Labor	Equipment	Total	Total Incl O&P
0010	**PLASTER PARTITION WALL**									
0400	Stud walls, 3.4 lb. metal lath, 3 coat gypsum plaster, 2 sides									
0600	2" x 4" wood studs, 16" O.C.	J-2	315	.152	S.F.	3.39	6.30	.44	10.13	13.60
0700	2-1/2" metal studs, 25 ga., 12" O.C.	"	325	.148	"	3.14	6.10	.43	9.67	13.05
0900	Gypsum lath, 2 coat vermiculite plaster, 2 sides									
1000	2" x 4" wood studs, 16" O.C.	J-2	355	.135	S.F.	3.77	5.60	.39	9.76	12.95
1200	2-1/2" metal studs, 25 ga., 12" O.C.	"	365	.132	"	3.35	5.45	.38	9.18	12.25

09 21 16 – Gypsum Board Assemblies

09 21 16.33 Partition Wall

		Crew	Daily Output	Labor-Hours	Unit	Material	2015 Bare Costs Labor	Equipment	Total	Total Incl O&P
0010	**PARTITION WALL** Stud wall, 8' to 12' high									
3200	5/8", interior, gypsum board, standard, tape & finish 2 sides									
3400	Installed on and including 2" x 4" wood studs, 16" O.C.	2 Carp	300	.053	S.F.	1.22	2.50		3.72	5.20
3800	Metal studs, NLB, 25 ga., 16" O.C., 3-5/8" wide		340	.047		1.12	2.21		3.33	4.63
4800	Water resistant, on 2" x 4" wood studs, 16" O.C.		300	.053		1.40	2.50		3.90	5.40
5200	Metal studs, NLB, 25 ga. 16" O.C., 3-5/8" wide		340	.047		1.30	2.21		3.51	4.83
6000	Fire resistant, 2 layers, 2 hr., on 2" x 4" wood studs, 16" O.C.		205	.078		1.82	3.66		5.48	7.65
6400	Metal studs, NLB, 25 ga., 16" O.C., 3-5/8" wide		245	.065		1.85	3.07		4.92	6.75
9600	Partitions, for work over 8' high, add	↓	1530	.010	↓		.49		.49	.76

09 23 Gypsum Plastering

09 23 20 – Gypsum Plaster

09 23 20.10 Gypsum Plaster On Walls and Ceilings

		Crew	Daily Output	Labor-Hours	Unit	Material	2015 Bare Costs Labor	Equipment	Total	Total Incl O&P
0010	**GYPSUM PLASTER ON WALLS AND CEILINGS**									
0020	80# bag, less than 1 ton				Bag	15.95			15.95	17.55
0100	Over 1 ton				"	13.95			13.95	15.35
0300	2 coats, no lath included, on walls	J-1	105	.381	S.Y.	3.61	15.60	1.34	20.55	29
0600	On and incl. 3/8" gypsum lath on steel, on walls	J-2	97	.495		6.65	20.50	1.45	28.60	39.50
0900	3 coats, no lath included, on walls	J-1	87	.460		5.20	18.85	1.61	25.66	36
1200	On and including painted metal lath, on wood studs	J-2	86	.558	↓	10.20	23	1.63	34.83	47.50

For customer support on your Site Work & Landscape Cost Data, call 877.737.1594.

171

09 24 Cement Plastering

09 24 23 – Cement Stucco

09 24 23.40 Stucco		Crew	Daily Output	Labor-Hours	Unit	Material	2015 Bare Costs Labor	Equipment	Total	Total Incl O&P
0010	**STUCCO**									
0015	3 coats 1" thick, float finish, with mesh, on wood frame	J-2	63	.762	S.Y.	6.25	31.50	2.22	39.97	56.50
0100	On masonry construction, no mesh incl.	J-1	67	.597		2.55	24.50	2.10	29.15	41.50
0300	For trowel finish, add	1 Plas	170	.047			2.02		2.02	3.03
1000	Exterior stucco, with bonding agent, 3 coats, on walls, no mesh incl.	J-1	200	.200		3.65	8.20	.70	12.55	17.10

09 26 Veneer Plastering

09 26 13 – Gypsum Veneer Plastering

09 26 13.80 Thin Coat Plaster

		Crew	Daily Output	Labor-Hours	Unit	Material	Labor	Equipment	Total	Total Incl O&P
0010	**THIN COAT PLASTER**									
0012	1 coat veneer, not incl. lath	J-1	3600	.011	S.F.	.11	.46	.04	.61	.84
1000	In 50 lb. bags				Bag	15.25			15.25	16.80

09 29 Gypsum Board

09 29 10 – Gypsum Board Panels

09 29 10.30 Gypsum Board

		Crew	Daily Output	Labor-Hours	Unit	Material	Labor	Equipment	Total	Total Incl O&P
0010	**GYPSUM BOARD** on walls & ceilings R092910-10									
0150	3/8" thick, on walls, standard, no finish included	2 Carp	2000	.008	S.F.	.34	.38		.72	.95
0300	1/2" thick, on walls, standard, no finish included		2000	.008		.30	.38		.68	.91
0350	Taped and finished (level 4 finish)		965	.017		.35	.78		1.13	1.58
0390	With compound skim coat (level 5 finish)		775	.021		.40	.97		1.37	1.93
2000	5/8" thick, on walls, standard, no finish included		2000	.008		.33	.38		.71	.94
2090	With compound skim coat (level 5 finish)		775	.021		.43	.97		1.40	1.96
2200	Water resistant, no finish included		2000	.008		.42	.38		.80	1.04
2290	With compound skim coat (level 5 finish)		775	.021		.52	.97		1.49	2.06
2510	Mold resistant, no finish included		2000	.008		.46	.38		.84	1.09
2530	With compound skim coat (level 5 finish)		775	.021		.56	.97		1.53	2.11
4000	Fireproofing, beams or columns, 2 layers, 1/2" thick, incl finish		330	.048		.79	2.28		3.07	4.37
4010	Mold resistant		330	.048		.97	2.28		3.25	4.57
4050	5/8" thick		300	.053		.77	2.50		3.27	4.70
4060	Mold resistant		300	.053		1.01	2.50		3.51	4.97
6010	1/2" thick on walls, multi-layer, light weight, no finish included		1500	.011		1.87	.50		2.37	2.83
6015	Taped and finished (level 4 finish)		725	.022		1.92	1.04		2.96	3.70
6025	5/8" thick on walls, for wood studs, no finish included		1500	.011		2.17	.50		2.67	3.16
6035	With compound skim coat (level 5 finish)		580	.028		2.27	1.30		3.57	4.49
6040	For metal stud, no finish included		1500	.011		2.06	.50		2.56	3.04
6050	With compound skim coat (level 5 finish)		580	.028		2.16	1.30		3.46	4.37
6055	Abuse resist, no finish included		1500	.011		3.75	.50		4.25	4.90
6065	With compound skim coat (level 5 finish)		580	.028		3.85	1.30		5.15	6.25
6070	Shear rated, no finish included		1500	.011		4.30	.50		4.80	5.50
6080	With compound skim coat (level 5 finish)		580	.028		4.40	1.30		5.70	6.85
6085	For SCIF applications, no finish included		1500	.011		4.72	.50		5.22	5.95
6095	With compound skim coat (level 5 finish)		580	.028		4.82	1.30		6.12	7.30
6100	1-3/8" thick on walls, THX Certified, no finish included		1500	.011		8.40	.50		8.90	10
6110	With compound skim coat (level 5 finish)		580	.028		8.50	1.30		9.80	11.35
6115	5/8" thick on walls, score & snap installation, no finish included		2000	.008		1.69	.38		2.07	2.44
6125	With compound skim coat (level 5 finish)		775	.021		1.79	.97		2.76	3.46
7020	5/8" thick on ceilings, for wood joists, no finish included		1200	.013		2.17	.63		2.80	3.35
7030	With compound skim coat (level 5 finish)		410	.039		2.27	1.83		4.10	5.30

09 29 Gypsum Board

09 29 10 – Gypsum Board Panels

09 29 10.30 Gypsum Board		Crew	Daily Output	Labor-Hours	Unit	Material	2015 Bare Costs Labor	Equipment	Total	Total Incl O&P
7035	For metal joists, no finish included	2 Carp	1200	.013	S.F.	2.06	.63		2.69	3.23
7045	With compound skim coat (level 5 finish)		410	.039		2.16	1.83		3.99	5.20
7050	Abuse resist, no finish included		1200	.013		3.75	.63		4.38	5.10
7060	With compound skim coat (level 5 finish)		410	.039		3.85	1.83		5.68	7.05
7065	Shear rated, no finish included		1200	.013		4.30	.63		4.93	5.70
7075	With compound skim coat (level 5 finish)		410	.039		4.40	1.83		6.23	7.65
7080	For SCIF applications, no finish included		1200	.013		4.72	.63		5.35	6.15
7090	With compound skim coat (level 5 finish)		410	.039		4.82	1.83		6.65	8.10
8010	5/8" thick on ceilings, score & snap installation, no finish included		1600	.010		1.69	.47		2.16	2.58
8020	With compound skim coat (level 5 finish)	▼	545	.029	▼	1.79	1.38		3.17	4.09

09 30 Tiling

09 30 13 – Ceramic Tiling

09 30 13.10 Ceramic Tile

		Crew	Daily Output	Labor-Hours	Unit	Material	2015 Bare Costs Labor	Equipment	Total	Total Incl O&P
0010	**CERAMIC TILE**									
3300	Porcelain type, 1 color, color group 2, 1" x 1"	D-7	183	.087	S.F.	5.20	3.34		8.54	10.65
3310	2" x 2" or 2" x 1", thin set		190	.084		6.10	3.22		9.32	11.45
5400	Walls, interior, thin set, 4-1/4" x 4-1/4" tile		190	.084		2.26	3.22		5.48	7.25
5700	8-1/2" x 4-1/4" tile		190	.084		4.86	3.22		8.08	10.10
6300	Exterior walls, frostproof, mud set, 4-1/4" x 4-1/4"		102	.157		7.15	6		13.15	16.70
6400	1-3/8" x 1-3/8"	▼	93	.172	▼	6.10	6.55		12.65	16.40

09 30 16 – Quarry Tiling

09 30 16.10 Quarry Tile

		Crew	Daily Output	Labor-Hours	Unit	Material	2015 Bare Costs Labor	Equipment	Total	Total Incl O&P
0010	**QUARRY TILE**									
0100	Base, cove or sanitary, mud set, to 5" high, 1/2" thick	D-7	110	.145	L.F.	5.35	5.55		10.90	14.10
0700	Floors, mud set, 1,000 S.F. lots, red, 4" x 4" x 1/2" thick		120	.133	S.F.	8.05	5.10		13.15	16.40
0900	6" x 6" x 1/2" thick	▼	140	.114	"	7.55	4.36		11.91	14.75

09 34 Waterproofing-Membrane Tiling

09 34 13 – Waterproofing-Membrane Ceramic Tiling

09 34 13.10 Ceramic Tile Waterproofing Membrane

		Crew	Daily Output	Labor-Hours	Unit	Material	2015 Bare Costs Labor	Equipment	Total	Total Incl O&P
0010	**CERAMIC TILE WATERPROOFING MEMBRANE**									
0020	On floors, including thinset									
0030	Fleece laminated polyethylene grid, 1/8" thick	D-7	250	.064	S.F.	2.26	2.44		4.70	6.10
0040	5/16" thick	"	250	.064	"	2.58	2.44		5.02	6.45
0050	On walls, including thinset									
0060	Fleece laminated polyethylene sheet, 8 mil thick	D-7	480	.033	S.F.	2.26	1.27		3.53	4.37
0070	Accessories, including thinset									
0080	Joint and corner sheet, 4 mils thick, 5" wide	1 Tilf	240	.033	L.F.	1.33	1.43		2.76	3.58
0090	7-1/4" wide		180	.044		1.69	1.90		3.59	4.67
0100	10" wide		120	.067	▼	2.06	2.85		4.91	6.50
0110	Pre-formed corners, inside		32	.250	Ea.	6.90	10.70		17.60	23.50
0120	Outside		32	.250		7.65	10.70		18.35	24.50
0130	2" flanged floor drain with 6" stainless steel grate		16	.500	▼	370	21.50		391.50	440
0140	EPS, sloped shower floor		480	.017	S.F.	4.95	.71		5.66	6.50
0150	Curb	▼	32	.250	L.F.	14	10.70		24.70	31.50

09 51 Acoustical Ceilings

09 51 23 – Acoustical Tile Ceilings

09 51 23.30 Suspended Ceilings, Complete	Crew	Daily Output	Labor-Hours	Unit	Material	2015 Bare Costs Labor	Equipment	Total	Total Incl O&P
0010 **SUSPENDED CEILINGS, COMPLETE**, including standard									
0100 suspension system but not incl. 1-1/2" carrier channels									
0600 Fiberglass ceiling board, 2' x 4' x 5/8", plain faced	1 Carp	500	.016	S.F.	1.97	.75		2.72	3.33
1800 Tile, Z bar suspension, 5/8" mineral fiber tile	"	150	.053	"	2.32	2.50		4.82	6.40

09 63 Masonry Flooring

09 63 13 – Brick Flooring

09 63 13.10 Miscellaneous Brick Flooring

		Crew	Daily Output	Labor-Hours	Unit	Material	2015 Bare Costs Labor	Equipment	Total	Total Incl O&P
0010	**MISCELLANEOUS BRICK FLOORING**									
0020	Acid-proof shales, red, 8" x 3-3/4" x 1-1/4" thick	D-7	.43	37.209	M	695	1,425		2,120	2,875
0050	2-1/4" thick	D-1	.40	40		965	1,675		2,640	3,625
0200	Acid-proof clay brick, 8" x 3-3/4" x 2-1/4" thick [G]	"	.40	40	↓	935	1,675		2,610	3,600
0260	Cast ceramic, pressed, 4" x 8" x 1/2", unglazed	D-7	100	.160	S.F.	6.35	6.10		12.45	16
0270	Glazed		100	.160		8.45	6.10		14.55	18.35
0280	Hand molded flooring, 4" x 8" x 3/4", unglazed		95	.168		8.35	6.45		14.80	18.70
0290	Glazed		95	.168		10.50	6.45		16.95	21
0300	8" hexagonal, 3/4" thick, unglazed		85	.188		9.20	7.20		16.40	21
0310	Glazed		85	.188		16.60	7.20		23.80	29
0400	Heavy duty industrial, cement mortar bed, 2" thick, not incl. brick	D-1	80	.200		1.06	8.40		9.46	14
0450	Acid-proof joints, 1/4" wide	"	65	.246		1.46	10.35		11.81	17.40
0500	Pavers, 8" x 4", 1" to 1-1/4" thick, red	D-7	95	.168		3.69	6.45		10.14	13.55
0510	Ironspot	"	95	.168		5.20	6.45		11.65	15.25
0540	1-3/8" to 1-3/4" thick, red	D-1	95	.168		3.56	7.10		10.66	14.75
0560	Ironspot		95	.168		5.15	7.10		12.25	16.55
0580	2-1/4" thick, red		90	.178		3.62	7.50		11.12	15.45
0590	Ironspot		90	.178		5.60	7.50		13.10	17.65
0700	Paver, adobe brick, 6" x 12", 1/2" joint [G]	↓	42	.381		1.30	16.05		17.35	26
0710	Mexican red, 12" x 12" [G]	1 Tilf	48	.167		1.66	7.15		8.81	12.40
0720	Saltillo, 12" x 12" [G]	"	48	.167	↓	1.40	7.15		8.55	12.10
0800	For sidewalks and patios with pavers, see Section 32 14 16.10									
0870	For epoxy joints, add	D-1	600	.027	S.F.	2.81	1.12		3.93	4.80
0880	For Furan underlayment, add	"	600	.027		2.33	1.12		3.45	4.27
0890	For waxed surface, steam cleaned, add	A-1H	1000	.008	↓	.20	.30	.08	.58	.76

09 65 Resilient Flooring

09 65 13 – Resilient Base and Accessories

09 65 13.13 Resilient Base

		Crew	Daily Output	Labor-Hours	Unit	Material	2015 Bare Costs Labor	Equipment	Total	Total Incl O&P
0010	**RESILIENT BASE**									
0800	1/8" rubber base, 2 1/2" H, straight or cove, standard colors	1 Tilf	315	.025	L.F.	1.13	1.09		2.22	2.85
1100	4" high	"	315	.025	"	1.02	1.09		2.11	2.73

09 65 13.23 Resilient Stair Treads and Risers

		Crew	Daily Output	Labor-Hours	Unit	Material	2015 Bare Costs Labor	Equipment	Total	Total Incl O&P
0010	**RESILIENT STAIR TREADS AND RISERS**									
0300	Rubber, molded tread, 12" wide, 5/16" thick, black	1 Tilf	115	.070	L.F.	14.75	2.98		17.73	20.50
1800	Risers, 7" high, 1/8" thick, flat		250	.032		7.70	1.37		9.07	10.50
2100	Vinyl, molded tread, 12" wide, colors, 1/8" thick		115	.070		5.35	2.98		8.33	10.25
2400	Riser, 7" high, 1/8" thick, coved	↓	175	.046	↓	2.70	1.96		4.66	5.85

09 65 Resilient Flooring

09 65 19 – Resilient Tile Flooring

09 65 19.10 Miscellaneous Resilient Tile Flooring

		Crew	Daily Output	Labor-Hours	Unit	Material	2015 Bare Costs Labor	Equipment	Total	Total Incl O&P
0010	**MISCELLANEOUS RESILIENT TILE FLOORING**									
6700	Synthetic turf, 3/8" thick	1 Tilf	90	.089	S.F.	4.54	3.80		8.34	10.65
6750	Interlocking 2' x 2' squares, 1/2" thick, not									
6810	cemented, for playgrounds, 3/8" thick	1 Tilf	210	.038	S.F.	4.69	1.63		6.32	7.55
6850	1/2" thick	"	190	.042	"	5.10	1.80		6.90	8.25

09 65 19.19 Vinyl Composition Tile Flooring

		Crew	Daily Output	Labor-Hours	Unit	Material	2015 Bare Costs Labor	Equipment	Total	Total Incl O&P
0010	**VINYL COMPOSITION TILE FLOORING**									
7000	Vinyl composition tile, 12" x 12", 1/16" thick	1 Tilf	500	.016	S.F.	1.18	.68		1.86	2.31
7350	1/8" thick, marbleized	"	500	.016	"	2.40	.68		3.08	3.65

09 65 19.23 Vinyl Tile Flooring

		Crew	Daily Output	Labor-Hours	Unit	Material	2015 Bare Costs Labor	Equipment	Total	Total Incl O&P
0010	**VINYL TILE FLOORING**									
7500	Vinyl tile, 12" x 12", 3/32" thick,	1 Tilf	500	.016	S.F.	3.59	.68		4.27	4.96
7550	3/32" thick, premium colors/patterns	"	500	.016	"	7.25	.68		7.93	9

09 66 Terrazzo Flooring

09 66 16 – Terrazzo Floor Tile

09 66 16.10 Tile or Terrazzo Base

		Crew	Daily Output	Labor-Hours	Unit	Material	2015 Bare Costs Labor	Equipment	Total	Total Incl O&P
0010	**TILE OR TERRAZZO BASE**									
0020	Scratch coat only	1 Mstz	150	.053	S.F.	.43	2.29		2.72	3.86
0500	Scratch and brown coat only	"	75	.107	"	.82	4.58		5.40	7.65

09 91 Painting

09 91 13 – Exterior Painting

09 91 13.60 Siding Exterior

		Crew	Daily Output	Labor-Hours	Unit	Material	2015 Bare Costs Labor	Equipment	Total	Total Incl O&P
0010	**SIDING EXTERIOR**, Alkyd (oil base)									
0450	Steel siding, oil base, paint 1 coat, brushwork	2 Pord	2015	.008	S.F.	.10	.32		.42	.59
0800	Paint 2 coats, brushwork		1300	.012		.20	.50		.70	.97
1200	Stucco, rough, oil base, paint 2 coats, brushwork		1300	.012		.20	.50		.70	.97
1400	Roller		1625	.010		.21	.40		.61	.83
1800	Texture 1-11 or clapboard, oil base, primer coat, brushwork		1300	.012		.15	.50		.65	.91
2400	Paint 2 coats, brushwork		810	.020		.30	.80		1.10	1.52
8000	For latex paint, deduct					10%				

09 91 23 – Interior Painting

09 91 23.52 Miscellaneous, Interior

		Crew	Daily Output	Labor-Hours	Unit	Material	2015 Bare Costs Labor	Equipment	Total	Total Incl O&P
0010	**MISCELLANEOUS, INTERIOR**									
2400	Floors, conc./wood, oil base, primer/sealer coat, brushwork	2 Pord	1950	.008	S.F.	.09	.33		.42	.60
2450	Roller	"	5200	.003		.10	.12		.22	.30
3800	Grilles, per side, oil base, primer coat, brushwork	1 Pord	520	.015		.14	.62		.76	1.09
3900	Spray	"	1140	.007		.24	.28		.52	.70
5000	Pipe, 1" - 4" diameter, primer or sealer coat, oil base, brushwork	2 Pord	1250	.013	L.F.	.10	.52		.62	.89
5350	Paint 2 coats, brushwork		775	.021		.19	.83		1.02	1.47
6300	13" - 16" diameter, primer or sealer coat, brushwork		310	.052		.39	2.08		2.47	3.57
6500	Paint 2 coats, brushwork		195	.082		.78	3.31		4.09	5.85
8900	Trusses and wood frames, primer coat, oil base, brushwork	1 Pord	800	.010	S.F.	.07	.40		.47	.69
9220	Paint 2 coats, brushwork		500	.016		.21	.65		.86	1.20
9260	Stain, brushwork, wipe off		600	.013		.09	.54		.63	.90
9280	Varnish, 3 coats, brushwork		275	.029		.28	1.17		1.45	2.08

For customer support on your Site Work & Landscape Cost Data, call 877.737.1594.

175

09 91 Painting

09 91 23 – Interior Painting

09 91 23.72 Walls and Ceilings, Interior		Crew	Daily Output	Labor-Hours	Unit	Material	2015 Bare Costs Labor	Equipment	Total	Total Incl O&P
0010	**WALLS AND CEILINGS, INTERIOR**									
0100	Concrete, drywall or plaster, latex , primer or sealer coat									
0200	Smooth finish, brushwork	1 Pord	1150	.007	S.F.	.06	.28		.34	.49
0800	Paint 2 coats, smooth finish, brushwork		680	.012		.13	.47		.60	.87
0880	Spray	↓	1625	.005	↓	.12	.20		.32	.44

09 91 23.74 Walls and Ceilings, Interior, Zero VOC Latex

			Crew	Daily Output	Labor-Hours	Unit	Material	Labor	Equipment	Total	Total Incl O&P
0010	**WALLS AND CEILINGS, INTERIOR, ZERO VOC LATEX**										
0100	Concrete, dry wall or plaster, latex, primer or sealer coat										
0200	Smooth finish, brushwork	G	1 Pord	1150	.007	S.F.	.06	.28		.34	.49
0800	Paint 2 coats, smooth finish, brushwork	G		680	.012		.15	.47		.62	.89
0880	Spray	G	↓	1625	.005	↓	.13	.20		.33	.45

09 91 23.75 Dry Fall Painting

		Crew	Daily Output	Labor-Hours	Unit	Material	Labor	Equipment	Total	Total Incl O&P
0010	**DRY FALL PAINTING**									
0100	Sprayed on walls, gypsum board or plaster									
0220	One coat	1 Pord	2600	.003	S.F.	.06	.12		.18	.25
0250	Two coats		1560	.005		.11	.21		.32	.43
0280	Concrete or textured plaster, one coat		1560	.005		.06	.21		.27	.37
0310	Two coats		1300	.006		.11	.25		.36	.49
0340	Concrete block, one coat		1560	.005		.06	.21		.27	.37
0370	Two coats		1300	.006		.11	.25		.36	.49
0400	Wood, one coat		877	.009		.06	.37		.43	.61
0430	Two coats	↓	650	.012	↓	.11	.50		.61	.87
0440	On ceilings, gypsum board or plaster									
0470	One coat	1 Pord	1560	.005	S.F.	.06	.21		.27	.37
0500	Two coats		1300	.006		.11	.25		.36	.49
0530	Concrete or textured plaster, one coat		1560	.005		.06	.21		.27	.37
0560	Two coats		1300	.006		.11	.25		.36	.49
0570	Structural steel, bar joists or metal deck, one coat		1560	.005		.06	.21		.27	.37
0580	Two coats	↓	1040	.008	↓	.11	.31		.42	.59

09 96 High-Performance Coatings

09 96 23 – Graffiti-Resistant Coatings

09 96 23.10 Graffiti Resistant Treatments

		Crew	Daily Output	Labor-Hours	Unit	Material	Labor	Equipment	Total	Total Incl O&P
0010	**GRAFFITI RESISTANT TREATMENTS**, sprayed on walls									
0100	Non-sacrificial, permanent non-stick coating, clear, on metals	1 Pord	2000	.004	S.F.	2.06	.16		2.22	2.51
0200	Concrete		2000	.004		2.35	.16		2.51	2.82
0300	Concrete block		2000	.004		3.03	.16		3.19	3.58
0400	Brick		2000	.004		3.44	.16		3.60	4.02
0500	Stone		2000	.004		3.44	.16		3.60	4.02
0600	Unpainted wood		2000	.004		3.97	.16		4.13	4.61
2000	Semi-permanent cross linking polymer primer, on metals		2000	.004		.70	.16		.86	1.01
2100	Concrete		2000	.004		.84	.16		1	1.16
2200	Concrete block		2000	.004		1.05	.16		1.21	1.39
2300	Brick		2000	.004		.84	.16		1	1.16
2400	Stone		2000	.004		.84	.16		1	1.16
2500	Unpainted wood		2000	.004		1.16	.16		1.32	1.52
3000	Top coat, on metals		2000	.004		.55	.16		.71	.84
3100	Concrete		2000	.004		.62	.16		.78	.93
3200	Concrete block		2000	.004		.87	.16		1.03	1.20
3300	Brick		2000	.004		.73	.16		.89	1.04

09 96 High-Performance Coatings

09 96 23 – Graffiti-Resistant Coatings

09 96 23.10 Graffiti Resistant Treatments	Crew	Daily Output	Labor-Hours	Unit	Material	2015 Bare Costs Labor	Equipment	Total	Total Incl O&P
3400	Stone	1 Pord	2000	.004	S.F.	.73	.16		.89	1.04
3500	Unpainted wood		2000	.004		.87	.16		1.03	1.20
5000	Sacrificial, water based, on metal		2000	.004		.32	.16		.48	.60
5100	Concrete		2000	.004		.32	.16		.48	.60
5200	Concrete block		2000	.004		.32	.16		.48	.60
5300	Brick		2000	.004		.32	.16		.48	.60
5400	Stone		2000	.004		.32	.16		.48	.60
5500	Unpainted wood		2000	.004		.32	.16		.48	.60
8000	Cleaner for use after treatment									
8100	Towels or wipes, per package of 30				Ea.	.63			.63	.70
8200	Aerosol spray, 24 oz. can				"	18			18	19.80

09 96 46 – Intumescent Coatings

09 96 46.10 Coatings, Intumescent

		Crew	Daily Output	Labor-Hours	Unit	Material	2015 Bare Costs Labor	Equipment	Total	Total Incl O&P
0010	**COATINGS, INTUMESCENT**, spray applied									
0100	On exterior structural steel, 0.25" d.f.t.	1 Pord	475	.017	S.F.	.41	.68		1.09	1.47
0150	0.51" d.f.t.		350	.023		.41	.92		1.33	1.84
0200	0.98" d.f.t.		280	.029		.41	1.15		1.56	2.19
0300	On interior structural steel, 0.108" d.f.t.		300	.027		.41	1.08		1.49	2.07
0350	0.310" d.f.t.		150	.053		.41	2.15		2.56	3.69
0400	0.670" d.f.t.		100	.080		.41	3.23		3.64	5.30

09 97 Special Coatings

09 97 10 – Coatings and Paints

09 97 10.10 Coatings and Paints

		Crew	Daily Output	Labor-Hours	Unit	Material	2015 Bare Costs Labor	Equipment	Total	Total Incl O&P
0010	**COATINGS & PAINTS** in 5 gallon lots									
0050	For 100 gallons or more, deduct					10%				
0100	Paint, Exterior alkyd (oil base)									
0200	Flat				Gal.	44.50			44.50	48.50
0300	Gloss					40.50			40.50	44.50
0400	Primer					37.50			37.50	41
0500	Latex (water base)									
0600	Acrylic stain				Gal.	35.50			35.50	39.50
0700	Gloss enamel					33			33	36.50
0800	Flat					27.50			27.50	30.50
0900	Primer					24			24	26.50
1000	Semi-gloss					30.50			30.50	33.50
2400	Masonry, Exterior									
2500	Alkali resistant primer				Gal.	28			28	30.50
2600	Block filler, epoxy					29.50			29.50	32.50
2700	Latex					21.50			21.50	23.50
2800	Latex, flat					21.50			21.50	24
2900	Semi-gloss					34			34	37
4000	Metal									
4100	Galvanizing paint				Gal.	93.50			93.50	103
4200	High heat					62.50			62.50	69
4300	Heat resistant					38.50			38.50	42.50
4400	Machinery enamel, alkyd					49.50			49.50	54
4500	Metal pretreatment (polyvinyl butyral)					112			112	123
4600	Rust inhibitor, ferrous metal					43			43	47.50
4700	Zinc chromate					151			151	166

For customer support on your Site Work & Landscape Cost Data, call 877.737.1594.

177

09 97 Special Coatings

09 97 10 – Coatings and Paints

09 97 10.10 Coatings and Paints	Crew	Daily Output	Labor-Hours	Unit	Material	2015 Bare Costs Labor	Equipment	Total	Total Incl O&P
4800	Zinc rich primer				Gal.	173			173	190
5500	Coatings									
5600	Heavy duty									
5700	Acrylic urethane				Gal.	56.50			56.50	62
5800	Chlorinated rubber					65			65	71.50
5900	Coal tar epoxy					76			76	83.50
6000	Polyamide epoxy, finish					65.50			65.50	72
6100	Primer					58.50			58.50	64.50
6200	Silicone alkyd					52.50			52.50	57.50
6300	2 component solvent based acrylic epoxy					83			83	91.50
6400	Polyester epoxy					83.50			83.50	92
6500	Vinyl					37.50			37.50	41
6600	Special/Miscellaneous									
6700	Aluminum				Gal.	45			45	49.50
6900	Dry fall out, flat					16.90			16.90	18.60
7000	Fire retardant, intumescent					50.50			50.50	56
7100	Linseed oil					21.50			21.50	23.50
7200	Shellac					43			43	47
7300	Swimming pool, epoxy or urethane base					53			53	58
7400	Rubber base					65			65	71.50
7500	Texture paint					21.50			21.50	24
7600	Turpentine					29			29	32
7700	Water repellent, 5% silicone					25			25	27.50

09 97 13 – Steel Coatings

09 97 13.23 Exterior Steel Coatings

0010	**EXTERIOR STEEL COATINGS**									
6100	Cold galvanizing, brush in field	1 Psst	1100	.007	S.F.	.23	.30		.53	.79
6510	Paints & protective coatings, sprayed in field									
6520	Alkyds, primer	2 Psst	3600	.004	S.F.	.09	.18		.27	.42
6540	Gloss topcoats		3200	.005		.08	.21		.29	.45
6560	Silicone alkyd		3200	.005		.15	.21		.36	.52
6610	Epoxy, primer		3000	.005		.29	.22		.51	.71
6630	Intermediate or topcoat		2800	.006		.26	.24		.50	.71
6650	Enamel coat		2800	.006		.33	.24		.57	.78
6810	Latex primer		3600	.004		.06	.18		.24	.39
6830	Topcoats		3200	.005		.07	.21		.28	.44
6910	Universal primers, one part, phenolic, modified alkyd		2000	.008		.37	.33		.70	.99
6940	Two part, epoxy spray		2000	.008		.33	.33		.66	.95
7000	Zinc rich primers, self cure, spray, inorganic		1800	.009		.86	.37		1.23	1.60
7010	Epoxy, spray, organic		1800	.009		.26	.37		.63	.94
7020	Above one story, spray painting simple structures, add						25%			
7030	Intricate structures, add						50%			

Estimating Tips
General

- The items in this division are usually priced per square foot or each.

- Many items in Division 10 require some type of support system or special anchors that are not usually furnished with the item. The required anchors must be added to the estimate in the appropriate division.

- Some items in Division 10, such as lockers, may require assembly before installation. Verify the amount of assembly required. Assembly can often exceed installation time.

10 20 00 Interior Specialties

- Support angles and blocking are not included in the installation of toilet compartments, shower/ dressing compartments, or cubicles. Appropriate line items from Divisions 5 or 6 may need to be added to support the installations.

- Toilet partitions are priced by the stall. A stall consists of a side wall, pilaster, and door with hardware. Toilet tissue holders and grab bars are extra.

- The required acoustical rating of a folding partition can have a significant impact on costs. Verify the sound transmission coefficient rating of the panel priced to the specification requirements.

- Grab bar installation does not include supplemental blocking or backing to support the required load. When grab bars are installed at an existing facility, provisions must be made to attach the grab bars to solid structure.

Reference Numbers

Reference numbers are shown in shaded boxes at the beginning of some major classifications. These numbers refer to related items in the Reference Section. The reference information may be an estimating procedure, an alternate pricing method, or technical information.

Note: Not all subdivisions listed here necessarily appear in this publication. ■

Division 10 – Specialties

10 05 Common Work Results for Specialties

10 05 05 – Selective Demolition for Specialties

10 05 05.10 Selective Demolition, Specialties	Crew	Daily Output	Labor-Hours	Unit	Material	2015 Bare Costs Labor	Equipment	Total	Total Incl O&P
0010 **SELECTIVE DEMOLITION, SPECIALTIES**									
3500 Flagpole, groundset, to 70' high, excluding base/foundation	K-1	1	16	Ea.		690	305	995	1,375
3555 To 30' high	"	2.50	6.400	"		275	121	396	555
4000 Removal of traffic signs, including supports									
4020 To 10 S.F.	B-80B	16	2	Ea.		80.50	15.25	95.75	141
4030 11 S.F. to 20 S.F.	"	5	6.400			258	49	307	450
4040 21 S.F. to 40 S.F.	B-14	1.80	26.667			1,050	202	1,252	1,850
4050 41 S.F. to 100 S.F.	B-13	1.30	43.077			1,775	565	2,340	3,325
4070 Remove traffic posts to 12'-0" high	B-6	100	.240			9.90	3.64	13.54	19.15
4310 Signs, street, reflective aluminum, including post and bracket	1 Clab	60	.133	▼		5		5	7.70

10 13 Directories

10 13 10 – Building Directories

10 13 10.10 Directory Boards

	Crew	Daily Output	Labor-Hours	Unit	Material	2015 Bare Costs Labor	Equipment	Total	Total Incl O&P
0010 **DIRECTORY BOARDS**									
0900 Outdoor, weatherproof, black plastic, 36" x 24"	2 Carp	2	8	Ea.	760	375		1,135	1,425
1000 36" x 36"	"	1.50	10.667	"	880	500		1,380	1,750

10 14 Signage

10 14 19 – Dimensional Letter Signage

10 14 19.10 Exterior Signs

	Crew	Daily Output	Labor-Hours	Unit	Material	2015 Bare Costs Labor	Equipment	Total	Total Incl O&P
0010 **EXTERIOR SIGNS**									
0020 Letters, 2" high, 3/8" deep, cast bronze	1 Carp	24	.333	Ea.	25	15.65		40.65	51.50
0140 1/2" deep, cast aluminum		18	.444		25	21		46	59.50
0160 Cast bronze		32	.250		30	11.75		41.75	51
0300 6" high, 5/8" deep, cast aluminum		24	.333		29	15.65		44.65	56
0400 Cast bronze		24	.333		62.50	15.65		78.15	93
0600 8" high, 3/4" deep, cast aluminum		14	.571		36	27		63	81
0700 Cast bronze		20	.400		88	18.80		106.80	126
0900 10" high, 1" deep, cast aluminum		18	.444		53	21		74	90
1000 Bronze		18	.444		104	21		125	146
1200 12" high, 1-1/4" deep, cast aluminum		12	.667		53.50	31.50		85	107
1500 Cast bronze		18	.444		127	21		148	171
1600 14" high, 2-5/16" deep, cast aluminum		12	.667		101	31.50		132.50	159
1800 Fabricated stainless steel, 6" high, 2" deep		20	.400		41.50	18.80		60.30	74.50
1900 12" high, 3" deep		18	.444		67	21		88	106
2100 18" high, 3" deep		12	.667		109	31.50		140.50	167
2200 24" high, 4" deep		10	.800		212	37.50		249.50	291
2700 Acrylic, on high density foam, 12" high, 2" deep		20	.400		19.80	18.80		38.60	51
2800 18" high, 2" deep	▼	18	.444		37.50	21		58.50	73
3900 Plaques, custom, 20" x 30", for up to 450 letters, cast aluminum	2 Carp	4	4		1,850	188		2,038	2,325
4000 Cast bronze		4	4		1,750	188		1,938	2,200
4200 30" x 36", up to 900 letters cast aluminum		3	5.333		2,625	250		2,875	3,275
4300 Cast bronze		3	5.333		4,025	250		4,275	4,800
4500 36" x 48", for up to 1300 letters, cast bronze		2	8		4,650	375		5,025	5,700
4800 Signs, reflective alum. directional signs, dbl. face, 2-way, w/bracket		30	.533		144	25		169	197
4900 4-way	▼	30	.533		231	25		256	293
5100 Exit signs, 24 ga. alum., 14" x 12" surface mounted	1 Carp	30	.267		47.50	12.50		60	72
5200 10" x 7"	▼	20	.400	▼	25.50	18.80		44.30	57

10 14 Signage

10 14 19 – Dimensional Letter Signage

10 14 19.10 Exterior Signs	Crew	Daily Output	Labor-Hours	Unit	Material	2015 Bare Costs Labor	Equipment	Total	Total Incl O&P
5400	Bracket mounted, double face, 12" x 10"	1 Carp	30	.267	Ea.	56	12.50		68.50	81.50
5500	Sticky back, stock decals, 14" x 10"	1 Clab	50	.160		26.50	6		32.50	38.50
6000	Interior elec., wall mount, fiberglass panels, 2 lamps, 6"	1 Elec	8	1		92	54.50		146.50	183
6100	8"	"	8	1		114	54.50		168.50	208
6400	Replacement sign faces, 6" or 8"	1 Clab	50	.160		62.50	6		68.50	78

10 14 53 – Traffic Signage

10 14 53.20 Traffic Signs

		Crew	Daily Output	Labor-Hours	Unit	Material	2015 Bare Costs Labor	Equipment	Total	Total Incl O&P
0010	**TRAFFIC SIGNS**									
0012	Stock, 24" x 24", no posts, .080" alum. reflectorized	B-80	70	.457	Ea.	85	18.85	10.30	114.15	134
0100	High intensity		70	.457		97.50	18.85	10.30	126.65	148
0300	30" x 30", reflectorized		70	.457		123	18.85	10.30	152.15	175
0400	High intensity		70	.457		135	18.85	10.30	164.15	188
0600	Guide and directional signs, 12" x 18", reflectorized		70	.457		34.50	18.85	10.30	63.65	78
0700	High intensity		70	.457		52	18.85	10.30	81.15	97.50
0900	18" x 24", stock signs, reflectorized		70	.457		47	18.85	10.30	76.15	92
1000	High intensity		70	.457		52	18.85	10.30	81.15	97.50
1200	24" x 24", stock signs, reflectorized		70	.457		57	18.85	10.30	86.15	103
1300	High intensity		70	.457		62	18.85	10.30	91.15	108
1500	Add to above for steel posts, galvanized, 10'-0" upright, bolted		200	.160		32.50	6.60	3.60	42.70	50
1600	12'-0" upright, bolted		140	.229		39	9.40	5.15	53.55	63
1800	Highway road signs, aluminum, over 20 S.F., reflectorized		350	.091	S.F.	33.50	3.77	2.06	39.33	45
2000	High intensity		350	.091		33.50	3.77	2.06	39.33	45
2200	Highway, suspended over road, 80 S.F. min., reflectorized		165	.194		32	8	4.37	44.37	52.50
2300	High intensity		165	.194		30.50	8	4.37	42.87	51
2350	Roadway delineators and reference markers		500	.064	Ea.	15.50	2.64	1.44	19.58	22.50
2360	Delineator post only, 6'		500	.064	"	18	2.64	1.44	22.08	25.50
5200	Remove and relocate signs, including supports									
5210	To 10 S.F.	B-80B	5	6.400	Ea.	350	258	49	657	835
5220	11 S.F. to 20 S.F.	"	1.70	18.824		790	760	143	1,693	2,200
5230	21 S.F. to 40 S.F.	B-14	.56	85.714		835	3,400	650	4,885	6,850
5240	41 S.F. to 100 S.F.	B-13	.32	175		1,375	7,175	2,300	10,850	15,100
8000	For temporary barricades and lights, see Section 01 56 23.10									

10 22 Partitions

10 22 16 – Folding Gates

10 22 16.10 Security Gates

		Crew	Daily Output	Labor-Hours	Unit	Material	2015 Bare Costs Labor	Equipment	Total	Total Incl O&P
0010	**SECURITY GATES**									
0300	Scissors type folding gate, ptd. steel, single, 6-1/2' high, 5-1/2' wide	2 Sswk	4	4	Opng.	226	211		437	615
0400	7-1/2' wide		4	4		237	211		448	625
0600	Double gate, 8' high, 8' wide		2.50	6.400		390	335		725	1,025
0750	14' wide		2	8		630	420		1,050	1,425

For customer support on your Site Work & Landscape Cost Data, call 877.737.1594.

181

10 26 Wall and Door Protection

10 26 13 – Corner Guards

10 26 13.10 Metal Corner Guards

		Crew	Daily Output	Labor-Hours	Unit	Material	2015 Bare Costs Labor	Equipment	Total	Total Incl O&P
0010	**METAL CORNER GUARDS**									
0020	Steel angle w/anchors, 1" x 1" x 1/4", 1.5#/L.F.	2 Carp	160	.100	L.F.	7.10	4.70		11.80	15.05
0100	2" x 2" x 1/4" angles, 3.2#/L.F.		150	.107		10.20	5		15.20	18.90
0200	3" x 3" x 5/16" angles, 6.1#/L.F.		140	.114		14.75	5.35		20.10	24.50
0300	4" x 4" x 5/16" angles, 8.2#/L.F.		120	.133		19.95	6.25		26.20	31.50
0350	For angles drilled and anchored to masonry, add					15%	120%			
0370	Drilled and anchored to concrete, add					20%	170%			
0400	For galvanized angles, add					35%				
0450	For stainless steel angles, add					100%				
0500	Steel door track/wheel guards, 4' - 0" high	E-4	22	1.455	Ea.	109	77.50	6.65	193.15	261
0800	Pipe bumper for truck doors, 8' long, 6" diameter, filled		20	1.600		625	85	7.30	717.30	845
0900	8" diameter		20	1.600		725	85	7.30	817.30	955

10 44 Fire Protection Specialties

10 44 16 – Fire Extinguishers

10 44 16.13 Portable Fire Extinguishers

		Crew	Daily Output	Labor-Hours	Unit	Material	2015 Bare Costs Labor	Equipment	Total	Total Incl O&P
0010	**PORTABLE FIRE EXTINGUISHERS**									
0140	CO_2, with hose and "H" horn, 10 lb.				Ea.	275			275	305
0160	15 lb.				"	355			355	390
1000	Dry chemical, pressurized									
1040	Standard type, portable, painted, 2-1/2 lb.				Ea.	37.50			37.50	41
1060	5 lb.					51			51	56.50
1080	10 lb.					81			81	89.50
1100	20 lb.					136			136	150
1120	30 lb.					425			425	470
1300	Standard type, wheeled, 150 lb.					2,425			2,425	2,650
2000	ABC all purpose type, portable, 2-1/2 lb.					21			21	23.50
2060	5 lb.					26.50			26.50	29
2080	9-1/2 lb.					44			44	48
2100	20 lb.					79.50			79.50	87.50
5000	Pressurized water, 2-1/2 gallon, stainless steel					102			102	112
5060	With anti-freeze					106			106	116
9400	Installation of extinguishers, 12 or more, on nailable surface	1 Carp	30	.267			12.50		12.50	19.25
9420	On masonry or concrete	"	15	.533			25		25	38.50

10 44 16.16 Wheeled Fire Extinguisher Units

		Crew	Daily Output	Labor-Hours	Unit	Material	2015 Bare Costs Labor	Equipment	Total	Total Incl O&P
0010	**WHEELED FIRE EXTINGUISHER UNITS**									
0350	CO_2, portable, with swivel horn									
0360	Wheeled type, cart mounted, 50 lb.				Ea.	1,125			1,125	1,250
0400	100 lb.				"	3,850			3,850	4,250
2200	ABC all purpose type									
2300	Wheeled, 45 lb.				Ea.	735			735	810
2360	150 lb.				"	1,850			1,850	2,025

10 57 Wardrobe and Closet Specialties

10 57 23 – Closet and Utility Shelving

10 57 23.19 Wood Closet and Utility Shelving

	10 57 23.19 Wood Closet and Utility Shelving	Crew	Daily Output	Labor-Hours	Unit	Material	2015 Bare Costs Labor	Equipment	Total	Total Incl O&P
0010	**WOOD CLOSET AND UTILITY SHELVING**									
0020	Pine, clear grade, no edge band, 1" x 8"	1 Carp	115	.070	L.F.	3.49	3.27		6.76	8.90
0100	1" x 10"		110	.073		4.34	3.41		7.75	10
0200	1" x 12"		105	.076		5.25	3.58		8.83	11.25

10 73 Protective Covers

10 73 13 – Awnings

10 73 13.10 Awnings, Fabric

	10 73 13.10 Awnings, Fabric	Crew	Daily Output	Labor-Hours	Unit	Material	2015 Bare Costs Labor	Equipment	Total	Total Incl O&P
0010	**AWNINGS, FABRIC**									
0020	Including acrylic canvas and frame, standard design									
0100	Door and window, slope, 3' high, 4' wide	1 Carp	4.50	1.778	Ea.	720	83.50		803.50	920
0110	6' wide		3.50	2.286		925	107		1,032	1,200
0120	8' wide		3	2.667		1,125	125		1,250	1,450
0200	Quarter round convex, 4' wide		3	2.667		1,125	125		1,250	1,425
0210	6' wide		2.25	3.556		1,450	167		1,617	1,850
0220	8' wide		1.80	4.444		1,775	209		1,984	2,275
0300	Dome, 4' wide		7.50	1.067		430	50		480	550
0310	6' wide		3.50	2.286		970	107		1,077	1,250
0320	8' wide		2	4		1,725	188		1,913	2,200
0350	Elongated dome, 4' wide		1.33	6.015		1,625	282		1,907	2,200
0360	6' wide		1.11	7.207		1,925	340		2,265	2,650
0370	8' wide		1	8		2,275	375		2,650	3,075
1000	Entry or walkway, peak, 12' long, 4' wide	2 Carp	.90	17.778		5,225	835		6,060	7,025
1010	6' wide		.60	26.667		8,050	1,250		9,300	10,800
1020	8' wide		.40	40		11,100	1,875		12,975	15,100
1100	Radius with dome end, 4' wide		1.10	14.545		3,950	685		4,635	5,400
1110	6' wide		.70	22.857		6,350	1,075		7,425	8,650
1120	8' wide		.50	32		9,050	1,500		10,550	12,300
2000	Retractable lateral arm awning, manual									
2010	To 12' wide, 8' - 6" projection	2 Carp	1.70	9.412	Ea.	1,175	440		1,615	1,975
2020	To 14' wide, 8' - 6" projection		1.10	14.545		1,375	685		2,060	2,575
2030	To 19' wide, 8' - 6" projection		.85	18.824		1,875	885		2,760	3,400
2040	To 24' wide, 8' - 6" projection		.67	23.881		2,350	1,125		3,475	4,325
2050	Motor for above, add	1 Carp	2.67	3		1,000	141		1,141	1,350
3000	Patio/deck canopy with frame									
3010	12' wide, 12' projection	2 Carp	2	8	Ea.	1,675	375		2,050	2,400
3020	16' wide, 14' projection	"	1.20	13.333		2,600	625		3,225	3,825
9000	For fire retardant canvas, add					7%				
9010	For lettering or graphics, add					35%				
9020	For painted or coated acrylic canvas, deduct					8%				
9030	For translucent or opaque vinyl canvas, add					10%				
9040	For 6 or more units, deduct					20%	15%			

10 73 16 – Canopies

10 73 16.20 Metal Canopies

	10 73 16.20 Metal Canopies	Crew	Daily Output	Labor-Hours	Unit	Material	2015 Bare Costs Labor	Equipment	Total	Total Incl O&P
0010	**METAL CANOPIES**									
0020	Wall hung, .032", aluminum, prefinished, 8' x 10'	K-2	1.30	18.462	Ea.	2,150	900	233	3,283	4,125
0300	8' x 20'		1.10	21.818		3,650	1,075	276	5,001	6,075
0500	10' x 10'		1.30	18.462		2,825	900	233	3,958	4,850
0700	10' x 20'		1.10	21.818		4,600	1,075	276	5,951	7,125
1000	12' x 20'		1	24		5,250	1,175	305	6,730	8,075

10 73 Protective Covers

10 73 16 – Canopies

10 73 16.20 Metal Canopies

		Crew	Daily Output	Labor-Hours	Unit	Material	2015 Bare Costs Labor	Equipment	Total	Total Incl O&P
1360	12' x 30'	K-2	.80	30	Ea.	7,875	1,475	380	9,730	11,500
1700	12' x 40'	↓	.60	40		10,500	1,950	505	12,955	15,400
1900	For free standing units, add				↓	20%	10%			
7000	Carport, baked vinyl finish, .032", 20' x 10', no foundations, flat panel	K-2	4	6	Car	4,000	293	76	4,369	4,975
7250	Insulated flat panel		2	12	"	6,300	585	152	7,037	8,075
7500	Walkway cover, to 12' wide, stl., vinyl finish, .032",no fndtns., flat		250	.096	S.F.	22.50	4.68	1.21	28.39	33.50
7750	Arched	↓	200	.120	"	55	5.85	1.52	62.37	72

10 74 Manufactured Exterior Specialties

10 74 46 – Window Wells

10 74 46.10 Area Window Wells

		Crew	Daily Output	Labor-Hours	Unit	Material	2015 Bare Costs Labor	Equipment	Total	Total Incl O&P
0010	**AREA WINDOW WELLS**, Galvanized steel									
0020	20 ga., 3'-2" wide, 1' deep	1 Sswk	29	.276	Ea.	17.45	14.50		31.95	44
0100	2' deep		23	.348		31	18.30		49.30	66.50
0300	16 ga., 3'-2" wide, 1' deep		29	.276		23	14.50		37.50	50.50
0400	3' deep		23	.348		47	18.30		65.30	83.50
0600	Welded grating for above, 15 lb., painted		45	.178		87.50	9.35		96.85	112
0700	Galvanized	↓	45	.178	↓	118	9.35		127.35	146

10 75 Flagpoles

10 75 16 – Ground-Set Flagpoles

10 75 16.10 Flagpoles

		Crew	Daily Output	Labor-Hours	Unit	Material	2015 Bare Costs Labor	Equipment	Total	Total Incl O&P
0010	**FLAGPOLES**, ground set									
0050	Not including base or foundation									
0100	Aluminum, tapered, ground set 20' high	K-1	2	8	Ea.	1,050	345	152	1,547	1,850
0200	25' high		1.70	9.412		1,100	405	178	1,683	2,050
0300	30' high		1.50	10.667		1,300	460	202	1,962	2,350
0400	35' high		1.40	11.429		1,800	490	217	2,507	3,000
0500	40' high		1.20	13.333		2,775	575	253	3,603	4,200
0600	50' high		1	16		3,175	690	305	4,170	4,875
0700	60' high		.90	17.778		4,950	765	335	6,050	6,975
0800	70' high		.80	20		8,375	860	380	9,615	11,000
1100	Counterbalanced, internal halyard, 20' high		1.80	8.889		2,450	380	168	2,998	3,475
1200	30' high		1.50	10.667		2,675	460	202	3,337	3,875
1300	40' high		1.30	12.308		6,475	530	233	7,238	8,200
1400	50' high		1	16		9,025	690	305	10,020	11,300
2820	Aluminum, electronically operated, 30' high		1.40	11.429		4,150	490	217	4,857	5,575
2840	35' high		1.30	12.308		4,950	530	233	5,713	6,500
2860	39' high		1.10	14.545		6,025	625	276	6,926	7,875
2880	45' high		1	16		6,350	690	305	7,345	8,375
2900	50' high		.90	17.778		8,175	765	335	9,275	10,500
3000	Fiberglass, tapered, ground set, 23' high		2	8		580	345	152	1,077	1,325
3100	29'-7" high		1.50	10.667		1,525	460	202	2,187	2,600
3200	36'-1" high		1.40	11.429		2,000	490	217	2,707	3,200
3300	39'-5" high		1.20	13.333		2,100	575	253	2,928	3,450
3400	49'-2" high		1	16		3,900	690	305	4,895	5,675
3500	59' high		.90	17.778	↓	4,825	765	335	5,925	6,850
4300	Steel, direct imbedded installation									
4400	Internal halyard, 20' high	K-1	2.50	6.400	Ea.	1,375	275	121	1,771	2,050

10 75 Flagpoles

10 75 16 – Ground-Set Flagpoles

10 75 16.10 Flagpoles		Crew	Daily Output	Labor-Hours	Unit	Material	2015 Bare Costs Labor	Equipment	Total	Total Incl O&P
4500	25' high	K-1	2.50	6.400	Ea.	2,050	275	121	2,446	2,800
4600	30' high		2.30	6.957		2,450	299	132	2,881	3,275
4700	40' high		2.10	7.619		3,725	330	144	4,199	4,750
4800	50' high		1.90	8.421		4,325	360	160	4,845	5,475
5000	60' high		1.80	8.889		7,200	380	168	7,748	8,700
5100	70' high		1.60	10		7,850	430	190	8,470	9,500
5200	80' high		1.40	11.429		10,100	490	217	10,807	12,100
5300	90' high		1.20	13.333		15,500	575	253	16,328	18,200
5500	100' high		1	16		17,600	690	305	18,595	20,800
6400	Wood poles, tapered, clear vertical grain fir with tilting									
6410	base, not incl. foundation, 4" butt, 25' high	K-1	1.90	8.421	Ea.	1,400	360	160	1,920	2,250
6800	6" butt, 30' high	"	1.30	12.308	"	2,600	530	233	3,363	3,925
7300	Foundations for flagpoles, including									
7400	excavation and concrete, to 35' high poles	C-1	10	3.200	Ea.	685	143		828	975
7600	40' to 50' high		3.50	9.143		1,275	410		1,685	2,025
7700	Over 60' high		2	16		1,575	715		2,290	2,825

10 75 23 – Wall-Mounted Flagpoles

10 75 23.10 Flagpoles		Crew	Daily Output	Labor-Hours	Unit	Material	2015 Bare Costs Labor	Equipment	Total	Total Incl O&P
0010	**FLAGPOLES**, structure mounted									
0100	Fiberglass, vertical wall set, 19'-8" long	K-1	1.50	10.667	Ea.	1,150	460	202	1,812	2,200
0200	23' long		1.40	11.429		1,425	490	217	2,132	2,550
0300	26'-3" long		1.30	12.308		2,050	530	233	2,813	3,325
0800	19'-8" long outrigger		1.30	12.308		1,325	530	233	2,088	2,525
1300	Aluminum, vertical wall set, tapered, with base, 20' high		1.20	13.333		1,075	575	253	1,903	2,325
1400	29'-6" high		1	16		2,650	690	305	3,645	4,300
2400	Outrigger poles with base, 12' long		1.30	12.308		1,100	530	233	1,863	2,275
2500	14' long		1	16		1,425	690	305	2,420	2,950

10 88 Scales

10 88 05 – Commercial Scales

10 88 05.10 Scales		Crew	Daily Output	Labor-Hours	Unit	Material	2015 Bare Costs Labor	Equipment	Total	Total Incl O&P
0010	**SCALES**									
0700	Truck scales, incl. steel weigh bridge,									
0800	not including foundation, pits									
1550	Digital, electronic, 100 ton capacity, steel deck 12' x 10' platform	3 Carp	.20	120	Ea.	14,100	5,625		19,725	24,200
1600	40' x 10' platform		.14	171		28,100	8,050		36,150	43,300
1640	60' x 10' platform		.13	184		37,100	8,675		45,775	54,000
1680	70' x 10' platform		.12	200		39,400	9,400		48,800	58,000
2000	For standard automatic printing device, add					1,250			1,250	1,375
2100	For remote reading electronic system, add					2,725			2,725	3,000
2300	Concrete foundation pits for above, 8' x 6', 5 C.Y. required	C-1	.50	64		1,075	2,850		3,925	5,575
2400	14' x 6' platform, 10 C.Y. required		.35	91.429		1,575	4,075		5,650	8,000
2600	50' x 10' platform, 30 C.Y. required		.25	128		2,125	5,700		7,825	11,100
2700	70' x 10' platform, 40 C.Y. required		.15	213		4,625	9,525		14,150	19,700
2750	Crane scales, dial, 1 ton capacity					1,150			1,150	1,275
2780	5 ton capacity					1,550			1,550	1,700
2800	Digital, 1 ton capacity					1,900			1,900	2,075
2850	10 ton capacity					4,800			4,800	5,300
3800	Portable, beam type, capacity 1000#, platform 18" x 24"					785			785	860
3900	Dial type, capacity 2000#, platform 24" x 24"					1,425			1,425	1,550

10 88 Scales

10 88 05 – Commercial Scales

10 88 05.10 Scales	Crew	Daily Output	Labor-Hours	Unit	Material	2015 Bare Costs Labor	Equipment	Total	Total Incl O&P
4000	Digital type, capacity 1000#, platform 24" x 30"				Ea.	2,275			2,275	2,500
4100	Portable contractor truck scales, 50 ton cap., 40' x 10' platform					33,600			33,600	37,000
4200	60' x 10' platform					31,600			31,600	34,800

Estimating Tips
General

- The items in this division are usually priced per square foot or each. Many of these items are purchased by the owner for installation by the contractor. Check the specifications for responsibilities and include time for receiving, storage, installation, and mechanical and electrical hookups in the appropriate divisions.

- Many items in Division 11 require some type of support system that is not usually furnished with the item. Examples of these systems include blocking for the attachment of casework and support angles for ceiling-hung projection screens. The required blocking or supports must be added to the estimate in the appropriate division.

- Some items in Division 11 may require assembly or electrical hookups. Verify the amount of assembly required or the need for a hard electrical connection and add the appropriate costs.

Reference Numbers

Reference numbers are shown in shaded boxes at the beginning of some major classifications. These numbers refer to related items in the Reference Section. The reference information may be an estimating procedure, an alternate pricing method, or technical information.

Note: Not all subdivisions listed here necessarily appear in this publication. ■

11 11 Vehicle Service Equipment

11 11 13 – Compressed-Air Vehicle Service Equipment

11 11 13.10 Compressed Air Equipment

		Crew	Daily Output	Labor-Hours	Unit	Material	2015 Bare Costs Labor	2015 Bare Costs Equipment	Total	Total Incl O&P
0010	**COMPRESSED AIR EQUIPMENT**									
0030	Compressors, electric, 1-1/2 H.P., standard controls	L-4	1.50	16	Ea.	455	710		1,165	1,600

11 11 19 – Vehicle Lubrication Equipment

11 11 19.10 Lubrication Equipment

		Crew	Daily Output	Labor-Hours	Unit	Material	Labor	Equipment	Total	Total Incl O&P
0010	**LUBRICATION EQUIPMENT**									
3000	Lube equipment, 3 reel type, with pumps, not including piping	L-4	.50	48	Set	8,800	2,125		10,925	13,000
3100	Hose reel, including hose, oil/lube, 1000 PSI	2 Sswk	2	8	Ea.	740	420		1,160	1,550

11 11 33 – Vehicle Spray Painting Equipment

11 11 33.10 Spray Painting Equipment

		Crew	Daily Output	Labor-Hours	Unit	Material	Labor	Equipment	Total	Total Incl O&P
0010	**SPRAY PAINTING EQUIPMENT**									
4000	Spray painting booth, 26' long, complete	L-4	.40	60	Ea.	16,400	2,650		19,050	22,100

11 12 Parking Control Equipment

11 12 13 – Parking Key and Card Control Units

11 12 13.10 Parking Control Units

		Crew	Daily Output	Labor-Hours	Unit	Material	Labor	Equipment	Total	Total Incl O&P
0010	**PARKING CONTROL UNITS**									
5100	Card reader	1 Elec	2	4	Ea.	1,950	219		2,169	2,475
5120	Proximity with customer display	2 Elec	1	16		5,575	875		6,450	7,425
6000	Parking control software, basic functionality	1 Elec	.50	16		23,900	875		24,775	27,500
6020	multi-function	"	.20	40		104,500	2,200		106,700	118,500

11 12 16 – Parking Ticket Dispensers

11 12 16.10 Ticket Dispensers

		Crew	Daily Output	Labor-Hours	Unit	Material	Labor	Equipment	Total	Total Incl O&P
0010	**TICKET DISPENSERS**									
5900	Ticket spitter with time/date stamp, standard	2 Elec	2	8	Ea.	6,200	440		6,640	7,475
5920	Mag stripe encoding	"	2	8	"	18,800	440		19,240	21,400

11 12 26 – Parking Fee Collection Equipment

11 12 26.13 Parking Fee Coin Collection Equipment

		Crew	Daily Output	Labor-Hours	Unit	Material	Labor	Equipment	Total	Total Incl O&P
0010	**PARKING FEE COIN COLLECTION EQUIPMENT**									
5200	Cashier booth, average	B-22	1	30	Ea.	10,400	1,325	207	11,932	13,800
5300	Collector station, pay on foot	2 Elec	.20	80		111,000	4,375		115,375	128,500
5320	Credit card only	"	.50	32		20,500	1,750		22,250	25,100

11 12 26.23 Fee Equipment

		Crew	Daily Output	Labor-Hours	Unit	Material	Labor	Equipment	Total	Total Incl O&P
0010	**FEE EQUIPMENT**									
5600	Fee computer	1 Elec	1.50	5.333	Ea.	14,200	292		14,492	16,000

11 12 33 – Parking Gates

11 12 33.13 Lift Arm Parking Gates

		Crew	Daily Output	Labor-Hours	Unit	Material	Labor	Equipment	Total	Total Incl O&P
0010	**LIFT ARM PARKING GATES**									
5000	Barrier gate with programmable controller	2 Elec	3	5.333	Ea.	3,400	292		3,692	4,150
5020	Industrial		3	5.333		5,050	292		5,342	5,975
5500	Exit verifier		1	16		17,600	875		18,475	20,700
5700	Full sign, 4" letters	1 Elec	2	4		1,225	219		1,444	1,675
5800	Inductive loop	2 Elec	4	4		171	219		390	520
5950	Vehicle detector, microprocessor based	1 Elec	3	2.667		425	146		571	690

11 13 Loading Dock Equipment

11 13 13 – Loading Dock Bumpers

11 13 13.10 Dock Bumpers

		Crew	Daily Output	Labor-Hours	Unit	Material	2015 Bare Costs Labor	Equipment	Total	Total Incl O&P
0010	**DOCK BUMPERS** Bolts not included									
0020	2" x 6" to 4" x 8", average	1 Carp	.30	26.667	M.B.F.	1,350	1,250		2,600	3,400
0050	Bumpers, rubber blocks 4-1/2" thick, 10" high, 14" long		26	.308	Ea.	64	14.45		78.45	92
0300	36" long		17	.471		78	22		100	120
0500	12" high, 14" long		25	.320		101	15		116	135
0600	36" long		15	.533		125	25		150	176
0800	Rubber blocks 6" thick, 10" high, 14" long		22	.364		104	17.05		121.05	141
0900	36" long		13	.615		188	29		217	252
0920	Extruded rubber bumpers, T section, 22" x 22" x 3" thick		41	.195		65.50	9.15		74.65	86
0940	Molded rubber bumpers, 24" x 12" x 3" thick		20	.400		57.50	18.80		76.30	92.50

11 14 Pedestrian Control Equipment

11 14 13 – Pedestrian Gates

11 14 13.13 Portable Posts and Railings

		Crew	Daily Output	Labor-Hours	Unit	Material	2015 Bare Costs Labor	Equipment	Total	Total Incl O&P
0010	**PORTABLE POSTS AND RAILINGS**									
0020	Portable for pedestrian traffic control, standard				Ea.	134			134	147
0300	Deluxe posts				"	210			210	231
0600	Ropes for above posts, plastic covered, 1-1/2" diameter				L.F.	17.25			17.25	19
0700	Chain core				"	11.65			11.65	12.80
1500	Portable security or safety barrier, black with 7' yellow strap				Ea.	213			213	234
1510	12' yellow strap					238			238	262
1550	Sign holder, standard design					76			76	83.50

11 14 13.19 Turnstiles

		Crew	Daily Output	Labor-Hours	Unit	Material	2015 Bare Costs Labor	Equipment	Total	Total Incl O&P
0010	**TURNSTILES**									
0020	One way, 4 arm, 46" diameter, economy, manual	2 Carp	5	3.200	Ea.	1,700	150		1,850	2,100
0100	Electric		1.20	13.333		2,050	625		2,675	3,250
0420	Three arm, 24" opening, light duty, manual		2	8		3,500	375		3,875	4,425
0450	Heavy duty		1.50	10.667		5,000	500		5,500	6,275
0460	Manual, with registering & controls, light duty		2	8		3,750	375		4,125	4,725
0470	Heavy duty		1.50	10.667		4,100	500		4,600	5,275

11 66 Athletic Equipment

11 66 43 – Interior Scoreboards

11 66 43.10 Scoreboards

		Crew	Daily Output	Labor-Hours	Unit	Material	2015 Bare Costs Labor	Equipment	Total	Total Incl O&P
0010	**SCOREBOARDS**									
7000	Baseball, minimum	R-3	1.30	15.385	Ea.	4,125	835	106	5,066	5,925
7200	Maximum		.05	400		18,100	21,700	2,750	42,550	55,500
7300	Football, minimum		.86	23.256		5,325	1,275	160	6,760	7,950
7400	Maximum		.20	100		15,900	5,425	690	22,015	26,400

For customer support on your Site Work & Landscape Cost Data, call 877.737.1594.

189

11 68 13 – Playground Equipment

11 68 13.10 Free-Standing Playground Equipment		Crew	Daily Output	Labor-Hours	Unit	Material	2015 Bare Costs Labor	Equipment	Total	Total Incl O&P
0010	**FREE-STANDING PLAYGROUND EQUIPMENT** See also individual items									
0200	Bike rack, 10' long, permanent **G**	B-1	12	2	Ea.	425	76.50		501.50	590
0240	Climber, arch, 6' high, 12' long, 5' wide		4	6		775	230		1,005	1,200
0260	Fitness trail, with signs, 9 to 10 stations, treated pine, minimum		.25	96		7,200	3,675		10,875	13,600
0270	Maximum		.17	141		16,900	5,400		22,300	26,900
0280	Metal, minimum		.25	96		12,000	3,675		15,675	18,900
0285	Maximum		.17	141		30,000	5,400		35,400	41,300
0300	Redwood, minimum		.25	96		10,900	3,675		14,575	17,700
0310	Maximum		.17	141		15,500	5,400		20,900	25,300
0320	16 to 20 station, treated pine, minimum		.17	141		11,400	5,400		16,800	20,900
0330	Maximum		.13	184		12,500	7,075		19,575	24,600
0340	Metal, minimum		.17	141		12,700	5,400		18,100	22,200
0350	Maximum		.13	184		16,100	7,075		23,175	28,600
0360	Redwood, minimum		.17	141		16,600	5,400		22,000	26,600
0370	Maximum		.13	184		25,500	7,075		32,575	38,900
0400	Horizontal monkey ladder, 14' long, 6' high		4	6		905	230		1,135	1,350
0590	Parallel bars, 10' long		4	6		320	230		550	705
0600	Posts, tether ball set, 2-3/8" O.D.		12	2	▼	455	76.50		531.50	620
0800	Poles, multiple purpose, 10'-6" long		12	2	Pr.	179	76.50		255.50	315
1000	Ground socket for movable posts, 2-3/8" post		10	2.400		102	92		194	253
1100	3-1/2" post		10	2.400	▼	167	92		259	325
1300	See-saw, spring, steel, 2 units		6	4	Ea.	740	153		893	1,050
1400	4 units		4	6		1,275	230		1,505	1,775
1500	6 units		3	8		1,675	305		1,980	2,325
1700	Shelter, fiberglass golf tee, 3 person		4.60	5.217		4,375	200		4,575	5,100
1900	Slides, stainless steel bed, 12' long, 6' high		3	8		3,325	305		3,630	4,125
2000	20' long, 10' high		2	12		3,675	460		4,135	4,750
2200	Swings, plain seats, 8' high, 4 seats		2	12		1,150	460		1,610	1,975
2300	8 seats		1.30	18.462		2,175	705		2,880	3,450
2500	12' high, 4 seats		2	12		2,150	460		2,610	3,075
2600	8 seats		1.30	18.462		3,525	705		4,230	4,950
2800	Whirlers, 8' diameter		3	8		2,775	305		3,080	3,525
2900	10' diameter ▼		3	8	▼	6,275	305		6,580	7,375

11 68 13.20 Modular Playground

		Crew	Daily Output	Labor-Hours	Unit	Material	Labor	Equipment	Total	Total Incl O&P
0010	**MODULAR PLAYGROUND** Basic components									
0100	Deck, square, steel, 48" x 48"	B-1	1	24	Ea.	520	920		1,440	2,000
0110	Recycled polyurethane		1	24		515	920		1,435	2,000
0120	Triangular, steel, 48" side		1	24	▼	680	920		1,600	2,175
0130	Post, steel, 5" square		18	1.333	L.F.	40.50	51		91.50	123
0140	Aluminum, 2-3/8" square		20	1.200		39.50	46		85.50	114
0150	5" square		18	1.333	▼	40.50	51		91.50	123
0160	Roof, square poly, 54" side		18	1.333	Ea.	1,400	51		1,451	1,625
0170	Wheelchair transfer module, for 3' high deck		3	8	"	2,950	305		3,255	3,725
0180	Guardrail, pipe, 36" high		60	.400	L.F.	198	15.30		213.30	242
0190	Steps, deck-to-deck, 3 – 8" steps		8	3	Ea.	1,125	115		1,240	1,400
0200	Activity panel, crawl through panel		2	12		500	460		960	1,250
0210	Alphabet/spelling panel		2	12		555	460		1,015	1,325
0360	With guardrails		3	8		1,850	305		2,155	2,500
0370	Crawl tunnel, straight, 56" long		4	6		1,200	230		1,430	1,675
0380	90°, 4' long		4	6		1,400	230		1,630	1,900
1200	Slide, tunnel, for 56" high deck		8	3		1,750	115		1,865	2,100
1210	Straight, poly ▼		8	3	▼	390	115		505	605

11 68 Play Field Equipment and Structures

11 68 13 – Playground Equipment

11 68 13.20 Modular Playground

		Crew	Daily Output	Labor-Hours	Unit	Material	2015 Bare Costs Labor	2015 Bare Costs Equipment	Total	Total Incl O&P
1220	Stainless steel, 54" high deck	B-1	6	4	Ea.	690	153		843	995
1230	Curved, poly, 40" high deck		6	4		865	153		1,018	1,200
1240	Spiral slide, 56" - 72" high		5	4.800		4,475	184		4,659	5,200
1300	Ladder, vertical, for 24" - 72" high deck		5	4.800		555	184		739	895
1310	Horizontal, 8' long		5	4.800		695	184		879	1,050
1320	Corkscrew climber, 6' high		3	8		1,125	305		1,430	1,725
1330	Fire pole for 72" high deck		6	4		655	153		808	955
1340	Bridge, ring climber, 8' long		4	6		1,900	230		2,130	2,425
1350	Suspension		4	6	L.F.	360	230		590	750

11 68 16 – Play Structures

11 68 16.10 Handball/Squash Court

		Crew	Daily Output	Labor-Hours	Unit	Material	2015 Bare Costs Labor	2015 Bare Costs Equipment	Total	Total Incl O&P
0010	**HANDBALL/SQUASH COURT**, outdoor									
0900	Handball or squash court, outdoor, wood	2 Carp	.50	32	Ea.	5,050	1,500		6,550	7,875
1000	Masonry handball/squash court	D-1	.30	53.333	"	25,100	2,250		27,350	31,000

11 68 16.30 Platform/Paddle Tennis Court

		Crew	Daily Output	Labor-Hours	Unit	Material	2015 Bare Costs Labor	2015 Bare Costs Equipment	Total	Total Incl O&P
0010	**PLATFORM/PADDLE TENNIS COURT** Complete with lighting, etc.									
0100	Aluminum slat deck with aluminum frame	B-1	.08	300	Court	60,500	11,500		72,000	84,500
0500	Aluminum slat deck with wood frame	C-1	.12	266		63,500	11,900		75,400	88,000
0800	Aluminum deck heater, add	B-1	1.18	20.339		2,575	780		3,355	4,050
0900	Douglas fir planking with wood frame 2" x 6" x 30'	C-1	.12	266		59,500	11,900		71,400	84,000
1000	Plywood deck with steel frame		.12	266		59,500	11,900		71,400	84,000
1100	Steel slat deck with wood frame		.12	266		39,300	11,900		51,200	61,500

11 68 33 – Athletic Field Equipment

11 68 33.13 Football Field Equipment

		Crew	Daily Output	Labor-Hours	Unit	Material	2015 Bare Costs Labor	2015 Bare Costs Equipment	Total	Total Incl O&P
0010	**FOOTBALL FIELD EQUIPMENT**									
0020	Goal posts, steel, football, double post	B-1	1.50	16	Pr.	3,800	610		4,410	5,125
0100	Deluxe, single post		1.50	16		2,625	610		3,235	3,850
0300	Football, convertible to soccer		1.50	16		2,825	610		3,435	4,075
0500	Soccer, regulation		2	12		1,425	460		1,885	2,250

11 82 Facility Solid Waste Handling Equipment

11 82 19 – Packaged Incinerators

11 82 19.10 Packaged Gas Fired Incinerators

		Crew	Daily Output	Labor-Hours	Unit	Material	2015 Bare Costs Labor	2015 Bare Costs Equipment	Total	Total Incl O&P
0010	**PACKAGED GAS FIRED INCINERATORS**									
4750	Large municipal incinerators, incl. stack, minimum	Q-3	.25	128	Ton/day	20,500	7,150		27,650	33,300
4850	Maximum	"	.10	320	"	54,500	17,900		72,400	87,000

11 82 26 – Facility Waste Compactors

11 82 26.10 Compactors

		Crew	Daily Output	Labor-Hours	Unit	Material	2015 Bare Costs Labor	2015 Bare Costs Equipment	Total	Total Incl O&P
0010	**COMPACTORS**									
0020	Compactors, 115 volt, 250#/hr., chute fed	L-4	1	24	Ea.	12,100	1,050		13,150	15,000
1400	For handling hazardous waste materials, 55 gallon drum packer, std.					19,700			19,700	21,700
1410	55 gallon drum packer w/HEPA filter					24,600			24,600	27,100
1420	55 gallon drum packer w/charcoal & HEPA filter					32,800			32,800	36,100
1430	All of the above made explosion proof, add					1,450			1,450	1,575
6000	Transfer station compactor, with power unit									
6050	and pedestal, not including pit, 50 ton per hour				Ea.	192,500			192,500	211,500

For customer support on your Site Work & Landscape Cost Data, call 877.737.1594.

191

Division Notes

	CREW	DAILY OUTPUT	LABOR-HOURS	UNIT	BARE COSTS				TOTAL INCL O&P
					MAT.	LABOR	EQUIP.	TOTAL	

Estimating Tips
General

- The items in this division are usually priced per square foot or each. Most of these items are purchased by the owner and installed by the contractor. Do not assume the items in Division 12 will be purchased and installed by the contractor. Check the specifications for responsibilities and include receiving, storage, installation, and mechanical and electrical hookups in the appropriate divisions.

- Some items in this division require some type of support system that is not usually furnished with the item. Examples of these systems include blocking for the attachment of casework and heavy drapery rods. The required blocking must be added to the estimate in the appropriate division.

Reference Numbers

Reference numbers are shown in shaded boxes at the beginning of some major classifications. These numbers refer to related items in the Reference Section. The reference information may be an estimating procedure, an alternate pricing method, or technical information.

Note: Not all subdivisions listed here necessarily appear in this publication. ■

12 23 Interior Shutters

12 23 10 - Wood Interior Shutters

12 23 10.10 Wood Interior Shutters	Crew	Daily Output	Labor-Hours	Unit	Material	2015 Bare Costs Labor	Equipment	Total	Total Incl O&P
0010 **WOOD INTERIOR SHUTTERS**, louvered									
0200 Two panel, 27" wide, 36" high	1 Carp	5	1.600	Set	150	75		225	281
0300 33" wide, 36" high		5	1.600		194	75		269	330
0500 47" wide, 36" high		5	1.600		260	75		335	400
1000 Four panel, 27" wide, 36" high		5	1.600		220	75		295	360
1100 33" wide, 36" high		5	1.600		282	75		357	425
1300 47" wide, 36" high		5	1.600		375	75		450	530

12 48 Rugs and Mats

12 48 13 - Entrance Floor Mats and Frames

12 48 13.13 Entrance Floor Mats

	Crew	Daily Output	Labor-Hours	Unit	Material	2015 Bare Costs Labor	Equipment	Total	Total Incl O&P
0010 **ENTRANCE FLOOR MATS**									
0020 Recessed, black rubber, 3/8" thick, solid	1 Clab	155	.052	S.F.	26	1.94		27.94	31.50

12 92 Interior Planters and Artificial Plants

12 92 13 - Interior Artificial Plants

12 92 13.10 Plants

	Crew	Daily Output	Labor-Hours	Unit	Material	2015 Bare Costs Labor	Equipment	Total	Total Incl O&P
0010 **PLANTS** Permanent only, weighted									
0020 Preserved or polyester leaf, natural wood									
0030 Or molded trunk. For pots see Section 12 92 33.10									
0040 For fill see Section 31 23 16.00									
0100 Plants, acuba, 5' high				Ea.	350			350	385
0200 Apidistra, 4' high					310			310	345
0300 Beech, variegated, 5' high					305			305	335
0400 Birds nest fern, 6' high					550			550	605
0500 Croton, 4' high					134			134	147
0600 Diffenbachia, 3' high					123			123	136
0700 Ficus Benjamina, 3' high					146			146	161
0720 6' high					370			370	405
0760 Nitida, 3' high					330			330	360
0780 6' high					575			575	635
0800 Helicona					305			305	335
1200 Palm, green date fan, 5' high					315			315	350
1220 7' high					400			400	440
1280 Green chamdora date, 5' high					288			288	315
1300 7' high					440			440	485
1400 Green giant, 7' high					685			685	750
1600 Rubber plant, 5' high					232			232	255
1800 Schefflera, 3' high					159			159	175
1820 4' high					190			190	209
1840 5' high					300			300	330
1860 6' high					415			415	455
1880 7' high					620			620	680
1900 Spathiphyllum, 3' high					220			220	242
4000 Trees, polyester or preserved, with									
4020 Natural trunks									
4100 Acuba, 10' high				Ea.	1,725			1,725	1,900
4120 12' high					2,425			2,425	2,675
4140 14' high					3,375			3,375	3,725

12 92 Interior Planters and Artificial Plants

12 92 13 – Interior Artificial Plants

12 92 13.10 Plants		Crew	Daily Output	Labor-Hours	Unit	Material	2015 Bare Costs Labor	Equipment	Total	Total Incl O&P
4400	Bamboo, 10' high				Ea.	755			755	830
4420	12' high					875			875	960
4800	Beech, 10' high					2,325			2,325	2,550
4820	12' high					2,675			2,675	2,925
4840	14' high					3,600			3,600	3,950
5000	Birch, 10' high					2,325			2,325	2,550
5020	12' high					2,675			2,675	2,925
5040	14' high					2,900			2,900	3,200
5060	16' high					3,600			3,600	3,950
5080	18' high					4,050			4,050	4,475
5500	Ficus Benjamina, 10' high					1,700			1,700	1,875
5520	12' high					2,175			2,175	2,400
5540	14' high					2,450			2,450	2,700
5560	16' high					3,425			3,425	3,750
5580	18' high					5,125			5,125	5,650
6000	Magnolia, 10' high					2,500			2,500	2,750
6020	12' high					3,550			3,550	3,900
6040	14' high					4,850			4,850	5,350
6500	Maple, 10' high					267			267	294
6520	12' high					400			400	440
6540	14' high					495			495	545
7000	Palms, chamadora, 10' high					490			490	535
7020	12' high					620			620	685
7040	Date, 10' high					670			670	740
7060	12' high					770			770	845

12 92 33 – Interior Planters

12 92 33.10 Planters

		Crew	Daily Output	Labor-Hours	Unit	Material	2015 Bare Costs Labor	Equipment	Total	Total Incl O&P
0010	**PLANTERS**									
1000	Fiberglass, hanging, 12" diameter, 7" high				Ea.	118			118	129
1100	15" diameter, 7" high					171			171	188
1200	36" diameter, 8" high					235			235	259
1500	Rectangular, 48" long, 16" high x 15" wide					665			665	735
1550	16" high x 24" wide					725			725	800
1600	24" high x 24" wide					1,075			1,075	1,175
1650	60" long, 30" high, 28" wide					1,025			1,025	1,125
1700	72" long, 16" high, 15" wide					850			850	935
1750	21" high, 24" wide					1,025			1,025	1,125
1800	30" high, 24" wide					1,175			1,175	1,300
2000	Round, 12" diameter, 13" high					154			154	170
2050	25" high					203			203	223
2150	14" diameter, 15" high					167			167	183
2200	16" diameter, 16" high					188			188	207
2250	18" diameter, 19" high					227			227	250
2300	23" high					295			295	325
2350	20" diameter, 16" high					205			205	226
2400	18" high					226			226	248
2450	21" high					291			291	320
2500	22" diameter, 10" high					239			239	263
2550	24" diameter, 16" high					285			285	315
2600	19" high					340			340	375
2650	25" high					395			395	430
2700	36" high					610			610	675

12 92 Interior Planters and Artificial Plants

12 92 33 – Interior Planters

12 92 33.10 Planters	Crew	Daily Output	Labor-Hours	Unit	Material	2015 Bare Costs Labor	Equipment	Total	Total Incl O&P
2750	48" high				Ea.	855			855	940
2800	30" diameter, 16" high					325			325	355
2850	18" high					325			325	360
2900	21" high					365			365	400
3000	24" high					375			375	415
3350	27" high					415			415	455
3400	36" diameter, 16" high					410			410	450
3450	18" high					425			425	470
3500	21" high					460			460	505
3550	24" high					490			490	540
3600	27" high					530			530	585
3650	30" high					575			575	635
3700	48" diameter, 16" high					675			675	745
3750	21" high					730			730	800
3800	24" high					815			815	900
3850	27" high					860			860	945
3900	30" high					930			930	1,025
3950	36" high					980			980	1,075
4000	60" diameter, 16" high					965			965	1,050
4100	21" high					1,100			1,100	1,200
4150	27" high					1,225			1,225	1,350
4200	30" high					1,350			1,350	1,475
4250	33" high					1,550			1,550	1,700
4300	36" high					1,875			1,875	2,075
4400	39" high					2,025			2,025	2,225
5000	Square, 10" side, 20" high					193			193	212
5100	14" side, 15" high					234			234	257
5200	18" side, 19" high					230			230	253
5300	20" side, 16" high					282			282	310
5320	18" high					475			475	520
5340	21" high					375			375	415
5400	24" side, 16" high					350			350	385
5420	21" high					540			540	590
5440	25" high					515			515	570
5460	30" side, 16" high					555			555	610
5480	24" high					665			665	730
5490	27" high					885			885	975
5500	Round, 36" diameter, 16" high					500			500	550
5510	18" high					695			695	765
5520	21" high					765			765	845
5530	24" high					850			850	935
5540	27" high					965			965	1,075
5550	30" high					1,325			1,325	1,475
5800	48" diameter, 16" high					670			670	740
5820	21" high					750			750	825
5840	24" high					935			935	1,025
5860	27" high					1,025			1,025	1,125
5880	30" high					305			305	335
5900	60" diameter, 16" high					665			665	730
5920	21" high					770			770	845
5940	27" high					840			840	925
5960	30" high					950			950	1,050
5980	36" high					1,025			1,025	1,125

196

12 92 Interior Planters and Artificial Plants

12 92 33 – Interior Planters

12 92 33.10 Planters		Crew	Daily Output	Labor-Hours	Unit	Material	2015 Bare Costs Labor	Equipment	Total	Total Incl O&P
6000	Metal bowl, 32" diameter, 8" high, minimum				Ea.	555			555	610
6050	Maximum					755			755	830
6100	Rectangle, 30" long x 12" wide, 6" high, minimum					430			430	475
6200	Maximum					600			600	660
6300	36" long 12" wide, 6" high, minimum					850			850	935
6400	Maximum					475			475	520
6500	Square, 15" side, minimum					605			605	665
6600	Maximum					935			935	1,025
6700	20" side, minimum					1,350			1,350	1,475
6800	Maximum					1,025			1,025	1,125
6900	Round, 6" diameter x 6" high, minimum					62.50			62.50	69
7000	Maximum					74.50			74.50	82
7100	8" diameter x 8" high, minimum					83.50			83.50	92
7200	Maximum					89.50			89.50	98.50
7300	10" diameter x 11" high, minimum					107			107	118
7400	Maximum					159			159	174
7420	12" diameter x 13" high, minimum					99			99	109
7440	Maximum					180			180	198
7500	14" diameter x 15" high, minimum					134			134	147
7550	Maximum					235			235	258
7580	16" diameter x 17" high, minimum					144			144	159
7600	Maximum					257			257	282
7620	18" diameter x 19" high, minimum					175			175	192
7640	Maximum					315			315	345
7680	22" diameter x 20" high, minimum					220			220	242
7700	Maximum					400			400	440
7750	24" diameter x 21" high, minimum					285			285	315
7800	Maximum					535			535	590
7850	31" diameter x 18" high, minimum					620			620	685
7900	Maximum					1,575			1,575	1,750
7950	38" diameter x 24" high, minimum					1,050			1,050	1,150
8000	Maximum					2,675			2,675	2,925
8050	48" diameter x 24" high, minimum					1,400			1,400	1,525
8150	Maximum				▼	2,750			2,750	3,025
8500	Plastic laminate faced, fiberglass liner, square									
8520	14" sq., 15" high				Ea.	630			630	690
8540	24" sq., 16" high					805			805	885
8580	36" sq., 21" high					1,100			1,100	1,200
8600	Rectangle 36" long, 12" wide, 10" high					680			680	750
8650	48" long, 12" wide, 10" high					755			755	830
8700	48" long, 12" wide, 24" high				▼	1,125			1,125	1,225
8750	Wood, fiberglass liner, square									
8780	14" square, 15" high, minimum				Ea.	455			455	500
8800	Maximum					560			560	615
8820	24" sq., 16" high, minimum					560			560	615
8840	Maximum					740			740	815
8860	36" sq., 21" high, minimum					720			720	790
8880	Maximum					1,075			1,075	1,200
9000	Rectangle, 36" long x 12" wide, 10" high, minimum					500			500	550
9050	Maximum					650			650	715
9100	48" long x 12" wide, 10" high, minimum					540			540	595
9120	Maximum					680			680	750
9200	48" long x 12" wide, 24" high, minimum					650			650	715

For customer support on your Site Work & Landscape Cost Data, call 877.737.1594.

197

12 92 Interior Planters and Artificial Plants

12 92 33 – Interior Planters

12 92 33.10 Planters

	12 92 33.10 Planters	Crew	Daily Output	Labor-Hours	Unit	Material	2015 Bare Costs Labor	Equipment	Total	Total Incl O&P
9300	Maximum				Ea.	950			950	1,050
9400	Plastic cylinder, molded, 10" diameter, 10" high					18.45			18.45	20.50
9500	11" diameter, 11" high					35			35	38.50
9600	13" diameter, 12" high					57			57	63
9700	16" diameter, 14" high					66.50			66.50	73

12 93 Interior Public Space Furnishings

12 93 23 – Trash and Litter Receptacles

12 93 23.10 Trash Receptacles

		Crew	Daily Output	Labor-Hours	Unit	Material	2015 Bare Costs Labor	Equipment	Total	Total Incl O&P
0010	**TRASH RECEPTACLES**									
0020	Fiberglass, 2' square, 18" high	2 Clab	30	.533	Ea.	560	20		580	645
0100	2' square, 2'-6" high		30	.533		795	20		815	905
0300	Circular , 2' diameter, 18" high		30	.533		475	20		495	550
0400	2' diameter, 2'-6" high		30	.533		530	20		550	615
1000	Alum. frame, hardboard panels, steel drum base,									
1020	30 gal. capacity, silk screen on plastic finish	2 Clab	25	.640	Ea.	460	24		484	540
1040	Aggregate finish		25	.640		590	24		614	685
1100	50 gal. capacity, silk screen on plastic finish		20	.800		695	30		725	810
1140	Aggregate finish		20	.800		750	30		780	870
1200	Formed plastic liner, 14 gal., silk screen on plastic finish		40	.400		390	15.05		405.05	455
1240	Aggregate finish		40	.400		430	15.05		445.05	495
1300	30 gal. capacity, silk screen on plastic finish		35	.457		510	17.20		527.20	585
1340	Aggregate finish		35	.457		560	17.20		577.20	640
1400	Redwood slats, plastic liner, leg base, 14 gal. capacity,									
1420	Varnish w/routed message	2 Clab	40	.400	Ea.	415	15.05		430.05	480
2000	Concrete, precast, 2' to 2-1/2' wide, 3' high, sandblasted	"	15	1.067	"	730	40		770	865
3000	Galv. steel frame and panels, leg base, poly bag retainer,									
3020	40 gal. capacity, silk screen on enamel finish	2 Clab	25	.640	Ea.	430	24		454	505
3040	Aggregate finish		25	.640		470	24		494	550
3200	Formed plastic liner, 50 gal., silk screen on enamel finish		20	.800		865	30		895	1,000
3240	Aggregate finish		20	.800		910	30		940	1,050
4000	Perforated steel, pole mounted, 12" diam., 10 gal., painted		25	.640		120	24		144	169
4040	Redwood slats		25	.640		360	24		384	430
4100	22 gal. capacity, painted		25	.640		160	24		184	213
4140	Redwood slats		25	.640		420	24		444	495
4500	Galvanized steel street basket, 52 gal. capacity, unpainted		40	.400		395	15.05		410.05	460

12 93 23.20 Trash Closure

		Crew	Daily Output	Labor-Hours	Unit	Material	2015 Bare Costs Labor	Equipment	Total	Total Incl O&P
0010	**TRASH CLOSURE**									
0020	Steel with pullover cover, 2'-3" wide, 4'-7" high, 6'-2" long	2 Clab	5	3.200	Ea.	1,950	120		2,070	2,325
0100	10'-1" long		4	4		2,425	150		2,575	2,900
0300	Wood, 10' wide, 6' high, 10' long		1.20	13.333		1,750	500		2,250	2,700

Estimating Tips
General

- The items and systems in this division are usually estimated, purchased, supplied, and installed as a unit by one or more subcontractors. The estimator must ensure that all parties are operating from the same set of specifications and assumptions, and that all necessary items are estimated and will be provided. Many times the complex items and systems are covered, but the more common ones, such as excavation or a crane, are overlooked for the very reason that everyone assumes nobody could miss them. The estimator should be the central focus and be able to ensure that all systems are complete.

- Another area where problems can develop in this division is at the interface between systems. The estimator must ensure, for instance, that anchor bolts, nuts, and washers are estimated and included for the air-supported structures and pre-engineered buildings to be bolted to their foundations. Utility supply is a common area where essential items or pieces of equipment can be missed or overlooked, because each subcontractor may feel it is another's responsibility. The estimator should also be aware of certain items which may be supplied as part of a package but installed by others, and ensure that the installing contractor's estimate includes the cost of installation. Conversely, the estimator must also ensure that items are not costed by two different subcontractors, resulting in an inflated overall estimate.

13 30 00 Special Structures

- The foundations and floor slab, as well as rough mechanical and electrical, should be estimated, as this work is required for the assembly and erection of the structure.

Generally, as noted in the book, the pre-engineered building comes as a shell. Pricing is based on the size and structural design parameters stated in the reference section. Additional features, such as windows and doors with their related structural framing, must also be included by the estimator. Here again, the estimator must have a clear understanding of the scope of each portion of the work and all the necessary interfaces.

Reference Numbers

Reference numbers are shown in shaded boxes at the beginning of some major classifications. These numbers refer to related items in the Reference Section. The reference information may be an estimating procedure, an alternate pricing method, or technical information.

Note: Not all subdivisions listed here necessarily appear in this publication. ∎

Division 13 – Special Construction

Did you know?
RSMeans Online gives you the same access to RSMeans' data with 24/7 access:

- Quickly locate costs in the searchable database.
- Build cost lists, estimates, and reports in minutes.
- Adjust costs to any location in the U.S. and Canada with the click of a button.

Start your free trial today at **www.rsmeansonline.com**

RSMeansOnline

13 05 Common Work Results for Special Construction

13 05 05 – Selective Demolition for Special Construction

13 05 05.25 Selective Demolition, Geodesic Domes

		Crew	Daily Output	Labor-Hours	Unit	Material	2015 Bare Costs Labor	Equipment	Total	Total Incl O&P
0010	**SELECTIVE DEMOLITION, GEODESIC DOMES**									
0050	Shell only, interlocking plywood panels, 30' diameter	F-5	3.20	10	Ea.		475		475	730
0060	34' diameter		2.30	13.913			660		660	1,025
0070	39' diameter		2	16			760		760	1,175
0080	45' diameter	F-3	2.20	18.182			870	297	1,167	1,650
0090	55' diameter		2	20			960	325	1,285	1,825
0100	60' diameter		2	20			960	325	1,285	1,825
0110	65' diameter		1.60	25			1,200	410	1,610	2,275

13 05 05.45 Selective Demolition, Lightning Protection

		Crew	Daily Output	Labor-Hours	Unit	Material	2015 Bare Costs Labor	Equipment	Total	Total Incl O&P
0010	**SELECTIVE DEMOLITION, LIGHTNING PROTECTION**									
0020	Air terminal & base, copper, 3/8" diam. x 10", to 75' h	1 Clab	16	.500	Ea.		18.80		18.80	29
0030	1/2" diam. x 12", over 75' h		16	.500			18.80		18.80	29
0050	Aluminum, 1/2" diam. x 12", to 75' h		16	.500			18.80		18.80	29
0060	5/8" diam. x 12", over 75' h		16	.500			18.80		18.80	29
0070	Cable, copper, 220 lb. per thousand feet, to 75' high		640	.013	L.F.		.47		.47	.72
0080	375 lb. per thousand feet, over 75' high		460	.017			.65		.65	1.01
0090	Aluminum, 101 lb. per thousand feet, to 75' high		560	.014			.54		.54	.83
0100	199 lb. per thousand feet, over 75' high		480	.017			.63		.63	.96
0110	Arrester, 175 V AC, to ground		16	.500	Ea.		18.80		18.80	29
0120	650 V AC, to ground		13	.615	"		23		23	35.50

13 05 05.50 Selective Demolition, Pre-Engineered Steel Buildings

		Crew	Daily Output	Labor-Hours	Unit	Material	2015 Bare Costs Labor	Equipment	Total	Total Incl O&P
0010	**SELECTIVE DEMOLITION, PRE-ENGINEERED STEEL BUILDINGS**									
0500	Pre-engd. steel bldgs., rigid frame, clear span & multi post, excl. salvage									
0550	3,500 to 7,500 S.F.	L-10	1000	.024	SF Flr.		1.27	.65	1.92	2.84
0600	7,501 to 12,500 S.F.		1500	.016			.85	.44	1.29	1.89
0650	12,500 S.F. or greater		1650	.015			.77	.40	1.17	1.72
0700	Pre-engd. steel building components									
0710	Entrance canopy, including frame 4' x 4'	E-24	8	4	Ea.		209	92	301	450
0720	4' x 8'	"	7	4.571			238	105	343	515
0730	HM doors, self framing, single leaf	2 Skwk	8	2			97.50		97.50	150
0740	Double leaf		5	3.200			156		156	240
0760	Gutter, eave type		600	.027	L.F.		1.30		1.30	2
0770	Sash, single slide, double slide or fixed		24	.667	Ea.		32.50		32.50	50
0780	Skylight, fiberglass, to 30 S.F.		16	1			48.50		48.50	75
0785	Roof vents, circular, 12" to 24" diameter		12	1.333			65		65	100
0790	Continuous, 10' long		8	2			97.50		97.50	150
0900	Shelters, aluminum frame									
0910	Acrylic glazing, 3' x 9' x 8' high	2 Skwk	2	8	Ea.		390		390	600
0920	9' x 12' x 8' high	"	1.50	10.667	"		520		520	800

13 05 05.60 Selective Demolition, Silos

		Crew	Daily Output	Labor-Hours	Unit	Material	2015 Bare Costs Labor	Equipment	Total	Total Incl O&P
0010	**SELECTIVE DEMOLITION, SILOS**									
0020	Conc stave, indstrl, conical/sloping bott, excl fndtn, 12' diam., 35' h	E-24	.18	177	Ea.		9,275	4,100	13,375	20,100
0030	16' diam., 45' h		.12	266			13,900	6,150	20,050	30,200
0040	25' diam., 75' h		.08	400			20,900	9,200	30,100	45,200
0050	Steel, factory fabricated, 30,000 gal. cap, painted or epoxy lined	L-5	2	28			1,475	370	1,845	2,925

13 05 05.75 Selective Demolition, Storage Tanks

		Crew	Daily Output	Labor-Hours	Unit	Material	2015 Bare Costs Labor	Equipment	Total	Total Incl O&P
0010	**SELECTIVE DEMOLITION, STORAGE TANKS**									
0500	Steel tank, single wall, above ground, not incl. fdn., pumps or piping									
0510	Single wall, 275 gallon R024119-10	Q-1	3	5.333	Ea.		282		282	425
0520	550 thru 2,000 gallon	B-34P	2	12			600	335	935	1,275
0530	5,000 thru 10,000 gallon	B-34Q	2	12			600	630	1,230	1,600
0540	15,000 thru 30,000 gallon	B-34S	2	16			845	1,775	2,620	3,225

For customer support on your Site Work & Landscape Cost Data, call 877.737.1594.

13 05 Common Work Results for Special Construction

13 05 05 – Selective Demolition for Special Construction

13 05 05.75 Selective Demolition, Storage Tanks	Crew	Daily Output	Labor-Hours	Unit	Material	2015 Bare Costs Labor	2015 Bare Costs Equipment	Total	Total Incl O&P
0600	Steel tank, double wall, above ground not incl. fdn., pumps & piping									
0620	500 thru 2,000 gallon	B-34P	2	12	Ea.		600	335	935	1,275

13 05 05.90 Selective Demolition, Tension Structures

		Crew	Daily Output	Labor-Hours	Unit	Material	Labor	Equipment	Total	Total Incl O&P
0010	**SELECTIVE DEMOLITION, TENSION STRUCTURES**									
0020	Steel/alum. frame, fabric shell, 60' clear span, 6,000 S.F.	B-41	2000	.022	SF Flr.		.86	.14	1	1.48
0030	12,000 S.F.		2200	.020			.78	.13	.91	1.34
0040	80' clear span, 20,800 S.F.		2440	.018			.70	.12	.82	1.21
0050	100' clear span, 10,000 S.F.	L-5	4350	.013			.68	.17	.85	1.35
0060	26,000 S.F.		4600	.012			.64	.16	.80	1.28
0070	36,000 S.F.		5000	.011			.59	.15	.74	1.17
0080	120' clear span, 24,000 S.F.		6000	.009			.49	.12	.61	.98
0090	150' clear span, 30,000 S.F.		7000	.008			.42	.11	.53	.84
0100	200' clear span, 40,000 S.F.	E-6	16000	.008			.42	.12	.54	.84
0110	For roll-up door, 12' x 14'	L-2	2	8	Ea.	330			330	510

13 11 Swimming Pools

13 11 13 – Below-Grade Swimming Pools

13 11 13.50 Swimming Pools

		Crew	Daily Output	Labor-Hours	Unit	Material	Labor	Equipment	Total	Total Incl O&P
0010	**SWIMMING POOLS** Residential in-ground, vinyl lined, concrete									
0020	Swimming pools, resi in-ground, vyl lined, conc sides, W/ equip, sand bot	B-52	300	.187	SF Surf	23.50	8.15	1.98	33.63	40
0100	Metal or polystyrene sides	B-14	410	.117		19.55	4.66	.89	25.10	29.50
0200	Add for vermiculite bottom					1.49			1.49	1.64
0500	Gunite bottom and sides, white plaster finish									
0600	12' x 30' pool	B-52	145	.386	SF Surf	43.50	16.85	4.10	64.45	78.50
0720	16' x 32' pool		155	.361		39	15.75	3.83	58.58	71
0750	20' x 40' pool		250	.224		35	9.75	2.38	47.13	56
0810	Concrete bottom and sides, tile finish									
0820	12' x 30' pool	B-52	80	.700	SF Surf	44	30.50	7.45	81.95	103
0830	16' x 32' pool		95	.589		36.50	25.50	6.25	68.25	86.50
0840	20' x 40' pool		130	.431		29	18.80	4.57	52.37	66
1100	Motel, gunite with plaster finish, incl. medium									
1150	capacity filtration & chlorination	B-52	115	.487	SF Surf	53.50	21	5.15	79.65	97
1200	Municipal, gunite with plaster finish, incl. high									
1250	capacity filtration & chlorination	B-52	100	.560	SF Surf	69.50	24.50	5.95	99.95	120
1350	Add for formed gutters				L.F.	102			102	112
1360	Add for stainless steel gutters				"	300			300	330
1700	Filtration and deck equipment only, as % of total				Total				20%	20%
1800	Deck equipment, rule of thumb, 20' x 40' pool				SF Pool				1.18	1.30
1900	5000 S.F. pool				"				1.73	1.90
3000	Painting pools, preparation + 3 coats, 20' x 40' pool, epoxy	2 Pord	.33	48.485	Total	1,775	1,950		3,725	4,900
3100	Rubber base paint, 18 gallons	"	.33	48.485		1,225	1,950		3,175	4,300
3500	42' x 82' pool, 75 gallons, epoxy paint	3 Pord	.14	171		7,500	6,925		14,425	18,700
3600	Rubber base paint	"	.14	171		5,075	6,925		12,000	16,000

13 11 46 – Swimming Pool Accessories

13 11 46.50 Swimming Pool Equipment

		Crew	Daily Output	Labor-Hours	Unit	Material	Labor	Equipment	Total	Total Incl O&P
0010	**SWIMMING POOL EQUIPMENT**									
0020	Diving stand, stainless steel, 3 meter	2 Carp	.40	40	Ea.	15,100	1,875		16,975	19,500
0300	1 meter		2.70	5.926		9,175	278		9,453	10,500
0600	Diving boards, 16' long, aluminum		2.70	5.926		3,950	278		4,228	4,775
0700	Fiberglass		2.70	5.926		3,250	278		3,528	4,000

For customer support on your Site Work & Landscape Cost Data, call 877.737.1594.

201

13 11 Swimming Pools

13 11 46 – Swimming Pool Accessories

13 11 46.50 Swimming Pool Equipment	Crew	Daily Output	Labor-Hours	Unit	Material	2015 Bare Costs Labor	Equipment	Total	Total Incl O&P
0800	14' long, aluminum	2 Carp	2.70	5.926	Ea.	3,575	278		3,853	4,350
0850	Fiberglass		2.70	5.926		3,225	278		3,503	3,950
1200	Ladders, heavy duty, stainless steel, 2 tread		7	2.286		810	107		917	1,050
1500	4 tread		6	2.667		1,075	125		1,200	1,375
1900	Portable					2,775			2,775	3,050
2100	Lights, underwater, 12 volt, with transformer, 300 watt	1 Elec	1	8		330	440		770	1,025
2200	110 volt, 500 watt, standard		1	8		294	440		734	980
2400	Low water cutoff type		1	8		300	440		740	985
3000	Pool covers, reinforced vinyl	3 Clab	1800	.013	S.F.	1.13	.50		1.63	2.01
3050	Automatic, electric								8.75	9.65
3100	Vinyl, for winter, 400 SF max pool surface	3 Clab	3200	.008		.26	.28		.54	.72
3200	With water tubes, 400SF max pool surface	"	3000	.008		.29	.30		.59	.78
3250	Sealed air bubble polyethylene solar blanket, 16 mils					.30			.30	.33
3300	Slides, tubular, fiberglass, aluminum handrails & ladder, 5'-0", straight	2 Carp	1.60	10	Ea.	3,575	470		4,045	4,675
3320	8'-0", curved		3	5.333		7,225	250		7,475	8,325
3400	10'-0", curved		1	16		22,000	750		22,750	25,400
3420	12'-0", straight with platform		1.20	13.333		13,800	625		14,425	16,200

13 12 Fountains

13 12 13 – Exterior Fountains

13 12 13.10 Yard Fountains

0010	YARD FOUNTAINS									
0100	Outdoor fountain, 48" high with bowl and figures	2 Clab	2	8	Ea.	570	300		870	1,100

13 18 Ice Rinks

13 18 13 – Ice Rink Floor Systems

13 18 13.50 Ice Skating

0010	ICE SKATING Equipment incl. refrigeration, plumbing & cooling									
0020	coils & concrete slab, 85' x 200' rink									
0300	55° system, 5 mos., 100 ton				Total	575,000			575,000	632,500
0700	90° system, 12 mos., 135 ton				"	650,000			650,000	715,000
1200	Subsoil heating system (recycled from compressor), 85' x 200'	Q-7	.27	118	Ea.	40,000	6,750		46,750	54,000
1300	Subsoil insulation, 2 lb. polystyrene with vapor barrier, 85' x 200'	2 Carp	.14	114	"	30,000	5,375		35,375	41,300

13 18 16 – Ice Rink Dasher Boards

13 18 16.50 Ice Rink Dasher Boards

0010	ICE RINK DASHER BOARDS									
1000	Dasher boards, 1/2" H.D. polyethylene faced steel frame, 3' acrylic									
1020	screen at sides, 5' acrylic ends, 85' x 200'	F-5	.06	533	Ea.	135,000	25,300		160,300	187,500
1100	Fiberglass & aluminum construction, same sides and ends	"	.06	533	"	155,000	25,300		180,300	209,500

13 31 Fabric Structures

13 31 13 – Air-Supported Fabric Structures

13 31 13.09 Air Supported Tank Covers

		Crew	Daily Output	Labor-Hours	Unit	Material	2015 Bare Costs Labor	Equipment	Total	Total Incl O&P
0010	**AIR SUPPORTED TANK COVERS**, vinyl polyester									
0100	Scrim, double layer, with hardware, blower, standby & controls									
0200	Round, 75' diameter	B-2	4500	.009	S.F.	11.75	.34		12.09	13.45
0300	100' diameter		5000	.008		10.70	.30		11	12.20
0400	150' diameter		5000	.008		8.45	.30		8.75	9.75
0500	Rectangular, 20' x 20'		4500	.009		23	.34		23.34	26
0600	30' x 40'		4500	.009		23	.34		23.34	26
0700	50' x 60'		4500	.009		23	.34		23.34	26
0800	For single wall construction, deduct, minimum					.79			.79	.87
0900	Maximum					2.33			2.33	2.56
1000	For maximum resistance to atmosphere or cold, add					1.14			1.14	1.25
1100	For average shipping charges, add				Total	1,975			1,975	2,175

13 31 13.13 Single-Walled Air-Supported Structures

		Crew	Daily Output	Labor-Hours	Unit	Material	2015 Bare Costs Labor	Equipment	Total	Total Incl O&P
0010	**SINGLE-WALLED AIR-SUPPORTED STRUCTURES**									
0020	Site preparation, incl. anchor placement and utilities	B-11B	1000	.016	SF Flr.	1.16	.69	.30	2.15	2.66
0030	For concrete, see Section 03 30 53.40									
0050	Warehouse, polyester/vinyl fabric, 28 oz., over 10 yr. life, welded									
0060	Seams, tension cables, primary & auxiliary inflation system,									
0070	airlock, personnel doors and liner									
0100	5,000 S.F.	4 Clab	5000	.006	SF Flr.	26.50	.24		26.74	29.50
0250	12,000 S.F.	"	6000	.005		18.85	.20		19.05	21.50
0400	24,000 S.F.	8 Clab	12000	.005		13.30	.20		13.50	14.90
0500	50,000 S.F.	"	12500	.005		12.30	.19		12.49	13.85
0700	12 oz. reinforced vinyl fabric, 5 yr. life, sewn seams,									
0710	accordion door, including liner									
0750	3000 S.F.	4 Clab	3000	.011	SF Flr.	13.20	.40		13.60	15.15
0800	12,000 S.F.	"	6000	.005		11.25	.20		11.45	12.65
0850	24,000 S.F.	8 Clab	12000	.005		9.50	.20		9.70	10.75
0950	Deduct for single layer					1.03			1.03	1.13
1000	Add for welded seams					1.50			1.50	1.65
1050	Add for double layer, welded seams included					3			3	3.30
1250	Tedlar/vinyl fabric, 28 oz., with liner, over 10 yr. life,									
1260	incl. overhead and personnel doors									
1300	3000 S.F.	4 Clab	3000	.011	SF Flr.	24.50	.40		24.90	27.50
1450	12,000 S.F.	"	6000	.005		17.20	.20		17.40	19.25
1550	24,000 S.F.	8 Clab	12000	.005		13.30	.20		13.50	14.95
1700	Deduct for single layer					2			2	2.20
2250	Greenhouse/shelter, woven polyethylene with liner, 2 yr. life,									
2260	sewn seams, including doors									
2300	3000 S.F.	4 Clab	3000	.011	SF Flr.	16	.40		16.40	18.20
2350	12,000 S.F.	"	6000	.005		14	.20		14.20	15.70
2450	24,000 S.F.	8 Clab	12000	.005		12	.20		12.20	13.50
2550	Deduct for single layer					.98			.98	1.08
2600	Tennis/gymnasium, polyester/vinyl fabric, 28 oz., over 10 yr. life,									
2610	including thermal liner, heat and lights									
2650	7,200 S.F.	4 Clab	6000	.005	SF Flr.	23.50	.20		23.70	26.50
2750	13,000 S.F.	"	6500	.005		18	.19		18.19	20
2850	Over 24,000 S.F.	8 Clab	12000	.005		16.45	.20		16.65	18.35
2860	For low temperature conditions, add					1.14			1.14	1.25
2870	For average shipping charges, add				Total	5,600			5,600	6,150
2900	Thermal liner, translucent reinforced vinyl				SF Flr.	1.14			1.14	1.25
2950	Metalized mylar fabric and mesh, double liner				"	2.33			2.33	2.56

For customer support on your Site Work & Landscape Cost Data, call 877.737.1594.

203

13 31 Fabric Structures

13 31 13 – Air-Supported Fabric Structures

13 31 13.13 Single-Walled Air-Supported Structures	Crew	Daily Output	Labor-Hours	Unit	Material	2015 Bare Costs Labor	Equipment	Total	Total Incl O&P
3050	Stadium/convention center, teflon coated fiberglass, heavy weight,									
3060	over 20 yr. life, incl. thermal liner and heating system									
3100	Minimum	9 Clab	26000	.003	SF Flr.	57.50	.10		57.60	63
3110	Maximum	"	19000	.004	"	68	.14		68.14	75
3400	Doors, air lock, 15' long, 10' x 10'	2 Carp	.80	20	Ea.	20,400	940		21,340	24,000
3600	15' x 15'	"	.50	32		30,300	1,500		31,800	35,700
3700	For each added 5' length, add					5,425			5,425	5,950
3900	Revolving personnel door, 6' diameter, 6'-6" high	2 Carp	.80	20	↓	15,200	940		16,140	18,200

13 31 23 – Tensioned Fabric Structures

13 31 23.50 Tension Structures

		Crew	Daily Output	Labor-Hours	Unit	Material	2015 Bare Costs Labor	Equipment	Total	Total Incl O&P
0010	**TENSION STRUCTURES** Rigid steel/alum. frame, vinyl coated poly									
0100	Fabric shell, 60' clear span, not incl. foundations or floors									
0200	6,000 S.F.	B-41	1000	.044	SF Flr.	13.80	1.71	.29	15.80	18.15
0300	12,000 S.F.		1100	.040		13.20	1.56	.26	15.02	17.25
0400	80' to 99' clear span, 20,800 S.F.	↓	1220	.036		13	1.40	.24	14.64	16.70
0410	100' to 119' clear span, 10,000 S.F.	L-5	2175	.026		13.70	1.36	.34	15.40	17.75
0430	26,000 S.F.		2300	.024		12.75	1.29	.32	14.36	16.60
0450	36,000 S.F.		2500	.022		12.60	1.18	.29	14.07	16.20
0460	120' to 149' clear span, 24,000 S.F.		3000	.019		13.90	.99	.25	15.14	17.20
0470	150' to 199' clear span, 30,000 S.F.	↓	6000	.009		14.45	.49	.12	15.06	16.85
0480	200' clear span, 40,000 S.F.	E-6	8000	.016	↓	17.75	.84	.23	18.82	21
0500	For roll-up door, 12' x 14', add	L-2	1	16	Ea.	5,500	660		6,160	7,075

13 34 Fabricated Engineered Structures

13 34 13 – Glazed Structures

13 34 13.13 Greenhouses

		Crew	Daily Output	Labor-Hours	Unit	Material	2015 Bare Costs Labor	Equipment	Total	Total Incl O&P
0010	**GREENHOUSES**, Shell only, stock units, not incl. 2' stub walls,									
0020	foundation, floors, heat or compartments									
0300	Residential type, free standing, 8'-6" long x 7'-6" wide	2 Carp	59	.271	SF Flr.	20	12.75		32.75	41.50
0400	10'-6" wide		85	.188		37	8.85		45.85	54
0600	13'-6" wide		108	.148		39	6.95		45.95	53
0700	17'-0" wide		160	.100		43.50	4.70		48.20	55.50
0900	Lean-to type, 3'-10" wide		34	.471		41.50	22		63.50	80
1000	6'-10" wide	↓	58	.276	↓	50	12.95		62.95	75
1100	Wall mounted to existing window, 3' x 3'	1 Carp	4	2	Ea.	1,575	94		1,669	1,900
1120	4' x 5'	"	3	2.667	"	2,025	125		2,150	2,425
1200	Deluxe quality, free standing, 7'-6" wide	2 Carp	55	.291	SF Flr.	81.50	13.65		95.15	111
1220	10'-6" wide		81	.198		61	9.25		70.25	81.50
1240	13'-6" wide		104	.154		55	7.20		62.20	71.50
1260	17'-0" wide		150	.107		56.50	5		61.50	70
1400	Lean-to type, 3'-10" wide		31	.516		105	24		129	154
1420	6'-10" wide		55	.291		66.50	13.65		80.15	94
1440	8'-0" wide	↓	97	.165	↓	56	7.75		63.75	73.50
1500	Commercial, custom, truss frame, incl. equip., plumbing, elec.,									
1550	benches and controls, under 2,000 S.F.				SF Flr.	13			13	14.30
1700	Over 5,000 S.F.				"	11.95			11.95	13.15
2000	Institutional, custom, rigid frame, including compartments and									
2050	multi-controls, under 500 S.F.				SF Flr.	25.50			25.50	28
2150	Over 2,000 S.F.				"	10.70			10.70	11.75
3700	For 1/4" tempered glass, add				SF Surf	1.34			1.34	1.47

13 34 13 – Glazed Structures

13 34 13.13 Greenhouses

		Crew	Daily Output	Labor-Hours	Unit	Material	2015 Bare Costs Labor	Equipment	Total	Total Incl O&P
3900	Cooling, 1200 CFM exhaust fan, add				Ea.	310			310	340
4000	7850 CFM					1,050			1,050	1,150
4200	For heaters, 10 MBH, add					215			215	237
4300	60 MBH, add					780			780	855
4500	For benches, 2' x 8', add					160			160	176
4600	4' x 10', add				↓	195			195	214
4800	For ventilation & humidity control w/ 4 integrated outlets, add				Total	240			240	264
4900	For environmental controls and automation, 8 outputs, 9 stages, add				"	765			765	840
5100	For humidification equipment, add				Ea.	299			299	330
5200	For vinyl shading, add				S.F.	.24			.24	.26
6000	Geodesic hemisphere, 1/8" plexiglass glazing									
6050	8' diameter	2 Carp	2	8	Ea.	6,250	375		6,625	7,450
6150	24' diameter	↓	.35	45.714		14,000	2,150		16,150	18,600
6250	48' diameter	↓	.20	80	↓	33,000	3,750		36,750	42,000

13 34 13.19 Swimming Pool Enclosures

		Crew	Daily Output	Labor-Hours	Unit	Material	2015 Bare Costs Labor	Equipment	Total	Total Incl O&P
0010	**SWIMMING POOL ENCLOSURES** Translucent, free standing R131113-20									
0020	not including foundations, heat or light									
0200	Economy	2 Carp	200	.080	SF Hor.	37	3.76		40.76	47
0600	Deluxe	"	70	.229		93	10.75		103.75	119
0700	For motorized roof, 40% opening, solid roof, add					21			21	23
0800	Skylight type roof, add				↓	13.50			13.50	14.85

13 34 16 – Grandstands and Bleachers

13 34 16.13 Grandstands

		Crew	Daily Output	Labor-Hours	Unit	Material	2015 Bare Costs Labor	Equipment	Total	Total Incl O&P
0010	**GRANDSTANDS** Permanent, municipal, including foundation									
0300	Steel, economy				Seat	19.90			19.90	22
0400	Steel, deluxe					22.50			22.50	24.50
0900	Composite, steel, wood and plastic, stock design, economy					38.50			38.50	42
1000	Deluxe				↓	68.50			68.50	75

13 34 16.53 Bleachers

		Crew	Daily Output	Labor-Hours	Unit	Material	2015 Bare Costs Labor	Equipment	Total	Total Incl O&P
0010	**BLEACHERS**									
0020	Bleachers, outdoor, portable, 5 tiers, 42 seats	2 Sswk	120	.133	Seat	90	7		97	111
0100	5 tiers, 54 seats		80	.200		81.50	10.55		92.05	108
0200	10 tiers, 104 seats		120	.133		92.50	7		99.50	114
0300	10 tiers, 144 seats	↓	80	.200	↓	83	10.55		93.55	109
0500	Permanent bleachers, aluminum seat, steel frame, 24" row									
0600	8 tiers, 80 seats	2 Sswk	60	.267	Seat	67	14.05		81.05	98.50
0700	8 tiers, 160 seats		48	.333		58	17.55		75.55	94.50
0925	15 tiers, 154 to 165 seats		60	.267		94	14.05		108.05	128
0975	15 tiers, 214 to 225 seats		60	.267		84.50	14.05		98.55	118
1050	15 tiers, 274 to 285 seats		60	.267		77	14.05		91.05	109
1200	Seat backs only, 30" row, fiberglass		160	.100		23	5.25		28.25	34.50
1300	Steel and wood	↓	160	.100	↓	22	5.25		27.25	33.50
1400	NOTE: average seating is 1.5' in width									

13 34 19 – Metal Building Systems

13 34 19.50 Pre-Engineered Steel Buildings

		Crew	Daily Output	Labor-Hours	Unit	Material	2015 Bare Costs Labor	Equipment	Total	Total Incl O&P
0010	**PRE-ENGINEERED STEEL BUILDINGS** R133419-10									
0100	Clear span rigid frame, 26 ga. colored roofing and siding									
0150	20' to 29' wide, 10' eave height	E-2	425	.132	SF Flr.	8.80	6.80	3.55	19.15	25
0160	14' eave height		350	.160		9.50	8.30	4.32	22.12	29
0170	16' eave height		320	.175		10.20	9.05	4.72	23.97	31.50
0180	20' eave height	↓	275	.204	↓	11.15	10.55	5.50	27.20	36

13 34 19.50 Pre-Engineered Steel Buildings		Crew	Daily Output	Labor-Hours	Unit	Material	2015 Bare Costs Labor	Equipment	Total	Total Incl O&P
0190	24' eave height	E-2	240	.233	SF Flr.	12.30	12.05	6.30	30.65	41
0200	30' to 49' wide, 10' eave height		535	.105		6.75	5.40	2.82	14.97	19.65
0300	14' eave height		450	.124		7.30	6.45	3.36	17.11	22.50
0400	16' eave height		415	.135		7.80	7	3.64	18.44	24.50
0500	20' eave height		360	.156		8.45	8.05	4.20	20.70	27.50
0600	24' eave height		320	.175		9.30	9.05	4.72	23.07	30.50
0700	50' to 100' wide, 10' eave height		770	.073		5.75	3.76	1.96	11.47	14.75
0900	16' eave height		600	.093		6.60	4.83	2.52	13.95	18.10
1000	20' eave height		490	.114		7.15	5.90	3.08	16.13	21
1100	24' eave height		435	.129		7.90	6.65	3.47	18.02	23.50
1200	Clear span tapered beam frame, 26 ga. colored roofing/siding									
1300	30' to 39' wide, 10' eave height	E-2	535	.105	SF Flr.	7.65	5.40	2.82	15.87	20.50
1400	14' eave height		450	.124		8.45	6.45	3.36	18.26	24
1500	16' eave height		415	.135		8.90	7	3.64	19.54	25.50
1600	20' eave height		360	.156		9.80	8.05	4.20	22.05	29
1700	40' wide, 10' eave height		600	.093		6.80	4.83	2.52	14.15	18.35
1800	14' eave height		510	.110		7.55	5.70	2.96	16.21	21
1900	16' eave height		475	.118		7.90	6.10	3.18	17.18	22.50
2000	20' eave height		415	.135		8.70	7	3.64	19.34	25.50
2100	50' to 79' wide, 10' eave height		770	.073		6.40	3.76	1.96	12.12	15.45
2200	14' eave height		675	.083		6.95	4.29	2.24	13.48	17.25
2300	16' eave height		635	.088		7.20	4.56	2.38	14.14	18.20
2400	20' eave height		490	.114		8	5.90	3.08	16.98	22
2410	80' to 100' wide, 10' eave height		935	.060		5.65	3.10	1.62	10.37	13.25
2420	14' eave height		750	.075		6.25	3.86	2.01	12.12	15.55
2430	16' eave height		685	.082		6.50	4.23	2.21	12.94	16.70
2440	20' eave height		560	.100		6.95	5.15	2.70	14.80	19.30
2460	101' to 120' wide, 10' eave height		950	.059		5.20	3.05	1.59	9.84	12.55
2470	14' eave height		770	.073		5.75	3.76	1.96	11.47	14.80
2480	16' eave height		675	.083		6.15	4.29	2.24	12.68	16.40
2490	20' eave height		560	.100		6.55	5.15	2.70	14.40	18.90
2500	Single post 2-span frame, 26 ga. colored roofing and siding									
2600	80' wide, 14' eave height	E-2	740	.076	SF Flr.	5.75	3.92	2.04	11.71	15.10
2700	16' eave height		695	.081		6.10	4.17	2.17	12.44	16.10
2800	20' eave height		625	.090		6.60	4.64	2.42	13.66	17.70
2900	24' eave height		570	.098		7.25	5.10	2.65	15	19.40
3000	100' wide, 14' eave height		835	.067		5.60	3.47	1.81	10.88	13.95
3100	16' eave height		795	.070		5.20	3.64	1.90	10.74	13.95
3200	20' eave height		730	.077		6.30	3.97	2.07	12.34	15.90
3300	24' eave height		670	.084		7	4.32	2.26	13.58	17.45
3400	120' wide, 14' eave height		870	.064		6.45	3.33	1.74	11.52	14.60
3500	16' eave height		830	.067		5.80	3.49	1.82	11.11	14.20
3600	20' eave height		765	.073		6.30	3.79	1.97	12.06	15.45
3700	24' eave height		705	.079		6.90	4.11	2.14	13.15	16.85
3800	Double post 3-span frame, 26 ga. colored roofing and siding									
3900	150' wide, 14' eave height	E-2	925	.061	SF Flr.	4.57	3.13	1.63	9.33	12.10
4000	16' eave height		890	.063		4.77	3.26	1.70	9.73	12.55
4100	20' eave height		820	.068		5.20	3.53	1.84	10.57	13.70
4200	24' eave height		765	.073		5.75	3.79	1.97	11.51	14.85
4300	Triple post 4-span frame, 26 ga. colored roofing and siding									
4400	160' wide, 14' eave height	E-2	970	.058	SF Flr.	4.50	2.99	1.56	9.05	11.65
4500	16' eave height		930	.060		4.69	3.12	1.62	9.43	12.20
4600	20' eave height		870	.064		4.62	3.33	1.74	9.69	12.60

13 34 Fabricated Engineered Structures

13 34 19 – Metal Building Systems

13 34 19.50 Pre-Engineered Steel Buildings

		Crew	Daily Output	Labor-Hours	Unit	Material	2015 Bare Costs Labor	Equipment	Total	Total Incl O&P
4700	24' eave height	E-2	815	.069	SF Flr.	5.25	3.56	1.85	10.66	13.80
4800	200' wide, 14' eave height		1030	.054		4.13	2.81	1.47	8.41	10.85
4900	16' eave height		995	.056		4.28	2.91	1.52	8.71	11.25
5000	20' eave height		935	.060		4.72	3.10	1.62	9.44	12.20
5100	24' eave height	▼	885	.063	▼	5.30	3.27	1.71	10.28	13.25
7635	Insulation installation, over the purlin, second layer, up to 4" thick, add						90%			
7640	Insulation installation, between the purlins, up to 4" thick, add						100%			

13 34 23 – Fabricated Structures

13 34 23.15 Domes

		Crew	Daily Output	Labor-Hours	Unit	Material	2015 Bare Costs Labor	Equipment	Total	Total Incl O&P
0010	**DOMES**									
1500	Domes, bulk storage, shell only, dual radius hemisphere, arch, steel									
1600	framing, corrugated steel covering, 150' diameter	E-2	550	.102	SF Flr.	35	5.25	2.75	43	50
1700	400' diameter	"	720	.078		28.50	4.02	2.10	34.62	40
1800	Wood framing, wood decking, to 400' diameter	F-4	400	.120	▼	37.50	5.70	2.82	46.02	53.50
1900	Radial framed wood (2" x 6"), 1/2" thick									
2000	plywood, asphalt shingles, 50' diameter	F-3	2000	.020	SF Flr.	72.50	.96	.33	73.79	81.50
2100	60' diameter		1900	.021		62	1.01	.34	63.35	70
2200	72' diameter		1800	.022		51.50	1.06	.36	52.92	58.50
2300	116' diameter		1730	.023		35	1.11	.38	36.49	40.50
2400	150' diameter	▼	1500	.027	▼	37.50	1.28	.44	39.22	44

13 34 23.16 Fabricated Control Booths

		Crew	Daily Output	Labor-Hours	Unit	Material	2015 Bare Costs Labor	Equipment	Total	Total Incl O&P
0010	**FABRICATED CONTROL BOOTHS**									
0100	Guard House, prefab conc. w/bullet resistant doors & windows, roof & wiring									
0110	8' x 8', Level III	L-10	1	24	Ea.	44,200	1,275	655	46,130	51,500
0120	8' x 8', Level IV	"	1	24	"	50,500	1,275	655	52,430	58,500

13 34 23.25 Garage Costs

		Crew	Daily Output	Labor-Hours	Unit	Material	2015 Bare Costs Labor	Equipment	Total	Total Incl O&P
0010	**GARAGE COSTS**									
0300	Residential, wood, 12' x 20', one car prefab shell, stock, economy	2 Carp	1	16	Total	5,375	750		6,125	7,075
0350	Custom		.67	23.881		5,975	1,125		7,100	8,300
0400	Two car, 24' x 20', economy		.67	23.881		10,100	1,125		11,225	12,800
0450	Custom	▼	.50	32	▼	12,100	1,500		13,600	15,600

13 34 23.30 Garden House

		Crew	Daily Output	Labor-Hours	Unit	Material	2015 Bare Costs Labor	Equipment	Total	Total Incl O&P
0010	**GARDEN HOUSE** Prefab wood, no floors or foundations									
0100	6' x 6'	2 Carp	200	.080	SF Flr.	51.50	3.76		55.26	62.50
0300	8' x 12'	"	48	.333	"	38	15.65		53.65	66

13 34 23.35 Geodesic Domes

		Crew	Daily Output	Labor-Hours	Unit	Material	2015 Bare Costs Labor	Equipment	Total	Total Incl O&P
0010	**GEODESIC DOMES** Shell only, interlocking plywood panels R133423-30									
0400	30' diameter	F-5	1.60	20	Ea.	23,000	950		23,950	26,800
0500	33' diameter		1.14	28.070		24,300	1,325		25,625	28,800
0600	40' diameter		1	32		28,200	1,525		29,725	33,300
0700	45' diameter	F-3	1.13	35.556		29,500	1,700	580	31,780	35,800
0750	56' diameter		1	40		53,000	1,925	655	55,580	62,000
0800	60' diameter		1	40		60,000	1,925	655	62,580	69,500
0850	67' diameter	▼	.80	50	▼	84,500	2,400	820	87,720	97,500
1100	Aluminum panel, with 6" insulation									
1200	100' diameter				SF Flr.	30.50			30.50	33.50
1300	500' diameter				"	29.50			29.50	32.50
1600	Aluminum framed, plexiglass closure panels									
1700	40' diameter				SF Flr.	75.50			75.50	83
1800	200' diameter				"	69.50			69.50	76.50
2100	Aluminum framed, aluminum closure panels									

For customer support on your Site Work & Landscape Cost Data, call 877.737.1594.

207

13 34 23 – Fabricated Structures

13 34 23.35 Geodesic Domes	Crew	Daily Output	Labor-Hours	Unit	Material	2015 Bare Costs Labor	Equipment	Total	Total Incl O&P
2200 40' diameter				SF Flr.	24.50			24.50	27
2300 100' diameter					23.50			23.50	26
2400 200' diameter					23.50			23.50	26
2500 For VRP faced bonded fiberglass insulation, add								10	10
2700 Aluminum framed, fiberglass sandwich panel closure									
2800 6' diameter	2 Carp	150	.107	SF Flr.	33	5		38	44
2900 28' diameter	"	350	.046	"	30	2.15		32.15	36.50

13 34 23.45 Kiosks

	Crew	Daily Output	Labor-Hours	Unit	Material	Labor	Equipment	Total	Total Incl O&P
0010 **KIOSKS**									
0020 Round, advertising type, 5' diameter, 7' high, aluminum wall, illuminated				Ea.	23,500			23,500	25,800
0100 Aluminum wall, non-illuminated					22,500			22,500	24,700
0500 Rectangular, 5' x 9', 7'-6" high, aluminum wall, illuminated					25,500			25,500	28,000
0600 Aluminum wall, non-illuminated					24,000			24,000	26,400

13 34 23.60 Portable Booths

	Crew	Daily Output	Labor-Hours	Unit	Material	Labor	Equipment	Total	Total Incl O&P
0010 **PORTABLE BOOTHS** Prefab. aluminum with doors, windows, ext. roof									
0100 lights wiring & insulation, 15 S.F. building, O.D., painted				S.F.	266			266	293
0300 30 S.F. building					214			214	235
0400 50 S.F. building					169			169	186
0600 80 S.F. building					147			147	161
0700 100 S.F. building					123			123	135
0900 Acoustical booth, 27 Db @ 1,000 Hz, 15 S.F. floor				Ea.	3,550			3,550	3,925
1000 7' x 7'-6", including light & ventilation					7,325			7,325	8,050
1200 Ticket booth, galv. steel, not incl. foundations., 4' x 4'					4,625			4,625	5,100
1300 4' x 6'					6,825			6,825	7,500

13 34 23.70 Shelters

	Crew	Daily Output	Labor-Hours	Unit	Material	Labor	Equipment	Total	Total Incl O&P
0010 **SHELTERS**									
0020 Aluminum frame, acrylic glazing, 3' x 9' x 8' high	2 Sswk	1.14	14.035	Ea.	3,075	740		3,815	4,650
0100 9' x 12' x 8' high	"	.73	21.918	"	7,300	1,150		8,450	10,000

13 34 43 – Aircraft Hangars

13 34 43.50 Hangars

	Crew	Daily Output	Labor-Hours	Unit	Material	Labor	Equipment	Total	Total Incl O&P
0010 **HANGARS** Prefabricated steel T hangars, Galv. steel roof &									
0100 walls, incl. electric bi-folding doors									
0110 not including floors or foundations, 4 unit	E-2	1275	.044	SF Flr.	12.75	2.27	1.19	16.21	19.15
0130 8 unit	"	1063	.053	"	11.60	2.73	1.42	15.75	18.90
1200 Alternate pricing method:									
1300 Galv. roof and walls, electric bi-folding doors, 4 plane	E-2	1.06	52.830	Plane	16,900	2,725	1,425	21,050	24,800
1500 8 plane		.91	61.538		13,800	3,175	1,650	18,625	22,400
1600 With bottom rolling doors, 4 plane		1.25	44.800		15,600	2,325	1,200	19,125	22,300
1800 8 plane		.97	57.732		12,600	2,975	1,550	17,125	20,600

13 34 53 – Agricultural Structures

13 34 53.50 Silos

	Crew	Daily Output	Labor-Hours	Unit	Material	Labor	Equipment	Total	Total Incl O&P
0010 **SILOS**									
0500 Steel, factory fab., 30,000 gallon cap., painted, economy	L-5	1	56	Ea.	22,100	2,950	735	25,785	30,200
0700 Deluxe	"	.50	112	"	35,100	5,925	1,475	42,500	50,500

13 47 Facility Protection

13 47 13 – Cathodic Protection

13 47 13.16 Cathodic Prot. for Underground Storage Tanks	Crew	Daily Output	Labor-Hours	Unit	Material	2015 Bare Costs Labor	Equipment	Total	Total Incl O&P
0010 **CATHODIC PROTECTION FOR UNDERGROUND STORAGE TANKS**									
1000 Anodes, magnesium type, 9 #	R-15	18.50	2.595	Ea.	41.50	140	16.30	197.80	273
1010 17 #		13	3.692		71.50	199	23	293.50	400
1020 32 #		10	4.800		124	258	30	412	555
1030 48 #	▼	7.20	6.667		164	360	42	566	765
1100 Graphite type w/epoxy cap, 3" x 60" (32 #)	R-22	8.40	4.438		128	206		334	455
1110 4" x 80" (68 #)		6	6.213		241	289		530	705
1120 6" x 72" (80 #)		5.20	7.169		1,500	335		1,835	2,150
1130 6" x 36" (45 #)	▼	9.60	3.883		760	181		941	1,100
2000 Rectifiers, silicon type, air cooled, 28 V/10 A	R-19	3.50	5.714		2,300	315		2,615	3,025
2010 20 V/20 A		3.50	5.714		2,375	315		2,690	3,075
2100 Oil immersed, 28 V/10 A		3	6.667		3,175	365		3,540	4,025
2110 20 V/20 A	▼	3	6.667	▼	3,175	365		3,540	4,050
3000 Anode backfill, coke breeze	R-22	3850	.010	Lb.	.22	.45		.67	.92
4000 Cable, HMWPE, No. 8		2.40	15.533	M.L.F.	500	720		1,220	1,650
4010 No. 6		2.40	15.533		745	720		1,465	1,925
4020 No. 4		2.40	15.533		1,125	720		1,845	2,350
4030 No. 2		2.40	15.533		1,750	720		2,470	3,025
4040 No. 1		2.20	16.945		2,400	790		3,190	3,850
4050 No. 1/0		2.20	16.945		2,975	790		3,765	4,475
4060 No. 2/0		2.20	16.945		4,625	790		5,415	6,300
4070 No. 4/0	▼	2	18.640	▼	6,000	865		6,865	7,925
5000 Test station, 7 terminal box, flush curb type w/lockable cover	R-19	12	1.667	Ea.	71.50	91.50		163	216
5010 Reference cell, 2" dia PVC conduit, cplg., plug, set flush	"	4.80	4.167	"	151	228		379	505

13 53 Meteorological Instrumentation

13 53 09 – Weather Instrumentation

13 53 09.50 Weather Station

	Crew	Daily Output	Labor-Hours	Unit	Material	2015 Bare Costs Labor	Equipment	Total	Total Incl O&P
0010 **WEATHER STATION**									
0020 Remote recording, solar powered, with rain gauge & display, 400 ft range				Ea.	775			775	850
0100 1 mile range				"	1,900			1,900	2,075

For customer support on your Site Work & Landscape Cost Data, call 877.737.1594.

209

Division Notes

	CREW	DAILY OUTPUT	LABOR-HOURS	UNIT	BARE COSTS				TOTAL INCL O&P
					MAT.	LABOR	EQUIP.	TOTAL	

Estimating Tips
22 10 00 Plumbing Piping and Pumps

This subdivision is primarily basic pipe and related materials. The pipe may be used by any of the mechanical disciplines, i.e., plumbing, fire protection, heating, and air conditioning.

Note: CPVC plastic piping approved for fire protection is located in 21 11 13.

- The labor adjustment factors listed in Subdivision 22 01 02.20 apply throughout Divisions 21, 22, and 23. CAUTION: the correct percentage may vary for the same items. For example, the percentage add for the basic pipe installation should be based on the maximum height that the craftsman must install for that particular section. If the pipe is to be located 14' above the floor but it is suspended on threaded rod from beams, the bottom flange of which is 18' high (4' rods), then the height is actually 18' and the add is 20%. The pipe coverer, however, does not have to go above the 14', and so the add should be 10%.

- Most pipe is priced first as straight pipe with a joint (coupling, weld, etc.) every 10' and a hanger usually every 10'. There are exceptions with hanger spacing such as for cast iron pipe (5') and plastic pipe (3 per 10'). Following each type of pipe there are several lines listing sizes and the amount to be subtracted to delete couplings and hangers. This is for pipe that is to be buried or supported together on trapeze hangers. The reason that the couplings are deleted is that these runs are usually long, and frequently longer lengths of pipe are used. By deleting the couplings, the estimator is expected to look up and add back the correct reduced number of couplings.

- When preparing an estimate, it may be necessary to approximate the fittings. Fittings usually run between 25% and 50% of the cost of the pipe. The lower percentage is for simpler runs, and the higher number is for complex areas, such as mechanical rooms.

- For historic restoration projects, the systems must be as invisible as possible, and pathways must be sought for pipes, conduit, and ductwork. While installations in accessible spaces (such as basements and attics) are relatively straightforward to estimate, labor costs may be more difficult to determine when delivery systems must be concealed.

22 40 00 Plumbing Fixtures

- Plumbing fixture costs usually require two lines: the fixture itself and its "rough-in, supply, and waste."

- In the Assemblies Section (Plumbing D2010) for the desired fixture, the System Components Group at the center of the page shows the fixture on the first line. The rest of the list (fittings, pipe, tubing, etc.) will total up to what we refer to in the Unit Price section as "Rough-in, supply, waste, and vent." Note that for most fixtures we allow a nominal 5' of tubing to reach from the fixture to a main or riser.

- Remember that gas- and oil-fired units need venting.

Reference Numbers

Reference numbers are shown in shaded boxes at the beginning of some major classifications. These numbers refer to related items in the Reference Section. The reference information may be an estimating procedure, an alternate pricing method, or technical information.

Note: Not all subdivisions listed here necessarily appear in this publication. ∎

Division 22 – Plumbing

22 01 Operation and Maintenance of Plumbing

22 01 02 – Labor Adjustments

22 01 02.20 Labor Adjustment Factors	Crew	Daily Output	Labor-Hours	Unit	Material	2015 Bare Costs Labor	Equipment	Total	Total Incl O&P
0010 **LABOR ADJUSTMENT FACTORS**, (For Div. 21, 22 and 23) R220102-20									
0100 Labor factors, The below are reasonable suggestions, however									
0110 each project must be evaluated for its own peculiarities, and									
0120 the adjustments be increased or decreased depending on the									
0130 severity of the special conditions.									
1000 Add to labor for elevated installation (Above floor level)									
1080 10' to 14.5' high						10%			
1100 15' to 19.5' high						20%			
1120 20' to 24.5' high						25%			
1140 25' to 29.5' high						35%			
1160 30' to 34.5' high						40%			
1180 35' to 39.5' high						50%			
1200 40' and higher						55%			
2000 Add to labor for crawl space									
2100 3' high						40%			
2140 4' high						30%			
3000 Add to labor for multi-story building									
3100 Add per floor for floors 3 thru 19						2%			
3140 Add per floor for floors 20 and up						4%			
4000 Add to labor for working in existing occupied buildings									
4100 Hospital						35%			
4140 Office building						25%			
4180 School						20%			
4220 Factory or warehouse						15%			
4260 Multi dwelling						15%			
5000 Add to labor, miscellaneous									
5100 Cramped shaft						35%			
5140 Congested area						15%			
5180 Excessive heat or cold						30%			
9000 Labor factors, The above are reasonable suggestions, however									
9010 each project should be evaluated for its own peculiarities.									
9100 Other factors to be considered are:									
9140 Movement of material and equipment through finished areas									
9180 Equipment room									
9220 Attic space									
9260 No service road									
9300 Poor unloading/storage area									
9340 Congested site area/heavy traffic									

22 05 Common Work Results for Plumbing

22 05 05 – Selective Demolition for Plumbing

22 05 05.10 Plumbing Demolition

	Crew	Daily Output	Labor-Hours	Unit	Material	2015 Bare Costs Labor	Equipment	Total	Total Incl O&P
0010 **PLUMBING DEMOLITION**									
1020 Fixtures, including 10' piping									
1100 Bathtubs, cast iron	1 Plum	4	2	Ea.		117		117	177
1120 Fiberglass		6	1.333			78.50		78.50	118
1140 Steel		5	1.600			94		94	142
1200 Lavatory, wall hung		10	.800			47		47	71
1220 Counter top		8	1			58.50		58.50	88.50
1300 Sink, single compartment		8	1			58.50		58.50	88.50
1320 Double compartment		7	1.143			67		67	101

22 05 Common Work Results for Plumbing

22 05 05 – Selective Demolition for Plumbing

22 05 05.10 Plumbing Demolition		Crew	Daily Output	Labor-Hours	Unit	Material	2015 Bare Costs Labor	Equipment	Total	Total Incl O&P
1400	Water closet, floor mounted	1 Plum	8	1	Ea.		58.50		58.50	88.50
1420	Wall mounted		7	1.143			67		67	101
1500	Urinal, floor mounted		4	2			117		117	177
1520	Wall mounted		7	1.143			67		67	101
1600	Water fountains, free standing		8	1			58.50		58.50	88.50
1620	Wall or deck mounted		6	1.333			78.50		78.50	118
2000	Piping, metal, up thru 1-1/2" diameter		200	.040	L.F.		2.35		2.35	3.55
2050	2" thru 3-1/2" diameter		150	.053			3.13		3.13	4.73
2100	4" thru 6" diameter	2 Plum	100	.160			9.40		9.40	14.20
2150	8" thru 14" diameter	"	60	.267			15.65		15.65	23.50
2153	16" thru 20" diameter	Q-18	70	.343			19.10	.82	19.92	30
2155	24" thru 26" diameter		55	.436			24.50	1.05	25.55	37.50
2156	30" thru 36" diameter		40	.600			33.50	1.44	34.94	52
2160	Plastic pipe with fittings, up thru 1-1/2" diameter	1 Plum	250	.032			1.88		1.88	2.84
2162	2" thru 3" diameter	"	200	.040			2.35		2.35	3.55
2164	4" thru 6" diameter	Q-1	200	.080			4.23		4.23	6.40
2166	8" thru 14" diameter		150	.107			5.65		5.65	8.50
2168	16" diameter		100	.160			8.45		8.45	12.75
2212	Deduct for salvage, aluminum scrap				Ton				700	770
2214	Brass scrap								2,450	2,675
2216	Copper scrap								3,200	3,525
2218	Lead scrap								520	570
2220	Steel scrap								180	200
2250	Water heater, 40 gal.	1 Plum	6	1.333	Ea.		78.50		78.50	118

22 05 23 – General-Duty Valves for Plumbing Piping

22 05 23.20 Valves, Bronze

		Crew	Daily Output	Labor-Hours	Unit	Material	Labor	Equipment	Total	Total Incl O&P
0010	**VALVES, BRONZE** R220523-80									
1020	Angle, 150 lb., rising stem, threaded									
1030	1/8"	1 Plum	24	.333	Ea.	128	19.55		147.55	170
1040	1/4"		24	.333		128	19.55		147.55	170
1050	3/8"		24	.333		130	19.55		149.55	173
1060	1/2"		22	.364		142	21.50		163.50	188
1070	3/4"		20	.400		193	23.50		216.50	249
1080	1"		19	.421		279	24.50		303.50	345
1100	1-1/2"		13	.615		470	36		506	570
1110	2"		11	.727		755	42.50		797.50	895
1750	Check, swing, class 150, regrinding disc, threaded									
1800	1/8"	1 Plum	24	.333	Ea.	66.50	19.55		86.05	103
1830	1/4"		24	.333		66.50	19.55		86.05	103
1840	3/8"		24	.333		70.50	19.55		90.05	107
1850	1/2"		24	.333		75.50	19.55		95.05	113
1860	3/4"		20	.400		100	23.50		123.50	146
1870	1"		19	.421		144	24.50		168.50	196
1880	1-1/4"		15	.533		208	31.50		239.50	277
1890	1-1/2"		13	.615		242	36		278	320
1900	2"		11	.727		355	42.50		397.50	455
1910	2-1/2"	Q-1	15	1.067		800	56.50		856.50	965
2000	For 200 lb., add					5%	10%			
2040	For 300 lb., add					15%	15%			
2850	Gate, N.R.S., soldered, 125 psi									
2900	3/8"	1 Plum	24	.333	Ea.	61	19.55		80.55	96.50
2920	1/2"		24	.333		54	19.55		73.55	89

For customer support on your Site Work & Landscape Cost Data, call 877.737.1594.

213

22 05 23.20 Valves, Bronze		Crew	Daily Output	Labor-Hours	Unit	Material	2015 Bare Costs Labor	2015 Bare Costs Equipment	Total	Total Incl O&P
2940	3/4"	1 Plum	20	.400	Ea.	63.50	23.50		87	106
2950	1"		19	.421		76.50	24.50		101	122
2960	1-1/4"		15	.533		126	31.50		157.50	187
2970	1-1/2"		13	.615		142	36		178	212
2980	2"		11	.727		185	42.50		227.50	269
2990	2-1/2"	Q-1	15	1.067		450	56.50		506.50	580
3000	3"	"	13	1.231		560	65		625	715
3850	Rising stem, soldered, 300 psi									
3950	1"	1 Plum	19	.421	Ea.	179	24.50		203.50	235
3980	2"	"	11	.727		480	42.50		522.50	595
4000	3"	Q-1	13	1.231		1,575	65		1,640	1,850
4250	Threaded, class 150									
4310	1/4"	1 Plum	24	.333	Ea.	68.50	19.55		88.05	105
4320	3/8"		24	.333		68.50	19.55		88.05	105
4330	1/2"		24	.333		63	19.55		82.55	98.50
4340	3/4"		20	.400		73.50	23.50		97	116
4350	1"		19	.421		98.50	24.50		123	146
4360	1-1/4"		15	.533		134	31.50		165.50	195
4370	1-1/2"		13	.615		169	36		205	240
4380	2"		11	.727		227	42.50		269.50	315
4390	2-1/2"	Q-1	15	1.067		530	56.50		586.50	670
4400	3"	"	13	1.231		740	65		805	910
4500	For 300 psi, threaded, add					100%	15%			
4540	For chain operated type, add					15%				
4850	Globe, class 150, rising stem, threaded									
4920	1/4"	1 Plum	24	.333	Ea.	97	19.55		116.55	136
4940	3/8"		24	.333		95.50	19.55		115.05	135
4950	1/2"		24	.333		95.50	19.55		115.05	135
4960	3/4"		20	.400		99	23.50		122.50	145
4970	1"		19	.421		154	24.50		178.50	207
4980	1-1/4"		15	.533		245	31.50		276.50	315
4990	1-1/2"		13	.615		320	36		356	410
5000	2"		11	.727		465	42.50		507.50	580
5010	2-1/2"	Q-1	15	1.067		1,175	56.50		1,231.50	1,350
5020	3"	"	13	1.231		1,675	65		1,740	1,925
5120	For 300 lb. threaded, add					50%	15%			
5600	Relief, pressure & temperature, self-closing, ASME, threaded									
5640	3/4"	1 Plum	28	.286	Ea.	253	16.75		269.75	305
5650	1"		24	.333		405	19.55		424.55	475
5660	1-1/4"		20	.400		895	23.50		918.50	1,025
5670	1-1/2"		18	.444		1,250	26		1,276	1,425
5680	2"		16	.500		1,350	29.50		1,379.50	1,550
5950	Pressure, poppet type, threaded									
6000	1/2"	1 Plum	30	.267	Ea.	78.50	15.65		94.15	110
6040	3/4"	"	28	.286	"	73.50	16.75		90.25	106
6400	Pressure, water, ASME, threaded									
6440	3/4"	1 Plum	28	.286	Ea.	116	16.75		132.75	153
6450	1"		24	.333		260	19.55		279.55	315
6460	1-1/4"		20	.400		390	23.50		413.50	465
6470	1-1/2"		18	.444		570	26		596	665
6480	2"		16	.500		820	29.50		849.50	950
6490	2-1/2"		15	.533		3,150	31.50		3,181.50	3,525
6900	Reducing, water pressure									

214

For customer support on your Site Work & Landscape Cost Data, call 877.737.1594.

22 05 Common Work Results for Plumbing

22 05 23 – General-Duty Valves for Plumbing Piping

22 05 23.20 Valves, Bronze		Crew	Daily Output	Labor-Hours	Unit	Material	2015 Bare Costs Labor	Equipment	Total	Total Incl O&P
6920	300 psi to 25-75 psi, threaded or sweat									
6940	1/2"	1 Plum	24	.333	Ea.	395	19.55		414.55	465
6950	3/4"		20	.400		405	23.50		428.50	485
6960	1"		19	.421		630	24.50		654.50	730
6970	1-1/4"		15	.533		1,100	31.50		1,131.50	1,250
6980	1-1/2"	↓	13	.615	↓	1,650	36		1,686	1,875
8350	Tempering, water, sweat connections									
8400	1/2"	1 Plum	24	.333	Ea.	98	19.55		117.55	138
8440	3/4"	"	20	.400	"	126	23.50		149.50	175
8650	Threaded connections									
8700	1/2"	1 Plum	24	.333	Ea.	126	19.55		145.55	169
8740	3/4"		20	.400		770	23.50		793.50	880
8750	1"		19	.421		865	24.50		889.50	995
8760	1-1/4"		15	.533		1,350	31.50		1,381.50	1,525
8770	1-1/2"		13	.615		1,475	36		1,511	1,650
8780	2"	↓	11	.727	↓	2,200	42.50		2,242.50	2,500

22 05 23.60 Valves, Plastic

22 05 23.60 Valves, Plastic		Crew	Daily Output	Labor-Hours	Unit	Material	2015 Bare Costs Labor	Equipment	Total	Total Incl O&P
0010	**VALVES, PLASTIC**									
1150	Ball, PVC, socket or threaded, true union									
1230	1/2"	1 Plum	26	.308	Ea.	40.50	18.05		58.55	72
1240	3/4"		25	.320		40.50	18.80		59.30	73
1250	1"		23	.348		48	20.50		68.50	84
1260	1-1/4"		21	.381		83.50	22.50		106	126
1270	1-1/2"		20	.400		83.50	23.50		107	128
1280	2"	↓	17	.471		110	27.50		137.50	163
1290	2-1/2"	Q-1	26	.615		188	32.50		220.50	256
1300	3"		24	.667		282	35		317	365
1310	4"	↓	20	.800		450	42.50		492.50	560
1360	For PVC, flanged, add				↓	100%	15%			
3150	Ball check, PVC, socket or threaded									
3200	1/4"	1 Plum	26	.308	Ea.	45.50	18.05		63.55	78
3220	3/8"		26	.308		45.50	18.05		63.55	78
3240	1/2"		26	.308		45.50	18.05		63.55	78
3250	3/4"		25	.320		51	18.80		69.80	84.50
3260	1"		23	.348		64	20.50		84.50	102
3270	1-1/4"		21	.381		107	22.50		129.50	152
3280	1-1/2"		20	.400		107	23.50		130.50	154
3290	2"	↓	17	.471		146	27.50		173.50	203
3310	3"	Q-1	24	.667		405	35		440	500
3320	4"	"	20	.800	↓	575	42.50		617.50	700
3360	For PVC, flanged, add					50%	15%			

22 05 76 – Facility Drainage Piping Cleanouts

22 05 76.10 Cleanouts

22 05 76.10 Cleanouts		Crew	Daily Output	Labor-Hours	Unit	Material	2015 Bare Costs Labor	Equipment	Total	Total Incl O&P
0010	**CLEANOUTS**									
0060	Floor type									
0080	Round or square, scoriated nickel bronze top									
0100	2" pipe size	1 Plum	10	.800	Ea.	197	47		244	288
0120	3" pipe size		8	1		295	58.50		353.50	415
0140	4" pipe size	↓	6	1.333	↓	295	78.50		373.50	445

For customer support on your Site Work & Landscape Cost Data, call 877.737.1594.

215

22 05 76.20 Cleanout Tees	Crew	Daily Output	Labor-Hours	Unit	Material	2015 Bare Costs Labor	Equipment	Total	Total Incl O&P
0010	**CLEANOUT TEES**								
0100	Cast iron, B&S, with countersunk plug								
0200	2" pipe size	1 Plum	4	2	Ea.	267	117		384	470
0220	3" pipe size		3.60	2.222		292	130		422	515
0240	4" pipe size		3.30	2.424		365	142		507	615
0260	5" pipe size	Q-1	5.50	2.909		790	154		944	1,100
0280	6" pipe size	"	5	3.200		980	169		1,149	1,325
0300	8" pipe size	Q-3	5	6.400		1,125	360		1,485	1,775
0500	For round smooth access cover, same price								
0600	For round scoriated access cover, same price								
0700	For square smooth access cover, add				Ea.	60%				
4000	Plastic, tees and adapters. Add plugs								
4010	ABS, DWV								
4020	Cleanout tee, 1-1/2" pipe size	1 Plum	15	.533	Ea.	23	31.50		54.50	72.50
4030	2" pipe size	Q-1	27	.593		25	31.50		56.50	75
4040	3" pipe size		21	.762		47	40.50		87.50	113
4050	4" pipe size		16	1		101	53		154	191
4100	Cleanout plug, 1-1/2" pipe size	1 Plum	32	.250		3.94	14.70		18.64	26.50
4110	2" pipe size	Q-1	56	.286		5.20	15.10		20.30	28.50
4120	3" pipe size		36	.444		8.35	23.50		31.85	44.50
4130	4" pipe size		30	.533		14.65	28		42.65	58.50
4180	Cleanout adapter fitting, 1-1/2" pipe size	1 Plum	32	.250		6.25	14.70		20.95	29
4190	2" pipe size	Q-1	56	.286		9.60	15.10		24.70	33.50
4200	3" pipe size		36	.444		24.50	23.50		48	62.50
4210	4" pipe size		30	.533		45	28		73	92
5000	PVC, DWV								
5010	Cleanout tee, 1-1/2" pipe size	1 Plum	15	.533	Ea.	17.10	31.50		48.60	66.50
5020	2" pipe size	Q-1	27	.593		19.95	31.50		51.45	69.50
5030	3" pipe size		21	.762		35.50	40.50		76	100
5040	4" pipe size		16	1		69.50	53		122.50	157
5090	Cleanout plug, 1-1/2" pipe size	1 Plum	32	.250		4.08	14.70		18.78	26.50
5100	2" pipe size	Q-1	56	.286		4.53	15.10		19.63	28
5110	3" pipe size		36	.444		8.10	23.50		31.60	44.50
5120	4" pipe size		30	.533		11.95	28		39.95	55.50
5130	6" pipe size		24	.667		39	35		74	96
5170	Cleanout adapter fitting, 1-1/2" pipe size	1 Plum	32	.250		5.45	14.70		20.15	28
5180	2" pipe size	Q-1	56	.286		7	15.10		22.10	30.50
5190	3" pipe size		36	.444		19.75	23.50		43.25	57
5200	4" pipe size		30	.533		32.50	28		60.50	78
5210	6" pipe size		24	.667		94.50	35		129.50	157

22 11 13.23 Pipe/Tube, Copper

		Crew	Daily Output	Labor-Hours	Unit	Material	2015 Bare Costs Labor	Equipment	Total	Total Incl O&P
0010	**PIPE/TUBE, COPPER**, Solder joints									
1000	Type K tubing, couplings & clevis hanger assemblies 10' O.C.									
1100	1/4" diameter	1 Plum	84	.095	L.F.	3.71	5.60		9.31	12.55
1120	3/8" diameter		82	.098		4.31	5.75		10.06	13.40
1140	1/2" diameter		78	.103		4.78	6		10.78	14.35
1160	5/8" diameter		77	.104		5.90	6.10		12	15.65
1180	3/4" diameter		74	.108		7.80	6.35		14.15	18.15
1200	1" diameter		66	.121		10.35	7.10		17.45	22
1220	1-1/4" diameter		56	.143		12.20	8.40		20.60	26
1240	1-1/2" diameter		50	.160		15.60	9.40		25	31.50
1260	2" diameter		40	.200		23.50	11.75		35.25	43.50
1280	2-1/2" diameter	Q-1	60	.267		35	14.10		49.10	60
1300	3" diameter	"	54	.296		48	15.65		63.65	76
1950	To delete cplgs. & hngrs., 1/4"-1" pipe, subtract					27%	60%			
1960	1-1/4"-3" pipe, subtract					14%	52%			

22 11 13.25 Pipe/Tube Fittings, Copper

		Crew	Daily Output	Labor-Hours	Unit	Material	2015 Bare Costs Labor	Equipment	Total	Total Incl O&P
0010	**PIPE/TUBE FITTINGS, COPPER**, Wrought unless otherwise noted									
0040	Solder joints, copper x copper									
0070	90° elbow, 1/4"	1 Plum	22	.364	Ea.	3.28	21.50		24.78	35.50
0090	3/8"		22	.364		3.11	21.50		24.61	35.50
0100	1/2"		20	.400		1.10	23.50		24.60	36.50
0110	5/8"		19	.421		2.46	24.50		26.96	40
0120	3/4"		19	.421		2.46	24.50		26.96	40
0130	1"		16	.500		6.05	29.50		35.55	51
0140	1-1/4"		15	.533		9	31.50		40.50	57.50
0150	1-1/2"		13	.615		14.05	36		50.05	70
0160	2"		11	.727		25.50	42.50		68	92.50
0180	3"	Q-1	11	1.455		64.50	77		141.50	187
0200	4"	"	9	1.778		152	94		246	310
0220	6"	Q-2	9	2.667		865	146		1,011	1,175
0250	45° elbow, 1/4"	1 Plum	22	.364		5.90	21.50		27.40	38.50
0270	3/8"		22	.364		5	21.50		26.50	37.50
0280	1/2"		20	.400		2.01	23.50		25.51	37.50
0290	5/8"		19	.421		9.55	24.50		34.05	48
0300	3/4"		19	.421		3.52	24.50		28.02	41.50
0310	1"		16	.500		8.85	29.50		38.35	54
0320	1-1/4"		15	.533		11.85	31.50		43.35	60.50
0340	2"		11	.727		24	42.50		66.50	90.50
0450	Tee, 1/4"		14	.571		6.55	33.50		40.05	57.50
0470	3/8"		14	.571		5.25	33.50		38.75	56.50
0480	1/2"		13	.615		1.87	36		37.87	56.50
0490	5/8"		12	.667		12.05	39		51.05	72.50
0500	3/4"		12	.667		4.51	39		43.51	64
0510	1"		10	.800		13.95	47		60.95	86.50
0520	1-1/4"		9	.889		18.85	52		70.85	99.50
0530	1-1/2"		8	1		29	58.50		87.50	121
0540	2"		7	1.143		45.50	67		112.50	151
0560	3"	Q-1	7	2.286		131	121		252	325
0580	4"	"	5	3.200		320	169		489	605
0600	6"	Q-2	6	4		1,325	219		1,544	1,800
0612	Tee, reducing on the outlet, 1/4"	1 Plum	15	.533		16.45	31.50		47.95	65.50
0613	3/8"		15	.533		15.40	31.50		46.90	64.50

For customer support on your Site Work & Landscape Cost Data, call 877.737.1594.

217

22 11 Facility Water Distribution

22 11 13 – Facility Water Distribution Piping

22 11 13.25 Pipe/Tube Fittings, Copper		Crew	Daily Output	Labor-Hours	Unit	Material	2015 Bare Costs Labor	Equipment	Total	Total Incl O&P
0614	1/2"	1 Plum	14	.571	Ea.	10.05	33.50		43.55	61.50
0615	5/8"		13	.615		32	36		68	90
0616	3/4"		12	.667		6.45	39		45.45	66
0617	1"		11	.727		18.50	42.50		61	85
0618	1-1/4"		10	.800		20.50	47		67.50	93.50
0619	1-1/2"		9	.889		21.50	52		73.50	103
0620	2"	▼	8	1		39	58.50		97.50	132
0621	2-1/2"	Q-1	9	1.778		107	94		201	259
0622	3"		8	2		110	106		216	281
0623	4"		6	2.667		203	141		344	435
0624	5"	▼	5	3.200		1,125	169		1,294	1,500
0625	6"	Q-2	7	3.429		1,550	188		1,738	1,975
0626	8"	"	6	4		5,950	219		6,169	6,875
0630	Tee, reducing on the run, 1/4"	1 Plum	15	.533		13.90	31.50		45.40	63
0631	3/8"		15	.533		19.60	31.50		51.10	69
0632	1/2"		14	.571		11.35	33.50		44.85	63
0633	5/8"		13	.615		19.40	36		55.40	76
0634	3/4"		12	.667		15.15	39		54.15	75.50
0635	1"		11	.727		16.65	42.50		59.15	83
0636	1-1/4"		10	.800		26	47		73	100
0637	1-1/2"		9	.889		46	52		98	130
0638	2"	▼	8	1		59	58.50		117.50	154
0639	2-1/2"	Q-1	9	1.778		152	94		246	310
0640	3"		8	2		202	106		308	380
0641	4"		6	2.667		425	141		566	680
0642	5"	▼	5	3.200		1,075	169		1,244	1,425
0643	6"	Q-2	7	3.429		1,625	188		1,813	2,075
0644	8"	"	6	4		5,950	219		6,169	6,875
0650	Coupling, 1/4"	1 Plum	24	.333		.75	19.55		20.30	30.50
0670	3/8"		24	.333		1	19.55		20.55	30.50
0680	1/2"		22	.364		.83	21.50		22.33	33
0690	5/8"		21	.381		2.50	22.50		25	37
0700	3/4"		21	.381		1.67	22.50		24.17	36
0710	1"		18	.444		5.55	26		31.55	45.50
0715	1-1/4"		17	.471		5.85	27.50		33.35	48
0716	1-1/2"		15	.533		7.70	31.50		39.20	56
0718	2"	▼	13	.615	▼	12.90	36		48.90	68.50

22 11 13.44 Pipe, Steel

		Crew	Daily Output	Labor-Hours	Unit	Material	2015 Bare Costs Labor	Equipment	Total	Total Incl O&P
0010	**PIPE, STEEL** R221113-50									
0020	All pipe sizes are to Spec. A-53 unless noted otherwise									
0050	Schedule 40, threaded, with couplings, and clevis hanger									
0060	assemblies sized for covering, 10' O.C.									
0540	Black, 1/4" diameter	1 Plum	66	.121	L.F.	6.55	7.10		13.65	17.95
0550	3/8" diameter		65	.123		7.30	7.20		14.50	18.95
0560	1/2" diameter		63	.127		3.32	7.45		10.77	14.90
0570	3/4" diameter		61	.131		3.91	7.70		11.61	15.95
0580	1" diameter	▼	53	.151		5.05	8.85		13.90	18.95
0590	1-1/4" diameter	Q-1	89	.180		6.20	9.50		15.70	21
0600	1-1/2" diameter		80	.200		7.10	10.55		17.65	24
0610	2" diameter		64	.250		9	13.20		22.20	30
0620	2-1/2" diameter		50	.320		14	16.90		30.90	41
0630	3" diameter	▼	43	.372	▼	17.80	19.65		37.45	49

For customer support on your Site Work & Landscape Cost Data, call 877.737.1594.

22 11 Facility Water Distribution

22 11 13 – Facility Water Distribution Piping

22 11 13.44 Pipe, Steel

		Crew	Daily Output	Labor-Hours	Unit	Material	2015 Bare Costs Labor	Equipment	Total	Total Incl O&P
0640	3-1/2" diameter	Q-1	40	.400	L.F.	24.50	21		45.50	59
0650	4" diameter		36	.444		27	23.50		50.50	65
1220	To delete coupling & hanger, subtract									
1230	1/4" diam. to 3/4" diam.					31%	56%			
1240	1" diam. to 1-1/2" diam.					23%	51%			
1250	2" diam. to 4" diam.					23%	41%			
1280	All pipe sizes are to Spec. A-53 unless noted otherwise									
1281	Schedule 40, threaded, with couplings and clevis hanger									
1282	assemblies sized for covering, 10' O. C.									
1290	Galvanized, 1/4" diameter	1 Plum	66	.121	L.F.	9.10	7.10		16.20	21
1300	3/8" diameter		65	.123		9.95	7.20		17.15	22
1310	1/2" diameter		63	.127		3.69	7.45		11.14	15.30
1320	3/4" diameter		61	.131		4.24	7.70		11.94	16.30
1330	1" diameter		53	.151		5.75	8.85		14.60	19.70
1340	1-1/4" diameter	Q-1	89	.180		7	9.50		16.50	22
1350	1-1/2" diameter		80	.200		8.05	10.55		18.60	25
1360	2" diameter		64	.250		10.35	13.20		23.55	31.50
1370	2-1/2" diameter		50	.320		16.30	16.90		33.20	43.50
1380	3" diameter		43	.372		20.50	19.65		40.15	52.50
1390	3-1/2" diameter		40	.400		26	21		47	61
1400	4" diameter		36	.444		30	23.50		53.50	68.50
1750	To delete coupling & hanger, subtract									
1760	1/4" diam. to 3/4" diam.					31%	56%			
1770	1" diam. to 1-1/2" diam.					23%	51%			
1780	2" diam. to 4" diam.					23%	41%			

22 11 13.45 Pipe Fittings, Steel, Threaded

		Crew	Daily Output	Labor-Hours	Unit	Material	2015 Bare Costs Labor	Equipment	Total	Total Incl O&P
0010	**PIPE FITTINGS, STEEL, THREADED**									
0020	Cast Iron									
1300	Extra heavy weight, black									
1310	Couplings, steel straight									
1320	1/4"	1 Plum	19	.421	Ea.	3.77	24.50		28.27	41.50
1330	3/8"		19	.421		4.10	24.50		28.60	42
1340	1/2"		19	.421		5.55	24.50		30.05	43.50
1350	3/4"		18	.444		5.90	26		31.90	46
1360	1"		15	.533		7.55	31.50		39.05	56
1370	1-1/4"	Q-1	26	.615		12.10	32.50		44.60	62.50
1380	1-1/2"		24	.667		12.10	35		47.10	66.50
1390	2"		21	.762		18.45	40.50		58.95	81.50
1400	2-1/2"		18	.889		27.50	47		74.50	101
1410	3"		14	1.143		32.50	60.50		93	127
1420	3-1/2"		12	1.333		43.50	70.50		114	154
1430	4"		10	1.600		51.50	84.50		136	185
1510	90° Elbow, straight									
1520	1/2"	1 Plum	15	.533	Ea.	31.50	31.50		63	82.50
1530	3/4"		14	.571		32	33.50		65.50	86
1540	1"		13	.615		39	36		75	97.50
1550	1-1/4"	Q-1	22	.727		58	38.50		96.50	122
1560	1-1/2"		20	.800		72	42.50		114.50	143
1580	2"		18	.889		89	47		136	169
1590	2-1/2"		14	1.143		216	60.50		276.50	330
1600	3"		10	1.600		285	84.50		369.50	445
1610	4"		6	2.667		585	141		726	855

For customer support on your Site Work & Landscape Cost Data, call 877.737.1594.

219

22 11 13 – Facility Water Distribution Piping

22 11 13.45 Pipe Fittings, Steel, Threaded	Crew	Daily Output	Labor-Hours	Unit	Material	2015 Bare Costs Labor	Equipment	Total	Total Incl O&P
1650	45° Elbow, straight									
1660	1/2"	1 Plum	15	.533	Ea.	45	31.50		76.50	97
1670	3/4"		14	.571		43.50	33.50		77	98.50
1680	1"		13	.615		52.50	36		88.50	112
1690	1-1/4"	Q-1	22	.727		86	38.50		124.50	153
1700	1-1/2"		20	.800		95	42.50		137.50	168
1710	2"		18	.889		135	47		182	219
1720	2-1/2"		14	1.143		233	60.50		293.50	345
1800	Tee, straight									
1810	1/2"	1 Plum	9	.889	Ea.	50	52		102	134
1820	3/4"		9	.889		49.50	52		101.50	134
1830	1"		8	1		59.50	58.50		118	154
1840	1-1/4"	Q-1	14	1.143		89	60.50		149.50	189
1850	1-1/2"		13	1.231		115	65		180	224
1860	2"		11	1.455		142	77		219	272
1870	2-1/2"		9	1.778		305	94		399	475
1880	3"		6	2.667		415	141		556	675
1890	4"		4	4		810	211		1,021	1,225
4000	Standard weight, black									
4010	Couplings, steel straight, merchants									
4030	1/4"	1 Plum	19	.421	Ea.	1.01	24.50		25.51	38.50
4040	3/8"		19	.421		1.22	24.50		25.72	39
4050	1/2"		19	.421		1.30	24.50		25.80	39
4060	3/4"		18	.444		1.64	26		27.64	41.50
4070	1"		15	.533		2.31	31.50		33.81	50
4080	1-1/4"	Q-1	26	.615		2.95	32.50		35.45	52.50
4090	1-1/2"		24	.667		3.73	35		38.73	57
4100	2"		21	.762		5.35	40.50		45.85	67
4110	2-1/2"		18	.889		16.75	47		63.75	89.50
4120	3"		14	1.143		23.50	60.50		84	117
4130	3-1/2"		12	1.333		41.50	70.50		112	152
4140	4"		10	1.600		41.50	84.50		126	174
4200	Standard weight, galvanized									
4210	Couplings, steel straight, merchants									
4230	1/4"	1 Plum	19	.421	Ea.	1.16	24.50		25.66	39
4240	3/8"		19	.421		1.49	24.50		25.99	39
4250	1/2"		19	.421		1.58	24.50		26.08	39
4260	3/4"		18	.444		1.99	26		27.99	41.50
4270	1"		15	.533		2.78	31.50		34.28	50.50
4280	1-1/4"	Q-1	26	.615		3.55	32.50		36.05	53
4290	1-1/2"		24	.667		4.41	35		39.41	58
4300	2"		21	.762		6.60	40.50		47.10	68.50
4310	2-1/2"		18	.889		20.50	47		67.50	93.50
4320	3"		14	1.143		27.50	60.50		88	121
4330	3-1/2"		12	1.333		48	70.50		118.50	159
4340	4"		10	1.600		48	84.50		132.50	181
5000	Malleable iron, 150 lb.									
5020	Black									
5040	90° elbow, straight									
5060	1/4"	1 Plum	16	.500	Ea.	4.78	29.50		34.28	50
5070	3/8"		16	.500		4.78	29.50		34.28	50
5080	1/2"		15	.533		3.30	31.50		34.80	51
5090	3/4"		14	.571		3.99	33.50		37.49	55

For customer support on your Site Work & Landscape Cost Data, call 877.737.1594.

22 11 Facility Water Distribution

22 11 13 – Facility Water Distribution Piping

22 11 13.45 Pipe Fittings, Steel, Threaded		Crew	Daily Output	Labor-Hours	Unit	Material	2015 Bare Costs Labor	Equipment	Total	Total Incl O&P
5100	1"	1 Plum	13	.615	Ea.	6.95	36		42.95	62
5110	1-1/4"	Q-1	22	.727		11.45	38.50		49.95	70.50
5120	1-1/2"		20	.800		15.05	42.50		57.55	80.50
5130	2"		18	.889		26	47		73	99.50
5140	2-1/2"		14	1.143		58	60.50		118.50	155
5150	3"		10	1.600		84.50	84.50		169	221
5160	3-1/2"		8	2		232	106		338	415
5170	4"	↓	6	2.667	↓	182	141		323	415
5250	45° elbow, straight									
5270	1/4"	1 Plum	16	.500	Ea.	7.20	29.50		36.70	52.50
5280	3/8"		16	.500		7.20	29.50		36.70	52.50
5290	1/2"		15	.533		5.45	31.50		36.95	53.50
5300	3/4"		14	.571		6.75	33.50		40.25	58
5310	1"	↓	13	.615		8.50	36		44.50	64
5320	1-1/4"	Q-1	22	.727		15.05	38.50		53.55	74.50
5330	1-1/2"		20	.800		18.60	42.50		61.10	84.50
5340	2"		18	.889		28	47		75	102
5350	2-1/2"		14	1.143		81.50	60.50		142	181
5360	3"		10	1.600		188	84.50		272.50	335
5370	3-1/2"		8	2		208	106		314	390
5380	4"	↓	6	2.667	↓	208	141		349	440
5450	Tee, straight									
5470	1/4"	1 Plum	10	.800	Ea.	6.95	47		53.95	78.50
5480	3/8"		10	.800		6.95	47		53.95	78.50
5490	1/2"		9	.889		4.42	52		56.42	84
5500	3/4"		9	.889		6.35	52		58.35	86
5510	1"	↓	8	1		10.85	58.50		69.35	100
5520	1-1/4"	Q-1	14	1.143		17.60	60.50		78.10	110
5530	1-1/2"		13	1.231		22	65		87	122
5540	2"		11	1.455		37.50	77		114.50	157
5550	2-1/2"		9	1.778		80.50	94		174.50	231
5560	3"		6	2.667		119	141		260	345
5570	3-1/2"		5	3.200		275	169		444	555
5580	4"	↓	4	4	↓	286	211		497	635
5650	Coupling									
5670	1/4"	1 Plum	19	.421	Ea.	5.95	24.50		30.45	44
5680	3/8"		19	.421		5.95	24.50		30.45	44
5690	1/2"		19	.421		4.58	24.50		29.08	42.50
5700	3/4"		18	.444		5.35	26		31.35	45.50
5710	1"	↓	15	.533		8	31.50		39.50	56.50
5720	1-1/4"	Q-1	26	.615		10.40	32.50		42.90	60.50
5730	1-1/2"		24	.667		14.05	35		49.05	68.50
5740	2"		21	.762		21	40.50		61.50	84
5750	2-1/2"		18	.889		57.50	47		104.50	134
5760	3"		14	1.143		77.50	60.50		138	177
5770	3-1/2"		12	1.333		156	70.50		226.50	278
5780	4"	↓	10	1.600	↓	156	84.50		240.50	300
6000	For galvanized elbows, tees, and couplings add					20%				

22 11 13.47 Pipe Fittings, Steel

0010	PIPE FITTINGS, STEEL, Flanged, Welded & Special									
0620	Gasket and bolt set, 150#, 1/2" pipe size	1 Plum	20	.400	Ea.	2.75	23.50		26.25	38.50
0622	3/4" pipe size	↓	19	.421	↓	2.90	24.50		27.40	40.50

22 11 13 – Facility Water Distribution Piping

22 11 13.47 Pipe Fittings, Steel	Crew	Daily Output	Labor-Hours	Unit	Material	2015 Bare Costs Labor	Equipment	Total	Total Incl O&P
0624	1" pipe size	1 Plum	18	.444	Ea.	2.96	26		28.96	43
0626	1-1/4" pipe size		17	.471		4.02	27.50		31.52	46
0628	1-1/2" pipe size		15	.533		4.16	31.50		35.66	52
0630	2" pipe size		13	.615		5.95	36		41.95	61
0640	2-1/2" pipe size		12	.667		6.15	39		45.15	66
0650	3" pipe size		11	.727		6.35	42.50		48.85	71.50
0660	3-1/2" pipe size		9	.889		13.05	52		65.05	93.50
0670	4" pipe size		8	1		14.50	58.50		73	104
0680	5" pipe size		7	1.143		18.85	67		85.85	122
0690	6" pipe size		6	1.333		21.50	78.50		100	142
0700	8" pipe size		5	1.600		21.50	94		115.50	166
0710	10" pipe size		4.50	1.778		45	104		149	208
0720	12" pipe size		4.20	1.905		41.50	112		153.50	215
0730	14" pipe size		4	2		40.50	117		157.50	222
0740	16" pipe size		3	2.667		46	157		203	287
0750	18" pipe size		2.70	2.963		88.50	174		262.50	360
0760	20" pipe size		2.30	3.478		144	204		348	470
0780	24" pipe size		1.90	4.211		180	247		427	575

22 11 13.48 Pipe, Fittings and Valves, Steel, Grooved-Joint

		Crew	Daily Output	Labor-Hours	Unit	Material	2015 Bare Costs Labor	Equipment	Total	Total Incl O&P
0010	**PIPE, FITTINGS AND VALVES, STEEL, GROOVED-JOINT**									
0012	Fittings are ductile iron. Steel fittings noted.									
0020	Pipe includes coupling & clevis type hanger assemblies, 10' O.C.									
1000	Schedule 40, black									
1040	3/4" diameter	1 Plum	71	.113	L.F.	5.50	6.60		12.10	16
1050	1" diameter		63	.127		5.30	7.45		12.75	17.05
1060	1-1/4" diameter		58	.138		6.60	8.10		14.70	19.50
1070	1-1/2" diameter		51	.157		7.35	9.20		16.55	22
1080	2" diameter		40	.200		8.70	11.75		20.45	27.50
1090	2-1/2" diameter	Q-1	57	.281		13.65	14.85		28.50	37.50
1100	3" diameter		50	.320		16.75	16.90		33.65	44
1110	4" diameter		45	.356		23.50	18.80		42.30	54.50
1120	5" diameter		37	.432		38	23		61	76.50
1130	6" diameter	Q-2	42	.571		48.50	31.50		80	101
1140	8" diameter		37	.649		78.50	35.50		114	140
1150	10" diameter		31	.774		106	42.50		148.50	181
1160	12" diameter		27	.889		118	48.50		166.50	204
1740	To delete coupling & hanger, subtract									
1750	3/4" diam. to 2" diam.					65%	27%			
1760	2-1/2" diam. to 5" diam.					41%	18%			
1770	6" diam. to 12" diam.					31%	13%			
1780	14" diam. to 24" diam.					35%	10%			
1800	Galvanized									
1840	3/4" diameter	1 Plum	71	.113	L.F.	5.80	6.60		12.40	16.35
1850	1" diameter		63	.127		7	7.45		14.45	18.95
1860	1-1/4" diameter		58	.138		8.95	8.10		17.05	22
1870	1-1/2" diameter		51	.157		10.10	9.20		19.30	25
1880	2" diameter		40	.200		12.50	11.75		24.25	31.50
1890	2-1/2" diameter	Q-1	57	.281		17.60	14.85		32.45	42
1900	3" diameter		50	.320		22.50	16.90		39.40	50
1910	4" diameter		45	.356		32	18.80		50.80	63.50
1920	5" diameter		37	.432		60	23		83	100
1930	6" diameter	Q-2	42	.571		64.50	31.50		96	119

22 11 13 – Facility Water Distribution Piping

22 11 13.48 Pipe, Fittings and Valves, Steel, Grooved-Joint		Crew	Daily Output	Labor-Hours	Unit	Material	2015 Bare Costs Labor	Equipment	Total	Total Incl O&P
1940	8" diameter	Q-2	37	.649	L.F.	76	35.50		111.50	137
1950	10" diameter		31	.774		122	42.50		164.50	198
1960	12" diameter		27	.889		148	48.50		196.50	237
2540	To delete coupling & hanger, subtract									
2550	3/4" diam. to 2" diam.					36%	27%			
2560	2-1/2" diam. to 5" diam.					19%	18%			
2570	6" diam. to 12" diam.					14%	13%			
4690	Tee, painted									
4700	3/4" diameter	1 Plum	38	.211	Ea.	64.50	12.35		76.85	89.50
4740	1" diameter		33	.242		50	14.25		64.25	76.50
4750	1-1/4" diameter		27	.296		50	17.40		67.40	81.50
4760	1-1/2" diameter		22	.364		50	21.50		71.50	87
4770	2" diameter		17	.471		50	27.50		77.50	96.50
4780	2-1/2" diameter	Q-1	27	.593		50	31.50		81.50	103
4790	3" diameter		22	.727		68	38.50		106.50	133
4800	4" diameter		17	.941		103	49.50		152.50	189
4810	5" diameter		13	1.231		241	65		306	365
4820	6" diameter	Q-2	17	1.412		278	77.50		355.50	420
4830	8" diameter		14	1.714		610	94		704	810
4840	10" diameter		12	2		1,225	110		1,335	1,525
4850	12" diameter		10	2.400		1,700	131		1,831	2,075
4900	For galvanized tees, add					24%				
4939	Couplings									
4940	Flexible, standard, painted									
4950	3/4" diameter	1 Plum	100	.080	Ea.	17.80	4.70		22.50	26.50
4960	1" diameter		100	.080		17.80	4.70		22.50	26.50
4970	1-1/4" diameter		80	.100		23.50	5.85		29.35	34.50
4980	1-1/2" diameter		67	.119		25.50	7		32.50	38.50
4990	2" diameter		50	.160		27	9.40		36.40	44
5000	2-1/2" diameter	Q-1	80	.200		31.50	10.55		42.05	51
5010	3" diameter		67	.239		35	12.60		47.60	57.50
5020	3-1/2" diameter		57	.281		50	14.85		64.85	77.50
5030	4" diameter		50	.320		50.50	16.90		67.40	81
5040	5" diameter		40	.400		76.50	21		97.50	117
5050	6" diameter	Q-2	50	.480		90.50	26.50		117	139
5070	8" diameter		42	.571		147	31.50		178.50	210
5090	10" diameter		35	.686		240	37.50		277.50	320
5110	12" diameter		32	.750		272	41		313	360
5200	For galvanized couplings, add					33%				
5750	Flange, w/groove gasket, black steel									
5754	See Line 22 11 13.47 0620 for gasket & bolt set									
5760	ANSI class 125 and 150, painted									
5780	2" pipe size	1 Plum	23	.348	Ea.	106	20.50		126.50	148
5790	2-1/2" pipe size	Q-1	37	.432		132	23		155	180
5800	3" pipe size		31	.516		142	27.50		169.50	197
5820	4" pipe size		23	.696		189	37		226	264
5830	5" pipe size		19	.842		220	44.50		264.50	310
5840	6" pipe size	Q-2	23	1.043		240	57		297	350
5850	8" pipe size		17	1.412		271	77.50		348.50	415
5860	10" pipe size		14	1.714		430	94		524	610
5870	12" pipe size		12	2		560	110		670	780
8000	Butterfly valve, 2 position handle, with standard trim									
8010	1-1/2" pipe size	1 Plum	50	.160	Ea.	257	9.40		266.40	297

22 11 13.48 Pipe, Fittings and Valves, Steel, Grooved-Joint	Crew	Daily Output	Labor-Hours	Unit	Material	2015 Bare Costs Labor	Equipment	Total	Total Incl O&P
8020	2" pipe size	1 Plum	38	.211	Ea.	257	12.35		269.35	300
8030	3" pipe size	Q-1	50	.320		370	16.90		386.90	430
8050	4" pipe size	"	38	.421		405	22		427	480
8070	6" pipe size	Q-2	38	.632		820	34.50		854.50	955
8080	8" pipe size		27	.889		1,100	48.50		1,148.50	1,300
8090	10" pipe size		20	1.200		1,800	65.50		1,865.50	2,100
8200	With stainless steel trim									
8240	1-1/2" pipe size	1 Plum	50	.160	Ea.	325	9.40		334.40	375
8250	2" pipe size	"	38	.211		325	12.35		337.35	380
8270	3" pipe size	Q-1	50	.320		440	16.90		456.90	505
8280	4" pipe size	"	38	.421		475	22		497	560
8300	6" pipe size	Q-2	38	.632		890	34.50		924.50	1,025
8310	8" pipe size		27	.889		2,200	48.50		2,248.50	2,500
8320	10" pipe size		20	1.200		3,675	65.50		3,740.50	4,125
9000	Cut one groove, labor									
9010	3/4" pipe size	Q-1	152	.105	Ea.		5.55		5.55	8.40
9020	1" pipe size		140	.114			6.05		6.05	9.10
9030	1-1/4" pipe size		124	.129			6.80		6.80	10.30
9040	1-1/2" pipe size		114	.140			7.40		7.40	11.20
9050	2" pipe size		104	.154			8.15		8.15	12.25
9060	2-1/2" pipe size		96	.167			8.80		8.80	13.30
9070	3" pipe size		88	.182			9.60		9.60	14.50
9080	3-1/2" pipe size		83	.193			10.20		10.20	15.40
9090	4" pipe size		78	.205			10.85		10.85	16.35
9100	5" pipe size		72	.222			11.75		11.75	17.75
9110	6" pipe size		70	.229			12.10		12.10	18.25
9120	8" pipe size		54	.296			15.65		15.65	23.50
9130	10" pipe size		38	.421			22		22	33.50
9140	12" pipe size		30	.533			28		28	42.50
9210	Roll one groove									
9220	3/4" pipe size	Q-1	266	.060	Ea.		3.18		3.18	4.80
9230	1" pipe size		228	.070			3.71		3.71	5.60
9240	1-1/4" pipe size		200	.080			4.23		4.23	6.40
9250	1-1/2" pipe size		178	.090			4.75		4.75	7.15
9260	2" pipe size		116	.138			7.30		7.30	11
9270	2-1/2" pipe size		110	.145			7.70		7.70	11.60
9280	3" pipe size		100	.160			8.45		8.45	12.75
9290	3-1/2" pipe size		94	.170			9		9	13.60
9300	4" pipe size		86	.186			9.85		9.85	14.85
9310	5" pipe size		84	.190			10.05		10.05	15.20
9320	6" pipe size		80	.200			10.55		10.55	15.95
9330	8" pipe size		66	.242			12.80		12.80	19.35
9340	10" pipe size		58	.276			14.55		14.55	22
9350	12" pipe size		46	.348			18.40		18.40	28

22 11 13.74 Pipe, Plastic

		Crew	Daily Output	Labor-Hours	Unit	Material	2015 Bare Costs Labor	Equipment	Total	Total Incl O&P
0010	**PIPE, PLASTIC**									
0020	Fiberglass reinforced, couplings 10' O.C., clevis hanger assy's, 3 per 10'									
0080	General service									
0120	2" diameter	Q-1	59	.271	L.F.	12.55	14.35		26.90	35.50
0140	3" diameter		52	.308		16.10	16.25		32.35	42.50
0150	4" diameter		48	.333		21	17.60		38.60	49.50
0160	6" diameter		39	.410		35.50	21.50		57	72

22 11 Facility Water Distribution

22 11 13 – Facility Water Distribution Piping

22 11 13.74 Pipe, Plastic		Crew	Daily Output	Labor-Hours	Unit	Material	2015 Bare Costs Labor	Equipment	Total	Total Incl O&P
0170	8" diameter	Q-2	49	.490	L.F.	55	27		82	101
0180	10" diameter		41	.585		80	32		112	137
0190	12" diameter	↓	36	.667	↓	103	36.50		139.50	168
1800	PVC, couplings 10' O.C., clevis hanger assemblies, 3 per 10'									
1820	Schedule 40									
1860	1/2" diameter	1 Plum	54	.148	L.F.	4.88	8.70		13.58	18.50
1870	3/4" diameter		51	.157		5.20	9.20		14.40	19.65
1880	1" diameter		46	.174		5.85	10.20		16.05	22
1890	1-1/4" diameter		42	.190		6.55	11.20		17.75	24
1900	1-1/2" diameter	↓	36	.222		6.85	13.05		19.90	27.50
1910	2" diameter	Q-1	59	.271		8.05	14.35		22.40	30.50
1920	2-1/2" diameter		56	.286		10.35	15.10		25.45	34.50
1930	3" diameter		53	.302		12.60	15.95		28.55	38
1940	4" diameter		48	.333		16.10	17.60		33.70	44
1950	5" diameter		43	.372		26.50	19.65		46.15	58.50
1960	6" diameter	↓	39	.410	↓	27.50	21.50		49	62.50
2340	To delete coupling & hangers, subtract									
2360	1/2" diam. to 1-1/4" diam.					65%	74%			
2370	1-1/2" diam. to 6" diam.					44%	57%			
4100	DWV type, schedule 40, couplings 10' O.C., clevis hanger assy's, 3 per 10'									
4210	ABS, schedule 40, foam core type									
4212	Plain end black									
4214	1-1/2" diameter	1 Plum	39	.205	L.F.	5.20	12.05		17.25	24
4216	2" diameter	Q-1	62	.258		5.60	13.65		19.25	26.50
4218	3" diameter		56	.286		8	15.10		23.10	32
4220	4" diameter		51	.314		10.20	16.55		26.75	36
4222	6" diameter	↓	42	.381	↓	18	20		38	50.50
4240	To delete coupling & hangers, subtract									
4244	1-1/2" diam. to 6" diam.					43%	48%			
4400	PVC									
4410	1-1/4" diameter	1 Plum	42	.190	L.F.	5.35	11.20		16.55	23
4420	1-1/2" diameter	"	36	.222		5.30	13.05		18.35	25.50
4460	2" diameter	Q-1	59	.271		5.65	14.35		20	27.50
4470	3" diameter		53	.302		8.05	15.95		24	33
4480	4" diameter		48	.333		10	17.60		27.60	37.50
4490	6" diameter	↓	39	.410	↓	16.40	21.50		37.90	50.50
4510	To delete coupling & hangers, subtract									
4520	1-1/4" diam. to 1-1/2" diam.					48%	60%			
4530	2" diam. to 8" diam.					42%	54%			
5300	CPVC, socket joint, couplings 10' O.C., clevis hanger assemblies, 3 per 10'									
5302	Schedule 40									
5304	1/2" diameter	1 Plum	54	.148	L.F.	5.90	8.70		14.60	19.65
5305	3/4" diameter		51	.157		6.75	9.20		15.95	21.50
5306	1" diameter		46	.174		8.10	10.20		18.30	24.50
5307	1-1/4" diameter		42	.190		9.65	11.20		20.85	27.50
5308	1-1/2" diameter	↓	36	.222		10.85	13.05		23.90	31.50
5309	2" diameter	Q-1	59	.271		12.85	14.35		27.20	35.50
5310	2-1/2" diameter		56	.286		19.90	15.10		35	45
5311	3" diameter	↓	53	.302	↓	23.50	15.95		39.45	50
5318	To delete coupling & hangers, subtract									
5319	1/2" diam. to 3/4" diam.					37%	77%			
5320	1" diam. to 1-1/4" diam.					27%	70%			
5321	1-1/2" diam. to 3" diam.					21%	57%			

22 11 13.74 Pipe, Plastic

		Crew	Daily Output	Labor-Hours	Unit	Material	2015 Bare Costs Labor	Equipment	Total	Total Incl O&P
5360	CPVC, threaded, couplings 10' O.C., clevis hanger assemblies, 3 per 10'									
5380	Schedule 40									
5460	1/2" diameter	1 Plum	54	.148	L.F.	6.70	8.70		15.40	20.50
5470	3/4" diameter		51	.157		8.15	9.20		17.35	23
5480	1" diameter		46	.174		9.55	10.20		19.75	26
5490	1-1/4" diameter		42	.190		10.80	11.20		22	29
5500	1-1/2" diameter		36	.222		11.80	13.05		24.85	32.50
5510	2" diameter	Q-1	59	.271		14	14.35		28.35	37
5520	2-1/2" diameter		56	.286		21	15.10		36.10	46
5530	3" diameter		53	.302		25.50	15.95		41.45	52
5730	To delete coupling & hangers, subtract									
5740	1/2" diam. to 3/4" diam.					37%	77%			
5750	1" diam. to 1-1/4" diam.					27%	70%			
5760	1-1/2" diam. to 3" diam.					21%	57%			
7280	PEX, flexible, no couplings or hangers									
7282	Note: For labor costs add 25% to the couplings and fittings labor total.									
7300	Non-barrier type, hot/cold tubing rolls									
7310	1/4" diameter x 100'				L.F.	.49			.49	.54
7350	3/8" diameter x 100'					.55			.55	.61
7360	1/2" diameter x 100'					.61			.61	.67
7370	1/2" diameter x 500'					.61			.61	.67
7380	1/2" diameter x 1000'					.61			.61	.67
7400	3/4" diameter x 100'					1.11			1.11	1.22
7410	3/4" diameter x 500'					1.11			1.11	1.22
7420	3/4" diameter x 1000'					1.11			1.11	1.22
7460	1" diameter x 100'					1.90			1.90	2.09
7470	1" diameter x 300'					1.90			1.90	2.09
7480	1" diameter x 500'					1.90			1.90	2.09
7500	1-1/4" diameter x 100'					3.23			3.23	3.55
7510	1-1/4" diameter x 300'					3.23			3.23	3.55
7540	1-1/2" diameter x 100'					4.39			4.39	4.83
7550	1-1/2" diameter x 300'					4.39			4.39	4.83
7596	Most sizes available in red or blue									

22 11 13.76 Pipe Fittings, Plastic

		Crew	Daily Output	Labor-Hours	Unit	Material	2015 Bare Costs Labor	Equipment	Total	Total Incl O&P
0010	**PIPE FITTINGS, PLASTIC**									
0030	Epoxy resin, fiberglass reinforced, general service									
0100	3"	Q-1	20.80	.769	Ea.	113	40.50		153.50	186
0110	4"		16.50	.970		115	51		166	204
0120	6"		10.10	1.584		225	83.50		308.50	375
0130	8"	Q-2	9.30	2.581		415	141		556	670
0140	10"		8.50	2.824		520	155		675	810
0150	12"		7.60	3.158		750	173		923	1,075
0380	Couplings									
0410	2"	Q-1	33.10	.483	Ea.	22.50	25.50		48	63.50
0420	3"		20.80	.769		24.50	40.50		65	88.50
0430	4"		16.50	.970		33	51		84	114
0440	6"		10.10	1.584		78.50	83.50		162	212
0450	8"	Q-2	9.30	2.581		133	141		274	360
0460	10"		8.50	2.824		195	155		350	450
0470	12"		7.60	3.158		262	173		435	550
0473	High corrosion resistant couplings, add					30%				
2100	PVC schedule 80, socket joint									

226

For customer support on your Site Work & Landscape Cost Data, call 877.737.1594.

22 11 13.76 Pipe Fittings, Plastic		Crew	Daily Output	Labor-Hours	Unit	Material	2015 Bare Costs Labor	Equipment	Total	Total Incl O&P
2110	90° elbow, 1/2"	1 Plum	30.30	.264	Ea.	2.48	15.50		17.98	26
2130	3/4"		26	.308		3.17	18.05		21.22	31
2140	1"		22.70	.352		4.95	20.50		25.45	36.50
2150	1-1/4"		20.20	.396		6.85	23.50		30.35	42.50
2160	1-1/2"		18.20	.440		7.30	26		33.30	47
2170	2"	Q-1	33.10	.483		8.85	25.50		34.35	48
2180	3"		20.80	.769		23.50	40.50		64	87
2190	4"		16.50	.970		35.50	51		86.50	117
2200	6"		10.10	1.584		101	83.50		184.50	237
2210	8"	Q-2	9.30	2.581		277	141		418	520
2250	45° elbow, 1/2"	1 Plum	30.30	.264		4.67	15.50		20.17	28.50
2270	3/4"		26	.308		7.15	18.05		25.20	35.50
2280	1"		22.70	.352		10.70	20.50		31.20	43
2290	1-1/4"		20.20	.396		13.60	23.50		37.10	50
2300	1-1/2"		18.20	.440		16.10	26		42.10	56.50
2310	2"	Q-1	33.10	.483		21	25.50		46.50	61.50
2320	3"		20.80	.769		53.50	40.50		94	120
2330	4"		16.50	.970		96	51		147	184
2340	6"		10.10	1.584		121	83.50		204.50	259
2350	8"	Q-2	9.30	2.581		262	141		403	500
2400	Tee, 1/2"	1 Plum	20.20	.396		7	23.50		30.50	42.50
2420	3/4"		17.30	.462		7.35	27		34.35	49
2430	1"		15.20	.526		9.15	31		40.15	56.50
2440	1-1/4"		13.50	.593		25.50	35		60.50	80.50
2450	1-1/2"		12.10	.661		25.50	39		64.50	86.50
2460	2"	Q-1	20	.800		31.50	42.50		74	98.50
2470	3"		13.90	1.151		43	61		104	139
2480	4"		11	1.455		49.50	77		126.50	171
2490	6"		6.70	2.388		169	126		295	375
2500	8"	Q-2	6.20	3.871		395	212		607	750
2510	Flange, socket, 150 lb., 1/2"	1 Plum	55.60	.144		13.60	8.45		22.05	27.50
2514	3/4"		47.60	.168		14.50	9.85		24.35	31
2518	1"		41.70	.192		16.15	11.25		27.40	35
2522	1-1/2"		33.30	.240		16.65	14.10		30.75	40
2526	2"	Q-1	60.60	.264		22.50	13.95		36.45	46
2530	4"		30.30	.528		49	28		77	96
2534	6"		18.50	.865		77	45.50		122.50	154
2538	8"	Q-2	17.10	1.404		138	77		215	267
2550	Coupling, 1/2"	1 Plum	30.30	.264		4.49	15.50		19.99	28.50
2570	3/4"		26	.308		6.05	18.05		24.10	34
2580	1"		22.70	.352		6.25	20.50		26.75	38
2590	1-1/4"		20.20	.396		9.50	23.50		33	45.50
2600	1-1/2"		18.20	.440		10.25	26		36.25	50.50
2610	2"	Q-1	33.10	.483		11	25.50		36.50	50.50
2620	3"		20.80	.769		31	40.50		71.50	95.50
2630	4"		16.50	.970		39	51		90	121
2640	6"		10.10	1.584		84	83.50		167.50	218
2650	8"	Q-2	9.30	2.581		114	141		255	340
2660	10"		8.50	2.824		400	155		555	675
2670	12"		7.60	3.158		450	173		623	755
2700	PVC (white), schedule 40, socket joints									
2810	2"	Q-1	36.40	.440	Ea.	2.89	23		25.89	38
2840	4"	"	18.20	.879	"	18.80	46.50		65.30	90.50

For customer support on your Site Work & Landscape Cost Data, call 877.737.1594.

227

22 11 13.76 Pipe Fittings, Plastic		Crew	Daily Output	Labor-Hours	Unit	Material	2015 Bare Costs Labor	Equipment	Total	Total Incl O&P
4500	DWV, ABS, non pressure, socket joints									
4540	1/4 Bend, 1-1/4"	1 Plum	20.20	.396	Ea.	2.57	23.50		26.07	38
4560	1-1/2"	"	18.20	.440		1.92	26		27.92	41
4570	2"	Q-1	33.10	.483		3.05	25.50		28.55	42
4580	3"	"	20.80	.769		7.70	40.50		48.20	70
4650	1/8 Bend, same as 1/4 Bend									
4800	Tee, sanitary									
4820	1-1/4"	1 Plum	13.50	.593	Ea.	3.42	35		38.42	56.50
4830	1-1/2"	"	12.10	.661		2.92	39		41.92	61.50
4840	2"	Q-1	20	.800		4.52	42.50		47.02	69
4850	3"		13.90	1.151		12.40	61		73.40	106
4860	4"		11	1.455		22	77		99	140
4862	Tee, sanitary, reducing, 2" x 1-1/2"		22	.727		3.94	38.50		42.44	62.50
4864	3" x 2"		15.30	1.046		9.05	55.50		64.55	93.50
4868	4" x 3"		12.10	1.322		20	70		90	127
4870	Combination Y and 1/8 bend									
4872	1-1/2"	1 Plum	12.10	.661	Ea.	7	39		46	66
4874	2"	Q-1	20	.800		7.85	42.50		50.35	72.50
4876	3"		13.90	1.151		18.50	61		79.50	113
4878	4"		11	1.455		35.50	77		112.50	155
4880	3" x 1-1/2"		15.50	1.032		18.05	54.50		72.55	102
4882	4" x 3"		12.10	1.322		28	70		98	136
4900	Wye, 1-1/4"	1 Plum	13.50	.593		3.94	35		38.94	57
4902	1-1/2"	"	12.10	.661		4.49	39		43.49	63.50
4904	2"	Q-1	20	.800		5.85	42.50		48.35	70.50
4906	3"		13.90	1.151		13.80	61		74.80	107
4908	4"		11	1.455		28	77		105	147
4910	6"		6.70	2.388		81	126		207	280
4918	3" x 1-1/2"		15.50	1.032		11.05	54.50		65.55	94.50
4920	4" x 3"		12.10	1.322		22	70		92	130
4922	6" x 4"		6.90	2.319		66.50	123		189.50	259
4930	Double Wye, 1-1/2"	1 Plum	9.10	.879		13.95	51.50		65.45	93.50
4932	2"	Q-1	16.60	.964		16.65	51		67.65	95.50
4934	3"		10.40	1.538		38	81.50		119.50	165
4936	4"		8.25	1.939		74	102		176	237
4940	2" x 1-1/2"		16.80	.952		14.55	50.50		65.05	92
4942	3" x 2"		10.60	1.509		28	79.50		107.50	151
4944	4" x 3"		8.45	1.893		58.50	100		158.50	216
4946	6" x 4"		7.25	2.207		90	117		207	275
4950	Reducer bushing, 2" x 1-1/2"		36.40	.440		1.56	23		24.56	36.50
4952	3" x 1-1/2"		27.30	.586		6.65	31		37.65	54.50
4954	4" x 2"		18.20	.879		12.70	46.50		59.20	84
4956	6" x 4"		11.10	1.441		34.50	76		110.50	153
4960	Couplings, 1-1/2"	1 Plum	18.20	.440		.95	26		26.95	40
4962	2"	Q-1	33.10	.483		1.28	25.50		26.78	40
4963	3"		20.80	.769		3.58	40.50		44.08	65.50
4964	4"		16.50	.970		6.45	51		57.45	84.50
4966	6"		10.10	1.584		27	83.50		110.50	156
4970	2" x 1-1/2"		33.30	.480		2.75	25.50		28.25	41.50
4972	3" x 1-1/2"		21	.762		7.65	40.50		48.15	69.50
4974	4" x 3"		16.70	.958		12.15	50.50		62.65	90
4978	Closet flange, 4"	1 Plum	32	.250		6.65	14.70		21.35	29.50
4980	4" x 3"	"	34	.235		7.55	13.80		21.35	29.50

22 11 13.76 Pipe Fittings, Plastic		Crew	Daily Output	Labor-Hours	Unit	Material	2015 Bare Costs Labor	2015 Bare Costs Equipment	Total	Total Incl O&P
5000	DWV, PVC, schedule 40, socket joints									
5040	1/4 bend, 1-1/4"	1 Plum	20.20	.396	Ea.	5.20	23.50		28.70	40.50
5060	1-1/2"	"	18.20	.440		1.48	26		27.48	40.50
5070	2"	Q-1	33.10	.483		2.33	25.50		27.83	41
5080	3"		20.80	.769		6.85	40.50		47.35	69
5090	4"		16.50	.970		13.05	51		64.05	92
5100	6"		10.10	1.584		46	83.50		129.50	177
5105	8"	Q-2	9.30	2.581		65	141		206	286
5110	1/4 bend, long sweep, 1-1/2"	1 Plum	18.20	.440		3.42	26		29.42	43
5112	2"	Q-1	33.10	.483		3.83	25.50		29.33	42.50
5114	3"		20.80	.769		8.75	40.50		49.25	71
5116	4"		16.50	.970		16.65	51		67.65	96
5150	1/8 bend, 1-1/4"	1 Plum	20.20	.396		3.40	23.50		26.90	38.50
5215	8"	Q-2	9.30	2.581		158	141		299	385
5250	Tee, sanitary 1-1/4"	1 Plum	13.50	.593		5.20	35		40.20	58.50
5254	1-1/2"	"	12.10	.661		2.58	39		41.58	61.50
5255	2"	Q-1	20	.800		3.80	42.50		46.30	68
5256	3"	"	13.90	1.151		10	61		71	103
5374	Coupling, 1-1/4"	1 Plum	20.20	.396		3.15	23.50		26.65	38.50
5376	1-1/2"	"	18.20	.440		.72	26		26.72	40
5378	2"	Q-1	33.10	.483		.95	25.50		26.45	39.50
5380	3"		20.80	.769		3.29	40.50		43.79	65
5390	4"		16.50	.970		5.65	51		56.65	83.50
5450	Solvent cement for PVC, industrial grade, per quart				Qt.	27.50			27.50	30.50
5500	CPVC, Schedule 80, threaded joints									
5540	90° Elbow, 1/4"	1 Plum	32	.250	Ea.	12.15	14.70		26.85	35.50
5560	1/2"		30.30	.264		7.05	15.50		22.55	31.50
5570	3/4"		26	.308		10.55	18.05		28.60	39
5580	1"		22.70	.352		14.80	20.50		35.30	47.50
5590	1-1/4"		20.20	.396		28.50	23.50		52	66.50
5600	1-1/2"		18.20	.440		30.50	26		56.50	73
5610	2"	Q-1	33.10	.483		41	25.50		66.50	83.50
5620	2-1/2"		24.20	.661		128	35		163	193
5630	3"		20.80	.769		137	40.50		177.50	212
5660	45° Elbow same as 90° Elbow									
5700	Tee, 1/4"	1 Plum	22	.364	Ea.	23.50	21.50		45	58
5704	3/4"		17.30	.462		34	27		61	78.50
5706	1"		15.20	.526		36.50	31		67.50	87
5708	1-1/4"		13.50	.593		37	35		72	93
5710	1-1/2"		12.10	.661		38.50	39		77.50	101
5712	2"	Q-1	20	.800		43	42.50		85.50	112
5714	2-1/2"		16.20	.988		211	52		263	310
5716	3"		13.90	1.151		245	61		306	360
5730	Coupling, 1/4"	1 Plum	32	.250		15.45	14.70		30.15	39
5732	1/2"		30.30	.264		12.75	15.50		28.25	37.50
5734	3/4"		26	.308		20.50	18.05		38.55	50
5736	1"		22.70	.352		23.50	20.50		44	57
5738	1-1/4"		20.20	.396		25	23.50		48.50	62
5740	1-1/2"		18.20	.440		26.50	26		52.50	68.50
5742	2"	Q-1	33.10	.483		31.50	25.50		57	73
5744	2-1/2"		24.20	.661		56.50	35		91.50	115
5746	3"		20.80	.769		65.50	40.50		106	134
5900	CPVC, Schedule 80, socket joints									

22 11 13.76 Pipe Fittings, Plastic		Crew	Daily Output	Labor-Hours	Unit	Material	2015 Bare Costs Labor	Equipment	Total	Total Incl O&P
5904	90° Elbow, 1/4"	1 Plum	32	.250	Ea.	11.55	14.70		26.25	34.50
5906	1/2"		30.30	.264		4.53	15.50		20.03	28.50
5908	3/4"		26	.308		5.80	18.05		23.85	34
5910	1"		22.70	.352		9.20	20.50		29.70	41
5912	1-1/4"		20.20	.396		19.85	23.50		43.35	57
5914	1-1/2"		18.20	.440		22	26		48	63.50
5916	2"	Q-1	33.10	.483		26.50	25.50		52	68
5918	2-1/2"		24.20	.661		61.50	35		96.50	121
5920	3"		20.80	.769		69.50	40.50		110	138
5930	45° Elbow, 1/4"	1 Plum	32	.250		17.20	14.70		31.90	41
5932	1/2"		30.30	.264		5.55	15.50		21.05	29.50
5934	3/4"		26	.308		7.95	18.05		26	36.50
5936	1"		22.70	.352		12.75	20.50		33.25	45
5938	1-1/4"		20.20	.396		25	23.50		48.50	62.50
5940	1-1/2"		18.20	.440		25.50	26		51.50	67
5942	2"	Q-1	33.10	.483		29	25.50		54.50	70.50
5944	2-1/2"		24.20	.661		59	35		94	118
5946	3"		20.80	.769		75.50	40.50		116	145
5960	Tee, 1/4"	1 Plum	22	.364		10.60	21.50		32.10	43.50
5964	3/4"		17.30	.462		10.80	27		37.80	53
5966	1"		15.20	.526		13.25	31		44.25	61
5968	1-1/4"		13.50	.593		28	35		63	83
5970	1-1/2"		12.10	.661		32	39		71	93.50
5972	2"	Q-1	20	.800		36	42.50		78.50	104
5974	2-1/2"		16.20	.988		90.50	52		142.50	179
5976	3"		13.90	1.151		90.50	61		151.50	192
5990	Coupling, 1/4"	1 Plum	32	.250		12.30	14.70		27	35.50
5992	1/2"		30.30	.264		4.79	15.50		20.29	29
5994	3/4"		26	.308		6.70	18.05		24.75	35
5996	1"		22.70	.352		9	20.50		29.50	41
5998	1-1/4"		20.20	.396		13.50	23.50		37	50
6000	1-1/2"		18.20	.440		17	26		43	57.50
6002	2"	Q-1	33.10	.483		19.75	25.50		45.25	60
6004	2-1/2"		24.20	.661		44	35		79	102
6006	3"		20.80	.769		47.50	40.50		88	114
6360	Solvent cement for CPVC, commercial grade, per quart				Qt.	45			45	49.50
7340	PVC flange, slip-on, Sch 80 std., 1/2"	1 Plum	22	.364	Ea.	13.60	21.50		35.10	47
7350	3/4"		21	.381		14.50	22.50		37	50
7360	1"		18	.444		16.15	26		42.15	57.50
7370	1-1/4"		17	.471		16.65	27.50		44.15	60
7380	1-1/2"		16	.500		17	29.50		46.50	63
7390	2"	Q-1	26	.615		22.50	32.50		55	74
7400	2-1/2"		24	.667		35	35		70	91.50
7410	3"		18	.889		38.50	47		85.50	114
7420	4"		15	1.067		49	56.50		105.50	139
7430	6"		10	1.600		77	84.50		161.50	213
7440	8"	Q-2	11	2.182		138	120		258	330
7550	Union, schedule 40, socket joints, 1/2"	1 Plum	19	.421		5.20	24.50		29.70	43.50
7560	3/4"		18	.444		5.35	26		31.35	45.50
7570	1"		15	.533		5.55	31.50		37.05	53.50
7580	1-1/4"		14	.571		16.65	33.50		50.15	69
7590	1-1/2"		13	.615		18.60	36		54.60	75
7600	2"	Q-1	20	.800		25	42.50		67.50	91.50

22 11 Facility Water Distribution

22 11 19 – Domestic Water Piping Specialties

22 11 19.38 Water Supply Meters	Crew	Daily Output	Labor-Hours	Unit	Material	2015 Bare Costs Labor	Equipment	Total	Total Incl O&P
0010 **WATER SUPPLY METERS**									
1000 Detector, serves dual systems such as fire and domestic or									
1020 process water, wide range cap., UL and FM approved									
1100 3" mainline x 2" by-pass, 400 GPM	Q-1	3.60	4.444	Ea.	7,450	235		7,685	8,525
1140 4" mainline x 2" by-pass, 700 GPM	"	2.50	6.400		7,450	340		7,790	8,675
1180 6" mainline x 3" by-pass, 1600 GPM	Q-2	2.60	9.231		11,400	505		11,905	13,300
1220 8" mainline x 4" by-pass, 2800 GPM		2.10	11.429		16,900	625		17,525	19,400
1260 10" mainline x 6" by-pass, 4400 GPM		2	12		24,100	655		24,755	27,500
1300 10" x 12" mainlines x 6" by-pass, 5400 GPM		1.70	14.118		32,700	775		33,475	37,200
2000 Domestic/commercial, bronze									
2020 Threaded									
2060 5/8" diameter, to 20 GPM	1 Plum	16	.500	Ea.	50	29.50		79.50	99.50
2080 3/4" diameter, to 30 GPM		14	.571		91	33.50		124.50	151
2100 1" diameter, to 50 GPM		12	.667		138	39		177	211
2300 Threaded/flanged									
2340 1-1/2" diameter, to 100 GPM	1 Plum	8	1	Ea.	340	58.50		398.50	460
2360 2" diameter, to 160 GPM	"	6	1.333	"	460	78.50		538.50	625
2600 Flanged, compound									
2640 3" diameter, 320 GPM	Q-1	3	5.333	Ea.	3,125	282		3,407	3,850
2660 4" diameter, to 500 GPM		1.50	10.667		5,000	565		5,565	6,350
2680 6" diameter, to 1,000 GPM		1	16		7,975	845		8,820	10,000
2700 8" diameter, to 1,800 GPM		.80	20		12,500	1,050		13,550	15,300
7000 Turbine									
7260 Flanged									
7300 2" diameter, to 160 GPM	1 Plum	7	1.143	Ea.	610	67		677	770
7320 3" diameter, to 450 GPM	Q-1	3.60	4.444		1,275	235		1,510	1,750
7340 4" diameter, to 650 GPM	"	2.50	6.400		2,100	340		2,440	2,825
7360 6" diameter, to 1800 GPM	Q-2	2.60	9.231		3,775	505		4,280	4,925
7380 8" diameter, to 2500 GPM		2.10	11.429		5,975	625		6,600	7,525
7400 10" diameter, to 5500 GPM		1.70	14.118		8,075	775		8,850	10,100

22 11 19.42 Backflow Preventers

22 11 19.42 Backflow Preventers	Crew	Daily Output	Labor-Hours	Unit	Material	2015 Bare Costs Labor	Equipment	Total	Total Incl O&P
0010 **BACKFLOW PREVENTERS**, Includes valves									
0020 and four test cocks, corrosion resistant, automatic operation									
1000 Double check principle									
1010 Threaded, with ball valves									
1020 3/4" pipe size	1 Plum	16	.500	Ea.	231	29.50		260.50	299
1030 1" pipe size		14	.571		264	33.50		297.50	340
1040 1-1/2" pipe size		10	.800		560	47		607	690
1050 2" pipe size		7	1.143		655	67		722	820
1080 Threaded, with gate valves									
1100 3/4" pipe size	1 Plum	16	.500	Ea.	1,075	29.50		1,104.50	1,250
1120 1" pipe size		14	.571		1,100	33.50		1,133.50	1,250
1140 1-1/2" pipe size		10	.800		1,400	47		1,447	1,625
1160 2" pipe size		7	1.143		1,725	67		1,792	2,000
1200 Flanged, valves are gate									
1210 3" pipe size	Q-1	4.50	3.556	Ea.	2,800	188		2,988	3,350
1220 4" pipe size	"	3	5.333		2,900	282		3,182	3,625
1230 6" pipe size	Q-2	3	8		4,275	440		4,715	5,350
1240 8" pipe size		2	12		7,775	655		8,430	9,550
1250 10" pipe size		1	24		11,500	1,325		12,825	14,700
1300 Flanged, valves are OS&Y									
1380 3" pipe size	Q-1	4.50	3.556	Ea.	2,875	188		3,063	3,425

22 11 19 – Domestic Water Piping Specialties

22 11 19.42 Backflow Preventers

		Crew	Daily Output	Labor-Hours	Unit	Material	2015 Bare Costs Labor	Equipment	Total	Total Incl O&P
1400	4" pipe size	Q-1	3	5.333	Ea.	3,475	282		3,757	4,250
1420	6" pipe size	Q-2	3	8	↓	5,450	440		5,890	6,650
4000	Reduced pressure principle									
4100	Threaded, bronze, valves are ball									
4120	3/4" pipe size	1 Plum	16	.500	Ea.	445	29.50		474.50	535
4140	1" pipe size		14	.571		480	33.50		513.50	575
4150	1-1/4" pipe size		12	.667		845	39		884	990
4160	1-1/2" pipe size		10	.800		960	47		1,007	1,125
4180	2" pipe size	↓	7	1.143	↓	1,075	67		1,142	1,300
5000	Flanged, bronze, valves are OS&Y									
5060	2-1/2" pipe size	Q-1	5	3.200	Ea.	4,025	169		4,194	4,675
5080	3" pipe size		4.50	3.556		4,650	188		4,838	5,375
5100	4" pipe size	↓	3	5.333		5,500	282		5,782	6,475
5120	6" pipe size	Q-2	3	8	↓	8,750	440		9,190	10,300
5200	Flanged, iron, valves are gate									
5210	2-1/2" pipe size	Q-1	5	3.200	Ea.	2,650	169		2,819	3,175
5220	3" pipe size		4.50	3.556		2,775	188		2,963	3,325
5230	4" pipe size	↓	3	5.333		3,750	282		4,032	4,550
5240	6" pipe size	Q-2	3	8		5,275	440		5,715	6,475
5250	8" pipe size		2	12		9,475	655		10,130	11,400
5260	10" pipe size		1	24	↓	13,400	1,325		14,725	16,700
5600	Flanged, iron, valves are OS&Y									
5660	2-1/2" pipe size	Q-1	5	3.200	Ea.	3,025	169		3,194	3,575
5680	3" pipe size		4.50	3.556		3,175	188		3,363	3,775
5700	4" pipe size	↓	3	5.333		3,975	282		4,257	4,800
5720	6" pipe size	Q-2	3	8		5,775	440		6,215	7,000
5740	8" pipe size		2	12		10,100	655		10,755	12,100
5760	10" pipe size	↓	1	24	↓	13,600	1,325		14,925	16,900

22 11 19.54 Water Hammer Arresters/Shock Absorbers

		Crew	Daily Output	Labor-Hours	Unit	Material	2015 Bare Costs Labor	Equipment	Total	Total Incl O&P
0010	**WATER HAMMER ARRESTERS/SHOCK ABSORBERS**									
0490	Copper									
0500	3/4" male I.P.S. For 1 to 11 fixtures	1 Plum	12	.667	Ea.	28	39		67	90
0600	1" male I.P.S. For 12 to 32 fixtures		8	1		45.50	58.50		104	139
0700	1-1/4" male I.P.S. For 33 to 60 fixtures		8	1		47	58.50		105.50	140
0800	1-1/2" male I.P.S. For 61 to 113 fixtures		8	1		67.50	58.50		126	163
0900	2" male I.P.S. For 114 to 154 fixtures		8	1		98.50	58.50		157	197
1000	2-1/2" male I.P.S. For 155 to 330 fixtures	↓	4	2	↓	305	117		422	510

22 11 19.64 Hydrants

		Crew	Daily Output	Labor-Hours	Unit	Material	2015 Bare Costs Labor	Equipment	Total	Total Incl O&P
0010	**HYDRANTS**									
0050	Wall type, moderate climate, bronze, encased									
0200	3/4" IPS connection	1 Plum	16	.500	Ea.	745	29.50		774.50	860
0300	1" IPS connection		14	.571		850	33.50		883.50	985
0500	Anti-siphon type, 3/4" connection	↓	16	.500	↓	640	29.50		669.50	750
1000	Non-freeze, bronze, exposed									
1100	3/4" IPS connection, 4" to 9" thick wall	1 Plum	14	.571	Ea.	500	33.50		533.50	600
1120	10" to 14" thick wall		•12	.667		545	39		584	660
1140	15" to 19" thick wall		12	.667		605	39		644	725
1160	20" to 24" thick wall	↓	10	.800	↓	640	47		687	775
1200	For 1" IPS connection, add					15%	10%			
1240	For 3/4" adapter type vacuum breaker, add				Ea.	63			63	69.50
1280	For anti-siphon type, add				"	132			132	145
2000	Non-freeze bronze, encased, anti-siphon type									

22 11 Facility Water Distribution

22 11 19 – Domestic Water Piping Specialties

22 11 19.64 Hydrants	Crew	Daily Output	Labor-Hours	Unit	Material	2015 Bare Costs Labor	Equipment	Total	Total Incl O&P
2100	3/4" IPS connection, 5" to 9" thick wall	1 Plum	14	.571	Ea.	1,275	33.50		1,308.50	1,450
2120	10" to 14" thick wall		12	.667		1,300	39		1,339	1,500
2140	15" to 19" thick wall		12	.667		1,375	39		1,414	1,550
2160	20" to 24" thick wall		10	.800		1,425	47		1,472	1,650
2200	For 1" IPS connection, add					10%	10%			
3000	Ground box type, bronze frame, 3/4" IPS connection									
3080	Non-freeze, all bronze, polished face, set flush									
3100	2 feet depth of bury	1 Plum	8	1	Ea.	950	58.50		1,008.50	1,150
3120	3 feet depth of bury		8	1		1,025	58.50		1,083.50	1,225
3140	4 feet depth of bury		8	1		1,075	58.50		1,133.50	1,300
3160	5 feet depth of bury		7	1.143		1,175	67		1,242	1,375
3180	6 feet depth of bury		7	1.143		1,250	67		1,317	1,475
3200	7 feet depth of bury		6	1.333		1,300	78.50		1,378.50	1,575
3220	8 feet depth of bury		5	1.600		1,375	94		1,469	1,675
3240	9 feet depth of bury		4	2		1,450	117		1,567	1,775
3260	10 feet depth of bury		4	2		1,525	117		1,642	1,850
3400	For 1" IPS connection, add					15%	10%			
3450	For 1-1/4" IPS connection, add					325%	14%			
3500	For 1-1/2" connection, add					370%	18%			
3550	For 2" connection, add					445%	24%			
3600	For tapped drain port in box, add					86			86	94.50
4000	Non-freeze, CI body, bronze frame & scoriated cover									
4010	with hose storage									
4100	2 feet depth of bury	1 Plum	7	1.143	Ea.	1,750	67		1,817	2,025
4120	3 feet depth of bury		7	1.143		1,825	67		1,892	2,100
4140	4 feet depth of bury		7	1.143		1,875	67		1,942	2,175
4160	5 feet depth of bury		6.50	1.231		1,925	72.50		1,997.50	2,200
4180	6 feet depth of bury		6	1.333		1,950	78.50		2,028.50	2,275
4200	7 feet depth of bury		5.50	1.455		2,025	85.50		2,110.50	2,350
4220	8 feet depth of bury		5	1.600		2,100	94		2,194	2,450
4240	9 feet depth of bury		4.50	1.778		2,150	104		2,254	2,525
4260	10 feet depth of bury		4	2		2,225	117		2,342	2,625
4280	For 1" IPS connection, add					390			390	425
4300	For tapped drain port in box, add					86			86	94.50
5000	Moderate climate, all bronze, polished face									
5020	and scoriated cover, set flush									
5100	3/4" IPS connection	1 Plum	16	.500	Ea.	655	29.50		684.50	770
5120	1" IPS connection	"	14	.571		810	33.50		843.50	940
5200	For tapped drain port in box, add					86			86	94.50
6000	Ground post type, all non-freeze, all bronze, aluminum casing									
6010	guard, exposed head, 3/4" IPS connection									
6100	2 feet depth of bury	1 Plum	8	1	Ea.	925	58.50		983.50	1,125
6120	3 feet depth of bury		8	1		1,000	58.50		1,058.50	1,200
6140	4 feet depth of bury		8	1		1,075	58.50		1,133.50	1,275
6160	5 feet depth of bury		7	1.143		1,150	67		1,217	1,375
6180	6 feet depth of bury		7	1.143		1,225	67		1,292	1,450
6200	7 feet depth of bury		6	1.333		1,325	78.50		1,403.50	1,575
6220	8 feet depth of bury		5	1.600		1,400	94		1,494	1,700
6240	9 feet depth of bury		4	2		1,500	117		1,617	1,825
6260	10 feet depth of bury		4	2		1,575	117		1,692	1,900
6300	For 1" IPS connection, add					40%	10%			
6350	For 1-1/4" IPS connection, add					140%	14%			
6400	For 1-1/2" IPS connection, add					225%	18%			

22 11 Facility Water Distribution

22 11 19 – Domestic Water Piping Specialties

22 11 19.64 Hydrants	Crew	Daily Output	Labor-Hours	Unit	Material	2015 Bare Costs Labor	Equipment	Total	Total Incl O&P
6450 For 2" IPS connection, add					315%	24%			

22 11 23 – Domestic Water Pumps

22 11 23.10 General Utility Pumps

		Crew	Daily Output	Labor-Hours	Unit	Material	Labor	Equipment	Total	Total Incl O&P
0010	**GENERAL UTILITY PUMPS**									
2000	Single stage									
3000	Double suction,									
3190	75 HP, to 2500 GPM	Q-3	.28	114	Ea.	20,100	6,375		26,475	31,800
3220	100 HP, to 3000 GPM		.26	123		25,500	6,875		32,375	38,500
3240	150 HP, to 4000 GPM		.24	133		36,000	7,450		43,450	51,000

22 12 Facility Potable-Water Storage Tanks

22 12 21 – Facility Underground Potable-Water Storage Tanks

22 12 21.13 Fiberglass, Undrgrnd Pot.-Water Storage Tanks

		Crew	Daily Output	Labor-Hours	Unit	Material	Labor	Equipment	Total	Total Incl O&P
0010	**FIBERGLASS, UNDERGROUND POTABLE-WATER STORAGE TANKS**									
0020	Excludes excavation, backfill, & piping									
0030	Single wall									
2000	600 gallon capacity	B-21B	3.75	10.667	Ea.	3,300	435	174	3,909	4,475
2010	1,000 gallon capacity		3.50	11.429		4,250	465	187	4,902	5,600
2020	2,000 gallon capacity		3.25	12.308		6,200	500	201	6,901	7,800
2030	4,000 gallon capacity		3	13.333		8,575	545	218	9,338	10,500
2040	6,000 gallon capacity		2.65	15.094		9,625	615	247	10,487	11,800
2050	8,000 gallon capacity		2.30	17.391		11,500	710	284	12,494	14,100
2060	10,000 gallon capacity		2	20		13,200	815	325	14,340	16,200
2070	12,000 gallon capacity		1.50	26.667		18,300	1,100	435	19,835	22,300
2080	15,000 gallon capacity		1	40		21,200	1,625	655	23,480	26,500
2090	20,000 gallon capacity		.75	53.333		27,300	2,175	870	30,345	34,300
2100	25,000 gallon capacity		.50	80		40,800	3,275	1,300	45,375	51,500
2110	30,000 gallon capacity		.35	114		49,400	4,675	1,875	55,950	63,500
2120	40,000 gallon capacity		.30	133		71,500	5,450	2,175	79,125	89,500

22 13 Facility Sanitary Sewerage

22 13 16 – Sanitary Waste and Vent Piping

22 13 16.20 Pipe, Cast Iron

		Crew	Daily Output	Labor-Hours	Unit	Material	Labor	Equipment	Total	Total Incl O&P
0010	**PIPE, CAST IRON**, Soil, on clevis hanger assemblies, 5' O.C.									
0020	Single hub, service wt., lead & oakum joints 10' O.C.									
2120	2" diameter	Q-1	63	.254	L.F.	11.35	13.40		24.75	33
2140	3" diameter		60	.267		15	14.10		29.10	38
2160	4" diameter		55	.291		18.55	15.35		33.90	43.50
2180	5" diameter	Q-2	76	.316		25.50	17.30		42.80	54
2200	6" diameter	"	73	.329		31	18		49	61.50
2220	8" diameter	Q-3	59	.542		47	30.50		77.50	98
2240	10" diameter		54	.593		74.50	33		107.50	132
2260	12" diameter		48	.667		105	37.50		142.50	173
2320	For service weight, double hub, add					10%				
2340	For extra heavy, single hub, add					48%	4%			
2360	For extra heavy, double hub, add					71%	4%			
2400	Lead for caulking, (1#/diam. in.)	Q-1	160	.100	Lb.	1.04	5.30		6.34	9.15
2420	Oakum for caulking, (1/8#/diam. in.)	"	40	.400	"	3.60	21		24.60	36
2960	To delete hangers, subtract									

22 13 16.20 Pipe, Cast Iron		Crew	Daily Output	Labor-Hours	Unit	Material	2015 Bare Costs Labor	Equipment	Total	Total Incl O&P
2970	2" diam. to 4" diam.					16%	19%			
2980	5" diam. to 8" diam.					14%	14%			
2990	10" diam. to 15" diam.					13%	19%			
3000	Single hub, service wt., push-on gasket joints 10' O.C.									
3010	2" diameter	Q-1	66	.242	L.F.	12.30	12.80		25.10	33
3020	3" diameter		63	.254		16.20	13.40		29.60	38.50
3030	4" diameter	↓	57	.281		20	14.85		34.85	44.50
3040	5" diameter	Q-2	79	.304		28	16.65		44.65	55.50
3050	6" diameter	"	75	.320		33.50	17.55		51.05	63.50
3060	8" diameter	Q-3	62	.516		52.50	29		81.50	102
3070	10" diameter		56	.571		84	32		116	141
3080	12" diameter		49	.653		118	36.50		154.50	184
3082	15" diameter	↓	40	.800	↓	171	44.50		215.50	256
3100	For service weight, double hub, add					65%				
3110	For extra heavy, single hub, add					48%	4%			
3120	For extra heavy, double hub, add					29%	4%			
3130	To delete hangers, subtract									
3140	2" diam. to 4" diam.					12%	21%			
3150	5" diam. to 8" diam.					10%	16%			
3160	10" diam. to 15" diam.					9%	21%			
4000	No hub, couplings 10' O.C.									
4100	1-1/2" diameter	Q-1	71	.225	L.F.	11.05	11.90		22.95	30
4120	2" diameter		67	.239		11.25	12.60		23.85	31.50
4140	3" diameter		64	.250		15.20	13.20		28.40	36.50
4160	4" diameter	↓	58	.276		19.10	14.55		33.65	43
4180	5" diameter	Q-2	83	.289		25.50	15.85		41.35	52
4200	6" diameter	"	79	.304		32	16.65		48.65	60.50
4220	8" diameter	Q-3	69	.464		54.50	26		80.50	99
4240	10" diameter		61	.525		88.50	29.50		118	142
4244	12" diameter		58	.552		110	31		141	168
4248	15" diameter	↓	52	.615	↓	163	34.50		197.50	231
4280	To delete hangers, subtract									
4290	1-1/2" diam. to 6" diam.					22%	47%			
4300	8" diam. to 10" diam.					21%	44%			
4310	12" diam. to 15" diam.					19%	40%			

22 13 16.30 Pipe Fittings, Cast Iron

		Crew	Daily Output	Labor-Hours	Unit	Material	2015 Bare Costs Labor	Equipment	Total	Total Incl O&P
0010	**PIPE FITTINGS, CAST IRON**, Soil									
0040	Hub and spigot, service weight, lead & oakum joints									
0080	1/4 bend, 2"	Q-1	16	1	Ea.	19.90	53		72.90	102
0120	3"		14	1.143		26.50	60.50		87	120
0140	4"	↓	13	1.231		41.50	65		106.50	144
0160	5"	Q-2	18	1.333		58	73		131	174
0180	6"	"	17	1.412		72	77.50		149.50	197
0200	8"	Q-3	11	2.909		217	163		380	485
0220	10"		10	3.200		320	179		499	620
0224	12"	↓	9	3.556		430	199		629	775
0266	Closet bend, 3" diameter with flange 10" x 16"	Q-1	14	1.143		127	60.50		187.50	231
0268	16" x 16"		12	1.333		141	70.50		211.50	262
0270	Closet bend, 4" diameter, 2-1/2" x 4" ring, 6" x 16"		13	1.231		118	65		183	228
0280	8" x 16"		13	1.231		106	65		171	215
0290	10" x 12"		12	1.333		102	70.50		172.50	218
0300	10" x 18"	↓	11	1.455		136	77		213	266

22 13 16.30 Pipe Fittings, Cast Iron		Crew	Daily Output	Labor-Hours	Unit	Material	2015 Bare Costs Labor	Equipment	Total	Total Incl O&P
0310	12" x 16"	Q-1	11	1.455	Ea.	119	77		196	247
0330	16" x 16"		10	1.600		148	84.50		232.50	291
0340	1/8 bend, 2"		16	1		14.15	53		67.15	95.50
0350	3"		14	1.143		22	60.50		82.50	116
0360	4"		13	1.231		33.50	65		98.50	135
0380	5"	Q-2	18	1.333		45.50	73		118.50	160
0400	6"	"	17	1.412		54.50	77.50		132	177
0420	8"	Q-3	11	2.909		164	163		327	425
0440	10"		10	3.200		236	179		415	530
0460	12"		9	3.556		445	199		644	790
0500	Sanitary tee, 2"	Q-1	10	1.600		27.50	84.50		112	159
0540	3"		9	1.778		45	94		139	192
0620	4"		8	2		55	106		161	221
0700	5"	Q-2	12	2		109	110		219	285
0800	6"	"	11	2.182		126	120		246	320
0880	8"	Q-3	7	4.571		330	256		586	745
1000	Tee, 2"	Q-1	10	1.600		40	84.50		124.50	172
1060	3"		9	1.778		59.50	94		153.50	208
1120	4"		8	2		76.50	106		182.50	244
1200	5"	Q-2	12	2		162	110		272	345
1300	6"	"	11	2.182		160	120		280	355
1380	8"	Q-3	7	4.571		293	256		549	710
1400	Combination Y and 1/8 bend									
1420	2"	Q-1	10	1.600	Ea.	34.50	84.50		119	166
1460	3"		9	1.778		52.50	94		146.50	200
1520	4"		8	2		72.50	106		178.50	240
1540	5"	Q-2	12	2		138	110		248	315
1560	6"		11	2.182		174	120		294	375
1580	8"		7	3.429		430	188		618	760
1582	12"	Q-3	6	5.333		880	298		1,178	1,425
1600	Double Y, 2"	Q-1	8	2		61.50	106		167.50	228
1610	3"		7	2.286		76.50	121		197.50	266
1620	4"		6.50	2.462		100	130		230	305
1630	5"	Q-2	9	2.667		183	146		329	425
1640	6"	"	8	3		262	164		426	535
1650	8"	Q-3	5.50	5.818		635	325		960	1,175
1660	10"		5	6.400		1,425	360		1,785	2,100
1670	12"		4.50	7.111		1,625	395		2,020	2,400
1740	Reducer, 3" x 2"	Q-1	15	1.067		19.45	56.50		75.95	107
1750	4" x 2"		14.50	1.103		22	58.50		80.50	113
1760	4" x 3"		14	1.143		25.50	60.50		86	119
1770	5" x 2"		14	1.143		53.50	60.50		114	150
1780	5" x 3"		13.50	1.185		56.50	62.50		119	157
1790	5" x 4"		13	1.231		32.50	65		97.50	134
1800	6" x 2"		13.50	1.185		51	62.50		113.50	151
1810	6" x 3"		13	1.231		51.50	65		116.50	155
1830	6" x 4"		12.50	1.280		51	67.50		118.50	158
1840	6" x 5"		11	1.455		55	77		132	177
1880	8" x 3"	Q-2	13.50	1.778		99	97.50		196.50	256
1900	8" x 4"		13	1.846		85	101		186	247
1920	8" x 5"		12	2		89.50	110		199.50	264
1940	8" x 6"		12	2		87.50	110		197.50	261
1960	Increaser, 2" x 3"	Q-1	15	1.067		46.50	56.50		103	136

236

22 13 16.30 Pipe Fittings, Cast Iron		Crew	Daily Output	Labor-Hours	Unit	Material	2015 Bare Costs Labor	Equipment	Total	Total Incl O&P
1980	2" x 4"	Q-1	14	1.143	Ea.	46.50	60.50		107	142
2000	2" x 5"		13	1.231		57	65		122	161
2020	3" x 4"		13	1.231		51	65		116	154
2040	3" x 5"		13	1.231		57	65		122	161
2060	3" x 6"		12	1.333		68.50	70.50		139	182
2070	4" x 5"		13	1.231		60.50	65		125.50	165
2080	4" x 6"		12	1.333		69	70.50		139.50	182
2090	4" x 8"	Q-2	13	1.846		143	101		244	310
2100	5" x 6"	Q-1	11	1.455		103	77		180	229
2110	5" x 8"	Q-2	12	2		166	110		276	345
2120	6" x 8"		12	2		166	110		276	345
2130	6" x 10"		8	3		299	164		463	580
2140	8" x 10"		6.50	3.692		305	202		507	640
2150	10" x 12"		5.50	4.364		540	239		779	955
2500	Y, 2"	Q-1	10	1.600		25.50	84.50		110	156
2510	3"		9	1.778		47	94		141	194
2520	4"		8	2		62.50	106		168.50	229
2530	5"	Q-2	12	2		111	110		221	287
2540	6"	"	11	2.182		144	120		264	340
2550	8"	Q-3	7	4.571		350	256		606	770
2560	10"		6	5.333		570	298		868	1,075
2570	12"		5	6.400		1,300	360		1,660	2,000
2580	15"		4	8		2,875	445		3,320	3,825
3000	For extra heavy, add					44%	4%			
3600	Hub and spigot, service weight gasket joint									
3605	Note: gaskets and joint labor have									
3606	been included with all listed fittings.									
3610	1/4 bend, 2"	Q-1	20	.800	Ea.	29.50	42.50		72	96
3620	3"		17	.941		38.50	49.50		88	118
3630	4"		15	1.067		56.50	56.50		113	148
3640	5"	Q-2	21	1.143		82	62.50		144.50	185
3650	6"	"	19	1.263		97	69		166	212
3660	8"	Q-3	12	2.667		272	149		421	525
3670	10"		11	2.909		415	163		578	700
3680	12"		10	3.200		550	179		729	880
3700	Closet bend, 3" diameter with ring 10" x 16"	Q-1	17	.941		139	49.50		188.50	228
3710	16" x 16"		15	1.067		154	56.50		210.50	254
3730	Closet bend, 4" diameter, 1" x 4" ring, 6" x 16"		15	1.067		133	56.50		189.50	232
3740	8" x 16"		15	1.067		121	56.50		177.50	218
3750	10" x 12"		14	1.143		117	60.50		177.50	220
3760	10" x 18"		13	1.231		152	65		217	265
3770	12" x 16"		13	1.231		134	65		199	246
3780	16" x 16"		12	1.333		163	70.50		233.50	286
3800	1/8 bend, 2"		20	.800		23.50	42.50		66	90
3810	3"		17	.941		34.50	49.50		84	113
3820	4"		15	1.067		48.50	56.50		105	139
3830	5"	Q-2	21	1.143		69.50	62.50		132	171
3840	6"	"	19	1.263		79.50	69		148.50	193
3850	8"	Q-3	12	2.667		219	149		368	465
3860	10"		11	2.909		330	163		493	610
3870	12"		10	3.200		570	179		749	895
3900	Sanitary Tee, 2"	Q-1	12	1.333		46.50	70.50		117	157
3910	3"		10	1.600		69	84.50		153.50	204

22 13 16.30 Pipe Fittings, Cast Iron		Crew	Daily Output	Labor-Hours	Unit	Material	2015 Bare Costs Labor	Equipment	Total	Total Incl O&P
3920	4"	Q-1	9	1.778	Ea.	85.50	94		179.50	236
3930	5"	Q-2	13	1.846		157	101		258	325
3940	6"	"	11	2.182		176	120		296	375
3950	8"	Q-3	8.50	3.765		440	210		650	800
3980	Tee, 2"	Q-1	12	1.333		59	70.50		129.50	171
3990	3"		10	1.600		84	84.50		168.50	221
4000	4"		9	1.778		107	94		201	260
4010	5"	Q-2	13	1.846		210	101		311	385
4020	6"	"	11	2.182		210	120		330	410
4030	8"	Q-3	8	4		405	224		629	785
4060	Combination Y and 1/8 bend									
4070	2"	Q-1	12	1.333	Ea.	53.50	70.50		124	165
4080	3"		10	1.600		77	84.50		161.50	213
4090	4"		9	1.778		103	94		197	256
4100	5"	Q-2	13	1.846		186	101		287	355
4110	6"	"	11	2.182		224	120		344	425
4120	8"	Q-3	8	4		540	224		764	935
4121	12"	"	7	4.571		1,125	256		1,381	1,625
4160	Double Y, 2"	Q-1	10	1.600		90	84.50		174.50	227
4170	3"		8	2		113	106		219	284
4180	4"		7	2.286		146	121		267	345
4190	5"	Q-2	10	2.400		255	131		386	480
4200	6"	"	9	2.667		335	146		481	590
4210	8"	Q-3	6	5.333		800	298		1,098	1,325
4220	10"		5	6.400		1,700	360		2,060	2,425
4230	12"		4.50	7.111		2,000	395		2,395	2,800
4260	Reducer, 3" x 2"	Q-1	17	.941		41	49.50		90.50	120
4270	4" x 2"		16.50	.970		47	51		98	129
4280	4" x 3"		16	1		53	53		106	138
4290	5" x 2"		16	1		87	53		140	176
4300	5" x 3"		15.50	1.032		93	54.50		147.50	185
4310	5" x 4"		15	1.067		72	56.50		128.50	164
4320	6" x 2"		15.50	1.032		85	54.50		139.50	176
4330	6" x 3"		15	1.067		88.50	56.50		145	183
4336	6" x 4"		14	1.143		91	60.50		151.50	191
4340	6" x 5"		13	1.231		104	65		169	212
4360	8" x 3"	Q-2	15	1.600		166	87.50		253.50	315
4370	8" x 4"		15	1.600		155	87.50		242.50	305
4380	8" x 5"		14	1.714		169	94		263	325
4390	8" x 6"		14	1.714		167	94		261	325
4430	Increaser, 2" x 3"	Q-1	17	.941		58.50	49.50		108	140
4440	2" x 4"		16	1		62	53		115	148
4450	2" x 5"		15	1.067		81	56.50		137.50	175
4460	3" x 4"		15	1.067		66.50	56.50		123	158
4470	3" x 5"		15	1.067		81	56.50		137.50	175
4480	3" x 6"		14	1.143		93.50	60.50		154	194
4490	4" x 5"		15	1.067		84.50	56.50		141	178
4500	4" x 6"		14	1.143		94	60.50		154.50	194
4510	4" x 8"	Q-2	15	1.600		198	87.50		285.50	350
4520	5" x 6"	Q-1	13	1.231		127	65		192	238
4530	5" x 8"	Q-2	14	1.714		221	94		315	385
4540	6" x 8"		14	1.714		221	94		315	385
4550	6" x 10"		10	2.400		395	131		526	635

22 13 16.30 Pipe Fittings, Cast Iron		Crew	Daily Output	Labor-Hours	Unit	Material	2015 Bare Costs Labor	Equipment	Total	Total Incl O&P
4560	8" x 10"	Q-2	8.50	2.824	Ea.	400	155		555	675
4570	10" x 12"		7.50	3.200		665	175		840	995
4600	Y, 2"	Q-1	12	1.333		44	70.50		114.50	155
4610	3"		10	1.600		71	84.50		155.50	207
4620	4"		9	1.778		93.50	94		187.50	245
4630	5"	Q-2	13	1.846		159	101		260	330
4640	6"	"	11	2.182		194	120		314	395
4650	8"	Q-3	8	4		460	224		684	850
4660	10"		7	4.571		760	256		1,016	1,225
4670	12"		6	5.333		1,550	298		1,848	2,150
4672	15"		5	6.400		3,150	360		3,510	4,025
4900	For extra heavy, add					44%	4%			
4940	Gasket and making push-on joint									
4950	2"	Q-1	40	.400	Ea.	9.40	21		30.40	42.50
4960	3"		35	.457		12.20	24		36.20	50
4970	4"		32	.500		15.30	26.50		41.80	57
4980	5"	Q-2	43	.558		24	30.50		54.50	72.50
4990	6"	"	40	.600		25	33		58	77
5000	8"	Q-3	32	1		55	56		111	145
5010	10"		29	1.103		95.50	61.50		157	198
5020	12"		25	1.280		122	71.50		193.50	242
5022	15"		21	1.524		146	85		231	290
5030	Note: gaskets and joint labor have									
5040	Been included with all listed fittings.									
5990	No hub									
6000	Cplg. & labor required at joints not incl. in fitting									
6010	price. Add 1 coupling per joint for installed price									
6020	1/4 Bend, 1-1/2"				Ea.	10.20			10.20	11.25
6060	2"					11.15			11.15	12.25
6080	3"					16.25			16.25	17.85
6120	4"					23			23	25.50
6140	5"					55.50			55.50	61
6160	6"					55.50			55.50	61
6180	8"					156			156	172
6184	1/4 Bend, long sweep, 1-1/2"					25.50			25.50	28
6186	2"					24.50			24.50	26.50
6188	3"					29.50			29.50	32.50
6189	4"					47			47	51.50
6190	5"					90.50			90.50	99.50
6191	6"					103			103	114
6192	8"					282			282	310
6193	10"					570			570	625
6200	1/8 Bend, 1-1/2"					8.60			8.60	9.45
6210	2"					9.60			9.60	10.55
6212	3"					12.80			12.80	14.10
6214	4"					16.80			16.80	18.50
6216	5"					35			35	38.50
6218	6"					37.50			37.50	41
6220	8"					108			108	118
6222	10"					204			204	225
6380	Sanitary Tee, tapped, 1-1/2"					20.50			20.50	22.50
6382	2" x 1-1/2"					17.95			17.95	19.70
6384	2"					19.25			19.25	21

For customer support on your Site Work & Landscape Cost Data, call 877.737.1594.

239

22 13 16.30 Pipe Fittings, Cast Iron		Crew	Daily Output	Labor-Hours	Unit	Material	2015 Bare Costs Labor	Equipment	Total	Total Incl O&P
6386	3" x 2"				Ea.	28.50			28.50	31.50
6388	3"					49.50			49.50	54.50
6390	4" x 1-1/2"					25.50			25.50	28
6392	4" x 2"					29			29	32
6393	4"					29			29	32
6394	6" x 1-1/2"					66			66	73
6396	6" x 2"					67.50			67.50	74
6459	Sanitary Tee, 1-1/2"					14.35			14.35	15.80
6460	2"					15.35			15.35	16.85
6470	3"					18.90			18.90	21
6472	4"					36			36	39.50
6474	5"					83.50			83.50	92
6476	6"					85.50			85.50	94
6478	8"					345			345	380
6730	Y, 1-1/2"					14.50			14.50	15.95
6740	2"					14.20			14.20	15.65
6750	3"					20.50			20.50	22.50
6760	4"					33			33	36.50
6762	5"					78.50			78.50	86
6764	6"					88			88	97
6768	8"					207			207	228
6769	10"					460			460	505
6770	12"					905			905	995
6771	15"					2,025			2,025	2,225
6791	Y, reducing, 3" x 2"					15.35			15.35	16.85
6792	4" x 2"					22			22	24.50
6793	5" x 2"					48.50			48.50	53.50
6794	6" x 2"					54			54	59.50
6795	6" x 4"					70			70	77
6796	8" x 4"					121			121	133
6797	8" x 6"					149			149	163
6798	10" x 6"					335			335	370
6799	10" x 8"					400			400	440
6800	Double Y, 2"					22.50			22.50	25
6920	3"					41.50			41.50	45.50
7000	4"					84.50			84.50	92.50
7100	6"					149			149	164
7120	8"					425			425	470
7200	Combination Y and 1/8 Bend									
7220	1-1/2"				Ea.	15.45			15.45	17
7260	2"					16.15			16.15	17.80
7320	3"					25.50			25.50	28
7400	4"					49			49	54
7480	5"					101			101	111
7500	6"					135			135	148
7520	8"					315			315	345
7800	Reducer, 3" x 2"					7.85			7.85	8.60
7820	4" x 2"					12.10			12.10	13.30
7840	4" x 3"					12.10			12.10	13.30
7842	6" x 3"					32.50			32.50	36
7844	6" x 4"					29.50			29.50	32.50
7846	6" x 5"					33.50			33.50	36.50
7848	8" x 2"					51.50			51.50	57

22 13 16.30 Pipe Fittings, Cast Iron	Crew	Daily Output	Labor-Hours	Unit	Material	2015 Bare Costs Labor	Equipment	Total	Total Incl O&P
7850	8" x 3"				Ea.	47.50			47.50	52.50
7852	8" x 4"					50.50			50.50	55.50
7854	8" x 5"					57			57	62.50
7856	8" x 6"					56			56	61.50
7858	10" x 4"					99			99	109
7860	10" x 6"					104			104	115
7862	10" x 8"					122			122	134
7864	12" x 4"					204			204	225
7866	12" x 6"					219			219	241
7868	12" x 8"					225			225	248
7870	12" x 10"					225			225	248
7872	15" x 4"					425			425	470
7874	15" x 6"					400			400	440
7876	15" x 8"					465			465	510
7878	15" x 10"					480			480	530
7880	15" x 12"					485			485	535
8000	Coupling, standard (by CISPI Mfrs.)									
8020	1-1/2"	Q-1	48	.333	Ea.	13.95	17.60		31.55	42
8040	2"		44	.364		15.25	19.20		34.45	46
8080	3"		38	.421		17.10	22		39.10	52.50
8120	4"		33	.485		20	25.50		45.50	60.50
8160	5"	Q-2	44	.545		41	30		71	90
8180	6"	"	40	.600		46.50	33		79.50	101
8200	8"	Q-3	33	.970		97	54		151	189
8220	10"	"	26	1.231		124	69		193	240
8300	Coupling, cast iron clamp & neoprene gasket (by MG)									
8310	1-1/2"	Q-1	48	.333	Ea.	6.40	17.60		24	33.50
8320	2"		44	.364		8.35	19.20		27.55	38
8330	3"		38	.421		12.65	22		34.65	47.50
8340	4"		33	.485		14.60	25.50		40.10	54.50
8350	5"	Q-2	44	.545		20.50	30		50.50	67.50
8360	6"	"	40	.600		32.50	33		65.50	85.50
8380	8"	Q-3	33	.970		116	54		170	210
8400	10"	"	26	1.231		189	69		258	310
8600	Coupling, Stainless steel, heavy duty									
8620	1-1/2"	Q-1	48	.333	Ea.	10	17.60		27.60	37.50
8630	2"		44	.364		10.40	19.20		29.60	40.50
8640	2" x 1-1/2"		44	.364		12.20	19.20		31.40	42.50
8650	3"		38	.421		11.30	22		33.30	46
8660	4"		33	.485		12.75	25.50		38.25	52.50
8670	4" x 3"		33	.485		18.40	25.50		43.90	58.50
8680	5"	Q-2	44	.545		24.50	30		54.50	72
8690	6"	"	40	.600		30.50	33		63.50	83.50
8700	8"	Q-3	33	.970		52	54		106	139
8710	10"		26	1.231		65.50	69		134.50	176
8712	12"		22	1.455		102	81.50		183.50	235
8715	15"		18	1.778		120	99.50		219.50	282

22 13 Facility Sanitary Sewerage

22 13 19 – Sanitary Waste Piping Specialties

22 13 19.13 Sanitary Drains

		Crew	Daily Output	Labor-Hours	Unit	Material	2015 Bare Costs Labor	Equipment	Total	Total Incl O&P
0010	**SANITARY DRAINS**									
0400	Deck, auto park, C.I., 13" top									
0440	3", 4", 5", and 6" pipe size	Q-1	8	2	Ea.	1,450	106		1,556	1,725
0480	For galvanized body, add				"	780			780	855
0800	Promenade, heelproof grate, C.I., 14" top									
0840	2", 3", and 4" pipe size	Q-1	10	1.600	Ea.	550	84.50		634.50	735
0860	5" and 6" pipe size		9	1.778		685	94		779	895
0880	8" pipe size	↓	8	2		810	106		916	1,050
0940	For galvanized body, add					400			400	440
0960	With polished bronze top, 2"-3"-4" diam.			↓		930			930	1,025
1200	Promenade, heelproof grate, C.I., lateral, 14" top									
1240	2", 3" and 4" pipe size	Q-1	10	1.600	Ea.	720	84.50		804.50	920
1260	5" and 6" pipe size		9	1.778		855	94		949	1,075
1280	8" pipe size	↓	8	2		980	106		1,086	1,225
1340	For galvanized body, add				↓	410			410	450
1360	For polished bronze top, add					375			375	415
1500	Promenade, slotted grate, C.I., 11" top									
1540	2", 3", 4", 5", and 6" pipe size	Q-1	12	1.333	Ea.	495	70.50		565.50	650
1600	For galvanized body, add				↓	230			230	253
1640	With polished bronze top					790			790	870
2000	Floor, medium duty, C.I., deep flange, 7" diam. top									
2040	2" and 3" pipe size	Q-1	12	1.333	Ea.	208	70.50		278.50	335
2080	For galvanized body, add			↓		96.50			96.50	106
2120	With polished bronze top				↓	315			315	345
2400	Heavy duty, with sediment bucket, C.I., 12" diam. loose grate									
2420	2", 3", 4", 5", and 6" pipe size	Q-1	9	1.778	Ea.	690	94		784	900
2460	With polished bronze top				"	975			975	1,075
2500	Heavy duty, cleanout & trap w/bucket, C.I., 15" top									
2540	2", 3", and 4" pipe size	Q-1	6	2.667	Ea.	6,575	141		6,716	7,450
2560	For galvanized body, add					1,675			1,675	1,850
2580	With polished bronze top			↓		7,300			7,300	8,025

22 13 23 – Sanitary Waste Interceptors

22 13 23.10 Interceptors

		Crew	Daily Output	Labor-Hours	Unit	Material	2015 Bare Costs Labor	Equipment	Total	Total Incl O&P
0010	**INTERCEPTORS**									
0150	Grease, fabricated steel, 4 GPM, 8 lb. fat capacity	1 Plum	4	2	Ea.	1,150	117		1,267	1,450
0200	7 GPM, 14 lb. fat capacity		4	2		1,600	117		1,717	1,950
1000	10 GPM, 20 lb. fat capacity		4	2		1,875	117		1,992	2,250
1040	15 GPM, 30 lb. fat capacity		4	2		2,800	117		2,917	3,250
1060	20 GPM, 40 lb. fat capacity	↓	3	2.667		3,425	157		3,582	3,975
1120	50 GPM, 100 lb. fat capacity	Q-1	2	8		6,300	425		6,725	7,575
1160	100 GPM, 200 lb. fat capacity	"	2	8	↓	15,100	425		15,525	17,200
1580	For seepage pan, add					7%				
3000	Hair, cast iron, 1-1/4" and 1-1/2" pipe connection	1 Plum	8	1	Ea.	435	58.50		493.50	565
3100	For chrome-plated cast iron, add					266			266	293
4000	Oil, fabricated steel, 10 GPM, 2" pipe size	1 Plum	4	2		2,575	117		2,692	3,000
4100	15 GPM, 2" or 3" pipe size		4	2		3,525	117		3,642	4,075
4120	20 GPM, 2" or 3" pipe size	↓	3	2.667		4,625	157		4,782	5,300
4220	100 GPM, 3" pipe size	Q-1	2	8		14,300	425		14,725	16,300
6000	Solids, precious metals recovery, C.I., 1-1/4" to 2" pipe	1 Plum	4	2		655	117		772	895
6100	Dental Lab., large, C.I., 1-1/2" to 2" pipe	"	3	2.667	↓	2,275	157		2,432	2,750

22 13 29.13 Wet-Pit-Mounted, Vertical Sewerage Pumps		Crew	Daily Output	Labor-Hours	Unit	Material	2015 Bare Costs Labor	Equipment	Total	Total Incl O&P
0010	**WET-PIT-MOUNTED, VERTICAL SEWERAGE PUMPS**									
0020	Controls incl. alarm/disconnect panel w/wire. Excavation not included									
0260	Simplex, 9 GPM at 60 PSIG, 91 gal. tank				Ea.	3,325			3,325	3,675
0300	Unit with manway, 26" I.D., 18" high					3,700			3,700	4,075
0340	26" I.D., 36" high					3,750			3,750	4,125
0380	43" I.D., 4' high					3,975			3,975	4,375
0600	Simplex, 9 GPM at 60 PSIG, 150 gal. tank, indoor					3,525			3,525	3,900
0700	Unit with manway, 26" I.D., 36" high					4,225			4,225	4,650
0740	26" I.D., 4' high					4,450			4,450	4,900
2000	Duplex, 18 GPM at 60 PSIG, 150 gal. tank, indoor					7,050			7,050	7,750
2060	Unit with manway, 43" I.D., 4' high					8,100			8,100	8,925
2400	For core only					1,875			1,875	2,050
3000	Indoor residential type installation									
3020	Simplex, 9 GPM at 60 PSIG, 91 gal. HDPE tank				Ea.	3,350			3,350	3,675

22 13 29.14 Sewage Ejector Pumps

		Crew	Daily Output	Labor-Hours	Unit	Material	2015 Bare Costs Labor	Equipment	Total	Total Incl O&P
0010	**SEWAGE EJECTOR PUMPS**, With operating and level controls									
0100	Simplex system incl. tank, cover, pump 15' head									
0500	37 gal. PE tank, 12 GPM, 1/2 HP, 2" discharge	Q-1	3.20	5	Ea.	480	264		744	925
0510	3" discharge		3.10	5.161		520	273		793	980
0530	87 GPM, .7 HP, 2" discharge		3.20	5		735	264		999	1,200
0540	3" discharge		3.10	5.161		795	273		1,068	1,275
0600	45 gal. coated stl. tank, 12 GPM, 1/2 HP, 2" discharge		3	5.333		855	282		1,137	1,375
0610	3" discharge		2.90	5.517		890	291		1,181	1,425
0630	87 GPM, .7 HP, 2" discharge		3	5.333		1,100	282		1,382	1,625
0640	3" discharge		2.90	5.517		1,150	291		1,441	1,725
0660	134 GPM, 1 HP, 2" discharge		2.80	5.714		1,175	300		1,475	1,750
0680	3" discharge		2.70	5.926		1,250	315		1,565	1,850
0700	70 gal. PE tank, 12 GPM, 1/2 HP, 2" discharge		2.60	6.154		920	325		1,245	1,525
0710	3" discharge		2.40	6.667		980	350		1,330	1,600
0730	87 GPM, 0.7 HP, 2" discharge		2.50	6.400		1,200	340		1,540	1,800
0740	3" discharge		2.30	6.957		1,275	370		1,645	1,950
0760	134 GPM, 1 HP, 2" discharge		2.20	7.273		1,300	385		1,685	2,000
0770	3" discharge		2	8		1,375	425		1,800	2,175
0800	75 gal. coated stl. tank, 12 GPM, 1/2 HP, 2" discharge		2.40	6.667		1,025	350		1,375	1,650
0810	3" discharge		2.20	7.273		1,075	385		1,460	1,750
0830	87 GPM, .7 HP, 2" discharge		2.30	6.957		1,300	370		1,670	1,975
0840	3" discharge		2.10	7.619		1,350	405		1,755	2,100
0860	134 GPM, 1 HP, 2" discharge		2	8		1,375	425		1,800	2,175
0880	3" discharge		1.80	8.889		1,450	470		1,920	2,300
1040	Duplex system incl. tank, covers, pumps									
1060	110 gal. fiberglass tank, 24 GPM, 1/2 HP, 2" discharge	Q-1	1.60	10	Ea.	1,850	530		2,380	2,825
1080	3" discharge		1.40	11.429		1,950	605		2,555	3,025
1100	174 GPM, .7 HP, 2" discharge		1.50	10.667		2,400	565		2,965	3,475
1120	3" discharge		1.30	12.308		2,475	650		3,125	3,700
1140	268 GPM, 1 HP, 2" discharge		1.20	13.333		2,600	705		3,305	3,925
1160	3" discharge		1	16		2,700	845		3,545	4,225
1260	135 gal. coated stl. tank, 24 GPM, 1/2 HP, 2" discharge	Q-2	1.70	14.118		1,900	775		2,675	3,275
2000	3" discharge		1.60	15		2,025	820		2,845	3,475
2640	174 GPM, .7 HP, 2" discharge		1.60	15		2,500	820		3,320	4,000
2660	3" discharge		1.50	16		2,625	875		3,500	4,225
2700	268 GPM, 1 HP, 2" discharge		1.30	18.462		2,700	1,000		3,700	4,500
3040	3" discharge		1.10	21.818		2,875	1,200		4,075	4,975

22 13 Facility Sanitary Sewerage

22 13 29 – Sanitary Sewerage Pumps

22 13 29.14 Sewage Ejector Pumps

		Crew	Daily Output	Labor-Hours	Unit	Material	2015 Bare Costs Labor	Equipment	Total	Total Incl O&P
3060	275 gal. coated stl. tank, 24 GPM, 1/2 HP, 2" discharge	Q-2	1.50	16	Ea.	2,375	875		3,250	3,950
3080	3" discharge		1.40	17.143		2,425	940		3,365	4,075
3100	174 GPM, .7 HP, 2" discharge		1.40	17.143		3,075	940		4,015	4,800
3120	3" discharge		1.30	18.462		3,250	1,000		4,250	5,100
3140	268 GPM, 1 HP, 2" discharge		1.10	21.818		3,375	1,200		4,575	5,500
3160	3" discharge	↓	.90	26.667	↓	3,550	1,450		5,000	6,100
3260	Pump system accessories, add									
3300	Alarm horn and lights, 115 V mercury switch	Q-1	8	2	Ea.	97	106		203	266
3340	Switch, mag. contactor, alarm bell, light, 3 level control		5	3.200		475	169		644	780
3380	Alternator, mercury switch activated	↓	4	4	↓	855	211		1,066	1,250

22 14 Facility Storm Drainage

22 14 23 – Storm Drainage Piping Specialties

22 14 23.33 Backwater Valves

		Crew	Daily Output	Labor-Hours	Unit	Material	2015 Bare Costs Labor	Equipment	Total	Total Incl O&P
0010	**BACKWATER VALVES**, C.I. Body									
6980	Bronze gate and automatic flapper valves									
7000	3" and 4" pipe size	Q-1	13	1.231	Ea.	2,050	65		2,115	2,350
7100	5" and 6" pipe size	"	13	1.231	"	3,125	65		3,190	3,550
7240	Bronze flapper valve, bolted cover									
7260	2" pipe size	Q-1	16	1	Ea.	595	53		648	735
7280	3" pipe size		14.50	1.103		935	58.50		993.50	1,125
7300	4" pipe size	↓	13	1.231		1,150	65		1,215	1,375
7320	5" pipe size	Q-2	18	1.333		1,650	73		1,723	1,925
7340	6" pipe size	"	17	1.412		1,650	77.50		1,727.50	1,950
7360	8" pipe size	Q-3	10	3.200		2,250	179		2,429	2,750
7380	10" pipe size	"	9	3.556	↓	3,700	199		3,899	4,350
7500	For threaded cover, same cost									
7540	Revolving disk type, same cost as flapper type									

22 14 26 – Facility Storm Drains

22 14 26.19 Facility Trench Drains

		Crew	Daily Output	Labor-Hours	Unit	Material	2015 Bare Costs Labor	Equipment	Total	Total Incl O&P
0010	**FACILITY TRENCH DRAINS**									
5980	Trench, floor, heavy duty, modular, C.I., 12" x 12" top									
6000	2", 3", 4", 5", & 6" pipe size	Q-1	8	2	Ea.	895	106		1,001	1,150
6100	For unit with polished bronze top		8	2		1,325	106		1,431	1,625
6200	For 12" extension section, C.I. top		8	2		895	106		1,001	1,150
6240	For 12" extension section, polished bronze top	↓	8	2	↓	1,400	106		1,506	1,700
6600	Trench, floor, for cement concrete encasement									
6610	Not including trenching or concrete									
6640	Polyester polymer concrete									
6650	4" internal width, with grate									
6660	Light duty steel grate	Q-1	120	.133	L.F.	35	7.05		42.05	49
6670	Medium duty steel grate		115	.139		40.50	7.35		47.85	55.50
6680	Heavy duty iron grate	↓	110	.145	↓	62	7.70		69.70	79.50
6700	12" internal width, with grate									
6770	Heavy duty galvanized grate	Q-1	80	.200	L.F.	169	10.55		179.55	201
6800	Fiberglass									
6810	8" internal width, with grate									
6820	Medium duty galvanized grate	Q-1	115	.139	L.F.	111	7.35		118.35	133
6830	Heavy duty iron grate	"	110	.145	"	106	7.70		113.70	128

22 14 Facility Storm Drainage

22 14 29 – Sump Pumps

22 14 29.13 Wet-Pit-Mounted, Vertical Sump Pumps

		Crew	Daily Output	Labor-Hours	Unit	Material	2015 Bare Costs Labor	Equipment	Total	Total Incl O&P
0010	**WET-PIT-MOUNTED, VERTICAL SUMP PUMPS**									
0400	Molded PVC base, 21 GPM at 15' head, 1/3 HP	1 Plum	5	1.600	Ea.	135	94		229	291
0800	Iron base, 21 GPM at 15' head, 1/3 HP		5	1.600		164	94		258	320
1200	Solid brass, 21 GPM at 15' head, 1/3 HP		5	1.600		289	94		383	460
2000	Sump pump, single stage									
2010	25 GPM, 1 HP, 1-1/2" discharge	Q-1	1.80	8.889	Ea.	3,825	470		4,295	4,925
2020	75 GPM, 1-1/2 HP, 2" discharge		1.50	10.667		4,050	565		4,615	5,300
2030	100 GPM, 2 HP, 2-1/2" discharge		1.30	12.308		4,125	650		4,775	5,525
2040	150 GPM, 3 HP, 3" discharge		1.10	14.545		4,125	770		4,895	5,700
2050	200 GPM, 3 HP, 3" discharge		1	16		4,375	845		5,220	6,100
2060	300 GPM, 10 HP, 4" discharge	Q-2	1.20	20		4,725	1,100		5,825	6,850
2070	500 GPM, 15 HP, 5" discharge		1.10	21.818		5,375	1,200		6,575	7,700
2080	800 GPM, 20 HP, 6" discharge		1	24		6,350	1,325		7,675	8,950
2090	1000 GPM, 30 HP, 6" discharge		.85	28.235		6,975	1,550		8,525	10,000
2100	1600 GPM, 50 HP, 8" discharge		.72	33.333		10,900	1,825		12,725	14,800
2110	2000 GPM, 60 HP, 8" discharge	Q-3	.85	37.647		11,100	2,100		13,200	15,400
2202	For general purpose float switch, copper coated float, add	Q-1	5	3.200		108	169		277	375

22 14 29.16 Submersible Sump Pumps

		Crew	Daily Output	Labor-Hours	Unit	Material	2015 Bare Costs Labor	Equipment	Total	Total Incl O&P
0010	**SUBMERSIBLE SUMP PUMPS**									
7000	Sump pump, automatic									
7100	Plastic, 1-1/4" discharge, 1/4 HP	1 Plum	6.40	1.250	Ea.	138	73.50		211.50	263
7140	1/3 HP		6	1.333		200	78.50		278.50	340
7160	1/2 HP		5.40	1.481		246	87		333	400
7180	1-1/2" discharge, 1/2 HP		5.20	1.538		281	90.50		371.50	445
7500	Cast iron, 1-1/4" discharge, 1/4 HP		6	1.333		194	78.50		272.50	330
7540	1/3 HP		6	1.333		229	78.50		307.50	370
7560	1/2 HP		5	1.600		277	94		371	445

22 14 53 – Rainwater Storage Tanks

22 14 53.13 Fiberglass, Rainwater Storage Tank

		Crew	Daily Output	Labor-Hours	Unit	Material	2015 Bare Costs Labor	Equipment	Total	Total Incl O&P
0010	**FIBERGLASS, RAINWATER STORAGE TANK**									
2000	600 gallon	B-21B	3.75	10.667	Ea.	3,300	435	174	3,909	4,475
2010	1,000 gallon		3.50	11.429		4,250	465	187	4,902	5,600
2020	2,000 gallon		3.25	12.308		6,200	500	201	6,901	7,800
2030	4,000 gallon		3	13.333		8,575	545	218	9,338	10,500
2040	6,000 gallon		2.65	15.094		9,625	615	247	10,487	11,800
2050	8,000 gallon		2.30	17.391		11,500	710	284	12,494	14,100
2060	10,000 gallon		2	20		13,200	815	325	14,340	16,200
2070	12,000 gallon		1.50	26.667		18,300	1,100	435	19,835	22,300
2080	15,000 gallon		1	40		21,200	1,625	655	23,480	26,500
2090	20,000 gallon		.75	53.333		27,300	2,175	870	30,345	34,300
2100	25,000 gallon		.50	80		40,800	3,275	1,300	45,375	51,500
2110	30,000 gallon		.35	114		49,400	4,675	1,875	55,950	63,500
2120	40,000 gallon		.30	133		71,500	5,450	2,175	79,125	89,500

For customer support on your Site Work & Landscape Cost Data, call 877.737.1594.

245

22 41 Residential Plumbing Fixtures

22 41 39 – Residential Faucets, Supplies and Trim

22 41 39.10 Faucets and Fittings	Crew	Daily Output	Labor-Hours	Unit	Material	2015 Bare Costs Labor	Equipment	Total	Total Incl O&P
0010 **FAUCETS AND FITTINGS**									
5000 Sillcock, compact, brass, IPS or copper to hose	1 Plum	24	.333	Ea.	9.70	19.55		29.25	40

22 47 Drinking Fountains and Water Coolers

22 47 13 – Drinking Fountains

22 47 13.10 Drinking Water Fountains

22 47 13.10 Drinking Water Fountains	Crew	Daily Output	Labor-Hours	Unit	Material	2015 Bare Costs Labor	Equipment	Total	Total Incl O&P
0010 **DRINKING WATER FOUNTAINS**, For connection to cold water supply									
1000 Wall mounted, non-recessed									
1400 Bronze, with no back	1 Plum	4	2	Ea.	1,000	117		1,117	1,275
1800 Cast aluminum, enameled, for correctional institutions		4	2		1,675	117		1,792	2,000
2000 Fiberglass, 12" back, single bubbler unit		4	2		1,925	117		2,042	2,300
2040 Dual bubbler		3.20	2.500		2,225	147		2,372	2,650
2400 Precast stone, no back		4	2		915	117		1,032	1,175
2700 Stainless steel, single bubbler, no back		4	2		1,050	117		1,167	1,325
2740 With back		4	2		565	117		682	795
2780 Dual handle & wheelchair projection type		4	2		745	117		862	995
2820 Dual level for handicapped type		3.20	2.500		1,575	147		1,722	1,950
3300 Vitreous china									
3340 7" back	1 Plum	4	2	Ea.	620	117		737	855
3940 For vandal-resistant bottom plate, add					77			77	84.50
3960 For freeze-proof valve system, add	1 Plum	2	4		705	235		940	1,125
3980 For rough-in, supply and waste, add	"	2.21	3.620		174	212		386	510
4000 Wall mounted, semi-recessed									
4200 Poly-marble, single bubbler	1 Plum	4	2	Ea.	955	117		1,072	1,225
4600 Stainless steel, satin finish, single bubbler		4	2		1,150	117		1,267	1,450
4900 Vitreous china, single bubbler		4	2		895	117		1,012	1,150
5980 For rough-in, supply and waste, add		1.83	4.372		174	257		431	580
6000 Wall mounted, fully recessed									
6400 Poly-marble, single bubbler	1 Plum	4	2	Ea.	1,600	117		1,717	1,925
6800 Stainless steel, single bubbler		4	2		1,550	117		1,667	1,875
7560 For freeze-proof valve system, add		2	4		795	235		1,030	1,225
7580 For rough-in, supply and waste, add		1.83	4.372		174	257		431	580
7600 Floor mounted, pedestal type									
7780 Wheelchair handicap unit	1 Plum	2	4	Ea.	1,625	235		1,860	2,125
8400 Stainless steel, architectural style		2	4		1,750	235		1,985	2,275
8600 Enameled iron, heavy duty service, 2 bubblers		2	4		2,575	235		2,810	3,200
8660 4 bubblers		2	4		3,950	235		4,185	4,675
8880 For freeze-proof valve system, add		2	4		705	235		940	1,125
8900 For rough-in, supply and waste, add		1.83	4.372		174	257		431	580
9100 Deck mounted									
9500 Stainless steel, circular receptor	1 Plum	4	2	Ea.	435	117		552	655
9760 White enameled steel, 14" x 9" receptor		4	2		375	117		492	590
9860 White enameled cast iron, 24" x 16" receptor		3	2.667		460	157		617	740
9980 For rough-in, supply and waste, add		1.83	4.372		174	257		431	580

22 51 Swimming Pool Plumbing Systems

22 51 19 – Swimming Pool Water Treatment Equipment

22 51 19.50 Swimming Pool Filtration Equipment	Crew	Daily Output	Labor-Hours	Unit	Material	2015 Bare Costs Labor	Equipment	Total	Total Incl O&P
0010 **SWIMMING POOL FILTRATION EQUIPMENT**									
0900 Filter system, sand or diatomite type, incl. pump, 6,000 gal./hr.	2 Plum	1.80	8.889	Total	1,975	520		2,495	2,975
1020 Add for chlorination system, 800 S.F. pool		3	5.333	Ea.	181	315		496	675
1040 5,000 S.F. pool		3	5.333	"	1,850	315		2,165	2,500

22 52 Fountain Plumbing Systems

22 52 16 – Fountain Pumps

22 52 16.10 Fountain Water Pumps

		Crew	Daily Output	Labor-Hours	Unit	Material	Labor	Equipment	Total	Total Incl O&P
0010	**FOUNTAIN WATER PUMPS**									
0100	Pump w/controls									
0200	Single phase, 100' cord, 1/2 H.P. pump	2 Skwk	4.40	3.636	Ea.	1,275	177		1,452	1,675
0300	3/4 H.P. pump		4.30	3.721		2,175	181		2,356	2,675
0400	1 H.P. pump		4.20	3.810		2,350	185		2,535	2,875
0500	1-1/2 H.P. pump		4.10	3.902		2,800	190		2,990	3,375
0600	2 H.P. pump		4	4		• 3,775	195		3,970	4,475
0700	Three phase, 200' cord, 5 H.P. pump		3.90	4.103		5,175	200		5,375	6,000
0800	7-1/2 H.P. pump		3.80	4.211		9,000	205		9,205	10,200
0900	10 H.P. pump		3.70	4.324		13,300	210		13,510	15,000
1000	15 H.P. pump		3.60	4.444		16,800	216		17,016	18,800
2000	DESIGN NOTE: Use two horsepower per surface acre.									

22 52 33 – Fountain Ancillary

22 52 33.10 Fountain Miscellaneous

		Crew	Daily Output	Labor-Hours	Unit	Material	Labor	Equipment	Total	Total Incl O&P
0010	**FOUNTAIN MISCELLANEOUS**									
1300	Lights w/mounting kits, 200 watt	2 Skwk	18	.889	Ea.	1,050	43		1,093	1,225
1400	300 watt		18	.889		1,275	43		1,318	1,475
1500	500 watt		18	.889		1,425	43		1,468	1,650
1600	Color blender		12	1.333		555	65		620	710

22 66 Chemical-Waste Systems for Lab. and Healthcare Facilities

22 66 53 – Laboratory Chemical-Waste and Vent Piping

22 66 53.30 Glass Pipe

		Crew	Daily Output	Labor-Hours	Unit	Material	Labor	Equipment	Total	Total Incl O&P
0010	**GLASS PIPE**, Borosilicate, couplings & clevis hanger assemblies, 10' O.C.									
0020	Drainage									
1100	1-1/2" diameter	Q-1	52	.308	L.F.	11.40	16.25		27.65	37
1120	2" diameter		44	.364		14.65	19.20		33.85	45
1140	3" diameter		39	.410		19.50	21.50		41	54
1160	4" diameter		30	.533		34	28		62	80
1180	6" diameter		26	.615		58.50	32.50		91	114

22 66 53.40 Pipe Fittings, Glass

		Crew	Daily Output	Labor-Hours	Unit	Material	Labor	Equipment	Total	Total Incl O&P
0010	**PIPE FITTINGS, GLASS**									
0020	Drainage, beaded ends									
0040	Coupling & labor required at joints not incl. in fitting									
0050	price. Add 1 per joint for installed price									
0070	90° Bend or sweep, 1-1/2"				Ea.	31.50			31.50	35
0110	4"				"	105			105	116

For customer support on your Site Work & Landscape Cost Data, call 877.737.1594.

247

22 66 53.60 Corrosion Resistant Pipe

22 66 53.60 Corrosion Resistant Pipe		Crew	Daily Output	Labor-Hours	Unit	Material	2015 Bare Costs Labor	Equipment	Total	Total Incl O&P
0010	**CORROSION RESISTANT PIPE**, No couplings or hangers									
0020	Iron alloy, drain, mechanical joint									
1000	1-1/2" diameter	Q-1	70	.229	L.F.	46	12.10		58.10	69
1100	2" diameter		66	.242		47	12.80		59.80	71
1120	3" diameter		60	.267		60.50	14.10		74.60	88
1140	4" diameter		52	.308		77.50	16.25		93.75	110
1980	Iron alloy, drain, B&S joint									
2000	2" diameter	Q-1	54	.296	L.F.	55.50	15.65		71.15	85
2100	3" diameter		52	.308		71	16.25		87.25	103
2120	4" diameter		48	.333		98	17.60		115.60	135
2140	6" diameter	Q-2	59	.407		158	22.50		180.50	207
2160	8" diameter	"	54	.444		297	24.50		321.50	360
2980	Plastic, epoxy, fiberglass filament wound, B&S joint									
3000	2" diameter	Q-1	62	.258	L.F.	12	13.65		25.65	33.50
3100	3" diameter		51	.314		14	16.55		30.55	40.50
3120	4" diameter		45	.356		20	18.80		38.80	50.50
3140	6" diameter		32	.500		28	26.50		54.50	71
3160	8" diameter	Q-2	38	.632		44	34.50		78.50	101
3980	Polyester, fiberglass filament wound, B&S joint									
4000	2" diameter	Q-1	62	.258	L.F.	13.05	13.65		26.70	35
4100	3" diameter		51	.314		17	16.55		33.55	43.50
4120	4" diameter		45	.356		25	18.80		43.80	56
4140	6" diameter		32	.500		36	26.50		62.50	79.50
4160	8" diameter	Q-2	38	.632		85.50	34.50		120	147
4980	Polypropylene, acid resistant, fire retardant, schedule 40									
5000	1-1/2" diameter	Q-1	68	.235	L.F.	7.90	12.45		20.35	27.50
5100	2" diameter		62	.258		12.45	13.65		26.10	34
5120	3" diameter		51	.314		22	16.55		38.55	49.50
5140	4" diameter		45	.356		28	18.80		46.80	59.50
5160	6" diameter		32	.500		56.50	26.50		83	102
5980	Proxylene, fire retardant, Schedule 40									
6000	1-1/2" diameter	Q-1	68	.235	L.F.	12.40	12.45		24.85	32.50
6100	2" diameter		62	.258		17	13.65		30.65	39
6120	3" diameter		51	.314		30.50	16.55		47.05	59
6140	4" diameter		45	.356		43.50	18.80		62.30	76
6820	For Schedule 80, add					35%	2%			

22 66 53.70 Pipe Fittings, Corrosion Resistant

		Crew	Daily Output	Labor-Hours	Unit	Material	Labor	Equipment	Total	Total Incl O&P
0010	**PIPE FITTINGS, CORROSION RESISTANT**									
0030	Iron alloy									
0050	Mechanical joint									
0060	1/4 Bend, 1-1/2"	Q-1	12	1.333	Ea.	77	70.50		147.50	191
0080	2"		10	1.600		126	84.50		210.50	267
0090	3"		9	1.778		151	94		245	310
0100	4"		8	2		174	106		280	350
0160	Tee and Y, sanitary, straight									
0170	1-1/2"	Q-1	8	2	Ea.	84	106		190	253
0180	2"		7	2.286		112	121		233	305
0190	3"		6	2.667		174	141		315	405
0200	4"		5	3.200		320	169		489	605
3000	Epoxy, filament wound									
3030	Quick-lock joint									
3040	90° Elbow, 2"	Q-1	28	.571	Ea.	97.50	30		127.50	153

248

For customer support on your Site Work & Landscape Cost Data, call 877.737.1594.

22 66 53 – Laboratory Chemical-Waste and Vent Piping

22 66 53.70 Pipe Fittings, Corrosion Resistant	Crew	Daily Output	Labor-Hours	Unit	Material	2015 Bare Costs Labor	2015 Bare Costs Equipment	Total	Total Incl O&P
3060	3"	Q-1	16	1	Ea.	112	53		165	203
3070	4"	↓	13	1.231	↓	153	65		218	266
4000	Polypropylene, acid resistant									
4020	Non-pressure, electrofusion joints									
4060	2"	Q-1	28	.571	Ea.	27	30		57	75.50
4090	4"	"	14	1.143	"	47.50	60.50		108	144

For customer support on your Site Work & Landscape Cost Data, call 877.737.1594.

249

Division Notes

	CREW	DAILY OUTPUT	LABOR-HOURS	UNIT	BARE COSTS				TOTAL INCL O&P
					MAT.	LABOR	EQUIP.	TOTAL	

Estimating Tips

The labor adjustment factors listed in Subdivision 22 01 02.20 also apply to Division 23.

23 10 00 Facility Fuel Systems

- The prices in this subdivision for above- and below-ground storage tanks do not include foundations or hold-down slabs, unless noted. The estimator should refer to Divisions 3 and 31 for foundation system pricing. In addition to the foundations, required tank accessories, such as tank gauges, leak detection devices, and additional manholes and piping, must be added to the tank prices.

23 50 00 Central Heating Equipment

- When estimating the cost of an HVAC system, check to see who is responsible for providing and installing the temperature control system. It is possible to overlook controls, assuming that they would be included in the electrical estimate.

- When looking up a boiler, be careful on specified capacity. Some manufacturers rate their products on output while others use input.

- Include HVAC insulation for pipe, boiler, and duct (wrap and liner).

- Be careful when looking up mechanical items to get the correct pressure rating and connection type (thread, weld, flange).

23 70 00 Central HVAC Equipment

- Combination heating and cooling units are sized by the air conditioning requirements. (See Reference No. R236000-20 for preliminary sizing guide.)

- A ton of air conditioning is nominally 400 CFM.

- Rectangular duct is taken off by the linear foot for each size, but its cost is usually estimated by the pound. Remember that SMACNA standards now base duct on internal pressure.

- Prefabricated duct is estimated and purchased like pipe: straight sections and fittings.

- Note that cranes or other lifting equipment are not included on any lines in Division 23. For example, if a crane is required to lift a heavy piece of pipe into place high above a gym floor, or to put a rooftop unit on the roof of a four-story building, etc., it must be added. Due to the potential for extreme variation—from nothing additional required to a major crane or helicopter—we feel that including a nominal amount for "lifting contingency" would be useless and detract from the accuracy of the estimate. When using equipment rental cost data from RSMeans, do not forget to include the cost of the operator(s).

Reference Numbers

Reference numbers are shown in shaded boxes at the beginning of some major classifications. These numbers refer to related items in the Reference Section. The reference information may be an estimating procedure, an alternate pricing method, or technical information.

Note: Not all subdivisions listed here necessarily appear in this publication. ■

*Note: **Trade Service**, in part, has been used as a reference source for some of the material prices used in Division 23.*

23 05 05 – Selective Demolition for HVAC

23 05 05.10 HVAC Demolition		Crew	Daily Output	Labor-Hours	Unit	Material	2015 Bare Costs Labor	Equipment	Total	Total Incl O&P
0010	**HVAC DEMOLITION**									
0100	Air conditioner, split unit, 3 ton	Q-5	2	8	Ea.		430		430	650
0150	Package unit, 3 ton	Q-6	3	8	"		445		445	675
0298	Boilers									
0300	Electric, up thru 148 kW	Q-19	2	12	Ea.		650		650	975
0310	150 thru 518 kW	"	1	24			1,300		1,300	1,950
0320	550 thru 2000 kW	Q-21	.40	80			4,450		4,450	6,700
0330	2070 kW and up	"	.30	106			5,925		5,925	8,925
0340	Gas and/or oil, up thru 150 MBH	Q-7	2.20	14.545			825		825	1,250
0350	160 thru 2000 MBH		.80	40			2,275		2,275	3,425
0360	2100 thru 4500 MBH		.50	64			3,650		3,650	5,500
0370	4600 thru 7000 MBH		.30	106			6,075		6,075	9,175
0380	7100 thru 12,000 MBH		.16	200			11,400		11,400	17,200
0390	12,200 thru 25,000 MBH		.12	266			15,200		15,200	22,900
1000	Ductwork, 4" high, 8" wide	1 Clab	200	.040	L.F.		1.50		1.50	2.31
1100	6" high, 8" wide		165	.048			1.82		1.82	2.80
1200	10" high, 12" wide		125	.064			2.41		2.41	3.70
1300	12"-14" high, 16"-18" wide		85	.094			3.54		3.54	5.45
1400	18" high, 24" wide		67	.119			4.49		4.49	6.90
1500	30" high, 36" wide		56	.143			5.35		5.35	8.25
1540	72" wide		50	.160			6		6	9.25
3000	Mechanical equipment, light items. Unit is weight, not cooling.	Q-5	.90	17.778	Ton		955		955	1,450
3600	Heavy items	"	1.10	14.545	"		780		780	1,175
5090	Remove refrigerant from system	1 Stpi	40	.200	Lb.		11.95		11.95	18.05

23 05 23 – General-Duty Valves for HVAC Piping

23 05 23.30 Valves, Iron Body

23 05 23.30 Valves, Iron Body		Crew	Daily Output	Labor-Hours	Unit	Material	2015 Bare Costs Labor	Equipment	Total	Total Incl O&P
0010	**VALVES, IRON BODY**	R220523-80								
1020	Butterfly, wafer type, gear actuator, 200 lb.									
1030	2"	1 Plum	14	.571	Ea.	96	33.50		129.50	156
1040	2-1/2"	Q-1	9	1.778		97.50	94		191.50	249
1050	3"		8	2		101	106		207	271
1060	4"		5	3.200		113	169		282	380
1070	5"	Q-2	5	4.800		126	263		389	535
1080	6"	"	5	4.800		143	263		406	555
1650	Gate, 125 lb., N.R.S.									
2150	Flanged									
2200	2"	1 Plum	5	1.600	Ea.	715	94		809	930
2240	2-1/2"	Q-1	5	3.200		735	169		904	1,075
2260	3"		4.50	3.556		825	188		1,013	1,200
2280	4"		3	5.333		1,175	282		1,457	1,725
2300	6"	Q-2	3	8		2,025	440		2,465	2,875
3550	OS&Y, 125 lb., flanged									
3600	2"	1 Plum	5	1.600	Ea.	475	94		569	665
3660	3"	Q-1	4.50	3.556		530	188		718	865
3680	4"	"	3	5.333		770	282		1,052	1,275
3700	6"	Q-2	3	8		1,250	440		1,690	2,025
3900	For 175 lb., flanged, add					200%	10%			
5450	Swing check, 125 lb., threaded									
5500	2"	1 Plum	11	.727	Ea.	430	42.50		472.50	540
5540	2-1/2"	Q-1	15	1.067		555	56.50		611.50	695
5550	3"		13	1.231		590	65		655	750
5560	4"		10	1.600		955	84.50		1,039.50	1,175

23 05 Common Work Results for HVAC

23 05 23 – General-Duty Valves for HVAC Piping

23 05 23.30 Valves, Iron Body

		Crew	Daily Output	Labor-Hours	Unit	Material	2015 Bare Costs Labor	Equipment	Total	Total Incl O&P
5950	Flanged									
6000	2"	1 Plum	5	1.600	Ea.	395	94		489	575
6040	2-1/2"	Q-1	5	3.200		380	169		549	675
6050	3"		4.50	3.556		410	188		598	735
6060	4"		3	5.333		605	282		887	1,100
6070	6"	Q-2	3	8		1,025	440		1,465	1,800

23 05 23.80 Valves, Steel

		Crew	Daily Output	Labor-Hours	Unit	Material	2015 Bare Costs Labor	Equipment	Total	Total Incl O&P
0010	**VALVES, STEEL** R220523-80									
0800	Cast									
1350	Check valve, swing type, 150 lb., flanged									
1370	1"	1 Plum	10	.800	Ea.	375	47		422	485
1400	2"	"	8	1		685	58.50		743.50	840
1440	2-1/2"	Q-1	5	3.200		890	169		1,059	1,225
1450	3"		4.50	3.556		805	188		993	1,175
1460	4"		3	5.333		1,225	282		1,507	1,750
1540	For 300 lb., flanged, add					50%	15%			
1548	For 600 lb., flanged, add					110%	20%			
1950	Gate valve, 150 lb., flanged									
2000	2"	1 Plum	8	1	Ea.	780	58.50		838.50	950
2040	2-1/2"	Q-1	5	3.200		1,100	169		1,269	1,475
2050	3"		4.50	3.556		1,100	188		1,288	1,500
2060	4"		3	5.333		1,350	282		1,632	1,925
2070	6"	Q-2	3	8		2,250	440		2,690	3,125
3650	Globe valve, 150 lb., flanged									
3700	2"	1 Plum	8	1	Ea.	980	58.50		1,038.50	1,175
3740	2-1/2"	Q-1	5	3.200		1,250	169		1,419	1,625
3750	3"		4.50	3.556		1,250	188		1,438	1,650
3760	4"		3	5.333		1,825	282		2,107	2,425
3770	6"	Q-2	3	8		2,875	440		3,315	3,800
5150	Forged									
5650	Check valve, class 800, horizontal, socket									
5651	,Socket									
5698	Threaded									
5700	1/4"	1 Plum	24	.333	Ea.	94.50	19.55		114.05	134
5720	3/8"		24	.333		94.50	19.55		114.05	134
5730	1/2"		24	.333		94.50	19.55		114.05	134
5740	3/4"		20	.400		101	23.50		124.50	147
5750	1"		19	.421		119	24.50		143.50	169
5760	1-1/4"		15	.533		233	31.50		264.50	305

23 05 93 – Testing, Adjusting, and Balancing for HVAC

23 05 93.50 Piping, Testing

		Crew	Daily Output	Labor-Hours	Unit	Material	2015 Bare Costs Labor	Equipment	Total	Total Incl O&P
0010	**PIPING, TESTING**									
0100	Nondestructive testing									
0110	Nondestructive hydraulic pressure test, isolate & 1 hr. hold									
0120	1" - 4" pipe									
0140	0 – 250 L.F.	1 Stpi	1.33	6.015	Ea.		360		360	545
0160	250 – 500 L.F.	"	.80	10			600		600	900
0180	500 – 1000 L.F.	Q-5	1.14	14.035			755		755	1,150
0200	1000 – 2000 L.F.	"	.80	20			1,075		1,075	1,625
0300	6" - 10" pipe									
0320	0 – 250 L.F.	Q-5	1	16	Ea.		860		860	1,300
0340	250 – 500 L.F.		.73	21.918			1,175		1,175	1,775

For customer support on your Site Work & Landscape Cost Data, call 877.737.1594.

253

23 05 93 – Testing, Adjusting, and Balancing for HVAC

23 05 93.50 Piping, Testing	Crew	Daily Output	Labor-Hours	Unit	Material	2015 Bare Costs Labor	Equipment	Total	Total Incl O&P
0360	500 – 1000 L.F.	Q-5	.53	30.189	Ea.		1,625		1,625	2,450
0380	1000 – 2000 L.F.	↓	.38	42.105	↓		2,275		2,275	3,425
1000	Pneumatic pressure test, includes soaping joints									
1120	1" - 4" pipe									
1140	0 – 250 L.F.	Q-5	2.67	5.993	Ea.	10.25	320		330.25	495
1160	250 – 500 L.F.		1.33	12.030		20.50	645		665.50	1,000
1180	500 – 1000 L.F.		.80	20		31	1,075		1,106	1,650
1200	1000 – 2000 L.F.	↓	.50	32	↓	41	1,725		1,766	2,650
1300	6" - 10" pipe									
1320	0 – 250 L.F.	Q-5	1.33	12.030	Ea.	10.25	645		655.25	985
1340	250 – 500 L.F.		.67	23.881		20.50	1,275		1,295.50	1,975
1360	500 – 1000 L.F.		.40	40		41	2,150		2,191	3,300
1380	1000 – 2000 L.F.	↓	.25	64	↓	51.50	3,450		3,501.50	5,250
2000	X-Ray of welds									
2110	2" diam.	1 Stpi	8	1	Ea.	13.50	60		73.50	105
2120	3" diam.		8	1		13.50	60		73.50	105
2130	4" diam.		8	1		20.50	60		80.50	113
2140	6" diam.		8	1		20.50	60		80.50	113
2150	8" diam.		6.60	1.212		20.50	72.50		93	132
2160	10" diam.	↓	6	1.333	↓	27	79.50		106.50	150
3000	Liquid penetration of welds									
3110	2" diam.	1 Stpi	14	.571	Ea.	4.50	34		38.50	56.50
3120	3" diam.		13.60	.588		4.50	35		39.50	58
3130	4" diam.		13.40	.597		4.50	35.50		40	59
3140	6" diam.		13.20	.606		4.50	36		40.50	59.50
3150	8" diam.		13	.615		6.75	37		43.75	63
3160	10" diam.	↓	12.80	.625	↓	6.75	37.50		44.25	64

23 13 Facility Fuel-Storage Tanks

23 13 13 – Facility Underground Fuel-Oil, Storage Tanks

23 13 13.09 Single-Wall Steel Fuel-Oil Tanks

		Crew	Daily Output	Labor-Hours	Unit	Material	2015 Bare Costs Labor	Equipment	Total	Total Incl O&P
0010	**SINGLE-WALL STEEL FUEL-OIL TANKS**									
5000	Tanks, steel ugnd., sti-p3, not incl. hold-down bars									
5500	Excavation, pad, pumps and piping not included									
5510	Single wall, 500 gallon capacity, 7 ga. shell	Q-5	2.70	5.926	Ea.	2,050	320		2,370	2,725
5520	1,000 gallon capacity, 7 ga. shell	"	2.50	6.400		3,825	345		4,170	4,725
5530	2,000 gallon capacity, 1/4" thick shell	Q-7	4.60	6.957		6,200	395		6,595	7,425
5535	2,500 gallon capacity, 7 ga. shell	Q-5	3	5.333		6,850	287		7,137	7,950
5540	5,000 gallon capacity, 1/4" thick shell	Q-7	3.20	10		11,500	570		12,070	13,600
5560	10,000 gallon capacity, 1/4" thick shell		2	16		12,300	910		13,210	15,000
5580	15,000 gallon capacity, 5/16" thick shell		1.70	18.824		19,000	1,075		20,075	22,500
5600	20,000 gallon capacity, 5/16" thick shell		1.50	21.333		26,700	1,225		27,925	31,100
5610	25,000 gallon capacity, 3/8" thick shell		1.30	24.615		37,900	1,400		39,300	43,800
5620	30,000 gallon capacity, 3/8" thick shell		1.10	29.091		38,400	1,650		40,050	44,700
5630	40,000 gallon capacity, 3/8" thick shell		.90	35.556		42,000	2,025		44,025	49,300
5640	50,000 gallon capacity, 3/8" thick shell	↓	.80	40	↓	46,600	2,275		48,875	55,000

23 13 13 – Facility Underground Fuel-Oil, Storage Tanks

23 13 13.23 Glass-Fiber-Reinfcd-Plastic, Fuel-Oil, Storage	Crew	Daily Output	Labor-Hours	Unit	Material	2015 Bare Costs Labor	Equipment	Total	Total Incl O&P
0010 **GLASS-FIBER-REINFCD-PLASTIC, UNDERGRND. FUEL-OIL, STORAGE**									
0210 Fiberglass, underground, single wall, U.L. listed, not including									
0220 manway or hold-down strap									
0225 550 gallon capacity	Q-5	2.67	5.993	Ea.	3,200	320		3,520	3,975
0230 1,000 gallon capacity	"	2.46	6.504		4,125	350		4,475	5,050
0240 2,000 gallon capacity	Q-7	4.57	7.002		5,950	400		6,350	7,150
0245 3,000 gallon capacity		3.90	8.205		7,125	465		7,590	8,550
0250 4,000 gallon capacity		3.55	9.014		8,275	515		8,790	9,875
0255 5,000 gallon capacity		3.20	10		9,200	570		9,770	11,000
0260 6,000 gallon capacity		2.67	11.985		9,400	680		10,080	11,300
0270 8,000 gallon capacity		2.29	13.974		11,200	795		11,995	13,600
0280 10,000 gallon capacity		2	16		12,800	910		13,710	15,500
0282 12,000 gallon capacity		1.88	17.021		14,500	970		15,470	17,500
0284 15,000 gallon capacity		1.68	19.048		20,500	1,075		21,575	24,100
0290 20,000 gallon capacity		1.45	22.069		26,300	1,250		27,550	30,900
0300 25,000 gallon capacity		1.28	25		54,000	1,425		55,425	61,500
0320 30,000 gallon capacity		1.14	28.070		77,500	1,600		79,100	87,500
0340 40,000 gallon capacity		.89	35.955		86,000	2,050		88,050	97,500
0360 48,000 gallon capacity		.81	39.506		128,000	2,250		130,250	144,000
0500 For manway, fittings and hold-downs, add					20%	15%			
1000 For helical heating coil, add	Q-5	2.50	6.400		4,775	345		5,120	5,775
2210 Fiberglass, underground, single wall, U.L. listed, including									
2220 hold-down straps, no manways									
2225 550 gallon capacity	Q-5	2	8	Ea.	3,625	430		4,055	4,650
2230 1,000 gallon capacity	"	1.88	8.511		4,575	460		5,035	5,725
2240 2,000 gallon capacity	Q-7	3.55	9.014		6,400	515		6,915	7,825
2250 4,000 gallon capacity		2.90	11.034		8,725	630		9,355	10,600
2260 6,000 gallon capacity		2	16		10,300	910		11,210	12,700
2270 8,000 gallon capacity		1.78	17.978		12,100	1,025		13,125	14,900
2280 10,000 gallon capacity		1.60	20		13,700	1,150		14,850	16,800
2282 12,000 gallon capacity		1.52	21.053		15,400	1,200		16,600	18,800
2284 15,000 gallon capacity		1.39	23.022		21,400	1,300		22,700	25,500
2290 20,000 gallon capacity		1.14	28.070		27,700	1,600		29,300	32,800
2300 25,000 gallon capacity		.96	33.333		56,000	1,900		57,900	64,500
2320 30,000 gallon capacity		.80	40		80,000	2,275		82,275	91,500

23 21 Hydronic Piping and Pumps

23 21 23 – Hydronic Pumps

23 21 23.13 In-Line Centrifugal Hydronic Pumps

	Crew	Daily Output	Labor-Hours	Unit	Material	2015 Bare Costs Labor	Equipment	Total	Total Incl O&P
0010 **IN-LINE CENTRIFUGAL HYDRONIC PUMPS**									
0600 Bronze, sweat connections, 1/40 HP, in line									
0640 3/4" size	Q-1	16	1	Ea.	218	53		271	320
1000 Flange connection, 3/4" to 1-1/2" size									
1040 1/12 HP	Q-1	6	2.667	Ea.	565	141		706	835
1060 1/8 HP		6	2.667		970	141		1,111	1,300
1100 1/3 HP		6	2.667		1,075	141		1,216	1,425
1140 2" size, 1/6 HP		5	3.200		1,400	169		1,569	1,775
1180 2-1/2" size, 1/4 HP		5	3.200		1,775	169		1,944	2,200
2000 Cast iron, flange connection									
2040 3/4" to 1-1/2" size, in line, 1/12 HP	Q-1	6	2.667	Ea.	365	141		506	615

For customer support on your Site Work & Landscape Cost Data, call 877.737.1594.

255

23 21 Hydronic Piping and Pumps

23 21 23 – Hydronic Pumps

23 21 23.13 In-Line Centrifugal Hydronic Pumps		Crew	Daily Output	Labor-Hours	Unit	Material	2015 Bare Costs		Total	Total Incl O&P
							Labor	Equipment		
2100	1/3 HP	Q-1	6	2.667	Ea.	680	141		821	960
2140	2" size, 1/6 HP		5	3.200		745	169		914	1,075
2180	2-1/2" size, 1/4 HP		5	3.200		960	169		1,129	1,300
2220	3" size, 1/4 HP		4	4		975	211		1,186	1,400
2600	For nonferrous impeller, add					3%				

23 55 Fuel-Fired Heaters

23 55 13 – Fuel-Fired Duct Heaters

23 55 13.16 Gas-Fired Duct Heaters

		Crew	Daily Output	Labor-Hours	Unit	Material	Labor	Equipment	Total	Total Incl O&P
0010	**GAS-FIRED DUCT HEATERS**, Includes burner, controls, stainless steel									
0020	heat exchanger. Gas fired, electric ignition									
1000	Outdoor installation, with power venter									
1020	75 MBH output	Q-5	4	4	Ea.	3,525	215		3,740	4,200
1060	120 MBH output		4	4		3,875	215		4,090	4,575
1100	187 MBH output		3	5.333		4,800	287		5,087	5,700
1140	300 MBH output		1.80	8.889		7,750	480		8,230	9,250
1180	450 MBH output		1.40	11.429		9,350	615		9,965	11,200

Estimating Tips

26 05 00 Common Work Results for Electrical

- Conduit should be taken off in three main categories—power distribution, branch power, and branch lighting—so the estimator can concentrate on systems and components, therefore making it easier to ensure all items have been accounted for.

- For cost modifications for elevated conduit installation, add the percentages to labor according to the height of installation, and only to the quantities exceeding the different height levels, not to the total conduit quantities.

- Remember that aluminum wiring of equal ampacity is larger in diameter than copper and may require larger conduit.

- If more than three wires at a time are being pulled, deduct percentages from the labor hours of that grouping of wires.

- When taking off grounding systems, identify separately the type and size of wire, and list each unique type of ground connection.

- The estimator should take the weights of materials into consideration when completing a takeoff. Topics to consider include: How will the materials be supported? What methods of support are available? How high will the support structure have to reach? Will the final support structure be able to withstand the total burden? Is the support material included or separate from the fixture, equipment, and material specified?

- Do not overlook the costs for equipment used in the installation. If scaffolding or highlifts are available in the field, contractors may use them in lieu of the proposed ladders and rolling staging.

26 20 00 Low-Voltage Electrical Transmission

- Supports and concrete pads may be shown on drawings for the larger equipment, or the support system may be only a piece of plywood for the back of a panelboard. In either case, it must be included in the costs.

26 40 00 Electrical and Cathodic Protection

- When taking off cathodic protections systems, identify the type and size of cable, and list each unique type of anode connection.

26 50 00 Lighting

- Fixtures should be taken off room by room, using the fixture schedule, specifications, and the ceiling plan. For large concentrations of lighting fixtures in the same area, deduct the percentages from labor hours.

Reference Numbers

Reference numbers are shown in shaded boxes at the beginning of some major classifications. These numbers refer to related items in the Reference Section. The reference information may be an estimating procedure, an alternate pricing method, or technical information.

Note: Not all subdivisions listed here necessarily appear in this publication. ■

Did you know?

RSMeans Online gives you the same access to RSMeans' data with 24/7 access:

- Quickly locate costs in the searchable database.
- Build cost lists, estimates, and reports in minutes.
- Adjust costs to any location in the U.S. and Canada with the click of a button.

Start your free trial today at **www.rsmeansonline.com**

RSMeansOnline

---

*Note: **Trade Service**, in part, has been used as a reference source for some of the material prices used in Division 26.*

26 05 Common Work Results for Electrical

26 05 05 – Selective Demolition for Electrical

26 05 05.10 Electrical Demolition

26 05 05.10 Electrical Demolition		Crew	Daily Output	Labor-Hours	Unit	Material	2015 Bare Costs Labor	Equipment	Total	Total Incl O&P
0010	**ELECTRICAL DEMOLITION**									
0020	Conduit to 15' high, including fittings & hangers									
0100	Rigid galvanized steel, 1/2" to 1" diameter	1 Elec	242	.033	L.F.		1.81		1.81	2.71
0120	1-1/4" to 2"	"	200	.040			2.19		2.19	3.28
0140	2-1/2" to 3-1/2"	2 Elec	302	.053			2.90		2.90	4.34
0160	4" to 6"	"	160	.100			5.45		5.45	8.20
0200	Electric metallic tubing (EMT), 1/2" to 1"	1 Elec	394	.020			1.11		1.11	1.66
0220	1-1/4" to 1-1/2"		326	.025			1.34		1.34	2.01
0240	2" to 3"		236	.034			1.85		1.85	2.78
0260	3-1/2" to 4"	2 Elec	310	.052			2.82		2.82	4.23
1300	Transformer, dry type, 1 phase, incl. removal of									
1320	supports, wire & conduit terminations									
1340	1 kVA	1 Elec	7.70	1.039	Ea.		57		57	85
1420	75 kVA	2 Elec	2.50	6.400	"		350		350	525
1440	3 phase to 600V, primary									
1460	3 kVA	1 Elec	3.87	2.067	Ea.		113		113	169
1520	75 kVA	2 Elec	2.69	5.948			325		325	485
1550	300 kVA	R-3	1.80	11.111			605	76.50	681.50	990
1570	750 kVA	"	1.10	18.182			985	125	1,110	1,625

26 05 13 – Medium-Voltage Cables

26 05 13.16 Medium-Voltage, Single Cable

26 05 13.16 Medium-Voltage, Single Cable		Crew	Daily Output	Labor-Hours	Unit	Material	2015 Bare Costs Labor	Equipment	Total	Total Incl O&P
0010	**MEDIUM-VOLTAGE, SINGLE CABLE** Splicing & terminations not included									
0040	Copper, XLP shielding, 5 kV, #6 R260533-22	2 Elec	4.40	3.636	C.L.F.	160	199		359	475
0050	#4		4.40	3.636		207	199		406	525
0100	#2		4	4		228	219		447	580
0200	#1		4	4		281	219		500	640
0400	1/0		3.80	4.211		315	230		545	690
0600	2/0		3.60	4.444		385	243		628	785
0800	4/0		3.20	5		520	274		794	980
1000	250 kcmil	3 Elec	4.50	5.333		595	292		887	1,100
1200	350 kcmil		3.90	6.154		780	335		1,115	1,375
1400	500 kcmil		3.60	6.667		955	365		1,320	1,600
1600	15 kV, ungrounded neutral, #1	2 Elec	4	4		340	219		559	705
1800	1/0		3.80	4.211		410	230		640	795
2000	2/0		3.60	4.444		465	243		708	875
2200	4/0		3.20	5		620	274		894	1,100
2400	250 kcmil	3 Elec	4.50	5.333		685	292		977	1,200
2600	350 kcmil		3.90	6.154		865	335		1,200	1,450
2800	500 kcmil		3.60	6.667		1,075	365		1,440	1,725
3000	25 kV, grounded neutral, #1/0	2 Elec	3.60	4.444		565	243		808	985
3200	2/0		3.40	4.706		620	257		877	1,075
3400	4/0		3	5.333		780	292		1,072	1,300
3600	250 kcmil	3 Elec	4.20	5.714		970	315		1,285	1,550
3800	350 kcmil		3.60	6.667		1,125	365		1,490	1,800
3900	500 kcmil		3.30	7.273		1,325	400		1,725	2,075
4000	35 kV, grounded neutral, #1/0	2 Elec	3.40	4.706		600	257		857	1,050
4200	2/0		3.20	5		705	274		979	1,175
4400	4/0		2.80	5.714		885	315		1,200	1,450
4600	250 kcmil	3 Elec	3.90	6.154		1,025	335		1,360	1,650
4800	350 kcmil		3.30	7.273		1,250	400		1,650	1,975
5000	500 kcmil		3	8		1,475	440		1,915	2,250
5050	Aluminum, XLP shielding, 5 kV, #2	2 Elec	5	3.200		170	175		345	450

26 05 Common Work Results for Electrical

26 05 13 – Medium-Voltage Cables

26 05 13.16 Medium-Voltage, Single Cable

		Crew	Daily Output	Labor-Hours	Unit	Material	2015 Bare Costs Labor	Equipment	Total	Total Incl O&P
5070	#1	2 Elec	4.40	3.636	C.L.F.	176	199		375	490
5090	1/0		4	4		204	219		423	555
5100	2/0		3.80	4.211		229	230		459	595
5150	4/0		3.60	4.444		271	243		514	665
5200	250 kcmil	3 Elec	4.80	5		330	274		604	770
5220	350 kcmil		4.50	5.333		385	292		677	860
5240	500 kcmil		3.90	6.154		495	335		830	1,050
5260	750 kcmil		3.60	6.667		655	365		1,020	1,275
5300	15 kV aluminum, XLP, #1	2 Elec	4.40	3.636		218	199		417	540
5320	1/0		4	4		226	219		445	580
5340	2/0		3.80	4.211		269	230		499	640
5360	4/0		3.60	4.444		299	243		542	695
5380	250 kcmil	3 Elec	4.80	5		355	274		629	800
5400	350 kcmil		4.50	5.333		400	292		692	875
5420	500 kcmil		3.90	6.154		555	335		890	1,125
5440	750 kcmil		3.60	6.667		735	365		1,100	1,350

26 05 19 – Low-Voltage Electrical Power Conductors and Cables

26 05 19.55 Non-Metallic Sheathed Cable

		Crew	Daily Output	Labor-Hours	Unit	Material	2015 Bare Costs Labor	Equipment	Total	Total Incl O&P
0010	**NON-METALLIC SHEATHED CABLE** 600 volt R260533-22									
0100	Copper with ground wire, (Romex)									
0150	#14, 2 conductor	1 Elec	2.70	2.963	C.L.F.	24	162		186	270
0200	3 conductor		2.40	3.333		34	182		216	310
0220	4 conductor		2.20	3.636		49	199		248	350
0250	#12, 2 conductor		2.50	3.200		36.50	175		211.50	300
0300	3 conductor		2.20	3.636		52	199		251	355
0320	4 conductor		2	4		76.50	219		295.50	415
0350	#10, 2 conductor		2.20	3.636		56.50	199		255.50	360
0400	3 conductor		1.80	4.444		82.50	243		325.50	455
0420	4 conductor		1.60	5		119	274		393	540
0430	#8, 2 conductor		1.60	5		88.50	274		362.50	510
0450	3 conductor		1.50	5.333		133	292		425	580
0500	#6, 3 conductor		1.40	5.714		215	315		530	705
0520	#4, 3 conductor	2 Elec	2.40	6.667		550	365		915	1,150
0540	#2, 3 conductor	"	2.20	7.273		790	400		1,190	1,475
0550	SE type SER aluminum cable, 3 RHW and									
0600	1 bare neutral, 3 #8 & 1 #8	1 Elec	1.60	5	C.L.F.	158	274		432	585
0650	3 #6 & 1 #6	"	1.40	5.714		179	315		494	665
0700	3 #4 & 1 #6	2 Elec	2.40	6.667		165	365		530	725
0750	3 #2 & 1 #4		2.20	7.273		296	400		696	920
0800	3 #1/0 & 1 #2		2	8		450	440		890	1,150
0850	3 #2/0 & 1 #1		1.80	8.889		530	485		1,015	1,300
0900	3 #4/0 & 1 #2/0		1.60	10		755	545		1,300	1,650
1000	URD - triplex underground distribution cable, alum. 2 #4 + #4 neutral		2.80	5.714		101	315		416	580
1010	2 #2 + #4 neutral		2.65	6.038		126	330		456	635
1020	2 #2 + #2 neutral		2.55	6.275		126	345		471	655
1030	2 1/0 + #2 neutral		2.40	6.667		152	365		517	715
1040	2 1/0 + 1/0 neutral		2.30	6.957		166	380		546	755
1050	2 2/0 + #1 neutral		2.20	7.273		181	400		581	795
1060	2 2/0 + 2/0 neutral		2.10	7.619		197	415		612	840
1070	2 3/0 + 1/0 neutral		1.95	8.205		218	450		668	910
1080	2 3/0 + 3/0 neutral		1.95	8.205		250	450		700	945
1090	2 4/0 + 2/0 neutral		1.85	8.649		261	475		736	995

For customer support on your Site Work & Landscape Cost Data, call 877.737.1594.

259

26 05 19 – Low-Voltage Electrical Power Conductors and Cables

26 05 19.55 Non-Metallic Sheathed Cable	Crew	Daily Output	Labor-Hours	Unit	Material	2015 Bare Costs Labor	Equipment	Total	Total Incl O&P
1100	2 4/0 + 4/0 neutral	2 Elec	1.85	8.649	C.L.F.	276	475		751	1,025
1450	UF underground feeder cable, copper with ground, #14, 2 conductor	1 Elec	4	2		27	109		136	194
1500	#12, 2 conductor		3.50	2.286		41.50	125		166.50	233
1550	#10, 2 conductor		3	2.667		63.50	146		209.50	289
1600	#14, 3 conductor		3.50	2.286		39.50	125		164.50	231
1650	#12, 3 conductor		3	2.667		59.50	146		205.50	285
1700	#10, 3 conductor		2.50	3.200		93.50	175		268.50	365
1710	#8, 3 conductor		2	4		154	219		373	500
1720	#6, 3 conductor		1.80	4.444		248	243		491	640
2400	SEU service entrance cable, copper 2 conductors, #8 + #8 neutral		1.50	5.333		115	292		407	560
2600	#6 + #8 neutral		1.30	6.154		170	335		505	690
2800	#6 + #6 neutral		1.30	6.154		193	335		528	715
3000	#4 + #6 neutral	2 Elec	2.20	7.273		266	400		666	890
3200	#4 + #4 neutral		2.20	7.273		300	400		700	925
3400	#3 + #5 neutral		2.10	7.619		370	415		785	1,025
3600	#3 + #3 neutral		2.10	7.619		400	415		815	1,075
3800	#2 + #4 neutral		2	8		430	440		870	1,125
4000	#1 + #1 neutral		1.90	8.421		470	460		930	1,200
4200	1/0 + 1/0 neutral		1.80	8.889		750	485		1,235	1,550
4400	2/0 + 2/0 neutral		1.70	9.412		935	515		1,450	1,800
4600	3/0 + 3/0 neutral		1.60	10		1,175	545		1,720	2,125
4620	4/0 + 4/0 neutral		1.45	11.034		1,325	605		1,930	2,350
4800	Aluminum 2 conductors, #8 + #8 neutral	1 Elec	1.60	5		131	274		405	555
5000	#6 + #6 neutral	"	1.40	5.714		132	315		447	615
5100	#4 + #6 neutral	2 Elec	2.50	6.400		155	350		505	695
5200	#4 + #4 neutral		2.40	6.667		169	365		534	730
5300	#2 + #4 neutral		2.30	6.957		207	380		587	800
5400	#2 + #2 neutral		2.20	7.273		226	400		626	845
5450	1/0 + #2 neutral		2.10	7.619		330	415		745	985
5500	1/0 + 1/0 neutral		2	8		345	440		785	1,025
5550	2/0 + #1 neutral		1.90	8.421		370	460		830	1,100
5600	2/0 + 2/0 neutral		1.80	8.889		395	485		880	1,175
5800	3/0 + 1/0 neutral		1.70	9.412		430	515		945	1,250
6000	3/0 + 3/0 neutral		1.70	9.412		470	515		985	1,300
6200	4/0 + 2/0 neutral		1.60	10		510	545		1,055	1,375
6400	4/0 + 4/0 neutral		1.60	10		555	545		1,100	1,425
6500	Service entrance cap for copper SEU									
6600	100 amp	1 Elec	12	.667	Ea.	8.75	36.50		45.25	64
6700	150 amp	"	10	.800	"	16.10	44		60.10	83

26 05 26 – Grounding and Bonding for Electrical Systems

26 05 26.80 Grounding

		Crew	Daily Output	Labor-Hours	Unit	Material	Labor	Equipment	Total	Total Incl O&P
0010	**GROUNDING**									
0030	Rod, copper clad, 8' long, 1/2" diameter	1 Elec	5.50	1.455	Ea.	20	79.50		99.50	141
0040	5/8" diameter		5.50	1.455		19.20	79.50		98.70	140
0050	3/4" diameter		5.30	1.509		33.50	82.50		116	161
0080	10' long, 1/2" diameter		4.80	1.667		22	91		113	162
0090	5/8" diameter		4.60	1.739		24	95		119	170
0100	3/4" diameter		4.40	1.818		38.50	99.50		138	192
0130	15' long, 3/4" diameter		4	2		54	109		163	224
0150	Coupling, bronze, 1/2" diameter					4.07			4.07	4.48
0160	5/8" diameter					5.35			5.35	5.90
0170	3/4" diameter					13.20			13.20	14.50

26 05 26 – Grounding and Bonding for Electrical Systems

26 05 26.80 Grounding		Crew	Daily Output	Labor-Hours	Unit	Material	2015 Bare Costs Labor	Equipment	Total	Total Incl O&P
0190	Drive studs, 1/2" diameter				Ea.	10.70			10.70	11.75
0210	5/8" diameter					15.55			15.55	17.10
0220	3/4" diameter					18.15			18.15	20
0230	Clamp, bronze, 1/2" diameter	1 Elec	32	.250		4.65	13.70		18.35	25.50
0240	5/8" diameter		32	.250		5.25	13.70		18.95	26.50
0250	3/4" diameter		32	.250		5.90	13.70		19.60	27
0260	Wire ground bare armored, #8-1 conductor		2	4	C.L.F.	76	219		295	415
0270	#6-1 conductor		1.80	4.444		91.50	243		334.50	465
0280	#4-1 conductor		1.60	5		128	274		402	550
0320	Bare copper wire, #14 solid		14	.571		7.35	31.50		38.85	55
0330	#12		13	.615		12.60	33.50		46.10	64.50
0340	#10		12	.667		18	36.50		54.50	74.50
0350	#8		11	.727		29	40		69	91.50
0360	#6		10	.800		51	44		95	122
0370	#4		8	1		117	54.50		171.50	210
0380	#2		5	1.600		130	87.50		217.50	274
0390	Bare copper wire, stranded, #8		11	.727		29.50	40		69.50	92
0400	#6		10	.800		52	44		96	123
0450	#4	2 Elec	16	1		87.50	54.50		142	179
0600	#2		10	1.600		138	87.50		225.50	283
0650	#1		9	1.778		182	97		279	345
0700	1/0		8	2		197	109		306	380
0750	2/0		7.20	2.222		248	122		370	455
0800	3/0		6.60	2.424		310	133		443	540
1000	4/0		5.70	2.807		395	154		549	665
1200	250 kcmil	3 Elec	7.20	3.333		465	182		647	785
1210	300 kcmil		6.60	3.636		525	199		724	880
1220	350 kcmil		6	4		660	219		879	1,050
1230	400 kcmil		5.70	4.211		770	230		1,000	1,200
1240	500 kcmil		5.10	4.706		945	257		1,202	1,425
1260	750 kcmil		3.60	6.667		1,600	365		1,965	2,325
1270	1000 kcmil		3	8		2,125	440		2,565	3,000
1360	Bare aluminum, stranded, #6	1 Elec	9	.889		14.60	48.50		63.10	89
1370	#4	2 Elec	16	1		25.50	54.50		80	111
1380	#2		13	1.231		36.50	67.50		104	142
1390	#1		10.60	1.509		40.50	82.50		123	169
1400	1/0		9	1.778		46.50	97		143.50	197
1410	2/0		8	2		59	109		168	229
1420	3/0		7.20	2.222		79.50	122		201.50	269
1430	4/0		6.60	2.424		91	133		224	299
1440	250 kcmil	3 Elec	9.30	2.581		119	141		260	340
1450	300 kcmil		8.70	2.759		140	151		291	380
1460	400 kcmil		7.50	3.200		180	175		355	460
1470	500 kcmil		6.90	3.478		214	190		404	520
1480	600 kcmil		6	4		243	219		462	600
1490	700 kcmil		5.70	4.211		267	230		497	640
1500	750 kcmil		5.10	4.706		277	257		534	690
1510	1000 kcmil		4.80	5		350	274		624	795
1800	Water pipe ground clamps, heavy duty									
2000	Bronze, 1/2" to 1" diameter	1 Elec	8	1	Ea.	24	54.50		78.50	108
2100	1-1/4" to 2" diameter		8	1		33	54.50		87.50	119
2200	2-1/2" to 3" diameter		6	1.333		44.50	73		117.50	158
2730	Exothermic weld, 4/0 wire to 1" ground rod		7	1.143		10.70	62.50		73.20	105

26 05 26.80 Grounding		Crew	Daily Output	Labor-Hours	Unit	Material	2015 Bare Costs Labor	Equipment	Total	Total Incl O&P
2740	4/0 wire to building steel	1 Elec	7	1.143	Ea.	10.70	62.50		73.20	105
2750	4/0 wire to motor frame		7	1.143		10.70	62.50		73.20	105
2760	4/0 wire to 4/0 wire		7	1.143		10.70	62.50		73.20	105
2770	4/0 wire to #4 wire		7	1.143		10.70	62.50		73.20	105
2780	4/0 wire to #8 wire	▼	7	1.143		10.70	62.50		73.20	105
2790	Mold, reusable, for above					138			138	152
2800	Brazed connections, #6 wire	1 Elec	12	.667		16.15	36.50		52.65	72.50
3000	#2 wire		10	.800		21.50	44		65.50	89.50
3100	3/0 wire		8	1		32.50	54.50		87	118
3200	4/0 wire		7	1.143		37	62.50		99.50	135
3400	250 kcmil wire		5	1.600		43.50	87.50		131	179
3600	500 kcmil wire		4	2	▼	53.50	109		162.50	223
3700	Insulated ground wire, copper #14		13	.615	C.L.F.	8.90	33.50		42.40	60.50
3710	#12		11	.727		13.30	40		53.30	74
3720	#10		10	.800		20.50	44		64.50	88
3730	#8		8	1		33.50	54.50		88	119
3740	#6	▼	6.50	1.231		57.50	67.50		125	165
3750	#4	2 Elec	10.60	1.509		87.50	82.50		170	220
3770	#2		9	1.778		140	97		237	300
3780	#1		8	2		181	109		290	365
3790	1/0		6.60	2.424		217	133		350	435
3800	2/0		5.80	2.759		271	151		422	525
3810	3/0		5	3.200		340	175		515	635
3820	4/0	▼	4.40	3.636		430	199		629	770
3830	250 kcmil	3 Elec	6	4		520	219		739	900
3840	300 kcmil		5.70	4.211		625	230		855	1,025
3850	350 kcmil		5.40	4.444		730	243		973	1,175
3860	400 kcmil		5.10	4.706		825	257		1,082	1,300
3870	500 kcmil		4.80	5		1,025	274		1,299	1,525
3880	600 kcmil		3.90	6.154		1,400	335		1,735	2,025
3890	750 kcmil		3.30	7.273		1,975	400		2,375	2,750
3900	1000 kcmil	▼	2.70	8.889		2,825	485		3,310	3,825
3960	Insulated ground wire, aluminum, #6	1 Elec	8	1		43	54.50		97.50	130
3970	#4	2 Elec	13	1.231		53.50	67.50		121	160
3980	#2		10.60	1.509		72.50	82.50		155	204
3990	#1		9	1.778		106	97		203	262
4000	1/0		8	2		127	109		236	305
4010	2/0		7.20	2.222		150	122		272	345
4020	3/0		6.60	2.424		186	133		319	405
4030	4/0	▼	6.20	2.581		207	141		348	440
4040	250 kcmil	3 Elec	8.70	2.759		253	151		404	505
4050	300 kcmil		8.10	2.963		350	162		512	630
4060	350 kcmil		7.50	3.200		355	175		530	650
4070	400 kcmil		6.90	3.478		415	190		605	740
4080	500 kcmil		6	4		460	219		679	835
4090	600 kcmil		5.70	4.211		580	230		810	985
4100	700 kcmil		5.10	4.706		670	257		927	1,125
4110	750 kcmil	▼	4.80	5	▼	695	274		969	1,175
5000	Copper Electrolytic ground rod system									
5010	Includes augering hole, mixing bentonite clay,									
5020	Installing rod, and terminating ground wire									
5100	Straight Vertical type, 2" diam.									
5120	8.5' long, clamp connection	1 Elec	2.67	2.996	Ea.	770	164		934	1,100

For customer support on your Site Work & Landscape Cost Data, call 877.737.1594.

26 05 Common Work Results for Electrical

26 05 26 – Grounding and Bonding for Electrical Systems

26 05 26.80 Grounding

		Crew	Daily Output	Labor-Hours	Unit	Material	2015 Bare Costs Labor	Equipment	Total	Total Incl O&P
5130	With exothermic weld connection	1 Elec	1.95	4.103	Ea.	770	224		994	1,175
5140	10' long		2.35	3.404		900	186		1,086	1,275
5150	With exothermic weld connection		1.78	4.494		900	246		1,146	1,350
5160	12' long		2.16	3.704		1,025	203		1,228	1,425
5170	With exothermic weld connection		1.67	4.790		1,025	262		1,287	1,525
5180	20' long		1.74	4.598		1,475	251		1,726	1,975
5190	With exothermic weld connection	▼	1.40	5.714		1,775	315		2,090	2,425
5195	40' long with exothermic weld connection	2 Elec	2	8	▼	3,075	440		3,515	4,025
5200	L-Shaped, 2" diam.									
5220	4' Vert. x 10' Horz., clamp connection	1 Elec	5.33	1.501	Ea.	1,275	82		1,357	1,550
5230	With exothermic weld connection	"	3.08	2.597	"	1,275	142		1,417	1,650
5300	Protective Box at grade level, with breather slots									
5320	Round 12" long, fiberlyte	1 Elec	32	.250	Ea.	65	13.70		78.70	92
5330	Concrete	"	16	.500		101	27.50		128.50	152
5400	Bentonite Clay, 50# bag, 1 per 10' of rod					41.50			41.50	45.50
5500	Equipotential earthing bar	1 Elec	2	4	▼	176	219		395	525

26 05 33 – Raceway and Boxes for Electrical Systems

26 05 33.13 Conduit

		Crew	Daily Output	Labor-Hours	Unit	Material	2015 Bare Costs Labor	Equipment	Total	Total Incl O&P
0010	**CONDUIT** To 15' high, includes 2 terminations, 2 elbows,									
0020	11 beam clamps, and 11 couplings per 100 L.F.									
9100	PVC, schedule 40, 1/2" diameter	1 Elec	190	.042	L.F.	.90	2.30		3.20	4.44
9110	3/4" diameter		145	.055		.98	3.02		4	5.60
9120	1" diameter		125	.064		2.11	3.50		5.61	7.55
9130	1-1/4" diameter		110	.073		2.63	3.98		6.61	8.85
9140	1-1/2" diameter		100	.080		2.99	4.38		7.37	9.85
9150	2" diameter		90	.089		3.90	4.86		8.76	11.60
9160	2-1/2" diameter	▼	65	.123		5.45	6.75		12.20	16.10
9170	3" diameter	2 Elec	110	.145		6.30	7.95		14.25	18.80
9180	3-1/2" diameter		100	.160		8.25	8.75		17	22
9190	4" diameter		90	.178		9.65	9.70		19.35	25
9200	5" diameter		70	.229		12.45	12.50		24.95	32.50
9210	6" diameter	▼	60	.267	▼	15.95	14.60		30.55	39.50
9220	Elbows, 1/2" diameter	1 Elec	50	.160	Ea.	.90	8.75		9.65	14.10
9225	3/4" diameter		42	.190		.88	10.40		11.28	16.55
9230	1" diameter		35	.229		1.33	12.50		13.83	20
9235	1-1/4" diameter		28	.286		2.04	15.65		17.69	25.50
9240	1-1/2" diameter		20	.400		2.65	22		24.65	36
9245	2" diameter		16	.500		3.59	27.50		31.09	45
9250	2-1/2" diameter		11	.727		6.45	40		46.45	66.50
9255	3" diameter		9	.889		10.85	48.50		59.35	85
9260	3-1/2" diameter		7	1.143		14	62.50		76.50	109
9265	4" diameter		6	1.333		17.25	73		90.25	128
9270	5" diameter		4	2		28	109		137	195
9275	6" diameter		3	2.667		64.50	146		210.50	290
9312	Couplings, 1/2" diameter		50	.160		.29	8.75		9.04	13.40
9314	3/4" diameter		42	.190		.32	10.40		10.72	15.95
9316	1" diameter		35	.229		.36	12.50		12.86	19.15
9318	1-1/4" diameter		28	.286		.51	15.65		16.16	24
9320	1-1/2" diameter		20	.400		.54	22		22.54	33.50
9322	2" diameter		16	.500		1.07	27.50		28.57	42
9324	2-1/2" diameter		11	.727		1.80	40		41.80	61.50
9326	3" diameter	▼	9	.889		1.97	48.50		50.47	75

For customer support on your Site Work & Landscape Cost Data, call 877.737.1594.

263

26 05 33.13 Conduit		Crew	Daily Output	Labor-Hours	Unit	Material	2015 Bare Costs Labor	Equipment	Total	Total Incl O&P
9328	3-1/2" diameter	1 Elec	7	1.143	Ea.	2.51	62.50		65.01	96.50
9330	4" diameter		6	1.333		3.07	73		76.07	112
9332	5" diameter		4	2		7.55	109		116.55	172
9334	6" diameter		3	2.667		10.60	146		156.60	231
9335	See note on line 26 05 33.13 9995									
9340	Field bends, 45° & 90°, 1/2" diameter	1 Elec	45	.178	Ea.		9.70		9.70	14.55
9350	3/4" diameter		40	.200			10.95		10.95	16.40
9360	1" diameter		35	.229			12.50		12.50	18.75
9370	1-1/4" diameter		32	.250			13.70		13.70	20.50
9380	1-1/2" diameter		27	.296			16.20		16.20	24.50
9390	2" diameter		20	.400			22		22	33
9400	2-1/2" diameter		16	.500			27.50		27.50	41
9410	3" diameter		13	.615			33.50		33.50	50.50
9420	3-1/2" diameter		12	.667			36.50		36.50	54.50
9430	4" diameter		10	.800			44		44	65.50
9440	5" diameter		9	.889			48.50		48.50	73
9450	6" diameter		8	1			54.50		54.50	82
9460	PVC adapters, 1/2" diameter		50	.160		.25	8.75		9	13.40
9470	3/4" diameter		42	.190		.41	10.40		10.81	16.05
9480	1" diameter		38	.211		.56	11.50		12.06	17.85
9490	1-1/4" diameter		35	.229		.74	12.50		13.24	19.55
9500	1-1/2" diameter		32	.250		.98	13.70		14.68	21.50
9510	2" diameter		27	.296		1.22	16.20		17.42	26
9520	2-1/2" diameter		23	.348		2.14	19.05		21.19	31
9530	3" diameter		18	.444		2.97	24.50		27.47	40
9540	3-1/2" diameter		13	.615		4.57	33.50		38.07	55.50
9550	4" diameter		11	.727		5.30	40		45.30	65.50
9560	5" diameter		8	1		11.20	54.50		65.70	94.50
9570	6" diameter		6	1.333		18.70	73		91.70	130
9580	PVC-LB, LR or LL fittings & covers									
9590	1/2" diameter	1 Elec	20	.400	Ea.	3.04	22		25.04	36.50
9600	3/4" diameter		16	.500		4.60	27.50		32.10	46
9610	1" diameter		12	.667		5.05	36.50		41.55	60
9620	1-1/4" diameter		9	.889		7.80	48.50		56.30	81.50
9630	1-1/2" diameter		7	1.143		9.30	62.50		71.80	104
9640	2" diameter		6	1.333		14.75	73		87.75	125
9650	2-1/2" diameter		6	1.333		52	73		125	167
9660	3" diameter		5	1.600		50.50	87.50		138	187
9670	3-1/2" diameter		4	2		53.50	109		162.50	223
9680	4" diameter		3	2.667		70.50	146		216.50	297
9690	PVC-tee fitting & cover									
9700	1/2"	1 Elec	14	.571	Ea.	5.85	31.50		37.35	53.50
9710	3/4"		13	.615		5.85	33.50		39.35	57
9720	1"		10	.800		6.55	44		50.55	72.50
9730	1-1/4"		9	.889		11.50	48.50		60	85.50
9740	1-1/2"		8	1		13.50	54.50		68	97
9750	2"		7	1.143		20.50	62.50		83	116
9760	PVC-reducers, 3/4" x 1/2" diameter					1.41			1.41	1.55
9770	1" x 1/2" diameter					3.09			3.09	3.40
9780	1" x 3/4" diameter					3.34			3.34	3.67
9790	1-1/4" x 3/4" diameter					4.10			4.10	4.51
9800	1-1/4" x 1" diameter					4.34			4.34	4.77
9810	1-1/2" x 1-1/4" diameter					4.53			4.53	4.98

26 05 33 – Raceway and Boxes for Electrical Systems

26 05 33.13 Conduit

		Crew	Daily Output	Labor-Hours	Unit	Material	2015 Bare Costs Labor	Equipment	Total	Total Incl O&P
9820	2" x 1-1/4" diameter				Ea.	5.45			5.45	5.95
9830	2-1/2" x 2" diameter					16.85			16.85	18.55
9840	3" x 2" diameter					17.40			17.40	19.15
9850	4" x 3" diameter					20			20	22
9860	Cement, quart					16.60			16.60	18.30
9870	Gallon					104			104	114
9880	Heat bender, to 6" diameter					1,850			1,850	2,025
9900	Add to labor for higher elevated installation									
9910	15' to 20' high, add						10%			
9920	20' to 25' high, add						20%			
9930	25' to 30' high, add						25%			
9940	30' to 35' high, add						30%			
9950	35' to 40' high, add						35%			
9960	Over 40' high, add						40%			
9995	Do not include labor when adding couplings to a fitting installation									

26 05 33.18 Pull Boxes

		Crew	Daily Output	Labor-Hours	Unit	Material	2015 Bare Costs Labor	Equipment	Total	Total Incl O&P
0010	**PULL BOXES**									
2100	Pull box, NEMA 3R, type SC, raintight & weatherproof									
2150	6" L x 6" W x 6" D	1 Elec	10	.800	Ea.	14.75	44		58.75	82
2200	8" L x 6" W x 6" D		8	1		20.50	54.50		75	105
2250	10" L x 6" W x 6" D		7	1.143		32	62.50		94.50	129
2300	12" L x 12" W x 6" D		5	1.600		54.50	87.50		142	191
2350	16" L x 16" W x 6" D		4.50	1.778		77.50	97		174.50	232
2400	20" L x 20" W x 6" D		4	2		101	109		210	275
2450	24" L x 18" W x 8" D		3	2.667		123	146		269	355
2500	24" L x 24" W x 10" D		2.50	3.200		291	175		466	580
2550	30" L x 24" W x 12" D		2	4		385	219		604	750
2600	36" L x 36" W x 12" D		1.50	5.333		430	292		722	910
2800	Cast iron, pull boxes for surface mounting									
3000	NEMA 4, watertight & dust tight									
3050	6" L x 6" W x 6" D	1 Elec	4	2	Ea.	257	109		366	445
3100	8" L x 6" W x 6" D		3.20	2.500		360	137		497	600
3150	10" L x 6" W x 6" D		2.50	3.200		400	175		575	700
3200	12" L x 12" W x 6" D		2.30	3.478		730	190		920	1,075
3250	16" L x 16" W x 6" D		1.30	6.154		960	335		1,295	1,550
3300	20" L x 20" W x 6" D		.80	10		1,800	545		2,345	2,800
3350	24" L x 18" W x 8" D		.70	11.429		2,625	625		3,250	3,825
3400	24" L x 24" W x 10" D		.50	16		4,975	875		5,850	6,775
3450	30" L x 24" W x 12" D		.40	20		5,450	1,100		6,550	7,650
3500	36" L x 36" W x 12" D		.20	40		5,975	2,200		8,175	9,850

26 05 39 – Underfloor Raceways for Electrical Systems

26 05 39.30 Conduit In Concrete Slab

		Crew	Daily Output	Labor-Hours	Unit	Material	2015 Bare Costs Labor	Equipment	Total	Total Incl O&P
0010	**CONDUIT IN CONCRETE SLAB** Including terminations,	R337119-30								
0020	fittings and supports									
3230	PVC, schedule 40, 1/2" diameter	1 Elec	270	.030	L.F.	.57	1.62		2.19	3.06
3250	3/4" diameter		230	.035		.66	1.90		2.56	3.57
3270	1" diameter		200	.040		.87	2.19		3.06	4.23
3300	1-1/4" diameter		170	.047		1.17	2.57		3.74	5.15
3330	1-1/2" diameter		140	.057		1.42	3.13		4.55	6.25
3350	2" diameter		120	.067		1.78	3.65		5.43	7.40
3370	2-1/2" diameter		90	.089		3.07	4.86		7.93	10.65
3400	3" diameter	2 Elec	160	.100		3.90	5.45		9.35	12.50

For customer support on your Site Work & Landscape Cost Data, call 877.737.1594.

265

26 05 Common Work Results for Electrical

26 05 39 – Underfloor Raceways for Electrical Systems

26 05 39.30 Conduit In Concrete Slab

		Crew	Daily Output	Labor-Hours	Unit	Material	2015 Bare Costs Labor	Equipment	Total	Total Incl O&P
3430	3-1/2" diameter	2 Elec	120	.133	L.F.	4.94	7.30		12.24	16.40
3440	4" diameter		100	.160		5.40	8.75		14.15	19.05
3450	5" diameter		80	.200		8.35	10.95		19.30	25.50
3460	6" diameter		60	.267		11.95	14.60		26.55	35
3530	Sweeps, 1" diameter, 30" radius	1 Elec	32	.250	Ea.	41	13.70		54.70	65.50
3550	1-1/4" diameter		24	.333		44.50	18.25		62.75	76.50
3570	1-1/2" diameter		21	.381		47	21		68	82.50
3600	2" diameter		18	.444		52	24.50		76.50	93.50
3630	2-1/2" diameter		14	.571		67.50	31.50		99	122
3650	3" diameter		10	.800		86	44		130	160
3670	3-1/2" diameter		8	1		105	54.50		159.50	198
3700	4" diameter		7	1.143		147	62.50		209.50	256
3710	5" diameter		6	1.333		168	73		241	294
3730	Couplings, 1/2" diameter					.21			.21	.23
3750	3/4" diameter					.24			.24	.26
3770	1" diameter					.36			.36	.40
3800	1-1/4" diameter					.55			.55	.61
3830	1-1/2" diameter					.68			.68	.75
3850	2" diameter					.88			.88	.97
3870	2-1/2" diameter					1.57			1.57	1.73
3900	3" diameter					2.54			2.54	2.79
3930	3-1/2" diameter					3.21			3.21	3.53
3950	4" diameter					3.59			3.59	3.95
3960	5" diameter					9.10			9.10	10
3970	6" diameter					12.35			12.35	13.60
4030	End bells 1" diameter, PVC	1 Elec	60	.133		3.90	7.30		11.20	15.25
4050	1-1/4" diameter		53	.151		4.80	8.25		13.05	17.65
4100	1-1/2" diameter		48	.167		5.95	9.10		15.05	20
4150	2" diameter		34	.235		7.15	12.85		20	27
4170	2-1/2" diameter		27	.296		7.90	16.20		24.10	33
4200	3" diameter		20	.400		8.30	22		30.30	42
4250	3-1/2" diameter		16	.500		9.90	27.50		37.40	52
4300	4" diameter		14	.571		10.75	31.50		42.25	59
4310	5" diameter		12	.667		11.35	36.50		47.85	67
4320	6" diameter		9	.889		13.55	48.50		62.05	88
4350	Rigid galvanized steel, 1/2" diameter		200	.040	L.F.	2.48	2.19		4.67	6
4400	3/4" diameter		170	.047		2.62	2.57		5.19	6.75
4450	1" diameter		130	.062		3.60	3.37		6.97	9
4500	1-1/4" diameter		110	.073		4.94	3.98		8.92	11.40
4600	1-1/2" diameter		100	.080		5.50	4.38		9.88	12.60
4800	2" diameter		90	.089		6.80	4.86		11.66	14.80

26 05 39.40 Conduit In Trench

		Crew	Daily Output	Labor-Hours	Unit	Material	2015 Bare Costs Labor	Equipment	Total	Total Incl O&P
0010	**CONDUIT IN TRENCH** Includes terminations and fittings R337119-30									
0020	Does not include excavation or backfill, see Section 31 23 16.00									
0200	Rigid galvanized steel, 2" diameter	1 Elec	150	.053	L.F.	6.40	2.92		9.32	11.40
0400	2-1/2" diameter	"	100	.080		12.45	4.38		16.83	20.50
0600	3" diameter	2 Elec	160	.100		14.55	5.45		20	24
0800	3-1/2" diameter		140	.114		19.20	6.25		25.45	30.50
1000	4" diameter		100	.160		21	8.75		29.75	36.50
1200	5" diameter		80	.200		44	10.95		54.95	64.50
1400	6" diameter		60	.267		61	14.60		75.60	89.50

26 12 Medium-Voltage Transformers

26 12 19 – Pad-Mounted, Liquid-Filled, Medium-Voltage Transformers

26 12 19.10 Transformer, Oil-Filled	Crew	Daily Output	Labor-Hours	Unit	Material	2015 Bare Costs Labor	Equipment	Total	Total Incl O&P
0010 **TRANSFORMER, OIL-FILLED** primary delta or Y,									
0050 Pad mounted 5 kV or 15 kV, with taps, 277/480 V secondary, 3 phase									
0100 150 kVA	R-3	.65	30.769	Ea.	9,250	1,675	212	11,137	12,900
0200 300 kVA	"	.45	44.444	"	13,200	2,425	305	15,930	18,500

26 24 Switchboards and Panelboards

26 24 16 – Panelboards

26 24 16.30 Panelboards Commercial Applications

	Crew	Daily Output	Labor-Hours	Unit	Material	2015 Bare Costs Labor	Equipment	Total	Total Incl O&P
0010 **PANELBOARDS COMMERCIAL APPLICATIONS**									
0050 NQOD, w/20 amp 1 pole bolt-on circuit breakers									
0100 3 wire, 120/240 volts, 100 amp main lugs									
0150 10 circuits	1 Elec	1	8	Ea.	545	440		985	1,250
0200 14 circuits		.88	9.091		660	495		1,155	1,475
0250 18 circuits		.75	10.667		720	585		1,305	1,675
0300 20 circuits		.65	12.308		805	675		1,480	1,875
0350 225 amp main lugs, 24 circuits	2 Elec	1.20	13.333		910	730		1,640	2,100
0400 30 circuits		.90	17.778		1,050	970		2,020	2,600
0450 36 circuits		.80	20		1,200	1,100		2,300	2,975
0500 38 circuits		.72	22.222		1,275	1,225		2,500	3,225
0550 42 circuits		.66	24.242		1,350	1,325		2,675	3,450
0600 4 wire, 120/208 volts, 100 amp main lugs, 12 circuits	1 Elec	1	8		640	440		1,080	1,350
0650 16 circuits		.75	10.667		730	585		1,315	1,675
0700 20 circuits		.65	12.308		845	675		1,520	1,925
0750 24 circuits		.60	13.333		875	730		1,605	2,075
0800 30 circuits		.53	15.094		1,050	825		1,875	2,375
0850 225 amp main lugs, 32 circuits	2 Elec	.90	17.778		1,175	970		2,145	2,750
0900 34 circuits		.84	19.048		1,200	1,050		2,250	2,875
0950 36 circuits		.80	20		1,225	1,100		2,325	3,000
1000 42 circuits		.68	23.529		1,375	1,275		2,650	3,425

26 27 Low-Voltage Distribution Equipment

26 27 13 – Electricity Metering

26 27 13.10 Meter Centers and Sockets

	Crew	Daily Output	Labor-Hours	Unit	Material	2015 Bare Costs Labor	Equipment	Total	Total Incl O&P
0010 **METER CENTERS AND SOCKETS**									
0100 Sockets, single position, 4 terminal, 100 amp	1 Elec	3.20	2.500	Ea.	43	137		180	253
0200 150 amp		2.30	3.478		48	190		238	340
0300 200 amp		1.90	4.211		92	230		322	445
0500 Double position, 4 terminal, 100 amp		2.80	2.857		204	156		360	460
0600 150 amp		2.10	3.810		240	208		448	575
0700 200 amp		1.70	4.706		450	257		707	880
1100 Meter centers and sockets, three phase, single pos, 7 terminal, 100 amp		2.80	2.857		164	156		320	415
1200 200 amp		2.10	3.810		295	208		503	635
1400 400 amp		1.70	4.706		720	257		977	1,175
2000 Meter center, main fusible switch, 1P 3W 120/240 volt									
2030 400 amp	2 Elec	1.60	10	Ea.	1,675	545		2,220	2,675
2040 600 amp		1.10	14.545		2,600	795		3,395	4,050
2050 800 amp		.90	17.778		4,325	970		5,295	6,225
2060 Rainproof 1P 3W 120/240 volt, 400 amp		1.60	10		1,625	545		2,170	2,600
2070 600 amp		1.10	14.545		2,825	795		3,620	4,300

26 27 Low-Voltage Distribution Equipment

26 27 13 – Electricity Metering

26 27 13.10 Meter Centers and Sockets	Crew	Daily Output	Labor-Hours	Unit	Material	2015 Bare Costs Labor	Equipment	Total	Total Incl O&P
2080	800 amp	2 Elec	.90	17.778	Ea.	4,400	970		5,370	6,300
2100	3P 4W 120/208 V, 400 amp		1.60	10		2,125	545		2,670	3,175
2110	600 amp		1.10	14.545		3,350	795		4,145	4,900
2120	800 amp		.90	17.778		5,425	970		6,395	7,425
2130	Rainproof 3P 4W 120/208 V, 400 amp		1.60	10		1,850	545		2,395	2,850
2140	600 amp		1.10	14.545		3,450	795		4,245	5,000
2150	800 amp		.90	17.778		6,425	970		7,395	8,500
2170	Main circuit breaker, 1P 3W 120/240 V									
2180	400 amp	2 Elec	1.60	10	Ea.	2,475	545		3,020	3,550
2190	600 amp		1.10	14.545		3,300	795		4,095	4,850
2200	800 amp		.90	17.778		5,225	970		6,195	7,200
2210	1000 amp		.80	20		6,250	1,100		7,350	8,525
2220	1200 amp		.76	21.053		8,700	1,150		9,850	11,300
2230	1600 amp		.68	23.529		18,900	1,275		20,175	22,700
2240	Rainproof 1P 3W 120/240 V, 400 amp		1.60	10		2,900	545		3,445	4,000
2250	600 amp		1.10	14.545		3,900	795		4,695	5,475
2260	800 amp		.90	17.778		4,550	970		5,520	6,450
2270	1000 amp		.80	20		6,250	1,100		7,350	8,525
2280	1200 amp		.76	21.053		8,450	1,150		9,600	11,000
2300	3P 4W 120/208 V, 400 amp		1.60	10		3,300	545		3,845	4,450
2310	600 amp		1.10	14.545		4,625	795		5,420	6,300
2320	800 amp		.90	17.778		5,500	970		6,470	7,525
2330	1000 amp		.80	20		7,250	1,100		8,350	9,625
2340	1200 amp		.76	21.053		9,250	1,150		10,400	11,900
2350	1600 amp		.68	23.529		18,900	1,275		20,175	22,700
2360	Rainproof 3P 4W 120/208 V, 400 amp		1.60	10		3,300	545		3,845	4,450
2370	600 amp		1.10	14.545		4,625	795		5,420	6,300
2380	800 amp		.90	17.778		5,500	970		6,470	7,525
2390	1000 amp		.76	21.053		7,250	1,150		8,400	9,700

26 28 Low-Voltage Circuit Protective Devices

26 28 16 – Enclosed Switches and Circuit Breakers

26 28 16.10 Circuit Breakers

		Crew	Daily Output	Labor-Hours	Unit	Material	Labor	Equipment	Total	Total Incl O&P
0010	**CIRCUIT BREAKERS** (in enclosure)									
2300	Enclosed (NEMA 7), explosion proof, 600 volt 3 pole, 50 amp	1 Elec	2.30	3.478	Ea.	1,525	190		1,715	1,950
2350	100 amp		1.50	5.333		1,575	292		1,867	2,175
2400	150 amp		1	8		3,825	440		4,265	4,850
2450	250 amp	2 Elec	1.60	10		4,775	545		5,320	6,075
2500	400 amp	"	1.20	13.333		5,300	730		6,030	6,925

26 28 16.20 Safety Switches

		Crew	Daily Output	Labor-Hours	Unit	Material	Labor	Equipment	Total	Total Incl O&P
0010	**SAFETY SWITCHES**									
0100	General duty 240 volt, 3 pole NEMA 1, fusible, 30 amp	1 Elec	3.20	2.500	Ea.	73.50	137		210.50	286
0200	60 amp		2.30	3.478		124	190		314	420
0300	100 amp		1.90	4.211		213	230		443	580
0400	200 amp		1.30	6.154		455	335		790	1,000
0500	400 amp	2 Elec	1.80	8.889		1,150	485		1,635	2,000
0600	600 amp	"	1.20	13.333		2,150	730		2,880	3,475
2900	Heavy duty, 240 volt, 3 pole NEMA 1 fusible									
2910	30 amp	1 Elec	3.20	2.500	Ea.	118	137		255	335
3000	60 amp		2.30	3.478		199	190		389	505
3300	100 amp		1.90	4.211		315	230		545	690

26 28 Low-Voltage Circuit Protective Devices

26 28 16 – Enclosed Switches and Circuit Breakers

26 28 16.20 Safety Switches		Crew	Daily Output	Labor-Hours	Unit	Material	2015 Bare Costs Labor	Equipment	Total	Total Incl O&P
3500	200 amp	1 Elec	1.30	6.154	Ea.	540	335		875	1,100
3700	400 amp	2 Elec	1.80	8.889		1,400	485		1,885	2,250
3900	600 amp	"	1.20	13.333	↓	2,800	730		3,530	4,175

26 32 Packaged Generator Assemblies

26 32 13 – Engine Generators

26 32 13.13 Diesel-Engine-Driven Generator Sets

		Crew	Daily Output	Labor-Hours	Unit	Material	2015 Bare Costs Labor	Equipment	Total	Total Incl O&P
0010	**DIESEL-ENGINE-DRIVEN GENERATOR SETS**									
2000	Diesel engine, including battery, charger,									
2010	muffler, & day tank, 30 kW	R-3	.55	36.364	Ea.	14,000	1,975	251	16,226	18,700
2100	50 kW		.42	47.619		19,800	2,575	330	22,705	26,000
2200	75 kW		.35	57.143		21,300	3,100	395	24,795	28,500
2300	100 kW		.31	64.516		29,900	3,500	445	33,845	38,600
2400	125 kW		.29	68.966		31,700	3,750	475	35,925	40,900
2500	150 kW		.26	76.923		33,800	4,175	530	38,505	44,100
2600	175 kW		.25	80		39,100	4,350	550	44,000	50,000
2700	200 kW		.24	83.333		42,200	4,525	575	47,300	54,000
2800	250 kW		.23	86.957		45,200	4,725	600	50,525	57,500
2900	300 kW		.22	90.909		49,100	4,925	625	54,650	62,000
3000	350 kW		.20	100		55,500	5,425	690	61,615	70,000
3100	400 kW		.19	105		68,500	5,725	725	74,950	85,000
3200	500 kW		.18	111		86,500	6,025	765	93,290	105,000
3220	600 kW	↓	.17	117		112,500	6,400	810	119,710	134,500
3240	750 kW	R-13	.38	110	↓	140,000	5,850	495	146,345	163,500

26 32 13.16 Gas-Engine-Driven Generator Sets

		Crew	Daily Output	Labor-Hours	Unit	Material	2015 Bare Costs Labor	Equipment	Total	Total Incl O&P
0010	**GAS-ENGINE-DRIVEN GENERATOR SETS**									
0020	Gas or gasoline operated, includes battery,									
0050	charger, & muffler									
0200	3 phase 4 wire, 277/480 volt, 7.5 kW	R-3	.83	24.096	Ea.	7,350	1,300	166	8,816	10,200
0300	11.5 kW		.71	28.169		10,400	1,525	194	12,119	14,000
0400	20 kW		.63	31.746		12,300	1,725	219	14,244	16,300
0500	35 kW		.55	36.364		14,600	1,975	251	16,826	19,400
0520	60 kW		.50	40		19,300	2,175	276	21,751	24,800
0600	80 kW		.40	50		24,000	2,725	345	27,070	30,900
0700	100 kW		.33	60.606		26,300	3,300	420	30,020	34,300
0800	125 kW		.28	71.429		54,000	3,875	490	58,365	65,500
0900	185 kW	↓	.25	80		71,000	4,350	550	75,900	85,000

26 36 Transfer Switches

26 36 13 – Manual Transfer Switches

26 36 13.10 Non-Automatic Transfer Switches

		Crew	Daily Output	Labor-Hours	Unit	Material	2015 Bare Costs Labor	Equipment	Total	Total Incl O&P
0010	**NON-AUTOMATIC TRANSFER SWITCHES** enclosed									
0100	Manual operated, 480 volt 3 pole, 30 amp	1 Elec	2.30	3.478	Ea.	1,375	190		1,565	1,800
0200	100 amp	"	1.30	6.154		2,750	335		3,085	3,525
0250	200 amp	2 Elec	2	8		3,650	440		4,090	4,675
0300	400 amp	"	1.60	10		5,300	545		5,845	6,675
1000	250 volt 3 pole, 30 amp	1 Elec	2.30	3.478		1,000	190		1,190	1,375
1150	100 amp	"	1.30	6.154		1,825	335		2,160	2,500
1200	200 amp	2 Elec	2	8	↓	3,600	440		4,040	4,625

For customer support on your Site Work & Landscape Cost Data, call 877.737.1594.

269

26 36 Transfer Switches

26 36 13 – Manual Transfer Switches

26 36 13.10 Non-Automatic Transfer Switches

		Crew	Daily Output	Labor-Hours	Unit	Material	2015 Bare Costs Labor	Equipment	Total	Total Incl O&P
1500	Electrically operated, 480 volt 3 pole, 60 amp	1 Elec	1.90	4.211	Ea.	2,375	230		2,605	2,975
1600	100 amp	"	1.30	6.154		2,375	335		2,710	3,125
1650	200 amp	2 Elec	2	8		3,925	440		4,365	4,975
1700	400 amp	"	1.60	10		5,500	545		6,045	6,875
2000	250 volt 3 pole, 30 amp	1 Elec	2.30	3.478		2,350	190		2,540	2,875
2050	60 amp	"	1.90	4.211		2,350	230		2,580	2,950
2150	200 amp	2 Elec	2	8		3,900	440		4,340	4,925
2200	400 amp	"	1.60	10		5,425	545		5,970	6,800
2500	NEMA 3R, 480 volt 3 pole, 60 amp	1 Elec	1.80	4.444		2,775	243		3,018	3,425
2550	100 amp	"	1.20	6.667		3,575	365		3,940	4,475
2650	400 amp	2 Elec	1.40	11.429		6,000	625		6,625	7,525

26 51 Interior Lighting

26 51 13 – Interior Lighting Fixtures, Lamps, and Ballasts

26 51 13.70 Residential Fixtures

		Crew	Daily Output	Labor-Hours	Unit	Material	2015 Bare Costs Labor	Equipment	Total	Total Incl O&P
0010	**RESIDENTIAL FIXTURES**									
2000	Incandescent, exterior lantern, wall mounted, 60 watt	1 Elec	16	.500	Ea.	55.50	27.50		83	102
2100	Post light, 150W, with 7' post		4	2		243	109		352	430
2500	Lamp holder, weatherproof with 150W PAR		16	.500		32	27.50		59.50	76
2550	With reflector and guard		12	.667		56	36.50		92.50	117

26 51 13.90 Ballast, Replacement HID

		Crew	Daily Output	Labor-Hours	Unit	Material	2015 Bare Costs Labor	Equipment	Total	Total Incl O&P
0010	**BALLAST, REPLACEMENT HID**									
7510	Multi-tap 120/208/240/277 volt									
7550	High pressure sodium, 70 watt	1 Elec	10	.800	Ea.	136	44		180	216
7560	100 watt		9.40	.851		142	46.50		188.50	226
7570	150 watt		9	.889		153	48.50		201.50	241
7580	250 watt		8.50	.941		227	51.50		278.50	325
7590	400 watt		7	1.143		258	62.50		320.50	380
7600	1000 watt		6	1.333		355	73		428	500
7610	Metal halide, 175 watt		8	1		83.50	54.50		138	174
7620	250 watt		8	1		108	54.50		162.50	201
7630	400 watt		7	1.143		135	62.50		197.50	242
7640	1000 watt		6	1.333		231	73		304	365
7650	1500 watt		5	1.600		286	87.50		373.50	445

26 56 Exterior Lighting

26 56 13 – Lighting Poles and Standards

26 56 13.10 Lighting Poles

		Crew	Daily Output	Labor-Hours	Unit	Material	2015 Bare Costs Labor	Equipment	Total	Total Incl O&P
0010	**LIGHTING POLES**									
2800	Light poles, anchor base									
2820	not including concrete bases									
2840	Aluminum pole, 8' high	1 Elec	4	2	Ea.	705	109		814	940
2850	10' high		4	2		745	109		854	985
2860	12' high		3.80	2.105		775	115		890	1,025
2870	14' high		3.40	2.353		805	129		934	1,075
2880	16' high		3	2.667		880	146		1,026	1,200
3000	20' high	R-3	2.90	6.897		935	375	47.50	1,357.50	1,625
3200	30' high		2.60	7.692		1,775	420	53	2,248	2,625
3400	35' high		2.30	8.696		1,925	470	60	2,455	2,900

26 56 Exterior Lighting

26 56 13 – Lighting Poles and Standards

26 56 13.10 Lighting Poles		Crew	Daily Output	Labor-Hours	Unit	Material	2015 Bare Costs Labor	Equipment	Total	Total Incl O&P
3600	40' high	R-3	2	10	Ea.	2,200	545	69	2,814	3,325
3800	Bracket arms, 1 arm	1 Elec	8	1		121	54.50		175.50	215
4000	2 arms		8	1		243	54.50		297.50	350
4200	3 arms		5.30	1.509		365	82.50		447.50	525
4400	4 arms		5.30	1.509		485	82.50		567.50	660
4500	Steel pole, galvanized, 8' high		3.80	2.105		610	115		725	845
4510	10' high		3.70	2.162		635	118		753	875
4520	12' high		3.40	2.353		690	129		819	950
4530	14' high		3.10	2.581		730	141		871	1,025
4540	16' high		2.90	2.759		775	151		926	1,075
4550	18' high		2.70	2.963		820	162		982	1,150
4600	20' high	R-3	2.60	7.692		1,100	420	53	1,573	1,875
4800	30' high		2.30	8.696		1,300	470	60	1,830	2,200
5000	35' high		2.20	9.091		1,425	495	62.50	1,982.50	2,375
5200	40' high		1.70	11.765		1,775	640	81	2,496	3,000
5400	Bracket arms, 1 arm	1 Elec	8	1		180	54.50		234.50	280
5600	2 arms		8	1		216	54.50		270.50	320
5800	3 arms		5.30	1.509		254	82.50		336.50	405
6000	4 arms		5.30	1.509		310	82.50		392.50	465
6100	Fiberglass pole, 1 or 2 fixtures, 20' high	R-3	4	5		675	272	34.50	981.50	1,200
6200	30' high		3.60	5.556		835	300	38.50	1,173.50	1,425
6300	35' high		3.20	6.250		1,300	340	43	1,683	1,975
6400	40' high		2.80	7.143		1,525	390	49	1,964	2,325
6420	Wood pole, 4-1/2" x 5-1/8", 8' high	1 Elec	6	1.333		330	73		403	475
6430	10' high		6	1.333		375	73		448	525
6440	12' high		5.70	1.404		475	77		552	640
6450	15' high		5	1.600		555	87.50		642.50	740
6460	20' high		4	2		670	109		779	905
7300	Transformer bases, not including concrete bases									
7320	Maximum pole size, steel, 40' high	1 Elec	2	4	Ea.	1,425	219		1,644	1,875
7340	Cast aluminum, 30' high		3	2.667		750	146		896	1,050
7350	40' high		2.50	3.200		1,150	175		1,325	1,500

26 56 16 – Parking Lighting

26 56 16.55 Parking LED Lighting

			Crew	Daily Output	Labor-Hours	Unit	Material	Labor	Equipment	Total	Total Incl O&P
0010	**PARKING LED LIGHTING**										
0100	Round pole mounting, 88 lamp watts	G	1 Elec	2	4	Ea.	995	219		1,214	1,425
0110	Square pole mounting, 223 lamp watts	G	"	2	4	"	1,750	219		1,969	2,250

26 56 19 – Roadway Lighting

26 56 19.20 Roadway Luminaire

			Crew	Daily Output	Labor-Hours	Unit	Material	Labor	Equipment	Total	Total Incl O&P
0010	**ROADWAY LUMINAIRE**										
2650	Roadway area luminaire, low pressure sodium, 135 watt		1 Elec	2	4	Ea.	650	219		869	1,050
2700	180 watt		"	2	4		700	219		919	1,100
2750	Metal halide, 400 watt		2 Elec	4.40	3.636		555	199		754	910
2760	1000 watt			4	4		625	219		844	1,025
2780	High pressure sodium, 400 watt			4.40	3.636		580	199		779	940
2790	1000 watt			4	4		660	219		879	1,050

26 56 19.55 Roadway LED Luminaire

			Crew	Daily Output	Labor-Hours	Unit	Material	Labor	Equipment	Total	Total Incl O&P
0010	**ROADWAY LED LUMINAIRE**										
0100	LED fixture, 72 LEDs, 120 V AC or 12 V DC, equal to 60 watt	G	1 Elec	2.70	2.963	Ea.	595	162		757	895
0110	108 LEDs, 120 V AC or 12 V DC, equal to 90 watt	G		2.70	2.963		695	162		857	1,000
0120	144 LEDs, 120 V AC or 12 V DC, equal to 120 watt	G		2.70	2.963		855	162		1,017	1,175

For customer support on your Site Work & Landscape Cost Data, call 877.737.1594.

271

26 56 19 – Roadway Lighting

26 56 19.55 Roadway LED Luminaire		Crew	Daily Output	Labor-Hours	Unit	Material	2015 Bare Costs Labor	Equipment	Total	Total Incl O&P
0130	252 LEDs, 120 V AC or 12 V DC, equal to 210 watt	G	2 Elec	4.40	3.636	Ea.	1,175	199		1,374	1,600
0140	Replaces high pressure sodium fixture, 75 watt	G	1 Elec	2.70	2.963		720	162		882	1,050
0150	125 watt	G		2.70	2.963		825	162		987	1,150
0160	150 watt	G		2.70	2.963		1,025	162		1,187	1,375
0170	175 watt	G		2.70	2.963		1,225	162		1,387	1,600
0180	200 watt	G		2.70	2.963		1,450	162		1,612	1,825
0190	250 watt	G	2 Elec	4.40	3.636		1,650	199		1,849	2,125
0200	320 watt	G	"	4.40	3.636		1,800	199		1,999	2,275

26 56 23 – Area Lighting

26 56 23.10 Exterior Fixtures

26 56 23.10 Exterior Fixtures		Crew	Daily Output	Labor-Hours	Unit	Material	2015 Bare Costs Labor	Equipment	Total	Total Incl O&P
0010	**EXTERIOR FIXTURES** With lamps									
0200	Wall mounted, incandescent, 100 watt	1 Elec	8	1	Ea.	35	54.50		89.50	121
0400	Quartz, 500 watt		5.30	1.509		50	82.50		132.50	179
0420	1500 watt		4.20	1.905		103	104		207	269
1100	Wall pack, low pressure sodium, 35 watt		4	2		227	109		336	415
1150	55 watt		4	2		270	109		379	460
1160	High pressure sodium, 70 watt		4	2		224	109		333	410
1170	150 watt		4	2		244	109		353	430
1180	Metal Halide, 175 watt		4	2		248	109		357	435
1190	250 watt		4	2		282	109		391	475
1195	400 watt		4	2		335	109		444	530
1250	Induction lamp, 40 watt		4	2		340	109		449	540
1260	80 watt		4	2		580	109		689	805
1278	LED, poly lens, 26 watt		4	2		330	109		439	525
1280	110 watt		4	2		1,300	109		1,409	1,625
1500	LED, glass lens, 13 watt		4	2		330	109		439	525

26 56 23.55 Exterior LED Fixtures

26 56 23.55 Exterior LED Fixtures		Crew	Daily Output	Labor-Hours	Unit	Material	2015 Bare Costs Labor	Equipment	Total	Total Incl O&P
0010	**EXTERIOR LED FIXTURES**									
0100	Wall mounted, indoor/outdoor, 12 watt	G	1 Elec	10	.800	Ea.	258	44		302	350
0110	32 watt	G		10	.800		350	44		394	450
0120	66 watt	G		10	.800		500	44		544	615
0200	outdoor, 110 watt	G		10	.800		765	44		809	905
0210	220 watt	G		10	.800		1,350	44		1,394	1,550
0300	modular, type IV, 120 V, 50 lamp watts	G		9	.889		930	48.50		978.50	1,100
0310	101 lamp watts	G		9	.889		1,050	48.50		1,098.50	1,225
0320	126 lamp watts	G		9	.889		1,325	48.50		1,373.50	1,525
0330	202 lamp watts	G		9	.889		1,500	48.50		1,548.50	1,725
0340	240 V, 50 lamp watts	G		8	1		970	54.50		1,024.50	1,150
0350	101 lamp watts	G		8	1		1,100	54.50		1,154.50	1,275
0360	126 lamp watts	G		8	1		1,350	54.50		1,404.50	1,575
0370	202 lamp watts	G		8	1		1,550	54.50		1,604.50	1,775
0400	wall pack, glass, 13 lamp watts	G		4	2		360	109		469	560
0410	poly w/photocell, 26 lamp watts	G		4	2		226	109		335	410
0420	50 lamp watts	G		4	2		530	109		639	745
0430	replacement, 40 watts	G		4	2		460	109		569	670
0440	60 watts	G		4	2		580	109		689	805

272

For customer support on your Site Work & Landscape Cost Data, call 877.737.1594.

26 56 26 – Landscape Lighting

26 56 26.20 Landscape Fixtures	Crew	Daily Output	Labor- Hours	Unit	Material	2015 Bare Costs Labor	Equipment	Total	Total Incl O&P
0010 **LANDSCAPE FIXTURES**									
0012 Incl. conduit, wire, trench									
0030 Bollards									
0040 Incandescent, 24"	1 Elec	2.50	3.200	Ea.	370	175		545	670
0050 36"		2	4		485	219		704	860
0060 42"		2	4		515	219		734	895
0070 H.I.D., 24"		2.50	3.200		430	175		605	735
0080 36"		2	4		480	219		699	860
0090 42"		2	4		630	219		849	1,025
0100 Concrete, 18" diam.		1.20	6.667		1,425	365		1,790	2,125
0110 24" diam.		.75	10.667		1,800	585		2,385	2,850
0120 Dry niche									
0130 300 W 120 Volt	1 Elec	4	2	Ea.	945	109		1,054	1,225
0140 1000 W 120 Volt		2	4		1,275	219		1,494	1,725
0150 300 W 12 Volt		4	2		945	109		1,054	1,225
0160 Low voltage									
0170 Recessed uplight	1 Elec	2.20	3.636	Ea.	360	199		559	695
0180 Walkway		4	2		325	109		434	525
0190 Malibu - 5 light set		3	2.667		238	146		384	480
0200 Mushroom 24" pier		4	2		243	109		352	430
0210 Recessed, adjustable									
0220 Incandescent, 150 W	1 Elec	2.50	3.200	Ea.	555	175		730	870
0230 300 W	"	2.50	3.200	"	640	175		815	965
0250 Recessed uplight									
0260 Incandescent, 50 W	1 Elec	2.50	3.200	Ea.	455	175		630	760
0270 150 W		2.50	3.200		470	175		645	780
0280 300 W		2.50	3.200		525	175		700	840
0310 Quartz 500 W		2.50	3.200		520	175		695	830
0400 Recessed wall light									
0410 Incandescent 100 W	1 Elec	4	2	Ea.	227	109		336	415
0420 Fluorescent		4	2		207	109		316	390
0430 H.I.D. 100 W		3	2.667		425	146		571	685
0500 Step lights									
0510 Incandescent	1 Elec	5	1.600	Ea.	203	87.50		290.50	355
0520 Fluorescent	"	5	1.600	"	215	87.50		302.50	370
0600 Tree lights, surface adjustable									
0610 Incandescent 50 W	1 Elec	3	2.667	Ea.	480	146		626	750
0620 Incandescent 100 W		3	2.667		500	146		646	770
0630 Incandescent 150 W		2	4		530	219		749	915
0700 Underwater lights									
0710 150 W 120 Volt	1 Elec	6	1.333	Ea.	850	73		923	1,050
0720 300 W 120 Volt		6	1.333		1,025	73		1,098	1,225
0730 1000 W 120 Volt		4	2		1,275	109		1,384	1,600
0740 50 W 12 Volt		6	1.333		970	73		1,043	1,175
0750 300 W 12 Volt		6	1.333		870	73		943	1,075
0800 Walkway, adjustable									
0810 Fluorescent, 2'	1 Elec	3	2.667	Ea.	380	146		526	635
0820 Fluorescent, 4'		3	2.667		400	146		546	660
0830 Fluorescent, 8'		2	4		785	219		1,004	1,200
0840 Incandescent, 50 W		4	2		355	109		464	560
0850 150 W		4	2		380	109		489	585
0900 Wet niche									

26 56 Exterior Lighting

26 56 26 – Landscape Lighting

26 56 26.20 Landscape Fixtures

		Crew	Daily Output	Labor-Hours	Unit	Material	2015 Bare Costs Labor	Equipment	Total	Total Incl O&P
0910	300 W 120 Volt	1 Elec	2.50	3.200	Ea.	780	175		955	1,125
0920	1000 W 120 Volt		1.50	5.333		940	292		1,232	1,450
0930	300 W 12 Volt		2.50	3.200		890	175		1,065	1,250
0960	Landscape lights, solar powered, 6" dia x 12" h, one piece w/stake [G]	1 Clab	80	.100		27.50	3.76		31.26	36.50
7380	Landscape recessed uplight, incl. housing, ballast, transformer									
7390	& reflector, not incl. conduit, wire, trench									
7420	Incandescent, 250 watt	1 Elec	5	1.600	Ea.	590	87.50		677.50	780
7440	Quartz, 250 watt		5	1.600		560	87.50		647.50	745
7460	500 watt		4	2		575	109		684	800

26 56 33 – Walkway Lighting

26 56 33.10 Walkway Luminaire

		Crew	Daily Output	Labor-Hours	Unit	Material	2015 Bare Costs Labor	Equipment	Total	Total Incl O&P
0010	**WALKWAY LUMINAIRE**									
6500	Bollard light, lamp & ballast, 42" high with polycarbonate lens									
6800	Metal halide, 175 watt	1 Elec	3	2.667	Ea.	815	146		961	1,125
6900	High pressure sodium, 70 watt		3	2.667		835	146		981	1,125
7000	100 watt		3	2.667		835	146		981	1,125
7100	150 watt		3	2.667		815	146		961	1,125
7200	Incandescent, 150 watt		3	2.667		595	146		741	875
7810	Walkway luminaire, square 16", metal halide 250 watt		2.70	2.963		635	162		797	945
7820	High pressure sodium, 70 watt		3	2.667		730	146		876	1,025
7830	100 watt		3	2.667		745	146		891	1,025
7840	150 watt		3	2.667		745	146		891	1,025
7850	200 watt		3	2.667		750	146		896	1,050
7910	Round 19", metal halide, 250 watt		2.70	2.963		930	162		1,092	1,275
7920	High pressure sodium, 70 watt		3	2.667		1,025	146		1,171	1,350
7930	100 watt		3	2.667		1,025	146		1,171	1,350
7940	150 watt		3	2.667		1,025	146		1,171	1,350
7950	250 watt		2.70	2.963		1,075	162		1,237	1,425
8000	Sphere 14" opal, incandescent, 200 watt		4	2		295	109		404	490
8020	Sphere 18" opal, incandescent, 300 watt		3.50	2.286		355	125		480	575
8040	Sphere 16" clear, high pressure sodium, 70 watt		3	2.667		615	146		761	900
8050	100 watt		3	2.667		660	146		806	945
8100	Cube 16" opal, incandescent, 300 watt		3.50	2.286		390	125		515	615
8120	High pressure sodium, 70 watt		3	2.667		570	146		716	850
8130	100 watt		3	2.667		585	146		731	865
8230	Lantern, high pressure sodium, 70 watt		3	2.667		510	146		656	785
8240	100 watt		3	2.667		550	146		696	825
8250	150 watt		3	2.667		515	146		661	785
8260	250 watt		2.70	2.963		720	162		882	1,050
8270	Incandescent, 300 watt		3.50	2.286		380	125		505	605
8330	Reflector 22" w/globe, high pressure sodium, 70 watt		3	2.667		490	146		636	760
8340	100 watt		3	2.667		500	146		646	770
8350	150 watt		3	2.667		505	146		651	775
8360	250 watt		2.70	2.963		645	162		807	955

26 56 33.55 Walkway LED Luminaire

		Crew	Daily Output	Labor-Hours	Unit	Material	2015 Bare Costs Labor	Equipment	Total	Total Incl O&P
0010	**WALKWAY LED LUMINAIRE**									
0100	Pole mounted, 86 watts, 4350 lumens [G]	1 Elec	3	2.667	Ea.	945	146		1,091	1,275
0110	4630 lumens [G]		3	2.667		1,575	146		1,721	1,975
0120	80 watts, 4000 lumens [G]		3	2.667		1,500	146		1,646	1,875

26 56 Exterior Lighting

26 56 36 – Flood Lighting

26 56 36.20 Floodlights

		Crew	Daily Output	Labor-Hours	Unit	Material	2015 Bare Costs Labor	Equipment	Total	Total Incl O&P
0010	**FLOODLIGHTS** with ballast and lamp,									
1290	floor mtd, mount with swivel bracket									
1300	Induction lamp, 40 watt	1 Elec	3	2.667	Ea.	450	146		596	715
1310	80 watt		3	2.667		685	146		831	975
1320	150 watt		3	2.667		1,250	146		1,396	1,600
1400	Pole mounted, pole not included									
1950	Metal halide, 175 watt	1 Elec	2.70	2.963	Ea.	340	162		502	615
2000	400 watt	2 Elec	4.40	3.636		420	199		619	765
2200	1000 watt		4	4		580	219		799	965
2210	1500 watt		3.70	4.324		605	237		842	1,025
2250	Low pressure sodium, 55 watt	1 Elec	2.70	2.963		585	162		747	890
2270	90 watt		2	4		645	219		864	1,050
2290	180 watt		2	4		820	219		1,039	1,225
2340	High pressure sodium, 70 watt		2.70	2.963		246	162		408	515
2360	100 watt		2.70	2.963		252	162		414	520
2380	150 watt		2.70	2.963		290	162		452	565
2400	400 watt	2 Elec	4.40	3.636		380	199		579	720
2600	1000 watt	"	4	4		650	219		869	1,050
9005	Solar powered floodlight, w/motion det, incl batt pack for cloudy days [G]	1 Elec	8	1		119	54.50		173.50	213
9020	Battery pack for [G]	"	8	1		13.55	54.50		68.05	97

26 56 36.55 LED Floodlights

		Crew	Daily Output	Labor-Hours	Unit	Material	2015 Bare Costs Labor	Equipment	Total	Total Incl O&P
0010	**LED FLOODLIGHTS** with ballast and lamp,									
0020	Pole mounted, pole not included									
0100	11 watt [G]	1 Elec	4	2	Ea.	345	109		454	545
0110	46 watt [G]		4	2		1,050	109		1,159	1,325
0120	90 watt [G]		4	2		1,725	109		1,834	2,075
0130	288 watt [G]		4	2		2,125	109		2,234	2,500

26 61 Lighting Systems and Accessories

26 61 23 – Lamps Applications

26 61 23.10 Lamps

		Crew	Daily Output	Labor-Hours	Unit	Material	2015 Bare Costs Labor	Equipment	Total	Total Incl O&P
0010	**LAMPS**									
0520	Very high output, 4' long, 110 watt	1 Elec	.90	8.889	C	2,175	485		2,660	3,125
0525	8' long, 195 watt energy saver [G]		.70	11.429		1,775	625		2,400	2,875
0550	8' long, 215 watt		.70	11.429		1,575	625		2,200	2,650
0600	Mercury vapor, mogul base, deluxe white, 100 watt		.30	26.667		3,650	1,450		5,100	6,200
0650	175 watt		.30	26.667		1,725	1,450		3,175	4,050
0700	250 watt		.30	26.667		3,000	1,450		4,450	5,475
0800	400 watt		.30	26.667		4,350	1,450		5,800	6,950
0900	1000 watt		.20	40		7,350	2,200		9,550	11,400
1000	Metal halide, mogul base, 175 watt		.30	26.667		2,550	1,450		4,000	5,000
1100	250 watt		.30	26.667		2,900	1,450		4,350	5,350
1200	400 watt		.30	26.667		4,750	1,450		6,200	7,400
1300	1000 watt		.20	40		6,625	2,200		8,825	10,600
1320	1000 watt, 125,000 initial lumens		.20	40		22,100	2,200		24,300	27,600
1330	1500 watt		.20	40		27,900	2,200		30,100	34,000
1350	High pressure sodium, 70 watt		.30	26.667		3,125	1,450		4,575	5,600
1360	100 watt		.30	26.667		3,250	1,450		4,700	5,750
1370	150 watt		.30	26.667		3,325	1,450		4,775	5,850
1380	250 watt		.30	26.667		4,225	1,450		5,675	6,825

For customer support on your Site Work & Landscape Cost Data, call 877.737.1594.

275

26 61 23.10 Lamps

26 61 23.10 Lamps		Crew	Daily Output	Labor-Hours	Unit	Material	2015 Bare Costs Labor	2015 Bare Costs Equipment	Total	Total Incl O&P
1400	400 watt	1 Elec	.30	26.667	C	5,525	1,450		6,975	8,250
1450	1000 watt		.20	40		10,000	2,200		12,200	14,300
1500	Low pressure sodium, 35 watt		.30	26.667		12,000	1,450		13,450	15,400
1550	55 watt		.30	26.667		11,900	1,450		13,350	15,300
1600	90 watt		.30	26.667		13,400	1,450		14,850	17,000
1650	135 watt		.20	40		20,000	2,200		22,200	25,300
1700	180 watt		.20	40		23,100	2,200		25,300	28,700
1750	Quartz line, clear, 500 watt		1.10	7.273		1,375	400		1,775	2,125
1760	1500 watt		.20	40		3,050	2,200		5,250	6,625
1762	Spot, MR 16, 50 watt		1.30	6.154		1,075	335		1,410	1,675
1800	Incandescent, interior, A21, 100 watt		1.60	5		233	274		507	665
2500	Exterior, PAR 38, 75 watt		1.30	6.154		1,850	335		2,185	2,550
2600	PAR 38, 150 watt		1.30	6.154		2,000	335		2,335	2,700
2700	PAR 46, 200 watt		1.10	7.273		3,875	400		4,275	4,850
2800	PAR 56, 300 watt		1.10	7.273		4,425	400		4,825	5,475

26 61 23.55 LED Lamps

			Crew	Daily Output	Labor-Hours	Unit	Material	2015 Bare Costs Labor	2015 Bare Costs Equipment	Total	Total Incl O&P
0010	**LED LAMPS**										
0100	LED lamp, interior, shape A60, equal to 60 watt	G	1 Elec	160	.050	Ea.	22.50	2.74		25.24	28.50
0200	Globe frosted A60, equal to 60 watt	G		160	.050		22.50	2.74		25.24	28.50
0300	Globe earth, equal to 100 watt	G		160	.050		74	2.74		76.74	85.50
1100	MR16, 3 watt, replacement of halogen lamp 25 watt	G		130	.062		21.50	3.37		24.87	28.50
1200	6 watt replacement of halogen lamp 45 watt	G		130	.062		47	3.37		50.37	56.50
2100	10 watt, PAR20, equal to 60 watt	G		130	.062		47.50	3.37		50.87	57.50
2200	15 watt, PAR30, equal to 100 watt	G		130	.062		79	3.37		82.37	92

Estimating Tips

27 20 00 Data Communications
27 30 00 Voice Communications
27 40 00 Audio-Video Communications

When estimating material costs for special systems, it is always prudent to obtain manufacturers' quotations for equipment prices and special installation requirements which will affect the total costs.

Reference Numbers

Reference numbers are shown in shaded boxes at the beginning of some major classifications. These numbers refer to related items in the Reference Section. The reference information may be an estimating procedure, an alternate pricing method, or technical information.

Note: Not all subdivisions listed here necessarily appear in this publication. ■

*Note: **Trade Service**, in part, has been used as a reference source for some of the material prices used in Division 27.*

27 13 23 – Communications Optical Fiber Backbone Cabling

27 13 23.13 Communications Optical Fiber	Crew	Daily Output	Labor-Hours	Unit	Material	2015 Bare Costs Labor	Equipment	Total	Total Incl O&P
0010 **COMMUNICATIONS OPTICAL FIBER**									
0040 Specialized tools & techniques cause installation costs to vary.									
0070 Fiber optic, cable, bulk simplex, single mode	1 Elec	8	1	C.L.F.	22.50	54.50		77	107
0080 Multi mode		8	1		42	54.50		96.50	129
0090 4 strand, single mode		7.34	1.090		38	59.50		97.50	131
0095 Multi mode		7.34	1.090		50.50	59.50		110	145
0100 12 strand, single mode		6.67	1.199		90	65.50		155.50	198
0105 Multi mode		6.67	1.199		96.50	65.50		162	205
0150 Jumper				Ea.	33			33	36.50
0200 Pigtail					33.50			33.50	37
0300 Connector	1 Elec	24	.333		23.50	18.25		41.75	53
0350 Finger splice		32	.250		32.50	13.70		46.20	56.50
0400 Transceiver (low cost bi-directional)		8	1		420	54.50		474.50	540
0450 Rack housing, 4 rack spaces, 12 panels (144 fibers)		2	4		500	219		719	880
0500 Patch panel, 12 ports		6	1.333		247	73		320	380

Estimating Tips
31 05 00 Common Work Results for Earthwork
- Estimating the actual cost of performing earthwork requires careful consideration of the variables involved. This includes items such as type of soil, whether water will be encountered, dewatering, whether banks need bracing, disposal of excavated earth, and length of haul to fill or spoil sites, etc. If the project has large quantities of cut or fill, consider raising or lowering the site to reduce costs, while paying close attention to the effect on site drainage and utilities.
- If the project has large quantities of fill, creating a borrow pit on the site can significantly lower the costs.
- It is very important to consider what time of year the project is scheduled for completion. Bad weather can create large cost overruns from dewatering, site repair, and lost productivity from cold weather.

Reference Numbers
Reference numbers are shown in shaded boxes at the beginning of some major classifications. These numbers refer to related items in the Reference Section. The reference information may be an estimating procedure, an alternate pricing method, or technical information.

Note: Not all subdivisions listed here necessarily appear in this publication. ∎

Division 31 – Earthwork

31 05 Common Work Results for Earthwork

31 05 13 – Soils for Earthwork

31 05 13.10 Borrow

	31 05 13.10 Borrow	Crew	Daily Output	Labor-Hours	Unit	Material	2015 Bare Costs Labor	Equipment	Total	Total Incl O&P
0010	**BORROW**									
0020	Spread, 200 H.P. dozer, no compaction, 2 mi. RT haul									
0200	Common borrow	B-15	600	.047	C.Y.	12.40	1.99	4.62	19.01	22
0700	Screened loam		600	.047		27.50	1.99	4.62	34.11	38.50
0800	Topsoil, weed free		600	.047		24.50	1.99	4.62	31.11	35
0900	For 5 mile haul, add	B-34B	200	.040			1.60	3.46	5.06	6.20

31 05 16 – Aggregates for Earthwork

31 05 16.10 Borrow

	31 05 16.10 Borrow	Crew	Daily Output	Labor-Hours	Unit	Material	2015 Bare Costs Labor	Equipment	Total	Total Incl O&P
0010	**BORROW**									
0020	Spread, with 200 H.P. dozer, no compaction, 2 mi. RT haul									
0100	Bank run gravel	B-15	600	.047	L.C.Y.	22	1.99	4.62	28.61	32.50
0300	Crushed stone (1.40 tons per CY) , 1-1/2"		600	.047		23.50	1.99	4.62	30.11	34
0320	3/4"		600	.047		23.50	1.99	4.62	30.11	34
0340	1/2"		600	.047		26.50	1.99	4.62	33.11	37
0360	3/8"		600	.047		27.50	1.99	4.62	34.11	38.50
0400	Sand, washed, concrete		600	.047		41	1.99	4.62	47.61	53
0500	Dead or bank sand		600	.047		17.85	1.99	4.62	24.46	27.50
0600	Select structural fill		600	.047		21	1.99	4.62	27.61	31
0610	Import 10 mi. RT select structural fill		408	.069		21	2.93	6.80	30.73	35
0900	For 5 mile haul, add	B-34B	200	.040			1.60	3.46	5.06	6.20
1000	For flowable fill, see Section 03 31 13.35									

31 05 23 – Cement and Concrete for Earthwork

31 05 23.30 Plant Mixed Bituminous Concrete

	31 05 23.30 Plant Mixed Bituminous Concrete	Crew	Daily Output	Labor-Hours	Unit	Material	2015 Bare Costs Labor	Equipment	Total	Total Incl O&P
0010	**PLANT MIXED BITUMINOUS CONCRETE**									
0020	Asphaltic concrete plant mix (145 lb. per C.F.)				Ton	70			70	77
0040	Asphaltic concrete less than 300 tons add trucking costs									
0050	See Section 31 23 23.20 for hauling costs									
0200	All weather patching mix, hot				Ton	69			69	76
0250	Cold patch					79.50			79.50	87.50
0300	Berm mix					69			69	76
0400	Base mix					70			70	77
0500	Binder mix					70			70	77
0600	Sand or sheet mix					67.50			67.50	74

31 05 23.40 Recycled Plant Mixed Bituminous Concrete

	31 05 23.40 Recycled Plant Mixed Bituminous Concrete	Crew	Daily Output	Labor-Hours	Unit	Material	2015 Bare Costs Labor	Equipment	Total	Total Incl O&P
0010	**RECYCLED PLANT MIXED BITUMINOUS CONCRETE**									
0200	Reclaimed pavement in stockpile	G			Ton	53			53	58.50
0400	Recycled pavement, at plant, ratio old: new, 70:30	G				58			58	63.50
0600	Ratio old: new, 30:70	G				64			64	70.50

31 06 Schedules for Earthwork

31 06 60 – Schedules for Special Foundations and Load Bearing Elements

31 06 60.14 Piling Special Costs

	31 06 60.14 Piling Special Costs	Crew	Daily Output	Labor-Hours	Unit	Material	2015 Bare Costs Labor	Equipment	Total	Total Incl O&P
0010	**PILING SPECIAL COSTS**									
0011	Piling special costs, pile caps, see Section 03 30 53.40									
0500	Cutoffs, concrete piles, plain	1 Pile	5.50	1.455	Ea.		67		67	106
0600	With steel thin shell, add		38	.211			9.70		9.70	15.35
0700	Steel pile or "H" piles		19	.421			19.40		19.40	30.50
0800	Wood piles		38	.211			9.70		9.70	15.35
0900	Pre-augering up to 30' deep, average soil, 24" diameter	B-43	180	.267	L.F.		11.10	14.10	25.20	32.50
0920	36" diameter		115	.417			17.35	22	39.35	51

31 06 60 – Schedules for Special Foundations and Load Bearing Elements

31 06 60.14 Piling Special Costs		Crew	Daily Output	Labor-Hours	Unit	Material	2015 Bare Costs Labor	2015 Bare Costs Equipment	Total	Total Incl O&P
0960	48" diameter	B-43	70	.686	L.F.		28.50	36.50	65	83.50
0980	60" diameter	▼	50	.960	▼		40	51	91	117
1000	Testing, any type piles, test load is twice the design load									
1050	50 ton design load, 100 ton test				Ea.				14,000	15,500
1100	100 ton design load, 200 ton test								20,000	22,000
1150	150 ton design load, 300 ton test								26,000	28,500
1200	200 ton design load, 400 ton test								28,000	31,000
1250	400 ton design load, 800 ton test				▼				32,000	35,000
1500	Wet conditions, soft damp ground									
1600	Requiring mats for crane, add								40%	40%
1700	Barge mounted driving rig, add								30%	30%

31 06 60.15 Mobilization

		Crew	Daily Output	Labor-Hours	Unit	Material	Labor	Equipment	Total	Total Incl O&P
0010	**MOBILIZATION**									
0020	Set up & remove, air compressor, 600 CFM	A-5	3.30	5.455	Ea.		206	18.60	224.60	335
0100	1200 CFM	"	2.20	8.182			310	28	338	505
0200	Crane, with pile leads and pile hammer, 75 ton	B-19	.60	106			5,075	2,900	7,975	11,100
0300	150 ton	"	.36	177			8,475	4,825	13,300	18,500
0500	Drill rig, for caissons, to 36", minimum	B-43	2	24			995	1,275	2,270	2,925
0520	Maximum		.50	96			4,000	5,075	9,075	11,700
0600	Up to 84"	▼	1	48			2,000	2,550	4,550	5,850
0800	Auxiliary boiler, for steam small	A-5	1.66	10.843			410	37	447	670
0900	Large	"	.83	21.687			820	74	894	1,325
1100	Rule of thumb: complete pile driving set up, small	B-19	.45	142			6,775	3,850	10,625	14,900
1200	Large	"	.27	237	▼		11,300	6,425	17,725	24,700
1300	Mobilization by water for barge driving rig									
1310	Minimum				Ea.				7,000	7,700
1320	Maximum				"				45,000	49,500
1500	Mobilization, barge, by tug boat	B-83	25	.640	Mile		28	35	63	81.50
1600	Standby time for shore pile driving crew				Hr.				715	890
1700	Standby time for barge driving rig				"				1,000	1,250

31 11 Clearing and Grubbing

31 11 10 – Clearing and Grubbing Land

31 11 10.10 Clear and Grub Site		Crew	Daily Output	Labor-Hours	Unit	Material	Labor	Equipment	Total	Total Incl O&P
0010	**CLEAR AND GRUB SITE**									
0020	Cut & chip light trees to 6" diam.	B-7	1	48	Acre		1,925	1,675	3,600	4,775
0150	Grub stumps and remove	B-30	2	12			525	1,200	1,725	2,125
0160	Clear & grub brush including stumps	"	.58	41.379			1,800	4,150	5,950	7,300
0200	Cut & chip medium, trees to 12" diam.	B-7	.70	68.571			2,750	2,375	5,125	6,850
0250	Grub stumps and remove	B-30	1	24			1,050	2,400	3,450	4,225
0260	Clear & grub dense brush including stumps	"	.47	51.064			2,225	5,125	7,350	9,025
0300	Cut & chip heavy, trees to 24" diam.	B-7	.30	160			6,425	5,575	12,000	16,000
0350	Grub stumps and remove	B-30	.50	48			2,100	4,825	6,925	8,475
0400	If burning is allowed, deduct cut & chip				▼				40%	40%
3000	Chipping stumps, to 18" deep, 12" diam.	B-86	20	.400	Ea.		20	9.30	29.30	40.50
3040	18" diameter		16	.500			25.50	11.60	37.10	51.50
3080	24" diameter		14	.571			29	13.25	42.25	58.50
3100	30" diameter		12	.667			33.50	15.45	48.95	68
3120	36" diameter		10	.800			40.50	18.55	59.05	82
3160	48" diameter	▼	8	1	▼		50.50	23	73.50	103
5000	Tree thinning, feller buncher, conifer									

31 11 Clearing and Grubbing

31 11 10 – Clearing and Grubbing Land

31 11 10.10 Clear and Grub Site	Crew	Daily Output	Labor-Hours	Unit	Material	2015 Bare Costs Labor	Equipment	Total	Total Incl O&P
5080	Up to 8" diameter	B-93	240	.033	Ea.		1.69	3.49	5.18	6.40
5120	12" diameter		160	.050			2.53	5.25	7.78	9.60
5240	Hardwood, up to 4" diameter		240	.033			1.69	3.49	5.18	6.40
5280	8" diameter		180	.044			2.25	4.66	6.91	8.50
5320	12" diameter	↓	120	.067	↓		3.37	7	10.37	12.80
7000	Tree removal, congested area, aerial lift truck									
7040	8" diameter	B-85	7	5.714	Ea.		233	147	380	515
7080	12" diameter		6	6.667			271	172	443	605
7120	18" diameter		5	8			325	206	531	720
7160	24" diameter		4	10			405	258	663	905
7240	36" diameter		3	13.333			545	345	890	1,200
7280	48" diameter	↓	2	20	↓		815	515	1,330	1,825

31 13 Selective Tree and Shrub Removal and Trimming

31 13 13 – Selective Tree and Shrub Removal

31 13 13.10 Selective Clearing

		Crew	Daily Output	Labor-Hours	Unit	Material	Labor	Equipment	Total	Total Incl O&P
0010	**SELECTIVE CLEARING**									
0020	Clearing brush with brush saw	A-1C	.25	32	Acre		1,200	125	1,325	1,975
0100	By hand	1 Clab	.12	66.667			2,500		2,500	3,850
0300	With dozer, ball and chain, light clearing	B-11A	2	8			355	695	1,050	1,300
0400	Medium clearing		1.50	10.667			470	925	1,395	1,750
0500	With dozer and brush rake, light		10	1.600			70.50	139	209.50	261
0550	Medium brush to 4" diameter		8	2			88	173	261	325
0600	Heavy brush to 4" diameter	↓	6.40	2.500	↓		110	217	327	405
1000	Brush mowing, tractor w/rotary mower, no removal									
1020	Light density	B-84	2	4	Acre		202	185	387	510
1040	Medium density		1.50	5.333			270	247	517	680
1080	Heavy density	↓	1	8	↓		405	370	775	1,025

31 13 13.20 Selective Tree Removal

		Crew	Daily Output	Labor-Hours	Unit	Material	Labor	Equipment	Total	Total Incl O&P
0010	**SELECTIVE TREE REMOVAL**									
0011	With tractor, large tract, firm									
0020	level terrain, no boulders, less than 12" diam. trees									
0300	300 HP dozer, up to 400 trees/acre, 0 to 25% hardwoods	B-10M	.75	16	Acre		740	2,525	3,265	3,900
0340	25% to 50% hardwoods		.60	20			925	3,150	4,075	4,875
0370	75% to 100% hardwoods		.45	26.667			1,225	4,225	5,450	6,500
0400	500 trees/acre, 0% to 25% hardwoods		.60	20			925	3,150	4,075	4,875
0440	25% to 50% hardwoods		.48	25			1,150	3,950	5,100	6,100
0470	75% to 100% hardwoods		.36	33.333			1,550	5,275	6,825	8,150
0500	More than 600 trees/acre, 0 to 25% hardwoods		.52	23.077			1,075	3,650	4,725	5,650
0540	25% to 50% hardwoods		.42	28.571			1,325	4,525	5,850	7,000
0570	75% to 100% hardwoods		.31	38.710	↓		1,800	6,125	7,925	9,450
0900	Large tract clearing per tree									
1500	300 HP dozer, to 12" diameter, softwood	B-10M	320	.038	Ea.		1.74	5.95	7.69	9.15
1550	Hardwood		100	.120			5.55	18.95	24.50	29.50
1600	12" to 24" diameter, softwood		200	.060			2.78	9.50	12.28	14.70
1650	Hardwood		80	.150			6.95	23.50	30.45	36.50
1700	24" to 36" diameter, softwood		100	.120			5.55	18.95	24.50	29.50
1750	Hardwood		50	.240			11.10	38	49.10	58.50
1800	36" to 48" diameter, softwood		70	.171			7.95	27	34.95	42
1850	Hardwood	↓	35	.343	↓		15.85	54	69.85	83.50
2000	Stump removal on site by hydraulic backhoe, 1-1/2 C.Y.									

For customer support on your Site Work & Landscape Cost Data, call 877.737.1594.

31 13 Selective Tree and Shrub Removal and Trimming

31 13 13 – Selective Tree and Shrub Removal

31 13 13.20 Selective Tree Removal	Crew	Daily Output	Labor-Hours	Unit	Material	2015 Bare Costs Labor	2015 Bare Costs Equipment	Total	Total Incl O&P
2040	4" to 6" diameter	B-17	60	.533	Ea.		22	12.90	34.90	47.50
2050	8" to 12" diameter	B-30	33	.727			31.50	73	104.50	129
2100	14" to 24" diameter		25	.960			42	96.50	138.50	170
2150	26" to 36" diameter		16	1.500			65.50	151	216.50	265
3000	Remove selective trees, on site using chain saws and chipper,									
3050	not incl. stumps, up to 6" diameter	B-7	18	2.667	Ea.		107	93	200	266
3100	8" to 12" diameter		12	4			160	139	299	400
3150	14" to 24" diameter		10	4.800			192	167	359	480
3200	26" to 36" diameter		8	6			241	209	450	600
3300	Machine load, 2 mile haul to dump, 12" diam. tree	A-3B	8	2			90.50	151	241.50	305

31 14 Earth Stripping and Stockpiling

31 14 13 – Soil Stripping and Stockpiling

31 14 13.23 Topsoil Stripping and Stockpiling

		Crew	Daily Output	Labor-Hours	Unit	Material	2015 Bare Costs Labor	2015 Bare Costs Equipment	Total	Total Incl O&P
0010	**TOPSOIL STRIPPING AND STOCKPILING**									
0020	200 H.P. dozer, ideal conditions	B-10B	2300	.005	C.Y.		.24	.60	.84	1.03
0100	Adverse conditions	"	1150	.010			.48	1.21	1.69	2.06
0200	300 H.P. dozer, ideal conditions	B-10M	3000	.004			.19	.63	.82	.98
0300	Adverse conditions	"	1650	.007			.34	1.15	1.49	1.77
0400	400 H.P. dozer, ideal conditions	B-10X	3900	.003			.14	.62	.76	.90
0500	Adverse conditions	"	2000	.006			.28	1.20	1.48	1.74
0600	Clay, dry and soft, 200 H.P. dozer, ideal conditions	B-10B	1600	.008			.35	.87	1.22	1.48
0700	Adverse conditions	"	800	.015			.69	1.73	2.42	2.97
1000	Medium hard, 300 H.P. dozer, ideal conditions	B-10M	2000	.006			.28	.95	1.23	1.46
1100	Adverse conditions	"	1100	.011			.50	1.72	2.22	2.67
1200	Very hard, 400 H.P. dozer, ideal conditions	B-10X	2600	.005			.21	.93	1.14	1.35
1300	Adverse conditions	"	1340	.009			.41	1.80	2.21	2.61
1400	Loam or topsoil, remove and stockpile on site									
1420	6" deep, 200' haul	B-10B	865	.014	C.Y.		.64	1.60	2.24	2.74
1430	300' haul		520	.023			1.07	2.67	3.74	4.56
1440	500' haul		225	.053			2.47	6.15	8.62	10.55
1450	Alternate method: 6" deep, 200' haul		5090	.002	S.Y.		.11	.27	.38	.47
1460	500' haul		1325	.009	"		.42	1.05	1.47	1.79
1500	Loam or topsoil, remove/stockpile on site									
1510	By hand, 6" deep, 50' haul, less than 100 S.Y.	B-1	100	.240	S.Y.		9.20		9.20	14.15
1520	By skid steer, 6" deep, 100' haul, 101-500 S.Y.	B-62	500	.048			1.98	.35	2.33	3.41
1530	100' haul, 501-900 S.Y.	"	900	.027			1.10	.19	1.29	1.89
1540	200' haul, 901-1100 S.Y.	B-63	1000	.040			1.59	.17	1.76	2.63
1550	By dozer, 200' haul, 1101-4000 S.Y.	B-10B	4000	.003			.14	.35	.49	.59

For customer support on your Site Work & Landscape Cost Data, call 877.737.1594.

283

31 22 Grading

31 22 13 – Rough Grading

31 22 13.20 Rough Grading Sites

		Crew	Daily Output	Labor-Hours	Unit	Material	2015 Bare Costs Labor	2015 Bare Costs Equipment	Total	Total Incl O&P
0010	**ROUGH GRADING SITES**									
0100	Rough grade sites 400 S.F. or less	B-1	2	12	Ea.		460		460	705
0120	410-1000 S.F.	"	1	24			920		920	1,425
0130	1100-3000 S.F.	B-62	1.50	16			660	116	776	1,125
0140	3100-5000 S.F.	"	1	24			990	174	1,164	1,725
0150	5100-8000 S.F.	B-63	1	40			1,600	174	1,774	2,650
0160	8100-10000 S.F.	"	.75	53.333			2,125	231	2,356	3,500
0170	8100-10000 S.F.	B-10L	1	12			555	470	1,025	1,375
0200	Rough grade open sites 10000-20000 S.F.	B-11L	1.80	8.889			390	410	800	1,050
0210	20100-25000 S.F.		1.40	11.429			505	525	1,030	1,350
0220	25100-30000 S.F.		1.20	13.333			590	615	1,205	1,575
0230	30100-35000 S.F.		1	16			705	735	1,440	1,875
0240	35100-40000 S.F.		.90	17.778			785	820	1,605	2,100
0250	40100-45000 S.F.		.80	20			880	920	1,800	2,350
0260	45100-50000 S.F.		.72	22.222			980	1,025	2,005	2,625
0270	50100-75000 S.F.		.50	32			1,400	1,475	2,875	3,775
0280	75100-100000 S.F.		.36	44.444			1,950	2,050	4,000	5,250

31 22 16 – Fine Grading

31 22 16.10 Finish Grading

		Crew	Daily Output	Labor-Hours	Unit	Material	2015 Bare Costs Labor	2015 Bare Costs Equipment	Total	Total Incl O&P
0010	**FINISH GRADING**									
0011	Finish grading granular subbase for highway paving	B-32C	8000	.006	S.Y.		.27	.30	.57	.73
0012	Finish grading area to be paved with grader, small area	B-11L	400	.040			1.76	1.84	3.60	4.71
0100	Large area		2000	.008			.35	.37	.72	.94
0200	Grade subgrade for base course, roadways		3500	.005			.20	.21	.41	.54
1020	For large parking lots	B-32C	5000	.010			.43	.47	.90	1.17
1100	Fine grade for slab on grade, machine	B-11L	1040	.015			.68	.71	1.39	1.82
1150	Hand grading	B-18	700	.034			1.31	.07	1.38	2.09
1200	Fine grade granular base for sidewalks and bikeways	B-62	1200	.020			.83	.14	.97	1.42
2550	Hand grade select gravel	2 Clab	60	.267	C.S.F.		10.05		10.05	15.45
3000	Hand grade select gravel, including compaction, 4" deep	B-18	555	.043	S.Y.		1.65	.08	1.73	2.64
3100	6" deep		400	.060			2.30	.12	2.42	3.66
3120	8" deep		300	.080			3.06	.16	3.22	4.88
3300	Finishing grading slopes, gentle	B-11L	8900	.002			.08	.08	.16	.21
3310	Steep slopes		7100	.002			.10	.10	.20	.26
3312	Steep slopes, large quantities		64	.250	M.S.F.		11.05	11.50	22.55	29.50
3500	Finish grading lagoon bottoms		4	4			176	184	360	470
3600	Fine grade, top of lagoon banks for compaction		30	.533			23.50	24.50	48	63

31 23 Excavation and Fill

31 23 16 – Excavation

31 23 16.13 Excavating, Trench

		Crew	Daily Output	Labor-Hours	Unit	Material	2015 Bare Costs Labor	2015 Bare Costs Equipment	Total	Total Incl O&P
0010	**EXCAVATING, TRENCH**	R312316-40								
0011	Or continuous footing									
0020	Common earth with no sheeting or dewatering included									
0050	1' to 4' deep, 3/8 C.Y. excavator	B-11C	150	.107	B.C.Y.		4.70	2.43	7.13	9.85
0060	1/2 C.Y. excavator	B-11M	200	.080			3.53	1.96	5.49	7.55
0062	3/4 C.Y. excavator	B-12F	270	.059			2.65	2.43	5.08	6.70
0090	4' to 6' deep, 1/2 C.Y. excavator	B-11M	200	.080			3.53	1.96	5.49	7.55
0100	5/8 C.Y. excavator	B-12Q	250	.064			2.86	2.36	5.22	6.95
0110	3/4 C.Y. excavator	B-12F	300	.053			2.38	2.18	4.56	6.05

31 23 16 – Excavation

31 23 16.13 Excavating, Trench	Crew	Daily Output	Labor-Hours	Unit	Material	2015 Bare Costs Labor	Equipment	Total	Total Incl O&P
0120	1 C.Y. hydraulic excavator	B-12A	400	.040	B.C.Y.		1.79	2.03	3.82	4.96
0130	1-1/2 C.Y. excavator	B-12B	540	.030			1.32	1.91	3.23	4.12
0300	1/2 C.Y. excavator, truck mounted	B-12J	200	.080			3.57	4.41	7.98	10.30
0500	6' to 10' deep, 3/4 C.Y. excavator	B-12F	225	.071			3.18	2.91	6.09	8.05
0510	1 C.Y. excavator	B-12A	400	.040			1.79	2.03	3.82	4.96
0600	1 C.Y. excavator, truck mounted	B-12K	400	.040			1.79	2.51	4.30	5.50
0610	1-1/2 C.Y. excavator	B-12B	600	.027			1.19	1.72	2.91	3.71
0620	2-1/2 C.Y. excavator	B-12S	1000	.016			.71	1.61	2.32	2.86
0900	10' to 14' deep, 3/4 C.Y. excavator	B-12F	200	.080			3.57	3.27	6.84	9.05
0910	1 C.Y. excavator	B-12A	360	.044			1.98	2.26	4.24	5.50
1000	1-1/2 C.Y. excavator	B-12B	540	.030			1.32	1.91	3.23	4.12
1020	2-1/2 C.Y. excavator	B-12S	900	.018			.79	1.78	2.57	3.17
1030	3 C.Y. excavator	B-12D	1400	.011			.51	1.74	2.25	2.70
1040	3-1/2 C.Y. excavator	"	1800	.009			.40	1.36	1.76	2.10
1300	14' to 20' deep, 1 C.Y. excavator	B-12A	320	.050			2.23	2.54	4.77	6.20
1310	1-1/2 C.Y. excavator	B-12B	480	.033			1.49	2.15	3.64	4.63
1320	2-1/2 C.Y. excavator	B-12S	765	.021			.93	2.10	3.03	3.74
1330	3 C.Y. excavator	B-12D	1000	.016			.71	2.44	3.15	3.77
1335	3-1/2 C.Y. excavator	"	1150	.014			.62	2.12	2.74	3.28
1340	20' to 24' deep, 1 C.Y. excavator	B-12A	288	.056			2.48	2.82	5.30	6.90
1342	1-1/2 C.Y. excavator	B-12B	432	.037			1.65	2.38	4.03	5.15
1344	2-1/2 C.Y. excavator	B-12S	685	.023			1.04	2.34	3.38	4.17
1346	3 C.Y. excavator	B-12D	900	.018			.79	2.71	3.50	4.19
1348	3-1/2 C.Y. excavator	"	1050	.015			.68	2.32	3	3.60
1352	4' to 6' deep, 1/2 C.Y. excavator w/trench box	B-13H	188	.085			3.80	5.10	8.90	11.45
1354	5/8 C.Y. excavator	"	235	.068			3.04	4.10	7.14	9.15
1356	3/4 C.Y. excavator	B-13G	282	.057			2.53	2.61	5.14	6.75
1358	1 C.Y. excavator	B-13D	376	.043			1.90	2.38	4.28	5.50
1360	1-1/2 C.Y. excavator	B-13E	508	.032			1.41	2.19	3.60	4.56
1362	6' to 10' deep, 3/4 C.Y. excavator w/trench box	B-13G	212	.075			3.37	3.47	6.84	8.95
1370	1 C.Y. excavator	B-13D	376	.043			1.90	2.38	4.28	5.50
1371	1-1/2 C.Y. excavator	B-13E	564	.028			1.27	1.97	3.24	4.10
1372	2-1/2 C.Y. excavator	B-13J	940	.017			.76	1.79	2.55	3.13
1374	10' to 14' deep, 3/4 C.Y. excavator w/trench box	B-13G	188	.085			3.80	3.91	7.71	10.10
1375	1 C.Y. excavator	B-13D	338	.047			2.11	2.64	4.75	6.15
1376	1-1/2 C.Y. excavator	B-13E	508	.032			1.41	2.19	3.60	4.56
1377	2-1/2 C.Y. excavator	B-13J	845	.019			.85	1.99	2.84	3.48
1378	3 C.Y. excavator	B-13F	1316	.012			.54	1.92	2.46	2.94
1380	3-1/2 C.Y. excavator	"	1692	.009			.42	1.49	1.91	2.28
1381	14' to 20' deep, 1 C.Y. excavator w/trench box	B-13D	301	.053			2.37	2.97	5.34	6.90
1382	1-1/2 C.Y. excavator	B-13E	451	.035			1.58	2.46	4.04	5.15
1383	2-1/2 C.Y. excavator	B-13J	720	.022			.99	2.34	3.33	4.09
1384	3 C.Y. excavator	B-13F	940	.017			.76	2.68	3.44	4.11
1385	3-1/2 C.Y. excavator	"	1081	.015			.66	2.33	2.99	3.58
1386	20' to 24' deep, 1 C.Y. excavator w/trench box	B-13D	271	.059			2.64	3.30	5.94	7.65
1387	1-1/2 C.Y. excavator	B-13E	406	.039			1.76	2.74	4.50	5.70
1388	2-1/2 C.Y. excavator	B-13J	645	.025			1.11	2.61	3.72	4.57
1389	3 C.Y. excavator	B-13F	846	.019			.84	2.98	3.82	4.57
1390	3-1/2 C.Y. excavator	"	987	.016			.72	2.55	3.27	3.91
1391	Shoring by S.F./day trench wall protected loose mat., 4' W	B-6	3200	.008	SF Wall	.53	.31	.11	.95	1.18
1392	Rent shoring per week per S.F. wall protected, loose mat., 4' W					1.46			1.46	1.60
1395	Hydraulic shoring, S.F. trench wall protected stable mat., 4' W	2 Clab	2700	.006		.19	.22		.41	.55
1397	semi-stable material, 4' W	"	2400	.007		.27	.25		.52	.69

31 23 Excavation and Fill

31 23 16 – Excavation

31 23 16.13 Excavating, Trench

		Crew	Daily Output	Labor-Hours	Unit	Material	2015 Bare Costs Labor	2015 Bare Costs Equipment	Total	Total Incl O&P
1398	Rent hydraulic shoring per day/S.F. wall, stable mat., 4' W				SF Wall	.32			.32	.35
1399	semi-stable material					.40			.40	.44
1400	By hand with pick and shovel 2' to 6' deep, light soil	1 Clab	8	1	B.C.Y.		37.50		37.50	58
1500	Heavy soil	"	4	2	"		75		75	116
1700	For tamping backfilled trenches, air tamp, add	A-1G	100	.080	E.C.Y.		3.01	.56	3.57	5.25
1900	Vibrating plate, add	B-18	180	.133	"		5.10	.26	5.36	8.15
2100	Trim sides and bottom for concrete pours, common earth	↓	1500	.016	S.F.		.61	.03	.64	.97
2300	Hardpan		600	.040	"		1.53	.08	1.61	2.45
2400	Pier and spread footing excavation, add to above				B.C.Y.				30%	30%
3000	Backfill trench, F.E. loader, wheel mtd., 1 C.Y. bucket									
3020	Minimal haul	B-10R	400	.030	L.C.Y.		1.39	.75	2.14	2.93
3040	100' haul		200	.060			2.78	1.50	4.28	5.85
3060	200' haul	↓	100	.120			5.55	2.99	8.54	11.75
3080	2-1/4 C.Y. bucket, minimum haul	B-10T	600	.020			.93	.87	1.80	2.36
3090	100' haul		300	.040			1.85	1.73	3.58	4.73
3100	200' haul	↓	150	.080	↓		3.70	3.47	7.17	9.45
4000	For backfill with dozer, see Section 31 23 23.14									
4010	For compaction of backfill, see Section 31 23 23.23									
5020	Loam & Sandy clay with no sheeting or dewatering included									
5050	1' to 4' deep, 3/8 C.Y. tractor loader/backhoe	B-11C	162	.099	B.C.Y.		4.36	2.25	6.61	9.10
5060	1/2 C.Y. excavator	B-11M	216	.074			3.27	1.81	5.08	7
5070	3/4 C.Y. excavator	B-12F	292	.055			2.45	2.24	4.69	6.20
5080	4' to 6' deep, 1/2 C.Y. excavator	B-11M	216	.074			3.27	1.81	5.08	7
5090	5/8 C.Y. excavator	B-12Q	276	.058			2.59	2.14	4.73	6.30
5100	3/4 C.Y. excavator	B-12F	324	.049			2.20	2.02	4.22	5.60
5110	1 C.Y. excavator	B-12A	432	.037			1.65	1.88	3.53	4.59
5120	1-1/2 C.Y. excavator	B-12B	583	.027			1.23	1.77	3	3.81
5130	1/2 C.Y. excavator, truck mounted	B-12J	216	.074			3.31	4.08	7.39	9.55
5140	6' to 10' deep, 3/4 C.Y. excavator	B-12F	243	.066			2.94	2.69	5.63	7.45
5150	1 C.Y. excavator	B-12A	432	.037			1.65	1.88	3.53	4.59
5160	1 C.Y. excavator, truck mounted	B-12K	432	.037			1.65	2.32	3.97	5.05
5170	1-1/2 C.Y. excavator	B-12B	648	.025			1.10	1.59	2.69	3.43
5180	2-1/2 C.Y. excavator	B-12S	1080	.015			.66	1.49	2.15	2.64
5190	10' to 14' deep, 3/4 C.Y. excavator	B-12F	216	.074			3.31	3.03	6.34	8.40
5200	1 C.Y. excavator	B-12A	389	.041			1.84	2.09	3.93	5.10
5210	1-1/2 C.Y. excavator	B-12B	583	.027			1.23	1.77	3	3.81
5220	2-1/2 C.Y. hydraulic backhoe	B-12S	970	.016			.74	1.65	2.39	2.94
5230	3 C.Y. excavator	B-12D	1512	.011			.47	1.61	2.08	2.49
5240	3-1/2 C.Y. excavator	"	1944	.008			.37	1.26	1.63	1.94
5250	14' to 20' deep, 1 C.Y. excavator	B-12A	346	.046			2.06	2.35	4.41	5.75
5260	1-1/2 C.Y. excavator	B-12B	518	.031			1.38	1.99	3.37	4.30
5270	2-1/2 C.Y. excavator	B-12S	826	.019			.86	1.94	2.80	3.46
5280	3 C.Y. excavator	B-12D	1080	.015			.66	2.26	2.92	3.49
5290	3-1/2 C.Y. excavator	"	1242	.013			.58	1.96	2.54	3.04
5300	20' to 24' deep, 1 C.Y. excavator	B-12A	311	.051			2.30	2.61	4.91	6.40
5310	1-1/2 C.Y. excavator	B-12B	467	.034			1.53	2.21	3.74	4.76
5320	2-1/2 C.Y. excavator	B-12S	740	.022			.97	2.17	3.14	3.86
5330	3 C.Y. excavator	B-12D	972	.016			.73	2.51	3.24	3.88
5340	3-1/2 C.Y. excavator	"	1134	.014			.63	2.15	2.78	3.33
5352	4' to 6' deep, 1/2 C.Y. excavator w/trench box	B-13H	205	.078			3.48	4.70	8.18	10.45
5354	5/8 C.Y. excavator	"	257	.062			2.78	3.75	6.53	8.35
5356	3/4 C.Y. excavator	B-13G	308	.052			2.32	2.39	4.71	6.15
5358	1 C.Y. excavator	B-13D	410	.039	↓		1.74	2.18	3.92	5.05

31 23 16.13 Excavating, Trench

		Crew	Daily Output	Labor-Hours	Unit	Material	2015 Bare Costs Labor	Equipment	Total	Total Incl O&P
5360	1-1/2 C.Y. excavator	B-13E	554	.029	B.C.Y.		1.29	2.01	3.30	4.18
5362	6' to 10' deep, 3/4 C.Y. excavator w/trench box	B-13G	231	.069			3.09	3.19	6.28	8.20
5364	1 C.Y. excavator	B-13D	410	.039			1.74	2.18	3.92	5.05
5366	1-1/2 C.Y. excavator	B-13E	616	.026			1.16	1.80	2.96	3.75
5368	2-1/2 C.Y. excavator	B-13J	1015	.016			.70	1.66	2.36	2.90
5370	10' to 14' deep, 3/4 C.Y. excavator w/trench box	B-13G	205	.078			3.48	3.59	7.07	9.25
5372	1 C.Y. excavator	B-13D	370	.043			1.93	2.42	4.35	5.60
5374	1-1/2 C.Y. excavator	B-13E	554	.029			1.29	2.01	3.30	4.18
5376	2-1/2 C.Y. excavator	B-13J	914	.018			.78	1.85	2.63	3.22
5378	3 C.Y. excavator	B-13F	1436	.011			.50	1.76	2.26	2.69
5380	3-1/2 C.Y. excavator	"	1847	.009			.39	1.36	1.75	2.09
5382	14' to 20' deep, 1 C.Y. excavator w/trench box	B-13D	329	.049			2.17	2.72	4.89	6.30
5384	1-1/2 C.Y. excavator	B-13E	492	.033			1.45	2.26	3.71	4.70
5386	2-1/2 C.Y. excavator	B-13J	780	.021			.92	2.16	3.08	3.78
5388	3 C.Y. excavator	B-13F	1026	.016			.70	2.46	3.16	3.76
5390	3-1/2 C.Y. excavator	"	1180	.014			.61	2.14	2.75	3.27
5392	20' to 24' deep, 1 C.Y. excavator w/trench box	B-13D	295	.054			2.42	3.03	5.45	7.05
5394	1-1/2 C.Y. excavator	B-13E	444	.036			1.61	2.50	4.11	5.20
5396	2-1/2 C.Y. excavator	B-13J	695	.023			1.03	2.43	3.46	4.24
5398	3 C.Y. excavator	B-13F	923	.017			.77	2.73	3.50	4.18
5400	3-1/2 C.Y. excavator	"	1077	.015			.66	2.34	3	3.59
6020	Sand & gravel with no sheeting or dewatering included									
6050	1' to 4' deep, 3/8 C.Y. excavator	B-11C	165	.097	B.C.Y.		4.28	2.21	6.49	9
6060	1/2 C.Y. excavator	B-11M	220	.073			3.21	1.78	4.99	6.85
6070	3/4 C.Y. excavator	B-12F	297	.054			2.41	2.20	4.61	6.10
6080	4' to 6' deep, 1/2 C.Y. excavator	B-11M	220	.073			3.21	1.78	4.99	6.85
6090	5/8 C.Y. excavator	B-12Q	275	.058			2.60	2.14	4.74	6.35
6100	3/4 C.Y. excavator	B-12F	330	.048			2.16	1.98	4.14	5.50
6110	1 C.Y. excavator	B-12A	440	.036			1.62	1.85	3.47	4.51
6120	1-1/2 C.Y. excavator	B-12B	594	.027			1.20	1.73	2.93	3.75
6130	1/2 C.Y. excavator, truck mounted	B-12J	220	.073			3.25	4.01	7.26	9.35
6140	6' to 10' deep, 3/4 C.Y. excavator	B-12F	248	.065			2.88	2.64	5.52	7.30
6150	1 C.Y. excavator	B-12A	440	.036			1.62	1.85	3.47	4.51
6160	1 C.Y. excavator, truck mounted	B-12K	440	.036			1.62	2.28	3.90	4.98
6170	1-1/2 C.Y. excavator	B-12B	660	.024			1.08	1.56	2.64	3.37
6180	2-1/2 C.Y. excavator	B-12S	1100	.015			.65	1.46	2.11	2.60
6190	10' to 14' deep, 3/4 C.Y. excavator	B-12F	220	.073			3.25	2.98	6.23	8.25
6200	1 C.Y. excavator	B-12A	396	.040			1.80	2.05	3.85	5
6210	1-1/2 C.Y. excavator	B-12B	594	.027			1.20	1.73	2.93	3.75
6220	2-1/2 C.Y. excavator	B-12S	990	.016			.72	1.62	2.34	2.88
6230	3 C.Y. excavator	B-12D	1540	.010			.46	1.58	2.04	2.45
6240	3-1/2 C.Y. excavator	"	1980	.008			.36	1.23	1.59	1.91
6250	14' to 20' deep, 1 C.Y. excavator	B-12A	352	.045			2.03	2.31	4.34	5.65
6260	1-1/2 C.Y. excavator	B-12B	528	.030			1.35	1.95	3.30	4.21
6270	2-1/2 C.Y. excavator	B-12S	840	.019			.85	1.91	2.76	3.40
6280	3 C.Y. excavator	B-12D	1100	.015			.65	2.22	2.87	3.43
6290	3-1/2 C.Y. excavator	"	1265	.013			.56	1.93	2.49	2.98
6300	20' to 24' deep, 1 C.Y. excavator	B-12A	317	.050			2.25	2.56	4.81	6.25
6310	1-1/2 C.Y. excavator	B-12B	475	.034			1.50	2.17	3.67	4.68
6320	2-1/2 C.Y. excavator	B-12S	755	.021			.95	2.13	3.08	3.78
6330	3 C.Y. excavator	B-12D	990	.016			.72	2.46	3.18	3.81
6340	3-1/2 C.Y. excavator	"	1155	.014			.62	2.11	2.73	3.26
6352	4' to 6' deep, 1/2 C.Y. excavator w/trench box	B-13H	209	.077			3.42	4.61	8.03	10.25

31 23 16.13 Excavating, Trench

		Crew	Daily Output	Labor-Hours	Unit	Material	2015 Bare Costs Labor	Equipment	Total	Total Incl O&P
6354	5/8 C.Y. excavator	B-13H	261	.061	B.C.Y.		2.74	3.69	6.43	8.25
6356	3/4 C.Y. excavator	B-13G	314	.051			2.28	2.34	4.62	6.05
6358	1 C.Y. excavator	B-13D	418	.038			1.71	2.14	3.85	4.96
6360	1-1/2 C.Y. excavator	B-13E	564	.028			1.27	1.97	3.24	4.10
6362	6' to 10' deep, 3/4 C.Y. excavator w/trench box	B-13G	236	.068			3.03	3.12	6.15	8.05
6364	1 C.Y. excavator	B-13D	418	.038			1.71	2.14	3.85	4.96
6366	1-1/2 C.Y. excavator	B-13E	627	.026			1.14	1.77	2.91	3.69
6368	2-1/2 C.Y. excavator	B-13J	1035	.015			.69	1.63	2.32	2.84
6370	10' to 14' deep, 3/4 C.Y. excavator w/trench box	B-13G	209	.077			3.42	3.52	6.94	9.05
6372	1 C.Y. excavator	B-13D	376	.043			1.90	2.38	4.28	5.50
6374	1-1/2 C.Y. excavator	B-13E	564	.028			1.27	1.97	3.24	4.10
6376	2-1/2 C.Y. excavator	B-13J	930	.017			.77	1.81	2.58	3.16
6378	3 C.Y. excavator	B-13F	1463	.011			.49	1.72	2.21	2.65
6380	3-1/2 C.Y. excavator	"	1881	.009			.38	1.34	1.72	2.06
6382	14' to 20' deep, 1 C.Y. excavator w/trench box	B-13D	334	.048			2.14	2.68	4.82	6.20
6384	1-1/2 C.Y. excavator	B-13E	502	.032			1.42	2.21	3.63	4.60
6386	2-1/2 C.Y. excavator	B-13J	790	.020			.90	2.13	3.03	3.73
6388	3 C.Y. excavator	B-13F	1045	.015			.68	2.41	3.09	3.69
6390	3-1/2 C.Y. excavator	"	1202	.013			.59	2.10	2.69	3.22
6392	20' to 24' deep, 1 C.Y. excavator w/trench box	B-13D	301	.053			2.37	2.97	5.34	6.90
6394	1-1/2 C.Y. excavator	B-13E	452	.035			1.58	2.46	4.04	5.10
6396	2-1/2 C.Y. excavator	B-13J	710	.023			1.01	2.38	3.39	4.15
6398	3 C.Y. excavator	B-13F	941	.017			.76	2.68	3.44	4.11
6400	3-1/2 C.Y. excavator	"	1097	.015			.65	2.30	2.95	3.52
7020	Dense hard clay with no sheeting or dewatering included									
7050	1' to 4' deep, 3/8 C.Y. excavator	B-11C	132	.121	B.C.Y.		5.35	2.76	8.11	11.20
7060	1/2 C.Y. excavator	B-11M	176	.091			4.01	2.23	6.24	8.55
7070	3/4 C.Y. excavator	B-12F	238	.067			3	2.75	5.75	7.60
7080	4' to 6' deep, 1/2 C.Y. excavator	B-11M	176	.091			4.01	2.23	6.24	8.55
7090	5/8 C.Y. excavator	B-12Q	220	.073			3.25	2.68	5.93	7.90
7100	3/4 C.Y. excavator	B-12F	264	.061			2.71	2.48	5.19	6.85
7110	1 C.Y. excavator	B-12A	352	.045			2.03	2.31	4.34	5.65
7120	1-1/2 C.Y. excavator	B-12B	475	.034			1.50	2.17	3.67	4.68
7130	1/2 C.Y. excavator, truck mounted	B-12J	176	.091			4.06	5	9.06	11.70
7140	6' to 10' deep, 3/4 C.Y. excavator	B-12F	198	.081			3.61	3.31	6.92	9.15
7150	1 C.Y. excavator	B-12A	352	.045			2.03	2.31	4.34	5.65
7160	1 C.Y. excavator, truck mounted	B-12K	352	.045			2.03	2.85	4.88	6.25
7170	1-1/2 C.Y. excavator	B-12B	528	.030			1.35	1.95	3.30	4.21
7180	2-1/2 C.Y. excavator	B-12S	880	.018			.81	1.82	2.63	3.25
7190	10' to 14' deep, 3/4 C.Y. excavator	B-12F	176	.091			4.06	3.72	7.78	10.30
7200	1 C.Y. excavator	B-12A	317	.050			2.25	2.56	4.81	6.25
7210	1-1/2 C.Y. excavator	B-12B	475	.034			1.50	2.17	3.67	4.68
7220	2-1/2 C.Y. excavator	B-12S	790	.020			.90	2.03	2.93	3.61
7230	3 C.Y. excavator	B-12D	1232	.013			.58	1.98	2.56	3.07
7240	3-1/2 C.Y. excavator	"	1584	.010			.45	1.54	1.99	2.38
7250	14' to 20' deep, 1 C.Y. excavator	B-12A	282	.057			2.53	2.88	5.41	7.05
7260	1-1/2 C.Y. excavator	B-12B	422	.038			1.69	2.44	4.13	5.25
7270	2-1/2 C.Y. excavator	B-12S	675	.024			1.06	2.38	3.44	4.24
7280	3 C.Y. excavator	B-12D	880	.018			.81	2.77	3.58	4.29
7290	3-1/2 C.Y. excavator	"	1012	.016			.71	2.41	3.12	3.73
7300	20' to 24' deep, 1 C.Y. excavator	B-12A	254	.063			2.81	3.20	6.01	7.80
7310	1-1/2 C.Y. excavator	B-12B	380	.042			1.88	2.71	4.59	5.85
7320	2-1/2 C.Y. excavator	B-12S	605	.026			1.18	2.65	3.83	4.72

31 23 Excavation and Fill

31 23 16 – Excavation

31 23 16.13 **Excavating, Trench**	Crew	Daily Output	Labor-Hours	Unit	Material	2015 Bare Costs Labor	2015 Bare Costs Equipment	Total	Total Incl O&P
7330	3 C.Y. excavator	B-12D	792	.020	B.C.Y.		.90	3.08	3.98	4.77
7340	3-1/2 C.Y. excavator	"	924	.017	↓		.77	2.64	3.41	4.09

31 23 16.14 Excavating, Utility Trench

	31 23 16.14	Crew	Daily Output	Labor-Hours	Unit	Material	Labor	Equipment	Total	Total Incl O&P
0010	**EXCAVATING, UTILITY TRENCH**									
0011	Common earth									
0050	Trenching with chain trencher, 12 H.P., operator walking									
0100	4" wide trench, 12" deep	B-53	800	.010	L.F.		.49	.09	.58	.83
0150	18" deep		750	.011			.52	.09	.61	.89
0200	24" deep		700	.011			.56	.10	.66	.95
0300	6" wide trench, 12" deep		650	.012			.60	.10	.70	1.03
0350	18" deep		600	.013			.65	.11	.76	1.10
0400	24" deep		550	.015			.71	.12	.83	1.21
0450	36" deep		450	.018			.86	.15	1.01	1.48
0600	8" wide trench, 12" deep		475	.017			.82	.14	.96	1.40
0650	18" deep		400	.020			.97	.17	1.14	1.67
0700	24" deep		350	.023			1.11	.19	1.30	1.90
0750	36" deep	↓	300	.027	↓		1.30	.23	1.53	2.22
0830	Fly wheel trencher, 18" wide trench, 6' deep, light soil	B-54A	1992	.005	B.C.Y.		.23	.60	.83	1.01
0840	Medium soil		1594	.006			.29	.75	1.04	1.26
0850	Heavy soil	↓	1295	.007			.35	.92	1.27	1.56
0860	24" wide trench, 9' deep, light soil	B-54B	4981	.002			.10	.38	.48	.57
0870	Medium soil		4000	.003			.12	.47	.59	.70
0880	Heavy soil	↓	3237	.003	↓		.15	.58	.73	.87
1000	Backfill by hand including compaction, add									
1050	4" wide trench, 12" deep	A-1G	800	.010	L.F.		.38	.07	.45	.66
1100	18" deep		530	.015			.57	.11	.68	.99
1150	24" deep		400	.020			.75	.14	.89	1.32
1300	6" wide trench, 12" deep		540	.015			.56	.10	.66	.97
1350	18" deep		405	.020			.74	.14	.88	1.29
1400	24" deep		270	.030			1.11	.21	1.32	1.94
1450	36" deep		180	.044			1.67	.31	1.98	2.91
1600	8" wide trench, 12" deep		400	.020			.75	.14	.89	1.32
1650	18" deep		265	.030			1.14	.21	1.35	1.98
1700	24" deep		200	.040			1.50	.28	1.78	2.62
1750	36" deep	↓	135	.059	↓		2.23	.42	2.65	3.89
2000	Chain trencher, 40 H.P. operator riding									
2050	6" wide trench and backfill, 12" deep	B-54	1200	.007	L.F.		.32	.28	.60	.80
2100	18" deep		1000	.008			.39	.34	.73	.96
2150	24" deep		975	.008			.40	.34	.74	.99
2200	36" deep		900	.009			.43	.37	.80	1.07
2250	48" deep		750	.011			.52	.45	.97	1.28
2300	60" deep		650	.012			.60	.52	1.12	1.48
2400	8" wide trench and backfill, 12" deep		1000	.008			.39	.34	.73	.96
2450	18" deep		950	.008			.41	.35	.76	1.01
2500	24" deep		900	.009			.43	.37	.80	1.07
2550	36" deep		800	.010			.49	.42	.91	1.20
2600	48" deep		650	.012			.60	.52	1.12	1.48
2700	12" wide trench and backfill, 12" deep		975	.008			.40	.34	.74	.99
2750	18" deep		860	.009			.45	.39	.84	1.12
2800	24" deep		800	.010			.49	.42	.91	1.20
2850	36" deep		725	.011			.54	.46	1	1.32
3000	16" wide trench and backfill, 12" deep		835	.010	↓		.47	.40	.87	1.15

For customer support on your Site Work & Landscape Cost Data, call 877.737.1594.

289

31 23 Excavation and Fill

31 23 16 – Excavation

31 23 16.14 Excavating, Utility Trench

		Crew	Daily Output	Labor-Hours	Unit	Material	2015 Bare Costs Labor	Equipment	Total	Total Incl O&P
3050	18" deep	B-54	750	.011	L.F.		.52	.45	.97	1.28
3100	24" deep	↓	700	.011	↓		.56	.48	1.04	1.37
3200	Compaction with vibratory plate, add								35%	35%
5100	Hand excavate and trim for pipe bells after trench excavation									
5200	8" pipe	1 Clab	155	.052	L.F.		1.94		1.94	2.99
5300	18" pipe	"	130	.062	"		2.31		2.31	3.56
5400	For clay or till, add up to								150%	150%
6000	Excavation utility trench, rock material									
6050	Note: assumption teeth change every 100 feet of trench									
6100	Chain trencher, 6" wide, 30" depth, rock saw	B-54D	400	.040	L.F.	19.60	1.76	.93	22.29	25
6200	Chain trencher, 18" wide, 8' depth, rock trencher	B-54E	280	.057	"	32.50	2.52	9.20	44.22	50

31 23 16.15 Excavating, Utility Trench, Plow

		Crew	Daily Output	Labor-Hours	Unit	Material	2015 Bare Costs Labor	Equipment	Total	Total Incl O&P
0010	**EXCAVATING, UTILITY TRENCH, PLOW**									
0100	Single cable, plowed into fine material	B-54C	3800	.004	L.F.		.19	.31	.50	.63
0200	Two cable		3200	.005			.22	.37	.59	.75
0300	Single cable, plowed into coarse material	↓	2000	.008	↓		.35	.60	.95	1.20

31 23 16.16 Structural Excavation for Minor Structures

		Crew	Daily Output	Labor-Hours	Unit	Material	2015 Bare Costs Labor	Equipment	Total	Total Incl O&P
0010	**STRUCTURAL EXCAVATION FOR MINOR STRUCTURES** R312316-40									
0015	Hand, pits to 6' deep, sandy soil	1 Clab	8	1	B.C.Y.		37.50		37.50	58
0020	Normal soil	B-2	16	2.500			95		95	146
0030	Medium clay		12	3.333			127		127	195
0040	Heavy clay		8	5			190		190	292
0050	Loose rock	↓	6	6.667			253		253	390
0100	Heavy soil or clay	1 Clab	4	2			75		75	116
0200	Pits to 2' deep, normal soil	B-2	24	1.667			63.50		63.50	97.50
0210	Sand and gravel		24	1.667			63.50		63.50	97.50
0220	Medium clay		18	2.222			84.50		84.50	130
0230	Heavy clay	↓	12	3.333			127		127	195
0300	Pits 6' to 12' deep, sandy soil	1 Clab	5	1.600			60		60	92.50
0500	Heavy soil or clay		3	2.667			100		100	154
0700	Pits 12' to 18' deep, sandy soil		4	2			75		75	116
0900	Heavy soil or clay	↓	2	4	↓		150		150	231
1000	Hand trimming, bottom of excavation	B-2	2400	.017	S.F.		.63		.63	.97
1010	Slopes and sides		2400	.017	"		.63		.63	.97
1030	Around obstructions	↓	8	5	B.C.Y.		190		190	292
1100	Hand loading trucks from stock pile, sandy soil	1 Clab	12	.667			25		25	38.50
1300	Heavy soil or clay	"	8	1	↓		37.50		37.50	58
1500	For wet or muck hand excavation, add to above								50%	50%
1550	Excavation rock by hand/air tool	B-9	3.40	11.765	B.C.Y.		445	68.50	513.50	765
6000	Machine excavation, for spread and mat footings, elevator pits,									
6001	and small building foundations									
6030	Common earth, hydraulic backhoe, 1/2 C.Y. bucket	B-12E	55	.291	B.C.Y.		13	8.15	21.15	29
6035	3/4 C.Y. bucket	B-12F	90	.178			7.95	7.30	15.25	20
6040	1 C.Y. bucket	B-12A	108	.148			6.60	7.50	14.10	18.40
6050	1-1/2 C.Y. bucket	B-12B	144	.111			4.96	7.15	12.11	15.40
6060	2 C.Y. bucket	B-12C	200	.080			3.57	5.90	9.47	11.90
6070	Sand and gravel, 3/4 C.Y. bucket	B-12F	100	.160			7.15	6.55	13.70	18.10
6080	1 C.Y. bucket	B-12A	120	.133			5.95	6.75	12.70	16.55
6090	1-1/2 C.Y. bucket	B-12B	160	.100			4.47	6.45	10.92	13.90
6100	2 C.Y. bucket	B-12C	220	.073			3.25	5.35	8.60	10.85
6110	Clay, till, or blasted rock, 3/4 C.Y. bucket	B-12F	80	.200			8.95	8.20	17.15	22.50
6120	1 C.Y. bucket	B-12A	95	.168			7.50	8.55	16.05	21

For customer support on your Site Work & Landscape Cost Data, call 877.737.1594.

31 23 16 – Excavation

31 23 16.16 Structural Excavation for Minor Structures

		Crew	Daily Output	Labor-Hours	Unit	Material	2015 Bare Costs Labor	Equipment	Total	Total Incl O&P
6130	1-1/2 C.Y. bucket	B-12B	130	.123	B.C.Y.		5.50	7.90	13.40	17.10
6140	2 C.Y. bucket	B-12C	175	.091			4.08	6.70	10.78	13.65
6230	Sandy clay & loam, hydraulic backhoe, 1/2 C.Y. bucket	B-12E	60	.267			11.90	7.45	19.35	26.50
6235	3/4 C.Y. bucket	B-12F	98	.163			7.30	6.70	14	18.50
6240	1 C.Y. bucket	B-12A	116	.138			6.15	7	13.15	17.10
6250	1-1/2 C.Y. bucket	B-12B	156	.103			4.58	6.60	11.18	14.25
6260	2 C.Y. bucket	B-12C	216	.074			3.31	5.45	8.76	11.05
6280	3 1/2 C.Y. bucket	B-12D	300	.053	▼		2.38	8.15	10.53	12.60
9010	For mobilization or demobilization, see Section 01 54 36.50									
9020	For dewatering, see Section 31 23 19.20									
9022	For larger structures, see Bulk Excavation, Section 31 23 16.42									
9024	For loading onto trucks, add								15%	15%
9026	For hauling, see Section 31 23 23.20									
9030	For sheeting or soldier bms/lagging, see Section 31 52 16.10									
9040	For trench excavation of strip ftgs, see Section 31 23 16.13									

31 23 16.26 Rock Removal

		Crew	Daily Output	Labor-Hours	Unit	Material	2015 Bare Costs Labor	Equipment	Total	Total Incl O&P
0010	**ROCK REMOVAL** R312316-40									
0015	Drilling only rock, 2" hole for rock bolts	B-47	316	.076	L.F.		3.18	5.10	8.28	10.45
0800	2-1/2" hole for pre-splitting		600	.040			1.68	2.68	4.36	5.50
4600	Quarry operations, 2-1/2" to 3-1/2" diameter	▼	715	.034	▼		1.41	2.25	3.66	4.62

31 23 16.30 Drilling and Blasting Rock

		Crew	Daily Output	Labor-Hours	Unit	Material	2015 Bare Costs Labor	Equipment	Total	Total Incl O&P
0010	**DRILLING AND BLASTING ROCK**									
0020	Rock, open face, under 1500 C.Y.	B-47	225	.107	B.C.Y.	3.20	4.47	7.15	14.82	18.20
0100	Over 1500 C.Y.		300	.080		3.20	3.35	5.35	11.90	14.55
0200	Areas where blasting mats are required, under 1500 C.Y.		175	.137		3.20	5.75	9.20	18.15	22.50
0250	Over 1500 C.Y.	▼	250	.096		3.20	4.03	6.45	13.68	16.75
0300	Bulk drilling and blasting, can vary greatly, average								9.65	12.20
0500	Pits, average								25.50	31.50
1300	Deep hole method, up to 1500 C.Y.	B-47	50	.480		3.20	20	32	55.20	70
1400	Over 1500 C.Y.		66	.364		3.20	15.25	24.50	42.95	54
1900	Restricted areas, up to 1500 C.Y.		13	1.846		3.20	77.50	124	204.70	258
2000	Over 1500 C.Y.		20	1.200		3.20	50.50	80.50	134.20	169
2200	Trenches, up to 1500 C.Y.		22	1.091		9.30	45.50	73	127.80	161
2300	Over 1500 C.Y.		26	.923		9.30	38.50	62	109.80	137
2500	Pier holes, up to 1500 C.Y.		22	1.091		3.20	45.50	73	121.70	154
2600	Over 1500 C.Y.	▼	31	.774		3.20	32.50	52	87.70	110
2800	Boulders under 1/2 C.Y., loaded on truck, no hauling	B-100	80	.150			6.95	11.95	18.90	23.50
2900	Boulders, drilled, blasted	B-47	100	.240	▼	3.20	10.05	16.10	29.35	36.50
3100	Jackhammer operators with foreman compressor, air tools	B-9	1	40	Day		1,525	233	1,758	2,600
3300	Track drill, compressor, operator and foreman	B-47	1	24	"		1,000	1,600	2,600	3,325
3500	Blasting caps				Ea.	6.25			6.25	6.90
3700	Explosives					.48			.48	.52
3900	Blasting mats, rent, for first day					137			137	151
4000	Per added day					47			47	51.50
4200	Preblast survey for 6 room house, individual lot, minimum	A-6	2.40	6.667			315	23	338	505
4300	Maximum	"	1.35	11.852	▼		555	40.50	595.50	900
4500	City block within zone of influence, minimum	A-8	25200	.001	S.F.		.06		.06	.10
4600	Maximum	"	15100	.002	"		.11		.11	.16
5000	Excavate and load boulders, less than 0.5 C.Y.	B-10T	80	.150	B.C.Y.		6.95	6.50	13.45	17.70
5020	0.5 C.Y. to 1 C.Y.	B-10U	100	.120			5.55	10.80	16.35	20.50
5200	Excavate and load blasted rock, 3 C.Y. power shovel	B-12T	1530	.010			.47	1.02	1.49	1.83
5400	Haul boulders, 25 Ton off-highway dump, 1 mile round trip	B-34E	330	.024	▼		.97	4.09	5.06	5.95

31 23 16 – Excavation

31 23 16.30 Drilling and Blasting Rock	Crew	Daily Output	Labor-Hours	Unit	Material	2015 Bare Costs Labor	2015 Bare Costs Equipment	Total	Total Incl O&P
5420	2 mile round trip	B-34E	275	.029	B.C.Y.		1.17	4.91	6.08	7.15
5440	3 mile round trip		225	.036			1.42	6	7.42	8.75
5460	4 mile round trip	↓	200	.040	↓		1.60	6.75	8.35	9.85
5600	Bury boulders on site, less than 0.5 C.Y., 300 H.P. dozer									
5620	150' haul	B-10M	310	.039	B.C.Y.		1.79	6.10	7.89	9.50
5640	300' haul		210	.057			2.64	9.05	11.69	14
5800	0.5 to 1 C.Y., 300 H.P. dozer, 150' haul		300	.040			1.85	6.30	8.15	9.75
5820	300' haul	↓	200	.060	↓		2.78	9.50	12.28	14.70

31 23 16.32 Ripping

	31 23 16.32 Ripping	Crew	Daily Output	Labor-Hours	Unit	Material	Labor	Equipment	Total	Total Incl O&P
0010	**RIPPING** R312316-40									
0020	Ripping, trap rock, soft, 300 HP dozer, ideal conditions	B-11S	700	.017	B.C.Y.		.79	2.83	3.62	4.32
1500	Adverse conditions		660	.018			.84	3	3.84	4.58
1600	Medium hard, 300 HP dozer, ideal conditons		600	.020			.93	3.30	4.23	5.05
1700	Adverse conditions	↓	540	.022			1.03	3.67	4.70	5.60
2000	Very hard, 410 HP dozer, ideal conditions	B-11T	350	.034			1.59	7.20	8.79	10.30
2100	Adverse conditions	"	310	.039			1.79	8.10	9.89	11.65
2200	Shale, soft, 300 HP dozer, ideal conditons	B-11S	1500	.008			.37	1.32	1.69	2.01
2300	Adverse conditions	"	1350	.009			.41	1.47	1.88	2.24
2310	Grader rear ripper, 180 H.P. ideal conditions	B-11J	740	.022			.95	1.11	2.06	2.68
2320	Adverse conditions	"	630	.025			1.12	1.30	2.42	3.14
2400	Medium hard, 300 HP dozer, ideal conditons	B-11S	1200	.010			.46	1.65	2.11	2.52
2500	Adverse conditions	"	1080	.011			.51	1.83	2.34	2.80
2510	Grader rear ripper, 180 H.P. ideal conditions	B-11J	625	.026			1.13	1.31	2.44	3.16
2520	Adverse conditions	"	530	.030			1.33	1.55	2.88	3.73
2600	Very hard, 410 HP dozer, ideal conditons	B-11T	800	.015			.69	3.14	3.83	4.52
2700	Adverse conditions	"	720	.017			.77	3.49	4.26	5
2800	Till, boulder clay/hardpan, soft, 300 H.P. dozer, ideal conditions	B-11S	7000	.002			.08	.28	.36	.43
2810	Adverse conditions	"	6300	.002			.09	.31	.40	.48
2815	Grader rear ripper, 180 H.P. ideal conditions	B-11J	1500	.011			.47	.55	1.02	1.32
2816	Adverse conditions	"	1275	.013			.55	.64	1.19	1.55
2820	Medium hard, 300 H.P. dozer, ideal conditions	B-11S	6000	.002			.09	.33	.42	.50
2830	Adverse conditions	"	5400	.002			.10	.37	.47	.56
2835	Grader rear ripper, 180 H.P. ideal conditions	B-11J	740	.022			.95	1.11	2.06	2.68
2836	Adverse conditions	"	630	.025			1.12	1.30	2.42	3.14
2840	Very hard, 410 H.P. dozer, ideal conditions	B-11T	5000	.002			.11	.50	.61	.72
2850	Adverse conditions	"	4500	.003			.12	.56	.68	.81
3000	Dozing ripped material, 200 HP, 100' haul	B-10B	700	.017			.79	1.98	2.77	3.39
3050	300' haul	"	250	.048			2.22	5.55	7.77	9.50
3200	300 HP, 100' haul	B-10M	1150	.010			.48	1.65	2.13	2.54
3250	300' haul	"	400	.030			1.39	4.74	6.13	7.30
3400	410 HP, 100' haul	B-10X	1680	.007			.33	1.43	1.76	2.07
3450	300' haul	"	600	.020	↓		.93	4.01	4.94	5.80

31 23 16.35 Hydraulic Rock Breaking and Loading

	31 23 16.35 Hydraulic Rock Breaking and Loading	Crew	Daily Output	Labor-Hours	Unit	Material	Labor	Equipment	Total	Total Incl O&P
0010	**HYDRAULIC ROCK BREAKING AND LOADING**									
0020	Solid rock mass excavation									
0022	Excavator/breaker and excavator/ bucket (into trucks)									
0024	Double costs for trenching									
0026	Mobilization costs to be repeated for demobilization									
0100	110 H.P. Excavator w/4,000 ft lb. breaker									
0120	Mobilization 2/20 ton									
0130	6,000 PSI rock	B-13K	640	.025	B.C.Y.		1.29	2.53	3.82	4.74
0140	12,000 PSI rock		240	.067	↓		3.45	6.75	10.20	12.65

For customer support on your Site Work & Landscape Cost Data, call 877.737.1594.

31 23 Excavation and Fill

31 23 16 – Excavation

31 23 16.35 Hydraulic Rock Breaking and Loading

		Crew	Daily Output	Labor-Hours	Unit	Material	2015 Bare Costs Labor	Equipment	Total	Total Incl O&P
0150	18,000 PSI rock	B-13K	80	.200	B.C.Y.		10.35	20	30.35	37.50
0200	170 H.P. Excavator w/5,000 ft lb. breaker									
0220	Mobilization 30 ton & 20 ton									
0240	12,000 PSI rock	B-13L	640	.025	B.C.Y.		1.29	3.21	4.50	5.50
0250	18,000 PSI rock	↓	240	.067	↓		3.45	8.55	12	14.65
0260	24,000 PSI rock	↓	80	.200	↓		10.35	25.50	35.85	44
0300	270 H.P. excavator w/8,000 ft lb. breaker									
0320	Mobilization 40 ton & 30 ton									
0350	18,000 PSI rock	B-13M	480	.033	B.C.Y.		1.72	6.65	8.37	9.90
0360	24,000 PSI rock		240	.067			3.45	13.25	16.70	19.85
0370	30,000 PSI rock	↓	80	.200	↓		10.35	40	50.35	59
0400	350 H.P. excavator w/12,000 ft lb. breaker									
0420	Mobilization 50 ton & 30 ton (may require disassembly & third hauler)									
0450	18,000 PSI rock	B-13N	640	.025	B.C.Y.		1.29	6.40	7.69	9
0460	24,000 PSI rock	↓	400	.040			2.07	10.25	12.32	14.45
0470	30,000 PSI rock	↓	240	.067	↓		3.45	17.10	20.55	24

31 23 16.42 Excavating, Bulk Bank Measure

		Crew	Daily Output	Labor-Hours	Unit	Material	2015 Bare Costs Labor	Equipment	Total	Total Incl O&P
0010	**EXCAVATING, BULK BANK MEASURE** R312316-40									
0011	Common earth piled									
0020	For loading onto trucks, add								15%	15%
0050	For mobilization and demobilization, see Section 01 54 36.50 R312316-45									
0100	For hauling, see Section 31 23 23.20									
0200	Excavator, hydraulic, crawler mtd., 1 C.Y. cap. = 100 C.Y./hr.	B-12A	800	.020	B.C.Y.		.89	1.02	1.91	2.48
0250	1-1/2 C.Y. cap. = 125 C.Y./hr.	B-12B	1000	.016			.71	1.03	1.74	2.22
0260	2 C.Y. cap. = 165 C.Y./hr.	B-12C	1320	.012			.54	.89	1.43	1.81
0300	3 C.Y. cap. = 260 C.Y./hr.	B-12D	2080	.008			.34	1.17	1.51	1.81
0305	3-1/2 C.Y. cap. = 300 C.Y./hr.	"	2400	.007			.30	1.02	1.32	1.57
0310	Wheel mounted, 1/2 C.Y. cap. = 40 C.Y./hr.	B-12E	320	.050			2.23	1.40	3.63	4.95
0360	3/4 C.Y. cap. = 60 C.Y./hr.	B-12F	480	.033			1.49	1.36	2.85	3.77
0500	Clamshell, 1/2 C.Y. cap. = 20 C.Y./hr.	B-12G	160	.100			4.47	4.43	8.90	11.65
0550	1 C.Y. cap. = 35 C.Y./hr.	B-12H	280	.057			2.55	4.28	6.83	8.60
0950	Dragline, 1/2 C.Y. cap. = 30 C.Y./hr.	B-12I	240	.067			2.98	3.68	6.66	8.60
1000	3/4 C.Y. cap. = 35 C.Y./hr.	"	280	.057			2.55	3.15	5.70	7.35
1050	1-1/2 C.Y. cap. = 65 C.Y./hr.	B-12P	520	.031			1.37	2.29	3.66	4.62
1100	3 C.Y. cap. = 112 C.Y./hr.	B-12V	900	.018			.79	1.68	2.47	3.06
1200	Front end loader, track mtd., 1-1/2 C.Y. cap. = 70 C.Y./hr.	B-10N	560	.021			.99	.93	1.92	2.54
1250	2-1/2 C.Y. cap. = 95 C.Y./hr.	B-10O	760	.016			.73	1.26	1.99	2.49
1300	3 C.Y. cap. = 130 C.Y./hr.	B-10P	1040	.012			.53	1.14	1.67	2.07
1350	5 C.Y. cap. = 160 C.Y./hr.	B-10Q	1280	.009			.43	1.22	1.65	2
1500	Wheel mounted, 3/4 C.Y. cap. = 45 C.Y./hr.	B-10R	360	.033			1.54	.83	2.37	3.26
1550	1-1/2 C.Y. cap. = 80 C.Y./hr.	B-10S	640	.019			.87	.59	1.46	1.97
1600	2-1/4 C.Y. cap. = 100 C.Y./hr.	B-10T	800	.015			.69	.65	1.34	1.77
1601	3 C.Y. cap. = 140 C.Y./hr.	"	1120	.011			.50	.46	.96	1.26
1650	5 C.Y. cap. = 185 C.Y./hr.	B-10U	1480	.008			.38	.73	1.11	1.37
1800	Hydraulic excavator, truck mtd. 1/2 C.Y. = 30 C.Y./hr.	B-12J	240	.067			2.98	3.68	6.66	8.60
1850	48 inch bucket, 1 C.Y. = 45 C.Y./hr.	B-12K	360	.044			1.98	2.78	4.76	6.10
3700	Shovel, 1/2 C.Y. capacity = 55 C.Y./hr.	B-12L	440	.036			1.62	1.66	3.28	4.30
3750	3/4 C.Y. capacity = 85 C.Y./hr.	B-12M	680	.024			1.05	1.36	2.41	3.10
3800	1 C.Y. capacity = 120 C.Y./hr.	B-12N	960	.017			.74	1.27	2.01	2.54
3850	1-1/2 C.Y. capacity = 160 C.Y./hr.	B-12O	1280	.013			.56	.97	1.53	1.91
3900	3 C.Y. cap. = 250 C.Y./hr.	B-12T	2000	.008			.36	.78	1.14	1.41
4000	For soft soil or sand, deduct								15%	15%

31 23 16 – Excavation

31 23 16.42 Excavating, Bulk Bank Measure

		Crew	Daily Output	Labor-Hours	Unit	Material	2015 Bare Costs Labor	2015 Bare Costs Equipment	Total	Total Incl O&P
4100	For heavy soil or stiff clay, add				B.C.Y.				60%	60%
4200	For wet excavation with clamshell or dragline, add								100%	100%
4250	All other equipment, add								50%	50%
4400	Clamshell in sheeting or cofferdam, minimum	B-12H	160	.100			4.47	7.50	11.97	15.05
4450	Maximum	"	60	.267	▼		11.90	19.95	31.85	40
5000	Excavating, bulk bank measure, sandy clay & loam piled									
5020	For loading onto trucks, add								15%	15%
5100	Excavator, hydraulic, crawler mtd., 1 C.Y. cap. = 120 C.Y./hr.	B-12A	960	.017	B.C.Y.		.74	.85	1.59	2.07
5150	1-1/2 C.Y. cap. = 150 C.Y./hr.	B-12B	1200	.013			.60	.86	1.46	1.85
5300	2 C.Y. cap. = 195 C.Y./hr.	B-12C	1560	.010			.46	.75	1.21	1.53
5400	3 C.Y. cap. = 300 C.Y./hr.	B-12D	2400	.007			.30	1.02	1.32	1.57
5500	3.5 C.Y. cap. = 350 C.Y./hr.	"	2800	.006			.26	.87	1.13	1.35
5610	Wheel mounted, 1/2 C.Y. cap. = 44 C.Y./hr.	B-12E	352	.045			2.03	1.27	3.30	4.50
5660	3/4 C.Y. cap. = 66 C.Y./hr.	B-12F	528	.030	▼		1.35	1.24	2.59	3.42
8000	For hauling excavated material, see Section 31 23 23.20									

31 23 16.43 Excavating, Large Volume Projects

		Crew	Daily Output	Labor-Hours	Unit	Material	2015 Bare Costs Labor	2015 Bare Costs Equipment	Total	Total Incl O&P
0010	**EXCAVATING, LARGE VOLUME PROJECTS**, various materials									
0050	Minimum project size 200,000 B.C.Y.									
0080	For hauling, see Section 31 23 23.20									
0100	Unrestricted means continous loading into hopper or railroad cars									
0200	Loader, 8 C.Y. bucket, 110% fill factor, unrestricted operation	B-14J	5280	.002	L.C.Y.		.11	.37	.48	.56
0250	10 C.Y. bucket	B-14K	7040	.002			.08	.42	.50	.58
0300	8 C.Y. bucket, 105% fill factor	B-14J	5040	.002			.11	.38	.49	.59
0350	10 C.Y. bucket	B-14K	6720	.002			.08	.44	.52	.61
0400	8 C.Y. bucket, 100% fill factor	B-14J	4800	.003			.12	.40	.52	.62
0450	10 C.Y. bucket	B-14K	6400	.002			.09	.46	.55	.64
0500	8 C.Y. bucket, 95% fill factor	B-14J	4560	.003			.12	.42	.54	.66
0550	10 C.Y. bucket	B-14K	6080	.002			.09	.48	.57	.67
0600	8 C.Y. bucket, 90% fill factor	B-14J	4320	.003			.13	.45	.58	.69
0650	10 C.Y. bucket	B-14K	5760	.002			.10	.51	.61	.71
0700	8 C.Y. bucket, 85% fill factor	B-14J	4080	.003			.14	.47	.61	.73
0750	10 C.Y. bucket	B-14K	5440	.002			.10	.54	.64	.76
0800	8 C.Y. bucket, 80% fill factor	B-14J	3840	.003			.14	.51	.65	.78
0850	10 C.Y. bucket	B-14K	5120	.002			.11	.57	.68	.79
0900	8 C.Y. bucket, 75% fill factor	B-14J	3600	.003			.15	.54	.69	.82
0950	10 C.Y. bucket	B-14K	4800	.003			.12	.61	.73	.85
1000	8 C.Y. bucket, 70% fill factor	B-14J	3360	.004			.17	.58	.75	.88
1050	10 C.Y. bucket	B-14K	4480	.003			.12	.66	.78	.91
1100	8 C.Y. bucket, 65% fill factor	B-14J	3120	.004			.18	.62	.80	.95
1150	10 C.Y. bucket	B-14K	4160	.003			.13	.71	.84	.98
1200	8 C.Y. bucket, 60% fill factor	B-14J	2880	.004			.19	.67	.86	1.03
1250	10 C.Y. bucket	B-14K	3840	.003	▼		.14	.77	.91	1.06
2100	Restricted loading trucks									
2200	Loader, 8 C.Y. bucket, 110% fill factor, loading trucks	B-14J	4400	.003	L.C.Y.		.13	.44	.57	.67
2250	10 C.Y. bucket	B-14K	5940	.002			.09	.50	.59	.68
2300	8 C.Y. bucket, 105% fill factor	B-14J	4200	.003			.13	.46	.59	.71
2350	10 C.Y. bucket	B-14K	5670	.002			.10	.52	.62	.72
2400	8 C.Y. bucket, 100% fill factor	B-14J	4000	.003			.14	.48	.62	.74
2450	10 C.Y. bucket	B-14K	5400	.002			.10	.54	.64	.76
2500	8 C.Y. bucket, 95% fill factor	B-14J	3800	.003			.15	.51	.66	.78
2550	10 C.Y. bucket	B-14K	5130	.002			.11	.57	.68	.79
2600	8 C.Y. bucket, 90% fill factor	B-14J	3600	.003			.15	.54	.69	.82

31 23 16.43 Excavating, Large Volume Projects	Crew	Daily Output	Labor-Hours	Unit	Material	2015 Bare Costs Labor	2015 Bare Costs Equipment	Total	Total Incl O&P
2650	10 C.Y. bucket	B-14K	4860	.002	L.C.Y.		.11	.61	.72	.84
2700	8 C.Y. bucket, 85% fill factor	B-14J	3400	.004			.16	.57	.73	.88
2750	10 C.Y. bucket	B-14K	4590	.003			.12	.64	.76	.88
2800	8 C.Y. bucket, 80% fill factor	B-14J	3200	.004			.17	.61	.78	.93
2850	10 C.Y. bucket	B-14K	4320	.003			.13	.68	.81	.95
2900	8 C.Y. bucket, 75% fill factor	B-14J	3000	.004			.19	.65	.84	.99
2950	10 C.Y. bucket	B-14K	4050	.003			.14	.73	.87	1.01
4000	8 C.Y. bucket, 70% fill factor	B-14J	2800	.004			.20	.69	.89	1.06
4050	10 C.Y. bucket	B-14K	3780	.003			.15	.78	.93	1.07
4100	8 C.Y. bucket, 65% fill factor	B-14J	2600	.005			.21	.75	.96	1.15
4150	10 C.Y. bucket	B-14K	3510	.003			.16	.84	1	1.16
4200	8 C.Y. bucket, 60% fill factor	B-14J	2400	.005			.23	.81	1.04	1.24
4250	10 C.Y. bucket	B-14K	3240	.004			.17	.91	1.08	1.26
4290	Continuous excavation with no truck loading									
4300	Excavator, 4.5 C.Y. bucket, 100% fill factor, no truck loading	B-14A	4000	.003	B.C.Y.		.14	.74	.88	1.02
4320	6 C.Y. bucket	B-14B	5900	.002			.10	.59	.69	.80
4330	7 C.Y. bucket	B-14C	6900	.002			.08	.52	.60	.69
4340	Shovel, 7 C.Y. bucket	B-14F	8900	.001			.06	.45	.51	.59
4360	12 C.Y. bucket	B-14G	14800	.001			.04	.39	.43	.49
4400	Excavator, 4.5 C.Y. bucket, 95% fill factor	B-14A	3800	.003			.15	.78	.93	1.09
4420	6 C.Y. bucket	B-14B	5605	.002			.10	.62	.72	.84
4430	7 C.Y. bucket	B-14C	6555	.002			.09	.55	.64	.73
4440	Shovel, 7 C.Y. bucket	B-14F	8455	.001			.07	.47	.54	.62
4460	12 C.Y. bucket	B-14G	14060	.001			.04	.41	.45	.51
4500	Excavator, 4.5 C.Y. bucket, 90% fill factor	B-14A	3600	.003			.16	.82	.98	1.14
4520	6 C.Y. bucket	B-14B	5310	.002			.11	.66	.77	.88
4530	7 C.Y. bucket	B-14C	6210	.002			.09	.58	.67	.78
4540	Shovel, 7 C.Y. bucket	B-14F	8010	.002			.07	.50	.57	.66
4560	12 C.Y. bucket	B-14G	13320	.001			.04	.43	.47	.53
4600	Excavator, 4.5 C.Y. bucket, 85% fill factor	B-14A	3400	.004			.17	.87	1.04	1.21
4620	6 C.Y. bucket	B-14B	5015	.002			.11	.70	.81	.94
4630	7 C.Y. bucket	B-14C	5865	.002			.10	.61	.71	.82
4640	Shovel, 7 C.Y. bucket	B-14F	7565	.002			.07	.53	.60	.69
4660	12 C.Y. bucket	B-14G	12580	.001			.04	.45	.49	.57
4700	Excavator, 4.5 C.Y. bucket, 80% fill factor	B-14A	3200	.004			.18	.93	1.11	1.29
4720	6 C.Y. bucket	B-14B	4720	.003			.12	.74	.86	.99
4730	7 C.Y. bucket	B-14C	5520	.002			.10	.65	.75	.87
4740	Shovel, 7 C.Y. bucket	B-14F	7120	.002			.08	.56	.64	.74
4760	12 C.Y. bucket	B-14G	11840	.001			.05	.48	.53	.60
5290	Excavation with truck loading									
5300	Excavator, 4.5 C.Y. bucket, 100% fill factor, with truck loading	B-14A	3400	.004	B.C.Y.		.17	.87	1.04	1.21
5320	6 C.Y. bucket	B-14B	5000	.002			.11	.70	.81	.94
5330	7 C.Y. bucket	B-14C	5800	.002			.10	.62	.72	.83
5340	Shovel, 7 C.Y. bucket	B-14F	7500	.002			.08	.53	.61	.70
5360	12 C.Y. bucket	B-14G	12500	.001			.05	.46	.51	.57
5400	Excavator, 4.5 C.Y. bucket, 95% fill factor	B-14A	3230	.004			.17	.92	1.09	1.28
5420	6 C.Y. bucket	B-14B	4750	.003			.12	.74	.86	.99
5430	7 C.Y. bucket	B-14C	5510	.002			.10	.65	.75	.88
5440	Shovel, 7 C.Y. bucket	B-14F	7125	.002			.08	.56	.64	.73
5460	12 C.Y. bucket	B-14G	11875	.001			.05	.48	.53	.60
5500	Excavator, 4.5 C.Y. bucket, 90% fill factor	B-14A	3060	.004			.18	.97	1.15	1.34
5520	6 C.Y. bucket	B-14B	4500	.003			.13	.78	.91	1.05
5530	7 C.Y. bucket	B-14C	5220	.002			.11	.69	.80	.92

For customer support on your Site Work & Landscape Cost Data, call 877.737.1594.

295

31 23 Excavation and Fill

31 23 16 – Excavation

31 23 16.43 Excavating, Large Volume Projects

		Crew	Daily Output	Labor-Hours	Unit	Material	2015 Bare Costs Labor	2015 Bare Costs Equipment	Total	Total Incl O&P
5540	Shovel, 7 C.Y. bucket	B-14F	6750	.002	B.C.Y.		.08	.59	.67	.78
5560	12 C.Y. bucket	B-14G	11250	.001			.05	.51	.56	.64
5600	Excavator, 4.5 C.Y. bucket, 85% fill factor	B-14A	2890	.004			.20	1.02	1.22	1.43
5620	6 C.Y. bucket	B-14B	4250	.003			.13	.82	.95	1.10
5630	7 C.Y. bucket	B-14C	4930	.002			.11	.73	.84	.97
5640	Shovel, 7 C.Y. bucket	B-14F	6375	.002			.09	.63	.72	.82
5660	12 C.Y. bucket	B-14G	10625	.001			.05	.54	.59	.67
5700	Excavator, 4.5 C.Y. bucket, 80% fill factor	B-14A	2720	.004			.21	1.09	1.30	1.52
5720	6 C.Y. bucket	B-14B	4000	.003			.14	.87	1.01	1.17
5740	Shovel, 7 C.Y. bucket	B-14F	6000	.002			.09	.67	.76	.87
5760	12 C.Y. bucket	B-14G	10000	.001			.06	.57	.63	.72
6000	Self propelled scraper, 1/4 push dozer, average productivity									
6100	31 C.Y. , 1500' haul	B-33K	2046	.007	B.C.Y.		.32	2.10	2.42	2.80
6200	44 C.Y.	B-33H	2640	.005	"		.25	2	2.25	2.58

31 23 16.46 Excavating, Bulk, Dozer

		Crew	Daily Output	Labor-Hours	Unit	Material	2015 Bare Costs Labor	2015 Bare Costs Equipment	Total	Total Incl O&P
0010	**EXCAVATING, BULK, DOZER**									
0011	Open site									
2000	80 H.P., 50' haul, sand & gravel	B-10L	460	.026	B.C.Y.		1.21	1.03	2.24	2.97
2010	Sandy clay & loam		440	.027			1.26	1.07	2.33	3.10
2020	Common earth		400	.030			1.39	1.18	2.57	3.41
2040	Clay		250	.048			2.22	1.89	4.11	5.45
2200	150' haul, sand & gravel		230	.052			2.41	2.05	4.46	5.95
2210	Sandy clay & loam		220	.055			2.52	2.15	4.67	6.20
2220	Common earth		200	.060			2.78	2.36	5.14	6.85
2240	Clay		125	.096			4.44	3.78	8.22	10.90
2400	300' haul, sand & gravel		120	.100			4.63	3.94	8.57	11.40
2410	Sandy clay & loam		115	.104			4.83	4.11	8.94	11.85
2420	Common earth		100	.120			5.55	4.72	10.27	13.65
2440	Clay		65	.185			8.55	7.25	15.80	21
3000	105 H.P., 50' haul, sand & gravel	B-10W	700	.017			.79	.86	1.65	2.16
3010	Sandy clay & loam		680	.018			.82	.89	1.71	2.22
3020	Common earth		610	.020			.91	.99	1.90	2.48
3040	Clay		385	.031			1.44	1.57	3.01	3.92
3200	150' haul, sand & gravel		310	.039			1.79	1.94	3.73	4.87
3210	Sandy clay & loam		300	.040			1.85	2.01	3.86	5.05
3220	Common earth		270	.044			2.06	2.23	4.29	5.60
3240	Clay		170	.071			3.27	3.55	6.82	8.85
3300	300' haul, sand & gravel		140	.086			3.97	4.31	8.28	10.80
3310	Sandy clay & loam		135	.089			4.11	4.46	8.57	11.15
3320	Common earth		120	.100			4.63	5	9.63	12.60
3340	Clay		100	.120			5.55	6.05	11.60	15.10
4000	200 H.P., 50' haul, sand & gravel	B-10B	1400	.009			.40	.99	1.39	1.69
4010	Sandy clay & loam		1360	.009			.41	1.02	1.43	1.74
4020	Common earth		1230	.010			.45	1.13	1.58	1.93
4040	Clay		770	.016			.72	1.80	2.52	3.08
4200	150' haul, sand & gravel		595	.020			.93	2.33	3.26	3.98
4210	Sandy clay & loam		580	.021			.96	2.39	3.35	4.09
4220	Common earth		516	.023			1.08	2.69	3.77	4.60
4240	Clay		325	.037			1.71	4.27	5.98	7.30
4400	300' haul, sand & gravel		310	.039			1.79	4.47	6.26	7.65
4410	Sandy clay & loam		300	.040			1.85	4.62	6.47	7.90
4420	Common earth		270	.044			2.06	5.15	7.21	8.80

For customer support on your Site Work & Landscape Cost Data, call 877.737.1594.

31 23 Excavation and Fill

31 23 16 – Excavation

31 23 16.46 Excavating, Bulk, Dozer

		Crew	Daily Output	Labor-Hours	Unit	Material	2015 Bare Costs Labor	2015 Bare Costs Equipment	Total	Total Incl O&P
4440	Clay	B-10B	170	.071	B.C.Y.		3.27	8.15	11.42	13.90
5000	300 H.P., 50' haul, sand & gravel	B-10M	1900	.006			.29	1	1.29	1.55
5010	Sandy clay & loam		1850	.006			.30	1.03	1.33	1.59
5020	Common earth		1650	.007			.34	1.15	1.49	1.77
5040	Clay		1025	.012			.54	1.85	2.39	2.87
5200	150' haul, sand & gravel		920	.013			.60	2.06	2.66	3.19
5210	Sandy clay & loam		895	.013			.62	2.12	2.74	3.27
5220	Common earth		800	.015			.69	2.37	3.06	3.67
5240	Clay		500	.024			1.11	3.79	4.90	5.85
5400	300' haul, sand & gravel		470	.026			1.18	4.04	5.22	6.25
5410	Sandy clay & loam		455	.026			1.22	4.17	5.39	6.45
5420	Common earth		410	.029			1.35	4.63	5.98	7.15
5440	Clay		250	.048			2.22	7.60	9.82	11.75
5500	460 H.P., 50' haul, sand & gravel	B-10X	1930	.006			.29	1.25	1.54	1.81
5506	Sandy clay & loam		1880	.006			.30	1.28	1.58	1.86
5510	Common earth		1680	.007			.33	1.43	1.76	2.07
5520	Clay		1050	.011			.53	2.29	2.82	3.33
5530	150' haul, sand & gravel		1290	.009			.43	1.86	2.29	2.71
5535	Sandy clay & loam		1250	.010			.44	1.92	2.36	2.80
5540	Common earth		1120	.011			.50	2.15	2.65	3.11
5550	Clay		700	.017			.79	3.44	4.23	4.99
5560	300' haul, sand & gravel		660	.018			.84	3.64	4.48	5.30
5565	Sandy clay & loam		640	.019			.87	3.76	4.63	5.45
5570	Common earth		575	.021			.97	4.18	5.15	6.05
5580	Clay		350	.034			1.59	6.85	8.44	9.95
6000	700 H.P., 50' haul, sand & gravel	B-10V	3500	.003			.16	1.42	1.58	1.81
6006	Sandy clay & loam		3400	.004			.16	1.46	1.62	1.86
6010	Common earth		3035	.004			.18	1.64	1.82	2.08
6020	Clay		1925	.006			.29	2.59	2.88	3.28
6030	150' haul, sand & gravel		2025	.006			.27	2.46	2.73	3.13
6035	Sandy clay & loam		1960	.006			.28	2.54	2.82	3.22
6040	Common earth		1750	.007			.32	2.85	3.17	3.61
6050	Clay		1100	.011			.50	4.53	5.03	5.75
6060	300' haul, sand & gravel		1030	.012			.54	4.83	5.37	6.10
6065	Sandy clay & loam		1005	.012			.55	4.95	5.50	6.30
6070	Common earth		900	.013			.62	5.55	6.17	7.05
6080	Clay		550	.022			1.01	9.05	10.06	11.50
6090	For dozer with ripper, see Section 31 23 16.32									

31 23 16.48 Excavation, Bulk, Dragline

		Crew	Daily Output	Labor-Hours	Unit	Material	2015 Bare Costs Labor	2015 Bare Costs Equipment	Total	Total Incl O&P
0010	**EXCAVATION, BULK, DRAGLINE**									
0011	Excavate and load on truck, bank measure									
0012	Bucket drag line, 3/4 C.Y., sand/gravel	B-12I	440	.036	B.C.Y.		1.62	2.01	3.63	4.69
0100	Light clay		310	.052			2.30	2.85	5.15	6.65
0110	Heavy clay		280	.057			2.55	3.15	5.70	7.35
0120	Unclassified soil		250	.064			2.86	3.53	6.39	8.25
0200	1-1/2 C.Y. bucket, sand/gravel	B-12P	575	.028			1.24	2.07	3.31	4.18
0210	Light clay		440	.036			1.62	2.70	4.32	5.45
0220	Heavy clay		352	.045			2.03	3.38	5.41	6.80
0230	Unclassified soil		300	.053			2.38	3.97	6.35	8
0300	3 C.Y., sand/gravel	B-12V	720	.022			.99	2.10	3.09	3.82
0310	Light clay		700	.023			1.02	2.16	3.18	3.94
0320	Heavy clay		600	.027			1.19	2.52	3.71	4.59

31 23 Excavation and Fill

31 23 16 – Excavation

31 23 16.48 Excavation, Bulk, Dragline	Crew	Daily Output	Labor-Hours	Unit	Material	2015 Bare Costs Labor	Equipment	Total	Total Incl O&P
0330 Unclassified soil	B-12V	550	.029	B.C.Y.		1.30	2.75	4.05	5

31 23 16.50 Excavation, Bulk, Scrapers

		Crew	Daily Output	Labor-Hours	Unit	Material	Labor	Equipment	Total	Total Incl O&P
0010	**EXCAVATION, BULK, SCRAPERS** R312316-40									
0100	Elev. scraper 11 C.Y., sand & gravel 1500' haul, 1/4 dozer	B-33F	690	.020	B.C.Y.		.95	2.37	3.32	4.06
0150	3000' haul R312316-45		610	.023			1.08	2.68	3.76	4.59
0200	5000' haul		505	.028			1.30	3.24	4.54	5.55
0300	Common earth, 1500' haul		600	.023			1.09	2.73	3.82	4.66
0350	3000' haul		530	.026			1.24	3.09	4.33	5.30
0400	5000' haul		440	.032			1.49	3.72	5.21	6.35
0410	Sandy clay & loam, 1500' haul		648	.022			1.01	2.53	3.54	4.32
0420	3000' haul		572	.024			1.15	2.86	4.01	4.90
0430	5000' haul		475	.029			1.38	3.45	4.83	5.90
0500	Clay, 1500' haul		375	.037			1.75	4.37	6.12	7.45
0550	3000' haul		330	.042			1.99	4.96	6.95	8.50
0600	5000' haul	↓	275	.051	↓		2.39	5.95	8.34	10.20
1000	Self propelled scraper, 14 C.Y. 1/4 push dozer, sand									
1050	Sand and gravel, 1500' haul	B-33D	920	.015	B.C.Y.		.71	2.56	3.27	3.91
1100	3000' haul		805	.017			.82	2.93	3.75	4.46
1200	5000' haul		645	.022			1.02	3.66	4.68	5.55
1300	Common earth, 1500' haul		800	.018			.82	2.95	3.77	4.49
1350	3000' haul		700	.020			.94	3.37	4.31	5.15
1400	5000' haul		560	.025			1.17	4.21	5.38	6.40
1420	Sandy clay & loam, 1500' haul		864	.016			.76	2.73	3.49	4.16
1430	3000' haul		786	.018			.84	3	3.84	4.57
1440	5000' haul		605	.023			1.09	3.90	4.99	5.95
1500	Clay, 1500' haul		500	.028			1.31	4.72	6.03	7.20
1550	3000' haul		440	.032			1.49	5.35	6.84	8.15
1600	5000' haul	↓	350	.040			1.88	6.75	8.63	10.25
2000	21 C.Y., 1/4 push dozer, sand & gravel, 1500' haul	B-33E	1180	.012			.56	2.68	3.24	3.80
2100	3000' haul		910	.015			.72	3.47	4.19	4.92
2200	5000' haul		750	.019			.88	4.22	5.10	5.95
2300	Common earth, 1500' haul		1030	.014			.64	3.07	3.71	4.35
2350	3000' haul		790	.018			.83	4	4.83	5.65
2400	5000' haul		650	.022			1.01	4.87	5.88	6.90
2420	Sandy clay & loam, 1500' haul		1112	.013			.59	2.84	3.43	4.03
2430	3000' haul		854	.016			.77	3.70	4.47	5.25
2440	5000' haul		702	.020			.94	4.50	5.44	6.35
2500	Clay, 1500' haul		645	.022			1.02	4.90	5.92	6.95
2550	3000' haul		495	.028			1.33	6.40	7.73	9.05
2600	5000' haul	↓	405	.035			1.62	7.80	9.42	11.05
2700	Towed, 10 C.Y., 1/4 push dozer, sand & gravel, 1500' haul	B-33B	560	.025			1.17	4.50	5.67	6.75
2720	3000' haul		450	.031			1.46	5.60	7.06	8.35
2730	5000' haul		365	.038			1.80	6.90	8.70	10.35
2750	Common earth, 1500' haul		420	.033			1.56	6	7.56	9
2770	3000' haul		400	.035			1.64	6.30	7.94	9.40
2780	5000' haul		310	.045			2.12	8.10	10.22	12.15
2785	Sandy clay & Loam, 1500' haul		454	.031			1.45	5.55	7	8.30
2790	3000' haul		432	.032			1.52	5.85	7.37	8.70
2795	5000' haul		340	.041			1.93	7.40	9.33	11.10
2800	Clay, 1500' haul		315	.044			2.08	8	10.08	11.95
2820	3000' haul		300	.047			2.19	8.40	10.59	12.60
2840	5000' haul	↓	225	.062	↓		2.92	11.20	14.12	16.75

31 23 Excavation and Fill

31 23 16 – Excavation

31 23 16.50 Excavation, Bulk, Scrapers

		Crew	Daily Output	Labor-Hours	Unit	Material	2015 Bare Costs Labor	2015 Bare Costs Equipment	Total	Total Incl O&P
2900	15 C.Y., 1/4 push dozer, sand & gravel, 1500' haul	B-33C	800	.018	B.C.Y.		.82	3.17	3.99	4.74
2920	3000' haul		640	.022			1.03	3.96	4.99	5.90
2940	5000' haul		520	.027			1.26	4.88	6.14	7.25
2960	Common earth, 1500' haul		600	.023			1.09	4.23	5.32	6.30
2980	3000' haul		560	.025			1.17	4.53	5.70	6.75
3000	5000' haul		440	.032			1.49	5.75	7.24	8.60
3005	Sandy clay & Loam, 1500' haul		648	.022			1.01	3.91	4.92	5.85
3010	3000' haul		605	.023			1.09	4.19	5.28	6.25
3015	5000' haul		475	.029			1.38	5.35	6.73	7.95
3020	Clay, 1500' haul		450	.031			1.46	5.65	7.11	8.40
3040	3000' haul		420	.033			1.56	6.05	7.61	9.05
3060	5000' haul		320	.044			2.05	7.95	10	11.80

31 23 19 – Dewatering

31 23 19.10 Cut Drainage Ditch

		Crew	Daily Output	Labor-Hours	Unit	Material	2015 Bare Costs Labor	2015 Bare Costs Equipment	Total	Total Incl O&P
0010	**CUT DRAINAGE DITCH**									
0020	Cut drainage ditch common earth, 30' wide x 1' deep	B-11L	6000	.003	L.F.		.12	.12	.24	.32
0200	Clay and till		4200	.004			.17	.18	.35	.45
0250	Clean wet drainage ditch, 30' wide		10000	.002			.07	.07	.14	.19

31 23 19.20 Dewatering Systems

		Crew	Daily Output	Labor-Hours	Unit	Material	2015 Bare Costs Labor	2015 Bare Costs Equipment	Total	Total Incl O&P
0010	**DEWATERING SYSTEMS**									
0020	Excavate drainage trench, 2' wide, 2' deep	B-11C	90	.178	C.Y.		7.85	4.05	11.90	16.40
0100	2' wide, 3' deep, with backhoe loader	"	135	.119			5.25	2.70	7.95	10.95
0200	Excavate sump pits by hand, light soil	1 Clab	7.10	1.127			42.50		42.50	65
0300	Heavy soil	"	3.50	2.286			86		86	132
0500	Pumping 8 hr., attended 2 hrs. per day, including 20 L.F.									
0550	of suction hose & 100 L.F. discharge hose									
0600	2" diaphragm pump used for 8 hours	B-10H	4	3	Day		139	18.70	157.70	232
0620	Add per additional pump							72	72	79
0650	4" diaphragm pump used for 8 hours	B-10I	4	3			139	30.50	169.50	245
0670	Add per additional pump							116	116	127
0800	8 hrs. attended, 2" diaphragm pump	B-10H	1	12			555	75	630	925
0820	Add per additional pump							72	72	79
0900	3" centrifugal pump	B-10J	1	12			555	84	639	940
0920	Add per additional pump							79	79	86.50
1000	4" diaphragm pump	B-10I	1	12			555	122	677	980
1020	Add per additional pump							116	116	127
1100	6" centrifugal pump	B-10K	1	12			555	370	925	1,250
1120	Add per additional pump							340	340	375
1300	CMP, incl. excavation 3' deep, 12" diameter	B-6	115	.209	L.F.	11.05	8.60	3.17	22.82	29
1400	18" diameter		100	.240	"	16.70	9.90	3.64	30.24	37.50
1600	Sump hole construction, incl. excavation and gravel, pit		1250	.019	C.F.	1.09	.79	.29	2.17	2.73
1700	With 12" gravel collar, 12" pipe, corrugated, 16 ga.		70	.343	L.F.	21.50	14.15	5.20	40.85	50.50
1800	15" pipe, corrugated, 16 ga.		55	.436		28	18	6.60	52.60	65.50
1900	18" pipe, corrugated, 16 ga.		50	.480		32	19.80	7.30	59.10	74
2000	24" pipe, corrugated, 14 ga.		40	.600		38.50	25	9.10	72.60	90.50
2200	Wood lining, up to 4' x 4', add		300	.080	SFCA	16.25	3.30	1.21	20.76	24.50
9950	See Section 31 23 19.40 for wellpoints									
9960	See Section 31 23 19.30 for deep well systems									
9970	See Section 22 11 23 for pumps									

For customer support on your Site Work & Landscape Cost Data, call 877.737.1594.

299

31 23 Excavation and Fill

31 23 19 – Dewatering

31 23 19.30 Wells

		Crew	Daily Output	Labor-Hours	Unit	Material	2015 Bare Costs Labor	2015 Bare Costs Equipment	Total	Total Incl O&P
0010	**WELLS**									
0011	For dewatering 10' to 20' deep, 2' diameter									
0020	with steel casing, minimum	B-6	165	.145	V.L.F.	38	6	2.21	46.21	53
0050	Average		98	.245		43	10.10	3.72	56.82	66.50
0100	Maximum	↓	49	.490	↓	47.50	20	7.45	74.95	91.50
0300	For dewatering pumps see 01 54 33 in Reference Section									
0500	For domestic water wells, see Section 33 21 13.10									

31 23 19.40 Wellpoints

		Crew	Daily Output	Labor-Hours	Unit	Material	2015 Bare Costs Labor	2015 Bare Costs Equipment	Total	Total Incl O&P
0010	**WELLPOINTS** R312319-90									
0011	For equipment rental, see 01 54 33 in Reference Section									
0100	Installation and removal of single stage system									
0110	Labor only, .75 labor-hours per L.F.	1 Clab	10.70	.748	LF Hdr		28		28	43.50
0200	2.0 labor-hours per L.F.	"	4	2	"		75		75	116
0400	Pump operation, 4 @ 6 hr. shifts									
0410	Per 24 hour day	4 Eqlt	1.27	25.197	Day		1,225		1,225	1,850
0500	Per 168 hour week, 160 hr. straight, 8 hr. double time		.18	177	Week		8,650		8,650	13,100
0550	Per 4.3 week month	↓	.04	800	Month		38,900		38,900	59,000
0600	Complete installation, operation, equipment rental, fuel &									
0610	removal of system with 2" wellpoints 5' O.C.									
0700	100' long header, 6" diameter, first month	4 Eqlt	3.23	9.907	LF Hdr	159	480		639	905
0800	Thereafter, per month		4.13	7.748		127	375		502	710
1000	200' long header, 8" diameter, first month		6	5.333		145	259		404	555
1100	Thereafter, per month		8.39	3.814		71.50	185		256.50	360
1300	500' long header, 8" diameter, first month		10.63	3.010		55.50	146		201.50	283
1400	Thereafter, per month		20.91	1.530		39.50	74.50		114	157
1600	1,000' long header, 10" diameter, first month		11.62	2.754		47.50	134		181.50	256
1700	Thereafter, per month	↓	41.81	.765	↓	24	37		61	82.50
1900	Note: above figures include pumping 168 hrs. per week									
1910	and include the pump operator and one stand-by pump.									

31 23 23 – Fill

31 23 23.13 Backfill

		Crew	Daily Output	Labor-Hours	Unit	Material	2015 Bare Costs Labor	2015 Bare Costs Equipment	Total	Total Incl O&P
0010	**BACKFILL** R312323-30									
0015	By hand, no compaction, light soil	1 Clab	14	.571	L.C.Y.		21.50		21.50	33
0100	Heavy soil		11	.727	"		27.50		27.50	42
0300	Compaction in 6" layers, hand tamp, add to above	↓	20.60	.388	E.C.Y.		14.60		14.60	22.50
0400	Roller compaction operator walking, add	B-10A	100	.120			5.55	1.80	7.35	10.45
0500	Air tamp, add	B-9D	190	.211			8	1.40	9.40	13.85
0600	Vibrating plate, add	A-1D	60	.133			5	.60	5.60	8.35
0800	Compaction in 12" layers, hand tamp, add to above	1 Clab	34	.235			8.85		8.85	13.60
0900	Roller compaction operator walking, add	B-10A	150	.080			3.70	1.20	4.90	6.95
1000	Air tamp, add	B-9	285	.140			5.35	.82	6.17	9.10
1100	Vibrating plate, add	A-1E	90	.089	↓		3.34	.52	3.86	5.70

31 23 23.14 Backfill, Structural

		Crew	Daily Output	Labor-Hours	Unit	Material	2015 Bare Costs Labor	2015 Bare Costs Equipment	Total	Total Incl O&P
0010	**BACKFILL, STRUCTURAL**									
0011	Dozer or F.E. loader									
0020	From existing stockpile, no compaction									
2000	80 H.P., 50' haul, sand & gravel	B-10L	1100	.011	L.C.Y.		.50	.43	.93	1.24
2010	Sandy clay & loam		1070	.011			.52	.44	.96	1.28
2020	Common earth		975	.012			.57	.48	1.05	1.40
2040	Clay		850	.014			.65	.56	1.21	1.60
2200	150' haul, sand & gravel	↓	550	.022	↓		1.01	.86	1.87	2.48

31 23 23.14 Backfill, Structural

		Crew	Daily Output	Labor-Hours	Unit	Material	2015 Bare Costs Labor	Equipment	Total	Total Incl O&P
2210	Sandy clay & loam	B-10L	535	.022	L.C.Y.		1.04	.88	1.92	2.55
2220	Common earth		490	.024			1.13	.96	2.09	2.79
2240	Clay		425	.028			1.31	1.11	2.42	3.21
2400	300' haul, sand & gravel		370	.032			1.50	1.28	2.78	3.68
2410	Sandy clay & loam		360	.033			1.54	1.31	2.85	3.79
2420	Common earth		330	.036			1.68	1.43	3.11	4.13
2440	Clay		290	.041			1.91	1.63	3.54	4.71
3000	105 H.P., 50' haul, sand & gravel	B-10W	1350	.009			.41	.45	.86	1.12
3010	Sandy clay & loam		1325	.009			.42	.46	.88	1.14
3020	Common earth		1225	.010			.45	.49	.94	1.23
3040	Clay		1100	.011			.50	.55	1.05	1.37
3200	150' haul, sand & gravel		670	.018			.83	.90	1.73	2.25
3210	Sandy clay & loam		655	.018			.85	.92	1.77	2.30
3220	Common earth		610	.020			.91	.99	1.90	2.48
3240	Clay		550	.022			1.01	1.10	2.11	2.75
3300	300' haul, sand & gravel		465	.026			1.19	1.30	2.49	3.25
3310	Sandy clay & loam		455	.026			1.22	1.32	2.54	3.32
3320	Common earth		415	.029			1.34	1.45	2.79	3.64
3340	Clay		370	.032			1.50	1.63	3.13	4.07
4000	200 H.P., 50' haul, sand & gravel	B-10B	2500	.005			.22	.55	.77	.95
4010	Sandy clay & loam		2435	.005			.23	.57	.80	.98
4020	Common earth		2200	.005			.25	.63	.88	1.07
4040	Clay		1950	.006			.28	.71	.99	1.21
4200	150' haul, sand & gravel		1225	.010			.45	1.13	1.58	1.94
4210	Sandy clay & loam		1200	.010			.46	1.16	1.62	1.97
4220	Common earth		1100	.011			.50	1.26	1.76	2.16
4240	Clay		975	.012			.57	1.42	1.99	2.44
4400	300' haul, sand & gravel		805	.015			.69	1.72	2.41	2.95
4410	Sandy clay & loam		790	.015			.70	1.76	2.46	3
4420	Common earth		735	.016			.76	1.89	2.65	3.23
4440	Clay		660	.018			.84	2.10	2.94	3.59
5000	300 H.P., 50' haul, sand & gravel	B-10M	3170	.004			.18	.60	.78	.93
5010	Sandy clay & loam		3110	.004			.18	.61	.79	.94
5020	Common earth		2900	.004			.19	.65	.84	1.01
5040	Clay		2700	.004			.21	.70	.91	1.08
5200	150' haul, sand & gravel		2200	.005			.25	.86	1.11	1.33
5210	Sandy clay & loam		2150	.006			.26	.88	1.14	1.36
5220	Common earth		1950	.006			.28	.97	1.25	1.50
5240	Clay		1700	.007			.33	1.12	1.45	1.73
5400	300' haul, sand & gravel		1500	.008			.37	1.26	1.63	1.95
5410	Sandy clay & loam		1470	.008			.38	1.29	1.67	1.99
5420	Common earth		1350	.009			.41	1.41	1.82	2.18
5440	Clay		1225	.010			.45	1.55	2	2.39
6000	For compaction, see Section 31 23 23.23									
6010	For trench backfill, see Section 31 23 16.13 and 31 23 16.14									

31 23 23.15 Borrow, Loading And/Or Spreading

		Crew	Daily Output	Labor-Hours	Unit	Material	2015 Bare Costs Labor	Equipment	Total	Total Incl O&P
0010	**BORROW, LOADING AND/OR SPREADING**									
4000	Common earth, shovel, 1 C.Y. bucket	B-12N	840	.019	B.C.Y.	16.75	.85	1.45	19.05	21.50
4010	1-1/2 C.Y. bucket	B-12O	1135	.014		16.75	.63	1.09	18.47	20.50
4020	3 C.Y. bucket	B-12T	1800	.009		16.75	.40	.87	18.02	19.95
4030	Front end loader, wheel mounted									
4050	3/4 C.Y. bucket	B-10R	550	.022	B.C.Y.	16.75	1.01	.54	18.30	20.50

For customer support on your Site Work & Landscape Cost Data, call 877.737.1594.

301

31 23 Excavation and Fill

31 23 23 – Fill

31 23 23.15 Borrow, Loading And/Or Spreading

		Crew	Daily Output	Labor-Hours	Unit	Material	2015 Bare Costs Labor	Equipment	Total	Total Incl O&P
4060	1-1/2 C.Y. bucket	B-10S	970	.012	B.C.Y.	16.75	.57	.39	17.71	19.70
4070	3 C.Y. bucket	B-10T	1575	.008		16.75	.35	.33	17.43	19.30
4080	5 C.Y. bucket	B-10U	2600	.005		16.75	.21	.42	17.38	19.20
5000	Select granular fill, shovel, 1 C.Y. bucket	B-12N	925	.017		21	.77	1.32	23.09	25.50
5010	1-1/2 C.Y. bucket	B-12O	1250	.013		21	.57	.99	22.56	25
5020	3 C.Y. bucket	B-12T	1980	.008		21	.36	.79	22.15	24.50
5030	Front end loader, wheel mounted									
5050	3/4 C.Y. bucket	B-10R	800	.015	B.C.Y.	21	.69	.37	22.06	24.50
5060	1-1/2 C.Y. bucket	B-10S	1065	.011		21	.52	.36	21.88	24
5070	3 C.Y. bucket	B-10T	1735	.007		21	.32	.30	21.62	24
5080	5 C.Y. bucket	B-10U	2850	.004		21	.19	.38	21.57	23.50
6000	Clay, till, or blasted rock, shovel, 1 C.Y. bucket	B-12N	715	.022		12.40	1	1.71	15.11	17.05
6010	1-1/2 C.Y. bucket	B-12O	965	.017		12.40	.74	1.28	14.42	16.20
6020	3 C.Y. bucket	B-12T	1530	.010		12.40	.47	1.02	13.89	15.50
6030	Front end loader, wheel mounted									
6035	3/4 C.Y. bucket	B-10R	465	.026	B.C.Y.	12.40	1.19	.64	14.23	16.20
6040	1-1/2 C.Y. bucket	B-10S	825	.015		12.40	.67	.46	13.53	15.20
6045	3 C.Y. bucket	B-10T	1340	.009		12.40	.41	.39	13.20	14.70
6050	5 C.Y. bucket	B-10U	2200	.005		12.40	.25	.49	13.14	14.55
6060	Front end loader, track mounted									
6065	1-1/2 C.Y. bucket	B-10N	715	.017	B.C.Y.	12.40	.78	.73	13.91	15.65
6070	3 C.Y. bucket	B-10P	1190	.010		12.40	.47	1	13.87	15.45
6075	5 C.Y. bucket	B-10Q	1835	.007		12.40	.30	.85	13.55	15.05
7000	Topsoil or loam from stockpile, shovel, 1 C.Y. bucket	B-12N	840	.019		24.50	.85	1.45	26.80	30
7010	1-1/2 C.Y. bucket	B-12O	1135	.014		24.50	.63	1.09	26.22	29
7020	3 C.Y. bucket	B-12T	1800	.009		24.50	.40	.87	25.77	28.50
7030	Front end loader, wheel mounted									
7050	3/4 C.Y. bucket	B-10R	550	.022	B.C.Y.	24.50	1.01	.54	26.05	29
7060	1-1/2 C.Y. bucket	B-10S	970	.012		24.50	.57	.39	25.46	28.50
7070	3 C.Y. bucket	B-10T	1575	.008		24.50	.35	.33	25.18	28
7080	5 C.Y. bucket	B-10U	2600	.005		24.50	.21	.42	25.13	28
8900	For larger hauling units, deduct from above						30%			30%
9000	Hauling only, excavated or borrow material, see Section 31 23 23.20									

31 23 23.16 Fill By Borrow and Utility Bedding

		Crew	Daily Output	Labor-Hours	Unit	Material	2015 Bare Costs Labor	Equipment	Total	Total Incl O&P
0010	**FILL BY BORROW AND UTILITY BEDDING**									
0049	Utility bedding, for pipe & conduit, not incl. compaction									
0050	Crushed or screened bank run gravel	B-6	150	.160	L.C.Y.	25.50	6.60	2.43	34.53	41
0100	Crushed stone 3/4" to 1/2"		150	.160		23.50	6.60	2.43	32.53	39
0200	Sand, dead or bank		150	.160		17.85	6.60	2.43	26.88	32.50
0500	Compacting bedding in trench	A-1D	90	.089	E.C.Y.		3.34	.40	3.74	5.60
0600	If material source exceeds 2 miles, add for extra mileage.									
0610	See Section 31 23 23.20 for hauling mileage add.									

31 23 23.17 General Fill

		Crew	Daily Output	Labor-Hours	Unit	Material	2015 Bare Costs Labor	Equipment	Total	Total Incl O&P
0010	**GENERAL FILL**									
0011	Spread dumped material, no compaction									
0020	By dozer, no compaction	B-10B	1000	.012	L.C.Y.		.56	1.39	1.95	2.38
0100	By hand	1 Clab	12	.667	"		25		25	38.50
0150	Spread fill, from stockpile with 2-1/2 C.Y. F.E. loader									
0170	130 H.P., 300' haul	B-10P	600	.020	L.C.Y.		.93	1.98	2.91	3.59
0190	With dozer 300 H.P., 300' haul	B-10M	600	.020	"		.93	3.16	4.09	4.89
0400	For compaction of embankment, see Section 31 23 23.23									
0500	Gravel fill, compacted, under floor slabs, 4" deep	B-37	10000	.005	S.F.	.42	.19	.02	.63	.77

31 23 23.17 General Fill

		Crew	Daily Output	Labor-Hours	Unit	Material	2015 Bare Costs Labor	2015 Bare Costs Equipment	Total	Total Incl O&P
0600	6" deep	B-37	8600	.006	S.F.	.63	.22	.02	.87	1.05
0700	9" deep		7200	.007		1.05	.27	.02	1.34	1.58
0800	12" deep		6000	.008	▼	1.47	.32	.03	1.82	2.14
1000	Alternate pricing method, 4" deep		120	.400	E.C.Y.	31.50	15.90	1.31	48.71	60.50
1100	6" deep		160	.300		31.50	11.95	.98	44.43	54
1200	9" deep		200	.240		31.50	9.55	.79	41.84	50
1300	12" deep	▼	220	.218	▼	31.50	8.70	.72	40.92	48.50
1500	For fill under exterior paving, see Section 32 11 23.23									
1600	For flowable fill, see Section 03 31 13.35									

31 23 23.20 Hauling

		Crew	Daily Output	Labor-Hours	Unit	Material	2015 Bare Costs Labor	2015 Bare Costs Equipment	Total	Total Incl O&P
0010	**HAULING**									
0011	Excavated or borrow, loose cubic yards									
0012	no loading equipment, including hauling, waiting, loading/dumping									
0013	time per cycle (wait, load, travel, unload or dump & return)									
0014	8 C.Y. truck, 15 MPH ave, cycle 0.5 miles, 10 min. wait/Ld./Uld.	B-34A	320	.025	L.C.Y.		1	1.29	2.29	2.92
0016	cycle 1 mile		272	.029			1.18	1.51	2.69	3.44
0018	cycle 2 miles		208	.038			1.54	1.98	3.52	4.50
0020	cycle 4 miles		144	.056			2.23	2.86	5.09	6.50
0022	cycle 6 miles		112	.071			2.86	3.67	6.53	8.35
0024	cycle 8 miles		88	.091			3.64	4.67	8.31	10.65
0026	20 MPH ave, cycle 0.5 mile		336	.024			.95	1.22	2.17	2.79
0028	cycle 1 mile		296	.027			1.08	1.39	2.47	3.17
0030	cycle 2 miles		240	.033			1.33	1.71	3.04	3.90
0032	cycle 4 miles		176	.045			1.82	2.34	4.16	5.30
0034	cycle 6 miles		136	.059			2.36	3.02	5.38	6.90
0036	cycle 8 miles		112	.071			2.86	3.67	6.53	8.35
0044	25 MPH ave, cycle 4 miles		192	.042			1.67	2.14	3.81	4.88
0046	cycle 6 miles		160	.050			2	2.57	4.57	5.85
0048	cycle 8 miles		128	.063			2.50	3.21	5.71	7.30
0050	30 MPH ave, cycle 4 miles		216	.037			1.48	1.90	3.38	4.33
0052	cycle 6 miles		176	.045			1.82	2.34	4.16	5.30
0054	cycle 8 miles		144	.056			2.23	2.86	5.09	6.50
0114	15 MPH ave, cycle 0.5 mile, 15 min. wait/Ld./Uld.		224	.036			1.43	1.84	3.27	4.18
0116	cycle 1 mile		200	.040			1.60	2.06	3.66	4.68
0118	cycle 2 miles		168	.048			1.91	2.45	4.36	5.55
0120	cycle 4 miles		120	.067			2.67	3.43	6.10	7.80
0122	cycle 6 miles		96	.083			3.34	4.28	7.62	9.75
0124	cycle 8 miles		80	.100			4.01	5.15	9.16	11.70
0126	20 MPH ave, cycle 0.5 mile		232	.034			1.38	1.77	3.15	4.04
0128	cycle 1 mile		208	.038			1.54	1.98	3.52	4.50
0130	cycle 2 miles		184	.043			1.74	2.23	3.97	5.10
0132	cycle 4 miles		144	.056			2.23	2.86	5.09	6.50
0134	cycle 6 miles		112	.071			2.86	3.67	6.53	8.35
0136	cycle 8 miles		96	.083			3.34	4.28	7.62	9.75
0144	25 MPH ave, cycle 4 miles		152	.053			2.11	2.71	4.82	6.15
0146	cycle 6 miles		128	.063			2.50	3.21	5.71	7.30
0148	cycle 8 miles		112	.071			2.86	3.67	6.53	8.35
0150	30 MPH ave, cycle 4 miles		168	.048			1.91	2.45	4.36	5.55
0152	cycle 6 miles		144	.056			2.23	2.86	5.09	6.50
0154	cycle 8 miles		120	.067			2.67	3.43	6.10	7.80
0214	15 MPH ave, cycle 0.5 mile, 20 min wait/Ld./Uld.		176	.045			1.82	2.34	4.16	5.30
0216	cycle 1 mile	▼	160	.050	▼		2	2.57	4.57	5.85

For customer support on your Site Work & Landscape Cost Data, call 877.737.1594.

303

31 23 23.20 Hauling		Crew	Daily Output	Labor-Hours	Unit	Material	2015 Bare Costs Labor	2015 Bare Costs Equipment	Total	Total Incl O&P
0218	cycle 2 miles	B-34A	136	.059	L.C.Y.		2.36	3.02	5.38	6.90
0220	cycle 4 miles		104	.077			3.08	3.95	7.03	9
0222	cycle 6 miles		88	.091			3.64	4.67	8.31	10.65
0224	cycle 8 miles		72	.111			4.45	5.70	10.15	13.05
0226	20 MPH ave, cycle 0.5 mile		176	.045			1.82	2.34	4.16	5.30
0228	cycle 1 mile		168	.048			1.91	2.45	4.36	5.55
0230	cycle 2 miles		144	.056			2.23	2.86	5.09	6.50
0232	cycle 4 miles		120	.067			2.67	3.43	6.10	7.80
0234	cycle 6 miles		96	.083			3.34	4.28	7.62	9.75
0236	cycle 8 miles		88	.091			3.64	4.67	8.31	10.65
0244	25 MPH ave, cycle 4 miles		128	.063			2.50	3.21	5.71	7.30
0246	cycle 6 miles		112	.071			2.86	3.67	6.53	8.35
0248	cycle 8 miles		96	.083			3.34	4.28	7.62	9.75
0250	30 MPH ave, cycle 4 miles		136	.059			2.36	3.02	5.38	6.90
0252	cycle 6 miles		120	.067			2.67	3.43	6.10	7.80
0254	cycle 8 miles		104	.077			3.08	3.95	7.03	9
0314	15 MPH ave, cycle 0.5 mile, 25 min wait/Ld./Uld.		144	.056			2.23	2.86	5.09	6.50
0316	cycle 1 mile		128	.063			2.50	3.21	5.71	7.30
0318	cycle 2 miles		112	.071			2.86	3.67	6.53	8.35
0320	cycle 4 miles		96	.083			3.34	4.28	7.62	9.75
0322	cycle 6 miles		80	.100			4.01	5.15	9.16	11.70
0324	cycle 8 miles		64	.125			5	6.45	11.45	14.60
0326	20 MPH ave, cycle 0.5 mile		144	.056			2.23	2.86	5.09	6.50
0328	cycle 1 mile		136	.059			2.36	3.02	5.38	6.90
0330	cycle 2 miles		120	.067			2.67	3.43	6.10	7.80
0332	cycle 4 miles		104	.077			3.08	3.95	7.03	9
0334	cycle 6 miles		88	.091			3.64	4.67	8.31	10.65
0336	cycle 8 miles		80	.100			4.01	5.15	9.16	11.70
0344	25 MPH ave, cycle 4 miles		112	.071			2.86	3.67	6.53	8.35
0346	cycle 6 miles		96	.083			3.34	4.28	7.62	9.75
0348	cycle 8 miles		88	.091			3.64	4.67	8.31	10.65
0350	30 MPH ave, cycle 4 miles		112	.071			2.86	3.67	6.53	8.35
0352	cycle 6 miles		104	.077			3.08	3.95	7.03	9
0354	cycle 8 miles		96	.083			3.34	4.28	7.62	9.75
0414	15 MPH ave, cycle 0.5 mile, 30 min wait/Ld./Uld.		120	.067			2.67	3.43	6.10	7.80
0416	cycle 1 mile		112	.071			2.86	3.67	6.53	8.35
0418	cycle 2 miles		96	.083			3.34	4.28	7.62	9.75
0420	cycle 4 miles		80	.100			4.01	5.15	9.16	11.70
0422	cycle 6 miles		72	.111			4.45	5.70	10.15	13.05
0424	cycle 8 miles		64	.125			5	6.45	11.45	14.60
0426	20 MPH ave, cycle 0.5 mile		120	.067			2.67	3.43	6.10	7.80
0428	cycle 1 mile		112	.071			2.86	3.67	6.53	8.35
0430	cycle 2 miles		104	.077			3.08	3.95	7.03	9
0432	cycle 4 miles		88	.091			3.64	4.67	8.31	10.65
0434	cycle 6 miles		80	.100			4.01	5.15	9.16	11.70
0436	cycle 8 miles		72	.111			4.45	5.70	10.15	13.05
0444	25 MPH ave, cycle 4 miles		96	.083			3.34	4.28	7.62	9.75
0446	cycle 6 miles		88	.091			3.64	4.67	8.31	10.65
0448	cycle 8 miles		80	.100			4.01	5.15	9.16	11.70
0450	30 MPH ave, cycle 4 miles		96	.083			3.34	4.28	7.62	9.75
0452	cycle 6 miles		88	.091			3.64	4.67	8.31	10.65
0454	cycle 8 miles		80	.100			4.01	5.15	9.16	11.70
0514	15 MPH ave, cycle 0.5 mile, 35 min wait/Ld./Uld.		104	.077			3.08	3.95	7.03	9

31 23 Excavation and Fill

31 23 23 — Fill

31 23 23.20 Hauling		Crew	Daily Output	Labor-Hours	Unit	Material	2015 Bare Costs Labor	Equipment	Total	Total Incl O&P
0516	cycle 1 mile	B-34A	96	.083	L.C.Y.		3.34	4.28	7.62	9.75
0518	cycle 2 miles		88	.091			3.64	4.67	8.31	10.65
0520	cycle 4 miles		72	.111			4.45	5.70	10.15	13.05
0522	cycle 6 miles		64	.125			5	6.45	11.45	14.60
0524	cycle 8 miles		56	.143			5.70	7.35	13.05	16.75
0526	20 MPH ave, cycle 0.5 mile		104	.077			3.08	3.95	7.03	9
0528	cycle 1 mile		96	.083			3.34	4.28	7.62	9.75
0530	cycle 2 miles		96	.083			3.34	4.28	7.62	9.75
0532	cycle 4 miles		80	.100			4.01	5.15	9.16	11.70
0534	cycle 6 miles		72	.111			4.45	5.70	10.15	13.05
0536	cycle 8 miles		64	.125			5	6.45	11.45	14.60
0544	25 MPH ave, cycle 4 miles		88	.091			3.64	4.67	8.31	10.65
0546	cycle 6 miles		80	.100			4.01	5.15	9.16	11.70
0548	cycle 8 miles		72	.111			4.45	5.70	10.15	13.05
0550	30 MPH ave, cycle 4 miles		88	.091			3.64	4.67	8.31	10.65
0552	cycle 6 miles		80	.100			4.01	5.15	9.16	11.70
0554	cycle 8 miles		72	.111			4.45	5.70	10.15	13.05
1014	12 C.Y. truck, cycle 0.5 mile, 15 MPH ave, 15 min. wait/Ld./Uld.	B-34B	336	.024			.95	2.06	3.01	3.70
1016	cycle 1 mile		300	.027			1.07	2.30	3.37	4.14
1018	cycle 2 miles		252	.032			1.27	2.74	4.01	4.94
1020	cycle 4 miles		180	.044			1.78	3.84	5.62	6.90
1022	cycle 6 miles		144	.056			2.23	4.80	7.03	8.65
1024	cycle 8 miles		120	.067			2.67	5.75	8.42	10.40
1025	cycle 10 miles		96	.083			3.34	7.20	10.54	12.95
1026	20 MPH ave, cycle 0.5 mile		348	.023			.92	1.99	2.91	3.57
1028	cycle 1 mile		312	.026			1.03	2.21	3.24	3.99
1030	cycle 2 miles		276	.029			1.16	2.50	3.66	4.51
1032	cycle 4 miles		216	.037			1.48	3.20	4.68	5.75
1034	cycle 6 miles		168	.048			1.91	4.11	6.02	7.40
1036	cycle 8 miles		144	.056			2.23	4.80	7.03	8.65
1038	cycle 10 miles		120	.067			2.67	5.75	8.42	10.40
1040	25 MPH ave, cycle 4 miles		228	.035			1.41	3.03	4.44	5.45
1042	cycle 6 miles		192	.042			1.67	3.60	5.27	6.50
1044	cycle 8 miles		168	.048			1.91	4.11	6.02	7.40
1046	cycle 10 miles		144	.056			2.23	4.80	7.03	8.65
1050	30 MPH ave, cycle 4 miles		252	.032			1.27	2.74	4.01	4.94
1052	cycle 6 miles		216	.037			1.48	3.20	4.68	5.75
1054	cycle 8 miles		180	.044			1.78	3.84	5.62	6.90
1056	cycle 10 miles		156	.051			2.05	4.43	6.48	8
1060	35 MPH ave, cycle 4 miles		264	.030			1.21	2.62	3.83	4.71
1062	cycle 6 miles		228	.035			1.41	3.03	4.44	5.45
1064	cycle 8 miles		204	.039			1.57	3.39	4.96	6.10
1066	cycle 10 miles		180	.044			1.78	3.84	5.62	6.90
1068	cycle 20 miles		120	.067			2.67	5.75	8.42	10.40
1069	cycle 30 miles		84	.095			3.81	8.25	12.06	14.80
1070	cycle 40 miles		72	.111			4.45	9.60	14.05	17.30
1072	40 MPH ave, cycle 6 miles		240	.033			1.33	2.88	4.21	5.20
1074	cycle 8 miles		216	.037			1.48	3.20	4.68	5.75
1076	cycle 10 miles		192	.042			1.67	3.60	5.27	6.50
1078	cycle 20 miles		120	.067			2.67	5.75	8.42	10.40
1080	cycle 30 miles		96	.083			3.34	7.20	10.54	12.95
1082	cycle 40 miles		72	.111			4.45	9.60	14.05	17.30
1084	cycle 50 miles		60	.133			5.35	11.50	16.85	20.50

31 23 Excavation and Fill

31 23 23 – Fill

31 23 23.20 Hauling	Crew	Daily Output	Labor-Hours	Unit	Material	2015 Bare Costs Labor	2015 Bare Costs Equipment	Total	Total Incl O&P
1094	45 MPH ave, cycle 8 miles	B-34B	216	.037	L.C.Y.		1.48	3.20	4.68	5.75
1096	cycle 10 miles		204	.039			1.57	3.39	4.96	6.10
1098	cycle 20 miles		132	.061			2.43	5.25	7.68	9.40
1100	cycle 30 miles		108	.074			2.97	6.40	9.37	11.55
1102	cycle 40 miles		84	.095			3.81	8.25	12.06	14.80
1104	cycle 50 miles		72	.111			4.45	9.60	14.05	17.30
1106	50 MPH ave, cycle 10 miles		216	.037			1.48	3.20	4.68	5.75
1108	cycle 20 miles		144	.056			2.23	4.80	7.03	8.65
1110	cycle 30 miles		108	.074			2.97	6.40	9.37	11.55
1112	cycle 40 miles		84	.095			3.81	8.25	12.06	14.80
1114	cycle 50 miles		72	.111			4.45	9.60	14.05	17.30
1214	15 MPH ave, cycle 0.5 mile, 20 min. wait/Ld./Uld.		264	.030			1.21	2.62	3.83	4.71
1216	cycle 1 mile		240	.033			1.33	2.88	4.21	5.20
1218	cycle 2 miles		204	.039			1.57	3.39	4.96	6.10
1220	cycle 4 miles		156	.051			2.05	4.43	6.48	8
1222	cycle 6 miles		132	.061			2.43	5.25	7.68	9.40
1224	cycle 8 miles		108	.074			2.97	6.40	9.37	11.55
1225	cycle 10 miles		96	.083			3.34	7.20	10.54	12.95
1226	20 MPH ave, cycle 0.5 mile		264	.030			1.21	2.62	3.83	4.71
1228	cycle 1 mile		252	.032			1.27	2.74	4.01	4.94
1230	cycle 2 miles		216	.037			1.48	3.20	4.68	5.75
1232	cycle 4 miles		180	.044			1.78	3.84	5.62	6.90
1234	cycle 6 miles		144	.056			2.23	4.80	7.03	8.65
1236	cycle 8 miles		132	.061			2.43	5.25	7.68	9.40
1238	cycle 10 miles		108	.074			2.97	6.40	9.37	11.55
1240	25 MPH ave, cycle 4 miles		192	.042			1.67	3.60	5.27	6.50
1242	cycle 6 miles		168	.048			1.91	4.11	6.02	7.40
1244	cycle 8 miles		144	.056			2.23	4.80	7.03	8.65
1246	cycle 10 miles		132	.061			2.43	5.25	7.68	9.40
1250	30 MPH ave, cycle 4 miles		204	.039			1.57	3.39	4.96	6.10
1252	cycle 6 miles		180	.044			1.78	3.84	5.62	6.90
1254	cycle 8 miles		156	.051			2.05	4.43	6.48	8
1256	cycle 10 miles		144	.056			2.23	4.80	7.03	8.65
1260	35 MPH ave, cycle 4 miles		216	.037			1.48	3.20	4.68	5.75
1262	cycle 6 miles		192	.042			1.67	3.60	5.27	6.50
1264	cycle 8 miles		168	.048			1.91	4.11	6.02	7.40
1266	cycle 10 miles		156	.051			2.05	4.43	6.48	8
1268	cycle 20 miles		108	.074			2.97	6.40	9.37	11.55
1269	cycle 30 miles		72	.111			4.45	9.60	14.05	17.30
1270	cycle 40 miles		60	.133			5.35	11.50	16.85	20.50
1272	40 MPH ave, cycle 6 miles		192	.042			1.67	3.60	5.27	6.50
1274	cycle 8 miles		180	.044			1.78	3.84	5.62	6.90
1276	cycle 10 miles		156	.051			2.05	4.43	6.48	8
1278	cycle 20 miles		108	.074			2.97	6.40	9.37	11.55
1280	cycle 30 miles		84	.095			3.81	8.25	12.06	14.80
1282	cycle 40 miles		72	.111			4.45	9.60	14.05	17.30
1284	cycle 50 miles		60	.133			5.35	11.50	16.85	20.50
1294	45 MPH ave, cycle 8 miles		180	.044			1.78	3.84	5.62	6.90
1296	cycle 10 miles		168	.048			1.91	4.11	6.02	7.40
1298	cycle 20 miles		120	.067			2.67	5.75	8.42	10.40
1300	cycle 30 miles		96	.083			3.34	7.20	10.54	12.95
1302	cycle 40 miles		72	.111			4.45	9.60	14.05	17.30
1304	cycle 50 miles		60	.133			5.35	11.50	16.85	20.50

31 23 Excavation and Fill

31 23 23 – Fill

31 23 23.20 Hauling		Crew	Daily Output	Labor-Hours	Unit	Material	2015 Bare Costs Labor	2015 Bare Costs Equipment	Total	Total Incl O&P
1306	50 MPH ave, cycle 10 miles	B-34B	180	.044	L.C.Y.		1.78	3.84	5.62	6.90
1308	cycle 20 miles		132	.061			2.43	5.25	7.68	9.40
1310	cycle 30 miles		96	.083			3.34	7.20	10.54	12.95
1312	cycle 40 miles		84	.095			3.81	8.25	12.06	14.80
1314	cycle 50 miles		72	.111			4.45	9.60	14.05	17.30
1414	15 MPH ave, cycle 0.5 mile, 25 min. wait/Ld./Uld.		204	.039			1.57	3.39	4.96	6.10
1416	cycle 1 mile		192	.042			1.67	3.60	5.27	6.50
1418	cycle 2 miles		168	.048			1.91	4.11	6.02	7.40
1420	cycle 4 miles		132	.061			2.43	5.25	7.68	9.40
1422	cycle 6 miles		120	.067			2.67	5.75	8.42	10.40
1424	cycle 8 miles		96	.083			3.34	7.20	10.54	12.95
1425	cycle 10 miles		84	.095			3.81	8.25	12.06	14.80
1426	20 MPH ave, cycle 0.5 mile		216	.037			1.48	3.20	4.68	5.75
1428	cycle 1 mile		204	.039			1.57	3.39	4.96	6.10
1430	cycle 2 miles		180	.044			1.78	3.84	5.62	6.90
1432	cycle 4 miles		156	.051			2.05	4.43	6.48	8
1434	cycle 6 miles		132	.061			2.43	5.25	7.68	9.40
1436	cycle 8 miles		120	.067			2.67	5.75	8.42	10.40
1438	cycle 10 miles		96	.083			3.34	7.20	10.54	12.95
1440	25 MPH ave, cycle 4 miles		168	.048			1.91	4.11	6.02	7.40
1442	cycle 6 miles		144	.056			2.23	4.80	7.03	8.65
1444	cycle 8 miles		132	.061			2.43	5.25	7.68	9.40
1446	cycle 10 miles		108	.074			2.97	6.40	9.37	11.55
1450	30 MPH ave, cycle 4 miles		168	.048			1.91	4.11	6.02	7.40
1452	cycle 6 miles		156	.051			2.05	4.43	6.48	8
1454	cycle 8 miles		132	.061			2.43	5.25	7.68	9.40
1456	cycle 10 miles		120	.067			2.67	5.75	8.42	10.40
1460	35 MPH ave, cycle 4 miles		180	.044			1.78	3.84	5.62	6.90
1462	cycle 6 miles		156	.051			2.05	4.43	6.48	8
1464	cycle 8 miles		144	.056			2.23	4.80	7.03	8.65
1466	cycle 10 miles		132	.061			2.43	5.25	7.68	9.40
1468	cycle 20 miles		96	.083			3.34	7.20	10.54	12.95
1469	cycle 30 miles		72	.111			4.45	9.60	14.05	17.30
1470	cycle 40 miles		60	.133			5.35	11.50	16.85	20.50
1472	40 MPH ave, cycle 6 miles		168	.048			1.91	4.11	6.02	7.40
1474	cycle 8 miles		156	.051			2.05	4.43	6.48	8
1476	cycle 10 miles		144	.056			2.23	4.80	7.03	8.65
1478	cycle 20 miles		96	.083			3.34	7.20	10.54	12.95
1480	cycle 30 miles		84	.095			3.81	8.25	12.06	14.80
1482	cycle 40 miles		60	.133			5.35	11.50	16.85	20.50
1484	cycle 50 miles		60	.133			5.35	11.50	16.85	20.50
1494	45 MPH ave, cycle 8 miles		156	.051			2.05	4.43	6.48	8
1496	cycle 10 miles		144	.056			2.23	4.80	7.03	8.65
1498	cycle 20 miles		108	.074			2.97	6.40	9.37	11.55
1500	cycle 30 miles		84	.095			3.81	8.25	12.06	14.80
1502	cycle 40 miles		72	.111			4.45	9.60	14.05	17.30
1504	cycle 50 miles		60	.133			5.35	11.50	16.85	20.50
1506	50 MPH ave, cycle 10 miles		156	.051			2.05	4.43	6.48	8
1508	cycle 20 miles		120	.067			2.67	5.75	8.42	10.40
1510	cycle 30 miles		96	.083			3.34	7.20	10.54	12.95
1512	cycle 40 miles		72	.111			4.45	9.60	14.05	17.30
1514	cycle 50 miles		60	.133			5.35	11.50	16.85	20.50
1614	15 MPH, cycle 0.5 mile, 30 min. wait/Ld./Uld.		180	.044			1.78	3.84	5.62	6.90

31 23 23.20 Hauling		Crew	Daily Output	Labor-Hours	Unit	Material	2015 Bare Costs Labor	2015 Bare Costs Equipment	Total	Total Incl O&P
1616	cycle 1 mile	B-34B	168	.048	L.C.Y.		1.91	4.11	6.02	7.40
1618	cycle 2 miles		144	.056			2.23	4.80	7.03	8.65
1620	cycle 4 miles		120	.067			2.67	5.75	8.42	10.40
1622	cycle 6 miles		108	.074			2.97	6.40	9.37	11.55
1624	cycle 8 miles		84	.095			3.81	8.25	12.06	14.80
1625	cycle 10 miles		84	.095			3.81	8.25	12.06	14.80
1626	20 MPH ave, cycle 0.5 mile		180	.044			1.78	3.84	5.62	6.90
1628	cycle 1 mile		168	.048			1.91	4.11	6.02	7.40
1630	cycle 2 miles		156	.051			2.05	4.43	6.48	8
1632	cycle 4 miles		132	.061			2.43	5.25	7.68	9.40
1634	cycle 6 miles		120	.067			2.67	5.75	8.42	10.40
1636	cycle 8 miles		108	.074			2.97	6.40	9.37	11.55
1638	cycle 10 miles		96	.083			3.34	7.20	10.54	12.95
1640	25 MPH ave, cycle 4 miles		144	.056			2.23	4.80	7.03	8.65
1642	cycle 6 miles		132	.061			2.43	5.25	7.68	9.40
1644	cycle 8 miles		108	.074			2.97	6.40	9.37	11.55
1646	cycle 10 miles		108	.074			2.97	6.40	9.37	11.55
1650	30 MPH ave, cycle 4 miles		144	.056			2.23	4.80	7.03	8.65
1652	cycle 6 miles		132	.061			2.43	5.25	7.68	9.40
1654	cycle 8 miles		120	.067			2.67	5.75	8.42	10.40
1656	cycle 10 miles		108	.074			2.97	6.40	9.37	11.55
1660	35 MPH ave, cycle 4 miles		156	.051			2.05	4.43	6.48	8
1662	cycle 6 miles		144	.056			2.23	4.80	7.03	8.65
1664	cycle 8 miles		132	.061			2.43	5.25	7.68	9.40
1666	cycle 10 miles		120	.067			2.67	5.75	8.42	10.40
1668	cycle 20 miles		84	.095			3.81	8.25	12.06	14.80
1669	cycle 30 miles		72	.111			4.45	9.60	14.05	17.30
1670	cycle 40 miles		60	.133			5.35	11.50	16.85	20.50
1672	40 MPH, cycle 6 miles		144	.056			2.23	4.80	7.03	8.65
1674	cycle 8 miles		132	.061			2.43	5.25	7.68	9.40
1676	cycle 10 miles		120	.067			2.67	5.75	8.42	10.40
1678	cycle 20 miles		96	.083			3.34	7.20	10.54	12.95
1680	cycle 30 miles		72	.111			4.45	9.60	14.05	17.30
1682	cycle 40 miles		60	.133			5.35	11.50	16.85	20.50
1684	cycle 50 miles		48	.167			6.70	14.40	21.10	26
1694	45 MPH ave, cycle 8 miles		144	.056			2.23	4.80	7.03	8.65
1696	cycle 10 miles		132	.061			2.43	5.25	7.68	9.40
1698	cycle 20 miles		96	.083			3.34	7.20	10.54	12.95
1700	cycle 30 miles		84	.095			3.81	8.25	12.06	14.80
1702	cycle 40 miles		60	.133			5.35	11.50	16.85	20.50
1704	cycle 50 miles		60	.133			5.35	11.50	16.85	20.50
1706	50 MPH ave, cycle 10 miles		132	.061			2.43	5.25	7.68	9.40
1708	cycle 20 miles		108	.074			2.97	6.40	9.37	11.55
1710	cycle 30 miles		84	.095			3.81	8.25	12.06	14.80
1712	cycle 40 miles		72	.111			4.45	9.60	14.05	17.30
1714	cycle 50 miles		60	.133			5.35	11.50	16.85	20.50
2000	Hauling, 8 C.Y. truck, small project cost per hour	B-34A	8	1	Hr.		40	51.50	91.50	117
2100	12 C.Y. Truck	B-34B	8	1			40	86.50	126.50	156
2150	16.5 C.Y. Truck	B-34C	8	1			40	91	131	161
2175	18 C.Y. 8 wheel Truck	B-34I	8	1			40	109	149	180
2200	20 C.Y. Truck	B-34D	8	1			40	92.50	132.50	163
2300	Grading at dump, or embankment if required, by dozer	B-10B	1000	.012	L.C.Y.		.56	1.39	1.95	2.38
2310	Spotter at fill or cut,.if required	1 Clab	8	1	Hr.		37.50		37.50	58

31 23 23.20 Hauling		Crew	Daily Output	Labor-Hours	Unit	Material	2015 Bare Costs Labor	2015 Bare Costs Equipment	Total	Total Incl O&P
2500	Dust control, light	B-59	1	8	Day		320	500	820	1,025
2510	Heavy	"	.50	16			640	1,000	1,640	2,075
2600	Haul road maintenance	B-86A	1	8	▼		405	735	1,140	1,425
3014	16.5 C.Y. truck, 15 min. wait/Ld./Uld., 15 MPH, cycle 0.5 mile	B-34C	462	.017	L.C.Y.		.69	1.57	2.26	2.78
3016	cycle 1 mile		413	.019			.78	1.76	2.54	3.10
3018	cycle 2 miles		347	.023			.92	2.09	3.01	3.70
3020	cycle 4 miles		248	.032			1.29	2.93	4.22	5.15
3022	cycle 6 miles		198	.040			1.62	3.67	5.29	6.50
3024	cycle 8 miles		165	.048			1.94	4.40	6.34	7.80
3025	cycle 10 miles		132	.061			2.43	5.50	7.93	9.70
3026	20 MPH ave, cycle 0.5 mile		479	.017			.67	1.52	2.19	2.68
3028	cycle 1 mile		429	.019			.75	1.69	2.44	2.99
3030	cycle 2 miles		380	.021			.84	1.91	2.75	3.37
3032	cycle 4 miles		281	.028			1.14	2.59	3.73	4.56
3034	cycle 6 miles		231	.035			1.39	3.14	4.53	5.55
3036	cycle 8 miles		198	.040			1.62	3.67	5.29	6.50
3038	cycle 10 miles		165	.048			1.94	4.40	6.34	7.80
3040	25 MPH ave, cycle 4 miles		314	.025			1.02	2.31	3.33	4.08
3042	cycle 6 miles		264	.030			1.21	2.75	3.96	4.86
3044	cycle 8 miles		231	.035			1.39	3.14	4.53	5.55
3046	cycle 10 miles		198	.040			1.62	3.67	5.29	6.50
3050	30 MPH ave, cycle 4 miles		347	.023			.92	2.09	3.01	3.70
3052	cycle 6 miles		281	.028			1.14	2.59	3.73	4.56
3054	cycle 8 miles		248	.032			1.29	2.93	4.22	5.15
3056	cycle 10 miles		215	.037			1.49	3.38	4.87	5.95
3060	35 MPH ave, cycle 4 miles		363	.022			.88	2	2.88	3.53
3062	cycle 6 miles		314	.025			1.02	2.31	3.33	4.08
3064	cycle 8 miles		264	.030			1.21	2.75	3.96	4.86
3066	cycle 10 miles		248	.032			1.29	2.93	4.22	5.15
3068	cycle 20 miles		149	.054			2.15	4.88	7.03	8.60
3070	cycle 30 miles		116	.069			2.76	6.25	9.01	11.10
3072	cycle 40 miles		83	.096			3.86	8.75	12.61	15.50
3074	40 MPH ave, cycle 6 miles		330	.024			.97	2.20	3.17	3.89
3076	cycle 8 miles		281	.028			1.14	2.59	3.73	4.56
3078	cycle 10 miles		264	.030			1.21	2.75	3.96	4.86
3080	cycle 20 miles		165	.048			1.94	4.40	6.34	7.80
3082	cycle 30 miles		132	.061			2.43	5.50	7.93	9.70
3084	cycle 40 miles		99	.081			3.24	7.35	10.59	12.95
3086	cycle 50 miles		83	.096			3.86	8.75	12.61	15.50
3094	45 MPH ave, cycle 8 miles		297	.027			1.08	2.45	3.53	4.32
3096	cycle 10 miles		281	.028			1.14	2.59	3.73	4.56
3098	cycle 20 miles		182	.044			1.76	3.99	5.75	7.05
3100	cycle 30 miles		132	.061			2.43	5.50	7.93	9.70
3102	cycle 40 miles		116	.069			2.76	6.25	9.01	11.10
3104	cycle 50 miles		99	.081			3.24	7.35	10.59	12.95
3106	50 MPH ave, cycle 10 miles		281	.028			1.14	2.59	3.73	4.56
3108	cycle 20 miles		198	.040			1.62	3.67	5.29	6.50
3110	cycle 30 miles		149	.054			2.15	4.88	7.03	8.60
3112	cycle 40 miles		116	.069			2.76	6.25	9.01	11.10
3114	cycle 50 miles		99	.081			3.24	7.35	10.59	12.95
3214	20 min. wait/Ld./Uld., 15 MPH, cycle 0.5 mile		363	.022			.88	2	2.88	3.53
3216	cycle 1 mile		330	.024			.97	2.20	3.17	3.89
3218	cycle 2 miles		281	.028	▼		1.14	2.59	3.73	4.56

31 23 23.20 Hauling		Crew	Daily Output	Labor-Hours	Unit	Material	2015 Bare Costs Labor	2015 Bare Costs Equipment	Total	Total Incl O&P
3220	cycle 4 miles	B-34C	215	.037	L.C.Y.		1.49	3.38	4.87	5.95
3222	cycle 6 miles		182	.044			1.76	3.99	5.75	7.05
3224	cycle 8 miles		149	.054			2.15	4.88	7.03	8.60
3225	cycle 10 miles		132	.061			2.43	5.50	7.93	9.70
3226	20 MPH ave, cycle 0.5 mile		363	.022			.88	2	2.88	3.53
3228	cycle 1 mile		347	.023			.92	2.09	3.01	3.70
3230	cycle 2 miles		297	.027			1.08	2.45	3.53	4.32
3232	cycle 4 miles		248	.032			1.29	2.93	4.22	5.15
3234	cycle 6 miles		198	.040			1.62	3.67	5.29	6.50
3236	cycle 8 miles		182	.044			1.76	3.99	5.75	7.05
3238	cycle 10 miles		149	.054			2.15	4.88	7.03	8.60
3240	25 MPH ave, cycle 4 miles		264	.030			1.21	2.75	3.96	4.86
3242	cycle 6 miles		231	.035			1.39	3.14	4.53	5.55
3244	cycle 8 miles		198	.040			1.62	3.67	5.29	6.50
3246	cycle 10 miles		182	.044			1.76	3.99	5.75	7.05
3250	30 MPH ave, cycle 4 miles		281	.028			1.14	2.59	3.73	4.56
3252	cycle 6 miles		248	.032			1.29	2.93	4.22	5.15
3254	cycle 8 miles		215	.037			1.49	3.38	4.87	5.95
3256	cycle 10 miles		198	.040			1.62	3.67	5.29	6.50
3260	35 MPH ave, cycle 4 miles		297	.027			1.08	2.45	3.53	4.32
3262	cycle 6 miles		264	.030			1.21	2.75	3.96	4.86
3264	cycle 8 miles		231	.035			1.39	3.14	4.53	5.55
3266	cycle 10 miles		215	.037			1.49	3.38	4.87	5.95
3268	cycle 20 miles		149	.054			2.15	4.88	7.03	8.60
3270	cycle 30 miles		99	.081			3.24	7.35	10.59	12.95
3272	cycle 40 miles		83	.096			3.86	8.75	12.61	15.50
3274	40 MPH ave, cycle 6 miles		264	.030			1.21	2.75	3.96	4.86
3276	cycle 8 miles		248	.032			1.29	2.93	4.22	5.15
3278	cycle 10 miles		215	.037			1.49	3.38	4.87	5.95
3280	cycle 20 miles		149	.054			2.15	4.88	7.03	8.60
3282	cycle 30 miles		116	.069			2.76	6.25	9.01	11.10
3284	cycle 40 miles		99	.081			3.24	7.35	10.59	12.95
3286	cycle 50 miles		83	.096			3.86	8.75	12.61	15.50
3294	45 MPH ave, cycle 8 miles		248	.032			1.29	2.93	4.22	5.15
3296	cycle 10 miles		231	.035			1.39	3.14	4.53	5.55
3298	cycle 20 miles		165	.048			1.94	4.40	6.34	7.80
3300	cycle 30 miles		132	.061			2.43	5.50	7.93	9.70
3302	cycle 40 miles		99	.081			3.24	7.35	10.59	12.95
3304	cycle 50 miles		83	.096			3.86	8.75	12.61	15.50
3306	50 MPH ave, cycle 10 miles		248	.032			1.29	2.93	4.22	5.15
3308	cycle 20 miles		182	.044			1.76	3.99	5.75	7.05
3310	cycle 30 miles		132	.061			2.43	5.50	7.93	9.70
3312	cycle 40 miles		116	.069			2.76	6.25	9.01	11.10
3314	cycle 50 miles		99	.081			3.24	7.35	10.59	12.95
3414	25 min. wait/Ld./Uld., 15 MPH, cycle 0.5 mile		281	.028			1.14	2.59	3.73	4.56
3416	cycle 1 mile		264	.030			1.21	2.75	3.96	4.86
3418	cycle 2 miles		231	.035			1.39	3.14	4.53	5.55
3420	cycle 4 miles		182	.044			1.76	3.99	5.75	7.05
3422	cycle 6 miles		165	.048			1.94	4.40	6.34	7.80
3424	cycle 8 miles		132	.061			2.43	5.50	7.93	9.70
3425	cycle 10 miles		116	.069			2.76	6.25	9.01	11.10
3426	20 MPH ave, cycle 0.5 mile		297	.027			1.08	2.45	3.53	4.32
3428	cycle 1 mile	↓	281	.028	↓		1.14	2.59	3.73	4.56

For customer support on your Site Work & Landscape Cost Data, call 877.737.1594.

31 23 23 – Fill

31 23 23.20 Hauling		Crew	Daily Output	Labor-Hours	Unit	Material	2015 Bare Costs Labor	Equipment	Total	Total Incl O&P
3430	cycle 2 miles	B-34C	248	.032	L.C.Y.		1.29	2.93	4.22	5.15
3432	cycle 4 miles		215	.037			1.49	3.38	4.87	5.95
3434	cycle 6 miles		182	.044			1.76	3.99	5.75	7.05
3436	cycle 8 miles		165	.048			1.94	4.40	6.34	7.80
3438	cycle 10 miles		132	.061			2.43	5.50	7.93	9.70
3440	25 MPH ave, cycle 4 miles		231	.035			1.39	3.14	4.53	5.55
3442	cycle 6 miles		198	.040			1.62	3.67	5.29	6.50
3444	cycle 8 miles		182	.044			1.76	3.99	5.75	7.05
3446	cycle 10 miles		165	.048			1.94	4.40	6.34	7.80
3450	30 MPH ave, cycle 4 miles		231	.035			1.39	3.14	4.53	5.55
3452	cycle 6 miles		215	.037			1.49	3.38	4.87	5.95
3454	cycle 8 miles		182	.044			1.76	3.99	5.75	7.05
3456	cycle 10 miles		165	.048			1.94	4.40	6.34	7.80
3460	35 MPH ave, cycle 4 miles		248	.032			1.29	2.93	4.22	5.15
3462	cycle 6 miles		215	.037			1.49	3.38	4.87	5.95
3464	cycle 8 miles		198	.040			1.62	3.67	5.29	6.50
3466	cycle 10 miles		182	.044			1.76	3.99	5.75	7.05
3468	cycle 20 miles		132	.061			2.43	5.50	7.93	9.70
3470	cycle 30 miles		99	.081			3.24	7.35	10.59	12.95
3472	cycle 40 miles		83	.096			3.86	8.75	12.61	15.50
3474	40 MPH, cycle 6 miles		231	.035			1.39	3.14	4.53	5.55
3476	cycle 8 miles		215	.037			1.49	3.38	4.87	5.95
3478	cycle 10 miles		198	.040			1.62	3.67	5.29	6.50
3480	cycle 20 miles		132	.061			2.43	5.50	7.93	9.70
3482	cycle 30 miles		116	.069			2.76	6.25	9.01	11.10
3484	cycle 40 miles		83	.096			3.86	8.75	12.61	15.50
3486	cycle 50 miles		83	.096			3.86	8.75	12.61	15.50
3494	45 MPH ave, cycle 8 miles		215	.037			1.49	3.38	4.87	5.95
3496	cycle 10 miles		198	.040			1.62	3.67	5.29	6.50
3498	cycle 20 miles		149	.054			2.15	4.88	7.03	8.60
3500	cycle 30 miles		116	.069			2.76	6.25	9.01	11.10
3502	cycle 40 miles		99	.081			3.24	7.35	10.59	12.95
3504	cycle 50 miles		83	.096			3.86	8.75	12.61	15.50
3506	50 MPH ave, cycle 10 miles		215	.037			1.49	3.38	4.87	5.95
3508	cycle 20 miles		165	.048			1.94	4.40	6.34	7.80
3510	cycle 30 miles		132	.061			2.43	5.50	7.93	9.70
3512	cycle 40 miles		99	.081			3.24	7.35	10.59	12.95
3514	cycle 50 miles		83	.096			3.86	8.75	12.61	15.50
3614	30 min. wait/Ld./Uld., 15 MPH, cycle 0.5 mile		248	.032			1.29	2.93	4.22	5.15
3616	cycle 1 mile		231	.035			1.39	3.14	4.53	5.55
3618	cycle 2 miles		198	.040			1.62	3.67	5.29	6.50
3620	cycle 4 miles		165	.048			1.94	4.40	6.34	7.80
3622	cycle 6 miles		149	.054			2.15	4.88	7.03	8.60
3624	cycle 8 miles		116	.069			2.76	6.25	9.01	11.10
3625	cycle 10 miles		116	.069			2.76	6.25	9.01	11.10
3626	20 MPH ave, cycle 0.5 mile		248	.032			1.29	2.93	4.22	5.15
3628	cycle 1 mile		231	.035			1.39	3.14	4.53	5.55
3630	cycle 2 miles		215	.037			1.49	3.38	4.87	5.95
3632	cycle 4 miles		182	.044			1.76	3.99	5.75	7.05
3634	cycle 6 miles		165	.048			1.94	4.40	6.34	7.80
3636	cycle 8 miles		149	.054			2.15	4.88	7.03	8.60
3638	cycle 10 miles		132	.061			2.43	5.50	7.93	9.70
3640	25 MPH ave, cycle 4 miles		198	.040			1.62	3.67	5.29	6.50

31 23 23.20 Hauling		Crew	Daily Output	Labor-Hours	Unit	Material	2015 Bare Costs Labor	2015 Bare Costs Equipment	Total	Total Incl O&P
3642	cycle 6 miles	B-34C	182	.044	L.C.Y.		1.76	3.99	5.75	7.05
3644	cycle 8 miles		149	.054			2.15	4.88	7.03	8.60
3646	cycle 10 miles		149	.054			2.15	4.88	7.03	8.60
3650	30 MPH ave, cycle 4 miles		198	.040			1.62	3.67	5.29	6.50
3652	cycle 6 miles		182	.044			1.76	3.99	5.75	7.05
3654	cycle 8 miles		165	.048			1.94	4.40	6.34	7.80
3656	cycle 10 miles		149	.054			2.15	4.88	7.03	8.60
3660	35 MPH ave, cycle 4 miles		215	.037			1.49	3.38	4.87	5.95
3662	cycle 6 miles		198	.040			1.62	3.67	5.29	6.50
3664	cycle 8 miles		182	.044			1.76	3.99	5.75	7.05
3666	cycle 10 miles		165	.048			1.94	4.40	6.34	7.80
3668	cycle 20 miles		116	.069			2.76	6.25	9.01	11.10
3670	cycle 30 miles		99	.081			3.24	7.35	10.59	12.95
3672	cycle 40 miles		83	.096			3.86	8.75	12.61	15.50
3674	40 MPH, cycle 6 miles		198	.040			1.62	3.67	5.29	6.50
3676	cycle 8 miles		182	.044			1.76	3.99	5.75	7.05
3678	cycle 10 miles		165	.048			1.94	4.40	6.34	7.80
3680	cycle 20 miles		132	.061			2.43	5.50	7.93	9.70
3682	cycle 30 miles		99	.081			3.24	7.35	10.59	12.95
3684	cycle 40 miles		83	.096			3.86	8.75	12.61	15.50
3686	cycle 50 miles		66	.121			4.85	11	15.85	19.45
3694	45 MPH ave, cycle 8 miles		198	.040			1.62	3.67	5.29	6.50
3696	cycle 10 miles		182	.044			1.76	3.99	5.75	7.05
3698	cycle 20 miles		132	.061			2.43	5.50	7.93	9.70
3700	cycle 30 miles		116	.069			2.76	6.25	9.01	11.10
3702	cycle 40 miles		83	.096			3.86	8.75	12.61	15.50
3704	cycle 50 miles		83	.096			3.86	8.75	12.61	15.50
3706	50 MPH ave, cycle 10 miles		182	.044			1.76	3.99	5.75	7.05
3708	cycle 20 miles		149	.054			2.15	4.88	7.03	8.60
3710	cycle 30 miles		116	.069			2.76	6.25	9.01	11.10
3712	cycle 40 miles		99	.081			3.24	7.35	10.59	12.95
3714	cycle 50 miles		83	.096			3.86	8.75	12.61	15.50
4014	20 C.Y. truck, 15 min. wait/Ld./Uld., 15 MPH, cycle 0.5 mile	B-34D	560	.014			.57	1.32	1.89	2.33
4016	cycle 1 mile		500	.016			.64	1.48	2.12	2.60
4018	cycle 2 miles		420	.019			.76	1.76	2.52	3.09
4020	cycle 4 miles		300	.027			1.07	2.47	3.54	4.33
4022	cycle 6 miles		240	.033			1.33	3.09	4.42	5.40
4024	cycle 8 miles		200	.040			1.60	3.71	5.31	6.50
4025	cycle 10 miles		160	.050			2	4.63	6.63	8.15
4026	20 MPH ave, cycle 0.5 mile		580	.014			.55	1.28	1.83	2.25
4028	cycle 1 mile		520	.015			.62	1.42	2.04	2.50
4030	cycle 2 miles		460	.017			.70	1.61	2.31	2.82
4032	cycle 4 miles		340	.024			.94	2.18	3.12	3.82
4034	cycle 6 miles		280	.029			1.14	2.65	3.79	4.64
4036	cycle 8 miles		240	.033			1.33	3.09	4.42	5.40
4038	cycle 10 miles		200	.040			1.60	3.71	5.31	6.50
4040	25 MPH ave, cycle 4 miles		380	.021			.84	1.95	2.79	3.41
4042	cycle 6 miles		320	.025			1	2.32	3.32	4.06
4044	cycle 8 miles		280	.029			1.14	2.65	3.79	4.64
4046	cycle 10 miles		240	.033			1.33	3.09	4.42	5.40
4050	30 MPH ave, cycle 4 miles		420	.019			.76	1.76	2.52	3.09
4052	cycle 6 miles		340	.024			.94	2.18	3.12	3.82
4054	cycle 8 miles		300	.027			1.07	2.47	3.54	4.33

31 23 Excavation and Fill

31 23 23 – Fill

31 23 23.20 Hauling		Crew	Daily Output	Labor-Hours	Unit	Material	2015 Bare Costs Labor	Equipment	Total	Total Incl O&P
4056	cycle 10 miles	B-34D	260	.031	L.C.Y.		1.23	2.85	4.08	5
4060	35 MPH ave, cycle 4 miles		440	.018			.73	1.68	2.41	2.95
4062	cycle 6 miles		380	.021			.84	1.95	2.79	3.41
4064	cycle 8 miles		320	.025			1	2.32	3.32	4.06
4066	cycle 10 miles		300	.027			1.07	2.47	3.54	4.33
4068	cycle 20 miles		180	.044			1.78	4.12	5.90	7.20
4070	cycle 30 miles		140	.057			2.29	5.30	7.59	9.25
4072	cycle 40 miles		100	.080			3.20	7.40	10.60	13
4074	40 MPH ave, cycle 6 miles		400	.020			.80	1.85	2.65	3.25
4076	cycle 8 miles		340	.024			.94	2.18	3.12	3.82
4078	cycle 10 miles		320	.025			1	2.32	3.32	4.06
4080	cycle 20 miles		200	.040			1.60	3.71	5.31	6.50
4082	cycle 30 miles		160	.050			2	4.63	6.63	8.15
4084	cycle 40 miles		120	.067			2.67	6.20	8.87	10.85
4086	cycle 50 miles		100	.080			3.20	7.40	10.60	13
4094	45 MPH ave, cycle 8 miles		360	.022			.89	2.06	2.95	3.61
4096	cycle 10 miles		340	.024			.94	2.18	3.12	3.82
4098	cycle 20 miles		220	.036			1.46	3.37	4.83	5.90
4100	cycle 30 miles		160	.050			2	4.63	6.63	8.15
4102	cycle 40 miles		140	.057			2.29	5.30	7.59	9.25
4104	cycle 50 miles		120	.067			2.67	6.20	8.87	10.85
4106	50 MPH ave, cycle 10 miles		340	.024			.94	2.18	3.12	3.82
4108	cycle 20 miles		240	.033			1.33	3.09	4.42	5.40
4110	cycle 30 miles		180	.044			1.78	4.12	5.90	7.20
4112	cycle 40 miles		140	.057			2.29	5.30	7.59	9.25
4114	cycle 50 miles		120	.067			2.67	6.20	8.87	10.85
4214	20 min. wait/Ld./Uld., 15 MPH, cycle 0.5 mile		440	.018			.73	1.68	2.41	2.95
4216	cycle 1 mile		400	.020			.80	1.85	2.65	3.25
4218	cycle 2 miles		340	.024			.94	2.18	3.12	3.82
4220	cycle 4 miles		260	.031			1.23	2.85	4.08	5
4222	cycle 6 miles		220	.036			1.46	3.37	4.83	5.90
4224	cycle 8 miles		180	.044			1.78	4.12	5.90	7.20
4225	cycle 10 miles		160	.050			2	4.63	6.63	8.15
4226	20 MPH ave, cycle 0.5 mile		440	.018			.73	1.68	2.41	2.95
4228	cycle 1 mile		420	.019			.76	1.76	2.52	3.09
4230	cycle 2 miles		360	.022			.89	2.06	2.95	3.61
4232	cycle 4 miles		300	.027			1.07	2.47	3.54	4.33
4234	cycle 6 miles		240	.033			1.33	3.09	4.42	5.40
4236	cycle 8 miles		220	.036			1.46	3.37	4.83	5.90
4238	cycle 10 miles		180	.044			1.78	4.12	5.90	7.20
4240	25 MPH ave, cycle 4 miles		320	.025			1	2.32	3.32	4.06
4242	cycle 6 miles		280	.029			1.14	2.65	3.79	4.64
4244	cycle 8 miles		240	.033			1.33	3.09	4.42	5.40
4246	cycle 10 miles		220	.036			1.46	3.37	4.83	5.90
4250	30 MPH ave, cycle 4 miles		340	.024			.94	2.18	3.12	3.82
4252	cycle 6 miles		300	.027			1.07	2.47	3.54	4.33
4254	cycle 8 miles		260	.031			1.23	2.85	4.08	5
4256	cycle 10 miles		240	.033			1.33	3.09	4.42	5.40
4260	35 MPH ave, cycle 4 miles		360	.022			.89	2.06	2.95	3.61
4262	cycle 6 miles		320	.025			1	2.32	3.32	4.06
4264	cycle 8 miles		280	.029			1.14	2.65	3.79	4.64
4266	cycle 10 miles		260	.031			1.23	2.85	4.08	5
4268	cycle 20 miles		180	.044			1.78	4.12	5.90	7.20

31 23 23.20 Hauling		Crew	Daily Output	Labor-Hours	Unit	Material	Labor	Equipment	Total	Total Incl O&P
							2015 Bare Costs			
4270	cycle 30 miles	B-34D	120	.067	L.C.Y.		2.67	6.20	8.87	10.85
4272	cycle 40 miles		100	.080			3.20	7.40	10.60	13
4274	40 MPH ave, cycle 6 miles		320	.025			1	2.32	3.32	4.06
4276	cycle 8 miles		300	.027			1.07	2.47	3.54	4.33
4278	cycle 10 miles		260	.031			1.23	2.85	4.08	5
4280	cycle 20 miles		180	.044			1.78	4.12	5.90	7.20
4282	cycle 30 miles		140	.057			2.29	5.30	7.59	9.25
4284	cycle 40 miles		120	.067			2.67	6.20	8.87	10.85
4286	cycle 50 miles		100	.080			3.20	7.40	10.60	13
4294	45 MPH ave, cycle 8 miles		300	.027			1.07	2.47	3.54	4.33
4296	cycle 10 miles		280	.029			1.14	2.65	3.79	4.64
4298	cycle 20 miles		200	.040			1.60	3.71	5.31	6.50
4300	cycle 30 miles		160	.050			2	4.63	6.63	8.15
4302	cycle 40 miles		120	.067			2.67	6.20	8.87	10.85
4304	cycle 50 miles		100	.080			3.20	7.40	10.60	13
4306	50 MPH ave., cycle 10 miles		300	.027			1.07	2.47	3.54	4.33
4308	cycle 20 miles		220	.036			1.46	3.37	4.83	5.90
4310	cycle 30 miles		180	.044			1.78	4.12	5.90	7.20
4312	cycle 40 miles		140	.057			2.29	5.30	7.59	9.25
4314	cycle 50 miles		120	.067			2.67	6.20	8.87	10.85
4414	25 min. wait/Ld./Uld., 15 MPH, cycle 0.5 mile		340	.024			.94	2.18	3.12	3.82
4416	cycle 1 mile		320	.025			1	2.32	3.32	4.06
4418	cycle 2 miles		280	.029			1.14	2.65	3.79	4.64
4420	cycle 4 miles		220	.036			1.46	3.37	4.83	5.90
4422	cycle 6 miles		200	.040			1.60	3.71	5.31	6.50
4424	cycle 8 miles		160	.050			2	4.63	6.63	8.15
4425	cycle 10 miles		140	.057			2.29	5.30	7.59	9.25
4426	20 MPH ave, cycle 0.5 mile		360	.022			.89	2.06	2.95	3.61
4428	cycle 1 mile		340	.024			.94	2.18	3.12	3.82
4430	cycle 2 miles		300	.027			1.07	2.47	3.54	4.33
4432	cycle 4 miles		260	.031			1.23	2.85	4.08	5
4434	cycle 6 miles		220	.036			1.46	3.37	4.83	5.90
4436	cycle 8 miles		200	.040			1.60	3.71	5.31	6.50
4438	cycle 10 miles		160	.050			2	4.63	6.63	8.15
4440	25 MPH ave, cycle 4 miles		280	.029			1.14	2.65	3.79	4.64
4442	cycle 6 miles		240	.033			1.33	3.09	4.42	5.40
4444	cycle 8 miles		220	.036			1.46	3.37	4.83	5.90
4446	cycle 10 miles		200	.040			1.60	3.71	5.31	6.50
4450	30 MPH ave, cycle 4 miles		280	.029			1.14	2.65	3.79	4.64
4452	cycle 6 miles		260	.031			1.23	2.85	4.08	5
4454	cycle 8 miles		220	.036			1.46	3.37	4.83	5.90
4456	cycle 10 miles		200	.040			1.60	3.71	5.31	6.50
4460	35 MPH ave, cycle 4 miles		300	.027			1.07	2.47	3.54	4.33
4462	cycle 6 miles		260	.031			1.23	2.85	4.08	5
4464	cycle 8 miles		240	.033			1.33	3.09	4.42	5.40
4466	cycle 10 miles		220	.036			1.46	3.37	4.83	5.90
4468	cycle 20 miles		160	.050			2	4.63	6.63	8.15
4470	cycle 30 miles		120	.067			2.67	6.20	8.87	10.85
4472	cycle 40 miles		100	.080			3.20	7.40	10.60	13
4474	40 MPH, cycle 6 miles		280	.029			1.14	2.65	3.79	4.64
4476	cycle 8 miles		260	.031			1.23	2.85	4.08	5
4478	cycle 10 miles		240	.033			1.33	3.09	4.42	5.40
4480	cycle 20 miles		160	.050			2	4.63	6.63	8.15

31 23 Excavation and Fill

31 23 23 – Fill

31 23 23.20 Hauling		Crew	Daily Output	Labor-Hours	Unit	Material	2015 Bare Costs Labor	Equipment	Total	Total Incl O&P
4482	cycle 30 miles	B-34D	140	.057	L.C.Y.		2.29	5.30	7.59	9.25
4484	cycle 40 miles		100	.080			3.20	7.40	10.60	13
4486	cycle 50 miles		100	.080			3.20	7.40	10.60	13
4494	45 MPH ave, cycle 8 miles		260	.031			1.23	2.85	4.08	5
4496	cycle 10 miles		240	.033			1.33	3.09	4.42	5.40
4498	cycle 20 miles		180	.044			1.78	4.12	5.90	7.20
4500	cycle 30 miles		140	.057			2.29	5.30	7.59	9.25
4502	cycle 40 miles		120	.067			2.67	6.20	8.87	10.85
4504	cycle 50 miles		100	.080			3.20	7.40	10.60	13
4506	50 MPH ave, cycle 10 miles		260	.031			1.23	2.85	4.08	5
4508	cycle 20 miles		200	.040			1.60	3.71	5.31	6.50
4510	cycle 30 miles		160	.050			2	4.63	6.63	8.15
4512	cycle 40 miles		120	.067			2.67	6.20	8.87	10.85
4514	cycle 50 miles		100	.080			3.20	7.40	10.60	13
4614	30 min. wait/Ld./Uld., 15 MPH, cycle 0.5 mile		300	.027			1.07	2.47	3.54	4.33
4616	cycle 1 mile		280	.029			1.14	2.65	3.79	4.64
4618	cycle 2 miles		240	.033			1.33	3.09	4.42	5.40
4620	cycle 4 miles		200	.040			1.60	3.71	5.31	6.50
4622	cycle 6 miles		180	.044			1.78	4.12	5.90	7.20
4624	cycle 8 miles		140	.057			2.29	5.30	7.59	9.25
4625	cycle 10 miles		140	.057			2.29	5.30	7.59	9.25
4626	20 MPH ave, cycle 0.5 mile		300	.027			1.07	2.47	3.54	4.33
4628	cycle 1 mile		280	.029			1.14	2.65	3.79	4.64
4630	cycle 2 miles		260	.031			1.23	2.85	4.08	5
4632	cycle 4 miles		220	.036			1.46	3.37	4.83	5.90
4634	cycle 6 miles		200	.040			1.60	3.71	5.31	6.50
4636	cycle 8 miles		180	.044			1.78	4.12	5.90	7.20
4638	cycle 10 miles		160	.050			2	4.63	6.63	8.15
4640	25 MPH ave, cycle 4 miles		240	.033			1.33	3.09	4.42	5.40
4642	cycle 6 miles		220	.036			1.46	3.37	4.83	5.90
4644	cycle 8 miles		180	.044			1.78	4.12	5.90	7.20
4646	cycle 10 miles		180	.044			1.78	4.12	5.90	7.20
4650	30 MPH ave, cycle 4 miles		240	.033			1.33	3.09	4.42	5.40
4652	cycle 6 miles		220	.036			1.46	3.37	4.83	5.90
4654	cycle 8 miles		200	.040			1.60	3.71	5.31	6.50
4656	cycle 10 miles		180	.044			1.78	4.12	5.90	7.20
4660	35 MPH ave, cycle 4 miles		260	.031			1.23	2.85	4.08	5
4662	cycle 6 miles		240	.033			1.33	3.09	4.42	5.40
4664	cycle 8 miles		220	.036			1.46	3.37	4.83	5.90
4666	cycle 10 miles		200	.040			1.60	3.71	5.31	6.50
4668	cycle 20 miles		140	.057			2.29	5.30	7.59	9.25
4670	cycle 30 miles		120	.067			2.67	6.20	8.87	10.85
4672	cycle 40 miles		100	.080			3.20	7.40	10.60	13
4674	40 MPH, cycle 6 miles		240	.033			1.33	3.09	4.42	5.40
4676	cycle 8 miles		220	.036			1.46	3.37	4.83	5.90
4678	cycle 10 miles		200	.040			1.60	3.71	5.31	6.50
4680	cycle 20 miles		160	.050			2	4.63	6.63	8.15
4682	cycle 30 miles		120	.067			2.67	6.20	8.87	10.85
4684	cycle 40 miles		100	.080			3.20	7.40	10.60	13
4686	cycle 50 miles		80	.100			4.01	9.25	13.26	16.25
4694	45 MPH ave, cycle 8 miles		220	.036			1.46	3.37	4.83	5.90
4696	cycle 10 miles		220	.036			1.46	3.37	4.83	5.90
4698	cycle 20 miles		160	.050			2	4.63	6.63	8.15

31 23 23.20 Hauling		Crew	Daily Output	Labor-Hours	Unit	Material	2015 Bare Costs Labor	2015 Bare Costs Equipment	Total	Total Incl O&P
4700	cycle 30 miles	B-34D	140	.057	L.C.Y.		2.29	5.30	7.59	9.25
4702	cycle 40 miles		100	.080			3.20	7.40	10.60	13
4704	cycle 50 miles		100	.080			3.20	7.40	10.60	13
4706	50 MPH ave, cycle 10 miles		220	.036			1.46	3.37	4.83	5.90
4708	cycle 20 miles		180	.044			1.78	4.12	5.90	7.20
4710	cycle 30 miles		140	.057			2.29	5.30	7.59	9.25
4712	cycle 40 miles		120	.067			2.67	6.20	8.87	10.85
4714	cycle 50 miles		100	.080			3.20	7.40	10.60	13
5000	22 C.Y. off-road, 15 min. wait/Ld./Uld., 5 MPH, cycle 2000 ft	B-34F	528	.015			.61	2.86	3.47	4.07
5010	cycle 3000 ft		484	.017			.66	3.12	3.78	4.44
5020	cycle 4000 ft		440	.018			.73	3.44	4.17	4.88
5030	cycle 0.5 mile		506	.016			.63	2.99	3.62	4.25
5040	cycle 1 mile		374	.021			.86	4.04	4.90	5.75
5050	cycle 2 miles		264	.030			1.21	5.75	6.96	8.15
5060	10 MPH, cycle 2000 ft		594	.013			.54	2.55	3.09	3.62
5070	cycle 3000 ft		572	.014			.56	2.64	3.20	3.76
5080	cycle 4000 ft		528	.015			.61	2.86	3.47	4.07
5090	cycle 0.5 mile		572	.014			.56	2.64	3.20	3.76
5100	cycle 1 mile		506	.016			.63	2.99	3.62	4.25
5110	cycle 2 miles		374	.021			.86	4.04	4.90	5.75
5120	cycle 4 miles		264	.030			1.21	5.75	6.96	8.15
5130	15 MPH, cycle 2000 ft		638	.013			.50	2.37	2.87	3.37
5140	cycle 3000 ft		594	.013			.54	2.55	3.09	3.62
5150	cycle 4000 ft		572	.014			.56	2.64	3.20	3.76
5160	cycle 0.5 mile		616	.013			.52	2.46	2.98	3.49
5170	cycle 1 mile		550	.015			.58	2.75	3.33	3.90
5180	cycle 2 miles		462	.017			.69	3.27	3.96	4.65
5190	cycle 4 miles		330	.024			.97	4.58	5.55	6.50
5200	20 MPH, cycle 2 miles		506	.016			.63	2.99	3.62	4.25
5210	cycle 4 miles		374	.021			.86	4.04	4.90	5.75
5220	25 MPH, cycle 2 miles		528	.015			.61	2.86	3.47	4.07
5230	cycle 4 miles		418	.019			.77	3.62	4.39	5.15
5300	20 min. wait/Ld./Uld., 5 MPH, cycle 2000 ft		418	.019			.77	3.62	4.39	5.15
5310	cycle 3000 ft		396	.020			.81	3.82	4.63	5.40
5320	cycle 4000 ft		352	.023			.91	4.30	5.21	6.10
5330	cycle 0.5 mile		396	.020			.81	3.82	4.63	5.40
5340	cycle 1 mile		330	.024			.97	4.58	5.55	6.50
5350	cycle 2 miles		242	.033			1.32	6.25	7.57	8.85
5360	10 MPH, cycle 2000 ft		462	.017			.69	3.27	3.96	4.65
5370	cycle 3000 ft		440	.018			.73	3.44	4.17	4.88
5380	cycle 4000 ft		418	.019			.77	3.62	4.39	5.15
5390	cycle 0.5 mile		462	.017			.69	3.27	3.96	4.65
5400	cycle 1 mile		396	.020			.81	3.82	4.63	5.40
5410	cycle 2 miles		330	.024			.97	4.58	5.55	6.50
5420	cycle 4 miles		242	.033			1.32	6.25	7.57	8.85
5430	15 MPH, cycle 2000 ft		484	.017			.66	3.12	3.78	4.44
5440	cycle 3000 ft		462	.017			.69	3.27	3.96	4.65
5450	cycle 4000 ft		462	.017			.69	3.27	3.96	4.65
5460	cycle 0.5 mile		484	.017			.66	3.12	3.78	4.44
5470	cycle 1 mile		440	.018			.73	3.44	4.17	4.88
5480	cycle 2 miles		374	.021			.86	4.04	4.90	5.75
5490	cycle 4 miles		286	.028			1.12	5.30	6.42	7.50
5500	20 MPH, cycle 2 miles		396	.020			.81	3.82	4.63	5.40

31 23 23 – Fill

31 23 23.20 Hauling		Crew	Daily Output	Labor-Hours	Unit	Material	2015 Bare Costs Labor	Equipment	Total	Total Incl O&P
5510	cycle 4 miles	B-34F	330	.024	L.C.Y.		.97	4.58	5.55	6.50
5520	25 MPH, cycle 2 miles		418	.019			.77	3.62	4.39	5.15
5530	cycle 4 miles		352	.023			.91	4.30	5.21	6.10
5600	25 min. wait/Ld./Uld., 5 MPH, cycle 2000 ft		352	.023			.91	4.30	5.21	6.10
5610	cycle 3000 ft		330	.024			.97	4.58	5.55	6.50
5620	cycle 4000 ft		308	.026			1.04	4.91	5.95	6.95
5630	cycle 0.5 mile		330	.024			.97	4.58	5.55	6.50
5640	cycle 1 mile		286	.028			1.12	5.30	6.42	7.50
5650	cycle 2 miles		220	.036			1.46	6.85	8.31	9.75
5660	10 MPH, cycle 2000 ft		374	.021			.86	4.04	4.90	5.75
5670	cycle 3000 ft		374	.021			.86	4.04	4.90	5.75
5680	cycle 4000 ft		352	.023			.91	4.30	5.21	6.10
5690	cycle 0.5 mile		374	.021			.86	4.04	4.90	5.75
5700	cycle 1 mile		330	.024			.97	4.58	5.55	6.50
5710	cycle 2 miles		286	.028			1.12	5.30	6.42	7.50
5720	cycle 4 miles		220	.036			1.46	6.85	8.31	9.75
5730	15 MPH, cycle 2000 ft		396	.020			.81	3.82	4.63	5.40
5740	cycle 3000 ft		374	.021			.86	4.04	4.90	5.75
5750	cycle 4000 ft		374	.021			.86	4.04	4.90	5.75
5760	cycle 0.5 mile		374	.021			.86	4.04	4.90	5.75
5770	cycle 1 mile		352	.023			.91	4.30	5.21	6.10
5780	cycle 2 miles		308	.026			1.04	4.91	5.95	6.95
5790	cycle 4 miles		242	.033			1.32	6.25	7.57	8.85
5800	20 MPH, cycle 2 miles		330	.024			.97	4.58	5.55	6.50
5810	cycle 4 miles		286	.028			1.12	5.30	6.42	7.50
5820	25 MPH, cycle 2 miles		352	.023			.91	4.30	5.21	6.10
5830	cycle 4 miles		308	.026			1.04	4.91	5.95	6.95
6000	34 C.Y. off-road, 15 min. wait/Ld./Uld., 5 MPH, cycle 2000 ft	B-34G	816	.010			.39	2.25	2.64	3.07
6010	cycle 3000 ft		748	.011			.43	2.46	2.89	3.35
6020	cycle 4000 ft		680	.012			.47	2.70	3.17	3.68
6030	cycle 0.5 mile		782	.010			.41	2.35	2.76	3.20
6040	cycle 1 mile		578	.014			.55	3.18	3.73	4.34
6050	cycle 2 miles		408	.020			.79	4.50	5.29	6.15
6060	10 MPH, cycle 2000 ft		918	.009			.35	2	2.35	2.73
6070	cycle 3000 ft		884	.009			.36	2.08	2.44	2.84
6080	cycle 4000 ft		816	.010			.39	2.25	2.64	3.07
6090	cycle 0.5 mile		884	.009			.36	2.08	2.44	2.84
6100	cycle 1 mile		782	.010			.41	2.35	2.76	3.20
6110	cycle 2 miles		578	.014			.55	3.18	3.73	4.34
6120	cycle 4 miles		408	.020			.79	4.50	5.29	6.15
6130	15 MPH, cycle 2000 ft		986	.008			.32	1.86	2.18	2.54
6140	cycle 3000 ft		918	.009			.35	2	2.35	2.73
6150	cycle 4000 ft		884	.009			.36	2.08	2.44	2.84
6160	cycle 0.5 mile		952	.008			.34	1.93	2.27	2.63
6170	cycle 1 mile		850	.009			.38	2.16	2.54	2.95
6180	cycle 2 miles		714	.011			.45	2.57	3.02	3.51
6190	cycle 4 miles		510	.016			.63	3.60	4.23	4.91
6200	20 MPH, cycle 2 miles		782	.010			.41	2.35	2.76	3.20
6210	cycle 4 miles		578	.014			.55	3.18	3.73	4.34
6220	25 MPH, cycle 2 miles		816	.010			.39	2.25	2.64	3.07
6230	cycle 4 miles		646	.012			.50	2.84	3.34	3.88
6300	20 min. wait/Ld./Uld., 5 MPH, cycle 2000 ft		646	.012			.50	2.84	3.34	3.88
6310	cycle 3000 ft		612	.013			.52	3	3.52	4.09

31 23 23.20 Hauling		Crew	Daily Output	Labor-Hours	Unit	Material	2015 Bare Costs Labor	Equipment	Total	Total Incl O&P
6320	cycle 4000 ft	B-34G	544	.015	L.C.Y.		.59	3.38	3.97	4.61
6330	cycle 0.5 mile		612	.013			.52	3	3.52	4.09
6340	cycle 1 mile		510	.016			.63	3.60	4.23	4.91
6350	cycle 2 miles		374	.021			.86	4.91	5.77	6.70
6360	10 MPH, cycle 2000 ft		714	.011			.45	2.57	3.02	3.51
6370	cycle 3000 ft		680	.012			.47	2.70	3.17	3.68
6380	cycle 4000 ft		646	.012			.50	2.84	3.34	3.88
6390	cycle 0.5 mile		714	.011			.45	2.57	3.02	3.51
6400	cycle 1 mile		612	.013			.52	3	3.52	4.09
6410	cycle 2 miles		510	.016			.63	3.60	4.23	4.91
6420	cycle 4 miles		374	.021			.86	4.91	5.77	6.70
6430	15 MPH, cycle 2000 ft		748	.011			.43	2.46	2.89	3.35
6440	cycle 3000 ft		714	.011			.45	2.57	3.02	3.51
6450	cycle 4000 ft		714	.011			.45	2.57	3.02	3.51
6460	cycle 0.5 mile		748	.011			.43	2.46	2.89	3.35
6470	cycle 1 mile		680	.012			.47	2.70	3.17	3.68
6480	cycle 2 miles		578	.014			.55	3.18	3.73	4.34
6490	cycle 4 miles		442	.018			.72	4.16	4.88	5.65
6500	20 MPH, cycle 2 miles		612	.013			.52	3	3.52	4.09
6510	cycle 4 miles		510	.016			.63	3.60	4.23	4.91
6520	25 MPH, cycle 2 miles		646	.012			.50	2.84	3.34	3.88
6530	cycle 4 miles		544	.015			.59	3.38	3.97	4.61
6600	25 min. wait/Ld./Uld., 5 MPH, cycle 2000 ft		544	.015			.59	3.38	3.97	4.61
6610	cycle 3000 ft		510	.016			.63	3.60	4.23	4.91
6620	cycle 4000 ft		476	.017			.67	3.86	4.53	5.25
6630	cycle 0.5 mile		510	.016			.63	3.60	4.23	4.91
6640	cycle 1 mile		442	.018			.72	4.16	4.88	5.65
6650	cycle 2 miles		340	.024			.94	5.40	6.34	7.35
6660	10 MPH, cycle 2000 ft		578	.014			.55	3.18	3.73	4.34
6670	cycle 3000 ft		578	.014			.55	3.18	3.73	4.34
6680	cycle 4000 ft		544	.015			.59	3.38	3.97	4.61
6690	cycle 0.5 mile		578	.014			.55	3.18	3.73	4.34
6700	cycle 1 mile		510	.016			.63	3.60	4.23	4.91
6710	cycle 2 miles		442	.018			.72	4.16	4.88	5.65
6720	cycle 4 miles		340	.024			.94	5.40	6.34	7.35
6730	15 MPH, cycle 2000 ft		612	.013			.52	3	3.52	4.09
6740	cycle 3000 ft		578	.014			.55	3.18	3.73	4.34
6750	cycle 4000 ft		578	.014			.55	3.18	3.73	4.34
6760	cycle 0.5 mile		612	.013			.52	3	3.52	4.09
6770	cycle 1 mile		544	.015			.59	3.38	3.97	4.61
6780	cycle 2 miles		476	.017			.67	3.86	4.53	5.25
6790	cycle 4 miles		374	.021			.86	4.91	5.77	6.70
6800	20 MPH, cycle 2 miles		510	.016			.63	3.60	4.23	4.91
6810	cycle 4 miles		442	.018			.72	4.16	4.88	5.65
6820	25 MPH, cycle 2 miles		544	.015			.59	3.38	3.97	4.61
6830	cycle 4 miles		476	.017			.67	3.86	4.53	5.25
7000	42 C.Y. off-road, 20 min. wait/Ld./Uld., 5 MPH, cycle 2000 ft	B-34H	798	.010			.40	2.34	2.74	3.18
7010	cycle 3000 ft		756	.011			.42	2.46	2.88	3.35
7020	cycle 4000 ft		672	.012			.48	2.77	3.25	3.77
7030	cycle 0.5 mile		756	.011			.42	2.46	2.88	3.35
7040	cycle 1 mile		630	.013			.51	2.96	3.47	4.02
7050	cycle 2 miles		462	.017			.69	4.03	4.72	5.50
7060	10 MPH, cycle 2000 ft		882	.009			.36	2.11	2.47	2.87

31 23 Excavation and Fill

31 23 23 – Fill

31 23 23.20 Hauling		Crew	Daily Output	Labor-Hours	Unit	Material	2015 Bare Costs Labor	Equipment	Total	Total Incl O&P
7070	cycle 3000 ft	B-34H	840	.010	L.C.Y.		.38	2.22	2.60	3.02
7080	cycle 4000 ft		798	.010			.40	2.34	2.74	3.18
7090	cycle 0.5 mile		882	.009			.36	2.11	2.47	2.87
7100	cycle 1 mile		798	.010			.40	2.34	2.74	3.18
7110	cycle 2 miles		630	.013			.51	2.96	3.47	4.02
7120	cycle 4 miles		462	.017			.69	4.03	4.72	5.50
7130	15 MPH, cycle 2000 ft		924	.009			.35	2.02	2.37	2.74
7140	cycle 3000 ft		882	.009			.36	2.11	2.47	2.87
7150	cycle 4000 ft		882	.009			.36	2.11	2.47	2.87
7160	cycle 0.5 mile		882	.009			.36	2.11	2.47	2.87
7170	cycle 1 mile		840	.010			.38	2.22	2.60	3.02
7180	cycle 2 miles		714	.011			.45	2.61	3.06	3.55
7190	cycle 4 miles		546	.015			.59	3.41	4	4.64
7200	20 MPH, cycle 2 miles		756	.011			.42	2.46	2.88	3.35
7210	cycle 4 miles		630	.013			.51	2.96	3.47	4.02
7220	25 MPH, cycle 2 miles		798	.010			.40	2.34	2.74	3.18
7230	cycle 4 miles		672	.012			.48	2.77	3.25	3.77
7300	25 min. wait/Ld./Uld., 5 MPH, cycle 2000 ft		672	.012			.48	2.77	3.25	3.77
7310	cycle 3000 ft		630	.013			.51	2.96	3.47	4.02
7320	cycle 4000 ft		588	.014			.55	3.17	3.72	4.31
7330	cycle 0.5 mile		630	.013			.51	2.96	3.47	4.02
7340	cycle 1 mile		546	.015			.59	3.41	4	4.64
7350	cycle 2 miles		378	.021			.85	4.93	5.78	6.70
7360	10 MPH, cycle 2000 ft		714	.011			.45	2.61	3.06	3.55
7370	cycle 3000 ft		714	.011			.45	2.61	3.06	3.55
7380	cycle 4000 ft		672	.012			.48	2.77	3.25	3.77
7390	cycle 0.5 mile		714	.011			.45	2.61	3.06	3.55
7400	cycle 1 mile		630	.013			.51	2.96	3.47	4.02
7410	cycle 2 miles		546	.015			.59	3.41	4	4.64
7420	cycle 4 miles		378	.021			.85	4.93	5.78	6.70
7430	15 MPH, cycle 2000 ft		756	.011			.42	2.46	2.88	3.35
7440	cycle 3000 ft		714	.011			.45	2.61	3.06	3.55
7450	cycle 4000 ft		714	.011			.45	2.61	3.06	3.55
7460	cycle 0.5 mile		714	.011			.45	2.61	3.06	3.55
7470	cycle 1 mile		672	.012			.48	2.77	3.25	3.77
7480	cycle 2 miles		588	.014			.55	3.17	3.72	4.31
7490	cycle 4 miles		462	.017			.69	4.03	4.72	5.50
7500	20 MPH, cycle 2 miles		630	.013			.51	2.96	3.47	4.02
7510	cycle 4 miles		546	.015			.59	3.41	4	4.64
7520	25 MPH, cycle 2 miles		672	.012			.48	2.77	3.25	3.77
7530	cycle 4 miles		588	.014			.55	3.17	3.72	4.31
8000	60 C.Y. off-road, 20 min. wait/Ld./Uld., 5 MPH, cycle 2000 ft	B-34J	1140	.007			.28	2.57	2.85	3.25
8010	cycle 3000 ft		1080	.007			.30	2.71	3.01	3.43
8020	cycle 4000 ft		960	.008			.33	3.05	3.38	3.85
8030	cycle 0.5 mile		1080	.007			.30	2.71	3.01	3.43
8040	cycle 1 mile		900	.009			.36	3.25	3.61	4.12
8050	cycle 2 miles		660	.012			.49	4.43	4.92	5.60
8060	10 MPH, cycle 2000 ft		1260	.006			.25	2.32	2.57	2.93
8070	cycle 3000 ft		1200	.007			.27	2.44	2.71	3.08
8080	cycle 4000 ft		1140	.007			.28	2.57	2.85	3.25
8090	cycle 0.5 mile		1260	.006			.25	2.32	2.57	2.93
8100	cycle 1 mile		1080	.007			.30	2.71	3.01	3.43
8110	cycle 2 miles		900	.009			.36	3.25	3.61	4.12

31 23 23.20 Hauling		Crew	Daily Output	Labor-Hours	Unit	Material	2015 Bare Costs Labor	Equipment	Total	Total Incl O&P
8120	cycle 4 miles	B-34J	660	.012	L.C.Y.		.49	4.43	4.92	5.60
8130	15 MPH, cycle 2000 ft		1320	.006			.24	2.22	2.46	2.81
8140	cycle 3000 ft		1260	.006			.25	2.32	2.57	2.93
8150	cycle 4000 ft		1260	.006			.25	2.32	2.57	2.93
8160	cycle 0.5 mile		1320	.006			.24	2.22	2.46	2.81
8170	cycle 1 mile		1200	.007			.27	2.44	2.71	3.08
8180	cycle 2 miles		1020	.008			.31	2.87	3.18	3.62
8190	cycle 4 miles		780	.010			.41	3.75	4.16	4.75
8200	20 MPH, cycle 2 miles		1080	.007			.30	2.71	3.01	3.43
8210	cycle 4 miles		900	.009			.36	3.25	3.61	4.12
8220	25 MPH, cycle 2 miles		1140	.007			.28	2.57	2.85	3.25
8230	cycle 4 miles		960	.008			.33	3.05	3.38	3.85
8300	25 min. wait/Ld./Uld., 5 MPH, cycle 2000 ft		960	.008			.33	3.05	3.38	3.85
8310	cycle 3000 ft		900	.009			.36	3.25	3.61	4.12
8320	cycle 4000 ft		840	.010			.38	3.48	3.86	4.41
8330	cycle 0.5 mile		900	.009			.36	3.25	3.61	4.12
8340	cycle 1 mile		780	.010			.41	3.75	4.16	4.75
8350	cycle 2 miles		600	.013			.53	4.87	5.40	6.15
8360	10 MPH, cycle 2000 ft		1020	.008			.31	2.87	3.18	3.62
8370	cycle 3000 ft		1020	.008			.31	2.87	3.18	3.62
8380	cycle 4000 ft		960	.008			.33	3.05	3.38	3.85
8390	cycle 0.5 mile		1020	.008			.31	2.87	3.18	3.62
8400	cycle 1 mile		900	.009			.36	3.25	3.61	4.12
8410	cycle 2 miles		780	.010			.41	3.75	4.16	4.75
8420	cycle 4 miles		600	.013			.53	4.87	5.40	6.15
8430	15 MPH, cycle 2000 ft		1080	.007			.30	2.71	3.01	3.43
8440	cycle 3000 ft		1020	.008			.31	2.87	3.18	3.62
8450	cycle 4000 ft		1020	.008			.31	2.87	3.18	3.62
8460	cycle 0.5 mile		1080	.007			.30	2.71	3.01	3.43
8470	cycle 1 mile		960	.008			.33	3.05	3.38	3.85
8480	cycle 2 miles		840	.010			.38	3.48	3.86	4.41
8490	cycle 4 miles		660	.012			.49	4.43	4.92	5.60
8500	20 MPH, cycle 2 miles		900	.009			.36	3.25	3.61	4.12
8510	cycle 4 miles		780	.010			.41	3.75	4.16	4.75
8520	25 MPH, cycle 2 miles		960	.008			.33	3.05	3.38	3.85
8530	cycle 4 miles		840	.010			.38	3.48	3.86	4.41
9014	18 C.Y. truck, 8 wheels,15 min. wait/Ld./Uld.,15 MPH, cycle 0.5 mi.	B-34I	504	.016			.64	1.72	2.36	2.86
9016	cycle 1 mile		450	.018			.71	1.93	2.64	3.20
9018	cycle 2 miles		378	.021			.85	2.30	3.15	3.81
9020	cycle 4 miles		270	.030			1.19	3.22	4.41	5.35
9022	cycle 6 miles		216	.037			1.48	4.02	5.50	6.65
9024	cycle 8 miles		180	.044			1.78	4.83	6.61	8
9025	cycle 10 miles		144	.056			2.23	6.05	8.28	10
9026	20 MPH ave, cycle 0.5 mile		522	.015			.61	1.67	2.28	2.76
9028	cycle 1 mile		468	.017			.68	1.86	2.54	3.07
9030	cycle 2 miles		414	.019			.77	2.10	2.87	3.48
9032	cycle 4 miles		324	.025			.99	2.68	3.67	4.45
9034	cycle 6 miles		252	.032			1.27	3.45	4.72	5.70
9036	cycle 8 miles		216	.037			1.48	4.02	5.50	6.65
9038	cycle 10 miles		180	.044			1.78	4.83	6.61	8
9040	25 MPH ave, cycle 4 miles		342	.023			.94	2.54	3.48	4.21
9042	cycle 6 miles		288	.028			1.11	3.02	4.13	5
9044	cycle 8 miles		252	.032			1.27	3.45	4.72	5.70

31 23 23 – Fill

31 23 23.20 **Hauling**	Crew	Daily Output	Labor-Hours	Unit	Material	2015 Bare Costs Labor	2015 Bare Costs Equipment	Total	Total Incl O&P
9046	cycle 10 miles	B-34I	216	.037	L.C.Y.		1.48	4.02	5.50	6.65
9050	30 MPH ave, cycle 4 miles		378	.021			.85	2.30	3.15	3.81
9052	cycle 6 miles		324	.025			.99	2.68	3.67	4.45
9054	cycle 8 miles		270	.030			1.19	3.22	4.41	5.35
9056	cycle 10 miles		234	.034			1.37	3.71	5.08	6.15
9060	35 MPH ave, cycle 4 miles		396	.020			.81	2.19	3	3.63
9062	cycle 6 miles		342	.023			.94	2.54	3.48	4.21
9064	cycle 8 miles		288	.028			1.11	3.02	4.13	5
9066	cycle 10 miles		270	.030			1.19	3.22	4.41	5.35
9068	cycle 20 miles		162	.049			1.98	5.35	7.33	8.90
9070	cycle 30 miles		126	.063			2.54	6.90	9.44	11.45
9072	cycle 40 miles		90	.089			3.56	9.65	13.21	16
9074	40 MPH ave, cycle 6 miles		360	.022			.89	2.41	3.30	4.01
9076	cycle 8 miles		324	.025			.99	2.68	3.67	4.45
9078	cycle 10 miles		288	.028			1.11	3.02	4.13	5
9080	cycle 20 miles		180	.044			1.78	4.83	6.61	8
9082	cycle 30 miles		144	.056			2.23	6.05	8.28	10
9084	cycle 40 miles		108	.074			2.97	8.05	11.02	13.35
9086	cycle 50 miles		90	.089			3.56	9.65	13.21	16
9094	45 MPH ave, cycle 8 miles		324	.025			.99	2.68	3.67	4.45
9096	cycle 10 miles		306	.026			1.05	2.84	3.89	4.70
9098	cycle 20 miles		198	.040			1.62	4.39	6.01	7.30
9100	cycle 30 miles		144	.056			2.23	6.05	8.28	10
9102	cycle 40 miles		126	.063			2.54	6.90	9.44	11.45
9104	cycle 50 miles		108	.074			2.97	8.05	11.02	13.35
9106	50 MPH ave, cycle 10 miles		324	.025			.99	2.68	3.67	4.45
9108	cycle 20 miles		216	.037			1.48	4.02	5.50	6.65
9110	cycle 30 miles		162	.049			1.98	5.35	7.33	8.90
9112	cycle 40 miles		126	.063			2.54	6.90	9.44	11.45
9114	cycle 50 miles		108	.074			2.97	8.05	11.02	13.35
9214	20 min. wait/Ld./Uld.,15 MPH, cycle 0.5 mi.		396	.020			.81	2.19	3	3.63
9216	cycle 1 mile		360	.022			.89	2.41	3.30	4.01
9218	cycle 2 miles		306	.026			1.05	2.84	3.89	4.70
9220	cycle 4 miles		234	.034			1.37	3.71	5.08	6.15
9222	cycle 6 miles		198	.040			1.62	4.39	6.01	7.30
9224	cycle 8 miles		162	.049			1.98	5.35	7.33	8.90
9225	cycle 10 miles		144	.056			2.23	6.05	8.28	10
9226	20 MPH ave, cycle 0.5 mile		396	.020			.81	2.19	3	3.63
9228	cycle 1 mile		378	.021			.85	2.30	3.15	3.81
9230	cycle 2 miles		324	.025			.99	2.68	3.67	4.45
9232	cycle 4 miles		270	.030			1.19	3.22	4.41	5.35
9234	cycle 6 miles		216	.037			1.48	4.02	5.50	6.65
9236	cycle 8 miles		198	.040			1.62	4.39	6.01	7.30
9238	cycle 10 miles		162	.049			1.98	5.35	7.33	8.90
9240	25 MPH ave, cycle 4 miles		288	.028			1.11	3.02	4.13	5
9242	cycle 6 miles		252	.032			1.27	3.45	4.72	5.70
9244	cycle 8 miles		216	.037			1.48	4.02	5.50	6.65
9246	cycle 10 miles		198	.040			1.62	4.39	6.01	7.30
9250	30 MPH ave, cycle 4 miles		306	.026			1.05	2.84	3.89	4.70
9252	cycle 6 miles		270	.030			1.19	3.22	4.41	5.35
9254	cycle 8 miles		234	.034			1.37	3.71	5.08	6.15
9256	cycle 10 miles		216	.037			1.48	4.02	5.50	6.65
9260	35 MPH ave, cycle 4 miles		324	.025			.99	2.68	3.67	4.45

31 23 23.20 Hauling		Crew	Daily Output	Labor-Hours	Unit	Material	2015 Bare Costs Labor	2015 Bare Costs Equipment	Total	Total Incl O&P
9262	cycle 6 miles	B-34I	288	.028	L.C.Y.		1.11	3.02	4.13	5
9264	cycle 8 miles		252	.032			1.27	3.45	4.72	5.70
9266	cycle 10 miles		234	.034			1.37	3.71	5.08	6.15
9268	cycle 20 miles		162	.049			1.98	5.35	7.33	8.90
9270	cycle 30 miles		108	.074			2.97	8.05	11.02	13.35
9272	cycle 40 miles		90	.089			3.56	9.65	13.21	16
9274	40 MPH ave, cycle 6 miles		288	.028			1.11	3.02	4.13	5
9276	cycle 8 miles		270	.030			1.19	3.22	4.41	5.35
9278	cycle 10 miles		234	.034			1.37	3.71	5.08	6.15
9280	cycle 20 miles		162	.049			1.98	5.35	7.33	8.90
9282	cycle 30 miles		126	.063			2.54	6.90	9.44	11.45
9284	cycle 40 miles		108	.074			2.97	8.05	11.02	13.35
9286	cycle 50 miles		90	.089			3.56	9.65	13.21	16
9294	45 MPH ave, cycle 8 miles		270	.030			1.19	3.22	4.41	5.35
9296	cycle 10 miles		252	.032			1.27	3.45	4.72	5.70
9298	cycle 20 miles		180	.044			1.78	4.83	6.61	8
9300	cycle 30 miles		144	.056			2.23	6.05	8.28	10
9302	cycle 40 miles		108	.074			2.97	8.05	11.02	13.35
9304	cycle 50 miles		90	.089			3.56	9.65	13.21	16
9306	50 MPH ave, cycle 10 miles		270	.030			1.19	3.22	4.41	5.35
9308	cycle 20 miles		198	.040			1.62	4.39	6.01	7.30
9310	cycle 30 miles		144	.056			2.23	6.05	8.28	10
9312	cycle 40 miles		126	.063			2.54	6.90	9.44	11.45
9314	cycle 50 miles		108	.074			2.97	8.05	11.02	13.35
9414	25 min. wait/Ld./Uld.,15 MPH, cycle 0.5 mi.		306	.026			1.05	2.84	3.89	4.70
9416	cycle 1 mile		288	.028			1.11	3.02	4.13	5
9418	cycle 2 miles		252	.032			1.27	3.45	4.72	5.70
9420	cycle 4 miles		198	.040			1.62	4.39	6.01	7.30
9422	cycle 6 miles		180	.044			1.78	4.83	6.61	8
9424	cycle 8 miles		144	.056			2.23	6.05	8.28	10
9425	cycle 10 miles		126	.063			2.54	6.90	9.44	11.45
9426	20 MPH ave, cycle 0.5 mile		324	.025			.99	2.68	3.67	4.45
9428	cycle 1 mile		306	.026			1.05	2.84	3.89	4.70
9430	cycle 2 miles		270	.030			1.19	3.22	4.41	5.35
9432	cycle 4 miles		234	.034			1.37	3.71	5.08	6.15
9434	cycle 6 miles		198	.040			1.62	4.39	6.01	7.30
9436	cycle 8 miles		180	.044			1.78	4.83	6.61	8
9438	cycle 10 miles		144	.056			2.23	6.05	8.28	10
9440	25 MPH ave, cycle 4 miles		252	.032			1.27	3.45	4.72	5.70
9442	cycle 6 miles		216	.037			1.48	4.02	5.50	6.65
9444	cycle 8 miles		198	.040			1.62	4.39	6.01	7.30
9446	cycle 10 miles		180	.044			1.78	4.83	6.61	8
9450	30 MPH ave, cycle 4 miles		252	.032			1.27	3.45	4.72	5.70
9452	cycle 6 miles		234	.034			1.37	3.71	5.08	6.15
9454	cycle 8 miles		198	.040			1.62	4.39	6.01	7.30
9456	cycle 10 miles		180	.044			1.78	4.83	6.61	8
9460	35 MPH ave, cycle 4 miles		270	.030			1.19	3.22	4.41	5.35
9462	cycle 6 miles		234	.034			1.37	3.71	5.08	6.15
9464	cycle 8 miles		216	.037			1.48	4.02	5.50	6.65
9466	cycle 10 miles		198	.040			1.62	4.39	6.01	7.30
9468	cycle 20 miles		144	.056			2.23	6.05	8.28	10
9470	cycle 30 miles		108	.074			2.97	8.05	11.02	13.35
9472	cycle 40 miles		90	.089			3.56	9.65	13.21	16

31 23 23 – Fill

31 23 23.20 Hauling		Crew	Daily Output	Labor-Hours	Unit	Material	2015 Bare Costs		Total	Total Incl O&P
							Labor	Equipment		
9474	40 MPH ave, cycle 6 miles	B-34I	252	.032	L.C.Y.		1.27	3.45	4.72	5.70
9476	cycle 8 miles		234	.034			1.37	3.71	5.08	6.15
9478	cycle 10 miles		216	.037			1.48	4.02	5.50	6.65
9480	cycle 20 miles		144	.056			2.23	6.05	8.28	10
9482	cycle 30 miles		126	.063			2.54	6.90	9.44	11.45
9484	cycle 40 miles		90	.089			3.56	9.65	13.21	16
9486	cycle 50 miles		90	.089			3.56	9.65	13.21	16
9494	45 MPH ave, cycle 8 miles		234	.034			1.37	3.71	5.08	6.15
9496	cycle 10 miles		216	.037			1.48	4.02	5.50	6.65
9498	cycle 20 miles		162	.049			1.98	5.35	7.33	8.90
9500	cycle 30 miles		126	.063			2.54	6.90	9.44	11.45
9502	cycle 40 miles		108	.074			2.97	8.05	11.02	13.35
9504	cycle 50 miles		90	.089			3.56	9.65	13.21	16
9506	50 MPH ave, cycle 10 miles		234	.034			1.37	3.71	5.08	6.15
9508	cycle 20 miles		180	.044			1.78	4.83	6.61	8
9510	cycle 30 miles		144	.056			2.23	6.05	8.28	10
9512	cycle 40 miles		108	.074			2.97	8.05	11.02	13.35
9514	cycle 50 miles		90	.089			3.56	9.65	13.21	16
9614	30 min. wait/Ld./Uld.,15 MPH, cycle 0.5 mi.		270	.030			1.19	3.22	4.41	5.35
9616	cycle 1 mile		252	.032			1.27	3.45	4.72	5.70
9618	cycle 2 miles		216	.037			1.48	4.02	5.50	6.65
9620	cycle 4 miles		180	.044			1.78	4.83	6.61	8
9622	cycle 6 miles		162	.049			1.98	5.35	7.33	8.90
9624	cycle 8 miles		126	.063			2.54	6.90	9.44	11.45
9625	cycle 10 miles		126	.063			2.54	6.90	9.44	11.45
9626	20 MPH ave, cycle 0.5 mile		270	.030			1.19	3.22	4.41	5.35
9628	cycle 1 mile		252	.032			1.27	3.45	4.72	5.70
9630	cycle 2 miles		234	.034			1.37	3.71	5.08	6.15
9632	cycle 4 miles		198	.040			1.62	4.39	6.01	7.30
9634	cycle 6 miles		180	.044			1.78	4.83	6.61	8
9636	cycle 8 miles		162	.049			1.98	5.35	7.33	8.90
9638	cycle 10 miles		144	.056			2.23	6.05	8.28	10
9640	25 MPH ave, cycle 4 miles		216	.037			1.48	4.02	5.50	6.65
9642	cycle 6 miles		198	.040			1.62	4.39	6.01	7.30
9644	cycle 8 miles		180	.044			1.78	4.83	6.61	8
9646	cycle 10 miles		162	.049			1.98	5.35	7.33	8.90
9650	30 MPH ave, cycle 4 miles		216	.037			1.48	4.02	5.50	6.65
9652	cycle 6 miles		198	.040			1.62	4.39	6.01	7.30
9654	cycle 8 miles		180	.044			1.78	4.83	6.61	8
9656	cycle 10 miles		162	.049			1.98	5.35	7.33	8.90
9660	35 MPH ave, cycle 4 miles		234	.034			1.37	3.71	5.08	6.15
9662	cycle 6 miles		216	.037			1.48	4.02	5.50	6.65
9664	cycle 8 miles		198	.040			1.62	4.39	6.01	7.30
9666	cycle 10 miles		180	.044			1.78	4.83	6.61	8
9668	cycle 20 miles		126	.063			2.54	6.90	9.44	11.45
9670	cycle 30 miles		108	.074			2.97	8.05	11.02	13.35
9672	cycle 40 miles		90	.089			3.56	9.65	13.21	16
9674	40 MPH ave, cycle 6 miles		216	.037			1.48	4.02	5.50	6.65
9676	cycle 8 miles		198	.040			1.62	4.39	6.01	7.30
9678	cycle 10 miles		180	.044			1.78	4.83	6.61	8
9680	cycle 20 miles		144	.056			2.23	6.05	8.28	10
9682	cycle 30 miles		108	.074			2.97	8.05	11.02	13.35
9684	cycle 40 miles		90	.089			3.56	9.65	13.21	16

31 23 23.20 Hauling

	Crew	Daily Output	Labor-Hours	Unit	Material	2015 Bare Costs Labor	2015 Bare Costs Equipment	Total	Total Incl O&P
9686	cycle 50 miles	B-34I	72	.111	L.C.Y.		4.45	12.05	16.50	20
9694	45 MPH ave, cycle 8 miles		216	.037			1.48	4.02	5.50	6.65
9696	cycle 10 miles		198	.040			1.62	4.39	6.01	7.30
9698	cycle 20 miles		144	.056			2.23	6.05	8.28	10
9700	cycle 30 miles		126	.063			2.54	6.90	9.44	11.45
9702	cycle 40 miles		108	.074			2.97	8.05	11.02	13.35
9704	cycle 50 miles		90	.089			3.56	9.65	13.21	16
9706	50 MPH ave, cycle 10 miles		198	.040			1.62	4.39	6.01	7.30
9708	cycle 20 miles		162	.049			1.98	5.35	7.33	8.90
9710	cycle 30 miles		126	.063			2.54	6.90	9.44	11.45
9712	cycle 40 miles		108	.074			2.97	8.05	11.02	13.35
9714	cycle 50 miles		90	.089			3.56	9.65	13.21	16

31 23 23.23 Compaction

	Crew	Daily Output	Labor-Hours	Unit	Material	2015 Bare Costs Labor	2015 Bare Costs Equipment	Total	Total Incl O&P
0010	**COMPACTION** R312323-30									
5000	Riding, vibrating roller, 6" lifts, 2 passes	B-10Y	3000	.004	E.C.Y.		.19	.18	.37	.48
5020	3 passes		2300	.005			.24	.24	.48	.63
5040	4 passes		1900	.006			.29	.29	.58	.77
5050	8" lifts, 2 passes		4100	.003			.14	.13	.27	.36
5060	12" lifts, 2 passes		5200	.002			.11	.11	.22	.28
5080	3 passes		3500	.003			.16	.16	.32	.41
5100	4 passes		2600	.005			.21	.21	.42	.56
5600	Sheepsfoot or wobbly wheel roller, 6" lifts, 2 passes	B-10G	2400	.005			.23	.50	.73	.90
5620	3 passes		1735	.007			.32	.70	1.02	1.26
5640	4 passes		1300	.009			.43	.93	1.36	1.67
5680	12" lifts, 2 passes		5200	.002			.11	.23	.34	.42
5700	3 passes		3500	.003			.16	.34	.50	.62
5720	4 passes		2600	.005			.21	.46	.67	.84
6000	Towed sheepsfoot or wobbly wheel roller, 6" lifts, 2 passes	B-10D	10000	.001			.06	.18	.24	.28
6020	3 passes		2000	.006			.28	.91	1.19	1.42
6030	4 passes		1500	.008			.37	1.21	1.58	1.89
6050	12" lifts, 2 passes		6000	.002			.09	.30	.39	.47
6060	3 passes		4000	.003			.14	.45	.59	.71
6070	4 passes		3000	.004			.19	.60	.79	.94
6200	Vibrating roller, 6" lifts, 2 passes	B-10C	2600	.005			.21	.69	.90	1.09
6210	3 passes		1735	.007			.32	1.03	1.35	1.62
6220	4 passes		1300	.009			.43	1.37	1.80	2.16
6250	12" lifts, 2 passes		5200	.002			.11	.34	.45	.54
6260	3 passes		3465	.003			.16	.51	.67	.81
6270	4 passes		2600	.005			.21	.69	.90	1.09
7000	Walk behind, vibrating plate 18" wide, 6" lifts, 2 passes	A-1D	200	.040			1.50	.18	1.68	2.51
7020	3 passes		185	.043			1.63	.20	1.83	2.72
7040	4 passes		140	.057			2.15	.26	2.41	3.59
7200	12" lifts, 2 passes, 21" wide	A-1E	560	.014			.54	.08	.62	.92
7220	3 passes		375	.021			.80	.12	.92	1.37
7240	4 passes		280	.029			1.07	.17	1.24	1.83
7500	Vibrating roller 24" wide, 6" lifts, 2 passes	B-10A	420	.029			1.32	.43	1.75	2.48
7520	3 passes		280	.043			1.98	.64	2.62	3.73
7540	4 passes		210	.057			2.64	.86	3.50	4.97
7600	12" lifts, 2 passes		840	.014			.66	.21	.87	1.25
7620	3 passes		560	.021			.99	.32	1.31	1.86
7640	4 passes		420	.029			1.32	.43	1.75	2.48
8000	Rammer tamper, 6" to 11", 4" lifts, 2 passes	A-1F	130	.062			2.31	.38	2.69	3.98

31 23 Excavation and Fill

31 23 23 – Fill

31 23 23.23 Compaction

31 23 23.23 Compaction		Crew	Daily Output	Labor-Hours	Unit	Material	2015 Bare Costs Labor	2015 Bare Costs Equipment	Total	Total Incl O&P
8050	3 passes	A-1F	97	.082	E.C.Y.		3.10	.52	3.62	5.35
8100	4 passes		65	.123			4.63	.77	5.40	7.95
8200	8" lifts, 2 passes		260	.031			1.16	.19	1.35	1.99
8250	3 passes		195	.041			1.54	.26	1.80	2.65
8300	4 passes		130	.062			2.31	.38	2.69	3.98
8400	13" to 18", 4" lifts, 2 passes	A-1G	390	.021			.77	.14	.91	1.35
8450	3 passes		290	.028			1.04	.19	1.23	1.81
8500	4 passes		195	.041			1.54	.29	1.83	2.69
8600	8" lifts, 2 passes		780	.010			.39	.07	.46	.67
8650	3 passes		585	.014			.51	.10	.61	.90
8700	4 passes		390	.021			.77	.14	.91	1.35
9000	Water, 3000 gal. truck, 3 mile haul	B-45	1888	.008		1.22	.38	.48	2.08	2.45
9010	6 mile haul		1444	.011		1.22	.50	.63	2.35	2.79
9020	12 mile haul		1000	.016		1.22	.73	.91	2.86	3.44
9030	6000 gal. wagon, 3 mile haul	B-59	2000	.004		1.22	.16	.25	1.63	1.86
9040	6 mile haul	"	1600	.005		1.22	.20	.31	1.73	1.98

31 23 23.24 Compaction, Structural

31 23 23.24 Compaction, Structural		Crew	Daily Output	Labor-Hours	Unit	Material	2015 Bare Costs Labor	2015 Bare Costs Equipment	Total	Total Incl O&P
0010	**COMPACTION, STRUCTURAL**									
0020	Steel wheel tandem roller, 5 tons	B-10E	8	1.500	Hr.		69.50	19.70	89.20	128
0100	10 tons	B-10F	8	1.500	"		69.50	29.50	99	139
0300	Sheepsfoot or wobbly wheel roller, 8" lifts, common fill	B-10G	1300	.009	E.C.Y.		.43	.93	1.36	1.67
0400	Select fill	"	1500	.008	"		.37	.80	1.17	1.44
0420	Static roller, riding 33" diam.	B-10A	2800	.004	S.Y.		.20	.06	.26	.37
0600	Vibratory plate, 8" lifts, common fill	A-1D	200	.040	E.C.Y.		1.50	.18	1.68	2.51
0700	Select fill	"	216	.037	"		1.39	.17	1.56	2.32

31 25 Erosion and Sedimentation Controls

31 25 14 – Stabilization Measures for Erosion and Sedimentation Control

31 25 14.16 Rolled Erosion Control Mats and Blankets

31 25 14.16 Rolled Erosion Control Mats and Blankets			Crew	Daily Output	Labor-Hours	Unit	Material	2015 Bare Costs Labor	2015 Bare Costs Equipment	Total	Total Incl O&P
0010	**ROLLED EROSION CONTROL MATS AND BLANKETS**										
0020	Jute mesh, 100 S.Y. per roll, 4' wide, stapled	G	B-80A	2400	.010	S.Y.	1.03	.38	.13	1.54	1.85
0060	Polyethylene 3 dimensional geomatrix, 50 mil thick	G		700	.034		2.28	1.29	.43	4	4.97
0062	120 mil thick	G		515	.047		2.53	1.75	.59	4.87	6.15
0068	Slope stakes (placed @ 3' - 5' intervals)	G				Ea.	.12			.12	.13
0070	Paper biodegradable mesh	G	B-1	2500	.010	S.Y.	.11	.37		.48	.69
0080	Paper mulch	G	B-64	20000	.001		.11	.03	.02	.16	.19
0100	Plastic netting, stapled, 2" x 1" mesh, 20 mil	G	B-1	2500	.010		.24	.37		.61	.83
0120	Revegetation mat, webbed	G	2 Clab	1000	.016		4.48	.60		5.08	5.85
0160	Underdrain fabric, 18" x 100' roll	G	"	32	.500	Roll	27	18.80		45.80	58.50
0200	Polypropylene mesh, stapled, 6.5 oz./S.Y.	G	B-1	2500	.010	S.Y.	2.30	.37		2.67	3.10
0300	Tobacco netting, or jute mesh #2, stapled	G	"	2500	.010		.19	.37		.56	.78
0400	Soil sealant, liquid sprayed from truck	G	B-81	5000	.005		.43	.21	.14	.78	.93
1000	Silt fence, install and maintain, remove	G	B-62	1300	.018	L.F.	.72	.76	.13	1.61	2.11
1100	Allow 25% per month for maintenance; 6-month max life										
1130	Cellular confinement, poly, 3-dimen, 8' x 20' panels, 4" deep cell	G	B-6	1600	.015	S.F.	2	.62	.23	2.85	3.40
1140	8" deep cells	G	"	1200	.020	"	2.72	.83	.30	3.85	4.58
1200	Place and remove hay bales	G	A-2	3	8	Ton	246	305	82	633	825
1250	Hay bales, staked	G	"	2500	.010	L.F.	9.85	.37	.10	10.32	11.45
1300	Soil cement, 7% portland cement	G	B-70A	40	1	E.C.Y.	12.05	48	63	123.05	155
1305	For less than 3 To 1 slope, add							15%			
1310	For greater than 3 To 1 slope, add							25%			

For customer support on your Site Work & Landscape Cost Data, call 877.737.1594.

325

31 25 Erosion and Sedimentation Controls

31 25 14 – Stabilization Measures for Erosion and Sedimentation Control

31 25 14.16 Rolled Erosion Control Mats and Blankets		Crew	Daily Output	Labor-Hours	Unit	Material	2015 Bare Costs Labor	Equipment	Total	Total Incl O&P
1400	Barriers, w/degradable component, 3' H, incl wd stakes	[G] 2 Clab	1600	.010	L.F.	3.25	.38		3.63	4.16

31 31 Soil Treatment

31 31 16 – Termite Control

31 31 16.13 Chemical Termite Control

		Crew	Daily Output	Labor-Hours	Unit	Material	2015 Bare Costs Labor	Equipment	Total	Total Incl O&P
0010	**CHEMICAL TERMITE CONTROL**									
0020	Slab and walls, residential	1 Skwk	1200	.007	SF Flr.	.32	.32		.64	.85
0030	SS mesh, no chemicals, avg 1400 S.F. home, min	[G]	1000	.008		.32	.39		.71	.95
0040	Max	[G]	500	.016		.32	.78		1.10	1.55
0100	Commercial, minimum		2496	.003		.33	.16		.49	.60
0200	Maximum		1645	.005		.50	.24		.74	.91
0400	Insecticides for termite control, minimum		14.20	.563	Gal.	68.50	27.50		96	118
0500	Maximum		11	.727	"	117	35.50		152.50	184
3000	Soil poisoning (sterilization)	1 Clab	4496	.002	S.F.	.44	.07		.51	.58
3100	Herbicide application from truck	B-59	19000	.001	S.Y.		.02	.03	.05	.06

31 32 Soil Stabilization

31 32 13 – Soil Mixing Stabilization

31 32 13.13 Asphalt Soil Stabilization

		Crew	Daily Output	Labor-Hours	Unit	Material	2015 Bare Costs Labor	Equipment	Total	Total Incl O&P
0010	**ASPHALT SOIL STABILIZATION**									
0011	Including scarifying and compaction									
0020	Asphalt, 1-1/2" deep, 1/2 gal/S.Y.	B-75	4000	.014	S.Y.	.95	.64	1.50	3.09	3.67
0040	3/4 gal/S.Y.		4000	.014		1.43	.64	1.50	3.57	4.19
0100	3" deep, 1 gal/S.Y.		3500	.016		1.90	.73	1.72	4.35	5.10
0140	1-1/2 gal/S.Y.		3500	.016		2.85	.73	1.72	5.30	6.15
0200	6" deep, 2 gal/S.Y.		3000	.019		3.80	.85	2	6.65	7.70
0240	3 gal/S.Y.		3000	.019		5.70	.85	2	8.55	9.75
0300	8" deep, 2-2/3 gal/S.Y.		2800	.020		5.05	.91	2.15	8.11	9.35
0340	4 gal/S.Y.		2800	.020		7.60	.91	2.15	10.66	12.10
0500	12" deep, 4 gal/S.Y.		5000	.011		7.60	.51	1.20	9.31	10.45
0540	6 gal/S.Y.		2600	.022		11.40	.98	2.31	14.69	16.60

31 32 13.16 Cement Soil Stabilization

		Crew	Daily Output	Labor-Hours	Unit	Material	2015 Bare Costs Labor	Equipment	Total	Total Incl O&P
0010	**CEMENT SOIL STABILIZATION**									
0011	Including scarifying and compaction									
1020	Cement, 4% mix, by volume, 6" deep	B-74	1100	.058	S.Y.	1.54	2.62	5.40	9.56	11.60
1030	8" deep		1050	.061		2.01	2.74	5.70	10.45	12.65
1060	12" deep		960	.067		3.01	3	6.20	12.21	14.70
1100	6% mix, 6" deep		1100	.058		2.21	2.62	5.40	10.23	12.35
1120	8" deep		1050	.061		2.88	2.74	5.70	11.32	13.60
1160	12" deep		960	.067		4.35	3	6.20	13.55	16.20
1200	9% mix, 6" deep		1100	.058		3.35	2.62	5.40	11.37	13.60
1220	8" deep		1050	.061		4.35	2.74	5.70	12.79	15.20
1260	12" deep		960	.067		6.55	3	6.20	15.75	18.60
1300	12% mix, 6" deep		1100	.058		4.35	2.62	5.40	12.37	14.70
1320	8" deep		1050	.061		5.80	2.74	5.70	14.24	16.80
1360	12" deep		960	.067		8.70	3	6.20	17.90	21

31 32 Soil Stabilization

31 32 13 – Soil Mixing Stabilization

31 32 13.19 Lime Soil Stabilization

	Crew	Daily Output	Labor-Hours	Unit	Material	2015 Bare Costs Labor	2015 Bare Costs Equipment	Total	Total Incl O&P
0010 **LIME SOIL STABILIZATION**									
0011 Including scarifying and compaction									
2020 Hydrated lime, for base, 2% mix by weight, 6" deep	B-74	1800	.036	S.Y.	2.34	1.60	3.31	7.25	8.65
2030 8" deep		1700	.038		3.35	1.69	3.51	8.55	10.10
2060 12" deep		1550	.041		4.73	1.86	3.85	10.44	12.25
2100 4% mix, 6" deep		1800	.036		3.49	1.60	3.31	8.40	9.90
2120 8" deep		1700	.038		4.72	1.69	3.51	9.92	11.65
2160 12" deep		1550	.041		7.05	1.86	3.85	12.76	14.80
2200 6% mix, 6" deep		1800	.036		5.30	1.60	3.31	10.21	11.85
2220 8" deep		1700	.038		7.05	1.69	3.51	12.25	14.20
2260 12" deep	▼	1550	.041	▼	10.50	1.86	3.85	16.21	18.60

31 32 13.30 Calcium Chloride

	Crew	Daily Output	Labor-Hours	Unit	Material	2015 Bare Costs Labor	2015 Bare Costs Equipment	Total	Total Incl O&P
0010 **CALCIUM CHLORIDE**									
0020 Calcium chloride delivered, 100 lb. bags, truckload lots				Ton	390			390	430
0030 Solution, 4 lb. flake per gallon, tank truck delivery				Gal.	1.48			1.48	1.63

31 32 19 – Geosynthetic Soil Stabilization and Layer Separation

31 32 19.16 Geotextile Soil Stabilization

	Crew	Daily Output	Labor-Hours	Unit	Material	2015 Bare Costs Labor	2015 Bare Costs Equipment	Total	Total Incl O&P
0010 **GEOTEXTILE SOIL STABILIZATION**									
1500 Geotextile fabric, woven, 200 lb. tensile strength	2 Clab	2500	.006	S.Y.	1.90	.24		2.14	2.46
1510 Heavy Duty, 600 lb. tensile strength		2400	.007		1.84	.25		2.09	2.41
1550 Non-woven, 120 lb. tensile strength	▼	2500	.006	▼	1.11	.24		1.35	1.59

31 32 36 – Soil Nailing

31 32 36.16 Grouted Soil Nailing

	Crew	Daily Output	Labor-Hours	Unit	Material	2015 Bare Costs Labor	2015 Bare Costs Equipment	Total	Total Incl O&P
0010 **GROUTED SOIL NAILING**									
0020 Soil nailing does not include guniting of surfaces									
0030 See Section 03 37 13.30 for guniting of surfaces									
0035 Layout and vertical and horizontal control per day	A-6	1	16	Day		750	55	805	1,200
0038 Layout and vertical and horizontal control average holes per day	"	60	.267	Ea.		12.50	.91	13.41	20
0050 For Grade 150 soil nail add $ 1.37/L.F. to base material cost									
0060 Material delivery add $ 1.83 to $ 2.00 per truck mile for shipping									
0090 Average Soil nailing, grade 75, 15 min setup per hole & 80'/hr. drilling									
0100 Soil nailing, drill hole, install # 8 nail, grout 20' depth average	B-47G	16	2	Ea.	140	81.50	124	345.50	415
0110 25' depth average		14.20	2.254		175	92	139	406	485
0120 30' depth average		12.80	2.500		288	102	155	545	640
0130 35' depth average		11.60	2.759		335	113	171	619	730
0140 40' depth average		10.70	2.991		385	122	185	692	810
0150 45' depth average		9.90	3.232		430	132	200	762	895
0160 50' depth average		9.10	3.516		495	144	218	857	1,000
0170 55' depth average		8.50	3.765		540	154	233	927	1,075
0180 60' depth average		8	4		590	163	248	1,001	1,175
0190 65' depth average		7.50	4.267		635	174	264	1,073	1,250
0200 70' depth average		7.10	4.507		685	184	279	1,148	1,350
0210 75' depth average	▼	6.70	4.776	▼	730	195	296	1,221	1,425
0290 Average Soil nailing, grade 75, 15 min setup per hole & 90'/hr. drilling									
0300 Soil nailing, drill hole, install # 8 nail, grout 20' depth average	B-47G	16.60	1.928	Ea.	140	79	119	338	405
0310 25' depth average		15	2.133		175	87	132	394	470
0320 30' depth average		13.70	2.336		288	95.50	145	528.50	620
0330 35' depth average		12.30	2.602		335	106	161	602	710
0340 40' depth average		11.40	2.807		385	115	174	674	785
0350 45' depth average		10.70	2.991		430	122	185	737	865
0360 50' depth average		9.80	3.265		495	133	202	830	970

31 32 36.16 Grouted Soil Nailing	Crew	Daily Output	Labor-Hours	Unit	Material	2015 Bare Costs Labor	2015 Bare Costs Equipment	Total	Total Incl O&P
0370	55' depth average	B-47G	9.20	3.478	Ea.	540	142	215	897	1,050
0380	60' depth average		8.70	3.678		590	150	228	968	1,125
0390	65' depth average		8.10	3.951		635	161	244	1,040	1,225
0400	70' depth average		7.70	4.156		685	170	257	1,112	1,300
0410	75' depth average	▼	7.40	4.324	▼	730	177	268	1,175	1,375
0490	Average Soil nailing, grade 75, 15 min setup per hole & 100'/hr. drilling									
0500	Soil nailing , drill hole, install # 8 nail, grout 20' depth average	B-47G	17.80	1.798	Ea.	140	73.50	111	324.50	390
0510	25' depth average		16	2		175	81.50	124	380.50	455
0520	30' depth average		14.60	2.192		288	89.50	136	513.50	600
0530	35' depth average		13.30	2.406		335	98.50	149	582.50	685
0540	40' depth average		12.30	2.602		385	106	161	652	760
0550	45' depth average		11.40	2.807		430	115	174	719	840
0560	50' depth average		10.70	2.991		495	122	185	802	935
0570	55' depth average		10	3.200		540	131	198	869	1,025
0580	60' depth average		9.40	3.404		590	139	211	940	1,100
0590	65' depth average		8.90	3.596		635	147	222	1,004	1,175
0600	70' depth average		8.40	3.810		685	156	236	1,077	1,250
0610	75' depth average	▼	8	4	▼	730	163	248	1,141	1,325
0690	Average Soil nailing, grade 75, 15 min setup per hole & 110'/hr. drilling									
0700	Soil nailing , drill hole, install # 8 nail, grout 20' depth average	B-47G	18.50	1.730	Ea.	140	70.50	107	317.50	380
0710	25' depth average		16.60	1.928		175	79	119	373	445
0720	30' depth average		15.50	2.065		288	84.50	128	500.50	585
0730	35' depth average		14.10	2.270		335	92.50	140	567.50	665
0740	40' depth average		13	2.462		385	101	152	638	740
0750	45' depth average		12	2.667		430	109	165	704	825
0760	50' depth average		11.40	2.807		495	115	174	784	910
0770	55' depth average		10.70	2.991		540	122	185	847	985
0780	60' depth average		10	3.200		590	131	198	919	1,075
0790	65' depth average		9.40	3.404		635	139	211	985	1,150
0800	70' depth average		9.10	3.516		685	144	218	1,047	1,225
0810	75' depth average	▼	8.60	3.721	▼	730	152	230	1,112	1,300
0890	Average Soil nailing, grade 75, 15 min setup per hole & 120'/hr. drilling									
0900	Soil nailing , drill hole, install # 8 nail, grout 20' depth average	B-47G	19.20	1.667	Ea.	140	68	103	311	370
0910	25' depth average		17.10	1.871		175	76.50	116	367.50	435
0920	30' depth average		16	2		288	81.50	124	493.50	575
0930	35' depth average		14.60	2.192		335	89.50	136	560.50	655
0940	40' depth average		13.70	2.336		385	95.50	145	625.50	725
0950	45' depth average		12.60	2.540		430	104	157	691	805
0960	50' depth average		12	2.667		495	109	165	769	895
0970	55' depth average		11.20	2.857		540	117	177	834	970
0980	60' depth average		10.70	2.991		590	122	185	897	1,050
0990	65' depth average		10	3.200		635	131	198	964	1,125
1000	70' depth average		9.60	3.333		685	136	206	1,027	1,200
1010	75' depth average	▼	9.10	3.516	▼	730	144	218	1,092	1,275
1190	Difficult Soil nailing, grade 75, 20 min setup per hole & 80'/hr. drilling									
1200	Soil nailing , drill hole, install # 8 nail, grout 20' depth difficult	B-47G	13.70	2.336	Ea.	140	95.50	145	380.50	460
1210	25' depth difficult		12.30	2.602		175	106	161	442	535
1220	30' depth difficult		11.20	2.857		288	117	177	582	690
1230	35' depth difficult		10.40	3.077		335	126	190	651	770
1240	40' depth difficult		9.60	3.333		385	136	206	727	855
1250	45' depth difficult		8.90	3.596		430	147	222	799	945
1260	50' depth difficult		8.30	3.855		495	157	239	891	1,050
1270	55' depth difficult		7.90	4.051		540	165	251	956	1,125

31 32 36.16 Grouted Soil Nailing	Crew	Daily Output	Labor-Hours	Unit	Material	2015 Bare Costs Labor	2015 Bare Costs Equipment	Total	Total Incl O&P
1280	60' depth difficult	B-47G	7.40	4.324	Ea.	590	177	268	1,035	1,225
1290	65' depth difficult		7	4.571		635	187	283	1,105	1,300
1300	70' depth difficult		6.60	4.848		685	198	300	1,183	1,400
1310	75' depth difficult		6.30	5.079		730	207	315	1,252	1,475
1390	Difficult soil nailing, grade 75, 20 min setup per hole & 90'/hr. drilling									
1400	Soil nailing , drill hole, install # 8 nail, grout 20' depth difficult	B-47G	14.10	2.270	Ea.	140	92.50	140	372.50	450
1410	25' depth difficult		13	2.462		175	101	152	428	515
1420	30' depth difficult		12	2.667		288	109	165	562	665
1430	35' depth difficult		10.90	2.936		335	120	182	637	755
1440	40' depth difficult		10.20	3.137		385	128	194	707	830
1450	45' depth difficult		9.60	3.333		430	136	206	772	910
1460	50' depth difficult		8.90	3.596		495	147	222	864	1,025
1470	55' depth difficult		8.40	3.810		540	156	236	932	1,100
1480	60' depth difficult		8	4		590	163	248	1,001	1,175
1490	65' depth difficult		7.50	4.267		635	174	264	1,073	1,250
1500	70' depth difficult		7.20	4.444		685	182	275	1,142	1,350
1510	75' depth difficult		6.90	4.638		730	189	287	1,206	1,400
1590	Difficult soil nailing, grade 75, 20 min setup per hole & 100'/hr. drilling									
1600	Soil nailing , drill hole, install # 8 nail, grout 20' depth difficult	B-47G	15	2.133	Ea.	140	87	132	359	435
1610	25' depth difficult		13.70	2.336		175	95.50	145	415.50	500
1620	30' depth difficult		12.60	2.540		288	104	157	549	645
1630	35' depth difficult		11.70	2.735		335	112	169	616	725
1640	40' depth difficult		10.90	2.936		385	120	182	687	805
1650	45' depth difficult		10.20	3.137		430	128	194	752	885
1660	50' depth difficult		9.60	3.333		495	136	206	837	980
1670	55' depth difficult		9.10	3.516		540	144	218	902	1,050
1680	60' depth difficult		8.60	3.721		590	152	230	972	1,125
1690	65' depth difficult		8.10	3.951		635	161	244	1,040	1,225
1700	70' depth difficult		7.70	4.156		685	170	257	1,112	1,300
1710	75' depth difficult		7.40	4.324		730	177	268	1,175	1,375
1790	Difficult soil nailing, grade 75, 20 min setup per hole & 110'/hr. drilling									
1800	Soil nailing , drill hole, install # 8 nail, grout 20' depth difficult	B-47G	15.50	2.065	Ea.	140	84.50	128	352.50	425
1810	25' depth difficult		14.10	2.270		175	92.50	140	407.50	490
1820	30' depth difficult		13.30	2.406		288	98.50	149	535.50	630
1830	35' depth difficult		12.30	2.602		335	106	161	602	710
1840	40' depth difficult		11.40	2.807		385	115	174	674	785
1850	45' depth difficult		10.70	2.991		430	122	185	737	865
1860	50' depth difficult		10.20	3.137		495	128	194	817	955
1870	55' depth difficult		9.60	3.333		540	136	206	882	1,025
1880	60' depth difficult		9.10	3.516		590	144	218	952	1,100
1890	65' depth difficult		8.60	3.721		635	152	230	1,017	1,175
1900	70' depth difficult		8.30	3.855		685	157	239	1,081	1,250
1910	75' depth difficult		7.90	4.051		730	165	251	1,146	1,325
1990	Difficult soil nailing, grade 75, 20 min setup per hole & 120'/hr. drilling									
2000	Soil nailing , drill hole, install # 8 nail, grout 20' depth difficult	B-47G	16	2	Ea.	140	81.50	124	345.50	415
2010	25' depth difficult		14.60	2.192		175	89.50	136	400.50	480
2020	30' depth difficult		13.70	2.336		288	95.50	145	528.50	620
2030	35' depth difficult		12.60	2.540		335	104	157	596	700
2040	40' depth difficult		12	2.667		385	109	165	659	770
2050	45' depth difficult		11.20	2.857		430	117	177	724	850
2060	50' depth difficult		10.70	2.991		495	122	185	802	935
2070	55' depth difficult		10	3.200		540	131	198	869	1,025
2080	60' depth naifficult		9.60	3.333		590	136	206	932	1,075

31 32 36.16 Grouted Soil Nailing	Crew	Daily Output	Labor-Hours	Unit	Material	2015 Bare Costs Labor	Equipment	Total	Total Incl O&P
2090 65' depth difficult	B-47G	9.10	3.516	Ea.	635	144	218	997	1,150
2100 70' depth difficult		8.70	3.678		685	150	228	1,063	1,225
2110 75' depth difficult		8.30	3.855		730	157	239	1,126	1,300
2990 Very difficult soil nailing, grade 75, 25 min setup & 80'/hr. drilling									
3000 Soil nailing, drill, install # 8 nail, grout 20' depth very difficult	B-47G	12	2.667	Ea.	140	109	165	414	505
3010 25' depth very difficult		10.90	2.936		175	120	182	477	575
3020 30' depth very difficult		10	3.200		288	131	198	617	735
3030 35' depth very difficult		9.40	3.404		335	139	211	685	815
3040 40' depth very difficult		8.70	3.678		385	150	228	763	900
3050 45' depth very difficult		8.10	3.951		430	161	244	835	990
3060 50' depth very difficult		7.60	4.211		495	172	261	928	1,100
3070 55' depth very difficult		7.30	4.384		540	179	271	990	1,175
3080 60' depth very difficult		6.90	4.638		590	189	287	1,066	1,250
3090 65' depth very difficult		6.50	4.923		635	201	305	1,141	1,350
3100 70' depth very difficult		6.20	5.161		685	211	320	1,216	1,425
3110 75' depth very difficult		5.90	5.424		730	222	335	1,287	1,525
3190 Very difficult soil nailing, grade 75, 25 min setup & 90'/hr. drilling									
3200 Soil nailing, drill, install # 8 nail, grout 20' depth very difficult	B-47G	12.30	2.602	Ea.	140	106	161	407	495
3210 25' depth very difficult		11.40	2.807		175	115	174	464	560
3220 30' depth very difficult		10.70	2.991		288	122	185	595	705
3230 35' depth very difficult		9.80	3.265		335	133	202	670	795
3240 40' depth very difficult		9.20	3.478		385	142	215	742	875
3250 45' depth very difficult		8.70	3.678		430	150	228	808	955
3260 50' depth very difficult		8.10	3.951		495	161	244	900	1,050
3270 55' depth very difficult		7.70	4.156		540	170	257	967	1,150
3280 60' depth very difficult		7.40	4.324		590	177	268	1,035	1,225
3290 65' depth very difficult		7	4.571		635	187	283	1,105	1,300
3300 70' depth very difficult		6.70	4.776		685	195	296	1,176	1,375
3310 75' depth very difficult		6.40	5		730	204	310	1,244	1,450
3390 Very difficult soil nailing, grade 75, 25 min setup & 100'/hr. drilling									
3400 Soil nailing, drill, install # 8 nail, grout 20' depth very difficult	B-47G	13	2.462	Ea.	140	101	152	393	475
3410 25' depth very difficult		12	2.667		175	109	165	449	540
3420 30' depth very difficult		11.20	2.857		288	117	177	582	690
3430 35' depth very difficult		10.40	3.077		335	126	190	651	770
3440 40' depth very difficult		9.80	3.265		385	133	202	720	845
3450 45' depth very difficult		9.20	3.478		430	142	215	787	930
3460 50' depth very difficult		8.70	3.678		495	150	228	873	1,025
3470 55' depth very difficult		8.30	3.855		540	157	239	936	1,100
3480 60' depth very difficult		7.90	4.051		590	165	251	1,006	1,175
3490 65' depth very difficult		7.50	4.267		635	174	264	1,073	1,250
3500 70' depth very difficult		7.20	4.444		685	182	275	1,142	1,350
3510 75' depth very difficult		6.90	4.638		730	189	287	1,206	1,400
3590 Very difficult soil nailing, grade 75, 25 min setup & 110'/hr. drilling									
3600 Soil nailing, drill, install # 8 nail, grout 20' depth very difficult	B-47G	13.30	2.406	Ea.	140	98.50	149	387.50	470
3610 25' depth very difficult		13.70	2.336		175	95.50	145	415.50	500
3620 30' depth very difficult		11.70	2.735		288	112	169	569	670
3630 35' depth very difficult		10.90	2.936		335	120	182	637	755
3640 40' depth very difficult		10.20	3.137		385	128	194	707	830
3650 45' depth very difficult		9.60	3.333		430	136	206	772	910
3660 50' depth very difficult		9.20	3.478		495	142	215	852	1,000
3670 55' depth very difficult		8.70	3.678		540	150	228	918	1,075
3680 60' depth very difficult		8.30	3.855		590	157	239	986	1,150
3690 65' depth very difficult		7.90	4.051		635	165	251	1,051	1,225

31 32 36 – Soil Nailing

31 32 36.16 Grouted Soil Nailing	Crew	Daily Output	Labor-Hours	Unit	Material	2015 Bare Costs Labor	2015 Bare Costs Equipment	Total	Total Incl O&P
3700	70' depth very difficult	B-47G	7.60	4.211	Ea.	685	172	261	1,118	1,300
3710	75' depth very difficult	↓	7.30	4.384	↓	730	179	271	1,180	1,375
3790	Very difficult soil nailing, grade 75, 25 min setup & 120'/hr. drilling									
3800	Soil nailing, drill, install # 8 nail, grout 20' depth very difficult	B-47G	13.70	2.336	Ea.	140	95.50	145	380.50	460
3810	25' depth very difficult		12.60	2.540		175	104	157	436	525
3820	30' depth very difficult		12	2.667		288	109	165	562	665
3830	35' depth very difficult		11.20	2.857		335	117	177	629	745
3840	40' depth very difficult		10.70	2.991		385	122	185	692	810
3850	45' depth very difficult		10	3.200		430	131	198	759	895
3860	50' depth very difficult		9.60	3.333		495	136	206	837	980
3870	55' depth very difficult		9.10	3.516		540	144	218	902	1,050
3880	60' depth very difficult		8.70	3.678		590	150	228	968	1,125
3890	65' depth very difficult		8.30	3.855		635	157	239	1,031	1,200
3900	70' depth very difficult		8	4		685	163	248	1,096	1,275
3910	75' depth very difficult	↓	7.60	4.211	↓	730	172	261	1,163	1,350
3990	Severe soil nailing, grade 75, 30 min setup per hole & 80'/hr. drilling									
4000	Soil nailing, drill hole, install # 8 nail, grout 20' depth severe	B-47G	10.70	2.991	Ea.	140	122	185	447	545
4010	25' depth severe		9.80	3.265		175	133	202	510	620
4020	30' depth severe		9.10	3.516		288	144	218	650	775
4030	35' depth severe		8.60	3.721		335	152	230	717	855
4040	40' depth severe		8	4		385	163	248	796	940
4050	45' depth severe		7.50	4.267		430	174	264	868	1,025
4060	50' depth severe		7.10	4.507		495	184	279	958	1,125
4070	55' depth severe		6.80	4.706		540	192	291	1,023	1,200
4080	60' depth severe		6.40	5		590	204	310	1,104	1,300
4090	65' depth severe		6.10	5.246		635	214	325	1,174	1,375
4100	70' depth severe		5.80	5.517		685	225	340	1,250	1,475
4110	75' depth severe	↓	5.60	5.714	↓	730	233	355	1,318	1,550
4190	Severe soil nailing, grade 75, 30 min setup per hole & 90'/hr. drilling									
4200	Soil nailing, drill hole, install # 8 nail, grout 20' depth severe	B-47G	10.90	2.936	Ea.	140	120	182	442	540
4210	25' depth severe		10.20	3.137		175	128	194	497	605
4220	30' depth severe		9.60	3.333		288	136	206	630	750
4230	35' depth severe		8.90	3.596		335	147	222	704	840
4240	40' depth severe		8.40	3.810		385	156	236	777	915
4250	45' depth severe		8	4		430	163	248	841	995
4260	50' depth severe		7.50	4.267		495	174	264	933	1,100
4270	55' depth severe		7.20	4.444		540	182	275	997	1,175
4280	60' depth severe		6.90	4.638		590	189	287	1,066	1,250
4290	65' depth severe		6.50	4.923		635	201	305	1,141	1,350
4300	70' depth severe		6.20	5.161		685	211	320	1,216	1,425
4310	75' depth severe	↓	6	5.333	↓	730	218	330	1,278	1,500
4390	Severe soil nailing, grade 75, 30 min setup per hole & 100'/hr. drilling									
4400	Soil nailing, drill hole, install # 8 nail, grout 20' depth severe	B-47G	11.40	2.807	Ea.	140	115	174	429	520
4410	25' depth severe		10.70	2.991		175	122	185	482	585
4420	30' depth severe		10	3.200		288	131	198	617	735
4430	35' depth severe		9.40	3.404		335	139	211	685	815
4440	40' depth severe		8.90	3.596		385	147	222	754	890
4450	45' depth severe		8.40	3.810		430	156	236	822	970
4460	50' depth severe		8	4		495	163	248	906	1,075
4470	55' depth severe		7.60	4.211		540	172	261	973	1,150
4480	60' depth severe		7.30	4.384		590	179	271	1,040	1,225
4490	65' depth severe		7	4.571		635	187	283	1,105	1,300
4500	70' depth Nailve		6.70	4.776		685	195	296	1,176	1,375

31 32 Soil Stabilization

31 32 36 – Soil Nailing

31 32 36.16 Grouted Soil Nailing		Crew	Daily Output	Labor-Hours	Unit	Material	2015 Bare Costs Labor	Equipment	Total	Total Incl O&P
4510	75' depth severe	B-47G	6.40	5	Ea.	730	204	310	1,244	1,450
4590	Severe soil nailing, grade 75, 30 min setup per hole & 110'/hr. drilling									
4600	Soil nailing , drill hole, install # 8 nail, grout 20' depth severe	B-47G	11.70	2.735	Ea.	140	112	169	421	510
4610	25' depth severe		10.90	2.936		175	120	182	477	575
4620	30' depth severe		10.40	3.077		288	126	190	604	715
4630	35' depth severe		9.80	3.265		335	133	202	670	795
4640	40' depth severe		9.20	3.478		385	142	215	742	875
4650	45' depth severe		8.70	3.678		430	150	228	808	955
4660	50' depth severe		8.40	3.810		495	156	236	887	1,050
4670	55' depth severe		8	4		540	163	248	951	1,125
4680	60' depth severe		7.60	4.211		590	172	261	1,023	1,200
4690	65' depth severe		7.30	4.384		635	179	271	1,085	1,275
4700	70' depth severe		7.10	4.507		685	184	279	1,148	1,350
4710	75' depth severe	↓	6.80	4.706	↓	730	192	291	1,213	1,425
4790	Severe soil nailing, grade 75, 30 min setup per hole & 120'/hr. drilling									
4800	Soil nailing , drill hole, install # 8 nail, grout 20' depth severe	B-47G	12	2.667	Ea.	140	109	165	414	505
4810	25' depth severe		11.20	2.857		175	117	177	469	565
4820	30' depth severe		10.70	2.991		288	122	185	595	705
4830	35' depth severe		10	3.200		335	131	198	664	790
4840	40' depth severe		9.60	3.333		385	136	206	727	855
4850	45' depth severe		9.10	3.516		430	144	218	792	935
4860	50' depth severe		8.70	3.678		495	150	228	873	1,025
4870	55' depth severe		8.30	3.855		540	157	239	936	1,100
4880	60' depth severe		8	4		590	163	248	1,001	1,175
4890	65' depth severe		7.60	4.211		635	172	261	1,068	1,250
4900	70' depth severe		7.40	4.324		685	177	268	1,130	1,325
4910	75' depth severe	↓	7.10	4.507	↓	730	184	279	1,193	1,400

31 36 Gabions

31 36 13 – Gabion Boxes

31 36 13.10 Gabion Box Systems

		Crew	Daily Output	Labor-Hours	Unit	Material	Labor	Equipment	Total	Total Incl O&P
0010	**GABION BOX SYSTEMS**									
0400	Gabions, galvanized steel mesh mats or boxes, stone filled, 6" deep	B-13	200	.280	S.Y.	26.50	11.50	3.68	41.68	50.50
0500	9" deep		163	.344		39	14.10	4.52	57.62	69.50
0600	12" deep		153	.366		52.50	15	4.81	72.31	86
0700	18" deep		102	.549		71.50	22.50	7.20	101.20	121
0800	36" deep	↓	60	.933	↓	98	38.50	12.25	148.75	180

31 37 Riprap

31 37 13 – Machined Riprap

31 37 13.10 Riprap and Rock Lining

		Crew	Daily Output	Labor-Hours	Unit	Material	Labor	Equipment	Total	Total Incl O&P
0010	**RIPRAP AND ROCK LINING**									
0011	Random, broken stone									
0100	Machine placed for slope protection	B-12G	62	.258	L.C.Y.	30	11.50	11.40	52.90	63
0110	3/8 to 1/4 C.Y. pieces, grouted	B-13	80	.700	S.Y.	59.50	28.50	9.20	97.20	120
0200	18" minimum thickness, not grouted	"	53	1.057	"	18.90	43.50	13.90	76.30	103
0300	Dumped, 50 lb. average	B-11A	800	.020	Ton	26.50	.88	1.73	29.11	32.50
0350	100 lb. average		700	.023		26.50	1.01	1.98	29.49	32.50
0370	300 lb. average	↓	600	.027	↓	26.50	1.18	2.31	29.99	33.50

31 41 Shoring

31 41 13 – Timber Shoring

31 41 13.10 Building Shoring		Crew	Daily Output	Labor-Hours	Unit	Material	2015 Bare Costs Labor	Equipment	Total	Total Incl O&P
0010	**BUILDING SHORING**									
0020	Shoring, existing building, with timber, no salvage allowance	B-51	2.20	21.818	M.B.F.	850	835	111	1,796	2,325
1000	On cribbing with 35 ton screw jacks, per box and jack	"	3.60	13.333	Jack	68.50	510	68	646.50	930

31 41 16 – Sheet Piling

31 41 16.10 Sheet Piling Systems

			Crew	Daily Output	Labor-Hours	Unit	Material	2015 Bare Costs Labor	Equipment	Total	Total Incl O&P
0010	**SHEET PILING SYSTEMS**										
0020	Sheet piling steel, not incl. wales, 22 psf, 15' excav., left in place		B-40	10.81	5.920	Ton	1,600	282	345	2,227	2,575
0100	Drive, extract & salvage	R314116-40		6	10.667		510	510	625	1,645	2,025
0300	20' deep excavation, 27 psf, left in place			12.95	4.942		1,600	235	289	2,124	2,425
0400	Drive, extract & salvage	R314116-45		6.55	9.771		510	465	570	1,545	1,925
0600	25' deep excavation, 38 psf, left in place			19	3.368		1,600	160	197	1,957	2,225
0700	Drive, extract & salvage			10.50	6.095		510	290	355	1,155	1,400
0900	40' deep excavation, 38 psf, left in place			21.20	3.019		1,600	144	177	1,921	2,175
1000	Drive, extract & salvage			12.25	5.224		510	249	305	1,064	1,275
1200	15' deep excavation, 22 psf, left in place			983	.065	S.F.	18.60	3.10	3.81	25.51	29.50
1300	Drive, extract & salvage			545	.117		5.70	5.60	6.85	18.15	22.50
1500	20' deep excavation, 27 psf, left in place			960	.067		23.50	3.18	3.90	30.58	34.50
1600	Drive, extract & salvage			485	.132		7.45	6.30	7.70	21.45	26.50
1800	25' deep excavation, 38 psf, left in place			1000	.064		34.50	3.05	3.74	41.29	47
1900	Drive, extract & salvage			553	.116		10.15	5.50	6.75	22.40	27.50
2100	Rent steel sheet piling and wales, first month					Ton	310			310	340
2200	Per added month						31			31	34
2300	Rental piling left in place, add to rental						1,150			1,150	1,275
2500	Wales, connections & struts, 2/3 salvage						480			480	530
2700	High strength piling, 50,000 psi, add						63.50			63.50	70
2800	55,000 psi, add						82			82	90
3000	Tie rod, not upset, 1-1/2" to 4" diameter with turnbuckle						2,125			2,125	2,325
3100	No turnbuckle						1,650			1,650	1,825
3300	Upset, 1-3/4" to 4" diameter with turnbuckle						2,400			2,400	2,625
3400	No turnbuckle						2,075			2,075	2,275
3600	Lightweight, 18" to 28" wide, 7 ga., 9.22 psf, and										
3610	9 ga., 8.6 psf, minimum					Lb.	.77			.77	.85
3700	Average						.87			.87	.96
3750	Maximum						1.04			1.04	1.14
3900	Wood, solid sheeting, incl. wales, braces and spacers,										
3910	drive, extract & salvage, 8' deep excavation		B-31	330	.121	S.F.	1.89	4.83	.66	7.38	10.25
4000	10' deep, 50 S.F./hr. in & 150 S.F./hr. out			300	.133		1.95	5.30	.73	7.98	11.15
4100	12' deep, 45 S.F./hr. in & 135 S.F./hr. out			270	.148		2	5.90	.81	8.71	12.20
4200	14' deep, 42 S.F./hr. in & 126 S.F./hr. out			250	.160		2.06	6.40	.88	9.34	13.05
4300	16' deep, 40 S.F./hr. in & 120 S.F./hr. out			240	.167		2.13	6.65	.91	9.69	13.60
4400	18' deep, 38 S.F./hr. in & 114 S.F./hr. out			230	.174		2.20	6.95	.95	10.10	14.10
4500	20' deep, 35 S.F./hr. in & 105 S.F./hr. out			210	.190		2.27	7.60	1.04	10.91	15.35
4520	Left in place, 8' deep, 55 S.F./hr.			440	.091		3.41	3.62	.50	7.53	9.90
4540	10' deep, 50 S.F./hr.			400	.100		3.58	3.99	.55	8.12	10.70
4560	12' deep, 45 S.F./hr.			360	.111		3.78	4.43	.61	8.82	11.65
4565	14' deep, 42 S.F./hr.			335	.119		4.01	4.76	.65	9.42	12.50
4570	16' deep, 40 S.F./hr.			320	.125		4.26	4.98	.68	9.92	13.10
4580	18' deep, 38 S.F./hr.			305	.131		4.54	5.25	.72	10.51	13.85
4590	20' deep, 35 S.F./hr.			280	.143		4.86	5.70	.78	11.34	14.95
4700	Alternate pricing, left in place, 8' deep			1.76	22.727	M.B.F.	765	905	124	1,794	2,375
4800	Drive, extract and salvage, 8' deep			1.32	30.303	"	680	1,200	166	2,046	2,775
5000	For treated lumber add cost of treatment to lumber										

For customer support on your Site Work & Landscape Cost Data, call 877.737.1594.

333

31 43 Concrete Raising

31 43 13 – Pressure Grouting

31 43 13.13 Concrete Pressure Grouting	Crew	Daily Output	Labor-Hours	Unit	Material	2015 Bare Costs Labor	Equipment	Total	Total Incl O&P
0010 **CONCRETE PRESSURE GROUTING**									
0020 Grouting, pressure, cement & sand, 1:1 mix, minimum	B-61	124	.323	Bag	12.10	12.95	2.83	27.88	36.50
0100 Maximum		51	.784	"	12.10	31.50	6.90	50.50	69.50
0200 Cement and sand, 1:1 mix, minimum		250	.160	C.F.	24	6.45	1.40	31.85	38
0300 Maximum		100	.400		36.50	16.10	3.51	56.11	68.50
0310 Grouting, cement and sand, 1:2 mix, geothermal wells		250	.160		9.70	6.45	1.40	17.55	22
0320 Bentonite mix 1:4		250	.160		10.95	6.45	1.40	18.80	23.50
0400 Epoxy cement grout, minimum		137	.292		700	11.75	2.56	714.31	790
0500 Maximum		57	.702		700	28	6.15	734.15	820
0700 Alternate pricing method: (Add for materials)									
0710 5 person crew and equipment	B-61	1	40	Day		1,600	350	1,950	2,850

31 43 19 – Mechanical Jacking

31 43 19.10 Slabjacking

	Crew	Daily Output	Labor-Hours	Unit	Material	2015 Bare Costs Labor	Equipment	Total	Total Incl O&P
0010 **SLABJACKING**									
0100 4" thick slab	D-4	1500	.021	S.F.	.31	.91	.09	1.31	1.83
0150 6" thick slab		1200	.027		.44	1.14	.11	1.69	2.34
0200 8" thick slab		1000	.032		.52	1.37	.13	2.02	2.80
0250 10" thick slab		900	.036		.56	1.52	.15	2.23	3.09
0300 12" thick slab		850	.038		.61	1.61	.16	2.38	3.29

31 45 Vibroflotation and Densification

31 45 13 – Vibroflotation

31 45 13.10 Vibroflotation Densification

	Crew	Daily Output	Labor-Hours	Unit	Material	2015 Bare Costs Labor	Equipment	Total	Total Incl O&P
0010 **VIBROFLOTATION DENSIFICATION**									
0900 Vibroflotation compacted sand cylinder, minimum	B-60	750	.075	V.L.F.		3.30	2.91	6.21	8.25
0950 Maximum		325	.172			7.60	6.70	14.30	19
1100 Vibro replacement compacted stone cylinder, minimum		500	.112			4.94	4.36	9.30	12.35
1150 Maximum		250	.224			9.90	8.70	18.60	24.50
1300 Mobilization and demobilization, minimum		.47	119	Total		5,250	4,650	9,900	13,100
1400 Maximum		.14	400	"		17,700	15,600	33,300	44,000

31 48 Underpinning

31 48 13 – Underpinning Piers

31 48 13.10 Underpinning Foundations

	Crew	Daily Output	Labor-Hours	Unit	Material	2015 Bare Costs Labor	Equipment	Total	Total Incl O&P
0010 **UNDERPINNING FOUNDATIONS**									
0011 Including excavation,									
0020 forming, reinforcing, concrete and equipment									
0100 5' to 16' below grade, 100 to 500 C.Y.	B-52	2.30	24.348	C.Y.	283	1,050	258	1,591	2,225
0200 Over 500 C.Y.		2.50	22.400		255	975	238	1,468	2,050
0400 16' to 25' below grade, 100 to 500 C.Y.		2	28		310	1,225	297	1,832	2,550
0500 Over 500 C.Y.		2.10	26.667		295	1,175	283	1,753	2,400
0700 26' to 40' below grade, 100 to 500 C.Y.		1.60	35		340	1,525	370	2,235	3,100
0800 Over 500 C.Y.		1.80	31.111		310	1,350	330	1,990	2,775
0900 For under 50 C.Y., add					10%	40%			
1000 For 50 C.Y. to 100 C.Y., add					5%	20%			

31 52 Cofferdams

31 52 16 – Timber Cofferdams

31 52 16.10 Cofferdams	Crew	Daily Output	Labor-Hours	Unit	Material	2015 Bare Costs Labor	2015 Bare Costs Equipment	Total	Total Incl O&P
0010 **COFFERDAMS**									
0011 Incl. mobilization and temporary sheeting									
0020 Shore driven	B-40	960	.067	S.F.	23	3.18	3.90	30.08	34
0060 Barge driven	"	550	.116	"	23	5.55	6.80	35.35	41
0080 Soldier beams & lagging H piles with 3" wood sheeting									
0090 horizontal between piles, including removal of wales & braces									
0100 No hydrostatic head, 15' deep, 1 line of braces, minimum	B-50	545	.206	S.F.	8.50	9.30	4.48	22.28	29
0200 Maximum		495	.226		9.45	10.25	4.93	24.63	32
0400 15' to 22' deep with 2 lines of braces, 10" H, minimum		360	.311		10	14.10	6.80	30.90	40.50
0500 Maximum		330	.339		11.35	15.35	7.40	34.10	44.50
0700 23' to 35' deep with 3 lines of braces, 12" H, minimum		325	.345		13.10	15.60	7.50	36.20	47
0800 Maximum		295	.380		14.20	17.20	8.30	39.70	51.50
1000 36' to 45' deep with 4 lines of braces, 14" H, minimum		290	.386		14.70	17.50	8.40	40.60	53
1100 Maximum		265	.423		15.50	19.15	9.20	43.85	57
1300 No hydrostatic head, left in place, 15' dp., 1 line of braces, min.		635	.176		11.35	8	3.85	23.20	29
1400 Maximum		575	.195		12.15	8.80	4.25	25.20	32
1600 15' to 22' deep with 2 lines of braces, minimum		455	.246		17.05	11.15	5.35	33.55	42
1700 Maximum		415	.270		18.95	12.25	5.90	37.10	46.50
1900 23' to 35' deep with 3 lines of braces, minimum		420	.267		20.50	12.10	5.80	38.40	48
2000 Maximum		380	.295		22.50	13.35	6.45	42.30	52.50
2200 36' to 45' deep with 4 lines of braces, minimum		385	.291		24.50	13.20	6.35	44.05	54.50
2300 Maximum		350	.320		28.50	14.50	7	50	61
2350 Lagging only, 3" thick wood between piles 8' O.C., minimum	B-46	400	.120		1.89	5.05	.11	7.05	10.10
2370 Maximum		250	.192		2.84	8.10	.18	11.12	15.95
2400 Open sheeting no bracing, for trenches to 10' deep, min.		1736	.028		.85	1.17	.03	2.05	2.79
2450 Maximum		1510	.032		.95	1.34	.03	2.32	3.17
2500 Tie-back method, add to open sheeting, add, minimum								20%	20%
2550 Maximum								60%	60%
2700 Tie-backs only, based on tie-backs total length, minimum	B-46	86.80	.553	L.F.	14.60	23.50	.52	38.62	53
2750 Maximum		38.50	1.247	"	25.50	52.50	1.17	79.17	112
3500 Tie-backs only, typical average, 25' long		2	24	Ea.	645	1,000	22.50	1,667.50	2,300
3600 35' long		1.58	30.380	"	855	1,275	28.50	2,158.50	2,975
4500 Trench box, 7' deep, 16' x 8', see 01 54 33 in Reference Section				Day				191	210
4600 20' x 10', see 01 54 33 in Reference Section				"				240	265
5200 Wood sheeting, in trench, jacks at 4' O.C., 8' deep	B-1	800	.030	S.F.	.66	1.15		1.81	2.49
5250 12' deep		700	.034		.77	1.31		2.08	2.87
5300 15' deep		600	.040		1.07	1.53		2.60	3.53
6000 See also Section 31 41 16.10									

31 56 Slurry Walls

31 56 23 – Lean Concrete Slurry Walls

31 56 23.20 Slurry Trench

	Crew	Daily Output	Labor-Hours	Unit	Material	Labor	Equipment	Total	Total Incl O&P
0010 **SLURRY TRENCH**									
0011 Excavated slurry trench in wet soils									
0020 backfilled with 3000 PSI concrete, no reinforcing steel									
0050 Minimum	C-7	333	.216	C.F.	7.55	8.85	3.65	20.05	26
0100 Maximum		200	.360	"	12.60	14.75	6.05	33.40	43
0200 Alternate pricing method, minimum		150	.480	S.F.	15.05	19.65	8.10	42.80	55.50
0300 Maximum		120	.600		22.50	24.50	10.10	57.10	73.50
0500 Reinforced slurry trench, minimum	B-48	177	.316		11.30	13.45	16.40	41.15	51
0600 Maximum	"	69	.812		37.50	34.50	42	114	141

For customer support on your Site Work & Landscape Cost Data, call 877.737.1594.

335

31 56 23 – Lean Concrete Slurry Walls

31 56 23.20 Slurry Trench	Crew	Daily Output	Labor-Hours	Unit	Material	2015 Bare Costs Labor	Equipment	Total	Total Incl O&P
0800 Haul for disposal, 2 mile haul, excavated material, add	B-34B	99	.081	C.Y.		3.24	7	10.24	12.60
0900 Haul bentonite castings for disposal, add	"	40	.200	"		8	17.30	25.30	31

31 62 Driven Piles

31 62 13 – Concrete Piles

31 62 13.23 Prestressed Concrete Piles

	Crew	Daily Output	Labor-Hours	Unit	Material	2015 Bare Costs Labor	Equipment	Total	Total Incl O&P
0010 **PRESTRESSED CONCRETE PILES**, 200 piles									
0020 Unless specified otherwise, not incl. pile caps or mobilization									
2200 Precast, prestressed, 50' long, 12" diam., 2-3/8" wall	B-19	720	.089	V.L.F.	23.50	4.23	2.41	30.14	35.50
2300 14" diameter, 2-1/2" wall		680	.094		32	4.48	2.55	39.03	45
2500 16" diameter, 3" wall		640	.100		45.50	4.76	2.71	52.97	60.50
2600 18" diameter, 3" wall	B-19A	600	.107		57	5.10	3.61	65.71	74.50
2800 20" diameter, 3-1/2" wall		560	.114		67.50	5.45	3.87	76.82	87
2900 24" diameter, 3-1/2" wall		520	.123		76	5.85	4.16	86.01	97
2920 36" diameter, 4-1/2" wall	B-19	400	.160		102	7.60	4.34	113.94	129
2940 54" diameter, 5" wall		340	.188		133	8.95	5.10	147.05	166
2960 66" diameter, 6" wall		220	.291		207	13.85	7.90	228.75	258
3100 Precast, prestressed, 40' long, 10" thick, square		700	.091		18.35	4.36	2.48	25.19	29.50
3200 12" thick, square		680	.094		22.50	4.48	2.55	29.53	34.50
3275 Shipping for 60 foot long concrete piles, add to material cost					.93			.93	1.02
3400 14" thick, square	B-19	600	.107		25.50	5.10	2.90	33.50	39
3500 Octagonal		640	.100		34.50	4.76	2.71	41.97	48.50
3700 16" thick, square		560	.114		41	5.45	3.10	49.55	57
3800 Octagonal		600	.107		41.50	5.10	2.90	49.50	57
4000 18" thick, square	B-19A	520	.123		47.50	5.85	4.16	57.51	65.50
4100 Octagonal	B-19	560	.114		49.50	5.45	3.10	58.05	66
4300 20" thick, square	B-19A	480	.133		60.50	6.35	4.51	71.36	81.50
4400 Octagonal	B-19	520	.123		54.50	5.85	3.34	63.69	73
4600 24" thick, square	B-19A	440	.145		72	6.95	4.92	83.87	95
4700 Octagonal	B-19	480	.133		78.50	6.35	3.62	88.47	100
4750 Mobilization for 10,000 L.F. pile job, add		3300	.019			.92	.53	1.45	2.02
4800 25,000 L.F. pile job, add		8500	.008			.36	.20	.56	.78
4850 Mobilization by water for barge driving rig, add								100%	100%

31 62 16 – Steel Piles

31 62 16.13 Steel Piles

	Crew	Daily Output	Labor-Hours	Unit	Material	2015 Bare Costs Labor	Equipment	Total	Total Incl O&P
0010 **STEEL PILES**									
0100 Step tapered, round, concrete filled									
0110 8" tip, 60 ton capacity, 30' depth	B-19	760	.084	V.L.F.	11.45	4.01	2.29	17.75	21.50
0120 60' depth		740	.086		12.95	4.12	2.35	19.42	23
0130 80' depth		700	.091		13.40	4.36	2.48	20.24	24.50
0150 10" tip, 90 ton capacity, 30' depth		700	.091		13.75	4.36	2.48	20.59	24.50
0160 60' depth		690	.093		14.20	4.42	2.52	21.14	25.50
0170 80' depth		670	.096		15.30	4.55	2.59	22.44	27
0190 12" tip, 120 ton capacity, 30' depth		660	.097		18.35	4.62	2.63	25.60	30
0200 60' depth, 12" diameter		630	.102		17.65	4.84	2.76	25.25	30
0210 80' depth		590	.108		17.15	5.15	2.94	25.24	30
0250 "H" Sections, 50' long, HP8 x 36		640	.100		16.05	4.76	2.71	23.52	28
0400 HP10 X 42		610	.105		18.35	5	2.85	26.20	31
0500 HP10 X 57		610	.105		25.50	5	2.85	33.35	39
0700 HP12 X 53		590	.108		25	5.15	2.94	33.09	39

31 62 Driven Piles

31 62 16 – Steel Piles

31 62 16.13 Steel Piles

31 62 16.13 Steel Piles	Crew	Daily Output	Labor-Hours	Unit	Material	2015 Bare Costs Labor	2015 Bare Costs Equipment	Total	Total Incl O&P
0800	HP12 X 74	B-19A	590	.108	V.L.F.	34.50	5.15	3.67	43.32	50
1000	HP14 X 73		540	.119		35	5.65	4.01	44.66	51.50
1100	HP14 X 89		540	.119		41	5.65	4.01	50.66	58
1300	HP14 X 102		510	.125		47	6	4.24	57.24	65.50
1400	HP14 X 117		510	.125		54	6	4.24	64.24	73
1600	Splice on standard points, not in leads, 8" or 10"	1 Sswl	5	1.600	Ea.	120	84		204	278
1700	12" or 14"		4	2		177	105		282	375
1900	Heavy duty points, not in leads, 10" wide		4	2		190	105		295	390
2100	14" wide		3.50	2.286		238	120		358	470

31 62 19 – Timber Piles

31 62 19.10 Wood Piles

31 62 19.10 Wood Piles	Crew	Daily Output	Labor-Hours	Unit	Material	2015 Bare Costs Labor	2015 Bare Costs Equipment	Total	Total Incl O&P
0010	**WOOD PILES**									
0011	Friction or end bearing, not including									
0050	mobilization or demobilization									
0100	Untreated piles, up to 30' long, 12" butts, 8" points	B-19	625	.102	V.L.F.	16.85	4.88	2.78	24.51	29
0200	30' to 39' long, 12" butts, 8" points		700	.091		16.85	4.36	2.48	23.69	28
0300	40' to 49' long, 12" butts, 7" points		720	.089		16.85	4.23	2.41	23.49	28
0400	50' to 59' long, 13" butts, 7" points		800	.080		16.85	3.81	2.17	22.83	27
0500	60' to 69' long, 13" butts, 7" points		840	.076		18.95	3.63	2.07	24.65	29
0600	70' to 80' long, 13" butts, 6" points		840	.076		21	3.63	2.07	26.70	31
0800	Treated piles, 12 lb. per C.F.,									
0810	friction or end bearing, ASTM class B									
1000	Up to 30' long, 12" butts, 8" points	B-19	625	.102	V.L.F.	15.85	4.88	2.78	23.51	28
1100	30' to 39' long, 12" butts, 8" points		700	.091		17.80	4.36	2.48	24.64	29
1200	40' to 49' long, 12" butts, 7" points		720	.089		19.35	4.23	2.41	25.99	31
1300	50' to 59' long, 13" butts, 7" points		800	.080		22	3.81	2.17	27.98	32.50
1400	60' to 69' long, 13" butts, 6" points	B-19A	840	.076		26	3.63	2.58	32.21	37
1500	70' to 80' long, 13" butts, 6" points	"	840	.076		28	3.63	2.58	34.21	39.50
1600	Treated piles, C.C.A., 2.5# per C.F.									
1610	8" butts, 10' long	B-19	400	.160	V.L.F.	18.40	7.60	4.34	30.34	36.50
1620	11' to 16' long		500	.128		18.40	6.10	3.47	27.97	33.50
1630	17' to 20' long		575	.111		18.40	5.30	3.02	26.72	31.50
1640	10" butts, 10' to 16' long		500	.128		18.40	6.10	3.47	27.97	33.50
1650	17' to 20' long		575	.111		18.40	5.30	3.02	26.72	31.50
1660	21' to 40' long		700	.091		18.40	4.36	2.48	25.24	29.50
1670	12" butts, 10' to 20' long		575	.111		18.40	5.30	3.02	26.72	31.50
1680	21' to 35' long		650	.098		18.40	4.69	2.67	25.76	30
1690	36' to 40' long		700	.091		18.40	4.36	2.48	25.24	29.50
1695	14" butts, to 40' long		700	.091		18.40	4.36	2.48	25.24	29.50
1700	Boot for pile tip, minimum	1 Pile	27	.296	Ea.	23	13.65		36.65	47
1800	Maximum		21	.381		69.50	17.55		87.05	105
2000	Point for pile tip, minimum		20	.400		23	18.45		41.45	54.50
2100	Maximum		15	.533		83.50	24.50		108	131
2300	Splice for piles over 50' long, minimum	B-46	35	1.371		57	58	1.29	116.29	155
2400	Maximum		20	2.400		68.50	101	2.26	171.76	236
2600	Concrete encasement with wire mesh and tube		331	.145	V.L.F.	10.60	6.10	.14	16.84	21.50
2700	Mobilization for 10,000 L.F. pile job, add	B-19	3300	.019			.92	.53	1.45	2.02
2800	25,000 L.F. pile job, add	"	8500	.008			.36	.20	.56	.78
2900	Mobilization by water for barge driving rig, add								100%	100%

For customer support on your Site Work & Landscape Cost Data, call 877.737.1594.

337

31 62 19.30 Marine Wood Piles	Crew	Daily Output	Labor-Hours	Unit	Material	2015 Bare Costs Labor	Equipment	Total	Total Incl O&P
0010 **MARINE WOOD PILES**									
0040 Friction or end bearing, not including									
0050 mobilization or demobilization									
0055 Marine piles includes production adjusted									
0060 due to thickness of silt layers									
0090 Shore driven piles with silt layer									
1000 Shore driven 50' untreated pile, 13" butts, 7" points, 10' silt	B-19	952	.067	V.L.F.	16.85	3.20	1.82	21.87	25.50
1050 55' untreated pile		936	.068		16.85	3.26	1.86	21.97	25.50
1075 60' untreated pile		969	.066		18.95	3.15	1.79	23.89	28
1100 65' untreated pile		958	.067		18.95	3.18	1.81	23.94	28
1125 70' untreated pile, 6" points		948	.068		21	3.22	1.83	26.05	30
1150 75' untreated pile, 6" points		940	.068		21	3.24	1.85	26.09	30
1175 80' untreated pile, 6" points		933	.069		21	3.27	1.86	26.13	30
1200 50' treated pile, 7" points		952	.067		22	3.20	1.82	27.02	31
1225 55' treated pile, 7" points		936	.068		22	3.26	1.86	27.12	31
1250 60' treated pile, 6" points		969	.066		26	3.15	1.79	30.94	35.50
1275 65' treated pile, 6" points		958	.067		26	3.18	1.81	30.99	35.50
1300 70' treated pile, 6" points		948	.068		28	3.22	1.83	33.05	38
1325 75' treated pile, 6" points		940	.068		28	3.24	1.85	33.09	38
1350 80' treated pile, 6" points		933	.069		28	3.27	1.86	33.13	38
1400 Shore driven 50' untreated pile, 13" butts, 7" points, 15' silt		1053	.061		16.85	2.90	1.65	21.40	25
1450 55' untreated pile		1023	.063		16.85	2.98	1.70	21.53	25
1475 60' untreated pile		1050	.061		18.95	2.90	1.65	23.50	27.50
1500 65' untreated pile		1030	.062		18.95	2.96	1.69	23.60	27.50
1525 70' untreated pile, 6" points		1013	.063		21	3.01	1.71	25.72	29.50
1550 75' untreated pile, 6" points		1000	.064		21	3.05	1.74	25.79	29.50
1575 80' untreated pile, 6" points		988	.065		21	3.09	1.76	25.85	29.50
1600 50' treated pile, 7" points		1053	.061		22	2.90	1.65	26.55	30.50
1625 55' treated pile, 7" points		1023	.063		22	2.98	1.70	26.68	30.50
1650 60' treated pile, 6" points		1050	.061		26	2.90	1.65	30.55	35
1675 65' treated pile, 6" points		1030	.062		26	2.96	1.69	30.65	35
1700 70' treated pile, 6" points		1014	.063		28	3.01	1.71	32.72	37.50
1725 75' treated pile, 6" points		1000	.064		28	3.05	1.74	32.79	37.50
1750 80' treated pile, 6" points		988	.065		28	3.09	1.76	32.85	37.50
1800 Shore driven 50' untreated pile, 13" butts, 7" points, 20' silt		1177	.054		16.85	2.59	1.48	20.92	24
1850 55' untreated pile		1128	.057		16.85	2.70	1.54	21.09	24.50
1875 60' untreated pile		1145	.056		18.95	2.66	1.52	23.13	27
1900 65' untreated pile		1114	.057		18.95	2.74	1.56	23.25	27
1925 70' untreated pile, 6" points		1089	.059		21	2.80	1.60	25.40	29
1950 75' untreated pile, 6" points		1068	.060		21	2.86	1.63	25.49	29
1975 80' untreated pile, 6" points		1050	.061		21	2.90	1.65	25.55	29.50
2000 50' treated pile, 7" points		1177	.054		22	2.59	1.48	26.07	29.50
2025 55' treated pile, 7" points		1128	.057		22	2.70	1.54	26.24	30
2050 60' treated pile, 6" points		1145	.056		26	2.66	1.52	30.18	34.50
2075 65' treated pile, 6" points		1114	.057		26	2.74	1.56	30.30	34.50
2100 70' treated pile, 6" points		1089	.059		28	2.80	1.60	32.40	37
2125 75' treated pile, 6" points		1068	.060		28	2.86	1.63	32.49	37
2150 80' treated pile, 6" points		1050	.061		28	2.90	1.65	32.55	37.50
2200 Shore driven 60' untreated pile, 13" butts, 7" points, 25' silt		1260	.051		18.95	2.42	1.38	22.75	26.50
2225 65' untreated pile		1213	.053		18.95	2.51	1.43	22.89	26.50
2250 70' untreated piles, 6" points		1176	.054		21	2.59	1.48	25.07	28.50
2275 75' untreated pile, 6" points		1146	.056		21	2.66	1.52	25.18	29

338

For customer support on your Site Work & Landscape Cost Data, call 877.737.1594.

31 62 Driven Piles

31 62 19 – Timber Piles

31 62 19.30 Marine Wood Piles

		Crew	Daily Output	Labor-Hours	Unit	Material	2015 Bare Costs Labor	Equipment	Total	Total Incl O&P
2300	80' untreated pile, 6" points	B-19	1120	.057	V.L.F.	21	2.72	1.55	25.27	29
2350	60' treated pile, 6" points		1260	.051		26	2.42	1.38	29.80	34
2375	65' treated pile, 6" points		1213	.053		26	2.51	1.43	29.94	34
2400	70' treated pile, 6" points		1176	.054		28	2.59	1.48	32.07	36.50
2425	75' treated pile, 6" points		1146	.056		28	2.66	1.52	32.18	37
2450	80' treated pile, 6" points		1120	.057		28	2.72	1.55	32.27	37
2500	Shore driven 70' untreated pile, 13" butts, 6" points, 30' silt		1278	.050		21	2.39	1.36	24.75	28
2525	75' untreated pile, 6" points		1235	.052		21	2.47	1.41	24.88	28.50
2550	80' untreated pile, 6" points		1200	.053		21	2.54	1.45	24.99	28.50
2600	70' treated pile, 6" points		1278	.050		28	2.39	1.36	31.75	36
2625	75' treated pile, 6" points		1235	.052		28	2.47	1.41	31.88	36.50
2650	80' treated pile, 6" points		1200	.053		28	2.54	1.45	31.99	36.50
2700	Shore driven 70' untreated pile, 13" butts, 6" points, 35' silt		1400	.046		21	2.18	1.24	24.42	28
2725	75' untreated pile, 6" points		1340	.048		21	2.28	1.30	24.58	28
2750	80' untreated pile, 6" points		1292	.050		21	2.36	1.34	24.70	28
2800	70' treated pile, 6" points		1400	.046		28	2.18	1.24	31.42	36
2825	75' treated pile, 6" points		1340	.048		28	2.28	1.30	31.58	36
2850	80' treated pile, 6" points		1292	.050		28	2.36	1.34	31.70	36
2875	Shore driven 75' untreated pile, 13" butts, 6" points, 40' silt		1465	.044		21	2.08	1.19	24.27	27.50
2900	80' untreated pile, 6" points		1400	.046		21	2.18	1.24	24.42	28
2925	75' treated pile, 6" points		1465	.044		28	2.08	1.19	31.27	35.50
2950	80' treated pile, 6" points		1400	.046		28	2.18	1.24	31.42	36
2990	Barge driven piles with silt layer									
3000	Barge driven 50' untreated pile, 13" butts, 7" points, 10' silt	B-19B	762	.084	V.L.F.	16.85	4	3.30	24.15	28.50
3050	55' untreated pile		749	.085		16.85	4.07	3.35	24.27	28.50
3075	60' untreated pile		775	.083		18.95	3.93	3.24	26.12	30.50
3100	65' untreated pile		766	.084		18.95	3.98	3.28	26.21	31
3125	70' untreated pile, 6" points		759	.084		21	4.02	3.31	28.33	33
3150	75' untreated pile, 6" points		752	.085		21	4.05	3.34	28.39	33
3175	80' untreated pile, 6" points		747	.086		21	4.08	3.36	28.44	33
3200	50' treated pile, 7" points		762	.084		22	4	3.30	29.30	34
3225	55' treated pile, 7" points		749	.085		22	4.07	3.35	29.42	34
3250	60' treated pile, 6" points		775	.083		26	3.93	3.24	33.17	38
3275	65' treated pile, 6" points		766	.084		26	3.98	3.28	33.26	38.50
3300	70' treated pile, 6" points		759	.084		28	4.02	3.31	35.33	41
3325	75' treated pile, 6" points		752	.085		28	4.05	3.34	35.39	41
3350	80' treated pile, 6" points		747	.086		28	4.08	3.36	35.44	41
3400	Barge driven 50' untreated pile, 13" butts, 7" points, 15' silt		842	.076		16.85	3.62	2.98	23.45	27.50
3450	55' untreated pile		819	.078		16.85	3.72	3.07	23.64	27.50
3475	60' untreated pile		840	.076		18.95	3.63	2.99	25.57	30
3500	65' untreated pile		824	.078		18.95	3.70	3.05	25.70	30
3525	70' untreated pile, 6" points		811	.079		21	3.76	3.10	27.86	32.50
3550	75' untreated pile, 6" points		800	.080		21	3.81	3.14	27.95	32.50
3575	80' untreated pile, 6" points		791	.081		21	3.85	3.18	28.03	32.50
3600	50' treated pile, 7" points		842	.076		22	3.62	2.98	28.60	33
3625	55' treated pile, 7" points		819	.078		22	3.72	3.07	28.79	33
3650	60' treated pile, 6" points		840	.076		26	3.63	2.99	32.62	37.50
3675	65' treated pile, 6" points		824	.078		26	3.70	3.05	32.75	37.50
3700	70' treated pile, 6" points		811	.079		28	3.76	3.10	34.86	40.50
3725	75' treated pile, 6" points		800	.080		28	3.81	3.14	34.95	40.50
3750	80' treated pile, 6" points		791	.081		28	3.85	3.18	35.03	40.50
3800	Barge driven 50' untreated pile, 13" butts, 7" points, 20' silt		941	.068		16.85	3.24	2.67	22.76	26.50
3850	55' untreated pile		903	.071		16.85	3.38	2.78	23.01	27

31 62 19 – Timber Piles

31 62 19.30 Marine Wood Piles		Crew	Daily Output	Labor-Hours	Unit	Material	2015 Bare Costs			Total Incl O&P
							Labor	Equipment	Total	
3875	60' untreated pile	B-19B	916	.070	V.L.F.	18.95	3.33	2.74	25.02	29
3900	65' untreated pile		891	.072		18.95	3.42	2.82	25.19	29.50
3925	70' untreated pile, 6" points		871	.073		21	3.50	2.88	27.38	31.50
3950	75' untreated pile, 6" points		854	.075		21	3.57	2.94	27.51	32
3975	80' untreated pile, 6" points		840	.076		21	3.63	2.99	27.62	32
4000	50' treated pile, 7" points		941	.068		22	3.24	2.67	27.91	32
4025	55' treated pile, 7" points		903	.071		22	3.38	2.78	28.16	32.50
4050	60' treated pile, 6" points		916	.070		26	3.33	2.74	32.07	36.50
4075	65' treated pile, 6" points		891	.072		26	3.42	2.82	32.24	37
4100	70' treated pile, 6" points		871	.073		28	3.50	2.88	34.38	39.50
4125	75' treated pile, 6" points		854	.075		28	3.57	2.94	34.51	40
4150	80' treated pile, 6" points		840	.076		28	3.63	2.99	34.62	40
4200	Barge driven 60' untreated pile, 13" butts, 7" points, 25' silt		1008	.063		18.95	3.02	2.49	24.46	28.50
4225	65' untreated pile		971	.066		18.95	3.14	2.59	24.68	28.50
4250	70' untreated pile, 6" points		941	.068		21	3.24	2.67	26.91	31
4275	75' untreated pile, 6" points		916	.070		21	3.33	2.74	27.07	31
4300	80' untreated pile, 6" points		896	.071		21	3.40	2.80	27.20	31.50
4350	60' treated pile, 6" points		1008	.063		26	3.02	2.49	31.51	36
4375	65' treated pile, 6" points		971	.066		26	3.14	2.59	31.73	36
4400	70' treated pile, 6" points		941	.068		28	3.24	2.67	33.91	39
4425	75' treated pile, 6" points		916	.070		28	3.33	2.74	34.07	39
4450	80' treated pile, 6" points		896	.071		28	3.40	2.80	34.20	39.50
4500	Barge driven 70' untreated pile, 13" butts, 6" points, 30' silt		1023	.063		21	2.98	2.46	26.44	30.50
4525	75' untreated pile, 6" points		988	.065		21	3.09	2.54	26.63	30.50
4550	80' untreated pile, 6" points		960	.067		21	3.18	2.62	26.80	31
4600	70' treated pile, 6" points		1023	.063		28	2.98	2.46	33.44	38.50
4625	75' treated pile, 6" points		988	.065		28	3.09	2.54	33.63	38.50
4650	80' treated pile, 6" points		960	.067		28	3.18	2.62	33.80	39
4700	Barge driven 70' untreated pile, 13" butts, 6" points, 35' silt		1120	.057		21	2.72	2.24	25.96	29.50
4725	75' untreated pile, 6" points		1072	.060		21	2.84	2.34	26.18	30
4750	80' untreated pile, 6" points		1034	.062		21	2.95	2.43	26.38	30.50
4800	70' treated pile, 6" points		1120	.057		28	2.72	2.24	32.96	37.50
4825	75' treated pile, 6" points		1072	.060		28	2.84	2.34	33.18	38
4850	80' treated pile, 6" points		1034	.062		28	2.95	2.43	33.38	38.50
4875	Barge driven 75' untreated pile, 13" butts, 6" points, 40' silt		1172	.055		21	2.60	2.14	25.74	29.50
4900	80' untreated pile, 6" points		1120	.057		21	2.72	2.24	25.96	29.50
4925	75' treated pile, 6" points		1172	.055		28	2.60	2.14	32.74	37.50
4950	80' treated pile, 6" points		1120	.057		28	2.72	2.24	32.96	37.50
5000	Piles, wood, treated, added undriven length, 13" butt					28			28	31
5020	Untreated pile, 13" butts					21			21	23

31 62 23 – Composite Piles

31 62 23.10 Recycled Plastic and Steel Piles

0010	**RECYCLED PLASTIC AND STEEL PILES**, 200 PILES		Crew	Daily Output	Labor-Hours	Unit	Material	Labor	Equipment	Total	Total Incl O&P
5000	Marine pilings, recycled plastic w/steel reinf, up to 90' long, 8" dia	G	B-19	500	.128	V.L.F.	31	6.10	3.47	40.57	47.50
5010	10" dia	G		500	.128		38	6.10	3.47	47.57	55.50
5020	13" dia	G		400	.160		53.50	7.60	4.34	65.44	75
5030	16" dia	G		400	.160		67.50	7.60	4.34	79.44	91
5040	20" dia	G		350	.183		94	8.70	4.96	107.66	123
5050	24" dia	G		350	.183		119	8.70	4.96	132.66	149

31 62 Driven Piles

31 62 23 – Composite Piles

31 62 23.12 Marine Recycled Plastic and Steel Piles, 200 Piles	Crew	Daily Output	Labor-Hours	Unit	Material	2015 Bare Costs Labor	Equipment	Total	Total Incl O&P
0010 **MARINE RECYCLED PLASTIC AND STEEL PILES, 200 PILES**									
0040 Friction or end bearing, not including									
0050 mobilization or demobilization									
0055 Marine piles includes production adjusted									
0060 due to thickness of silt layers									
0090 Shore driven piles with silt layer									
0100 Marine pilings, recycled plastic w/steel, 50' long, 8" dia,10' silt G	B-19	595	.108	V.L.F.	31	5.10	2.92	39.02	45
0110 50' long, 10" dia G		595	.108		38	5.10	2.92	46.02	53
0120 50' long, 13" dia G		476	.134		53.50	6.40	3.65	63.55	72.50
0130 50' long, 16" dia G		476	.134		67.50	6.40	3.65	77.55	88.50
0140 50' long, 20" dia G		417	.153		94	7.30	4.17	105.47	120
0150 50' long, 24" dia G		417	.153		119	7.30	4.17	130.47	146
0210 55' long, 8" dia G		585	.109		31	5.20	2.97	39.17	45.50
0220 55' long, 10" dia G		585	.109		38	5.20	2.97	46.17	53.50
0230 55' long, 13" dia G		468	.137		53.50	6.50	3.71	63.71	72.50
0240 55' long, 16" dia G		468	.137		67.50	6.50	3.71	77.71	88.50
0250 55' long, 20" dia G		410	.156		94	7.45	4.24	105.69	120
0260 55' long, 24" dia G		410	.156		119	7.45	4.24	130.69	146
0310 60' long, 8" dia G		576	.111		31	5.30	3.02	39.32	45.50
0320 60' long, 10" dia G		577	.111		38	5.30	3.01	46.31	53.50
0330 60' long, 13" dia G		462	.139		53.50	6.60	3.76	63.86	73
0340 60' long, 16" dia G		462	.139		67.50	6.60	3.76	77.86	89
0350 60' long, 20" dia G		404	.158		94	7.55	4.30	105.85	120
0360 60' long, 24" dia G		404	.158		119	7.55	4.30	130.85	146
0410 65' long, 8" dia G		570	.112		31	5.35	3.05	39.40	45.50
0420 65' long, 10" dia G		570	.112		38	5.35	3.05	46.40	53.50
0430 65' long, 13" dia G		456	.140		53.50	6.70	3.81	64.01	73
0440 65' long, 16" dia G		456	.140		67.50	6.70	3.81	78.01	89
0450 65' long, 20" dia G		399	.160		94	7.65	4.35	106	121
0460 65' long, 24" dia G		399	.160		119	7.65	4.35	131	147
0510 70' long, 8" dia G		565	.113		31	5.40	3.07	39.47	46
0520 70' long, 10" dia G		565	.113		38	5.40	3.07	46.47	54
0530 70' long, 13" dia G		452	.142		53.50	6.75	3.84	64.09	73
0540 70' long, 16" dia G		452	.142		67.50	6.75	3.84	78.09	89
0550 70' long, 20" dia G		395	.162		94	7.70	4.40	106.10	121
0560 70' long, 24" dia G		399	.160		119	7.65	4.35	131	147
0610 75' long, 8" dia G		560	.114		31	5.45	3.10	39.55	46
0620 75' long, 10" dia G		560	.114		38	5.45	3.10	46.55	54
0630 75' long, 13" dia G		448	.143		53.50	6.80	3.88	64.18	73.50
0640 75' long, 16" dia G		448	.143		67.50	6.80	3.88	78.18	89.50
0650 75' long, 20" dia G		392	.163		94	7.80	4.43	106.23	121
0660 75' long, 24" dia G		392	.163		119	7.80	4.43	131.23	147
0710 80' long, 8" dia G		556	.115		31	5.50	3.12	39.62	46
0720 80' long, 10" dia G		556	.115		38	5.50	3.12	46.62	54
0730 80' long, 13" dia G		444	.144		53.50	6.85	3.91	64.26	73.50
0740 80' long, 16" dia G		444	.144		67.50	6.85	3.91	78.26	89.50
0750 80' long, 20" dia G		389	.165		94	7.85	4.47	106.32	121
0760 80' long, 24" dia G		389	.165		119	7.85	4.47	131.32	147
1000 Marine pilings, recycled plastic w/steel, 50' long, 8" dia,15' silt G		658	.097		31	4.63	2.64	38.27	44
1010 50' long, 10" dia G		658	.097		38	4.63	2.64	45.27	52
1020 50' long, 13" dia G		526	.122		53.50	5.80	3.30	62.60	71
1030 50' long, 16" dia G		526	.122		67.50	5.80	3.30	76.60	87

For customer support on your Site Work & Landscape Cost Data, call 877.737.1594.

341

31 62 23.12 Marine Recycled Plastic and Steel Piles, 200 Piles	Crew	Daily Output	Labor-Hours	Unit	Material	2015 Bare Costs Labor	Equipment	Total	Total Incl O&P
1040	50' long, 20" dia	G	B-19	461	.139	V.L.F.	94	6.60	3.77	104.37	118
1050	50' long, 24" dia	G		461	.139		119	6.60	3.77	129.37	144
1210	55' long, 8" dia	G		640	.100		31	4.76	2.71	38.47	44.50
1220	55' long, 10" dia	G		640	.100		38	4.76	2.71	45.47	52.50
1230	55' long, 13" dia	G		512	.125		53.50	5.95	3.39	62.84	71.50
1240	55' long, 16" dia	G		512	.125		67.50	5.95	3.39	76.84	87.50
1250	55' long, 20" dia	G		448	.143		94	6.80	3.88	104.68	119
1260	55' long, 24" dia	G		448	.143		119	6.80	3.88	129.68	145
1310	60' long, 8" dia	G		625	.102		31	4.88	2.78	38.66	44.50
1320	60' long, 10" dia	G		625	.102		38	4.88	2.78	45.66	52.50
1330	60' long, 13" dia	G		500	.128		53.50	6.10	3.47	63.07	72
1340	60' long, 16" dia	G		500	.128		67.50	6.10	3.47	77.07	88
1350	60' long, 20" dia	G		438	.146		94	6.95	3.97	104.92	119
1360	60' long, 24" dia	G		438	.146		119	6.95	3.97	129.92	145
1410	65' long, 8" dia	G		613	.104		31	4.97	2.83	38.80	45
1420	65' long, 10" dia	G		613	.104		38	4.97	2.83	45.80	53
1430	65' long, 13" dia	G		491	.130		53.50	6.20	3.54	63.24	72
1440	65' long, 16" dia	G		491	.130		67.50	6.20	3.54	77.24	88
1450	65' long, 20" dia	G		429	.149		94	7.10	4.05	105.15	120
1460	65' long, 24" dia	G		429	.149		119	7.10	4.05	130.15	146
1510	70' long, 8" dia	G		603	.106		31	5.05	2.88	38.93	45
1520	70' long, 10" dia	G		603	.106		38	5.05	2.88	45.93	53
1530	70' long, 13" dia	G		483	.133		53.50	6.30	3.60	63.40	72.50
1540	70' long, 16" dia	G		483	.133		67.50	6.30	3.60	77.40	88.50
1550	70' long, 20" dia	G		422	.152		94	7.25	4.12	105.37	120
1560	70' long, 24" dia	G		422	.152		119	7.25	4.12	130.37	146
1610	75' long, 8" dia	G		595	.108		31	5.10	2.92	39.02	45
1620	75' long, 10" dia	G		595	.108		38	5.10	2.92	46.02	53
1630	75' long, 13" dia	G		476	.134		53.50	6.40	3.65	63.55	72.50
1640	75' long, 16" dia	G		476	.134		67.50	6.40	3.65	77.55	88.50
1650	75' long, 20" dia	G		417	.153		94	7.30	4.17	105.47	120
1660	75' long, 24" dia	G		417	.153		119	7.30	4.17	130.47	146
1710	80' long, 8" dia	G		588	.109		31	5.20	2.95	39.15	45.50
1720	80' long, 10" dia	G		588	.109		38	5.20	2.95	46.15	53.50
1730	80' long, 13" dia	G		471	.136		53.50	6.45	3.69	63.64	72.50
1740	80' long, 16" dia	G		471	.136		67.50	6.45	3.69	77.64	88.50
1750	80' long, 20" dia	G		412	.155		94	7.40	4.22	105.62	120
1760	80' long, 24" dia	G		412	.155		119	7.40	4.22	130.62	146
2000	Marine pilings, recycled plastic w/steel, 50' long, 8" dia, 20' silt	G		735	.087		31	4.15	2.36	37.51	43
2010	50' long, 10" dia	G		735	.087		38	4.15	2.36	44.51	51
2020	50' long, 13" dia	G		588	.109		53.50	5.20	2.95	61.65	70
2030	50' long, 16" dia	G		588	.109		67.50	5.20	2.95	75.65	86
2040	50' long, 20" dia	G		515	.124		94	5.90	3.37	103.27	117
2050	50' long, 24" dia	G		515	.124		119	5.90	3.37	128.27	143
2210	55' long, 8" dia	G		705	.091		31	4.32	2.46	37.78	43.50
2220	55' long, 10" dia	G		705	.091		38	4.32	2.46	44.78	51.50
2230	55' long, 13" dia	G		564	.113		53.50	5.40	3.08	61.98	70.50
2240	55' long, 16" dia	G		564	.113		67.50	5.40	3.08	75.98	86.50
2250	55' long, 20" dia	G		494	.130		94	6.15	3.52	103.67	117
2260	55' long, 24" dia	G		494	.130		119	6.15	3.52	128.67	143
2310	60' long, 8" dia	G		682	.094		31	4.47	2.55	38.02	44
2320	60' long, 10" dia	G		682	.094		38	4.47	2.55	45.02	52
2330	60' long, 13" dia	G		546	.117		53.50	5.60	3.18	62.28	70.50

31 62 23.12 Marine Recycled Plastic and Steel Piles, 200 Piles		Crew	Daily Output	Labor-Hours	Unit	Material	2015 Bare Costs Labor	Equipment	Total	Total Incl O&P
2340	60' long, 16" dia	G B-19	546	.117	V.L.F.	67.50	5.60	3.18	76.28	86.50
2350	60' long, 20" dia	G	477	.134		94	6.40	3.64	104.04	118
2360	60' long, 24" dia	G	477	.134		119	6.40	3.64	129.04	144
2410	65' long, 8" dia	G	663	.097		31	4.60	2.62	38.22	44
2420	65' long, 10" dia	G	663	.097		38	4.60	2.62	45.22	52
2430	65' long, 13" dia	G	531	.121		53.50	5.75	3.27	62.52	71
2440	65' long, 16" dia	G	531	.121		67.50	5.75	3.27	76.52	87
2450	65' long, 20" dia	G	464	.138		94	6.55	3.74	104.29	118
2460	65' long, 24" dia	G	464	.138		119	6.55	3.74	129.29	144
2510	70' long, 8" dia	G	648	.099		31	4.71	2.68	38.39	44.50
2520	70' long, 10" dia	G	648	.099		38	4.71	2.68	45.39	52.50
2530	70' long, 13" dia	G	518	.124		53.50	5.90	3.35	62.75	71.50
2540	70' long, 16" dia	G	518	.124		67.50	5.90	3.35	76.75	87.50
2550	70' long, 20" dia	G	454	.141		94	6.70	3.83	104.53	119
2560	70' long, 24" dia	G	454	.141		119	6.70	3.83	129.53	145
2610	75' long, 8" dia	G	636	.101		31	4.79	2.73	38.52	44.50
2620	75' long, 10" dia	G	636	.101		38	4.79	2.73	45.52	52.50
2630	75' long, 13" dia	G	508	.126		53.50	6	3.42	62.92	71.50
2640	75' long, 16" dia	G	508	.126		67.50	6	3.42	76.92	87.50
2650	75' long, 20" dia	G	445	.144		94	6.85	3.90	104.75	119
2660	75' long, 24" dia	G	445	.144		119	6.85	3.90	129.75	145
2710	80' long, 8" dia	G	625	.102		31	4.88	2.78	38.66	44.50
2720	80' long, 10" dia	G	625	.102		38	4.88	2.78	45.66	52.50
2730	80' long, 13" dia	G	500	.128		53.50	6.10	3.47	63.07	72
2740	80' long, 16" dia	G	500	.128		67.50	6.10	3.47	77.07	88
2750	80' long, 20" dia	G	437	.146		94	7	3.97	104.97	119
2760	80' long, 24" dia	G	437	.146		119	7	3.97	129.97	145
4990	Barge driven piles with silt layer									
5100	Marine pilings, recycled plastic w/steel, 50' long, 8" dia,10' silt	G B-19B	476	.134	V.L.F.	31	6.40	5.30	42.70	50
5110	50' long, 10" dia	G	476	.134		38	6.40	5.30	49.70	58
5120	50' long, 13" dia	G	381	.168		53.50	8	6.60	68.10	78
5130	50' long, 16" dia	G	381	.168		67.50	8	6.60	82.10	94
5140	50' long, 20" dia	G	333	.192		94	9.15	7.55	110.70	127
5150	50' long, 24" dia	G	333	.192		119	9.15	7.55	135.70	153
5210	55' long, 8" dia	G	468	.137		31	6.50	5.35	42.85	50
5220	55' long, 10" dia	G	468	.137		38	6.50	5.35	49.85	58
5230	55' long, 13" dia	G	374	.171		53.50	8.15	6.70	68.35	78.50
5240	55' long, 16" dia	G	374	.171		67.50	8.15	6.70	82.35	94.50
5250	55' long, 20" dia	G	328	.195		94	9.30	7.65	110.95	127
5260	55' long, 24" dia	G	328	.195		119	9.30	7.65	135.95	153
5310	60' long, 8" dia	G	461	.139		31	6.60	5.45	43.05	50.50
5320	60' long, 10" dia	G	461	.139		38	6.60	5.45	50.05	58.50
5330	60' long, 13" dia	G	369	.173		53.50	8.25	6.80	68.55	79
5340	60' long, 16" dia	G	369	.173		67.50	8.25	6.80	82.55	95
5350	60' long, 20" dia	G	323	.198		94	9.45	7.80	111.25	127
5360	60' long, 24" dia	G	323	.198		119	9.45	7.80	136.25	153
5410	65' long, 8" dia	G	456	.140		31	6.70	5.50	43.20	50.50
5420	65' long, 10" dia	G	456	.140		38	6.70	5.50	50.20	58.50
5430	65' long, 13" dia	G	365	.175		53.50	8.35	6.90	68.75	79
5440	65' long, 16" dia	G	365	.175		67.50	8.35	6.90	82.75	95
5450	65' long, 20" dia	G	319	.201		94	9.55	7.90	111.45	128
5460	65' long, 24" dia	G	319	.201		119	9.55	7.90	136.45	154
5510	70' long, 8" dia	G	452	.142		31	6.75	5.55	43.30	50.50

For customer support on your Site Work & Landscape Cost Data, call 877.737.1594.

343

31 62 23.12 Marine Recycled Plastic and Steel Piles, 200 Piles		Crew	Daily Output	Labor-Hours	Unit	Material	2015 Bare Costs Labor	Equipment	Total	Total Incl O&P
5520	70' long, 10" dia	G	B-19B	452	.142	V.L.F.	38	6.75	5.55	50.30	58.50
5530	70' long, 13" dia	G		361	.177		53.50	8.45	6.95	68.90	79.50
5540	70' long, 16" dia	G		361	.177		67.50	8.45	6.95	82.90	95.50
5550	70' long, 20" dia	G		316	.203		94	9.65	7.95	111.60	128
5560	70' long, 24" dia	G		316	.203		119	9.65	7.95	136.60	154
5610	75' long, 8" dia	G		448	.143		31	6.80	5.60	43.40	51
5620	75' long, 10" dia	G		448	.143		38	6.80	5.60	50.40	59
5630	75' long, 13" dia	G		358	.179		53.50	8.50	7	69	79.50
5640	75' long, 16" dia	G		358	.179		67.50	8.50	7	83	95.50
5650	75' long, 20" dia	G		313	.204		94	9.75	8.05	111.80	128
5660	75' long, 24" dia	G		313	.204		119	9.75	8.05	136.80	154
5710	80' long, 8" dia	G		444	.144		31	6.85	5.65	43.50	51
5720	80' long, 10" dia	G		444	.144		38	6.85	5.65	50.50	59
5730	80' long, 13" dia	G		356	.180		53.50	8.55	7.05	69.10	79.50
5740	80' long, 16" dia	G		356	.180		67.50	8.55	7.05	83.10	95.50
5750	80' long, 20" dia	G		311	.206		94	9.80	8.10	111.90	128
5760	80' long, 24" dia	G		311	.206		119	9.80	8.10	136.90	154
6100	Marine pilings, recycled plastic w/steel, 50' long, 8" dia,15' silt	G		526	.122		31	5.80	4.78	41.58	48.50
6110	50' long, 10" dia	G		526	.122		38	5.80	4.78	48.58	56.50
6120	50' long, 13" dia	G		421	.152		53.50	7.25	5.95	66.70	76.50
6130	50' long, 16" dia	G		421	.152		67.50	7.25	5.95	80.70	92.50
6140	50' long, 20" dia	G		368	.174		94	8.30	6.85	109.15	124
6150	50' long, 24" dia	G		368	.174		119	8.30	6.85	134.15	150
6210	55' long, 8" dia	G		512	.125		31	5.95	4.91	41.86	48.50
6220	55' long, 10" dia	G		512	.125		38	5.95	4.91	48.86	56.50
6230	55' long, 13" dia	G		409	.156		53.50	7.45	6.15	67.10	77
6240	55' long, 16" dia	G		409	.156		67.50	7.45	6.15	81.10	93
6250	55' long, 20" dia	G		358	.179		94	8.50	7	109.50	125
6260	55' long, 24" dia	G		358	.179		119	8.50	7	134.50	151
6310	60' long, 8" dia	G		500	.128		31	6.10	5.05	42.15	49
6320	60' long, 10" dia	G		500	.128		38	6.10	5.05	49.15	57
6330	60' long, 13" dia	G		400	.160		53.50	7.60	6.30	67.40	77.50
6340	60' long, 16" dia	G		400	.160		67.50	7.60	6.30	81.40	93.50
6350	60' long, 20" dia	G		350	.183		94	8.70	7.20	109.90	125
6360	60' long, 24" dia	G		350	.183		119	8.70	7.20	134.90	151
6410	65' long, 8" dia	G		491	.130		31	6.20	5.10	42.30	49.50
6420	65' long, 10" dia	G		491	.130		38	6.20	5.10	49.30	57.50
6430	65' long, 13" dia	G		392	.163		53.50	7.80	6.40	67.70	77.50
6440	65' long, 16" dia	G		392	.163		67.50	7.80	6.40	81.70	93.50
6450	65' long, 20" dia	G		343	.187		94	8.90	7.35	110.25	126
6460	65' long, 24" dia	G		343	.187		119	8.90	7.35	135.25	152
6510	70' long, 8" dia	G		483	.133		31	6.30	5.20	42.50	49.50
6520	70' long, 10" dia	G		483	.133		38	6.30	5.20	49.50	57.50
6530	70' long, 13" dia	G		386	.166		53.50	7.90	6.50	67.90	78
6540	70' long, 16" dia	G		386	.166		67.50	7.90	6.50	81.90	94
6550	70' long, 20" dia	G		338	.189		94	9	7.45	110.45	126
6560	70' long, 24" dia	G		338	.189		119	9	7.45	135.45	152
6610	75' long, 8" dia	G		476	.134		31	6.40	5.30	42.70	50
6620	75' long, 10" dia	G		476	.134		38	6.40	5.30	49.70	58
6630	75' long, 13" dia	G		381	.168		53.50	8	6.60	68.10	78
6640	75' long, 16" dia	G		381	.168		67.50	8	6.60	82.10	94
6650	75' long, 20" dia	G		333	.192		94	9.15	7.55	110.70	127
6660	75' long, 24" dia	G		333	.192		119	9.15	7.55	135.70	153

For customer support on your Site Work & Landscape Cost Data, call 877.737.1594.

31 62 23 – Composite Piles

31 62 23.12 Marine Recycled Plastic and Steel Piles, 200 Piles	Crew	Daily Output	Labor-Hours	Unit	Material	2015 Bare Costs Labor	Equipment	Total	Total Incl O&P
6710	80' long, 8" dia	B-19B	471	.136	V.L.F.	31	6.45	5.35	42.80	50
6720	80' long, 10" dia G		471	.136		38	6.45	5.35	49.80	58
6730	80' long, 13" dia G		376	.170		53.50	8.10	6.70	68.30	78.50
6740	80' long, 16" dia G		376	.170		67.50	8.10	6.70	82.30	94.50
6750	80' long, 20" dia G		329	.195		94	9.25	7.65	110.90	127
6760	80' long, 24" dia G		329	.195		119	9.25	7.65	135.90	153
7100	Marine pilings, recycled plastic w/steel, 50' long, 8" dia,20' silt G		588	.109		31	5.20	4.27	40.47	47
7110	50' long, 10" dia G		588	.109		38	5.20	4.27	47.47	55
7120	50' long, 13" dia G		471	.136		53.50	6.45	5.35	65.30	74.50
7130	50' long, 16" dia G		471	.136		67.50	6.45	5.35	79.30	90.50
7140	50' long, 20" dia G		412	.155		94	7.40	6.10	107.50	122
7150	50' long, 24" dia G		412	.155		119	7.40	6.10	132.50	148
7210	55' long, 8" dia G		564	.113		31	5.40	4.46	40.86	47.50
7220	55' long, 10" dia G		564	.113		38	5.40	4.46	47.86	55.50
7230	55' long, 13" dia G		451	.142		53.50	6.75	5.55	65.80	75
7240	55' long, 16" dia G		451	.142		67.50	6.75	5.55	79.80	91
7250	55' long, 20" dia G		395	.162		94	7.70	6.35	108.05	123
7260	55' long, 24" dia G		395	.162		119	7.70	6.35	133.05	149
7310	60' long, 8" dia G		545	.117		31	5.60	4.61	41.21	48
7320	60' long, 10" dia G		545	.117		38	5.60	4.61	48.21	56
7330	60' long, 13" dia G		436	.147		53.50	7	5.75	66.25	76
7340	60' long, 16" dia G		436	.147		67.50	7	5.75	80.25	92
7350	60' long, 20" dia G		382	.168		94	8	6.60	108.60	124
7360	60' long, 24" dia G		382	.168		119	8	6.60	133.60	150
7410	65' long, 8" dia G		531	.121		31	5.75	4.73	41.48	48
7420	65' long, 10" dia G		531	.121		38	5.75	4.73	48.48	56
7430	65' long, 13" dia G		424	.151		53.50	7.20	5.95	66.65	76
7440	65' long, 16" dia G		424	.151		67.50	7.20	5.95	80.65	92
7450	65' long, 20" dia G		371	.173		94	8.20	6.75	108.95	124
7460	65' long, 24" dia G		371	.173		119	8.20	6.75	133.95	150
7510	70' long, 8" dia G		518	.124		31	5.90	4.85	41.75	48.50
7520	70' long, 10" dia G		518	.124		38	5.90	4.85	48.75	56.50
7530	70' long, 13" dia G		415	.154		53.50	7.35	6.05	66.90	76.50
7540	70' long, 16" dia G		415	.154		67.50	7.35	6.05	80.90	92.50
7550	70' long, 20" dia G		363	.176		94	8.40	6.90	109.30	125
7560	70' long, 24" dia G		363	.176		119	8.40	6.90	134.30	151
7610	75' long, 8" dia G		508	.126		31	6	4.95	41.95	49
7620	75' long, 10" dia G		508	.126		38	6	4.95	48.95	57
7630	75' long, 13" dia G		407	.157		53.50	7.50	6.15	67.15	77
7640	75' long, 16" dia G		407	.157		67.50	7.50	6.15	81.15	93
7650	75' long, 20" dia G		356	.180		94	8.55	7.05	109.60	125
7660	75' long, 24" dia G		356	.180		119	8.55	7.05	134.60	151
7710	80' long, 8" dia G		500	.128		31	6.10	5.05	42.15	49
7720	80' long, 10" dia G		500	.128		38	6.10	5.05	49.15	57
7730	80' long, 13" dia G		400	.160		53.50	7.60	6.30	67.40	77.50
7740	80' long, 16" dia G		400	.160		67.50	7.60	6.30	81.40	93.50
7750	80' long, 20" dia G		350	.183		94	8.70	7.20	109.90	125
7760	80' long, 24" dia G		350	.183		119	8.70	7.20	134.90	151

31 62 23.13 Concrete-Filled Steel Piles

		Crew	Daily Output	Labor-Hours	Unit	Material	Labor	Equipment	Total	Total Incl O&P
0010	**CONCRETE-FILLED STEEL PILES** no mobilization or demobilization									
2600	Pipe piles, 50' lg. 8" diam., 29 lb. per L.F., no concrete	B-19	500	.128	V.L.F.	20.50	6.10	3.47	30.07	36
2700	Concrete filled		460	.139		21.50	6.65	3.78	31.93	38

For customer support on your Site Work & Landscape Cost Data, call 877.737.1594.

345

31 62 Driven Piles

31 62 23 – Composite Piles

31 62 23.13 Concrete-Filled Steel Piles

		Crew	Daily Output	Labor-Hours	Unit	Material	2015 Bare Costs Labor	Equipment	Total	Total Incl O&P
2900	10" diameter, 34 lb. per L.F., no concrete	B-19	500	.128	V.L.F.	27	6.10	3.47	36.57	43.50
3000	Concrete filled		450	.142		29	6.80	3.86	39.66	47
3200	12" diameter, 44 lb. per L.F., no concrete		475	.135		33	6.40	3.66	43.06	50.50
3300	Concrete filled		415	.154		37	7.35	4.19	48.54	57
3500	14" diameter, 46 lb. per L.F., no concrete		430	.149		35.50	7.10	4.04	46.64	55
3600	Concrete filled		355	.180		41.50	8.60	4.89	54.99	64.50
3800	16" diameter, 52 lb. per L.F., no concrete		385	.166		39	7.90	4.51	51.41	60.50
3900	Concrete filled		335	.191		45.50	9.10	5.20	59.80	70
4100	18" diameter, 59 lb. per L.F., no concrete		355	.180		48.50	8.60	4.89	61.99	72.50
4200	Concrete filled	▼	310	.206	▼	54.50	9.85	5.60	69.95	81.50
4400	Splices for pipe piles, not in leads, 8" diameter	1 Sswl	4.67	1.713	Ea.	90.50	90		180.50	257
4500	14" diameter		3.79	2.111		119	111		230	325
4600	16" diameter		3.03	2.640		147	139		286	400
4650	18" diameter		4.50	1.778		194	93.50		287.50	375
4800	Points, standard, 8" diameter		4.61	1.735		148	91.50		239.50	320
4900	14" diameter		4.05	1.975		206	104		310	405
5000	16" diameter		3.37	2.374		251	125		376	495
5050	18" diameter		5	1.600		390	84		474	575
5200	Points, heavy duty, 10" diameter		2.89	2.768		296	146		442	580
5300	14" or 16" diameter		2.02	3.960	▼	475	209		684	880
5500	For reinforcing steel, add	▼	1150	.007	Lb.	.93	.37		1.30	1.66
5700	For thick wall sections, add				"	.96			.96	1.06
6020	Steel pipe pile end plates, 8" diameter	1 Sswl	14	.571	Ea.	78	30		108	139
6050	10" diameter		14	.571		82	30		112	143
6100	12" diameter		12	.667		87	35		122	157
6150	14" diameter		10	.800		90	42		132	172
6200	16" diameter		9	.889		96	47		143	188
6250	18" diameter		8	1		108	52.50		160.50	211
6300	Steel pipe pile shoes, 8" diameter		12	.667		160	35		195	237
6350	10" diameter		12	.667		166	35		201	243
6400	12" diameter		10	.800		177	42		219	268
6450	14" diameter		9	.889		204	47		251	305
6500	16" diameter		8	1		227	52.50		279.50	340
6550	18" diameter	▼	6	1.333	▼	254	70		324	400

31 62 33 – Drilled Micropiles

31 62 33.10 Drilled Micropiles Metal Pipe

		Crew	Daily Output	Labor-Hours	Unit	Material	2015 Bare Costs Labor	Equipment	Total	Total Incl O&P
0010	**DRILLED MICROPILES METAL PIPE**									
0011	No mobilization or demobilization									
5000	Pressure grouted pin pile, 5" diam., cased, up to 50 ton,									
5040	End bearing, less than 20'	B-48	90	.622	V.L.F.	49.50	26.50	32.50	108.50	130
5080	More than 40'		135	.415		29.50	17.65	21.50	68.65	82.50
5120	Friction, loose sand and gravel		107	.523		49.50	22.50	27	99	118
5160	Dense sand and gravel		135	.415		29.50	17.65	21.50	68.65	82.50
5200	Uncased, up to 10 ton capacity, 20'	▼	135	.415	▼	29	17.65	21.50	68.15	82.50

31 63 26.13 Fixed End Caisson Piles		Crew	Daily Output	Labor-Hours	Unit	Material	2015 Bare Costs Labor	Equipment	Total	Total Incl O&P
0010	**FIXED END CAISSON PILES** R316326-60									
0015	Including excavation, concrete, 50 lb. reinforcing									
0020	per C.Y., not incl. mobilization, boulder removal, disposal									
0100	Open style, machine drilled, to 50' deep, in stable ground, no									
0110	casings or ground water, 18" diam., 0.065 C.Y./L.F.	B-43	200	.240	V.L.F.	8.15	9.95	12.70	30.80	38
0200	24" diameter, 0.116 C.Y./L.F.		190	.253		14.60	10.50	13.40	38.50	47
0300	30" diameter, 0.182 C.Y./L.F.		150	.320		23	13.30	16.95	53.25	64
0400	36" diameter, 0.262 C.Y./L.F.		125	.384		33	15.95	20.50	69.45	83
0500	48" diameter, 0.465 C.Y./L.F.		100	.480		58.50	19.95	25.50	103.95	123
0600	60" diameter, 0.727 C.Y./L.F.		90	.533		91.50	22	28.50	142	166
0700	72" diameter, 1.05 C.Y./L.F.		80	.600		132	25	32	189	218
0800	84" diameter, 1.43 C.Y./L.F.		75	.640		180	26.50	34	240.50	276
1000	For bell excavation and concrete, add									
1020	4' bell diameter, 24" shaft, 0.444 C.Y.	B-43	20	2.400	Ea.	45	99.50	127	271.50	345
1040	6' bell diameter, 30" shaft, 1.57 C.Y.		5.70	8.421		160	350	445	955	1,200
1060	8' bell diameter, 36" shaft, 3.72 C.Y.		2.40	20		380	830	1,050	2,260	2,875
1080	9' bell diameter, 48" shaft, 4.48 C.Y.		2	24		455	995	1,275	2,725	3,425
1100	10' bell diameter, 60" shaft, 5.24 C.Y.		1.70	28.235		535	1,175	1,500	3,210	4,025
1120	12' bell diameter, 72" shaft, 8.74 C.Y.		1	48		890	2,000	2,550	5,440	6,825
1140	14' bell diameter, 84" shaft, 13.6 C.Y.		.70	68.571		1,375	2,850	3,625	7,850	9,875
1200	Open style, machine drilled, to 50' deep, in wet ground, pulled									
1300	casing and pumping, 18" diameter, 0.065 C.Y./L.F.	B-48	160	.350	V.L.F.	8.15	14.90	18.15	41.20	52
1400	24" diameter, 0.116 C.Y./L.F.		125	.448		14.60	19.05	23.50	57.15	70.50
1500	30" diameter, 0.182 C.Y./L.F.		85	.659		23	28	34	85	106
1600	36" diameter, 0.262 C.Y./L.F.		60	.933		33	39.50	48.50	121	150
1700	48" diameter, 0.465 C.Y./L.F.	B-49	55	1.600		58.50	71	66	195.50	247
1800	60" diameter, 0.727 C.Y./L.F.		35	2.514		91.50	111	104	306.50	385
1900	72" diameter, 1.05 C.Y./L.F.		30	2.933		132	130	121	383	480
2000	84" diameter, 1.43 C.Y./L.F.		25	3.520		180	156	146	482	595
2100	For bell excavation and concrete, add									
2120	4' bell diameter, 24" shaft, 0.444 C.Y.	B-48	19.80	2.828	Ea.	45	120	147	312	395
2140	6' bell diameter, 30" shaft, 1.57 C.Y.		5.70	9.825		160	420	510	1,090	1,375
2160	8' bell diameter, 36" shaft, 3.72 C.Y.		2.40	23.333		380	995	1,200	2,575	3,275
2180	9' bell diameter, 48" shaft, 4.48 C.Y.	B-49	3.30	26.667		455	1,175	1,100	2,730	3,550
2200	10' bell diameter, 60" shaft, 5.24 C.Y.		2.80	31.429		535	1,400	1,300	3,235	4,150
2220	12' bell diameter, 72" shaft, 8.74 C.Y.		1.60	55		890	2,425	2,275	5,590	7,225
2240	14' bell diameter, 84" shaft, 13.6 C.Y.		1	88		1,375	3,900	3,650	8,925	11,500
2300	Open style, machine drilled, to 50' deep, in soft rocks and									
2400	medium hard shales, 18" diameter, 0.065 C.Y./L.F.	B-49	50	1.760	V.L.F.	8.15	78	73	159.15	209
2500	24" diameter, 0.116 C.Y./L.F.		30	2.933		14.60	130	121	265.60	350
2600	30" diameter, 0.182 C.Y./L.F.		20	4.400		23	195	182	400	525
2700	36" diameter, 0.262 C.Y./L.F.		15	5.867		33	260	243	536	705
2800	48" diameter, 0.465 C.Y./L.F.		10	8.800		58.50	390	365	813.50	1,075
2900	60" diameter, 0.727 C.Y./L.F.		7	12.571		91.50	555	520	1,166.50	1,525
3000	72" diameter, 1.05 C.Y./L.F.		6	14.667		132	650	605	1,387	1,825
3100	84" diameter, 1.43 C.Y./L.F.		5	17.600		180	780	730	1,690	2,200
3200	For bell excavation and concrete, add									
3220	4' bell diameter, 24" shaft, 0.444 C.Y.	B-49	10.90	8.073	Ea.	45	355	335	735	970
3240	6' bell diameter, 30" shaft, 1.57 C.Y.		3.10	28.387		160	1,250	1,175	2,585	3,400
3260	8' bell diameter, 36" shaft, 3.72 C.Y.		1.30	67.692		380	3,000	2,800	6,180	8,100
3280	9' bell diameter, 48" shaft, 4.48 C.Y.		1.10	80		455	3,550	3,300	7,305	9,600
3300	10' bell diameter, 60" shaft, 5.24 C.Y.		.90	97.778		535	4,325	4,050	8,910	11,700
3320	12' bell diameter, 72" shaft, 8.74 C.Y.		.60	146		890	6,500	6,075	13,465	17,600

31 63 Bored Piles

31 63 26 – Drilled Caissons

31 63 26.13 Fixed End Caisson Piles

		Crew	Daily Output	Labor-Hours	Unit	Material	2015 Bare Costs Labor	Equipment	Total	Total Incl O&P
3340	14' bell diameter, 84" shaft, 13.6 C.Y.	B-49	.40	220	Ea.	1,375	9,750	9,100	20,225	26,500
3600	For rock excavation, sockets, add, minimum		120	.733	C.F.		32.50	30.50	63	83.50
3650	Average		95	.926			41	38.50	79.50	105
3700	Maximum		48	1.833			81	76	157	209
3900	For 50' to 100' deep, add				V.L.F.				7%	7%
4000	For 100' to 150' deep, add								25%	25%
4100	For 150' to 200' deep, add								30%	30%
4200	For casings left in place, add				Lb.	1.19			1.19	1.31
4300	For other than 50 lb. reinf. per C.Y., add or deduct				"	1.16			1.16	1.28
4400	For steel "I" beam cores, add	B-49	8.30	10.602	Ton	2,125	470	440	3,035	3,525
4500	Load and haul excess excavation, 2 miles	B-34B	178	.045	L.C.Y.		1.80	3.88	5.68	7
4600	For mobilization, 50 mile radius, rig to 36"	B-43	2	24	Ea.		995	1,275	2,270	2,925
4650	Rig to 84"	B-48	1.75	32			1,350	1,650	3,000	3,900
4700	For low headroom, add								50%	50%
4750	For difficult access, add								25%	25%
5000	Bottom inspection	1 Skwk	1.20	6.667			325		325	500

31 63 26.16 Concrete Caissons for Marine Construction

		Crew	Daily Output	Labor-Hours	Unit	Material	2015 Bare Costs Labor	Equipment	Total	Total Incl O&P
0010	**CONCRETE CAISSONS FOR MARINE CONSTRUCTION**									
0100	Caissons, incl. mobilization and demobilization, up to 50 miles									
0200	Uncased shafts, 30 to 80 tons cap., 17" diam., 10' depth	B-44	88	.727	V.L.F.	20.50	34	20.50	75	98
0300	25' depth		165	.388		14.55	18.10	11	43.65	56.50
0400	80-150 ton capacity, 22" diameter, 10' depth		80	.800		25.50	37.50	22.50	85.50	112
0500	20' depth		130	.492		20.50	23	14	57.50	74
0700	Cased shafts, 10 to 30 ton capacity, 10-5/8" diam., 20' depth		175	.366		14.55	17.10	10.40	42.05	54
0800	30' depth		240	.267		13.55	12.45	7.55	33.55	42.50
0850	30 to 60 ton capacity, 12" diameter, 20' depth		160	.400		20.50	18.70	11.35	50.55	64
0900	40' depth		230	.278		15.65	13	7.90	36.55	46.50
1000	80 to 100 ton capacity, 16" diameter, 20' depth		160	.400		29	18.70	11.35	59.05	73.50
1100	40' depth		230	.278		27	13	7.90	47.90	59
1200	110 to 140 ton capacity, 17-5/8" diameter, 20' depth		160	.400		31.50	18.70	11.35	61.55	76
1300	40' depth		230	.278		29	13	7.90	49.90	61
1400	140 to 175 ton capacity, 19" diameter, 20' depth		130	.492		34	23	14	71	89
1500	40' depth		210	.305		31.50	14.25	8.65	54.40	66
1700	Over 30' long, L.F. cost tends to be lower									
1900	Maximum depth is about 90'									

31 63 29 – Drilled Concrete Piers and Shafts

31 63 29.13 Uncased Drilled Concrete Piers

		Crew	Daily Output	Labor-Hours	Unit	Material	2015 Bare Costs Labor	Equipment	Total	Total Incl O&P
0010	**UNCASED DRILLED CONCRETE PIERS**									
0020	Unless specified otherwise, not incl. pile caps or mobilization									
0050	Cast in place augered piles, no casing or reinforcing									
0060	8" diameter	B-43	540	.089	V.L.F.	4.06	3.69	4.71	12.46	15.30
0065	10" diameter		480	.100		6.45	4.16	5.30	15.91	19.30
0070	12" diameter		420	.114		9.10	4.75	6.05	19.90	24
0075	14" diameter		360	.133		12.25	5.55	7.05	24.85	30
0080	16" diameter		300	.160		16.50	6.65	8.45	31.60	37.50
0085	18" diameter		240	.200		20.50	8.30	10.60	39.40	47
0100	Cast in place, thin wall shell pile, straight sided,									
0110	not incl. reinforcing, 8" diam., 16 ga., 5.8 lb./L.F.	B-19	700	.091	V.L.F.	9.10	4.36	2.48	15.94	19.55
0200	10" diameter, 16 ga. corrugated, 7.3 lb./L.F.		650	.098		11.90	4.69	2.67	19.26	23.50
0300	12" diameter, 16 ga. corrugated, 8.7 lb./L.F.		600	.107		15.45	5.10	2.90	23.45	28
0400	14" diameter, 16 ga. corrugated, 10.0 lb./L.F.		550	.116		18.20	5.55	3.16	26.91	32
0500	16" diameter, 16 ga. corrugated, 11.6 lb./L.F.		500	.128		22.50	6.10	3.47	32.07	38

31 63 Bored Piles

31 63 29 – Drilled Concrete Piers and Shafts

31 63 29.13 Uncased Drilled Concrete Piers	Crew	Daily Output	Labor-Hours	Unit	Material	2015 Bare Costs Labor	Equipment	Total	Total Incl O&P
0800	Cast in place friction pile, 50' long, fluted,									
0810	tapered steel, 4000 psi concrete, no reinforcing									
0900	12" diameter, 7 ga.	B-19	600	.107	V.L.F.	29	5.10	2.90	37	43
1000	14" diameter, 7 ga.		560	.114		31.50	5.45	3.10	40.05	47
1100	16" diameter, 7 ga.		520	.123		37.50	5.85	3.34	46.69	54
1200	18" diameter, 7 ga.		480	.133		43.50	6.35	3.62	53.47	62
1300	End bearing, fluted, constant diameter,									
1320	4000 psi concrete, no reinforcing									
1340	12" diameter, 7 ga.	B-19	600	.107	V.L.F.	30.50	5.10	2.90	38.50	44.50
1360	14" diameter, 7 ga.		560	.114		38	5.45	3.10	46.55	54
1380	16" diameter, 7 ga.		520	.123		44	5.85	3.34	53.19	61.50
1400	18" diameter, 7 ga.		480	.133		48.50	6.35	3.62	58.47	67.50

31 63 29.20 Cast In Place Piles, Adds

		Crew	Daily Output	Labor-Hours	Unit	Material	2015 Bare Costs Labor	Equipment	Total	Total Incl O&P
0010	**CAST IN PLACE PILES, ADDS**									
1500	For reinforcing steel, add				Lb.	.97			.97	1.06
1700	For ball or pedestal end, add	B-19	11	5.818	C.Y.	146	277	158	581	765
1900	For lengths above 60', concrete, add	"	11	5.818	"	152	277	158	587	770
2000	For steel thin shell, pipe only				Lb.	1.26			1.26	1.39

For customer support on your Site Work & Landscape Cost Data, call 877.737.1594.

349

Division Notes

	CREW	DAILY OUTPUT	LABOR-HOURS	UNIT	BARE COSTS				TOTAL INCL O&P
					MAT.	LABOR	EQUIP.	TOTAL	

Estimating Tips

32 01 00 Operations and Maintenance of Exterior Improvements

- Recycling of asphalt pavement is becoming very popular and is an alternative to removal and replacement. It can be a good value engineering proposal if removed pavement can be recycled, either at the project site or at another site that is reasonably close to the project site. Sections on repair of flexible and rigid pavement are included.

32 10 00 Bases, Ballasts, and Paving

- When estimating paving, keep in mind the project schedule. Also note that prices for asphalt and concrete are generally higher in the cold seasons. Lines for pavement markings, including tactile warning systems and fence lines, are included.

32 90 00 Planting

- The timing of planting and guarantee specifications often dictate the costs for establishing tree and shrub growth and a stand of grass or ground cover. Establish the work performance schedule to coincide with the local planting season. Maintenance and growth guarantees can add from 20%–100% to the total landscaping cost and can be contractually cumbersome. The cost to replace trees and shrubs can be as high as 5% of the total cost, depending on the planting zone, soil conditions, and time of year.

Reference Numbers

Reference numbers are shown in shaded boxes at the beginning of some major classifications. These numbers refer to related items in the Reference Section. The reference information may be an estimating procedure, an alternate pricing method, or technical information.

Note: Not all subdivisions listed here necessarily appear in this publication. ■

Division 32 – Exterior Improvements

---

32 01 13 – Flexible Paving Surface Treatment

32 01 13.61 Slurry Seal (Latex Modified)	Crew	Daily Output	Labor-Hours	Unit	Material	2015 Bare Costs Labor	Equipment	Total	Total Incl O&P
0010 **SLURRY SEAL (LATEX MODIFIED)**									
3600 Waterproofing, membrane, tar and fabric, small area	B-63	233	.172	S.Y.	14.05	6.85	.75	21.65	27
3640 Large area		1435	.028		12.95	1.11	.12	14.18	16.10
3680 Preformed rubberized asphalt, small area		100	.400		19.15	15.90	1.74	36.79	47.50
3720 Large area	↓	367	.109		17.45	4.34	.47	22.26	26.50
3780 Rubberized asphalt (latex) seal	B-45	5000	.003	↓	2.81	.15	.18	3.14	3.51

32 01 13.62 Asphalt Surface Treatment

	Crew	Daily Output	Labor-Hours	Unit	Material	Labor	Equipment	Total	Total Incl O&P
0010 **ASPHALT SURFACE TREATMENT**									
3000 Pavement overlay, polypropylene									
3040 6 oz. per S.Y., ideal conditions	B-63	10000	.004	S.Y.	.98	.16	.02	1.16	1.34
3080 Adverse conditions		1000	.040		1.31	1.59	.17	3.07	4.07
3120 4 oz. per S.Y., ideal conditions		10000	.004		.80	.16	.02	.98	1.14
3160 Adverse conditions	↓	1000	.040		1.03	1.59	.17	2.79	3.77
3200 Tack coat, emulsion, .05 gal. per S.Y., 1000 S.Y.	B-45	2500	.006		.29	.29	.36	.94	1.16
3240 10,000 S.Y.		10000	.002		.23	.07	.09	.39	.47
3270 .10 gal. per S.Y., 1000 S.Y.		2500	.006		.54	.29	.36	1.19	1.44
3275 10,000 S.Y.		10000	.002		.44	.07	.09	.60	.69
3280 .15 gal. per S.Y., 1000 S.Y.		2500	.006		.80	.29	.36	1.45	1.72
3320 10,000 S.Y.	↓	10000	.002	↓	.64	.07	.09	.80	.91

32 01 13.64 Sand Seal

	Crew	Daily Output	Labor-Hours	Unit	Material	Labor	Equipment	Total	Total Incl O&P
0010 **SAND SEAL**									
2080 Sand sealing, sharp sand, asphalt emulsion, small area	B-91	10000	.006	S.Y.	1.48	.29	.23	2	2.33
2120 Roadway or large area	"	18000	.004	"	1.27	.16	.13	1.56	1.78
3000 Sealing random cracks, min 1/2" wide, to 1-1/2", 1,000 L.F.	B-77	2800	.014	L.F.	1.53	.55	.20	2.28	2.74
3040 10,000 L.F.		4000	.010	"	1.06	.38	.14	1.58	1.92
3080 Alternate method, 1,000 L.F.		200	.200	Gal.	39.50	7.65	2.83	49.98	58.50
3120 10,000 L.F.	↓	325	.123	"	32	4.71	1.74	38.45	44
3200 Multi-cracks (flooding), 1 coat, small area	B-92	460	.070	S.Y.	2.34	2.65	1.38	6.37	8.15
3240 Large area		2850	.011		2.08	.43	.22	2.73	3.19
3280 2 coat, small area		230	.139		14.50	5.30	2.76	22.56	27
3320 Large area	↓	1425	.022	↓	13.20	.86	.45	14.51	16.30
3360 Alternate method, small area		115	.278	Gal.	14.50	10.60	5.50	30.60	38.50
3400 Large area	↓	715	.045	"	13.65	1.71	.89	16.25	18.60

32 01 13.66 Fog Seal

	Crew	Daily Output	Labor-Hours	Unit	Material	Labor	Equipment	Total	Total Incl O&P
0010 **FOG SEAL**									
0012 Sealcoating, 2 coat coal tar pitch emulsion over 10,000 S.Y.	B-45	5000	.003	S.Y.	.90	.15	.18	1.23	1.41
0030 1000 to 10,000 S.Y.	"	3000	.005		.90	.24	.30	1.44	1.69
0100 Under 1000 S.Y.	B-1	1050	.023		.90	.87		1.77	2.34
0300 Petroleum resistant, over 10,000 S.Y.	B-45	5000	.003		1.30	.15	.18	1.63	1.85
0320 1000 to 10,000 S.Y.	"	3000	.005		1.30	.24	.30	1.84	2.13
0400 Under 1000 S.Y.	B-1	1050	.023		1.30	.87		2.17	2.78
0600 Non-skid pavement renewal, over 10,000 S.Y.	B-45	5000	.003		1.37	.15	.18	1.70	1.93
0620 1000 to 10,000 S.Y.	"	3000	.005		1.37	.24	.30	1.91	2.21
0700 Under 1000 S.Y.	B-1	1050	.023		1.37	.87		2.24	2.86
0800 Prepare and clean surface for above	A-2	8545	.003	↓		.11	.03	.14	.19
1000 Hand seal asphalt curbing	B-1	4420	.005	L.F.	.62	.21		.83	1
1900 Asphalt surface treatment, single course, small area									
1901 0.30 gal/S.Y. asphalt material, 20#/S.Y. aggregate	B-91	5000	.013	S.Y.	1.30	.57	.46	2.33	2.81
1910 Roadway or large area		10000	.006		1.20	.29	.23	1.72	2.02
1950 Asphalt surface treatment, dbl. course for small area		3000	.021		2.94	.95	.77	4.66	5.55
1960 Roadway or large area		6000	.011		2.65	.48	.39	3.52	4.07
1980 Asphalt surface treatment, single course, for shoulders	↓	7500	.009	↓	1.46	.38	.31	2.15	2.53

32 01 13 – Flexible Paving Surface Treatment

32 01 13.68 Slurry Seal

		Crew	Daily Output	Labor-Hours	Unit	Material	2015 Bare Costs Labor	Equipment	Total	Total Incl O&P
0010	**SLURRY SEAL**									
0100	Slurry seal, type I, 8 lb. agg./S.Y., 1 coat, small or irregular area	B-90	2800	.023	S.Y.	1.86	.94	.79	3.59	4.36
0150	Roadway or large area		10000	.006		1.86	.26	.22	2.34	2.69
0200	Type II, 12 lb. aggregate/S.Y., 2 coats,small or irregular area		2000	.032		3.72	1.32	1.10	6.14	7.30
0250	Roadway or large area		8000	.008		3.72	.33	.28	4.33	4.89
0300	Type III, 20 lb. aggregate/S.Y., 2 coats, small or irregular area		1800	.036		4.39	1.47	1.23	7.09	8.40
0350	Roadway or large area		6000	.011		4.39	.44	.37	5.20	5.90
0400	Slurry seal, thermoplastic coal-tar, type I, small or irregular area		2400	.027		3.76	1.10	.92	5.78	6.85
0450	Roadway or large area		8000	.008		3.76	.33	.28	4.37	4.94
0500	Type II, small or irregular area		2400	.027		4.80	1.10	.92	6.82	8
0550	Roadway or large area		7800	.008		4.80	.34	.28	5.42	6.15

32 01 16 – Flexible Paving Rehabilitation

32 01 16.71 Cold Milling Asphalt Paving

		Crew	Daily Output	Labor-Hours	Unit	Material	2015 Bare Costs Labor	Equipment	Total	Total Incl O&P
0010	**COLD MILLING ASPHALT PAVING**									
5200	Cold planing & cleaning, 1" to 3" asphalt pavmt., over 25,000 S.Y.	B-71	6000	.009	S.Y.		.41	1.14	1.55	1.87
5280	5,000 S.Y. to 10,000 S.Y.	"	4000	.014	"		.61	1.71	2.32	2.81
5300	Asphalt pavement removal from conc. base, no haul									
5320	Rip, load & sweep 1" to 3"	B-70	8000	.007	S.Y.		.30	.23	.53	.72
5330	3" to 6" deep	"	5000	.011			.49	.37	.86	1.15
5340	Profile grooving, asphalt pavement load & sweep, 1" deep	B-71	12500	.004			.19	.55	.74	.90
5350	3" deep		9000	.006			.27	.76	1.03	1.25
5360	6" deep		5000	.011			.49	1.37	1.86	2.25
5400	Mixing material in windrow, 180 H.P. grader	B-11L	9400	.002	C.Y.		.08	.08	.16	.20
5450	For cold laid asphalt pavement, see Section 32 12 16.19									
7400	(Over 3") 5K-25K S.F.	B-71	7500	.007	S.F.		.32	.91	1.23	1.50
7410	25001-100000 S.F.		27000	.002			.09	.25	.34	.42
7420	More than 100000 S.F.		50000	.001			.05	.14	.19	.22

32 01 16.73 In Place Cold Reused Asphalt Paving

		Crew	Daily Output	Labor-Hours	Unit	Material	2015 Bare Costs Labor	Equipment	Total	Total Incl O&P
0010	**IN PLACE COLD REUSED ASPHALT PAVING**									
5000	Reclamation, pulverizing and blending with existing base									
5040	Aggregate base, 4" thick pavement, over 15,000 S.Y.	B-73	2400	.027	S.Y.		1.23	2.18	3.41	4.26
5080	5,000 S.Y. to 15,000 S.Y.		2200	.029			1.34	2.37	3.71	4.65
5120	8" thick pavement, over 15,000 S.Y.		2200	.029			1.34	2.37	3.71	4.65
5160	5,000 S.Y. to 15,000 S.Y.		2000	.032			1.47	2.61	4.08	5.10

32 01 16.74 In Place Hot Reused Asphalt Paving

			Crew	Daily Output	Labor-Hours	Unit	Material	2015 Bare Costs Labor	Equipment	Total	Total Incl O&P
0010	**IN PLACE HOT REUSED ASPHALT PAVING**										
5500	Recycle asphalt pavement at site										
5520	Remove, rejuvenate and spread 4" deep	G	B-72	2500	.026	S.Y.	4.73	1.14	4.56	10.43	11.95
5521	6" deep	G	"	2000	.032	"	6.95	1.42	5.70	14.07	16

32 01 17 – Flexible Paving Repair

32 01 17.10 Repair of Asphalt Pavement Holes

		Crew	Daily Output	Labor-Hours	Unit	Material	2015 Bare Costs Labor	Equipment	Total	Total Incl O&P
0010	**REPAIR OF ASPHALT PAVEMENT HOLES** (cold patch)									
0100	Flexible pavement repair holes, roadway,light traffic, 1 C.F. size	B-37A	24	1	Ea.	9	38	15.75	62.75	85.50
0150	Group of two, 1 C.F. size each		16	1.500	Set	18	57	23.50	98.50	133
0200	Group of three, 1 C.F. size each		12	2	"	27	76	31.50	134.50	181
0300	Medium traffic, 1 C.F. size each	B-37B	24	1.333	Ea.	9	50.50	15.70	75.20	105
0350	Group of two, 1 C.F. size each		16	2	Set	18	76	23.50	117.50	162
0400	Group of three, 1 C.F. size each		12	2.667	"	27	101	31.50	159.50	219
0500	Highway/heavy traffic, 1 C.F. size each	B-37C	24	1.333	Ea.	9	51	26	86	116
0550	Group of two, 1 C.F. size each		16	2	Set	18	76.50	39	133.50	180

32 01 17.10 Repair of Asphalt Pavement Holes

		Crew	Daily Output	Labor-Hours	Unit	Material	2015 Bare Costs Labor	2015 Bare Costs Equipment	Total	Total Incl O&P
0600	Group of three, 1 C.F. size each	B-37C	12	2.667	Set	27	102	52	181	243
0700	Add police officer and car for traffic control				Hr.	45.50			45.50	50
1000	Flexible pavement repair holes, parking lot, bag material, 1 C.F. size each	B-37D	18	.889	Ea.	64.50	34	8	106.50	132
1010	Economy bag material, 1 C.F. each		18	.889	"	42	34	8	84	107
1100	Group of two, 1 C.F. size each		12	1.333	Set	129	51	12	192	233
1110	Group of two, economy bag, 1 C.F. size each		12	1.333		84	51	12	147	184
1200	Group of three 1 C.F. size each		10	1.600		193	61.50	14.40	268.90	320
1210	Economy bag, group of three, 1 C.F. size each		10	1.600		126	61.50	14.40	201.90	248
1300	Flexible pavement repair holes, parking lot, 1 C.F. single hole	A-3A	4	2	Ea.	64.50	97	39	200.50	262
1310	Economy material, 1 C.F. single hole		4	2	"	42	97	39	178	238
1400	Flexible pavement repair holes, parking lot, 1 C.F. four holes		2	4	Set	258	194	78	530	665
1410	Economy material, 1 C.F. four holes		2	4	"	168	194	78	440	565
1500	Flexible pavement repair holes, large parking lot, bulk matl, 1 C.F. size	B-37A	32	.750	Ea.	9	28.50	11.80	49.30	66.50

32 01 17.20 Repair of Asphalt Pavement Patches

		Crew	Daily Output	Labor-Hours	Unit	Material	2015 Bare Costs Labor	2015 Bare Costs Equipment	Total	Total Incl O&P
0010	**REPAIR OF ASPHALT PAVEMENT PATCHES**									
0100	Flexible pavement patches, roadway, light traffic, sawcut 10-25 S.F.	B-89	12	1.333	Ea.		58.50	40.50	99	133
0150	Sawcut 26-60 S.F.		10	1.600			70	49	119	160
0200	Sawcut 61-100 S.F.		8	2			87.50	61	148.50	200
0210	Sawcut groups of small size patches		24	.667			29	20.50	49.50	67
0220	Large size patches		16	1			44	30.50	74.50	100
0300	Flexible pavement patches, roadway, light traffic, digout 10-25 S.F.	B-6	16	1.500			62	23	85	120
0350	Digout 26-60 S.F.		12	2			82.50	30.50	113	160
0400	Digout 61-100 S.F.		8	3			124	45.50	169.50	239
0450	Add 8 C.Y. truck, small project debris haulaway	B-34A	8	1	Hr.		40	51.50	91.50	117
0460	Add 12 C.Y. truck, small project debris haulaway	B-34B	8	1			40	86.50	126.50	156
0480	Add flagger for non-intersection medium traffic	1 Clab	8	1			37.50		37.50	58
0490	Add flasher truck for intersection medium traffic or heavy traffic	A-2B	8	1			39	30.50	69.50	92.50
0500	Flexible pavement patches, roadway, repave, cold, 15 S.F., 4" D	B-37	8	6	Ea.	43	239	19.70	301.70	435
0510	6" depth		8	6		65	239	19.70	323.70	460
0520	Repave, cold, 20 S.F., 4" depth		8	6		57	239	19.70	315.70	450
0530	6" depth		8	6		86.50	239	19.70	345.20	480
0540	Repave, cold, 25 S.F., 4" depth		8	6		71.50	239	19.70	330.20	465
0550	6" depth		8	6		108	239	19.70	366.70	505
0600	Repave, cold, 30 S.F., 4" depth		8	6		85.50	239	19.70	344.20	480
0610	6" depth		8	6		130	239	19.70	388.70	530
0640	Repave, cold, 40 S.F., 4" depth		8	6		114	239	19.70	372.70	510
0650	6" depth		8	6		173	239	19.70	431.70	575
0680	Repave, cold, 50 S.F., 4" depth		8	6		143	239	19.70	401.70	545
0690	6" depth		8	6		216	239	19.70	474.70	625
0720	Repave, cold, 60 S.F., 4" depth		8	6		171	239	19.70	429.70	575
0730	6" depth		8	6		259	239	19.70	517.70	670
0800	Repave, cold, 70 S.F., 4" depth		7	6.857		199	273	22.50	494.50	665
0810	6" depth		7	6.857		300	273	22.50	595.50	775
0820	Repave, cold, 75 S.F., 4" depth		7	6.857		213	273	22.50	508.50	680
0830	6" depth		7	6.857		325	273	22.50	620.50	800
0900	Repave, cold, 80 S.F., 4" depth		6	8		228	320	26	574	770
0910	6" depth		6	8		345	320	26	691	900
0940	Repave, cold, 90 S.F., 4" depth		6	8		256	320	26	602	800
0950	6" depth		6	8		390	320	26	736	950
0980	Repave, cold, 100 S.F., 4" depth		6	8		285	320	26	631	835
0990	6" depth		6	8		430	320	26	776	995
1000	Add flasher truck for paving operations in medium or heavy traffic	A-2B	8	1	Hr.		39	30.50	69.50	92.50

32 01 17 – Flexible Paving Repair

32 01 17.20 Repair of Asphalt Pavement Patches

		Crew	Daily Output	Labor-Hours	Unit	Material	2015 Bare Costs Labor	2015 Bare Costs Equipment	Total	Total Incl O&P
1100	Prime coat for repair 15-40 S.F., 25% overspray	B-37A	48	.500	Ea.	7.25	19.05	7.85	34.15	45.50
1150	41-60 S.F.		40	.600		14.50	23	9.45	46.95	61.50
1175	61-80 S.F.		32	.750		19.65	28.50	11.80	59.95	78
1200	81-100 S.F.		32	.750		24	28.50	11.80	64.30	83
1210	Groups of patches w/25% overspray		3600	.007	S.F.	.24	.25	.10	.59	.78
1300	Flexible pavement repair patches, street repave, hot, 60 S.F., 4" D	B-37	8	6	Ea.	101	239	19.70	359.70	500
1310	6" depth		8	6		153	239	19.70	411.70	555
1320	Repave, hot, 70 S.F., 4" depth		7	6.857		118	273	22.50	413.50	575
1330	6" depth		7	6.857		179	273	22.50	474.50	640
1340	Repave, hot, 75 S.F., 4" depth		7	6.857		126	273	22.50	421.50	585
1350	6" depth		7	6.857		192	273	22.50	487.50	655
1360	Repave, hot, 80 S.F., 4" depth		6	8		135	320	26	481	665
1370	6" depth		6	8		205	320	26	551	745
1380	Repave, hot, 90 S.F., 4" depth		6	8		152	320	26	498	685
1390	6" depth		6	8		230	320	26	576	775
1400	Repave, hot, 100 S.F., 4" depth		6	8		169	320	26	515	705
1410	6" depth		6	8		256	320	26	602	800
1420	Pave hot groups of patches, 4" depth		900	.053	S.F.	1.68	2.12	.17	3.97	5.30
1430	6" depth		900	.053	"	2.56	2.12	.17	4.85	6.25
1500	Add 8 C.Y. truck for hot asphalt paving operations	B-34A	1	8	Day		320	410	730	935
1550	Add flasher truck for hot paving operations in med/heavy traffic	A-2B	8	1	Hr.		39	30.50	69.50	92.50
2000	Add police officer and car for traffic control				"	45.50			45.50	50

32 01 17.61 Sealing Cracks In Asphalt Paving

		Crew	Daily Output	Labor-Hours	Unit	Material	2015 Bare Costs Labor	2015 Bare Costs Equipment	Total	Total Incl O&P
0010	**SEALING CRACKS IN ASPHALT PAVING**									
0100	Sealing cracks in asphalt paving, 1/8" wide x 1/2" depth, slow set	B-37A	2000	.012	L.F.	.17	.46	.19	.82	1.10
0110	1/4" wide x 1/2" depth		2000	.012		.20	.46	.19	.85	1.13
0130	3/8" wide x 1/2" depth		2000	.012		.23	.46	.19	.88	1.16
0140	1/2" wide x 1/2" depth		1800	.013		.26	.51	.21	.98	1.29
0150	3/4" wide x 1/2" depth		1600	.015		.31	.57	.24	1.12	1.47
0160	1" wide x 1/2" depth		1600	.015		.37	.57	.24	1.18	1.53
0165	1/8" wide x 1" depth, rapid set	B-37F	2000	.016		.25	.61	.29	1.15	1.52
0170	1/4" wide x 1" depth		2000	.016		.48	.61	.29	1.38	1.78
0175	3/8" wide x 1" depth		1800	.018		.72	.68	.32	1.72	2.18
0180	1/2" wide x 1" depth		1800	.018		.97	.68	.32	1.97	2.44
0185	5/8" wide x 1" depth		1800	.018		1.21	.68	.32	2.21	2.71
0190	3/4" wide x 1" depth		1600	.020		1.45	.76	.36	2.57	3.15
0195	1" wide x 1" depth		1600	.020		1.93	.76	.36	3.05	3.68
0200	1/8" wide x 2" depth, rapid set		2000	.016		.48	.61	.29	1.38	1.78
0210	1/4" wide x 2" depth		2000	.016		.97	.61	.29	1.87	2.31
0220	3/8" wide x 2" depth		1800	.018		1.45	.68	.32	2.45	2.97
0230	1/2" wide x 2" depth		1800	.018		1.93	.68	.32	2.93	3.50
0240	5/8" wide x 2" depth		1800	.018		2.41	.68	.32	3.41	4.03
0250	3/4" wide x 2" depth		1600	.020		2.89	.76	.36	4.01	4.74
0260	1" wide x 2" depth		1600	.020		3.86	.76	.36	4.98	5.80
0300	Add flagger for non-intersection medium traffic	1 Clab	8	1	Hr.		37.50		37.50	58
0400	Add flasher truck for intersection medium traffic or heavy traffic	A-2B	8	1	"		39	30.50	69.50	92.50

32 01 29 – Rigid Paving Repair

32 01 29.61 Partial Depth Patching of Rigid Pavement

		Crew	Daily Output	Labor-Hours	Unit	Material	2015 Bare Costs Labor	2015 Bare Costs Equipment	Total	Total Incl O&P
0010	**PARTIAL DEPTH PATCHING OF RIGID PAVEMENT**									
0100	Rigid pavement repair, roadway, light traffic, 25% pitting 15 S.F.	B-37F	16	2	Ea.	27	76	36	139	186
0110	Pitting 20 S.F.		16	2		36	76	36	148	196
0120	Pitting 25 S.F.		16	2		45	76	36	157	206

For customer support on your Site Work & Landscape Cost Data, call 877.737.1594.

355

32 01 29.61 Partial Depth Patching of Rigid Pavement

		Crew	Daily Output	Labor-Hours	Unit	Material	2015 Bare Costs Labor	2015 Bare Costs Equipment	Total	Total Incl O&P
0130	Pitting 30 S.F.	B-37F	16	2	Ea.	54	76	36	166	216
0140	Pitting 40 S.F.		16	2		72	76	36	184	236
0150	Pitting 50 S.F.		12	2.667		90	101	48.50	239.50	310
0160	Pitting 60 S.F.		12	2.667		108	101	48.50	257.50	325
0170	Pitting 70 S.F.		12	2.667		126	101	48.50	275.50	345
0180	Pitting 75 S.F.		12	2.667		135	101	48.50	284.50	355
0190	Pitting 80 S.F.		8	4		144	152	72.50	368.50	470
0200	Pitting 90 S.F.		8	4		162	152	72.50	386.50	490
0210	Pitting 100 S.F.		8	4		180	152	72.50	404.50	510
0300	Roadway, light traffic, 50% pitting 15 S.F.		12	2.667		54	101	48.50	203.50	268
0310	Pitting 20 S.F.		12	2.667		72	101	48.50	221.50	288
0320	Pitting 25 S.F.		12	2.667		90	101	48.50	239.50	310
0330	Pitting 30 S.F.		12	2.667		108	101	48.50	257.50	325
0340	Pitting 40 S.F.		12	2.667		144	101	48.50	293.50	365
0350	Pitting 50 S.F.		8	4		180	152	72.50	404.50	510
0360	Pitting 60 S.F.		8	4		217	152	72.50	441.50	550
0370	Pitting 70 S.F.		8	4		253	152	72.50	477.50	590
0380	Pitting 75 S.F.		8	4		271	152	72.50	495.50	610
0390	Pitting 80 S.F.		6	5.333		289	203	96.50	588.50	735
0400	Pitting 90 S.F.		6	5.333		325	203	96.50	624.50	770
0410	Pitting 100 S.F.		6	5.333		360	203	96.50	659.50	810
1000	Rigid pavement repair, light traffic, surface patch, 2" deep, 15 S.F.		8	4		108	152	72.50	332.50	430
1010	Surface patch, 2" deep, 20 S.F.		8	4		144	152	72.50	368.50	470
1020	Surface patch, 2" deep, 25 S.F.		8	4		180	152	72.50	404.50	510
1030	Surface patch, 2" deep, 30 S.F.		8	4		217	152	72.50	441.50	550
1040	Surface patch, 2" deep, 40 S.F.		8	4		289	152	72.50	513.50	635
1050	Surface patch, 2" deep, 50 S.F.		6	5.333		360	203	96.50	659.50	810
1060	Surface patch, 2" deep, 60 S.F.		6	5.333		435	203	96.50	734.50	890
1070	Surface patch, 2" deep, 70 S.F.		6	5.333		505	203	96.50	804.50	970
1080	Surface patch, 2" deep, 75 S.F.		6	5.333		540	203	96.50	839.50	1,000
1090	Surface patch, 2" deep, 80 S.F.		5	6.400		580	243	116	939	1,125
1100	Surface patch, 2" deep, 90 S.F.		5	6.400		650	243	116	1,009	1,225
1200	Surface patch, 2" deep, 100 S.F.		5	6.400		720	243	116	1,079	1,300
2000	Add flagger for non-intersection medium traffic	1 Clab	8	1	Hr.		37.50		37.50	58
2100	Add flasher truck for intersection medium traffic or heavy traffic	A-2B	8	1			39	30.50	69.50	92.50
2200	Add police officer and car for traffic control						45.50		45.50	50

32 01 29.70 Full Depth Patching of Rigid Pavement

		Crew	Daily Output	Labor-Hours	Unit	Material	2015 Bare Costs Labor	2015 Bare Costs Equipment	Total	Total Incl O&P
0010	**FULL DEPTH PATCHING OF RIGID PAVEMENT**									
0015	Pavement preparation includes sawcut, remove pavement and replace									
0020	6 inches of subbase and one layer of reinforcement									
0030	Trucking and haulaway of debris excluded									
0100	Rigid pavement replace, light traffic, prep, 15 S.F., 6" depth	B-37E	16	3.500	Ea.	19.65	145	64	228.65	315
0110	Replacement preparation 20 S.F., 6" depth		16	3.500		26	145	64	235	320
0115	25 S.F., 6" depth		16	3.500		32.50	145	64	241.50	330
0120	30 S.F., 6" depth		14	4		39.50	166	73	278.50	375
0125	35 S.F., 6" depth		14	4		46	166	73	285	385
0130	40 S.F., 6" depth		14	4		52.50	166	73	291.50	390
0135	45 S.F., 6" depth		14	4		59	166	73	298	400
0140	50 S.F., 6" depth		12	4.667		65.50	193	85	343.50	460
0145	55 S.F., 6" depth		12	4.667		72	193	85	350	470
0150	60 S.F., 6" depth		10	5.600		78.50	232	102	412.50	555
0155	65 S.F., 6" depth		10	5.600		85	232	102	419	560

356

For customer support on your Site Work & Landscape Cost Data, call 877.737.1594.

32 01 29.70 Full Depth Patching of Rigid Pavement	Crew	Daily Output	Labor-Hours	Unit	Material	2015 Bare Costs Labor	2015 Bare Costs Equipment	Total	Total Incl O&P
0160 70 S.F., 6" depth	B-37E	10	5.600	Ea.	91.50	232	102	425.50	570
0165 75 S.F., 6" depth		10	5.600		98	232	102	432	575
0170 80 S.F., 6" depth		8	7		105	290	128	523	695
0175 85 S.F., 6" depth		8	7		111	290	128	529	705
0180 90 S.F., 6" depth		8	7		118	290	128	536	710
0185 95 S.F., 6" depth		8	7		124	290	128	542	720
0190 100 S.F., 6" depth	↓	8	7	↓	131	290	128	549	725
0200 Pavement preparation for 8 inch rigid paving same as 6 inch									
0290 Pavement preparation for 9 inch rigid paving same as 10 inch									
0300 Rigid pavement replace, light traffic,prep, 15 S.F.,10" depth	B-37E	16	3.500	Ea.	32.50	145	64	241.50	330
0302 Pavement preparation 10 inch includes sawcut, remove pavement and									
0304 replace 6 inches of subbase and two layers of reinforcement									
0306 Trucking and haulaway of debris excluded									
0310 Replacement preparation 20 S.F., 10" depth	B-37E	16	3.500	Ea.	43.50	145	64	252.50	340
0315 25 S.F., 10" depth		16	3.500		54.50	145	64	263.50	350
0320 30 S.F., 10" depth		14	4		65.50	166	73	304.50	405
0325 35 S.F., 10" depth		14	4		50	166	73	289	390
0330 40 S.F., 10" depth		14	4		87	166	73	326	430
0335 45 S.F., 10" depth		12	4.667		98	193	85	376	495
0340 50 S.F., 10" depth		12	4.667		109	193	85	387	510
0345 55 S.F., 10" depth		12	4.667		120	193	85	398	520
0350 60 S.F., 10" depth		10	5.600		131	232	102	465	610
0355 65 S.F., 10" depth		10	5.600		142	232	102	476	625
0360 70 S.F., 10" depth		10	5.600		153	232	102	487	635
0365 75 S.F., 10" depth		8	7		163	290	128	581	760
0370 80 S.F., 10" depth		8	7		174	290	128	592	775
0375 85 S.F., 10" depth		8	7		185	290	128	603	785
0380 90 S.F., 10" depth		8	7		196	290	128	614	795
0385 95 S.F., 10" depth		8	7		207	290	128	625	810
0390 100 S.F., 10" depth	↓	8	7	↓	218	290	128	636	820
0500 Add 8 C.Y. truck, small project debris haulaway	B-34A	8	1	Hr.		40	51.50	91.50	117
0550 Add 12 C.Y. truck, small project debris haulaway	B-34B	8	1			40	86.50	126.50	156
0600 Add flagger for non-intersection medium traffic	1 Clab	8	1			37.50		37.50	58
0650 Add flasher truck for intersection medium traffic or heavy traffic	A-2B	8	1			39	30.50	69.50	92.50
0700 Add police officer and car for traffic control				↓	45.50			45.50	50
0990 Concrete will replaced using quick set mix with aggregate									
1000 Rigid pavement replace, light traffic,repour, 15 S.F.,6" depth	B-37F	18	1.778	Ea.	161	67.50	32	260.50	315
1010 20 S.F., 6" depth		18	1.778		214	67.50	32	313.50	375
1015 25 S.F., 6" depth		18	1.778		268	67.50	32	367.50	435
1020 30 S.F., 6" depth		16	2		320	76	36	432	510
1025 35 S.F., 6" depth		16	2		375	76	36	487	570
1030 40 S.F., 6" depth		16	2		430	76	36	542	625
1035 45 S.F., 6" depth		16	2		480	76	36	592	685
1040 50 S.F., 6" depth		16	2		535	76	36	647	745
1045 55 S.F., 6" depth		12	2.667		590	101	48.50	739.50	860
1050 60 S.F., 6" depth		12	2.667		645	101	48.50	794.50	915
1055 65 S.F., 6" depth		12	2.667		695	101	48.50	844.50	975
1060 70 S.F., 6" depth		12	2.667		750	101	48.50	899.50	1,025
1065 75 S.F., 6" depth		10	3.200		805	122	58	985	1,125
1070 80 S.F., 6" depth		10	3.200		855	122	58	1,035	1,200
1075 85 S.F., 6" depth		8	4		910	152	72.50	1,134.50	1,325
1080 90 S.F., 6" depth		8	4		965	152	72.50	1,189.50	1,375
1085 95 S.F., 6" depth	↓	8	4		1,025	152	72.50	1,249.50	1,450

For customer support on your Site Work & Landscape Cost Data, call 877.737.1594.

357

32 01 Operation and Maintenance of Exterior Improvements

32 01 29 – Rigid Paving Repair

32 01 29.70 Full Depth Patching of Rigid Pavement

		Crew	Daily Output	Labor-Hours	Unit	Material	2015 Bare Costs Labor	Equipment	Total	Total Incl O&P
1090	100 S.F., 6" depth	B-37F	8	4	Ea.	1,075	152	72.50	1,299.50	1,500
1099	Concrete will be replaced using 4500 PSI Concrete ready mix									
1100	Rigid pavement replace, light traffic, repour, 15 S.F., 6" depth	A-2	12	2	Ea.	278	76	20.50	374.50	445
1110	20-50 S.F., 6" depth		12	2		278	76	20.50	374.50	445
1120	55-65 S.F., 6" depth		10	2.400		310	91.50	24.50	426	505
1130	70-80 S.F., 6" depth		10	2.400		340	91.50	24.50	456	535
1140	85-100 S.F., 6" depth		8	3		395	114	30.50	539.50	645
1200	Repour 15-40 S.F., 8" depth		12	2		278	76	20.50	374.50	445
1210	45-50 S.F., 8" depth		12	2		310	76	20.50	406.50	480
1220	55-60 S.F., 8" depth		10	2.400		340	91.50	24.50	456	535
1230	65-80 S.F., 8" depth		10	2.400		395	91.50	24.50	511	600
1240	85-90 S.F., 8" depth		8	3		430	114	30.50	574.50	680
1250	95-100 S.F., 8" depth		8	3		455	114	30.50	599.50	710
1300	Repour 15-30 S.F., 10" depth		12	2		278	76	20.50	374.50	445
1310	35-40 S.F., 10" depth		12	2		310	76	20.50	406.50	480
1320	45 S.F., 10" depth		12	2		340	76	20.50	436.50	510
1330	50-65 S.F., 10" depth		10	2.400		395	91.50	24.50	511	600
1340	70 S.F., 10" depth		10	2.400		430	91.50	24.50	546	635
1350	75-80 S.F., 10" depth		10	2.400		455	91.50	24.50	571	665
1360	85-95 S.F., 10" depth		8	3		515	114	30.50	659.50	780
1370	100 S.F., 10" depth		8	3		550	114	30.50	694.50	815

32 01 30 – Operation and Maintenance of Site Improvements

32 01 30.10 Site Maintenance

		Crew	Daily Output	Labor-Hours	Unit	Material	2015 Bare Costs Labor	Equipment	Total	Total Incl O&P
0010	**SITE MAINTENANCE**									
0800	Flower bed maintenance									
0810	Cultivate bed, no mulch	1 Clab	14	.571	M.S.F.		21.50		21.50	33
0830	Fall clean-up of flower bed, including pick-up mulch for re-use		1	8			300		300	465
0840	Fertilize flower bed, dry granular 3 lb./C.S.F.		85	.094		8.75	3.54		12.29	15.10
1130	Police, hand pickup		30	.267			10.05		10.05	15.45
1140	Vacuum (outside)		48	.167			6.25		6.25	9.65
1200	Spring prepare		2	4			150		150	231
1300	Weed mulched bed		20	.400			15.05		15.05	23
1310	Unmulched bed		8	1			37.50		37.50	58
3000	Lawn maintenance									
3010	Aerate lawn, 18" cultivating width, walk behind	A-1K	95	.084	M.S.F.		3.17	.76	3.93	5.70
3040	48" cultivating width	B-66	750	.011			.52	.35	.87	1.18
3060	72" cultivating width	"	1100	.007			.35	.24	.59	.80
3100	Edge lawn, by hand at walks	1 Clab	16	.500	C.L.F.		18.80		18.80	29
3150	At planting beds		7	1.143			43		43	66
3200	Using gas powered edger at walks		88	.091			3.42		3.42	5.25
3250	At planting beds		24	.333			12.55		12.55	19.30
3260	Vacuum, 30" gas, outdoors with hose		96	.083	M.L.F.		3.13		3.13	4.82
3400	Weed lawn, by hand		3	2.667	M.S.F.		100		100	154
3800	Lawn bed preparation see Section 32 91 13.23									
4510	Power rake	1 Clab	45	.178	M.S.F.		6.70		6.70	10.30
4700	Seeding lawn, see Section 32 92 19.14									
4750	Sodding, see Section 32 92 23.10									
5900	Road & walk maintenance									
5910	Asphaltic concrete paving, cold patch, 2" thick	B-37	350	.137	S.Y.	11.35	5.45	.45	17.25	21.50
5913	3" thick	"	260	.185	"	17.05	7.35	.61	25.01	30.50
5915	De-icing roads and walks									
5920	Calcium Chloride in truckload lots see Section 31 32 13.30									

358

For customer support on your Site Work & Landscape Cost Data, call 877.737.1594.

32 01 Operation and Maintenance of Exterior Improvements

32 01 30 – Operation and Maintenance of Site Improvements

32 01 30.10 Site Maintenance

		Crew	Daily Output	Labor-Hours	Unit	Material	2015 Bare Costs Labor	2015 Bare Costs Equipment	Total	Total Incl O&P
6000	Ice melting comp., 90% Calc. Chlor., effec. to -30°F									
6010	50-80 lb. poly bags, med. applic. 19 lb./M.S.F., by hand	1 Clab	60	.133	M.S.F.	21.50	5		26.50	31
6050	With hand operated rotary spreader		110	.073		21	2.73		23.73	27
6100	Rock salt, med. applic. on road & walkway, by hand		60	.133		10	5		15	18.70
6110	With hand operated rotary spreader		110	.073		10	2.73		12.73	15.20
6130	Hosing, sidewalks & other paved areas		30	.267			10.05		10.05	15.45
6260	Sidewalk, brick pavers, steam cleaning	A-1H	950	.008	S.F.	.12	.32	.08	.52	.71
6400	Sweep walk by hand	1 Clab	15	.533	M.S.F.		20		20	31
6410	Power vacuum		100	.080			3.01		3.01	4.63
6420	Drives & parking areas with power vacuum		120	.067			2.51		2.51	3.86
6600	Shrub maintenance									
6640	Shrub bed fertilize dry granular 3 lb./M.S.F.	1 Clab	85	.094	M.S.F.	6.60	3.54		10.14	12.75
6800	Weed, by handhoe		8	1			37.50		37.50	58
6810	Spray out		32	.250			9.40		9.40	14.45
6820	Spray after mulch		48	.167			6.25		6.25	9.65
7100	Tree maintenance									
7200	Fertilize, tablets, slow release, 30 gram/tree	1 Clab	100	.080	Ea.	.58	3.01		3.59	5.25
7420	Pest control, spray		24	.333		26.50	12.55		39.05	48.50
7430	Systemic		48	.167		26.50	6.25		32.75	39

32 01 30.20 Snow Removal

		Crew	Daily Output	Labor-Hours	Unit	Material	2015 Bare Costs Labor	2015 Bare Costs Equipment	Total	Total Incl O&P
0010	**SNOW REMOVAL**									
0020	Plowing, 12 ton truck, 2"-4" deep	B-34A	250	.032	M.S.F.		1.28	1.64	2.92	3.75
0040	4"-10" deep		200	.040			1.60	2.06	3.66	4.68
0060	10"-15" deep		150	.053			2.14	2.74	4.88	6.25
0080	Pickup truck, 2"-4" deep	A-3A	175	.046			2.22	.89	3.11	4.35
0100	4"-10" deep		130	.062			2.99	1.20	4.19	5.85
0120	10"-15" deep		75	.107			5.20	2.07	7.27	10.15
0140	Load and haul snow, 1 mile round trip	A-3B	230	.070	C.Y.		3.15	5.25	8.40	10.60
0160	2 mile round trip		175	.091			4.14	6.90	11.04	13.90
0180	3 mile round trip		150	.107			4.84	8.05	12.89	16.20
0200	4 mile round trip		130	.123			5.60	9.30	14.90	18.70
0220	5 mile round trip		120	.133			6.05	10.10	16.15	20.50
0240	Clearing with wheeled skid steer loader, 1 C.Y.	A-3C	240	.033			1.62	1.33	2.95	3.92
0260	Spread sand and salt mix	B-34A	375	.021	M.S.F.	6.30	.85	1.10	8.25	9.45
0280	Sidewalks and drives, by hand	1 Clab	1200	.007	C.F.		.25		.25	.39
0300	Power, 24" blower	A-1M	7000	.001	"		.04	.01	.05	.08
0320	2"-4" deep, single driveway (10' x 50')		16	.500	Ea.		18.80	4.20	23	33.50
0340	Double driveway (20' x 50')		16	.500			18.80	4.20	23	33.50
0360	4"-10" deep, single driveway		16	.500			18.80	4.20	23	33.50
0380	Double driveway		16	.500			18.80	4.20	23	33.50
0400	10"-15" deep, single driveway		12	.667			25	5.60	30.60	44.50
0420	Double driveway		12	.667			25	5.60	30.60	44.50
0440	For heavy wet snow, add								20%	20%

32 01 90 – Operation and Maintenance of Planting

32 01 90.13 Fertilizing

		Crew	Daily Output	Labor-Hours	Unit	Material	2015 Bare Costs Labor	2015 Bare Costs Equipment	Total	Total Incl O&P
0010	**FERTILIZING**									
0100	Dry granular, 4#/M.S.F., hand spread	1 Clab	24	.333	M.S.F.	2.78	12.55		15.33	22.50
0110	Push rotary	"	140	.057		2.78	2.15		4.93	6.35
0120	Tractor towed spreader, 8'	B-66	500	.016		2.78	.78	.53	4.09	4.82
0130	12' spread		800	.010		2.78	.49	.33	3.60	4.16
0140	Truck whirlwind spreader		1200	.007		2.78	.32	.22	3.32	3.79
0180	Water soluable, hydro spread, 1.5#/M.S.F.	B-64	600	.027		2.85	1.02	.66	4.53	5.45

For customer support on your Site Work & Landscape Cost Data, call 877.737.1594.

359

32 01 Operation and Maintenance of Exterior Improvements

32 01 90 – Operation and Maintenance of Planting

32 01 90.13 Fertilizing

	Crew	Daily Output	Labor-Hours	Unit	Material	2015 Bare Costs Labor	2015 Bare Costs Equipment	Total	Total Incl O&P
0190	Add for weed control				M.S.F.	.48			.48	.53

32 01 90.19 Mowing

		Crew	Daily Output	Labor-Hours	Unit	Material	Labor	Equipment	Total	Total Incl O&P
0010	**MOWING**									
1650	Mowing brush, tractor with rotary mower									
1660	Light density	B-84	22	.364	M.S.F.		18.40	16.85	35.25	46.50
1670	Medium density		13	.615			31	28.50	59.50	78.50
1680	Heavy density		9	.889			45	41	86	114
2000	Mowing, brush/grass, tractor, rotary mower, highway/airport median		13	.615			31	28.50	59.50	78.50
2010	Traffic safety flashing truck for highway/airport median mowing	A-2B	1	8	Day		315	245	560	745
4050	Lawn mowing, power mower, 18" - 22"	1 Clab	65	.123	M.S.F.		4.63		4.63	7.10
4100	22" - 30"		110	.073			2.73		2.73	4.21
4150	30" - 32"		140	.057			2.15		2.15	3.31
4160	Riding mower, 36" - 44"	B-66	300	.027			1.30	.88	2.18	2.94
4170	48" - 58"	"	480	.017			.81	.55	1.36	1.83
4175	Mowing with tractor & attachments									
4180	3 gang reel, 7'	B-66	930	.009	M.S.F.		.42	.28	.70	.94
4190	5 gang reel, 12'		1200	.007			.32	.22	.54	.73
4200	Cutter or sickle-bar, 5', rough terrain		210	.038			1.85	1.25	3.10	4.19
4210	Cutter or sickle-bar, 5', smooth terrain		340	.024			1.14	.77	1.91	2.59
4220	Drainage channel, 5' sickle bar		5	1.600	Mile		78	52.50	130.50	176
4250	Lawnmower, rotary type, sharpen (all sizes)	1 Clab	10	.800	Ea.		30		30	46.50
4260	Repair or replace part		7	1.143	"		43		43	66
5000	Edge trimming with weed whacker		5760	.001	L.F.		.05		.05	.08

32 01 90.23 Pruning

		Crew	Daily Output	Labor-Hours	Unit	Material	Labor	Equipment	Total	Total Incl O&P
0010	**PRUNING**									
0020	1-1/2" caliper	1 Clab	84	.095	Ea.		3.58		3.58	5.50
0030	2" caliper		70	.114			4.30		4.30	6.60
0040	2-1/2" caliper		50	.160			6		6	9.25
0050	3" caliper		30	.267			10.05		10.05	15.45
0060	4" caliper, by hand	2 Clab	21	.762			28.50		28.50	44
0070	Aerial lift equipment	B-85	38	1.053			43	27	70	95.50
0100	6" caliper, by hand	2 Clab	12	1.333			50		50	77
0110	Aerial lift equipment	B-85	20	2			81.50	51.50	133	181
0200	9" caliper, by hand	2 Clab	7.50	2.133			80		80	123
0210	Aerial lift equipment	B-85	12.50	3.200			130	82.50	212.50	290
0300	12" caliper, by hand	2 Clab	6.50	2.462			92.50		92.50	142
0310	Aerial lift equipment	B-85	10.80	3.704			151	95.50	246.50	335
0400	18" caliper by hand	2 Clab	5.60	2.857			107		107	165
0410	Aerial lift equipment	B-85	9.30	4.301			175	111	286	390
0500	24" caliper, by hand	2 Clab	4.60	3.478			131		131	201
0510	Aerial lift equipment	B-85	7.70	5.195			211	134	345	470
0600	30" caliper, by hand	2 Clab	3.70	4.324			163		163	250
0610	Aerial lift equipment	B-85	6.20	6.452			263	167	430	585
0700	36" caliper, by hand	2 Clab	2.70	5.926			223		223	345
0710	Aerial lift equipment	B-85	4.50	8.889			360	229	589	805
0800	48" caliper, by hand	2 Clab	1.70	9.412			355		355	545
0810	Aerial lift equipment	B-85	2.80	14.286			580	370	950	1,300

32 01 90.24 Shrub Pruning

		Crew	Daily Output	Labor-Hours	Unit	Material	Labor	Equipment	Total	Total Incl O&P
0010	**SHRUB PRUNING**									
6700	Prune, shrub bed	1 Clab	7	1.143	M.S.F.		43		43	66
6710	Shrub under 3' height		190	.042	Ea.		1.58		1.58	2.44
6720	4' height		90	.089			3.34		3.34	5.15

32 01 Operation and Maintenance of Exterior Improvements

32 01 90 – Operation and Maintenance of Planting

32 01 90.24 Shrub Pruning

		Crew	Daily Output	Labor-Hours	Unit	Material	2015 Bare Costs Labor	Equipment	Total	Total Incl O&P
6730	Over 6'	1 Clab	50	.160	Ea.		6		6	9.25
7350	Prune trees from ground		20	.400			15.05		15.05	23
7360	High work	↓	8	1	↓		37.50		37.50	58

32 01 90.26 Watering

		Crew	Daily Output	Labor-Hours	Unit	Material	2015 Bare Costs Labor	Equipment	Total	Total Incl O&P
0010	**WATERING**									
4900	Water lawn or planting bed with hose, 1" of water	1 Clab	16	.500	M.S.F.		18.80		18.80	29
4910	50' soaker hoses, in place		82	.098			3.67		3.67	5.65
4920	60' soaker hoses, in place		89	.090	↓		3.38		3.38	5.20
7500	Water trees or shrubs, under 1" caliper		32	.250	Ea.		9.40		9.40	14.45
7550	1" - 3" caliper		17	.471			17.70		17.70	27
7600	3" - 4" caliper		12	.667			25		25	38.50
7650	Over 4" caliper	↓	10	.800	↓		30		30	46.50
9000	For sprinkler irrigation systems, see Section 32 84 23.10									

32 01 90.29 Topsoil Preservation

		Crew	Daily Output	Labor-Hours	Unit	Material	2015 Bare Costs Labor	Equipment	Total	Total Incl O&P
0010	**TOPSOIL PRESERVATION**									
0100	Weed planting bed	1 Clab	800	.010	S.Y.		.38		.38	.58

32 06 Schedules for Exterior Improvements

32 06 10 – Schedules for Bases, Ballasts, and Paving

32 06 10.10 Sidewalks, Driveways and Patios

		Crew	Daily Output	Labor-Hours	Unit	Material	2015 Bare Costs Labor	Equipment	Total	Total Incl O&P
0010	**SIDEWALKS, DRIVEWAYS AND PATIOS** No base									
0020	Asphaltic concrete, 2" thick	B-37	720	.067	S.Y.	7.40	2.65	.22	10.27	12.45
0100	2-1/2" thick	"	660	.073	"	9.40	2.89	.24	12.53	15.05
0110	Bedding for brick or stone, mortar, 1" thick	D-1	300	.053	S.F.	.89	2.25		3.14	4.40
0120	2" thick	"	200	.080		2.21	3.37		5.58	7.60
0130	Sand, 2" thick	B-18	8000	.003		.28	.11	.01	.40	.50
0140	4" thick	"	4000	.006	↓	.56	.23	.01	.80	.98
0300	Concrete, 3000 psi, CIP, 6 x 6 - W1.4 x W1.4 mesh,									
0310	broomed finish, no base, 4" thick	B-24	600	.040	S.F.	1.69	1.73		3.42	4.48
0350	5" thick		545	.044		2.26	1.90		4.16	5.40
0400	6" thick	↓	510	.047	↓	2.64	2.03		4.67	6
0440	For other finishes, see Section 03 35 29.30									
0450	For bank run gravel base, 4" thick, add	B-18	2500	.010	S.F.	.52	.37	.02	.91	1.16
0520	8" thick, add	"	1600	.015		1.04	.57	.03	1.64	2.06
0550	Exposed aggregate finish, add to above, minimum	B-24	1875	.013		.11	.55		.66	.96
0600	Maximum		455	.053		.36	2.28		2.64	3.86
0700	Patterned surface, add to above min.		1200	.020			.86		.86	1.31
0710	Maximum	↓	500	.048	↓		2.07		2.07	3.15
0850	Splash block, precast concrete	1 Clab	150	.053	Ea.	11.65	2.01		13.66	15.90
0950	Concrete tree grate, 5' square	B-6	25	.960		420	39.50	14.55	474.05	540
0955	Tree well & cover, concrete, 3' square		25	.960		320	39.50	14.55	374.05	425
0960	Cast iron tree grate with frame, 2 piece, round, 5' diameter		25	.960		1,100	39.50	14.55	1,154.05	1,275
0980	Square, 5' side	↓	25	.960	↓	1,100	39.50	14.55	1,154.05	1,275
1000	Crushed stone, 1" thick, white marble	2 Clab	1700	.009	S.F.	.44	.35		.79	1.03
1050	Bluestone		1700	.009		.13	.35		.48	.68
1070	Granite chips	↓	1700	.009		.22	.35		.57	.79
1200	For 2" asphaltic conc. base and tack coat, add to above	B-37	7200	.007		1.09	.27	.02	1.38	1.63
1660	Limestone pavers, 3" thick	D-1	72	.222		10.05	9.35		19.40	25.50
1670	4" thick		70	.229		13.30	9.60		22.90	29.50
1680	5" thick	↓	68	.235	↓	16.65	9.90		26.55	33.50

For customer support on your Site Work & Landscape Cost Data, call 877.737.1594.

361

32 06 10 – Schedules for Bases, Ballasts, and Paving

32 06 10.10 Sidewalks, Driveways and Patios

		Crew	Daily Output	Labor-Hours	Unit	Material	2015 Bare Costs Labor	2015 Bare Costs Equipment	Total	Total Incl O&P
1700	Redwood, prefabricated, 4' x 4' sections	2 Carp	316	.051	S.F.	4.77	2.38		7.15	8.90
1750	Redwood planks, 1" thick, on sleepers	"	240	.067		4.77	3.13		7.90	10.05
1830	1-1/2" thick	B-28	167	.144		7.65	6.30		13.95	18.10
1840	2" thick		167	.144		9.85	6.30		16.15	20.50
1850	3" thick		150	.160		14.50	7		21.50	27
1860	4" thick		150	.160		19.05	7		26.05	32
1870	5" thick		150	.160		24	7		31	37.50
2100	River or beach stone, stock	B-1	18	1.333	Ton	30	51		81	112
2150	Quarried	"	18	1.333	"	52	51		103	136
2160	Load, dump, and spread stone with skid steer, 100' haul	B-62	24	1	C.Y.		41.50	7.25	48.75	71
2165	200' haul		18	1.333			55	9.65	64.65	94.50
2168	300' haul		12	2			82.50	14.45	96.95	142
2170	Shale paver, 2-1/4" thick	D-1	200	.080	S.F.	3.13	3.37		6.50	8.60
2200	Coarse washed sand bed, 1"	B-62	1350	.018	S.Y.	1.77	.73	.13	2.63	3.21
2250	Stone dust, 4" thick	"	900	.027	"	3.33	1.10	.19	4.62	5.55
2300	Tile thinset pavers, 3/8" thick	D-1	300	.053	S.F.	3.53	2.25		5.78	7.30
2350	3/4" thick	"	280	.057	"	5.65	2.41		8.06	9.85
2400	Wood rounds, cypress	B-1	175	.137	Ea.	9.95	5.25		15.20	19

32 06 10.20 Steps

		Crew	Daily Output	Labor-Hours	Unit	Material	2015 Bare Costs Labor	2015 Bare Costs Equipment	Total	Total Incl O&P
0010	**STEPS**									
0011	Incl. excav., borrow & concrete base as required									
0100	Brick steps	B-24	35	.686	LF Riser	15.35	29.50		44.85	62
0200	Railroad ties	2 Clab	25	.640		3.59	24		27.59	41
0300	Bluestone treads, 12" x 2" or 12" x 1-1/2"	B-24	30	.800		33.50	34.50		68	89
0500	Concrete, cast in place, see Section 03 30 53.40									
0600	Precast concrete, see Section 03 41 23.50									
4000	Edging, redwood, 2" x 4"	2 Carp	330	.048	L.F.	2.43	2.28		4.71	6.15
4025	Steel edge strips, incl. stakes, 1/4" x 5"	B-1	390	.062		3.92	2.36		6.28	7.95
4050	Edging, landscape timber or railroad ties, 6" x 8"	2 Carp	170	.094		2.79	4.42		7.21	9.85

32 11 Base Courses

32 11 23 – Aggregate Base Courses

32 11 23.23 Base Course Drainage Layers

		Crew	Daily Output	Labor-Hours	Unit	Material	2015 Bare Costs Labor	2015 Bare Costs Equipment	Total	Total Incl O&P
0010	**BASE COURSE DRAINAGE LAYERS**									
0011	For roadways and large areas									
0050	Crushed 3/4" stone base, compacted, 3" deep	B-36C	5200	.008	S.Y.	2.30	.36	.81	3.47	3.96
0100	6" deep		5000	.008		4.61	.37	.84	5.82	6.55
0200	9" deep		4600	.009		6.90	.40	.91	8.21	9.20
0300	12" deep		4200	.010		9.20	.44	1	10.64	11.90
0301	Crushed 1-1/2" stone base, compacted to 4" deep	B-36B	6000	.011		4.46	.48	.80	5.74	6.50
0302	6" deep		5400	.012		6.70	.53	.89	8.12	9.15
0303	8" deep		4500	.014		8.90	.64	1.07	10.61	11.95
0304	12" deep		3800	.017		13.35	.75	1.27	15.37	17.25
0350	Bank run gravel, spread and compacted									
0370	6" deep	B-32	6000	.005	S.Y.	4.33	.25	.39	4.97	5.55
0390	9" deep		4900	.007		6.50	.31	.48	7.29	8.15
0400	12" deep		4200	.008		8.65	.36	.56	9.57	10.65
0600	Cold laid asphalt pavement, see Section 32 12 16.19									
1500	Alternate method to figure base course									
1510	Crushed stone, 3/4", compacted, 3" deep	B-36C	435	.092	E.C.Y.	23.50	4.26	9.65	37.41	43
1511	6" deep	B-36B	835	.077		23.50	3.42	5.75	32.67	37.50

32 11 Base Courses

32 11 23 – Aggregate Base Courses

32 11 23.23 Base Course Drainage Layers

		Crew	Daily Output	Labor-Hours	Unit	Material	2015 Bare Costs Labor	Equipment	Total	Total Incl O&P
1512	9" deep	B-36B	1150	.056	E.C.Y.	23.50	2.49	4.19	30.18	34.50
1513	12" deep		1400	.046		23.50	2.04	3.44	28.98	33
1520	Crushed stone, 1-1/2", compacted 4" deep		665	.096		23.50	4.30	7.25	35.05	40.50
1521	6" deep		900	.071		23.50	3.18	5.35	32.03	36.50
1522	8" deep		1000	.064		23.50	2.86	4.82	31.18	35.50
1523	12" deep		1265	.051		23.50	2.26	3.81	29.57	33.50
1530	Gravel, bank run, compacted, 6" deep	B-36C	835	.048		22	2.22	5	29.22	33.50
1531	9" deep		1150	.035		22	1.61	3.64	27.25	31
1532	12" deep		1400	.029		22	1.32	2.99	26.31	30
2010	Crushed stone, 3/4" maximum size, 3" deep	B-36	540	.074	Ton	14.30	3.20	3.08	20.58	24
2011	6" deep		1625	.025		14.30	1.06	1.02	16.38	18.45
2012	9" deep		1785	.022		14.30	.97	.93	16.20	18.20
2013	12" deep		1950	.021		14.30	.89	.85	16.04	18
2020	Crushed stone, 1-1/2" maximum size, 4" deep		720	.056		14.30	2.40	2.31	19.01	22
2021	6" deep		815	.049		14.30	2.12	2.04	18.46	21
2022	8" deep		835	.048		14.30	2.07	1.99	18.36	21
2023	12" deep		975	.041		14.30	1.77	1.71	17.78	20.50
2030	Bank run gravel, 6" deep	B-32A	875	.027		14.95	1.27	1.63	17.85	20
2031	9" deep		970	.025		14.95	1.14	1.47	17.56	19.80
2032	12" deep		1060	.023		14.95	1.05	1.34	17.34	19.55
6000	Stabilization fabric, polypropylene, 6 oz./S.Y.	B-6	10000	.002	S.Y.	1.28	.10	.04	1.42	1.60
6900	For small and irregular areas, add						50%	50%		
7000	Prepare and roll sub-base, small areas to 2500 S.Y.	B-32A	1500	.016	S.Y.		.74	.95	1.69	2.17
8000	Large areas over 2500 S.Y.	"	3500	.007			.32	.41	.73	.93
8050	For roadways	B-32	4000	.008			.38	.59	.97	1.23

32 11 26 – Asphaltic Base Courses

32 11 26.13 Plant Mix Asphaltic Base Courses

		Crew	Daily Output	Labor-Hours	Unit	Material	2015 Bare Costs Labor	Equipment	Total	Total Incl O&P
0010	**PLANT MIX ASPHALTIC BASE COURSES**									
0011	Roadways and large paved areas									
0500	Bituminous concrete, 4" thick	B-25	4545	.019	S.Y.	15.75	.80	.60	17.15	19.25
0550	6" thick		3700	.024		23	.98	.73	24.71	28
0560	8" thick		3000	.029		31	1.21	.90	33.11	37
0570	10" thick		2545	.035		38	1.43	1.07	40.50	45.50
1600	Macadam base, crushed stone or slag, dry-bound	B-36D	1400	.023	E.C.Y.	67.50	1.09	2.37	70.96	79
1610	Water-bound	B-36C	1400	.029	"	67.50	1.32	2.99	71.81	80
2000	Alternate method to figure base course									
2005	Bituminous concrete, 4" thick	B-25	1000	.088	Ton	70	3.64	2.71	76.35	85.50
2006	6" thick		1220	.072		70	2.98	2.22	75.20	84
2007	8" thick		1320	.067		70	2.76	2.06	74.82	83.50
2008	10" thick		1400	.063		70	2.60	1.94	74.54	83
8900	For small and irregular areas, add						50%	50%		

32 11 26.19 Bituminous-Stabilized Base Courses

		Crew	Daily Output	Labor-Hours	Unit	Material	2015 Bare Costs Labor	Equipment	Total	Total Incl O&P
0010	**BITUMINOUS-STABILIZED BASE COURSES**									
0020	And large paved areas									
0700	Liquid application to gravel base, asphalt emulsion	B-45	6000	.003	Gal.	4.29	.12	.15	4.56	5.05
0800	Prime and seal, cut back asphalt		6000	.003	"	5.05	.12	.15	5.32	5.90
1000	Macadam penetration crushed stone, 2 gal. per S.Y., 4" thick		6000	.003	S.Y.	8.60	.12	.15	8.87	9.80
1100	6" thick, 3 gal. per S.Y.		4000	.004		12.85	.18	.23	13.26	14.65
1200	8" thick, 4 gal. per S.Y.		3000	.005		17.15	.24	.30	17.69	19.60
8900	For small and irregular areas, add						50%	50%		

For customer support on your Site Work & Landscape Cost Data, call 877.737.1594.

363

32 12 16.13 Plant-Mix Asphalt Paving		Crew	Daily Output	Labor-Hours	Unit	Material	2015 Bare Costs Labor	Equipment	Total	Total Incl O&P
0010	**PLANT-MIX ASPHALT PAVING**									
0020	And large paved areas with no hauling included									
0025	See Section 31 23 23.20 for hauling costs									
0080	Binder course, 1-1/2" thick	B-25	7725	.011	S.Y.	5.70	.47	.35	6.52	7.40
0120	2" thick		6345	.014		7.60	.57	.43	8.60	9.70
0130	2-1/2" thick		5620	.016		9.50	.65	.48	10.63	11.95
0160	3" thick		4905	.018		11.40	.74	.55	12.69	14.30
0170	3-1/2" thick		4520	.019		13.30	.80	.60	14.70	16.55
0200	4" thick		4140	.021		15.25	.88	.66	16.79	18.80
0300	Wearing course, 1" thick	B-25B	10575	.009		3.78	.38	.28	4.44	5.05
0340	1-1/2" thick		7725	.012		6.35	.52	.38	7.25	8.20
0380	2" thick		6345	.015		8.50	.64	.46	9.60	10.90
0420	2-1/2" thick		5480	.018		10.50	.74	.54	11.78	13.25
0460	3" thick		4900	.020		12.55	.82	.60	13.97	15.70
0470	3-1/2" thick		4520	.021		14.70	.89	.65	16.24	18.30
0480	4" thick		4140	.023		16.80	.98	.71	18.49	21
0500	Open graded friction course	B-25C	5000	.010		2.13	.41	.47	3.01	3.48
0800	Alternate method of figuring paving costs									
0810	Binder course, 1-1/2" thick	B-25	630	.140	Ton	70	5.75	4.31	80.06	90.50
0811	2" thick		690	.128		70	5.25	3.93	79.18	89.50
0812	3" thick		800	.110		70	4.55	3.39	77.94	87.50
0813	4" thick		900	.098		70	4.04	3.01	77.05	86.50
0850	Wearing course, 1" thick	B-25B	575	.167		69	7.05	5.15	81.20	92.50
0851	1-1/2" thick		630	.152		69	6.40	4.68	80.08	91
0852	2" thick		690	.139		69	5.85	4.28	79.13	89.50
0853	2-1/2" thick		765	.125		69	5.30	3.86	78.16	88.50
0854	3" thick		800	.120		69	5.05	3.69	77.74	88
1000	Pavement replacement over trench, 2" thick	B-37	90	.533	S.Y.	7.85	21	1.75	30.60	43
1050	4" thick		70	.686		15.55	27.50	2.25	45.30	61.50
1080	6" thick		55	.873		25	34.50	2.86	62.36	83.50
1100	Turnouts and driveway entrances to highways									
1110	Binder course, 1-1/2" thick	B-25	315	.279	Ton	70	11.55	8.60	90.15	104
1120	2" thick		345	.255		70	10.55	7.85	88.40	102
1130	3" thick		400	.220		70	9.10	6.80	85.90	98.50
1140	4" thick		450	.196		70	8.10	6.05	84.15	96
1150	Binder course, 1-1/2" thick		3860	.023	S.Y.	5.70	.94	.70	7.34	8.50
1160	2" thick		3175	.028		7.60	1.15	.85	9.60	11.05
1170	2-1/2" thick		2810	.031		9.50	1.29	.97	11.76	13.50
1180	3" thick		2455	.036		11.40	1.48	1.11	13.99	16.05
1190	3-1/2" thick		2260	.039		13.30	1.61	1.20	16.11	18.45
1195	4" thick		2070	.043		15.25	1.76	1.31	18.32	21
1200	Wearing course, 1" thick	B-25B	290	.331	Ton	69	13.95	10.15	93.10	109
1210	1-1/2" thick		315	.305		69	12.85	9.35	91.20	106
1220	2" thick		345	.278		69	11.70	8.55	89.25	103
1230	2-1/2" thick		385	.249		69	10.50	7.65	87.15	101
1240	3" thick		400	.240		69	10.10	7.40	86.50	99.50
1250	Wearing course, 1" thick		5290	.018	S.Y.	3.78	.76	.56	5.10	5.95
1260	1-1/2" thick		3860	.025		6.35	1.05	.76	8.16	9.45
1270	2" thick		3175	.030		8.50	1.27	.93	10.70	12.35
1280	2-1/2" thick		2740	.035		10.50	1.48	1.08	13.06	15
1285	3" thick		2450	.039		12.55	1.65	1.20	15.40	17.65
1290	3-1/2" thick		2260	.042		14.70	1.79	1.31	17.80	20.50
1295	4" thick		2070	.046		16.80	1.95	1.43	20.18	23

For customer support on your Site Work & Landscape Cost Data, call 877.737.1594.

32 12 16.13 Plant-Mix Asphalt Paving	Crew	Daily Output	Labor-Hours	Unit	Material	2015 Bare Costs Labor	Equipment	Total	Total Incl O&P
1400	Bridge approach less than 300 tons								
1410	Binder course, 1-1/2" thick	B-25	330	.267	Ton	70	11	8.20	89.20	103
1420	2" thick		360	.244		70	10.10	7.55	87.65	101
1430	3" thick		420	.210		70	8.65	6.45	85.10	97.50
1440	4" thick		470	.187		70	7.75	5.75	83.50	95
1450	Binder course, 1-1/2" thick		4055	.022	S.Y.	5.70	.90	.67	7.27	8.40
1460	2" thick		3330	.026		7.60	1.09	.81	9.50	10.90
1470	2-1/2" thick		2950	.030		9.50	1.23	.92	11.65	13.35
1480	3" thick		2575	.034		11.40	1.41	1.05	13.86	15.85
1490	3-1/2" thick		2370	.037		13.30	1.53	1.14	15.97	18.25
1495	4" thick		2175	.040		15.25	1.67	1.25	18.17	20.50
1500	Wearing course, 1" thick	B-25B	300	.320	Ton	69	13.45	9.85	92.30	107
1510	1-1/2" thick		330	.291		69	12.25	8.95	90.20	105
1520	2" thick		360	.267		69	11.25	8.20	88.45	102
1530	2-1/2" thick		400	.240		69	10.10	7.40	86.50	99.50
1540	3" thick		420	.229		69	9.60	7	85.60	98.50
1550	Wearing course, 1" thick		5555	.017	S.Y.	3.78	.73	.53	5.04	5.85
1560	1-1/2" thick		4055	.024		6.35	1	.73	8.08	9.30
1570	2" thick		3330	.029		8.50	1.21	.89	10.60	12.25
1580	2-1/2" thick		2875	.033		10.50	1.41	1.03	12.94	14.85
1585	3" thick		2570	.037		12.55	1.57	1.15	15.27	17.45
1590	3-1/2" thick		2375	.040		14.70	1.70	1.24	17.64	20
1595	4" thick		2175	.044		16.80	1.86	1.36	20.02	23
1600	Bridge approach 300-800 tons								
1610	Binder course, 1-1/2" thick	B-25	390	.226	Ton	70	9.35	6.95	86.30	99
1620	2" thick		430	.205		70	8.45	6.30	84.75	97
1630	3" thick		500	.176		70	7.25	5.45	82.70	94
1640	4" thick		560	.157		70	6.50	4.84	81.34	92.50
1650	Binder course, 1-1/2" thick		4815	.018	S.Y.	5.70	.76	.56	7.02	8.10
1660	2" thick		3955	.022		7.60	.92	.69	9.21	10.50
1670	2-1/2" thick		3500	.025		9.50	1.04	.78	11.32	12.90
1680	3" thick		3060	.029		11.40	1.19	.89	13.48	15.35
1690	3-1/2" thick		2820	.031		13.30	1.29	.96	15.55	17.70
1695	4" thick		2580	.034		15.25	1.41	1.05	17.71	20
1700	Wearing course, 1" thick	B-25B	360	.267	Ton	69	11.25	8.20	88.45	102
1710	1-1/2" thick		390	.246		69	10.35	7.55	86.90	100
1720	2" thick		430	.223		69	9.40	6.85	85.25	98
1730	2-1/2" thick		475	.202		69	8.50	6.20	83.70	96
1740	3" thick		500	.192		69	8.10	5.90	83	95
1750	Wearing course, 1" thick		6590	.015	S.Y.	3.78	.61	.45	4.84	5.60
1760	1-1/2" thick		4815	.020		6.35	.84	.61	7.80	8.95
1770	2" thick		3955	.024		8.50	1.02	.75	10.27	11.80
1780	2-1/2" thick		3415	.028		10.50	1.18	.86	12.54	14.30
1785	3" thick		3055	.031		12.55	1.32	.97	14.84	16.90
1790	3-1/2" thick		2820	.034		14.70	1.43	1.05	17.18	19.55
1795	4" thick		2580	.037		16.80	1.57	1.14	19.51	22
1800	Bridge approach over 800 tons								
1810	Binder course, 1-1/2" thick	B-25	525	.168	Ton	70	6.95	5.15	82.10	93.50
1820	2" thick		575	.153		70	6.35	4.72	81.07	92
1830	3" thick		670	.131		70	5.45	4.05	79.50	90
1840	4" thick		750	.117		70	4.85	3.62	78.47	88.50
1850	Binder course, 1-1/2" thick		6450	.014	S.Y.	5.70	.56	.42	6.68	7.60
1860	2" thick		5300	.017		7.60	.69	.51	8.80	9.95

32 12 16 – Asphalt Paving

32 12 16.13 Plant-Mix Asphalt Paving

		Crew	Daily Output	Labor-Hours	Unit	Material	2015 Bare Costs Labor	2015 Bare Costs Equipment	Total	Total Incl O&P
1870	2-1/2" thick	B-25	4690	.019	S.Y.	9.50	.78	.58	10.86	12.30
1880	3" thick		4095	.021		11.40	.89	.66	12.95	14.65
1890	3-1/2" thick		3775	.023		13.30	.96	.72	14.98	16.90
1895	4" thick		3455	.025		15.25	1.05	.79	17.09	19.20
1900	Wearing course, 1" thick	B-25B	480	.200	Ton	69	8.40	6.15	83.55	95.50
1910	1-1/2" thick		525	.183		69	7.70	5.60	82.30	94
1920	2" thick		575	.167		69	7.05	5.15	81.20	92.50
1930	2-1/2" thick		640	.150		69	6.30	4.61	79.91	90.50
1940	3" thick		670	.143		69	6.05	4.40	79.45	90
1950	Wearing course, 1" thick		8830	.011	S.Y.	3.78	.46	.33	4.57	5.20
1960	1-1/2" thick		6450	.015		6.35	.63	.46	7.44	8.45
1970	2" thick		5300	.018		8.50	.76	.56	9.82	11.20
1980	2-1/2" thick		4575	.021		10.50	.88	.64	12.02	13.60
1985	3" thick		4090	.023		12.55	.99	.72	14.26	16.10
1990	3-1/2" thick		3775	.025		14.70	1.07	.78	16.55	18.70
1995	4" thick		3455	.028		16.80	1.17	.85	18.82	21
2000	Intersections									
2010	Binder course, 1-1/2" thick	B-25	440	.200	Ton	70	8.25	6.15	84.40	96.50
2020	2" thick		485	.181		70	7.50	5.60	83.10	94.50
2030	3" thick		560	.157		70	6.50	4.84	81.34	92.50
2040	4" thick		630	.140		70	5.75	4.31	80.06	90.50
2050	Binder course, 1-1/2" thick		5410	.016	S.Y.	5.70	.67	.50	6.87	7.90
2060	2" thick		4440	.020		7.60	.82	.61	9.03	10.25
2070	2-1/2" thick		3935	.022		9.50	.92	.69	11.11	12.65
2080	3" thick		3435	.026		11.40	1.06	.79	13.25	15.05
2090	3-1/2" thick		3165	.028		13.30	1.15	.86	15.31	17.35
2095	4" thick		2900	.030		15.25	1.25	.94	17.44	19.70
2100	Wearing course, 1" thick	B-25B	400	.240	Ton	69	10.10	7.40	86.50	99.50
2110	1-1/2" thick		440	.218		69	9.20	6.70	84.90	97.50
2120	2" thick		485	.198		69	8.35	6.10	83.45	95.50
2130	2-1/2" thick		535	.179		69	7.55	5.50	82.05	93.50
2140	3" thick		560	.171		69	7.20	5.25	81.45	93
2150	Wearing course, 1" thick		7400	.013	S.Y.	3.78	.55	.40	4.73	5.45
2160	1-1/2" thick		5410	.018		6.35	.75	.55	7.65	8.75
2170	2" thick		4440	.022		8.50	.91	.66	10.07	11.50
2180	2-1/2" thick		3835	.025		10.50	1.05	.77	12.32	14
2185	3" thick		3430	.028		12.55	1.18	.86	14.59	16.55
2190	3-1/2" thick		3165	.030		14.70	1.28	.93	16.91	19.20
2195	4" thick		2900	.033		16.80	1.39	1.02	19.21	22
3000	Prime coat, emulsion, .30 gal. per S.Y., 1000 S.Y.	B-45	2500	.006		1.74	.29	.36	2.39	2.75
3100	Tack coat, emulsion, .10 gal. per S.Y., 1000 S.Y.	"	2500	.006		.58	.29	.36	1.23	1.48

32 12 16.14 Asphaltic Concrete Paving

		Crew	Daily Output	Labor-Hours	Unit	Material	2015 Bare Costs Labor	2015 Bare Costs Equipment	Total	Total Incl O&P
0011	**ASPHALTIC CONCRETE PAVING**, parking lots & driveways									
0015	No asphalt hauling included									
0018	Use 6.05 C.Y. per inch per M.S.F. for hauling									
0020	6" stone base, 2" binder course, 1" topping	B-25C	9000	.005	S.F.	1.86	.23	.26	2.35	2.68
0025	2" binder course, 2" topping		9000	.005		2.28	.23	.26	2.77	3.14
0030	3" binder course, 2" topping		9000	.005		2.71	.23	.26	3.20	3.61
0035	4" binder course, 2" topping		9000	.005		3.13	.23	.26	3.62	4.07
0040	1.5" binder course, 1" topping		9000	.005		1.65	.23	.26	2.14	2.45
0042	3" binder course, 1" topping		9000	.005		2.29	.23	.26	2.78	3.15
0045	3" binder course, 3" topping		9000	.005		3.13	.23	.26	3.62	4.07

32 12 Flexible Paving

32 12 16 – Asphalt Paving

32 12 16.14 Asphaltic Concrete Paving

		Crew	Daily Output	Labor-Hours	Unit	Material	2015 Bare Costs Labor	2015 Bare Costs Equipment	Total	Total Incl O&P
0050	4" binder course, 3" topping	B-25C	9000	.005	S.F.	3.55	.23	.26	4.04	4.53
0055	4" binder course, 4" topping		9000	.005		3.96	.23	.26	4.45	4.99
0300	Binder course, 1-1/2" thick		35000	.001		.64	.06	.07	.77	.86
0400	2" thick		25000	.002		.82	.08	.09	.99	1.13
0500	3" thick		15000	.003		1.27	.14	.16	1.57	1.78
0600	4" thick		10800	.004		1.67	.19	.22	2.08	2.36
0800	Sand finish course, 3/4" thick		41000	.001		.32	.05	.06	.43	.49
0900	1" thick	▼	34000	.001		.40	.06	.07	.53	.61
1000	Fill pot holes, hot mix, 2" thick	B-16	4200	.008		.85	.30	.16	1.31	1.57
1100	4" thick		3500	.009		1.25	.35	.20	1.80	2.13
1120	6" thick	▼	3100	.010		1.67	.40	.22	2.29	2.70
1140	Cold patch, 2" thick	B-51	3000	.016		.99	.61	.08	1.68	2.12
1160	4" thick		2700	.018		1.89	.68	.09	2.66	3.22
1180	6" thick		1900	.025	▼	2.94	.96	.13	4.03	4.86
2000	From 60% recycled content, base course 3" thick ⒢	B-25	800	.110	Ton	45.50	4.55	3.39	53.44	60.50
3000	Prime coat, emulsion, .30 gal. per S.Y., 1000 S.Y.	B-45	2500	.006	S.Y.	1.74	.29	.36	2.39	2.75
3100	Tack coat, emulsion, .10 gal. per S.Y., 1000 S.Y.	"	2500	.006	"	.58	.29	.36	1.23	1.48

32 12 16.19 Cold-Mix Asphalt Paving

		Crew	Daily Output	Labor-Hours	Unit	Material	2015 Bare Costs Labor	2015 Bare Costs Equipment	Total	Total Incl O&P
0010	**COLD-MIX ASPHALT PAVING** 0.5 gal. asphalt/S.Y.per in depth									
0020	Well graded granular aggregate									
0100	Blade mixed in windrows, spread & compacted 4" course	B-90A	1600	.035	S.Y.	15.90	1.59	1.28	18.77	21.50
0200	Traveling plant mixed in windrows, compacted 4" course	B-90B	3000	.016		15.90	.71	.76	17.37	19.40
0300	Rotary plant mixed in place, compacted 4" course	"	3500	.014		15.90	.61	.65	17.16	19.15
0400	Central stationary plant, mixed, compacted 4" course	B-36	7200	.006	▼	32	.24	.23	32.47	35.50

32 13 Rigid Paving

32 13 13 – Concrete Paving

32 13 13.23 Concrete Paving Surface Treatment

		Crew	Daily Output	Labor-Hours	Unit	Material	2015 Bare Costs Labor	2015 Bare Costs Equipment	Total	Total Incl O&P
0010	**CONCRETE PAVING SURFACE TREATMENT**									
0015	Including joints, finishing and curing									
0020	Fixed form, 12' pass, unreinforced, 6" thick	B-26	3000	.029	S.Y.	22	1.24	1.18	24.42	27
0030	7" thick		2850	.031		27	1.30	1.24	29.54	33
0100	8" thick		2750	.032		30	1.35	1.28	32.63	36.50
0110	8" thick, small area		1375	.064		30	2.70	2.57	35.27	40
0200	9" thick		2500	.035		34.50	1.48	1.41	37.39	41.50
0300	10" thick		2100	.042		37.50	1.77	1.68	40.95	46
0310	10" thick, small area		1050	.084		37.50	3.54	3.36	44.40	50.50
0400	12" thick		1800	.049		43	2.06	1.96	47.02	53
0410	Conc. pavement, w/jt.,fnsh.&curing,fix form,24' pass,unreinforced,6"T		6000	.015		21	.62	.59	22.21	24.50
0420	7" thick		5700	.015		25	.65	.62	26.27	29.50
0430	8" thick		5500	.016		28.50	.67	.64	29.81	33
0440	9" thick		5000	.018		32.50	.74	.71	33.95	38
0450	10" thick		4200	.021		36	.88	.84	37.72	42
0460	12" thick		3600	.024		41.50	1.03	.98	43.51	48
0470	15" thick		3000	.029		54.50	1.24	1.18	56.92	62.50
0500	Fixed form 12' pass 15" thick	▼	1500	.059	▼	55	2.47	2.35	59.82	67
0510	For small irregular areas, add				%	10%	100%	100%		
0520	Welded wire fabric, sheets for rigid paving 2.33 lb./S.Y.	2 Rodm	389	.041	S.Y.	1.31	2.16		3.47	4.82
0530	Reinforcing steel for rigid paving 12 lb./S.Y.		666	.024		6.10	1.26		7.36	8.65
0540	Reinforcing steel for rigid paving 18 lb./S.Y.	▼	444	.036	▼	9.15	1.89		11.04	13
0610	For under 10' pass, add				%	10%	100%	100%		

For customer support on your Site Work & Landscape Cost Data, call 877.737.1594.

367

32 13 Rigid Paving

32 13 13 – Concrete Paving

32 13 13.23 Concrete Paving Surface Treatment

		Crew	Daily Output	Labor-Hours	Unit	Material	2015 Bare Costs Labor	Equipment	Total	Total Incl O&P
0620	Slip form, 12' pass, unreinforced, 6" thick	B-26A	5600	.016	S.Y.	21	.66	.66	22.32	24.50
0622	7" thick		5600	.016		26	.66	.66	27.32	30
0624	8" thick		5300	.017		29	.70	.70	30.40	34
0626	9" thick		4820	.018		33	.77	.77	34.54	38.50
0628	10" thick		4050	.022		36.50	.92	.91	38.33	42.50
0630	12" thick		3470	.025		42	1.07	1.07	44.14	49
0632	15" thick		2890	.030		53	1.28	1.28	55.56	62
0640	Slip form, 24' pass, unreinforced, 6" thick		11200	.008		20.50	.33	.33	21.16	24
0642	7" thick		11200	.008		24.50	.33	.33	25.16	28
0644	8" thick		10600	.008		28	.35	.35	28.70	31.50
0646	9" thick		9640	.009		32	.39	.38	32.77	36
0648	10" thick		8100	.011		35	.46	.46	35.92	40
0650	12" thick		6940	.013		41	.53	.53	42.06	46.50
0652	15" thick	▼	5780	.015		51.50	.64	.64	52.78	58
0700	Finishing, broom finish small areas	2 Cefi	120	.133	▼		6		6	8.90
0730	Transverse expansion joints, incl. premolded bit. jt. filler	C-1	150	.213	L.F.	2.35	9.50		11.85	17.25
0740	Transverse construction joint using bulkhead	"	73	.438	"	3.41	19.55		22.96	34
0750	Longitudinal joint tie bars, grouted	B-23	70	.571	Ea.	5.30	21.50	40.50	67.30	84
1000	Curing, with sprayed membrane by hand	2 Clab	1500	.011	S.Y.	1	.40		1.40	1.71

32 14 Unit Paving

32 14 13 – Precast Concrete Unit Paving

32 14 13.13 Interlocking Precast Concrete Unit Paving

		Crew	Daily Output	Labor-Hours	Unit	Material	2015 Bare Costs Labor	Equipment	Total	Total Incl O&P
0010	**INTERLOCKING PRECAST CONCRETE UNIT PAVING**									
0020	"V" blocks for retaining soil	D-1	205	.078	S.F.	10	3.29		13.29	16

32 14 13.16 Precast Concrete Unit Paving Slabs

		Crew	Daily Output	Labor-Hours	Unit	Material	2015 Bare Costs Labor	Equipment	Total	Total Incl O&P
0010	**PRECAST CONCRETE UNIT PAVING SLABS**									
0710	Precast concrete patio blocks, 2-3/8" thick, colors, 8" x 16"	D-1	265	.060	S.F.	1.85	2.54		4.39	5.90
0715	12" x 12"		300	.053		2.41	2.25		4.66	6.10
0720	16" x 16"		335	.048		2.65	2.01		4.66	6
0730	24" x 24"		510	.031		3.29	1.32		4.61	5.65
0740	Green, 8" x 16"	▼	265	.060		2.39	2.54		4.93	6.50
0750	Exposed local aggregate, natural	2 Bric	250	.064		7.30	2.95		10.25	12.55
0800	Colors		250	.064		7.30	2.95		10.25	12.55
0850	Exposed granite or limestone aggregate		250	.064		7.30	2.95		10.25	12.55
0900	Exposed white tumblestone aggregate	▼	250	.064		5.70	2.95		8.65	10.75

32 14 13.18 Precast Concrete Plantable Pavers

		Crew	Daily Output	Labor-Hours	Unit	Material	2015 Bare Costs Labor	Equipment	Total	Total Incl O&P
0010	**PRECAST CONCRETE PLANTABLE PAVERS** (50% grass)									
0015	Subgrade preparation and grass planting not included									
0100	Precast concrete plantable pavers with topsoil, 24" x 16"	B-63	800	.050	S.F.	4.15	1.99	.22	6.36	7.85
0200	Less than 600 Square Feet or irregular area	"	500	.080	"	4.15	3.18	.35	7.68	9.85
0300	3/4" crushed stone base for plantable pavers, 6 inch depth	B-62	1000	.024	S.Y.	4.61	.99	.17	5.77	6.75
0400	8 inch depth		900	.027		6.15	1.10	.19	7.44	8.70
0500	10 inch depth		800	.030		7.70	1.24	.22	9.16	10.60
0600	12 inch depth	▼	700	.034	▼	9.20	1.42	.25	10.87	12.60
0700	Hydro seeding plantable pavers	B-81A	20	.800	M.S.F.	12.45	30.50	21.50	64.45	84
0800	Apply fertilizer and seed to plantable pavers	1 Clab	8	1	"	50.50	37.50		88	114

32 14 Unit Paving

32 14 16 - Brick Unit Paving

32 14 16.10 Brick Paving

		Crew	Daily Output	Labor-Hours	Unit	Material	2015 Bare Costs Labor	Equipment	Total	Total Incl O&P
0010	**BRICK PAVING**									
0012	4" x 8" x 1-1/2", without joints (4.5 brick/S.F.)	D-1	110	.145	S.F.	2.21	6.10		8.31	11.80
0100	Grouted, 3/8" joint (3.9 brick/S.F.)		90	.178		1.95	7.50		9.45	13.60
0200	4" x 8" x 2-1/4", without joints (4.5 bricks/S.F.)		110	.145		2.25	6.10		8.35	11.85
0300	Grouted, 3/8" joint (3.9 brick/S.F.)		90	.178		1.95	7.50		9.45	13.60
0400	4" x 8" x 2-1/4", dry, on edge (8/S.F.)		140	.114		4	4.81		8.81	11.75
0450	Grouted, 3/8" joint (6.5/S.F.)		85	.188		3.25	7.90		11.15	15.70
0455	Pervious brick paving, 4" x 8" x 3-1/4", without joints (4.5 bricks/S.F.)		110	.145		3.38	6.10		9.48	13.05
0500	Bedding, asphalt, 3/4" thick	B-25	5130	.017		.70	.71	.53	1.94	2.44
0540	Course washed sand bed, 1" thick	B-18	5000	.005		.32	.18	.01	.51	.64
0580	Mortar, 1" thick	D-1	300	.053		.74	2.25		2.99	4.24
0620	2" thick		200	.080		1.48	3.37		4.85	6.75
2000	Brick pavers, laid on edge, 7.2 per S.F.		70	.229		3.86	9.60		13.46	18.95
2500	For 4" thick concrete bed and joints, add		595	.027		1.19	1.13		2.32	3.04
2800	For steam cleaning, add	A-1H	950	.008		.09	.32	.08	.49	.68

32 14 23 - Asphalt Unit Paving

32 14 23.10 Asphalt Blocks

		Crew	Daily Output	Labor-Hours	Unit	Material	2015 Bare Costs Labor	Equipment	Total	Total Incl O&P
0010	**ASPHALT BLOCKS**									
0020	Rectangular, 6" x 12" x 1-1/4", w/bed & neopr. adhesive	D-1	135	.119	S.F.	9.30	4.99		14.29	17.80
0100	3" thick		130	.123		13	5.20		18.20	22
0300	Hexagonal tile, 8" wide, 1-1/4" thick		135	.119		9.30	4.99		14.29	17.80
0400	2" thick		130	.123		13	5.20		18.20	22
0500	Square, 8" x 8", 1-1/4" thick		135	.119		9.30	4.99		14.29	17.80
0600	2" thick		130	.123		13	5.20		18.20	22
0900	For exposed aggregate (ground finish) add					.62			.62	.68
0910	For colors, add					.47			.47	.52

32 14 40 - Stone Paving

32 14 40.10 Stone Pavers

		Crew	Daily Output	Labor-Hours	Unit	Material	2015 Bare Costs Labor	Equipment	Total	Total Incl O&P
0010	**STONE PAVERS**									
1100	Flagging, bluestone, irregular, 1" thick,	D-1	81	.198	S.F.	6.40	8.30		14.70	19.75
1110	1-1/2" thick		90	.178		7.55	7.50		15.05	19.75
1120	Pavers, 1/2" thick		110	.145		10.65	6.10		16.75	21
1130	3/4" thick		95	.168		13.60	7.10		20.70	26
1140	1" thick		81	.198		14.55	8.30		22.85	28.50
1150	Snapped random rectangular, 1" thick		92	.174		9.70	7.30		17	22
1200	1-1/2" thick		85	.188		11.65	7.90		19.55	25
1250	2" thick		83	.193		13.60	8.10		21.70	27.50
1300	Slate, natural cleft, irregular, 3/4" thick		92	.174		9.20	7.30		16.50	21.50
1310	1" thick		85	.188		10.70	7.90		18.60	24
1350	Random rectangular, gauged, 1/2" thick		105	.152		19.85	6.40		26.25	32
1400	Random rectangular, butt joint, gauged, 1/4" thick		150	.107		21.50	4.49		25.99	30.50
1450	For sand rubbed finish, add					9.30			9.30	10.20
1500	For interior setting, add					25%			25%	25%
1550	Granite blocks, 3-1/2" x 3-1/2" x 3-1/2"	D-1	92	.174	S.F.	12	7.30		19.30	24.50
1560	4" x 4" x 4"		95	.168		12.70	7.10		19.80	25
1600	4" to 12" long, 3" to 5" wide, 3" to 5" thick		98	.163		10	6.85		16.85	21.50
1650	6" to 15" long, 3" to 6" wide, 3" to 5" thick		105	.152		5.35	6.40		11.75	15.70
2000	Granite paver, sawn with thermal finish, white, 4" x 4" x 2"	D-2	80	.550		30.50	24		54.50	70
2005	4" x 4" x 3"		80	.550		32.50	24		56.50	72
2010	4" x 4" x 4"		80	.550		34.50	24		58.50	74.50
2015	4" x 8" x 2"		170	.259		26	11.20		37.20	45.50

For customer support on your Site Work & Landscape Cost Data, call 877.737.1594.

369

32 14 Unit Paving

32 14 40 – Stone Paving

32 14 40.10 Stone Pavers

		Crew	Daily Output	Labor-Hours	Unit	Material	2015 Bare Costs Labor	Equipment	Total	Total Incl O&P
2020	4" x 8" x 3"	D-2	170	.259	S.F.	31.50	11.20		42.70	52
2025	4" x 8" x 4"		170	.259		32.50	11.20		43.70	52.50
2030	8" x 8" x 2"		300	.147		23.50	6.35		29.85	35
2035	8" x 8" x 3"		300	.147		30	6.35		36.35	42.50
2040	8" x 8" x 4"		300	.147		34	6.35		40.35	46.50
2045	12" x 12" x 2"		725	.061		21.50	2.63		24.13	27.50
2050	12" x 12" x 3"		725	.061		23	2.63		25.63	29.50
2055	12" x 12" x 4"		725	.061		29	2.63		31.63	35.50

32 16 Curbs, Gutters, Sidewalks, and Driveways

32 16 13 – Curbs and Gutters

32 16 13.13 Cast-in-Place Concrete Curbs and Gutters

		Crew	Daily Output	Labor-Hours	Unit	Material	2015 Bare Costs Labor	Equipment	Total	Total Incl O&P
0010	**CAST-IN-PLACE CONCRETE CURBS AND GUTTERS**									
0290	Forms only, no concrete									
0300	Concrete, wood forms, 6" x 18", straight	C-2	500	.096	L.F.	2.99	4.39		7.38	10.05
0400	6" x 18", radius	"	200	.240	"	3.11	11		14.11	20.50
0402	Forms and concrete complete									
0404	Concrete, wood forms, 6" x 18", straight & concrete	C-2A	500	.096	L.F.	5.85	4.36		10.21	13.05
0406	6" x 18", radius		200	.240		5.95	10.90		16.85	23
0410	Steel forms, 6" x 18", straight		700	.069		4.40	3.11		7.51	9.60
0411	6" x 18", radius		400	.120		3.61	5.45		9.06	12.35
0415	Machine formed, 6" x 18", straight	B-69A	2000	.024		3.52	.99	.50	5.01	5.95
0416	6" x 18", radius	"	900	.053		3.55	2.20	1.11	6.86	8.50
0421	Curb and gutter, straight									
0422	with 6" high curb and 6" thick gutter, wood forms									
0430	24" wide, .055 C.Y. per L.F.	C-2A	375	.128	L.F.	15.35	5.80		21.15	26
0435	30" wide, .066 C.Y. per L.F.		340	.141		16.85	6.40		23.25	28.50
0440	Steel forms, 24" wide, straight		700	.069		6.80	3.11		9.91	12.20
0441	Radius		500	.096		6.75	4.36		11.11	14.10
0442	30" wide, straight		700	.069		7.90	3.11		11.01	13.45
0443	Radius		500	.096		7.70	4.36		12.06	15.10
0445	Machine formed, 24" wide, straight	B-69A	2000	.024		5.70	.99	.50	7.19	8.30
0446	Radius		900	.053		5.70	2.20	1.11	9.01	10.85
0447	30" wide, straight		2000	.024		6.60	.99	.50	8.09	9.30
0448	Radius		900	.053		6.60	2.20	1.11	9.91	11.85
0451	Median mall, machine formed, 2' x 9" high, straight		2200	.022		5.70	.90	.45	7.05	8.10
0452	Radius	B-69B	900	.053		5.70	2.20	.86	8.76	10.55
0453	4' x 9" high, straight		2000	.024		11.40	.99	.39	12.78	14.50
0454	Radius		800	.060		11.40	2.48	.97	14.85	17.40

32 16 13.23 Precast Concrete Curbs and Gutters

		Crew	Daily Output	Labor-Hours	Unit	Material	2015 Bare Costs Labor	Equipment	Total	Total Incl O&P
0010	**PRECAST CONCRETE CURBS AND GUTTERS**									
0550	Precast, 6" x 18", straight	B-29	700	.080	L.F.	10.30	3.28	1.26	14.84	17.75
0600	6" x 18", radius	"	325	.172	"	10.80	7.05	2.71	20.56	25.50

32 16 13.33 Asphalt Curbs

		Crew	Daily Output	Labor-Hours	Unit	Material	2015 Bare Costs Labor	Equipment	Total	Total Incl O&P
0010	**ASPHALT CURBS**									
0012	Curbs, asphaltic, machine formed, 8" wide, 6" high, 40 L.F./ton	B-27	1000	.032	L.F.	1.82	1.22	.30	3.34	4.21
0100	8" wide, 8" high, 30 L.F. per ton		900	.036		2.43	1.35	.33	4.11	5.10
0150	Asphaltic berm, 12" W, 3"-6" H, 35 L.F./ton, before pavement		700	.046		.04	1.74	.42	2.20	3.19
0200	12" W, 1-1/2" to 4" H, 60 L.F. per ton, laid with pavement	B-2	1050	.038		.02	1.45		1.47	2.26

32 16 13.43 Stone Curbs	Crew	Daily Output	Labor-Hours	Unit	Material	2015 Bare Costs Labor	2015 Bare Costs Equipment	Total	Total Incl O&P
0010 **STONE CURBS**									
1000 Granite, split face, straight, 5" x 16"	D-13	275	.175	L.F.	11.65	7.85	1.72	21.22	26.50
1100 6" x 18"	"	250	.192		15.35	8.60	1.89	25.84	32
1300 Radius curbing, 6" x 18", over 10' radius	B-29	260	.215		18.75	8.85	3.39	30.99	37.50
1400 Corners, 2' radius	"	80	.700	Ea.	63	28.50	11.05	102.55	126
1600 Edging, 4-1/2" x 12", straight	d-13	300	.160	L.F.	5.85	7.15	1.58	14.58	19.10
1800 Curb inlets, (guttermouth) straight	B-29	41	1.366	Ea.	140	56	21.50	217.50	263
2000 Indian granite (belgian block)									
2100 Jumbo, 10-1/2" x 7-1/2" x 4", grey	D-1	150	.107	L.F.	6.15	4.49		10.64	13.60
2150 Pink		150	.107		7.75	4.49		12.24	15.35
2200 Regular, 9" x 4-1/2" x 4-1/2", grey		160	.100		4.67	4.21		8.88	11.60
2250 Pink		160	.100		6.15	4.21		10.36	13.20
2300 Cubes, 4" x 4" x 4", grey		175	.091		3.96	3.85		7.81	10.25
2350 Pink		175	.091		3.81	3.85		7.66	10.10
2400 6" x 6" x 6", pink		155	.103		12.60	4.35		16.95	20.50
2500 Alternate pricing method for indian granite									
2550 Jumbo, 10-1/2" x 7-1/2" x 4" (30 lb.), grey				Ton	350			350	385
2600 Pink					450			450	495
2650 Regular, 9" x 4-1/2" x 4-1/2" (20 lb.), grey					330			330	365
2700 Pink					430			430	475
2750 Cubes, 4" x 4" x 4" (5 lb.), grey					480			480	530
2800 Pink					490			490	540
2850 6" x 6" x 6" (25 lb.), pink					490			490	540
2900 For pallets, add					22			22	24

32 17 Paving Specialties
32 17 13 – Parking Bumpers

32 17 13.13 Metal Parking Bumpers	Crew	Daily Output	Labor-Hours	Unit	Material	Labor	Equipment	Total	Total Incl O&P
0010 **METAL PARKING BUMPERS**									
0015 Bumper rails for garages, 12 Ga. rail, 6" wide, with steel									
0020 posts 12'-6" O.C., minimum	E-4	190	.168	L.F.	18.25	8.95	.77	27.97	36.50
0030 Average		165	.194		23	10.30	.88	34.18	44
0100 Maximum		140	.229		27.50	12.15	1.04	40.69	52
0300 12" channel rail, minimum		160	.200		23	10.65	.91	34.56	44.50
0400 Maximum		120	.267		34	14.15	1.22	49.37	63.50
1300 Pipe bollards, conc. filled/paint, 8' L x 4' D hole, 6" diam.	B-6	20	1.200	Ea.	600	49.50	18.20	667.70	755
1400 8" diam.		15	1.600		685	66	24.50	775.50	880
1500 12" diam.		12	2		965	82.50	30.50	1,078	1,200
2030 Folding with individual padlocks	B-2	50	.800		605	30.50		635.50	710

32 17 13.16 Plastic Parking Bumpers									
0010 **PLASTIC PARKING BUMPERS**									
1200 Thermoplastic, 6" x 10" x 6'-0"	B-2	120	.333	Ea.	52.50	12.65		65.15	77.50

32 17 13.19 Precast Concrete Parking Bumpers									
0010 **PRECAST CONCRETE PARKING BUMPERS**									
1000 Wheel stops, precast concrete incl. dowels, 6" x 10" x 6'-0"	B-2	120	.333	Ea.	39.50	12.65		52.15	63
1100 8" x 13" x 6'-0"	"	120	.333	"	46	12.65		58.65	70

32 17 Paving Specialties

32 17 13 – Parking Bumpers

32 17 13.26 Wood Parking Bumpers

		Crew	Daily Output	Labor-Hours	Unit	Material	2015 Bare Costs Labor	Equipment	Total	Total Incl O&P
0010	**WOOD PARKING BUMPERS**									
0020	Parking barriers, timber w/saddles, treated type									
0100	4" x 4" for cars	B-2	520	.077	L.F.	2.92	2.92		5.84	7.70
0200	6" x 6" for trucks		520	.077	"	6.10	2.92		9.02	11.20
0600	Flexible fixed stanchion, 2' high, 3" diameter		100	.400	Ea.	40.50	15.20		55.70	68

32 17 23 – Pavement Markings

32 17 23.13 Painted Pavement Markings

		Crew	Daily Output	Labor-Hours	Unit	Material	2015 Bare Costs Labor	Equipment	Total	Total Incl O&P
0010	**PAINTED PAVEMENT MARKINGS**									
0020	Acrylic waterborne, white or yellow, 4" wide, less than 3000 L.F.	B-78	20000	.002	L.F.	.15	.09	.03	.27	.34
0030	3000-16000 L.F.		20000	.002		.09	.09	.03	.21	.27
0040	over 16000 L.F.		20000	.002		.09	.09	.03	.21	.27
0200	6" wide, less than 3000 L.F.		11000	.004		.23	.17	.05	.45	.57
0220	3000-16000 L.F.		11000	.004		.14	.17	.05	.36	.47
0230	over 16000 L.F.		11000	.004		.14	.17	.05	.36	.47
0500	8" wide, less than 3000 L.F.		10000	.005		.31	.18	.06	.55	.69
0520	3000-16000 L.F.		10000	.005		.18	.18	.06	.42	.55
0530	over 16000 L.F.		10000	.005		.18	.18	.06	.42	.55
0600	12" wide, less than 3000 L.F.		4000	.012		.46	.46	.15	1.07	1.37
0604	3000-16000 L.F.		4000	.012		.27	.46	.15	.88	1.16
0608	over 16000 L.F.		4000	.012		.27	.46	.15	.88	1.16
0620	Arrows or gore lines		2300	.021	S.F.	.22	.80	.26	1.28	1.75
0640	Temporary paint, white or yellow, less than 3000 L.F.		15000	.003	L.F.	.08	.12	.04	.24	.32
0642	3000-16000 L.F.		15000	.003		.07	.12	.04	.23	.31
0644	Over 16000 L.F.		15000	.003		.06	.12	.04	.22	.30
0660	Removal	1 Clab	300	.027			1		1	1.54
0680	Temporary tape	2 Clab	1500	.011		.48	.40		.88	1.15
0710	Thermoplastic, white or yellow, 4" wide, less than 6000 L.F.	B-79	15000	.003		.31	.10	.10	.51	.61
0715	6000 L.F. or more		15000	.003		.29	.10	.10	.49	.59
0730	6" wide, less than 6000 L.F.		14000	.003		.47	.11	.11	.69	.80
0735	6000 L.F. or more		14000	.003		.44	.11	.11	.66	.77
0740	8" wide, less than 6000 L.F.		12000	.003		.62	.13	.12	.87	1.02
0745	6000 L.F. or more		12000	.003		.58	.13	.12	.83	.98
0750	12" wide, less than 6000 L.F.		6000	.007		.91	.26	.25	1.42	1.67
0755	6000 L.F. or more		6000	.007		.86	.26	.25	1.37	1.60
0760	Arrows		660	.061	S.F.	.61	2.32	2.24	5.17	6.70
0770	Gore lines		2500	.016		.61	.61	.59	1.81	2.26
0780	Letters		660	.061		.61	2.32	2.24	5.17	6.70
0782	Thermoplastic material, small users				Ton	1,700			1,700	1,875
0784	Glass beads, highway use, add				Lb.	.59			.59	.65
0786	Thermoplastic material, highway departments				Ton	1,475			1,475	1,625
1000	Airport painted markings									
1050	Traffic safety flashing truck for airport painting	A-2B	1	8	Day		315	245	560	745
1100	Painting, white or yellow, taxiway markings	B-78	4000	.012	S.F.	.27	.46	.15	.88	1.16
1110	with 12 lb. beads per 100 S.F.		4000	.012		.53	.46	.15	1.14	1.44
1200	Runway markings		3500	.014		.27	.52	.17	.96	1.29
1210	with 12 lb. beads per 100 S.F.		3500	.014		.53	.52	.17	1.22	1.57
1300	Pavement location or direction signs		2500	.019		.27	.73	.24	1.24	1.68
1310	with 12 lb. beads per 100 S.F.		2500	.019		.53	.73	.24	1.50	1.96
1350	Mobilization airport pavement painting		4	12	Ea.		460	150	610	870
1400	Paint markings or pavement signs removal daytime	B-78B	400	.045	S.F.		1.75	.94	2.69	3.71
1500	Removal nighttime		335	.054	"		2.09	1.12	3.21	4.43
1600	Mobilization pavement paint removal		4	4.500	Ea.		175	94	269	370

372

32 17 Paving Specialties

32 17 23 – Pavement Markings

32 17 23.14 Pavement Parking Markings

		Crew	Daily Output	Labor-Hours	Unit	Material	2015 Bare Costs Labor	Equipment	Total	Total Incl O&P
0010	**PAVEMENT PARKING MARKINGS**									
0790	Layout of pavement marking	A-2	25000	.001	L.F.		.04	.01	.05	.07
0800	Lines on pvmt., parking stall, paint, white, 4" wide	B-78B	400	.045	Stall	4.44	1.75	.94	7.13	8.60
0825	Parking stall, small quantities	2 Pord	80	.200		8.90	8.05		16.95	22
0830	Lines on pvmt., parking stall, thermoplastic, white, 4" wide	B-79	300	.133	↓	13.50	5.10	4.92	23.52	28
1000	Street letters and numbers	B-78B	1600	.011	S.F.	.67	.44	.23	1.34	1.67
1100	Pavement marking letter, 6"	2 Pord	400	.040	Ea.	10.60	1.61		12.21	14.10
1110	12" letter		272	.059		13.35	2.37		15.72	18.25
1120	24" letter		160	.100		29.50	4.04		33.54	38.50
1130	36" letter		84	.190		38.50	7.70		46.20	54
1140	42" letter		84	.190		51	7.70		58.70	67.50
1150	72" letter		40	.400		42	16.15		58.15	70.50
1200	Handicap symbol	↓	40	.400		31	16.15		47.15	58.50
1210	Handicap Parking sign 12" x 18 " and post	A-2	12	2	↓	124	76	20.50	220.50	276
1300	Pavement marking, thermoplastic tape including layout, 4 inch width	B-79B	320	.025	L.F.	2.53	.94	.48	3.95	4.75
1310	12 inch width		192	.042	"	6.80	1.57	.79	9.16	10.80
1320	Letters including layout, 4 inch		240	.033	Ea.	12.35	1.25	.63	14.23	16.25
1330	6 inch		160	.050		15.15	1.88	.95	17.98	20.50
1340	12 inch		120	.067		19.20	2.51	1.27	22.98	26.50
1350	48 inch		64	.125		71.50	4.70	2.38	78.58	89
1360	96 inch		32	.250		91	9.40	4.75	105.15	120
1380	4 letter words, 8 feet tall	↓	8	1	↓	340	37.50	19	396.50	455
1385	Sample words: "BUMP, FIRE, LANE"									

32 17 23.33 Plastic Pavement Markings

		Crew	Daily Output	Labor-Hours	Unit	Material	2015 Bare Costs Labor	Equipment	Total	Total Incl O&P
0010	**PLASTIC PAVEMENT MARKINGS**									
0020	Thermoplastic markings with glass beads									
0100	Thermoplastic striping, 6# beads per 100 S.F, white or yellow, 4" wide	B-79	15000	.003	L.F.	.32	.10	.10	.52	.62
0110	8# beads per 100 S.F		15000	.003		.33	.10	.10	.53	.63
0120	10# beads per 100 S.F		15000	.003		.33	.10	.10	.53	.63
0130	12# beads per 100 S.F		15000	.003		.33	.10	.10	.53	.64
0200	6# beads per 100 S.F, white or yellow, 6" wide		14000	.003		.48	.11	.11	.70	.82
0210	8# beads per 100 S.F		14000	.003		.49	.11	.11	.71	.83
0220	10# beads per 100 S.F		14000	.003		.49	.11	.11	.71	.83
0230	12# beads per 100 S.F		14000	.003		.50	.11	.11	.72	.84
0300	6# beads per 100 S.F, white or yellow, 8" wide		12000	.003		.64	.13	.12	.89	1.05
0310	8# beads per 100 S.F		12000	.003		.65	.13	.12	.90	1.06
0320	10# beads per 100 S.F		12000	.003		.66	.13	.12	.91	1.07
0330	12# beads per 100 S.F		12000	.003		.67	.13	.12	.92	1.07
0400	6# beads per 100 S.F, white or yellow, 12" wide		6000	.007		.97	.26	.25	1.48	1.72
0410	8# beads per 100 S.F		6000	.007		.98	.26	.25	1.49	1.73
0420	10# beads per 100 S.F		6000	.007		.99	.26	.25	1.50	1.75
0430	12# beads per 100 S.F		6000	.007	↓	1	.26	.25	1.51	1.76
0500	Gore lines with 6# beads per 100 S.F.		2500	.016	S.F.	.65	.61	.59	1.85	2.30
0510	8# beads per 100 S.F.		2500	.016		.66	.61	.59	1.86	2.31
0520	10# beads per 100 S.F.		2500	.016		.67	.61	.59	1.87	2.33
0530	12# beads per 100 S.F.		2500	.016		.68	.61	.59	1.88	2.34
0600	Arrows with 6# beads per100 S.F.		660	.061		.65	2.32	2.24	5.21	6.75
0610	8# beads per100 S.F.		660	.061		.66	2.32	2.24	5.22	6.75
0620	10# beads per100 S.F.		660	.061		.67	2.32	2.24	5.23	6.75
0630	12# beads per100 S.F.		660	.061		.68	2.32	2.24	5.24	6.75
0700	Letters with 6# beads per 100 S.F.		660	.061		.65	2.32	2.24	5.21	6.75
0710	8# beads per 100 S.F.		660	.061		.66	2.32	2.24	5.22	6.75

32 17 Paving Specialties

32 17 23 – Pavement Markings

32 17 23.33 Plastic Pavement Markings

32 17 23.33 Plastic Pavement Markings	Crew	Daily Output	Labor-Hours	Unit	Material	2015 Bare Costs Labor	Equipment	Total	Total Incl O&P
0720	10# beads per 100 S.F.	B-79	660	.061	S.F.	.67	2.32	2.24	5.23	6.75
0730	12# beads per 100 S.F.	↓	660	.061	↓	.68	2.32	2.24	5.24	6.75
1000	Airport thermoplastic markings									
1050	Traffic safety flashing truck for airport markings	A-2B	1	8	Day		315	245	560	745
1100	Thermoplastic taxiway markings with 24# beads per 100 S.F.	B-79	2500	.016	S.F.	1.11	.61	.59	2.31	2.82
1200	Runway markings		2100	.019		1.11	.73	.70	2.54	3.12
1250	Location or direction signs		1500	.027	↓	1.11	1.02	.98	3.11	3.88
1350	Mobilization airport pavement marking	↓	4	10	Ea.		385	370	755	990
1400	Thermostatic markings or pavement signs removal daytime	B-78B	400	.045	S.F.		1.75	.94	2.69	3.71
1500	Removal nighttime		335	.054	"		2.09	1.12	3.21	4.43
1600	Mobilization thermostatic marking removal	↓	4	4.500	Ea.		175	94	269	370
1700	Thermoplastic road marking material, small users				Ton	1,700			1,700	1,875
1710	Highway departments					1,475			1,475	1,625
1720	Thermoplastic airport marking material, small users					1,800			1,800	1,975
1730	Large users				↓	1,575			1,575	1,750
1800	Glass beads material for highway use, type II				Lb.	.59			.59	.65
1900	Glass beads material for airport use, type III				"	2.16			2.16	2.38

32 18 Athletic and Recreational Surfacing

32 18 13 – Synthetic Grass Surfacing

32 18 13.10 Artificial Grass Surfacing

32 18 13.10 Artificial Grass Surfacing	Crew	Daily Output	Labor-Hours	Unit	Material	2015 Bare Costs Labor	Equipment	Total	Total Incl O&P
0010	ARTIFICIAL GRASS SURFACING									
0015	Not including asphalt base or drainage,									
0020	but including cushion pad, over 50,000 S.F.									
0200	1/2" pile and 5/16" cushion pad, standard	C-17	3200	.025	S.F.	10.15	1.23		11.38	13.10
0300	Deluxe		2560	.031	↓	15	1.53		16.53	18.85
0500	1/2" pile and 5/8" cushion pad, standard		2844	.028		14.60	1.38		15.98	18.20
0600	Deluxe	↓	2327	.034	↓	16.10	1.69		17.79	20.50
0700	Acrylic emulsion texture coat, sand filled	B-1	5200	.005	S.Y.	2.46	.18		2.64	2.98
0710	Rubber filled	"	5200	.005	"	2.57	.18		2.75	3.10
0720	Acrylic emulsion color coat									
0730	Brown, red, or tan	B-1	6000	.004	S.Y.	2.46	.15		2.61	2.95
0740	Green		6000	.004		2.46	.15		2.61	2.95
0750	Blue		6000	.004		2.46	.15		2.61	2.95
0760	Rubber acrylic cushion base coat	↓	2600	.009	↓	3.32	.35		3.67	4.19
0800	For asphaltic concrete base, 2-1/2" thick,									
0900	with 6" crushed stone sub-base, add	B-25	12000	.007	S.F.	1.69	.30	.23	2.22	2.57

32 18 16 – Synthetic Resilient Surfacing

32 18 16.13 Playground Protective Surfacing

32 18 16.13 Playground Protective Surfacing	Crew	Daily Output	Labor-Hours	Unit	Material	2015 Bare Costs Labor	Equipment	Total	Total Incl O&P
0010	PLAYGROUND PROTECTIVE SURFACING									
0100	Resilient rubber surface, poured in place, 4" thick, black	2 Skwk	300	.053	S.F.	13.35	2.59		15.94	18.70
0150	2" thick topping, colors	"	2800	.006		7.25	.28		7.53	8.40
0200	Wood chip mulch, 6" deep	1 Clab	300	.027	↓	.76	1		1.76	2.38

32 18 23 – Athletic Surfacing

32 18 23.33 Running Track Surfacing

32 18 23.33 Running Track Surfacing	Crew	Daily Output	Labor-Hours	Unit	Material	2015 Bare Costs Labor	Equipment	Total	Total Incl O&P
0010	RUNNING TRACK SURFACING									
0020	Running track, asphalt, incl base, 3" thick	B-37	300	.160	S.Y.	13	6.35	.52	19.87	24.50
0102	Surface, latex rubber system, 1/2" thick, black	B-20	115	.209		41	8.75		49.75	59
0152	Colors		115	.209		50.50	8.75		59.25	69
0302	Urethane rubber system, 1/2" thick, black	↓	110	.218	↓	30.50	9.15		39.65	47.50

374

32 18 Athletic and Recreational Surfacing

32 18 23 – Athletic Surfacing

32 18 23.33 Running Track Surfacing

		Crew	Daily Output	Labor-Hours	Unit	Material	2015 Bare Costs Labor	Equipment	Total	Total Incl O&P
0402	Color coating	B-20	110	.218	S.Y.	37.50	9.15		46.65	55

32 18 23.53 Tennis Court Surfacing

		Crew	Daily Output	Labor-Hours	Unit	Material	2015 Bare Costs Labor	Equipment	Total	Total Incl O&P
0010	**TENNIS COURT SURFACING**									
0020	Tennis court, asphalt, incl. base, 2-1/2" thick, one court	B-37	450	.107	S.Y.	37.50	4.24	.35	42.09	48.50
0200	Two courts		675	.071		15.85	2.83	.23	18.91	22
0300	Clay courts		360	.133		42	5.30	.44	47.74	55
0400	Pulverized natural greenstone with 4" base, fast dry		250	.192		39.50	7.65	.63	47.78	56
0800	Rubber-acrylic base resilient pavement		600	.080		56	3.18	.26	59.44	66.50
1000	Colored sealer, acrylic emulsion, 3 coats	2 Clab	800	.020		6.05	.75		6.80	7.80
1100	3 coat, 2 colors	"	900	.018		8.45	.67		9.12	10.30
1200	For preparing old courts, add	1 Clab	825	.010			.36		.36	.56
1400	Posts for nets, 3-1/2" diameter with eye bolts	B-1	3.40	7.059	Pr.	305	270		575	750
1500	With pulley & reel		3.40	7.059	"	780	270		1,050	1,275
1700	Net, 42' long, nylon thread with binder		50	.480	Ea.	254	18.35		272.35	310
1800	All metal		6.50	3.692	"	490	141		631	755
2000	Paint markings on asphalt, 2 coats	1 Pord	1.78	4.494	Court	187	181		368	480
2200	Complete court with fence, etc., asphaltic conc., minimum	B-37	.20	240		28,700	9,550	785	39,035	47,000
2300	Maximum		.16	300		56,500	11,900	985	69,385	82,000
2800	Clay courts, minimum		.20	240		31,500	9,550	785	41,835	50,000
2900	Maximum		.16	300		58,000	11,900	985	70,885	83,500

32 31 Fences and Gates

32 31 13 – Chain Link Fences and Gates

32 31 13.10 Chain Link Gates and Fences

		Crew	Daily Output	Labor-Hours	Unit	Material	2015 Bare Costs Labor	Equipment	Total	Total Incl O&P
0010	**CHAIN LINK GATES AND FENCES**									
4750	Gate, transom for 10' fence, galv. steel, single, 3' x 7'	B-80A	52	.462	Ea.	390	17.35	5.85	413.20	465
4752	4' x 7'		10	2.400		425	90	30.50	545.50	645
4754	3' x 10'		8	3		390	113	38	541	645
4756	4' x 10'		10	2.400		420	90	30.50	540.50	640
4758	Double transom, 10' x 7'	B-80B	10	3.200		745	129	24.50	898.50	1,050
4760	12' x 7'		6	5.333		785	215	40.50	1,040.50	1,250
4762	14' x 7'		5	6.400		855	258	49	1,162	1,400
4764	10' x 10'		4	8		1,075	325	61	1,461	1,725
4766	12' x 10'		7	4.571		1,200	184	35	1,419	1,625
4768	14' x 10'		7	4.571		1,275	184	35	1,494	1,725
4780	Vinyl clad, single transom, 3' x 7'		10	3.200		510	129	24.50	663.50	785
4782	4' x 7'		10	3.200		555	129	24.50	708.50	835
4784	3' x 10'		8	4		610	161	30.50	801.50	950
4786	4' x 10'		8	4		690	161	30.50	881.50	1,025
4788	Double transom, 10' x 7'		10	3.200		855	129	24.50	1,008.50	1,175
4790	12' x 7'		6	5.333		875	215	40.50	1,130.50	1,350
4792	14' x 7'		5	6.400		1,075	258	49	1,382	1,625
4794	10' x 10'		4	8		1,050	325	61	1,436	1,700
4798	12' x 12'		7	4.571		1,300	184	35	1,519	1,775
4799	14' x 14'		7	4.571		1,925	184	35	2,144	2,425

For customer support on your Site Work & Landscape Cost Data, call 877.737.1594.

375

32 31 Fences and Gates

32 31 13 – Chain Link Fences and Gates

32 31 13.20 Fence, Chain Link Industrial

		Crew	Daily Output	Labor-Hours	Unit	Material	2015 Bare Costs Labor	Equipment	Total	Total Incl O&P
0010	**FENCE, CHAIN LINK INDUSTRIAL**									
0011	Schedule 40, including concrete									
0020	3 strands barb wire, 2" post @ 10' O.C., set in concrete, 6' H									
0200	9 ga. wire, galv. steel, in concrete	B-80C	240	.100	L.F.	19.10	3.81	1.06	23.97	28
0248	Fence, add for vinyl coated fabric				S.F.	.66			.66	.73
0300	Aluminized steel	B-80C	240	.100	L.F.	20.50	3.81	1.06	25.37	29.50
0500	6 ga. wire, galv. steel		240	.100		21	3.81	1.06	25.87	30
0600	Aluminized steel		240	.100		30	3.81	1.06	34.87	40
0800	6 ga. wire, 6' high but omit barbed wire, galv. steel		250	.096		19.55	3.66	1.02	24.23	28
0900	Aluminized steel, in concrete		250	.096		23.50	3.66	1.02	28.18	32.50
0920	8' H, 6 ga. wire, 2-1/2" line post, galv. steel, in concrete		180	.133		31	5.10	1.41	37.51	43.50
0940	Aluminized steel, in concrete		180	.133		38	5.10	1.41	44.51	51
1400	Gate for 6' high fence, 1-5/8" frame, 3' wide, galv. steel		10	2.400	Ea.	203	91.50	25.50	320	390
1500	Aluminized steel, in concrete		10	2.400	"	205	91.50	25.50	322	395
2000	5'-0" high fence, 9 ga., no barbed wire, 2" line post, in concrete									
2010	10' O.C., 1-5/8" top rail, in concrete									
2100	Galvanized steel, in concrete	B-80C	300	.080	L.F.	18.45	3.05	.85	22.35	26
2200	Aluminized steel, in concrete		300	.080	"	18.75	3.05	.85	22.65	26
2400	Gate, 4' wide, 5' high, 2" frame, galv. steel, in concrete		10	2.400	Ea.	188	91.50	25.50	305	375
2500	Aluminized steel, in concrete		10	2.400	"	200	91.50	25.50	317	390
3100	Overhead slide gate, chain link, 6' high, to 18' wide, in concrete		38	.632	L.F.	97	24	6.70	127.70	151
3105	8' high, in concrete	B-80	30	1.067		99.50	44	24	167.50	204
3108	10' high, in concrete		24	1.333		156	55	30	241	288
3110	Cantilever type, in concrete		48	.667		129	27.50	15	171.50	201
3120	8' high, in concrete		24	1.333		155	55	30	240	288
3130	10' high, in concrete		18	1.778		190	73.50	40	303.50	365
5000	Double swing gates, incl. posts & hardware, in concrete									
5010	5' high, 12' opening, in concrete	B-80C	3.40	7.059	Opng.	395	269	74.50	738.50	925
5020	20' opening, in concrete		2.80	8.571		520	325	90.50	935.50	1,175
5060	6' high, 12' opening, in concrete		3.20	7.500		455	286	79.50	820.50	1,025
5070	20' opening, in concrete		2.60	9.231		655	350	97.50	1,102.50	1,375
5080	8' high, 12' opening, in concrete	B-80	2.13	15.002		460	620	340	1,420	1,825
5090	20' opening, in concrete		1.45	22.069		685	910	495	2,090	2,700
5100	10' high, 12' opening, in concrete		1.31	24.427		825	1,000	550	2,375	3,025
5110	20' opening, in concrete		1.03	31.068		865	1,275	700	2,840	3,675
5120	12' high, 12' opening, in concrete		1.05	30.476		1,175	1,250	685	3,110	3,975
5130	20' opening, in concrete		.85	37.647		1,225	1,550	845	3,620	4,650
5190	For aluminized steel add					20%				
7055	Braces, galv. steel	B-80A	960	.025	L.F.	2.56	.94	.32	3.82	4.61
7056	Aluminized steel	"	960	.025	"	3.07	.94	.32	4.33	5.20
7071	Privacy slats, vertical, vinyl	1 Clab	500	.016	S.F.	1.44	.60		2.04	2.51
7072	Redwood		450	.018		1.41	.67		2.08	2.58
7073	Diagonal, aluminum		300	.027		4.55	1		5.55	6.55

32 31 13.25 Fence, Chain Link Residential

		Crew	Daily Output	Labor-Hours	Unit	Material	2015 Bare Costs Labor	Equipment	Total	Total Incl O&P
0010	**FENCE, CHAIN LINK RESIDENTIAL**									
0011	Schedule 20, 11 ga. wire, 1-5/8" post									
0020	10' O.C., 1-3/8" top rail, 2" corner post, galv. stl. 3' high	B-80C	500	.048	L.F.	2.12	1.83	.51	4.46	5.70
0050	4' high		400	.060		7.10	2.29	.63	10.02	12
0100	6' high		200	.120		9.45	4.57	1.27	15.29	18.80
0150	Add for gate 3' wide, 1-3/8" frame, 3' high		12	2	Ea.	81.50	76	21	178.50	230
0170	4' high		10	2.400		87.50	91.50	25.50	204.50	264
0190	6' high		10	2.400		109	91.50	25.50	226	288

32 31 13 – Chain Link Fences and Gates

32 31 13.25 Fence, Chain Link Residential

		Crew	Daily Output	Labor-Hours	Unit	Material	2015 Bare Costs Labor	Equipment	Total	Total Incl O&P
0200	Add for gate 4' wide, 1-3/8" frame, 3' high	B-80C	9	2.667	Ea.	91.50	102	28	221.50	287
0220	4' high		9	2.667		97.50	102	28	227.50	293
0240	6' high		8	3	▼	123	114	31.50	268.50	345
0350	Aluminized steel, 11 ga. wire, 3' high		500	.048	L.F.	8.80	1.83	.51	11.14	13.05
0380	4' high		400	.060		9.25	2.29	.63	12.17	14.35
0400	6' high		200	.120	▼	11.15	4.57	1.27	16.99	20.50
0450	Add for gate 3' wide, 1-3/8" frame, 3' high		12	2	Ea.	95	76	21	192	245
0470	4' high		10	2.400		101	91.50	25.50	218	279
0490	6' high		10	2.400		125	91.50	25.50	242	305
0500	Add for gate 4' wide, 1-3/8" frame, 3' high		10	2.400		105	91.50	25.50	222	284
0520	4' high		9	2.667		121	102	28	251	320
0540	6' high		8	3	▼	130	114	31.50	275.50	355
0620	Vinyl covered, 9 ga. wire, 3' high		500	.048	L.F.	7.80	1.83	.51	10.14	11.95
0640	4' high		400	.060		8.15	2.29	.63	11.07	13.20
0660	6' high		200	.120	▼	10.15	4.57	1.27	15.99	19.55
0720	Add for gate 3' wide, 1-3/8" frame, 3' high		12	2	Ea.	94.50	76	21	191.50	245
0740	4' high		10	2.400		101	91.50	25.50	218	279
0760	6' high		10	2.400		120	91.50	25.50	237	300
0780	Add for gate 4' wide, 1-3/8" frame, 3' high		10	2.400		99.50	91.50	25.50	216.50	277
0800	4' high		9	2.667		103	102	28	233	299
0820	6' high	▼	8	3	▼	128	114	31.50	273.50	350
7076	Fence, for small jobs 100 L.F. fence or less w/or wo gate, add				S.F.	20%				

32 31 13.26 Tennis Court Fences and Gates

		Crew	Daily Output	Labor-Hours	Unit	Material	2015 Bare Costs Labor	Equipment	Total	Total Incl O&P
0010	**TENNIS COURT FENCES AND GATES**									
0860	Tennis courts, 11 ga. wire, 2-1/2" post set									
0870	in concrete, 10' O.C., 1-5/8" top rail									
0900	10' high	B-80	190	.168	L.F.	22.50	6.95	3.79	33.24	39.50
0920	12' high		170	.188	"	23.50	7.75	4.24	35.49	42.50
1000	Add for gate 4' wide, 1-5/8" frame 7' high		10	3.200	Ea.	242	132	72	446	545
1040	Aluminized steel, 11 ga. wire 10' high		190	.168	L.F.	21	6.95	3.79	31.74	38
1100	12' high		170	.188	"	23	7.75	4.24	34.99	41.50
1140	Add for gate 4' wide, 1-5/8" frame, 7' high		10	3.200	Ea.	262	132	72	466	570
1250	Vinyl covered, 9 ga. wire, 10' high		190	.168	L.F.	21.50	6.95	3.79	32.24	38.50
1300	12' high	▼	170	.188	"	25.50	7.75	4.24	37.49	44.50
1310	Fence, CL, tennis court, transom gate, single, galv., 4' x 7'	B-80A	8.72	2.752	Ea.	310	103	35	448	540
1400	Add for gate 4' wide, 1-5/8" frame, 7' high	B-80	10	3.200	"	315	132	72	519	625

32 31 13.30 Fence, Chain Link, Gates and Posts

		Crew	Daily Output	Labor-Hours	Unit	Material	2015 Bare Costs Labor	Equipment	Total	Total Incl O&P
0010	**FENCE, CHAIN LINK, GATES & POSTS**									
0011	(1/3 post length in ground)									
6580	Line posts, galvanized, 2-1/2" OD, set in conc., 4'	B-80	80	.400	Ea.	27.50	16.50	9	53	65.50
6585	5'		76	.421		34.50	17.35	9.50	61.35	75
6590	6'		74	.432		36.50	17.85	9.75	64.10	77.50
6595	7'		72	.444		44.50	18.30	10	72.80	87.50
6600	8'		69	.464		48.50	19.10	10.45	78.05	94
6610	H-beam, 1-7/8", 4'		83	.386		34.50	15.90	8.70	59.10	72
6615	5'		81	.395		40	16.30	8.90	65.20	79
6620	6'		78	.410		45.50	16.90	9.25	71.65	86.50
6625	7'		75	.427		50	17.60	9.60	77.20	92.50
6630	8'		73	.438		56	18.05	9.85	83.90	100
6635	Vinyl coated, 2-1/2" OD, set in conc., 4'		79	.405		39	16.70	9.10	64.80	78.50
6640	5'		77	.416		39.50	17.15	9.35	66	80
6645	6'	▼	74	.432	▼	53.50	17.85	9.75	81.10	96

For customer support on your Site Work & Landscape Cost Data, call 877.737.1594.

377

32 31 13.30 Fence, Chain Link, Gates and Posts	Crew	Daily Output	Labor-Hours	Unit	Material	2015 Bare Costs Labor	Equipment	Total	Total Incl O&P
6650	7'	B-80	72	.444	Ea.	65	18.30	10	93.30	111
6655	8'		69	.464		73	19.10	10.45	102.55	121
6660	End gate post, steel, 3" OD, set in conc.,4'		68	.471		45.50	19.40	10.60	75.50	91.50
6665	5'		65	.492		49	20.50	11.10	80.60	97
6670	6'		63	.508		51	21	11.45	83.45	101
6675	7'		61	.525		62	21.50	11.80	95.30	114
6680	8'		59	.542		70.50	22.50	12.20	105.20	125
6685	Vinyl, 4'		68	.471		50.50	19.40	10.60	80.50	96.50
6690	5'		65	.492		59	20.50	11.10	90.60	108
6695	6'		63	.508		92.50	21	11.45	124.95	147
6700	7'		61	.525		111	21.50	11.80	144.30	168
6705	8'		59	.542		124	22.50	12.20	158.70	184
6710	Corner post, galv. steel, 4" OD, set in conc., 4'		65	.492		97	20.50	11.10	128.60	150
6715	6'		63	.508		106	21	11.45	138.45	162
6720	7'		61	.525		131	21.50	11.80	164.30	190
6725	8'		65	.492		141	20.50	11.10	172.60	198
6730	Vinyl, 5'		65	.492		91.50	20.50	11.10	123.10	143
6735	6'		63	.508		140	21	11.45	172.45	199
6740	7'		61	.525		163	21.50	11.80	196.30	225
6745	8'		59	.542		182	22.50	12.20	216.70	247
7031	For corner, end, & pull post bracing, add					20%	15%			
7770	Gates, sliding w/overhead support, 4' high	B-80B	35	.914	L.F.	150	37	6.95	193.95	229
7775	5' high		32	1		168	40.50	7.60	216.10	255
7780	6' high		28	1.143		151	46	8.70	205.70	246
7785	7' high		25	1.280		194	51.50	9.75	255.25	305
7790	8' high		23	1.391		208	56	10.60	274.60	325
7795	Cantilever, manual, exp. roller, (pr) 40' wide x 8' high	B-22	1	30	Ea.	5,500	1,325	207	7,032	8,300
7800	30' wide x 8' high		1	30		4,125	1,325	207	5,657	6,775
7805	24' wide x 8' high		1	30		3,375	1,325	207	4,907	5,975
7810	Motor operators for gates, (no elec wiring), 3' wide swing	2 Skwk	.50	32		1,150	1,550		2,700	3,675
7815	Up to 20' wide swing		.50	32		1,500	1,550		3,050	4,050
7820	Up to 45' sliding		.50	32		2,675	1,550		4,225	5,350
7825	Overhead gate, 6' to 18' wide, sliding/cantilever		45	.356	L.F.	293	17.30		310.30	345
7830	Gate operators, digital receiver		7	2.286	Ea.	74	111		185	253
7835	Two button transmitter		24	.667		23	32.50		55.50	75.50
7840	3 button station		14	1.143		39	55.50		94.50	129
7845	Master slave system		4	4		168	195		363	485
7900	Auger fence post hole, 3' deep, medium soil, by hand	1 Clab	30	.267			10.05		10.05	15.45
7925	By machine	B-80	175	.183			7.55	4.12	11.67	16.05
7950	Rock, with jackhammer	B-9	32	1.250			47.50	7.30	54.80	81
7975	With rock drill	B-47C	65	.246			10.60	25	35.60	43.50

32 31 13.33 Chain Link Backstops

		Crew	Daily Output	Labor-Hours	Unit	Material	2015 Bare Costs Labor	Equipment	Total	Total Incl O&P
0010	**CHAIN LINK BACKSTOPS**									
0015	Backstops, baseball, prefabricated, 30' wide, 12' high & 1 overhang	B-1	1	24	Ea.	2,575	920		3,495	4,275
0100	40' wide, 12' high & 2 overhangs	"	.75	32		6,775	1,225		8,000	9,325
0300	Basketball, steel, single goal	B-13	3.04	18.421		1,425	755	242	2,422	3,000
0400	Double goal	"	1.92	29.167		1,925	1,200	385	3,510	4,375
0600	Tennis, wire mesh with pair of ends	B-1	2.48	9.677	Set	2,650	370		3,020	3,475
0700	Enclosed court	"	1.30	18.462	Ea.	8,975	705		9,680	10,900

32 31 13.40 Fence, Fabric and Accessories	Crew	Daily Output	Labor-Hours	Unit	Material	2015 Bare Costs Labor	Equipment	Total	Total Incl O&P
0010 **FENCE, FABRIC & ACCESSORIES**									
1000 Fabric, 9 ga., galv., 1.2 oz. coat, 2" chain link, 4'	B-80A	304	.079	L.F.	3.44	2.97	1	7.41	9.45
1150 5'		285	.084		4.15	3.17	1.06	8.38	10.60
1200 6'		266	.090		8.05	3.39	1.14	12.58	15.30
1250 7'		247	.097		9.70	3.65	1.23	14.58	17.65
1300 8'		228	.105		12.40	3.96	1.33	17.69	21
1400 9 ga., fused, 4'		304	.079		4.04	2.97	1	8.01	10.10
1450 5'		285	.084		4.60	3.17	1.06	8.83	11.10
1500 6'		266	.090		4.72	3.39	1.14	9.25	11.65
1550 7'		247	.097		5.95	3.65	1.23	10.83	13.50
1600 8'		228	.105		9.20	3.96	1.33	14.49	17.65
1650 Barbed wire, galv., cost per strand		2280	.011		.13	.40	.13	.66	.90
1700 Vinyl coated		2280	.011	↓	.17	.40	.13	.70	.95
1750 Extension arms, 3 strands		143	.168	Ea.	4.13	6.30	2.12	12.55	16.55
1800 6 strands, 2-3/8"		119	.202		10.15	7.60	2.55	20.30	25.50
1850 Eye tops, 2-3/8"		143	.168	↓	1.72	6.30	2.12	10.14	13.90
1900 Top rail, incl. tie wires, 1-5/8", galv.		912	.026	L.F.	4.65	.99	.33	5.97	7
1950 Vinyl coated		912	.026		5.25	.99	.33	6.57	7.70
2100 Rail, middle/bottom, w/tie wire, 1-5/8", galv.		912	.026		4.65	.99	.33	5.97	7
2150 Vinyl coated		912	.026		5.25	.99	.33	6.57	7.70
2200 Reinforcing wire, coiled spring, 7 ga. galv.		2279	.011		.17	.40	.13	.70	.95
2250 9 ga., vinyl coated		2282	.011	↓	.52	.40	.13	1.05	1.33
2300 Steel T-post, galvanized with clips, 5', common earth, flat		200	.120	Ea.	9.60	4.51	1.52	15.63	19.15
2310 Clay		176	.136		9.60	5.15	1.72	16.47	20.50
2320 Soil & rock		144	.167		9.60	6.25	2.11	17.96	22.50
2330 5.5', common earth, flat		200	.120		10.80	4.51	1.52	16.83	20.50
2340 Clay		176	.136		10.80	5.15	1.72	17.67	21.50
2350 Soil & rock		144	.167		10.80	6.25	2.11	19.16	24
2360 6', common earth, flat		200	.120		11.25	4.51	1.52	17.28	21
2370 Clay		176	.136		11.25	5.15	1.72	18.12	22
2375 Soil & rock		144	.167		11.25	6.25	2.11	19.61	24.50
2385 6.5', common earth, flat		200	.120		12	4.51	1.52	18.03	22
2390 Clay		176	.136		12	5.15	1.72	18.87	23
2395 Soil & rock		144	.167		12	6.25	2.11	20.36	25
2400 7', common earth, flat		184	.130		12.75	4.90	1.65	19.30	23.50
2410 Clay		160	.150		12.75	5.65	1.89	20.29	25
2420 Soil & rock		128	.188		12.75	7.05	2.37	22.17	27.50
2430 8', common earth, flat		184	.130		14.20	4.90	1.65	20.75	25
2440 Clay		160	.150		14.20	5.65	1.89	21.74	26.50
2450 Soil & rock		128	.188		14.20	7.05	2.37	23.62	29
2460 9', common earth, flat		184	.130		16.20	4.90	1.65	22.75	27
2470 Clay		160	.150		16.20	5.65	1.89	23.74	28.50
2480 Soil & rock		128	.188		16.20	7.05	2.37	25.62	31.50
2485 10', common earth, flat		168	.143		17.85	5.35	1.80	25	30
2490 Clay		144	.167		17.85	6.25	2.11	26.21	31.50
2495 Soil & rock		112	.214		17.85	8.05	2.71	28.61	35
2500 11', common earth, flat		168	.143		19.15	5.35	1.80	26.30	31
2510 Clay		144	.167		19.15	6.25	2.11	27.51	33
2530 Soil & rock		112	.214		19.15	8.05	2.71	29.91	36.50
2540 12', common earth, flat		168	.143		21.50	5.35	1.80	28.65	34
2550 Clay		144	.167		21.50	6.25	2.11	29.86	36
2560 Soil & rock		112	.214		21.50	8.05	2.71	32.26	39.50

32 31 Fences and Gates

32 31 13 – Chain Link Fences and Gates

32 31 13.40 Fence, Fabric and Accessories

		Crew	Daily Output	Labor-Hours	Unit	Material	2015 Bare Costs Labor	Equipment	Total	Total Incl O&P
2600	Steel T-post, galvanized with clips, 5', common earth, hills	B-80A	180	.133	Ea.	9.60	5	1.68	16.28	20
2610	Clay		160	.150		9.60	5.65	1.89	17.14	21.50
2620	Soil & rock		130	.185		9.60	6.95	2.33	18.88	24
2630	5.5', common earth, hills		180	.133		10.80	5	1.68	17.48	21.50
2640	Clay		160	.150		10.80	5.65	1.89	18.34	22.50
2650	Soil & rock		130	.185		10.80	6.95	2.33	20.08	25
2660	6', common earth, hills		180	.133		11.25	5	1.68	17.93	22
2670	Clay		160	.150		11.25	5.65	1.89	18.79	23
2675	Soil & rock		130	.185		11.25	6.95	2.33	20.53	25.50
2685	6.5', common earth, hills		180	.133		12	5	1.68	18.68	23
2690	Clay		160	.150		12	5.65	1.89	19.54	24
2695	Soil & rock		130	.185		12	6.95	2.33	21.28	26.50
2700	7', common earth, hills		166	.145		12.75	5.45	1.83	20.03	24.50
2710	Clay		144	.167		12.75	6.25	2.11	21.11	26
2720	Soil & rock		116	.207		12.75	7.80	2.61	23.16	29
2730	8', common earth, hills		166	.145		14.20	5.45	1.83	21.48	26
2740	Clay		144	.167		14.20	6.25	2.11	22.56	27.50
2750	Soil & rock		116	.207		14.20	7.80	2.61	24.61	30.50
2760	9', common earth, hills		166	.145		16.20	5.45	1.83	23.48	28
2770	Clay		144	.167		16.20	6.25	2.11	24.56	30
2780	Soil & rock		116	.207		16.20	7.80	2.61	26.61	32.50
2785	10', common earth, hills		152	.158		17.85	5.95	1.99	25.79	31
2790	Clay		130	.185		17.85	6.95	2.33	27.13	33
2795	Soil & rock		101	.238		17.85	8.95	3	29.80	36.50
2800	11', common earth, hills		152	.158		19.15	5.95	1.99	27.09	32.50
2810	Clay		130	.185		19.15	6.95	2.33	28.43	34.50
2830	Soil & rock		101	.238		19.15	8.95	3	31.10	38
2840	12', common earth, hills		152	.158		21.50	5.95	1.99	29.44	35.50
2850	Clay		130	.185		21.50	6.95	2.33	30.78	37.50
2860	Soil & rock		101	.238		21.50	8.95	3	33.45	41

32 31 13.53 High-Security Chain Link Fences, Gates and Sys.

		Crew	Daily Output	Labor-Hours	Unit	Material	2015 Bare Costs Labor	Equipment	Total	Total Incl O&P
0010	**HIGH-SECURITY CHAIN LINK FENCES, GATES AND SYSTEMS**									
0100	Fence, chain link, security, 7' H, standard FE-7, incl excavation & posts	B-80C	480	.050	L.F.	44	1.91	.53	46.44	52
0200	Fence, barbed wire, security, 7' high, with 3 wire barbed wire arm	"	400	.060	"	7.75	2.29	.63	10.67	12.70
0300	Complete systems, including material and installation									
0310	Taunt wire fence detection system				M.L.F.				25,100	27,600
0410	Microwave fence detection system								41,300	45,400
0510	Passive magnetic fence detection system								19,500	21,400
0610	Infrared fence detection system								12,900	14,400
0710	Strain relief fence detection system								25,100	27,600
0810	Electro-shock fence detection system								35,900	39,500
0910	Photo-electric fence detection system								16,300	18,000

32 31 19 – Decorative Metal Fences and Gates

32 31 19.10 Decorative Fence

		Crew	Daily Output	Labor-Hours	Unit	Material	2015 Bare Costs Labor	Equipment	Total	Total Incl O&P
0010	**DECORATIVE FENCE**									
5300	Tubular picket, steel, 6' sections, 1-9/16" posts, 4' high	B-80C	300	.080	L.F.	31	3.05	.85	34.90	39.50
5400	2" posts, 5' high		240	.100		35	3.81	1.06	39.87	45.50
5600	2" posts, 6' high		200	.120		42	4.57	1.27	47.84	55
5700	Staggered picket 1-9/16" posts, 4' high		300	.080		31	3.05	.85	34.90	39.50
5800	2" posts, 5' high		240	.100		35	3.81	1.06	39.87	45.50
5900	2" posts, 6' high		200	.120		42	4.57	1.27	47.84	55
6200	Gates, 4' high, 3' wide	B-1	10	2.400	Ea.	282	92		374	450

32 31 Fences and Gates

32 31 19 – Decorative Metal Fences and Gates

32 31 19.10 Decorative Fence		Crew	Daily Output	Labor-Hours	Unit	Material	2015 Bare Costs Labor	Equipment	Total	Total Incl O&P
6300	5' high, 3' wide	B-1	10	2.400	Ea.	350	92		442	525
6400	6' high, 3' wide		10	2.400		415	92		507	595
6500	4' wide	↓	10	2.400	↓	420	92		512	605

32 31 23 – Plastic Fences and Gates

32 31 23.10 Fence, Vinyl

		Crew	Daily Output	Labor-Hours	Unit	Material	Labor	Equipment	Total	Total Incl O&P
0010	**FENCE, VINYL**									
0011	White, steel reinforced, stainless steel fasteners									
0020	Picket, 4" x 4" posts @ 6' - 0" OC, 3' high	B-1	140	.171	L.F.	22.50	6.55		29.05	34.50
0030	4' high		130	.185		24.50	7.05		31.55	38
0040	5' high		120	.200		27.50	7.65		35.15	42
0100	Board (semi-privacy), 5" x 5" posts @ 7' - 6" OC, 5' high		130	.185		25	7.05		32.05	38.50
0120	6' high		125	.192		28.50	7.35		35.85	42.50
0200	Basketweave, 5" x 5" posts @ 7' - 6" OC, 5' high		160	.150		25.50	5.75		31.25	37
0220	6' high		150	.160		28.50	6.10		34.60	40.50
0300	Privacy, 5" x 5" posts @ 7' - 6" OC, 5' high		130	.185		24.50	7.05		31.55	38
0320	6' high		150	.160	↓	28	6.10		34.10	40.50
0350	Gate, 5' high		9	2.667	Ea.	310	102		412	495
0360	6' high		9	2.667	↓	355	102		457	545
0400	For posts set in concrete, add		25	.960	↓	8.45	36.50		44.95	66
0500	Post and rail fence, 2 rail		150	.160	L.F.	5.90	6.10		12	15.90
0510	3 rail		150	.160		7.60	6.10		13.70	17.75
0515	4 rail	↓	150	.160	↓	9.85	6.10		15.95	20.50

32 31 23.20 Fence, Recycled Plastic

			Crew	Daily Output	Labor-Hours	Unit	Material	Labor	Equipment	Total	Total Incl O&P
0010	**FENCE, RECYCLED PLASTIC**										
9015	Fence rail, made from recycled plastic, various colors, 2 rail	G	B-1	150	.160	L.F.	10.10	6.10		16.20	20.50
9018	3 rail	G		150	.160		12.85	6.10		18.95	23.50
9020	4 rail	G		150	.160	↓	15.60	6.10		21.70	26.50
9030	Fence pole, made from recycled plastic, various colors, 7'	G	↓	96	.250	Ea.	49.50	9.55		59.05	69
9040	Stockade fence, made from recycled plastic, various colors, 4' high	G	B-80C	160	.150	L.F.	34.50	5.70	1.59	41.79	48.50
9050	6' high	G		160	.150	"	36.50	5.70	1.59	43.79	51
9060	6' pole	G		96	.250	Ea.	39	9.55	2.65	51.20	60.50
9070	9' pole	G		96	.250	"	44.50	9.55	2.65	56.70	66.50
9080	Picket fence, made from recycled plastic, various colors, 3' high	G		160	.150	L.F.	23	5.70	1.59	30.29	36
9090	4' high	G		160	.150	"	34	5.70	1.59	41.29	47.50
9100	3' high gate	G		8	3	Ea.	23	114	31.50	168.50	235
9110	4' high gate	G		8	3		29.50	114	31.50	175	243
9120	5' high pole	G		96	.250		37	9.55	2.65	49.20	58.50
9130	6' high pole	G	↓	96	.250		43	9.55	2.65	55.20	65
9140	Pole cap only	G					5.30			5.30	5.85
9150	Keeper pins only	G				↓	.42			.42	.46

32 31 26 – Wire Fences and Gates

32 31 26.10 Fences, Misc. Metal

		Crew	Daily Output	Labor-Hours	Unit	Material	Labor	Equipment	Total	Total Incl O&P
0010	**FENCES, MISC. METAL**									
0012	Chicken wire, posts @ 4', 1" mesh, 4' high	B-80C	410	.059	L.F.	3.30	2.23	.62	6.15	7.70
0100	2" mesh, 6' high		350	.069		3.82	2.61	.73	7.16	9
0200	Galv. steel, 12 ga., 2" x 4" mesh, posts 5' O.C., 3' high		300	.080		2.78	3.05	.85	6.68	8.65
0300	5' high		300	.080		3.38	3.05	.85	7.28	9.30
0400	14 ga., 1" x 2" mesh, 3' high		300	.080		3.42	3.05	.85	7.32	9.35
0500	5' high	↓	300	.080	↓	4.57	3.05	.85	8.47	10.65
1000	Kennel fencing, 1-1/2" mesh, 6' long, 3'-6" wide, 6'-2" high	2 Clab	4	4	Ea.	510	150		660	790
1050	12' long		4	4		720	150		870	1,025

For customer support on your Site Work & Landscape Cost Data, call 877.737.1594.

381

32 31 Fences and Gates

32 31 26 – Wire Fences and Gates

32 31 26.10 Fences, Misc. Metal

		Crew	Daily Output	Labor-Hours	Unit	Material	2015 Bare Costs Labor	Equipment	Total	Total Incl O&P
1200	Top covers, 1-1/2" mesh, 6' long	2 Clab	15	1.067	Ea.	136	40		176	212
1250	12' long	↓	12	1.333	↓	191	50		241	287
4500	Security fence, prison grade, set in concrete, 12' high	B-80	25	1.280	L.F.	61.50	53	29	143.50	180
4600	16' high	"	20	1.600	"	79	66	36	181	228

32 31 26.20 Wire Fencing, General

		Crew	Daily Output	Labor-Hours	Unit	Material	2015 Bare Costs Labor	Equipment	Total	Total Incl O&P
0010	**WIRE FENCING, GENERAL**									
0015	Barbed wire, galvanized, domestic steel, hi-tensile 15-1/2 ga.				M.L.F.	98.50			98.50	108
0020	Standard, 12-3/4 ga.					111			111	122
0210	Barbless wire, 2-strand galvanized, 12-1/2 ga.				↓	111			111	122
0500	Helical razor ribbon, stainless steel, 18" dia x 18" spacing				C.L.F.	164			164	180
0600	Hardware cloth galv., 1/4" mesh, 23 ga., 2' wide				C.S.F.	60			60	66
0700	3' wide					43.50			43.50	48
0900	1/2" mesh, 19 ga., 2' wide					35.50			35.50	39
1000	4' wide					23.50			23.50	26
1200	Chain link fabric, steel, 2" mesh, 6 ga., galvanized					152			152	167
1300	9 ga., galvanized					86			86	94.50
1350	Vinyl coated					82			82	90
1360	Aluminized					79.50			79.50	87.50
1400	2-1/4" mesh, 11.5 ga., galvanized					54.50			54.50	60
1600	1-3/4" mesh (tennis courts), 11.5 ga. (core), vinyl coated					61			61	67
1700	9 ga., galvanized					82.50			82.50	90.50
2100	Welded wire fabric, galvanized, 1" x 2", 14 ga.					59.50			59.50	65.50
2200	2" x 4", 12-1/2 ga.				↓	57			57	62.50

32 31 29 – Wood Fences and Gates

32 31 29.10 Fence, Wood

		Crew	Daily Output	Labor-Hours	Unit	Material	2015 Bare Costs Labor	Equipment	Total	Total Incl O&P
0010	**FENCE, WOOD**									
0011	Basket weave, 3/8" x 4" boards, 2" x 4"									
0020	stringers on spreaders, 4" x 4" posts									
0050	No. 1 cedar, 6' high	B-80C	160	.150	L.F.	26	5.70	1.59	33.29	39
0070	Treated pine, 6' high	"	150	.160	"	34.50	6.10	1.69	42.29	49
0200	Board fence, 1" x 4" boards, 2" x 4" rails, 4" x 4" post									
0220	Preservative treated, 2 rail, 3' high	B-80C	145	.166	L.F.	9.30	6.30	1.75	17.35	22
0240	4' high		135	.178		10.90	6.75	1.88	19.53	24.50
0260	3 rail, 5' high		130	.185		11.85	7.05	1.95	20.85	26
0300	6' high		125	.192		13.35	7.30	2.03	22.68	28
0320	No. 2 grade western cedar, 2 rail, 3' high		145	.166		10.20	6.30	1.75	18.25	23
0340	4' high		135	.178		11.25	6.75	1.88	19.88	25
0360	3 rail, 5' high		130	.185		12.60	7.05	1.95	21.60	27
0400	6' high		125	.192		13.45	7.30	2.03	22.78	28
0420	No. 1 grade cedar, 2 rail, 3' high		145	.166		12.30	6.30	1.75	20.35	25
0440	4' high		135	.178		13.95	6.75	1.88	22.58	28
0460	3 rail, 5' high		130	.185		17	7.05	1.95	26	31.50
0500	6' high	↓	125	.192	↓	18.75	7.30	2.03	28.08	34
0540	Shadow box, 1" x 6" board, 2" x 4" rail, 4" x 4"post									
0560	Pine, pressure treated, 3 rail, 6' high	B-80C	150	.160	L.F.	17.20	6.10	1.69	24.99	30
0600	Gate, 3'-6" wide		8	3	Ea.	107	114	31.50	252.50	330
0620	No. 1 cedar, 3 rail, 4' high		130	.185	L.F.	18	7.05	1.95	27	32.50
0640	6' high		125	.192		23	7.30	2.03	32.33	38.50
0860	Open rail fence, split rails, 2 rail 3' high, no. 1 cedar		160	.150		11.75	5.70	1.59	19.04	23.50
0870	No. 2 cedar		160	.150		10.75	5.70	1.59	18.04	22.50
0880	3 rail, 4' high, no. 1 cedar		150	.160		12.10	6.10	1.69	19.89	24.50
0890	No. 2 cedar	↓	150	.160		8.55	6.10	1.69	16.34	20.50

32 31 29 – Wood Fences and Gates

32 31 29.10 Fence, Wood

		Crew	Daily Output	Labor-Hours	Unit	Material	2015 Bare Costs Labor	Equipment	Total	Total Incl O&P
0920	Rustic rails, 2 rail 3' high, no. 1 cedar	B-80C	160	.150	L.F.	9.35	5.70	1.59	16.64	20.50
0930	No. 2 cedar		160	.150		8.75	5.70	1.59	16.04	20
0940	3 rail, 4' high		150	.160		8.95	6.10	1.69	16.74	21
0950	No. 2 cedar		150	.160		7.30	6.10	1.69	15.09	19.20
0960	Picket fence, gothic, pressure treated pine									
1000	2 rail, 3' high	B-80C	140	.171	L.F.	7.15	6.55	1.81	15.51	19.90
1020	3 rail, 4' high		130	.185	"	8.15	7.05	1.95	17.15	22
1040	Gate, 3'-6" wide		9	2.667	Ea.	68	102	28	198	261
1060	No. 2 cedar, 2 rail, 3' high		140	.171	L.F.	8.25	6.55	1.81	16.61	21
1100	3 rail, 4' high		130	.185	"	8.35	7.05	1.95	17.35	22
1120	Gate, 3'-6" wide		9	2.667	Ea.	72.50	102	28	202.50	266
1140	No. 1 cedar, 2 rail 3' high		140	.171	L.F.	12.55	6.55	1.81	20.91	26
1160	3 rail, 4' high		130	.185	"	16.35	7.05	1.95	25.35	31
1170	Gate, 3'-6" wide		9	2.667	Ea.	232	102	28	362	440
1200	Rustic picket, molded pine, 2 rail, 3' high		140	.171	L.F.	7.75	6.55	1.81	16.11	20.50
1220	No. 1 cedar, 2 rail, 3' high		140	.171		8.95	6.55	1.81	17.31	22
1240	Stockade fence, no. 1 cedar, 3-1/4" rails, 6' high		160	.150		12.05	5.70	1.59	19.34	23.50
1260	8' high		155	.155		16.60	5.90	1.64	24.14	29
1270	Gate, 3'-6" wide		9	2.667	Ea.	238	102	28	368	450
1300	No. 2 cedar, treated wood rails, 6' high		160	.150	L.F.	12.35	5.70	1.59	19.64	24
1320	Gate, 3'-6" wide		8	3	Ea.	82	114	31.50	227.50	300
1360	Treated pine, treated rails, 6' high		160	.150	L.F.	12.80	5.70	1.59	20.09	24.50
1400	8' high		150	.160	"	19	6.10	1.69	26.79	32
1420	Gate, 3'-6" wide		9	2.667	Ea.	92	102	28	222	287

32 31 29.20 Fence, Wood Rail

		Crew	Daily Output	Labor-Hours	Unit	Material	2015 Bare Costs Labor	Equipment	Total	Total Incl O&P
0010	**FENCE, WOOD RAIL**									
0012	Picket, No. 2 cedar, Gothic, 2 rail, 3' high	B-1	160	.150	L.F.	7.60	5.75		13.35	17.20
0050	Gate, 3'-6" wide	B-80C	9	2.667	Ea.	77	102	28	207	271
0400	3 rail, 4' high		150	.160	L.F.	8.50	6.10	1.69	16.29	20.50
0500	Gate, 3'-6" wide		9	2.667	Ea.	95	102	28	225	290
5000	Fence rail, redwood, 2" x 4", merch. grade 8'	B-1	2400	.010	L.F.	2.42	.38		2.80	3.25
5050	Select grade, 8'		2400	.010	"	5.35	.38		5.73	6.45
6000	Fence post, select redwood, earthpacked & treated, 4" x 4" x 6'		96	.250	Ea.	13.60	9.55		23.15	29.50
6010	4" x 4" x 8'		96	.250		18.70	9.55		28.25	35
6020	Set in concrete, 4" x 4" x 6'		50	.480		21	18.35		39.35	52
6030	4" x 4" x 8'		50	.480		22.50	18.35		40.85	53
6040	Wood post, 4' high, set in concrete, incl. concrete		50	.480		13.80	18.35		32.15	43.50
6050	Earth packed		96	.250		16.70	9.55		26.25	33
6060	6' high, set in concrete, incl. concrete		50	.480		17.20	18.35		35.55	47.50
6070	Earth packed		96	.250		13.10	9.55		22.65	29

For customer support on your Site Work & Landscape Cost Data, call 877.737.1594.

383

32 32 Retaining Walls

32 32 13 – Cast-in-Place Concrete Retaining Walls

32 32 13.10 Retaining Walls, Cast Concrete

32 32 13.10 Retaining Walls, Cast Concrete	Crew	Daily Output	Labor-Hours	Unit	Material	2015 Bare Costs Labor	Equipment	Total	Total Incl O&P
0010 **RETAINING WALLS, CAST CONCRETE**									
1800 Concrete gravity wall with vertical face including excavation & backfill									
1850 No reinforcing									
1900 6' high, level embankment	C-17C	36	2.306	L.F.	74.50	113	16.90	204.40	276
2000 33° slope embankment		32	2.594		86.50	127	19.05	232.55	315
2200 8' high, no surcharge		27	3.074		92.50	151	22.50	266	360
2300 33° slope embankment		24	3.458		112	170	25.50	307.50	415
2500 10' high, level embankment		19	4.368		132	215	32	379	510
2600 33° slope embankment		18	4.611		183	227	34	444	590
2800 Reinforced concrete cantilever, incl. excavation, backfill & reinf.									
2900 6' high, 33° slope embankment	C-17C	35	2.371	L.F.	68	117	17.40	202.40	274
3000 8' high, 33° slope embankment		29	2.862		78	141	21	240	325
3100 10' high, 33° slope embankment		20	4.150		102	204	30.50	336.50	460
3200 20' high, 500 lb. per L.F. surcharge		7.50	11.067		305	545	81	931	1,275
3500 Concrete cribbing, incl. excavation and backfill									
3700 12' high, open face	B-13	210	.267	S.F.	34	10.95	3.51	48.46	58
3900 Closed face	"	210	.267	"	32	10.95	3.51	46.46	55.50
4100 Concrete filled slurry trench, see Section 31 56 23.20									

32 32 23 – Segmental Retaining Walls

32 32 23.13 Segmental Conc. Unit Masonry Retaining Walls

	Crew	Daily Output	Labor-Hours	Unit	Material	2015 Bare Costs Labor	Equipment	Total	Total Incl O&P
0010 **SEGMENTAL CONC. UNIT MASONRY RETAINING WALLS**									
7100 Segmental Retaining Wall system, incl. pins, and void fill									
7120 base and backfill not included									
7140 Large unit, 8" high x 18" wide x 20" deep, 3 plane split	B-62	300	.080	S.F.	13.50	3.30	.58	17.38	20.50
7150 Straight split		300	.080		13.60	3.30	.58	17.48	20.50
7160 Medium, lt. wt., 8" high x 18" wide x 12" deep, 3 plane split		400	.060		10.50	2.48	.43	13.41	15.80
7170 Straight split		400	.060		10.40	2.48	.43	13.31	15.70
7180 Small unit, 4" x 18" x 10" deep, 3 plane split		400	.060		13.40	2.48	.43	16.31	19
7190 Straight split		400	.060		13.20	2.48	.43	16.11	18.75
7200 Cap unit, 3 plane split		300	.080		13.80	3.30	.58	17.68	21
7210 Cap unit, straight split		300	.080		13.80	3.30	.58	17.68	21
7250 Geo-grid soil reinforcement 4' x 50'	2 Clab	22500	.001		.76	.03		.79	.88
7255 Geo-grid soil reinforcement 6' x 150'	"	22500	.001		.60	.03		.63	.70
8000 For higher walls, add components as necessary									

32 32 26 – Metal Crib Retaining Walls

32 32 26.10 Metal Bin Retaining Walls

	Crew	Daily Output	Labor-Hours	Unit	Material	2015 Bare Costs Labor	Equipment	Total	Total Incl O&P
0010 **METAL BIN RETAINING WALLS**									
0011 Aluminized steel bin, excavation									
0020 and backfill not included, 10' wide									
0100 4' high, 5.5' deep	B-13	650	.086	S.F.	27	3.53	1.13	31.66	36
0200 8' high, 5.5' deep		615	.091		31	3.73	1.20	35.93	41
0300 10' high, 7.7' deep		580	.097		34.50	3.96	1.27	39.73	45.50
0400 12' high, 7.7' deep		530	.106		37	4.33	1.39	42.72	49
0500 16' high, 7.7' deep		515	.109		39.50	4.46	1.43	45.39	51.50
0600 16' high, 9.9' deep		500	.112		41.50	4.59	1.47	47.56	54
0700 20' high, 9.9' deep		470	.119		46.50	4.88	1.57	52.95	60.50
0800 20' high, 12.1' deep		460	.122		42	4.99	1.60	48.59	55.50
0900 24' high, 12.1' deep		455	.123		44.50	5.05	1.62	51.17	58.50
1000 24' high, 14.3' deep		450	.124		52.50	5.10	1.64	59.24	67
1100 28' high, 14.3' deep		440	.127		54.50	5.20	1.67	61.37	70
1300 For plain galvanized bin type walls, deduct					10%				

32 32 29 – Timber Retaining Walls

32 32 29.10 Landscape Timber Retaining Walls	Crew	Daily Output	Labor-Hours	Unit	Material	2015 Bare Costs Labor	Equipment	Total	Total Incl O&P
0010	**LANDSCAPE TIMBER RETAINING WALLS**									
0100	Treated timbers, 6" x 6"	1 Clab	265	.030	L.F.	2.01	1.14		3.15	3.96
0110	6" x 8"	"	200	.040	"	2.65	1.50		4.15	5.25
0120	Drilling holes in timbers for fastening, 1/2"	1 Carp	450	.018	Inch		.83		.83	1.28
0130	5/8"	"	450	.018	"		.83		.83	1.28
0140	Reinforcing rods for fastening, 1/2"	1 Clab	312	.026	L.F.	.36	.96		1.32	1.87
0150	5/8"	"	312	.026	"	.56	.96		1.52	2.09
0160	Reinforcing fabric	2 Clab	2500	.006	S.Y.	1.90	.24		2.14	2.46
0170	Gravel backfill		28	.571	C.Y.	20	21.50		41.50	55
0180	Perforated pipe, 4" diameter with silt sock		1200	.013	L.F.	1.25	.50		1.75	2.15
0190	Galvanized 60d common nails	1 Clab	625	.013	Ea.	.16	.48		.64	.92
0200	20d common nails	"	3800	.002	"	.04	.08		.12	.16

32 32 36 – Gabion Retaining Walls

32 32 36.10 Stone Gabion Retaining Walls

		Crew	Daily Output	Labor-Hours	Unit	Material	2015 Bare Costs Labor	Equipment	Total	Total Incl O&P
0010	**STONE GABION RETAINING WALLS**									
4300	Stone filled gabions, not incl. excavation,									
4310	Stone, delivered, 3' wide									
4340	Galvanized, 6' long, 1' high	B-13	113	.496	Ea.	105	20.50	6.50	132	154
4400	1'-6" high		50	1.120		164	46	14.75	224.75	267
4490	3'-0" high		13	4.308		244	177	56.50	477.50	600
4590	9' long, 1' high		50	1.120		198	46	14.75	258.75	305
4650	1'-6" high		22	2.545		212	104	33.50	349.50	430
4690	3'-0" high		6	9.333		375	385	123	883	1,125
4890	12' long, 1' high		28	2		238	82	26.50	346.50	415
4950	1'-6" high		13	4.308		315	177	56.50	548.50	680
4990	3'-0" high		3	18.667		450	765	245	1,460	1,950
5200	PVC coated, 6' long, 1' high		113	.496		110	20.50	6.50	137	159
5250	1'-6" high		50	1.120		168	46	14.75	228.75	272
5300	3' high		13	4.308		261	177	56.50	494.50	620
5500	9' long, 1' high		50	1.120		209	46	14.75	269.75	315
5550	1'-6" high		22	2.545		233	104	33.50	370.50	455
5600	3' high		6	9.333		410	385	123	918	1,175
5800	12' long, 1' high		28	2		278	82	26.50	386.50	460
5850	1'-6" high		13	4.308		335	177	56.50	568.50	705
5900	3' high		3	18.667		480	765	245	1,490	1,975
6000	Galvanized, 6' long, 1' high		75	.747	C.Y.	95.50	30.50	9.80	135.80	163
6010	1'-6" high		50	1.120		164	46	14.75	224.75	267
6020	3'-0" high		25	2.240		122	92	29.50	243.50	310
6030	9' long, 1' high		50	1.120		198	46	14.75	258.75	305
6040	1'-6" high		33.30	1.682		141	69	22	232	286
6050	3'-0" high		16.70	3.353		125	137	44	306	395
6060	12' long, 1' high		37.50	1.493		178	61	19.65	258.65	310
6070	1'-6" high		25	2.240		157	92	29.50	278.50	345
6080	3'-0" high		12.50	4.480		112	184	59	355	470
6100	PVC coated, 6' long, 1' high		75	.747		165	30.50	9.80	205.30	240
6110	1'-6" high		50	1.120		168	46	14.75	228.75	272
6120	3' high		25	2.240		130	92	29.50	251.50	320
6130	9' long, 1' high		50	1.120		209	46	14.75	269.75	315
6140	1'-6" high		33.30	1.682		155	69	22	246	300
6150	3' high		16.67	3.359		136	138	44	318	410
6160	12' long, 1' high		37.50	1.493		209	61	19.65	289.65	345
6170	1'-6" high		25	2.240		149	92	29.50	270.50	340

32 32 Retaining Walls

32 32 36 – Gabion Retaining Walls

32 32 36.10 Stone Gabion Retaining Walls	Crew	Daily Output	Labor-Hours	Unit	Material	2015 Bare Costs Labor	Equipment	Total	Total Incl O&P
6180	3' high	B-13	12.50	4.480	C.Y.	120	184	59	363	480

32 32 53 – Stone Retaining Walls

32 32 53.10 Retaining Walls, Stone

		Crew	Daily Output	Labor-Hours	Unit	Material	Labor	Equipment	Total	Total Incl O&P
0010	**RETAINING WALLS, STONE**									
0015	Including excavation, concrete footing and									
0020	stone 3' below grade. Price is exposed face area.									
0200	Decorative random stone, to 6' high, 1'-6" thick, dry set	D-1	35	.457	S.F.	58.50	19.25		77.75	94
0300	Mortar set		40	.400		60.50	16.85		77.35	92
0500	Cut stone, to 6' high, 1'-6" thick, dry set		35	.457		60.50	19.25		79.75	96.50
0600	Mortar set		40	.400		61.50	16.85		78.35	93
0800	Random stone, 6' to 10' high, 2' thick, dry set		45	.356		66.50	14.95		81.45	96
0900	Mortar set		50	.320		69	13.45		82.45	96
1100	Cut stone, 6' to 10' high, 2' thick, dry set		45	.356		67	14.95		81.95	96.50
1200	Mortar set		50	.320		69	13.45		82.45	96.50
5100	Setting stone, dry		100	.160	C.F.		6.75		6.75	10.30
5600	With mortar	▼	120	.133	"		5.60		5.60	8.55

32 33 Site Furnishings

32 33 33 – Site Manufactured Planters

32 33 33.10 Planters

		Crew	Daily Output	Labor-Hours	Unit	Material	Labor	Equipment	Total	Total Incl O&P
0010	**PLANTERS**									
0012	Concrete, sandblasted, precast, 48" diameter, 24" high	2 Clab	15	1.067	Ea.	630	40		670	755
0100	Fluted, precast, 7' diameter, 36" high		10	1.600		1,575	60		1,635	1,825
0300	Fiberglass, circular, 36" diameter, 24" high		15	1.067		725	40		765	855
0400	60" diameter, 24" high		10	1.600		1,125	60		1,185	1,325
0600	Square, 24" side, 36" high		15	1.067		620	40		660	740
0700	48" side, 36" high		15	1.067		1,025	40		1,065	1,175
0900	Planter/bench, 72" square, 36" high		5	3.200		1,800	120		1,920	2,150
1000	96" square, 27" high		5	3.200		2,225	120		2,345	2,625
1200	Wood, square, 48" side, 24" high		15	1.067		1,400	40		1,440	1,600
1300	Circular, 48" diameter, 30" high		10	1.600		985	60		1,045	1,175
1500	72" diameter, 30" high		10	1.600		1,725	60		1,785	2,000
1600	Planter/bench, 72"	▼	5	3.200	▼	3,275	120		3,395	3,775

32 33 43 – Site Seating and Tables

32 33 43.13 Site Seating

		Crew	Daily Output	Labor-Hours	Unit	Material	Labor	Equipment	Total	Total Incl O&P
0010	**SITE SEATING**									
0012	Seating, benches, park, precast conc., w/backs, wood rails, 4' long	2 Clab	5	3.200	Ea.	595	120		715	840
0100	8' long		4	4		955	150		1,105	1,275
0300	Fiberglass, without back, one piece, 4' long		10	1.600		620	60		680	775
0400	8' long		7	2.286		815	86		901	1,025
0500	Steel barstock pedestals w/backs, 2" x 3" wood rails, 4' long		10	1.600		1,125	60		1,185	1,325
0510	8' long		7	2.286		1,425	86		1,511	1,700
0520	3" x 8" wood plank, 4' long		10	1.600		1,200	60		1,260	1,425
0530	8' long		7	2.286		1,500	86		1,586	1,775
0540	Backless, 4" x 4" wood plank, 4' square		10	1.600		940	60		1,000	1,125
0550	8' long		7	2.286		1,000	86		1,086	1,225
0600	Aluminum pedestals, with backs, aluminum slats, 8' long		8	2		480	75		555	640
0610	15' long		5	3.200		975	120		1,095	1,250
0620	Portable, aluminum slats, 8' long		8	2		465	75		540	625
0630	15' long	▼	5	3.200	▼	570	120		690	815

32 33 Site Furnishings

32 33 43 – Site Seating and Tables

32 33 43.13 Site Seating

	32 33 43.13 Site Seating	Crew	Daily Output	Labor-Hours	Unit	Material	2015 Bare Costs Labor	Equipment	Total	Total Incl O&P
0800	Cast iron pedestals, back & arms, wood slats, 4' long	2 Clab	8	2	Ea.	385	75		460	535
0820	8' long		5	3.200		1,075	120		1,195	1,350
0840	Backless, wood slats, 4' long		8	2		590	75		665	760
0860	8' long		5	3.200		1,150	120		1,270	1,450
1700	Steel frame, fir seat, 10' long		10	1.600		355	60		415	490

32 34 Fabricated Bridges

32 34 10 – Fabricated Highway Bridges

32 34 10.10 Bridges, Highway

		Crew	Daily Output	Labor-Hours	Unit	Material	2015 Bare Costs Labor	Equipment	Total	Total Incl O&P
0010	**BRIDGES, HIGHWAY**									
0020	Structural steel, rolled beams	E-5	8.50	9.412	Ton	2,650	490	195	3,335	3,975
0500	Built up, plate girders	E-6	10.50	12.190	"	3,050	635	176	3,861	4,650
1000	Concrete in place, no reinforcing, abutment footings	C-17B	30	2.733	C.Y.	224	134	13.95	371.95	470
1100	Walls, stems and wing walls		20	4.100		300	201	21	522	665
1200	Decks		17	4.824		475	237	24.50	736.50	915
1300	Sidewalks and parapets		11	7.455		945	365	38	1,348	1,650
2000	Reinforcing, in place	4 Rodm	3	10.667	Ton	2,175	560		2,735	3,275
2050	Galvanized coated		3	10.667		2,875	560		3,435	4,050
2100	Epoxy coated		3	10.667		2,725	560		3,285	3,875
3000	Expansion dams, steel, double upset 4" x 8" angles welded to									
3010	double 8" x 8" angles, 1-3/4" compression seal	C-22	30	1.400	L.F.	575	74	3.07	652.07	755
3040	Double 8" x 8" angles only, 1-3/4" compression seal		35	1.200		430	63.50	2.63	496.13	575
3050	Galvanized		35	1.200		535	63.50	2.63	601.13	685
3060	Double 8" x 6" angles only, 1-3/4" compression seal		35	1.200		330	63.50	2.63	396.13	465
3100	Double 10" channels, 1-3/4" compression seal		35	1.200		300	63.50	2.63	366.13	435
3420	For 3" compression seal, add					62			62	68.50
3440	For double slotted extrusions with seal strip, add					284			284	310
3490	For galvanizing, add				Lb.	.44			.44	.48
4000	Approach railings, steel, galv. pipe, 2 line	C-22	140	.300	L.F.	220	15.80	.66	236.46	267
4200	Bridge railings, steel, galv. pipe, 3 line w/screen		85	.494		310	26	1.08	337.08	380
4220	4 line w/screen		75	.560		350	29.50	1.23	380.73	430
4300	Aluminum, pipe, 3 line w/screen		95	.442		212	23.50	.97	236.47	271
8000	For structural excavation, see Section 31 23 16.16									
8010	For dewatering, see Section 31 23 19.20									

32 34 20 – Fabricated Pedestrian Bridges

32 34 20.10 Bridges, Pedestrian

		Crew	Daily Output	Labor-Hours	Unit	Material	2015 Bare Costs Labor	Equipment	Total	Total Incl O&P
0010	**BRIDGES, PEDESTRIAN**									
0011	Spans over streams, roadways, etc.									
0020	including erection, not including foundations									
0050	Precast concrete, complete in place, 8' wide, 60' span	E-2	215	.260	S.F.	116	13.50	7.05	136.55	158
0100	100' span		185	.303		127	15.65	8.15	150.80	176
0150	120' span		160	.350		138	18.10	9.45	165.55	193
0200	150' span		145	.386		144	20	10.40	174.40	203
0300	Steel, trussed or arch spans, compl. in place, 8' wide, 40' span		320	.175		117	9.05	4.72	130.77	149
0400	50' span		395	.142		105	7.35	3.83	116.18	133
0500	60' span		465	.120		105	6.25	3.25	114.50	130
0600	80' span		570	.098		125	5.10	2.65	132.75	149
0700	100' span		465	.120		176	6.25	3.25	185.50	208
0800	120' span		365	.153		223	7.95	4.14	235.09	263
0900	150' span		310	.181		237	9.35	4.87	251.22	281

For customer support on your Site Work & Landscape Cost Data, call 877.737.1594.

387

32 34 Fabricated Bridges

32 34 20 – Fabricated Pedestrian Bridges

32 34 20.10 Bridges, Pedestrian		Crew	Daily Output	Labor-Hours	Unit	Material	2015 Bare Costs Labor	Equipment	Total	Total Incl O&P
1000	160' span	E-2	255	.220	S.F.	237	11.35	5.95	254.30	286
1100	10' wide, 80' span		640	.088		125	4.53	2.36	131.89	147
1200	120' span		415	.135		162	7	3.64	172.64	194
1300	150' span		445	.126		182	6.50	3.40	191.90	215
1400	200' span		205	.273		194	14.15	7.35	215.50	245
1600	Wood, laminated type, complete in place, 80' span	C-12	203	.236		86.50	11	3.22	100.72	116
1700	130' span	"	153	.314		90.50	14.60	4.27	109.37	127

32 35 Screening Devices

32 35 16 – Sound Barriers

32 35 16.10 Traffic Barriers, Highway Sound Barriers

		Crew	Daily Output	Labor-Hours	Unit	Material	2015 Bare Costs Labor	Equipment	Total	Total Incl O&P
0010	**TRAFFIC BARRIERS, HIGHWAY SOUND BARRIERS**									
0020	Highway sound barriers, not including footing									
0100	Precast concrete, concrete columns @ 30' OC, 8" T, 8' H	C-12	400	.120	L.F.	131	5.60	1.63	138.23	154
0110	12' H		265	.181		197	8.45	2.47	207.92	232
0120	16' H		200	.240		262	11.15	3.27	276.42	310
0130	20' H		160	.300		330	13.95	4.09	348.04	385
0400	Lt. Wt. composite panel, cementitious face, St. posts @ 12' OC, 8' H	B-80B	190	.168		156	6.80	1.28	164.08	184
0410	12' H		125	.256		235	10.35	1.95	247.30	276
0420	16' H		95	.337		315	13.60	2.57	331.17	370
0430	20' H		75	.427		390	17.20	3.25	410.45	460

32 84 Planting Irrigation

32 84 13 – Drip Irrigation

32 84 13.10 Subsurface Drip Irrigation

			Crew	Daily Output	Labor-Hours	Unit	Material	2015 Bare Costs Labor	Equipment	Total	Total Incl O&P
0010	**SUBSURFACE DRIP IRRIGATION**										
0011	Looped grid, pressure compensating										
0100	Preinserted PE emitter, line, hand bury, irregular area, small	G	3 Skwk	1200	.020	L.F.	.29	.97		1.26	1.82
0150	Medium	G		1800	.013		.29	.65		.94	1.32
0200	Large	G		2520	.010		.29	.46		.75	1.04
0250	Rectangular area, small	G		2040	.012		.29	.57		.86	1.20
0300	Medium	G		2640	.009		.29	.44		.73	1
0350	Large	G		3600	.007		.29	.32		.61	.82
0400	Install in trench, irregular area, small	G		4050	.006		.29	.29		.58	.77
0450	Medium	G		7488	.003		.29	.16		.45	.56
0500	Large	G		16560	.001		.29	.07		.36	.43
0550	Rectangular area, small	G		8100	.003		.29	.14		.43	.54
0600	Medium			21960	.001		.29	.05		.34	.40
0650	Large	G		33264	.001		.29	.04		.33	.37
0700	Trenching and backfill	G	B-53	500	.016			.78	.14	.92	1.33
0750	For vinyl tubing, 1/4", add to above						25%	10%			
0800	Vinyl tubing, 1/4", material only	G					.05			.05	.06
0850	Supply tubing, 1/2", material only, 100' coil	G					.12			.12	.13
0900	500' coil	G					.11			.11	.12
0950	Compression fittings	G	1 Skwk	90	.089	Ea.	.72	4.32		5.04	7.50
1000	Barbed fittings, 1/4"	G		360	.022		.16	1.08		1.24	1.85
1100	Flush risers	G		60	.133		3.40	6.50		9.90	13.75
1150	Flush ends, figure eight	G		180	.044		.52	2.16		2.68	3.91
1200	Ball valve, 4-1/2"	G		20	.400		9.25	19.45		28.70	40

32 84 Planting Irrigation

32 84 13 – Drip Irrigation

32 84 13.10 Subsurface Drip Irrigation

		Crew	Daily Output	Labor-Hours	Unit	Material	2015 Bare Costs Labor	Equipment	Total	Total Incl O&P
1250	4-3/4" **G**	1 Skwk	20	.400	Ea.	7.25	19.45		26.70	38
1300	Auto flush, spring loaded **G**		90	.089		2.20	4.32		6.52	9.10
1350	Volumetric **G**		90	.089		7.50	4.32		11.82	14.95
1400	Air relief valve, inline with compensation tee, 1/2" **G**		45	.178		16	8.65		24.65	31
1450	1" **G**		30	.267		17	12.95		29.95	38.50
1500	Round box for flush ends, 6" **G**		30	.267		7.75	12.95		20.70	28.50
1550	Fertilizer injector, non-proportional **G**		4	2		12	97.50		109.50	163
1600	Screen filter, 3/4" screen **G**		12	.667		10.35	32.50		42.85	61.50
1650	1" disk **G**		8	1		26	48.50		74.50	104
1700	1-1/2" disk **G**		4	2		70	97.50		167.50	227
1750	2" disk **G**		3	2.667		121	130		251	335
1800	Typical installation 18" O.C., small, minimum				S.F.				1.53	2.35
1850	Maximum								1.78	2.75
1900	Large, minimum								1.48	2.28
2000	Maximum								1.71	2.64
2100	For non-pressure compensating systems, deduct								10%	10%
2150	For supply piping, see Section 33 11 13.45									
2680	Install PVC or hose bib to PE drip adapter fittings	1 Skwk	40	.200	Ea.	.99	9.75		10.74	16.15
2690	Install three outlet manual manifold		4	2		21	97.50		118.50	173
2700	Install four zone control module		4	2		90	97.50		187.50	249
2710	Install six zone control module		4	2		126	97.50		223.50	289

32 84 23 – Underground Sprinklers

32 84 23.10 Sprinkler Irrigation System

		Crew	Daily Output	Labor-Hours	Unit	Material	2015 Bare Costs Labor	Equipment	Total	Total Incl O&P
0010	**SPRINKLER IRRIGATION SYSTEM**									
0011	For lawns									
0100	Golf course with fully automatic system	C-17	.05	1600	9 holes	100,000	78,500		178,500	231,000
0200	24' diam. head at 15' O.C. incl. piping, auto oper., minimum	B-20	70	.343	Head	27	14.40		41.40	51.50
0300	Maximum		40	.600		45	25		70	88.50
0600	Sprinkler irrigation sys, golf course, auto sys, 60' dia HD		23	1.043		150	44		194	233
0800	Residential system, custom, 1" supply		2000	.012	S.F.	.26	.50		.76	1.07
0900	1-1/2" supply		1800	.013	"	.49	.56		1.05	1.40
0990	For renovation work, add to above						50%			
1020	Pop up spray head w/risers, hi-pop, full circle pattern, 4"	2 Skwk	76	.211	Ea.	5.15	10.25		15.40	21.50
1030	1/2 circle pattern, 4"		76	.211		5.15	10.25		15.40	21.50
1040	6", full circle pattern		76	.211		9.50	10.25		19.75	26.50
1050	1/2 circle pattern, 6"		76	.211		9.50	10.25		19.75	26.50
1060	12", full circle pattern		76	.211		11.15	10.25		21.40	28
1070	1/2 circle pattern, 12"		76	.211		13.75	10.25		24	31
1080	Pop up bubbler head w/risers, hi-pop bubbler head, 4"		76	.211		4.40	10.25		14.65	20.50
1090	6"		76	.211		9.20	10.25		19.45	26
1100	12"		76	.211		11	10.25		21.25	28
1110	Impact full/part circle sprinklers, 28'-54' 25-60 PSI		37	.432		17.65	21		38.65	52
1120	Spaced 37'-49' @ 25-50 PSI		37	.432		22	21		43	57
1130	Spaced 43'-61' @ 30-60 PSI		37	.432		61.50	21		82.50	100
1140	Spaced 54'-78' @ 40-80 PSI		37	.432		106	21		127	150
1145	Impact rotor pop-up full/part commercial circle sprinklers									
1150	Spaced 42'-65' 35-80 PSI	2 Skwk	25	.640	Ea.	15.30	31		46.30	65
1160	Spaced 48'-76' 45-85 PSI	"	25	.640	"	16.85	31		47.85	66.50
1165	Impact rotor pop-up part. circle comm., 53'-75', 55-100 PSI, w/accessories									
1170	Plastic case, metal cover	2 Skwk	25	.640	Ea.	74	31		105	129
1180	Rubber cover		25	.640		56.50	31		87.50	111
1190	Iron case, metal cover		22	.727		122	35.50		157.50	189

For customer support on your Site Work & Landscape Cost Data, call 877.737.1594.

389

32 84 23.10 Sprinkler Irrigation System	Crew	Daily Output	Labor-Hours	Unit	Material	2015 Bare Costs Labor	Equipment	Total	Total Incl O&P
1200	Rubber cover	2 Skwk	22	.727	Ea.	129	35.50		164.50	197
1250	Plastic case, 2 nozzle, metal cover		25	.640		89.50	31		120.50	146
1260	Rubber cover		25	.640		91.50	31		122.50	148
1270	Iron case, 2 nozzle, metal cover		22	.727		130	35.50		165.50	197
1280	Rubber cover		22	.727		130	35.50		165.50	197
1282	Impact rotor pop-up full circle commercial, 39'-99', 30-100 PSI									
1284	Plastic case, metal cover	2 Skwk	25	.640	Ea.	83	31		114	139
1286	Rubber cover		25	.640		94.50	31		125.50	152
1288	Iron case, metal cover		22	.727		122	35.50		157.50	189
1290	Rubber cover		22	.727		126	35.50		161.50	194
1292	Plastic case, 2 nozzle, metal cover		22	.727		90	35.50		125.50	154
1294	Rubber cover		22	.727		90	35.50		125.50	154
1296	Iron case, 2 nozzle, metal cover		20	.800		119	39		158	190
1298	Rubber cover		20	.800		123	39		162	195
1305	Electric remote control valve, plastic, 3/4"		18	.889		23.50	43		66.50	93
1310	1"		18	.889		23.50	43		66.50	93
1320	1-1/2"		18	.889		91	43		134	167
1330	2"		18	.889		109	43		152	187
1335	Quick coupling valves, brass, locking cover									
1340	Inlet coupling valve, 3/4"	2 Skwk	18.75	.853	Ea.	21.50	41.50		63	87.50
1350	1"		18.75	.853		30	41.50		71.50	97
1360	Controller valve boxes, 6" round boxes		18.75	.853		7.10	41.50		48.60	72
1370	10" round boxes		14.25	1.123		11.40	54.50		65.90	97
1380	12" square box		9.75	1.641		16.05	80		96.05	141
1388	Electromech. control, 14 day 3-60 min., auto start to 23/day									
1390	4 station	2 Skwk	1.04	15.385	Ea.	75	750		825	1,225
1400	7 station		.64	25		140	1,225		1,365	2,025
1410	12 station		.40	40		170	1,950		2,120	3,175
1420	Dual programs, 18 station		.24	66.667		200	3,250		3,450	5,225
1430	23 station		.16	100		220	4,875		5,095	7,775
1435	Backflow preventer, bronze, 0-175 PSI, w/valves, test cocks									
1440	3/4"	2 Skwk	6	2.667	Ea.	82	130		212	290
1450	1"		6	2.667		94	130		224	305
1460	1-1/2"		6	2.667		224	130		354	445
1470	2"		6	2.667		276	130		406	505
1475	Pressure vacuum breaker, brass, 15-150 PSI									
1480	3/4"	2 Skwk	6	2.667	Ea.	25	130		155	228
1490	1"		6	2.667		30	130		160	233
1500	1-1/2"		6	2.667		70	130		200	277
1510	2"		6	2.667		120	130		250	330

32 91 Planting Preparation

32 91 13 – Soil Preparation

32 91 13.16 Mulching

		Crew	Daily Output	Labor-Hours	Unit	Material	2015 Bare Costs Labor	2015 Bare Costs Equipment	Total	Total Incl O&P
0010	**MULCHING**									
0100	Aged barks, 3" deep, hand spread	1 Clab	100	.080	S.Y.	3.55	3.01		6.56	8.55
0150	Skid steer loader	B-63	13.50	2.963	M.S.F.	395	118	12.85	525.85	630
0200	Hay, 1" deep, hand spread	1 Clab	475	.017	S.Y.	.52	.63		1.15	1.54
0250	Power mulcher, small	B-64	180	.089	M.S.F.	58	3.41	2.21	63.62	71
0350	Large	B-65	530	.030	"	58	1.16	1.07	60.23	66.50
0370	Fiber mulch recycled newsprint hand spread	1 Clab	500	.016	S.Y.	.23	.60		.83	1.18
0380	Power mulcher small	B-64	200	.080	M.S.F.	25.50	3.07	1.99	30.56	35
0390	Power mulcher large	B-65	600	.027	"	25.50	1.02	.94	27.46	30.50
0400	Humus peat, 1" deep, hand spread	1 Clab	700	.011	S.Y.	2.42	.43		2.85	3.32
0450	Push spreader	"	2500	.003	"	2.42	.12		2.54	2.85
0550	Tractor spreader	B-66	700	.011	M.S.F.	269	.56	.38	269.94	297
0600	Oat straw, 1" deep, hand spread	1 Clab	475	.017	S.Y.	.60	.63		1.23	1.63
0650	Power mulcher, small	B-64	180	.089	M.S.F.	66.50	3.41	2.21	72.12	81
0700	Large	B-65	530	.030	"	66.50	1.16	1.07	68.73	76.50
0750	Add for asphaltic emulsion	B-45	1770	.009	Gal.	5.80	.41	.51	6.72	7.60
0760	Pine straw, 1" deep, hand spread	1 Clab	1950	.004	S.F.	.09	.15		.24	.34
0800	Peat moss, 1" deep, hand spread		900	.009	S.Y.	2.80	.33		3.13	3.59
0850	Push spreader		2500	.003	"	2.80	.12		2.92	3.27
0950	Tractor spreader	B-66	700	.011	M.S.F.	310	.56	.38	310.94	340
1000	Polyethylene film, 6 mil	2 Clab	2000	.008	S.Y.	.46	.30		.76	.97
1010	4 mil		2300	.007		.38	.26		.64	.82
1020	1-1/2 mil		2500	.006		.25	.24		.49	.65
1050	Filter fabric weed barrier		2000	.008		.73	.30		1.03	1.26
1100	Redwood nuggets, 3" deep, hand spread	1 Clab	150	.053		2.77	2.01		4.78	6.15
1150	Skid steer loader	B-63	13.50	2.963	M.S.F.	310	118	12.85	440.85	535
1200	Stone mulch, hand spread, ceramic chips, economy	1 Clab	125	.064	S.Y.	6.85	2.41		9.26	11.25
1250	Deluxe	"	95	.084	"	10.60	3.17		13.77	16.50
1300	Granite chips	B-1	10	2.400	C.Y.	64	92		156	212
1400	Marble chips		10	2.400		152	92		244	310
1600	Pea gravel		28	.857		108	33		141	169
1700	Quartz		10	2.400		188	92		280	350
1760	Landscape mulch, 100% recycld tires, var colors, hand spread, 3" deep		10	2.400		273	92		365	440
1800	Tar paper, 15 lb. felt	1 Clab	800	.010	S.Y.	.49	.38		.87	1.11
1900	Wood chips, 2" deep, hand spread	"	220	.036	"	1.60	1.37		2.97	3.86
1950	Skid steer loader	B-63	20.30	1.970	M.S.F.	178	78.50	8.55	265.05	325

32 91 13.23 Structural Soil Mixing

		Crew	Daily Output	Labor-Hours	Unit	Material	2015 Bare Costs Labor	2015 Bare Costs Equipment	Total	Total Incl O&P
0010	**STRUCTURAL SOIL MIXING**									
0100	Rake topsoil, site material, harley rock rake, ideal	B-6	33	.727	M.S.F.		30	11.05	41.05	58
0200	Adverse	"	7	3.429			142	52	194	274
0250	By hand (raking)	1 Clab	10	.800			30		30	46.50
0300	Screened loam, york rake and finish, ideal	B-62	24	1			41.50	7.25	48.75	71
0400	Adverse	"	20	1.200			49.50	8.70	58.20	85.50
0450	By hand (raking)	1 Clab	15	.533			20		20	31
1000	Remove topsoil & stock pile on site, 75 HP dozer, 6" deep, 50' haul	B-10L	30	.400			18.50	15.75	34.25	45.50
1050	300' haul		6.10	1.967			91	77.50	168.50	224
1100	12" deep, 50' haul		15.50	.774			36	30.50	66.50	88
1150	300' haul		3.10	3.871			179	152	331	440
1200	200 HP dozer, 6" deep, 50' haul	B-10B	125	.096			4.44	11.10	15.54	18.95
1250	300' haul		30.70	.391			18.10	45	63.10	77
1300	12" deep, 50' haul		62	.194			8.95	22.50	31.45	38
1350	300' haul		15.40	.779			36	90	126	154

For customer support on your Site Work & Landscape Cost Data, call 877.737.1594.

391

32 91 13.23 Structural Soil Mixing		Crew	Daily Output	Labor-Hours	Unit	Material	2015 Bare Costs Labor	2015 Bare Costs Equipment	Total	Total Incl O&P
1400	Alternate method, 75 HP dozer, 50' haul	B-10L	860	.014	C.Y.		.65	.55	1.20	1.58
1450	300' haul	"	114	.105			4.87	4.14	9.01	11.95
1500	200 HP dozer, 50' haul	B-10B	2660	.005			.21	.52	.73	.89
1600	300' haul	"	570	.021			.97	2.43	3.40	4.16
1800	Rolling topsoil, hand push roller	1 Clab	3200	.003	S.F.		.09		.09	.14
1850	Tractor drawn roller	B-66	10666	.001	"		.04	.02	.06	.09
1900	Remove rocks & debris from grade, by hand	B-62	80	.300	M.S.F.		12.40	2.17	14.57	21.50
1920	With rock picker	B-10S	140	.086			3.97	2.70	6.67	9
2000	Root raking and loading, residential, no boulders	B-6	53.30	.450			18.60	6.85	25.45	36
2100	With boulders		32	.750			31	11.40	42.40	60
2200	Municipal, no boulders		200	.120			4.95	1.82	6.77	9.60
2300	With boulders		120	.200			8.25	3.04	11.29	16
2400	Large commercial, no boulders	B-10B	400	.030			1.39	3.47	4.86	5.90
2500	With boulders	"	240	.050			2.31	5.80	8.11	9.85
2600	Rough grade & scarify subsoil to receive topsoil, common earth									
2610	200 H.P. dozer with scarifier	B-11A	80	.200	M.S.F.		8.80	17.35	26.15	32.50
2620	180 H.P. grader with scarifier	B-11L	110	.145			6.40	6.70	13.10	17.15
2700	Clay and till, 200 H.P. dozer with scarifier	B-11A	50	.320			14.10	27.50	41.60	52
2710	180 H.P. grader with scarifier	B-11L	40	.400			17.65	18.40	36.05	47
3000	Scarify subsoil, residential, skid steer loader w/scarifiers, 50 HP	B-66	32	.250			12.15	8.25	20.40	27.50
3050	Municipal, skid steer loader w/scarifiers, 50 HP	"	120	.067			3.24	2.19	5.43	7.35
3100	Large commercial, 75 HP, dozer w/scarifier	B-10L	240	.050			2.31	1.97	4.28	5.70
3200	Grader with scarifier, 135 H.P.	B-11L	280	.057			2.52	2.63	5.15	6.75
3500	Screen topsoil from stockpile, vibrating screen, wet material (organic)	B-10P	200	.060	C.Y.		2.78	5.95	8.73	10.80
3550	Dry material	"	300	.040			1.85	3.96	5.81	7.20
3600	Mixing with conditioners, manure and peat	B-10R	550	.022			1.01	.54	1.55	2.14
3650	Mobilization add for 2 days or less operation	B-34K	3	2.667	Job		107	315	422	510
3800	Spread conditioned topsoil, 6" deep, by hand	B-1	360	.067	S.Y.	5.45	2.55		8	9.95
3850	300 HP dozer	B-10M	27	.444	M.S.F.	590	20.50	70.50	681	755
3900	4" deep, by hand	B-1	470	.051	S.Y.	4.90	1.95		6.85	8.40
3920	300 H.P. dozer	B-10M	34	.353	M.S.F.	440	16.35	56	512.35	570
3940	180 H.P. grader	B-11L	37	.432	"	440	19.05	19.90	478.95	535
4000	Spread soil conditioners, alum. sulfate, 1#/S.Y., hand push spreader	1 Clab	17500	.001	S.Y.	20	.02		20.02	22
4050	Tractor spreader	B-66	700	.011	M.S.F.	2,225	.56	.38	2,225.94	2,450
4100	Fertilizer, 0.2#/S.Y., push spreader	1 Clab	17500	.001	S.Y.	.12	.02		.14	.16
4150	Tractor spreader	B-66	700	.011	M.S.F.	13.35	.56	.38	14.29	15.90
4200	Ground limestone, 1#/S.Y., push spreader	1 Clab	17500	.001	S.Y.	.11	.02		.13	.15
4250	Tractor spreader	B-66	700	.011	M.S.F.	12.20	.56	.38	13.14	14.70
4400	Manure, 18#/S.Y., push spreader	1 Clab	2500	.003	S.Y.	8.15	.12		8.27	9.15
4450	Tractor spreader	B-66	280	.029	M.S.F.	905	1.39	.94	907.33	1,000
4500	Perlite, 1" deep, push spreader	1 Clab	17500	.001	S.Y.	10.35	.02		10.37	11.45
4550	Tractor spreader	B-66	700	.011	M.S.F.	1,150	.56	.38	1,150.94	1,275
4600	Vermiculite, push spreader	1 Clab	17500	.001	S.Y.	8.45	.02		8.47	9.35
4650	Tractor spreader	B-66	700	.011	M.S.F.	940	.56	.38	940.94	1,025
5000	Spread topsoil, skid steer loader and hand dress	B-62	270	.089	C.Y.	24.50	3.67	.64	28.81	33.50
5100	Articulated loader and hand dress	B-100	320	.038		24.50	1.74	2.99	29.23	33
5200	Articulated loader and 75HP dozer	B-10M	500	.024		24.50	1.11	3.79	29.40	33
5300	Road grader and hand dress	B-11L	1000	.016		24.50	.71	.74	25.95	29
6000	Tilling topsoil, 20 HP tractor, disk harrow, 2" deep	B-66	450	.018	M.S.F.		.86	.59	1.45	1.95
6050	4" deep		360	.022			1.08	.73	1.81	2.44
6100	6" deep		270	.030			1.44	.97	2.41	3.26
6150	26" rototiller, 2" deep	A-1J	1250	.006	S.Y.		.24	.04	.28	.41
6200	4" deep		1000	.008			.30	.05	.35	.51

32 91 Planting Preparation

32 91 13 – Soil Preparation

32 91 13.23 Structural Soil Mixing

		Crew	Daily Output	Labor-Hours	Unit	Material	2015 Bare Costs Labor	2015 Bare Costs Equipment	Total	Total Incl O&P
6250	6" deep	A-1J	750	.011	S.Y.		.40	.06	.46	.69

32 91 13.26 Planting Beds

		Crew	Daily Output	Labor-Hours	Unit	Material	Labor	Equipment	Total	Total Incl O&P
0010	**PLANTING BEDS**									
0100	Backfill planting pit, by hand, on site topsoil	2 Clab	18	.889	C.Y.		33.50		33.50	51.50
0200	Prepared planting mix, by hand	"	24	.667			25		25	38.50
0300	Skid steer loader, on site topsoil	B-62	340	.071			2.91	.51	3.42	5
0400	Prepared planting mix	"	410	.059			2.42	.42	2.84	4.17
1000	Excavate planting pit, by hand, sandy soil	2 Clab	16	1			37.50		37.50	58
1100	Heavy soil or clay	"	8	2			75		75	116
1200	1/2 C.Y. backhoe, sandy soil	B-11C	150	.107			4.70	2.43	7.13	9.85
1300	Heavy soil or clay	"	115	.139			6.15	3.17	9.32	12.85
2000	Mix planting soil, incl. loam, manure, peat, by hand	2 Clab	60	.267		43	10.05		53.05	62.50
2100	Skid steer loader	B-62	150	.160		43	6.60	1.16	50.76	58.50
3000	Pile sod, skid steer loader	"	2800	.009	S.Y.		.35	.06	.41	.61
3100	By hand	2 Clab	400	.040			1.50		1.50	2.31
4000	Remove sod, F.E. loader	B-10S	2000	.006			.28	.19	.47	.63
4100	Sod cutter	B-12K	3200	.005			.22	.31	.53	.68
4200	By hand	2 Clab	240	.067			2.51		2.51	3.86
6000	For planting bed edging, see Section 32 94 13.20									

32 91 19 – Landscape Grading

32 91 19.13 Topsoil Placement and Grading

		Crew	Daily Output	Labor-Hours	Unit	Material	Labor	Equipment	Total	Total Incl O&P
0010	**TOPSOIL PLACEMENT AND GRADING**									
0300	Fine grade, base course for paving, see Section 32 11 23.23									
0400	Spread from pile to rough finish grade, F.E. loader, 1.5 C.Y.	B-10S	200	.060	C.Y.		2.78	1.89	4.67	6.30
0500	Up to 200' radius, by hand	1 Clab	14	.571			21.50		21.50	33
0600	Top dress by hand, 1 C.Y. for 600 S.F.	"	11.50	.696		27.50	26		53.50	70.50
0700	Furnish and place, truck dumped, screened, 4" deep	B-10S	1300	.009	S.Y.	3.44	.43	.29	4.16	4.75
0800	6" deep	"	820	.015	"	4.40	.68	.46	5.54	6.40
0900	Fine grading and seeding, incl. lime, fertilizer & seed,									
1000	With equipment	B-14	1000	.048	S.Y.	.46	1.91	.36	2.73	3.83

32 92 Turf and Grasses

32 92 19 – Seeding

32 92 19.13 Mechanical Seeding

		Crew	Daily Output	Labor-Hours	Unit	Material	Labor	Equipment	Total	Total Incl O&P
0010	**MECHANICAL SEEDING**									
0020	Mechanical seeding, 215 lb./acre	B-66	1.50	5.333	Acre	560	259	175	994	1,200
0100	44 lb./M.S.Y.	"	2500	.003	S.Y.	.18	.16	.11	.45	.56
0101	$2.00/lb., 44 lb./M.S.Y.	1 Clab	13950	.001	S.F.	.02	.02		.04	.05
0300	Fine grading and seeding incl. lime, fertilizer & seed,									
0310	with equipment	B-14	1000	.048	S.Y.	.44	1.91	.36	2.71	3.81
0400	Fertilizer hand push spreader, 35 lb. per M.S.F.	1 Clab	200	.040	M.S.F.	9.80	1.50		11.30	13.10
0600	Limestone hand push spreader, 50 lb. per M.S.F.		180	.044		5.40	1.67		7.07	8.45
0800	Grass seed hand push spreader, 4.5 lb. per M.S.F.		180	.044		20	1.67		21.67	24.50
1000	Hydro or air seeding for large areas, incl. seed and fertilizer	B-81	8900	.003	S.Y.	.43	.12	.08	.63	.74
1100	With wood fiber mulch added	"	8900	.003	"	1.76	.12	.08	1.96	2.21
1300	Seed only, over 100 lb., field seed, minimum				Lb.	1.75			1.75	1.93
1400	Maximum					1.75			1.75	1.93
1500	Lawn seed, minimum					1.41			1.41	1.55
1600	Maximum					2.46			2.46	2.71
1800	Aerial operations, seeding only, field seed	B-58	50	.480	Acre	570	19.80	63	652.80	725

For customer support on your Site Work & Landscape Cost Data, call 877.737.1594.

393

32 92 Turf and Grasses

32 92 19 – Seeding

32 92 19.13 Mechanical Seeding	Crew	Daily Output	Labor-Hours	Unit	Material	2015 Bare Costs Labor	Equipment	Total	Total Incl O&P
1900 Lawn seed	B-58	50	.480	Acre	460	19.80	63	542.80	605
2100 Seed and liquid fertilizer, field seed		50	.480		690	19.80	63	772.80	860
2200 Lawn seed		50	.480		580	19.80	63	662.80	735

32 92 19.14 Seeding, Athletic Fields

	Crew	Daily Output	Labor-Hours	Unit	Material	2015 Bare Costs Labor	Equipment	Total	Total Incl O&P
0010 **SEEDING, ATHLETIC FIELDS** R329219-50									
0020 Seeding, athletic fields, athletic field mix, 8#/M.S.F. push spreader	1 Clab	8	1	M.S.F.	11.30	37.50		48.80	70.50
0100 Tractor spreader	B-66	52	.154		11.30	7.50	5.05	23.85	29.50
0200 Hydro or air seeding, with mulch and fertilizer	B-81	80	.300		12.45	12.85	8.65	33.95	42.50
0400 Birdsfoot trefoil, .45#/M.S.F., push spreader	1 Clab	8	1		4	37.50		41.50	62.50
0500 Tractor spreader	B-66	52	.154		4	7.50	5.05	16.55	21.50
0600 Hydro or air seeding, with mulch and fertilizer	B-81	80	.300		7.70	12.85	8.65	29.20	37.50
0800 Bluegrass, 4#/M.S.F., common, push spreader	1 Clab	8	1		12.80	37.50		50.30	72
0900 Tractor spreader	B-66	52	.154		12.80	7.50	5.05	25.35	31
1000 Hydro or air seeding, with mulch and fertilizer	B-81	80	.300		21	12.85	8.65	42.50	52
1100 Baron, push spreader	1 Clab	8	1		13.30	37.50		50.80	72.50
1200 Tractor spreader	B-66	52	.154		13.30	7.50	5.05	25.85	31.50
1300 Hydro or air seeding, with mulch and fertilizer	B-81	80	.300		18.30	12.85	8.65	39.80	49
1500 Clover, 0.67#/M.S.F., white, push spreader	1 Clab	8	1		3.08	37.50		40.58	61.50
1600 Tractor spreader	B-66	52	.154		3.08	7.50	5.05	15.63	20.50
1700 Hydro or air seeding, with mulch and fertilizer	B-81	80	.300		16.95	12.85	8.65	38.45	47.50
1800 Ladino, push spreader	1 Clab	8	1		3.08	37.50		40.58	61.50
1900 Tractor spreader	B-66	52	.154		3.08	7.50	5.05	15.63	20.50
2000 Hydro or air seeding, with mulch and fertilizer	B-81	80	.300		13.55	12.85	8.65	35.05	44
2200 Fescue 5.5#/M.S.F., tall, push spreader	1 Clab	8	1		7.75	37.50		45.25	66.50
2300 Tractor spreader	B-66	52	.154		7.75	7.50	5.05	20.30	25.50
2400 Hydro or air seeding, with mulch and fertilizer	B-81	80	.300		25.50	12.85	8.65	47	57
2500 Chewing, push spreader	1 Clab	8	1		8.25	37.50		45.75	67
2600 Tractor spreader	B-66	52	.154		8.25	7.50	5.05	20.80	26
2700 Hydro or air seeding, with mulch and fertilizer	B-81	80	.300		27	12.85	8.65	48.50	59
2800 Creeping, push spreader	1 Clab	8	1		7.30	37.50		44.80	66
2810 Tractor spreader	B-66	26	.308		7.30	14.95	10.10	32.35	41.50
2820 Hydro or air seeding, with mulch and fertilizer	B-81	80	.300		24	12.85	8.65	45.50	55.50
2900 Crown vetch, 4#/M.S.F., push spreader	1 Clab	8	1		105	37.50		142.50	174
3000 Tractor spreader	B-66	52	.154		105	7.50	5.05	117.55	133
3100 Hydro or air seeding, with mulch and fertilizer	B-81	80	.300		144	12.85	8.65	165.50	188
3300 Rye, 10#/M.S.F., annual, push spreader	1 Clab	8	1		15.15	37.50		52.65	74.50
3400 Tractor spreader	B-66	52	.154		15.15	7.50	5.05	27.70	33.50
3500 Hydro or air seeding, with mulch and fertilizer	B-81	80	.300		33.50	12.85	8.65	55	65.50
3600 Fine textured, push spreader	1 Clab	8	1		13.20	37.50		50.70	72.50
3700 Tractor spreader	B-66	52	.154		13.20	7.50	5.05	25.75	31.50
3800 Hydro or air seeding, with mulch and fertilizer	B-81	80	.300		29	12.85	8.65	50.50	61
4000 Shade mix, 6#/M.S.F., push spreader	1 Clab	8	1		10.45	37.50		47.95	69.50
4100 Tractor spreader	B-66	52	.154		10.45	7.50	5.05	23	28.50
4200 Hydro or air seeding, with mulch and fertilizer	B-81	80	.300		23	12.85	8.65	44.50	54.50
4400 Slope mix, 6#/M.S.F., push spreader	1 Clab	8	1		11.75	37.50		49.25	71
4500 Tractor spreader	B-66	52	.154		11.75	7.50	5.05	24.30	30
4600 Hydro or air seeding, with mulch and fertilizer	B-81	80	.300		29.50	12.85	8.65	51	61.50
4800 Turf mix, 4#/M.S.F., push spreader	1 Clab	8	1		11.25	37.50		48.75	70.50
4900 Tractor spreader	B-66	52	.154		11.25	7.50	5.05	23.80	29.50
5000 Hydro or air seeding, with mulch and fertilizer	B-81	80	.300		28	12.85	8.65	49.50	60
5200 Utility mix, 7#/M.S.F., push spreader	1 Clab	8	1		9.40	37.50		46.90	68.50
5300 Tractor spreader	B-66	52	.154		9.40	7.50	5.05	21.95	27.50

32 92 Turf and Grasses

32 92 19 – Seeding

32 92 19.14 Seeding, Athletic Fields

		Crew	Daily Output	Labor-Hours	Unit	Material	2015 Bare Costs Labor	Equipment	Total	Total Incl O&P
5400	Hydro or air seeding, with mulch and fertilizer	B-81	80	.300	M.S.F.	35.50	12.85	8.65	57	68
5600	Wildflower, .10#/M.S.F., push spreader	1 Clab	8	1		1.86	37.50		39.36	60
5700	Tractor spreader	B-66	52	.154		1.86	7.50	5.05	14.41	18.95
5800	Hydro or air seeding, with mulch and fertilizer	B-81	80	.300	▼	10.25	12.85	8.65	31.75	40.50
7000	Apply fertilizer, 800 lb./acre	B-66	4	2	Ton	980	97	66	1,143	1,300
7025	Fertilizer, mechanical spread	1 Clab	1.75	4.571	Acre	5.40	172		177.40	270
7050	Apply limestone, 800 lb./acre	B-66	4.25	1.882	Ton	170	91.50	62	323.50	395
7060	Limestone, mechanical spread	1 Clab	1.74	4.598	Acre	86	173		259	360
7100	Apply mulch, see Section 32 91 13.16									

32 92 23 – Sodding

32 92 23.10 Sodding Systems

		Crew	Daily Output	Labor-Hours	Unit	Material	2015 Bare Costs Labor	Equipment	Total	Total Incl O&P
0010	**SODDING SYSTEMS**									
0020	Sodding, 1" deep, bluegrass sod, on level ground, over 8 M.S.F.	B-63	22	1.818	M.S.F.	243	72.50	7.90	323.40	390
0200	4 M.S.F.		17	2.353		254	93.50	10.20	357.70	435
0300	1000 S.F.		13.50	2.963		295	118	12.85	425.85	520
0500	Sloped ground, over 8 M.S.F.		6	6.667		243	265	29	537	705
0600	4 M.S.F.		5	8		254	320	34.50	608.50	805
0700	1000 S.F.		4	10		295	400	43.50	738.50	985
1000	Bent grass sod, on level ground, over 6 M.S.F.		20	2		252	79.50	8.70	340.20	410
1100	3 M.S.F.		18	2.222		261	88.50	9.65	359.15	435
1200	Sodding 1000 S.F. or less		14	2.857		286	114	12.40	412.40	505
1500	Sloped ground, over 6 M.S.F.		15	2.667		252	106	11.55	369.55	455
1600	3 M.S.F.		13.50	2.963		261	118	12.85	391.85	480
1700	1000 S.F.	▼	12	3.333	▼	286	133	14.45	433.45	535

32 92 26 – Sprigging

32 92 26.13 Stolonizing

		Crew	Daily Output	Labor-Hours	Unit	Material	2015 Bare Costs Labor	Equipment	Total	Total Incl O&P
0010	**STOLONIZING**									
0100	6" O.C., by hand	1 Clab	4	2	M.S.F.	51.50	75		126.50	173
0110	Walk behind sprig planter	"	80	.100		51.50	3.76		55.26	62.50
0120	Towed sprig planter	B-66	350	.023		51.50	1.11	.75	53.36	59
0130	9" O.C., by hand	1 Clab	5.20	1.538		23	58		81	115
0140	Walk behind sprig planter	"	92	.087		23	3.27		26.27	30.50
0150	Towed sprig planter	B-66	420	.019		23	.93	.63	24.56	27.50
0160	12" O.C., by hand	1 Clab	6	1.333		12.85	50		62.85	91
0170	Walk behind sprig planter	"	110	.073		12.85	2.73		15.58	18.35
0180	Towed sprig planter	B-66	500	.016		12.85	.78	.53	14.16	15.90
0200	Broadcast, by hand, 2 Bu. per M.S.F.	1 Clab	15	.533		5.15	20		25.15	36.50
0210	4 Bu. per M.S.F.		10	.800		10.30	30		40.30	58
0220	6 Bu. per M.S.F.	▼	6.50	1.231		15.50	46.50		62	88
0300	Hydro planter, 6 Bu. per M.S.F.	B-64	100	.160		15.50	6.15	3.97	25.62	31
0320	Manure spreader planting 6 Bu. per M.S.F.	B-66	200	.040	▼	15.50	1.94	1.32	18.76	21.50

For customer support on your Site Work & Landscape Cost Data, call 877.737.1594.

395

32 93 13.30 Ground Covers	Crew	Daily Output	Labor-Hours	Unit	Material	2015 Bare Costs Labor	Equipment	Total	Total Incl O&P
0010 **GROUND COVERS**									
0011 Vines and climbing plants									
1000 Achillea tomentosa, (Woolly Yarrow), zone 4, cont									
1010 1 qt.				Ea.	7			7	7.70
1020 2 gal.				"	11			11	12.10
1100 Aegopodium podagaria, (Snow-on-the-Mountain Goutweed), zone 3, cont									
1110 1 qt.				Ea.	7			7	7.70
1120 1 gal.					9			9	9.90
1130 Flat/24 plants					33.50			33.50	37
1200 Ajuga reptans, (Carpet Bugle), zone 4, cont									
1210 4" Pot				Ea.	4			4	4.40
1220 1 qt.					8.90			8.90	9.80
1230 1 gal.					16.75			16.75	18.40
1240 Flat/24 plants					40			40	44
1300 Akebia quinata, (Five-Leaf Akebia), zone 4, container									
1310 1 gal.				Ea.	11.65			11.65	12.80
1320 5 gal.				"	41			41	45
1400 Alchemilla vulgaris, (Common Lady's-Mantle), zone 3, cont									
1410 1 qt.				Ea.	7			7	7.70
1420 1 gal.				"	24			24	26.50
1500 Ampelopsis brevipedunculata elegans, (Ampelopsis), zone 4, cont									
1510 1 gal.				Ea.	9.35			9.35	10.25
1520 3 gal.				"	17.70			17.70	19.50
1600 Arctostaphylos uva-ursi, (Bearberry), zone 2, container									
1610 3" Pot				Ea.	10.20			10.20	11.25
1620 1 gal.					28.50			28.50	31
1630 5 gal.					90.50			90.50	100
1700 Aristolochia durior, (Dutchman's Pipe), Z5, cont									
1710 2 gal.				Ea.	23.50			23.50	25.50
1720 5 gal.				"	25			25	27.50
1800 Armeria maritima, (Thrift, Sea Pink), Z6, cont									
1810 1 qt.				Ea.	7			7	7.70
1820 1 gal.				"	9			9	9.90
1900 Artemisia schmitdiana, (Silver Mound/Satiny Wormwood), Z3, cont									
1910 1 qt.				Ea.	7			7	7.70
1920 1 gal.				"	9			9	9.90
2000 Artemisia stellerana, (Dusty Miller), Z2, cont									
2010 1 qt.				Ea.	9			9	9.90
2020 1 gal.				"	44.50			44.50	49
2100 Asarum europaeum, (European Wild Ginger), Z4, cont									
2110 4" Pot				Ea.	21.50			21.50	24
2120 1 gal.				"	51.50			51.50	56.50
2200 Baccharis pilularis, (Dwarf Coyote Bush), Z7, cont									
2210 1 qt.				Ea.	7			7	7.70
2220 1 gal.				"	8.90			8.90	9.80
2300 Bergenia cordifolia, (Heartleaf Bergenia), Z3, cont									
2310 1 qt.				Ea.	15.25			15.25	16.80
2320 1 gal.				"	23.50			23.50	26
2400 Bougainvillea glabra, Z10, cont									
2410 1 gal.				Ea.	15.95			15.95	17.50
2420 5 gal.				"	21			21	23.50
2500 Calluna vulgaris cultivars, (Scotch Heather), Z4, cont									
2510 3" Pot				Ea.	6.50			6.50	7.15

32 93 13.30 Ground Covers		Crew	Daily Output	Labor-Hours	Unit	2015 Bare Costs Material	Labor	Equipment	Total	Total Incl O&P
2520	1 qt.				Ea.	12.10			12.10	13.35
2530	1 gal.					24.50			24.50	26.50
2540	2 gal.				↓	47.50			47.50	52
2600	Campsis radicans, (Trumpet Creeper), Z5, cont									
2610	1 gal.				Ea.	17.15			17.15	18.90
2620	2 gal.					17.35			17.35	19.05
2630	5 gal.				↓	25.50			25.50	28
2700	Celastrus scandens, (American Bittersweet), Z2, cont									
2710	1 gal.				Ea.	9			9	9.90
2720	2 gal.				"	22			22	24
2800	Cerastium tomentosum, (Snow-in-Summer), Z2, cont									
2810	1 qt.				Ea.	18.45			18.45	20.50
2820	1 gal.				"	37			37	40.50
2900	Ceratostigma, (Dwarf Plumbago), Z6, cont									
2910	1 qt.				Ea.	10.50			10.50	11.55
2920	1 gal.				"	21			21	23
3000	Cissus antartica, (Kangeroo Vine), Z8, cont									
3010	1 gal.				Ea.	9			9	9.90
3020	5 gal.				"	18.15			18.15	19.95
3100	Cistus crispus, (Wrinkleleaf Rock Rose), Z7, cont									
3110	1 gal.				Ea.	9			9	9.90
3120	5 gal.				"	15			15	16.50
3200	Clematis, (Hybrids & Clones), Z6, cont									
3210	1 gal.				Ea.	10.90			10.90	12
3220	2 gal.					17.40			17.40	19.15
3230	5 gal.				↓	26.50			26.50	29.50
3300	Cocculus laurifolius, (Laurel-leaf Snailseed), Z8, cont									
3310	1 gal.				Ea.	9			9	9.90
3320	5 gal.				"	13.75			13.75	15.15
3400	Conuallaria majalis, (Lily-of-the-Valley), Z3, cont									
3410	1 qt.				Ea.	7			7	7.70
3420	1 gal.				"	9			9	9.90
3500	Coprosma prostrata, (Prostrate Coprosma), Z7, cont									
3510	1 gal.				Ea.	9			9	9.90
3520	5 gal.				"	14.85			14.85	16.35
3600	Coronilla varia, (Crown Vetch), Z3, cont									
3610	2-1/4" Pot				Ea.	4			4	4.40
3620	Flat/50 plants				"	71.50			71.50	79
3700	Cotoneaster dammeri, (Bearberry Cotoneaster), Z5, cont									
3710	1 gal.				Ea.	9			9	9.90
3720	2 gal.					11			11	12.10
3730	5 gal.				↓	13.35			13.35	14.65
3800	Cytisus decumbens, (Prostrate Broom), Z5, cont									
3810	1 gal.				Ea.	15			15	16.50
3820	2 gal.				"	13.90			13.90	15.30
3900	Dianthus plumarius, (Grass Pinks), Z4, cont									
3910	1 qt.				Ea.	9.25			9.25	10.20
3920	1 gal.				"	28			28	30.50
4000	Dicentra formosa, (Western Bleeding Heart), Z3, cont									
4010	2 qt.				Ea.	10.30			10.30	11.35
4020	1 gal.				"	14.95			14.95	16.40
4100	Distictis buccinatoria, (Blood Red Trumpet Vine), Z9, cont									
4110	1 gal.				Ea.	10			10	11

32 93 13 – Ground Covers

32 93 13.30 Ground Covers	Crew	Daily Output	Labor- Hours	Unit	Material	2015 Bare Costs Labor	Equipment	Total	Total Incl O&P
4120	5 gal.				Ea.	26			26	28.50
4200	Epimedium grandiflorum, (Barrenwort, Bishopshat), Z3, cont									
4210	1 qt.				Ea.	6.35			6.35	6.95
4220	1 gal.				"	11.35			11.35	12.50
4300	Euonymus fortunei colorata, (Purple-Leaf Wintercreeper), Z5, cont									
4310	1 qt.				Ea.	7.15			7.15	7.90
4320	1 gal.					12.70			12.70	13.95
4330	Flat/24 plants					31.50			31.50	35
4400	Euonymus fortunei kewensis, (Euonymus), Z5, cont									
4410	1 gal.				Ea.	9			9	9.90
4420	2 gal.				"	18.85			18.85	20.50
4500	Fragaria vesca, (Alpine Strawberry), Z6, cont									
4510	4" Pot				Ea.	6.65			6.65	7.35
4520	1 qt.					8.50			8.50	9.35
4530	1 gal.					14.45			14.45	15.90
4600	Galium odoratum, (Sweet Woodruff), Z4, cont									
4610	4" Pot				Ea.	8.90			8.90	9.80
4620	1 gal.				"	26.50			26.50	29.50
4700	Gardenia jasminoides "Radicans", (Creeping Gardenia), Z8, cont									
4710	1 gal.				Ea.	8.35			8.35	9.20
4720	5 gal.				"	20			20	22
4800	Gelsemium sempervirens, (Carolina Jessamine), Z7, cont									
4810	1 gal.				Ea.	8.35			8.35	9.15
4820	5 gal.				"	20			20	22
4900	Genista pilosa, (Silky-leaf Woadwaxen), Z5, cont									
4910	1 gal.				Ea.	11.10			11.10	12.25
4920	2 gal.				"	24			24	26.50
5000	Hardenbergia violacea, (Happy Wanderer), Z9, cont									
5010	1 gal.				Ea.	11			11	12.10
5020	5 gal.				"	22.50			22.50	24.50
5100	Hedera helix varieties, (English Ivy), Z5, cont									
5110	3" Pot				Ea.	4			4	4.40
5120	5 gal.					30			30	33
5130	Flat/50 plants					51			51	56.50
5200	Helianthemum nummularium, (Sun-Rose), Z5, cont									
5210	1 qt.				Ea.	7			7	7.70
5220	1 gal.				"	9			9	9.90
5300	Hemerocallis hybrids, (Assorted Daylilies), Z4, cont									
5310	2 qt.				Ea.	8.90			8.90	9.80
5320	1 gal.					13.35			13.35	14.65
5330	5 gal.					20			20	22
5400	Hosta assorted, (Plantain Lily), Z4, cont									
5410	2 qt.				Ea.	16.70			16.70	18.35
5420	1 gal.					27.50			27.50	30
5430	2 gal.					40			40	44
5500	Hydrangea petiolaris, (Climbing Hydrangea), Z4, cont									
5510	1 gal.				Ea.	25			25	27.50
5520	2 gal.					40			40	44
5530	5 gal.					77			77	84.50
5600	Hypericum calycinum, (St. John's Wort), Z6, cont									
5610	1 qt.				Ea.	9.45			9.45	10.40
5620	1 gal.					40			40	44
5630	5 gal.					58			58	63.50

32 93 Plants

32 93 13 – Ground Covers

32 93 13.30 Ground Covers	Crew	Daily Output	Labor-Hours	Unit	Material	2015 Bare Costs Labor	Equipment	Total	Total Incl O&P
5700	Iberis sempervirens, (Candytuft), Z4, cont								
5710	1 qt.				Ea.	7			7	7.70
5720	1 gal.				"	9.75			9.75	10.70
5800	Jasminum nudiflorum, (Winter Jasmine), Z5, cont								
5810	1 gal.				Ea.	9.35			9.35	10.25
5820	2 gal.					26			26	28.50
5830	5 gal.				▼	18.35			18.35	20
5900	Juniperus horizontalis varieties, (Prostrate Juniper), Z2, cont								
5910	1 gal.				Ea.	24			24	26.50
5920	2 gal.					35.50			35.50	39
5930	5 gal.				▼	53.50			53.50	59
6000	Lamium maculatum, (Dead Nettle), Z6, cont								
6010	1 qt.				Ea.	7			7	7.70
6020	1 gal.					8.80			8.80	9.70
6030	Flat/24 plants				▼	60.50			60.50	66.50
6100	Lantana camara, (Common Lantana), Z8, cont								
6110	3" Pot				Ea.	9.90			9.90	10.90
6120	1 gal.				"	17.65			17.65	19.40
6200	Lantana montevidensis, (Trailing Lantana), Z10, cont								
6210	1 gal.				Ea.	17.65			17.65	19.40
6220	5 gal.				"	26.50			26.50	29
6300	Lavandula angustifolia, (English Lavender), Z5, cont								
6310	4" Pot				Ea.	4			4	4.40
6320	1 qt.					7			7	7.70
6330	1 gal.				▼	6.85			6.85	7.50
6400	Liriope spicata, (Creeping Lilyturf), Z6, cont								
6410	2 qt.				Ea.	8			8	8.80
6420	1 gal.					9			9	9.90
6430	5 gal.				▼	15.95			15.95	17.55
6500	Lonicera heckrotti, (Gold Flame Honeysuckle), Z5, cont								
6510	1 gal.				Ea.	35.50			35.50	39
6520	2 gal.				"	53			53	58
6600	Lonicera japonica "Halliana", (Halls Honeysuckle), Z4, cont								
6610	3" Pot				Ea.	11.55			11.55	12.70
6620	1 gal.					32.50			32.50	36
6630	2 gal.				▼	49.50			49.50	54.50
6700	Lysimachia nummularia aurea, (Creeping Jenny), Z3, cont								
6710	2 qt.				Ea.	8			8	8.80
6720	1 gal.				"	8.75			8.75	9.65
6800	Macfadyena unguis-cali, (Cat Claw Vine), Z8, cont								
6810	1 gal.				Ea.	7.95			7.95	8.75
6820	5 gal.				"	15			15	16.50
6900	Myoporum parvifolium, (Prostrate Myoporum), Z9, cont								
6910	1 gal.				Ea.	6.15			6.15	6.80
6920	5 gal.				"	19			19	21
7000	Nepeta, (Persian Catmint), Z5, cont								
7010	1 qt.				Ea.	20			20	22
7020	1 gal.				"	27			27	29.50
7100	Ophiupogon japonicus, (Mondo-Grass), Z7, cont								
7110	4" Pot				Ea.	4			4	4.40
7120	1 gal.					9			9	9.90
7130	5 gal.				▼	11			11	12.10
7200	Pachysandra terminalis, (Japanese Spurge), Z5, cont								

For customer support on your Site Work & Landscape Cost Data, call 877.737.1594.

399

32 93 13.30 Ground Covers		Crew	Daily Output	Labor-Hours	Unit	Material	2015 Bare Costs Labor	Equipment	Total	Total Incl O&P
7210	2-1/2" Pot				Ea.	8.20			8.20	9
7220	1 gal.					29			29	32
7230	Tray/50 plants					113			113	125
7240	Tray/100 plants				↓	196			196	216
7300	Parthenocissus quinquefolia, (Virginia Creeper), Z3, cont									
7310	3" Pot				Ea.	9.35			9.35	10.30
7320	1 gal.				"	30.50			30.50	34
7400	Parthenocissus tricuspidata veitchi, (Boston Ivy), Z4, cont									
7410	3" Pot				Ea.	8.20			8.20	9
7420	1 gal.				↓	26			26	28.50
7430	5 gal.				↓	45.50			45.50	50.50
7500	Phlox subulata, (Moss Phlox, Creeping Phlox), Z4, cont									
7510	1 qt.				Ea.	15.60			15.60	17.15
7520	1 gal.				"	26			26	28.50
7600	Polygonum auberti, (Silver Fleece Vine), Z4, cont									
7610	1 qt.				Ea.	14.30			14.30	15.75
7620	1 gal.				"	24.50			24.50	27
7700	Polygonum cuspidatum compactum, (Fleece Flower), Z4, cont									
7710	1 qt.				Ea.	14.70			14.70	16.15
7720	1 gal.				"	24.50			24.50	27
7800	Potentilla verna, (Spring Cinquefoil), Z6, cont									
7810	1 qt.				Ea.	15.80			15.80	17.40
7820	1 gal.				"	24.50			24.50	27
7900	Rosmarinus officinalis "Prostratus", (Creeping Rosemary), Z8, cont									
7910	3" Pot				Ea.	9.20			9.20	10.10
7920	1 gal.				"	28			28	31
8000	Sagina subulata, (Irish Moss, Scotch Moss), Z6, cont									
8010	3" Pot				Ea.	7.70			7.70	8.50
8020	4" Pot				↓	9.05			9.05	9.95
8030	1 qt.				↓	20.50			20.50	22.50
8100	Sedum, (Stonecrop), Z4, cont									
8110	1 qt.				Ea.	7.70			7.70	8.50
8120	1 gal.				"	14.70			14.70	16.15
8200	Solanum jasminoides, (Jasmine Nightshade), Z9, cont									
8210	1 gal.				Ea.	15.60			15.60	17.15
8220	5 gal.				"	90			90	99
8300	Stachys byzantina, (Lambs'-ears), Z4, cont									
8310	1 qt.				Ea.	19.40			19.40	21.50
8320	1 gal.				"	24			24	26.50
8400	Thymus pseudolanuginosus, (Wooly Thyme), Z5, cont									
8410	3" Pot				Ea.	7.50			7.50	8.25
8420	1 qt.					12.60			12.60	13.85
8430	1 gal.				↓	15.40			15.40	16.95
8500	Vaccinium crassifolium procumbent, (Creeping Blueberry), Z7, cont									
8510	1 gal.				Ea.	16.90			16.90	18.60
8520	3 gal.				"	45			45	49.50
8600	Verbena peruviana "St. Paul", Z8, cont									
8610	2 qt.				Ea.	7.60			7.60	8.35
8620	1 gal.				"	12.65			12.65	13.90
8700	Veronica repens, (Creeping Speedwell), Z5, cont									
8710	1 qt.				Ea.	15.40			15.40	16.95
8720	1 gal.				"	21.50			21.50	23.50
8800	Vinca major variegata, (Variegated Greater Periwinkle), Z7, cont									

32 93 Plants

32 93 13 – Ground Covers

32 93 13.30 Ground Covers

		Crew	Daily Output	Labor-Hours	Unit	Material	2015 Bare Costs Labor	Equipment	Total	Total Incl O&P
8810	2-1/4" Pot				Ea.	6.10			6.10	6.70
8820	4" Pot					11.45			11.45	12.60
8830	Bare Root				↓	1.36			1.36	1.50
8900	Vinca minor, (Periwinkle), Z4, cont									
8910	2-1/4" Pot				Ea.	5.10			5.10	5.60
8920	4" Pot					8.80			8.80	9.70
8930	Bare Root				↓	1.60			1.60	1.76
9000	Waldsteinia sibirica, (Barren Strawberry), Z4, cont									
9010	1 qt.				Ea.	11.20			11.20	12.30
9020	1 gal.				"	11.20			11.20	12.35
9100	Wisteria sinensis, (Chinese Wisteria), Z5, cont									
9110	1 gal.				Ea.	33			33	36
9120	3 gal.				"	50.50			50.50	55.50

32 93 13.40 Ornamental Grasses

		Crew	Daily Output	Labor-Hours	Unit	Material	2015 Bare Costs Labor	Equipment	Total	Total Incl O&P
0010	**ORNAMENTAL GRASSES**									
2000	Acorus gramineus, (Japanese Sweet Flag), Z7, cont									
2010	1 gal.				Ea.	7.35			7.35	8.05
2100	Arundo donax, (Giant Reed), Z7, cont									
2110	1 qt.				Ea.	7.30			7.30	8.05
2120	1 gal.				"	30.50			30.50	33.50
2200	Calamagrostis acutiflora stricta, (Feather Reed Grass), Z5, cont									
2210	1 qt.				Ea.	7.35			7.35	8.05
2220	1 gal.				↓	17.85			17.85	19.65
2230	2 gal.					23			23	25.50
2300	Carex elata "Bowles Golden", (Variegated Sedge), Z5, cont									
2310	1 qt.				Ea.	6.10			6.10	6.70
2320	1 gal.				"	12.20			12.20	13.40
2400	Carex morrowii "aureo variegata", (Japanese Sedge), Z5, cont									
2410	1 qt.				Ea.	6.10			6.10	6.70
2420	1 gal.					11			11	12.10
2430	2 gal.				↓	19.25			19.25	21
2500	Cortaderia selloana, (Pampas Grass), Z8, cont									
2510	1 gal.				Ea.	8			8	8.80
2520	2 gal.					14.65			14.65	16.10
2530	3 gal.					24.50			24.50	27
2540	5 gal.				↓	49			49	53.50
2600	Deschampsia caespitosa, (Tufted Hair Grass), Z4, cont									
2610	1 qt.				Ea.	6			6	6.60
2620	1 gal.				"	7.55			7.55	8.30
2700	Elymus glaucus, (Blue Wild Rye), Z4, cont									
2710	1 qt.				Ea.	6			6	6.60
2720	1 gal.				"	9.75			9.75	10.75
2800	Erianthus ravennae, (Ravenna Grass), Z6, cont									
2810	1 gal.				Ea.	20.50			20.50	23
2820	2 gal.				↓	23			23	25.50
2830	7 gal.					39			39	43
2900	Festuca cineria "Sea Urchin", (Sea Urchin Blue Fescue), Z6, cont									
2910	1 qt.				Ea.	6			6	6.60
2920	1 gal.					9.15			9.15	10.10
2930	2 gal.				↓	9.75			9.75	10.75
3000	Glyceria maxima variegata, (Manna Grass), Z5, cont									
3010	1 qt.				Ea.	12.80			12.80	14.10

For customer support on your Site Work & Landscape Cost Data, call 877.737.1594.

401

32 93 Plants

32 93 13 – Ground Covers

32 93 13.40 Ornamental Grasses	Crew	Daily Output	Labor-Hours	Unit	Material	2015 Bare Costs Labor	Equipment	Total	Total Incl O&P
3020	1 gal.				Ea.	18.65			18.65	20.50
3100	Hakonechloa macra aureola, (Variegated Hakonechloa), Z7, cont									
3110	1 qt.				Ea.	12.20			12.20	13.40
3120	1 gal.				"	19.50			19.50	21.50
3200	Helictotrichon sempervirens, (Blue Oat Grass), Z4, cont									
3210	1 qt.				Ea.	6			6	6.60
3220	1 gal.					5.25			5.25	5.80
3230	2 gal.				▼	14.65			14.65	16.10
3300	Imperata cylindrica rubra, (Japanese Blood Grass), Z7, cont									
3310	1 qt.				Ea.	6			6	6.60
3320	1 gal.					8			8	8.80
3330	2 gal.				▼	8.65			8.65	9.55
3400	Juncus effusus spiralis, (Corkscrew Rush), Z4, cont									
3410	1 qt.				Ea.	6			6	6.60
3420	2 gal.				"	9.75			9.75	10.75
3500	Koeleria glauca, (Blue Hair Grass), Z6, cont									
3510	1 qt.				Ea.	6			6	6.60
3520	1 gal.					8			8	8.80
3530	3 gal.				▼	19.85			19.85	22
3600	Miscanthus sinensis gracillimus, (Maiden Grass), Z6, cont									
3610	1 gal.				Ea.	7.30			7.30	8.05
3620	2 gal.					11			11	12.10
3630	5 gal.				▼	20.50			20.50	23
3700	Miscanthus sinensis zebrinus, (Zebra Grass), Z6, cont									
3710	1 gal.				Ea.	7.30			7.30	8.05
3720	2 gal.					11			11	12.10
3730	5 gal.				▼	20.50			20.50	23
3800	Molinia caerulea arundinacea, (Tall Purple Moor Grass), Z5, cont									
3810	1 gal.				Ea.	16.80			16.80	18.45
3820	3 gal.				"	27.50			27.50	30
3900	Molinia caerulea variegata, (Variegated Moor Grass), Z5, cont									
3910	1 qt.				Ea.	8.80			8.80	9.65
3920	1 gal.				"	16.80			16.80	18.45
4000	Pennisetum alopecuroides, (Fountain Grass), Z6, cont									
4010	1 qt.				Ea.	6.85			6.85	7.50
4020	1 gal.					16.60			16.60	18.25
4030	2 gal.				▼	19.50			19.50	21.50
4100	Phalaris arundinacea "Picta", (Ribbon Grass), Z4, cont									
4110	1 qt.				Ea.	6			6	6.60
4120	1 gal.					7.30			7.30	8.05
4130	2 gal.				▼	12.20			12.20	13.40
4200	Sesleria autumnalis, (Autumn Moor Grass), Z5, cont									
4210	1 qt.				Ea.	6.85			6.85	7.50
4220	1 gal.				"	11.70			11.70	12.90
4300	Spartina pectinata "Aureomarginata", (Cord Grass), Z5, cont									
4310	1 gal.				Ea.	11.70			11.70	12.90
4320	2 gal.				"	17.55			17.55	19.35
4400	Stipa gigantea, (Giant Feather Grass), Z7, cont									
4410	1 gal.				Ea.	8.80			8.80	9.65
4420	2 gal.				"	12.20			12.20	13.40

32 93 23.10 Perennials	Crew	Daily Output	Labor-Hours	Unit	Material	2015 Bare Costs Labor	Equipment	Total	Total Incl O&P
0010	**PERENNIALS**									
0100	Achillea filipendulina, (Fernleaf Yarrow), Z2, cont									
0110	1 gal.				Ea.	9			9	9.90
0120	2 gal.					11			11	12.10
0130	3 gal.				↓	13			13	14.30
0200	Agapanthus africanus, (Lily-of-the-Nile), Z9, cont									
0210	1 gal.				Ea.	9			9	9.90
0220	5 gal.				"	15			15	16.50
0300	Amsonia ciliata, (Blue Star), zone 7, container									
0310	1 qt.				Ea.	16.40			16.40	18.05
0320	1 gal.				"	26			26	29
0400	Amsonia tabernaemontana, (Willow Amsonia), Z3, cont									
0410	1 qt.				Ea.	14.20			14.20	15.60
0420	1 gal.				"	18.60			18.60	20.50
0500	Anchusa azurea, (Italian Bugloss), Z3, cont									
0510	4" Pot				Ea.	12.50			12.50	13.75
0520	1 qt.					19.70			19.70	21.50
0530	1 gal.				↓	28.50			28.50	31
0600	Anemone x hybrida, (Japanese Anemone), Z5, cont									
0610	4" Pot				Ea.	8.50			8.50	9.35
0620	1 qt.					9.80			9.80	10.80
0630	2 gal.				↓	15.80			15.80	17.40
0700	Anthemis tinctoria, (Golden Marguerite), Z3, cont									
0710	4" Pot				Ea.	4.16			4.16	4.58
0720	1 qt.					6.80			6.80	7.50
0730	1 gal.				↓	12.45			12.45	13.70
0800	Aonitum napellus, (Aconite Monkshood), Z2, cont									
0810	4" Pot				Ea.	4.82			4.82	5.30
0820	1 qt.					7.80			7.80	8.60
0830	1 gal.				↓	14.90			14.90	16.40
0900	Aquilegia species and hybrids, (Columbine), Z2, cont									
0910	2" Pot				Ea.	4.48			4.48	4.93
0920	1 qt.					7.75			7.75	8.50
0930	1 gal.				↓	9.65			9.65	10.60
1000	Aruncus dioicus, (Goatsbeard), Z4, cont									
1010	1 qt.				Ea.	9.60			9.60	10.55
1020	1 gal.					11.80			11.80	13
1030	2 gal.				↓	13.80			13.80	15.15
1100	Asclepias tuberosa, (Butterfly Flower), Z4, cont									
1110	1 gal.				Ea.	15.65			15.65	17.20
1120	2 gal.				"	23			23	25
1200	Aster species and hybrids, (Aster, Michaelemas Daisy), Z4, cont									
1210	1 gal.				Ea.	12.65			12.65	13.90
1220	2 gal.					18			18	19.80
1230	3 gal.				↓	26.50			26.50	29
1300	Astilbe species and hybrids, (False Spirea), Z4, cont									
1310	4" Pot				Ea.	5			5	5.50
1320	1 gal.					9			9	9.90
1330	2 gal.				↓	11			11	12.10
1400	Aubrieta deltoidea, (Purple Rock-cress), Z4, cont									
1410	4" Pot				Ea.	5.20			5.20	5.70
1420	1 qt.					7.40			7.40	8.15

For customer support on your Site Work & Landscape Cost Data, call 877.737.1594.

403

32 93 Plants

32 93 23 – Plants and Bulbs

32 93 23.10 Perennials	Crew	Daily Output	Labor-Hours	Unit	Material	2015 Bare Costs Labor	Equipment	Total	Total Incl O&P
1430	1 gal.				Ea.	16.85			16.85	18.50
1500	Aurinia saxatilis, (Basket of Gold), Z3, cont									
1510	4" Pot				Ea.	9.20			9.20	10.10
1520	1 qt.					18.10			18.10	19.90
1530	1 gal.				↓	22.50			22.50	24.50
1600	Baptisia australis, (False Indigo), Z3, cont									
1610	1 qt.				Ea.	7			7	7.70
1620	1 gal.				"	8.85			8.85	9.75
1700	Begonia grandis, (Evans Begonia), Z6, cont									
1710	1 qt.				Ea.	10.40			10.40	11.45
1720	1 gal.				"	22.50			22.50	25
1800	Belamcanda chinensis, (Blackberry Lily), Z5, cont									
1810	1 qt.				Ea.	10.10			10.10	11.10
1820	1 gal.				"	22			22	24
1900	Boltonia asteroides "Snowbank", (White Boltonia), Z3, cont									
1910	1 qt.				Ea.	10.40			10.40	11.45
1920	1 gal.				"	22.50			22.50	24.50
2000	Brunnera macrophylla, (Siberian Bugloss), Z3, cont									
2010	1 qt.				Ea.	7			7	7.70
2020	1 gal.				"	9			9	9.90
2100	Caltha palustris, (Marsh Marigold), Z3, cont									
2110	1 qt.				Ea.	11.30			11.30	12.45
2120	1 gal.				"	22			22	24.50
2200	Campanula carpatica "Blue Chips", (Bellflower), Z3, cont									
2210	1 gal.				Ea.	9.05			9.05	9.95
2220	2 gal.				"	11			11	12.10
2300	Ceratostigma plumbaginoides, (Blue Plumbago), Z6, cont									
2310	1 qt.				Ea.	14.40			14.40	15.85
2320	1 gal.				"	21.50			21.50	24
2400	Chrysanthemum hybrids, (Hardy Chrysanthemum), Z5, cont									
2410	1 qt.				Ea.	9.40			9.40	10.35
2420	6" to 8" Pot					14.80			14.80	16.30
2430	1 gal.				↓	14.80			14.80	16.30
2500	Chrysogonum virginianum, (Golden Star), Z6, cont									
2510	1 gal.				Ea.	13.10			13.10	14.40
2520	2 gal.				"	18.20			18.20	20
2600	Cimicifuga racemosa, (Bugbane), Z5, cont									
2610	4" Pot				Ea.	7.20			7.20	7.90
2620	1 qt.				↓	11.40			11.40	12.55
2630	1 gal.					19.80			19.80	22
2700	Coreopsis verticillata, (Threadleaf Coreopsis), Z5, cont									
2710	2" Pot				Ea.	9.60			9.60	10.55
2720	1 gal.				"	13.50			13.50	14.85
2800	Delphinium elatum and hybrids, (Delphinium), Z2, cont									
2810	1 qt.				Ea.	7			7	7.70
2820	1 gal.				↓	26			26	29
2830	2 gal.				↓	10.40			10.40	11.45
2900	Dianthus species and hybrids, (Cottage Pink/Scotch Pink), Z3, cont									
2910	1 gal.				Ea.	9			9	9.90
2920	2 gal.				"	11			11	12.10
3000	Dicentra spectabilis, (Bleeding Heart), Z3, cont									
3010	2 qt.				Ea.	12.70			12.70	13.95
3020	1 gal.				↓	13.75			13.75	15.15

32 93 23.10 Perennials		Crew	Daily Output	Labor-Hours	Unit	Material	2015 Bare Costs Labor	Equipment	Total	Total Incl O&P
3030	2 gal.				Ea.	18.30			18.30	20
3100	Dictamnus, (Gas Plant), Z3, cont									
3110	1 gal.				Ea.	23			23	25
3120	2 gal.					28.50			28.50	31
3130	3 gal.				↓	36.50			36.50	40.50
3200	Digitalis purpurea, (Foxglove), Z4, cont									
3210	1 gal.				Ea.	16.20			16.20	17.85
3220	2 gal.					47			47	52
3230	3 gal.				↓	56			56	61.50
3300	Doronicum cordatun, (Leopards Bane), Z4, cont									
3310	2 qt.				Ea.	7.90			7.90	8.65
3320	1 gal.				"	12.20			12.20	13.45
3400	Echinacea purpurea, (Purple Coneflower), Z3, cont									
3410	2 qt.				Ea.	10.45			10.45	11.50
3420	1 gal.					13.90			13.90	15.30
3430	2 gal.				↓	15.05			15.05	16.60
3500	Echinops exaltatus, (Globe Thistle), Z3, cont									
3510	1 qt.				Ea.	7.40			7.40	8.15
3520	1 gal.				"	13.60			13.60	14.95
3600	Erigeron speciosus, (Oregon Fleabane), Z3, cont									
3610	1 qt.				Ea.	7.20			7.20	7.95
3620	1 gal.				"	13.40			13.40	14.75
3700	Euphorbia epithymoides, (Cushion Spurge), Z4, cont									
3710	1 qt.				Ea.	7			7	7.70
3720	1 gal.				"	9			9	9.90
3800	Filipendula hexapetala, (Meadowsweet), Z5, cont									
3810	1 qt.				Ea.	7			7	7.70
3820	1 gal.				"	9			9	9.90
3900	Gaillardia aristata, (Blanket Flower), Z2, cont									
3910	1 qt.				Ea.	7			7	7.70
3920	1 gal.					9.20			9.20	10.10
3930	2 gal.				↓	10.60			10.60	11.65
4000	Geranium sanguineum, (Bloodred Geranium), Z3, cont									
4010	2" Pot				Ea.	4.23			4.23	4.65
4020	1 gal.				"	9			9	9.90
4100	Geum x borisii, (Boris Avens), Z3, cont									
4110	1 qt.				Ea.	7			7	7.70
4120	1 gal.				"	9.15			9.15	10.05
4200	Gypsophila paniculata, (Baby's Breath), Z3, cont									
4210	2 qt.				Ea.	8			8	8.80
4220	1 gal.					9			9	9.90
4230	3 gal.				↓	32.50			32.50	36
4300	Helenium autumnale, (Sneezeweed), Z3, cont									
4310	2 qt.				Ea.	8			8	8.80
4320	1 gal.					9.40			9.40	10.35
4330	2 gal.				↓	13.40			13.40	14.75
4400	Helianthus salicifolius, (Willow Leaf Sunflower), Z5, cont									
4410	1 qt.				Ea.	6.30			6.30	6.95
4420	1 gal.					11.45			11.45	12.60
4430	2 gal.				↓	17.80			17.80	19.60
4500	Heliopsis helianthoides, (False Sunflower), Z3, cont									
4510	2 qt.				Ea.	8			8	8.80
4520	1 gal.				↓	8.80			8.80	9.70

32 93 23.10 Perennials	Crew	Daily Output	Labor-Hours	Unit	Material	2015 Bare Costs Labor	Equipment	Total	Total Incl O&P
4530	2 gal.				Ea.	11.35			11.35	12.45
4600	Helleborus niger, (Christmas Rose), Z3, cont									
4610	2 qt.				Ea.	9.40			9.40	10.35
4620	1 gal.				"	18.10			18.10	19.90
4700	Hemerocallis hybrids (Diploid), (Day Lilly), Z3, cont									
4710	1 qt.				Ea.	7			7	7.70
4720	1 gal.					9			9	9.90
4730	3 gal.				↓	16.50			16.50	18.15
4800	Hemerocallis hybrids (Tetraploid), Z3, cont									
4810	1 qt.				Ea.	7			7	7.70
4820	1 gal.					11.20			11.20	12.35
4830	3 gal.				↓	18.45			18.45	20.50
4900	Hibiscus moscheutos, (Rose Mallow), Z5, cont									
4910	1 qt.				Ea.	7			7	7.70
4920	2 gal.					36			36	39.50
4930	3 gal.				↓	42			42	46
5000	Hosta species and hybrids, (Plantain Lily), Z3, cont									
5010	1 gal.				Ea.	9			9	9.90
5020	2 gal.					11			11	12.10
5030	3 gal.				↓	16.80			16.80	18.50
5100	Iris hybrids, (Pacific Coast Iris), Z6, cont									
5110	1 gal.				Ea.	9			9	9.90
5120	3 gal.				"	13			13	14.30
5200	Iris sibiricu and hybrids, (Siberian Iris), Z3, cont									
5210	1 gal.				Ea.	8.45			8.45	9.30
5220	4 gal.					15.60			15.60	17.15
5230	3" Pot				↓	4.45			4.45	4.90
5300	Kniphofia uvaria and hybrids, (Torch Lily), Z7, cont									
5310	1 qt.				Ea.	7			7	7.70
5320	1 gal.				"	9			9	9.90
5400	Liatris spicata, (Blazing Star, Gayfeather), Z3, cont									
5410	1 gal.				Ea.	9			9	9.90
5420	2 gal.				"	12.80			12.80	14.10
5500	Ligularia dentata, (Golden Groundsel), Z5, cont									
5510	2 qt.				Ea.	8.40			8.40	9.25
5520	2 gal.				"	11			11	12.10
5600	Linum perenne, (Perennial Flax), Z4, cont									
5610	1 qt.				Ea.	7			7	7.70
5620	1 gal.				"	9			9	9.90
5700	Lobelia cardinalis, (Cardinal Flower), Z3, cont									
5710	1 qt.				Ea.	7			7	7.70
5720	1 gal.				"	9			9	9.90
5800	Lupinus "Rusell Hybrids", (Russell Lupines), Z3, cont									
5810	1 gal.				Ea.	9			9	9.90
5820	2 gal.					11			11	12.10
5830	3 gal.				↓	13			13	14.30
5900	Lychnis chalcedonica, (Maltese Cross), Z3, cont									
5910	1 qt.				Ea.	7			7	7.70
5920	1 gal.				"	9			9	9.90
6000	Lysimachia clethroides, (Gooseneck Loosestrife), Z3, cont									
6010	1 qt.				Ea.	7			7	7.70
6020	1 gal.				"	9			9	9.90
6100	Lythrum salicaria, (Purple Loosestrife), Z3, cont									

32 93 23.10 Perennials		Crew	Daily Output	Labor-Hours	Unit	Material	2015 Bare Costs Labor	Equipment	Total	Total Incl O&P
6110	1 qt.				Ea.	7			7	7.70
6120	1 gal.				"	8.30			8.30	9.15
6200	Macleaya cordata, (Plume Poppy), Z3, cont									
6210	1 qt.				Ea.	7			7	7.70
6220	1 gal.				"	8.20			8.20	9
6300	Mertensia virginica, (Virginia Bluebells), Z3, cont									
6310	1 qt.				Ea.	6.10			6.10	6.70
6320	1 gal.				"	9.20			9.20	10.10
6400	Paeonia hybrids, (Herbaceous Peony), Z5, cont									
6410	1 gal.				Ea.	11.15			11.15	12.25
6420	2 gal.					13.40			13.40	14.75
6430	3 gal.					71			71	78.50
6500	Papaver orientalis, (Oriental Poppy), Z3, cont									
6510	1 qt.				Ea.	7			7	7.70
6520	1 gal.				"	8.70			8.70	9.55
6600	Penstemon azureus, (Azure Penstemon), Z8, cont									
6610	2" Pot				Ea.	4.10			4.10	4.51
6620	1 gal.				"	8.85			8.85	9.75
6700	Phlox paniculata, (Garden Phlox), Z4, cont									
6710	1 qt.				Ea.	8.30			8.30	9.15
6720	1 gal.				"	14.70			14.70	16.15
6800	Physostegia virginiana, (False Dragonhead), Z3, cont									
6810	4" Pot				Ea.	4.20			4.20	4.62
6820	1 gal.				"	8.90			8.90	9.80
6900	Platycodon grandiflorus, (Balloon Flower), Z3, cont									
6910	2" Pot				Ea.	4.10			4.10	4.51
6920	1 gal.				"	9.40			9.40	10.35
7000	Pulmonaria saccharata, (Bethlehem Sage), Z4, cont									
7010	4" Pot				Ea.	5			5	5.50
7020	1 qt.					7			7	7.70
7030	1 gal.					9.45			9.45	10.35
7100	Rudbeckia fulgida "Goldstrum", (Black-eyed Susan), Z4, cont									
7110	1 qt.				Ea.	7			7	7.70
7120	1 gal.					9			9	9.90
7130	2 gal.					11			11	12.10
7200	Salvia x superba, (Perennial Salvia), Z5, cont									
7210	4" Pot				Ea.	5			5	5.50
7220	1 qt.					8.10			8.10	8.95
7230	1 gal.					9			9	9.90
7300	Scabiosa caucasica, (Pincushion Flower), Z3, cont									
7310	1 qt.				Ea.	7			7	7.70
7320	1 gal.				"	9			9	9.90
7400	Sedum spectabile, (Showy Sedum), Z3, cont									
7410	4" Pot				Ea.	4.90			4.90	5.40
7420	2" Pot					4.73			4.73	5.20
7430	1 gal.					9.15			9.15	10.05
7500	Solidago hybrids, (Goldenrod), Z3, cont									
7510	1 qt.				Ea.	7			7	7.70
7520	1 gal.				"	9			9	9.90
7700	Trollius europaeus, (Common Globeflower), Z4, cont									
7710	1 qt.				Ea.	7			7	7.70
7720	1 gal.				"	12.10			12.10	13.30
7800	Veronica hybrids, (Speedwell), Z4, cont									

32 93 23 – Plants and Bulbs

32 93 23.10 Perennials		Crew	Daily Output	Labor-Hours	Unit	Material	2015 Bare Costs Labor	Equipment	Total	Total Incl O&P
7810	1 gal.				Ea.	10.95			10.95	12.05
7820	2 gal.				"	13.10			13.10	14.40

32 93 33 – Shrubs

32 93 33.40 Shrubs

		Crew	Daily Output	Labor-Hours	Unit	Material	Labor	Equipment	Total	Total Incl O&P
0010	**SHRUBS**, Temperate zones 2 – 6									
1000	Abelia grandiflora, (Abelia), Z6, cont									
1002	15" to 18"				Ea.	30			30	33
1003	18" to 21"				"	47.50			47.50	52.50
1050	Acanthopanax sieboldianus, (Five-Leaved Azalia), Z5, cont/B&B									
1051	15" to 18"				Ea.	31.50			31.50	34.50
1052	3' to 4'					32			32	35
1053	4' to 5'					32			32	35
1100	Aronia arbutifolia brilliantissima, (Brilliant Chokeberry), Z5, B&B									
1101	2' to 3'				Ea.	26.50			26.50	29.50
1102	3' to 4'					37.50			37.50	41
1103	4' to 5'					42.50			42.50	47
1104	5' to 6'					53.50			53.50	58.50
1150	Aronia melancarpa "Elata", (Elata Black Chokeberry), Z3, B&B									
1151	2' to 3'				Ea.	14.95			14.95	16.45
1152	3' to 4'				"	17.60			17.60	19.35
1200	Azalea arborescens, (Sweet Azalia), Z5, cont									
1201	15" to 18"				Ea.	16.65			16.65	18.30
1202	18" to 24"				"	37			37	41
1250	Azalea Evergreen Hybrids, (Azalea Evergreen), Z6, cont/B&B									
1251	1 gal.				Ea.	6.75			6.75	7.40
1252	2 gal.					10.20			10.20	11.25
1253	3 gal.					15.10			15.10	16.60
1254	5 gal.					20			20	22.50
1255	15" to 18"					15.10			15.10	16.60
1256	18" to 24"					20			20	22.50
1257	2' to 2-1/2'					42			42	46.50
1258	2-1/2' to 3'					50.50			50.50	55.50
1300	Azalea exbury, Ilam Hybrids, (Azalea exbury), Z5, cont/B&B									
1301	1 gal.				Ea.	6.75			6.75	7.40
1302	2 gal.					10.20			10.20	11.25
1303	15" to 18"					15.10			15.10	16.60
1304	18" to 24"					20			20	22.50
1305	2' to 2-1/2'					42			42	46.50
1306	2-1/2' to 3'					50.50			50.50	55.50
1307	4' to 5'					72			72	79
1350	Azalea gandavensis, (Ghent Azalea), Z4, B&B									
1351	15" to 18"				Ea.	26.50			26.50	29.50
1352	18" to 24"					33.50			33.50	37
1353	2' to 3'					38			38	42
1354	3' to 4'					46.50			46.50	51
1355	4' to 5'					63			63	69.50
1356	5' to 6'					80			80	88
1400	Azalea kaempferi, (Torch Azalea), Z6, cont/B&B									
1401	12" to 15"				Ea.	10.20			10.20	11.25
1402	15" to 18"					15.10			15.10	16.60
1403	18" to 24"					20			20	22.50
1404	2' to 3'					38			38	41.50

32 93 Plants

32 93 33 – Shrubs

32 93 33.40 Shrubs		Crew	Daily Output	Labor-Hours	Unit	Material	2015 Bare Costs Labor	Equipment	Total	Total Incl O&P
1450	Berberis julianae "Nana", (Dwarf Wintergreen Barberry), Z6, B&B									
1451	18" to 24"				Ea.	20.50			20.50	23
1452	2' to 2-1/2'					23			23	25.50
1453	2-1/2' to 3'				↓	28			28	30.50
1500	Berberis mentorensis, (Mentor Barberry), Z6, cont/B&B									
1501	1 gal.				Ea.	8.20			8.20	9
1502	5 gal.					15.95			15.95	17.55
1503	2' to 3'					22.50			22.50	24.50
1504	3' to 4'				↓	25.50			25.50	28
1550	Berberis thumbergii (Crimson Pygmy Barberry), Z5, cont									
1551	10" to 12".				Ea.	8.20			8.20	9.05
1552	12" to 15"					13.60			13.60	14.95
1553	15" to 18"				↓	19.95			19.95	22
1600	Berberis thunbergi, (Japanese Green Barberry), Z5, cont/B&B									
1601	9" to 12"				Ea.	4			4	4.40
1602	12" to 15"					12.65			12.65	13.95
1603	15" to 18"					15.30			15.30	16.85
1604	18" to 24"					23			23	25.50
1605	2' to 3'				↓	29			29	31.50
1650	Berberis verruculosa, (Barberry), Z5, cont/B&B									
1651	15" to 18"				Ea.	19.55			19.55	21.50
1652	18" to 24"				"	28			28	31
1700	Buddleia davidii, (Orange-Eye Butterfly Bush), Z5, cont									
1701	9" to 12"				Ea.	11.75			11.75	12.95
1702	15" to 18"				"	17			17	18.70
1750	Buxus microphylla japonica, (Japanese Boxwood), Z5, cont/B&B									
1751	1 gal.				Ea.	4.80			4.80	5.30
1752	8" to 10"					9.55			9.55	10.50
1753	12" to 15"					12.60			12.60	13.85
1754	15" to 18"					37.50			37.50	41
1755	18" to 24"					49			49	53.50
1756	24" to 30"					71			71	78
1757	30" to 36"				↓	78			78	86
1800	Buxus sempervirens, (Common Boxwood), Z5, cont/B&B									
1801	10" to 12"				Ea.	9.60			9.60	10.55
1802	15" to 18"					20.50			20.50	22.50
1803	18" to 24"					40			40	44
1804	24" to 30"				↓	51.50			51.50	57
1850	Callicarpa japonica, (Japanese Beautyberry), Z6, B&B									
1851	2' to 3'				Ea.	19.55			19.55	21.50
1852	3' to 4'					24			24	26.50
1853	4' to 5'				↓	31			31	34
1900	Caragana arborescens, (Siberian Peashrub), Z2, B&B									
1901	18" to 24"				Ea.	14.50			14.50	15.95
1902	2' to 3'					25.50			25.50	28
1903	5' to 6'					54.50			54.50	60
1904	6' to 8'				↓	81.50			81.50	89.50
1950	Caragana arborescens, (Walkers Weeping Peashrub), Z3, B&B									
1951	1-1/2" to 1-3/4" Cal.				Ea.	127			127	140
1952	1-3/4" to 2" Cal.				"	140			140	154
2000	Caryopteris x clandonensis, (Bluebeard), Z5, cont									
2001	12" to 15"				Ea.	11.70			11.70	12.90
2002	1 gal.				↓	19.55			19.55	21.50

For customer support on your Site Work & Landscape Cost Data, call 877.737.1594.

409

32 93 33.40 Shrubs		Crew	Daily Output	Labor-Hours	Unit	Material	2015 Bare Costs Labor	Equipment	Total	Total Incl O&P
2003	18" to 24"				Ea.	29.50			29.50	32
2050	Chaenomeles speciosa, (Flowering Quince), Z5, cont/B&B									
2051	10" to 12"				Ea.	12.30			12.30	13.55
2052	2' to 3'					16.70			16.70	18.40
2053	3' to 4'				▼	22			22	24
2100	Clethra alnifolia rosea, (Pink Summersweet), Z4, B&B									
2101	2' to 3'				Ea.	23.50			23.50	25.50
2102	3' to 4'					28			28	31
2103	4' to 5'				▼	32.50			32.50	36
2150	Cornus alba siberica, (Siberian Dogwood), Z3, B&B									
2151	3' to 4'				Ea.	24			24	26.50
2152	4' to 5'					34			34	37.50
2153	5' to 6'					52			52	57.50
2154	6' to 7'				▼	54			54	59.50
2200	Cornus alternifolia, (Alternate Leaved Dogwood), Z3, B&B									
2201	4' to 5'				Ea.	70			70	77
2202	5' to 6'					84.50			84.50	92.50
2203	6' to 8'				▼	130			130	144
2250	Cornus mas, (Cornelian Cherry), Z5, B&B									
2251	2' to 3'				Ea.	63.50			63.50	69.50
2252	3' to 4'					81			81	89
2253	4' to 5'					92.50			92.50	102
2254	5' to 6'				▼	101			101	111
2300	Cornus racemosa, (Gray Dogwood), Z4, B&B									
2301	18" to 24"				Ea.	26.50			26.50	29.50
2302	2' to 3'					35.50			35.50	39
2303	3' to 4'				▼	44.50			44.50	49
2350	Cornus stolonifera flaviramea, (Goldentwig Dogwood), Z3, cont/B&B									
2351	2' to 3'				Ea.	26.50			26.50	29.50
2352	3' to 4'					35.50			35.50	39
2353	4' to 5'					44.50			44.50	49
2354	5' to 6'					53.50			53.50	58.50
2355	6' to 7'				▼	62			62	68.50
2400	Corylus americana, (Filbert, American Hazelnut), Z4, B&B									
2401	2-1/2' to 3'				Ea.	14.65			14.65	16.10
2402	3' to 4'					25.50			25.50	28
2403	4' to 5'				▼	48			48	52.50
2450	Cotinus coggygria, (Smoke Tree), Z5, B&B									
2451	5 gal.				Ea.	41			41	45
2452	6' to 8'					59.50			59.50	65.50
2453	8' to 10'				▼	96			96	105
2500	Cotoneaster acutifolius, (Peking Cotoneaster), Z4, B&B									
2501	2' to 3'				Ea.	11.40			11.40	12.55
2502	3' to 4'					20.50			20.50	22.50
2503	4' to 5'				▼	22.50			22.50	24.50
2550	Cotoneaster adpressa, (Creeping Cotoneaster), Z5, cont									
2551	15" to 18" Spread				Ea.	12.75			12.75	14
2600	Cotoneaster adpressa praecox, (Early Cotoneaster), Z5, cont									
2601	12" to 15"				Ea.	18.75			18.75	20.50
2602	15" to 18"					28			28	31
2603	18" to 24"				▼	22.50			22.50	25
2650	Cotoneaster divaricatus, (Spreading Cotoneaster), Z5, cont/B&B									
2651	1 gal.				Ea.	22.50			22.50	25

32 93 33.40 Shrubs	Crew	Daily Output	Labor-Hours	Unit	Material	2015 Bare Costs Labor	Equipment	Total	Total Incl O&P
2652	2 gal.				Ea.	26.50			26.50	29
2653	2' to 3'					22.50			22.50	25
2654	3' to 4'					27			27	29.50
2655	4' to 5'				↓	33			33	36.50
2700	Cotoneaster horizontalis, (Rock Cotoneaster), Z5, cont									
2701	12" to 15"				Ea.	11.30			11.30	12.40
2702	15" to 18"					29.50			29.50	32.50
2703	18" to 21"				↓	32			32	35
2750	Cytisus praecox, (Warminster Broom), Z6, cont									
2751	1 gal.				Ea.	5.15			5.15	5.70
2752	2 gal.					10.35			10.35	11.40
2753	5 gal.				↓	20.50			20.50	23
2800	Daphne burkwoodi somerset, (Burkwood Daphne), Z6, cont									
2801	15" to 18"				Ea.	23.50			23.50	26
2802	18" to 24"				"	32			32	35
2850	Deutzia gracilis, (Slender Deutzia), Z5, cont									
2851	1 gal.				Ea.	9.70			9.70	10.65
2852	2 gal.				"	12.30			12.30	13.55
2900	Diervilla sessilifolia, (Southern Bush Honeysuckle), Z5, B&B									
2901	18" to 24"				Ea.	26			26	28.50
2902	2' to 3'					27			27	30
2903	3' to 4'				↓	40.50			40.50	45
2950	Elaeagnus angustifolia, (Russian Olive), Z3, B&B									
2951	5 gal.				Ea.	25.50			25.50	28
3000	Elaeagnus umbellata, (Autumn Olive), Z3, B&B									
3001	3' to 4'				Ea.	44			44	48.50
3002	4' to 5'					91.50			91.50	101
3003	5' to 6'				↓	137			137	151
3050	Enkianthus campanulatus, (Bellflowertree), Z5, cont/B&B									
3051	2' to 3'				Ea.	41.50			41.50	45.50
3052	3' to 4'					52			52	57
3053	4' to 5'					56.50			56.50	62
3054	5' to 6'				↓	68			68	74.50
3100	Euonymus alatus, (Winged Burning Bush), Z4, B&B									
3101	18" to 24"				Ea.	20.50			20.50	22.50
3102	2' to 2-1/2'					25			25	27.50
3103	2-1/2' to 3'					40			40	44
3104	3' to 3-1/2'					48			48	52.50
3105	3-1/2' to 4'					58.50			58.50	64.50
3106	4' to 5'					64			64	70.50
3107	5' to 6'					69			69	76
3108	6' to 8'				↓	74.50			74.50	82
3150	Euonymus alatus compacta, (Dwarf Winged Burning Bush), Z4, B&B									
3151	15" to 18"				Ea.	23			23	25
3152	18" to 24"					26.50			26.50	29.50
3153	2' to 2-1/2'					31.50			31.50	34.50
3154	2-1/2' to 3'					44			44	48.50
3155	3' to 3-1/2'					41			41	45.50
3156	3-1/2' to 4'					51.50			51.50	56.50
3157	4' to 5'					67			67	73.50
3158	5' to 6'				↓	69			69	76
3200	Euonymus europaeus aldenhamensis, (Spindletree), Z4, B&B									
3201	3' to 4'				Ea.	17.45			17.45	19.20

32 93 33.40 Shrubs		Crew	Daily Output	Labor-Hours	Unit	Material	2015 Bare Costs Labor	Equipment	Total	Total Incl O&P
3202	4' to 5'				Ea.	21.50			21.50	24
3203	5' to 6'					35			35	38.50
3204	6' to 8'				↓	55.50			55.50	61
3250	Euonymus fortunei, (Wintercreeper), Z5, cont/B&B									
3251	1 gal.				Ea.	9.40			9.40	10.35
3252	2 gal.					15.10			15.10	16.60
3253	5 gal.					24.50			24.50	27
3254	24" to 30"				↓	23			23	25.50
3300	Euonymus fortunei "Emerald 'n Gold", (Wintercreeper), Z5, cont									
3301	10" to 12"				Ea.	6.70			6.70	7.35
3302	12" to 15"					10.25			10.25	11.30
3303	15" to 18"					21			21	23
3304	5 gal.				↓	21			21	23
3350	Euonymus fortunei emerald gaiety, (Gaiety Wintercreeper), Z5, cont									
3351	10" to 12"				Ea.	9			9	9.90
3352	12" to 15"					13.50			13.50	14.85
3353	15" to 18"					13.95			13.95	15.35
3354	18" to 21"				↓	21			21	23
3400	Forsythia intermedia, (Border Goldenbells), Z5, cont/B&B									
3401	5 gal.				Ea.	14.95			14.95	16.45
3402	2' to 3'					14.30			14.30	15.70
3403	3' to 4'					17.10			17.10	18.80
3404	4' to 5'					33.50			33.50	37
3405	5' to 6'					46.50			46.50	51
3406	6' to 8'				↓	51.50			51.50	56.50
3450	Forsythia ovata robusta, (Korean Forsythia), Z5, B&B									
3451	2' to 3'				Ea.	20			20	22
3452	3' to 4'					21.50			21.50	23.50
3453	4' to 5'				↓	27.50			27.50	30
3500	Hamamelis vernalis, (Vernal Witch-Hazel), Z4, B&B									
3501	2' to 3'				Ea.	39			39	43
3502	3' to 4'				↓	48.50			48.50	53
3503	4' to 5'				↓	66			66	72.50
3550	Hibiscus syriacus, (Rose of Sharon), Z6, cont/B&B									
3551	18" to 24"				Ea.	17.60			17.60	19.35
3552	2' to 3'					19.35			19.35	21.50
3553	3' to 4'					22			22	24
3554	4' to 5'					41			41	45
3555	5' to 6'				↓	52.50			52.50	58
3600	Hydrangea arborescens, (Smooth Hydrangea), Z4, cont									
3601	15" to 18"				Ea.	22.50			22.50	25
3602	18" to 24"				"	19.55			19.55	21.50
3650	Hydrangea macrophylla nikko blue, (Blue Hydrangea), Z6, cont									
3651	18" to 24"				Ea.	18.30			18.30	20
3652	24" to 30"				"	54.50			54.50	60
3700	Hydrangea paniculata grandiflora, (Peegee Hydrangea), Z5, B&B									
3701	2' to 3'				Ea.	24.50			24.50	27
3702	3' to 4'				"	45			45	49.50
3750	Hydrangea quercifolia, (Oakleaf Hydrangea), Z6, cont									
3751	18" to 24"				Ea.	24.50			24.50	27
3800	Hypericum hidcote, (St. John's Wort), Z6, cont									
3801	12" to 15"				Ea.	24.50			24.50	26.50
3850	Ilex cornuta "Carissa", (Carissa Holly), Z7, cont									

32 93 33 — Shrubs

32 93 33.40 Shrubs		Crew	Daily Output	Labor-Hours	Unit	Material	2015 Bare Costs Labor	Equipment	Total	Total Incl O&P
3851	1 gal.				Ea.	21.50			21.50	24
3852	2 gal.					27			27	30
3853	5 gal.				↓	45.50			45.50	50
3900	Ilex cornuta rotunda, (Dwarf Chinese Holly), Z6, cont									
3901	1 gal.				Ea.	21			21	23
3902	2 gal.					31.50			31.50	35
3903	5 gal.				↓	40.50			40.50	45
3950	Ilex crenata "Helleri", (Hellers Japanese Holly), Z6, cont									
3951	24" to 30"				Ea.	21.50			21.50	23.50
3952	30" to 36"					36			36	40
3953	3' to 4'				↓	44.50			44.50	49
4000	Ilex crenata "Hetzi", (Hetzi Japanese Holly), Z6, cont/B&B									
4001	2 gal.				Ea.	19			19	21
4002	3 gal.					27			27	30
4003	2' to 3'					68			68	74.50
4004	3' to 4'				↓	93			93	102
4050	Ilex glabra compacta, (Compact Inkberry), Z4, B&B									
4051	15" to 18"				Ea.	22			22	24
4052	18" to 24"					30			30	33
4053	2' to 2-1/2'				↓	41			41	45
4100	Ilex meserve blue holly hybrids, (Blue Holly), Z5, cont/B&B									
4101	15" to 18"				Ea.	19.30			19.30	21.50
4102	18" to 24"					21			21	23
4103	24" to 30"					39			39	43
4104	2-1/2' to 3'					48			48	52.50
4105	3-1/2' to 4'					55.50			55.50	61.50
4106	4' to 5'					84.50			84.50	93
4107	5' to 6'				↓	130			130	143
4150	Ilex opaca, (American Holly), Z6, B&B									
4151	2' to 3'				Ea.	32.50			32.50	36
4152	3' to 4'					58.50			58.50	64.50
4153	4' to 5'					74			74	81.50
4154	5' to 6'					141			141	155
4155	6' to 7'					215			215	236
4156	7' to 8'					275			275	305
4157	8' to 10'					375			375	415
4158	10' to 12'					730			730	800
4159	12' to 14'				↓	765			765	840
4200	Ilex verticillata female, (Winterberry), Z4, B&B									
4201	2' to 3'				Ea.	27			27	29.50
4202	3' to 4'				"	37.50			37.50	41
4250	Ilex verticillata male, (Winterberry), Z4, B&B									
4251	2' to 3'				Ea.	33.50			33.50	36.50
4252	3' to 4'					37.50			37.50	41
4253	4' to 5'				↓	53			53	58.50
4300	Ilex x attenuata "Fosteri", (Foster Holly), Z6, B&B									
4301	4' to 5'				Ea.	140			140	154
4302	5' to 6'					186			186	205
4303	6' to 7'					263			263	289
4304	7' to 8'				↓	375			375	410
4350	Itea virginica, (Virginia Sweetspire), Z6, B&B									
4351	21" to 30"				Ea.	26.50			26.50	29
4400	Kalmia latifolia, (Mountain Laurel), Z5, cont/B&B									

32 93 Plants

32 93 33 – Shrubs

32 93 33.40 Shrubs	Crew	Daily Output	Labor-Hours	Unit	Material	2015 Bare Costs Labor	Equipment	Total	Total Incl O&P
4401	15" to 18"				Ea.	44.50			44.50	49
4402	18" to 24"					62			62	68.50
4403	2' to 3'					80			80	88
4404	4' to 5'					130			130	143
4405	5' to 6'					176			176	193
4406	6' to 8'					195			195	215
4450	Kerria japonica, (Kerria), Z6, cont									
4451	12" to 15"				Ea.	16			16	17.60
4452	5 gal.				"	27			27	30
4500	Kolkwitzia amabilis, (Beautybush), Z5, cont/B&B									
4501	2 gal.				Ea.	17.20			17.20	18.90
4502	15" to 18"					21.50			21.50	23.50
4503	2' to 3'					26.50			26.50	29.50
4504	3' to 4'					35.50			35.50	39
4505	4' to 5'					44			44	48.50
4506	5' to 6'					70			70	77
4507	6' to 8'					78.50			78.50	86
4550	Leucothoe axillaris, (Coast Leucothoe), Z6, cont									
4551	15" to 18"				Ea.	15.50			15.50	17.05
4552	18" to 24"					21.50			21.50	23.50
4553	3 gal.					35.50			35.50	39
4600	Leucothoe fontanesiana, (Drooping Leucothoe), Z6, cont/B&B									
4601	2 gal.				Ea.	23			23	25.50
4602	12" to 15"				"	23			23	25.50
4650	Ligistrum obtusifolium regelianum, (Regal Privet), Z4, cont/B&B									
4651	18" to 24"				Ea.	23			23	25.50
4652	2' to 3'					14.95			14.95	16.45
4653	Bare root, 18" to 24"					8			8	8.80
4654	2' to 2-1/2'					9.30			9.30	10.25
4700	Ligustrum amurense, (Amur Privet), Z4, Bare Root									
4701	2' to 3'				Ea.	10.65			10.65	11.70
4702	3' to 4'				"	14.20			14.20	15.60
4750	Lindera benzoin, (Spicebush), Z5, cont/B&B									
4751	18" to 24"				Ea.	21			21	23
4752	24" to 30"				"	36.50			36.50	40
4800	Lonicera fragrantissima, (Winter Honeysuckle), Z6, cont/B&B									
4801	2' to 3'				Ea.	29.50			29.50	32.50
4802	3' to 4'				"	38.50			38.50	42
4850	Lonicera xylosteum, (Emerald Mound Honeysuckle), Z4, cont									
4851	15" to 18"				Ea.	22.50			22.50	24.50
4852	3 gal.					27			27	30
4853	5 gal.					38.50			38.50	42
4900	Mahonia aquifolium, (Oregon Grape Holly), Z6, cont/B&B									
4901	1 gal.				Ea.	5.15			5.15	5.65
4902	2 gal.					14.95			14.95	16.45
4903	5 gal.					16.80			16.80	18.45
4950	Myrica pensylvanica, (Northern Bayberry), Z2, B&B									
4951	15" to 18"				Ea.	19.10			19.10	21
4952	2' to 2-1/2'					28			28	31
4953	2-1/2' to 3'					42			42	46.50
5000	Osmanthus heterophyllus "Gulftide", (Gulftide Sweet Holly), Z6, B&B									
5001	18" to 24"				Ea.	19.55			19.55	21.50
5002	2' to 2-1/2'					40			40	44

32 93 33.40 Shrubs		Crew	Daily Output	Labor-Hours	Unit	Material	2015 Bare Costs Labor	Equipment	Total	Total Incl O&P
5003	2-1/2' to 3'				Ea.	45.50			45.50	50.50
5004	3' to 3-1/2'				↓	47.50			47.50	52.50
5050	Paxistima canbyi, (Canby Paxistima), Z5, B&B									
5051	6" to 9"				Ea.	8.15			8.15	9
5052	9" to 12"					10.95			10.95	12.05
5053	12" to 15"				↓	13.90			13.90	15.30
5100	Philadelphus coronarius, (Sweet Mockorange), Z5, cont/B&B									
5101	2' to 3'				Ea.	26.50			26.50	29.50
5102	3' to 4'					44.50			44.50	49
5103	4' to 5'					71			71	78
5104	5' to 6'				↓	97.50			97.50	107
5150	Philadelphus virginalis, (Hybrid Mockorange), Z6, cont/B&B									
5151	18" to 24"				Ea.	17.50			17.50	19.25
5152	2' to 3'					26.50			26.50	29.50
5153	3' to 4'					44.50			44.50	49
5154	4' to 5'				↓	71			71	78
5200	Physocarpus opulifolius luteus, (Golden Ninebark), Z3, cont/B&B									
5201	5 gal.				Ea.	17.60			17.60	19.35
5202	3' to 4'					19.35			19.35	21.50
5203	4' to 5'				↓	23			23	25
5250	Pieris floribunda, (Mountain Andromeda), Z5, cont									
5251	12" to 15" spread				Ea.	14.40			14.40	15.85
5252	15" to 18" spread				"	26			26	28.50
5300	Pieris japonica, (Japanese Andromeda), Z6, cont/B&B									
5301	9" to 12""				Ea.	12.60			12.60	13.90
5302	12" to 15"					29.50			29.50	32.50
5303	18" to 24"					49			49	53.50
5304	24" to 30"					52.50			52.50	58
5305	2-1/2' to 3'				↓	69			69	76
5350	Potentilla fruticosa, (Shrubby Cinquefoil), Z2, cont/B&B									
5351	1 gal.				Ea.	10.85			10.85	11.90
5352	10" to 12"					12.60			12.60	13.85
5353	12" to 15"					5.30			5.30	5.85
5354	15" to 18"					14.70			14.70	16.15
5355	18" to 24"					17			17	18.70
5356	2' to 3'				↓	43			43	47.50
5400	Prunus cistena, (Purple-Leaf Sand Cherry), Z3, cont/B&B									
5401	5 gal.				Ea.	12.30			12.30	13.55
5402	18" to 24"					15.85			15.85	17.40
5403	2' to 3'					17.60			17.60	19.35
5404	3' to 4'					24			24	26.50
5405	4' to 5'					30			30	33
5406	5' to 6'				↓	71			71	78
5450	Prunus glandulosa albo plena, (Flowering Almond), Z6, cont/B&B									
5451	15" to 18"				Ea.	29.50			29.50	32.50
5452	18" to 24"					45.50			45.50	50
5453	2' to 3'					51.50			51.50	56.50
5454	3' to 4'				↓	79			79	87
5500	Prunus glandulosa sinensis, (Pink Flowering Almond), Z6, cont/B&B									
5501	5 gal.				Ea.	23			23	25.50
5502	18" to 24"					29			29	32
5503	2' to 3'				↓	24			24	26.50
5550	Prunus laurocerasus 'Schiphaewsis, (Cherry Laurel), Z5, B&B									

32 93 33.40 Shrubs	Crew	Daily Output	Labor-Hours	Unit	Material	2015 Bare Costs Labor	Equipment	Total	Total Incl O&P
5551	5 gal.				Ea.	18.65			18.65	20.50
5552	18" to 24"					29			29	32
5553	24" to 30"				↓	54			54	59
5600	Prunus maritima, (Beach Plum), Z4, cont/B&B									
5601	1 gal.				Ea.	21			21	23
5602	18" to 24"					49.50			49.50	54.50
5603	2' to 3'				↓	71			71	78
5650	Pyracantha coccinea, (LaLande Firethorn), Z6, cont/B&B									
5651	1 gal.				Ea.	44.50			44.50	49
5652	5 gal.					71			71	78
5653	5 gal. Espalier					133			133	146
5654	10 gal. Espalier				↓	178			178	195
5700	Rhamus frangula columnaris, (Tallhedge), Z2, B&B									
5701	2' to 3'				Ea.	22			22	24.50
5702	3' to 4'					35.50			35.50	39
5703	4' to 5'					31			31	34
5704	5' to 6'					42			42	46
5750	Rhododendron carolinianum, (Carolina Rhododendron), Z5, cont/B&B									
5751	15" to 18"				Ea.	15.95			15.95	17.55
5752	18" to 24"					35.50			35.50	39
5753	24" to 30"				↓	49.50			49.50	54.50
5800	Rhododendron catawbiense hybrids, (Rhododendron), Z5, cont/B&B									
5801	1 gal.				Ea.	9.75			9.75	10.75
5802	2 gal.					21.50			21.50	23.50
5803	5 gal.					38			38	42
5804	12" to 15"					24			24	26.50
5805	15" to 18"					25.50			25.50	28.50
5806	18" to 24"					44.50			44.50	49
5807	24" to 30"					53.50			53.50	59
5808	30" to 36"					63			63	69
5809	36" to 42"				↓	75			75	82.50
5850	Rhododendron PJM, (PJM Rhododendron), Z4, cont/B&B									
5851	15" to 18"				Ea.	24.50			24.50	27
5852	18" to 24"					33.50			33.50	37
5853	2' to 2-1/2'					46.50			46.50	51.50
5854	2-1/2' to 3'					63			63	69.50
5855	3' to 3-1/2'				↓	79			79	87
5900	Rhus aromatica "Gro-Low", (Fragrant Sumac), Z3, cont									
5901	15" to 18"				Ea.	17.55			17.55	19.30
5902	3 gal.					15.85			15.85	17.40
5903	5 gal.				↓	19.35			19.35	21.50
5950	Rhus glabra cismontana, (Dwarf Smooth Sumac), Z2, cont									
5951	1 gal.				Ea.	14.20			14.20	15.60
5952	5 gal.				"	35.50			35.50	39
6000	Rhus typhina lacianata, (Cut-Leaf Staghorn Sumac), Z4, cont/B&B									
6001	5 gal.				Ea.	24.50			24.50	27
6002	7 gal.					30			30	33
6003	6' to 7'				↓	53			53	58
6050	Ribes alpinum, (Alpine Currant), Z3, cont/B&B									
6051	18" to 24"				Ea.	11.50			11.50	12.65
6052	2' to 3'				"	20.50			20.50	22.50
6100	Rosa hugonis, (Father Hugo Rose), Z6, cont									
6101	1 gal.				Ea.	9.45			9.45	10.40

32 93 33.40 Shrubs	Crew	Daily Output	Labor-Hours	Unit	Material	2015 Bare Costs Labor	Equipment	Total	Total Incl O&P
6102	2 gal.				Ea.	13.30			13.30	14.65
6150	Rosa meidiland hybrids, Z6, cont									
6151	9" to 12"				Ea.	18.80			18.80	20.50
6152	12" to 15"				"	21.50			21.50	23.50
6200	Rosa multiflora, (Japanese Rose), Z6, cont									
6201	1 gal.				Ea.	6.70			6.70	7.35
6202	2 gal.				"	12.45			12.45	13.70
6250	Rosa rugosa and hybrids, Z4, cont									
6251	18" to 24"				Ea.	21			21	23
6252	2' to 3'				"	19			19	21
6300	Rosa: hybrid teas, grandifloras and climbers, Zna, cont									
6301	2 gal. Non Pat.				Ea.	17.95			17.95	19.75
6302	2 gal. Patented				"	14.30			14.30	15.75
6350	Salix caprea, (French Pussy Willow), Z5, B&B									
6351	4' to 5'				Ea.	33.50			33.50	37
6352	5' to 6'				"	35.50			35.50	39
6400	Salix discolor, (Pussy Willow), Z2, cont									
6401	2' to 3'				Ea.	24			24	26.50
6450	Sambucus canadensis, (American Elder), Z4, B&B									
6451	2' to 3'				Ea.	24			24	26.50
6500	Skimmia japonica, (Japanese Skimmia), Z6, cont									
6501	1 gal.				Ea.	8.50			8.50	9.35
6502	2 gal.					16.10			16.10	17.70
6503	5 gal.					23.50			23.50	26
6550	Spiraea arguta compacta, (Garland Spirea), Z5, B&B									
6551	3' to 4'				Ea.	26.50			26.50	29.50
6552	4' to 5'				"	46			46	51
6600	Spirea bumalda, (Bumalda Spirea), Z5, cont/B&B									
6601	1 gal.				Ea.	8.50			8.50	9.35
6602	5 gal.					28			28	30.50
6603	15" to 18"					14.55			14.55	16
6604	18" to 24"					15.75			15.75	17.35
6650	Spirea japonica, (Japanese Spirea), Z5, cont									
6651	15" to 18"				Ea.	13.40			13.40	14.75
6652	18" to 24"					29			29	32
6653	3 gal.					14.10			14.10	15.50
6654	5 gal.					17.60			17.60	19.35
6700	Spirea nipponica snowmound, (Snowmound Spirea), Z5, cont/B&B									
6701	15" to 18"				Ea.	14.65			14.65	16.15
6702	18" to 24"					24			24	26.50
6703	2' to 3'					32			32	35.50
6704	3' to 4'					45			45	49.50
6705	4' to 5'					59			59	65
6750	Spirea vanhouttei, (Van Houtte Spirea), Z4, cont/B&B									
6751	15" to 18"				Ea.	17			17	18.70
6752	2' to 3'					29			29	32
6753	3' to 4'					33			33	36.50
6754	4' to 5'					38.50			38.50	42
6755	5' to 6'					53.50			53.50	59
6800	Symphoricarpos albus, (Common Snowberry), Z4, cont/B&B									
6801	18" to 24"				Ea.	10.35			10.35	11.35
6802	2' to 3'					14.85			14.85	16.35
6803	3' to 4'					16.15			16.15	17.75

32 93 33.40 Shrubs		Crew	Daily Output	Labor-Hours	Unit	Material	2015 Bare Costs Labor	Equipment	Total	Total Incl O&P
6850	Syringa chinensis, (Roven Lilac), Z6, B&B									
6851	3' to 4'				Ea.	25.50			25.50	28
6852	4' to 5'					41			41	45
6853	5' to 6'				▼	72			72	79.50
6900	Syringa hugo koster, (Hugo Koster Lilac), Z4, B&B									
6901	2' to 3'				Ea.	27.50			27.50	30.50
6902	3' to 4'					33			33	36.50
6903	4' to 5'					46			46	50.50
6904	5' to 6'				▼	52.50			52.50	58
6950	Syringa meyeri, (Meyer Lilac), Z6, cont/B&B									
6951	12" to 15"				Ea.	15.85			15.85	17.40
6952	15" to 18"					21			21	23
6953	18" to 24"					24.50			24.50	27
6954	2' to 3'					31			31	34
6955	3' to 4'				▼	48.50			48.50	53
7000	Syringa persica, (Persian Lilac), Z5, cont									
7001	5 gal.				Ea.	47			47	51.50
7050	Syringa prestonae hybrids, (Preston Lilac), Z3, B&B									
7051	2' to 3'				Ea.	36.50			36.50	40
7052	3' to 4'					75			75	82.50
7053	4' to 5'					125			125	138
7054	5' to 6'					160			160	176
7055	6' to 7'				▼	166			166	183
7100	Syringa vulgaris and Mixed Hybrids, (Common Lilac), Z4, cont/B&B									
7101	5 gal.				Ea.	26.50			26.50	29
7102	3' to 4'					31			31	34
7103	4' to 5'					53			53	58
7104	5' to 6'					79			79	87
7105	6' to 8'				▼	106			106	116
7200	Vaccinium corymbosum, (Highbush Blueberry), Z4, cont/B&B									
7201	15" to 18"				Ea.	21.50			21.50	23.50
7202	18" to 24"					28.50			28.50	31
7203	2' to 3'					29.50			29.50	32
7204	3' to 4'				▼	36.50			36.50	40
7250	Viburnum bodnantense, (Bodnant Viburnum), Z5, cont/B&B									
7251	18" to 24"				Ea.	13			13	14.30
7252	3' to 4'					16.95			16.95	18.65
7253	4' to 5'					43.50			43.50	48
7254	5' to 6'				▼	63			63	69.50
7300	Viburnum carlcephalum, (Fragrant Snowball), Z6, cont/B&B									
7301	2' to 3'				Ea.	25.50			25.50	28.50
7302	3' to 4'					18.90			18.90	21
7303	4' to 5'				▼	45.50			45.50	50
7350	Viburnum carlesi, (Korean Spice Viburnum), Z4, B&B									
7351	18" to 24"				Ea.	23			23	25.50
7352	2' to 2-1/2'					26.50			26.50	29
7353	2-1/2' to 3'					30.50			30.50	33.50
7354	3' to 4'				▼	38			38	42
7400	Viburnum dilatatum, (Linden Viburnum), Z6, B&B									
7401	3' to 4'				Ea.	29.50			29.50	32
7402	4' to 5'					33			33	36
7403	5' to 6'				▼	45			45	49.50
7450	Viburnum juddii, (Judd Viburnum), Z5, B&B									

32 93 33.40 Shrubs		Crew	Daily Output	Labor-Hours	Unit	Material	2015 Bare Costs Labor	Equipment	Total	Total Incl O&P
7451	18" to 24"				Ea.	17.60			17.60	19.35
7452	2' to 2-1/2'					26.50			26.50	29
7453	2-1/2' to 3'					35			35	38.50
7454	3' to 4'					44			44	48.50
7500	Viburnum opulus sterile, (Common Snowball), Z4, cont/B&B									
7501	2 gal.				Ea.	16.85			16.85	18.55
7502	5 gal.					21			21	23
7503	2' to 3'					32			32	35
7504	3' to 4'					45.50			45.50	50
7550	Viburnum plicatum, (Japanese Snowball), Z6, cont/B&B									
7551	18" to 21"				Ea.	27.50			27.50	30
7552	5' to 6'				"	58.50			58.50	64
7600	Viburnum plicatum var. tomentosum, (Viburnum), Z5, cont/B&B									
7601	18" to 21"				Ea.	17.60			17.60	19.35
7602	2' to 3'					26.50			26.50	29
7603	3' to 4'					35			35	38.50
7604	4' to 5'					41.50			41.50	45.50
7650	Viburnum prunifolium, (Blackhaw), Z4, B&B									
7651	3' to 4'				Ea.	33.50			33.50	37
7652	4' to 5'					61.50			61.50	68
7653	5' to 6'					70.50			70.50	77.50
7654	6' to 7'					123			123	136
7700	Viburnum rhytidophyllum, (Leatherleaf Viburnum), Z6, B&B									
7701	2' to 3'				Ea.	26			26	28.50
7702	3' to 4'					26.50			26.50	29
7703	4' to 5'					35			35	38.50
7750	Viburnum sieboldi, (Siebold Viburnum), Z5, B&B									
7751	3' to 4'				Ea.	28.50			28.50	31
7752	4' to 5'					56			56	61.50
7753	5' to 6'					26.50			26.50	29.50
7754	6' to 7'					80			80	88
7800	Viburnum trilobum, (American Cranberry Bush), Z2, cont/B&B									
7801	2' to 3'				Ea.	19.35			19.35	21.50
7802	3' to 4'					24.50			24.50	27
7803	5' to 6'					31.50			31.50	35
7804	6' to 8'					39.50			39.50	43.50
7805	8' to 10'					53			53	58
7850	Weigela florida and Hybrids, (Old Fashioned Weigela), Z6, cont/B&B									
7851	2' to 3'				Ea.	16.80			16.80	18.50
7852	3' to 4'					25			25	27.50
7853	4' to 5'					39.50			39.50	43.50
7854	5' to 6'					45			45	49.50
7900	Xanthorhiza simplicissima, (Yellowroot), Z4, cont									
7901	4" Pot				Ea.	6.65			6.65	7.30
7902	1 gal.				"	16.40			16.40	18.05
7950	Yucca filamentosa, (Adams Needle), Z4, cont									
7951	9" to 12"				Ea.	10			10	11
7952	15" to 18"					19.10			19.10	21
7953	18" to 24"					24			24	26.50

32 93 33.50 Shrubs	Crew	Daily Output	Labor-Hours	Unit	2015 Bare Costs			Total	Total Incl O&P
					Material	Labor	Equipment	Total	
0010 **SHRUBS**, Warm temperate									
0011 & subtropical, zones 7 – 10									
1000 Aspidistra elatior, (Cast Iron Plant), Z7, cont									
1010 1 gal.				Ea.	6.70			6.70	7.35
1020 2 gal.				"	17.30			17.30	19.05
1100 Aucuba japonica "Variegata", (Gold Dust Plant), Z7, cont									
1110 1 gal.				Ea.	7.60			7.60	8.35
1120 3 gal.					15.60			15.60	17.15
1130 5 gal.					26.50			26.50	29.50
1200 Azara microphylla, (Boxleaf Azara), Z8, cont									
1210 5 gal.				Ea.	25			25	27.50
1220 15 gal.				"	80			80	88
1300 Boronia megastigma, (Sweet Boronia), Z9, cont									
1310 1 gal.				Ea.	8.05			8.05	8.85
1320 5 gal.				"	17.90			17.90	19.70
1400 Brunfelsia pauciflora calycina, (Brazil Raisin-tree), Z10, cont									
1410 1 gal.				Ea.	7.40			7.40	8.15
1420 5 gal.				"	22			22	24.50
1500 Calliandra haematocephala, (Pink Powerpuff), Z10, cont									
1510 1 gal.				Ea.	6.75			6.75	7.45
1520 5 gal.					14.80			14.80	16.30
1530 15 gal.					57			57	63
1600 Callistemon citrinus, (Lemon Bottlebrush), Z9, cont									
1610 1 gal.				Ea.	6.90			6.90	7.60
1620 5 gal.					22.50			22.50	25
1630 10 gal.					46			46	51
1640 20 gal.					69.50			69.50	76.50
1700 Camellia japonica, (Japanese Camellia), Z7, cont									
1710 1 gal.				Ea.	8.60			8.60	9.45
1720 3 gal.					11.85			11.85	13.05
1730 5 gal.					23			23	25.50
1800 Camellia sasanqua, (Sasanqua Camellia), Z7, cont									
1810 1 gal.				Ea.	9.85			9.85	10.80
1820 3 gal.					10.70			10.70	11.80
1830 5 gal.					24.50			24.50	27
1900 Carissa grandiflora, (Natal Plum), Z9, cont									
1910 1 gal.				Ea.	4.69			4.69	5.15
1920 5 gal.					11.30			11.30	12.40
1930 15 gal.					52			52	57.50
2000 Carpenteria californica, (Evergreen Mockorange), Z8, cont									
2010 1 gal.				Ea.	8.30			8.30	9.15
2020 5 gal.				"	27.50			27.50	30
2100 Cassia artemisioides, (Feathery Cassia), Z9, cont									
2110 1 gal.				Ea.	5.50			5.50	6.05
2120 5 gal.					15.15			15.15	16.65
2130 15 gal.					60.50			60.50	66.50
2200 Ceanothus concha, (Concha Wild Lilac), Z8, cont									
2210 1 gal.				Ea.	6.70			6.70	7.35
2220 5 gal.				"	21.50			21.50	23.50
2300 Choisa ternata, (Mexican Orange), Z7, cont									
2310 1 gal.				Ea.	9.80			9.80	10.80
2320 5 gal.				"	22.50			22.50	25

32 93 33.50 Shrubs		Crew	Daily Output	Labor-Hours	Unit	Material	2015 Bare Costs Labor	Equipment	Total	Total Incl O&P
2400	Cistus Hybridus, (White Rockrose), Z7, cont									
2410	1 gal.				Ea.	4.80			4.80	5.30
2420	5 gal.				"	12.10			12.10	13.30
2500	Coprosma repens, (Mirror Plant), Z9, cont									
2510	1 gal.				Ea.	5.30			5.30	5.85
2520	5 gal.				"	12.90			12.90	14.20
2600	Correa pulchella "Carminebells", (Australian Fuchsia), Z9, cont									
2610	1 gal.				Ea.	6.80			6.80	7.50
2620	5 gal.				"	15.40			15.40	16.95
2700	Cyrtomium falcatum, (Japanese Holly Fern), Z10, cont									
2710	1 gal.				Ea.	8.75			8.75	9.65
2720	5 gal.				"	18.30			18.30	20
2800	Daphne odora "Marginata", (Variegated Winter Daphne), Z7, cont									
2810	2 gal.				Ea.	29			29	32
2820	5 gal.					63			63	69.50
2830	15 gal.					88.50			88.50	97
2900	Dizygotheca elegantissima, (False Aralia), Z10, cont									
2910	1 gal.				Ea.	5.20			5.20	5.70
2920	5 gal.					15.10			15.10	16.60
2930	15 gal.					51			51	56.50
3000	Dodonaea viscosa, (Akeake), Z10, cont									
3010	1 gal.				Ea.	4.90			4.90	5.40
3020	5 gal.					11.30			11.30	12.45
3030	15 gal.					47			47	51.50
3100	Eleagnus ebbingei "Gilt Edge", (Variegated Silverberry), Z7, cont									
3110	1 gal.				Ea.	4.20			4.20	4.62
3120	5 gal.					12.80			12.80	14.10
3130	15 gal.					46			46	50.50
3200	Eleagnus pungens, (Silverberry), Z7, cont									
3210	1 gal.				Ea.	4.30			4.30	4.73
3220	3 gal.					8.70			8.70	9.55
3230	5 gal.					12.80			12.80	14.10
3300	Escallonia rubra, (Red Escallonia), Z8, cont									
3310	1 gal.				Ea.	4.75			4.75	5.25
3320	5 gal.					12.60			12.60	13.85
3330	15 gal.					47			47	51.50
3400	Euonymus japonica "Aureo-Variegata", (Gold Euonymus), Z7, cont									
3410	1 gal.				Ea.	4.70			4.70	5.15
3420	2 gal.					17.90			17.90	19.70
3430	5 gal.					26			26	28.50
3500	Fatsia japonica, (Japanese Fatsia), Z8, cont									
3510	1 gal.				Ea.	4.96			4.96	5.45
3520	3 gal.					9.10			9.10	10
3530	5 gal.					12.55			12.55	13.80
3540	15 gal.					46			46	51
3600	Fremontodendron californicum, (Pacific "Fremontia"), Z9, cont									
3610	2 gal.				Ea.	19.80			19.80	22
3620	5 gal.					39.50			39.50	43.50
3630	15 gal.					115			115	126
3700	Gardenia jasminoides, (Cape Jasmine), Z8, cont									
3710	1 gal.				Ea.	7.30			7.30	8.05
3720	3 gal.					12.90			12.90	14.20
3730	5 gal.					17.40			17.40	19.15

32 93 33.50 Shrubs	Crew	Daily Output	Labor-Hours	Unit	Material	2015 Bare Costs Labor	Equipment	Total	Total Incl O&P
3800 Garrya elliptica, (Silk Tassel), Z8, cont									
3810 1 gal.				Ea.	10.45			10.45	11.50
3820 5 gal.				"	13.10			13.10	14.40
3900 Grewia caffra, (Lavender Starflower), Z9, cont									
3910 5 gal.				Ea.	13.40			13.40	14.75
3920 15 gal.				"	46.50			46.50	51.50
4000 Hebe buxifolia, (Boxleaf Hebe), Z7, cont									
4010 1 gal.				Ea.	4.20			4.20	4.62
4020 5 gal.				"	12.60			12.60	13.85
4100 Heteromeles arbutifolia, (Toyon), Z9, cont									
4110 1 gal.				Ea.	8.30			8.30	9.15
4120 5 gal.					23.50			23.50	26
4130 15 gal.					81			81	89.50
4200 Hibiscus rosa-sinensis, (Chinese Hibiscus), Z9, cont									
4210 1 gal.				Ea.	5.40			5.40	5.95
4220 5 gal.					18.60			18.60	20.50
4230 15 gal.					56			56	61.50
4300 Ilex vomitoria, (Yaupon Holly), Z7, cont									
4310 1 gal.				Ea.	9.35			9.35	10.25
4320 3 gal.					33			33	36.50
4330 10 gal.					88			88	97
4400 Illicium parvifolium, (Florida Anise Tree), Z8, cont									
4410 1 gal.				Ea.	8.20			8.20	9
4420 5 gal.				"	19.60			19.60	21.50
4500 Lagerstroemia indica, (Crapemyrtle), Z7, cont									
4510 1 gal.				Ea.	5.40			5.40	5.95
4520 5 gal.					15.90			15.90	17.50
4530 3' to 4'					59.50			59.50	65.50
4540 4' to 5'					67			67	73.50
4550 5' to 6'					87			87	95.50
4600 Ligustrum japonicum texanum, (Wax Leaf Privet), Z7, cont									
4610 1 gal.				Ea.	6.70			6.70	7.35
4620 2 gal.					14.20			14.20	15.60
4630 5 gal.					20.50			20.50	22.50
4700 Ligustrum lucidum, (Glossy Privet), Z7, cont									
4710 1 gal.				Ea.	6.60			6.60	7.25
4720 5 gal.					14.30			14.30	15.75
4730 15 gal.					64.50			64.50	71
4800 Ligustrum sinensis "Variegatum", (Variegated Privet), Z7, cont									
4810 1 gal.				Ea.	6.70			6.70	7.35
4820 2 gal.					14.40			14.40	15.85
4830 3 gal.					19.40			19.40	21.50
4900 Mahonia lomariifolia, (Burmese Grape), Z8, cont									
4910 1 gal.				Ea.	6.35			6.35	7
4920 5 gal.					18.10			18.10	19.90
4930 15 gal.					51			51	56
5000 Myoporum laetum, (Coast Sandalwood), Z9, cont									
5010 1 gal.				Ea.	6.30			6.30	6.90
5020 5 gal.					18.20			18.20	20
5030 15 gal.					51.50			51.50	56.50
5100 Myrica californica, (Pacific Wax Myrtle), Z7, cont									
5110 1 gal.				Ea.	10			10	11
5120 5 gal.				"	29.50			29.50	32.50

For customer support on your Site Work & Landscape Cost Data, call 877.737.1594.

32 93 33.50 Shrubs	Crew	Daily Output	Labor-Hours	Unit	2015 Bare Costs Material	Labor	Equipment	Total	Total Incl O&P
5200	Myrtus communis "Compacta", (Dwarf Roman Myrtle), Z8, cont								
5210	1 gal.				Ea.	9.60			9.60	10.55
5220	5 gal.				"	29			29	32
5300	Nandina domestica, (Heavenly Bamboo), Z7, cont								
5310	1 gal.				Ea.	9			9	9.90
5320	2 gal.					16			16	17.60
5330	5 gal.				▼	25			25	27.50
5400	Nerium oleander, (Oleander), Z8, cont								
5410	1 gal.				Ea.	4.60			4.60	5.05
5420	3 gal.					8.80			8.80	9.70
5430	5 gal.				▼	12.80			12.80	14.10
5500	Osmanthus fragrans, (Fragrant Tea Olive), Z8, cont								
5510	1 gal.				Ea.	5.60			5.60	6.15
5520	3 gal.				"	13.65			13.65	15.05
5600	Philodendron selloum, (Selloum), Z10, cont								
5610	1 gal.				Ea.	5.60			5.60	6.15
5620	5 gal.					12.40			12.40	13.65
5630	15 gal.				▼	45.50			45.50	50
5700	Photinia fraseri, (Christmas Berry), Z7, cont								
5710	1 gal.				Ea.	7.90			7.90	8.70
5720	2 gal.					12.80			12.80	14.10
5730	5 gal.					24.50			24.50	27
5740	15 gal.				▼	81.50			81.50	89.50
5800	Phyllostachys aurea, (Golden Bamboo), Z7, cont								
5810	1 gal.				Ea.	9			9	9.90
5820	5 gal.					25			25	27.50
5830	15 gal.				▼	55			55	60.50
5900	Pittosporum tobira, (Japanese Pittosporum), Z8, cont								
5910	1 gal.				Ea.	4.50			4.50	4.95
5920	3 gal.					8.70			8.70	9.55
5930	5 gal.				▼	12.90			12.90	14.20
6000	Plumbago auriculata, (Cape Plumbago), Z9, cont								
6010	1 gal.				Ea.	4.70			4.70	5.15
6020	5 gal.					11.80			11.80	13
6030	15 gal.				▼	46.50			46.50	51
6100	Prunus carolina, (Carolina Cherry Laurel), Z7, cont								
6110	1 gal.				Ea.	8.40			8.40	9.25
6120	3 gal.					18.70			18.70	20.50
6130	15 gal.				▼	98			98	108
6200	Punica granatum "nana", (Dwarf Pomegranate), Z7, cont								
6210	1 gal.				Ea.	4.05			4.05	4.46
6220	5 gal.					12.70			12.70	13.95
6230	7 gal.				▼	25			25	27.50
6300	Pyracantha koidzumii "Santa Cruz", (Pyracantha), Z8, cont								
6310	1 gal.				Ea.	5.20			5.20	5.70
6320	5 gal.					11.10			11.10	12.20
6330	5 gal. Espalier				▼	16.30			16.30	17.95
6400	Raphiolepis indica, (India Hawthorne), Z8, cont								
6410	1 gal.				Ea.	12.10			12.10	13.30
6420	2 gal.					37			37	40.50
6430	5 gal.				▼	53			53	58.50
6500	Rhamnus alaternus, (Italian Buckthorn), Z7, cont								
6510	1 gal.				Ea.	4.20			4.20	4.62

For customer support on your Site Work & Landscape Cost Data, call 877.737.1594.

423

32 93 33.50 Shrubs	Crew	Daily Output	Labor-Hours	Unit	Material	2015 Bare Costs Labor	Equipment	Total	Total Incl O&P
6520	5 gal.				Ea.	12.45			12.45	13.70
6530	15 gal.				▼	46.50			46.50	51.50
6600	Sarcococca hookerana humilis, (Himalayan Sarcococca), Z8, cont									
6610	1 gal.				Ea.	5.60			5.60	6.15
6620	2 gal.				"	10.70			10.70	11.75
6700	Sarcococca ruscifolia, (Fragrant Sarcococca), Z7, cont									
6710	1 gal.				Ea.	5.40			5.40	5.95
6720	5 gal.				"	10.70			10.70	11.75
6800	Solanum rantonnetii, (Paraguay Nightshade), Z9, cont									
6810	1 gal.				Ea.	6.10			6.10	6.70
6820	5 gal.				"	18.60			18.60	20.50
6900	Ternstroemia gymnanthera, (Japanese Cleyera), Z7, cont									
6910	1 gal.				Ea.	7			7	7.70
6920	3 gal.					24			24	26.50
6930	5 gal.				▼	27.50			27.50	30.50
7000	Viburnum davidii, (David Viburnum), Z8, cont									
7010	1 gal.				Ea.	6.60			6.60	7.25
7020	3 gal.				"	11.90			11.90	13.10
7100	Viburnum japonicum, (Japanese Viburnum), Z8, cont									
7110	1 gal.				Ea.	6.80			6.80	7.50
7120	3 gal.				"	11.80			11.80	13
7200	Viburnum tinus, (Spring Bouquet Laurustinis), Z7, cont									
7210	1 gal.				Ea.	4.60			4.60	5.05
7220	5 gal.				"	12.70			12.70	13.95
7300	Vitex agnus castus, (Chastetree), Z7, cont									
7310	5 gal.				Ea.	12.60			12.60	13.85
7400	Xylosma congestum, (Shiny Xylosma), Z8, cont									
7410	1 gal.				Ea.	4.40			4.40	4.84
7420	5 gal.					12.40			12.40	13.65
7430	15 gal.				▼	46			46	50.50
7500	Yucca aloifolia, (Spanish Bayonet), Z7, cont									
7510	1 gal.				Ea.	7			7	7.70
7520	3 gal.				"	13.20			13.20	14.50

		Crew	Daily Output	Labor-Hours	Unit	Material	2015 Bare Costs Labor	Equipment	Total	Total Incl O&P
0010	**CACTI**									
1000	Column cactus, Cereus species, Z8, cont									
1020	5 gal.				Ea.	31			31	34
1030	regular size, 15 gal.					76.50			76.50	84.50
1032	large size, 15 gal.				▼	128			128	141
1100	Golden barrel cactus, Echinocactus grusonii, Z8, cont									
1130	14"				Ea.	67			67	73.50
1200	Orchid cactus,Epiphyllum Varieties, Z8, cont									
1210	1 gal.				Ea.	12.90			12.90	14.20
1212	2 gal.				"	21			21	23
1300	Cluster cactus, Mammillaria species, Z8, cont									
1310	1 gal.				Ea.	10			10	11
1312	2 gal.					20			20	22
1320	5 gal.				▼	25			25	27.50
1400	Burbank spineless Prickly Pear, Opuntia fiscus-indica, Z8, cont									
1420	5 gal.				Ea.	15.30			15.30	16.85
1430	15 gal.				"	50			50	55
1500	Bunny ears, Opuntia microdasys, Z8, cont									

32 93 33 – Shrubs

32 93 33.60 Cacti		Crew	Daily Output	Labor-Hours	Unit	Material	2015 Bare Costs Labor	Equipment	Total	Total Incl O&P
1510	1 gal.				Ea.	4.50			4.50	4.95
1520	5 gal.				"	16			16	17.60
1600	Prickly Pear, Opuntia species, Z8, cont									
1610	1 gal.				Ea.	5			5	5.50
1620	5 gal.					20			20	22
1630	15 gal.				↓	50			50	55
1700	Giant Saguaro Cactus, Carnegia gigantea, Z8, cont									
1713	3 gal.				Ea.	40			40	44
1720	5 gal.				"	61.50			61.50	67.50

32 93 43 – Trees

32 93 43.10 Planting		Crew	Daily Output	Labor-Hours	Unit	Material	2015 Bare Costs Labor	Equipment	Total	Total Incl O&P
0010	**PLANTING**									
0011	Trees, shrubs and ground cover									
0100	Light soil									
0110	Bare root seedlings, 3" to 5" height	1 Clab	960	.008	Ea.		.31		.31	.48
0120	6" to 10"		520	.015			.58		.58	.89
0130	11" to 16"		370	.022			.81		.81	1.25
0140	17" to 24"		210	.038			1.43		1.43	2.20
0200	Potted, 2-1/4" diameter		840	.010			.36		.36	.55
0210	3" diameter		700	.011			.43		.43	.66
0220	4" diameter		620	.013			.49		.49	.75
0300	Container, 1 gallon	2 Clab	84	.190			7.15		7.15	11
0310	2 gallon		52	.308			11.55		11.55	17.80
0320	3 gallon		40	.400			15.05		15.05	23
0330	5 gallon		29	.552			20.50		20.50	32
0400	Bagged and burlapped, 12" diameter ball, by hand	↓	19	.842			31.50		31.50	48.50
0410	Backhoe/loader, 48 H.P.	B-6	40	.600			25	9.10	34.10	48
0415	15" diameter, by hand	2 Clab	16	1			37.50		37.50	58
0416	Backhoe/loader, 48 H.P.	B-6	30	.800			33	12.15	45.15	64
0420	18" diameter by hand	2 Clab	12	1.333			50		50	77
0430	Backhoe/loader, 48 H.P.	B-6	27	.889			36.50	13.50	50	71
0440	24" diameter by hand	2 Clab	9	1.778			67		67	103
0450	Backhoe/loader 48 H.P.	B-6	21	1.143			47	17.35	64.35	91
0470	36" diameter, backhoe/loader, 48 H.P.	"	17	1.412	↓		58.50	21.50	80	113
0550	Medium soil									
0560	Bare root seedlings, 3" to 5"	1 Clab	672	.012	Ea.		.45		.45	.69
0561	6" to 10"		364	.022			.83		.83	1.27
0562	11" to 16"		260	.031			1.16		1.16	1.78
0563	17" to 24"		145	.055			2.07		2.07	3.19
0570	Potted, 2-1/4" diameter		590	.014			.51		.51	.78
0572	3" diameter		490	.016			.61		.61	.94
0574	4" diameter		435	.018			.69		.69	1.06
0590	Container, 1 gallon	2 Clab	59	.271			10.20		10.20	15.70
0592	2 gallon		36	.444			16.70		16.70	25.50
0594	3 gallon		28	.571			21.50		21.50	33
0595	5 gallon		20	.800			30		30	46.50
0600	Bagged and burlapped, 12" diameter ball, by hand	↓	13	1.231			46.50		46.50	71
0605	Backhoe/loader, 48 H.P.	B-6	28	.857			35.50	13	48.50	68.50
0607	15" diameter, by hand	2 Clab	11.20	1.429			53.50		53.50	82.50
0608	Backhoe/loader, 48 H.P.	B-6	21	1.143			47	17.35	64.35	91
0610	18" diameter, by hand	2 Clab	8.50	1.882			71		71	109
0615	Backhoe/loader, 48 H.P.	B-6	19	1.263	↓		52	19.15	71.15	101

32 93 43.10 Planting	Crew	Daily Output	Labor-Hours	Unit	Material	2015 Bare Costs Labor	2015 Bare Costs Equipment	Total	Total Incl O&P
0620 — 24" diameter, by hand	2 Clab	6.30	2.540	Ea.		95.50		95.50	147
0625 — Backhoe/loader, 48 H.P.	B-6	14.70	1.633			67.50	25	92.50	131
0630 — 36" diameter, backhoe/loader, 48 H.P.	"	12	2			82.50	30.50	113	160
0700 Heavy or stoney soil									
0710 — Bare root seedlings, 3" to 5"	1 Clab	470	.017	Ea.		.64		.64	.98
0711 — 6" to 10"		255	.031			1.18		1.18	1.81
0712 — 11" to 16"		182	.044			1.65		1.65	2.54
0713 — 17" to 24"		101	.079			2.98		2.98	4.58
0720 — Potted, 2-1/4" diameter		360	.022			.84		.84	1.29
0722 — 3" diameter		343	.023			.88		.88	1.35
0724 — 4" diameter		305	.026			.99		.99	1.52
0730 — Container, 1 gallon	2 Clab	41.30	.387			14.55		14.55	22.50
0732 — 2 gallon		25.20	.635			24		24	36.50
0734 — 3 gallon		19.60	.816			30.50		30.50	47
0735 — 5 gallon		14	1.143			43		43	66
0750 — Bagged and burlapped, 12" diameter ball, by hand		9.10	1.758			66		66	102
0751 — Backhoe/loader	B-6	19.60	1.224			50.50	18.60	69.10	98
0752 — 15" diameter, by hand	2 Clab	7.80	2.051			77		77	119
0753 — Backhoe/loader, 48 H.P.	B-6	14.70	1.633			67.50	25	92.50	131
0754 — 18" diameter, by hand	2 Clab	5.60	2.857			107		107	165
0755 — Backhoe/loader, 48 H.P.	B-6	13.30	1.805			74.50	27.50	102	144
0756 — 24" diameter, by hand	2 Clab	4.40	3.636			137		137	210
0757 — Backhoe/loader, 48 H.P.	B-6	10.30	2.330			96	35.50	131.50	186
0758 — 36" diameter backhoe/loader, 48 H.P.	"	8.40	2.857			118	43.50	161.50	228
2000 Stake out tree and shrub locations	2 Clab	220	.073			2.73		2.73	4.21

32 93 43.30 Trees, Deciduous	Crew	Daily Output	Labor-Hours	Unit	Material	2015 Bare Costs Labor	2015 Bare Costs Equipment	Total	Total Incl O&P
0010 **TREES, DECIDUOUS**									
0011 Zones 2 – 6									
0100 Acer campestre, (Hedge Maple), Z4, B&B									
0110 — 4' to 5'				Ea.	70.50			70.50	77.50
0120 — 5' to 6'					80			80	88
0130 — 1-1/2" to 2" Cal.					140			140	154
0140 — 2" to 2-1/2" Cal.					225			225	248
0150 — 2-1/2" to 3" Cal.					310			310	340
0200 Acer ginnala, (Amur Maple), Z2, cont/BB									
0210 — 8' to 10'				Ea.	141			141	155
0220 — 10' to 12'					210			210	231
0230 — 12' to 14'					206			206	227
0300 Acer griseum, (Paperbark Maple), Z5, B&B									
0310 — 1-1/2" to 1-3/4" Cal.				Ea.	260			260	287
0320 — 1-3/4" to 2" cal.				"	271			271	298
0400 Acer palmatum, (Japanese Maple), Z6, cont/BB									
0410 — 2-1/2' to 3'				Ea.	79			79	87
0420 — 4' to 5'					88			88	97
0430 — 5' to 6'					110			110	121
0440 — 6' to 7'					141			141	155
0450 — 7' to 8'					172			172	189
0460 — 8' to 10'					233			233	257
0470 — 10' to 12'					255			255	281
0500 Acer palmatum atropurpureum, (Bloodgood Japan Maple), Z5, B&B									
0510 — 3' to 3-1/2'				Ea.	80.50			80.50	88.50
0520 — 3-1/2' to 4'					83.50			83.50	92

32 93 Plants

32 93 43 – Trees

32 93 43.30 Trees, Deciduous		Crew	Daily Output	Labor-Hours	Unit	Material	2015 Bare Costs Labor	Equipment	Total	Total Incl O&P
0530	4' to 4-1/2'				Ea.	123			123	135
0540	4-1/2' to 5'					150			150	165
0550	5' to 6'				▼	145			145	160
0600	Acer platanoides, (Norway Maple), Z4, B&B									
0610	8' to 10'				Ea.	189			189	208
0620	1-1/2" to 2" Cal.					120			120	132
0630	2" to 2-1/2" Cal.					143			143	158
0640	2-1/2" to 3" Cal.					175			175	193
0650	3" to 3-1/2" Cal.					200			200	220
0660	Bare root, 8' to 10'					300			300	330
0670	10' to 12'					330			330	365
0680	12' to 14'				▼	365			365	400
0700	Acer platanoides columnare, (Column maple), Z4, B&B									
0710	2" to 2-1/2" Cal.				Ea.	170			170	187
0720	2-1/2" to 3" Cal.					185			185	204
0730	3" to 3-1/2" Cal.					200			200	220
0740	3-1/2" to 4" Cal.					225			225	248
0750	4" to 4-1/2" Cal.					260			260	286
0760	4-1/2" to 5" Cal.					1,500			1,500	1,650
0770	5" to 5-1/2" Cal.				▼	1,925			1,925	2,125
0800	Acer rubrum, (Red Maple), Z4, B&B									
0810	1-1/2" to 2" Cal.				Ea.	125			125	138
0820	2" to 2-1/2" Cal.					190			190	209
0830	2-1/2" to 3" Cal.					230			230	253
0840	Bare Root, 8' to 10'					220			220	242
0850	10' to 12'				▼	282			282	310
0900	Acer saccharum, (Sugar Maple), Z3, B&B									
0910	1-1/2" to 2" Cal.				Ea.	130			130	143
0920	2" to 2-1/2" Cal.					175			175	193
0930	2-1/2" to 3" Cal.					200			200	220
0940	3" to 3-1/2" Cal.					230			230	253
0950	3-1/2" to 4" Cal.					260			260	286
0960	Bare Root, 8' to 10'					126			126	138
0970	10' to 12'					193			193	212
0980	12' to 14'				▼	246			246	271
1000	Aesculus carnea biroti, (Ruby Horsechestnut), Z3, B&B									
1010	2' to 3'				Ea.	81			81	89
1020	3' to 4'					113			113	124
1030	4' to 5'					143			143	158
1040	5' to 6'				▼	180			180	197
1100	Amelanchier canadensis, (shadblow), Z4, B&B									
1110	3' to 4'				Ea.	43.50			43.50	48
1120	4' to 5'					85.50			85.50	94
1130	5' to 6'					117			117	128
1140	6' to 8'					116			116	128
1150	8' to 10'				▼	167			167	184
1200	Betula maximowicziana, (monarch birch), Z5, B&B									
1210	6' to 8'				Ea.	40.50			40.50	44.50
1220	1-1/2" to 2" Cal.					185			185	203
1230	2" to 2-1/2" Cal.				▼	222			222	244
1300	Betula nigra, (river birch), Z5, B&B									
1310	1-1/2" to 2" Cal.				Ea.	88			88	97
1320	2" to 2-1/2" Cal.				▼	106			106	117

32 93 43.30 Trees, Deciduous	Crew	Daily Output	Labor-Hours	Unit	Material	2015 Bare Costs Labor	Equipment	Total	Total Incl O&P
1330 2-1/2" to 3" Cal.				Ea.	149			149	164
1340 3" to 3-1/2" Cal.				▼	258			258	284
1400 Betula papyrifera, (canoe or paper birch), Z2, B&B									
1410 4' to 5'				Ea.	84.50			84.50	93
1420 1-1/2" to 2" Cal.					108			108	119
1430 2" to 2-1/2" Cal.					127			127	140
1440 2-1/2" to 3" Cal.					135			135	148
1450 3" to 3-1/2" Cal.					149			149	164
1460 3-1/2" to 4" Cal.					184			184	203
1470 4" to 4-1/2" Cal.					200			200	220
1480 4-1/2" to 5" Cal.				▼	249			249	274
1500 Castanea mollissima, (Chinese Chestnut), Z5, B&B									
1510 2' to 3'				Ea.	8.60			8.60	9.45
1520 6' to 8'					58.50			58.50	64
1530 8' to 10'					108			108	119
1540 10' to 12'				▼	136			136	150
1600 Catalpa speciosa, (northern catalpa), Z5, B&B									
1610 6' to 8'				Ea.	88			88	97
1620 2" Cal.				"	242			242	266
1700 Cercidiphyllum japonica, (katsura tree), Z5, B&B									
1710 6' to 8'				Ea.	113			113	124
1720 1-1/2" to 2" Cal.					170			170	187
1730 2" to 2-1/2" Cal.					170			170	187
1740 2-1/2" to 3" Cal.					209			209	229
1750 3-1/2" to 4" Cal.					226			226	249
1760 4" to 4-1/2" Cal.				▼	235			235	258
1800 Cercis canadensis, (eastern redbud), Z5, B&B									
1810 5 gal.				Ea.	61.50			61.50	68
1820 7 gal.					106			106	116
1830 4' to 5'					75			75	82.50
1840 5' to 6'					88			88	97
1850 6' to 8'				▼	134			134	147
1900 Chionanthus virginicus, (fringetree), Z4, B&B									
1910 5 gal.				Ea.	39.50			39.50	43.50
1920 5' to 6'					75			75	82.50
1930 6' to 8'				▼	101			101	111
2000 Cladrastis lutea, (yellowood), Z4, B&B									
2010 1-1/2" to 2" Cal.				Ea.	143			143	157
2020 2" to 2-1/2" Cal.					172			172	190
2030 2-1/2" to 3" Cal.					203			203	224
2040 3" to 3-1/2" Cal.					234			234	257
2050 3-1/2" to 4" Cal.				▼	330			330	360
2100 Cornus florida, (white flowering dogwood), Z5, B&B									
2110 4' to 5'				Ea.	44.50			44.50	49
2120 5' to 6'					75			75	82.50
2130 6' to 7'				▼	93.50			93.50	103
2200 Cornus florida rubra, (pink flowering dogwood), Z6, B&B									
2210 4' to 5'				Ea.	53.50			53.50	59
2220 5' to 6'					93.50			93.50	103
2230 6' to 7'					133			133	146
2240 7' to 8'				▼	145			145	160
2300 Cornus kousa, (Kousa Dogwood), Z5, B&B									
2310 3' to 4'				Ea.	53			53	58

32 93 43.30 Trees, Deciduous	Crew	Daily Output	Labor-Hours	Unit	Material	2015 Bare Costs Labor	Equipment	Total	Total Incl O&P
2320 4' to 5'				Ea.	52.50			52.50	58
2330 5' to 6'					74			74	81.50
2340 6' to 8'					167			167	184
2350 8' to 10'					229			229	252
2400 Crataegus crus-galli, (Cockspur Hawthorn), Z5, B&B									
2410 55 gal.				Ea.	123			123	135
2420 5' to 6'				"	95			95	105
2500 Crataegus oxyacantha superba, (Crimson Hawthorn), Z5, B&B									
2510 5' to 6'				Ea.	71			71	78
2520 6' to 8'					81			81	89
2530 1-1/2" to 2" Cal.					95			95	105
2540 2" to 2-1/2" Cal.					107			107	118
2550 2-1/2" to 3" Cal.					129			129	142
2560 3" to 3-1/2" Cal.					216			216	238
2570 3-1/2" to 4" Cal.					233			233	257
2580 4" to 5" Cal.					246			246	270
2600 Crataegus phaenopyrum, (Washington Hawthorn), Z5, B&B									
2610 5' to 6'				Ea.	135			135	149
2620 6' to 7'					165			165	182
2630 1-3/4" to 2" Cal.					125			125	138
2640 2" to 2-1/2" Cal.					150			150	165
2650 2-1/2" to 3" Cal.					210			210	231
2660 3" to 3-1/2" Cal.					240			240	264
2700 Cydonia oblonga orange, (Orange Quince), Z5, B&B									
2710 5' to 6'				Ea.	53			53	58
2720 6' to 8'				"	79			79	87
2800 Diospyros virginiana, (Persimmon), Z4, B&B									
2810 3' to 4'				Ea.	28.50			28.50	31.50
2820 4' to 5'					37.50			37.50	41
2830 1-1/2" to 2" Cal.					106			106	116
2840 2" to 2-1/2" Cal.					264			264	290
2850 2-1/2" to 3" Cal.					310			310	340
2900 Eleagnus angustifolia, (Russian Olive, tree form), Z3, B&B									
2910 1-1/2" to 2" Cal.				Ea.	211			211	232
2920 2" to 2-1/2" Cal.					425			425	470
2930 2-1/2" to 3" Cal.					640			640	705
3000 Eucommia ulmoides, (Hardy Rubber Tree), Z4, B&B									
3010 6' to 8'				Ea.	119			119	131
3020 8' to 10'					136			136	150
3030 1-1/2" to 2" Cal.					119			119	131
3040 2" to 2-1/2" Cal.					136			136	150
3050 2-1/2" to 3" Cal.					176			176	194
3100 Fagus grandiflora, (American Beech), Z3, B&B									
3110 1-1/2" to 1-3/4" Cal.				Ea.	217			217	239
3120 1-3/4" to 2" Cal.					287			287	315
3130 2" to 2-1/2" Cal.					320			320	350
3200 Fagus sylvatica, (European Beech), Z5, B&B									
3210 6' to 8'				Ea.	189			189	208
3220 1-1/2" to 2" Cal.					375			375	410
3230 2" to 2-1/2" Cal.					225			225	248
3300 Fagus sylvatica pendula, (Weeping European Beech), Z4, B&B									
3310 1-3/4" to 2" cal.				Ea.	190			190	209
3320 2" to 2-1/2" Cal.					190			190	209

32 93 43.30 Trees, Deciduous	Crew	Daily Output	Labor-Hours	Unit	Material	2015 Bare Costs Labor	Equipment	Total	Total Incl O&P
3330	2-1/2" to 3" Cal.				Ea.	265			265	291
3340	3" to 3-1/2" Cal.				▼	335			335	365
3400	Franklinia alatamaha, (Franklin Tree), Z5, B&B									
3410	3 gal.				Ea.	28			28	31
3420	7 gal.					79			79	87
3430	15 gal.					159			159	175
3440	5' to 6'					188			188	207
3450	6' to 8'				▼	161			161	177
3500	Fraxinus americana, (Autumn Purple Ash), Z3, B&B									
3510	5 gal.				Ea.	45			45	49.50
3520	1-1/2" to 2" Cal.					151			151	167
3530	2" to 2-1/2" Cal.				▼	189			189	208
3600	Fraxinus pensylvanica, (Seedless Green Ash), Z3, B&B									
3610	5 gal.				Ea.	34.50			34.50	38
3615	20 gal.					97			97	106
3620	55 gal.					128			128	140
3625	6' to 8'					79			79	87
3630	1-1/2" to 2" Cal.					114			114	126
3635	2" to 2-1/2" Cal.					144			144	159
3640	2-1/2" to 3" Cal.					172			172	190
3645	3" to 3-1/2" Cal.					216			216	237
3650	3-1/2" to 4" Cal.					260			260	286
3655	4" to 4-1/2" Cal.					260			260	286
3660	4-1/2" to 5" Cal.					430			430	475
3665	Bare root, 8' to 10'					86			86	95
3670	10' to 12'					101			101	111
3675	12' to 14'				▼	144			144	159
3700	Ginkgo biloba, (Maidenhair Tree), Z5, B&B									
3710	5 gal.				Ea.	63.50			63.50	69.50
3720	1-1/2" to 2" Cal.					180			180	198
3730	2" to 2-1/2" Cal.					230			230	253
3740	2-1/2" to 3" Cal.					270			270	297
3750	3" to 3-1/2" Cal.				▼	360			360	395
3800	Gleditsia triacanthos inermis, (Thornless Honeylocust), Z5, B&B									
3810	20 gal.				Ea.	37			37	40.50
3815	55 gal.					92.50			92.50	102
3820	8' to 10'					136			136	149
3825	1-1/2" to 2" Cal.					169			169	186
3830	2" to 2-1/2" Cal.					203			203	224
3835	2-1/2" to 3" Cal.					271			271	298
3840	3" to 3-1/2" Cal.					305			305	335
3845	3-1/2" to 4" Cal.					340			340	375
3850	4" to 4-1/2" Cal.					405			405	445
3855	4-1/2" to 5" Cal.					405			405	445
3860	Bare root, 10' to 12'					242			242	266
3865	12' to 14'					290			290	320
3870	14' to 16'				▼	385			385	425
3900	Gymnocladus dioicus, (Kentucky Coffee Tree), Z5, B&B									
3910	1-3/4" Cal.				Ea.	136			136	149
3920	2" Cal.					227			227	250
3930	2-1/2" Cal.				▼	290			290	320
4000	Halesia carolina, (Silverbell), Z6, B&B									
4010	4' to 5'				Ea.	66			66	72.50

32 93 43.30 Trees, Deciduous	Crew	Daily Output	Labor-Hours	Unit	Material	2015 Bare Costs Labor	Equipment	Total	Total Incl O&P
4020	5' to 6'				Ea.	71.50			71.50	78.50
4030	6' to 8'					85.50			85.50	94
4040	8' to 10'					117			117	129
4050	10' to 12'					162			162	178
4100	Hippophae rhamnoides, (Common Sea Buckthorn), Z3, B&B									
4110	3 gal.				Ea.	17.40			17.40	19.10
4120	5' to 6'					91.50			91.50	101
4130	6' to 8'					106			106	116
4200	Juglans cinera, (Butternut), Z4, B&B									
4210	4' to 5'				Ea.	31			31	34
4220	5' to 6'					41.50			41.50	45.50
4230	6' to 8'					55.50			55.50	61
4300	Juglans nigra, (Black Walnut), Z5, B&B									
4310	4' to 5'				Ea.	44			44	48.50
4320	5' to 6'					53			53	58
4330	1-1/2" to 2" Cal.					150			150	165
4340	2" to 2-1/2" Cal.					176			176	194
4350	2-1/2" to 3" Cal.					211			211	232
4400	Koelreuteria paniculata, (Goldenrain Tree), Z6, B&B									
4410	5 gal.				Ea.	19.70			19.70	21.50
4420	15 gal.					52			52	57
4430	20 gal.					135			135	148
4440	55 gal.					162			162	178
4450	1-1/2" to 2" Cal.					269			269	296
4460	2" to 2-1/2" Cal.					315			315	345
4470	2-1/2" to 3" Cal.					405			405	445
4500	Laburnum x watereri, (Goldenchain tree), Z5, B&B									
4510	6' to 8'				Ea.	63			63	69
4520	8' to 9'					88			88	97
4530	1-3/4" to 2" Cal.					192			192	211
4540	2" to 2-1/2" Cal.					194			194	213
4550	2-1/2" to 3" Cal.					187			187	205
4600	Larix decidua pendula, (Weeping European Larch), Z2, B&B									
4610	3' to 4'				Ea.	81			81	89
4620	4' to 5'					98.50			98.50	108
4630	5' to 6'					142			142	156
4640	6' to 7'					264			264	290
4700	Larix kaempferi, (Japanese Larch), Z4, B&B									
4710	5' to 6'				Ea.	142			142	156
4720	6' to 8'					171			171	188
4730	8' to 10'					188			188	207
4800	Liquidambar styraciflua, (Sweetgum), Z6, B&B									
4810	6' to 8'				Ea.	76.50			76.50	84
4820	8' to 10'					85			85	93.50
4830	1-1/2" to 2" Cal.					98.50			98.50	108
4840	2" to 2-1/2" Cal.					124			124	137
4850	2-1/2" to 3" Cal.					142			142	156
4900	Liriodendron tulipifera, (Tuliptree), Z5, B&B									
4910	7' to 8'				Ea.	54			54	59.50
4920	1-1/2" to 2" Cal.					154			154	169
4930	2" to 2-1/2" Cal.					176			176	193
4940	2-1/2" to 3" Cal.					216			216	237
5000	Maclura pomifera, (Osage Orange), Z5, B&B									

For customer support on your Site Work & Landscape Cost Data, call 877.737.1594.

431

32 93 43.30 Trees, Deciduous	Crew	Daily Output	Labor-Hours	Unit	Material	2015 Bare Costs Labor	Equipment	Total	Total Incl O&P
5010	3' to 4'				Ea.	41.50			41.50	45.50
5020	4' to 5'					59			59	65
5030	6' to 8'				▼	70.50			70.50	77.50
5100	Magnolia loebneri merrill, (Merrill Magnolia), Z5, B&B									
5110	4' to 5'				Ea.	72			72	79
5120	5' to 6'					91.50			91.50	101
5130	6' to 7'					144			144	158
5140	7' to 8'				▼	165			165	182
5200	Magnolia soulangena, (Saucer Magnolia), Z6, B&B									
5210	3' to 4'				Ea.	49.50			49.50	54
5220	4' to 5'					72			72	79
5230	5' to 6'					90			90	99
5240	6' to 7'				▼	144			144	158
5300	Magnolia stellata, (Star Magnolia), Z6, B&B									
5310	2' to 3'				Ea.	31.50			31.50	35
5320	3' to 4'					40.50			40.50	44.50
5330	4' to 5'					76.50			76.50	84
5340	5' to 6'				▼	107			107	118
5400	Magnolia virginiana, (Sweetbay Magnolia), Z5, B&B									
5410	2' to 3'				Ea.	39			39	43
5420	3' to 4'					50.50			50.50	56
5430	4' to 5'					79			79	87
5440	5' to 6'				▼	111			111	122
5500	Magnolia x galaxy, (Galaxy Magnolia), Z6, B&B									
5510	5 gal.				Ea.	68			68	74.50
5520	7 gal.					90			90	98.50
5530	2-1/2" to 3" Cal.				▼	180			180	197
5600	Malus, (Crabapple), Z5, B&B									
5610	5 gal.				Ea.	15.40			15.40	16.95
5615	15 gal.					34.50			34.50	38
5620	20 gal.					52.50			52.50	57.50
5625	55 gal.					105			105	115
5630	6' to 8'					61.50			61.50	68
5635	1-1/2" to 2" Cal.					111			111	122
5640	2" to 2-1/2" Cal.					136			136	149
5645	2-1/2" to 3" Cal.					185			185	203
5650	3" to 3-1/2" Cal.					234			234	257
5655	3-1/2" to 4" Cal.					268			268	295
5660	4" to 5" Cal.					300			300	330
5665	Bare root, 5' to 6'				▼	61.50			61.50	68
5700	Metasequoia glyptostroboides, (Dawn Redwood), Z5, B&B									
5710	5' to 6'				Ea.	134			134	148
5720	6' to 8'					215			215	237
5730	8' to 10'				▼	280			280	310
5800	Morus alba, (White Mulberry), Z4, B&B									
5810	5 gal.				Ea.	23			23	25
5900	Morus alba tatarica, (Russian Mulberry), Z4, B&B									
5910	6' to 8'				Ea.	61.50			61.50	68
5920	10' to 12'					141			141	155
5930	2-1/2" to 3" Cal.				▼	310			310	340
6000	Nyssa sylvatica, (Tupelo), Z4, B&B									
6010	5' to 6'				Ea.	71			71	78
6020	1-1/2" to 2" Cal.				▼	188			188	207

32 93 Plants

32 93 43 – Trees

		32 93 43.30 Trees, Deciduous	Crew	Daily Output	Labor-Hours	Unit	Material	2015 Bare Costs Labor	Equipment	Total	Total Incl O&P
6030		2" to 2-1/2" Cal.				Ea.	249			249	274
6040		2-1/2" to 3" Cal.				▼	310			310	340
6100		Ostrya virginiana, (Hop Hornbeam), Z5, B&B									
6110		2" to 2-1/2" Cal.				Ea.	188			188	207
6120		2-1/2" to 3" Cal.				"	249			249	274
6200		Oxydendron arboreum, (Sourwood), Z4, B&B									
6210		4' to 5'				Ea.	103			103	114
6220		5' to 6'					85.50			85.50	94
6230		6' to 7'					145			145	160
6240		7' to 8'				▼	148			148	163
6300		Parrotia persica, (Persian Parrotia), Z6, B&B									
6310		5 gal.				Ea.	31			31	34
6320		3' to 4'				"	90			90	98.50
6400		Phellodendron amurense, (Amur Corktree), Z3, B&B									
6410		6' to 8'				Ea.	79			79	87
6420		8' to 10'					101			101	111
6430		2" to 2-1/2" Cal.					150			150	166
6440		2-1/2" to 3" Cal.					200			200	220
6450		3" to 3-1/2" Cal.				▼	226			226	249
6500		Platanus acerifolia, (London Plane Tree), Z5, B&B									
6510		15 gal.				Ea.	32			32	35
6520		20 gal.					61.50			61.50	68
6530		8' to 10'					80			80	88
6540		1-1/2" to 2" Cal.					157			157	173
6550		2" to 2-1/2" Cal.					189			189	207
6560		2-1/2" to 3" Cal.					220			220	242
6570		3" to 3-1/2" Cal.				▼	251			251	276
6600		Platanus occidentalis, (Buttonwood, Sycamore), Z4, B&B									
6610		30" box				Ea.	232			232	255
6620		36" Box					350			350	385
6630		42" Box					755			755	830
6640		1-1/2" to 2" Cal.					157			157	173
6650		2" to 2-1/2" Cal.					189			189	207
6660		2-1/2" to 3" Cal.					220			220	242
6670		3" to 3-1/2" Cal.				▼	267			267	293
6700		Populus alba pyramidalis, (Bolleana Poplar), Z3, cont/BB									
6710		5 gal.				Ea.	31.50			31.50	35
6720		15 gal.					46.50			46.50	51.50
6730		20 gal.				▼	90			90	98.50
6800		Populus canadensis, (Hybrid Black Poplar), Z5, B&B									
6810		6' to 8'				Ea.	106			106	116
6820		1-1/2" to 2" Cal.					220			220	242
6830		2" to 2-1/2" Cal.				▼	310			310	340
6900		Populus nigra italica, (Lombardy Poplar), Z4, cont									
6910		5 gal.				Ea.	20			20	22.50
6920		20 gal.					67			67	73.50
6930		6' to 8' Potted				▼	79			79	87
7000		Prunus cerasifera pissardi, (Flowering Plum), Z5, cont/BB									
7010		5 gal.				Ea.	25.50			25.50	28
7020		15 gal.					82.50			82.50	91
7030		20 gal.					154			154	169
7040		5' to 6'					66			66	72.50
7050		6' to 8'				▼	141			141	155

For customer support on your Site Work & Landscape Cost Data, call 877.737.1594.

433

32 93 43.30 Trees, Deciduous	Crew	Daily Output	Labor-Hours	Unit	Material	2015 Bare Costs Labor	Equipment	Total	Total Incl O&P
7060	1-1/2" to 2" Cal.				Ea.	224			224	247
7070	2" to 2-1/2" Cal.				↓	286			286	315
7100	Prunus sargenti columnaris, (Columnar Cherry), Z4, cont/BB									
7110	6' to 8'				Ea.	88			88	97
7120	1-1/2" to 2" Cal.					175			175	193
7130	2" to 2-1/2" Cal.					246			246	271
7140	2-1/2" to 3" Cal.				▼	420			420	460
7200	Prunus serrulata kwanzan, (Flowering Cherry), Z6, cont/BB									
7210	20 gal.				Ea.	141			141	155
7220	1-1/2" to 2" Cal.					117			117	129
7230	2" to 2-1/2" Cal.					200			200	220
7240	3" to 3-1/2" Cal.					277			277	305
7250	3-1/2" to 4" Cal.					340			340	375
7260	4" to 5" Cal.				▼	400			400	440
7300	Prunus subhirtella pendula, (Weeping Cherry), Z5, B&B									
7310	1-1/4" to 1-1/2" Cal.				Ea.	92.50			92.50	102
7320	1-1/2" to 1-3/4" Cal.					111			111	122
7330	1-3/4" to 2" Cal.					166			166	183
7340	2" to 2-1/2" Cal.					185			185	203
7350	2-1/2" to 3" Cal.				▼	216			216	237
7400	Prunus yedoensis, (Yoshino Cherry), Z5, B&B									
7410	5 gal.				Ea.	154			154	169
7420	1-1/2" to 2" Cal.					238			238	261
7430	2" to 2-1/2" Cal.					286			286	315
7440	2-1/2" to 3" Cal.				▼	330			330	365
7500	Pyrus calleryana aristocrat, (Aristocrat Flwrng Pear), Z5, cont/BB									
7510	15 gal.				Ea.	36.50			36.50	40.50
7520	20 gal.					66.50			66.50	73.50
7530	6' to 8'					53.50			53.50	58.50
7540	1-1/2" to 2" Cal.					122			122	134
7550	2" to 2-1/2" Cal.					150			150	166
7560	2-1/2" to 3" Cal.					211			211	232
7570	3" to 3-1/2" Cal.					225			225	248
7580	3-1/2" to 4" Cal.				▼	250			250	275
7600	Pyrus calleryana bradford, (Bradford Flowering Pear), Z5, cont/BB									
7610	5 gal.				Ea.	18.65			18.65	20.50
7620	8 to 9'					78			78	85.50
7630	1-1/2" to 2" Cal.					134			134	147
7640	2" to 2-1/2" Cal.					222			222	244
7650	2-1/2" to 3" Cal.					310			310	340
7660	3" to 3-1/2" Cal.					445			445	490
7670	3-1/2" to 4" Cal.				▼	535			535	585
7700	Quercus acutissima, (Sawtooth Oak), Z5, B&B									
7710	6' to 8'				Ea.	61.50			61.50	68
7720	8' to 10'					80			80	88
7730	10' to 12'					98			98	108
7740	1-1/2" to 2" Cal.					98			98	108
7750	2" to 2-1/2" Cal.				▼	123			123	136
7800	Quercus coccinea, (Scarlet Oak), Z4, B&B									
7810	1-1/2" to 2" cal.				Ea.	154			154	169
7820	2" to 2-1/2" Cal.				"	216			216	237
7900	Quercus palustris, (Pin Oak), Z5, B&B									
7910	5 gal.				Ea.	13.55			13.55	14.90

32 93 43.30 Trees, Deciduous	Crew	Daily Output	Labor-Hours	Unit	Material	2015 Bare Costs Labor	Equipment	Total	Total Incl O&P
7920	1-1/2" to 2" Cal.				Ea.	114			114	125
7930	2" to 2-1/2" Cal.					166			166	183
7940	2-1/2" to 3" Cal.					216			216	237
7950	3" to 3-1/2" Cal.					277			277	305
7960	3-1/2" to 4" Cal.					310			310	340
7970	4" to 4-1/2" Cal.					415			415	455
7980	4-1/2" to 5" Cal.					350			350	390
7985	6" to 7" Cal.					690			690	755
7990	8" to 9" Cal.					830			830	910
8000	Quercus prinus, (Chestnut Oak), Z4, B&B									
8010	6' to 8'				Ea.	97			97	106
8020	8' to 10'				"	141			141	155
8100	Quercus robur fastigiata, (Columnar English Oak), Z4, B&B									
8110	6' to 8'				Ea.	68			68	74.50
8120	8' to 10'					98.50			98.50	108
8130	1-1/2" to 2" Cal.					139			139	152
8140	2" to 2-1/2" Cal.					228			228	251
8150	2-1/2" to 3" Cal.					262			262	288
8200	Quercus rubra, (Red Oak), Z4, cont/BB									
8210	5 gal.				Ea.	16.95			16.95	18.65
8220	1-1/2" to 2" Cal.					123			123	136
8230	2" to 2-1/2" Cal.					185			185	203
8240	2-1/2" to 3" Cal.					231			231	254
8300	Robinia pseudoacacia, (Black Locust), Z5, cont									
8310	24" Box				Ea.	113			113	125
8320	30" Box					234			234	257
8330	36" Box					350			350	385
8400	Salix babylonica, (Weeping Willow), Z5, cont/BB									
8410	24" Box				Ea.	127			127	139
8420	36" Box					395			395	435
8430	1-1/2" to 2" Cal.					113			113	124
8440	2" to 2-1/2" Cal.					157			157	172
8450	2-1/2" to 3" Cal.					166			166	183
8500	Sophora japonica "Regent", (Regent Scholartree), Z4, B&B									
8510	1-3/4" to 2" Cal.				Ea.	282			282	310
8520	2" to 2-1/2" Cal.					325			325	360
8530	2-1/2" to 3" Cal.					375			375	410
8600	Sorbus alnifolia, (Korean Mountain Ash), Z5, B&B									
8610	8' to 10'				Ea.	88			88	97
8620	1-1/2" to 2" Cal.					123			123	136
8630	2" to 2-1/2" Cal.					141			141	155
8640	2-1/2" to 3" Cal.					172			172	189
8700	Sorbus aucuparia, (European Mountain Ash), Z2, cont/BB									
8710	15 gal.				Ea.	53			53	58
8715	20 gal.					164			164	180
8720	1-1/2" to 2" Cal.					141			141	155
8725	2" to 2-1/2" Cal.					255			255	281
8730	2-1/2" to 3" Cal.					330			330	365
8735	3" to 3-1/2" Cal.					450			450	495
8740	3-1/2" to 4" Cal.					450			450	495
8745	4" to 5" Cal.					585			585	645
8750	5" to 6" Cal.					825			825	905
8755	Bare root, 8' to 10'					88			88	97

For customer support on your Site Work & Landscape Cost Data, call 877.737.1594.

435

32 93 43.30 Trees, Deciduous	Crew	Daily Output	Labor-Hours	Unit	Material	2015 Bare Costs Labor	Equipment	Total	Total Incl O&P
8760 — 10' to 12'				Ea.	101			101	111
8800 — Stewartia pseudocamellia, (Japanese Stewartia), Z5, B&B									
8810 — 2' to 3'				Ea.	66			66	72.50
8820 — 3' to 4'					132			132	145
8830 — 6' to 8'				↓	264			264	290
8900 — Styrax japonica, (Japanese Snowbell), Z6, B&B									
8910 — 4' to 5'				Ea.	137			137	151
8920 — 5' to 6'					206			206	227
8930 — 6' to 8'				↓	289			289	320
9000 — Syringa japonica, (Japanese Tree, Lilac), Z4, B&B									
9010 — 5' to 6'				Ea.	79			79	87
9020 — 6' to 8'					101			101	111
9030 — 8' to 10'					264			264	290
9040 — 10' to 12'				↓	335			335	370
9100 — Taxodium distichum, (Bald Cypress), Z4, B&B									
9110 — 5' to 6'				Ea.	98.50			98.50	108
9120 — 6' to 7'					123			123	136
9130 — 7' to 8'					148			148	163
9140 — 8' to 10'				↓	185			185	203
9200 — Tilia americana "Redmond", (Redmond Linden), Z3, B&B									
9210 — 8' to 10'				Ea.	157			157	173
9220 — 10' to 12'					191			191	210
9230 — 1-1/2" to 2" Cal.					157			157	173
9240 — 2" to 2-1/2" Cal.					194			194	213
9250 — 2-1/2" to 3" Cal.				↓	222			222	244
9300 — Tilia cordata greenspire, (Littleleaf Linden), Z4, B&B									
9310 — 1-1/2" to 2" Cal.				Ea.	187			187	205
9315 — 2" to 2-1/2" Cal.					234			234	257
9320 — 2-1/2" to 3" Cal.					296			296	325
9325 — 3" to 3-1/2" Cal.					345			345	380
9330 — 3-1/2" to 4" Cal.					395			395	430
9335 — 4" to 4-1/2" Cal.					440			440	485
9340 — 4-1/2" to 5" Cal.					485			485	535
9345 — 5" to 5-1/2" Cal.					535			535	585
9350 — Bare root, 10' to 12'					187			187	205
9355 — 12' to 14'				↓	218			218	240
9400 — Tilia tomentosa, (Silver Linden), Z4, B&B									
9410 — 6' to 8'				Ea.	139			139	152
9420 — 8' to 10'					157			157	173
9430 — 10' to 12'					191			191	210
9440 — 2" to 2-1/2" Cal.					231			231	254
9450 — 2-1/2" to 3" Cal.				↓	293			293	320
9500 — Ulmus americana, (American Elm), Z3, B&B									
9510 — 6' to 8'				Ea.	56			56	61.50
9600 — Zeklova serrata, (Japanese Keaki Tree), Z4, B&B									
9610 — 1-1/2" to 2" Cal.				Ea.	154			154	169
9620 — 2" to 2-1/2" Cal.					209			209	230
9630 — 2-1/2" to 3" Cal.				↓	234			234	257

32 93 43.40 Trees, Conifers	Crew	Daily Output	Labor-Hours	Unit	Material	2015 Bare Costs Labor	Equipment	Total	Total Incl O&P
0010	**TREES, CONIFERS**									
0011	Zone 2-7									
1000	Abies balsamea nana, (Dwarf Balsam Fir), Z3, cont									
1001	1 gal.				Ea.	18.55			18.55	20.50
1002	15" to 18"					42			42	46
1003	18" to 24"					64			64	70.50
1050	Abies concolor, (White Fir), Z4, B&B									
1051	2' to 3'				Ea.	42			42	46
1052	3' to 4'					51			51	56
1053	4' to 5'					116			116	127
1054	5' to 6'					148			148	163
1055	6' to 8'					195			195	214
1100	Abies concolor violacea, Z4, cont/BB									
1101	5' to 6'				Ea.	159			159	175
1102	6' to 7'				"	200			200	220
1150	Abies fraseri, (Fraser Balsam Fir), Z5, B&B									
1151	5' to 6'				Ea.	148			148	163
1152	6' to 7'				"	186			186	204
1200	Abies iasiocarpa arizonica, (Cork Fir), Z5, cont/BB									
1201	2' to 3'				Ea.	46.50			46.50	51
1202	3' to 4'					65			65	71.50
1203	4' to 5'					111			111	123
1204	5' to 6'					149			149	163
1205	6' to 7'					195			195	214
1206	8' to 10'					232			232	255
1207	10' to 12'					315			315	345
1250	Abies iasiocarpa compacta, (Dwarf Alpine Fir), Z5, cont/BB									
1251	18" to 24"				Ea.	93			93	102
1252	2' to 3'					111			111	123
1253	3' to 4'					139			139	153
1254	4' to 5'					186			186	204
1255	5' to 6'					232			232	255
1300	Abies koreana, (Korean Fir), Z5, B&B									
1301	10' to 12'				Ea.	440			440	485
1302	12' to 14'				"	535			535	585
1350	Abies pinsapo glauca, (Blue Spanish Fir), Z6, cont									
1351	2' to 3' Spread				Ea.	83.50			83.50	92
1352	3' to 4'					139			139	153
1353	4' to 5'					162			162	179
1400	Abies procera (nobilis) glauca, (Noble Fir), Z5, B&B									
1401	15" to 18" Spread				Ea.	43.50			43.50	48
1402	18" to 24" Spread					67			67	73.50
1403	2' to 3'					83.50			83.50	92
1404	3' to 4'					139			139	153
1450	Abies veitchi, (Veitch Fir), Z3, cont/BB									
1451	4' to 5'				Ea.	125			125	138
1452	5' to 6'				"	149			149	163
1500	Cedrus atlantica glauca, (Blue Atlas Cedar), Z6, cont/BB									
1501	2' to 3'				Ea.	86			86	94.50
1502	3' to 4'					143			143	158
1503	4' to 5'					191			191	210
1504	5' to 6'					239			239	263

For customer support on your Site Work & Landscape Cost Data, call 877.737.1594.

437

32 93 43.40 Trees, Conifers		Crew	Daily Output	Labor-Hours	Unit	Material	2015 Bare Costs Labor	Equipment	Total	Total Incl O&P
1505	7' to 8'				Ea.	310			310	340
1550	Cedrus deodara, (Indian Cedar), Z7, cont/BB									
1551	5 gal.				Ea.	21			21	23
1552	6' to 8'					251			251	276
1553	8' to 10'					284			284	310
1554	10' to 12'					330			330	365
1555	12' to 14'					615			615	675
1556	14' to 16'					615			615	675
1600	Cedrus deodara kashmir, (Hardy Deodar Cedar), Z6, cont/BB									
1601	3' to 4'				Ea.	142			142	156
1602	4' to 5'					189			189	208
1603	5' to 6'					232			232	255
1650	Cedrus deodara shalimar, (Hardy Deodar Cedar), Z6, cont/BB									
1651	2' to 3'				Ea.	114			114	125
1652	3' to 4'				"	127			127	140
1700	Cedrus libani sargenti, (Weeping Cedar of Lebanon), Z6, cont									
1701	2' to 3'				Ea.	95.50			95.50	105
1702	3' to 4'				"	142			142	156
1750	Chamaecyparis lawsoniana, (Dwarf Lawson's Cypress), Z6, cont									
1751	18" to 24"				Ea.	77.50			77.50	85
1752	2' to 2-1/2'				"	123			123	135
1800	Chamaecyparis nootkatensis glauca, (Alaska Cedar), Z6, cont/BB									
1801	2' to 3'				Ea.	86			86	95
1802	3' to 4'					143			143	158
1803	4' to 5'					191			191	210
1804	5' to 6'					239			239	263
1850	Chamaecyparis nootkatensis lutea, (Gold Cedar), Z6, cont/BB									
1851	3' to 4'				Ea.	122			122	134
1852	4' to 5'					131			131	144
1853	5' to 6'					157			157	172
1900	Chamaecyparis nootkatensis pendula, (Alaska Cedar), Z6, cont/BB									
1901	2' to 3'				Ea.	81.50			81.50	89.50
1902	4' to 5'					115			115	126
1903	5' to 6'					154			154	169
1904	6' to 7'					158			158	174
1950	Chamaecyparis obtusa coralliformis, (Torulosa), Z5, cont/BB									
1951	1 gal.				Ea.	4.78			4.78	5.25
1952	2 gal.					9.45			9.45	10.40
1953	5 gal.					14.20			14.20	15.60
1954	7 gal.					23.50			23.50	26
1955	4 to 5'					61.50			61.50	67.50
1956	7' to 8'					128			128	141
2000	Chamaecyparis obtusa crippsi, (Gold Hinoki Cypress), Z6, cont/BB									
2001	1 gal.				Ea.	20			20	22
2002	5 gal.					41			41	45
2003	2' to 3'					54.50			54.50	60
2004	3' to 4'					63.50			63.50	70
2005	4' to 5'					95.50			95.50	105
2050	Chamaecyparis obtusa filiciodes, (Fernspray Cypress), Z5, cont/BB									
2051	5 gal.				Ea.	25.50			25.50	28
2052	2' to 3'					86.50			86.50	95
2053	3' to 4'					109			109	120
2100	Chamaecyparis obtusa gracilis, (Hinoki Cypress), Z5, cont/BB									

32 93 43.40 Trees, Conifers	Crew	Daily Output	Labor-Hours	Unit	Material	2015 Bare Costs Labor	Equipment	Total	Total Incl O&P
2101	2' to 3'				Ea.	74.50			74.50	81.50
2102	3' to 4'					121			121	133
2103	10' to 12'					274			274	300
2150	Chamaecyparis obtusa gracilis compacta, (Cypress), Z5, cont/BB									
2151	15" to 18"				Ea.	43.50			43.50	48
2152	18" to 24"					60.50			60.50	66.50
2153	2' to 3'					97.50			97.50	107
2154	3' to 4'					167			167	184
2200	Chamaecyparis obtusa gracilis nana, (Hinoki Cypress), Z5, cont/BB									
2201	10" to 12"				Ea.	21.50			21.50	23.50
2202	12" to 15"					29.50			29.50	32.50
2203	15" to 18"					68			68	74.50
2204	18" to 24"					76			76	83.50
2250	Chamaecyparis obtusa lycopodioides, (Cypress), Z5, cont/BB									
2251	18" to 24"				Ea.	26			26	28.50
2252	2' to 3'					74.50			74.50	81.50
2253	3' to 4'					121			121	133
2254	4' to 5'					139			139	153
2255	5' to 6'					161			161	177
2256	6' to 7'					182			182	200
2257	7' to 8'					211			211	232
2300	Chamaecyparis obtusa magnifica, (Hinoki Cypress), Z5, cont/BB									
2301	2' to 3'				Ea.	63			63	69.50
2302	3' to 4'					63			63	69.50
2303	4' to 5'					157			157	173
2304	5' to 6'					190			190	209
2305	6' to 7'					212			212	233
2350	Chamaecyparis pisifera, (Sawara Cypress), Z5, cont/BB									
2351	4' to 5'				Ea.	46.50			46.50	51
2352	5' to 6'					64.50			64.50	71
2353	6' to 7'					126			126	138
2354	7' to 8'					135			135	148
2400	Chamaecyparis pisifera aurea, (Sawara Cypress), Z4, cont/BB									
2401	4' to 5'				Ea.	51			51	56
2402	5' to 6'					71.50			71.50	78.50
2403	6' to 7'					139			139	153
2404	7' to 8'					148			148	163
2450	Chamaecyparis pisifera boulevard, (Moss Cypress), Z5, cont/BB									
2451	18" to 24"				Ea.	21			21	23
2452	2' to 3'					63			63	69.50
2453	3' to 4'					80			80	88
2454	4' to 5'					102			102	112
2455	5' to 6'					147			147	161
2456	6' to 7'					187			187	206
2500	Chamaecyparis pisifera compacta, (Sawara Cypress), Z4, cont									
2501	15" to 18" Spread				Ea.	29.50			29.50	32.50
2502	18" to 24" Spread					43.50			43.50	48
2503	2' to 2-1/2' Spread					67			67	73.50
2504	2-1/2' to 3' Spread					104			104	114
2550	Chamaecyparis pisifera filifera, (Thread Cypress), Z4, cont/BB									
2551	18" to 24"				Ea.	35.50			35.50	39
2552	2' to 3'					65			65	71.50
2553	3' to 4'					104			104	114

32 93 Plants

32 93 43 – Trees

32 93 43.40 Trees, Conifers	Crew	Daily Output	Labor-Hours	Unit	Material	2015 Bare Costs Labor	Equipment	Total	Total Incl O&P
2554	4' to 5'				Ea.	126			126	138
2555	5' to 6'					147			147	161
2556	6' to 7'				▼	187			187	206
2600	Chamaecyparis pisifera filifera aurea, (Thread Cypress), Z4, cont									
2601	8 to 10"				Ea.	16.85			16.85	18.55
2602	10 to 12"					24			24	26.50
2603	15 to 18"				▼	25.50			25.50	28
2650	Chamaecyparis pisifera filifera nana, (Thread Cypress), Z5, cont									
2651	15" to 18"				Ea.	35.50			35.50	39
2652	18" to 24"					53			53	58
2653	2' to 2-1/2'					71.50			71.50	78.50
2654	2-1/2' to 3'					88			88	97
2655	3' to 4'					117			117	129
2671	Gold Spangle, 12" to 15"					32.50			32.50	35.50
2672	18" to 24"				▼	46.50			46.50	51
2673	Bare root, 2' to 3'				▼	63			63	69.50
2700	Chamaecyparis pisifera plumosa aurea, (Plumed Cypress), Z6, B&B									
2701	18" to 24"				Ea.	56.50			56.50	62.50
2702	3' to 4'					65			65	71.50
2703	4' to 5'				▼	83.50			83.50	92
2750	Chamaecyparis pisifera plumosa compress., Z6, cont/BB									
2751	12" to 15"				Ea.	27			27	29.50
2752	15" to 18"					35.50			35.50	39
2753	18" to 24"					46.50			46.50	51
2754	2' to 2-1/2'					56.50			56.50	62.50
2755	2-1/2' to 3'				▼	70.50			70.50	77.50
2800	Chamaecyparis pisifera squarrosa, (Cypress), Z5, cont/BB									
2801	1 gal.				Ea.	8.35			8.35	9.20
2802	2 gal.					16.70			16.70	18.35
2803	4' to 5'					21			21	23
2804	5' to 6'				▼	70.50			70.50	77.50
2850	Chamaecyparis pisifera squarrosa pygmaea, (Cypress), Z6, cont									
2851	12" to 15"				Ea.	27			27	29.50
2852	15" to 18"					35.50			35.50	39
2853	18" to 24"				▼	43.50			43.50	48
2900	Chamaecyparis thyoides Andelyensis, (White Cedar), Z5, cont/BB									
2901	2' to 3'				Ea.	8.65			8.65	9.50
2902	5 gal.					57			57	63
2903	4' to 5'					106			106	117
2904	5' to 6'					128			128	141
2905	6' to 7'				▼	150			150	164
2950	Cryptomeria japonica cristata, (Japanese Cedar), Z6, B&B									
2951	5' to 6'				Ea.	106			106	117
2952	6' to 8'				"	175			175	193
3000	Cryptomeria japonica lobbi, (Lobb Cryptomeria), Z6, B&B									
3001	6' to 8'				Ea.	191			191	210
3002	8' to 10'					239			239	263
3003	10' to 12'				▼	287			287	315
3050	Cupressocyparis leylandi blue, (Leylandi Cypress), Z6, B&B									
3051	5' to 6'				Ea.	137			137	150
3052	6' to 7'				"	159			159	175
3100	Cupressocyparis leylandii, (Leylandi Cypress), Z6, cont/BB									
3101	1 gal.				Ea.	9.10			9.10	10

440

32 93 43.40 Trees, Conifers	Crew	Daily Output	Labor-Hours	Unit	Material	2015 Bare Costs Labor	Equipment	Total	Total Incl O&P
3102	5 gal.				Ea.	25.50			25.50	28
3103	4' to 5'					86.50			86.50	95
3104	5' to 6'					137			137	150
3105	6' to 7'					159			159	175
3106	Box, 24"				↓	16.40			16.40	18
3150	Cupressus arizonica, (Arizona Cypress), Z6, cont									
3151	5 gal.				Ea.	41			41	45
3152	7 gal.				"	54.50			54.50	60
3200	Cupressus macrocarpa, (Monterey Cypress), Z8,									
3201	1 gal.				Ea.	6.35			6.35	7
3202	5 gal.					27.50			27.50	30
3203	15 gal.				↓	59			59	65
3250	Cupressus sempervirens, (Italian Cypress), Z7, cont									
3251	5 gal.				Ea.	27.50			27.50	30
3252	15 gal.				"	59			59	65
3300	Juniperus chinensis, (Green Clmnr Chinese Juniper), Z4, cont/BB									
3301	24 to 30"				Ea.	32.50			32.50	36
3302	30 to 36"					37			37	40.50
3303	3' to 4'					55			55	60.50
3304	4' to 5'					68			68	75
3305	5' to 6'				↓	90			90	99
3350	Juniperus chinensis "Armstrongii", (Armstrong Juniper), Z4, cont									
3351	1 gal.				Ea.	5.50			5.50	6.05
3352	2 gal.					17			17	18.70
3353	5 gal.				↓	27			27	29.50
3400	Juniperus chinensis "Blue Point", (Blue Point Juniper), Z4, cont/BB									
3401	1 gal.				Ea.	9.10			9.10	10
3402	5 gal.					20			20	22
3403	4' to 5'					52			52	57.50
3404	5' to 6'					115			115	127
3405	6' to 8'				↓	130			130	143
3450	Juniperus chinensis "Keteleeri", (Keteleer Juniper), Z5, cont/BB									
3451	3-1/2 to 4'				Ea.	52			52	57.50
3452	4 to 4-1/2'				"	133			133	146
3500	Juniperus chinensis "Sargenti Glauca", (Sargent Juniper), Z4, cont									
3501	12 to 15"				Ea.	13.40			13.40	14.75
3502	15 to 18"					16.85			16.85	18.50
3503	2 to 2-1/2'					42.50			42.50	47
3504	2-1/2 to 3'				↓	42.50			42.50	47
3550	Juniperus chinensis "Sea Green", (Sea Green Juniper), Z4, cont									
3555	15 to 18"				Ea.	17.65			17.65	19.40
3556	18 to 24"					28			28	30.50
3557	2 to 2-1/2'					44.50			44.50	49
3558	2-1/2 to 3'				↓	44.50			44.50	49
3600	Juniperus chinensis blaauwi, (Blaauwi Juniper), Z4, B&B									
3601	18" to 24"				Ea.	28			28	30.50
3602	2' to 3'					44.50			44.50	49
3603	3' to 4'					63			63	69.50
3604	4' to 5'					111			111	122
3605	5' to 6'				↓	145			145	159
3650	Juniperus chinensis columnaris, (Chinese Juniper), Z4, B&B									
3651	4' to 5'				Ea.	111			111	122
3652	5' to 6'				↓	145			145	159

For customer support on your Site Work & Landscape Cost Data, call 877.737.1594.

441

32 93 43.40 Trees, Conifers	Crew	Daily Output	Labor-Hours	Unit	Material	2015 Bare Costs Labor	Equipment	Total	Total Incl O&P
3653	6' to 7'				Ea.	168			168	185
3700	Juniperus chinensis densaerecta, (Spartan Juniper), Z5, cont								
3701	1 gal.				Ea.	5.10			5.10	5.60
3702	5 gal.					20.50			20.50	22.50
3703	15 gal.					45.50			45.50	50
3704	3' to 4'					54			54	59
3705	4' to 5'					106			106	117
3706	5' to 6'					144			144	158
3707	6' to 8'				▼	162			162	179
3750	Juniperus chinensis Hetzii, (Hetz Juniper), Z4, cont/BB								
3751	2-1/2 to 3'				Ea.	45.50			45.50	50
3752	3 to 3-1/2'					60.50			60.50	66.50
3753	2' to 2-1/2'					66			66	72.50
3754	4 to 4-1/2'					106			106	117
3755	4-1/2 to 5'				▼	116			116	128
3800	Juniperus chinensis iowa, (Chinese Juniper), Z4, cont/BB								
3801	24 to 30"				Ea.	45.50			45.50	50
3802	3' to 4'					63			63	69.50
3803	4' to 5'					111			111	123
3804	5' to 6'				▼	145			145	159
3850	Juniperus chinensis mountbatten, (Chinese Juniper), Z4, cont/BB								
3851	2' to 3'				Ea.	44.50			44.50	49
3852	3' to 4'					63			63	69.50
3853	4' to 5'					111			111	123
3854	5' to 6'					145			145	159
3855	6' to 7'					157			157	173
3856	7' to 8'					167			167	184
3857	8' to 10'				▼	186			186	204
3900	Juniperus chinensis obelisk, (Chinese Juniper), Z5, cont/BB								
3901	2' to 3'				Ea.	46			46	50.50
3902	3' to 4'					65			65	71.50
3903	4' to 5'					115			115	126
3904	5' to 6'					149			149	164
3905	6' to 7'				▼	162			162	179
3950	Juniperus chinensis pfitzeriana, (Pfitzer Juniper), Z4, cont/BB								
3951	1 gal.				Ea.	5.75			5.75	6.30
3952	2 gal.					16.25			16.25	17.85
3953	5 gal.					24			24	26.50
3954	9" to 12"					10.50			10.50	11.55
3955	15" to 18"					18.15			18.15	19.95
3956	18" to 24"					22			22	24
3957	2' to 2-1/2'					33.50			33.50	37
3958	2-1/2' to 3'					47			47	51.50
3959	3' to 3-1/2'				▼	47			47	51.50
3970	Juniperus chinensis pfitzeriana aurea, (Pfitzer Juniper), Z4, cont								
3971	1 gal.				Ea.	8			8	8.80
3972	2 gal.					19.10			19.10	21
3973	5 gal.				▼	27			27	30
4000	Juniperus chinensis pfitzeriana compact, (Pfitzer Juniper), Z4, cont								
4001	5 gal.				Ea.	27			27	29.50
4002	15" to 18"					21			21	23
4003	18" to 24"					21			21	23
4004	2' to 2-1/2'				▼	38			38	42

32 93 43.40 Trees, Conifers		Crew	Daily Output	Labor-Hours	Unit	Material	2015 Bare Costs Labor	Equipment	Total	Total Incl O&P
4005	2-1/2' to 3'				Ea.	38			38	42
4050	Juniperus chinensis robusta green, (Green Juniper), Z5, cont/BB									
4051	15 to 18"				Ea.	20			20	22
4052	2' to 3'					36.50			36.50	40
4053	3' to 4'					48.50			48.50	53.50
4054	4' to 5'					119			119	131
4055	5' to 6'					153			153	168
4056	6' to 7'					167			167	184
4057	7' to 8'					180			180	198
4058	8' to 10'				↓	180			180	198
4100	Juniperus chinensis torulosa, (Hollywood Juniper), Z6, cont/BB									
4101	1 gal.				Ea.	5.75			5.75	6.30
4102	5 gal.					24			24	26.50
4103	15 gal.					54.50			54.50	60
4104	4' to 5'					110			110	121
4105	5' to 6'				↓	147			147	162
4150	Juniperus horizontalis "Bar Harbor", (Bar Harbor Juniper), Z4, cont									
4151	9 to 12"				Ea.	15.90			15.90	17.50
4152	15 to 18"					23.50			23.50	26
4153	18 to 21"					30.50			30.50	33.50
4154	5 gal.				↓	23			23	25
4200	Juniperus horizontalis "Wiltoni", (Blue Rug Juniper), Z3, cont									
4201	12 to 15"				Ea.	18.10			18.10	19.90
4202	15 to 18"					22.50			22.50	25
4203	18 to 24"					25			25	27.50
4204	24 to 30"				↓	34.50			34.50	38
4250	Juniperus horizontalis Plumosa Compacta, (Juniper), Z3, cont									
4251	18 to 24"				Ea.	25.50			25.50	28
4252	24 to 30"					30			30	33
4253	30 to 36"					44			44	48.50
4254	3 to 3-1/2'				↓	79			79	87
4300	Juniperus procumbens "Nana", (Procumbens Juniper), Z4, cont									
4301	10" to 12"				Ea.	14.45			14.45	15.90
4302	12 to 15"					19.55			19.55	21.50
4303	15 to 18"					24			24	26.50
4304	18 to 24"				↓	26.50			26.50	29
4350	Juniperus sabina "Broadmoor", (Broadmoor Juniper), Z3, cont									
4351	10 to 12"				Ea.	15.45			15.45	17
4352	12 to 15"					19.10			19.10	21
4353	15 to 18"					26.50			26.50	29
4354	18 to 24"				↓	32			32	35
4400	Juniperus sabina Tamariscifolia New Blue, (Tam Juniper), Z4, cont									
4401	9 to 12"				Ea.	8.40			8.40	9.25
4402	15 to 18"					13.65			13.65	15
4403	18 to 21"				↓	16.40			16.40	18
4450	Juniperus scopulorum "Gray Gleam", (Gray Gleam Juniper), Z3, cont									
4451	3-1/2 to 4'				Ea.	70.50			70.50	77.50
4452	4 to 4-1/2'				"	100			100	110
4500	Juniperus scopulorum blue heaven, (Blue Heaven Juniper), Z4, B&B									
4501	4' to 5'				Ea.	109			109	119
4502	5' to 6'					134			134	148
4503	6' to 7'					155			155	170
4504	7' to 8'				↓	173			173	190

32 93 Plants

32 93 43 – Trees

32 93 43.40 Trees, Conifers	Crew	Daily Output	Labor-Hours	Unit	Material	2015 Bare Costs Labor	Equipment	Total	Total Incl O&P
4550	Juniperus scopulorum cologreen, (Cologreen Juniper), Z5, cont								
4551	5 gal.				Ea.	36.50			36.50	40
4600	Juniperus scopulorum hillburn's silver globe, (Juniper), Z5, BB								
4601	3' to 4'				Ea.	68.50			68.50	75
4602	4' to 5'				"	91			91	100
4650	Juniperus scopulorum pathfinder, (Pathfinder Juniper), Z5, B&B								
4651	4' to 5'				Ea.	100			100	110
4652	5' to 6'					114			114	125
4653	7' to 8'					159			159	175
4700	Juniperus scopulorum, (Rocky Mountain Juniper), Z5, cont/BB								
4701	20 gal.				Ea.	118			118	130
4702	3' to 4'					36.50			36.50	40
4703	4' to 5'					71			71	78
4704	5' to 6'					93			93	102
4750	Juniperus scopulorum welchii, (Welchi Juniper), Z3, cont								
4751	5 gal.				Ea.	76.50			76.50	84
4752	15 gal.				"	95.50			95.50	105
4800	Juniperus scopulorum wichita blue, (Wichita Blue Juniper), Z5, cont								
4801	3' to 4'				Ea.	78.50			78.50	86.50
4802	4' to 5'				"	123			123	135
4850	Juniperus squamata "Parsonii", (Parson's Juniper), Z4, cont								
4851	1 gal.				Ea.	7.75			7.75	8.50
4852	2 gal.					14.80			14.80	16.25
4853	3 gal.					18.20			18.20	20
4854	5 gal.					23.50			23.50	26
4900	Juniperus squamata Blue Star, (Blue Juniper), Z4, cont/BB								
4901	12" to 15"				Ea.	19.85			19.85	22
4902	15" to 18"				"	23			23	25
4950	Juniperus squamata meyeri, (Meyer's Juniper), Z5, cont/BB								
4951	3 gal.				Ea.	22			22	24.50
4952	5 gal.					29			29	32
4953	2' to 3'					41			41	45
5000	Juniperus virginiana, (Eastern Red Cedar), Z2, B&B								
5001	2' to 3'				Ea.	40			40	44
5002	3' to 4'					48			48	52.50
5003	4' to 5'					87.50			87.50	96
5004	5' to 6'					121			121	134
5050	Juniperus virginiana burkii, (Burki Juniper), Z2, cont								
5051	4' to 4-1/2'				Ea.	98.50			98.50	108
5052	4-1/2' to 5'				"	123			123	135
5100	Juniperus virginiana canaerti, (Canaert Red Cedar), Z4, B&B								
5101	2' to 3'				Ea.	38			38	42
5102	3' to 4'					51			51	56
5103	4' to 5'					56.50			56.50	62
5104	5' to 6'					123			123	135
5150	Juniperus virginiana glauca, (Silver Cedar), Z4, cont/BB								
5151	2' to 3'				Ea.	38			38	42
5152	3' to 4'					38			38	42
5153	4' to 5'					73.50			73.50	81
5200	Juniperus virginiana globusa, (Globe Red Cedar), Z4, cont/BB								
5201	2' to 3'				Ea.	41			41	45
5250	Juniperus virginiana gray owl, (Gray Owl Juniper), Z4, cont								
5251	18" to 24"				Ea.	24.50			24.50	27

32 93 43.40 Trees, Conifers	Crew	Daily Output	Labor-Hours	Unit	Material	2015 Bare Costs Labor	Equipment	Total	Total Incl O&P
5252	2' to 2-1/2'				Ea.	50			50	55
5300	Juniperus virginiana skyrocket, (Skyrocket Juniper), Z5, cont/BB									
5301	5 gal.				Ea.	75			75	82.50
5302	15 gal.					79.50			79.50	87.50
5303	2' to 3'					75			75	82.50
5304	3' to 4'					85			85	93.50
5305	4' to 5'					93			93	102
5306	5' to 6'					107			107	118
5307	6' to 8'					139			139	153
5350	Picea abies, (Norway Spruce), Z2, cont/BB									
5351	2' to 3'				Ea.	37.50			37.50	41
5352	3' to 4'					65.50			65.50	72
5353	4' to 5'					93.50			93.50	103
5354	5' to 6'					120			120	132
5355	6' to 7'					155			155	171
5356	7' to 8'					190			190	209
5400	Picea abies clanbrasiliana, (Barry Spruce), Z4, cont/BB									
5401	2' to 3'				Ea.	37.50			37.50	41
5402	3' to 4'				"	65.50			65.50	72
5450	Picea abies gregoryana, (Gregory's Dwarf Spruce), Z4, cont/BB									
5451	18" to 24"				Ea.	74.50			74.50	82
5452	2' to 2-1/2'				"	126			126	139
5500	Picea abies nidiformis, (Nest Spruce), Z4, cont/BB									
5501	12" to 15"				Ea.	20			20	22
5502	15" to 18"					30			30	33
5503	18" to 24"					35			35	38.50
5504	2' to 3'					45.50			45.50	50
5505	3' to 4'					68.50			68.50	75
5506	4' to 5'					105			105	115
5550	Picea abies pendula, (Weeping Norway Spruce), Z4, cont/BB									
5551	2' to 3'				Ea.	50			50	55
5552	3' to 4'					70.50			70.50	77.50
5553	4' to 5'					109			109	120
5554	6' to 7'					190			190	209
5555	7' to 8'					220			220	242
5600	Picea abies remonti, (Remont Spruce), Z4, cont/BB									
5601	2' to 3'				Ea.	73			73	80
5650	Picea glauca, (White or Canadian Spruce), Z3, cont/BB									
5651	3' to 4'				Ea.	64.50			64.50	71
5652	4' to 5'					93			93	102
5653	5' to 6'					140			140	154
5654	6' to 7'					175			175	193
5655	7' to 8'					200			200	220
5700	Picea glauca conica, (Dwarf Alberta Spruce), Z3, cont/BB									
5701	9" to 12"				Ea.	19.55			19.55	21.50
5702	15" to 18"					35			35	38.50
5703	18" to 24"					60			60	66
5704	2' to 2-1/2'					77			77	84.50
5705	2-1/2' to 3'					93			93	102
5750	Picea omorika, (Serbian Spruce), Z4, cont/BB									
5751	2' to 3'				Ea.	45.50			45.50	50.50
5752	3' to 4'					82			82	90
5753	4' to 5'					146			146	160

32 93 43.40 Trees, Conifers		Crew	Daily Output	Labor-Hours	Unit	Material	2015 Bare Costs Labor	Equipment	Total	Total Incl O&P
5754	5' to 6'				Ea.	173			173	190
5755	6' to 7'				↓	200			200	220
5800	Picea omorika nana, (Dwarf Serbian Spruce), Z4, cont									
5801	9" to 12"				Ea.	25			25	27.50
5802	12" to 15"					37			37	41
5803	18" to 24"				↓	50.50			50.50	55.50
5850	Picea omorika pendula, (Weeping Serbian Spruce), Z4, cont/BB									
5851	3' to 4'				Ea.	90			90	99
5900	Picea pungens, (Colorado Spruce), Z3, cont/BB									
5901	18" to 24"				Ea.	41			41	45
5902	2' to 3'					59			59	65
5903	3' to 4'					82			82	90
5904	4' to 5'					116			116	128
5905	5' to 6'					152			152	167
5906	6' to 7'					192			192	211
5907	7' to 8'				↓	200			200	220
5950	Picea pungens glauca, (Blue Colorado Spruce), Z3, cont/BB									
5951	18" to 24"				Ea.	41			41	45
5952	2' to 3'					59			59	65
5953	3' to 4'					82			82	90
5954	4' to 5'					123			123	135
5955	5' to 6'					164			164	180
5956	6' to 7'				↓	200			200	220
6000	Picea pungens hoopsi, (Hoops Blue Spruce), Z3, cont/BB									
6001	2' to 3'				Ea.	84.50			84.50	93
6002	3' to 4'					69			69	75.50
6003	4' to 5'					144			144	158
6004	5' to 6'					143			143	158
6005	14' to 16'					245			245	269
6006	16' to 18'					380			380	415
6007	18' to 20'				↓	675			675	745
6050	Picea pungens hunnewelliana, (Dwarf Blue Spruce), Z4, cont/BB									
6051	12" to 15"				Ea.	30			30	33
6052	15" to 18"					42			42	46.50
6053	18" to 24"					55			55	60.50
6054	2' to 2-1/2'				↓	97.50			97.50	107
6100	Picea pungens kosteriana, (Koster's Blue Spruce), Z3, cont/BB									
6101	2' to 3'				Ea.	67.50			67.50	74
6102	3' to 4'					71.50			71.50	79
6103	4' to 5'					126			126	139
6104	5' to 6'					139			139	153
6105	6' to 7'					222			222	244
6106	7' to 8'				↓	241			241	265
6150	Picea pungens montgomery, (Dwarf Blue Spruce), Z4, cont/BB									
6151	12" to 15"				Ea.	35			35	38.50
6152	15" to 18"					51			51	56
6153	18" to 24"					69			69	75.50
6154	4' to 5'					182			182	200
6155	5' to 6'				↓	590			590	650
6200	Pinus albicaulis, (White Bark Pine), Z4, cont/BB									
6201	2' to 3'				Ea.	41			41	45.50
6202	3' to 4'					75			75	82.50
6203	5' to 6'				↓	167			167	184

32 93 43.40 Trees, Conifers		Crew	Daily Output	Labor-Hours	Unit	Material	2015 Bare Costs Labor	Equipment	Total	Total Incl O&P
6204	6' to 8'				Ea.	252			252	277
6205	8' to 10'					420			420	465
6206	10' to 12'					465			465	510
6207	12' to 14'					465			465	510
6208	14' to 16'				↓	590			590	650
6250	Pinus aristata, (Bristlecone Pine), Z5, cont/BB									
6251	15" to 18"				Ea.	39			39	43
6252	18" to 24"					56			56	62
6253	2' to 3'					60			60	66
6254	3' to 4'					159			159	175
6255	4' to 5'				↓	330			330	360
6300	Pinus banksiana, (Jack Pine), Z3, cont/BB									
6301	5' to 6'				Ea.	36.50			36.50	40
6302	6' to 8'					45.50			45.50	50
6303	8' to 10'				↓	54.50			54.50	60
6350	Pinus bungeana, (Lacebark Pine), Z5, cont/BB									
6351	2' to 3'				Ea.	43			43	47.50
6352	3' to 4'					79.50			79.50	87.50
6353	4' to 5'					159			159	175
6354	5' to 6'					177			177	195
6355	6' to 7'					267			267	293
6356	7' to 8'				↓	355			355	390
6400	Pinus canariensis, (Canary Island Pine), Z8, cont									
6401	1 gal.				Ea.	6.35			6.35	7
6402	5 gal.					12.65			12.65	13.90
6403	15 gal.				↓	59			59	65
6450	Pinus cembra, (Swiss Stone Pine), Z3, cont/BB									
6451	1 gal.				Ea.	21			21	23
6452	2 gal.					36.50			36.50	40
6453	18" to 24"					73			73	80
6454	2' to 3'				↓	134			134	148
6500	Pinus densiflora umbraculifera, (Tanyosho Pine), Z5, cont/BB									
6501	18" to 24"				Ea.	57.50			57.50	63
6502	2' to 3'					164			164	180
6503	3' to 4'					205			205	225
6504	4' to 5'					246			246	270
6505	5' to 6'					282			282	310
6506	7' to 8'				↓	395			395	435
6550	Pinus flexilis, (Limber Pine), Z4, B&B									
6551	5 gal.				Ea.	63.50			63.50	70
6552	4' to 5'					141			141	155
6553	5' to 6'				↓	173			173	190
6600	Pinus koraiensis, (Korean Pine), Z4, cont/BB									
6601	3' to 4'				Ea.	241			241	265
6602	4' to 5'					305			305	340
6603	5' to 6'				↓	390			390	430
6650	Pinus lambertiana, (Sugar Pine), Z6, cont/BB									
6651	3' to 4'				Ea.	49			49	54
6652	4' to 5'					59			59	65
6653	7' to 8'					141			141	155
6654	8' to 10'				↓	209			209	230
6700	Pinus monticola, (Western White Pine), Z6, B&B									
6701	5' to 6'				Ea.	36			36	39.50

32 93 43.40 Trees, Conifers		Crew	Daily Output	Labor-Hours	Unit	Material	2015 Bare Costs Labor	Equipment	Total	Total Incl O&P
6702	6' to 7'				Ea.	45			45	49.50
6703	7' to 8'					54			54	59.50
6704	8' to 10'				↓	90			90	99
6750	Pinus mugo var. mugo, (Mugho Pine), Z3, cont/BB									
6751	12" to 15"				Ea.	20			20	22
6752	15" to 18"					22.50			22.50	25
6753	18" to 24"					25.50			25.50	28
6754	2' to 2-1/2'					31			31	34
6755	2-1/2' to 3'					40.50			40.50	44.50
6756	3' to 3-1/2' Spread					48			48	53
6757	3-1/2' to 4'					67.50			67.50	74.50
6758	1 gal.					6.85			6.85	7.50
6759	2 gal.				↓	9.10			9.10	10
6800	Pinus nigra, (Austrian Pine), Z5, cont/BB									
6801	5 gal.				Ea.	25.50			25.50	28
6802	3' to 4'					59.50			59.50	65.50
6803	4' to 5'					68.50			68.50	75
6804	5' to 6'					137			137	150
6805	6' to 7'					181			181	199
6806	7' to 8'					214			214	235
6807	8' to 9'					237			237	260
6808	9' to 10'					350			350	385
6809	10' to 12'				↓	420			420	460
6850	Pinus parviflora, (Japanese White Pine), Z5, cont									
6851	12' to 14'				Ea.	565			565	620
6900	Pinus parviflora glauca, (Silver Japanese White Pine), Z5, cont/BB									
6901	5 gal.				Ea.	63.50			63.50	70
6902	3' to 4'					82			82	90
6903	4' to 5'					218			218	240
6904	5' to 6'					320			320	350
6905	6' to 7'				↓	345			345	380
6950	Pinus ponderosa, (Western Yellow Pine), Z6, B&B									
6951	16' to 20'				Ea.	935			935	1,025
7000	Pinus radiata, (Monterey Pine), Z8, cont									
7001	1 gal.				Ea.	9.10			9.10	10
7002	5 gal.					22.50			22.50	25
7003	15 gal.					91			91	100
7004	24" Box				↓	284			284	310
7050	Pinus resinosa, (Red Pine), Z3, cont/BB									
7051	2' to 3'				Ea.	40			40	44
7052	3' to 4'					60			60	66
7053	4' to 5'					75			75	82.50
7054	5' to 6'					146			146	160
7055	6' to 8'					173			173	190
7056	8' to 10'					228			228	250
7057	10' to 12'					345			345	380
7058	12' to 14'				↓	410			410	450
7100	Pinus rigida, (Pitch Pine), Z5, cont/BB									
7101	2' to 3'				Ea.	36.50			36.50	40
7150	Pinus strobus, (White Pine), Z3, cont/BB									
7151	2' to 3'				Ea.	29.50			29.50	32.50
7152	3' to 4'					45.50			45.50	50
7153	4' to 5'				↓	73			73	80

For customer support on your Site Work & Landscape Cost Data, call 877.737.1594.

32 93 Plants

32 93 43 – Trees

32 93 43.40 Trees, Conifers	Crew	Daily Output	Labor-Hours	Unit	Material	2015 Bare Costs Labor	Equipment	Total	Total Incl O&P
7154	5' to 6'				Ea.	105			105	115
7155	6' to 8'					127			127	140
7156	8' to 10'					223			223	245
7157	10' to 12'					330			330	365
7158	12' to 14'					415			415	455
7200	Pinus strobus fastigiata, (Upright White Pine), Z3, B&B									
7201	5' to 6'				Ea.	109			109	120
7250	Pinus strobus nana, (Dwarf White Pine), Z3, cont/BB									
7251	5 gal.				Ea.	50			50	55
7252	15" to 18" Spread					52			52	57
7253	18" to 24" Spread					62.50			62.50	68.50
7254	2' to 2-1/2' Spread					68.50			68.50	75
7255	2-1/2' to 3' Spread					73.50			73.50	80.50
7256	3' to 4' Spread					105			105	115
7257	4' to 5' Spread					315			315	345
7258	5' to 6' Spread					410			410	450
7300	Pinus strobus pendula, (Weeping White Pine), Z3, cont/BB									
7301	3' to 4'				Ea.	69			69	76
7302	4' to 5'					85			85	93.50
7303	6' to 8'					191			191	210
7304	8' to 10'					300			300	330
7305	10' to 12'					445			445	490
7350	Pinus sylvestris, (Scotch Pine), Z3, cont/BB									
7351	Seedlings				Ea.	6.15			6.15	6.75
7352	3' to 4'					64.50			64.50	71
7353	4' to 5'					78.50			78.50	86
7354	5' to 6'					120			120	132
7355	6' to 7'					165			165	181
7356	7' to 8'					178			178	196
7400	Pinus sylvestris beauvronensis, (Mini Scotch Pine), Z4, cont/BB									
7401	12" to 15"				Ea.	54.50			54.50	60
7402	15" to 18"					61			61	67
7403	2' to 2-1/2'					96.50			96.50	106
7450	Pinus sylvestris fastigiata, (Pyramidal Scotch Pine), Z3, cont/BB									
7451	5 gal.				Ea.	59			59	65
7452	7 gal.				"	93			93	102
7500	Pinus thumbergi, (Japanese Black Pine), Z5, cont/BB									
7501	1 gal.				Ea.	7.05			7.05	7.75
7502	5 gal.					21			21	23
7503	7 gal.					37.50			37.50	41
7504	2' to 3'					50			50	55
7505	3' to 4'					68.50			68.50	75
7506	4' to 5'					91			91	100
7507	5' to 6'					173			173	190
7508	6' to 7'					196			196	215
7509	7' to 8'					205			205	225
7550	Podocarpus macrophyllus "Maki", (Podocarpus), Z7, cont/BB									
7551	1 gal.				Ea.	6.35			6.35	7
7552	5 gal.					20			20	22
7553	7 gal.					38			38	42
7554	15 gal.					53			53	58
7555	4' to 5'					64.50			64.50	71
7600	Pseudotsuga menziesii, (Douglas Fir), Z5, cont/BB									

For customer support on your Site Work & Landscape Cost Data, call 877.737.1594.

449

32 93 43.40 Trees, Conifers	Crew	Daily Output	Labor-Hours	Unit	Material	2015 Bare Costs Labor	Equipment	Total	Total Incl O&P
7601	5 gal.				Ea.	25			25	27.50
7602	3' to 4'					55.50			55.50	61
7603	4' to 5'					84.50			84.50	93
7604	5' to 6'					123			123	135
7605	6' to 7'					173			173	190
7650	Sciadopitys verticillata, (Umbrella Pine), Z6, B&B									
7651	2 gal.				Ea.	33			33	36
7652	2' to 2-1/2'					54.50			54.50	60
7653	6' to 7'					273			273	300
7654	7' to 8'					350			350	385
7700	Sequoia sempervirens, (Coast Redwood), Z7, cont									
7701	5 gal.				Ea.	19.55			19.55	21.50
7702	15 gal.					45.50			45.50	50
7703	24" Box					166			166	182
7750	Taxus baccata adpressa fowle, (Midget Boxleaf Yew), Z5, cont/BB									
7751	15" to 18"				Ea.	24			24	26.50
7752	18" to 24"					25			25	27.50
7753	2' to 2-1/2'					46			46	51
7754	2-1/2' to 3'					59			59	65
7755	3' to 4'					65			65	71.50
7756	4' to 5'					127			127	140
7800	Taxus baccata repandens, (Spreading English Yew), Z5, B&B									
7801	12" to 15"				Ea.	20			20	22
7802	15" to 18"					40			40	44
7803	2' to 2-1/2'					82			82	90
7804	2-1/2' to 3'					100			100	110
7805	3' to 3-1/2'					130			130	143
7850	Taxus cuspidata, (Spreading Japanese Yew), Z4, cont/BB									
7851	15" to 18"				Ea.	40			40	44
7852	18" to 24"					50			50	55
7853	2' to 2-1/2'					82			82	90
7854	2-1/2' to 3'					100			100	110
7855	3' to 3-1/2'					130			130	143
7900	Taxus cuspidata capitata, (Upright Japanese Yew), Z4, cont/BB									
7901	15" to 18"				Ea.	36			36	39.50
7902	18" to 24"					45.50			45.50	50
7903	2' to 2-1/2'					76			76	83.50
7904	2-1/2' to 3'					91			91	100
7905	3' to 4'					118			118	130
7906	4' to 5'					165			165	181
7907	5' to 6'					330			330	360
7908	6' to 7'					360			360	395
7909	7' to 8'					430			430	470
7950	Taxus cuspidata densiformis, (Dense Spreading Yew), Z5, cont/BB									
7951	15" to 18"				Ea.	45.50			45.50	50
7952	18" to 24"					54.50			54.50	60
7953	2' to 2-1/2'					65			65	71.50
7954	2-1/2' to 3'					74.50			74.50	82
7955	3' to 3-1/2'					85.50			85.50	94
8000	Taxus cuspidata hicksi, (Hick's Yew), Z4, cont/BB									
8001	15" to 18"				Ea.	33			33	36
8002	18" to 24"					54.50			54.50	60
8003	2' to 2-1/2'					68.50			68.50	75

32 93 43.40 Trees, Conifers		Crew	Daily Output	Labor-Hours	Unit	Material	2015 Bare Costs Labor	Equipment	Total	Total Incl O&P
8004	2-1/2' to 3'				Ea.	77.50			77.50	85
8050	Taxus cuspidata nana, (Dwarf Yew), Z4, cont/BB									
8051	15" to 18"				Ea.	33			33	36
8052	18" to 24"					54.50			54.50	60
8053	3' to 4'					86.50			86.50	95
8054	4' to 5'					109			109	120
8055	5' to 6'					127			127	140
8100	Thuja occidentalis "Smaragd", (Emerald Arborvitae), Z3, cont/BB									
8101	3' to 3-1/2'				Ea.	51			51	56
8102	3-1/2' to 4'					51			51	56
8103	4' to 4-1/2'					73			73	80
8104	4-1/2' to 5'					73			73	80
8105	5' to 6'					87.50			87.50	96
8150	Thuja occidentalis "Woodwardii", (Globe Arborvitae), Z2, B&B									
8151	15" to 18"				Ea.	20.50			20.50	22.50
8152	18" to 24"					25.50			25.50	28
8153	2' to 2-1/2'					33			33	36
8154	2-1/2' to 3'					40			40	44
8200	Thuja occidentalis douglasi pyramidalis, (Arborvitae), Z4, cont/BB									
8201	2' to 3'				Ea.	43.50			43.50	48
8202	3' to 4'					58			58	64
8203	4' to 5'					87.50			87.50	96
8204	5' to 6'					90			90	99
8205	6' to 7'					120			120	132
8206	7' to 8'					140			140	154
8250	Thuja occidentalis nigra, (Dark American Arborvitae), Z4, cont/BB									
8251	2' to 3'				Ea.	33			33	36
8252	3' to 4'					40			40	44
8253	4' to 5'					54.50			54.50	60
8254	5' to 6'					91			91	100
8255	6' to 8'					131			131	144
8256	8' to 10'					182			182	200
8300	Thuja occidentalis techney, (Mission Arborvitae), Z4, cont/BB									
8301	2' to 3'				Ea.	36.50			36.50	40
8302	3' to 4'					45.50			45.50	50
8303	4' to 5'					59			59	65
8304	5' to 6'					100			100	110
8305	6' to 7'					118			118	130
8306	7' to 8'					155			155	170
8350	Thuja orientalis "aurea nana"', (Gold Arborvitae), Z4, cont									
8351	1 gal.				Ea.	7.30			7.30	8
8352	5 gal.				"	20			20	22
8400	Thuja orientalis "blue cone", (Blue Cone Arborvitae), Z6, cont									
8401	1 gal.				Ea.	4.55			4.55	5
8402	5 gal.				"	13.65			13.65	15
8450	Tsuga canadensis, (Canadian Hemlock), Z4, cont/BB									
8451	2' to 2-1/2'				Ea.	54.50			54.50	60
8452	2-1/2' to 3'					69			69	76
8453	3' to 3-1/2'					83.50			83.50	92
8454	3-1/2' to 4'					91			91	100
8455	4' to 5'					127			127	140
8456	5' to 5-1/2'					146			146	160
8457	5-1/2' to 6'					167			167	184

For customer support on your Site Work & Landscape Cost Data, call 877.737.1594.

451

32 93 43.40 Trees, Conifers	Crew	Daily Output	Labor-Hours	Unit	Material	2015 Bare Costs Labor	Equipment	Total	Total Incl O&P
8458	6' to 7'				Ea.	178			178	196
8459	7' to 8'				↓	200			200	220
8500	Tsuga canadensis sargentii, (Sargents Weeping Hemlock), Z8, cont									
8501	1 gal.				Ea.	8.35			8.35	9.20
8502	3 gal.					21			21	23
8503	30" to 36"					90			90	99
8504	3' to 4'					105			105	116
8505	4' to 5'					125			125	138
8506	5' to 6'				↓	190			190	209
8550	Tsuga caroliniana, (Caroline Hemlock), Z5, B&B									
8551	2-1/2' to 3'				Ea.	87.50			87.50	96
8552	3' to 3-1/2'					106			106	116
8553	3-1/2' to 4'					115			115	126
8554	4' to 5'				↓	160			160	176
8600	Tsuga diversifolia, (Northern Japanese Hemlock), Z6, cont/BB									
8601	3' to 4'				Ea.	128			128	141
8602	4' to 5'				"	142			142	156

32 93 43.50 Trees and Palms

		Crew	Daily Output	Labor-Hours	Unit	Material	Labor	Equipment	Total	Total Incl O&P
0010	**TREES & PALMS**									
0011	Warm temperate and subtropical									
0100	Acacia baileyana, (Bailey Acacia), Z9, cont									
0110	1 gal.				Ea.	6.10			6.10	6.70
0120	5 gal.					20.50			20.50	23
0130	15 gal.				↓	51.50			51.50	57
0200	Acacia latifolia, (Broadleaf Acacia (multistem)), Z10, cont									
0210	1 gal.				Ea.	6.10			6.10	6.70
0220	5 gal.					20.50			20.50	23
0230	15 gal.				↓	51.50			51.50	57
0300	Acacia melanoxylon, (Blackwood Acacia), Z9, cont									
0310	1 gal.				Ea.	6.10			6.10	6.70
0320	5 gal.					20.50			20.50	23
0330	15 gal.				↓	51.50			51.50	57
0400	Agonis flexuosa, (Willow Myrtle), Z9, cont									
0410	5 gal.				Ea.	21.50			21.50	24
0420	15 gal.				"	55.50			55.50	61
0500	Albizzia julibrissin, (Silk Tree), Z7, cont									
0510	5 gal.				Ea.	21.50			21.50	24
0520	15 gal.					52.50			52.50	58
0530	20 gal.					88.50			88.50	97
0540	24" Box				↓	170			170	187
0600	Arbutus menziesii, (Pacific Madrone), Z7, cont									
0610	1 gal.				Ea.	7.60			7.60	8.35
0620	5 gal.					21			21	23
0630	15 gal.				↓	55.50			55.50	61
0700	Arbutus unedo, (Strawberry Tree), Z7, cont									
0710	1 gal.				Ea.	7.60			7.60	8.35
0720	5 gal.					21			21	23.50
0730	15 gal.				↓	55.50			55.50	61
0800	Archontophoenix cunninghamiana, (King Palm), Z10, cont									
0810	5 gal.				Ea.	34			34	37
0820	15 gal.					118			118	130
0830	24" Box				↓	266			266	292

452

32 93 43.50 Trees and Palms	Crew	Daily Output	Labor-Hours	Unit	Material	2015 Bare Costs Labor	Equipment	Total	Total Incl O&P
0900 Arecastrum romanzoffianum, (Queen Palm), Z10, cont									
0910 5 gal.				Ea.	19.75			19.75	21.50
0920 15 gal.					45			45	49.50
0930 24" Box				↓	180			180	199
1000 Bauhinia variegata, (Orchid Tree), Z9, cont									
1010 1 gal.				Ea.	17.40			17.40	19.15
1020 5 gal.					44.50			44.50	49
1030 24" Box				↓	155			155	171
1100 Brachychiton populneus, (Kurrajong), Z9, cont									
1110 5 gal.				Ea.	17.40			17.40	19.15
1120 15 gal.					44.50			44.50	49
1130 24" Box				↓	165			165	181
1200 Callistemon citroides, (Lemon Bottlebrush (Tree Form)), Z9, cont									
1210 15 gal.				Ea.	42.50			42.50	46.50
1220 24" Box					155			155	171
1230 36" Box				↓	470			470	515
1300 Casuarina stricta, (Mountain She-Oak), Z9, cont									
1310 5 gal.				Ea.	22			22	24.50
1320 15 gal.				"	67.50			67.50	74.50
1400 Ceratoma siliqua, (Carob), Z10, cont									
1410 5 gal.				Ea.	18.80			18.80	20.50
1420 15 gal.					51			51	56
1430 24" Box				↓	165			165	181
1500 Chamaerops humilis, (Mediterranean Fan Palm), Z9, cont									
1510 5 gal.				Ea.	19.50			19.50	21.50
1520 15 gal.					81.50			81.50	90
1530 24" Box				↓	225			225	248
1600 Chrysobalanus icaco, (Coco-plum), Z10, cont									
1610 1 gal.				Ea.	3.53			3.53	3.88
1620 3 gal.					4.70			4.70	5.15
1630 10 gal.					18.80			18.80	20.50
1640 20 gal.				↓	56.50			56.50	62
1700 Cinnamonum camphora, (Camphor Tree), Z9, cont									
1710 5 gal.				Ea.	21			21	23
1720 15 gal.					55.50			55.50	61
1730 24" Box				↓	172			172	190
1800 Cornus nattali, (California Laurel), Z7, B&B									
1810 5' to 6'				Ea.	28.50			28.50	31.50
1820 6' to 8'					62.50			62.50	68.50
1830 8' to 10'				↓	95			95	104
2000 Eriobotrya japonica, (Loquat), Z8, cont									
2010 3 gal.				Ea.	18.55			18.55	20.50
2020 10 gal.					31.50			31.50	35
2030 15 gal.					50.50			50.50	55.50
2040 15 gal. Espalier				↓	85			85	93.50
2100 Erythrina caffra, (Kaffirboom Coral Tree), Z10, cont									
2110 5 gal.				Ea.	17.40			17.40	19.15
2120 15 gal.					51.50			51.50	57
2130 24" Box				↓	165			165	181
2200 Eucalyptus camaldulensis, (Red Gum), Z9, cont									
2210 5 gal.				Ea.	17.40			17.40	19.15
2220 15 gal.					44.50			44.50	49
2230 24" Box				↓	155			155	171

32 93 43.50 Trees and Palms		Crew	Daily Output	Labor- Hours	Unit	Material	2015 Bare Costs Labor	Equipment	Total	Total Incl O&P
2300	Eucalyptus ficifolia, (Flaming Gum), Z10, cont									
2310	5 gal.				Ea.	17.40			17.40	19.15
2320	15 gal.					44.50			44.50	49
2330	24" Box				↓	155			155	171
2400	Feijoa sellowiana, (Guava), Z8, cont									
2410	1 gal.				Ea.	3.76			3.76	4.14
2420	5 gal.					14.10			14.10	15.50
2430	15 gal.				↓	47			47	51.50
2500	Ficus benjamina, (Benjamin Fig), Z10, cont									
2510	1 gal.				Ea.	5.15			5.15	5.70
2520	5 gal.					17.40			17.40	19.15
2530	24" Box				↓	165			165	181
2600	Ficus retusa nitida, (India Laurel Fig), Z10, cont									
2610	5 gal.				Ea.	17.40			17.40	19.15
2620	15 gal.					51.50			51.50	57
2630	24" Box				↓	165			165	181
2700	Fraxinus uhdei, (Shamel Ash), Z9, cont									
2710	5 gal.				Ea.	17.40			17.40	19.15
2720	15 gal.					44.50			44.50	49
2730	24" Box					155			155	171
2740	36" Box				↓	430			430	475
2800	Fraxinus velutina, (Velvet Ash), Z7, cont									
2810	5 gal.				Ea.	17.40			17.40	19.15
2820	15 gal.					44.50			44.50	49
2830	24" Box				↓	155			155	171
2900	Gordonia lasianthus, (Loblolly Bay Gordonia), Z8, cont									
2910	5 gal.				Ea.	17.85			17.85	19.65
2920	7 gal.				"	63			63	69.50
3000	Grevillea robusta, (Silk Oak), Z10, cont									
3010	5 gal.				Ea.	17.40			17.40	19.15
3020	15 gal.				"	45			45	49.50
3100	Hakea suaveolens, (Sea Urchin Tree), Z10, cont									
3110	1 gal.				Ea.	3.62			3.62	3.98
3120	5 gal.				↓	11.30			11.30	12.40
3130	15 gal.				↓	42.50			42.50	46.50
3200	Harpephyllum caffrum, (Kaffir Plum), Z10, cont									
3210	5 gal.				Ea.	17.15			17.15	18.90
3220	15 gal.					48			48	52.50
3230	24" Box				↓	193			193	212
3300	Hymenosporum flavum, (Sweetshade), Z10, cont									
3310	5 gal.				Ea.	17.40			17.40	19.15
3320	15 gal.				↓	44.50			44.50	49
3330	24" Box				↓	155			155	171
3400	Jacaranda mimosifolia, (Jacaranda), Z10, cont									
3410	5 gal.				Ea.	17.40			17.40	19.15
3420	15 gal.					46.50			46.50	51
3430	24" Box				↓	160			160	176
3500	Jatropha curcas, (Barbados Nut), Z10, cont/BB									
3510	3 gal.				Ea.	7.30			7.30	8
3520	10 gal.					32.50			32.50	35.50
3530	6' to 7'				↓	49			49	54
3600	Laurus nobilis, (Sweet Bay), Z8, cont									
3610	1 gal.				Ea.	5.65			5.65	6.20

32 93 43.50 Trees and Palms	Crew	Daily Output	Labor-Hours	Unit	Material	2015 Bare Costs Labor	Equipment	Total	Total Incl O&P
3620	5 gal.				Ea.	16			16	17.60
3630	15 gal.					48.50			48.50	53.50
3640	24" Box				↓	162			162	178
3700	Leptospermum laevigatum, (Australian Tea Tree), Z9, cont									
3710	1 gal.				Ea.	5.65			5.65	6.20
3720	5 gal.					14.10			14.10	15.50
3730	15 gal.				↓	50			50	55
3800	Leptospermum scoparium Ruby Glow, (Tea Tree), Z9, cont									
3810	1 gal.				Ea.	4			4	4.40
3820	5 gal.				"	11.30			11.30	12.40
3900	Magnolia grandiflora, (Southern Magnolia), Z7, B&B									
3910	4' to 5'				Ea.	45			45	49.50
3920	5' to 6'					55.50			55.50	61
3930	6' to 7'					89			89	97.50
3940	7' to 8'				↓	122			122	134
4000	Malaleuca linariifolia, (Flaxleaf Paperbark), Z9, cont									
4010	5 gal.				Ea.	17.85			17.85	19.65
4020	15 gal.					51			51	56
4030	24" Box				↓	167			167	184
4100	Maytenus boaria, (Mayten Tree), Z9, cont									
4110	5 gal.				Ea.	18.80			18.80	20.50
4120	15 gal.				"	60			60	66
4200	Metrosideros excelsus, (New Zealand Christmas Tree), Z10, cont									
4210	5 gal.				Ea.	19.75			19.75	21.50
4220	15 gal.					48.50			48.50	53.50
4230	24" Box				↓	188			188	207
4300	Olea europea, (Olive), Z9, cont									
4310	1 gal.				Ea.	9.70			9.70	10.65
4320	5 gal.					20.50			20.50	22.50
4330	15 gal.				↓	53			53	58
4400	Parkinsonia aculeata, (Jerusalem Thorn), Z9, cont									
4410	5 gal.				Ea.	19.25			19.25	21
4420	15 gal.					52.50			52.50	58
4430	24" Box				↓	172			172	190
4500	Pistachia chinensis, (Chinese Pistache), Z9, cont									
4510	5 gal.				Ea.	17.85			17.85	19.65
4520	15 gal.					45			45	49.50
4530	24" Box				↓	160			160	176
4600	Pyrus Kawakamii, (Evergreen Pear), Z8, cont									
4610	5 gal.				Ea.	28			28	31
4620	15 gal.					56.50			56.50	62
4630	15 gal. Espalier					70.50			70.50	77.50
4640	24" Box				↓	174			174	191
4700	Quercus agrifolia, (Coast Live Oak), Z9, cont									
4710	5 gal.				Ea.	17.85			17.85	19.65
4720	15 gal.					47			47	51.50
4730	20 gal.				↓	166			166	183
4800	Sapium sebiferum, (Chinese Tallow Tree), Z8, cont									
4810	5 gal.				Ea.	21.50			21.50	24
4820	15 gal.					46			46	50.50
4830	24" Box				↓	165			165	181
4900	Schinus molle, (Pepper Tree), Z9, cont									
4910	5 gal.				Ea.	19.05			19.05	21

For customer support on your Site Work & Landscape Cost Data, call 877.737.1594.

455

32 93 43.50 Trees and Palms	Crew	Daily Output	Labor-Hours	Unit	Material	2015 Bare Costs Labor	Equipment	Total	Total Incl O&P
4920	15 gal.				Ea.	49.50			49.50	54.50
4930	24" Box				↓	162			162	178
5000	Strelitzia nicolai, (Giant Bird of Paradise), Z10, cont									
5010	5 gal.				Ea.	18.80			18.80	20.50
5020	15 gal.					56.50			56.50	62
5030	24" Box				↓	183			183	202
5100	Syzygium paniculatum, (Brush Cherry), Z9, cont									
5110	1 gal.				Ea.	5.55			5.55	6.10
5120	5 gal.					16.60			16.60	18.25
5130	15 gal.				↓	48			48	52.50
5200	Tabebuia chrysotricha, (Golden Trumpet Tree), Z10, cont									
5210	5 gal.				Ea.	17.65			17.65	19.40
5220	15 gal.					46			46	50.50
5230	24" Box				↓	166			166	183
5300	Thevetia peruviana, (Yellow Oleander), Z10, cont									
5310	1 gal.				Ea.	7.50			7.50	8.25
5320	5 gal.					23.50			23.50	26
5330	15 gal.				↓	61			61	67
5400	Tipuana tipi, (Common Tiputree), Z10, cont									
5410	1 gal.				Ea.	5.80			5.80	6.35
5420	5 gal.					17.95			17.95	19.75
5430	15 gal.					46			46	50.50
5440	24" Box				↓	160			160	176
5500	Tristania conferta, (Brisbane Box), Z10, cont									
5510	5 gal.				Ea.	17.95			17.95	19.75
5520	15 gal.				"	46			46	50.50
5600	Umbellularia californica, (California Laurel), Z7, cont									
5610	1 gal.				Ea.	5.80			5.80	6.35
5620	5 gal.					19.20			19.20	21
5630	15 gal.				↓	57.50			57.50	63.50

32 93 43.60 Trees, Fruits and Nuts

		Crew	Daily Output	Labor-Hours	Unit	Material	2015 Bare Costs Labor	Equipment	Total	Total Incl O&P
0010	**TREES, FRUITS AND NUTS**									
1000	Apple, Different Varieties, Z4, cont									
1010	5 gal.				Ea.	26			26	28.50
1020	Standard, 2-3 yr.					29			29	32
1030	Semidwarf, 2-3 yr.				↓	27			27	29.50
1500	Apricot, Z5, cont/BB									
1510	5 gal.				Ea.	16.05			16.05	17.65
1520	Standard, 2-3 yr.					26			26	28.50
1530	Semidwarf, 2-3 yr.				↓	29			29	32
2000	Carya ovata, Z4, bare root									
2010	Bare root, 2 yr.				Ea.	51			51	56
2500	Castanea mollissima, (Chinese Chestnut), Z4, bare root									
2510	Bare root, 2 yr.				Ea.	41			41	45
3000	Cherry, Z4, B&B									
3010	Standard, 2-3 yr.				Ea.	22.50			22.50	25
3020	Semidwarf, 2-3 yr.				"	28.50			28.50	31.50
3500	Corylus americana, (Filbert, American Hazelnut), Z5, B&B									
3510	2' to 3'				Ea.	9.60			9.60	10.55
3520	3' to 4'				"	17			17	18.70
4500	Grape, (Different Varieties), Z5, potted									
4510	Potted				Ea.	10.60			10.60	11.65

32 93 Plants

32 93 43 – Trees

32 93 43.60 Trees, Fruits and Nuts	Crew	Daily Output	Labor-Hours	Unit	Material	2015 Bare Costs Labor	Equipment	Total	Total Incl O&P
5000 Juglans cinera, (Butternut), Z4, bare root									
5010 Bare Root, 2 yr.				Ea.	26			26	29
5500 Juglans nigra, (Black Walnut), Z4, bare root									
5510 Bare Root, 2'				Ea.	29			29	32
6000 Peach, Z6, cont/BB									
6010 5 gal.				Ea.	24			24	26.50
6020 Standard, 2-3 yr.					24.50			24.50	27
6030 Semidwarf, 2-3 yr.				↓	28.50			28.50	31.50
6500 Pear, zone 5, B&B									
6510 Standard, 2-3 yr.				Ea.	15.40			15.40	16.95
6520 Semidwarf, 2-3 yr.				"	17			17	18.70
7000 Plum, zone 5, container or B&B									
7010 5 gal.				Ea.	24			24	26.50
7020 Standard, 2-3 yr.					24			24	26.50
7030 Semidwarf, 2-3 yr.				↓	29			29	32
7500 Raspberry, (Everbearing), Zone 4									
7510 package of 5				Ea.	24			24	26.50
8000 Strawberry, (Hybrid), zone 5									
8010 25 per box				Ea.	11.05			11.05	12.15
8020 50 per box				"	21.50			21.50	24

32 94 Planting Accessories

32 94 13 – Landscape Edging

32 94 13.20 Edging

		Crew	Daily Output	Labor-Hours	Unit	Material	2015 Bare Costs Labor	Equipment	Total	Total Incl O&P
0010	**EDGING**									
0050	Aluminum alloy, including stakes, 1/8" x 4", mill finish	B-1	390	.062	L.F.	2.30	2.36		4.66	6.15
0051	Black paint		390	.062		2.67	2.36		5.03	6.55
0052	Black anodized		390	.062		3.08	2.36		5.44	7
0060	3/16" x 4", mill finish		380	.063		3.31	2.42		5.73	7.35
0061	Black paint		380	.063		3.82	2.42		6.24	7.90
0062	Black anodized		380	.063		4.46	2.42		6.88	8.65
0070	1/8" x 5-1/2" mill finish		370	.065		3.34	2.48		5.82	7.50
0071	Black paint		370	.065		3.96	2.48		6.44	8.15
0072	Black anodized		370	.065		4.53	2.48		7.01	8.80
0080	3/16" x 5-1/2" mill finish		360	.067		4.46	2.55		7.01	8.85
0081	Black paint		360	.067		5.05	2.55		7.60	9.50
0082	Black anodized	↓	360	.067		5.80	2.55		8.35	10.35
0100	Brick, set horizontally, 1-1/2 bricks per L.F.	D-1	370	.043		1.22	1.82		3.04	4.13
0150	Set vertically, 3 bricks per L.F.	"	135	.119		3.68	4.99		8.67	11.65
0200	Corrugated aluminum, roll, 4" wide	1 Carp	650	.012		1.93	.58		2.51	3.01
0250	6" wide	"	550	.015	↓	2.41	.68		3.09	3.70
0300	Concrete, cast in place, see Section 03 30 53.40									
0350	Granite, 5" x 16", straight	B-29	300	.187	L.F.	11.65	7.65	2.94	22.24	28
0400	Polyethylene grass barrier, 5" x 1/8"	D-1	400	.040		.81	1.68		2.49	3.46
0410	5" x 1/4"		400	.040		.93	1.68		2.61	3.59
0420	5" x 5/32"		400	.040		1.08	1.68		2.76	3.76
0430	6" x 3/32"		400	.040		.87	1.68		2.55	3.52
0500	Precast scallops, green, 2" x 8" x 16"		400	.040		2.08	1.68		3.76	4.86
0550	2" x 8" x 16" other than green		400	.040		1.66	1.68		3.34	4.40
0600	Railroad ties, 6" x 8"	2 Carp	170	.094		2.79	4.42		7.21	9.85
0650	7" x 9"		136	.118	↓	3.10	5.50		8.60	11.90

32 94 Planting Accessories

32 94 13 – Landscape Edging

32 94 13.20 Edging		Crew	Daily Output	Labor-Hours	Unit	Material	2015 Bare Costs Labor	Equipment	Total	Total Incl O&P
0750	Redwood 2" x 4"	2 Carp	330	.048	L.F.	2.25	2.28		4.53	5.95
0780	Landscape timbers, 100% recycled plastic, var colors, 4" x 4" x 8' **G**		250	.064		4.60	3		7.60	9.65
0790	6" x 6" x 8' **G**		250	.064		9.80	3		12.80	15.40
0800	Steel edge strips, incl. stakes, 1/4" x 5"	B-1	390	.062		3.92	2.36		6.28	7.95
0850	3/16" x 4"	"	390	.062		3.10	2.36		5.46	7.05
0900	Hardwood, pressure treated, 4" x 6"	2 Carp	250	.064		2.12	3		5.12	6.95
0940	6" x 6"		200	.080		3.03	3.76		6.79	9.15
0980	6" x 8"		170	.094		3.46	4.42		7.88	10.60
1000	Pine, pressure treated, 1" x 4"		500	.032		.54	1.50		2.04	2.90
1040	2" x 4"		330	.048		.91	2.28		3.19	4.50
1080	4" x 6"		250	.064		3.02	3		6.02	7.95
1100	6" x 6"		200	.080		4.54	3.76		8.30	10.80
1140	6" x 8"		170	.094		5.95	4.42		10.37	13.35
1200	Edging, lawn, made from recycled tires, black, 1" x 6"	B-1	390	.062		1.10	2.36		3.46	4.83

32 94 50 – Tree Guying

32 94 50.10 Tree Guying Systems

		Crew	Daily Output	Labor-Hours	Unit	Material	Labor	Equipment	Total	Total Incl O&P
0010	**TREE GUYING SYSTEMS**									
0015	Tree guying Including stakes, guy wire and wrap									
0100	Less than 3" caliper, 2 stakes	2 Clab	35	.457	Ea.	14.25	17.20		31.45	42
0200	3" to 4" caliper, 3 stakes	"	21	.762		19.25	28.50		47.75	65
0300	6" to 8" caliper, 3 stakes	B-1	8	3		36.50	115		151.50	218
1000	Including arrowhead anchor, cable, turnbuckles and wrap									
1100	Less than 3" caliper, 3 anchors	2 Clab	20	.800	Ea.	44.50	30		74.50	95.50
1200	3" to 6" caliper, 4 anchors		15	1.067		38.50	40		78.50	104
1300	6" caliper, 6" anchors		12	1.333		44.50	50		94.50	126
1400	8" caliper, 8" anchors		9	1.778		129	67		196	245
2000	Tree guard, preformed plastic, 36" high		168	.095		2.34	3.58		5.92	8.05
2010	Snow fence		140	.114		32	4.30		36.30	41.50

32 96 Transplanting

32 96 23 – Plant and Bulb Transplanting

32 96 23.23 Planting

		Crew	Daily Output	Labor-Hours	Unit	Material	Labor	Equipment	Total	Total Incl O&P
0010	**PLANTING**									
0012	Moving shrubs on site, 12" ball	B-62	28	.857	Ea.		35.50	6.20	41.70	61
0100	24" ball	"	22	1.091	"		45	7.90	52.90	77.50

32 96 23.43 Moving Trees

		Crew	Daily Output	Labor-Hours	Unit	Material	Labor	Equipment	Total	Total Incl O&P
0010	**MOVING TREES**, On site									
0300	Moving trees on site, 36" ball	B-6	3.75	6.400	Ea.		264	97	361	510
0400	60" ball	"	1	24	"		990	365	1,355	1,925

32 96 43 – Tree Transplanting

32 96 43.20 Tree Removal

		Crew	Daily Output	Labor-Hours	Unit	Material	Labor	Equipment	Total	Total Incl O&P
0010	**TREE REMOVAL**									
0100	Dig & lace, shrubs, broadleaf evergreen, 18"-24" high	B-1	55	.436	Ea.		16.70		16.70	25.50
0200	2'-3'	"	35	.686			26		26	40.50
0300	3'-4'	B-6	30	.800			33	12.15	45.15	64
0400	4'-5'	"	20	1.200			49.50	18.20	67.70	96
1000	Deciduous, 12"-15"	B-1	110	.218			8.35		8.35	12.85
1100	18"-24"		65	.369			14.15		14.15	21.50
1200	2'-3'		55	.436			16.70		16.70	25.50
1300	3'-4'	B-6	50	.480			19.80	7.30	27.10	38.50

32 96 43.20 Tree Removal		Crew	Daily Output	Labor-Hours	Unit	Material	2015 Bare Costs Labor	Equipment	Total	Total Incl O&P
2000	Evergreen, 18"-24"	B-1	55	.436	Ea.		16.70		16.70	25.50
2100	2'-0" to 2'-6"		50	.480			18.35		18.35	28.50
2200	2'-6" to 3'-0"		35	.686			26		26	40.50
2300	3'-0" to 3'-6"		20	1.200			46		46	70.50
3000	Trees, deciduous, small, 2'-3'		55	.436			16.70		16.70	25.50
3100	3'-4'	B-6	50	.480			19.80	7.30	27.10	38.50
3200	4'-5'		35	.686			28.50	10.40	38.90	55
3300	5'-6'		30	.800			33	12.15	45.15	64
4000	Shade, 5'-6'		50	.480			19.80	7.30	27.10	38.50
4100	6'-8'		35	.686			28.50	10.40	38.90	55
4200	8'-10'		25	.960			39.50	14.55	54.05	76.50
4300	2" caliper		12	2			82.50	30.50	113	160
5000	Evergreen, 4'-5'		35	.686			28.50	10.40	38.90	55
5100	5'-6'		25	.960			39.50	14.55	54.05	76.50
5200	6'-7'		19	1.263			52	19.15	71.15	101
5300	7'-8'		15	1.600			66	24.50	90.50	128
5400	8'-10'		11	2.182			90	33	123	175

For customer support on your Site Work & Landscape Cost Data, call 877.737.1594.

459

Division Notes

	CREW	DAILY OUTPUT	LABOR-HOURS	UNIT	BARE COSTS				TOTAL INCL O&P
					MAT.	LABOR	EQUIP.	TOTAL	

Estimating Tips
33 10 00 Water Utilities
33 30 00 Sanitary
Sewerage Utilities
33 40 00 Storm
Drainage Utilities

- Never assume that the water, sewer, and drainage lines will go in at the early stages of the project. Consider the site access needs before dividing the site in half with open trenches, loose pipe, and machinery obstructions. Always inspect the site to establish that the site drawings are complete. Check off all existing utilities on your drawings as you locate them. Be especially careful with underground utilities because appurtenances are sometimes buried during regrading or repaving operations. If you find any discrepancies, mark up the site plan for further research. Differing site conditions can be very costly if discovered later in the project.

- See also Section 33 01 00 for restoration of pipe where removal/replacement may be undesirable. Use of new types of piping materials can reduce the overall project cost. Owners/design engineers should consider the installing contractor as a valuable source of current information on utility products and local conditions that could lead to significant cost savings.

Reference Numbers
Reference numbers are shown in shaded boxes at the beginning of some major classifications. These numbers refer to related items in the Reference Section. The reference information may be an estimating procedure, an alternate pricing method, or technical information.

Note: Not all subdivisions listed here necessarily appear in this publication. ■

*Note: **Trade Service**, in part, has been used as a reference source for some of the material prices used in Division 33.*

33 01 Operation and Maintenance of Utilities

33 01 10 – Operation and Maintenance of Water Utilities

33 01 10.10 Corrosion Resistance	Crew	Daily Output	Labor-Hours	Unit	Material	2015 Bare Costs Labor	Equipment	Total	Total Incl O&P
0010 **CORROSION RESISTANCE**									
0012 Wrap & coat, add to pipe, 4" diameter				L.F.	2.21			2.21	2.43
0020 5" diameter					2.66			2.66	2.93
0040 6" diameter					3.28			3.28	3.61
0060 8" diameter					4.04			4.04	4.44
0080 10" diameter					4.91			4.91	5.40
0100 12" diameter					6.20			6.20	6.80
0120 14" diameter					7.30			7.30	8
0140 16" diameter					9.75			9.75	10.70
0160 18" diameter					10			10	11
0180 20" diameter					10.50			10.50	11.55
0200 24" diameter					12.95			12.95	14.25
0220 Small diameter pipe, 1" diameter, add					1.02			1.02	1.12
0240 2" diameter					1.38			1.38	1.52
0260 2-1/2" diameter					1.62			1.62	1.78
0280 3" diameter				↓	2.01			2.01	2.21
0300 Fittings, field covered, add				S.F.	10.40			10.40	11.45
0500 Coating, bituminous, per diameter inch, 1 coat, add				L.F.	.63			.63	.69
0540 3 coat					1.92			1.92	2.11
0560 Coal tar epoxy, per diameter inch, 1 coat, add					.22			.22	.24
0600 3 coat					.68			.68	.75
1000 Polyethylene H.D. extruded, .025" thk., 1/2" diameter add					.10			.10	.11
1020 3/4" diameter					.15			.15	.17
1040 1" diameter					.20			.20	.22
1060 1-1/4" diameter					.25			.25	.28
1080 1-1/2" diameter					.30			.30	.33
1100 .030" thk., 2" diameter					.40			.40	.44
1120 2-1/2" diameter					.50			.50	.55
1140 .035" thk., 3" diameter					.60			.60	.66
1160 3-1/2" diameter					.70			.70	.77
1180 4" diameter					.80			.80	.88
1200 .040" thk, 5" diameter					1			1	1.10
1220 6" diameter					1.20			1.20	1.32
1240 8" diameter					1.60			1.60	1.76
1260 10" diameter					2			2	2.20
1280 12" diameter					2.40			2.40	2.64
1300 .060" thk., 14" diameter					2.80			2.80	3.08
1320 16" diameter					3.20			3.20	3.52
1340 18" diameter					3.60			3.60	3.96
1360 20" diameter				↓	4			4	4.40
1380 Fittings, field wrapped, add				S.F.	4.79			4.79	5.25

33 01 10.20 Pipe Repair

	Crew	Daily Output	Labor-Hours	Unit	Material	2015 Bare Costs Labor	Equipment	Total	Total Incl O&P
0010 **PIPE REPAIR**									
0020 Not including excavation or backfill									
0100 Clamp, stainless steel, lightweight, for steel pipe									
0110 3" long, 1/2" diameter pipe	1 Plum	34	.235	Ea.	12.80	13.80		26.60	35
0120 3/4" diameter pipe		32	.250		13.05	14.70		27.75	36.50
0130 1" diameter pipe		30	.267		14.25	15.65		29.90	39
0140 1-1/4" diameter pipe		28	.286		14.45	16.75		31.20	41.50
0150 1-1/2" diameter pipe		26	.308		15.35	18.05		33.40	44.50
0160 2" diameter pipe		24	.333		16.50	19.55		36.05	47.50
0170 2-1/2" diameter pipe	↓	23	.348	↓	17.50	20.50		38	50.50

33 01 Operation and Maintenance of Utilities

33 01 10 – Operation and Maintenance of Water Utilities

33 01 10.20 Pipe Repair		Crew	Daily Output	Labor-Hours	Unit	Material	2015 Bare Costs Labor	Equipment	Total	Total Incl O&P
0180	3" diameter pipe	1 Plum	22	.364	Ea.	21	21.50		42.50	55
0190	3-1/2" diameter pipe	↓	21	.381		25	22.50		47.50	61.50
0200	4" diameter pipe	B-20	44	.545		25	23		48	63
0210	5" diameter pipe		42	.571		29.50	24		53.50	69.50
0220	6" diameter pipe		38	.632		34	26.50		60.50	78.50
0230	8" diameter pipe		30	.800		40.50	33.50		74	96
0240	10" diameter pipe		28	.857		115	36		151	183
0250	12" diameter pipe		24	1		120	42		162	197
0260	14" diameter pipe		22	1.091		125	46		171	209
0270	16" diameter pipe		20	1.200		135	50.50		185.50	227
0280	18" diameter pipe		18	1.333		145	56		201	246
0290	20" diameter pipe		16	1.500		150	63		213	262
0300	24" diameter pipe	↓	14	1.714		170	72		242	298
0360	For 6" long, add					100%	40%			
0370	For 9" long, add					200%	100%			
0380	For 12" long, add					300%	150%			
0390	For 18" long, add				↓	500%	200%			
0400	Pipe Freezing for live repairs of systems 3/8 inch to 6 inch									
0410	Note: Pipe Freezing can also be used to install a valve into a live system									
0420	Pipe Freezing each side 3/8 inch	2 Skwk	8	2	Ea.	540	97.50		637.50	745
0425	Pipe Freezing each side 3/8 inch, second location same kit		8	2		22.50	97.50		120	175
0430	Pipe Freezing each side 3/4 inch		8	2		495	97.50		592.50	695
0435	Pipe Freezing each side 3/4 inch, second location same kit		8	2		22.50	97.50		120	175
0440	Pipe Freezing each side 1-1/2 inch		6	2.667		495	130		625	745
0445	Pipe Freezing each side 1-1/2 inch , second location same kit		6	2.667		22.50	130		152.50	225
0450	Pipe Freezing each side 2 inch		6	2.667		890	130		1,020	1,175
0455	Pipe Freezing each side 2 inch, second location same kit		6	2.667		22.50	130		152.50	225
0460	Pipe Freezing each side 2-1/2 inch-3 inch		6	2.667		925	130		1,055	1,225
0465	Pipe Freeze each side 2-1/2 -3 inch, second location same kit		6	2.667		45.50	130		175.50	250
0470	Pipe Freezing each side 4 inch		4	4		1,475	195		1,670	1,925
0475	Pipe Freezing each side 4 inch, second location same kit		4	4		72	195		267	380
0480	Pipe Freezing each side 5-6 inch	↓	4	4		4,000	195		4,195	4,700
0485	Pipe Freezing each side 5-6 inch, second location same kit		4	4		216	195		411	540
0490	Pipe Freezing extra 20 lb. CO₂ cylinders (3/8" to 2" - 1 ea, 3" -2 ea)					222			222	244
0500	Pipe Freezing extra 50 lb. CO₂ cylinders (4" - 2 ea, 5"-6" -6 ea)				↓	440			440	485
1000	Clamp, stainless steel, with threaded service tap									
1040	Full seal for iron, steel, PVC pipe									
1100	6" long, 2" diameter pipe	1 Plum	17	.471	Ea.	87	27.50		114.50	137
1110	2-1/2" diameter pipe		16	.500		90	29.50		119.50	144
1120	3" diameter pipe		15.60	.513		104	30		134	161
1130	3-1/2" diameter pipe	↓	15	.533		110	31.50		141.50	169
1140	4" diameter pipe	B-20	32	.750		117	31.50		148.50	177
1150	6" diameter pipe		28	.857		145	36		181	216
1160	8" diameter pipe		21	1.143		171	48		219	262
1170	10" diameter pipe		20	1.200		224	50.50		274.50	325
1180	12" diameter pipe	↓	17	1.412		261	59		320	380
1200	8" long, 2" diameter pipe	1 Plum	11.72	.683		178	40		218	257
1210	2-1/2" diameter pipe		11	.727		183	42.50		225.50	266
1220	3" diameter pipe		10.75	.744		189	43.50		232.50	274
1230	3-1/2" diameter pipe	↓	10.34	.774		199	45.50		244.50	288
1240	4" diameter pipe	B-20	22	1.091		206	46		252	297
1250	6" diameter pipe		19.31	1.243		234	52		286	340
1260	8" diameter pipe	↓	14.48	1.657	↓	264	69.50		333.50	400

For customer support on your Site Work & Landscape Cost Data, call 877.737.1594.

463

33 01 10.20 Pipe Repair	Crew	Daily Output	Labor-Hours	Unit	Material	2015 Bare Costs Labor	Equipment	Total	Total Incl O&P
1270	10" diameter pipe	B-20	13.80	1.739	Ea.	330	73		403	475
1280	12" diameter pipe	▼	11.72	2.048		370	86		456	535
1300	12" long, 2" diameter pipe	1 Plum	9.44	.847		257	50		307	360
1310	2-1/2" diameter pipe		8.89	.900		262	53		315	370
1320	3" diameter pipe		8.67	.923		269	54		323	380
1330	3-1/2" diameter pipe	▼	8.33	.960		280	56.50		336.50	395
1340	4" diameter pipe	B-20	17.78	1.350		450	56.50		506.50	585
1350	6" diameter pipe		15.56	1.542		340	64.50		404.50	470
1360	8" diameter pipe		11.67	2.057		390	86.50		476.50	560
1370	10" diameter pipe		11.11	2.160		485	90.50		575.50	675
1380	12" diameter pipe	▼	9.44	2.542		555	107		662	775
1400	20" long, 2" diameter pipe	1 Plum	8.10	.988		299	58		357	420
1410	2-1/2" diameter pipe		7.62	1.050		325	61.50		386.50	450
1420	3" diameter pipe		7.43	1.077		365	63		428	495
1430	3-1/2" diameter pipe	▼	7.14	1.120		380	66		446	520
1440	4" diameter pipe	B-20	15.24	1.575		450	66		516	595
1450	6" diameter pipe		13.33	1.800		525	75.50		600.50	690
1460	8" diameter pipe		10	2.400		590	101		691	805
1470	10" diameter pipe		9.52	2.521		715	106		821	950
1480	12" diameter pipe	▼	8.10	2.963	▼	835	124		959	1,100
1600	Clamp, stainless steel, single section									
1640	Full seal for iron, steel, PVC pipe									
1700	6" long, 2" diameter pipe	1 Plum	17	.471	Ea.	87	27.50		114.50	137
1710	2-1/2" diameter pipe		16	.500		90	29.50		119.50	144
1720	3" diameter pipe		15.60	.513		104	30		134	161
1730	3-1/2" diameter pipe	▼	15	.533		110	31.50		141.50	169
1740	4" diameter pipe	B-20	32	.750		117	31.50		148.50	177
1750	6" diameter pipe		27	.889		145	37.50		182.50	218
1760	8" diameter pipe		21	1.143		171	48		219	262
1770	10" diameter pipe		20	1.200		224	50.50		274.50	325
1780	12" diameter pipe	▼	17	1.412		261	59		320	380
1800	8" long, 2" diameter pipe	1 Plum	11.72	.683		118	40		158	191
1805	2-1/2" diameter pipe		11.03	.725		123	42.50		165.50	200
1810	3" diameter pipe		10.76	.743		129	43.50		172.50	208
1815	3-1/2" diameter pipe	▼	10.34	.774		139	45.50		184.50	222
1820	4" diameter pipe	B-20	22.07	1.087		146	45.50		191.50	231
1825	6" diameter pipe		19.31	1.243		174	52		226	273
1830	8" diameter pipe		14.48	1.657		204	69.50		273.50	330
1835	10" diameter pipe		13.79	1.740		272	73		345	410
1840	12" diameter pipe	▼	11.72	2.048		310	86		396	470
1850	12" long, 2" diameter pipe	1 Plum	9.44	.847		197	50		247	291
1855	2-1/2" diameter pipe		8.89	.900		201	53		254	300
1860	3" diameter pipe		8.67	.923		209	54		263	310
1865	3-1/2" diameter pipe	▼	8.33	.960		220	56.50		276.50	325
1870	4" diameter pipe	B-20	17.78	1.350		231	56.50		287.50	340
1875	6" diameter pipe		15.56	1.542		278	64.50		342.50	405
1880	8" diameter pipe		11.67	2.057		330	86.50		416.50	495
1885	10" diameter pipe		11.11	2.160		425	90.50		515.50	610
1890	12" diameter pipe	▼	9.44	2.542		495	107		602	710
1900	20" long, 2" diameter pipe	1 Plum	8.10	.988		239	58		297	350
1905	2-1/2" diameter pipe		7.62	1.050		264	61.50		325.50	385
1910	3" diameter pipe		7.43	1.077		305	63		368	430
1915	3-1/2" diameter pipe	▼	7.14	1.120		320	66		386	450

464

For customer support on your Site Work & Landscape Cost Data, call 877.737.1594.

33 01 Operation and Maintenance of Utilities

33 01 10 – Operation and Maintenance of Water Utilities

33 01 10.20 Pipe Repair

33 01 10.20 Pipe Repair		Crew	Daily Output	Labor-Hours	Unit	Material	2015 Bare Costs Labor	Equipment	Total	Total Incl O&P
1920	4" diameter pipe	B-20	15.24	1.575	Ea.	390	66		456	530
1925	6" diameter pipe		13.33	1.800		465	75.50		540.50	625
1930	8" diameter pipe		10	2.400		530	101		631	740
1935	10" diameter pipe		9.52	2.521		655	106		761	885
1940	12" diameter pipe		8.10	2.963		775	124		899	1,050
2000	Clamp, stainless steel, two section									
2040	Full seal, for iron, steel, PVC pipe									
2100	6" long, 4" diameter pipe	B-20	24	1	Ea.	230	42		272	320
2110	6" diameter pipe		20	1.200		264	50.50		314.50	370
2120	8" diameter pipe		13	1.846		300	77.50		377.50	450
2130	10" diameter pipe		12	2		305	84		389	465
2140	12" diameter pipe		10	2.400		390	101		491	585
2200	9" long, 4" diameter pipe		16	1.500		300	63		363	425
2210	6" diameter pipe		13	1.846		340	77.50		417.50	495
2220	8" diameter pipe		9	2.667		375	112		487	585
2230	10" diameter pipe		8	3		495	126		621	740
2240	12" diameter pipe		7	3.429		565	144		709	845
2250	14" diameter pipe		6.40	3.750		760	157		917	1,075
2260	16" diameter pipe		6	4		705	168		873	1,050
2270	18" diameter pipe		5	4.800		800	201		1,001	1,200
2280	20" diameter pipe		4.60	5.217		885	219		1,104	1,300
2290	24" diameter pipe		4	6		1,175	252		1,427	1,700
2320	For 12" long, add to 9"					15%	25%			
2330	For 18" long, add to 9"					70%	55%			
8000	For internal cleaning and inspection, see Section 33 01 30.16									
8100	For pipe testing, see Section 23 05 93.50									

33 01 30 – Operation and Maintenance of Sewer Utilities

33 01 30.16 TV Inspection of Sewer Pipelines

		Crew	Daily Output	Labor-Hours	Unit	Material	2015 Bare Costs Labor	Equipment	Total	Total Incl O&P
0010	**TV INSPECTION OF SEWER PIPELINES**									
0100	Pipe internal cleaning & inspection, cleaning, pressure pipe systems									
0120	Pig method, lengths 1000' to 10,000'									
0140	4" diameter thru 24" diameter, minimum				L.F.				3.60	4.14
0160	Maximum				"				18	21
6000	Sewage/sanitary systems									
6100	Power rodder with header & cutters									
6110	Mobilization charge, minimum				Total				695	800
6120	Mobilization charge, maximum				"				9,125	10,600
6140	Cleaning 4"-12" diameter				L.F.				3.39	3.90
6190	14"-24" diameter								3.98	4.59
6240	30" diameter								5.80	6.65
6250	36" diameter								6.75	7.75
6260	48" diameter								7.70	8.85
6270	60" diameter								8.70	9.95
6280	72" diameter								9.65	11.10
9000	Inspection, television camera with video									
9060	up to 500 linear feet				Total				715	820

33 01 30.71 Rehabilitation of Sewer Utilities

		Crew	Daily Output	Labor-Hours	Unit	Material	2015 Bare Costs Labor	Equipment	Total	Total Incl O&P
0010	**REHABILITATION OF SEWER UTILITIES**									
0011	300' runs, replace with HDPE pipe									
0020	Not including excavation, backfill, shoring, or dewatering									
0100	6" to 15" diameter, minimum				L.F.				104	114
0200	Maximum								214	236

For customer support on your Site Work & Landscape Cost Data, call 877.737.1594.

465

33 01 Operation and Maintenance of Utilities

33 01 30 – Operation and Maintenance of Sewer Utilities

33 01 30.71 Rehabilitation of Sewer Utilities

		Crew	Daily Output	Labor-Hours	Unit	Material	2015 Bare Costs Labor	Equipment	Total	Total Incl O&P
0300	18" to 36" diameter, minimum				L.F.				208	229
0400	Maximum				↓				435	510
0500	Mobilize and demobilize, minimum				Job				3,000	3,300
0600	Maximum				"				32,100	35,400

33 01 30.72 Relining Sewers

		Crew	Daily Output	Labor-Hours	Unit	Material	2015 Bare Costs Labor	Equipment	Total	Total Incl O&P
0010	**RELINING SEWERS**									
0011	With cement incl. bypass & cleaning									
0020	Less than 10,000 L.F., urban, 6" to 10"	C-17E	130	.615	L.F.	9.55	30	.74	40.29	58
0050	10" to 12"		125	.640		11.70	31.50	.77	43.97	62.50
0070	12" to 16"		115	.696		12.05	34	.84	46.89	66.50
0100	16" to 20"		95	.842		14.15	41.50	1.02	56.67	80.50
0200	24" to 36"		90	.889		15.25	43.50	1.08	59.83	85.50
0300	48" to 72"		80	1		24.50	49	1.21	74.71	104
0500	Rural, 6" to 10"		180	.444		9.55	22	.54	32.09	44.50
0550	10" to 12"		175	.457		11.70	22.50	.55	34.75	48
0570	12" to 16"		160	.500		12.05	24.50	.61	37.16	52
0600	16" to 20"		135	.593		14.15	29	.72	43.87	61.50
0700	24" to 36"		125	.640		15.25	31.50	.77	47.52	66
0800	48" to 72"		100	.800		24.50	39	.97	64.47	88
1000	Greater than 10,000 L.F., urban, 6" to 10"		160	.500		9.55	24.50	.61	34.66	49
1050	10" to 12"		155	.516		11.70	25.50	.62	37.82	52.50
1070	12" to 16"		140	.571		12.05	28	.69	40.74	57.50
1100	16" to 20"		120	.667		14.15	32.50	.81	47.46	67
1200	24" to 36"		115	.696		15.25	34	.84	50.09	70
1300	48" to 72"		95	.842		24.50	41.50	1.02	67.02	91.50
1500	Rural, 6" to 10"		215	.372		9.55	18.25	.45	28.25	39
1550	10" to 12"		210	.381		11.70	18.70	.46	30.86	42.50
1570	12" to 16"		185	.432		12.05	21	.52	33.57	47
1600	16" to 20"		150	.533		14.15	26	.65	40.80	57
1700	24" to 36"		140	.571		15.25	28	.69	43.94	61
1800	48" to 72"	↓	120	.667	↓	24.50	32.50	.81	57.81	78
2000	Cured in place pipe, non-pressure, flexible felt resin, 400' runs									
2100	6" diameter				L.F.				25.50	28
2200	8" diameter								26.50	29
2300	10" diameter								29	32
2400	12" diameter								34.50	38
2500	15" diameter								59	65
2600	18" diameter								82	90
2700	21" diameter								105	115
2800	24" diameter								177	195
2900	30" diameter								195	215
3000	36" diameter								205	225
3100	48" diameter				↓				218	240

33 01 30.74 HDPE Pipe Lining

		Crew	Daily Output	Labor-Hours	Unit	Material	2015 Bare Costs Labor	Equipment	Total	Total Incl O&P
0010	**HDPE PIPE LINING**, excludes cleaning and video inspection									
0020	Pipe relined with one pipe size smaller than original (4" for 6")									
0100	6" diameter, original size	B-6B	600	.080	L.F.	2.47	3.06	1.50	7.03	9.10
0150	8" diameter, original size		600	.080		5.85	3.06	1.50	10.41	12.80
0200	10" diameter, original size		600	.080		8.55	3.06	1.50	13.11	15.75
0250	12" diameter, original size		400	.120		14.65	4.59	2.26	21.50	25.50
0300	14" diameter, original size	↓	400	.120		17.75	4.59	2.26	24.60	29
0350	16" diameter, original size	B-6C	300	.160	↓	27.50	6.10	5.35	38.95	45.50

33 01 Operation and Maintenance of Utilities

33 01 30 – Operation and Maintenance of Sewer Utilities

33 01 30.74 HDPE Pipe Lining	Crew	Daily Output	Labor-Hours	Unit	Material	2015 Bare Costs Labor	Equipment	Total	Total Incl O&P
0400	18" diameter, original size	B-6C	300	.160	L.F.	32.50	6.10	5.35	43.95	51
1000	Pipe HDPE lining, make service line taps	B-6	4	6	Ea.	97	248	91	436	585

33 05 Common Work Results for Utilities

33 05 16 – Utility Structures

33 05 16.13 Precast Concrete Utility Boxes

		Crew	Daily Output	Labor-Hours	Unit	Material	2015 Bare Costs Labor	Equipment	Total	Total Incl O&P
0010	**PRECAST CONCRETE UTILITY BOXES,** 6" thick									
0040	4' x 6' x 6' high, I.D.	B-13	2	28	Ea.	3,025	1,150	370	4,545	5,475
0050	5' x 10' x 6' high, I.D.		2	28		3,750	1,150	370	5,270	6,275
0100	6' x 10' x 6' high, I.D.		2	28		3,900	1,150	370	5,420	6,425
0150	5' x 12' x 6' high, I.D.		2	28		4,125	1,150	370	5,645	6,675
0200	6' x 12' x 6' high, I.D.		1.80	31.111		4,600	1,275	410	6,285	7,475
0250	6' x 13' x 6' high, I.D.		1.50	37.333		6,050	1,525	490	8,065	9,550
0300	8' x 14' x 7' high, I.D.		1	56		6,525	2,300	735	9,560	11,500
0350	Hand hole, precast concrete, 1-1/2" thick									
0400	1'-0" x 2'-0" x 1'-9", I.D., light duty	B-1	4	6	Ea.	400	230		630	795
0450	4'-6" x 3'-2" x 2'-0", O.D., heavy duty	B-6	3	8		1,475	330	121	1,926	2,250
0460	Meter pit, 4' x 4', 4' deep		2	12		1,400	495	182	2,077	2,500
0470	6' deep		1.60	15		2,000	620	228	2,848	3,400
0480	8' deep		1.40	17.143		2,650	705	260	3,615	4,250
0490	10' deep		1.20	20		3,350	825	305	4,480	5,300
0500	15' deep		1	24		4,900	990	365	6,255	7,325
0510	6' x 6', 4' deep		1.40	17.143		2,275	705	260	3,240	3,850
0520	6' deep		1.20	20		3,425	825	305	4,555	5,375
0530	8' deep		1	24		4,575	990	365	5,930	6,950
0540	10' deep		.80	30		5,700	1,250	455	7,405	8,675
0550	15' deep		.60	40		8,675	1,650	605	10,930	12,700

33 05 23 – Trenchless Utility Installation

33 05 23.19 Microtunneling

		Crew	Daily Output	Labor-Hours	Unit	Material	2015 Bare Costs Labor	Equipment	Total	Total Incl O&P
0010	**MICROTUNNELING**									
0011	Not including excavation, backfill, shoring,									
0020	or dewatering, average 50'/day, slurry method									
0100	24" to 48" outside diameter, minimum				L.F.				875	965
0110	Adverse conditions, add				%				50%	50%
1000	Rent microtunneling machine, average monthly lease				Month				97,500	107,000
1010	Operating technician				Day				630	705
1100	Mobilization and demobilization, minimum				Job				41,200	45,900
1110	Maximum				"				445,500	490,500

33 05 23.20 Horizontal Boring

		Crew	Daily Output	Labor-Hours	Unit	Material	2015 Bare Costs Labor	Equipment	Total	Total Incl O&P
0010	**HORIZONTAL BORING**									
0011	Casing only, 100' minimum,									
0020	not incl. jacking pits or dewatering									
0100	Roadwork, 1/2" thick wall, 24" diameter casing	B-42	20	3.200	L.F.	121	136	68	325	420
0200	36" diameter		16	4		223	170	85	478	605
0300	48" diameter		15	4.267		310	181	90.50	581.50	725
0500	Railroad work, 24" diameter		15	4.267		121	181	90.50	392.50	515
0600	36" diameter		14	4.571		223	194	97	514	655
0700	48" diameter		12	5.333		310	226	113	649	820
0900	For ledge, add								20%	20%
1000	Small diameter boring, 3", sandy soil	B-82	900	.018		22	.77	.09	22.86	25.50

For customer support on your Site Work & Landscape Cost Data, call 877.737.1594.

467

33 05 Common Work Results for Utilities

33 05 23 – Trenchless Utility Installation

33 05 23.20 Horizontal Boring

		Crew	Daily Output	Labor-Hours	Unit	Material	2015 Bare Costs Labor	2015 Bare Costs Equipment	Total	Total Incl O&P
1040	Rocky soil	B-82	500	.032	L.F.	22	1.38	.17	23.55	26.50
1100	Prepare jacking pits, incl. mobilization & demobilization, minimum				Ea.				3,225	3,700
1101	Maximum				"				22,000	25,500

33 05 23.22 Directional Drilling

		Crew	Daily Output	Labor-Hours	Unit	Material	2015 Bare Costs Labor	2015 Bare Costs Equipment	Total	Total Incl O&P
0010	**DIRECTIONAL DRILLING**									
0011	Excluding access and splice pits (if required) and conduit (required)									
0012	Drilled Hole diameters shown should be 50% larger than conduit									
0013	Assume access to H2O & removal of spoil/drilling mud as non-hazard material									
0014	Actual production rates adj. to account for risk factors for each soil type									
0100	Sand, silt, clay, common earth									
0110	Mobilization or demobilization	B-82A	1	32	Ea.		1,375	2,425	3,800	4,775
0120	6" diameter		480	.067	L.F.		2.87	5.05	7.92	10
0130	12" diameter		270	.119			5.10	9	14.10	17.70
0140	18" diameter		180	.178			7.65	13.50	21.15	26.50
0150	24" diameter		135	.237			10.20	18.05	28.25	35.50
0200	Hard clay, cobble, random boulders									
0210	Mobilization or demobilization	B-82B	1	32	Ea.		1,375	2,700	4,075	5,075
0220	6" diameter		400	.080	L.F.		3.45	6.80	10.25	12.70
0230	12" diameter		220	.145			6.25	12.30	18.55	23
0240	18" diameter		145	.221			9.50	18.70	28.20	35
0250	24" diameter		105	.305			13.15	26	39.15	48.50
0260	30" diameter		80	.400			17.25	34	51.25	64
0270	36" diameter		60	.533			23	45	68	84.50
0300	Hard rock (solid bed, 24,000+ psi)									
0310	Mobilization or Demobilization	B-82C	1	32	Ea.		1,375	3,025	4,400	5,425
0320	6" diameter		75	.427	L.F.		18.40	40	58.40	72.50
0330	12" diameter		40	.800			34.50	75.50	110	136
0340	18" diameter		25	1.280			55	121	176	217
0350	24" diameter		20	1.600			69	151	220	271
0360	30" diameter		15	2.133			92	201	293	360
0370	36" diameter		12	2.667			115	251	366	450

33 05 26 – Utility Identification

33 05 26.05 Utility Connection

		Crew	Daily Output	Labor-Hours	Unit	Material	2015 Bare Costs Labor	2015 Bare Costs Equipment	Total	Total Incl O&P
0010	**UTILITY CONNECTION**									
0020	Water, sanitary, stormwater, gas, single connection	B-14	1	48	Ea.	3,225	1,900	365	5,490	6,875
0030	Telecommunication	"	1	48	"	395	1,900	365	2,660	3,750

33 05 26.10 Utility Accessories

		Crew	Daily Output	Labor-Hours	Unit	Material	2015 Bare Costs Labor	2015 Bare Costs Equipment	Total	Total Incl O&P
0010	**UTILITY ACCESSORIES**									
0400	Underground tape, detectable, reinforced, alum. foil core, 2"	1 Clab	150	.053	C.L.F.	6.50	2.01		8.51	10.25
0500	6"	"	140	.057	"	27.50	2.15		29.65	33.50

33 11 13.10 Water Supply, Concrete Pipe

		Daily Output	Labor-Hours	Unit	Material	2015 Bare Costs Labor	Equipment	Total	Total Incl O&P
		Crew							
0010	**WATER SUPPLY, CONCRETE PIPE**								
0020	Not including excavation or backfill								
3000	Prestressed Conc. Pipe (PCCP), 150 PSI, 12" diam.	B-13	192	.292	L.F.	45	11.95	3.84	60.79	72
3010	24" diameter	"	128	.438		45	17.95	5.75	68.70	83.50
3040	36" diameter	B-13B	96	.583		70	24	11.75	105.75	126
3050	48" diameter		64	.875		100	36	17.60	153.60	184
3070	72" diameter		60	.933		195	38.50	18.80	252.30	294
3080	84" diameter		40	1.400		252	57.50	28	337.50	395
3090	96" diameter	B-13C	40	1.400		370	57.50	41.50	469	540
3100	108" diameter		32	1.750		525	71.50	52	648.50	750
3102	120" diameter		16	3.500		940	143	104	1,187	1,350
3104	144" diameter		16	3.500		920	143	104	1,167	1,325
3110	Prestressed Concrete Pipe (PCCP), 150 PSI, elbow, 90°, 12" diameter	B-13	24	2.333	Ea.	890	95.50	30.50	1,016	1,150
3140	24" diameter	"	6	9.333		1,750	385	123	2,258	2,650
3150	36" diameter	B-13B	4	14		3,400	575	282	4,257	4,950
3160	48" diameter		3	18.667		6,725	765	375	7,865	9,000
3180	72" diameter		1.60	35		19,200	1,425	705	21,330	24,100
3190	84" diameter		1.30	43.077		23,300	1,775	870	25,945	29,400
3200	96" diameter		1	56		31,300	2,300	1,125	34,725	39,200
3210	108" diameter	B-13C	.66	84.848		46,700	3,475	2,525	52,700	59,500
3220	120" diameter		.40	140		47,200	5,750	4,175	57,125	65,500
3225	144" diameter		.30	184		74,500	7,550	5,475	87,525	99,500
3230	Precast Concrete Pipe (PCCP), 150 PSI, elbow, 45°, 12" diameter	B-13	24	2.333		555	95.50	30.50	681	790
3250	24" diameter	"	6	9.333		1,125	385	123	1,633	1,975
3260	36" diameter	B-13B	4	14		1,900	575	282	2,757	3,300
3270	48" diameter		3	18.667		3,475	765	375	4,615	5,425
3290	72" diameter		1.60	35		11,900	1,425	705	14,030	16,100
3300	84" diameter		1.30	42.945		18,200	1,750	865	20,815	23,700
3310	96" diameter		1	56		22,500	2,300	1,125	25,925	29,600
3320	108" diameter	B-13C	.66	84.337		28,400	3,450	2,500	34,350	39,300
3330	120" diameter		.40	140		28,700	5,750	4,175	38,625	45,000
3340	144" diameter		.30	184		45,900	7,550	5,475	58,925	68,000

33 11 13.15 Water Supply, Ductile Iron Pipe

		Crew	Daily Output	Labor-Hours	Unit	Material	2015 Bare Costs Labor	Equipment	Total	Total Incl O&P
0010	**WATER SUPPLY, DUCTILE IRON PIPE**									
0011	Cement lined									
0020	Not including excavation or backfill									
2000	Pipe, class 50 water piping, 18' lengths									
2020	Mechanical joint, 4" diameter	B-21A	200	.200	L.F.	30.50	9.40	2.37	42.27	50.50
2040	6" diameter		160	.250		32	11.75	2.96	46.71	56
2060	8" diameter		133.33	.300		44.50	14.05	3.55	62.10	74.50
2080	10" diameter		114.29	.350		58.50	16.40	4.14	79.04	93.50
2100	12" diameter		105.26	.380		79	17.85	4.50	101.35	119
2120	14" diameter		100	.400		93	18.75	4.74	116.49	136
2140	16" diameter		72.73	.550		94.50	26	6.50	127	151
2160	18" diameter		68.97	.580		126	27	6.85	159.85	188
2170	20" diameter		57.14	.700		127	33	8.30	168.30	199
2180	24" diameter		47.06	.850		141	40	10.05	191.05	227
3000	Push-on joint, 4" diameter		400	.100		21	4.69	1.18	26.87	31.50
3020	6" diameter		333.33	.120		17	5.65	1.42	24.07	29
3040	8" diameter		200	.200		23	9.40	2.37	34.77	42.50
3060	10" diameter		181.82	.220		36.50	10.30	2.60	49.40	59
3080	12" diameter		160	.250		38.50	11.75	2.96	53.21	63.50

33 11 13.15 Water Supply, Ductile Iron Pipe	Crew	Daily Output	Labor-Hours	Unit	Material	2015 Bare Costs Labor	Equipment	Total	Total Incl O&P
3100	14" diameter	B-21A	133.33	.300	L.F.	42.50	14.05	3.55	60.10	72.50
3120	16" diameter		114.29	.350		51.50	16.40	4.14	72.04	86
3140	18" diameter		100	.400		57	18.75	4.74	80.49	96
3160	20" diameter		88.89	.450		59.50	21	5.35	85.85	103
3180	24" diameter		76.92	.520		59	24.50	6.15	89.65	109
6170	Cap, 4" diameter	B-20A	32	1	Ea.	96	45.50		141.50	175
6180	6" diameter		25.60	1.250		126	57		183	225
6190	8" diameter		21.33	1.500		172	68.50		240.50	293
6200	12" diameter		16.84	1.900		385	87		472	550
6210	18" diameter		11	2.909		995	133		1,128	1,300
6220	24" diameter	B-21A	9.41	4.251		1,875	199	50.50	2,124.50	2,425
6230	30" diameter		8	5		4,025	235	59	4,319	4,850
6240	36" diameter		6.90	5.797		4,850	272	68.50	5,190.50	5,825
8000	Piping, fittings, mechanical joint, AWWA C110									
8006	90° bend, 4" diameter	B-20A	16	2	Ea.	155	91.50		246.50	310
8020	6" diameter		12.80	2.500		229	114		343	425
8040	8" diameter		10.67	2.999		450	137		587	705
8060	10" diameter	B-21A	11.43	3.500		620	164	41.50	825.50	975
8080	12" diameter		10.53	3.799		880	178	45	1,103	1,300
8100	14" diameter		10	4		1,200	188	47.50	1,435.50	1,650
8120	16" diameter		7.27	5.502		1,525	258	65	1,848	2,150
8140	18" diameter		6.90	5.797		2,125	272	68.50	2,465.50	2,850
8160	20" diameter		5.71	7.005		2,650	330	83	3,063	3,525
8180	24" diameter		4.70	8.511		4,200	400	101	4,701	5,325
8200	Wye or tee, 4" diameter	B-20A	10.67	2.999		355	137		492	600
8220	6" diameter		8.53	3.751		535	171		706	850
8240	8" diameter		7.11	4.501		850	206		1,056	1,250
8260	10" diameter	B-21A	7.62	5.249		1,225	246	62	1,533	1,800
8280	12" diameter		7.02	5.698		1,625	267	67.50	1,959.50	2,250
8300	14" diameter		6.67	5.997		2,600	281	71	2,952	3,375
8320	16" diameter		4.85	8.247		2,900	385	97.50	3,382.50	3,875
8340	18" diameter		4.60	8.696		3,900	410	103	4,413	5,025
8360	20" diameter		3.81	10.499		5,475	490	124	6,089	6,900
8380	24" diameter		3.14	12.739		9,275	600	151	10,026	11,300
8398	45° bends, 4" diameter	B-20A	16	2		255	91.50		346.50	420
8400	6" diameter		12.80	2.500		199	114		313	395
8405	8" diameter		10.67	2.999		291	137		428	530
8410	12" diameter	B-21A	10.53	3.799		730	178	45	953	1,125
8420	16" diameter		7.27	5.502		1,275	258	65	1,598	1,875
8430	20" diameter		5.71	7.005		2,075	330	83	2,488	2,875
8440	24" diameter		4.70	8.511		2,900	400	101	3,401	3,900
8450	Decreaser, 6" x 4" diameter	B-20A	14.22	2.250		207	103		310	385
8460	8" x 6" diameter	"	11.64	2.749		310	126		436	530
8470	10" x 6" diameter	B-21A	13.33	3.001		390	141	35.50	566.50	685
8480	12" x 6" diameter		12.70	3.150		550	148	37.50	735.50	870
8490	16" x 6" diameter		10	4		890	188	47.50	1,125.50	1,325
8500	20" x 6" diameter		8.42	4.751		1,625	223	56.50	1,904.50	2,175
8552	For water utility valves see Section 33 12 16									
8700	Joint restraint, ductile iron mechanical joints									
8710	4" diameter	B-20A	32	1	Ea.	29	45.50		74.50	102
8720	6" diameter		25.60	1.250		31.50	57		88.50	122
8730	8" diameter		21.33	1.500		30	68.50		98.50	137
8740	10" diameter		18.28	1.751		38.50	80		118.50	165

33 11 13 – Public Water Utility Distribution Piping

33 11 13.15 Water Supply, Ductile Iron Pipe

		Crew	Daily Output	Labor-Hours	Unit	Material	2015 Bare Costs Labor	Equipment	Total	Total Incl O&P
8750	12" diameter	B-20A	16.84	1.900	Ea.	50	87		137	187
8760	14" diameter		16	2		53	91.50		144.50	198
8770	16" diameter		11.64	2.749		58	126		184	255
8780	18" diameter		11.03	2.901		73	133		206	282
8785	20" diameter		9.14	3.501		78	160		238	330
8790	24" diameter	▼	7.53	4.250		104	194		298	410
9600	Steel sleeve with tap, 4" diameter	B-20	3	8		435	335		770	995
9620	6" diameter		2	12		475	505		980	1,300
9630	8" diameter	▼	2	12	▼	515	505		1,020	1,350

33 11 13.20 Water Supply, Polyethylene Pipe, C901

		Crew	Daily Output	Labor-Hours	Unit	Material	2015 Bare Costs Labor	Equipment	Total	Total Incl O&P
0010	**WATER SUPPLY, POLYETHYLENE PIPE, C901**									
0020	Not including excavation or backfill									
1000	Piping, 160 PSI, 3/4" diameter	Q-1A	525	.019	L.F.	.46	1.13		1.59	2.21
1120	1" diameter		485	.021		.60	1.22		1.82	2.50
1140	1-1/2" diameter		450	.022		1.35	1.31		2.66	3.47
1160	2" diameter	▼	365	.027	▼	2.20	1.62		3.82	4.87
2000	Fittings, insert type, nylon, 160 & 250 psi, cold water									
2220	Clamp ring, stainless steel, 3/4" diameter	Q-1A	345	.029	Ea.	1.27	1.71		2.98	3.99
2240	1" diameter		321	.031		1.47	1.84		3.31	4.40
2260	1-1/2" diameter		285	.035		2.64	2.07		4.71	6.05
2280	2" diameter		255	.039		3.47	2.32		5.79	7.30
2300	Coupling, 3/4" diameter		66	.152		1.40	8.95		10.35	15.05
2320	1" diameter		57	.175		1.63	10.35		11.98	17.45
2340	1-1/2" diameter		51	.196		3.30	11.60		14.90	21
2360	2" diameter		48	.208		5.15	12.30		17.45	24.50
2400	Elbow, 90°, 3/4" diameter		66	.152		2.27	8.95		11.22	16
2420	1" diameter		57	.175		2.74	10.35		13.09	18.65
2440	1-1/2" diameter		51	.196		4.51	11.60		16.11	22.50
2460	2" diameter		48	.208		6.35	12.30		18.65	25.50
2500	Tee, 3/4" diameter		42	.238		2.74	14.05		16.79	24.50
2520	1" diameter		39	.256		3.80	15.15		18.95	27
2540	1-1/2" diameter		33	.303		7.45	17.90		25.35	35
2560	2" diameter	▼	30	.333	▼	14.10	19.70		33.80	45.50

33 11 13.25 Water Supply, Polyvinyl Chloride Pipe

		Crew	Daily Output	Labor-Hours	Unit	Material	2015 Bare Costs Labor	Equipment	Total	Total Incl O&P
0010	**WATER SUPPLY, POLYVINYL CHLORIDE PIPE**									
0020	Not including excavation or backfill, unless specified									
2100	PVC pipe, Class 150, 1-1/2" diameter	Q-1A	750	.013	L.F.	.45	.79		1.24	1.69
2120	2" diameter		686	.015		.68	.86		1.54	2.05
2140	2-1/2" diameter	▼	500	.020		1.30	1.18		2.48	3.22
2160	3" diameter	B-20	430	.056	▼	1.40	2.34		3.74	5.15
3010	AWWA C905, PR 100, DR 25									
3030	14" diameter	B-20A	213	.150	L.F.	13.65	6.85		20.50	25.50
3040	16" diameter		200	.160		19.25	7.30		26.55	32
3050	18" diameter		160	.200		24.50	9.15		33.65	40.50
3060	20" diameter		133	.241		30	11		41	50
3070	24" diameter		107	.299		43	13.65		56.65	68.50
3080	30" diameter		80	.400		81	18.30		99.30	117
3090	36" diameter		80	.400		126	18.30		144.30	166
3100	42" diameter		60	.533		168	24.50		192.50	222
3200	48" diameter		60	.533		220	24.50		244.50	279
3960	Pressure pipe, class 200, ASTM 2241, SDR 21, 3/4" diameter	Q-1A	1000	.010		.23	.59		.82	1.14
3980	1" diameter		900	.011		.33	.66		.99	1.35

For customer support on your Site Work & Landscape Cost Data, call 877.737.1594.

471

33 11 13.25 Water Supply, Polyvinyl Chloride Pipe		Crew	Daily Output	Labor-Hours	Unit	Material	2015 Bare Costs Labor	Equipment	Total	Total Incl O&P
4000	1-1/2" diameter	Q-1A	750	.013	L.F.	.72	.79		1.51	1.98
4010	2" diameter		686	.015		.88	.86		1.74	2.27
4020	2-1/2" diameter	▼	500	.020		1.37	1.18		2.55	3.30
4030	3" diameter	B-20A	430	.074		1.61	3.40		5.01	6.95
4040	4" diameter		375	.085		2.48	3.90		6.38	8.70
4050	6" diameter		316	.101		4.85	4.63		9.48	12.40
4060	8" diameter		260	.123		8.40	5.65		14.05	17.80
4090	Including trenching to 3' deep, 3/4" diameter	Q-1C	300	.080		.23	4.17	11.35	15.75	19
4100	1" diameter		280	.086		.33	4.46	12.15	16.94	20.50
4110	1-1/2" diameter		260	.092		.72	4.81	13.10	18.63	22.50
4120	2" diameter		220	.109		.88	5.70	15.45	22.03	26.50
4130	2-1/2" diameter		200	.120		1.37	6.25	17	24.62	29.50
4140	3" diameter		175	.137		1.61	7.15	19.45	28.21	34
4150	4" diameter		150	.160		2.48	8.35	22.50	33.33	40.50
4160	6" diameter	▼	125	.192	▼	4.85	10	27	41.85	50.50
4165	Fittings									
4170	Elbow, 90°, 3/4"	Q-1A	114	.088	Ea.	1.58	5.20		6.78	9.60
4180	1"		100	.100		4.58	5.90		10.48	14
4190	1-1/2"		80	.125		16.25	7.40		23.65	29
4200	2"	▼	72	.139		26	8.20		34.20	41
4210	3"	B-20A	46	.696		31	32		63	82.50
4220	4"		36	.889		38.50	40.50		79	105
4230	6"		24	1.333		70.50	61		131.50	171
4240	8"	▼	14	2.286		145	104		249	320
4250	Elbow, 45°, 3/4"	Q-1A	114	.088		2.65	5.20		7.85	10.75
4260	1"		100	.100		6.35	5.90		12.25	15.95
4270	1-1/2"		80	.125		18.75	7.40		26.15	31.50
4280	2"		72	.139		19.95	8.20		28.15	34.50
4290	2-1/2"	▼	54	.185		21	10.95		31.95	39.50
4300	3"	B-20A	46	.696		25	32		57	76
4310	4"		36	.889		37	40.50		77.50	103
4320	6"		24	1.333		75.50	61		136.50	176
4330	8"	▼	14	2.286		136	104		240	310
4340	Tee, 3/4"	Q-1A	76	.132		3.40	7.80		11.20	15.50
4350	1"		66	.152		16.80	8.95		25.75	32
4360	1-1/2"		54	.185		24.50	10.95		35.45	43.50
4370	2"		48	.208		29.50	12.30		41.80	51
4380	2-1/2"	▼	36	.278		32	16.40		48.40	60.50
4390	3"	B-20A	30	1.067		33.50	49		82.50	111
4400	4"		24	1.333		53.50	61		114.50	152
4410	6"		14.80	2.162		117	99		216	279
4420	8"	▼	9	3.556		210	163		373	480
4430	Coupling, 3/4"	Q-1A	114	.088		1.50	5.20	.	6.70	9.50
4440	1"		100	.100		6.65	5.90		12.55	16.25
4450	1-1/2"		80	.125		10.75	7.40		18.15	23
4460	2"		72	.139		11.65	8.20		19.85	25.50
4470	2-1/2"	▼	54	.185		12.85	10.95		23.80	30.50
4480	3"	B-20A	46	.696		16.35	32		48.35	66.50
4490	4"		36	.889		25	40.50		65.50	89.50
4500	6"		24	1.333		38	61		99	135
4510	8"	▼	14	2.286	▼	87	104		191	255
4520	Pressure pipe Class 150, SDR 18, AWWA C900, 4" diameter		380	.084	L.F.	2.73	3.85		6.58	8.85
4530	6" diameter	▼	316	.101	▼	5.35	4.63		9.98	12.95

472

33 11 13 – Public Water Utility Distribution Piping

33 11 13.25 Water Supply, Polyvinyl Chloride Pipe		Crew	Daily Output	Labor-Hours	Unit	Material	2015 Bare Costs Labor	Equipment	Total	Total Incl O&P
4540	8" diameter	B-20A	264	.121	L.F.	8.80	5.55		14.35	18.10
4550	10" diameter		220	.145		14.05	6.65		20.70	25.50
4560	12" diameter		186	.172		19.90	7.85		27.75	34
8000	Fittings with rubber gasket									
8003	Class 150, DR 18									
8006	90° Bend , 4" diameter	B-20	100	.240	Ea.	42.50	10.05		52.55	62
8020	6" diameter		90	.267		75	11.20		86.20	100
8040	8" diameter		80	.300		145	12.60		157.60	178
8060	10" diameter		50	.480		330	20		350	395
8080	12" diameter		30	.800		425	33.50		458.50	515
8100	Tee, 4" diameter		90	.267		58.50	11.20		69.70	82
8120	6" diameter		80	.300		144	12.60		156.60	177
8140	8" diameter		70	.343		185	14.40		199.40	225
8160	10" diameter		40	.600		590	25		615	690
8180	12" diameter		20	1.200		765	50.50		815.50	920
8200	45° Bend, 4" diameter		100	.240		42	10.05		52.05	62
8220	6" diameter		90	.267		73	11.20		84.20	97.50
8240	8" diameter		50	.480		139	20		159	183
8260	10" diameter		50	.480		278	20		298	335
8280	12" diameter		30	.800		360	33.50		393.50	445
8300	Reducing tee 6" x 4"		100	.240		104	10.05		114.05	131
8320	8" x 6"		90	.267		166	11.20		177.20	199
8330	10" x 6"		90	.267		196	11.20		207.20	232
8340	10" x 8"		90	.267		216	11.20		227.20	255
8350	12" x 6"		90	.267		245	11.20		256.20	286
8360	12" x 8"		90	.267		265	11.20		276.20	310
8400	Tapped service tee (threaded type) 6" x 6" x 3/4"		100	.240		95.50	10.05		105.55	121
8430	6" x 6" x 1"		90	.267		95.50	11.20		106.70	122
8440	6" x 6" x 1-1/2"		90	.267		95.50	11.20		106.70	122
8450	6" x 6" x 2"		90	.267		95.50	11.20		106.70	122
8460	8" x 8" x 3/4"		90	.267		140	11.20		151.20	171
8470	8" x 8" x 1"		90	.267		140	11.20		151.20	171
8480	8" x 8" x 1-1/2"		90	.267		140	11.20		151.20	171
8490	8" x 8" x 2"		90	.267		140	11.20		151.20	171
8500	Repair coupling 4"		100	.240		26	10.05		36.05	44
8520	6" diameter		90	.267		40.50	11.20		51.70	62
8540	8" diameter		50	.480		96.50	20		116.50	137
8560	10" diameter		50	.480		203	20		223	254
8580	12" diameter		50	.480		296	20		316	355
8600	Plug end 4"		100	.240		23	10.05		33.05	41
8620	6" diameter		90	.267		41	11.20		52.20	62.50
8640	8" diameter		50	.480		69	20		89	107
8660	10" diameter		50	.480		97	20		117	137
8680	12" diameter		50	.480		119	20		139	162
8700	PVC pipe, joint restraint									
8710	4" diameter	B-20A	32	1	Ea.	45.50	45.50		91	120
8720	6" diameter		25.60	1.250		56	57		113	149
8730	8" diameter		21.33	1.500		74.50	68.50		143	186
8740	10" diameter		18.28	1.751		130	80		210	265
8750	12" diameter		16.84	1.900		145	87		232	291
8760	14" diameter		16	2		204	91.50		295.50	365
8770	16" diameter		11.64	2.749		265	126		391	485
8780	18" diameter		11.03	2.901		340	133		473	575

33 11 13.25 Water Supply, Polyvinyl Chloride Pipe

		Crew	Daily Output	Labor-Hours	Unit	Material	2015 Bare Costs Labor	Equipment	Total	Total Incl O&P
8785	20" diameter	B-20A	9.14	3.501	Ea.	420	160		580	705
8790	24" diameter	↓	7.53	4.250	↓	490	194		684	835

33 11 13.35 Water Supply, HDPE

		Crew	Daily Output	Labor-Hours	Unit	Material	2015 Bare Costs Labor	Equipment	Total	Total Incl O&P
0010	**WATER SUPPLY, HDPE**									
0011	Butt fusion joints, SDR 21 40' lengths not including excavation or backfill									
0100	4" diameter	B-22A	400	.100	L.F.	2.47	4.30	1.64	8.41	11.15
0200	6" diameter		380	.105		5.85	4.53	1.73	12.11	15.30
0300	8" diameter	↓	320	.125		8.55	5.40	2.06	16.01	19.90
0400	10" diameter		300	.133		14.65	5.75	2.19	22.59	27.50
0500	12" diameter	↓	260	.154		17.75	6.60	2.53	26.88	32.50
0600	14" diameter	B-22B	220	.182		27.50	7.80	5	40.30	47.50
0700	16" diameter		180	.222		32.50	9.55	6.15	48.20	57
0800	18" diameter		140	.286		38	12.30	7.90	58.20	69
0900	24" diameter	↓	100	.400	↓	59	17.20	11.05	87.25	104
1000	Fittings									
1100	Elbows, 90 degrees									
1200	4" diameter	B-22A	32	1.250	Ea.	18.45	54	20.50	92.95	126
1300	6" diameter		28	1.429		59	61.50	23.50	144	186
1400	8" diameter		24	1.667		121	71.50	27.50	220	274
1500	10" diameter		18	2.222		385	95.50	36.50	517	610
1600	12" diameter	↓	12	3.333		400	143	55	598	720
1700	14" diameter	B-22B	9	4.444		490	191	123	804	965
1800	16" diameter		6	6.667		570	287	184	1,041	1,275
1900	18" diameter		4	10		660	430	276	1,366	1,700
2000	24" diameter	↓	3	13.333	↓	985	575	370	1,930	2,350
2100	Tees									
2200	4" diameter	B-22A	30	1.333	Ea.	23.50	57.50	22	103	138
2300	6" diameter		26	1.538		58	66	25.50	149.50	194
2400	8" diameter		22	1.818		146	78	30	254	315
2500	10" diameter		15	2.667		193	115	44	352	435
2600	12" diameter	↓	10	4		545	172	66	783	935
2700	14" diameter	B-22B	8	5		640	215	138	993	1,175
2800	16" diameter		6	6.667		755	287	184	1,226	1,475
2900	18" diameter		4	10		985	430	276	1,691	2,050
3000	24" diameter	↓	2	20	↓	1,500	860	555	2,915	3,575
4100	Caps									
4110	4" diameter	B-22A	34	1.176	Ea.	13.60	50.50	19.35	83.45	114
4120	6" diameter		30	1.333		35.50	57.50	22	115	151
4130	8" diameter		26	1.538		52	66	25.50	143.50	187
4150	10" diameter		20	2		111	86	33	230	290
4160	12" diameter	↓	14	2.857	↓	124	123	47	294	380

33 11 13.40 Water Supply, Black Steel Pipe

		Crew	Daily Output	Labor-Hours	Unit	Material	2015 Bare Costs Labor	Equipment	Total	Total Incl O&P
0010	**WATER SUPPLY, BLACK STEEL PIPE**									
0011	Not including excavation or backfill									
1000	Pipe, black steel, plain end, welded, 1/4" wall thk, 8" diam.	B-35A	208	.269	L.F.	32	12.25	7.70	51.95	62.50
1010	10" diameter		204	.275		40	12.50	7.85	60.35	72
1020	12" diameter		195	.287		49.50	13.10	8.25	70.85	83.50
1030	18" diameter		175	.320		72	14.60	9.15	95.75	112
1040	5/16" wall thickness, 12" diameter		195	.287		60	13.10	8.25	81.35	95
1050	18" diameter		175	.320		89.50	14.60	9.15	113.25	131
1060	36" diameter		28.96	1.934		179	88	55.50	322.50	395
1070	3/8" wall thickness, 18" diameter		43.20	1.296	↓	108	59	37	204	251

33 11 Water Utility Distribution Piping

33 11 13 – Public Water Utility Distribution Piping

33 11 13.40 Water Supply, Black Steel Pipe

		Crew	Daily Output	Labor-Hours	Unit	Material	2015 Bare Costs Labor	2015 Bare Costs Equipment	Total	Total Incl O&P
1080	24" diameter	B-35A	36	1.556	L.F.	148	71	44.50	263.50	320
1090	30" diameter		30.40	1.842		180	84	53	317	385
1100	1/2" wall thickness, 36" diameter		26.08	2.147		283	98	61.50	442.50	530
1110	48" diameter		21.68	2.583		380	118	74	572	680
1135	7/16" wall thickness, 48" diameter		20.80	2.692		345	123	77	545	650
1140	5/8" wall thickness, 48" diameter	↓	21.68	2.583	↓	490	118	74	682	800

33 11 13.45 Water Supply, Copper Pipe

		Crew	Daily Output	Labor-Hours	Unit	Material	2015 Bare Costs Labor	2015 Bare Costs Equipment	Total	Total Incl O&P
0010	**WATER SUPPLY, COPPER PIPE**									
0020	Not including excavation or backfill									
2000	Tubing, type K, 20' joints, 3/4" diameter	Q-1	400	.040	L.F.	6.30	2.11		8.41	10.15
2200	1" diameter		320	.050		8.40	2.64		11.04	13.25
3000	1-1/2" diameter		265	.060		13.40	3.19		16.59	19.50
3020	2" diameter		230	.070		20.50	3.68		24.18	28
3040	2-1/2" diameter		146	.110		30.50	5.80		36.30	42.50
3060	3" diameter		134	.119		42	6.30		48.30	56
4012	4" diameter		95	.168		69.50	8.90		78.40	90
4014	5" diameter	↓	80	.200		131	10.55		141.55	160
4016	6" diameter	Q-2	80	.300	↓	150	16.45		166.45	190
5000	Tubing, type L									
5108	2" diameter	Q-1	230	.070	L.F.	16.05	3.68		19.73	23
6010	3" diameter		134	.119		31.50	6.30		37.80	44
6012	4" diameter	↓	95	.168		55.50	8.90		64.40	74.50
6016	6" diameter	Q-2	80	.300	↓	132	16.45		148.45	170
7165	Fittings, brass, corporation stops, no lead, 3/4" diameter	1 Plum	19	.421	Ea.	82	24.50		106.50	128
7166	1" diameter		16	.500		108	29.50		137.50	164
7167	1-1/2" diameter		13	.615		240	36		276	320
7168	2" diameter		11	.727		350	42.50		392.50	450
7170	Curb stops, no lead, 3/4" diameter		19	.421		112	24.50		136.50	161
7171	1" diameter		16	.500		156	29.50		185.50	217
7172	1-1/2" diameter		13	.615		296	36		332	380
7173	2" diameter		11	.727		315	42.50		357.50	410
7180	Curb box, cast iron, 1/2" to 1" curb stops		12	.667		51.50	39		90.50	116
7200	1-1/4" to 2" curb stops	↓	8	1		84.50	58.50		143	182
7220	Saddles, 3/4" & 1" diameter, add					76.50			76.50	84.50
7240	1-1/2" to 2" diameter, add				↓	117			117	129
7250	For copper fittings, see Section 22 11 13.25									

33 11 13.90 Water Supply, Thrust Blocks

		Crew	Daily Output	Labor-Hours	Unit	Material	2015 Bare Costs Labor	2015 Bare Costs Equipment	Total	Total Incl O&P
0010	**WATER SUPPLY, THRUST BLOCKS**									
0015	Piping, not including excavation or backfill									
0110	Thrust block for 90 elbow, 4" Diameter	C-30	41	.195	Ea.	17.15	7.35	4.20	28.70	35
0115	6" Diameter		23	.348		29.50	13.10	7.50	50.10	60.50
0120	8" Diameter		14	.571		45	21.50	12.30	78.80	96
0125	10" Diameter		9	.889		64.50	33.50	19.15	117.15	144
0130	12" Diameter		7	1.143		87.50	43	24.50	155	189
0135	14" Diameter		5	1.600		117	60	34.50	211.50	260
0140	16" Diameter		4	2		148	75	43	266	325
0145	18" Diameter		3	2.667		182	100	57.50	339.50	415
0150	20" Diameter		2.50	3.200		219	120	69	408	500
0155	24" Diameter		2	4		315	150	86	551	670
0210	Thrust block for tee or deadend, 4" Diameter		65	.123		11.85	4.63	2.65	19.13	23
0215	6" Diameter		35	.229		21	8.60	4.93	34.53	41.50
0220	8" Diameter	↓	21	.381		32.50	14.30	8.20	55	66.50

For customer support on your Site Work & Landscape Cost Data, call 877.737.1594.

475

33 11 Water Utility Distribution Piping

33 11 13 – Public Water Utility Distribution Piping

33 11 13.90 Water Supply, Thrust Blocks

		Crew	Daily Output	Labor-Hours	Unit	Material	2015 Bare Costs Labor	Equipment	Total	Total Incl O&P
0225	10" Diameter	C-30	14	.571	Ea.	46.50	21.50	12.30	80.30	97.50
0230	12" Diameter		10	.800		63	30	17.25	110.25	135
0235	14" Diameter		7	1.143		84.50	43	24.50	152	186
0240	16" Diameter		5	1.600		106	60	34.50	200.50	248
0245	18" Diameter		4	2		131	75	43	249	310
0250	20" Diameter		3.50	2.286		158	86	49.50	293.50	360
0255	24" Diameter	↓	2.50	3.200	↓	223	120	69	412	505

33 12 Water Utility Distribution Equipment

33 12 13 – Water Service Connections

33 12 13.15 Tapping, Crosses and Sleeves

		Crew	Daily Output	Labor-Hours	Unit	Material	2015 Bare Costs Labor	Equipment	Total	Total Incl O&P
0010	**TAPPING, CROSSES AND SLEEVES**									
4000	Drill and tap pressurized main (labor only)									
4100	6" main, 1" to 2" service	Q-1	3	5.333	Ea.		282		282	425
4150	8" main, 1" to 2" service	"	2.75	5.818	"		305		305	465
4500	Tap and insert gate valve									
4600	8" main, 4" branch	B-21	3.20	8.750	Ea.		380	43	423	635
4650	6" branch		2.70	10.370			450	51	501	745
4700	10" Main, 4" branch		2.70	10.370			450	51	501	745
4750	6" branch		2.35	11.915			515	58.50	573.50	860
4800	12" main, 6" branch		2.35	11.915			515	58.50	573.50	860
4850	8" branch	↓	2.35	11.915	↓		515	58.50	573.50	860
7000	Tapping crosses, sleeves, valves; with rubber gaskets									
7020	Crosses, 4" x 4"	B-21	37	.757	Ea.	1,375	33	3.72	1,411.72	1,550
7030	6" x 4"		25	1.120		1,150	48.50	5.50	1,204	1,350
7040	6" x 6"		25	1.120		1,175	48.50	5.50	1,229	1,375
7060	8" x 6"		21	1.333		1,500	58	6.55	1,564.55	1,750
7080	8" x 8"		21	1.333		1,800	58	6.55	1,864.55	2,075
7100	10" x 6"		21	1.333		2,600	58	6.55	2,664.55	2,950
7120	10" x 10"		21	1.333		2,650	58	6.55	2,714.55	3,025
7140	12" x 6"		18	1.556		2,600	67.50	7.65	2,675.15	2,950
7160	12" x 12"		18	1.556		3,575	67.50	7.65	3,650.15	4,050
7180	14" x 6"		16	1.750		6,475	76	8.60	6,559.60	7,250
7200	14" x 14"		16	1.750		6,900	76	8.60	6,984.60	7,700
7220	16" x 6"		14	2		6,900	86.50	9.85	6,996.35	7,750
7240	16" x 10"		14	2		7,000	86.50	9.85	7,096.35	7,850
7260	16" x 16"		14	2		7,425	86.50	9.85	7,521.35	8,325
7280	18" x 6"		10	2.800		9,875	121	13.80	10,009.80	11,100
7300	18" x 12"		10	2.800		10,100	121	13.80	10,234.80	11,300
7320	18" x 18"		10	2.800		9,650	121	13.80	9,784.80	10,800
7340	20" x 6"		8	3.500		8,475	152	17.20	8,644.20	9,575
7360	20" x 12"		8	3.500		8,800	152	17.20	8,969.20	9,925
7380	20" x 20"		8	3.500		13,400	152	17.20	13,569.20	15,000
7400	24" x 6"		6	4.667		12,400	202	23	12,625	13,900
7420	24" x 12"		6	4.667		11,600	202	23	11,825	13,100
7440	24" x 18"		6	4.667		17,400	202	23	17,625	19,500
7460	24" x 24"		6	4.667		18,000	202	23	18,225	20,100
7600	Cut-in sleeves with rubber gaskets, 4"		18	1.556		430	67.50	7.65	505.15	585
7620	6"		12	2.333		505	101	11.50	617.50	725
7640	8"		10	2.800		650	121	13.80	784.80	915
7660	10"	↓	10	2.800	↓	960	121	13.80	1,094.80	1,250

33 12 13 – Water Service Connections

33 12 13.15 Tapping, Crosses and Sleeves

		Crew	Daily Output	Labor-Hours	Unit	Material	2015 Bare Costs Labor	2015 Bare Costs Equipment	Total	Total Incl O&P
7680	12"	B-21	9	3.111	Ea.	1,225	135	15.30	1,375.30	1,575
7800	Cut-in valves with rubber gaskets, 4"		18	1.556		505	67.50	7.65	580.15	665
7820	6"		12	2.333		675	101	11.50	787.50	910
7840	8"		10	2.800		1,050	121	13.80	1,184.80	1,375
7860	10"		10	2.800		1,150	121	13.80	1,284.80	1,450
7880	12"		9	3.111		1,300	135	15.30	1,450.30	1,650
7900	Tapping Valve 4 inch, MJ, ductile iron		18	1.556		555	67.50	7.65	630.15	720
7920	6 inch, MJ, ductile iron		12	2.333		780	101	11.50	892.50	1,025
8000	Sleeves with rubber gaskets, 4" x 4"		37	.757		845	33	3.72	881.72	985
8010	6" x 4"		25	1.120		900	48.50	5.50	954	1,075
8020	6" x 6"		25	1.120		1,125	48.50	5.50	1,179	1,325
8030	8" x 4"		21	1.333		960	58	6.55	1,024.55	1,150
8040	8" x 6"		21	1.333		1,075	58	6.55	1,139.55	1,275
8060	8" x 8"		21	1.333		1,250	58	6.55	1,314.55	1,475
8070	10" x 4"		21	1.333		1,075	58	6.55	1,139.55	1,300
8080	10" x 6"		21	1.333		1,200	58	6.55	1,264.55	1,425
8090	10" x 8"		21	1.333		1,325	58	6.55	1,389.55	1,550
8100	10" x 10"		21	1.333		1,950	58	6.55	2,014.55	2,250
8110	12" x 4"		18	1.556		1,150	67.50	7.65	1,225.15	1,375
8120	12" x 6"		18	1.556		1,175	67.50	7.65	1,250.15	1,400
8130	12" x 8"		18	1.556		1,475	67.50	7.65	1,550.15	1,725
8135	12" x 10"		18	1.556		2,325	67.50	7.65	2,400.15	2,650
8140	12" x 12"		18	1.556		2,350	67.50	7.65	2,425.15	2,700
8160	14" x 6"		16	1.750		1,900	76	8.60	1,984.60	2,225
8180	14" x 14"		16	1.750		2,500	76	8.60	2,584.60	2,875
8200	16" x 6"		14	2		2,100	86.50	9.85	2,196.35	2,450
8220	16" x 10"		14	2		3,525	86.50	9.85	3,621.35	4,025
8240	16" x 16"		14	2		8,650	86.50	9.85	8,746.35	9,675
8260	18" x 6"		10	2.800		2,250	121	13.80	2,384.80	2,675
8280	18" x 12"		10	2.800		3,625	121	13.80	3,759.80	4,175
8300	18" x 18"		10	2.800		11,600	121	13.80	11,734.80	13,000
8320	20" x 6"		8	3.500		2,550	152	17.20	2,719.20	3,075
8340	20" x 12"		8	3.500		4,400	152	17.20	4,569.20	5,100
8360	20" x 20"		8	3.500		11,000	152	17.20	11,169.20	12,400
8380	24" x 6"		6	4.667		2,700	202	23	2,925	3,300
8400	24" x 12"		6	4.667		4,400	202	23	4,625	5,175
8420	24" x 18"		6	4.667		11,700	202	23	11,925	13,200
8440	24" x 24"		6	4.667		14,800	202	23	15,025	16,600
8800	Hydrant valve box, 6' long	B-20	20	1.200		280	50.50		330.50	390
8820	8' long		18	1.333		355	56		411	475
8830	Valve box w/lid 4' deep		14	1.714		107	72		179	228
8840	Valve box and large base w/lid		14	1.714		325	72		397	470

33 12 16 – Water Utility Distribution Valves

33 12 16.10 Valves

		Crew	Daily Output	Labor-Hours	Unit	Material	2015 Bare Costs Labor	2015 Bare Costs Equipment	Total	Total Incl O&P
0010	**VALVES**, water distribution									
0011	See Sections 22 05 23.20 and 22 05 23.60									
3000	Butterfly valves with boxes, cast iron, mech. jt.									
3100	4" diameter	B-6	6	4	Ea.	575	165	60.50	800.50	955
3140	6" diameter		6	4		750	165	60.50	975.50	1,150
3180	8" diameter		6	4		940	165	60.50	1,165.50	1,350
3300	10" diameter		6	4		1,275	165	60.50	1,500.50	1,725
3340	12" diameter		6	4		1,700	165	60.50	1,925.50	2,200

For customer support on your Site Work & Landscape Cost Data, call 877.737.1594.

477

33 12 16 – Water Utility Distribution Valves

33 12 16.10 Valves		Crew	Daily Output	Labor-Hours	Unit	Material	2015 Bare Costs Labor	2015 Bare Costs Equipment	Total	Total Incl O&P
3400	14" diameter	B-6	4	6	Ea.	3,400	248	91	3,739	4,200
3440	16" diameter		4	6		5,025	248	91	5,364	6,000
3460	18" diameter		4	6		6,225	248	91	6,564	7,325
3480	20" diameter		4	6		8,200	248	91	8,539	9,475
3500	24" diameter	↓	4	6	↓	13,700	248	91	14,039	15,600
3600	With lever operator									
3610	4" diameter	B-6	6	4	Ea.	470	165	60.50	695.50	835
3614	6" diameter		6	4		645	165	60.50	870.50	1,025
3616	8" diameter		6	4		835	165	60.50	1,060.50	1,250
3618	10" diameter		6	4		1,175	165	60.50	1,400.50	1,600
3620	12" diameter		6	4		1,600	165	60.50	1,825.50	2,100
3622	14" diameter		4	6		3,075	248	91	3,414	3,850
3624	16" diameter		4	6		4,700	248	91	5,039	5,625
3626	18" diameter		4	6		5,900	248	91	6,239	6,950
3628	20" diameter		4	6		7,875	248	91	8,214	9,125
3630	24" diameter	↓	4	6	↓	13,400	248	91	13,739	15,200
3700	Check valves, flanged									
3710	4" diameter	B-6	6	4	Ea.	605	165	60.50	830.50	985
3712	5" diameter		6	4		775	165	60.50	1,000.50	1,175
3714	6" diameter		6	4		1,025	165	60.50	1,250.50	1,475
3716	8" diameter		6	4		1,950	165	60.50	2,175.50	2,475
3718	10" diameter		6	4		3,325	165	60.50	3,550.50	3,975
3720	12" diameter		6	4		5,175	165	60.50	5,400.50	6,025
3726	18" diameter		4	6		23,700	248	91	24,039	26,600
3730	24" diameter	↓	4	6	↓	52,000	248	91	52,339	58,000
3800	Gate valves, C.I., 250 PSI, mechanical joint, w/boxes									
3810	4" diameter	B-6	6	4	Ea.	880	165	60.50	1,105.50	1,275
3814	6" diameter		6	4		1,350	165	60.50	1,575.50	1,800
3816	8" diameter		6	4		2,300	165	60.50	2,525.50	2,850
3818	10" diameter		6	4		4,150	165	60.50	4,375.50	4,875
3820	12" diameter		6	4		5,625	165	60.50	5,850.50	6,500
3822	14" diameter		4	6		12,300	248	91	12,639	14,100
3824	16" diameter		4	6		17,300	248	91	17,639	19,500
3826	18" diameter		4	6		21,100	248	91	21,439	23,700
3828	20" diameter		4	6		23,200	248	91	23,539	26,000
3830	24" diameter		4	6		25,200	248	91	25,539	28,200
3831	30" diameter		4	6		39,200	248	91	39,539	43,600
3832	36" diameter	↓	4	6		57,000	248	91	57,339	63,000
3880	Sleeve, for tapping mains, 8" x 4", add					960			960	1,050
3884	10" x 6", add					1,200			1,200	1,325
3888	12" x 6", add					1,175			1,175	1,300
3892	12" x 8", add				↓	1,475			1,475	1,625

33 12 16.20 Valves

		Crew	Daily Output	Labor-Hours	Unit	Material	2015 Bare Costs Labor	2015 Bare Costs Equipment	Total	Total Incl O&P
0010	**VALVES**									
0011	Special trim or use									
0150	Altitude valve, single acting, modulating, 2.5" diameter	B-6	6	4	Ea.	2,925	165	60.50	3,150.50	3,550
0155	3" diameter		6	4		2,950	165	60.50	3,175.50	3,575
0160	4" diameter		6	4		3,450	165	60.50	3,675.50	4,125
0165	6" diameter		6	4		4,275	165	60.50	4,500.50	5,050
0170	8" diameter		6	4		6,150	165	60.50	6,375.50	7,100
0175	10" diameter		6	4		6,800	165	60.50	7,025.50	7,800
0180	12" diameter		6	4		10,300	165	60.50	10,525.50	11,700

33 12 16.20 Valves		Crew	Daily Output	Labor-Hours	Unit	Material	2015 Bare Costs Labor	Equipment	Total	Total Incl O&P
0250	Altitude valve, single acting, non-modulating, 2.5" diameter	B-6	6	4	Ea.	2,925	165	60.50	3,150.50	3,550
0255	3" diameter		6	4		2,950	165	60.50	3,175.50	3,575
0260	4" diameter		6	4		3,200	165	60.50	3,425.50	3,825
0265	6" diameter		6	4		4,275	165	60.50	4,500.50	5,050
0270	8" diameter		6	4		6,150	165	60.50	6,375.50	7,100
0275	10" diameter		6	4		6,800	165	60.50	7,025.50	7,800
0280	12" diameter		6	4		10,300	165	60.50	10,525.50	11,700
0350	Altitude valve, double acting, non-modulating, 2.5" diameter		6	4		3,800	165	60.50	4,025.50	4,500
0355	3" diameter		6	4		39,800	165	60.50	40,025.50	44,100
0360	4" diameter		6	4		4,500	165	60.50	4,725.50	5,275
0365	6" diameter		6	4		5,550	165	60.50	5,775.50	6,425
0370	8" diameter		6	4		8,000	165	60.50	8,225.50	9,125
0375	10" diameter		6	4		8,825	165	60.50	9,050.50	10,000
0380	12" diameter		6	4		13,400	165	60.50	13,625.50	15,100
1000	Air release valve for water, 1/2" inlet	1 Plum	16	.500		60.50	29.50		90	112
1005	3/4" inlet		16	.500		60.50	29.50		90	112
1010	1" inlet		14	.571		60.50	33.50		94	118
1020	2" inlet		9	.889		182	52		234	279
1100	Air release & vacuum valve for water, 1/2" inlet		16	.500		266	29.50		295.50	335
1105	3/4" inlet		16	.500		266	29.50		295.50	335
1110	1" inlet		14	.571		266	33.50		299.50	345
1120	2" inlet		9	.889		395	52		447	510
1130	3" inlet	Q-1	8	2		1,500	106		1,606	1,800
1140	4" inlet	"	5	3.200		1,875	169		2,044	2,325
9000	Valves, gate valve, N.R.S. PIV with post, 4" diameter	B-6	6	4		1,875	165	60.50	2,100.50	2,375
9020	6" diameter		6	4		2,350	165	60.50	2,575.50	2,900
9040	8" diameter		6	4		3,275	165	60.50	3,500.50	3,950
9060	10" diameter		6	4		5,150	165	60.50	5,375.50	5,975
9080	12" diameter		6	4		6,600	165	60.50	6,825.50	7,600
9100	14" diameter		6	4		13,100	165	60.50	13,325.50	14,700
9120	OS&Y, 4" diameter		6	4		730	165	60.50	955.50	1,125
9140	6" diameter		6	4		990	165	60.50	1,215.50	1,425
9160	8" diameter		6	4		1,550	165	60.50	1,775.50	2,025
9180	10" diameter		6	4		2,475	165	60.50	2,700.50	3,025
9200	12" diameter		6	4		3,725	165	60.50	3,950.50	4,425
9220	14" diameter		4	6		5,075	248	91	5,414	6,075
9400	Check valves, rubber disc, 2-1/2" diameter		6	4		710	165	60.50	935.50	1,100
9420	3" diameter		6	4		725	165	60.50	950.50	1,125
9440	4" diameter		6	4		605	165	60.50	830.50	985
9480	6" diameter		6	4		1,025	165	60.50	1,250.50	1,475
9500	8" diameter		6	4		1,950	165	60.50	2,175.50	2,475
9520	10" diameter		6	4		3,325	165	60.50	3,550.50	3,975
9540	12" diameter		6	4		5,175	165	60.50	5,400.50	6,025
9542	14" diameter		4	6		5,250	248	91	5,589	6,250
9700	Detector check valves, reducing, 4" diameter		6	4		1,350	165	60.50	1,575.50	1,800
9720	6" diameter		6	4		2,075	165	60.50	2,300.50	2,625
9740	8" diameter		6	4		3,050	165	60.50	3,275.50	3,675
9760	10" diameter		6	4		5,400	165	60.50	5,625.50	6,275
9800	Galvanized, 4" diameter		6	4		1,575	165	60.50	1,800.50	2,075
9820	6" diameter		6	4		2,125	165	60.50	2,350.50	2,675
9840	8" diameter		6	4		3,350	165	60.50	3,575.50	4,000
9860	10" diameter		6	4		5,125	165	60.50	5,350.50	5,975

For customer support on your Site Work & Landscape Cost Data, call 877.737.1594.

479

33 12 Water Utility Distribution Equipment

33 12 19 – Water Utility Distribution Fire Hydrants

33 12 19.10 Fire Hydrants	Crew	Daily Output	Labor-Hours	Unit	Material	2015 Bare Costs Labor	Equipment	Total	Total Incl O&P
0010 **FIRE HYDRANTS**									
0020 Mechanical joints unless otherwise noted									
1000 Fire hydrants, two way; excavation and backfill not incl.									
1100 4-1/2" valve size, depth 2'-0"	B-21	10	2.800	Ea.	1,650	121	13.80	1,784.80	2,025
1120 2'-6"		10	2.800		1,750	121	13.80	1,884.80	2,125
1140 3'-0"		10	2.800		1,875	121	13.80	2,009.80	2,275
1160 3'-6"		9	3.111		1,900	135	15.30	2,050.30	2,325
1170 4'-0"		9	3.111		1,950	135	15.30	2,100.30	2,375
1200 4'-6"		9	3.111		1,975	135	15.30	2,125.30	2,400
1220 5'-0"		8	3.500		2,025	152	17.20	2,194.20	2,475
1240 5'-6"		8	3.500		2,050	152	17.20	2,219.20	2,500
1260 6'-0"		7	4		2,100	173	19.70	2,292.70	2,600
1280 6'-6"		7	4		2,100	173	19.70	2,292.70	2,600
1300 7'-0"		6	4.667		2,150	202	23	2,375	2,700
1340 8'-0"		6	4.667		2,225	202	23	2,450	2,775
1420 10'-0"		5	5.600		2,375	243	27.50	2,645.50	3,025
2000 5-1/4" valve size, depth 2'-0"		10	2.800		1,775	121	13.80	1,909.80	2,150
2080 4'-0"		9	3.111		1,900	135	15.30	2,050.30	2,325
2160 6'-0"		7	4		2,050	173	19.70	2,242.70	2,550
2240 8'-0"		6	4.667		2,175	202	23	2,400	2,725
2320 10'-0"	▼	5	5.600		2,500	243	27.50	2,770.50	3,150
2350 For threeway valves, add					7%				
2400 Lower barrel extensions with stems, 1'-0"	B-20	14	1.714		320	72		392	460
2440 2'-0"		13	1.846		390	77.50		467.50	550
2480 3'-0"		12	2		770	84		854	975
2520 4'-0"	▼	10	2.400		740	101		841	970
3200 Yard hydrant, flush, non freeze, 4' depth of bury, 3/4" conn.	2 Plum	4	4		113	235		348	480
4000 Above ground, 1" connection	1 Plum	8	1	▼	135	58.50		193.50	238
5000 Indicator post									
5020 Adjustable, valve size 4" to 14", 4' bury	B-21	10	2.800	Ea.	815	121	13.80	949.80	1,100
5060 8' bury		7	4		1,100	173	19.70	1,292.70	1,500
5080 10' bury		6	4.667		1,150	202	23	1,375	1,600
5100 12' bury		5	5.600		1,400	243	27.50	1,670.50	1,950
5120 14' bury		4	7		1,525	305	34.50	1,864.50	2,175
5500 Non-adjustable, valve size 4" to 14", 3' bury		10	2.800		815	121	13.80	949.80	1,100
5520 3'-6" bury		10	2.800		815	121	13.80	949.80	1,100
5540 4' bury	▼	9	3.111	▼	815	135	15.30	965.30	1,125

33 16 Water Utility Storage Tanks

33 16 13 – Aboveground Water Utility Storage Tanks

33 16 13.13 Steel Water Storage Tanks

	Crew	Daily Output	Labor-Hours	Unit	Material	Labor	Equipment	Total	Total Incl O&P
0010 **STEEL WATER STORAGE TANKS**									
0910 Steel, ground level, ht./diam. less than 1, not incl. fdn., 100,000 gallons				Ea.				202,000	244,500
1000 250,000 gallons								295,500	324,000
1200 500,000 gallons								417,000	458,500
1250 750,000 gallons								538,000	591,500
1300 1,000,000 gallons								558,000	725,500
1500 2,000,000 gallons								1,043,000	1,148,000
1600 4,000,000 gallons								2,121,000	2,333,000
1800 6,000,000 gallons								3,095,000	3,405,000

33 16 Water Utility Storage Tanks

33 16 13 – Aboveground Water Utility Storage Tanks

33 16 13.13 Steel Water Storage Tanks

		Crew	Daily Output	Labor-Hours	Unit	Material	2015 Bare Costs Labor	Equipment	Total	Total Incl O&P
1850	8,000,000 gallons				Ea.				4,068,000	4,475,000
1910	10,000,000 gallons								5,050,000	5,554,500
2100	Steel standpipes, ht./diam. more than 1, 100' to overflow, no fdn.									
2200	500,000 gallons				Ea.				546,500	600,500
2400	750,000 gallons								722,500	794,500
2500	1,000,000 gallons								1,060,500	1,167,000
2700	1,500,000 gallons								1,749,000	1,923,000
2800	2,000,000 gallons								2,327,000	2,559,000

33 16 13.16 Prestressed Conc. Water Storage Tanks

		Crew	Daily Output	Labor-Hours	Unit	Material	2015 Bare Costs Labor	Equipment	Total	Total Incl O&P
0010	**PRESTRESSED CONC. WATER STORAGE TANKS**									
0020	Not including fdn., pipe or pumps, 250,000 gallons				Ea.				299,000	329,500
0100	500,000 gallons								487,000	536,000
0300	1,000,000 gallons								707,000	807,500
0400	2,000,000 gallons								1,072,000	1,179,000
0600	4,000,000 gallons								1,706,000	1,877,000
0700	6,000,000 gallons								2,266,000	2,493,000
0750	8,000,000 gallons								2,924,000	3,216,000
0800	10,000,000 gallons								3,533,000	3,886,000

33 16 13.23 Plastic-Coated Fabric Pillow Water Tanks

		Crew	Daily Output	Labor-Hours	Unit	Material	2015 Bare Costs Labor	Equipment	Total	Total Incl O&P
0010	**PLASTIC-COATED FABRIC PILLOW WATER TANKS**									
7000	Water tanks, vinyl coated fabric pillow tanks, freestanding, 5,000 gallons	4 Clab	4	8	Ea.	3,675	300		3,975	4,525
7100	Supporting embankment not included, 25,000 gallons	6 Clab	2	24		13,200	900		14,100	15,900
7200	50,000 gallons	8 Clab	1.50	42.667		18,500	1,600		20,100	22,800
7300	100,000 gallons	9 Clab	.90	80		42,300	3,000		45,300	51,000
7400	150,000 gallons		.50	144		60,500	5,425		65,925	75,500
7500	200,000 gallons		.40	180		75,000	6,775		81,775	93,000
7600	250,000 gallons		.30	240		105,500	9,025		114,525	130,000

33 16 19 – Elevated Water Utility Storage Tanks

33 16 19.50 Elevated Water Storage Tanks

		Crew	Daily Output	Labor-Hours	Unit	Material	2015 Bare Costs Labor	Equipment	Total	Total Incl O&P
0010	**ELEVATED WATER STORAGE TANKS**									
0011	Not incl. pipe, pumps or foundation									
3000	Elevated water tanks, 100' to bottom capacity line, incl. painting									
3010	50,000 gallons				Ea.				185,000	204,000
3300	100,000 gallons								280,000	307,500
3400	250,000 gallons								751,500	826,500
3600	500,000 gallons								1,336,000	1,470,000
3700	750,000 gallons								1,622,000	1,783,500
3900	1,000,000 gallons								2,322,000	2,556,000

33 21 Water Supply Wells

33 21 13 – Public Water Supply Wells

33 21 13.10 Wells and Accessories

		Crew	Daily Output	Labor-Hours	Unit	Material	2015 Bare Costs Labor	Equipment	Total	Total Incl O&P
0010	**WELLS & ACCESSORIES**									
0011	Domestic									
0100	Drilled, 4" to 6" diameter	B-23	120	.333	L.F.		12.65	23.50	36.15	45.50
0200	8" diameter	"	95.20	.420	"		15.95	30	45.95	57.50
0400	Gravel pack well, 40' deep, incl. gravel & casing, complete									
0500	24" diameter casing x 18" diameter screen	B-23	.13	307	Total	38,800	11,700	21,900	72,400	85,000
0600	36" diameter casing x 18" diameter screen		.12	333	"	40,000	12,700	23,700	76,400	89,500
0800	Observation wells, 1-1/4" riser pipe		163	.245	V.L.F.	20.50	9.35	17.45	47.30	56

33 21 13 – Public Water Supply Wells

33 21 13.10 Wells and Accessories	Crew	Daily Output	Labor-Hours	Unit	Material	2015 Bare Costs Labor	Equipment	Total	Total Incl O&P
0900 For flush Buffalo roadway box, add	1 Skwk	16.60	.482	Ea.	51	23.50		74.50	92
1200 Test well, 2-1/2" diameter, up to 50' deep (15 to 50 GPM)	B-23	1.51	26.490	"	805	1,000	1,875	3,680	4,525
1300 Over 50' deep, add	"	121.80	.328	L.F.	21.50	12.50	23.50	57.50	68
1400 Remove & reset pump, minimum	B-21	4	7	Ea.		305	34.50	339.50	505
1420 Maximum	"	2	14	"		605	69	674	1,000
1500 Pumps, installed in wells to 100' deep, 4" submersible									
1510 1/2 H.P.	Q-1	3.22	4.969	Ea.	350	263		613	780
1520 3/4 H.P.		2.66	6.015		400	320		720	920
1600 1 H.P.		2.29	6.987		425	370		795	1,025
1700 1-1/2 H.P.	Q-22	1.60	10		800	530	410	1,740	2,125
1800 2 H.P.		1.33	12.030		830	635	490	1,955	2,425
1900 3 H.P.		1.14	14.035		1,150	740	575	2,465	3,025
2000 5 H.P.		1.14	14.035		1,600	740	575	2,915	3,500
2050 Remove and install motor only, 4 H.P.		1.14	14.035		1,100	740	575	2,415	2,950
3000 Pump, 6" submersible, 25' to 150' deep, 25 H.P., 249 to 297 GPM		.89	17.978		3,350	950	735	5,035	5,900
3100 25' to 500' deep, 30 H.P., 100 to 300 GPM		.73	21.918		4,100	1,150	895	6,145	7,225
5000 Wells to 180 ft. deep, 4" submersible, 1 HP	B-21	1.10	25.455		2,350	1,100	125	3,575	4,425
5500 2 HP		1.10	25.455		3,275	1,100	125	4,500	5,450
6000 3 HP		1	28		4,375	1,225	138	5,738	6,850
7000 5 HP		.90	31.111		6,025	1,350	153	7,528	8,875
8000 Steel well casing	B-23A	3020	.008	Lb.	1.21	.34	.89	2.44	2.83
8110 Well screen assembly, stainless steel, 2" diameter		273	.088	L.F.	81	3.75	9.85	94.60	106
8120 3" diameter		253	.095		142	4.04	10.60	156.64	174
8130 4" diameter		200	.120		177	5.10	13.45	195.55	217
8140 5" diameter		168	.143		187	6.10	16	209.10	232
8150 6" diameter		126	.190		212	8.10	21.50	241.60	269
8160 8" diameter		98.50	.244		288	10.40	27.50	325.90	360
8170 10" diameter		73	.329		360	14	37	411	455
8180 12" diameter		62.50	.384		410	16.35	43	469.35	525
8190 14" diameter		54.30	.442		460	18.85	49.50	528.35	590
8200 16" diameter		48.30	.497		510	21	55.50	586.50	655
8210 18" diameter		39.20	.612		635	26	68.50	729.50	815
8220 20" diameter		31.20	.769		710	33	86	829	930
8230 24" diameter		23.80	1.008		855	43	113	1,011	1,125
8240 26" diameter		21	1.143		930	48.50	128	1,106.50	1,250
8244 Well casing or drop pipe, PVC, 0.5" dia		550	.044		1.55	1.86	4.88	8.29	9.90
8245 0.75" diameter		550	.044		1.13	1.86	4.88	7.87	9.45
8246 1" diameter		550	.044		1.17	1.86	4.88	7.91	9.50
8247 1.25" diameter		520	.046		1.35	1.97	5.15	8.47	10.20
8248 1.5" diameter		490	.049		1.58	2.09	5.50	9.17	11
8249 1.75" diameter		380	.063		1.48	2.69	7.05	11.22	13.55
8250 2" diameter		280	.086		1.65	3.65	9.60	14.90	17.95
8252 3" diameter		260	.092		3.39	3.93	10.35	17.67	21
8254 4" diameter		205	.117		4.90	4.99	13.10	22.99	27.50
8255 5" diameter		170	.141		3.20	6	15.80	25	30
8256 6" diameter		130	.185		8.50	7.85	20.50	36.85	44
8258 8" diameter		100	.240		12.95	10.20	27	50.15	59.50
8260 10" diameter		73	.329		9	14	37	60	72
8262 12" diameter		62	.387		12	16.50	43.50	72	85.50
8300 Slotted PVC, 1-1/4" diameter		521	.046		2.40	1.96	5.15	9.51	11.30
8310 1-1/2" diameter		488	.049		2.85	2.10	5.50	10.45	12.40
8320 2" diameter		273	.088		3.67	3.75	9.85	17.27	20.50
8330 3" diameter		253	.095		5.85	4.04	10.60	20.49	24.50

33 21 Water Supply Wells

33 21 13 – Public Water Supply Wells

33 21 13.10 Wells and Accessories

		Crew	Daily Output	Labor-Hours	Unit	Material	2015 Bare Costs Labor	Equipment	Total	Total Incl O&P
8340	4" diameter	B-23A	200	.120	L.F.	6.75	5.10	13.45	25.30	30
8350	5" diameter		168	.143		14.05	6.10	16	36.15	42.50
8360	6" diameter		126	.190		16.65	8.10	21.50	46.25	54.50
8370	8" diameter	▼	98.50	.244		26	10.40	27.50	63.90	74.50
8400	Artificial gravel pack, 2" screen, 6" casing	B-23B	174	.138		3.60	5.90	17.45	26.95	32
8405	8" casing		111	.216		4.63	9.20	27.50	41.33	49
8410	10" casing		74.50	.322		6.60	13.70	40.50	60.80	73.50
8415	12" casing		60	.400		9.25	17.05	50.50	76.80	91.50
8420	14" casing		50.20	.478		10.75	20.50	60.50	91.75	109
8425	16" casing		40.70	.590		13.65	25	74.50	113.15	136
8430	18" casing		36	.667		16.40	28.50	84.50	129.40	154
8435	20" casing		29.50	.814		19.25	34.50	103	156.75	187
8440	24" casing		25.70	.934		22	40	118	180	215
8445	26" casing		24.60	.976		24.50	41.50	123	189	227
8450	30" casing		20	1.200		28	51	152	231	276
8455	36" casing	▼	16.40	1.463	▼	31.50	62.50	185	279	335
8500	Develop well		8	3	Hr.	262	128	380	770	900
8550	Pump test well	▼	8	3		82.50	128	380	590.50	700
8560	Standby well	B-23A	8	3		78	128	335	541	650
8570	Standby, drill rig		8	3	▼		128	335	463	565
8580	Surface seal well, concrete filled	▼	1	24	Ea.	850	1,025	2,675	4,550	5,450
8590	Well test pump, install & remove	B-23	1	40			1,525	2,850	4,375	5,475
8600	Well sterilization, chlorine	2 Clab	1	16		122	600		722	1,050
8610	Well water pressure switch	1 Clab	12	.667		50.50	25		75.50	94
8630	Well, water pressure switch with manual reset	"	12	.667	▼	35.50	25		60.50	77.50
9950	See Section 31 23 19.40 for wellpoints									
9960	See Section 31 23 19.30 for drainage wells									

33 21 13.20 Water Supply Wells, Pumps

		Crew	Daily Output	Labor-Hours	Unit	Material	2015 Bare Costs Labor	Equipment	Total	Total Incl O&P
0010	**WATER SUPPLY WELLS, PUMPS**									
0011	With pressure control									
1000	Deep well, jet, 42 gal. galvanized tank									
1040	3/4 HP	1 Plum	.80	10	Ea.	1,100	585		1,685	2,100
3000	Shallow well, jet, 30 gal. galvanized tank									
3040	1/2 HP	1 Plum	2	4	Ea.	895	235		1,130	1,350

33 31 Sanitary Utility Sewerage Piping

33 31 13 – Public Sanitary Utility Sewerage Piping

33 31 13.10 Sewage Collection, Valves

		Crew	Daily Output	Labor-Hours	Unit	Material	2015 Bare Costs Labor	Equipment	Total	Total Incl O&P
0010	**SEWAGE COLLECTION, VALVES**									
1300	PVC swing check backwater valve									
1310	3" size	2 Skwk	15	1.067	Ea.	42.50	52		94.50	127
1315	4" size		15	1.067		47.50	52		99.50	132
1320	6" size	▼	13	1.231	▼	199	60		259	310
2000	Sewer relief valve									
2010	Plug style popper for outside cleanout									
2025	2" size	2 Skwk	56	.286	Ea.	2.10	13.90		16	24
2030	3" size		36	.444		3.15	21.50		24.65	37
2040	4" size	▼	30	.533	▼	3.94	26		29.94	44.50
3000	Air release valves for sewer pipes									
3020	2" size inlet connection	1 Plum	9	.889	Ea.	370	52		422	485
3030	3" size inlet connection	Q-1	8	2	▼	590	106		696	810

For customer support on your Site Work & Landscape Cost Data, call 877.737.1594.

483

33 31 13 – Public Sanitary Utility Sewerage Piping

33 31 13.10 Sewage Collection, Valves

	33 31 13.10 Sewage Collection, Valves	Crew	Daily Output	Labor-Hours	Unit	Material	2015 Bare Costs Labor	Equipment	Total	Total Incl O&P
3040	4" size inlet connection	Q-1	5	3.200	Ea.	575	169		744	885
3100	Air release valves for sewer pipes with backwash valve and fittings									
3120	2" size inlet connection	1 Plum	9	.889	Ea.	480	52		532	610
3130	3" size inlet connection	Q-1	8	2		880	106		986	1,125
3140	4" size inlet connection	"	5	3.200	↓	1,125	169		1,294	1,500
3200	Air release & vacuum valves for sewer pipes									
3220	2" size inlet connection	1 Plum	9	.889	Ea.	365	52		417	480
3230	3" size inlet connection	Q-1	8	2	"	2,525	106		2,631	2,925

33 31 13.13 Sewage Collection, Vent Cast Iron Pipe

	33 31 13.13 Sewage Collection, Vent Cast Iron Pipe	Crew	Daily Output	Labor-Hours	Unit	Material	2015 Bare Costs Labor	Equipment	Total	Total Incl O&P
0010	**SEWAGE COLLECTION, VENT CAST IRON PIPE**									
0020	Not including excavation or backfill									
2022	Sewage vent cast iron, B&S, 4" diameter	Q-1	66	.242	L.F.	15.95	12.80		28.75	37
2024	5" diameter	Q-2	88	.273		23.50	14.95		38.45	48.50
2026	6" diameter	"	84	.286		28	15.65		43.65	54.50
2028	8" diameter	Q-3	70	.457		46	25.50		71.50	89
2030	10" diameter		66	.485		76	27		103	125
2032	12" diameter		57	.561		109	31.50		140.50	168
2034	15" diameter	↓	49	.653	↓	156	36.50		192.50	226
8001	Fittings, bends and elbows									
8110	4" diameter	Q-1	13	1.231	Ea.	56.50	65		121.50	161
8112	5" diameter	Q-2	18	1.333		82	73		155	200
8114	6" diameter	"	17	1.412		97	77.50		174.50	224
8116	8" diameter	Q-3	11	2.909		272	163		435	545
8118	10" diameter		10	3.200		415	179		594	725
8120	12" diameter		9	3.556		550	199		749	910
8122	15" diameter	↓	7	4.571	↓	1,625	256		1,881	2,175
8500	Wyes and tees									
8510	4" diameter	Q-1	8	2	Ea.	93.50	106		199.50	263
8512	5" diameter	Q-2	12	2		159	110		269	340
8514	6" diameter	"	11	2.182		194	120		314	395
8516	8" diameter	Q-3	7	4.571		460	256		716	895
8518	10" diameter		6	5.333		760	298		1,058	1,275
8520	12" diameter		4	8		1,550	445		1,995	2,375
8522	15" diameter	↓	3	10.667	↓	3,150	595		3,745	4,375

33 31 13.15 Sewage Collection, Concrete Pipe

	33 31 13.15 Sewage Collection, Concrete Pipe	Crew	Daily Output	Labor-Hours	Unit	Material	2015 Bare Costs Labor	Equipment	Total	Total Incl O&P
0010	**SEWAGE COLLECTION, CONCRETE PIPE**									
0020	See Section 33 41 13.60 for sewage/drainage collection, concrete pipe									

33 31 13.20 Sewage Collection, Plastic Pipe

	33 31 13.20 Sewage Collection, Plastic Pipe	Crew	Daily Output	Labor-Hours	Unit	Material	2015 Bare Costs Labor	Equipment	Total	Total Incl O&P
0010	**SEWAGE COLLECTION, PLASTIC PIPE**									
0020	Not including excavation & backfill									
3000	Piping, HDPE Corrugated Type S with watertight gaskets, 4" diameter	B-20	425	.056	L.F.	.92	2.37		3.29	4.66
3020	6" diameter		400	.060		2.19	2.52		4.71	6.30
3040	8" diameter		380	.063		4.58	2.65		7.23	9.15
3060	10" diameter		370	.065		6.55	2.72		9.27	11.40
3080	12" diameter		340	.071		7.35	2.96		10.31	12.65
3100	15" diameter	↓	300	.080		8.75	3.36		12.11	14.75
3120	18" diameter	B-21	275	.102		13.90	4.41	.50	18.81	22.50
3140	24" diameter		250	.112		18.45	4.85	.55	23.85	28.50
3160	30" diameter		200	.140		24	6.05	.69	30.74	36.50
3180	36" diameter		180	.156		32.50	6.75	.77	40.02	46.50
3200	42" diameter		175	.160		43.50	6.95	.79	51.24	59.50
3220	48" diameter	↓	170	.165	↓	53.50	7.15	.81	61.46	71

484

For customer support on your Site Work & Landscape Cost Data, call 877.737.1594.

33 31 Sanitary Utility Sewerage Piping

33 31 13 – Public Sanitary Utility Sewerage Piping

33 31 13.20 Sewage Collection, Plastic Pipe

		Crew	Daily Output	Labor-Hours	Unit	Material	2015 Bare Costs Labor	Equipment	Total	Total Incl O&P
3240	54" diameter	B-21	160	.175	L.F.	97	7.60	.86	105.46	120
3260	60" diameter	↓	150	.187		142	8.10	.92	151.02	169
3300	Watertight elbows 12" diameter	B-20	11	2.182	Ea.	72	91.50		163.50	221
3320	15" diameter	"	9	2.667		110	112		222	293
3340	18" diameter	B-21	9	3.111		181	135	15.30	331.30	425
3360	24" diameter		9	3.111		380	135	15.30	530.30	645
3380	30" diameter		8	3.500		610	152	17.20	779.20	920
3400	36" diameter		8	3.500		785	152	17.20	954.20	1,100
3420	42" diameter		6	4.667		990	202	23	1,215	1,425
3440	48" diameter	↓	6	4.667		1,775	202	23	2,000	2,300
3460	Watertight tee 12" diameter	B-20	7	3.429		123	144		267	355
3480	15" diameter	"	6	4		184	168		352	460
3500	18" diameter	B-21	6	4.667		258	202	23	483	620
3520	24" diameter		5	5.600		355	243	27.50	625.50	795
3540	30" diameter		5	5.600		705	243	27.50	975.50	1,175
3560	36" diameter		4	7		795	305	34.50	1,134.50	1,375
3580	42" diameter		4	7		870	305	34.50	1,209.50	1,450
3600	48" diameter	↓	4	7	↓	1,500	305	34.50	1,839.50	2,150

33 31 13.25 Sewage Collection, Polyvinyl Chloride Pipe

		Crew	Daily Output	Labor-Hours	Unit	Material	2015 Bare Costs Labor	Equipment	Total	Total Incl O&P
0010	**SEWAGE COLLECTION, POLYVINYL CHLORIDE PIPE**									
0020	Not including excavation or backfill									
2000	20' lengths, SDR 35, B&S, 4" diameter	B-20	375	.064	L.F.	1.45	2.68		4.13	5.75
2040	6" diameter		350	.069		3.28	2.88		6.16	8.05
2080	13' lengths , SDR 35, B&S, 8" diameter	↓	335	.072		6.90	3.01		9.91	12.25
2120	10" diameter	B-21	330	.085		11.40	3.68	.42	15.50	18.60
2160	12" diameter		320	.088		12.75	3.79	.43	16.97	20.50
2200	15" diameter		240	.117		12.95	5.05	.57	18.57	22.50
2300	18" diameter		200	.140		15	6.05	.69	21.74	26.50
2400	21" diameter		190	.147		21	6.40	.73	28.13	33.50
2500	24" diameter	↓	180	.156	↓	27	6.75	.77	34.52	40.50
3040	Fittings, bends or elbows, 4" diameter	2 Skwk	24	.667	Ea.	9.80	32.50		42.30	61
3080	6" diameter		24	.667		32	32.50		64.50	85
3120	Tees, 4" diameter		16	1		13.45	48.50		61.95	90
3160	6" diameter		16	1		43	48.50		91.50	123
3200	Wyes, 4" diameter		16	1		16.65	48.50		65.15	93.50
3240	6" diameter		16	1		46	48.50		94.50	126
3661	Cap, 4"		48	.333		7.65	16.20		23.85	33.50
3670	6"		48	.333		12.20	16.20		28.40	38.50
3671	8"		40	.400		28.50	19.45		47.95	61.50
3672	10"		24	.667		88	32.50		120.50	147
3673	12"		20	.800		125	39		164	197
3674	15"		18	.889		215	43		258	305
3675	18"		18	.889		315	43		358	410
3676	21"		18	.889		680	43		723	815
3677	24"		18	.889		785	43		828	930
3745	Elbow, 90 degree, 8" diameter		20	.800		55	39		94	121
3750	10" diameter		12	1.333		184	65		249	300
3755	12" diameter		10	1.600		238	78		316	380
3760	15" diameter		9	1.778		500	86.50		586.50	685
3765	18" diameter		9	1.778		850	86.50		936.50	1,075
3770	21" diameter		9	1.778		1,450	86.50		1,536.50	1,725
3775	24" diameter		9	1.778		1,950	86.50		2,036.50	2,275

For customer support on your Site Work & Landscape Cost Data, call 877.737.1594.

485

33 31 Sanitary Utility Sewerage Piping

33 31 13 – Public Sanitary Utility Sewerage Piping

33 31 13.25 Sewage Collection, Polyvinyl Chloride Pipe	Crew	Daily Output	Labor-Hours	Unit	Material	2015 Bare Costs Labor	Equipment	Total	Total Incl O&P
3795	Elbow, 45 degree, 8" diameter	2 Skwk	20	.800	Ea.	49	39		88	114
3805	12" diameter		10	1.600		183	78		261	320
3810	15" diameter		9	1.778		410	86.50		496.50	585
3815	18" diameter		9	1.778		655	86.50		741.50	855
3820	21" diameter		9	1.778		1,100	86.50		1,186.50	1,350
3825	24" diameter		9	1.778		1,525	86.50		1,611.50	1,800
3875	Elbow, 22 1/2 degree, 8" diameter		20	.800		49	39		88	114
3880	10" diameter		12	1.333		134	65		199	247
3885	12" diameter		12	1.333		175	65		240	292
3890	15" diameter		9	1.778		460	86.50		546.50	645
3895	18" diameter		9	1.778		675	86.50		761.50	875
3900	21" diameter		9	1.778		960	86.50		1,046.50	1,175
3905	24" diameter		9	1.778		1,375	86.50		1,461.50	1,650
3910	Tee, 8" diameter		13	1.231		80	60		140	181
3915	10" diameter		8	2		290	97.50		387.50	470
3920	12" diameter		7	2.286		415	111		526	625
3925	15" diameter		6	2.667		685	130		815	955
3930	18" diameter		6	2.667		1,125	130		1,255	1,450
3935	21" diameter		6	2.667		2,750	130		2,880	3,225
3940	24" diameter	▼	6	2.667	▼	4,450	130		4,580	5,100
4000	Piping, DWV PVC, no exc./bkfill., 10' L, Sch 40, 4" diameter	B-20	375	.064	L.F.	3.84	2.68		6.52	8.35
4010	6" diameter		350	.069		7.65	2.88		10.53	12.85
4020	8" diameter		335	.072	▼	12	3.01		15.01	17.85
4030	Piping, fittings, 1/4 bend DWV PVC, 4" diameter		19	1.263	Ea.	13.05	53		66.05	96
4040	Piping, fittings, 1/4 bend DWV PVC, 6" diameter		12	2		65	84		149	201
4050	Piping, fittings, 1/4 bend DWV PVC, 8" diameter		11	2.182		65	91.50		156.50	213
4060	Piping, fittings, 1/8 bend DWV PVC, 4" diameter		19	1.263		10.40	53		63.40	93
4070	Piping, fittings, 1/8 bend DWV PVC, 6" diameter		12	2		42	84		126	175
4080	Piping, fittings, 1/8 bend DWV PVC, 8" diameter		11	2.182		158	91.50		249.50	315
4090	Piping, fittings, Tee DWV PVC, 4" diameter		12	2		17.75	84		101.75	149
4100	Piping, fittings, Tee DWV PVC, 6" diameter		10	2.400		74	101		175	237
4110	Piping, fittings, Tee DWV PVC, 8" diameter	▼	9	2.667	▼	173	112		285	360

33 32 Wastewater Utility Pumping Stations

33 32 13 – Packaged Utility Lift Stations

33 32 13.13 Packaged Sewage Lift Stations

		Crew	Daily Output	Labor-Hours	Unit	Material	2015 Bare Costs Labor	Equipment	Total	Total Incl O&P
0010	**PACKAGED SEWAGE LIFT STATIONS**									
2500	Sewage lift station, 200,000 GPD	E-8	.20	520	Ea.	220,000	27,000	10,500	257,500	299,000
2510	500,000 GPD		.15	684		250,500	35,600	13,800	299,900	350,500
2520	800,000 GPD	▼	.13	812	▼	300,000	42,300	16,400	358,700	419,500

33 36 Utility Septic Tanks

33 36 13 – Utility Septic Tank and Effluent Wet Wells

33 36 13.13 Concrete Utility Septic Tank	Crew	Daily Output	Labor-Hours	Unit	Material	2015 Bare Costs Labor	Equipment	Total	Total Incl O&P
0010 **CONCRETE UTILITY SEPTIC TANK**									
0011 Not including excavation or piping									
0015 Septic tanks, precast, 1,000 gallon	B-21	8	3.500	Ea.	1,000	152	17.20	1,169.20	1,350
0020 1,250 gallon		8	3.500		1,050	152	17.20	1,219.20	1,400
0060 1,500 gallon		7	4		1,325	173	19.70	1,517.70	1,775
0100 2,000 gallon		5	5.600		1,925	243	27.50	2,195.50	2,500
0140 2,500 gallon		5	5.600		2,025	243	27.50	2,295.50	2,625
0180 4,000 gallon		4	7		5,550	305	34.50	5,889.50	6,600
0200 5,000 gallon	B-13	3.50	16		9,500	655	210	10,365	11,700
0220 5,000 gal., 4 piece	"	3	18.667		9,575	765	245	10,585	11,900
0300 15,000 gallon, 4 piece	B-13B	1.70	32.941		20,000	1,350	665	22,015	24,800
0400 25,000 gallon, 4 piece		1.10	50.909		38,800	2,075	1,025	41,900	47,000
0500 40,000 gallon, 4 piece		.80	70		49,700	2,875	1,400	53,975	60,500
0520 50,000 gallon, 5 piece	B-13C	.60	93.333		57,000	3,825	2,775	63,600	72,000
0640 75,000 gallon, cast in place	C-14C	.25	448		69,500	20,200	125	89,825	107,500
0660 100,000 gallon	"	.15	746		86,000	33,700	209	119,909	146,500
0800 Septic tanks, precast, 2 compartment, 1,000 gallon	B-21	8	3.500		675	152	17.20	844.20	995
0805 1,250 gallon		8	3.500		875	152	17.20	1,044.20	1,225
0810 1,500 gallon		7	4		1,650	173	19.70	1,842.70	2,100
0815 2,000 gallon		5	5.600		2,025	243	27.50	2,295.50	2,625
0820 2,500 gallon		5	5.600		2,675	243	27.50	2,945.50	3,325
0890 Septic tanks, butyl rope sealant				L.F.	.40			.40	.44
0900 Concrete riser 24" X 12" with standard lid	1 Clab	6	1.333	Ea.	83	50		133	169
0905 24" X 12" with heavy duty lid		6	1.333		105	50		155	193
0910 24" X 8" with standard lid		6	1.333		78	50		128	163
0915 24" X 8" with heavy duty lid		6	1.333		100	50		150	187
0917 24" X 12" extension		12	.667		56	25		81	100
0920 24" X 8" extension		12	.667		51	25		76	94.50
0950 HDPE riser 20" X 12" with standard lid		8	1		122	37.50		159.50	192
0951 HDPE 20" X 12" with heavy duty lid		8	1		136	37.50		173.50	208
0955 HDPE 24" X 12" with standard lid		8	1		117	37.50		154.50	187
0956 HDPE 24" X 12" with heavy duty lid		8	1		140	37.50		177.50	212
0960 HDPE 20" X 6" extension		48	.167		27	6.25		33.25	39
0962 HDPE 20" X 12" extension		48	.167		48	6.25		54.25	62
0965 HDPE 24" X 6" extension		48	.167		28.50	6.25		34.75	40.50
0967 HDPE 24" X 12" extension		48	.167		46.50	6.25		52.75	60.50
1150 Leaching field chambers, 13' x 3'-7" x 1'-4", standard	B-13	16	3.500		485	143	46	674	800
1200 Heavy duty, 8' x 4' x 1'-6"		14	4		284	164	52.50	500.50	620
1300 13' x 3'-9" x 1'-6"		12	4.667		1,125	191	61.50	1,377.50	1,575
1350 20' x 4' x 1'-6"		5	11.200		1,175	460	147	1,782	2,150
1400 Leaching pit, precast concrete, 3' diameter, 3' deep	B-21	8	3.500		710	152	17.20	879.20	1,025
1500 6' diameter, 3' section		4.70	5.957		885	258	29.50	1,172.50	1,400
1600 Leaching pit, 6'-6" diameter, 6' deep		5	5.600		1,025	243	27.50	1,295.50	1,525
1620 8' deep		4	7		1,200	305	34.50	1,539.50	1,825
1700 8' diameter, H-20 load, 6' deep		4	7		1,500	305	34.50	1,839.50	2,150
1720 8' deep		3	9.333		2,500	405	46	2,951	3,425
2000 Velocity reducing pit, precast conc., 6' diameter, 3' deep		4.70	5.957		1,600	258	29.50	1,887.50	2,175

33 36 13.19 Polyethylene Utility Septic Tank

	Crew	Daily Output	Labor-Hours	Unit	Material	2015 Bare Costs Labor	Equipment	Total	Total Incl O&P
0010 **POLYETHYLENE UTILITY SEPTIC TANK**									
0015 High density polyethylene, 1,000 gallon	B-21	8	3.500	Ea.	1,550	152	17.20	1,719.20	1,950
0020 1,250 gallon		8	3.500		1,200	152	17.20	1,369.20	1,575
0025 1,500 gallon		7	4		1,475	173	19.70	1,667.70	1,925

For customer support on your Site Work & Landscape Cost Data, call 877.737.1594.

487

33 36 Utility Septic Tanks

33 36 13 – Utility Septic Tank and Effluent Wet Wells

33 36 13.19 Polyethylene Utility Septic Tank

		Crew	Daily Output	Labor-Hours	Unit	Material	2015 Bare Costs Labor	2015 Bare Costs Equipment	Total	Total Incl O&P
1015	Septic tanks, HDPE, 2 compartment, 1,000 gallon	B-21	8	3.500	Ea.	1,650	152	17.20	1,819.20	2,075
1020	1,500 gallon	↓	7	4	↓	2,100	173	19.70	2,292.70	2,600

33 36 19 – Utility Septic Tank Effluent Filter

33 36 19.13 Utility Septic Tank Effluent Tube Filter

		Crew	Daily Output	Labor-Hours	Unit	Material	Labor	Equipment	Total	Total Incl O&P
0010	**UTILITY SEPTIC TANK EFFLUENT TUBE FILTER**									
3000	Effluent filter, 4" diameter	1 Skwk	8	1	Ea.	42	48.50		90.50	121
3020	6" diameter		7	1.143		249	55.50		304.50	360
3030	8" diameter		7	1.143		225	55.50		280.50	335
3040	8" diameter, very fine		7	1.143		460	55.50		515.50	590
3050	10" diameter, very fine		6	1.333		235	65		300	360
3060	10" diameter		6	1.333		280	65		345	410
3080	12" diameter		6	1.333		670	65		735	840
3090	15" diameter		5	1.600	↓	1,150	78		1,228	1,375

33 36 33 – Utility Septic Tank Drainage Field

33 36 33.13 Utility Septic Tank Tile Drainage Field

		Crew	Daily Output	Labor-Hours	Unit	Material	Labor	Equipment	Total	Total Incl O&P
0010	**UTILITY SEPTIC TANK TILE DRAINAGE FIELD**									
0015	Distribution box, concrete, 5 outlets	2 Clab	20	.800	Ea.	80.50	30		110.50	135
0020	7 outlets		16	1		80.50	37.50		118	147
0025	9 outlets		8	2		490	75		565	655
0115	Distribution boxes, HDPE, 5 outlets		20	.800		64.50	30		94.50	118
0117	6 outlets		15	1.067		65	40		105	133
0118	7 outlets		15	1.067		65	40		105	133
0120	8 outlets	↓	10	1.600		68	60		128	168
0240	Distribution boxes, Outlet Flow Leveler	1 Clab	50	.160		2.25	6		8.25	11.75
0260	Bull Run Valve 4" dia.	2 Skwk	16	1		70.50	48.50		119	153
0261	Bull Run Valve Key					20.50			20.50	22.50
0300	Precast concrete, galley, 4' x 4' x 4'	B-21	16	1.750	↓	250	76	8.60	334.60	400
0350	HDPE infiltration chamber 12" H X 15" W	2 Clab	300	.053	L.F.	7.30	2.01		9.31	11.15
0351	12" H X 15" W End Cap	1 Clab	32	.250	Ea.	19.75	9.40		29.15	36
0355	chamber 12" H X 22" W	2 Clab	300	.053	L.F.	6.70	2.01		8.71	10.45
0356	12" H X 22" W End Cap	1 Clab	32	.250	Ea.	16.85	9.40		26.25	33
0360	chamber 13" H X 34" W	2 Clab	300	.053	L.F.	15	2.01		17.01	19.60
0361	13" H X 34" W End Cap	1 Clab	32	.250	Ea.	53.50	9.40		62.90	73
0365	chamber 16" H X 34" W	2 Clab	300	.053	L.F.	10.70	2.01		12.71	14.90
0366	16" H X 34" W End Cap	1 Clab	32	.250	Ea.	8	9.40		17.40	23.50
0370	chamber 8" H X 16" W	2 Clab	300	.053	L.F.	9.65	2.01		11.66	13.70
0371	8" H X 16" W End Cap	1 Clab	32	.250	Ea.	10.80	9.40		20.20	26.50

33 36 50 – Drainage Field Systems

33 36 50.10 Drainage Field Excavation and Fill

		Crew	Daily Output	Labor-Hours	Unit	Material	Labor	Equipment	Total	Total Incl O&P
0010	**DRAINAGE FIELD EXCAVATION AND FILL**									
2200	Septic tank & drainage field excavation with 3/4 c.y backhoe	B-12F	145	.110	C.Y.		4.93	4.52	9.45	12.45
2400	4' trench for disposal field, 3/4 C.Y. backhoe	"	335	.048	L.F.		2.13	1.95	4.08	5.40
2600	Gravel fill, run of bank	B-6	150	.160	C.Y.	20	6.60	2.43	29.03	35
2800	Crushed stone, 3/4"	"	150	.160	"	36.50	6.60	2.43	45.53	53

33 41 13 – Public Storm Utility Drainage Piping

33 41 13.40 Piping, Storm Drainage, Corrugated Metal	Crew	Daily Output	Labor-Hours	Unit	Material	2015 Bare Costs Labor	Equipment	Total	Total Incl O&P
0010 **PIPING, STORM DRAINAGE, CORRUGATED METAL**									
0020 Not including excavation or backfill									
2000 Corrugated metal pipe, galvanized									
2020 Bituminous coated with paved invert, 20' lengths									
2040 8" diameter, 16 ga.	B-14	330	.145	L.F.	8.65	5.80	1.10	15.55	19.60
2060 10" diameter, 16 ga.		260	.185		9	7.35	1.40	17.75	22.50
2080 12" diameter, 16 ga.		210	.229		11.05	9.10	1.73	21.88	28
2100 15" diameter, 16 ga.		200	.240		15.15	9.55	1.82	26.52	33.50
2120 18" diameter, 16 ga.		190	.253		16.70	10.05	1.92	28.67	36
2140 24" diameter, 14 ga.		160	.300		21.50	11.95	2.28	35.73	44.50
2160 30" diameter, 14 ga.	B-13	120	.467		27.50	19.15	6.15	52.80	67
2180 36" diameter, 12 ga.		120	.467		35.50	19.15	6.15	60.80	75.50
2200 48" diameter, 12 ga.		100	.560		52.50	23	7.35	82.85	101
2220 60" diameter, 10 ga.	B-13B	75	.747		80	30.50	15.05	125.55	151
2240 72" diameter, 8 ga.	"	45	1.244		95.50	51	25	171.50	211
2250 End sections, 8" diameter, 16 ga.	B-14	20	2.400	Ea.	43.50	95.50	18.20	157.20	214
2255 10" diameter, 16 ga.		20	2.400		60	95.50	18.20	173.70	232
2260 12" diameter, 16 ga.		18	2.667		120	106	20	246	320
2265 15" diameter, 16 ga.		18	2.667		205	106	20	331	410
2270 18" diameter, 16 ga.		16	3		240	119	23	382	470
2275 24" diameter, 16 ga.	B-13	16	3.500		280	143	46	469	580
2280 30" diameter, 16 ga.		14	4		490	164	52.50	706.50	845
2285 36" diameter, 14 ga.		14	4		730	164	52.50	946.50	1,100
2290 48" diameter, 14 ga.		10	5.600		1,850	230	73.50	2,153.50	2,450
2292 60" diameter, 14 ga.		6	9.333		1,950	385	123	2,458	2,875
2294 72" diameter, 14 ga.	B-13B	5	11.200		3,125	460	226	3,811	4,400
2300 Bends or elbows, 8" diameter	B-14	28	1.714		117	68	13	198	248
2320 10" diameter		25	1.920		146	76.50	14.55	237.05	293
2340 12" diameter, 16 ga.		23	2.087		169	83	15.85	267.85	330
2342 18" diameter, 16 ga.		20	2.400		244	95.50	18.20	357.70	435
2344 24" diameter, 14 ga.		16	3		335	119	23	477	580
2346 30" diameter, 14 ga.		15	3.200		430	127	24.50	581.50	690
2348 36" diameter, 14 ga.	B-13	15	3.733		580	153	49	782	925
2350 48" diameter, 12 ga.	"	12	4.667		805	191	61.50	1,057.50	1,250
2352 60" diameter, 10 ga.	B-13B	10	5.600		1,075	230	113	1,418	1,650
2354 72" diameter, 10 ga.	"	6	9.333		1,325	385	188	1,898	2,275
2360 Wyes or tees, 8" diameter	B-14	25	1.920		164	76.50	14.55	255.05	315
2380 10" diameter		21	2.286		205	91	17.35	313.35	385
2400 12" diameter, 16 ga.		19	2.526		244	100	19.15	363.15	445
2410 18" diameter, 16 ga.		16	3		325	119	23	467	565
2412 24" diameter, 14 ga.		16	3		485	119	23	627	745
2414 30" diameter, 14 ga.	B-13	12	4.667		645	191	61.50	897.50	1,075
2416 36" diameter, 14 ga.		11	5.091		795	209	67	1,071	1,275
2418 48" diameter, 12 ga.		10	5.600		1,175	230	73.50	1,478.50	1,700
2420 60" diameter, 10 ga.	B-13B	8	7		1,700	287	141	2,128	2,475
2422 72" diameter, 10 ga.	"	5	11.200		2,050	460	226	2,736	3,200
2500 Galvanized, uncoated, 20' lengths									
2520 8" diameter, 16 ga.	B-14	355	.135	L.F.	7.80	5.40	1.03	14.23	18
2540 10" diameter, 16 ga.		280	.171		8.95	6.80	1.30	17.05	21.50
2560 12" diameter, 16 ga.		220	.218		9.95	8.70	1.66	20.31	26
2580 15" diameter, 16 ga.		220	.218		12.45	8.70	1.66	22.81	29
2600 18" diameter, 16 ga.		205	.234		15.05	9.30	1.78	26.13	33
2610 21" diameter, 16 ga.		205	.234		17.95	9.30	1.78	29.03	36

For customer support on your Site Work & Landscape Cost Data, call 877.737.1594.

489

33 41 Storm Utility Drainage Piping

33 41 13 – Public Storm Utility Drainage Piping

33 41 13.40 Piping, Storm Drainage, Corrugated Metal

		Crew	Daily Output	Labor-Hours	Unit	Material	2015 Bare Costs Labor	Equipment	Total	Total Incl O&P
2620	24" diameter, 14 ga.	B-14	175	.274	L.F.	18.95	10.90	2.08	31.93	40
2630	27" diameter, 14 ga.	↓	170	.282		22	11.25	2.14	35.39	43.50
2640	30" diameter, 14 ga.	B-13	130	.431		25	17.65	5.65	48.30	61
2660	36" diameter, 12 ga.		130	.431		32	17.65	5.65	55.30	68.50
2680	48" diameter, 12 ga.	↓	110	.509		47.50	21	6.70	75.20	91.50
2690	60" diameter, 10 ga.	B-13B	78	.718		72	29.50	14.45	115.95	140
2695	72" diameter, 10 ga.	"	60	.933	↓	86	38.50	18.80	143.30	174
2711	Bends or elbows, 12" diameter, 16 ga.	B-14	30	1.600	Ea.	145	63.50	12.15	220.65	271
2712	15" diameter, 16 ga.		25.04	1.917		180	76	14.55	270.55	330
2714	18" diameter, 16 ga.		20	2.400		202	95.50	18.20	315.70	390
2716	24" diameter, 14 ga.		16	3		293	119	23	435	530
2718	30" diameter, 14 ga.	↓	15	3.200		340	127	24.50	491.50	595
2720	36" diameter, 14 ga.	B-13	15	3.733		515	153	49	717	855
2722	48" diameter, 12 ga.		12	4.667		680	191	61.50	932.50	1,100
2724	60" diameter, 10 ga.		10	5.600		1,050	230	73.50	1,353.50	1,575
2726	72" diameter, 10 ga.	↓	6	9.333		1,350	385	123	1,858	2,200
2728	Wyes or tees, 12" diameter, 16 ga.	B-14	22.48	2.135		193	85	16.20	294.20	360
2730	18" diameter, 16 ga.		15	3.200		282	127	24.50	433.50	530
2732	24" diameter, 14 ga.		15	3.200		450	127	24.50	601.50	715
2734	30" diameter, 14 ga.	↓	14	3.429		580	136	26	742	875
2736	36" diameter, 14 ga.	B-13	14	4		755	164	52.50	971.50	1,150
2738	48" diameter, 12 ga.		12	4.667		1,075	191	61.50	1,327.50	1,550
2740	60" diameter, 10 ga.		10	5.600		1,575	230	73.50	1,878.50	2,150
2742	72" diameter, 10 ga.	↓	6	9.333		1,850	385	123	2,358	2,775
2780	End sections, 8" diameter	B-14	35	1.371		73	54.50	10.40	137.90	175
2785	10" diameter		35	1.371		77	54.50	10.40	141.90	179
2790	12" diameter		35	1.371		114	54.50	10.40	178.90	220
2800	18" diameter	↓	30	1.600		115	63.50	12.15	190.65	237
2810	24" diameter	B-13	25	2.240		215	92	29.50	336.50	410
2820	30" diameter		25	2.240		330	92	29.50	451.50	535
2825	36" diameter		20	2.800		480	115	37	632	745
2830	48" diameter	↓	10	5.600		950	230	73.50	1,253.50	1,475
2835	60" diameter	B-13B	5	11.200		1,650	460	226	2,336	2,750
2840	72" diameter	"	4	14		1,975	575	282	2,832	3,350
2850	Couplings, 12" diameter					10.55			10.55	11.60
2855	18" diameter					15.10			15.10	16.60
2860	24" diameter					19.95			19.95	22
2865	30" diameter					25			25	27.50
2870	36" diameter					32			32	35
2875	48" diameter					47.50			47.50	52
2880	60" diameter					60			60	66
2885	72" diameter				↓	72.50			72.50	79.50

33 41 13.50 Piping, Drainage & Sewage, Corrug. HDPE Type S

		Crew	Daily Output	Labor-Hours	Unit	Material	2015 Bare Costs Labor	Equipment	Total	Total Incl O&P
0010	**PIPING, DRAINAGE & SEWAGE, CORRUGATED HDPE TYPE S**									
0020	Not including excavation & backfill, bell & spigot									
1000	With gaskets, 4" diameter	B-20	425	.056	L.F.	.80	2.37		3.17	4.53
1010	6" diameter		400	.060		1.90	2.52		4.42	5.95
1020	8" diameter		380	.063		3.98	2.65		6.63	8.45
1030	10" diameter		370	.065		5.70	2.72		8.42	10.45
1040	12" diameter		340	.071		6.40	2.96		9.36	11.60
1050	15" diameter	↓	300	.080		7.60	3.36		10.96	13.50
1060	18" diameter	B-21	275	.102	↓	12.10	4.41	.50	17.01	20.50

33 41 Storm Utility Drainage Piping

33 41 13 – Public Storm Utility Drainage Piping

33 41 13.50 Piping, Drainage & Sewage, Corrug. HDPE Type S	Crew	Daily Output	Labor-Hours	Unit	Material	2015 Bare Costs Labor	Equipment	Total	Total Incl O&P
1070 24" diameter	B-21	250	.112	L.F.	16.05	4.85	.55	21.45	25.50
1080 30" diameter		200	.140		21	6.05	.69	27.74	33
1090 36" diameter		180	.156		28	6.75	.77	35.52	42
1100 42" diameter		175	.160		38	6.95	.79	45.74	53.50
1110 48" diameter		170	.165		46.50	7.15	.81	54.46	63
1120 54" diameter		160	.175		84.50	7.60	.86	92.96	106
1130 60" diameter	▼	150	.187	▼	124	8.10	.92	133.02	149
1135 Add 15% to material pipe cost for water tight connection bell & spigot									
1140 HDPE type S, elbows 12" diameter	B-20	11	2.182	Ea.	63	91.50		154.50	210
1150 15" diameter	"	9	2.667		96	112		208	277
1160 18" diameter	B-21	9	3.111		158	135	15.30	308.30	395
1170 24" diameter		9	3.111		335	135	15.30	485.30	590
1180 30" diameter		8	3.500		530	152	17.20	699.20	830
1190 36" diameter		8	3.500		680	152	17.20	849.20	1,000
1200 42" diameter		6	4.667		860	202	23	1,085	1,275
1220 48" diameter	▼	6	4.667	▼	1,550	202	23	1,775	2,025
1240 HDPE type S, Tee 12" diameter	B-20	7	3.429		107	144		251	340
1260 15" diameter	"	6	4		160	168		328	435
1280 18" diameter	B-21	6	4.667		224	202	23	449	585
1300 24" diameter		5	5.600		310	243	27.50	580.50	745
1320 30" diameter		5	5.600		615	243	27.50	885.50	1,075
1340 36" diameter		4	7		690	305	34.50	1,029.50	1,275
1360 42" diameter		4	7		755	305	34.50	1,094.50	1,325
1380 48" diameter	▼	4	7	▼	1,300	305	34.50	1,639.50	1,925
1400 Add to basic installation cost for each split coupling joint									
1402 HDPE type S, split coupling, 12" diameter	B-20	17	1.412	Ea.	7.45	59		66.45	99.50
1420 15" diameter		15	1.600		12.45	67		79.45	117
1440 18" diameter		13	1.846		22	77.50		99.50	143
1460 24" diameter		12	2		31.50	84		115.50	164
1480 30" diameter		10	2.400		70	101		171	232
1500 36" diameter		9	2.667		133	112		245	320
1520 42" diameter		8	3		157	126		283	365
1540 48" diameter	▼	8	3	▼	168	126		294	380

33 41 13.60 Sewage/Drainage Collection, Concrete Pipe

	Crew	Daily Output	Labor-Hours	Unit	Material	2015 Bare Costs Labor	Equipment	Total	Total Incl O&P
0010 **SEWAGE/DRAINAGE COLLECTION, CONCRETE PIPE**									
0020 Not including excavation or backfill									
0050 Box culvert, cast in place, 6' x 6'	C-15	16	4.500	L.F.	233	199		432	560
0060 8' x 8'		14	5.143		340	228		568	725
0070 12' x 12'	▼	10	7.200		670	320		990	1,225
0100 Box culvert, precast, base price, 8' long, 6' x 3'	B-69	140	.343		254	14.25	11.60	279.85	315
0150 6' x 7'		125	.384		320	15.95	13	348.95	395
0200 8' x 3'		113	.425		315	17.65	14.40	347.05	395
0250 8' x 8'		100	.480		385	19.95	16.25	421.20	475
0300 10' x 3'		110	.436		440	18.15	14.75	472.90	530
0350 10' x 8'		80	.600		510	25	20.50	555.50	620
0400 12' x 3'		100	.480		660	19.95	16.25	696.20	775
0450 12' x 8'	▼	67	.716	▼	845	30	24.50	899.50	1,000
0500 Set up charge at plant, add to base price				Job	5,875			5,875	6,475
0510 Inserts and keyway, add				Ea.	545			545	600
0520 Sloped or skewed end, add				"	830			830	915
1000 Non-reinforced pipe, extra strength, B&S or T&G joints									
1010 6" diameter	B-14	265.04	.181	L.F.	6	7.20	1.37	14.57	19.15

33 41 13 – Public Storm Utility Drainage Piping

33 41 13.60 Sewage/Drainage Collection, Concrete Pipe		Crew	Daily Output	Labor-Hours	Unit	Material	2015 Bare Costs Labor	Equipment	Total	Total Incl O&P
1020	8" diameter	B-14	224	.214	L.F.	6.60	8.50	1.63	16.73	22
1030	10" diameter		216	.222		7.30	8.85	1.69	17.84	23.50
1040	12" diameter		200	.240		8.20	9.55	1.82	19.57	25.50
1050	15" diameter		180	.267		12	10.60	2.02	24.62	31.50
1060	18" diameter		144	.333		15	13.25	2.53	30.78	40
1070	21" diameter		112	.429		17	17.05	3.25	37.30	48.50
1080	24" diameter		100	.480		22	19.10	3.64	44.74	57.50
1560	Reinforced culvert, class 2, no gaskets									
1590	27" diameter	B-21	88	.318	L.F.	37	13.80	1.57	52.37	63
1592	30" diameter	B-13	80	.700		40	28.50	9.20	77.70	98
1594	36" diameter	"	72	.778		56	32	10.25	98.25	122
2000	Reinforced culvert, class 3, no gaskets									
2010	12" diameter	B-14	150	.320	L.F.	11	12.75	2.43	26.18	34.50
2020	15" diameter		150	.320		14	12.75	2.43	29.18	37.50
2030	18" diameter		132	.364		18	14.45	2.76	35.21	45
2035	21" diameter		120	.400		22	15.90	3.04	40.94	52
2040	24" diameter		100	.480		26	19.10	3.64	48.74	62
2045	27" diameter	B-13	92	.609		37	25	8	70	87.50
2050	30" diameter		88	.636		42	26	8.35	76.35	95
2060	36" diameter		72	.778		56	32	10.25	98.25	122
2070	42" diameter	B-13B	72	.778		75	32	15.65	122.65	149
2080	48" diameter		64	.875		89	36	17.60	142.60	172
2090	60" diameter		48	1.167		136	48	23.50	207.50	249
2100	72" diameter		40	1.400		206	57.50	28	291.50	345
2120	84" diameter		32	1.750		275	71.50	35.50	382	455
2140	96" diameter		24	2.333		330	95.50	47	472.50	565
2200	With gaskets, class 3, 12" diameter	B-21	168	.167		12.10	7.20	.82	20.12	25.50
2220	15" diameter		160	.175		15.40	7.60	.86	23.86	29.50
2230	18" diameter		152	.184		19.80	8	.91	28.71	35.50
2240	24" diameter		136	.206		33	8.90	1.01	42.91	51.50
2260	30" diameter	B-13	88	.636		50	26	8.35	84.35	104
2270	36" diameter	"	72	.778		65.50	32	10.25	107.75	132
2290	48" diameter	B-13B	64	.875		102	36	17.60	155.60	186
2310	72" diameter	"	40	1.400		225	57.50	28	310.50	365
2330	Flared ends, 12" diameter	B-21	31	.903	Ea.	226	39	4.44	269.44	315
2340	15" diameter		25	1.120		267	48.50	5.50	321	375
2400	18" diameter		20	1.400		305	60.50	6.90	372.40	440
2420	24" diameter		14	2		370	86.50	9.85	466.35	555
2440	36" diameter	B-13	10	5.600		790	230	73.50	1,093.50	1,300
2500	Class 4									
2510	12" diameter	B-21	168	.167	L.F.	13	7.20	.82	21.02	26.50
2512	15" diameter		160	.175		17	7.60	.86	25.46	31.50
2514	18" diameter		152	.184		21	8	.91	29.91	36.50
2516	21" diameter		144	.194		27	8.45	.96	36.41	43.50
2518	24" diameter		136	.206		32	8.90	1.01	41.91	50
2520	27" diameter		120	.233		43	10.10	1.15	54.25	64.50
2522	30" diameter	B-13	88	.636		49	26	8.35	83.35	103
2524	36" diameter	"	72	.778		66	32	10.25	108.25	133
2600	Class 5									
2610	12" diameter	B-21	168	.167	L.F.	15	7.20	.82	23.02	28.50
2612	15" diameter		160	.175		19	7.60	.86	27.46	33.50
2614	18" diameter		152	.184		23.50	8	.91	32.41	39.50
2616	21" diameter		144	.194		29.50	8.45	.96	38.91	46.50

33 41 13 – Public Storm Utility Drainage Piping

33 41 13.60 Sewage/Drainage Collection, Concrete Pipe		Crew	Daily Output	Labor-Hours	Unit	Material	2015 Bare Costs Labor	Equipment	Total	Total Incl O&P
2618	24" diameter	B-21	136	.206	L.F.	36.50	8.90	1.01	46.41	55
2620	27" diameter	↓	120	.233		47.50	10.10	1.15	58.75	69.50
2622	30" diameter	B-13	88	.636		55	26	8.35	89.35	110
2624	36" diameter	"	72	.778		74	32	10.25	116.25	142
2800	Add for rubber joints 12"- 36" diameter					12%				
3080	Radius pipe, add to pipe prices, 12" to 60" diameter					50%				
3090	Over 60" diameter, add				↓	20%				
3500	Reinforced elliptical, 8' lengths, C507 class 3									
3520	14" x 23" inside, round equivalent 18" diameter	B-21	82	.341	L.F.	41	14.80	1.68	57.48	70
3530	24" x 38" inside, round equivalent 30" diameter	B-13	58	.966		62	39.50	12.70	114.20	142
3540	29" x 45" inside, round equivalent 36" diameter		52	1.077		78	44	14.15	136.15	169
3550	38" x 60" inside, round equivalent 48" diameter		38	1.474		134	60.50	19.40	213.90	261
3560	48" x 76" inside, round equivalent 60" diameter		26	2.154		186	88.50	28.50	303	370
3570	58" x 91" inside, round equivalent 72" diameter	↓	22	2.545	↓	272	104	33.50	409.50	495
3780	Concrete slotted pipe, class 4 mortar joint									
3800	12" diameter	B-21	168	.167	L.F.	28	7.20	.82	36.02	43
3840	18" diameter	"	152	.184	"	32	8	.91	40.91	48.50
3900	Concrete slotted pipe, Class 4 O-ring joint									
3940	12" diameter	B-21	168	.167	L.F.	28	7.20	.82	36.02	43
3960	18" diameter	"	152	.184	"	32	8	.91	40.91	48.50
6200	Gasket, conc. pipe joint, 12"				Ea.	4			4	4.40
6220	24"					7			7	7.70
6240	36"					9.50			9.50	10.45
6260	48"					13			13	14.30
6270	60"					15.50			15.50	17.05
6280	72"				↓	19			19	21

33 42 Culverts

33 42 13 – Pipe Culverts

33 42 13.13 Public Pipe Culverts

0010	**PUBLIC PIPE CULVERTS**									
0020	Headwall, concrete									
0520	Precast, 12" diameter pipe	B-6	12	2	Ea.	1,675	82.50	30.50	1,788	1,975
0530	18" diameter pipe		10	2.400		1,750	99	36.50	1,885.50	2,125
0540	24" diameter pipe		10	2.400		2,225	99	36.50	2,360.50	2,650
0550	30" diameter pipe		8	3		2,325	124	45.50	2,494.50	2,825
0560	36" diameter pipe	↓	8	3		2,450	124	45.50	2,619.50	2,950
0570	48" diameter pipe	B-69	7	6.857		6,450	285	232	6,967	7,800
0580	60" diameter pipe	"	6	8	↓	10,500	330	271	11,101	12,400

33 42 16 – Concrete Culverts

33 42 16.15 Oval Arch Culverts

0010	**OVAL ARCH CULVERTS**									
3000	Corrugated galvanized or aluminum, coated & paved									
3020	17" x 13", 16 ga., 15" equivalent	B-14	200	.240	L.F.	13.20	9.55	1.82	24.57	31
3040	21" x 15", 16 ga., 18" equivalent		150	.320		16.05	12.75	2.43	31.23	40
3060	28" x 20", 14 ga., 24" equivalent		125	.384		24	15.25	2.91	42.16	53
3080	35" x 24", 14 ga., 30" equivalent	↓	100	.480		29.50	19.10	3.64	52.24	66
3100	42" x 29", 12 ga., 36" equivalent	B-13	100	.560		35.50	23	7.35	65.85	82
3120	49" x 33", 12 ga., 42" equivalent		90	.622		41	25.50	8.20	74.70	93.50
3140	57" x 38", 12 ga., 48" equivalent	↓	75	.747	↓	57	30.50	9.80	97.30	120

For customer support on your Site Work & Landscape Cost Data, call 877.737.1594.

493

33 42 Culverts

33 42 16 – Concrete Culverts

33 42 16.15 Oval Arch Culverts	Crew	Daily Output	Labor-Hours	Unit	Material	2015 Bare Costs Labor	Equipment	Total	Total Incl O&P
3160	Steel, plain oval arch culverts, plain								
3180	17" x 13", 16 ga., 15" equivalent	B-14	225	.213	L.F.	11.95	8.50	1.62	22.07	28
3200	21" x 15", 16 ga., 18" equivalent		175	.274		14.45	10.90	2.08	27.43	35
3220	28" x 20", 14 ga., 24" equivalent	↓	150	.320		21.50	12.75	2.43	36.68	45.50
3240	35" x 24", 14 ga., 30" equivalent	B-13	108	.519		26.50	21.50	6.80	54.80	69
3260	42" x 29", 12 ga., 36" equivalent		108	.519		32	21.50	6.80	60.30	75.50
3280	49" x 33", 12 ga., 42" equivalent		92	.609		37	25	8	70	88
3300	57" x 38", 12 ga., 48" equivalent		75	.747	↓	51.50	30.50	9.80	91.80	114
3320	End sections, 17" x 13"		22	2.545	Ea.	144	104	33.50	281.50	355
3340	42" x 29"	↓	17	3.294	"	395	135	43.50	573.50	690
3360	Multi-plate arch, steel	B-20	1690	.014	Lb.	1.25	.60		1.85	2.30
8000	Bends or elbows, 6" diameter		30	.800	Ea.	77.50	33.50		111	137
8020	8" diameter		28	.857		96	36		132	161
8040	10" diameter	↓	25	.960		119	40.50		159.50	193
8060	12" diameter	B-21	20	1.400		146	60.50	6.90	213.40	261
8100	Wyes or tees, 6" diameter	B-20	27	.889		118	37.50		155.50	188
8120	8" diameter		25	.960		149	40.50		189.50	226
8140	10" diameter	↓	21	1.143		176	48		224	268
8160	12" diameter	B-21	18	1.556	↓	193	67.50	7.65	268.15	325

33 44 Storm Utility Water Drains

33 44 13 – Utility Area Drains

33 44 13.13 Catchbasins

		Crew	Daily Output	Labor-Hours	Unit	Material	Labor	Equipment	Total	Total Incl O&P
0010	**CATCHBASINS**									
0011	Not including footing & excavation									
1510	Grates only, for pipe bells, plastic, 4" diameter pipe	1 Clab	50	.160	Ea.	3.40	6		9.40	13
1514	6" diameter pipe		50	.160		10.90	6		16.90	21
1516	8" diameter pipe	↓	50	.160		11.05	6		17.05	21.50
1520	For beehive type grate, add					60%				
1550	Gray iron, 4" diam. pipe, light duty	1 Clab	50	.160		22	6		28	33.50
1551	Heavy duty		50	.160		28	6		34	40.50
1552	6" diameter, pipe, light duty		50	.160		38	6		44	51.50
1553	Heavy duty		50	.160		40	6		46	53.50
1554	8" diameter pipe, light duty		50	.160		53	6		59	68
1555	Heavy duty		50	.160		83	6		89	101
1556	10" diameter pipe, light duty		40	.200		73	7.50		80.50	92
1557	Heavy duty		40	.200		123	7.50		130.50	147
1558	12" diameter pipe, light duty		40	.200		87	7.50		94.50	107
1559	Heavy duty		40	.200		153	7.50		160.50	180
1560	15" diameter pipe, light duty		32	.250		150	9.40		159.40	179
1561	Heavy duty		32	.250		215	9.40		224.40	251
1562	18" diameter pipe, light duty		32	.250		162	9.40		171.40	192
1563	Heavy duty	↓	32	.250		275	9.40		284.40	320
1568	For beehive type grate, add					60%				
1570	Covers only for pipe bells, gray iron, med. duty									
1571	4" diameter pipe	1 Clab	50	.160	Ea.	21	6		27	32.50
1572	6" diameter pipe		50	.160		36	6		42	49
1573	8" diameter pipe		50	.160		70	6		76	86.50
1574	10" diameter pipe		40	.200		82	7.50		89.50	102
1575	12" diameter pipe		40	.200		100	7.50		107.50	122
1576	15" diameter pipe	↓	32	.250		138	9.40		147.40	166

33 44 Storm Utility Water Drains

33 44 13 – Utility Area Drains

33 44 13.13 Catchbasins

		Crew	Daily Output	Labor-Hours	Unit	Material	2015 Bare Costs Labor	Equipment	Total	Total Incl O&P
1577	18" diameter pipe	1 Clab	32	.250	Ea.	162	9.40		171.40	192
1578	24" diameter pipe	2 Clab	24	.667		215	25		240	276
1579	36" diameter pipe	"	24	.667	↓	291	25		316	360
1580	Curb inlet frame, grate, and curb box									
1582	Large 24" x 36" heavy duty	B-24	2	12	Ea.	520	520		1,040	1,350
1590	Small 10" x 21" medium duty	"	2	12		365	520		885	1,200
1600	Frames & grates, C.I., 24" square, 500 lb.	B-6	7.80	3.077		340	127	46.50	513.50	620
1700	26" D shape, 600 lb.		7	3.429		505	142	52	699	830
1800	Light traffic, 18" diameter, 100 lb.		10	2.400		123	99	36.50	258.50	325
1900	24" diameter, 300 lb.		8.70	2.759		196	114	42	352	435
2000	36" diameter, 900 lb.		5.80	4.138		570	171	63	804	955
2100	Heavy traffic, 24" diameter, 400 lb.		7.80	3.077		244	127	46.50	417.50	515
2200	36" diameter, 1150 lb.		3	8		795	330	121	1,246	1,525
2300	Mass. State standard, 26" diameter, 475 lb.		7	3.429		266	142	52	460	565
2400	30" diameter, 620 lb.		7	3.429		345	142	52	539	655
2500	Watertight, 24" diameter, 350 lb.		7.80	3.077		320	127	46.50	493.50	595
2600	26" diameter, 500 lb.		7	3.429		425	142	52	619	745
2700	32" diameter, 575 lb.	↓	6	4	↓	850	165	60.50	1,075.50	1,250
2800	3 piece cover & frame, 10" deep,									
2900	1200 lb., for heavy equipment	B-6	3	8	Ea.	1,050	330	121	1,501	1,825
3000	Raised for paving 1-1/4" to 2" high									
3100	4 piece expansion ring									
3200	20" to 26" diameter	1 Clab	3	2.667	Ea.	158	100		258	330
3300	30" to 36" diameter	"	3	2.667	"	217	100		317	395
3320	Frames and covers, existing, raised for paving, 2", including									
3340	row of brick, concrete collar, up to 12" wide frame	B-6	18	1.333	Ea.	45	55	20	120	156
3360	20" to 26" wide frame		11	2.182		67.50	90	33	190.50	249
3380	30" to 36" wide frame	↓	9	2.667		83.50	110	40.50	234	305
3400	Inverts, single channel brick	D-1	3	5.333		97	225		322	450
3500	Concrete		5	3.200		104	135		239	320
3600	Triple channel, brick		2	8		148	335		483	680
3700	Concrete	↓	3	5.333	↓	139	225		364	500

33 44 13.15 Remove and Replace Catch Basin Cover

		Crew	Daily Output	Labor-Hours	Unit	Material	2015 Bare Costs Labor	Equipment	Total	Total Incl O&P
0010	**REMOVE AND REPLACE CATCH BASIN COVER**									
0023	Remove catch basin cover	1 Clab	80	.100	Ea.		3.76		3.76	5.80
0033	Replace catch basin cover	"	80	.100	"		3.76		3.76	5.80

33 44 13.50 Stormwater Management

		Crew	Daily Output	Labor-Hours	Unit	Material	2015 Bare Costs Labor	Equipment	Total	Total Incl O&P
0010	**STORMWATER MANAGEMENT**									
0020	Allowance, add per SF of impervious surface				S.F.				3	3

33 46 Subdrainage

33 46 16 – Subdrainage Piping

33 46 16.25 Piping, Subdrainage, Corrugated Metal

		Crew	Daily Output	Labor-Hours	Unit	Material	2015 Bare Costs Labor	Equipment	Total	Total Incl O&P
0010	**PIPING, SUBDRAINAGE, CORRUGATED METAL**									
0021	Not including excavation and backfill									
2010	Aluminum, perforated									
2020	6" diameter, 18 ga.	B-20	380	.063	L.F.	6.50	2.65		9.15	11.25
2200	8" diameter, 16 ga.	"	370	.065		8.55	2.72		11.27	13.60
2220	10" diameter, 16 ga.	B-21	360	.078		10.70	3.37	.38	14.45	17.35
2240	12" diameter, 16 ga.	↓	285	.098	↓	11.95	4.26	.48	16.69	20

For customer support on your Site Work & Landscape Cost Data, call 877.737.1594.

495

33 46 16 – Subdrainage Piping

33 46 16.25 Piping, Subdrainage, Corrugated Metal	Crew	Daily Output	Labor-Hours	Unit	Material	2015 Bare Costs Labor	Equipment	Total	Total Incl O&P
2260 18" diameter, 16 ga.	B-21	205	.137	L.F.	17.95	5.90	.67	24.52	29.50
3000 Uncoated galvanized, perforated									
3020 6" diameter, 18 ga.	B-20	380	.063	L.F.	6.05	2.65		8.70	10.75
3200 8" diameter, 16 ga.	"	370	.065		8.30	2.72		11.02	13.35
3220 10" diameter, 16 ga.	B-21	360	.078		8.80	3.37	.38	12.55	15.30
3240 12" diameter, 16 ga.		285	.098		9.80	4.26	.48	14.54	17.85
3260 18" diameter, 16 ga.		205	.137		15	5.90	.67	21.57	26.50
4000 Steel, perforated, asphalt coated									
4020 6" diameter 18 ga.	B-20	380	.063	L.F.	6.50	2.65		9.15	11.25
4030 8" diameter 18 ga.	"	370	.065		8.55	2.72		11.27	13.60
4040 10" diameter 16 ga.	B-21	360	.078		10.05	3.37	.38	13.80	16.65
4050 12" diameter 16 ga.		285	.098		11.05	4.26	.48	15.79	19.25
4060 18" diameter 16 ga.		205	.137		17.10	5.90	.67	23.67	28.50

33 46 16.30 Piping, Subdrainage, Plastic

		Crew	Daily Output	Labor-Hours	Unit	Material	2015 Bare Costs Labor	Equipment	Total	Total Incl O&P
0010	PIPING, SUBDRAINAGE, PLASTIC									
0020	Not including excavation and backfill									
2100	Perforated PVC, 4" diameter	B-14	314	.153	L.F.	1.45	6.10	1.16	8.71	12.25
2110	6" diameter		300	.160		3.28	6.35	1.21	10.84	14.70
2120	8" diameter		290	.166		6.30	6.60	1.26	14.16	18.40
2130	10" diameter		280	.171		9.10	6.80	1.30	17.20	22
2140	12" diameter		270	.178		12.75	7.05	1.35	21.15	26.50

33 46 16.35 Piping, Subdrain., Corr. Plas. Tubing, Perf. or Plain

		Crew	Daily Output	Labor-Hours	Unit	Material	2015 Bare Costs Labor	Equipment	Total	Total Incl O&P
0010	PIPING, SUBDRAINAGE, CORR. PLASTIC TUBING, PERF. OR PLAIN									
0020	In rolls, not including excavation and backfill									
0030	3" diameter	2 Clab	1200	.013	L.F.	.45	.50		.95	1.27
0040	4" diameter		1200	.013		.50	.50		1	1.32
0041	With silt sock		1200	.013		1.25	.50		1.75	2.15
0050	5" diameter		900	.018		1.35	.67		2.02	2.52
0060	6" diameter		900	.018		1.43	.67		2.10	2.60
0080	8" diameter		700	.023		2.70	.86		3.56	4.29
0200	Fittings									
0230	Elbows, 3" diameter	1 Clab	32	.250	Ea.	4.65	9.40		14.05	19.55
0240	4" diameter		32	.250		5.20	9.40		14.60	20
0250	5" diameter		32	.250		6.50	9.40		15.90	21.50
0260	6" diameter		32	.250		9.25	9.40		18.65	24.50
0280	8" diameter		32	.250		12.20	9.40		21.60	28
0330	Tees, 3" diameter		27	.296		3.90	11.15		15.05	21.50
0340	4" diameter		27	.296		5.35	11.15		16.50	23
0350	5" diameter		27	.296		6.45	11.15		17.60	24.50
0360	6" diameter		27	.296		10	11.15		21.15	28
0370	6" x 6" x 4"		27	.296		9.95	11.15		21.10	28
0380	8" diameter		27	.296		16.05	11.15		27.20	35
0390	8" x 8" x 6"		27	.296		16.05	11.15		27.20	35
0430	End cap, 3" diameter		32	.250		2	9.40		11.40	16.65
0440	4" diameter		32	.250		2.48	9.40		11.88	17.20
0460	6" diameter		32	.250		5.75	9.40		15.15	21
0480	8" diameter		32	.250		6.40	9.40		15.80	21.50
0530	Coupler, 3" diameter		32	.250		2.25	9.40		11.65	16.95
0540	4" diameter		32	.250		1.98	9.40		11.38	16.65
0550	5" diameter		32	.250		2.50	9.40		11.90	17.20
0560	6" diameter		32	.250		4.23	9.40		13.63	19.10
0580	8" diameter		32	.250		5.90	9.40		15.30	21

33 46 16 – Subdrainage Piping

33 46 16.35 Piping, Subdrain., Corr. Plas. Tubing, Perf. or Plain	Crew	Daily Output	Labor-Hours	Unit	Material	2015 Bare Costs Labor	Equipment	Total	Total Incl O&P
0590	Heavy duty highway type, add				Ea.	10%				
0660	Reducer, 6" to 4"	1 Clab	32	.250		6	9.40		15.40	21
0680	8" to 6"		32	.250		10.30	9.40		19.70	26
0730	"Y" fitting, 3" diameter		27	.296		5	11.15		16.15	22.50
0740	4" diameter		27	.296		7.70	11.15		18.85	25.50
0750	5" diameter		27	.296		9.90	11.15		21.05	28
0760	6" diameter		27	.296		12.25	11.15		23.40	30.50
0780	8" diameter		27	.296		26	11.15		37.15	45.50
0860	Silt sock only for above tubing, 6" diameter				L.F.	3.65			3.65	4.02
0880	8" diameter				"	6			6	6.60

33 46 26 – Geotextile Subsurface Drainage Filtration

33 46 26.10 Geotextiles for Subsurface Drainage

		Crew	Daily Output	Labor-Hours	Unit	Material	Labor	Equipment	Total	Total Incl O&P
0010	**GEOTEXTILES FOR SUBSURFACE DRAINAGE**									
0100	Fabric, laid in trench, polypropylene, ideal conditions	2 Clab	2400	.007	S.Y.	1.50	.25		1.75	2.04
0110	Adverse conditions		1600	.010	"	1.50	.38		1.88	2.23
0170	Fabric ply bonded to 3 dimen. nylon mat, .4" thick, ideal conditions		2000	.008	S.F.	.23	.30		.53	.71
0180	Adverse conditions		1200	.013	"	.29	.50		.79	1.08
0185	Soil drainage mat on vertical wall, 0.44" thick		265	.060	S.Y.	1.84	2.27		4.11	5.50
0188	0.25" thick		300	.053	"	.81	2.01		2.82	3.98
0190	0.8" thick, ideal conditions		2400	.007	S.F.	.22	.25		.47	.63
0200	Adverse conditions		1600	.010	"	.37	.38		.75	.98
0300	Drainage material, 3/4" gravel fill in trench	B-6	260	.092	C.Y.	24	3.81	1.40	29.21	34
0400	Pea stone	"	260	.092	"	23.50	3.81	1.40	28.71	33.50

33 47 13 – Pond and Reservoir Liners

33 47 13.53 Reservoir Liners HDPE

		Crew	Daily Output	Labor-Hours	Unit	Material	Labor	Equipment	Total	Total Incl O&P
0010	**RESERVOIR LINERS HDPE**									
0011	Membrane lining									
1100	30 mil thick	3 Skwk	1850	.013	S.F.	.50	.63		1.13	1.52
1200	60 mil thick		1600	.015	"	.57	.73		1.30	1.76
1220	60 mil thick		1.60	15	M.S.F.	570	730		1,300	1,750
1300	120 mil thick		1440	.017	S.F.	.70	.81		1.51	2.02

33 49 13 – Storm Drainage Manholes, Frames, and Covers

33 49 13.10 Storm Drainage Manholes, Frames and Covers

		Crew	Daily Output	Labor-Hours	Unit	Material	Labor	Equipment	Total	Total Incl O&P
0010	**STORM DRAINAGE MANHOLES, FRAMES & COVERS**									
0020	Excludes footing, excavation, backfill (See line items for frame & cover)									
0050	Brick, 4' inside diameter, 4' deep	D-1	1	16	Ea.	520	675		1,195	1,600
0100	6' deep		.70	22.857		740	960		1,700	2,300
0150	8' deep		.50	32		955	1,350		2,305	3,100
0200	For depths over 8', add		4	4	V.L.F.	83.50	168		251.50	350
0400	Concrete blocks (radial), 4' I.D., 4' deep		1.50	10.667	Ea.	415	450		865	1,150
0500	6' deep		1	16		565	675		1,240	1,650
0600	8' deep		.70	22.857		710	960		1,670	2,250
0700	For depths over 8', add		5.50	2.909	V.L.F.	77	122		199	272
0800	Concrete, cast in place, 4' x 4', 8" thick, 4' deep	C-14H	2	24	Ea.	505	1,100	15.60	1,620.60	2,275
0900	6' deep		1.50	32		730	1,475	21	2,226	3,100

For customer support on your Site Work & Landscape Cost Data, call 877.737.1594.

497

33 49 Storm Drainage Structures

33 49 13 – Storm Drainage Manholes, Frames, and Covers

33 49 13.10 Storm Drainage Manholes, Frames and Covers

		Crew	Daily Output	Labor-Hours	Unit	Material	2015 Bare Costs Labor	Equipment	Total	Total Incl O&P
1000	8' deep	C-14H	1	48	Ea.	1,050	2,225	31	3,306	4,575
1100	For depths over 8', add	↓	8	6	V.L.F.	119	278	3.90	400.90	560
1110	Precast, 4' I.D., 4' deep	B-22	4.10	7.317	Ea.	725	320	50.50	1,095.50	1,350
1120	6' deep		3	10		925	440	69	1,434	1,775
1130	8' deep		2	15		1,075	660	103	1,838	2,300
1140	For depths over 8', add		16	1.875	V.L.F.	127	82.50	12.90	222.40	280
1150	5' I.D., 4' deep	B-6	3	8	Ea.	1,650	330	121	2,101	2,450
1160	6' deep		2	12		1,925	495	182	2,602	3,075
1170	8' deep		1.50	16		2,400	660	243	3,303	3,925
1180	For depths over 8', add		12	2	V.L.F.	280	82.50	30.50	393	470
1190	6' I.D., 4' deep		2	12	Ea.	2,150	495	182	2,827	3,325
1200	6' deep		1.50	16		2,600	660	243	3,503	4,125
1210	8' deep		1	24		3,200	990	365	4,555	5,425
1220	For depths over 8', add	↓	8	3	V.L.F.	380	124	45.50	549.50	655
1250	Slab tops, precast, 8" thick									
1300	4' diameter manhole	B-6	8	3	Ea.	252	124	45.50	421.50	515
1400	5' diameter manhole		7.50	3.200		410	132	48.50	590.50	710
1500	6' diameter manhole	↓	7	3.429		635	142	52	829	975
3800	Steps, heavyweight cast iron, 7" x 9"	1 Bric	40	.200		19.25	9.25		28.50	35
3900	8" x 9"		40	.200		23	9.25		32.25	39.50
3928	12" x 10-1/2"		40	.200		27	9.25		36.25	43.50
4000	Standard sizes, galvanized steel		40	.200		22	9.25		31.25	38
4100	Aluminum		40	.200		24	9.25		33.25	40.50
4150	Polyethylene		40	.200		26	9.25		35.25	42.50
4210	Rubber boot 6" diam. or smaller	1 Clab	32	.250		82	9.40		91.40	104
4215	8" diam.		24	.333		93.50	12.55		106.05	122
4220	10" diam.		19	.421		107	15.85		122.85	143
4225	12" diam.		16	.500		136	18.80		154.80	179
4230	16" diam.		15	.533		174	20		194	222
4235	18" diam.		15	.533		201	20		221	252
4240	24" diam.		14	.571		230	21.50		251.50	286
4245	30" diam.	↓	12	.667	↓	300	25		325	370

33 49 23 – Storm Drainage Water Retention Structures

33 49 23.10 HDPE Storm Water Infiltration Chamber

		Crew	Daily Output	Labor-Hours	Unit	Material	2015 Bare Costs Labor	Equipment	Total	Total Incl O&P
0010	**HDPE STORM WATER INFILTRATION CHAMBER**									
0020	Not including excavation or backfill									
0100	11" H X 16" W	2 Clab	300	.053	L.F.	7	2.01		9.01	10.80
0110	12" H X 22" W		300	.053		9.50	2.01		11.51	13.55
0120	12" H X 34" W		300	.053		11.25	2.01		13.26	15.50
0130	16" H X 34" W		300	.053		23	2.01		25.01	28
0140	30" H X 52" W	↓	270	.059	↓	38.50	2.23		40.73	46

498

For customer support on your Site Work & Landscape Cost Data, call 877.737.1594.

33 51 Natural-Gas Distribution

33 51 13 – Natural-Gas Piping

33 51 13.10 Piping, Gas Service and Distribution, P.E.

		Crew	Daily Output	Labor-Hours	Unit	Material	2015 Bare Costs Labor	Equipment	Total	Total Incl O&P
0010	**PIPING, GAS SERVICE AND DISTRIBUTION, POLYETHYLENE**									
0020	Not including excavation or backfill									
1000	60 psi coils, compression coupling @ 100', 1/2" diameter, SDR 11	B-20A	608	.053	L.F.	.45	2.41		2.86	4.16
1010	1" diameter, SDR 11		544	.059		1.05	2.69		3.74	5.25
1040	1-1/4" diameter, SDR 11		544	.059		1.62	2.69		4.31	5.85
1100	2" diameter, SDR 11		488	.066		2.82	3		5.82	7.65
1160	3" diameter, SDR 11		408	.078		6.45	3.59		10.04	12.55
1500	60 PSI 40' joints with coupling, 3" diameter, SDR 11	B-21A	408	.098		10.05	4.60	1.16	15.81	19.35
1540	4" diameter, SDR 11		352	.114		14.25	5.35	1.35	20.95	25
1600	6" diameter, SDR 11		328	.122		33.50	5.70	1.44	40.64	47.50
1640	8" diameter, SDR 11		272	.147		51.50	6.90	1.74	60.14	69

33 51 13.20 Piping, Gas Service and Distribution, Steel

		Crew	Daily Output	Labor-Hours	Unit	Material	2015 Bare Costs Labor	Equipment	Total	Total Incl O&P
0010	**PIPING, GAS SERVICE & DISTRIBUTION, STEEL**									
0020	Not including excavation or backfill, tar coated and wrapped									
4000	Pipe schedule 40, plain end									
4040	1" diameter	Q-4	300	.107	L.F.	4.75	5.95	.19	10.89	14.45
4080	2" diameter		280	.114		7.45	6.40	.21	14.06	18.10
4120	3" diameter		260	.123		12.35	6.90	.22	19.47	24
4160	4" diameter	B-35	255	.188		16.05	8.85	2.79	27.69	34
4200	5" diameter		220	.218		23.50	10.25	3.24	36.99	44.50
4240	6" diameter		180	.267		28.50	12.50	3.96	44.96	55
4280	8" diameter		140	.343		45	16.10	5.10	66.20	79.50
4320	10" diameter		100	.480		117	22.50	7.10	146.60	171
4360	12" diameter		80	.600		130	28	8.90	166.90	196
4400	14" diameter		75	.640		139	30	9.50	178.50	208
4440	16" diameter		70	.686		152	32	10.20	194.20	227
4480	18" diameter		65	.738		195	34.50	10.95	240.45	279
4520	20" diameter		60	.800		305	37.50	11.85	354.35	405
4560	24" diameter		50	.960		345	45	14.25	404.25	465
6000	Schedule 80, plain end									
6002	4" diameter	B-35	144	.333	L.F.	46.50	15.65	4.95	67.10	81
6004	5" diameter		140	.343		68	16.10	5.10	89.20	105
6006	6" diameter		126	.381		93.50	17.85	5.65	117	137
6008	8" diameter		108	.444		125	21	6.60	152.60	176
6010	10" diameter		90	.533		187	25	7.90	219.90	253
6012	12" diameter		72	.667		250	31.50	9.90	291.40	335
8008	Elbow, weld joint, standard weight									
8020	4" diameter	Q-16	6.80	3.529	Ea.	96	193	8.45	297.45	405
8022	5" diameter		5.40	4.444		207	243	10.65	460.65	610
8024	6" diameter		4.50	5.333		212	292	12.80	516.80	685
8026	8" diameter		3.40	7.059		400	385	16.95	801.95	1,050
8028	10" diameter		2.70	8.889		595	485	21.50	1,101.50	1,425
8030	12" diameter		2.30	10.435		885	570	25	1,480	1,875
8032	14" diameter		1.80	13.333		1,450	730	32	2,212	2,725
8034	16" diameter		1.50	16		2,000	875	38.50	2,913.50	3,575
8036	18" diameter		1.40	17.143		2,300	940	41	3,281	4,000
8038	20" diameter		1.20	20		3,675	1,100	48	4,823	5,750
8040	24" diameter		1.02	23.529		5,200	1,300	56.50	6,556.50	7,725
8100	Extra heavy									
8102	4" diameter	Q-16	5.30	4.528	Ea.	192	248	10.85	450.85	600
8104	5" diameter		4.20	5.714		415	315	13.70	743.70	945
8106	6" diameter		3.50	6.857		425	375	16.45	816.45	1,050

For customer support on your Site Work & Landscape Cost Data, call 877.737.1594.

499

33 51 Natural-Gas Distribution

33 51 13 – Natural-Gas Piping

33 51 13.20 Piping, Gas Service and Distribution, Steel		Crew	Daily Output	Labor-Hours	Unit	Material	2015 Bare Costs Labor	Equipment	Total	Total Incl O&P
8108	8" diameter	Q-16	2.60	9.231	Ea.	600	505	22	1,127	1,450
8110	10" diameter		2.10	11.429		795	625	27.50	1,447.50	1,850
8112	12" diameter		1.80	13.333		1,175	730	32	1,937	2,425
8114	14" diameter		1.40	17.143		1,950	940	41	2,931	3,600
8116	16" diameter		1.20	20		2,675	1,100	48	3,823	4,650
8118	18" diameter		1.10	21.818		3,075	1,200	52.50	4,327.50	5,225
8120	20" diameter		.94	25.532		4,900	1,400	61.50	6,361.50	7,550
8122	24" diameter		.80	30		6,925	1,650	72	8,647	10,200
8200	Malleable, standard weight									
8202	4" diameter	B-20	12	2	Ea.	545	84		629	730
8204	5" diameter		9	2.667		625	112		737	860
8206	6" diameter		8	3		790	126		916	1,075
8208	8" diameter		6	4		1,475	168		1,643	1,875
8210	10" diameter		5	4.800		1,425	201		1,626	1,850
8212	12" diameter		4	6		1,575	252		1,827	2,125
8300	Extra heavy									
8302	4" diameter	B-20	12	2	Ea.	1,100	84		1,184	1,325
8304	5" diameter	B-21	9	3.111		1,250	135	15.30	1,400.30	1,600
8306	6" diameter		8	3.500		1,500	152	17.20	1,669.20	1,900
8308	8" diameter		6	4.667		1,875	202	23	2,100	2,375
8310	10" diameter		5	5.600		2,250	243	27.50	2,520.50	2,875
8312	12" diameter		4	7		2,525	305	34.50	2,864.50	3,275
8500	Tee weld, standard weight									
8510	4" diameter	Q-16	4.50	5.333	Ea.	177	292	12.80	481.80	650
8512	5" diameter		3.60	6.667		292	365	16	673	890
8514	6" diameter		3	8		305	440	19.20	764.20	1,025
8516	8" diameter		2.30	10.435		530	570	25	1,125	1,475
8518	10" diameter		1.80	13.333		1,050	730	32	1,812	2,275
8520	12" diameter		1.50	16		1,450	875	38.50	2,363.50	2,975
8522	14" diameter		1.20	20		2,550	1,100	48	3,698	4,525
8524	16" diameter		1	24		2,875	1,325	57.50	4,257.50	5,200
8526	18" diameter		.90	26.667		4,525	1,450	64	6,039	7,250
8528	20" diameter		.80	30		7,150	1,650	72	8,872	10,400
8530	24" diameter		.70	34.286		9,225	1,875	82.50	11,182.50	13,000
8810	Malleable, standard weight									
8812	4" diameter	B-20	8	3	Ea.	925	126		1,051	1,225
8814	5"	B-21	6	4.667		1,275	202	23	1,500	1,725
8816	6"		5.30	5.283		1,100	229	26	1,355	1,600
8818	8" diameter		4	7		1,600	305	34.50	1,939.50	2,250
8820	10"		3.30	8.485		2,500	370	42	2,912	3,325
8822	12" diameter		2.70	10.370		2,925	450	51	3,426	3,950
8900	Extra heavy									
8902	4" diameter	B-20	8	3	Ea.	1,400	126		1,526	1,725
8904	5"	B-21	6	4.667		1,900	202	23	2,125	2,425
8906	6"		5.30	5.283		1,650	229	26	1,905	2,200
8908	8" diameter		4	7		2,000	305	34.50	2,339.50	2,675
8910	10"		3.30	8.485		2,500	370	42	2,912	3,325
8912	12" diameter		2.70	10.370		2,925	450	51	3,426	3,950

33 51 Natural-Gas Distribution

33 51 33 – Natural-Gas Metering

33 51 33.10 Piping, Valves and Meters, Gas Distribution	Crew	Daily Output	Labor-Hours	Unit	Material	2015 Bare Costs Labor	Equipment	Total	Total Incl O&P
0010 **PIPING, VALVES & METERS, GAS DISTRIBUTION**									
0020 Not including excavation or backfill									
0100 Gas stops, with or without checks									
0140 1-1/4" size	1 Plum	12	.667	Ea.	64	39		103	130
0180 1-1/2" size		10	.800		80.50	47		127.50	160
0200 2" size	↓	8	1	↓	129	58.50		187.50	231
0600 Pressure regulator valves, iron and bronze									
0640 1-1/2" diameter	1 Plum	13	.615	Ea.	150	36		186	220
0680 2" diameter	"	11	.727		284	42.50		326.50	375
0700 3" diameter	Q-1	13	1.231		570	65		635	730
0740 4" diameter	"	8	2	↓	1,925	106		2,031	2,275
2000 Lubricated semi-steel plug valve									
2040 3/4" diameter	1 Plum	16	.500	Ea.	560	29.50		589.50	660
2080 1" diameter		14	.571		375	33.50		408.50	460
2100 1-1/4" diameter		12	.667		415	39		454	515
2140 1-1/2" diameter		11	.727		440	42.50		482.50	550
2180 2" diameter	↓	8	1		535	58.50		593.50	680
2300 2-1/2" diameter	Q-1	5	3.200		590	169		759	900
2340 3" diameter	"	4.50	3.556	↓	845	188		1,033	1,225

33 52 Liquid Fuel Distribution

33 52 16 – Gasoline Distribution

33 52 16.13 Gasoline Piping

	Crew	Daily Output	Labor-Hours	Unit	Material	2015 Bare Costs Labor	Equipment	Total	Total Incl O&P
0010 **GASOLINE PIPING**									
0020 Primary containment pipe, fiberglass-reinforced									
0030 Plastic pipe 15' & 30' lengths									
0040 2" diameter	Q-6	425	.056	L.F.	5.95	3.15		9.10	11.25
0050 3" diameter		400	.060		10.35	3.35		13.70	16.45
0060 4" diameter	↓	375	.064	↓	13.65	3.57		17.22	20.50
0100 Fittings									
0110 Elbows, 90° & 45°, bell-ends, 2"	Q-6	24	1	Ea.	43.50	56		99.50	132
0120 3" diameter		22	1.091		55	61		116	153
0130 4" diameter		20	1.200		70	67		137	178
0200 Tees, bell ends, 2"		21	1.143		60.50	63.50		124	163
0210 3" diameter		18	1.333		64	74.50		138.50	183
0220 4" diameter		15	1.600		84	89		173	228
0230 Flanges bell ends, 2"		24	1		33.50	56		89.50	121
0240 3" diameter		22	1.091		39	61		100	135
0250 4" diameter		20	1.200		45	67		112	151
0260 Sleeve couplings, 2"		21	1.143		12.40	63.50		75.90	110
0270 3" diameter		18	1.333		17.80	74.50		92.30	132
0280 4" diameter		15	1.600		23	89		112	160
0290 Threaded adapters 2"		21	1.143		17.95	63.50		81.45	116
0300 3" diameter		18	1.333		34	74.50		108.50	150
0310 4" diameter		15	1.600		38	89		127	177
0320 Reducers, 2"		27	.889		27.50	49.50		77	105
0330 3" diameter		22	1.091		27.50	61		88.50	122
0340 4" diameter	↓	20	1.200	↓	37	67		104	142
1010 Gas station product line for secondary containment (double wall)									
1100 Fiberglass reinforced plastic pipe 25' lengths									

For customer support on your Site Work & Landscape Cost Data, call 877.737.1594.

501

33 52 16 – Gasoline Distribution

33 52 16.13 Gasoline Piping		Crew	Daily Output	Labor-Hours	Unit	Material	2015 Bare Costs Labor	Equipment	Total	Total Incl O&P
1120	Pipe, plain end, 3" diameter	Q-6	375	.064	L.F.	26.50	3.57		30.07	34.50
1130	4" diameter		350	.069		32	3.82		35.82	41.50
1140	5" diameter		325	.074		35.50	4.12		39.62	45
1150	6" diameter		300	.080		39	4.46		43.46	50
1200	Fittings									
1230	Elbows, 90° & 45°, 3" diameter	Q-6	18	1.333	Ea.	136	74.50		210.50	262
1240	4" diameter		16	1.500		167	83.50		250.50	310
1250	5" diameter		14	1.714		184	95.50		279.50	345
1260	6" diameter		12	2		204	112		316	390
1270	Tees, 3" diameter		15	1.600		166	89		255	315
1280	4" diameter		12	2		202	112		314	390
1290	5" diameter		9	2.667		315	149		464	575
1300	6" diameter		6	4		375	223		598	750
1310	Couplings, 3" diameter		18	1.333		55	74.50		129.50	173
1320	4" diameter		16	1.500		119	83.50		202.50	257
1330	5" diameter		14	1.714		214	95.50		309.50	380
1340	6" diameter		12	2		315	112		427	520
1350	Cross-over nipples, 3" diameter		18	1.333		10.60	74.50		85.10	124
1360	4" diameter		16	1.500		12.70	83.50		96.20	140
1370	5" diameter		14	1.714		15.90	95.50		111.40	162
1380	6" diameter		12	2		19.05	112		131.05	189
1400	Telescoping, reducers, concentric 4" x 3"		18	1.333		48	74.50		122.50	165
1410	5" x 4"		17	1.412		95.50	78.50		174	224
1420	6" x 5"		16	1.500		234	83.50		317.50	385

33 61 Hydronic Energy Distribution

33 61 13 – Underground Hydronic Energy Distribution

33 61 13.10 Chilled/HVAC Hot Water Distribution

		Crew	Daily Output	Labor-Hours	Unit	Material	2015 Bare Costs Labor	Equipment	Total	Total Incl O&P
0010	**CHILLED/HVAC HOT WATER DISTRIBUTION**									
1005	Pipe, black steel w/2" polyurethane insul, 20' lengths									
1010	Align & tackweld on sleepers (NIC), 1-1/4" diameter	B-35	864	.056	L.F.	30	2.61	.82	33.43	38
1020	1-1/2"		824	.058		33.50	2.73	.86	37.09	42
1030	2"		680	.071		35	3.31	1.05	39.36	44.50
1040	2-1/2"		560	.086		38	4.02	1.27	43.29	49
1050	3"		528	.091		39	4.26	1.35	44.61	50.50
1060	4"		384	.125		42.50	5.85	1.86	50.21	58
1070	5"		360	.133		63	6.25	1.98	71.23	80.50
1080	6"		296	.162		68.50	7.60	2.41	78.51	90
1090	8"		264	.182		91.50	8.55	2.70	102.75	117
1100	12"		216	.222		153	10.40	3.30	166.70	188
1110	On trench bottom, 18" diameter		176.13	.273		236	12.80	4.04	252.84	284
1120	24"	B-35A	145	.386		335	17.60	11.05	363.65	405
1130	30"		121	.463		510	21	13.25	544.25	605
1140	36"		100	.560		680	25.50	16.05	721.55	805
1150	Elbows, on sleepers, 1-1/2" diameter	Q-17	21	.762	Ea.	780	41	2.75	823.75	925
1160	3"		9.36	1.709		1,025	92	6.15	1,123.15	1,275
1170	4"		8	2		1,250	108	7.20	1,365.20	1,550
1180	6"		6	2.667		1,625	143	9.65	1,777.65	2,000
1190	8"		4.64	3.448		1,975	185	12.45	2,172.45	2,450
1200	Tees, 1-1/2" diameter		17	.941		1,550	50.50	3.40	1,603.90	1,775
1210	3"		8.50	1.882		1,925	101	6.80	2,032.80	2,275

33 61 Hydronic Energy Distribution

33 61 13 – Underground Hydronic Energy Distribution

33 61 13.10 Chilled/HVAC Hot Water Distribution		Crew	Daily Output	Labor-Hours	Unit	Material	2015 Bare Costs Labor	2015 Bare Costs Equipment	Total	Total Incl O&P
1220	4"	Q-17	6	2.667	Ea.	2,075	143	9.65	2,227.65	2,500
1230	6"	Q-17A	6.72	3.571		2,600	190	106	2,896	3,250
1240	8"	"	6.40	3.750		3,050	199	111	3,360	3,775
1250	Reducer, 3" diameter	Q-17	16	1		410	54	3.61	467.61	535
1260	4"		12	1.333		490	71.50	4.81	566.31	650
1270	6"		12	1.333		695	71.50	4.81	771.31	880
1280	8"	↓	10	1.600		900	86	5.80	991.80	1,125
1290	Anchor, 4" diameter	Q-17A	12	2		1,200	106	59.50	1,365.50	1,525
1300	6"		10.50	2.286		1,375	121	68	1,564	1,750
1310	8"	↓	10	2.400		1,525	127	71	1,723	1,975
1320	Cap, 1-1/2" diameter	Q-17	42	.381		125	20.50	1.38	146.88	170
1330	3"		14.64	1.093		169	59	3.95	231.95	279
1340	4"		16	1		194	54	3.61	251.61	298
1350	6"		16	1		335	54	3.61	392.61	450
1360	8"		13.50	1.185		425	63.50	4.28	492.78	565
1365	12"	↓	11	1.455		625	78	5.25	708.25	810
1370	Elbow, fittings on trench bottom, 12" diameter	Q-17A	12	2		3,000	106	59.50	3,165.50	3,525
1380	18"		8	3		5,375	159	89	5,623	6,250
1390	24"		6	4		7,650	212	119	7,981	8,850
1400	30"		5.36	4.478		10,500	238	133	10,871	12,000
1410	36"		4	6		14,200	320	178	14,698	16,300
1420	Tee, 12" diameter		6.72	3.571		3,950	190	106	4,246	4,750
1430	18"		6	4		6,600	212	119	6,931	7,700
1440	24"		4.64	5.172		10,300	275	153	10,728	11,900
1450	30"		4.16	5.769		15,800	305	171	16,276	18,000
1460	36"		3.36	7.143		23,200	380	212	23,792	26,300
1470	Reducer, 12" diameter		10.64	2.256		1,250	120	67	1,437	1,625
1480	18"		9.68	2.479		2,000	132	73.50	2,205.50	2,475
1490	24"		8	3		3,075	159	89	3,323	3,725
1500	30"		7.04	3.409		4,775	181	101	5,057	5,625
1510	36"		5.36	4.478		6,800	238	133	7,171	7,975
1520	Anchor, 12" diameter		11	2.182		1,600	116	64.50	1,780.50	2,000
1530	18"		6.72	3.571		1,700	190	106	1,996	2,275
1540	24"		6.32	3.797		2,375	202	113	2,690	3,025
1550	30"		4.64	5.172		2,875	275	153	3,303	3,750
1560	36"	↓	4	6	↓	3,525	320	178	4,023	4,550
1565	Weld in place and install shrink collar									
1570	On sleepers, 1-1/2" diameter	Q-17A	18.50	1.297	Ea.	29	69	38.50	136.50	179
1580	3"		6.72	3.571		49.50	190	106	345.50	460
1590	4"		5.36	4.478		49.50	238	133	420.50	560
1600	6"		4	6		58	320	178	556	740
1610	8"		3.36	7.143		89.50	380	212	681.50	905
1620	12"		2.64	9.091		116	485	270	871	1,150
1630	On trench bottom, 18" diameter		2	12		174	635	355	1,164	1,550
1640	24"		1.36	17.647		232	935	525	1,692	2,250
1650	30"		1.04	23.077		290	1,225	685	2,200	2,925
1660	36"	↓	1	24	↓	350	1,275	710	2,335	3,100

For customer support on your Site Work & Landscape Cost Data, call 877.737.1594.

503

33 61 13.20 Pipe Conduit, Prefabricated/Preinsulated		Crew	Daily Output	Labor-Hours	Unit	Material	2015 Bare Costs			Total	Total Incl O&P
							Labor	Equipment		Total	
0010	**PIPE CONDUIT, PREFABRICATED/PREINSULATED**										
0020	Does not include trenching, fittings or crane.										
0300	For cathodic protection, add 12 to 14%										
0310	of total built-up price (casing plus service pipe)										
0580	Polyurethane insulated system, 250°F. max. temp.										
0620	Black steel service pipe, standard wt., 1/2" insulation										
0660	3/4" diam. pipe size	Q-17	54	.296	L.F.	57	15.95	1.07	74.02	88
0670	1" diam. pipe size		50	.320		63	17.20	1.16	81.36	96.50
0680	1-1/4" diam. pipe size		47	.340		70	18.30	1.23	89.53	106
0690	1-1/2" diam. pipe size		45	.356		76	19.10	1.28	96.38	114
0700	2" diam. pipe size		42	.381		79	20.50	1.38	100.88	119
0710	2-1/2" diam. pipe size		34	.471		80	25.50	1.70	107.20	128
0720	3" diam. pipe size		28	.571		93	30.50	2.06	125.56	151
0730	4" diam. pipe size		22	.727		117	39	2.63	158.63	191
0740	5" diam. pipe size		18	.889		149	48	3.21	200.21	240
0750	6" diam. pipe size	Q-18	23	1.043		173	58	2.50	233.50	282
0760	8" diam. pipe size		19	1.263		254	70.50	3.03	327.53	390
0770	10" diam. pipe size		16	1.500		320	83.50	3.60	407.10	485
0780	12" diam. pipe size		13	1.846		400	103	4.43	507.43	600
0790	14" diam. pipe size		11	2.182		445	122	5.25	572.25	680
0800	16" diam. pipe size		10	2.400		510	134	5.75	649.75	775
0810	18" diam. pipe size		8	3		590	167	7.20	764.20	910
0820	20" diam. pipe size		7	3.429		655	191	8.25	854.25	1,025
0830	24" diam. pipe size		6	4		805	223	9.60	1,037.60	1,225
0900	For 1" thick insulation, add					10%				
0940	For 1-1/2" thick insulation, add					13%				
0980	For 2" thick insulation, add					20%				
1500	Gland seal for system, 3/4" diam. pipe size	Q-17	32	.500	Ea.	775	27	1.81	803.81	890
1510	1" diam. pipe size		32	.500		775	27	1.81	803.81	890
1540	1-1/4" diam. pipe size		30	.533		825	28.50	1.93	855.43	955
1550	1-1/2" diam. pipe size		30	.533		825	28.50	1.93	855.43	955
1560	2" diam. pipe size		28	.571		980	30.50	2.06	1,012.56	1,125
1570	2-1/2" diam. pipe size		26	.615		1,050	33	2.22	1,085.22	1,225
1580	3" diam. pipe size		24	.667		1,125	36	2.41	1,163.41	1,300
1590	4" diam. pipe size		22	.727		1,350	39	2.63	1,391.63	1,525
1600	5" diam. pipe size		19	.842		1,650	45.50	3.04	1,698.54	1,900
1610	6" diam. pipe size	Q-18	26	.923		1,750	51.50	2.22	1,803.72	2,000
1620	8" diam. pipe size		25	.960		2,050	53.50	2.30	2,105.80	2,325
1630	10" diam. pipe size		23	1.043		2,375	58	2.50	2,435.50	2,725
1640	12" diam. pipe size		21	1.143		2,625	63.50	2.74	2,691.24	3,000
1650	14" diam. pipe size		19	1.263		2,950	70.50	3.03	3,023.53	3,350
1660	16" diam. pipe size		18	1.333		3,500	74.50	3.20	3,577.70	3,975
1670	18" diam. pipe size		16	1.500		3,700	83.50	3.60	3,787.10	4,200
1680	20" diam. pipe size		14	1.714		4,200	95.50	4.11	4,299.61	4,775
1690	24" diam. pipe size		12	2		4,675	112	4.80	4,791.80	5,325
2000	Elbow, 45° for system									
2020	3/4" diam. pipe size	Q-17	14	1.143	Ea.	485	61.50	4.13	550.63	635
2040	1" diam. pipe size		13	1.231		500	66	4.44	570.44	655
2050	1-1/4" diam. pipe size		11	1.455		570	78	5.25	653.25	750
2060	1-1/2" diam. pipe size		9	1.778		595	95.50	6.40	696.90	805
2070	2" diam. pipe size		6	2.667		620	143	9.65	772.65	915
2080	2-1/2" diam. pipe size		4	4		670	215	14.45	899.45	1,075

33 61 Hydronic Energy Distribution

33 61 13 – Underground Hydronic Energy Distribution

33 61 13.20 Pipe Conduit, Prefabricated/Preinsulated	Crew	Daily Output	Labor-Hours	Unit	Material	2015 Bare Costs Labor	Equipment	Total	Total Incl O&P
2090	3" diam. pipe size	Q-17	3.50	4.571	Ea.	775	246	16.50	1,037.50	1,250
2100	4" diam. pipe size		3	5.333		905	287	19.25	1,211.25	1,450
2110	5" diam. pipe size		2.80	5.714		1,175	305	20.50	1,500.50	1,775
2120	6" diam. pipe size	Q-18	4	6		1,325	335	14.40	1,674.40	1,975
2130	8" diam. pipe size		3	8		1,925	445	19.20	2,389.20	2,800
2140	10" diam. pipe size		2.40	10		2,350	560	24	2,934	3,450
2150	12" diam. pipe size		2	12		3,075	670	29	3,774	4,425
2160	14" diam. pipe size		1.80	13.333		3,825	745	32	4,602	5,375
2170	16" diam. pipe size		1.60	15		4,550	835	36	5,421	6,350
2180	18" diam. pipe size		1.30	18.462		5,725	1,025	44.50	6,794.50	7,900
2190	20" diam. pipe size		1	24		7,200	1,350	57.50	8,607.50	10,000
2200	24" diam. pipe size		.70	34.286		9,050	1,900	82.50	11,032.50	12,900
2260	For elbow, 90°, add					25%				
2300	For tee, straight, add					85%	30%			
2340	For tee, reducing, add					170%	30%			
2380	For weldolet, straight, add					50%				

33 63 Steam Energy Distribution

33 63 13 – Underground Steam and Condensate Distribution Piping

33 63 13.10 Calcium Silicate Insulated System

		Crew	Daily Output	Labor-Hours	Unit	Material	2015 Bare Costs Labor	Equipment	Total	Total Incl O&P
0010	**CALCIUM SILICATE INSULATED SYSTEM**									
0011	High temp. (1200 degrees F)									
2840	Steel casing with protective exterior coating									
2850	6-5/8" diameter	Q-18	52	.462	L.F.	106	25.50	1.11	132.61	157
2860	8-5/8" diameter		50	.480		115	27	1.15	143.15	169
2870	10-3/4" diameter		47	.511		135	28.50	1.23	164.73	193
2880	12-3/4" diameter		44	.545		147	30.50	1.31	178.81	209
2890	14" diameter		41	.585		166	32.50	1.40	199.90	234
2900	16" diameter		39	.615		178	34.50	1.48	213.98	250
2910	18" diameter		36	.667		196	37	1.60	234.60	274
2920	20" diameter		34	.706		221	39.50	1.69	262.19	305
2930	22" diameter		32	.750		305	42	1.80	348.80	400
2940	24" diameter		29	.828		350	46	1.99	397.99	455
2950	26" diameter		26	.923		400	51.50	2.22	453.72	520
2960	28" diameter		23	1.043		495	58	2.50	555.50	635
2970	30" diameter		21	1.143		530	63.50	2.74	596.24	685
2980	32" diameter		19	1.263		595	70.50	3.03	668.53	765
2990	34" diameter		18	1.333		600	74.50	3.20	677.70	775
3000	36" diameter		16	1.500		645	83.50	3.60	732.10	840
3040	For multi-pipe casings, add					10%				
3060	For oversize casings, add					2%				
3400	Steel casing gland seal, single pipe									
3420	6-5/8" diameter	Q-18	25	.960	Ea.	1,475	53.50	2.30	1,530.80	1,700
3440	8-5/8" diameter		23	1.043		1,725	58	2.50	1,785.50	2,000
3450	10-3/4" diameter		21	1.143		1,925	63.50	2.74	1,991.24	2,225
3460	12-3/4" diameter		19	1.263		2,275	70.50	3.03	2,348.53	2,600
3470	14" diameter		17	1.412		2,525	78.50	3.39	2,606.89	2,900
3480	16" diameter		16	1.500		2,950	83.50	3.60	3,037.10	3,375
3490	18" diameter		15	1.600		3,275	89	3.84	3,367.84	3,750
3500	20" diameter		13	1.846		3,625	103	4.43	3,732.43	4,150
3510	22" diameter		12	2		4,075	112	4.80	4,191.80	4,650

For customer support on your Site Work & Landscape Cost Data, call 877.737.1594.

505

33 63 13 – Underground Steam and Condensate Distribution Piping

33 63 13.10 Calcium Silicate Insulated System		Crew	Daily Output	Labor-Hours	Unit	Material	2015 Bare Costs Labor	Equipment	Total	Total Incl O&P
3520	24" diameter	Q-18	11	2.182	Ea.	4,575	122	5.25	4,702.25	5,225
3530	26" diameter		10	2.400		5,225	134	5.75	5,364.75	5,950
3540	28" diameter		9.50	2.526		5,900	141	6.05	6,047.05	6,725
3550	30" diameter		9	2.667		6,000	149	6.40	6,155.40	6,825
3560	32" diameter		8.50	2.824		6,750	157	6.80	6,913.80	7,675
3570	34" diameter		8	3		7,350	167	7.20	7,524.20	8,325
3580	36" diameter		7	3.429		7,825	191	8.25	8,024.25	8,900
3620	For multi-pipe casings, add					5%				
4000	Steel casing anchors, single pipe									
4020	6-5/8" diameter	Q-18	8	3	Ea.	1,325	167	7.20	1,499.20	1,700
4040	8-5/8" diameter		7.50	3.200		1,375	178	7.70	1,560.70	1,800
4050	10-3/4" diameter		7	3.429		1,800	191	8.25	1,999.25	2,275
4060	12-3/4" diameter		6.50	3.692		1,925	206	8.85	2,139.85	2,450
4070	14" diameter		6	4		2,275	223	9.60	2,507.60	2,850
4080	16" diameter		5.50	4.364		2,625	243	10.45	2,878.45	3,275
4090	18" diameter		5	4.800		2,975	268	11.50	3,254.50	3,700
4100	20" diameter		4.50	5.333		3,275	297	12.80	3,584.80	4,075
4110	22" diameter		4	6		3,650	335	14.40	3,999.40	4,550
4120	24" diameter		3.50	6.857		3,975	380	16.45	4,371.45	4,975
4130	26" diameter		3	8		4,500	445	19.20	4,964.20	5,650
4140	28" diameter		2.50	9.600		4,950	535	23	5,508	6,275
4150	30" diameter		2	12		5,250	670	29	5,949	6,800
4160	32" diameter		1.50	16		6,275	890	38.50	7,203.50	8,300
4170	34" diameter		1	24		7,050	1,350	57.50	8,457.50	9,850
4180	36" diameter		1	24		7,675	1,350	57.50	9,082.50	10,500
4220	For multi-pipe, add					5%	20%			
4800	Steel casing elbow									
4820	6-5/8" diameter	Q-18	15	1.600	Ea.	1,800	89	3.84	1,892.84	2,125
4830	8-5/8" diameter		15	1.600		1,925	89	3.84	2,017.84	2,275
4850	10-3/4" diameter		14	1.714		2,325	95.50	4.11	2,424.61	2,700
4860	12-3/4" diameter		13	1.846		2,750	103	4.43	2,857.43	3,175
4870	14" diameter		12	2		2,950	112	4.80	3,066.80	3,425
4880	16" diameter		11	2.182		3,225	122	5.25	3,352.25	3,750
4890	18" diameter		10	2.400		3,675	134	5.75	3,814.75	4,250
4900	20" diameter		9	2.667		3,925	149	6.40	4,080.40	4,550
4910	22" diameter		8	3		4,225	167	7.20	4,399.20	4,900
4920	24" diameter		7	3.429		4,650	191	8.25	4,849.25	5,425
4930	26" diameter		6	4		5,100	223	9.60	5,332.60	5,950
4940	28" diameter		5	4.800		5,500	268	11.50	5,779.50	6,475
4950	30" diameter		4	6		5,525	335	14.40	5,874.40	6,600
4960	32" diameter		3	8		6,275	445	19.20	6,739.20	7,600
4970	34" diameter		2	12		6,900	670	29	7,599	8,625
4980	36" diameter		2	12		7,350	670	29	8,049	9,100
5500	Black steel service pipe, std. wt., 1" thick insulation									
5510	3/4" diameter pipe size	Q-17	54	.296	L.F.	62	15.95	1.07	79.02	93
5540	1" diameter pipe size		50	.320		64	17.20	1.16	82.36	98
5550	1-1/4" diameter pipe size		47	.340		70	18.30	1.23	89.53	106
5560	1-1/2" diameter pipe size		45	.356		74	19.10	1.28	94.38	112
5570	2" diameter pipe size		42	.381		81	20.50	1.38	102.88	122
5580	2-1/2" diameter pipe size		34	.471		85	25.50	1.70	112.20	133
5590	3" diameter pipe size		28	.571		93	30.50	2.06	125.56	151
5600	4" diameter pipe size		22	.727		98	39	2.63	139.63	170
5610	5" diameter pipe size		18	.889		107	48	3.21	158.21	194

33 63 13 – Underground Steam and Condensate Distribution Piping

33 63 13.10 Calcium Silicate Insulated System	Crew	Daily Output	Labor-Hours	Unit	Material	2015 Bare Costs Labor	Equipment	Total	Total Incl O&P
5620	6" diameter pipe size	Q-18	23	1.043	L.F.	115	58	2.50	175.50	218
6000	Black steel service pipe, std. wt., 1-1/2" thick insul.									
6010	3/4" diameter pipe size	Q-17	54	.296	L.F.	62	15.95	1.07	79.02	93
6040	1" diameter pipe size		50	.320		67	17.20	1.16	85.36	101
6050	1-1/4" diameter pipe size		47	.340		73	18.30	1.23	92.53	109
6060	1-1/2" diameter pipe size		45	.356		79	19.10	1.28	99.38	117
6070	2" diameter pipe size		42	.381		85	20.50	1.38	106.88	126
6080	2-1/2" diameter pipe size		34	.471		89	25.50	1.70	116.20	138
6090	3" diameter pipe size		28	.571		99	30.50	2.06	131.56	158
6100	4" diameter pipe size		22	.727		107	39	2.63	148.63	180
6110	5" diameter pipe size		18	.889		115	48	3.21	166.21	203
6120	6" diameter pipe size	Q-18	23	1.043		130	58	2.50	190.50	234
6130	8" diameter pipe size		19	1.263		180	70.50	3.03	253.53	305
6140	10" diameter pipe size		16	1.500		240	83.50	3.60	327.10	395
6150	12" diameter pipe size		13	1.846		300	103	4.43	407.43	490
6190	For 2" thick insulation, add					15%				
6220	For 2-1/2" thick insulation, add					25%				
6260	For 3" thick insulation, add					30%				
6800	Black steel service pipe, ex. hvy. wt., 1" thick insul.									
6820	3/4" diameter pipe size	Q-17	50	.320	L.F.	64	17.20	1.16	82.36	98
6840	1" diameter pipe size		47	.340		68	18.30	1.23	87.53	104
6850	1-1/4" diameter pipe size		44	.364		76	19.55	1.31	96.86	114
6860	1-1/2" diameter pipe size		42	.381		78	20.50	1.38	99.88	119
6870	2" diameter pipe size		40	.400		85	21.50	1.44	107.94	128
6880	2-1/2" diameter pipe size		31	.516		89	28	1.86	118.86	142
6890	3" diameter pipe size		27	.593		97	32	2.14	131.14	157
6900	4" diameter pipe size		21	.762		102	41	2.75	145.75	177
6910	5" diameter pipe size		17	.941		110	50.50	3.40	163.90	201
6920	6" diameter pipe size	Q-18	22	1.091		120	61	2.62	183.62	227
7400	Black steel service pipe, ex. hvy. wt., 1-1/2" thick insul.									
7420	3/4" diameter pipe size	Q-17	50	.320	L.F.	55	17.20	1.16	73.36	88
7440	1" diameter pipe size		47	.340		60	18.30	1.23	79.53	95
7450	1-1/4" diameter pipe size		44	.364		67	19.55	1.31	87.86	104
7460	1-1/2" diameter pipe size		42	.381		72	20.50	1.38	93.88	112
7470	2" diameter pipe size		40	.400		77	21.50	1.44	99.94	119
7480	2-1/2" diameter pipe size		31	.516		82	28	1.86	111.86	134
7490	3" diameter pipe size		27	.593		91	32	2.14	125.14	150
7500	4" diameter pipe size		21	.762		110	41	2.75	153.75	186
7510	5" diameter pipe size		17	.941		152	50.50	3.40	205.90	247
7520	6" diameter pipe size	Q-18	22	1.091		160	61	2.62	223.62	271
7530	8" diameter pipe size		18	1.333		215	74.50	3.20	292.70	355
7540	10" diameter pipe size		15	1.600		275	89	3.84	367.84	445
7550	12" diameter pipe size		13	1.846		330	103	4.43	437.43	525
7590	For 2" thick insulation, add					13%				
7640	For 2-1/2" thick insulation, add					18%				
7680	For 3" thick insulation, add					24%				

33 71 Electrical Utility Transmission and Distribution

33 71 16 – Electrical Utility Poles

33 71 16.23 Steel Electrical Utility Poles

		Crew	Daily Output	Labor-Hours	Unit	Material	2015 Bare Costs Labor	2015 Bare Costs Equipment	Total	Total Incl O&P
0010	**STEEL ELECTRICAL UTILITY POLES**									
6000	Digging holes in earth, average	R-5	25.14	3.500	Ea.		167	58.50	225.50	315
6010	In rock, average	"	4.51	19.512	"		930	325	1,255	1,750
6020	Formed plate pole structure									
6030	Material handling and spotting	R-7	2.40	20	Ea.		775	86	861	1,300
6040	Erect steel plate pole	R-5	1.95	45.128		9,150	2,150	750	12,050	14,200
6050	Guys, anchors and hardware for pole, in earth		7.04	12.500		555	595	208	1,358	1,750
6060	In rock	↓	17.96	4.900	↓	665	234	81.50	980.50	1,175
6070	Foundations for line poles									
6080	Excavation, in earth	R-5	135.38	.650	C.Y.		31	10.85	41.85	59
6090	In rock		20	4.400			210	73.50	283.50	400
6110	Concrete foundations	↓	11	8	↓	134	380	133	647	875

33 71 16.33 Wood Electrical Utility Poles

		Crew	Daily Output	Labor-Hours	Unit	Material	2015 Bare Costs Labor	2015 Bare Costs Equipment	Total	Total Incl O&P
0010	**WOOD ELECTRICAL UTILITY POLES**									
0011	Excludes excavation, backfill and cast-in-place concrete									
6200	Electric & tel sitework, 20' high, treated wd., see Section 26 56 13.10	R-3	3.10	6.452	Ea.	224	350	44.50	618.50	820
6400	25' high		2.90	6.897		265	375	47.50	687.50	905
6600	30' high		2.60	7.692		435	420	53	908	1,150
6800	35' high		2.40	8.333		495	455	57.50	1,007.50	1,300
7000	40' high		2.30	8.696		710	470	60	1,240	1,550
7200	45' high	↓	1.70	11.765	↓	865	640	81	1,586	2,000
7400	Cross arms with hardware & insulators									
7600	4' long	1 Elec	2.50	3.200	Ea.	150	175		325	425
7800	5' long		2.40	3.333		172	182		354	460
8000	6' long	↓	2.20	3.636	↓	166	199		365	480
9000	Disposal of pole & hardware surplus material	R-7	20.87	2.300	Mile		89	9.90	98.90	148
9100	Disposal of crossarms & hardware surplus material	"	40	1.200	"		46.50	5.15	51.65	77

33 71 19 – Electrical Underground Ducts and Manholes

33 71 19.15 Underground Ducts and Manholes

		Crew	Daily Output	Labor-Hours	Unit	Material	2015 Bare Costs Labor	2015 Bare Costs Equipment	Total	Total Incl O&P
0010	**UNDERGROUND DUCTS AND MANHOLES**									
0011	Not incl. excavation, backfill and concrete, in slab or duct bank									
1000	Direct burial									
1010	PVC, schedule 40, w/coupling, 1/2" diameter	1 Elec	340	.024	L.F.	.35	1.29		1.64	2.32
1020	3/4" diameter		290	.028		.47	1.51		1.98	2.78
1030	1" diameter		260	.031		.75	1.68		2.43	3.35
1040	1-1/2" diameter		210	.038		1.14	2.08		3.22	4.37
1050	2" diameter	↓	180	.044		1.48	2.43		3.91	5.25
1060	3" diameter	2 Elec	240	.067		2.82	3.65		6.47	8.55
1070	4" diameter		160	.100		3.95	5.45		9.40	12.55
1080	5" diameter		120	.133		5.75	7.30		13.05	17.25
1090	6" diameter	↓	90	.178	↓	7.60	9.70		17.30	23
1110	Elbows, 1/2" diameter	1 Elec	48	.167	Ea.	.90	9.10		10	14.65
1120	3/4" diameter		38	.211		.88	11.50		12.38	18.20
1130	1" diameter		32	.250		1.33	13.70		15.03	22
1140	1-1/2" diameter		21	.381		2.65	21		23.65	34
1150	2" diameter		16	.500		3.59	27.50		31.09	45
1160	3" diameter		12	.667		10.85	36.50		47.35	66.50
1170	4" diameter		9	.889		17.25	48.50		65.75	92
1180	5" diameter		8	1		28	54.50		82.50	113
1190	6" diameter		5	1.600		64.50	87.50		152	202
1210	Adapters, 1/2" diameter		52	.154		.25	8.40		8.65	12.90
1220	3/4" diameter	↓	43	.186	↓	.41	10.20		10.61	15.70

508

33 71 Electrical Utility Transmission and Distribution

33 71 19 – Electrical Underground Ducts and Manholes

33 71 19.15 Underground Ducts and Manholes	Crew	Daily Output	Labor-Hours	Unit	Material	2015 Bare Costs Labor	Equipment	Total	Total Incl O&P
1230	1" diameter	1 Elec	39	.205	Ea.	.56	11.20		11.76	17.40
1240	1-1/2" diameter		35	.229		.98	12.50		13.48	19.85
1250	2" diameter		26	.308		1.22	16.85		18.07	26.50
1260	3" diameter		20	.400		2.97	22		24.97	36.50
1270	4" diameter		14	.571		5.30	31.50		36.80	53
1280	5" diameter		12	.667		11.20	36.50		47.70	67
1290	6" diameter		9	.889		18.70	48.50		67.20	93.50
1340	Bell end & cap, 1-1/2" diameter		35	.229		8.55	12.50		21.05	28
1350	Bell end & plug, 2" diameter		26	.308		9.65	16.85		26.50	35.50
1360	3" diameter		20	.400		11.70	22		33.70	46
1370	4" diameter		14	.571		14.75	31.50		46.25	63.50
1380	5" diameter		12	.667		16.75	36.50		53.25	73
1390	6" diameter		9	.889		20	48.50		68.50	95
1450	Base spacer, 2" diameter		56	.143		1.55	7.80		9.35	13.40
1460	3" diameter		46	.174		1.58	9.50		11.08	16
1470	4" diameter		41	.195		1.64	10.65		12.29	17.80
1480	5" diameter		37	.216		2.02	11.85		13.87	19.90
1490	6" diameter		34	.235		2.75	12.85		15.60	22.50
1550	Intermediate spacer, 2" diameter		60	.133		1.50	7.30		8.80	12.60
1560	3" diameter		46	.174		1.69	9.50		11.19	16.10
1570	4" diameter		41	.195		1.55	10.65		12.20	17.70
1580	5" diameter		37	.216		1.85	11.85		13.70	19.75
1590	6" diameter		34	.235		2.70	12.85		15.55	22.50
4010	PVC, schedule 80, w/coupling, 1/2" diameter		215	.037	L.F.	.92	2.04		2.96	4.06
4020	3/4" diameter		180	.044		1.24	2.43		3.67	5
4030	1" diameter		145	.055		1.76	3.02		4.78	6.45
4040	1-1/2" diameter		120	.067		2.93	3.65		6.58	8.65
4050	2" diameter		100	.080		4.05	4.38		8.43	11
4060	3" diameter	2 Elec	130	.123		8.25	6.75		15	19.20
4070	4" diameter		90	.178		12	9.70		21.70	28
4080	5" diameter		70	.229		17.25	12.50		29.75	37.50
4090	6" diameter		50	.320		21.50	17.50		39	50
4110	Elbows, 1/2" diameter	1 Elec	29	.276	Ea.	1.33	15.10		16.43	24
4120	3/4" diameter		23	.348		2.57	19.05		21.62	31.50
4130	1" diameter		20	.400		3.18	22		25.18	36.50
4140	1-1/2" diameter		16	.500		6.95	27.50		34.45	48.50
4150	2" diameter		12	.667		8.25	36.50		44.75	63.50
4160	3" diameter		9	.889		23	48.50		71.50	98.50
4170	4" diameter		7	1.143		46.50	62.50		109	145
4180	5" diameter		6	1.333		195	73		268	325
4190	6" diameter		4	2		231	109		340	420
4210	Adapter, 1/2" diameter		39	.205		.25	11.20		11.45	17.10
4220	3/4" diameter		33	.242		.41	13.25		13.66	20.50
4230	1" diameter		29	.276		.56	15.10		15.66	23
4240	1-1/2" diameter		26	.308		.98	16.85		17.83	26
4250	2" diameter		23	.348		1.22	19.05		20.27	30
4260	3" diameter		18	.444		2.97	24.50		27.47	40
4270	4" diameter		13	.615		5.30	33.50		38.80	56.50
4280	5" diameter		11	.727		11.20	40		51.20	72
4290	6" diameter		8	1		18.70	54.50		73.20	103
4310	Bell end & cap, 1-1/2" diameter		26	.308		8.55	16.85		25.40	34.50
4320	Bell end & plug, 2" diameter		23	.348		9.65	19.05		28.70	39
4330	3" diameter		18	.444		11.70	24.50		36.20	49.50

For customer support on your Site Work & Landscape Cost Data, call 877.737.1594.

509

33 71 19 – Electrical Underground Ducts and Manholes

33 71 19.15 Underground Ducts and Manholes	Crew	Daily Output	Labor-Hours	Unit	Material	2015 Bare Costs Labor	Equipment	Total	Total Incl O&P
4340	4" diameter	1 Elec	13	.615	Ea.	14.75	33.50		48.25	67
4350	5" diameter		11	.727		16.75	40		56.75	78
4360	6" diameter		8	1		20	54.50		74.50	104
4370	Base spacer, 2" diameter		42	.190		1.55	10.40		11.95	17.30
4380	3" diameter		33	.242		1.58	13.25		14.83	21.50
4390	4" diameter		29	.276		1.64	15.10		16.74	24.50
4400	5" diameter		26	.308		2.02	16.85		18.87	27
4410	6" diameter		25	.320		2.75	17.50		20.25	29
4420	Intermediate spacer, 2" diameter		45	.178		1.50	9.70		11.20	16.20
4430	3" diameter		34	.235		1.69	12.85		14.54	21
4440	4" diameter		31	.258		1.55	14.10		15.65	22.50
4450	5" diameter		28	.286		1.85	15.65		17.50	25.50
4460	6" diameter		25	.320		2.70	17.50		20.20	29

33 71 19.17 Electric and Telephone Underground

		Crew	Daily Output	Labor-Hours	Unit	Material	2015 Bare Costs Labor	Equipment	Total	Total Incl O&P
0010	**ELECTRIC AND TELEPHONE UNDERGROUND**									
0011	Not including excavation									
0200	backfill and cast in place concrete									
0250	For bedding, see Section 31 23 23.16									
0400	Hand holes, precast concrete, with concrete cover									
0600	2' x 2' x 3' deep	R-3	2.40	8.333	Ea.	405	455	57.50	917.50	1,200
0800	3' x 3' x 3' deep		1.90	10.526		525	570	72.50	1,167.50	1,525
1000	4' x 4' x 4' deep		1.40	14.286		1,400	775	98.50	2,273.50	2,825
1200	Manholes, precast with iron racks & pulling irons, C.I. frame									
1400	and cover, 4' x 6' x 7' deep	B-13	2	28	Ea.	6,050	1,150	370	7,570	8,800
1600	6' x 8' x 7' deep		1.90	29.474		6,800	1,200	390	8,390	9,750
1800	6' x 10' x 7' deep		1.80	31.111		7,625	1,275	410	9,310	10,800
4200	Underground duct, banks ready for concrete fill, min. of 7.5"									
4400	between conduits, center to center									
4580	PVC, type EB, 1 @ 2" diameter	2 Elec	480	.033	L.F.	.71	1.82		2.53	3.51
4600	2 @ 2" diameter		240	.067		1.41	3.65		5.06	7
4800	4 @ 2" diameter		120	.133		2.82	7.30		10.12	14.05
4900	1 @ 3" diameter		400	.040		.98	2.19		3.17	4.36
5000	2 @ 3" diameter		200	.080		1.96	4.38		6.34	8.70
5200	4 @ 3" diameter		100	.160		3.91	8.75		12.66	17.40
5300	1 @ 4" diameter		320	.050		1.52	2.74		4.26	5.80
5400	2 @ 4" diameter		160	.100		3.05	5.45		8.50	11.55
5600	4 @ 4" diameter		80	.200		6.10	10.95		17.05	23
5800	6 @ 4" diameter		54	.296		9.15	16.20		25.35	34.50
5810	1 @ 5" diameter		260	.062		2.24	3.37		5.61	7.50
5820	2 @ 5" diameter		130	.123		4.48	6.75		11.23	15.05
5840	4 @ 5" diameter		70	.229		8.95	12.50		21.45	28.50
5860	6 @ 5" diameter		50	.320		13.45	17.50		30.95	41
5870	1 @ 6" diameter		200	.080		3.21	4.38		7.59	10.10
5880	2 @ 6" diameter		100	.160		6.40	8.75		15.15	20
5900	4 @ 6" diameter		50	.320		12.80	17.50		30.30	40
5920	6 @ 6" diameter		30	.533		19.25	29		48.25	64.50
6200	Rigid galvanized steel, 2 @ 2" diameter		180	.089		12.90	4.86		17.76	21.50
6400	4 @ 2" diameter		90	.178		26	9.70		35.70	43
6800	2 @ 3" diameter		100	.160		29	8.75		37.75	44.50
7000	4 @ 3" diameter		50	.320		57.50	17.50		75	89.50
7200	2 @ 4" diameter		70	.229		41.50	12.50		54	64.50
7400	4 @ 4" diameter		34	.471		83	25.50		108.50	130

33 71 Electrical Utility Transmission and Distribution

33 71 19 – Electrical Underground Ducts and Manholes

33 71 19.17 Electric and Telephone Underground	Crew	Daily Output	Labor-Hours	Unit	Material	2015 Bare Costs Labor	Equipment	Total	Total Incl O&P
7600	6 @ 4" diameter	2 Elec	22	.727	L.F.	124	40		164	197
7620	2 @ 5" diameter		60	.267		85.50	14.60		100.10	116
7640	4 @ 5" diameter		30	.533		171	29		200	232
7660	6 @ 5" diameter		18	.889		257	48.50		305.50	355
7680	2 @ 6" diameter		40	.400		116	22		138	161
7700	4 @ 6" diameter		20	.800		232	44		276	320
7720	6 @ 6" diameter		14	1.143		350	62.50		412.50	480
7800	For cast-in-place concrete - Add									
7801	For cable, see Section 26 05 19.55									
7810	Under 1 C.Y.	C-6	16	3	C.Y.	163	118	3.90	284.90	360
7820	1 C.Y. - 5 C.Y.		19.20	2.500		147	98	3.25	248.25	315
7830	Over 5 C.Y.		24	2		122	78.50	2.60	203.10	257
7850	For reinforcing rods - Add									
7860	#4 to #7	2 Rodm	1.10	14.545	Ton	970	765		1,735	2,275
7870	#8 to #14	"	1.50	10.667	"	970	560		1,530	1,950
8000	Fittings, PVC type EB, elbow, 2" diameter	1 Elec	16	.500	Ea.	15.90	27.50		43.40	58.50
8200	3" diameter		14	.571		20.50	31.50		52	69.50
8400	4" diameter		12	.667		28.50	36.50		65	86
8420	5" diameter		10	.800		152	44		196	233
8440	6" diameter		9	.889		173	48.50		221.50	263
8500	Coupling, 2" diameter					.72			.72	.79
8600	3" diameter					3.23			3.23	3.55
8700	4" diameter					3.53			3.53	3.88
8720	5" diameter					6.65			6.65	7.30
8740	6" diameter					22.50			22.50	24.50
8800	Adapter, 2" diameter	1 Elec	26	.308		1.02	16.85		17.87	26
9000	3" diameter		20	.400		2.90	22		24.90	36
9200	4" diameter		16	.500		4.23	27.50		31.73	45.50
9220	5" diameter		13	.615		10.25	33.50		43.75	62
9240	6" diameter		10	.800		13.30	44		57.30	80
9400	End bell, 2" diameter		16	.500		1.30	27.50		28.80	42.50
9600	3" diameter		14	.571		6.65	31.50		38.15	54.50
9800	4" diameter		12	.667		4.26	36.50		40.76	59
9810	5" diameter		10	.800		13	44		57	80
9820	6" diameter		8	1		66	54.50		120.50	155
9830	5° angle coupling, 2" diameter		26	.308		19.60	16.85		36.45	46.50
9840	3" diameter		20	.400		29.50	22		51.50	65.50
9850	4" diameter		16	.500		15.25	27.50		42.75	58
9860	5" diameter		13	.615		14.75	33.50		48.25	66.50
9870	6" diameter		10	.800		23	44		67	90.50
9880	Expansion joint, 2" diameter		16	.500		33.50	27.50		61	78
9890	3" diameter		18	.444		64	24.50		88.50	107
9900	4" diameter		12	.667		85	36.50		121.50	148
9910	5" diameter		10	.800		114	44		158	192
9920	6" diameter		8	1		143	54.50		197.50	239
9930	Heat bender, 2" diameter					545			545	600
9940	6" diameter					1,850			1,850	2,025
9950	Cement, quart					16.60			16.60	18.30

For customer support on your Site Work & Landscape Cost Data, call 877.737.1594.

511

33 81 Communications Structures

33 81 13 – Communications Transmission Towers

33 81 13.10 Radio Towers	Crew	Daily Output	Labor-Hours	Unit	Material	2015 Bare Costs Labor	Equipment	Total	Total Incl O&P
0010 **RADIO TOWERS**									
0020 Guyed, 50' H, 40 lb. sect., 70 MPH basic wind spd.	2 Sswk	1	16	Ea.	2,750	840		3,590	4,500
0100 Wind load 90 MPH basic wind speed	"	1	16		3,700	840		4,540	5,550
0300 190' high, 40 lb. section, wind load 70 MPH basic wind speed	K-2	.33	72.727		9,550	3,550	920	14,020	17,500
0400 200' high, 70 lb. section, wind load 90 MPH basic wind speed		.33	72.727		15,900	3,550	920	20,370	24,500
0600 300' high, 70 lb. section, wind load 70 MPH basic wind speed		.20	120		25,500	5,850	1,525	32,875	39,500
0700 270' high, 90 lb. section, wind load 90 MPH basic wind speed		.20	120		27,600	5,850	1,525	34,975	41,800
0800 400' high, 100 lb. section, wind load 70 MPH basic wind speed		.14	171		38,100	8,375	2,175	48,650	58,500
0900 Self-supporting, 60' high, wind load 70 MPH basic wind speed		.80	30		4,500	1,475	380	6,355	7,825
0910 60' high, wind load 90 MPH basic wind speed		.45	53.333		5,275	2,600	675	8,550	10,900
1000 120' high, wind load 70 MPH basic wind speed		.40	60		10,000	2,925	760	13,685	16,700
1200 190' high, wind load 90 MPH basic wind speed		.20	120		28,300	5,850	1,525	35,675	42,600
2000 For states west of Rocky Mountains, add for shipping					10%				

Estimating Tips

34 11 00 Rail Tracks

This subdivision includes items that may involve either repair of existing, or construction of new, railroad tracks. Additional preparation work, such as the roadbed earthwork, would be found in Division 31. Additional new construction siding and turnouts are found in Subdivision 34 72. Maintenance of railroads is found under 34 01 23 Operation and Maintenance of Railways.

34 40 00 Traffic Signals

This subdivision includes traffic signal systems. Other traffic control devices such as traffic signs are found in Subdivision 10 14 53 Traffic Signage.

34 70 00 Vehicle Barriers

This subdivision includes security vehicle barriers, guide and guard rails, crash barriers, and delineators. The actual maintenance and construction of concrete and asphalt pavement is found in Division 32.

Reference Numbers

Reference numbers are shown in shaded boxes at the beginning of some major classifications. These numbers refer to related items in the Reference Section. The reference information may be an estimating procedure, an alternate pricing method, or technical information.

Note: Not all subdivisions listed here necessarily appear in this publication. ■

Division 34 – Transportation

Did you know?

RSMeans Online gives you the same access to RSMeans' data with 24/7 access:
- Quickly locate costs in the searchable database.
- Build cost lists, estimates, and reports in minutes.
- Adjust costs to any location in the U.S. and Canada with the click of a button.

Start your free trial today at **www.rsmeansonline.com**

RSMeansOnline

34 01 13.10 Maintenance Grading of Roadways	Crew	Daily Output	Labor-Hours	Unit	Material	2015 Bare Costs Labor	Equipment	Total	Total Incl O&P
0010 **MAINTENANCE GRADING OF ROADWAYS**									
0100 Maintenance grading mob/demob of equipment per hour	B-11L	8	2	Hr.		88	92	180	236
0200 Maintenance grading of ditches one ditch slope only 1.0 MPH average		5	3.200	Mile		141	147	288	375
0210 1.5 MPH		7.50	2.133			94	98	192	252
0220 2.0 MPH		10	1.600			70.50	73.50	144	189
0230 2.5 MPH		12.50	1.280			56.50	59	115.50	151
0240 3.0 MPH		15	1.067			47	49	96	126
0300 Maintenance grading of roadway, 3 passes, 3.0 MPH average		5	3.200			141	147	288	375
0310 4 passes		3.80	4.211			186	194	380	495
0320 3 passes, 3.5 MPH average		5.80	2.759			122	127	249	325
0330 4 passes		4.40	3.636			160	167	327	430
0340 3 passes, 4 MPH average		6.70	2.388			105	110	215	282
0350 4 passes		5	3.200			141	147	288	375
0360 3 passes, 4.5 MPH average		7.50	2.133			94	98	192	252
0370 4 passes		5.60	2.857			126	131	257	335
0380 3 passes, 5 MPH average		8.30	1.928			85	88.50	173.50	228
0390 4 passes		6.30	2.540			112	117	229	300
0400 3 passes, 5.5 MPH average		9.20	1.739			76.50	80	156.50	205
0410 4 passes		6.90	2.319			102	107	209	273
0420 3 passes, 6 MPH average		10	1.600			70.50	73.50	144	189
0430 4 passes		7.50	2.133			94	98	192	252
0440 3 passes, 6.5 MPH average		10.80	1.481			65.50	68	133.50	175
0450 4 passes		8.10	1.975			87	91	178	233
0460 3 passes, 7 MPH average		11.70	1.368			60.50	63	123.50	161
0470 4 passes		8.80	1.818			80	83.50	163.50	214
0480 3 passes, 7.5 MPH average		12.50	1.280			56.50	59	115.50	151
0490 4 passes		9.40	1.702			75	78.50	153.50	201
0500 3 passes, 8 MPH average		13.30	1.203			53	55.50	108.50	142
0510 4 passes		10	1.600			70.50	73.50	144	189
0520 3 passes, 8.5 MPH average		14.20	1.127			49.50	52	101.50	133
0530 4 passes		10.60	1.509			66.50	69.50	136	179
0540 3 passes, 9 MPH average		15	1.067			47	49	96	126
0550 4 passes		11.30	1.416			62.50	65	127.50	167
0560 3 passes, 9.5 MPH average		15.80	1.013			44.50	46.50	91	120
0570 4 passes		11.90	1.345			59.50	62	121.50	159
0600 Maintenance grading of roadway, 8' wide pass, 3.0 MPH average		15	1.067			47	49	96	126
0610 3.5 MPH average		17.50	.914			40.50	42	82.50	108
0620 4 MPH average		20	.800			35.50	37	72.50	94.50
0630 4.5 MPH average		22.50	.711			31.50	32.50	64	84
0640 5 MPH average		25	.640			28	29.50	57.50	75.50
0650 5.5 MPH average		27.50	.582			25.50	27	52.50	68.50
0660 6 MPH average		30	.533			23.50	24.50	48	63
0670 6.5 MPH average		32.50	.492			21.50	22.50	44	58
0680 7 MPH average		35	.457			20	21	41	54
0690 7.5 MPH average		37.50	.427			18.80	19.65	38.45	50
0700 8 MPH average		40	.400			17.65	18.40	36.05	47
0710 8.5 MPH average		42.50	.376			16.60	17.30	33.90	44.50
0720 9 MPH average		45	.356			15.70	16.35	32.05	42
0730 9.5 MPH average		47.50	.337			14.85	15.50	30.35	39.50

514

For customer support on your Site Work & Landscape Cost Data, call 877.737.1594.

34 01 Operation and Maintenance of Transportation

34 01 23 – Operation and Maintenance of Railways

34 01 23.51 Maintenance of Railroads	Crew	Daily Output	Labor-Hours	Unit	Material	2015 Bare Costs Labor	Equipment	Total	Total Incl O&P
0010 **MAINTENANCE OF RAILROADS**									
0400 Resurface and realign existing track	B-14	200	.240	L.F.		9.55	1.82	11.37	16.65
0600 For crushed stone ballast, add	"	500	.096	"	13.40	3.82	.73	17.95	21.50

34 11 Rail Tracks

34 11 13 – Track Rails

34 11 13.23 Heavy Rail Track

	Crew	Daily Output	Labor-Hours	Unit	Material	2015 Bare Costs Labor	Equipment	Total	Total Incl O&P
0010 **HEAVY RAIL TRACK** R347216-10									
1000 Rail, 100 lb. prime grade				L.F.	35			35	38.50
1500 Relay rail				"	17.55			17.55	19.30

34 11 33 – Track Cross Ties

34 11 33.13 Concrete Track Cross Ties

	Crew	Daily Output	Labor-Hours	Unit	Material	2015 Bare Costs Labor	Equipment	Total	Total Incl O&P
0010 **CONCRETE TRACK CROSS TIES**									
1400 Ties, concrete, 8'-6" long, 30" O.C.	B-14	80	.600	Ea.	173	24	4.55	201.55	232

34 11 33.16 Timber Track Cross Ties

	Crew	Daily Output	Labor-Hours	Unit	Material	2015 Bare Costs Labor	Equipment	Total	Total Incl O&P
0010 **TIMBER TRACK CROSS TIES**									
1600 Wood, pressure treated, 6" x 8" x 8'-6", C.L. lots	B-14	90	.533	Ea.	52	21	4.05	77.05	94
1700 L.C.L. lots		90	.533		54.50	21	4.05	79.55	97
1900 Heavy duty, 7" x 9" x 8'-6", C.L. lots		70	.686		57	27.50	5.20	89.70	110
2000 L.C.L. lots		70	.686		57	27.50	5.20	89.70	110

34 11 33.17 Timber Switch Ties

	Crew	Daily Output	Labor-Hours	Unit	Material	2015 Bare Costs Labor	Equipment	Total	Total Incl O&P
0010 **TIMBER SWITCH TIES**									
1200 Switch timber, for a #8 switch, pressure treated	B-14	3.70	12.973	M.B.F.	3,100	515	98.50	3,713.50	4,325
1300 Complete set of timbers, 3.7 MBF for #8 switch	"	1	48	Total	12,000	1,900	365	14,265	16,500

34 11 93 – Track Appurtenances and Accessories

34 11 93.50 Track Accessories

	Crew	Daily Output	Labor-Hours	Unit	Material	2015 Bare Costs Labor	Equipment	Total	Total Incl O&P
0010 **TRACK ACCESSORIES**									
0020 Car bumpers, test	B-14	2	24	Ea.	3,750	955	182	4,887	5,800
0100 Heavy duty R347216-20		2	24		7,100	955	182	8,237	9,500
0200 Derails hand throw (sliding)		10	4.800		1,250	191	36.50	1,477.50	1,700
0300 Hand throw with standard timbers, open stand & target		8	6		1,350	239	45.50	1,634.50	1,900
2400 Wheel stops, fixed		18	2.667	Pr.	920	106	20	1,046	1,200
2450 Hinged		14	3.429	"	1,250	136	26	1,412	1,625

34 11 93.60 Track Material

	Crew	Daily Output	Labor-Hours	Unit	Material	2015 Bare Costs Labor	Equipment	Total	Total Incl O&P
0010 **TRACK MATERIAL**									
0020 Track bolts				Ea.	4.17			4.17	4.59
0100 Joint bars				Pr.	93			93	103
0200 Spikes				Ea.	2			2	2.20
0300 Tie plates				"	15.60			15.60	17.15

For customer support on your Site Work & Landscape Cost Data, call 877.737.1594.

515

34 41 Roadway Signaling and Control Equipment

34 41 13 – Traffic Signals

34 41 13.10 Traffic Signals Systems	Crew	Daily Output	Labor-Hours	Unit	Material	2015 Bare Costs Labor	Equipment	Total	Total Incl O&P
0010 **TRAFFIC SIGNALS SYSTEMS**									
0020 Component costs									
0600 Crew employs crane / directional driller as required									
1000 Vertical mast with foundation									
1010 Mast sized for single arm to 40'; no lighting or power function	R-11	.50	112	Signal	10,000	5,825	1,725	17,550	21,700
1100 Horizontal arm									
1110 Per linear foot of arm	R-11	50	1.120	Signal	200	58	17.20	275.20	325
1200 Traffic signal									
1210 Includes signal, bracket, sensor, and wiring	R-11	2.50	22.400	Signal	1,000	1,175	345	2,520	3,225
1300 Pedestrian signals and callers									
1310 Includes four signals with brackets and two call buttons	R-11	2.50	22.400	Signal	3,000	1,175	345	4,520	5,425
1400 Controller, design, and underground conduit									
1410 Includes miscellaneous signage and adjacent surface work	R-11	.25	224	Signal	20,000	11,600	3,450	35,050	43,300

34 71 Roadway Construction

34 71 13 – Vehicle Barriers

34 71 13.17 Security Vehicle Barriers

	Crew	Daily Output	Labor-Hours	Unit	Material	2015 Bare Costs Labor	Equipment	Total	Total Incl O&P
0010 **SECURITY VEHICLE BARRIERS**									
0020 Security planters excludes filling material									
0100 Concrete security planter, exposed aggregate 36" diam. x 30" high	B-11M	8	2	Ea.	565	88	49	702	810
0200 48" diam. x 36" high		8	2		845	88	49	982	1,125
0300 53" diam. x 18" high		8	2		945	88	49	1,082	1,250
0400 72" diam. x 18" high with seats		8	2		2,275	88	49	2,412	2,700
0450 84" diam. x 36" high		8	2		2,250	88	49	2,387	2,675
0500 36" x 36" x 24" high square		8	2		510	88	49	647	755
0600 36" x 36" x 30" high square		8	2		820	88	49	957	1,100
0700 48" L x 24" W x 30" H rectangle		8	2		525	88	49	662	765
0800 72" L x 24" W x 30" H rectangle		8	2		610	88	49	747	865
0900 96" L x 24" W x 30" H rectangle		8	2		780	88	49	917	1,050
0950 Decorative geometric concrete barrier, 96" L x 24" W x 36" H		8	2		830	88	49	967	1,100
1000 Concrete security planter, filling with washed sand or gravel <1 C.Y.		8	2		39	88	49	176	232
1050 2 C.Y. or less		6	2.667		78	118	65.50	261.50	335
1200 Jersey concrete barrier, 10' L x 2' by 0.5' W x 30" H	B-21B	16	2.500		385	102	41	528	620
1300 10 or more same site		24	1.667		385	68	27.50	480.50	555
1400 10' L x 2' by 0.5' W x 32" H		16	2.500		405	102	41	548	645
1500 10 or more same site		24	1.667		405	68	27.50	500.50	580
1600 20' L x 2' by 0.5' W x 30" H		12	3.333		565	136	54.50	755.50	890
1700 10 or more same site		18	2.222		565	90.50	36.50	692	800
1800 20' L x 2' by 0.5' W x 32" H		12	3.333		680	136	54.50	870.50	1,025
1900 10 or more same site		18	2.222		680	90.50	36.50	807	930
2000 GFRC decorative security barrier per 10 feet section including concrete		4	10		3,200	410	164	3,774	4,300
2100 Per 12 feet section including concrete		4	10		3,825	410	164	4,399	5,025
2210 GFRC decorative security barrier will stop 30 MPH, 4000 lb. vehicle									
2300 High security barrier base prep per 12 feet section on bare ground	B-11C	4	4	Ea.	21.50	176	91	288.50	395
2310 GFRC barrier base prep does not include haul away of excavated matl.									
2400 GFRC decorative high security barrier per 12 feet section w/concrete	B-21B	3	13.333	Ea.	6,025	545	218	6,788	7,700
2410 GFRC decorative high security barrier will stop 50 MPH, 15000 lb. vehicle									
2500 GFRC decorative impaler security barrier per 10 feet section w/prep	B-6	4	6	Ea.	2,300	248	91	2,639	3,000
2600 Per 12 feet section w/prep	"	4	6	"	2,750	248	91	3,089	3,500
2610 Impaler barrier should stop 50 MPH, 15000 lb. vehicle w/some penetr.									
2700 Pipe bollards, steel, concrete filled/painted, 8' L x 4' D hole, 8" diam.	B-6	10	2.400	Ea.	875	99	36.50	1,010.50	1,150

516

34 71 13 – Vehicle Barriers

34 71 13.17 Security Vehicle Barriers

		Crew	Daily Output	Labor-Hours	Unit	Material	2015 Bare Costs Labor	Equipment	Total	Total Incl O&P
2710	Schedule 80 concrete bollards will stop 4000 lb. vehicle @ 30 MPH									
2800	GFRC decorative jersey barrier cover per 10 feet section excludes soil	B-6	8	3	Ea.	990	124	45.50	1,159.50	1,350
2900	Per 12 feet section excludes soil		8	3		1,175	124	45.50	1,344.50	1,550
3000	GFRC decorative 8" diameter bollard cover		12	2		515	82.50	30.50	628	725
3100	GFRC decorative barrier face 10 foot section excludes earth backing	↓	10	2.400	↓	1,075	99	36.50	1,210.50	1,400
3200	Drop arm crash barrier, 15000 lb. vehicle @ 50 MPH									
3205	Includes all material, labor for complete installation									
3210	12' width				Ea.				64,500	71,000
3310	24' width								86,000	95,000
3410	Wedge crash barrier, 10' width								98,000	108,000
3510	12.5' width								108,000	119,000
3520	15' width								118,500	130,000
3610	Sliding crash barrier, 12' width								178,500	196,000
3710	Sliding roller crash barrier, 20' width								198,000	217,500
3810	Sliding cantilever crash barrier, 20' width				↓				198,000	217,500
3890	Note: Raised bollard crash barriers should be used w/tire shredders									
3910	Raised bollard crash barrier, 10' width				Ea.				38,800	42,900
4010	12' width								44,900	49,000
4110	Raised bollard crash barrier, 10' width, solar powered								46,900	52,000
4210	12' width								53,000	58,000
4310	In ground tire shredder, 16' width				↓				43,900	47,900

34 71 13.26 Vehicle Guide Rails

		Crew	Daily Output	Labor-Hours	Unit	Material	2015 Bare Costs Labor	Equipment	Total	Total Incl O&P
0010	**VEHICLE GUIDE RAILS**									
0012	Corrugated stl., galv. stl. posts, 6'-3" O.C.	B-80	850	.038	L.F.	23	1.55	.85	25.40	28.50
0100	Double face		570	.056	"	33.50	2.31	1.26	37.07	42
0200	End sections, galvanized, flared		50	.640	Ea.	98.50	26.50	14.40	139.40	164
0300	Wrap around end		50	.640		141	26.50	14.40	181.90	211
0350	Anchorage units	↓	15	2.133		1,225	88	48	1,361	1,500
0365	End section, flared	B-80A	78	.308		46	11.55	3.89	61.44	72.50
0370	End section, wrap-around, corrugated steel	"	78	.308	↓	58.50	11.55	3.89	73.94	86.50
0400	Timber guide rail, 4" x 8" with 6" x 8" wood posts, treated	B-80	960	.033	L.F.	12.05	1.37	.75	14.17	16.20
0600	Cable guide rail, 3 at 3/4" cables, steel posts, single face		900	.036		10.75	1.47	.80	13.02	14.95
0650	Double face		635	.050		22	2.08	1.13	25.21	29
0700	Wood posts		950	.034		12.95	1.39	.76	15.10	17.20
0750	Double face		650	.049	↓	22.50	2.03	1.11	25.64	29.50
0760	Breakaway wood posts		195	.164	Ea.	350	6.75	3.69	360.44	400
0800	Anchorage units, breakaway		15	2.133	"	1,550	88	48	1,686	1,900
0900	Guide rail, steel box beam, 6" x 6"	↓	120	.267	L.F.	34	11	6	51	61
0950	End assembly	B-80A	48	.500	Ea.	345	18.80	6.30	370.10	410
1100	Median barrier, steel box beam, 6" x 8"	B-80	215	.149	L.F.	45	6.15	3.35	54.50	62.50
1120	Shop curved	B-80A	92	.261	"	57.50	9.80	3.29	70.59	81.50
1140	End assembly		48	.500	Ea.	520	18.80	6.30	545.10	605
1150	Corrugated beam	↓	400	.060	L.F.	42.50	2.26	.76	45.52	51.50
1400	Resilient guide fence and light shield, 6' high	B-2	130	.308	"	38	11.70		49.70	60
1500	Concrete posts, individual, 6'-5", triangular	B-80	110	.291	Ea.	72.50	12	6.55	91.05	106
1550	Square		110	.291		78	12	6.55	96.55	112
1600	Wood guide posts	↓	150	.213	↓	51	8.80	4.80	64.60	74.50
2000	Median, precast concrete, 3'-6" high, 2' wide, single face	B-29	380	.147	L.F.	54.50	6.05	2.32	62.87	71.50
2200	Double face	"	340	.165		62.50	6.75	2.59	71.84	81.50
2300	Cast in place, steel forms	C-2	170	.282		49	12.90		61.90	74
2320	Slipformed	C-7	352	.205	↓	46	8.35	3.45	57.80	67
2400	Speed bumps, thermoplastic, 10-1/2" x 2-1/4" x 48" long	B-2	120	.333	Ea.	138	12.65		150.65	171

34 71 Roadway Construction

34 71 13 – Vehicle Barriers

34 71 13.26 Vehicle Guide Rails

		Crew	Daily Output	Labor-Hours	Unit	Material	2015 Bare Costs Labor	Equipment	Total	Total Incl O&P
3000	Energy absorbing terminal, 10 bay, 3' wide	B-80B	.10	320	Ea.	43,200	12,900	2,450	58,550	70,000
3010	7 bay, 2' - 6" wide		.20	160		32,200	6,450	1,225	39,875	46,800
3020	5 bay, 2' wide		.20	160		24,600	6,450	1,225	32,275	38,400
3030	Impact barrier, UTMCD, barrel type	B-16	30	1.067		510	41.50	23	574.50	655
3100	Wide hazard protection, foam sandwich, 7 bay, 7' - 6" wide	B-80B	.14	228		32,200	9,225	1,750	43,175	51,500
3110	5' wide		.15	213		26,800	8,600	1,625	37,025	44,500
3120	3' wide		.18	177		24,600	7,175	1,350	33,125	39,600

34 71 19 – Vehicle Delineators

34 71 19.13 Fixed Vehicle Delineators

		Crew	Daily Output	Labor-Hours	Unit	Material	2015 Bare Costs Labor	Equipment	Total	Total Incl O&P
0010	**FIXED VEHICLE DELINEATORS**									
0020	Crash barriers									
0100	Traffic channelizing pavement markers, layout only	A-7	2000	.012	Ea.		.62	.03	.65	.98
0110	13" x 7-1/2" x 2-1/2" high, non-plowable install	2 Clab	96	.167		24.50	6.25		30.75	36
0200	8" x 8" x 3-1/4" high, non-plowable, install		96	.167		22.50	6.25		28.75	34.50
0230	4" x 4" x 3/4" high, non-plowable, install		120	.133		1.79	5		6.79	9.65
0240	9-1/4" x 5-7/8" x 1/4" high, plowable, concrete pavmt.	A-2A	70	.343		18.20	13.05	5.90	37.15	46.50
0250	9-1/4" x 5-7/8" x 1/4" high, plowable, asphalt pav't	"	120	.200		3.83	7.60	3.44	14.87	19.65
0300	Barrier and curb delineators, reflectorized, 2" x 4"	2 Clab	150	.107		2.04	4.01		6.05	8.40
0310	3" x 5"	"	150	.107		3.98	4.01		7.99	10.55
0500	Rumble strip, polycarbonate									
0510	24" x 3-1/2" x 1/2" high	2 Clab	50	.320	Ea.	8.40	12.05		20.45	28

34 72 Railway Construction

34 72 16 – Railway Siding

34 72 16.50 Railroad Sidings

		Crew	Daily Output	Labor-Hours	Unit	Material	2015 Bare Costs Labor	Equipment	Total	Total Incl O&P
0010	**RAILROAD SIDINGS** R347216-10									
0800	Siding, yard spur, level grade									
0808	Wood ties and ballast, 80 lb. new rail	B-14	57	.842	L.F.	117	33.50	6.40	156.90	187
0809	80 lb. relay rail		57	.842		83	33.50	6.40	122.90	150
0812	90 lb. new rail		57	.842		125	33.50	6.40	164.90	196
0813	90 lb. relay rail		57	.842		85	33.50	6.40	124.90	152
0820	100 lb. new rail		57	.842		133	33.50	6.40	172.90	205
0822	100 lb. relay rail		57	.842		89	33.50	6.40	128.90	157
0830	110 lb. new rail		57	.842		142	33.50	6.40	181.90	215
0832	110 lb. relay rail		57	.842		94.50	33.50	6.40	134.40	163
1002	Steel ties in concrete, incl. fasteners & plates									
1003	80 lb. new rail	B-14	22	2.182	L.F.	168	87	16.55	271.55	335
1005	80 lb. relay rail		22	2.182		138	87	16.55	241.55	305
1012	90 lb. new rail		22	2.182		175	87	16.55	278.55	345
1015	90 lb. relay rail		22	2.182		142	87	16.55	245.55	305
1020	100 lb. new rail		22	2.182		181	87	16.55	284.55	350
1025	100 lb. relay rail		22	2.182		145	87	16.55	248.55	310
1030	110 lb. new rail		22	2.182		191	87	16.55	294.55	360
1035	110 lb. relay rail		22	2.182		150	87	16.55	253.55	315

34 72 16.60 Railroad Turnouts		Crew	Daily Output	Labor-Hours	Unit	Material	2015 Bare Costs Labor	Equipment	Total	Total Incl O&P
0010	**RAILROAD TURNOUTS**									
2200	Turnout, #8 complete, w/rails, plates, bars, frog, switch point,									
2250	timbers, and ballast to 6" below bottom of ties									
2280	90 lb. rails	B-13	.25	224	Ea.	40,300	9,175	2,950	52,425	61,500
2290	90 lb. relay rails		.25	224		27,100	9,175	2,950	39,225	47,200
2300	100 lb. rails		.25	224		44,900	9,175	2,950	57,025	67,000
2310	100 lb. relay rails		.25	224		30,200	9,175	2,950	42,325	50,500
2320	110 lb. rails		.25	224		49,500	9,175	2,950	61,625	72,000
2330	110 lb. relay rails		.25	224		33,300	9,175	2,950	45,425	54,000
2340	115 lb. rails		.25	224		54,500	9,175	2,950	66,625	77,000
2350	115 lb. relay rails		.25	224		36,100	9,175	2,950	48,225	57,000
2360	132 lb. rails		.25	224		62,000	9,175	2,950	74,125	85,500
2370	132 lb. relay rails	↓	.25	224	↓	41,100	9,175	2,950	53,225	62,500

For customer support on your Site Work & Landscape Cost Data, call 877.737.1594.

519

Division Notes

	CREW	DAILY OUTPUT	LABOR-HOURS	UNIT	BARE COSTS				TOTAL INCL O&P
					MAT.	LABOR	EQUIP.	TOTAL	

Estimating Tips

35 01 50 Operation and Maintenance of Marine Construction

Includes unit price lines for pile cleaning and pile wrapping for protection.

35 20 16 Hydraulic Gates

This subdivision includes various types of gates that are commonly used in waterway and canal construction. Various earthwork items and structural support is found in Division 31, and concrete work in Division 3.

35 20 23 Dredging

This subdivision includes barge and shore dredging systems for rivers, canals, and channels.

35 31 00 Shoreline Protection

This subdivision includes breakwaters, bulkheads, and revetments for ocean and river inlets. Additional earthwork may be required from Division 31, and concrete work from Division 3.

35 41 00 Levees

Information on levee construction, including estimated cost of clay cone material.

35 49 00 Waterway Structures

This subdivision includes breakwaters and bulkheads for canals.

35 51 00 Floating Construction

This section includes floating piers, docks, and dock accessories. Fixed Pier Timber Construction is found in 06 13 33. Driven piles are found in Division 31, as well as sheet piling, cofferdams, and riprap.

Reference Numbers

Reference numbers are shown in shaded boxes at the beginning of some major classifications. These numbers refer to related items in the Reference Section. The reference information may be an estimating procedure, an alternate pricing method, or technical information.

Note: Not all subdivisions listed here necessarily appear in this publication. ■

35 01 50.10 Cleaning of Marine Pier Piles		Crew	Daily Output	Labor-Hours	Unit	Material	2015 Bare Costs Labor	Equipment	Total	Total Incl O&P
0010	**CLEANING OF MARINE PIER PILES**									
0015	Exposed piles pressure washing from boat									
0100	Clean wood piles from boat, 8" diam., 5' length	G	B-1D	17	.941	Ea.		35.50	15.35	50.85	71.50
0110	6-10' long	G		9	1.778			67	29	96	135
0120	11-15' long	G		6.50	2.462			92.50	40	132.50	186
0130	10" diam., 5' length	G		13.75	1.164			44	18.95	62.95	88.50
0140	6-10' long	G		7.25	2.207			83	36	119	168
0150	11-15' long	G		5	3.200			120	52	172	243
0160	12" diam., 5' length	G		11.50	1.391			52.50	22.50	75	106
0170	6-10' long	G		6	2.667			100	43.50	143.50	202
0180	11-15' long	G		4.25	3.765			142	61.50	203.50	286
0190	13" diam., 5' length	G		10.50	1.524			57.50	25	82.50	116
0200	6-10' long	G		5.50	2.909			109	47.50	156.50	220
0210	11-15' long	G		4	4			150	65	215	305
0220	14" diam., 5' length	G		9.75	1.641			61.50	27	88.50	125
0230	6-10' long	G		5.25	3.048			115	49.50	164.50	231
0240	11-15' long	G		3.75	4.267			160	69.50	229.50	325
0300	Clean concrete piles from boat, 12" diam., 5' length	G		14	1.143			43	18.65	61.65	86.50
0310	6-10' long	G		7.25	2.207			83	36	119	168
0320	11-15' long	G		5	3.200			120	52	172	243
0330	14" diam., 5' length	G		12	1.333			50	21.50	71.50	101
0340	6-10' long	G		6.25	2.560			96.50	41.50	138	194
0350	11-15' long	G		4.50	3.556			134	58	192	270
0360	16" diam., 5' length	G		10.50	1.524			57.50	25	82.50	116
0370	6-10' long	G		5.50	2.909			109	47.50	156.50	220
0380	11-15' long	G		4	4			150	65	215	305
0390	18" diam., 5' length	G		9.25	1.730			65	28	93	131
0400	6-10' long	G		5	3.200			120	52	172	243
0410	11-15' long	G		3.50	4.571			172	74.50	246.50	345
0420	20" diam., 5' length	G		8.50	1.882			71	30.50	101.50	143
0430	6-10' long	G		4.50	3.556			134	58	192	270
0440	11-15' long	G		3	5.333			201	87	288	405
0450	24" diam., 5' length	G		7	2.286			86	37.50	123.50	173
0460	6-10' long	G		3.75	4.267			160	69.50	229.50	325
0470	11-15' long	G		2.50	6.400			241	104	345	485
0480	36" diam., 5' length	G		4.75	3.368			127	55	182	256
0490	6-10' long	G		2.50	6.400			241	104	345	485
0500	11-15' long	G		1.75	9.143			345	149	494	695
0510	54" diam., 5' length	G		3	5.333			201	87	288	405
0520	6-10' long	G		1.75	9.143			345	149	494	695
0530	11-15' long	G		1.25	12.800			480	209	689	970
0540	66" diam., 5' length	G		2.50	6.400			241	104	345	485
0550	6-10' long	G		1.50	10.667			400	174	574	805
0560	11-15' long	G		1	16			600	261	861	1,200
0600	10" square pile, 5' length	G		13.25	1.208			45.50	19.70	65.20	91.50
0610	6-10' long	G		7	2.286			86	37.50	123.50	173
0620	11-15' long	G		4.75	3.368			127	55	182	256
0630	12" square pile, 5' length	G		11	1.455			54.50	23.50	78	110
0640	6-10' long	G		5.75	2.783			105	45.50	150.50	211
0650	11-15' long	G		4	4			150	65	215	305
0660	14" square pile, 5' length	G		9.50	1.684			63.50	27.50	91	128
0670	6-10' long	G		5	3.200			120	52	172	243
0680	11-15' long	G		3.50	4.571			172	74.50	246.50	345

35 01 Operation and Maint. of Waterway & Marine Construction

35 01 50 – Operation and Maintenance of Marine Construction

35 01 50.10 Cleaning of Marine Pier Piles		Crew	Daily Output	Labor-Hours	Unit	Material	2015 Bare Costs Labor	Equipment	Total	Total Incl O&P
0690	16" square pile, 5' length	G	B-1D	8.25	1.939	Ea.		73	31.50	104.50	147
0700	6-10' long	G		4.25	3.765			142	61.50	203.50	286
0710	11-15' long	G		3	5.333			201	87	288	405
0720	18" square pile, 5' length	G		7.25	2.207			83	36	119	168
0730	6-10' long	G		3.75	4.267			160	69.50	229.50	325
0740	11-15' long	G		2.75	5.818			219	95	314	440
0750	20" square pile, 5' length	G		6.50	2.462			92.50	40	132.50	186
0760	6-10' long	G		3.50	4.571			172	74.50	246.50	345
0770	11-15' long	G		2.50	6.400			241	104	345	485
0780	24" square pile, 5' length	G		5.50	2.909			109	47.50	156.50	220
0790	6-10' long	G		3	5.333			201	87	288	405
0800	11-15' long	G		2	8			300	130	430	610
0810	14" diameter Octagonal piles, 5' length	G		12.50	1.280			48	21	69	97
0820	6-10' long	G		6.50	2.462			92.50	40	132.50	186
0830	11-15' long	G		4.50	3.556			134	58	192	270
0840	16" diameter Octagonal piles, 5' length	G		11	1.455			54.50	23.50	78	110
0850	6-10' long	G		5.75	2.783			105	45.50	150.50	211
0860	11-15' long	G		4	4			150	65	215	305
0870	18" diameter Octagonal piles, 5' length	G		9.75	1.641			61.50	27	88.50	125
0880	6-10' long	G		5	3.200			120	52	172	243
0890	11-15' long	G		3.50	4.571			172	74.50	246.50	345
0900	20" diameter Octagonal piles, 5' length	G		8.75	1.829			69	30	99	139
0910	6-10' long	G		4.50	3.556			134	58	192	270
0920	11-15' long	G		3.25	4.923			185	80.50	265.50	375
0930	24" diameter Octagonal piles, 5' length	G		7.25	2.207			83	36	119	168
0940	6-10' long	G		3.75	4.267			160	69.50	229.50	325
0950	11-15' long	G		2.75	5.818			219	95	314	440
1000	Clean steel piles from boat, 8" diam., 5' length	G		14.50	1.103			41.50	18	59.50	84
1010	6-10' long	G		7.75	2.065			77.50	33.50	111	156
1020	11-15' long	G		5.50	2.909			109	47.50	156.50	220
1030	10" diam., 5' length	G		11.50	1.391			52.50	22.50	75	106
1040	6-10' long	G		6	2.667			100	43.50	143.50	202
1050	11-15' long	G		4.50	3.556			134	58	192	270
1060	12" diam., 5' length	G		9.50	1.684			63.50	27.50	91	128
1070	6-10' long	G		5	3.200			120	52	172	243
1080	11-15' long	G		3.75	4.267			160	69.50	229.50	325
1100	HP 8 x 36, 5' length	G		7.50	2.133			80	35	115	162
1110	6-10' long	G		4	4			150	65	215	305
1120	11-15' long	G		3	5.333			201	87	288	405
1130	HP 10 x 42, 5' length	G		6.25	2.560			96.50	41.50	138	194
1140	6-10' long	G		3.25	4.923			185	80.50	265.50	375
1150	11-15' long	G		2.30	6.957			262	113	375	525
1160	HP 10 x 57, 5' length	G		6	2.667			100	43.50	143.50	202
1170	6-10' long	G		3.25	4.923			185	80.50	265.50	375
1180	11-15' long	G		2.30	6.957			262	113	375	525
1200	HP 12 x 53, 5' length	G		5	3.200			120	52	172	243
1210	6-10' long	G		2.75	5.818			219	95	314	440
1220	11-15' long	G		2	8			300	130	430	610
1230	HP 12 x 74, 5' length	G		5	3.200			120	52	172	243
1240	6-10' long	G		2.75	5.818			219	95	314	440
1250	11-15' long	G		1.90	8.421			315	137	452	635
1300	HP 14 x 73, 5' length	G		4.25	3.765			142	61.50	203.50	286
1310	6-10' long	G		2.33	6.867			258	112	370	520

For customer support on your Site Work & Landscape Cost Data, call 877.737.1594.

523

35 01 50.10 Cleaning of Marine Pier Piles

		Crew	Daily Output	Labor-Hours	Unit	Material	2015 Bare Costs Labor	Equipment	Total	Total Incl O&P
1320	11-15' long	G B-1D	1.60	10	Ea.		375	163	538	760
1330	HP 14 x 89, 5' length	G	4.25	3.765			142	61.50	203.50	286
1340	6-10' long	G	2.33	6.867			258	112	370	520
1350	11-15' long	G	1.60	10			375	163	538	760
1360	HP 14 x 102, 5' length	G	4.25	3.765			142	61.50	203.50	286
1370	6-10' long	G	2.33	6.867			258	112	370	520
1380	11-15' long	G	1.60	10			375	163	538	760
1385	HP 14 x 117, 5' length	G	4.25	3.765			142	61.50	203.50	286
1390	6-10' long	G	2.33	6.867			258	112	370	520
1395	11-15' long	G	1.60	10			375	163	538	760

35 01 50.20 Protective Wrapping of Marine Pier Piles

		Crew	Daily Output	Labor-Hours	Unit	Material	2015 Bare Costs Labor	Equipment	Total	Total Incl O&P
0010	**PROTECTIVE WRAPPING OF MARINE PIER PILES**									
0015	Exposed piles wrapped using boat									
0020	Note: piles must be cleaned before wrapping									
0100	Wrap protective material on wood piles with nails 8" diameter	G B-1G	162	.099	V.L.F.	16.75	3.71	1.07	21.53	25.50
0110	10" diameter	G	130	.123		21	4.63	1.33	26.96	31.50
0120	12" diameter	G	108	.148		25	5.55	1.60	32.15	38
0130	13" diameter	G	99	.162		27.50	6.10	1.75	35.35	41.50
0140	14" diameter	G	93	.172		29.50	6.45	1.86	37.81	44.50
0150	Wrap protective material on wood piles, straps, 8" diam.	G	180	.089		26	3.34	.96	30.30	34.50
0160	10" diameter	G	144	.111		32.50	4.18	1.20	37.88	43.50
0170	12" diameter	G	120	.133		39	5	1.44	45.44	52
0180	13" diameter	G	110	.145		42	5.45	1.58	49.03	56
0190	14" diameter	G	103	.155		45	5.85	1.68	52.53	60.50
0200	Wrap protective material on concrete piles, straps, 12" diam.	G	120	.133		39	5	1.44	45.44	52
0210	14" diam.	G	103	.155		45	5.85	1.68	52.53	60.50
0220	16" diam.	G	90	.178		51.50	6.70	1.93	60.13	69.50
0230	18" diam.	G	80	.200		58	7.50	2.17	67.67	78
0240	20" diam.	G	72	.222		64.50	8.35	2.41	75.26	86.50
0250	24" diam.	G	60	.267		77.50	10.05	2.89	90.44	104
0260	36" diam.	G	40	.400		116	15.05	4.33	135.38	156
0270	54" diam.	G	27	.593		174	22.50	6.40	202.90	234
0280	66" diam.	G	22	.727		213	27.50	7.90	248.40	285
0300	Wrap protective material on concrete piles, straps, 10" square	G	113	.142		41	5.30	1.53	47.83	55.50
0310	12" square	G	94	.170		49.50	6.40	1.84	57.74	66
0320	14" square	G	81	.198		57.50	7.45	2.14	67.09	77.50
0330	16" square	G	71	.225		66	8.45	2.44	76.89	88
0340	18" square	G	63	.254		74	9.55	2.75	86.30	99
0350	20" square	G	63	.254		82	9.55	2.75	94.30	108
0360	24" square	G	47	.340		98.50	12.80	3.69	114.99	133
0400	Wrap protective material, concrete piles, straps, 14" octagon	G	107	.150		43.50	5.60	1.62	50.72	58
0410	16" octagon	G	94	.170		49.50	6.40	1.84	57.74	66.50
0420	18" octagon	G	83	.193		56	7.25	2.09	65.34	75
0430	20" octagon	G	75	.213		62	8	2.31	72.31	83
0440	24" octagon	G	62	.258		74.50	9.70	2.79	86.99	100
0500	Wrap protective material, steel piles, straps, HP 8 x 36	G	90	.178		65.50	6.70	1.93	74.13	84.50
0510	HP 10 x 42	G	72	.222		80.50	8.35	2.41	91.26	104
0520	HP 10 x 57	G	72	.222		82	8.35	2.41	92.76	106
0530	HP 12 x 53	G	60	.267		97	10.05	2.89	109.94	126
0540	HP 12 x 74	G	60	.267		98.50	10.05	2.89	111.44	127
0550	HP 14 x 73	G	52	.308		115	11.55	3.33	129.88	147
0560	HP 14 x 89	G	52	.308		117	11.55	3.33	131.88	149

524

For customer support on your Site Work & Landscape Cost Data, call 877.737.1594.

35 01 Operation and Maint. of Waterway & Marine Construction

35 01 50 – Operation and Maintenance of Marine Construction

35 01 50.20 Protective Wrapping of Marine Pier Piles		Crew	Daily Output	Labor-Hours	Unit	Material	2015 Bare Costs Labor	Equipment	Total	Total Incl O&P
0570	HP 14 x 102	[G] B-1G	52	.308	V.L.F.	117	11.55	3.33	131.88	149
0580	HP 14 x 117	[G]	52	.308		118	11.55	3.33	132.88	151

35 20 Waterway and Marine Construction and Equipment

35 20 16 – Hydraulic Gates

35 20 16.26 Hydraulic Sluice Gates

		Crew	Daily Output	Labor-Hours	Unit	Material	2015 Bare Costs Labor	Equipment	Total	Total Incl O&P
0010	**HYDRAULIC SLUICE GATES**									
0100	Heavy duty, self contained w/crank oper. gate, 18" x 18"	L-5A	1.70	18.824	Ea.	8,750	995	355	10,100	11,700
0110	24" x 24"		1.20	26.667		12,800	1,400	500	14,700	17,000
0120	30" x 30"		1	32		13,600	1,700	600	15,900	18,400
0130	36" x 36"		.90	35.556		16,400	1,875	665	18,940	22,000
0140	42" x 42"		.80	40		18,900	2,125	750	21,775	25,100
0150	48" x 48"		.50	64		20,800	3,375	1,200	25,375	29,900
0160	54" x 54"		.40	80		28,200	4,225	1,500	33,925	39,900
0170	60" x 60"		.30	106		30,900	5,650	2,000	38,550	45,600
0180	66" x 66"		.30	106		36,200	5,650	2,000	43,850	51,500
0190	72" x 72"		.20	160		40,200	8,475	3,000	51,675	62,000
0200	78" x 78"		.20	160		51,500	8,475	3,000	62,975	74,000
0210	84" x 84"		.10	320		56,000	16,900	6,000	78,900	97,000
0220	90" x 90"	E-20	.30	213		67,000	11,100	3,875	81,975	96,500
0230	96" x 96"		.30	213		71,000	11,100	3,875	85,975	101,500
0240	108" x 108"		.20	320		81,000	16,600	5,825	103,425	123,500
0250	120" x 120"		.10	640		89,500	33,200	11,600	134,300	167,500
0260	132" x 132"		.10	640		110,000	33,200	11,600	154,800	190,000

35 20 16.63 Canal Gates

		Crew	Daily Output	Labor-Hours	Unit	Material	2015 Bare Costs Labor	Equipment	Total	Total Incl O&P
0010	**CANAL GATES**									
0011	Cast iron body, fabricated frame									
0100	12" diameter	L-5A	4.60	6.957	Ea.	1,250	370	130	1,750	2,150
0110	18" diameter		4	8		1,450	425	150	2,025	2,475
0120	24" diameter		3.50	9.143		2,700	485	171	3,356	3,950
0130	30" diameter		2.80	11.429		3,075	605	214	3,894	4,650
0140	36" diameter		2.30	13.913		5,750	735	261	6,746	7,850
0150	42" diameter		1.70	18.824		11,000	995	355	12,350	14,200
0160	48" diameter		1.20	26.667		12,000	1,400	500	13,900	16,100
0170	54" diameter		.90	35.556		12,600	1,875	665	15,140	17,800
0180	60" diameter		.50	64		14,400	3,375	1,200	18,975	22,800
0190	66" diameter		.50	64		18,000	3,375	1,200	22,575	26,800
0200	72" diameter		.40	80		24,000	4,225	1,500	29,725	35,200

35 20 16.66 Flap Gates

		Crew	Daily Output	Labor-Hours	Unit	Material	2015 Bare Costs Labor	Equipment	Total	Total Incl O&P
0010	**FLAP GATES**									
0100	Aluminum, 18" diameter	L-5A	5	6.400	Ea.	2,250	340	120	2,710	3,175
0110	24" diameter		4	8		2,850	425	150	3,425	4,000
0120	30" diameter		3.50	9.143		3,900	485	171	4,556	5,300
0130	36" diameter		2.80	11.429		4,850	605	214	5,669	6,575
0140	42" diameter		2.30	13.913		5,575	735	261	6,571	7,650
0150	48" diameter		1.70	18.824		6,375	995	355	7,725	9,100
0160	54" diameter		1.20	26.667		7,050	1,400	500	8,950	10,700
0170	60" diameter		.80	40		7,850	2,125	750	10,725	13,000
0180	66" diameter		.50	64		8,425	3,375	1,200	13,000	16,300
0190	72" diameter		.40	80		9,925	4,225	1,500	15,650	19,700

For customer support on your Site Work & Landscape Cost Data, call 877.737.1594.

525

35 20 16 – Hydraulic Gates

35 20 16.69 Knife Gates		Crew	Daily Output	Labor-Hours	Unit	Material	2015 Bare Costs Labor	2015 Bare Costs Equipment	Total	Total Incl O&P
0010	**KNIFE GATES**									
0100	Incl. handwheel operator for hub, 6" diameter	Q-23	7.70	3.117	Ea.	1,400	177	123	1,700	1,925
0110	8" diameter		7.20	3.333		1,725	189	132	2,046	2,325
0120	10" diameter		4.80	5		2,525	283	198	3,006	3,425
0130	12" diameter		3.60	6.667		3,525	380	264	4,169	4,725
0140	14" diameter		3.40	7.059		4,850	400	279	5,529	6,250
0150	16" diameter		3.20	7.500		6,500	425	297	7,222	8,125
0160	18" diameter		3	8		8,850	455	315	9,620	10,800
0170	20" diameter		2.70	8.889		12,200	505	350	13,055	14,600
0180	24" diameter		2.40	10		15,800	565	395	16,760	18,700
0190	30" diameter		1.80	13.333		32,800	755	525	34,080	37,800
0200	36" diameter		1.20	20		43,200	1,125	790	45,115	50,000

35 20 16.73 Slide Gates

	35 20 16.73 Slide Gates	Crew	Daily Output	Labor-Hours	Unit	Material	Labor	Equipment	Total	Total Incl O&P
0010	**SLIDE GATES**									
0100	Steel, self contained incl. anchor bolts and grout, 12" x 12"	L-5A	4.60	6.957	Ea.	4,950	370	130	5,450	6,225
0110	18" x 18"		4	8		5,125	425	150	5,700	6,500
0120	24" x 24"		3.50	9.143		5,825	485	171	6,481	7,400
0130	30" x 30"		2.80	11.429		6,250	605	214	7,069	8,125
0140	36" x 36"		2.30	13.913		6,575	735	261	7,571	8,775
0150	42" x 42"		1.70	18.824		7,225	995	355	8,575	10,000
0160	48" x 48"		1.20	26.667		7,725	1,400	500	9,625	11,400
0170	54" x 54"		.90	35.556		8,400	1,875	665	10,940	13,100
0180	60" x 60"		.55	58.182		8,600	3,075	1,100	12,775	15,900
0190	72" x 72"		.36	88.889		10,900	4,700	1,675	17,275	21,800

35 20 23 – Dredging

35 20 23.13 Mechanical Dredging

	35 20 23.13 Mechanical Dredging	Crew	Daily Output	Labor-Hours	Unit	Material	Labor	Equipment	Total	Total Incl O&P
0010	**MECHANICAL DREDGING**									
0020	Dredging mobilization and demobilization, add to below, minimum	B-8	.53	120	Total		5,150	6,250	11,400	14,700
0100	Maximum	"	.10	640	"		27,300	33,100	60,400	78,000
0300	Barge mounted clamshell excavation into scows									
0310	Dumped 20 miles at sea, minimum	B-57	310	.155	B.C.Y.		6.70	5.40	12.10	16.20
0400	Maximum	"	213	.225	"		9.80	7.90	17.70	23.50
0500	Barge mounted dragline or clamshell, hopper dumped,									
0510	pumped 1000' to shore dump, minimum	B-57	340	.141	B.C.Y.		6.10	4.94	11.04	14.80
0525	All pumping uses 2000 gallons of water per cubic yard									
0600	Maximum	B-57	243	.198	B.C.Y.		8.55	6.90	15.45	20.50

35 20 23.23 Hydraulic Dredging

	35 20 23.23 Hydraulic Dredging	Crew	Daily Output	Labor-Hours	Unit	Material	Labor	Equipment	Total	Total Incl O&P
0010	**HYDRAULIC DREDGING**									
1000	Hydraulic method, pumped 1000' to shore dump, minimum	B-57	460	.104	B.C.Y.		4.53	3.65	8.18	10.90
1100	Maximum		310	.155			6.70	5.40	12.10	16.20
1400	Into scows dumped 20 miles, minimum		425	.113			4.90	3.95	8.85	11.85
1500	Maximum		243	.198			8.55	6.90	15.45	20.50
1600	For inland rivers and canals in South, deduct							30%		30%

526

For customer support on your Site Work & Landscape Cost Data, call 877.737.1594.

35 31 Shoreline Protection

35 31 16 – Seawalls

35 31 16.13 Concrete Seawalls

35 31 16.13 Concrete Seawalls	Crew	Daily Output	Labor-Hours	Unit	Material	2015 Bare Costs Labor	Equipment	Total	Total Incl O&P
0010 **CONCRETE SEAWALLS**									
0011 Reinforced concrete									
0015 include footing and tie-backs									
0020 Up to 6' high, minimum	C-17C	28	2.964	L.F.	51	146	22	219	305
0060 Maximum		24.25	3.423		81.50	168	25	274.50	375
0100 12' high, minimum		20	4.150		132	204	30.50	366.50	495
0160 Maximum		18.50	4.486		153	221	33	407	545
0180 Precast bulkhead, complete, including									
0190 vertical and battered piles, face panels, and cap									
0195 Using 16' vertical piles				L.F.				445	515
0196 Using 20' vertical piles				"				475	550

35 31 16.19 Steel Sheet Piling Seawalls

	Crew	Daily Output	Labor-Hours	Unit	Material	2015 Bare Costs Labor	Equipment	Total	Total Incl O&P
0010 **STEEL SHEET PILING SEAWALLS**									
0200 Steel sheeting, with 4' x 4' x 8" concrete deadmen, @ 10' O.C.									
0210 12' high, shore driven	B-40	27	2.370	L.F.	107	113	139	359	445
0260 Barge driven	B-76	15	4.800	"	160	228	221	609	775
6000 Crushed stone placed behind bulkhead by clam bucket	B-12H	120	.133	L.C.Y.	20	5.95	10	35.95	42

35 31 19 – Revetments

35 31 19.18 Revetments, Concrete

	Crew	Daily Output	Labor-Hours	Unit	Material	2015 Bare Costs Labor	Equipment	Total	Total Incl O&P
0010 **REVETMENTS, CONCRETE**									
0100 Concrete revetment matt 8' x 20' x 4 1/2" excluding site preparation									
0110 Includes all labor, material and equip. for complete installation				Ea.	3,350			3,350	3,700

35 49 Waterway Structures

35 49 13 – Floodwalls

35 49 13.30 Breakwaters, Bulkheads, Residential Canal

	Crew	Daily Output	Labor-Hours	Unit	Material	2015 Bare Costs Labor	Equipment	Total	Total Incl O&P
0010 **BREAKWATERS, BULKHEADS, RESIDENTIAL CANAL**									
0020 Aluminum panel sheeting, incl. concrete cap and anchor									
0030 Coarse compact sand, 4'-0" high, 2'-0" embedment	B-40	200	.320	L.F.	63	15.25	18.70	96.95	113
0040 3'-6" embedment		140	.457		74	22	26.50	122.50	145
0060 6'-0" embedment		90	.711		94.50	34	41.50	170	203
0120 6'-0" high, 2'-6" embedment		170	.376		80	17.95	22	119.95	140
0140 4'-0" embedment		125	.512		94.50	24.50	30	149	175
0160 5'-6" embedment		95	.674		124	32	39.50	195.50	231
0220 8'-0" high, 3'-6" embedment		140	.457		108	22	26.50	156.50	182
0240 5'-0" embedment		100	.640		108	30.50	37.50	176	207
0420 Medium compact sand, 3'-0" high, 2'-0" embedment		235	.272		138	12.95	15.95	166.90	190
0440 4'-0" embedment		150	.427		170	20.50	25	215.50	246
0460 5'-6" embedment		115	.557		206	26.50	32.50	265	305
0520 5'-0" high, 3'-6" embedment		165	.388		192	18.50	22.50	233	265
0540 5'-0" embedment		120	.533		221	25.50	31	277.50	320
0560 6'-6" embedment		105	.610		288	29	35.50	352.50	400
0620 7'-0" high, 4'-6" embedment		135	.474		250	22.50	27.50	300	340
0640 6'-0" embedment		110	.582		276	27.50	34	337.50	385
0720 Loose silty sand, 3'-0" high, 3'-0" embedment		205	.312		138	14.85	18.25	171.10	195
0740 4'-6" embedment		155	.413		167	19.65	24	210.65	240
0760 6'-0" embedment		125	.512		195	24.50	30	249.50	286
0820 4'-6" high, 4'-6" embedment		155	.413		192	19.65	24	235.65	268
0840 6'-0" embedment		125	.512		222	24.50	30	276.50	315
0860 7'-0" embedment		115	.557		269	26.50	32.50	328	375

35 49 Waterway Structures

35 49 13 – Floodwalls

35 49 13.30 Breakwaters, Bulkheads, Residential Canal	Crew	Daily Output	Labor-Hours	Unit	Material	2015 Bare Costs Labor	Equipment	Total	Total Incl O&P
0920	6'-0" high, 5'-6" embedment	B-40	130	.492	L.F.	250	23.50	29	302.50	345
0940	7'-0" embedment		115	.557		276	26.50	32.50	335	385

35 51 Floating Construction

35 51 13 – Floating Piers

35 51 13.23 Floating Wood Piers

		Crew	Daily Output	Labor-Hours	Unit	Material	2015 Bare Costs Labor	Equipment	Total	Total Incl O&P
0010	**FLOATING WOOD PIERS**									
0020	Polyethylene encased polystyrene, no pilings included	F-3	330	.121	S.F.	29	5.80	1.98	36.78	43
0030	See Section 06 13 33.50 or Section 06 13 33.52 for fixed docks									
0200	Pile supported, shore constructed, bare, 3" decking	F-3	130	.308	S.F.	28	14.75	5.05	47.80	58.50
0250	4" decking		120	.333		29	15.95	5.45	50.40	62.50
0400	Floating, small boat, prefab, no shore facilities, minimum		250	.160		24.50	7.65	2.62	34.77	41.50
0500	Maximum		150	.267		52	12.75	4.36	69.11	81.50
0700	Per slip, minimum (180 S.F. each)		1.59	25.157	Ea.	5,000	1,200	410	6,610	7,800
0800	Maximum		1.40	28.571	"	8,400	1,375	465	10,240	11,900

35 51 13.24 Jetties, Docks

		Crew	Daily Output	Labor-Hours	Unit	Material	2015 Bare Costs Labor	Equipment	Total	Total Incl O&P
0010	**JETTIES, DOCKS**									
0011	Floating including anchors									
0030	See Section 06 13 33.50 or Section 06 13 33.52 for fixed docks									
1000	Polystyrene flotation, minimum	F-3	200	.200	S.F.	27.50	9.60	3.27	40.37	48.50
1040	Maximum		135	.296	"	35.50	14.20	4.84	54.54	66.50
1100	Alternate method of figuring, minimum		1.13	35.398	Slip	5,025	1,700	580	7,305	8,750
1140	Maximum		.70	57.143	"	7,200	2,725	935	10,860	13,100
1200	Galv. steel frame and wood deck, 3' wide, minimum		320	.125	S.F.	17.10	6	2.04	25.14	30.50
1240	Maximum		200	.200		27.50	9.60	3.27	40.37	49
1300	4' wide, minimum		320	.125		17.35	6	2.04	25.39	30.50
1340	Maximum		200	.200		27.50	9.60	3.27	40.37	49
1500	8' wide, minimum		250	.160		18.90	7.65	2.62	29.17	35.50
1540	Maximum		160	.250		28.50	12	4.09	44.59	54.50
1700	Treated wood frames and deck, 3' wide, minimum		250	.160		19.20	7.65	2.62	29.47	35.50
1740	Maximum		125	.320		66	15.35	5.25	86.60	102
2000	Polyethylene drums, treated wood frame and deck									
2100	6' wide, minimum	F-3	250	.160	S.F.	32.50	7.65	2.62	42.77	50.50
2140	Maximum		125	.320		43.50	15.35	5.25	64.10	77
2200	8' wide, minimum		233	.172		26.50	8.20	2.81	37.51	44.50
2240	Maximum		120	.333		36.50	15.95	5.45	57.90	70.50
2300	10' wide, minimum		200	.200		29	9.60	3.27	41.87	50.50
2340	Maximum		110	.364		40	17.40	5.95	63.35	77
2400	Concrete pontoons, treated wood frame and deck									
2500	Breakwater, concrete pontoon, 50' L x 8' W x 6.5' D	F-4	4	12	Ea.	46,200	570	282	47,052	52,000
2600	Inland breakwater, concrete pontoon, 50' L x 8' W x 4' D		4	12	"	44,100	570	282	44,952	49,700
2700	Docks, concrete pontoon w/treated wood deck		2400	.020	S.F.	110	.95	.47	111.42	123
2800	Docks, concrete pontoons docks 400 S.F. minimum order									

35 51 13.28 Jetties, Floating Dock Accessories

		Crew	Daily Output	Labor-Hours	Unit	Material	2015 Bare Costs Labor	Equipment	Total	Total Incl O&P
0010	**JETTIES, FLOATING DOCK ACCESSORIES**									
0200	Dock connectors, stressed cables with rubber spacers									
0220	25" long, 3' wide dock	1 Clab	2	4	Joint	209	150		359	460
0240	5' wide dock		2	4		244	150		394	500
0400	38" long, 4' wide dock		1.75	4.571		229	172		401	515
0440	6' wide dock		1.45	5.517		260	207		467	605

35 51 Floating Construction

35 51 13 – Floating Piers

35 51 13.28 Jetties, Floating Dock Accessories		Crew	Daily Output	Labor-Hours	Unit	Material	2015 Bare Costs Labor	Equipment	Total	Total Incl O&P
1000	Gangway, aluminum, one end rolling, no hand rails									
1020	3' wide, minimum	1 Clab	67	.119	L.F.	199	4.49		203.49	226
1040	Maximum		32	.250		229	9.40		238.40	266
1100	4' wide, minimum		40	.200		211	7.50		218.50	244
1140	Maximum		24	.333		243	12.55		255.55	286
1180	For handrails, add					71			71	78.50
2000	Pile guides, beads on stainless cable	1 Clab	4	2	Ea.	182	75		257	315
2020	Rod type, 8" diameter piles, minimum		4	2		49.50	75		124.50	171
2040	Maximum		2	4		72.50	150		222.50	310
2100	10" to 14" diameter piles minimum		3.20	2.500		57.50	94		151.50	208
2140	Maximum		1.75	4.571		100	172		272	375
2200	Roller type, 4 rollers, minimum		4	2		164	75		239	296
2240	Maximum		1.75	4.571		234	172		406	520

35 59 Marine Specialties

35 59 33 – Marine Bollards and Cleats

35 59 33.50 Jetties, Dock Accessories		Crew	Daily Output	Labor-Hours	Unit	Material	2015 Bare Costs Labor	Equipment	Total	Total Incl O&P
0010	**JETTIES, DOCK ACCESSORIES**									
0100	Cleats, aluminum, "S" type, 12" long	1 Clab	8	1	Ea.	25.50	37.50		63	86
0140	10" long		6.70	1.194		61.50	45		106.50	137
0180	15" long		6	1.333		81	50		131	166
0400	Dock wheel for corners and piles, vinyl, 12" diameter		4	2		74	75		149	198
1000	Electrical receptacle with circuit breaker,									
1020	Pile mounted, double 30 amp, 125 volt	1 Elec	2	4	Unit	805	219		1,024	1,225
1060	Double 50 amp, 125/240 volt		1.60	5		1,075	274		1,349	1,600
1120	Free standing, add		4	2		198	109		307	380
1140	Double free standing, add		2.70	2.963		184	162		346	445
1160	Light, 2 louvered, with photo electric switch, add		8	1		201	54.50		255.50	305
1180	Telephone jack on stanchion		8	1		200	54.50		254.50	300
1300	Fender, Vinyl, 4" high	1 Clab	160	.050	L.F.	13.40	1.88		15.28	17.60
1380	Corner piece		80	.100	Ea.	16.85	3.76		20.61	24.50
1400	Hose holder, cast aluminum		16	.500	"	51	18.80		69.80	85
1500	Ladder, aluminum, heavy duty									
1520	Crown top, 5 to 7 step, minimum	1 Clab	5.30	1.509	Ea.	163	57		220	268
1560	Maximum		2	4		263	150		413	520
1580	Bracket for portable clamp mounting		8	1		9.35	37.50		46.85	68.50
1800	Line holder, treated wood, small		16	.500		8.75	18.80		27.55	38.50
1840	Large		13.30	.602		14.90	22.50		37.40	51.50
2000	Mooring whip, fiberglass bolted to dock,									
2020	1200 lb. boat	1 Clab	8.80	.909	Pr.	345	34		379	435
2040	10,000 lb. boat		6.70	1.194		700	45		745	840
2080	60,000 lb. boat		4	2		815	75		890	1,025
2400	Shock absorbing tubing, vertical bumpers									
2420	3" diam., vinyl, white	1 Clab	80	.100	L.F.	4.76	3.76		8.52	11.05
2440	Polybutyl, clear		80	.100	"	5.30	3.76		9.06	11.60
2480	Mounts, polybutyl		20	.400	Ea.	5.55	15.05		20.60	29
2490	Deluxe		20	.400	"	12.40	15.05		27.45	36.50

For customer support on your Site Work & Landscape Cost Data, call 877.737.1594.

529

Division Notes

		CREW	DAILY OUTPUT	LABOR-HOURS	UNIT	BARE COSTS				TOTAL INCL O&P
						MAT.	LABOR	EQUIP.	TOTAL	

Estimating Tips

Products such as conveyors, material handling cranes and hoists, as well as other items specified in this division, require trained installers. The general contractor may not have any choice as to who will perform the installation or when it will be performed. Long lead times are often required for these products, making early decisions in purchasing and scheduling necessary. The installation of this type of equipment may require the embedment of mounting hardware during construction of floors, structural walls, or interior walls/partitions. Electrical connections will require coordination with the electrical contractor.

Reference Numbers

Reference numbers are shown in shaded boxes at the beginning of some major classifications. These numbers refer to related items in the Reference Section. The reference information may be an estimating procedure, an alternate pricing method, or technical information.

Note: Not all subdivisions listed here necessarily appear in this publication. ■

Did you know?

RSMeans Online gives you the same access to RSMeans' data with 24/7 access:
- Quickly locate costs in the searchable database.
- Build cost lists, estimates, and reports in minutes.
- Adjust costs to any location in the U.S. and Canada with the click of a button.

Start your free trial today at **www.rsmeansonline.com**

RSMeansOnline

41 21 Conveyors

41 21 23 – Piece Material Conveyors

41 21 23.16 Container Piece Material Conveyors	Crew	Daily Output	Labor-Hours	Unit	Material	2015 Bare Costs Labor	Equipment	Total	Total Incl O&P
0010 **CONTAINER PIECE MATERIAL CONVEYORS**									
0020 Gravity fed, 2" rollers, 3" O.C.									
0050 10' sections with 2 supports, 600 lb. capacity, 18" wide				Ea.	480			480	530
0350 Horizontal belt, center drive and takeup, 60 fpm									
0400 16" belt, 26.5' length	2 Mill	.50	32	Ea.	3,350	1,575		4,925	6,025
0600 Inclined belt, 10' rise with horizontal loader and									
0620 End idler assembly, 27.5' length, 18" belt	2 Mill	.30	53.333	Ea.	7,300	2,625		9,925	11,900

41 22 Cranes and Hoists

41 22 13 – Cranes

41 22 13.10 Crane Rail

		Crew	Daily Output	Labor-Hours	Unit	Material	2015 Bare Costs Labor	Equipment	Total	Total Incl O&P
0010	**CRANE RAIL**									
0020	Box beam bridge, no equipment included	E-4	3400	.009	Lb.	1.33	.50	.04	1.87	2.38
0200	Running track only, 104 lb. per yard	"	5600	.006	"	.66	.30	.03	.99	1.29

41 22 23 – Hoists

41 22 23.10 Material Handling

		Crew	Daily Output	Labor-Hours	Unit	Material	2015 Bare Costs Labor	Equipment	Total	Total Incl O&P
0010	**MATERIAL HANDLING**, cranes, hoists and lifts									
2100	Hoists, electric overhead, chain, hook hung, 15' lift, 1 ton cap.				Ea.	2,500			2,500	2,750
2500	5 ton capacity				"	6,925			6,925	7,625

For customer support on your Site Work & Landscape Cost Data, call 877.737.1594.

Estimating Tips

This division contains information about water and wastewater equipment and systems, which was formerly located in Division 44. The main areas of focus are total wastewater treatment plants and components of wastewater treatment plants. In addition, there are assemblies such as sewage treatment lagoons that can be found in some publications under G30 Site Mechanical Utilities. Also included in this section are oil/water separators for wastewater treatment.

Reference Numbers

Reference numbers are shown in shaded boxes at the beginning of some major classifications. These numbers refer to related items in the Reference Section. The reference information may be an estimating procedure, an alternate pricing method, or technical information.

Note: Not all subdivisions listed here necessarily appear in this publication. ■

46 07 Packaged Water and Wastewater Treatment Equipment

46 07 53 – Packaged Wastewater Treatment Equipment

46 07 53.10 Biological Pkg. Wastewater Treatment Plants	Crew	Daily Output	Labor-Hours	Unit	Material	2015 Bare Costs Labor	Equipment	Total	Total Incl O&P
0010 **BIOLOGICAL PACKAGED WASTEWATER TREATMENT PLANTS**									
0011 Not including fencing or external piping									
0020 Steel packaged, blown air aeration plants									
0100 1,000 GPD				Gal.				55	60.50
0200 5,000 GPD								22	24
0300 15,000 GPD								22	24
0400 30,000 GPD								15.40	16.95
0500 50,000 GPD								11	12.10
0600 100,000 GPD								9.90	10.90
0700 200,000 GPD								8.80	9.70
0800 500,000 GPD								7.70	8.45
1000 Concrete, extended aeration, primary and secondary treatment									
1010 10,000 GPD				Gal.				22	24
1100 30,000 GPD								15.40	16.95
1200 50,000 GPD								11	12.10
1400 100,000 GPD								9.90	10.90
1500 500,000 GPD								7.70	8.45
1700 Municipal wastewater treatment facility									
1720 1.0 MGD				Gal.				11	12.10
1740 1.5 MGD								10.60	11.65
1760 2.0 MGD								10	11
1780 3.0 MGD								7.80	8.60
1800 5.0 MGD								5.80	6.70
2000 Holding tank system, not incl. excavation or backfill									
2010 Recirculating chemical water closet	2 Plum	4	4	Ea.	530	235		765	940
2100 For voltage converter, add	"	16	1		300	58.50		358.50	420
2200 For high level alarm, add	1 Plum	7.80	1.026		117	60		177	219

46 07 53.20 Wastewater Treatment System

	Crew	Daily Output	Labor-Hours	Unit	Material	Labor	Equipment	Total	Total Incl O&P
0010 **WASTEWATER TREATMENT SYSTEM**									
0020 Fiberglass, 1,000 gallon	B-21	1.29	21.705	Ea.	4,250	940	107	5,297	6,250
0100 1,500 gallon	"	1.03	27.184	"	8,475	1,175	134	9,784	11,300

46 23 Grit Removal And Handling Equipment

46 23 23 – Vortex Grit Removal Equipment

46 23 23.10 Rainwater Filters

	Crew	Daily Output	Labor-Hours	Unit	Material	Labor	Equipment	Total	Total Incl O&P
0010 **RAINWATER FILTERS**									
0100 42 gal./min	B-21	3.50	8	Ea.	45,100	345	39.50	45,484.50	50,000
0200 65 gal./min		3.50	8		45,200	345	39.50	45,584.50	50,500
0300 208 gal./min		3.50	8		45,200	345	39.50	45,584.50	50,500

46 25 Oil and Grease Separation and Removal Equipment

46 25 13 – Coalescing Oil-Water Separators

46 25 13.20 Oil/Water Separators	Crew	Daily Output	Labor-Hours	Unit	Material	2015 Bare Costs Labor	Equipment	Total	Total Incl O&P
0010 **OIL/WATER SEPARATORS**									
0020 Underground, tank only									
0030 Excludes excavation, backfill, & piping									
0100 200 GPM	B-21	3.50	8	Ea.	44,900	345	39.50	45,284.50	50,000
0110 400 GPM		3.25	8.615		62,500	375	42.50	62,917.50	69,500
0120 600 GPM		2.75	10.182		70,000	440	50	70,490	77,500
0130 800 GPM		2.50	11.200		79,000	485	55	79,540	88,000
0140 1000 GPM		2	14		88,500	605	69	89,174	98,500
0150 1200 GPM		1.50	18.667		101,000	810	92	101,902	112,500
0160 1500 GPM		1	28		119,500	1,225	138	120,863	133,000

46 25 16 – API Oil-Water Separators

46 25 16.10 Oil/Water Separators	Crew	Daily Output	Labor-Hours	Unit	Material	2015 Bare Costs Labor	Equipment	Total	Total Incl O&P
0010 **OIL/WATER SEPARATORS**									
0020 Complete system, not including excavation and backfill									
0100 · Treated capacity 0.2 cubic feet per second	B-22	1	30	Ea.	5,200	1,325	207	6,732	7,950
0200 0.5 cubic foot per second	B-13	.75	74.667		8,300	3,050	980	12,330	14,900
0300 1.0 cubic foot per second		.60	93.333		15,400	3,825	1,225	20,450	24,100
0400 2.4 – 3 cubic feet per second		.30	186		23,500	7,650	2,450	33,600	40,200
0500 11 cubic feet per second		.17	329		84,000	13,500	4,325	101,825	118,000
0600 22 cubic feet per second		.10	560		126,500	23,000	7,375	156,875	182,000

46 51 Air and Gas Diffusion Equipment

46 51 13 – Floating Mechanical Aerators

46 51 13.10 Aeration Equipment

46 51 13.10 Aeration Equipment	Crew	Daily Output	Labor-Hours	Unit	Material	2015 Bare Costs Labor	Equipment	Total	Total Incl O&P
0010 **AERATION EQUIPMENT**									
0020 Aeration equipment includes floats and excludes power supply and anchorage									
4320 Surface aerator, 50 lb. oxygen/hr, 30 HP, 900 RPM, inc floats, no anchoring	B-21B	1	40	Ea.	33,600	1,625	655	35,880	40,200
4322 Anchoring aerators per cell, 6 anchors per cell	B-6	.50	48		3,600	1,975	730	6,305	7,800
4324 Anchoring aerators per cell, 8 anchors per cell	"	.33	72.727		4,975	3,000	1,100	9,075	11,300

46 51 20 – Air and Gas Handling Equipment

46 51 20.10 Blowers and System Components

46 51 20.10 Blowers and System Components	Crew	Daily Output	Labor-Hours	Unit	Material	2015 Bare Costs Labor	Equipment	Total	Total Incl O&P
0010 **BLOWERS AND SYSTEM COMPONENTS**									
0020 Rotary Lobe Blowers									
0030 Medium Pressure (7 to 14 psig)									
0120 38CFM, 2.1 BHP	Q-2	2.50	9.600	Ea.	1,250	525		1,775	2,175
0130 125 CFM, 5.5 BHP		2.40	10		1,400	550		1,950	2,375
0140 245 CFM, 10.2 BHP		2	12		1,750	655		2,405	2,925
0150 363 CFM, 14.5 BHP		1.80	13.333		2,475	730		3,205	3,825
0160 622 CFM, 24.5 BHP		1.40	17.143		4,125	940		5,065	5,950
0170 1125 CFM, 42.8 BHP		1.10	21.818		6,525	1,200		7,725	8,975
0180 1224 CFM, 47.4 BHP		1	24		9,275	1,325		10,600	12,200
0400 Prepackaged Medium Pressure (7 to 14 PSIG) Blower									
0405 incl. 3 ph. motor, filter, silencer, valves, check valve, press. gage									
0420 38CFM, 2.1 BHP	Q-2	2.50	9.600	Ea.	2,975	525		3,500	4,075
0430 125 CFM, 5.5 BHP		2.40	10		3,800	550		4,350	5,000
0440 245 CFM, 10.2 BHP		2	12		5,075	655		5,730	6,600
0450 363 CFM, 14.5 BHP		1.80	13.333		7,850	730		8,580	9,750
0460 521 CFM, 20 BHP		1.50	16		7,900	875		8,775	10,000
1010 Filters and Silencers									
1100 Silencer with paper filter									

For customer support on your Site Work & Landscape Cost Data, call 877.737.1594.

535

46 51 Air and Gas Diffusion Equipment

46 51 20 – Air and Gas Handling Equipment

46 51 20.10 Blowers and System Components

		Crew	Daily Output	Labor-Hours	Unit	Material	2015 Bare Costs Labor	Equipment	Total	Total Incl O&P
1105	1" Connection	1 Plum	14	.571	Ea.	31.50	33.50		65	85
1110	1.5" Connection		11	.727		37	42.50		79.50	106
1115	2" Connection		9	.889		127	52		179	219
1120	2.5" Connection		8	1		137	58.50		195.50	240
1125	3" Connection	Q-1	8	2		135	106		241	310
1130	4" Connection	"	5	3.200		279	169		448	560
1135	5" Connection	Q-2	5	4.800		325	263		588	750
1140	6" Connection	"	5	4.800		340	263		603	765
1300	Silencer with polyester filter									
1305	1" Connection	1 Plum	14	.571	Ea.	41	33.50		74.50	96
1310	1.5" Connection		11	.727		45	42.50		87.50	114
1315	2" Connection		9	.889		157	52		209	251
1320	2.5" Connection		8	1		157	58.50		215.50	261
1325	3" Connection	Q-1	8	2		162	106		268	340
1330	4" Connection	"	5	3.200		305	169		474	590
1335	5" Connection	Q-2	5	4.800		370	263		633	800
1340	6" Connection	"	5	4.800		415	263		678	855
1500	Chamber Silencers									
1505	1" Connection	1 Plum	14	.571	Ea.	77	33.50		110.50	135
1510	1.5" Connection		11	.727		102	42.50		144.50	177
1515	2" Connection		9	.889		135	52		187	228
1520	2.5" Connection		8	1		209	58.50		267.50	320
1525	3" Connection	Q-1	8	2		282	106		388	470
1530	4" Connection	"	5	3.200		385	169		554	675
1700	Blower Couplings									
1701	Blower Flexible Coupling									
1710	1.5" Connection	Q-1	71	.225	Ea.	30.50	11.90		42.40	51.50
1715	2" Connection		67	.239		33.50	12.60		46.10	56
1720	2.5" Connection		65	.246		39	13		52	62
1725	3" Connection		64	.250		52	13.20		65.20	77
1730	4" Connection		58	.276		62	14.55		76.55	90.50
1735	5" Connection	Q-2	83	.289		64	15.85		79.85	94.50
1740	6" Connection		79	.304		88	16.65		104.65	122
1745	8" Connection	"	69	.348		147	19.05		166.05	191

46 51 20.20 Aeration System Air Process Piping

		Crew	Daily Output	Labor-Hours	Unit	Material	2015 Bare Costs Labor	Equipment	Total	Total Incl O&P
0010	**AERATION SYSTEM AIR PROCESS PIPING**									
0100	Blower Pressure Relief Valves-adjustable									
0105	1" Diameter	1 Plum	14	.571	Ea.	108	33.50		141.50	170
0110	2" Diameter		9	.889		118	52		170	209
0115	2.5" Diameter		8	1		167	58.50		225.50	273
0120	3" Diameter	Q-1	8	2		167	106		273	345
0125	4" Diameter	"	5	3.200		187	169		356	460
0200	Blower Pressure Relief Valves-weight loaded									
0205	1" Diameter	1 Plum	14	.571	Ea.	136	33.50		169.50	201
0210	2" Diameter	"	9	.889		184	52		236	281
0220	3" Diameter	Q-1	8	2		420	106		526	625
0225	4" Diameter	"	5	3.200		610	169		779	930
0300	Pressure Relief Valves-preset high flow									
0310	2" Diameter	1 Plum	9	.889	Ea.	246	52		298	350
0320	3" Diameter	Q-1	8	2	"	530	106		636	740
1000	Check Valves, Wafer Style									
1110	2" Diameter	1 Plum	9	.889	Ea.	122	52		174	213

46 51 20.20 Aeration System Air Process Piping

		Crew	Daily Output	Labor-Hours	Unit	Material	2015 Bare Costs Labor	Equipment	Total	Total Incl O&P
1120	3" Diameter	Q-1	8	2	Ea.	146	106		252	320
1125	4" Diameter	"	5	3.200		183	169		352	455
1130	5" Diameter	Q-2	6	4		260	219		479	615
1135	6" Diameter		5	4.800		340	263		603	770
1140	8" Diameter	↓	4.50	5.333	↓	450	292		742	935
1200	Check Valves, Flanged Steel									
1210	2" Diameter	1 Plum	8	1	Ea.	282	58.50		340.50	400
1220	3" Diameter	Q-1	4.50	3.556		340	188		528	660
1225	4" Diameter	"	3	5.333		410	282		692	880
1230	5" Diameter	Q-2	3	8		610	440		1,050	1,325
1235	6" Diameter		3	8		610	440		1,050	1,325
1240	8" Diameter	↓	2.50	9.600	↓	950	525		1,475	1,850
2100	Butterfly Valves, Lever Operated-Wafer Style									
2110	2" Diameter	1 Plum	14	.571	Ea.	50	33.50		83.50	106
2120	3" Diameter	Q-1	8	2		64	106		170	231
2125	4" Diameter	"	5	3.200		102	169		271	365
2130	5" Diameter	Q-2	6	4		122	219		341	465
2135	6" Diameter		5	4.800		134	263		397	540
2140	8" Diameter		4.50	5.333		191	292		483	650
2145	10" Diameter	↓	4	6	↓	252	330		582	770
2200	Butterfly Valves, Gear Operated-Wafer Style									
2210	2" Diameter	1 Plum	14	.571	Ea.	88	33.50		121.50	148
2220	3" Diameter	Q-1	8	2		98	106		204	268
2225	4" Diameter	"	5	3.200		132	169		301	400
2230	5" Diameter	Q-2	6	4		146	219		365	490
2235	6" Diameter		5	4.800		165	263		428	575
2240	8" Diameter		4.50	5.333		248	292		540	715
2245	10" Diameter		4	6		290	330		620	815
2250	12" Diameter	↓	3	8		365	440		805	1,050

46 51 20.30 Aeration System Blower Control Panels

		Crew	Daily Output	Labor-Hours	Unit	Material	2015 Bare Costs Labor	Equipment	Total	Total Incl O&P
0010	**AERATION SYSTEM BLOWER CONTROL PANELS**									
0020	Single Phase simplex									
0030	7 to 10 overload amp range	1 Elec	2.70	2.963	Ea.	755	162		917	1,075
0040	9 to 13 overload amp range		2.70	2.963		755	162		917	1,075
0050	12 to 18 overload amp range		2.70	2.963		755	162		917	1,075
0060	16 to 24 overload amp range		2.70	2.963		755	162		917	1,075
0070	23 to 32 overload amp range		2.70	2.963		810	162		972	1,150
0080	30 to 40 overload amp range	↓	2.70	2.963	↓	810	162		972	1,150
0090	Single Phase duplex									
0100	7 to 10 overload amp range	1 Elec	2	4	Ea.	1,225	219		1,444	1,675
0110	9 to 13 overload amp range		2	4		1,225	219		1,444	1,675
0120	12 to 18 overload amp range		2	4		1,225	219		1,444	1,675
0130	16 to 24 overload amp range		2	4		1,350	219		1,569	1,825
0140	23 to 32 overload amp range		2	4		1,350	219		1,569	1,825
0150	30 to 40 overload amp range	↓	2	4	↓	1,400	219		1,619	1,850
0160	Three Phase simplex									
0170	1.6 to 2.5 overload amp range	1 Elec	2.50	3.200	Ea.	880	175		1,055	1,225
0180	2.5 to 4 overload amp range		2.50	3.200		880	175		1,055	1,225
0190	4 to 6.3 overload amp range		2.50	3.200		880	175		1,055	1,225
0200	6 to 10 overload amp range		2.50	3.200		880	175		1,055	1,225
0210	9 to 14 overload amp range		2.50	3.200		910	175		1,085	1,250
0220	13 to 18 overload amp range	↓	2.50	3.200	↓	910	175		1,085	1,250

46 51 Air and Gas Diffusion Equipment

46 51 20 – Air and Gas Handling Equipment

46 51 20.30 Aeration System Blower Control Panels	Crew	Daily Output	Labor-Hours	Unit	Material	2015 Bare Costs Labor	Equipment	Total	Total Incl O&P
0230	17 to 23 overload amp range	1 Elec	2.50	3.200	Ea.	920	175		1,095	1,275
0240	20 to 25 overload amp range		2.50	3.200		920	175		1,095	1,275
0250	23 to 32 overload amp range		2.50	3.200		1,050	175		1,225	1,400
0260	37 to 50 overload amp range		2.50	3.200		1,150	175		1,325	1,525
0270	Three Phase duplex									
0280	1.6 to 2.5 overload amp range	1 Elec	1.90	4.211	Ea.	1,225	230		1,455	1,700
0290	2.5 to 4 overload amp range		1.90	4.211		1,325	230		1,555	1,800
0300	4 to 6.3 overload amp range		1.90	4.211		1,325	230		1,555	1,800
0310	6 to 10 overload amp range		1.90	4.211		1,325	230		1,555	1,800
0320	9 to 14 overload amp range		1.90	4.211		1,325	230		1,555	1,800
0330	13 to 18 overload amp range		1.90	4.211		1,375	230		1,605	1,850
0340	17 to 23 overload amp range		1.90	4.211		1,375	230		1,605	1,875
0350	20 to 25 overload amp range		1.90	4.211		1,375	230		1,605	1,875
0360	23 to 32 overload amp range		1.90	4.211		1,625	230		1,855	2,125
0370	37 to 50 overload amp range		1.90	4.211		1,825	230		2,055	2,350

46 51 36 – Ceramic Disc Fine Bubble Diffusers

46 51 36.10 Ceramic Disc Air Diffuser Systems

		Crew	Daily Output	Labor-Hours	Unit	Material	2015 Bare Costs Labor	Equipment	Total	Total Incl O&P
0010	**CERAMIC DISC AIR DIFFUSER SYSTEMS**									
0020	Price for air diffuser pipe system by cell size excluding concrete work									
0030	Price for air diffuser pipe system by cell size excluding air supply									
0040	Depth of 12 feet is the waste depth not the cell dimensions									
0100	Ceramic disc air diffuser system, cell size 20' x 20' x 12'	2 Plum	.38	42.667	Ea.	12,200	2,500		14,700	17,300
0120	20' x 30' x 12'		.26	61.326		18,200	3,600		21,800	25,400
0140	20' x 40' x 12'		.20	80		24,100	4,700		28,800	33,600
0160	20' x 50' x 12'		.16	98.644		30,000	5,800		35,800	41,800
0180	20' x 60' x 12'		.14	117		36,000	6,875		42,875	50,000
0200	20' x 70' x 12'		.12	136		41,900	7,975		49,875	58,000
0220	20' x 80' x 12'		.10	154		47,800	9,075		56,875	66,000
0240	20' x 90' x 12'		.09	173		53,500	10,200		63,700	74,500
0260	20' x 100' x 12'		.08	192		59,500	11,300		70,800	82,500
0280	20' x 120' x 12'		.07	229		71,500	13,500		85,000	99,000
0300	20' x 140' x 12'		.06	266		83,500	15,700		99,200	115,000
0320	20' x 160' x 12'		.05	304		95,500	17,900		113,400	132,000
0340	20' x 180' x 12'		.05	341		107,000	20,000		127,000	148,000
0360	20' x 200' x 12'		.04	378		119,000	22,200		141,200	164,500
0380	20' x 250' x 12'		.03	471		148,500	27,700		176,200	205,500
0400	20' x 300' x 12'		.03	565		178,500	33,200		211,700	246,000
0420	20' x 350' x 12'		.02	658		208,000	38,700		246,700	287,000
0440	20' x 400' x 12'		.02	751		237,500	44,100		281,600	328,000
0460	20' x 450' x 12'		.02	846		267,000	49,700		316,700	369,000
0480	20' x 500' x 12'		.02	941		297,000	55,000		352,000	410,000

46 53 17 - Activated Sludge Treatment

46 53 17.10 Activated Sludge Treatment Cells	Crew	Daily Output	Labor-Hours	Unit	Material	2015 Bare Costs Labor	Equipment	Total	Total Incl O&P
0010 **ACTIVATED SLUDGE TREATMENT CELLS**									
0015 Price for cell construction excluding aerator piping & drain									
0020 Cell construction by dimensions									
0100 Treatment cell, end or single, 20' x 20' x 14' high (2' freeboard)	C-14D	.46	434	Ea.	17,000	20,300	1,625	38,925	52,000
0120 20' x 30' x 14' high		.35	568		22,100	26,600	2,125	50,825	67,500
0140 20' x 40' x 14' high		.29	701		27,200	32,800	2,650	62,650	83,500
0160 20' x 50' x 14' high		.24	835		32,300	39,100	3,150	74,550	99,000
0180 20' x 60' x 14' high		.21	969		37,400	45,400	3,650	86,450	115,000
0200 20' x 70' x 14' high		.18	1103		42,500	51,500	4,150	98,150	131,000
0220 20' x 80' x 14' high		.16	1236		47,600	58,000	4,650	110,250	146,500
0240 20' x 90' x 14' high		.15	1370		52,500	64,000	5,150	121,650	162,000
0260 20' x 100' x 14' high		.13	1503		58,000	70,500	5,650	134,150	177,500
0280 20' x 120' x 14' high		.11	1771		68,000	83,000	6,650	157,650	210,000
0300 20' x 140' x 14' high		.10	2038		78,000	95,500	7,675	181,175	241,000
0320 20' x 160' x 14' high		.09	2306		88,500	108,000	8,675	205,175	272,500
0340 20' x 180' x 14' high		.08	2574		98,500	120,500	9,675	228,675	304,500
0360 20' x 200' x 14' high		.07	2840		108,500	133,000	10,700	252,200	335,500
0380 20' x 250' x 14' high		.06	3508		134,000	164,000	13,200	311,200	414,500
0400 20' x 300' x 14' high		.05	4175		159,500	195,500	15,700	370,700	493,000
0420 20' x 350' x 14' high		.04	4842		185,000	226,500	18,200	429,700	572,000
0440 20' x 400' x 14' high		.04	5509		210,500	258,000	20,700	489,200	651,000
0460 20' x 450' x 14' high		.03	6191		236,000	290,000	23,300	549,300	730,500
0480 20' x 500' x 14' high		.03	6849		261,500	320,500	25,800	607,800	809,000
0500 Treatment cell, end or single, 20' x 20' x 12' high (2' freeboard)		.48	414		16,100	19,400	1,550	37,050	49,200
0520 20' x 30' x 12' high		.37	543		21,000	25,400	2,050	48,450	64,500
0540 20' x 40' x 12' high		.30	671		25,800	31,400	2,525	59,725	79,500
0560 20' x 50' x 12' high		.25	800		30,700	37,500	3,000	71,200	94,500
0580 20' x 60' x 12' high		.22	928		35,500	43,500	3,500	82,500	110,000
0600 20' x 70' x 12' high		.19	1057		40,400	49,500	3,975	93,875	125,000
0620 20' x 80' x 12' high		.17	1186		45,300	55,500	4,450	105,250	140,000
0640 20' x 90' x 12' high		.15	1314		50,000	61,500	4,950	116,450	155,000
0660 20' x 100' x 12' high		.14	1444		55,000	67,500	5,425	127,925	170,500
0680 20' x 120' x 12' high		.12	1700		64,500	79,500	6,400	150,400	200,500
0700 20' x 140' x 12' high		.10	1958		74,500	91,500	7,375	173,375	231,000
0720 20' x 160' x 12' high		.09	2214		84,000	103,500	8,325	195,825	261,000
0740 20' x 180' x 12' high		.08	2472		94,000	115,500	9,300	218,800	291,000
0760 20' x 200' x 12' high		.07	2732		103,500	128,000	10,300	241,800	322,000
0780 20' x 250' x 12' high		.06	3372		128,000	158,000	12,700	298,700	397,000
0800 20' x 300' x 12' high		.05	4016		152,000	188,000	15,100	355,100	473,000
0820 20' x 350' x 12' high		.04	4662		176,500	218,000	17,500	412,000	549,000
0840 20' x 400' x 12' high		.04	5305		200,500	248,500	19,900	468,900	625,000
0860 20' x 450' x 12' high		.03	5952		225,000	278,500	22,400	525,900	700,500
0880 20' x 500' x 12' high		.03	6600		249,500	309,000	24,800	583,300	776,500
1100 Treatment cell, connecting, 20' x 20' x 14' high (2' freeboard)		.57	350		13,600	16,400	1,325	31,325	41,800
1120 20' x 30' x 14' high		.45	442		17,000	20,700	1,675	39,375	52,500
1140 20' x 40' x 14' high		.37	534		20,400	25,000	2,000	47,400	63,000
1160 20' x 50' x 14' high		.32	626		23,800	29,300	2,350	55,450	74,000
1180 20' x 60' x 14' high		.28	718		27,100	33,600	2,700	63,400	84,500
1200 20' x 70' x 14' high		.25	810		30,500	37,900	3,050	71,450	95,500
1220 20' x 80' x 14' high		.22	902		33,900	42,200	3,400	79,500	106,000
1240 20' x 90' x 14' high		.20	994		37,200	46,500	3,750	87,450	116,500
1260 20' x 100' x 14' high		.18	1086		40,600	51,000	4,075	95,675	127,000
1280 20' x 120' x 14' high		.16	1270		47,400	59,500	4,775	111,675	149,000

46 53 Biological Treatment Systems

46 53 17 – Activated Sludge Treatment

46 53 17.10 Activated Sludge Treatment Cells		Crew	Daily Output	Labor-Hours	Unit	Material	2015 Bare Costs Labor	Equipment	Total	Total Incl O&P
1300	20' x 140' x 14' high	C-14D	.14	1454	Ea.	54,000	68,000	5,475	127,475	170,000
1320	20' x 160' x 14' high		.12	1638		61,000	76,500	6,150	143,650	192,000
1340	20' x 180' x 14' high		.11	1823		67,500	85,500	6,850	159,850	213,000
1360	20' x 200' x 14' high		.10	2006		74,500	94,000	7,550	176,050	235,000
1380	20' x 250' x 14' high		.08	2466		91,000	115,500	9,275	215,775	288,000
1400	20' x 300' x 14' high		.07	2923		108,000	137,000	11,000	256,000	341,500
1420	20' x 350' x 14' high		.06	3384		125,000	158,500	12,700	296,200	395,000
1440	20' x 400' x 14' high		.05	3846		142,000	180,000	14,500	336,500	449,000
1460	20' x 450' x 14' high		.05	4301		158,500	201,500	16,200	376,200	502,000
1480	20' x 500' x 14' high		.04	4761		175,500	223,000	17,900	416,400	555,000
1500	Treatment cell, connecting, 20' x 20' x 12' high (2' freeboard)		.60	335		12,900	15,700	1,275	29,875	39,800
1520	20' x 30' x 12' high		.47	425		16,200	19,900	1,600	37,700	50,000
1540	20' x 40' x 12' high		.39	514		19,400	24,100	1,925	45,425	60,500
1560	20' x 50' x 12' high		.33	604		22,700	28,300	2,275	53,275	71,000
1580	20' x 60' x 12' high		.29	693		26,000	32,500	2,600	61,100	81,500
1600	20' x 70' x 12' high		.26	783		29,200	36,600	2,950	68,750	92,000
1620	20' x 80' x 12' high		.23	872		32,500	40,800	3,275	76,575	102,500
1640	20' x 90' x 12' high		.21	962		35,700	45,000	3,625	84,325	112,500
1660	20' x 100' x 12' high		.19	1051		39,000	49,200	3,950	92,150	123,000
1680	20' x 120' x 12' high		.16	1230		45,500	57,500	4,625	107,625	143,500
1700	20' x 140' x 12' high		.14	1409		52,000	66,000	5,300	123,300	164,500
1720	20' x 160' x 12' high		.13	1588		58,500	74,500	5,975	138,975	185,500
1740	20' x 180' x 12' high		.11	1766		65,000	82,500	6,650	154,150	206,000
1760	20' x 200' x 12' high		.10	1945		71,500	91,000	7,325	169,825	226,500
1780	20' x 250' x 12' high		.08	2392		88,000	112,000	9,000	209,000	278,500
1800	20' x 300' x 12' high		.07	2840		104,000	133,000	10,700	247,700	330,500
1820	20' x 350' x 12' high		.06	3289		120,500	154,000	12,400	286,900	382,500
1840	20' x 400' x 12' high		.05	3738		136,500	175,000	14,100	325,600	435,000
1860	20' x 450' x 12' high		.05	4184		153,000	196,000	15,700	364,700	487,000
1880	20' x 500' x 12' high		.04	5571		169,500	260,500	20,900	450,900	610,000
1996	Price for aerator curb per cell excluding aerator piping & drain									
2000	Treatment cell, 20' x 20' aerator curb	F-7	1.88	17.067	Ea.	590	720		1,310	1,750
2010	20' x 30'		1.25	25.600		885	1,075		1,960	2,650
2020	20' x 40'		.94	34.133		1,175	1,450		2,625	3,525
2030	20' x 50'		.75	42.667		1,475	1,800		3,275	4,400
2040	20' x 60'		.63	51.200		1,775	2,175		3,950	5,275
2050	20' x 70'		.54	59.735		2,050	2,525		4,575	6,150
2060	20' x 80'		.47	68.259		2,350	2,875		5,225	7,050
2070	20' x 90'		.42	76.794		2,650	3,250		5,900	7,925
2080	20' x 100'		.38	85.333		2,950	3,600		6,550	8,800
2090	20' x 120'		.31	102		3,525	4,325		7,850	10,600
2100	20' x 140'		.27	119		4,125	5,050		9,175	12,300
2110	20' x 160'		.23	136		4,725	5,775		10,500	14,100
2120	20' x 180'		.21	153		5,300	6,500		11,800	15,800
2130	20' x 200'		.19	170		5,900	7,225		13,125	17,600
2160	20' x 250'		.15	213		7,375	9,025		16,400	22,000
2190	20' x 300'		.13	256		8,850	10,800		19,650	26,400
2220	20' x 350'		.11	298		10,300	12,600		22,900	30,700
2250	20' x 400'		.09	341		11,800	14,400		26,200	35,200
2280	20' x 450'		.08	384		13,300	16,200		29,500	39,600
2310	20' x 500'		.08	426		14,700	18,000		32,700	44,000

540

Assemblies Section

Table of Contents

Table of Contents

How RSMeans Assemblies Data Works

Assemblies estimating provides a fast and reasonably accurate way to develop construction costs. An assembly is the grouping of individual work items, with appropriate quantities, to provide a cost for a major construction component in a convenient unit of measure.

An assemblies estimate is often used during early stages of design development to compare the cost impact of various design alternatives on total building cost.

Assemblies estimates are also used as an efficient tool to verify construction estimates.

Assemblies estimates do not require a completed design or detailed drawings. Instead, they are based on the general size of the structure and other known parameters of the project. The degree of accuracy of an assemblies estimate is generally within +/- 15%.

NARRATIVE FORMAT

G20 Site Improvements

G2040 Site Development

There are four basic types of Concrete Retaining Wall Systems: reinforced concrete with level backfill; reinforced concrete with sloped backfill or surcharge; unreinforced with level backfill; and unreinforced with sloped backfill or surcharge. System elements include: all necessary forms (4 uses); 3,000 p.s.i. concrete with an 8" chute; all necessary reinforcing steel; and underdrain. Exposed concrete is patched and rubbed.

The Expanded System Listing shows walls that range in thickness from 10" to 18" for reinforced concrete walls with level backfill and 12" to 24" for reinforced walls with sloped backfill. Walls range from a height of 4' to 20'. Unreinforced level and sloped backfill walls range from a height of 3' to 10'.

RSMeans assemblies are identified by a **unique 12-character identifier**. The assemblies are numbered using UNIFORMAT II, ASTM Standard E1557. The first 6 characters represent this system to Level 4. The last 6 characters represent further breakdown by RSMeans in order to arrange items in understandable groups of similar tasks. Line numbers are consistent across all RSMeans publications, so a line number in any RSMeans assemblies data set will always refer to the same work.

System Components	QUANTITY	UNIT	COST PER L.F. MAT.	COST PER L.F. INST.	COST PER L.F. TOTAL
SYSTEM G2040 210 1000					
CONC. RETAIN. WALL REINFORCED, LEVEL BACKFILL, 4' HIGH					
Forms in place, cont. wall footing & keyway, 4 uses	2.000	S.F.	4.88	9.06	13.94
Forms in place, retaining wall forms, battered to 8' high, 4 uses	8.000	SFCA	5.84	69.20	75.04
Reinforcing in place, walls, #3 to #7	.004	Ton	4.30	3.50	7.80
Concrete ready mix, regular weight, 3000 psi	.204	C.Y.	22.85		22.85
Placing concrete and vibrating footing con., shallow direct chute	.074	C.Y.		1.82	1.82
Placing concrete and vibrating walls, 8" thick, direct chute	.130	C.Y.		4.26	4.26
Pipe bedding, crushed or screened bank run gravel	1.000	L.F.	3.08	1.40	4.48
Pipe, subdrainage, corrugated plastic, 4" diameter	1.000	L.F.	.55	.77	1.32
Finish walls and break ties, patch walls	4.000	S.F.	.16	3.96	4.12
TOTAL			41.66	93.97	135.63

RSMeans assemblies descriptions appear in two formats: narrative and table. **Narrative descriptions** are shown in a hierarchical structure to make them readable. In order to read a complete description, read up through the indents to the top of the section. Include everything that is above and to the left that is not contradicted by information below.

G2040 210	Concrete Retaining Walls	COST PER L.F. MAT.	COST PER L.F. INST.	COST PER L.F. TOTAL
1000	Conc. retain. wall, reinforced, level backfill, 4' high x 2'-2" base, 10" thick	41.50	94	135.50
1200	6' high x 3'-3" base, 10" thick	60	136	196
1400	8' high x 4'-3" base, 10" thick	77.50	178	255.50
1600	10' high x 5'-4" base, 13" thick	101	261	362
1800	12' high x 6'-6" base, 14" thick	124	310	434
2200	16' high x 8'-6" base, 16" thick	188	420	608
2600	20' high x 10'-5" base, 18" thick	276	550	826
3000	Sloped backfill, 4' high x 3'-2" base, 12" thick	50.50	97.50	148
3200	6' high x 4'-6" base, 12" thick	71	140	211
3400	8' high x 5'-11" base, 12" thick	94	184	278
3600	10' high x 7'-5" base, 16" thick	134	274	408
3800	12' high x 8'-10" base, 18" thick	174	330	504
4200	16' high x 11'-10" base, 21" thick	291	470	761
4600	20' high x 15'-0" base, 24" thick	450	640	1,090
5000	Unreinforced, level backfill, 3'-0" high x 1'-6" base	21.50	63	84.50
5200	4'-0" high x 2'-0" base	33.50	84	117.50
5400	6'-0" high x 3'-0" base	62.50	131	193.50
5600	8'-0" high x 4'-0" base	99.50	174	273.50

For supplemental customizable square foot estimating forms, visit: **http://www.reedconstructiondata.com/rsmeans/assemblies**

544

Most assemblies consist of three major elements: a graphic, the system components, and the cost data itself. The **Graphic** is a visual representation showing the typical appearance of the assembly in question, frequently accompanied by additional explanatory technical information describing the class of items. The **System Components** is a listing of the individual tasks that make up the assembly, including the quantity and unit of measure for each item, along with the cost of material and installation. The **Assemblies Data** below lists prices for other similar systems with dimensional and/or size variations.

All RSMeans assemblies costs represent the cost for the installing contractor. An allowance for profit has been added to all material, labor, and equipment rental costs. A markup for labor burdens, including workers' compensation, fixed overhead, and business overhead, is included with installation costs.

The data published in RSMeans print books represents a "national average" cost. This data should be modified to the project location using the **City Cost Indexes** or **Location Factors** tables found in the Reference Section in the back of the book.

TABLE FORMAT

A20 Basement Construction

A2020 Basement Walls

The Foundation Bearing Wall System includes: forms up to 16' high (four uses); 3,000 p.s.i. concrete placed and vibrated; and form removal with breaking form ties and patching walls. The wall systems list walls from 6" to 16" thick and are designed with minimum reinforcement.

Excavation and backfill are not included.

Please see the reference section for further design and cost information.

All RSMeans assemblies data includes a typical **Unit of Measure** used for estimating that item. For instance, for continuous footings or foundation walls the unit is linear feet (L.F.). For spread footings the unit is each (Ea.). The estimator needs to take special care that the unit in the data matches the unit in the takeoff. Abbreviations and unit conversions can be found in the Reference Section.

System components are listed separately to detail what is included in the development of the total system price.

System Components		QUANTITY	UNIT	COST PER L.F.		
				MAT.	INST.	TOTAL
SYSTEM A2020 110 1500						
FOUNDATION WALL, CAST IN PLACE, DIRECT CHUTE, 4' HIGH, 6" THICK						
Formwork		8.000	SFCA	6.56	45.20	51.76
Reinforcing		3.300	Lb.	1.77	1.44	3.21
Unloading & sorting reinforcing		3.300	Lb.		.08	.08
Concrete, 3,000 psi		.074	C.Y.	8.29		8.29
Place concrete, direct chute		.074	C.Y.		2.43	2.43
Finish walls, break ties and patch voids, one side		4.000	S.F.	.16	3.96	4.12
	TOTAL			16.78	53.11	69.89

Table descriptions work in a similar fashion, except that if there is a blank in the column at a particular line number, read up to the description above in the same column.

A2020 110			Walls, Cast in Place					
	WALL HEIGHT (FT.)	PLACING METHOD	CONCRETE (C.Y. per L.F.)	REINFORCING (LBS. per L.F.)	WALL THICKNESS (IN.)	COST PER L.F.		
						MAT.	INST.	TOTAL
1500	4'	direct chute	.074	3.3	6	16.80	53	69.80
1520			.099	4.8	8	20.50	54.50	75
1540			.123	6.0	10	23.50	55.50	79
1560			.148	7.2	12	27	56.50	83.50
1580			.173	8.1	14	30.50	57.50	88
1600			.197	9.44	16	34	59	93
1700	4'	pumped	.074	3.3	6	16.80	54	70.80
1720			.099	4.8	8	20.50	56.50	77
1740			.123	6.0	10	23.50	57.50	81
1760			.148	7.2	12	27	59	86
1780			.173	8.1	14	30.50	60	90.50
1800			.197	9.44	16	34	61.50	95.50
3000	6'	direct chute	.111	4.95	6	25	79.50	104.50
3020			.149	7.20	8	30.50	82	112.50
3040			.184	9.00	10	35.50	83	118.50
3060			.222	10.8	12	41	85	126
3080			.260	12.15	14	45.50	86.50	132
3100			.300	14.39	16	51.50	89	140.50

How RSMeans Assemblies Data Works (Continued)

Sample Estimate

This sample demonstrates the elements of an estimate, including a tally of the RSMeans data lines. Published assemblies costs include all markups for labor burden and profit for the installing contractor. This estimate adds a summary of the markups applied by a general contractor on the installing contractors' work. These figures represent the total cost to the owner. The RSMeans location factor is added at the bottom of the estimate to adjust the cost of the work to a specific location. **NOTE: The following assemblies are not found in this book and are used here for example only.**

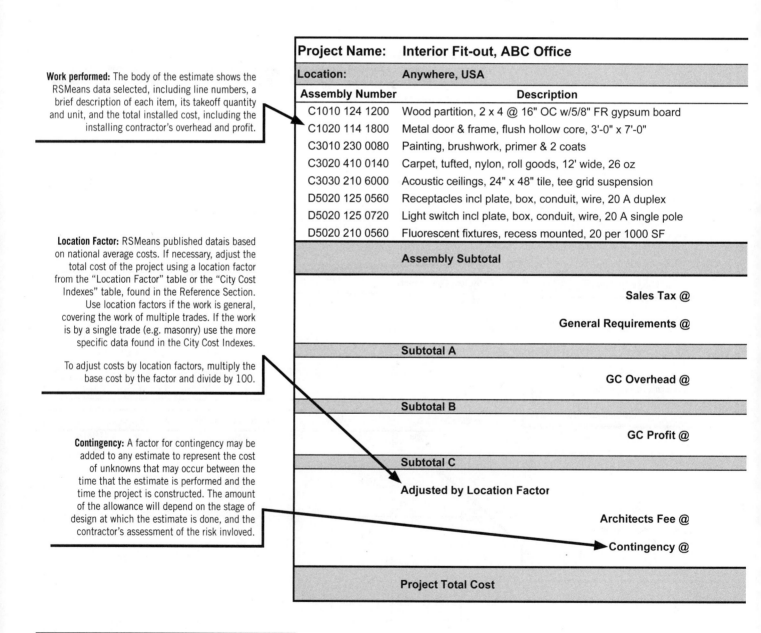

Work performed: The body of the estimate shows the RSMeans data selected, including line numbers, a brief description of each item, its takeoff quantity and unit, and the total installed cost, including the installing contractor's overhead and profit.

Location Factor: RSMeans published data is based on national average costs. If necessary, adjust the total cost of the project using a location factor from the "Location Factor" table or the "City Cost Indexes" table, found in the Reference Section. Use location factors if the work is general, covering the work of multiple trades. If the work is by a single trade (e.g. masonry) use the more specific data found in the City Cost Indexes.

To adjust costs by location factors, multiply the base cost by the factor and divide by 100.

Contingency: A factor for contingency may be added to any estimate to represent the cost of unknowns that may occur between the time that the estimate is performed and the time the project is constructed. The amount of the allowance will depend on the stage of design at which the estimate is done, and the contractor's assessment of the risk invloved.

Project Name:	Interior Fit-out, ABC Office
Location:	**Anywhere, USA**
Assembly Number	**Description**
C1010 124 1200	Wood partition, 2 x 4 @ 16" OC w/5/8" FR gypsum board
C1020 114 1800	Metal door & frame, flush hollow core, 3'-0" x 7'-0"
C3010 230 0080	Painting, brushwork, primer & 2 coats
C3020 410 0140	Carpet, tufted, nylon, roll goods, 12' wide, 26 oz
C3030 210 6000	Acoustic ceilings, 24" x 48" tile, tee grid suspension
D5020 125 0560	Receptacles incl plate, box, conduit, wire, 20 A duplex
D5020 125 0720	Light switch incl plate, box, conduit, wire, 20 A single pole
D5020 210 0560	Fluorescent fixtures, recess mounted, 20 per 1000 SF
Assembly Subtotal	
Sales Tax @	
General Requirements @	
Subtotal A	
GC Overhead @	
Subtotal B	
GC Profit @	
Subtotal C	
Adjusted by Location Factor	
Architects Fee @	
Contingency @	
Project Total Cost	

This estimate is based on an interactive spreadsheet. A copy of this spreadsheet is located on the RSMeans website at **http://www.reedconstructiondata.com/rsmeans/extras/546011.** You are free to download it and adjust it to your methodology.

546

Date: 1/1/2015		STD
Qty.	Unit	Subtotal
560.000	S.F.	$2,693.60
2.000	Ea.	$2,450.00
1,120.000	S.F.	$1,344.00
240.000	S.F.	$1,003.20
200.000	S.F.	$1,140.00
8.000	Ea.	$2,164.00
2.000	Ea.	$545.00
200.000	S.F.	$2,140.00
		$13,479.80
5 %		$ 337.00
7 %		$ 943.59
		$14,760.38
5 %		$ 738.02
		$15,498.40
5 %		$ 774.92
		$16,273.32
118.1		$ 19,218.79
8 %		$ 1,537.50
15 %		$ 2,882.82
		$ 23,639.11

Sales Tax: If the work is subject to state or local sales taxes, the amount must be added to the estimate. In a conceptual estimate it can be assumed that one half of the total represents material costs. Therefore, apply the sales tax rate to 50% of the assembly subtotal.

General Requirements: This item covers project-wide needs provided by the General Contractor. These items vary by project, but may include temporary facilities and utilities, security, testing, project cleanup, etc. In assemblies estimates a percentage is used, typically between 5% and 15% of project cost.

General Contractor Overhead: This entry represents the General Contractor's markup on all work to cover project administration costs.

General Contractor Profit: This entry represents the GC's profit on all work performed. The value included here can vary widely by project, and is influenced by the GC's perception of the project's financial risk and market conditions.

Architects Fee: If appropriate, add the design cost to the project estimate. These fees vary based on project complexity and size. Typical design and engineering fees can be found in the reference section.

A10 Foundations

A1010 Standard Foundations

The Strip Footing System includes: excavation; hand trim; all forms needed for footing placement; forms for 2″ x 6″ keyway (four uses); dowels; and 3,000 p.s.i. concrete.

The footing size required varies for different soils. Soil bearing capacities are listed for 3 KSF and 6 KSF. Depths of the system range from 8″ and deeper. Widths range from 16″ and wider. Smaller strip footings may not require reinforcement.

Please see the reference section for further design and cost information.

System Components			COST PER L.F.		
	QUANTITY	UNIT	MAT.	INST.	TOTAL
SYSTEM A1010 110 2500					
STRIP FOOTING, LOAD 5.1 KLF, SOIL CAP. 3 KSF, 24″ WIDE X 12″ DEEP, REINF.					
Trench excavation	.148	C.Y.		1.47	1.47
Hand trim	2.000	S.F.		1.94	1.94
Compacted backfill	.074	C.Y.		.30	.30
Formwork, 4 uses	2.000	S.F.	4.88	9.06	13.94
Keyway form, 4 uses	1.000	L.F.	.36	1.16	1.52
Reinforcing, fy = 60000 psi	3.000	Lb.	1.65	1.89	3.54
Dowels	2.000	Ea.	1.56	5.48	7.04
Concrete, f'c = 3000 psi	.074	C.Y.	8.29		8.29
Place concrete, direct chute	.074	C.Y.		1.82	1.82
Screed finish	2.000	S.F.		.76	.76
TOTAL			16.74	23.88	40.62

A1010 110	Strip Footings	COST PER L.F.		
		MAT.	INST.	TOTAL
2100	Strip footing, load 2.6 KLF, soil capacity 3 KSF, 16″ wide x 8″ deep, plain	8.65	14.30	22.95
2300	Load 3.9 KLF, soil capacity, 3 KSF, 24″ wide x 8″ deep, plain	10.55	15.70	26.25
2500	Load 5.1 KLF, soil capacity 3 KSF, 24″ wide x 12″ deep, reinf.	16.75	23.50	40.25
2700	Load 11.1 KLF, soil capacity 6 KSF, 24″ wide x 12″ deep, reinf.	16.75	23.50	40.25
2900	Load 6.8 KLF, soil capacity 3 KSF, 32″ wide x 12″ deep, reinf.	20	26	46
3100	Load 14.8 KLF, soil capacity 6 KSF, 32″ wide x 12″ deep, reinf.	20	26	46
3300	Load 9.3 KLF, soil capacity 3 KSF, 40″ wide x 12″ deep, reinf.	23.50	28	51.50
3500	Load 18.4 KLF, soil capacity 6 KSF, 40″ wide x 12″ deep, reinf.	23.50	28	51.50
3700	Load 10.1 KLF, soil capacity 3 KSF, 48″ wide x 12″ deep, reinf.	26	30.50	56.50
3900	Load 22.1 KLF, soil capacity 6 KSF, 48″ wide x 12″ deep, reinf.	27.50	32	59.50
4100	Load 11.8 KLF, soil capacity 3 KSF, 56″ wide x 12″ deep, reinf.	30.50	33.50	64
4300	Load 25.8 KLF, soil capacity 6 KSF, 56″ wide x 12″ deep, reinf.	33	36.50	69.50
4500	Load 10 KLF, soil capacity 3 KSF, 48″ wide x 16″ deep, reinf.	33	35.50	68.50
4700	Load 22 KLF, soil capacity 6 KSF, 48″ wide, 16″ deep, reinf.	34	36.50	70.50
4900	Load 11.6 KLF, soil capacity 3 KSF, 56″ wide x 16″ deep, reinf.	37.50	51	88.50
5100	Load 25.6 KLF, soil capacity 6 KSF, 56″ wide x 16″ deep, reinf.	39.50	53.50	93
5300	Load 13.3 KLF, soil capacity 3 KSF, 64″ wide x 16″ deep, reinf.	43	42	85
5500	Load 29.3 KLF, soil capacity 6 KSF, 64″ wide x 16″ deep, reinf.	45.50	45	90.50
5700	Load 15 KLF, soil capacity 3 KSF, 72″ wide x 20″ deep, reinf.	57	50.50	107.50
5900	Load 33 KLF, soil capacity 6 KSF, 72″ wide x 20″ deep, reinf.	60	54	114
6100	Load 18.3 KLF, soil capacity 3 KSF, 88″ wide x 24″ deep, reinf.	80	64.50	144.50
6300	Load 40.3 KLF, soil capacity 6 KSF, 88″ wide x 24″ deep, reinf.	86.50	71.50	158
6500	Load 20 KLF, soil capacity 3 KSF, 96″ wide x 24″ deep, reinf.	87	68	155
6700	Load 44 KLF, soil capacity 6 KSF, 96″ wide x 24″ deep, reinf.	91.50	73.50	165

A10 Foundations

A1010 Standard Foundations

The Spread Footing System includes: excavation; backfill; forms (four uses); all reinforcement; 3,000 p.s.i. concrete (chute placed); and float finish.

Footing systems are priced per individual unit. The Expanded System Listing at the bottom shows various footing sizes. It is assumed that excavation is done by a truck mounted hydraulic excavator with an operator and oiler.

Backfill is with a dozer, and compaction by air tamp. The excavation and backfill equipment is assumed to operate at 30 C.Y. per hour.

Please see the reference section for further design and cost information.

System Components	QUANTITY	UNIT	COST EACH		
			MAT.	INST.	TOTAL
SYSTEM A1010 210 2200					
SPREAD FOOTINGS, 3'-0" SQ. X 12" DEEP, 3 KSF SOIL CAP., 25K LOAD					
Excavation, Gradall, 30" bucket, 30 CY/Hr	.590	C.Y.		5.06	5.06
Trim sides & bottom	9.000	S.F.		8.73	8.73
Dozer backfill & roller compaction	.260	C.Y.		1.04	1.04
Forms in place, spread footing, 4 uses	12.000	S.F.	9.84	63.60	73.44
Reinforcing in place footings, #4 to #7	.006	Ton	6.45	7.50	13.95
Supports for dowels in footings, walls, and beams	6.000	L.F.	6.18	26.34	32.52
Concrete ready mix, regular weight, 3000 psi	.330	C.Y.	36.96		36.96
Place and vibrate concrete for spread footings over 5 CY, direct chute	.330	C.Y.		8.11	8.11
Float finish	9.000	S.F.		3.42	3.42
TOTAL			59.43	123.80	183.23

A1010 210	Spread Footings	COST EACH		
		MAT.	INST.	TOTAL
2200	Spread footings, 3'-0 square x 12" deep, 3 KSF soil cap., 25K load	59.50	124	183.50
2210	4'-0" sq. x 12" deep, 6 KSF soil cap., 75K load	102	183	285
2400	4'-6" sq. x 12" deep, 3 KSF soil capacity, 50K load	126	213	339
2600	15" deep, 6 KSF soil capacity, 100K load	155	251	406
2800	5'-0" sq. x 12" deep, 3 KSF soil capacity, 62K load	155	261	416
3000	16" deep, 6 KSF soil capacity, 125K load	223	315	538
3200	5'-6" sq. x 13" deep, 3 KSF soil capacity, 75K load	200	300	500
3400	18" deep, 6 KSF soil capacity, 150K load	266	380	646
3600	6'-0" sq. x 14" deep, 3 KSF soil capacity, 100K load	253	360	613
3800	20" deep, 6 KSF soil capacity, 200K load	350	465	815
4000	7'-6" sq. x 18" deep, 3 KSF soil capacity, 150K load	485	600	1,085
4200	25" deep, 6 KSF soil capacity, 300K load	660	775	1,435
4400	8'-6" sq. x 20" deep, 3 KSF soil capacity, 200K load	690	795	1,485
4600	27" deep, 6 KSF soil capacity, 400K load	920	1,025	1,945
4800	9'-6" sq. x 24" deep, 3 KSF soil capacity, 250K load	1,000	1,075	2,075
5000	30" deep, 6 KSF soil capacity, 500K load	1,275	1,325	2,600
5200	10'-6" sq. x 26" deep, 3 KSF soil capacity, 300K load	1,275	1,300	2,575
5400	33" deep, 6 KSF soil capacity, 600K load	1,700	1,700	3,400
5600	12'-0" sq. x 28" deep, 3 KSF soil capacity, 400K load	2,050	1,950	4,000
5800	38" deep, 6 KSF soil capacity, 800K load	2,450	2,300	4,750
6200	13'-6" sq. x 30" deep, 3 KSF soil capacity, 500K load	2,525	2,300	4,825
6400	42" deep, 6 KSF soil capacity, 1000K load	3,425	3,050	6,475

A1010 Standard Foundations

These pile cap systems include excavation with a truck mounted hydraulic excavator, hand trimming, compacted backfill, forms for concrete, templates for dowels or anchor bolts, reinforcing steel and concrete placed and floated.

Pile embedment is assumed as 6″. Design is consistent with the Concrete Reinforcing Steel Institute Handbook f'c = 3000 psi, fy = 60,000.

Please see the reference section for further design and cost information.

System Components	QUANTITY	UNIT	COST EACH MAT.	COST EACH INST.	COST EACH TOTAL
SYSTEM A1010 250 5100					
CAP FOR 2 PILES, 6'-6″X3'-6″X20″, 15 TON PILE, 8″ MIN. COL., 45K COL. LOAD					
Excavation, bulk, hyd excavator, truck mtd. 30″ bucket 1/2 CY	2.890	C.Y.		24.80	24.80
Trim sides and bottom of trench, regular soil	23.000	S.F.		22.31	22.31
Dozer backfill & roller compaction	1.500	C.Y.		6.02	6.02
Forms in place pile cap, square or rectangular, 4 uses	33.000	SFCA	34.32	189.75	224.07
Templates for dowels or anchor bolts	8.000	Ea.	8.24	35.12	43.36
Reinforcing in place footings, #8 to #14	.025	Ton	26.88	18.25	45.13
Concrete ready mix, regular weight, 3000 psi	1.400	C.Y.	156.80		156.80
Place and vibrate concrete for pile caps, under 5 CY, direct chute	1.400	C.Y.		45.86	45.86
Float finish	23.000	S.F.		8.74	8.74
TOTAL			226.24	350.85	577.09

A1010 250		Pile Caps						
	NO. PILES	SIZE FT-IN X FT-IN X IN	PILE CAPACITY (TON)	COLUMN SIZE (IN)	COLUMN LOAD (K)	COST EACH MAT.	COST EACH INST.	COST EACH TOTAL
5100	2	6-6x3-6x20	15	8	45	226	355	581
5150		26	40	8	155	277	430	707
5200		34	80	11	314	375	550	925
5250		37	120	14	473	405	590	995
5300	3	5-6x5-1x23	15	8	75	271	405	676
5350		28	40	10	232	300	460	760
5400		32	80	14	471	350	520	870
5450		38	120	17	709	405	595	1,000
5500	4	5-6x5-6x18	15	10	103	305	405	710
5550		30	40	11	308	445	580	1,025
5600		36	80	16	626	525	680	1,205
5650		38	120	19	945	555	710	1,265
5700	6	8-6x5-6x18	15	12	156	515	585	1,100
5750		37	40	14	458	825	865	1,690
5800		40	80	19	936	945	965	1,910
5850		45	120	24	1413	1,050	1,050	2,100
5900	8	8-6x7-9x19	15	12	205	775	795	1,570
5950		36	40	16	610	1,100	1,050	2,150
6000		44	80	22	1243	1,375	1,250	2,625
6050		47	120	27	1881	1,475	1,350	2,825

A10 Foundations

A1010 Standard Foundations

A1010 250					Pile Caps				

	NO. PILES	SIZE FT-IN X FT-IN X IN	PILE CAPACITY (TON)	COLUMN SIZE (IN)	COLUMN LOAD (K)	COST EACH		
						MAT.	INST.	TOTAL
6100	10	11-6x7-9x21	15	14	250	1,100	970	2,070
6150		39	40	17	756	1,650	1,375	3,025
6200		47	80	25	1547	2,025	1,650	3,675
6250		49	120	31	2345	2,125	1,750	3,875
6300	12	11-6x8-6x22	15	15	316	1,400	1,175	2,575
6350		49	40	19	900	2,175	1,775	3,950
6400		52	80	27	1856	2,425	1,925	4,350
6450		55	120	34	2812	2,625	2,075	4,700
6500	14	11-6x10-9x24	15	16	345	1,800	1,450	3,250
6550		41	40	21	1056	2,350	1,825	4,175
6600		55	80	29	2155	3,075	2,275	5,350
6700	16	11-6x11-6x26	15	18	400	2,175	1,675	3,850
6750		48	40	22	1200	2,875	2,150	5,025
6800		60	80	31	2460	3,600	2,600	6,200
6900	18	13-0x11-6x28	15	20	450	2,475	1,850	4,325
6950		49	40	23	1349	3,350	2,375	5,725
7000		56	80	33	2776	3,975	2,800	6,775
7100	20	14-6x11-6x30	15	20	510	3,025	2,200	5,225
7150		52	40	24	1491	4,050	2,800	6,850

A1010 Standard Foundations

General: Footing drains can be placed either inside or outside of foundation walls depending upon the source of water to be intercepted. If the source of subsurface water is principally from grade or a subsurface stream above the bottom of the footing, outside drains should be used. For high water tables, use inside drains or both inside and outside.

The effectiveness of underdrains depends on good waterproofing. This must be carefully installed and protected during construction.

Costs below include the labor and materials for the pipe and 6" of crushed stone around pipe. Excavation and backfill are not included.

System Components			QUANTITY	UNIT	COST PER L.F.		
					MAT.	INST.	TOTAL
SYSTEM A1010 310 1000							
FOUNDATION UNDERDRAIN, OUTSIDE ONLY, PVC, 4" DIAM.							
PVC pipe 4" diam. S.D.R. 35			1.000	L.F.	1.60	4.14	5.74
Crushed stone 3/4" to 1/2"			.070	C.Y.	1.82	.90	2.72
		TOTAL			3.42	5.04	8.46

A1010 310	Foundation Underdrain	COST PER L.F.		
		MAT.	INST.	TOTAL
1000	Foundation underdrain, outside only, PVC, 4" diameter	3.42	5.05	8.47
1100	6" diameter	5.95	5.60	11.55
1400	Perforated HDPE, 6" diameter	3.91	2.18	6.09
1450	8" diameter	5.85	2.72	8.57
1500	12" diameter	11.20	6.65	17.85
1600	Corrugated metal, 16 ga. asphalt coated, 6" diameter	9.50	5.25	14.75
1650	8" diameter	12.25	5.60	17.85
1700	10" diameter	15.15	7.25	22.40
3000	Outside and inside, PVC, 4" diameter	6.85	10.05	16.90
3100	6" diameter	11.90	11.20	23.10
3400	Perforated HDPE, 6" diameter	7.80	4.36	12.16
3450	8" diameter	11.65	5.45	17.10
3500	12" diameter	22.50	13.20	35.70
3600	Corrugated metal, 16 ga., asphalt coated, 6" diameter	19	10.50	29.50
3650	8" diameter	24.50	11.20	35.70
3700	10" diameter	30.50	14.60	45.10

A1010 Standard Foundations

General: Apply foundation wall dampproofing over clean concrete giving particular attention to the joint between the wall and the footing. Use care in backfilling to prevent damage to the dampproofing.

Costs for four types of dampproofing are listed below.

System Components	QUANTITY	UNIT	COST PER L.F.		
			MAT.	INST.	TOTAL
SYSTEM A1010 320 1000					
FOUNDATION DAMPPROOFING, BITUMINOUS, 1 COAT, 4' HIGH					
Bituminous asphalt dampproofing brushed on below grade, 1 coat	4.000	S.F.	1	3.28	4.28
Labor for protection of dampproofing during backfilling	4.000	S.F.		1.40	1.40
TOTAL			1	4.68	5.68

A1010 320	Foundation Dampproofing	COST PER L.F.		
		MAT.	INST.	TOTAL
1000	Foundation dampproofing, bituminous, 1 coat, 4' high	1	4.68	5.68
1400	8' high	2	9.35	11.35
1800	12' high	3	14.50	17.50
2000	2 coats, 4' high	1.96	5.80	7.76
2400	8' high	3.92	11.60	15.52
2800	12' high	5.90	17.85	23.75
3000	Asphalt with fibers, 1/16" thick, 4' high	1.60	5.80	7.40
3400	8' high	3.20	11.60	14.80
3800	12' high	4.80	17.85	22.65
4000	1/8" thick, 4' high	2.80	6.90	9.70
4400	8' high	5.60	13.75	19.35
4800	12' high	8.40	21	29.40
5000	Asphalt coated board and mastic, 1/4" thick, 4' high	5.10	6.30	11.40
5400	8' high	10.25	12.55	22.80
5800	12' high	15.35	19.30	34.65
6000	1/2" thick, 4' high	7.70	8.70	16.40
6400	8' high	15.35	17.45	32.80
6800	12' high	23	26.50	49.50
7000	Cementitious coating, on walls, 1/8" thick coating, 4' high	3.20	8.85	12.05
7400	8' high	6.40	17.65	24.05
7800	12' high	9.60	26.50	36.10
8000	Cementitious/metallic slurry, 4 coat, 1/2"thick, 2' high	.70	8.90	9.60
8400	4' high	1.40	17.80	19.20
8800	6' high	2.10	26.50	28.60

The Cast-in-Place Concrete Pile System includes: a defined number of 4,000 p.s.i. concrete piles with thin-wall, straight-sided, steel shells that have a standard steel plate driving point. An allowance for cutoffs is included.

The Expanded System Listing shows costs per cluster of piles. Clusters range from one pile to twenty piles. Loads vary from 50 Kips to 1,600 Kips. Both end-bearing and friction-type piles are shown.

Please see the reference section for cost of mobilization of the pile driving equipment and other design and cost information.

System Components	QUANTITY	UNIT	COST EACH MAT.	COST EACH INST.	COST EACH TOTAL
SYSTEM A1020 110 2220					
CIP SHELL CONCRETE PILE, 25′ LONG, 50K LOAD, END BEARING, 1 PILE					
7 Ga. shell, 12″ diam.	27.000	V.L.F.	904.50	299.16	1,203.66
Steel pipe pile standard point, 12″ or 14″ diameter pile	1.000	Ea.	113	90.50	203.50
Pile cutoff, conc. pile with thin steel shell	1.000	Ea.		15.35	15.35
TOTAL			1,017.50	405.01	1,422.51

A1020 110	C.I.P. Concrete Piles	COST EACH MAT.	COST EACH INST.	COST EACH TOTAL
2220	CIP shell concrete pile, 25′ long, 50K load, end bearing, 1 pile	1,025	405	1,430
2240	100K load, end bearing, 2 pile cluster	2,025	810	2,835
2260	200K load, end bearing, 4 pile cluster	4,075	1,625	5,700
2280	400K load, end bearing, 7 pile cluster	7,125	2,825	9,950
2300	10 pile cluster	10,200	4,050	14,250
2320	800K load, end bearing, 13 pile cluster	22,200	7,425	29,625
2340	17 pile cluster	29,000	9,700	38,700
2360	1200K load, end bearing, 14 pile cluster	23,900	7,975	31,875
2380	19 pile cluster	32,400	10,900	43,300
2400	1600K load, end bearing, 19 pile cluster	32,400	10,900	43,300
2420	50′ long, 50K load, end bearing, 1 pile	1,900	695	2,595
2440	Friction type, 2 pile cluster	3,625	1,375	5,000
2460	3 pile cluster	5,425	2,075	7,500
2480	100K load, end bearing, 2 pile cluster	3,775	1,375	5,150
2500	Friction type, 4 pile cluster	7,225	2,775	10,000
2520	6 pile cluster	10,900	4,150	15,050
2540	200K load, end bearing, 4 pile cluster	7,550	2,775	10,325
2560	Friction type, 8 pile cluster	14,500	5,550	20,050
2580	10 pile cluster	18,100	6,925	25,025
2600	400K load, end bearing, 7 pile cluster	13,200	4,850	18,050
2620	Friction type, 16 pile cluster	28,900	11,100	40,000
2640	19 pile cluster	34,400	13,200	47,600
2660	800K load, end bearing, 14 pile cluster	43,300	13,100	56,400
2680	20 pile cluster	62,000	18,600	80,600
2700	1200K load, end bearing, 15 pile cluster	46,400	14,000	60,400
2720	1600K load, end bearing, 20 pile cluster	62,000	18,600	80,600
3740	75′ long, 50K load, end bearing, 1 pile	2,900	1,175	4,075
3760	Friction type, 2 pile cluster	5,550	2,350	7,900

A1020 Special Foundations

A1020 110	C.I.P. Concrete Piles	COST EACH		
		MAT.	INST.	TOTAL
3780	3 pile cluster	8,325	3,525	11,850
3800	100K load, end bearing, 2 pile cluster	5,775	2,350	8,125
3820	Friction type, 3 pile cluster	8,325	3,525	11,850
3840	5 pile cluster	13,900	5,875	19,775
3860	200K load, end bearing, 4 pile cluster	11,600	4,700	16,300
3880	6 pile cluster	17,300	7,050	24,350
3900	Friction type, 6 pile cluster	16,600	7,050	23,650
3910	7 pile cluster	19,400	8,200	27,600
3920	400K load, end bearing, 7 pile cluster	20,200	8,200	28,400
3930	11 pile cluster	31,800	13,000	44,800
3940	Friction type, 12 pile cluster	33,300	14,100	47,400
3950	14 pile cluster	38,800	16,400	55,200
3960	800K load, end bearing, 15 pile cluster	69,500	23,000	92,500
3970	20 pile cluster	93,000	30,700	123,700
3980	1200K load, end bearing, 17 pile cluster	79,000	26,100	105,100

For customer support on your Site Work & Landscape Cost Data, call 877.737.1594.

A1020 Special Foundations

The Precast Concrete Pile System includes: pre-stressed concrete piles; standard steel driving point; and an allowance for cutoffs.

The Expanded System Listing shows costs per cluster of piles. Clusters range from one pile to twenty piles. Loads vary from 50 Kips to 1,600 Kips. Both end-bearing and friction type piles are listed.

Please see the reference section for cost of mobilization of the pile driving equipment and other design and cost information.

System Components	QUANTITY	UNIT	COST EACH		
			MAT.	INST.	TOTAL
SYSTEM A1020 120 2220					
PRECAST CONCRETE PILE, 50′ LONG, 50K LOAD, END BEARING, 1 PILE					
Precast, prestressed conc. piles, 10″ square, no mobil.	53.000	V.L.F.	1,060	505.09	1,565.09
Steel pipe pile standard point, 8″ to 10″ diameter	1.000	Ea.	81.50	79.50	161
Piling special costs cutoffs concrete piles plain	1.000	Ea.		106	106
TOTAL			1,141.50	690.59	1,832.09

A1020 120	Precast Concrete Piles	COST EACH		
		MAT.	INST.	TOTAL
2220	Precast conc pile, 50′ long, 50K load, end bearing, 1 pile	1,150	690	1,840
2240	Friction type, 2 pile cluster	2,825	1,425	4,250
2260	4 pile cluster	5,650	2,875	8,525
2280	100K load, end bearing, 2 pile cluster	2,275	1,400	3,675
2300	Friction type, 2 pile cluster	2,825	1,425	4,250
2320	4 pile cluster	5,650	2,875	8,525
2340	7 pile cluster	9,875	5,025	14,900
2360	200K load, end bearing, 3 pile cluster	3,425	2,075	5,500
2380	4 pile cluster	4,575	2,750	7,325
2400	Friction type, 8 pile cluster	11,300	5,750	17,050
2420	9 pile cluster	12,700	6,450	19,150
2440	14 pile cluster	19,800	10,000	29,800
2460	400K load, end bearing, 6 pile cluster	6,850	4,150	11,000
2480	8 pile cluster	9,125	5,525	14,650
2500	Friction type, 14 pile cluster	19,800	10,000	29,800
2520	16 pile cluster	22,600	11,500	34,100
2540	18 pile cluster	25,400	12,900	38,300
2560	800K load, end bearing, 12 pile cluster	14,800	8,975	23,775
2580	16 pile cluster	18,300	11,100	29,400
2600	1200K load, end bearing, 19 pile cluster	57,000	16,000	73,000
2620	20 pile cluster	60,000	16,900	76,900
2640	1600K load, end bearing, 19 pile cluster	57,000	16,000	73,000
4660	100′ long, 50K load, end bearing, 1 pile	2,175	1,175	3,350
4680	Friction type, 1 pile	2,675	1,225	3,900

A10 Foundations

A1020 Special Foundations

A1020 120	Precast Concrete Piles	COST EACH		
		MAT.	INST.	TOTAL
4700	2 pile cluster	5,375	2,475	7,850
4720	100K load, end bearing, 2 pile cluster	4,375	2,375	6,750
4740	Friction type, 2 pile cluster	5,375	2,475	7,850
4760	3 pile cluster	8,050	3,675	11,725
4780	4 pile cluster	10,700	4,900	15,600
4800	200K load, end bearing, 3 pile cluster	6,550	3,550	10,100
4820	4 pile cluster	8,725	4,750	13,475
4840	Friction type, 3 pile cluster	8,050	3,675	11,725
4860	5 pile cluster	13,400	6,125	19,525
4880	400K load, end bearing, 6 pile cluster	13,100	7,125	20,225
4900	8 pile cluster	17,500	9,500	27,000
4910	Friction type, 8 pile cluster	21,500	9,800	31,300
4920	10 pile cluster	26,900	12,300	39,200
4930	800K load, end bearing, 13 pile cluster	28,400	15,400	43,800
4940	16 pile cluster	34,900	19,000	53,900
4950	1200K load, end bearing, 19 pile cluster	110,500	27,800	138,300
4960	20 pile cluster	116,000	29,300	145,300
4970	1600K load, end bearing, 19 pile cluster	110,500	27,800	138,300

559

A1020 Special Foundations

The Steel Pipe Pile System includes: steel pipe sections filled with 4,000 p.s.i. concrete; a standard steel driving point; splices when required and an allowance for cutoffs.

The Expanded System Listing shows costs per cluster of piles. Clusters range from one pile to twenty piles. Loads vary from 50 Kips to 1,600 Kips. Both end-bearing and friction-type piles are shown.

Please see the reference section for cost of mobilization of the pile driving equipment and other design and cost information.

System Components	QUANTITY	UNIT	COST EACH		
			MAT.	INST.	TOTAL
SYSTEM A1020 130 2220					
CONC. FILL STEEL PIPE PILE, 50' LONG, 50K LOAD, END BEARING, 1 PILE					
Piles, steel, pipe, conc. filled, 12" diameter	53.000	V.L.F.	2,173	850.65	3,023.65
Steel pipe pile, standard point, for 12" or 14" diameter pipe	1.000	Ea.	226	181	407
Pile cut off, concrete pile, thin steel shell	1.000	Ea.		15.35	15.35
TOTAL			2,399	1,047	3,446

A1020 130	Steel Pipe Piles	COST EACH		
		MAT.	INST.	TOTAL
2220	Conc. fill steel pipe pile, 50' long, 50K load, end bearing, 1 pile	2,400	1,050	3,450
2240	Friction type, 2 pile cluster	4,800	2,100	6,900
2250	100K load, end bearing, 2 pile cluster	4,800	2,100	6,900
2260	3 pile cluster	7,200	3,125	10,325
2300	Friction type, 4 pile cluster	9,600	4,200	13,800
2320	5 pile cluster	12,000	5,250	17,250
2340	10 pile cluster	24,000	10,500	34,500
2360	200K load, end bearing, 3 pile cluster	7,200	3,125	10,325
2380	4 pile cluster	9,600	4,200	13,800
2400	Friction type, 4 pile cluster	9,600	4,200	13,800
2420	8 pile cluster	19,200	8,375	27,575
2440	9 pile cluster	21,600	9,425	31,025
2460	400K load, end bearing, 6 pile cluster	14,400	6,300	20,700
2480	7 pile cluster	16,800	7,325	24,125
2500	Friction type, 9 pile cluster	21,600	9,425	31,025
2520	16 pile cluster	38,400	16,800	55,200
2540	19 pile cluster	45,600	19,900	65,500
2560	800K load, end bearing, 11 pile cluster	26,400	11,500	37,900
2580	14 pile cluster	33,600	14,600	48,200
2600	15 pile cluster	36,000	15,700	51,700
2620	Friction type, 17 pile cluster	40,800	17,900	58,700
2640	1200K load, end bearing, 16 pile cluster	38,400	16,800	55,200
2660	20 pile cluster	48,000	21,000	69,000
2680	1600K load, end bearing, 17 pile cluster	40,800	17,900	58,700
3700	100' long, 50K load, end bearing, 1 pile	4,650	2,075	6,725
3720	Friction type, 1 pile	4,650	2,075	6,725

A1020 Special Foundations

A1020 130	Steel Pipe Piles	COST EACH		
		MAT.	INST.	TOTAL
3740	2 pile cluster	9,325	4,150	13,475
3760	100K load, end bearing, 2 pile cluster	9,325	4,150	13,475
3780	Friction type, 2 pile cluster	9,325	4,150	13,475
3800	3 pile cluster	14,000	6,225	20,225
3820	200K load, end bearing, 3 pile cluster	14,000	6,225	20,225
3840	4 pile cluster	18,600	8,300	26,900
3860	Friction type, 3 pile cluster	14,000	6,225	20,225
3880	4 pile cluster	18,600	8,300	26,900
3900	400K load, end bearing, 6 pile cluster	28,000	12,500	40,500
3910	7 pile cluster	32,600	14,500	47,100
3920	Friction type, 5 pile cluster	23,300	10,400	33,700
3930	8 pile cluster	37,300	16,600	53,900
3940	800K load, end bearing, 11 pile cluster	51,500	22,800	74,300
3950	14 pile cluster	65,500	29,100	94,600
3960	15 pile cluster	70,000	31,200	101,200
3970	1200K load, end bearing, 16 pile cluster	74,500	33,200	107,700
3980	20 pile cluster	93,000	41,500	134,500
3990	1600K load, end bearing, 17 pile cluster	79,000	35,300	114,300

561

A1020 Special Foundations

A Steel "H" Pile System includes: steel H sections; heavy duty driving point; splices where applicable and allowance for cutoffs.

The Expanded System Listing shows costs per cluster of piles. Clusters range from one pile to eighteen piles. Loads vary from 50 Kips to 2,000 Kips. All loads for Steel H Pile systems are given in terms of end bearing capacity.

Steel sections range from 10" x 10" to 14" x 14" in the Expanded System Listing. The 14" x 14" steel section is used for all H piles used in applications requiring a working load over 800 Kips.

Please see the reference section for cost of mobilization of the pile driving equipment and other design and cost information.

System Components	QUANTITY	UNIT	COST EACH		
			MAT.	INST.	TOTAL
SYSTEM A1020 140 2220					
STEEL H PILES, 50' LONG, 100K LOAD, END BEARING, 1 PILE					
Steel H piles 10" x 10", 42 #/L.F.	53.000	V.L.F.	1,060	579.29	1,639.29
Heavy duty point, 10"	1.000	Ea.	209	183	392
Pile cut off, steel pipe or H piles	1.000	Ea.		30.50	30.50
TOTAL			1,269	792.79	2,061.79

A1020 140	Steel H Piles	COST EACH		
		MAT.	INST.	TOTAL
2220	Steel H piles, 50' long, 100K load, end bearing, 1 pile	1,275	790	2,065
2260	2 pile cluster	2,550	1,575	4,125
2280	200K load, end bearing, 2 pile cluster	2,550	1,575	4,125
2300	3 pile cluster	3,800	2,375	6,175
2320	400K load, end bearing, 3 pile cluster	3,800	2,375	6,175
2340	4 pile cluster	5,075	3,175	8,250
2360	6 pile cluster	7,625	4,750	12,375
2380	800K load, end bearing, 5 pile cluster	6,350	3,950	10,300
2400	7 pile cluster	8,875	5,550	14,425
2420	12 pile cluster	15,200	9,525	24,725
2440	1200K load, end bearing, 8 pile cluster	10,200	6,350	16,550
2460	11 pile cluster	14,000	8,725	22,725
2480	17 pile cluster	21,600	13,500	35,100
2500	1600K load, end bearing, 10 pile cluster	16,900	8,300	25,200
2520	14 pile cluster	23,600	11,600	35,200
2540	2000K load, end bearing, 12 pile cluster	20,200	9,950	30,150
2560	18 pile cluster	30,400	15,000	45,400
3580	100' long, 50K load, end bearing, 1 pile	4,500	1,825	6,325
3600	100K load, end bearing, 1 pile	4,500	1,825	6,325
3620	2 pile cluster	9,000	3,625	12,625
3640	200K load, end bearing, 2 pile cluster	9,000	3,625	12,625
3660	3 pile cluster	13,500	5,450	18,950
3680	400K load, end bearing, 3 pile cluster	13,500	5,450	18,950
3700	4 pile cluster	18,000	7,225	25,225
3720	6 pile cluster	27,000	10,900	37,900
3740	800K load, end bearing, 5 pile cluster	22,500	9,050	31,550

A10 Foundations

A1020 Special Foundations

A1020 140	Steel H Piles	COST EACH		
		MAT.	INST.	TOTAL
3760	7 pile cluster	31,500	12,700	44,200
3780	12 pile cluster	54,000	21,800	75,800
3800	1200K load, end bearing, 8 pile cluster	36,000	14,500	50,500
3820	11 pile cluster	49,500	19,900	69,400
3840	17 pile cluster	76,500	30,800	107,300
3860	1600K load, end bearing, 10 pile cluster	45,000	18,100	63,100
3880	14 pile cluster	63,000	25,400	88,400
3900	2000K load, end bearing, 12 pile cluster	54,000	21,800	75,800
3920	18 pile cluster	81,000	32,500	113,500

A1020 Special Foundations

The Step Tapered Steel Pile System includes: step tapered piles filled with 4,000 p.s.i. concrete. The cost for splices and pile cutoffs is included.

The Expanded System Listing shows costs per cluster of piles. Clusters range from one pile to twenty-four piles. Both end bearing piles and friction piles are listed. Loads vary from 50 Kips to 1,600 Kips.

Please see the reference section for cost of mobilization of the pile driving equipment and other design and cost information.

System Components	QUANTITY	UNIT	COST EACH MAT.	COST EACH INST.	COST EACH TOTAL
SYSTEM A1020 150 1000					
STEEL PILE, STEP TAPERED, 50' LONG, 50K LOAD, END BEARING, 1 PILE					
Steel shell step tapered conc. filled piles, 8" tip 60 ton capacity to 60'	53.000	V.L.F.	755.25	475.94	1,231.19
Pile cutoff, steel pipe or H piles	1.000	Ea.		30.50	30.50
TOTAL			755.25	506.44	1,261.69

A1020 150	Step-Tapered Steel Piles	COST EACH MAT.	COST EACH INST.	COST EACH TOTAL
1000	Steel pile, step tapered, 50' long, 50K load, end bearing, 1 pile	755	505	1,260
1200	Friction type, 3 pile cluster	2,275	1,500	3,775
1400	100K load, end bearing, 2 pile cluster	1,500	1,025	2,525
1600	Friction type, 4 pile cluster	3,025	2,025	5,050
1800	200K load, end bearing, 4 pile cluster	3,025	2,025	5,050
2000	Friction type, 6 pile cluster	4,525	3,050	7,575
2200	400K load, end bearing, 7 pile cluster	5,275	3,550	8,825
2400	Friction type, 10 pile cluster	7,550	5,075	12,625
2600	800K load, end bearing, 14 pile cluster	10,600	7,100	17,700
2800	Friction type, 18 pile cluster	13,600	9,100	22,700
3000	1200K load, end bearing, 16 pile cluster	13,200	8,700	21,900
3200	Friction type, 21 pile cluster	17,400	11,400	28,800
3400	1600K load, end bearing, 18 pile cluster	14,900	9,775	24,675
3600	Friction type, 24 pile cluster	19,800	13,000	32,800
5000	100' long, 50K load, end bearing, 1 pile	1,525	1,000	2,525
5200	Friction type, 2 pile cluster	3,050	2,000	5,050
5400	100K load, end bearing, 2 pile cluster	3,050	2,000	5,050
5600	Friction type, 3 pile cluster	4,550	3,050	7,600
5800	200K load, end bearing, 4 pile cluster	6,075	4,050	10,125
6000	Friction type, 5 pile cluster	7,600	5,050	12,650
6200	400K load, end bearing, 7 pile cluster	10,600	7,100	17,700
6400	Friction type, 8 pile cluster	12,200	8,100	20,300
6600	800K load, end bearing, 15 pile cluster	22,800	15,200	38,000
6800	Friction type, 16 pile cluster	24,300	16,200	40,500
7000	1200K load, end bearing, 17 pile cluster	43,700	26,400	70,100
7200	Friction type, 19 pile cluster	32,900	20,100	53,000
7400	1600K load, end bearing, 20 pile cluster	34,600	21,100	55,700
7600	Friction type, 22 pile cluster	38,100	23,300	61,400

A1020 Special Foundations

The Treated Wood Pile System includes: creosoted wood piles; a standard steel driving point; and an allowance for cutoffs.

The Expanded System Listing shows costs per cluster of piles. Clusters range from two piles to twenty piles. Loads vary from 50 Kips to 400 Kips. Both end-bearing and friction type piles are listed.

Please see the reference section for cost of mobilization of the pile driving equipment and other design and cost information.

System Components	QUANTITY	UNIT	COST EACH		
			MAT.	INST.	TOTAL
SYSTEM A1020 160 2220					
WOOD PILES, 25' LONG, 50K LOAD, END BEARING, 3 PILE CLUSTER					
Wood piles, treated, 12" butt, 8" tip, up to 30' long	81.000	V.L.F.	1,409.40	863.46	2,272.86
Point for driving wood piles	3.000	Ea.	76.50	87	163.50
Pile cutoff, wood piles	3.000	Ea.		46.05	46.05
TOTAL			1,485.90	996.51	2,482.41

A1020 160	Treated Wood Piles	COST EACH		
		MAT.	INST.	TOTAL
2220	Wood piles, 25' long, 50K load, end bearing, 3 pile cluster	1,475	1,000	2,475
2240	Friction type, 3 pile cluster	1,400	910	2,310
2260	5 pile cluster	2,350	1,525	3,875
2280	100K load, end bearing, 4 pile cluster	1,975	1,325	3,300
2300	5 pile cluster	2,475	1,675	4,150
2320	6 pile cluster	2,975	2,000	4,975
2340	Friction type, 5 pile cluster	2,350	1,525	3,875
2360	6 pile cluster	2,825	1,825	4,650
2380	10 pile cluster	4,700	3,025	7,725
2400	200K load, end bearing, 8 pile cluster	3,950	2,650	6,600
2420	10 pile cluster	4,950	3,325	8,275
2440	12 pile cluster	5,950	4,000	9,950
2460	Friction type, 10 pile cluster	4,700	3,025	7,725
2480	400K load, end bearing, 16 pile cluster	7,925	5,325	13,250
2500	20 pile cluster	9,900	6,650	16,550
4520	50' long, 50K load, end bearing, 3 pile cluster	3,850	1,475	5,325
4540	4 pile cluster	5,150	1,975	7,125
4560	Friction type, 2 pile cluster	2,500	900	3,400
4580	3 pile cluster	3,750	1,350	5,100
4600	100K load, end bearing, 5 pile cluster	6,425	2,475	8,900
4620	8 pile cluster	10,300	3,950	14,250
4640	Friction type, 3 pile cluster	3,750	1,350	5,100
4660	5 pile cluster	6,250	2,250	8,500
4680	200K load, end bearing, 9 pile cluster	11,600	4,450	16,050
4700	10 pile cluster	12,900	4,925	17,825
4720	15 pile cluster	19,300	7,400	26,700
4740	Friction type, 5 pile cluster	6,250	2,250	8,500
4760	6 pile cluster	7,500	2,700	10,200

A1020   Special Foundations

A1020 160	Treated Wood Piles	COST EACH		
		MAT.	INST.	TOTAL
4780	10 pile cluster	12,500	4,500	17,000
4800	400K load, end bearing, 18 pile cluster	23,200	8,850	32,050
4820	20 pile cluster	25,700	9,850	35,550
4840	Friction type, 9 pile cluster	11,200	4,050	15,250
4860	10 pile cluster	12,500	4,500	17,000
9000	Add for boot for driving tip, each pile	25.50	21.50	47

A1020 Special Foundations

The Grade Beam System includes: excavation with a truck mounted backhoe; hand trim; backfill; forms (four uses); reinforcing steel; and 3,000 p.s.i. concrete placed from chute.

Superimposed loads vary in the listing from 1 Kip per linear foot (KLF) and above. In the Expanded System Listing, the span of the beams varies from 15' to 40'. Depth varies from 28" to 52". Width varies from 12" and wider.

Please see the reference section for further design and cost information.

System Components	QUANTITY	UNIT	COST PER L.F.		
			MAT.	INST.	TOTAL
SYSTEM A1020 210 2220					
GRADE BEAM, 15' SPAN, 28" DEEP, 12" WIDE, 8 KLF LOAD					
Excavation, trench, hydraulic backhoe, 3/8 CY bucket	.260	C.Y.		2.56	2.56
Trim sides and bottom of trench, regular soil	2.000	S.F.		1.94	1.94
Backfill, by hand, compaction in 6" layers, using vibrating plate	.170	C.Y.		1.42	1.42
Forms in place, grade beam, 4 uses	4.700	SFCA	5.26	26.32	31.58
Reinforcing in place, beams & girders, #8 to #14	.019	Ton	20.43	18.53	38.96
Concrete ready mix, regular weight, 3000 psi	.090	C.Y.	10.08		10.08
Place and vibrate conc. for grade beam, direct chute	.090	C.Y.		1.76	1.76
TOTAL			35.77	52.53	88.30

A1020 210	Grade Beams	COST PER L.F.		
		MAT.	INST.	TOTAL
2220	Grade beam, 15' span, 28" deep, 12" wide, 8 KLF load	36	52.50	88.50
2240	14" wide, 12 KLF load	37	53	90
2260	40" deep, 12" wide, 16 KLF load	37	65.50	102.50
2280	20 KLF load	42.50	70.50	113
2300	52" deep, 12" wide, 30 KLF load	49	88.50	137.50
2320	40 KLF load	60	98	158
3360	20' span, 28" deep, 12" wide, 2 KLF load	23	41	64
3380	16" wide, 4 KLF load	30	45.50	75.50
3400	40" deep, 12" wide, 8 KLF load	37	65.50	102.50
3440	14" wide, 16 KLF load	56.50	81.50	138
3460	52" deep, 12" wide, 20 KLF load	61	99	160
3480	14" wide, 30 KLF load	83.50	118	201.50
4540	30' span, 28" deep, 12" wide, 1 KLF load	24	42	66
4560	14" wide, 2 KLF load	38	57.50	95.50
4580	40" deep, 12" wide, 4 KLF load	45	69.50	114.50
4600	18" wide, 8 KLF load	63	84	147
4620	52" deep, 14" wide, 12 KLF load	80.50	115	195.50
4640	20" wide, 16 KLF load	98	125	223
4660	24" wide, 20 KLF load	121	142	263
5720	40' span, 40" deep, 12" wide, 1 KLF load	33	61.50	94.50
5740	2 KLF load	40.50	68.50	109
5760	52" deep, 12" wide, 4 KLF load	60	98	158
5780	20" wide, 8 KLF load	95	122	217
5800	28" wide, 12 KLF load	130	147	277

A10 Foundations

A1020 Special Foundations

Caisson Systems are listed for three applications: stable ground, wet ground and soft rock. Concrete used is 3,000 p.s.i. placed from chute. Included are a bell at the bottom of the caisson shaft (if applicable) along with required excavation and disposal of excess excavated material up to two miles from job site.

The Expanded System lists cost per caisson. End-bearing loads vary from 200 Kips to 3,200 Kips. The dimensions of the caissons range from 2' x 50' to 7' x 200'.

Please see the reference section for further design and cost information.

System Components	QUANTITY	UNIT	COST EACH MAT.	COST EACH INST.	COST EACH TOTAL
SYSTEM A1020 310 2200					
CAISSON, STABLE GROUND, 3000 PSI CONC., 10 KSF BRNG, 200K LOAD, 2'X50'					
Caissons, drilled, to 50', 24" shaft diameter, .116 C.Y./L.F.	50.000	V.L.F.	802.50	1,537.50	2,340
Reinforcing in place, columns, #3 to #7	.060	Ton	64.50	105	169.50
4' bell diameter, 24" shaft, 0.444 C.Y.	1.000	Ea.	49.50	293	342.50
Load & haul excess excavation, 2 miles	6.240	C.Y.		43.61	43.61
TOTAL			916.50	1,979.11	2,895.61

A1020 310	Caissons	COST EACH MAT.	COST EACH INST.	COST EACH TOTAL
2200	Caisson, stable ground, 3000 PSI conc, 10 KSF brng, 200K load, 2'-0"x50'-0	915	1,975	2,890
2400	400K load, 2'-6"x50'-0"	1,500	3,175	4,675
2600	800K load, 3'-0"x100'-0"	4,125	7,550	11,675
2800	1200K load, 4'-0"x100'-0"	7,175	9,525	16,700
3000	1600K load, 5'-0"x150'-0"	16,200	14,700	30,900
3200	2400K load, 6'-0"x150'-0"	23,500	19,200	42,700
3400	3200K load, 7'-0"x200'-0"	42,300	28,000	70,300
5000	Wet ground, 3000 PSI conc., 10 KSF brng, 200K load, 2'-0"x50'-0"	795	2,825	3,620
5200	400K load, 2'-6"x50'-0"	1,325	4,825	6,150
5400	800K load, 3'-0"x100'-0"	3,600	13,000	16,600
5600	1200K load, 4'-0"x100'-0"	6,225	19,300	25,525
5800	1600K load, 5'-0"x150'-0"	13,900	41,600	55,500
6000	2400K load, 6'-0"x150'-0"	20,200	51,000	71,200
6200	3200K load, 7'-0"x200'-0"	36,400	82,000	118,400
7800	Soft rock, 3000 PSI conc., 10 KSF brng, 200K load, 2'-0"x50'-0"	795	15,300	16,095
8000	400K load, 2'-6"x50'-0"	1,325	24,700	26,025
8200	800K load, 3'-0"x100'-0"	3,600	65,000	68,600
8400	1200K load, 4'-0"x100'-0"	6,225	95,000	101,225
8600	1600K load, 5'-0"x150'-0"	13,900	195,000	208,900
8800	2400K load, 6'-0"x150'-0"	20,200	232,000	252,200
9000	3200K load, 7'-0"x200'-0"	36,400	369,500	405,900

A1020 Special Foundations

Pressure Injected Piles are usually uncased up to 25' and cased over 25' depending on soil conditions.

These costs include excavation and hauling of excess materials; steel casing over 25'; reinforcement; 3,000 p.s.i. concrete; plus mobilization and demobilization of equipment for a distance of up to fifty miles to and from the job site.

The Expanded System lists cost per cluster of piles. Clusters range from one pile to eight piles. End-bearing loads range from 50 Kips to 1,600 Kips.

Please see the reference section for further design and cost information.

System Components	QUANTITY	UNIT	COST EACH MAT.	COST EACH INST.	COST EACH TOTAL
SYSTEM A1020 710 4200					
PRESSURE INJECTED FOOTING, END BEARING, 50' LONG, 50K LOAD, 1 PILE					
Pressure injected footings, cased, 30-60 ton cap., 12" diameter	50.000	V.L.F.	860	1,460	2,320
Pile cutoff, concrete pile with thin steel shell	1.000	Ea.		15.35	15.35
TOTAL			860	1,475.35	2,335.35

A1020 710	Pressure Injected Footings	MAT.	INST.	TOTAL
2200	Pressure injected footing, end bearing, 25' long, 50K load, 1 pile	400	1,025	1,425
2400	100K load, 1 pile	400	1,025	1,425
2600	2 pile cluster	800	2,050	2,850
2800	200K load, 2 pile cluster	800	2,050	2,850
3200	400K load, 4 pile cluster	1,600	4,100	5,700
3400	7 pile cluster	2,800	7,225	10,025
3800	1200K load, 6 pile cluster	3,375	7,800	11,175
4000	1600K load, 7 pile cluster	3,950	9,075	13,025
4200	50' long, 50K load, 1 pile	860	1,475	2,335
4400	100K load, 1 pile	1,500	1,475	2,975
4600	2 pile cluster	3,000	2,950	5,950
4800	200K load, 2 pile cluster	3,000	2,950	5,950
5000	4 pile cluster	6,000	5,900	11,900
5200	400K load, 4 pile cluster	6,000	5,900	11,900
5400	8 pile cluster	12,000	11,800	23,800
5600	800K load, 7 pile cluster	10,500	10,300	20,800
5800	1200K load, 6 pile cluster	9,600	8,850	18,450
6000	1600K load, 7 pile cluster	11,200	10,300	21,500

A1030 Slab on Grade

There are four types of Slab on Grade Systems listed: Non-industrial, Light industrial, Industrial and Heavy industrial. Each type is listed two ways: reinforced and non-reinforced. A Slab on Grade system includes three passes with a grader; 6" of compacted gravel fill; polyethylene vapor barrier; 3500 p.s.i. concrete placed by chute; bituminous fibre expansion joint; all necessary edge forms (4 uses); steel trowel finish; and sprayed-on membrane curing compound.

The Expanded System Listing shows costs on a per square foot basis. Thicknesses of the slabs range from 4" and above. Non-industrial applications are for foot traffic only with negligible abrasion. Light industrial applications are for pneumatic wheels and light abrasion. Industrial applications are for solid rubber wheels and moderate abrasion. Heavy industrial applications are for steel wheels and severe abrasion. All slabs are either shown unreinforced or reinforced with welded wire fabric.

System Components	QUANTITY	UNIT	COST PER S.F.		
			MAT.	INST.	TOTAL
SYSTEM A1030 120 2220					
SLAB ON GRADE, 4″ THICK, NON INDUSTRIAL, NON REINFORCED					
Fine grade, 3 passes with grader and roller	.110	S.Y.		.52	.52
Gravel under floor slab, 6″ deep, compacted	1.000	S.F.	.46	.31	.77
Polyethylene vapor barrier, standard, 6 mil	1.000	S.F.	.04	.16	.20
Concrete ready mix, regular weight, 3500 psi	.012	C.Y.	1.38		1.38
Place and vibrate concrete for slab on grade, 4″ thick, direct chute	.012	C.Y.		.32	.32
Expansion joint, premolded bituminous fiber, 1/2″ x 6″	.100	L.F.	.11	.34	.45
Edge forms in place for slab on grade to 6″ high, 4 uses	.030	L.F.	.01	.11	.12
Cure with sprayed membrane curing compound	1.000	S.F.	.12	.10	.22
Finishing floor, monolithic steel trowel	1.000	S.F.		.92	.92
TOTAL			2.12	2.78	4.90

A1030 120	Plain & Reinforced	COST PER S.F.		
		MAT.	INST.	TOTAL
2220	Slab on grade, 4″ thick, non industrial, non reinforced	2.12	2.78	4.90
2240	Reinforced	2.28	3.16	5.44
2260	Light industrial, non reinforced	2.75	3.41	6.16
2280	Reinforced	2.91	3.79	6.70
2300	Industrial, non reinforced	3.39	7.10	10.49
2320	Reinforced	3.55	7.50	11.05
3340	5″ thick, non industrial, non reinforced	2.47	2.86	5.33
3360	Reinforced	2.63	3.24	5.87
3380	Light industrial, non reinforced	3.10	3.49	6.59
3400	Reinforced	3.26	3.87	7.13
3420	Heavy industrial, non reinforced	4.42	8.45	12.87
3440	Reinforced	4.52	8.90	13.42
4460	6″ thick, non industrial, non reinforced	2.93	2.80	5.73
4480	Reinforced	3.16	3.31	6.47
4500	Light industrial, non reinforced	3.57	3.43	7
4520	Reinforced	3.93	4.12	8.05
4540	Heavy industrial, non reinforced	4.90	8.55	13.45
4560	Reinforced	5.15	9.10	14.25

A2010 Basement Excavation

Pricing Assumptions: Two-thirds of excavation is by 2-1/2 C.Y. wheel mounted front end loader and one-third by 1-1/2 C.Y. hydraulic excavator.

Two-mile round trip haul by 12 C.Y. tandem trucks is included for excavation wasted and storage of suitable fill from excavated soil. For excavation in clay, all is wasted and the cost of suitable backfill with two-mile haul is included.

Sand and gravel assumes 15% swell and compaction; common earth assumes 25% swell and 15% compaction; clay assumes 40% swell and 15% compaction (non-clay).

In general, the following items are accounted for in the costs in the table below.

1. Excavation for building or other structure to depth and extent indicated.
2. Backfill compacted in place.
3. Haul of excavated waste.
4. Replacement of unsuitable material with bank run gravel.

Note: Additional excavation and fill beyond this line of general excavation for the building (as required for isolated spread footings, strip footings, etc.) are included in the cost of the appropriate component systems.

System Components	QUANTITY	UNIT	COST PER S.F. MAT.	COST PER S.F. INST.	COST PER S.F. TOTAL
SYSTEM A2010 110 2280					
EXCAVATE & FILL, 1000 S.F., 8' DEEP, SAND, ON SITE STORAGE					
Excavating bulk shovel, 1.5 C.Y. bucket, 150 cy/hr	.262	C.Y.		.50	.50
Excavation, front end loader, 2-1/2 C.Y.	.523	C.Y.		1.30	1.30
Haul earth, 12 C.Y. dump truck	.341	L.C.Y.		2.36	2.36
Backfill, dozer bulk push 300', including compaction	.562	C.Y.		2.25	2.25
TOTAL				6.41	6.41

A2010 110	Building Excavation & Backfill	COST PER S.F. MAT.	COST PER S.F. INST.	COST PER S.F. TOTAL
2220	Excav & fill, 1000 S.F., 4' deep sand, gravel, or common earth, on site storage		1.07	1.07
2240	Off site storage		1.61	1.61
2260	Clay excavation, bank run gravel borrow for backfill	2.45	2.48	4.93
2280	8' deep, sand, gravel, or common earth, on site storage		6.40	6.40
2300	Off site storage		14.15	14.15
2320	Clay excavation, bank run gravel borrow for backfill	9.95	11.60	21.55
2340	16' deep, sand, gravel, or common earth, on site storage		17.55	17.55
2350	Off site storage		35.50	35.50
2360	Clay excavation, bank run gravel borrow for backfill	27.50	29.50	57
3380	4000 S.F., 4' deep, sand, gravel, or common earth, on site storage		.57	.57
3400	Off site storage		1.12	1.12
3420	Clay excavation, bank run gravel borrow for backfill	1.25	1.25	2.50
3440	8' deep, sand, gravel, or common earth, on site storage		4.53	4.53
3460	Off site storage		7.95	7.95
3480	Clay excavation, bank run gravel borrow for backfill	4.53	6.90	11.43
3500	16' deep, sand, gravel, or common earth, on site storage		10.85	10.85
3520	Off site storage		21.50	21.50
3540	Clay, excavation, bank run gravel borrow for backfill	12.15	16.50	28.65
4560	10,000 S.F., 4' deep, sand gravel, or common earth, on site storage		.32	.32
4580	Off site storage		.66	.66
4600	Clay excavation, bank run gravel borrow for backfill	.76	.76	1.52
4620	8' deep, sand, gravel, or common earth, on site storage		3.93	3.93
4640	Off site storage		5.95	5.95
4660	Clay excavation, bank run gravel borrow for backfill	2.74	5.40	8.14
4680	16' deep, sand, gravel, or common earth, on site storage		8.85	8.85
4700	Off site storage		15.15	15.15
4720	Clay excavation, bank run gravel borrow for backfill	7.30	12.30	19.60

A2010 Basement Excavation

A2010 110	Building Excavation & Backfill	COST PER S.F.		
		MAT.	INST.	TOTAL
5740	30,000 S.F., 4' deep, sand, gravel, or common earth, on site storage		.18	.18
5760	Off site storage		.39	.39
5780	Clay excavation, bank run gravel borrow for backfill	.44	.44	.88
5800	8' deep, sand & gravel, or common earth, on site storage		3.53	3.53
5820	Off site storage		4.66	4.66
5840	Clay excavation, bank run gravel borrow for backfill	1.54	4.36	5.90
5860	16' deep, sand, gravel, or common earth, on site storage		7.60	7.60
5880	Off site storage		11.05	11.05
5900	Clay excavation, bank run gravel borrow for backfill	4.04	9.55	13.59
6910	100,000 S.F., 4' deep, sand, gravel, or common earth, on site storage		.11	.11
6920	Off site storage		.22	.22
6930	Clay excavation, bank run gravel borrow for backfill	.22	.24	.46
6940	8' deep, sand, gravel, or common earth, on site storage		3.31	3.31
6950	Off site storage		3.91	3.91
6960	Clay excavation, bank run gravel borrow for backfill	.83	3.75	4.58
6970	16' deep, sand, gravel, or common earth, on site storage		6.90	6.90
6980	Off site storage		8.70	8.70
6990	Clay excavation, bank run gravel borrow for backfill	2.18	7.95	10.13

A20 Basement Construction

A2020 Basement Walls

The Foundation Bearing Wall System includes: forms up to 16′ high (four uses); 3,000 p.s.i. concrete placed and vibrated; and form removal with breaking form ties and patching walls. The wall systems list walls from 6″ to 16″ thick and are designed with minimum reinforcement.

Excavation and backfill are not included.

Please see the reference section for further design and cost information.

System Components			COST PER L.F.		
	QUANTITY	UNIT	MAT.	INST.	TOTAL
SYSTEM A2020 110 1500					
FOUNDATION WALL, CAST IN PLACE, DIRECT CHUTE, 4′ HIGH, 6″ THICK					
Formwork	8.000	SFCA	6.56	45.20	51.76
Reinforcing	3.300	Lb.	1.77	1.44	3.21
Unloading & sorting reinforcing	3.300	Lb.		.08	.08
Concrete, 3,000 psi	.074	C.Y.	8.29		8.29
Place concrete, direct chute	.074	C.Y.		2.43	2.43
Finish walls, break ties and patch voids, one side	4.000	S.F.	.16	3.96	4.12
TOTAL			16.78	53.11	69.89

A2020 110			Walls, Cast in Place						
	WALL HEIGHT (FT.)	PLACING METHOD	CONCRETE (C.Y. per L.F.)	REINFORCING (LBS. per L.F.)	WALL THICKNESS (IN.)	COST PER L.F.		
						MAT.	INST.	TOTAL
1500	4′	direct chute	.074	3.3	6	16.80	53	69.80
1520			.099	4.8	8	20.50	54.50	75
1540			.123	6.0	10	23.50	55.50	79
1560			.148	7.2	12	27	56.50	83.50
1580			.173	8.1	14	30.50	57.50	88
1600			.197	9.44	16	34	59	93
1700	4′	pumped	.074	3.3	6	16.80	54	70.80
1720			.099	4.8	8	20.50	56.50	77
1740			.123	6.0	10	23.50	57.50	81
1760			.148	7.2	12	27	59	86
1780			.173	8.1	14	30.50	60	90.50
1800			.197	9.44	16	34	61.50	95.50
3000	6′	direct chute	.111	4.95	6	25	79.50	104.50
3020			.149	7.20	8	30.50	82	112.50
3040			.184	9.00	10	35.50	83	118.50
3060			.222	10.8	12	41	85	126
3080			.260	12.15	14	45.50	86.50	132
3100			.300	14.39	16	51.50	89	140.50

573

A2020 Basement Walls

A2020 110	Walls, Cast in Place

	WALL HEIGHT (FT.)	PLACING METHOD	CONCRETE (C.Y. per L.F.)	REINFORCING (LBS. per L.F.)	WALL THICKNESS (IN.)	COST PER L.F.		
						MAT.	INST.	TOTAL
3200	6'	pumped	.111	4.95	6	25	81.50	106.50
3220			.149	7.20	8	30.50	84.50	115
3240			.184	9.00	10	35.50	86	121.50
3260			.222	10.8	12	41	88.50	129.50
3280			.260	12.15	14	45.50	90	135.50
3300			.300	14.39	16	51.50	92.50	144
5000	8'	direct chute	.148	6.6	6	33.50	106	139.50
5020			.199	9.6	8	41	109	150
5040			.250	12	10	48	111	159
5060			.296	14.39	12	54.50	113	167.50
5080			.347	16.19	14	56.50	114	170.50
5100			.394	19.19	16	68	118	186
5200	8'	pumped	.148	6.6	6	33.50	108	141.50
5220			.199	9.6	8	41	113	154
5240			.250	12	10	48	115	163
5260			.296	14.39	12	54.50	118	172.50
5280			.347	16.19	14	56.50	118	174.50
5300			.394	19.19	16	68	123	191
6020	10'	direct chute	.248	12	8	51	136	187
6040			.307	14.99	10	59	139	198
6060			.370	17.99	12	68	142	210
6080			.433	20.24	14	76	144	220
6100			.493	23.99	16	85	148	233
6220	10'	pumped	.248	12	8	51	140	191
6240			.307	14.99	10	59	143	202
6260			.370	17.99	12	68	147	215
6280			.433	20.24	14	76	150	226
6300			.493	23.99	16	85	154	239
7220	12'	pumped	.298	14.39	8	61.50	169	230.50
7240			.369	17.99	10	71	172	243
7260			.444	21.59	12	81.50	177	258.50
7280			.52	24.29	14	91.50	180	271.50
7300			.591	28.79	16	102	184	286
7420	12'	crane & bucket	.298	14.39	8	61.50	176	237.50
7440			.369	17.99	10	71	180	251
7460			.444	21.59	12	81.50	187	268.50
7480			.52	24.29	14	91.50	190	281.50
7500			.591	28.79	16	102	199	301
8220	14'	pumped	.347	16.79	8	71.50	197	268.50
8240			.43	20.99	10	83	200	283
8260			.519	25.19	12	95	206	301
8280			.607	28.33	14	107	209	316
8300			.69	33.59	16	119	215	334
8420	14'	crane & bucket	.347	16.79	8	71.50	205	276.50
8440			.43	20.99	10	83	210	293
8460			.519	25.19	12	95	218	313
8480			.607	28.33	14	107	223	330
8500			.69	33.59	16	119	230	349
9220	16'	pumped	.397	19.19	8	81.50	224	305.50
9240			.492	23.99	10	95	229	324
9260			.593	28.79	12	109	236	345
9280			.693	32.39	14	122	239	361
9300			.788	38.38	16	136	246	382

A20 Basement Construction

A2020 Basement Walls

A2020 110				Walls, Cast in Place				

	WALL HEIGHT (FT.)	PLACING METHOD	CONCRETE (C.Y. per L.F.)	REINFORCING (LBS. per L.F.)	WALL THICKNESS (IN.)	COST PER L.F.		
						MAT.	INST.	TOTAL
9420	16'	crane & bucket	.397	19.19	8	81.50	235	316.50
9440			.492	23.99	10	95	239	334
9460			.593	28.79	12	109	249	358
9480			.693	32.39	14	122	254	376
9500			.788	38.38	16	136	263	399

For customer support on your Site Work & Landscape Cost Data, call 877.737.1594.

A2020 Basement Walls

The Wood Wall Foundations System includes: all required pressure treated wood framing members; sheathing (treated and bonded with CDX-grade glue); asphalt paper; polyethylene vapor barrier; and 3-1/2" R11 fiberglass insulation.

The Expanded System Listing shows various walls fabricated with 2" x 4", 2" x 6", 2" x 8", or 2" x 10" studs. Wall height varies from 2' to 8'. The insulation is standard, fiberglass batt type for all walls listed.

System Components	QUANTITY	UNIT	COST PER S.F.		
			MAT.	INST.	TOTAL
SYSTEM A2020 150 2000					
WOOD WALL FOUNDATION, 2" X 4" STUDS, 12" O.C., 1/2" SHEATHING, 2' HIGH					
Framing plates & studs, 2" x 4" treated	.550	B.F.	1.32	2.57	3.89
Sheathing, 1/2" thick CDX, treated	1.005	S.F.	.90	1.03	1.93
Building paper, asphalt felt sheathing paper 15 lb	1.100	S.F.	.07	.17	.24
Polyethylene vapor barrier, standard, 6 mil	1.000	S.F.	.04	.16	.20
Fiberglass insulation, 3-1/2" thick, 11" wide	1.000	S.F.	.33	.50	.83
TOTAL			2.66	4.43	7.09

A2020 150	Wood Wall Foundations	COST PER S.F.		
		MAT.	INST.	TOTAL
2000	Wood wall foundation, 2" x 4" studs, 12" O.C., 1/2" sheathing, 2' high	2.66	4.43	7.09
2008	4' high	2.28	3.69	5.97
2012	6' high	2.16	3.45	5.61
2020	8' high	2.10	3.33	5.43
2500	2" x 6" studs, 12" O.C., 1/2" sheathing, 2' high	3.33	5.30	8.63
2508	4' high	2.77	4.32	7.09
2512	6' high	2.58	3.99	6.57
2520	8' high	2.49	3.84	6.33
3000	2" x 8" studs, 12" O.C., 1/2" sheathing, 2' high	4.02	4.69	8.71
3008	4' high	3.26	3.89	7.15
3016	6' high	3	3.62	6.62
3024	8' high	2.88	3.49	6.37
3032	16" O.C., 3/4" sheathing, 2' high	4.34	4.61	8.95
3040	4' high	3.56	3.78	7.34
3048	6' high	3.29	3.49	6.78
3056	8' high	3.16	3.35	6.51
4000	2" x 10" studs, 12" O.C., 1/2" sheathing, 2' high	4.93	4.83	9.76
4008	4' high	3.91	3.99	7.90
4012	6' high	3.57	3.71	7.28
4040	8' high	3.40	3.57	6.97
4048	16" O.C., 3/4" sheathing, 2' high	5.15	4.73	9.88
4056	4' high	4.11	3.85	7.96
4070	6' high	3.77	3.57	7.34
4080	8' high	3.59	3.42	7.01

D Services

Geothermal System

System Components

System Components	QUANTITY	UNIT	COST EACH		
			MAT.	INST.	TOTAL
SYSTEM D3050 248 1000					
GEOTHERMAL HEAT PUMP SYSTEM 50 TON, VERTICAL LOOP, 200 LF PER TON					
Mobilization excavator	2.000	Ea.		1,590	1,590
Mobilization support crew and equipment	2.000	Ea.		590	590
Mobilization drill rig	2.000	Ea.		314	314
Drill wells 6" diameter	100.000	C.L.F.		68,300	68,300
Pipe loops 1 1/2" diameter	200.000	C.L.F.	29,800	39,600	69,400
Pipe headers 2" diameter	1600.000	L.F.	3,872	3,920	7,792
U-fittings for pipe loops	50.000	Ea.	248	875	1,123
Header tee fittings	100.000	Ea.	1,550	3,000	4,550
Header elbow fittings	10.000	Ea.	69.50	186	255.50
Excavate trench for pipe header	475.000	B.C.Y.		3,591	3,591
Backfill trench for pipe header	655.000	L.C.Y.		1,919.15	1,919.15
Compact trench for pipe header	475.000	E.C.Y.		1,192.25	1,192.25
Circulation pump 5 HP	1.000	Ea.	10,800	850	11,650
Pump control system	1.000	Ea.	1,325	1,075	2,400
Pump gauges	2.000	Ea.	22.80	45	67.80
Pump gauge fittings	2.000	Ea.	153	45	198
Pipe insulation for pump connection	12.000	L.F.	31.32	82.80	114.12
Pipe for pump connection	12.000	L.F.	204	371.76	575.76
Pipe fittings for pump connection	1.000	Ea.	32	191.05	223.05
Install thermostat wells	2.000	Ea.	15.60	116.52	132.12
Install gauge wells	2.000	Ea.	15.60	121.78	137.38
Thermometers, stem type, 9" case, 8" stem, 3/4" NPT	8.000	Ea.	308	764.32	1,072.32
Gauges, pressure or vacuum, 3-1/2" diameter dial	1.000	Ea.	905	284	1,189
Pipe strainer for pump	1.000	Ea.	204	289	493
Shut valve for pump	1.000	Ea.	630	310	940
Expansion joints for pump	2.000	Ea.	660	228	888
Heat pump 50 tons	1.000	Ea.	40,000	13,500	53,500
TOTAL			90,845.82	143,351.63	234,197.45

D3050 248		Geothermal Heat Pump System	COST EACH		
			MAT.	INST.	TOTAL
0990	Geothermal heat pump system, vertical loops 200' depth, 200 LF/4 gpm per ton				
1000	50 tons, vertical loops 200' depth, soft soil		91,000	143,500	234,500

D30 HVAC

D3050 Terminal & Package Units

D3050 248	Geothermal Heat Pump System	COST EACH		
		MAT.	INST.	TOTAL
1050	50 tons common soil	91,000	166,000	257,000
1075	50 tons dense soil	91,000	211,500	302,500
1100	40 tons, vertical loops 200' depth, soft soil	79,500	116,500	196,000
1150	40 tons common soil	85,500	160,500	246,000
1175	40 tons dense soil	79,500	171,000	250,500
1200	30 tons, vertical loops 200' depth, soft soil	60,000	91,500	151,500
1250	30 tons, common soil	60,000	105,000	165,000
1275	30 tons, dense soil	60,000	132,500	192,500
1300	25 tons, vertical loops 200' depth, soft soil	54,500	77,500	132,000
1350	25 tons, common soil	54,500	89,000	143,500
1375	25 tons, dense soil	54,500	111,500	166,000
1390	Geothermal heat pump system, vertical loops 250' depth, 250 LF/4 gpm per ton			
1400	50 tons, vertical loops 250' depth, soft soil	98,500	170,500	269,000
1450	50 tons common soil	98,500	199,000	297,500
1475	50 tons dense soil	98,500	255,500	354,000
1500	40 tons, vertical loops 250' depth, soft soil	85,500	138,000	223,500
1550	40 tons common soil	85,500	160,500	246,000
1575	40 tons dense soil	85,500	206,000	291,500
1600	30 tons, vertical loops 250' depth, soft soil	64,500	107,500	172,000
1650	30 tons, common soil	64,500	124,500	189,000
1675	30 tons, dense soil	64,500	158,500	223,000
1700	25 tons, vertical loops 250' depth, soft soil	58,500	91,000	149,500
1750	25 tons, common soil	58,500	105,000	163,500
1775	25 tons, dense soil	58,500	134,000	192,500
1998	Geothermal heat pump system, vertical loops 200' depth, 200 LF/4 gpm per ton			
1999	Includes pumping of wells and adding 1:1 cement grout mix with 5% waste factor			
2000	50 tons, vertical loops 200' depth, soft soil	110,000	166,000	276,000
2050	50 tons common soil	110,000	188,500	298,500
2075	50 tons dense soil	110,000	234,000	344,000
2100	40 tons, vertical loops 200' depth, soft soil	95,000	134,500	229,500
2150	40 tons common soil	101,000	178,500	279,500
2175	40 tons dense soil	95,000	189,000	284,000
2200	30 tons, vertical loops 200' depth, soft soil	72,000	105,000	177,000
2250	30 tons, common soil	72,000	118,500	190,500
2275	30 tons, dense soil	72,000	145,500	217,500
2300	25 tons, vertical loops 200' depth, soft soil	64,500	88,500	153,000
2350	25 tons, common soil	64,500	100,000	164,500
2375	25 tons, dense soil	64,500	123,000	187,500
2390	Geothermal heat pump system, vertical loops 250' depth, 250 LF/4 gpm per ton			
2391	Includes pumping of wells and adding 1:1 cement grout mix with 5% waste factor			
2400	50 tons, vertical loops 250' depth, soft soil	122,500	198,500	321,000
2450	50 tons common soil	122,500	226,500	349,000
2475	50 tons dense soil	122,500	283,500	406,000
2500	40 tons, vertical loops 250' depth, soft soil	105,000	160,500	265,500
2550	40 tons common soil	105,000	183,000	288,000
2575	40 tons dense soil	105,000	228,500	333,500
2600	30 tons, vertical loops 250' depth, soft soil	79,000	124,000	203,000
2650	30 tons, common soil	79,000	141,500	220,500
2675	30 tons, dense soil	79,000	175,500	254,500
2700	25 tons, vertical loops 250' depth, soft soil	70,500	105,000	175,500
2750	25 tons, common soil	70,500	119,500	190,000
2775	25 tons, dense soil	70,500	147,500	218,000
2998	Geothermal heat pump system, vertical loops 200' depth, 200 LF/4 gpm per ton			
2999	Includes pumping of wells and adding bentonite mix with 5% waste factor			
3000	50 tons, vertical loops 200' depth, soft soil	112,500	166,000	278,500
3050	50 tons common soil	112,500	188,500	301,000
3075	50 tons dense soil	112,500	234,000	346,500
3100	40 tons, vertical loops 200' depth, soft soil	97,000	134,500	231,500

579

D30 HVAC

D3050 Terminal & Package Units

D3050 248	Geothermal Heat Pump System	COST EACH		
		MAT.	INST.	TOTAL
3150	40 tons common soil	103,000	178,500	281,500
3175	40 tons dense soil	97,000	189,000	286,000
3200	30 tons, vertical loops 200' depth, soft soil	73,500	105,000	178,500
3250	30 tons, common soil	73,500	118,500	192,000
3275	30 tons, dense soil	73,500	145,500	219,000
3300	25 tons, vertical loops 200' depth, soft soil	65,500	88,500	154,000
3350	25 tons, common soil	65,500	100,000	165,500
3375	25 tons, dense soil	65,500	123,000	188,500
3390	Geothermal heat pump system, vertical loops 250' depth, 250 LF/4 gpm per ton			
3391	Includes pumping of wells and adding bentonite mix with 5% waste factor			
3400	50 tons, vertical loops 250' depth, soft soil	125,500	198,500	324,000
3450	50 tons common soil	125,500	226,500	352,000
3475	50 tons dense soil	125,500	283,500	409,000
3500	40 tons, vertical loops 250' depth, soft soil	107,500	160,500	268,000
3550	40 tons common soil	107,500	183,000	290,500
3575	40 tons dense soil	107,500	228,500	336,000
3600	30 tons, vertical loops 250' depth, soft soil	81,000	124,000	205,000
3650	30 tons, common soil	81,000	141,500	222,500
3675	30 tons, dense soil	81,000	175,500	256,500
3700	25 tons, vertical loops 250' depth, soft soil	72,000	105,000	177,000
3750	25 tons, common soil	72,000	119,500	191,500
3775	25 tons, dense soil	72,000	147,500	219,500

G Building Sitework

System Components	QUANTITY	UNIT	COST PER ACRE		
			MAT.	INST.	TOTAL
SYSTEM G1010 120 1000					
REMOVE TREES & STUMPS UP TO 6″ DIA. BY CUT & CHIP & STUMP HAUL AWAY					
Cut & chip light trees to 6″ dia	1.000	Acre		4,775	4,775
Grub stumps & remove, ideal conditions	1.000	Acre		2,115	2,115
TOTAL				6,890	6,890

G1010 120	Clear & Grub Site	COST PER ACRE		
		MAT.	INST.	TOTAL
0980	Clear & grub includes removal and haulaway of tree stumps			
1000	Remove trees & stumps up to 6 ″ in dia. by cut & chip & remove stumps		6,900	6,900
1100	Up to 12 ″ in diameter		11,100	11,100
1990	Removal of brush includes haulaway of cut material			
1992	Percentage of vegetation is actual plant coverage			
2000	Remove brush by saw, 4′ tall, 10 mile haul cycle		4,225	4,225

G10 Site Preparation

G1010 Site Clearing

Stripping and stock piling top soil can be done with a variety of equipment depending on the size of the job. For small jobs you can do by hand. Larger jobs can be done with a loader or skid steer. Even larger jobs can be done by a dozer.

System Components	QUANTITY	UNIT	COST PER S.Y.		
			MAT.	INST.	TOTAL
SYSTEM G1010 122 1100 **STRIP TOPSOIL AND STOCKPILE, 6 INCH DEEP BY SKID STEER** By skid steer, 6″ deep, 100′ haul, 101-500 S.Y.	1.000	S.Y. S.Y.		3.41	3.41
TOTAL				3.41	3.41

G1010 122	Strip Topsoil	COST PER S.Y.		
		MAT.	INST.	TOTAL
1000	Strip topsoil & stockpile, 6 inch deep by hand, 50′ haul		14.15	14.15
1100	100′ haul, 101-500 S.Y., by skid steer		3.41	3.41
1200	100′ haul, 501-900 S.Y.		1.89	1.89
1300	200′ haul , 901-1100 S.Y.		2.63	2.63
1400	200′ haul, 1101-4000 S.Y., by dozer		.59	.59

G10 Site Preparation

G1020 Site Demolitions and Relocations

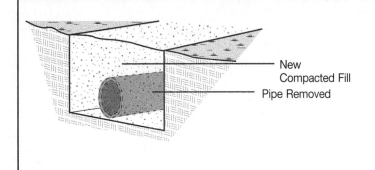

New Compacted Fill
Pipe Removed

Demolition of utility lines includes excavation, pipe removal, backfill, compaction and one day trucking cost for loading and disposal of pipe. No waste disposal fees are included.

Demolition of utility lines @ 6' depth include hydraulic shoring.

Demolition of utility lines @ 7' to 10' depth include a trench box.

Structural fill required after removal:

14″ diameter pipe:	5.15 LCY per 100 LF
16″ diameter pipe:	6.72 LCY per 100 LF
18″ diameter pipe:	8.53 LCY per 100 LF
24″ diameter pipe:	15.1 LCY per 100 LF

System Components	QUANTITY	UNIT	COST PER L.F.		
			MAT.	INST.	TOTAL
SYSTEM G1020 205 1000					
REMOVE 4″ D. I. WATER PIPE, 4′ DEPTH, EXCAVATE, BACKFILL, COMPACT & HAUL					
Excavate trench 4' depth	.593	B.C.Y.		3.98	3.98
Backfill trench	.770	L.C.Y.		2.25	2.25
Compact trench	.593	E.C.Y.		2.95	2.95
Demolition of 4 inch D.I. pipe	1.000	L.F.		16.10	16.10
Truck for waste and hauling	.040	Hr.		6.22	6.22
TOTAL				31.50	31.50

G1020 205	Remove Underground Water Pipe Including Earthwork	COST PER L.F.		
		MAT.	INST.	TOTAL
1000	Remove D.I. pipe 4' depth, excavate & backfill, hauling, no dump fee, 4″		31.50	31.50
1010	6″ to 12″ diameter		34.50	34.50
1020	Plastic pipe, 3/4″ to 4″ diameter		13.70	13.70
1030	6″ to 8″ diameter		15.50	15.50
1040	10″ to 12″ diameter		19.75	19.75
1050	Concrete water pipe, 4″ to 10″ diameter		22	22
1060	12″ diameter		27	27
1070	Welded steel water pipe, 4″ to 6″ diameter		29	29
1080	8″ to 10″ diameter		49	49
1090	Copper pipe, 3/4″ to 2″ diameter		14.25	14.25
1100	2-1/2″ to 3″ diameter		17.60	17.60
1110	4″ to 6″ diameter		22	22
1200	D.I. pipe 5' depth, 4″ diameter		33	33
1210	6″ to 12″ diameter		36.50	36.50
1220	Plastic pipe, 3/4″ to 4″ diameter		15.50	15.50
1230	6″ to 8″ diameter		17.30	17.30
1240	10″ to 12″ diameter		21.50	21.50
1250	Concrete water pipe, 4″ to 10″ diameter		23.50	23.50
1260	12″ diameter		29	29
1270	Welded steel water pipe, 4″ to 6″ diameter		30.50	30.50
1280	8″ to 10″ diameter		50.50	50.50
1290	Copper pipe, 3/4″ to 2″ diameter		16.05	16.05
1300	2-1/2″ to 3″ diameter		19.40	19.40
1310	4″ to 6 ″ diameter		23.50	23.50
1400	D.I. pipe 6' depth, 4″ diameter with hydraulic shoring	2.52	40	42.52
1410	6″ to 12″ diameter	2.52	43	45.52
1420	Plastic pipe, 3/4″ to 4″ diameter	2.52	22	24.52
1430	6″ to 8″ diameter	2.52	23.50	26.02
1440	10″ to 12″ diameter	2.52	28	30.52
1450	Concrete water pipe, 4″ to 10″ diameter	2.52	30	32.52

G1020 Site Demolitions and Relocations

G1020 205	Remove Underground Water Pipe Including Earthwork	COST PER L.F.		
		MAT.	INST.	TOTAL
1460	12" diameter	2.52	35	37.52
1470	Welded steel water pipe, 4" to 6" diameter	2.52	37	39.52
1480	8" to 10" diameter	2.52	57	59.52
1490	Copper pipe, 3/4" to 2" diameter	2.52	22.50	25.02
1500	2-1/2" to 3" diameter	2.52	25.50	28.02
1510	4" to 6" diameter	2.52	29.50	32.02
1600	D.I. pipe, trench 7' deep by 6' wide, with trench box, 4" diameter pipe		42.50	42.50
1610	6" to 12" diameter		45.50	45.50
1620	Plastic pipe, 3/4" to 4" diameter		26.50	26.50
1630	6" to 8" diameter		27.50	27.50
1640	10" to 12" diameter		30.50	30.50
1650	Concrete water pipe, 4" to 10" diameter		32.50	32.50
1660	12" diameter		38	38
1670	Welded steel water pipe, 4" to 6" diameter		40	40
1680	8" to 10" diameter		59.50	59.50
1690	Copper pipe, 3/4" to 2" diameter		26.50	26.50
1700	2-1/2" to 3" diameter		28.50	28.50
1710	4" to 6" diameter		33	33
1800	D.I. pipe, trench 8' deep by 6' wide, with trench box, 4" diameter pipe		45.50	45.50
1810	6" to 12" diameter		48.50	48.50
1820	Plastic pipe, 3/4" to 4" diameter		26.50	26.50
1830	6" to 8" diameter		27.50	27.50
1840	10" to 12" diameter		33.50	33.50
1850	Concrete water pipe, 4" to 10" diameter		35.50	35.50
1860	12" diameter		41	41
1870	Welded steel water pipe, 4" to 6" diameter		42.50	42.50
1880	8" to 10" diameter		62.50	62.50
1890	Copper pipe, 3/4" to 2" diameter		26.50	26.50
1900	2-1/2" to 3" diameter		31.50	31.50
1910	4" to 6" diameter		36	36
2000	D.I. pipe, trench 9' deep by 6' wide, with trench box, 4" diameter pipe		46.50	46.50
2010	6" to 12" diameter		49.50	49.50
2020	Plastic pipe, 3/4" to 4" diameter		30	30
2030	6" to 8" diameter		31.50	31.50
2040	10" to 12" diameter		34.50	34.50
2050	Concrete water pipe, 4" to 10" diameter		36.50	36.50
2060	12" diameter		42	42
2070	Welded steel water pipe, 4" to 6" diameter		43.50	43.50
2080	8" to 10" diameter		63.50	63.50
2090	Copper pipe, 3/4" to 2" diameter		30	30
2100	2-1/2" to 3" diameter		32	32
2110	4" to 6" diameter		36.50	36.50
2200	D.I. pipe, trench 10' deep by 6' wide, with trench box, 4" diameter pipe		49	49
2210	6" to 12" diameter		52	52
2220	Plastic pipe, 3/4" to 4" diameter		32.50	32.50
2230	6" to 8" diameter		34	34
2240	10" to 12" diameter		37	37
2250	Concrete water pipe, 4" to 10" diameter		39	39
2260	12" diameter		44.50	44.50
2270	Welded steel water pipe, 4" to 6" diameter		46	46
2280	8" to 10" diameter		66	66
2290	Copper pipe, 3/4" to 2" diameter		32.50	32.50
2300	2-1/2" to 3" diameter		35	35
2310	4" to 6" diameter		39	39
2400	Concrete water pipe 5' depth, 15" to 18" diameter		39	39
2410	21" to 24" diameter		47	47
2420	D.I. water pipe, 14" to 24" diameter		46	46
2430	Plastic water pipe, 14" to 18" diameter		19.80	19.80

585

G1020 Site Demolitions and Relocations

G1020 205	Remove Underground Water Pipe Including Earthwork	COST PER L.F.		
		MAT.	INST.	TOTAL
2440	20" to 24" diameter		25	25
2500	Concrete water pipe, 6' depth, 15" to 18" diameter with hydraulic shoring	2.52	44.50	47.02
2510	21" to 24" diameter	2.52	52.50	55.02
2520	D. I. water pipe, 14" to 24" diameter	2.52	51.50	54.02
2530	Plastic water pipe, 14" to 18" diameter	2.52	26	28.52
2540	20" to 24" diameter	2.52	31	33.52
2600	Concrete water pipe, 7' deep by 6' wide, w/trench box, 15" to 18" diameter		49	49
2610	21" to 24" diameter		56.50	56.50
2620	D. I. water pipe, 14" to 24" diameter		56	56
2630	Plastic water pipe, 14" to 18" inch diameter		29	29
2640	20" to 24" diameter		34.50	34.50
2700	Concrete water pipe, 8' deep by 6' wide, w/trench box, 15" to 18" diameter		51.50	51.50
2710	21" to 24" diameter		59	59
2720	D. I. water pipe, 14" to 24" diameter		58.50	58.50
2730	Plastic water pipe, 14" to 18" diameter		32	32
2740	20" to 24" diameter		37	37
2800	Concrete water pipe, 9' deep by 6' wide, w/trench box, 15" to 18" diameter		54.50	54.50
2810	21" to 24" diameter		62	62
2820	D. I. water pipe, 14" to 24" diameter		61.50	61.50
2830	Plastic water pipe, 14" to 18" diameter		34.50	34.50
2840	20" to 24" diameter		40	40
2900	Concrete water pipe, 10' deep by 6' wide, w/trench box, 15" to 18" diameter		56.50	56.50
2910	21" to 24" diameter		64.50	64.50
2920	D. I. water pipe, 14" to 24" diameter		63.50	63.50
2930	Plastic water pipe, 14" to 18" diameter		37	37
2940	20" to 24" diameter		42	42
3000	Import stuctural fill 10 miles round trip per cubic yard	23	11.90	34.90

G1020   Site Demolitions and Relocations

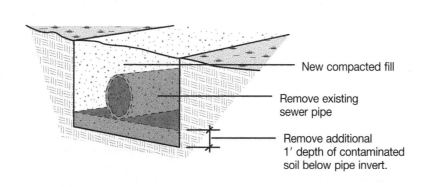

New compacted fill

Remove existing
sewer pipe

Remove additional
1' depth of contaminated
soil below pipe invert.

Demolition of utility lines includes excavation, pipe removal, backfill, compaction and one day trucking cost for loading and disposal of waste pipe and soil. No disposal fees are included.

Excavation is one foot deeper than pipe invert. For pipes to 12″ diameter, two feet of excavated soil is waste. For pipes 15″ to 18″ diameter, 2.5 feet of excavated soil is waste. For pipes 21″ to 24″ diameter, 3 feet of excavated soil is waste.

Demolition of utility lines @ 5′ to 6′ depth includes hydraulic shoring.

Demolition of utility lines @ 7′ to 10′ depth includes trench box. Trench box requires 6′ minimum trench width.

System Components	QUANTITY	UNIT	COST PER L.F.		
			MAT.	INST.	TOTAL
SYSTEM G1020 206 1000					
REMOVE 4 INCH PLASTIC SEWER PIPE, 4′ DEPTH, EXCAVATE,					
BACKFILL, COMPACT & HAUL WASTE SOIL AND PIPE					
Excavate trench 5′ depth (one foot over)	.741	B.C.Y.		4.47	4.47
Backfill trench	.963	L.C.Y.		2.82	2.82
Compact trench	.741	E.C.Y.		3.69	3.69
Demolition of 4 inch plastic sewer pipe	1.000	L.F.		2.74	2.74
Truck for waste hauling	.012	Hr.		1.87	1.87
TOTAL				15.59	15.59

G1020 206	Remove Underground Sewer Pipe Including Earthwork	COST PER L.F.		
		MAT.	INST.	TOTAL
1000	Remove plastic sewer, 4′ depth, excavate, backfill, haul waste, 4″ diameter		15.60	15.60
1010	6″ to 8″ diameter		17.30	17.30
1020	10″ to 12″ diameter		21.50	21.50
1030	Cast iron sewer, 4″ diameter		23.50	23.50
1040	5″ to 6″ diameter		27	27
1050	8″ to 12″ diameter		30.50	30.50
1060	Concrete sewer, 4″ to 10″ diameter		23.50	23.50
1070	12″ diameter		29	29
1100	Plastic sewer, 5′ depth, with hydraulic shoring, 4″ diameter	2.52	22	24.52
1110	6″ to 8″ diameter	2.52	23.50	26.02
1120	10″ to 12″ diameter	2.52	28	30.52
1130	Cast iron sewer, 4″ diameter	2.52	29.50	32.02
1140	5″ to 6″ diameter	2.52	33	35.52
1150	8″ to 12″ diameter	2.52	37	39.52
1160	Concrete sewer, 4″ to 10″ inch diameter	2.52	30	32.52
1170	12″ diameter	2.52	35.50	38.02
1200	Plastic sewer, 6′ depth, with hydraulic shoring, 4″ diameter	2.94	23.50	26.44
1210	6″ to 8″ diameter	2.94	25.50	28.44
1220	10″ to 12″ diameter	2.94	30	32.94
1230	Cast iron sewer, 4″ diameter	2.94	31.50	34.44
1240	5″ to 6″ diameter	2.94	35	37.94
1250	8″ to 12″ diameter	2.94	38.50	41.44
1260	Concrete sewer, 4″ to 10″ diameter	2.94	31.50	34.44
1270	12″ diameter	2.94	37	39.94
1300	Plastic sewer, 7′ depth, with trench box, 4″ diameter		27.50	27.50
1310	6″ to 8″ diameter		30	30

G1020 Site Demolitions and Relocations

G1020 206	Remove Underground Sewer Pipe Including Earthwork	COST PER L.F.		
		MAT.	INST.	TOTAL
1320	10" to 12" diameter		32	32
1330	Cast iron sewer, 4" diameter		34	34
1340	5" to 6" diameter		37.50	37.50
1350	8" to 12" diameter		41	41
1360	Concrete sewer, 4" to 10" diameter		33.50	33.50
1370	12" diameter		39.50	39.50
1400	Plastic sewer, 8' depth, with trench box, 4" diameter		30.50	30.50
1410	6" to 8" diameter		33	33
1420	10" to 12" diameter		36.50	36.50
1430	Cast iron sewer, 4" diameter		36.50	36.50
1440	5" to 6" diameter		40	40
1450	8" to 12" diameter		44	44
1460	Concrete sewer, 4" to 10" diameter		36.50	36.50
1470	12" diameter		42	42
1500	Plastic sewer, 9' depth, with trench box, 4" diameter		33	33
1510	6" to 8" diameter		35	35
1520	10" to 12" diameter		39	39
1530	Cast iron sewer, 4" diameter		39	39
1540	5" to 6" diameter		42.50	42.50
1550	8" to 12" diameter		46	46
1560	Concrete sewer, 4" to 10" diameter		39	39
1570	12" diameter		44.50	44.50
1600	Plastic sewer, 10' depth, with trench box, 4" diameter		35.50	35.50
1610	6" to 8" diameter		38	38
1620	10" to 12" diameter		42	42
1630	Cast iron sewer, 4" diameter		41.50	41.50
1640	5" to 6" diameter		45.50	45.50
1650	8" to 12" diameter		49	49
1660	Concrete sewer, 4" to 10" diameter		42	42
1670	12" diameter		47.50	47.50
1700	Concrete sewer, 5' depth, with hydraulic shoring, 15" to 18" diameter	2.52	47.50	50.02
1710	21" to 24" diameter	2.52	55.50	58.02
1720	Plastic sewer, 15" to 18" diameter	2.52	28	30.52
1730	21" to 24" diameter	2.52	33	35.52
1800	6' depth, 15" to 18" diameter	2.94	49	51.94
1810	21" to 24" diameter	2.94	58	60.94
1820	Plastic sewer, 15" to 18" diameter	2.94	30.50	33.44
1830	21" to 24" diameter	2.94	36	38.94
1900	7' depth, with trench box, 15" to 18" diameter		51.50	51.50
1910	21" to 24" diameter		59	59
1920	Plastic sewer, 15" to 18" diameter		32	32
1930	21" to 24" diameter		37	37
2000	8' depth, with trench box, 15" to 18" diameter		54.50	54.50
2010	21" to 24" diameter		62	62
2020	Plastic sewer, 15" to 18" diameter		34.50	34.50
2030	21" to 24" diameter		40	40
2100	9' depth, with trench box, 15" to 18" diameter		56.50	56.50
2110	21" to 24" diameter		64.50	64.50
2120	Plastic sewer, 15" to 18" diameter		37	37
2130	21" to 24" diameter		42	42
2200	10' depth, with trench box, 15" to 18" diameter		60.50	60.50
2210	21" to 24" diameter		68	68
2220	Plastic sewer, 15" to 18" diameter		40.50	40.50
2230	21" to 24" diameter		45.50	45.50

G10 Site Preparation

G1020 Site Demolitions and Relocations

G1020 210	Demolition Bituminous Sidewalk	COST PER S.Y.		
		MAT.	INST.	TOTAL
0990	Demolition of bituminous sidewalk & haulaway by truck			
1000	Sidewalk demolition, bituminous, 2 inch thick & trucking		9	9
1100	2-1/2 inch thick		9.70	9.70

G1020 212	Demolition Concrete Sidewalk	COST PER S.Y.		
		MAT.	INST.	TOTAL
0990	Demolition of concrete sidewalk & haulaway by truck			
1000	Sidewalk demolition, plain concrete, 4 inch thick & trucking		19.75	19.75
1100	Plain 5 inch thick		22.50	22.50
1200	Plain 6 inch thick		26.50	26.50
1300	Mesh reinforced, 4 inch thick		21	21
1400	Mesh reinforced, 5 inch thick		24	24
1500	Mesh reinforced, 6 inch thick		28	28

G1030 Site Earthwork

The Cut and Fill Gravel System includes: moving gravel cut from an area above the specified grade to an area below the specified grade utilizing a bulldozer and/or scraper with the addition of compaction equipment, plus a water wagon to adjust the moisture content of the soil.

The Expanded System Listing shows Cut and Fill operations with hauling distances that vary from 50' to 5000'. Lifts for compaction in the filled area vary from 6" to 12". There is no waste included in the assumptions.

System Components	QUANTITY	UNIT	COST PER C.Y.		
			EQUIP.	LABOR	TOTAL
SYSTEM G1030 105 1000					
GRAVEL CUT & FILL, 80 HP DOZER & COMPACT, 50' HAUL, 6" LIFT, 2 PASSES					
Excavating, bulk, dozer, 80 H.P. 50' haul sand and gravel	1.000	C.Y.	1.13	1.84	2.97
Water wagon rent per day	.003	Hr.	.21	.18	.39
Backfill, dozer, 50' haul sand and gravel	1.000	C.Y.	.54	.89	1.43
Compaction, vibrating roller, 6" lifts, 2 passes	1.000	C.Y.	.20	.28	.48
TOTAL			2.08	3.19	5.27

G1030 105	Cut & Fill Gravel	COST PER C.Y.		
		EQUIP.	LABOR	TOTAL
1000	Gravel cut & fill, 80HP dozer & roller compact, 50' haul, 6" lift, 2 passes	2.08	3.19	5.27
1050	4 passes	2.20	3.36	5.56
1100	12" lift, 2 passes	2	3.07	5.07
1150	4 passes	2.11	3.24	5.35
1200	150' haul, 6" lift, 2 passes	3.75	5.90	9.65
1250	4 passes	3.87	6.10	9.97
1300	12" lift, 2 passes	3.67	5.80	9.47
1350	4 passes	3.78	5.95	9.73
1400	300' haul, 6" lift, 2 passes	6.35	10.15	16.50
1450	4 passes	6.45	10.30	16.75
1500	12" lift, 2 passes	6.25	10	16.25
1550	4 passes	6.40	10.20	16.60
1600	105 HP dozer & roller compactor, 50' haul, 6" lift, 2 passes	1.92	2.39	4.31
1650	4 passes	2.04	2.56	4.60
1700	12" lift, 2 passes	1.84	2.27	4.11
1750	4 passes	1.95	2.44	4.39
1800	150' haul, 6" lift, 2 passes	3.69	4.64	8.33
1850	4 passes	3.81	4.81	8.62
1900	12" lift, 2 passes	3.61	4.52	8.13
1950	4 passes	3.72	4.69	8.41
2000	300' haul, 6" lift, 2 passes	6.80	8.60	15.40
2050	4 passes	6.90	8.75	15.65
2100	12" lift, 2 passes	6.70	8.50	15.20
2150	4 passes	6.80	8.65	15.45
2200	200 HP dozer & roller compactor, 150' haul, 6" lift, 2 passes	4.41	2.67	7.08
2250	4 passes	4.53	2.84	7.37
2300	12" lift, 2 passes	4.33	2.55	6.88
2350	4 passes	4.44	2.72	7.16

G1030 Site Earthwork

G1030 105	Cut & Fill Gravel	COST PER C.Y.		
		EQUIP.	LABOR	TOTAL
2600	300' haul, 6" lift, 2 passes	7.50	4.40	11.90
2650	4 passes	7.65	4.57	12.22
2700	12" lift, 2 passes	7.45	4.28	11.73
2750	4 passes	7.55	4.45	12
3000	300 HP dozer & roller compactors, 150' haul, 6" lift, 2 passes	3.77	1.82	5.59
3050	4 passes	3.89	1.99	5.88
3100	12" lift, 2 passes	3.69	1.70	5.39
3150	4 passes	3.80	1.87	5.67
3200	300' haul, 6" lift, 2 passes	6.45	2.90	9.35
3250	4 passes	6.55	3.07	9.62
3300	12" lift, 2 passes	6.35	2.78	9.13
3350	4 passes	6.50	2.95	9.45
4200	10 C.Y. elevating scraper & roller compacter, 1500' haul, 6" lift, 2 passes	4.59	3.98	8.57
4250	4 passes	5	4.42	9.42
4300	12" lift, 2 passes	4.48	3.84	8.32
4350	4 passes	4.58	4	8.58
4800	5000' haul, 6" lift, 2 passes	6.20	5.35	11.55
4850	4 passes	6.45	5.60	12.05
4900	12" lift, 2 passes	5.90	4.99	10.89
4950	4 passes	6.15	5.40	11.55
5000	15 C.Y. S.P. scraper & roller compactor, 1500' haul, 6" lift, 2 passes	4.30	2.94	7.24
5050	4 passes	4.58	3.19	7.77
5100	12" lift, 2 passes	4.18	2.81	6.99
5150	4 passes	4.30	2.95	7.25
5400	5000' haul, 6" lift, 2 passes	6	4.07	10.07
5450	4 passes	6.30	4.33	10.63
5500	12" lift, 2 passes	5.90	3.94	9.84
5550	4 passes	6	4.10	10.10
5600	21 C.Y. S.P. scraper & roller compactor, 1500' haul, 6" lift, 2 passes	4.16	2.34	6.50
5650	4 passes	4.44	2.59	7.03
5700	12" lift, 2 passes	4.04	2.21	6.25
5750	4 passes	4.16	2.35	6.51
6000	5000' haul, 6" lift, 2 passes	6.40	3.52	9.92
6050	4 passes	6.65	3.78	10.43
6100	12" lift, 2 passes	6.25	3.39	9.64
6150	4 passes	6.35	3.54	9.89

G10 Site Preparation

G1030 Site Earthwork

The Excavation of Sand and Gravel System balances the productivity of the Excavating equipment to the hauling equipment. It is assumed that the hauling equipment will encounter light traffic and will move up no considerable grades on the haul route. No mobilization cost is included. All costs given in these systems include a swell factor of 15%.

The Expanded System Listing shows excavation systems using backhoes ranging from 1/2 Cubic Yard capacity to 3-1/2 Cubic Yards. Power shovels indicated range from 1/2 Cubic Yard to 3 Cubic Yards. Dragline bucket rigs used range from 1/2 Cubic Yard to 3 Cubic Yards. Truck capacities indicated range from 8 Cubic Yards to 20 Cubic Yards. Each system lists the number of trucks involved and the distance (round trip) that each must travel.

System Components	QUANTITY	UNIT	COST PER C.Y.		
			EQUIP.	LABOR	TOTAL
SYSTEM G1030 110 1000					
EXCAVATE SAND & GRAVEL, 1/2 CY BACKHOE, TWO 8 CY DUMP TRUCKS 2 MRT					
Excavating, bulk, hyd. backhoe, wheel mtd., 1-1/2 CY	1.000	B.C.Y.	1.13	2.51	3.64
Haul earth, 8 CY dump truck, 2 mile round trip, 2.6 loads/hr	1.150	L.C.Y.	4.34	4.65	8.99
Spotter at earth fill dump or in cut	.020	Hr.		1.04	1.04
TOTAL			5.47	8.20	13.67

G1030 110	Excavate and Haul Sand & Gravel	COST PER C.Y.		
		EQUIP.	LABOR	TOTAL
1000	Excavate sand & gravel, 1/2 C.Y. backhoe, two 8 C.Y. dump trucks, 2 MRT	5.45	8.20	13.65
1200	Three 8 C.Y. dumptruck, 4 mile round trip	7.60	10.40	18
1400	Two 12 C.Y. dumptrucks, 4 mile round trip	7	6.75	13.75
1600	3/4 C.Y.backhoe, four 8 C.Y. dump trucks, 2 mile round trip	5.15	6.95	12.10
1700	Six 8 C.Y. dump trucks, 4 mile round trip	7.30	9.20	16.50
1800	Three 12 C.Y. dump trucks, 4 mile round trip	7	5.80	12.80
1900	Two 16 C.Y. dump trailers, 3 mile round trip	5.50	4.72	10.22
2000	Two 20 C.Y. dump trailers, 4 mile round trip	5.10	4.42	9.52
2200	1-1/2 C.Y. backhoe, four 12 C.Y. dump trucks, 2 mile round trip	5.60	4.09	9.69
2300	Six 12 C.Y. dump trucks, 4 mile round trip	6.80	4.57	11.37
2400	Three 16 C.Y. dump trailers, 3 mile round trip	5.55	4.01	9.56
2600	Three 20 C.Y. dump trailers, 4 mile round trip	5.15	3.72	8.87
2800	2-1/2 C.Y. backhoe, six 12 C.Y. dump trucks, 2 mile round trip	5.75	4.26	10.01
2900	Eight 12 C.Y. dump trucks, 4 mile round trip	7.05	5.05	12.10
3000	Four 16 C.Y. dump trailers, 2 mile round trip	4.73	3.34	8.07
3100	Six 16 C.Y. dump trailers, 4 mile round trip	5.95	4.23	10.18
3200	Four 20 C.Y. dump trailers, 3 mile round trip	4.96	3.44	8.40
3400	3-1/2 C.Y. backhoe, eight 16 C.Y. dump trailers, 3 mile round trip	5.60	3.49	9.09
3500	Ten 16 C.Y. dump trailers, 4 mile round trip	5.90	3.63	9.53
3700	Six 20 C.Y. dump trailers, 2 mile round trip	4.06	2.51	6.57
3800	Nine 20 C.Y. dump trailers, 4 mile round trip	5.10	3.09	8.19
4000	1/2 C.Y. pwr. shovel, four 8 C.Y. dump trucks, 2 mile round trip	5.35	6.55	11.90
4100	Six 8 C.Y. dump trucks, 3 mile round trip	6.25	7.80	14.05
4200	Two 12 C.Y. dump trucks, 1 mile round trip	4.44	4.05	8.49
4300	Four 12 C.Y. dump trucks, 4 mile round trip	6.90	5.40	12.30
4400	Two 16 C.Y. dump trailers, 2 mile round trip	4.61	3.94	8.55
4500	Two 20 C.Y. dump trailers, 3 mile round trip	4.83	4.04	8.87
4600	Three 20 C.Y. dump trailers, 4 mile round trip	4.96	3.83	8.79
4800	3/4 C.Y. pwr. shovel, six 8 C.Y. dump trucks, 2 mile round trip	5.25	6.35	11.60
4900	Four 12 C.Y. dump trucks, 2 mile round trip	5.65	4.25	9.90
5000	Six 12 C.Y. dump trucks, 4 mile round trip	6.85	5.25	12.10
5100	Four 16 C.Y. dump trailers, 4 mile round trip	5.85	4.22	10.07

592

G1030 Site Earthwork

G1030 110	Excavate and Haul Sand & Gravel	COST PER C.Y.		
		EQUIP.	LABOR	TOTAL
5200	Two 20 C.Y. dump trailers, 1 mile round trip	3.62	2.90	6.52
5400	1-1/2 C.Y. pwr. shovel, six 12 C.Y. dump trucks, 2 mile round trip	5.55	4.06	9.61
5600	Four 16 C.Y. dump trailers, 1 mile round trip	3.91	2.66	6.57
5700	Six 16 C.Y. dump trailers, 3 mile round trip	5.25	3.66	8.91
5800	Six 20 C.Y. dump trailers, 4 mile round trip	4.87	3.37	8.24
6000	3 C.Y. pwr. shovel, eight 16 C.Y. dump trailers, 1 mile round trip	3.70	2.43	6.13
6200	Eight 20 C.Y. dump trailers, 2 mile round trip	3.59	2.38	5.97
6400	Twelve 20 C.Y. dump trailers, 4 mile round trip	4.68	2.97	7.65
6600	1/2 C.Y. dragline bucket, three 8 C.Y. dump trucks, 1 mile round trip	4.59	5.60	10.19
6700	Five 8 C.Y. dump trucks, 4 mile round trip	9.10	11.10	20.20
6800	Two 12 C.Y. dump trucks, 2 mile round trip	7.50	6.70	14.20
6900	Three 12 C.Y. dump trucks, 4 mile round trip	8.55	7.15	15.70
7000	Two 16 C.Y. dump trailers, 4 mile round trip	7.70	6.65	14.35
7200	3/4 C.Y. dragline bucket, four 8 C.Y. dump trucks, 1 mile round trip	4.89	6	10.89
7300	Six 8 C.Y. dump trucks, 3 mile round trip	7.25	8.75	16
7400	Four 12 C.Y. dump trucks, 4 mile round trip	7.90	6.75	14.65
7500	Two 16 C.Y. dump trailers, 2 mile round trip	5.70	4.96	10.66
7600	Three 16 C.Y. dump trailers, 4 mile round trip	6.80	5.45	12.25
7800	1-1/2 C.Y. dragline bucket, six 8 C.Y. dump trucks, 1 mile round trip	3.83	4.30	8.13
7900	Ten 8 C.Y. dump trucks, 3 mile round trip	6.90	7.60	14.50
8000	Six 12 C.Y. dump trucks, 2 mile round trip	6.05	4.49	10.54
8100	Eight 12 C.Y. dump trucks, 4 mile round trip	7.30	5.30	12.60
8200	Four 16 C.Y. dump trailers, 2 mile round trip	5.05	3.60	8.65
8300	Three 20 C.Y. dump trailers, 2 mile round trip	4.70	3.74	8.44
8400	3 C.Y. dragline bucket, eight 12 C.Y. dump trucks, 2 mile round trip	6	4.12	10.12
8500	Six 16 C.Y. dump trailers, 2 mile round trip	4.86	3.35	8.21
8600	Nine 16 C.Y. dump trailers, 4 mile round trip	6.05	4.01	10.06
8700	Eight 20 C.Y. dump trailers, 4 mile round trip	5.25	3.47	8.72

G1030 Site Earthwork

The Cut and Fill Common Earth System includes: moving common earth cut from an area above the specified grade to an area below the specified grade utilizing a bulldozer and/or scraper, with the addition of compaction equipment, plus a water wagon to adjust the moisture content of the soil.

The Expanded System Listing shows Cut and Fill operations with hauling distances that vary from 50' to 5000'. Lifts for compaction in the filled area vary from 4" to 8". There is no waste included in the assumptions.

System Components	QUANTITY	UNIT	COST PER C.Y. EQUIP.	COST PER C.Y. LABOR	COST PER C.Y. TOTAL
SYSTEM G1030 115 1000					
EARTH CUT & FILL, 80 HP DOZER & COMPACTOR, 50′ HAUL, 4″ LIFT, 2 PASSES					
Excavating, bulk, dozer, 50′ haul, common earth	1.000	C.Y.	1.85	3	4.85
Water wagon, rent per day	.008	Hr.	.55	.48	1.03
Backfill dozer, from existing stockpile, 75 H.P., 50′ haul	1.000	C.Y.	.69	1.14	1.83
Compaction, roller, 4″ lifts, 2 passes	1.000	C.Y.	.09	.42	.51
TOTAL			3.18	5.04	8.22

G1030 115	Cut & Fill Common Earth	COST PER C.Y. EQUIP.	COST PER C.Y. LABOR	COST PER C.Y. TOTAL
1000	Earth cut & fill, 80 HP dozer & roller compact, 50′ haul, 4″ lift, 2 passes	3.18	5.05	8.25
1050	4 passes	2.71	4.58	7.30
1100	8″ lift, 2 passes	2.63	4.15	6.80
1150	4 passes	2.71	4.58	7.30
1200	150′ haul, 4″ lift, 2 passes	5.10	8.10	13.20
1250	4 passes	5.25	8.85	14.10
1300	8″ lift, 2 passes	5.10	8.10	13.20
1350	4 passes	5.25	8.85	14.10
1400	300′ haul, 4″ lift, 2 passes	9.20	14.50	23.50
1450	4 passes	9.45	15.80	25.50
1500	8″ lift, 2 passes	9.20	14.50	23.50
1550	4 passes	9.45	15.80	25.50
1600	105 H.P. dozer and roller compactor, 50′ haul, 4″ lift, 2 passes	2.12	2.74	4.86
1650	4 passes	2.17	2.95	5.10
1700	8″ lift, 2 passes	2.12	2.74	4.86
1750	4 passes	2.17	2.95	5.10
1800	150′ haul, 4″ lift, 2 passes	4.62	6	10.60
1850	4 passes	4.70	6.45	11.15
1900	8″ lift, 2 passes	4.60	5.90	10.50
1950	4 passes	4.68	6.35	11.05
2000	300′ haul, 4″ lift, 2 passes	8.55	11.40	19.95
2050	4 passes	8.75	12.45	21
2100	8″ lift, 2 passes	8.20	11.10	19.30
2150	4 passes	8.55	11.40	19.95
2200	200 H.P. dozer & roller compactor, 150′ haul, 4″ lift, 2 passes	5.20	3.16	8.35
2250	4 passes	5.25	3.37	8.60
2300	8″ lift, 2 passes	5.15	3.06	8.20
2350	4 passes	5.20	3.16	8.35
2600	300′ haul, 4″ lift, 2 passes	9.15	5.70	14.85
2650	4 passes	9.30	6.15	15.45

G1030 Site Earthwork

G1030 115	Cut & Fill Common Earth	COST PER C.Y.		
		EQUIP.	LABOR	TOTAL
2700	8" lift, 2 passes	9.10	5.50	14.60
2750	4 passes	9.05	5.35	14.40
3000	300 H.P. dozer & roller compactor, 150' haul, 4" lifts, 2 passes	4.52	2.30	6.80
3050	4 passes	4.62	2.62	7.25
3100	8" lift, 2 passes	4.47	2.14	6.60
3150	4 passes	4.52	2.30	6.80
3200	300' haul, 4" lifts, 2 passes	7.80	3.69	11.50
3250	4 passes	7.90	4.01	11.90
3300	8" lifts, 2 passes	7.75	3.53	11.30
3350	4 passes	7.80	3.69	11.50
4200	10 C.Y. elevating scraper & roller compact, 1500' haul, 4" lifts, 2 passes	4.31	3.42	7.75
4250	4 passes	4.39	3.85	8.25
4300	8" lifts, 2 passes	4.26	3.21	7.45
4350	4 passes	4.31	3.42	7.75
4800	5000' haul, 4" lifts, 2 passes	5.65	4.36	10
4850	4 passes	5.75	4.79	10.55
4900	8" lifts, 2 passes	5.60	4.15	9.75
4950	4 passes	5.65	4.36	10
5000	15 C.Y. S.P. scraper & roller compact, 1500' haul, 4" lifts, 2 passes	4.56	2.82	7.40
5050	4 passes	4.64	3.08	7.70
5100	8" lifts, 2 passes	4.64	3.08	7.70
5150	4 passes	4.52	2.69	7.20
5400	5000' haul, 4" lifts, 2 passes	5.65	3	8.65
5450	4 passes	5.70	3.21	8.90
5500	8" lifts, 2 passes	6.10	3.55	9.65
5550	4 passes	6.10	3.49	9.60
5600	21 C.Y. S.P. scraper & roller compact, 1500' haul, 4" lifts, 2 passes	4.59	2.39	7
5650	4 passes	4.65	2.60	7.25
5700	8" lifts, 2 passes	4.74	2.54	7.30
5750	4 passes	4.78	2.64	7.40
6000	5000' haul, 4" lifts, 2 passes	6.55	3.07	9.60
6050	4 passes	6.65	3.39	10.05
6100	8" lifts, 2 passes	6.50	2.91	9.40
6150	4 passes	6.55	3.07	9.60

G10 Site Preparation

G1030 Site Earthwork

The Excavation of Common Earth System balances the productivity of the excavating equipment to the hauling equipment. It is assumed that the hauling equipment will encounter light traffic and will move up no considerable grades on the haul route. No mobilization cost is included. All costs given in these systems include a swell factor of 25% for hauling.

The Expanded System Listing shows Excavation systems using backhoes ranging from 1/2 Cubic Yard capacity to 3-1/2 Cubic Yards. Power shovels indicated range from 1/2 Cubic Yard to 3 Cubic Yards. Dragline bucket rigs range from 1/2 Cubic Yard to 3 Cubic Yards. Truck capacities range from 8 Cubic Yards to 20 Cubic Yards. Each system lists the number of trucks involved and the distance (round trip) that each must travel.

System Components	QUANTITY	UNIT	COST PER C.Y.		
			EQUIP.	LABOR	TOTAL
SYSTEM G1030 120 1000					
EXCAVATE COMMON EARTH, 1/2 CY BACKHOE, TWO 8 CY DUMP TRUCKS, 1 MRT					
Excavating, bulk hyd. backhoe wheel mtd., 1/2 C.Y.	1.000	B.C.Y.	.97	2.16	3.13
Hauling, 8 CY truck, cycle 0.5 mile, 20 MPH, 15 min. wait/Ld./Uld.	1.280	L.C.Y.	2.50	2.68	5.18
Spotter at earth fill dump or in cut	.020	Hr.		.93	.93
TOTAL			3.47	5.77	9.24

G1030 120	Excavate and Haul Common Earth	COST PER C.Y.		
		EQUIP.	LABOR	TOTAL
1000	Excavate common earth, 1/2 C.Y. backhoe, two 8 C.Y. dump trucks, 1 mile RT	3.47	5.75	9.22
1200	Three 8 C.Y. dump trucks, 3 mile round trip	7.05	9.70	16.75
1400	Two 12 C.Y. dump trucks, 4 mile round trip	7.80	7.45	15.25
1600	3/4 C.Y. backhoe, three 8 C.Y. dump trucks, 1 mile round trip	3.45	4.75	8.20
1700	Five 8 C.Y. dump trucks, 3 mile round trip	6.95	9	15.95
1800	Two 12 C.Y. dump trucks, 2 mile round trip	6.45	5.75	12.20
1900	Two 16 C.Y. dump trailers, 3 mile round trip	6	4.89	10.89
2000	Two 20 C.Y. dump trailers, 4 mile round trip	5.70	4.82	10.52
2200	1-1/2 C.Y. backhoe, eight 8 C.Y. dump trucks, 3 mile round trip	6.85	7.95	14.80
2300	Four 12 C.Y. dump trucks, 2 mile round trip	6.20	4.91	11.11
2400	Six 12 C.Y. dump trucks, 4 mile round trip	7.50	5.65	13.15
2500	Three 16 C.Y. dump trailers, 2 mile round trip	4.94	3.64	8.58
2600	Two 20 C.Y. dump trailers, 1 mile round trip	3.92	2.99	6.91
2700	Three 20 C.Y. dump trailer, 3 mile round trip	5.20	3.74	8.94
2800	2-1/2 C.Y. excavator, six 12 C.Y. dump trucks, 1 mile round trip	4.47	3.32	7.79
2900	Eight 12 C.Y. dump trucks, 3 mile round trip	6.45	4.64	11.09
3000	Four 16 C.Y. dump trailers, 1 mile round trip	4.32	3	7.32
3100	Six 16 C.Y. dump trailers, 3 mile round trip	5.80	4.10	9.90
3200	Six 20 C.Y. dump trailers, 4 mile round trip	5.40	3.78	9.18
3400	3-1/2 C.Y. backhoe, six 16 C.Y. dump trailers, 1 mile round trip	4.58	2.87	7.45
3600	Ten 16 C.Y. dump trailers, 4 mile round trip	6.55	4.06	10.61
3800	Eight 20 C.Y. dump trailers, 3 mile round trip	5.25	3.24	8.49
4000	1/2 C.Y. pwr. shovel, four 8 C.Y. dump trucks, 2 mile round trip	5.90	7.25	13.15
4100	Two 12 C.Y. dump trucks, 1 mile round trip	4.92	4.47	9.39
4200	Four 12 C.Y. dump trucks, 4 mile round trip	7.65	6	13.65
4300	Two 16 C.Y. dump trailers, 2 mile round trip	5.10	4.37	9.47
4400	Two 20 C.Y. dump trailers, 4 mile round trip	5.90	5.05	10.95
4800	3/4 C.Y. pwr. shovel, six 8 C.Y. dump trucks, 2 mile round trip	5.85	7	12.85
4900	Three 12 C.Y. dump trucks, 1 mile round trip	4.84	3.84	8.68
5000	Five 12 C.Y. dump trucks, 4 mile round trip	7.75	5.75	13.50
5100	Three 16 C.Y. dump trailers, 3 mile round trip	6.20	4.67	10.87
5200	Three 20 C.Y. dump trailers, 4 mile round trip	5.80	4.34	10.14
5400	1-1/2 C.Y. pwr. shovel, six 12 C.Y. dump trucks, 1 mile round trip	4.48	3.30	7.78
5500	Ten 12 C.Y. dump trucks, 4 mile round trip	7.40	5.20	12.60

G10 Site Preparation

G1030 Site Earthwork

G1030 120	Excavate and Haul Common Earth	COST PER C.Y.		
		EQUIP.	LABOR	TOTAL
5600	Six 16 C.Y. dump trailers, 3 mile round trip	5.85	4.09	9.94
5700	Four 20 C.Y. dump trailers, 2 mile round trip	4.23	3.12	7.35
5800	Six 20 C.Y. dump trailers, 4 mile round trip	5.40	3.76	9.16
6000	3 C.Y. pwr. shovel, ten 12 C.Y. dump trucks, 1 mile round trip	4.37	3.01	7.38
6200	Twelve 16 C.Y. dump trailers, 4 mile round trip	6.15	3.96	10.11
6400	Eight 20 C.Y. dump trailers, 2 mile round trip	3.98	2.61	6.59
6600	1/2 C.Y. dragline bucket, three 8 C.Y. dump trucks, 2 mile round trip	8.05	9.55	17.60
6700	Two 12 C.Y. dump trucks, 3 mile round trip	9.15	8.25	17.40
6800	Three 12 C.Y. dump trucks, 4 mile round trip	9.45	7.90	17.35
7000	Two 16 C.Y. dump trailers, 4 mile round trip	8.50	7.30	15.80
7200	3/4 C.Y. dragline bucket, four 8 C.Y. dump trucks, 1 mile round trip	4.42	5.30	9.72
7300	Six 8 C.Y. dump trucks, 3 mile round trip	8.05	9.65	17.70
7400	Two 12 C.Y. dump trucks, 1 mile round trip	6.20	5.65	11.85
7500	Four 12 C.Y. dump trucks, 4 mile round trip	8.75	7	15.75
7600	Two 16 C.Y. dump trailers, 2 mile round trip	6.35	5.50	11.85
7800	1-1/2 C.Y. dragline bucket, four 12 C.Y. dump trucks, 1 mile round trip	5.45	4.06	9.51
7900	Six 12 C.Y. dump trucks, 3 mile round trip	7.20	5.40	12.60
8000	Four 16 C.Y. dump trucks, 2 mile round trip	5.60	4.02	9.62
8200	Five 16 C.Y. dump trucks, 4 mile round trip	7.15	4.98	12.13
8400	3 C.Y. dragline bucket, eight 12 C.Y. dump trucks, 2 mile round trip	6.65	4.60	11.25
8500	Twelve 12 C.Y. dump trucks, 4 mile round trip	7.90	5.35	13.25
8600	Eight 16 C.Y. dump trailers, 3 mile round trip	6.25	4.15	10.40
8700	Six 20 C.Y. dump trailers, 2 mile round trip	4.56	3.06	7.62

597

G10 Site Preparation

G1030 Site Earthwork

The Cut and Fill Clay System includes: moving clay from an area above the specified grade to an area below the specified grade utilizing a bulldozer and compaction equipment; plus a water wagon to adjust the moisture content of the soil.

The Expanded System Listing shows Cut and Fill operations with hauling distances that vary from 50' to 5000'. Lifts for compaction in the filled areas vary from 4" to 8". There is no waste included in the assumptions.

System Components			COST PER C.Y.		
	QUANTITY	UNIT	EQUIP.	LABOR	TOTAL
SYSTEM G1030 125 1000					
CLAY CUT & FILL, 80 HP DOZER & COMPACTOR, 50' HAUL, 4" LIFTS, 2 PASSES					
Excavating , bulk, dozer, 50' haul, clay	1.000	C.Y.	2.08	3.38	5.46
Water wagon, rent per day	.004	Hr.	.28	.24	.52
Backfill dozer, from existing, stock pile, 75 H.P., 50' haul, clay	1.330	C.Y.	.81	1.32	2.13
Compaction, tamper, 4" lifts, 2 passes	245.000	S.F.	.55	.35	.90
TOTAL			3.72	5.29	9.01

G1030 125	Cut & Fill Clay	COST PER C.Y.		
		EQUIP.	LABOR	TOTAL
1000	Clay cut & fill, 80 HP dozer & compactor, 50' haul, 4" lifts, 2 passes	3.72	5.30	9.02
1050	4 passes	4.46	5.85	10.31
1100	8" lifts, 2 passes	3.29	4.98	8.27
1150	4 passes	3.68	5.25	8.93
1200	150' haul, 4" lifts, 2 passes	6.60	10	16.60
1250	4 passes	7.35	10.55	17.90
1300	8" lifts, 2 passes	6.20	9.70	15.90
1350	4 passes	6.55	9.95	16.50
1400	300' haul, 4" lifts, 2 passes	11.20	17.45	28.65
1450	4 passes	11.95	18	29.95
1500	8" lifts, 2 passes	10.80	17.15	27.95
1550	4 passes	11.15	17.45	28.60
1600	105 HP dozer & sheeps foot compactors, 50' haul, 4" lifts, 2 passes	3.35	3.81	7.16
1650	4 passes	4.09	4.35	8.44
1700	8" lifts, 2 passes	2.92	3.50	6.42
1750	4 passes	3.31	3.79	7.10
1800	150' haul, 4" lifts, 2 passes	6.35	7.60	13.95
1850	4 passes	7.10	8.15	15.25
1900	8" lifts, 2 passes	5.90	7.30	13.20
1950	4 passes	6.30	7.60	13.90
2000	300' haul, 4" lifts, 2 passes	9.85	12.05	21.90
2050	4 passes	10.60	12.60	23.20
2100	8" lifts, 2 passes	9.45	11.75	21.20
2150	4 passes	9.80	12.05	21.85
2200	200 HP dozer & sheepsfoot compactors, 150' haul, 4" lifts, 2 passes	7.60	4.35	11.95
2250	4 passes	8.35	4.89	13.24
2300	8" lifts, 2 passes	7.20	4.04	11.24
2350	4 passes	7.55	4.33	11.88
2600	300' haul, 4" lifts, 2 passes	12.85	7.25	20.10
2650	4 passes	13.60	7.80	21.40

G1030 Site Earthwork

G1030 125	Cut & Fill Clay	COST PER C.Y.		
		EQUIP.	LABOR	TOTAL
2700	8" lifts, 2 passes	12.40	6.95	19.35
2750	4 passes	12.80	7.25	20.05
3000	300 HP dozer & sheepsfoot compactors, 150' haul, 4" lifts, 2 passes	6.65	2.95	9.60
3050	4 passes	7.40	3.49	10.89
3100	8" lifts, 2 passes	6.20	2.64	8.84
3150	4 passes	6.60	2.93	9.53
3200	300' haul, 4" lifts, 2 passes	11.45	4.89	16.34
3250	4 passes	12.20	5.45	17.65
3300	8" lifts, 2 passes	11	4.58	15.58
3350	4 passes	11.40	4.87	16.27
4200	10 C.Y. elev. scraper & sheepsfoot rollers, 1500' haul, 4" lifts, 2 passes	10.30	6.10	16.40
4250	4 passes	10.60	6.35	16.95
4300	8" lifts, 2 passes	10.25	5.95	16.20
4350	4 passes	10.35	6.15	16.50
4800	5000' haul, 4" lifts, 2 passes	14	8.20	22.20
4850	4 passes	14.25	8.45	22.70
4900	8" lifts, 2 passes	13.95	8.05	22
4950	4 passes	14	8.30	22.30
5000	15 C.Y. SP scraper & sheepsfoot rollers, 1500' haul, 4" lifts, 2 passes	8.75	4.21	12.96
5050	4 passes	9.05	4.46	13.51
5100	8" lifts, 2 passes	8.65	4.08	12.73
5150	4 passes	8.75	4.24	12.99
5400	5000' haul, 4" lifts, 2 passes	12.45	5.95	18.40
5450	4 passes	12.70	6.20	18.90
5500	8" lifts, 2 passes	12.35	5.80	18.15
5550	4 passes	12.45	6	18.45
5600	21 C.Y. SP scraper & sheepsfoot rollers, 1500' haul, 4" lifts, 2 passes	8.20	3.32	11.52
5650	4 passes	8.50	3.57	12.07
5700	8" lifts, 2 passes	8.10	3.19	11.29
5750	4 passes	8.25	3.34	11.59
6000	5000' haul, 4" lift, 2 passes	12.90	5.15	18.05
6050	4 passes	13.20	5.40	18.60
6100	8" lift, 2 passes	12.85	5	17.85
6150	4 passes	12.95	5.20	18.15

G1030 Site Earthwork

The Excavation of Clay System balances the productivity of excavating equipment to hauling equipment. It is assumed that the hauling equipment will encounter light traffic and will move up no considerable grades on the haul route. No mobilization cost is included. All costs given in these systems include a swell factor of 40%.

The Expanded System Listing shows Excavation systems using backhoes ranging from 1/2 Cubic Yard capacity to 3-1/2 Cubic Yards. Power shovels indicated range from 1/2 Cubic Yard to 3 Cubic Yards. Dragline bucket rigs range from 1/2 Cubic Yard to 3 Cubic Yards. Truck capacities range from 8 Cubic Yards to 20 Cubic Yards. Each system lists the number of trucks involved and the distance (round trip) that each must travel.

System Components	QUANTITY	UNIT	COST PER C.Y.		
			EQUIP.	LABOR	TOTAL
SYSTEM G1030 130 1000					
EXCAVATE CLAY, 1/2 CY BACKHOE, TWO 8 CY DUMP TRUCKS, 2 MI ROUND TRIP					
Excavating bulk hyd. backhoe, wheel mtd. 1/2 C.Y.	1.000	B.C.Y.	1.38	3.07	4.45
Haul earth, 8 C.Y. dump truck, 2 mile round trip, 2.6 loads/hr	1.350	L.C.Y.	5.09	5.45	10.54
Spotter at earth fill dump or in cut	.020	Hr.		1.33	1.33
TOTAL			6.47	9.85	16.32

G1030 130	Excavate and Haul Clay	COST PER C.Y.		
		EQUIP.	LABOR	TOTAL
1000	Excavate clay, 1/2 C.Y. backhoe, two 8 C.Y. dump trucks, 2 mile round trip	6.45	9.85	16.30
1200	Three 8 C.Y. dump trucks, 4 mile round trip	8.95	12.40	21.35
1400	Two 12 C.Y. dump trucks, 4 mile round trip	8.30	8.05	16.35
1600	3/4 C.Y. backhoe, three 8 C.Y. dump trucks, 2 mile round trip	6.45	8.35	14.80
1700	Five 8 C.Y. dump trucks, 4 mile round trip	8.80	10.70	19.50
1800	Two 12 C.Y. dump trucks, 2 mile round trip	6.90	6.20	13.10
1900	Three 12 C.Y. dump trucks, 4 mile round trip	8.25	6.90	15.15
2000	1-1/2 C.Y. backhoe, eight 8 C.Y. dump trucks, 3 mile round trip	7.30	8.15	15.45
2100	Three 12 C.Y. dump trucks, 1 mile round trip	5.05	3.94	8.99
2200	Six 12 C.Y. dump trucks, 4 mile round trip	8	6.05	14.05
2300	Three 16 C.Y. dump trailers, 2 mile round trip	5.25	3.92	9.17
2400	Four 16 C.Y. dump trailers, 4 mile round trip	6.85	4.87	11.72
2600	Two 20 C.Y. dump trailers, 1 mile round trip	4.19	3.25	7.44
2800	2-1/2 C.Y. backhoe, eight 12 C.Y. dump trucks, 3 mile round trip	6.80	4.95	11.75
2900	Four 16 C.Y. dump trailers, 1 mile round trip	4.59	3.19	7.78
3000	Six 16 C.Y. dump trailers, 3 mile round trip	6.20	4.39	10.59
3100	Four 20 C.Y. dump trailers, 2 mile round trip	4.39	3.24	7.63
3200	Six 20 C.Y. dump trailers, 4 mile round trip	5.70	4.04	9.74
3400	3-1/2 C.Y. backhoe, ten 12 C.Y. dump trucks, 2 mile round trip	6.75	4.33	11.08
3500	Six 16 C.Y. dump trailers, 1 mile round trip	4.88	3.03	7.91
3600	Ten 16 C.Y. dump trailers, 4 mile round trip	6.95	4.29	11.24
3800	Eight 20 C.Y. dump trailers, 3 mile round trip	5.60	3.42	9.02
4000	1/2 C.Y. pwr. shovel, three 8 C.Y. dump trucks, 1 mile round trip	5.75	7.15	12.90
4100	Six 8 C.Y. dump trucks, 4 mile round trip	8.80	11.05	19.85
4200	Two 12 C.Y. dump trucks, 1 mile round trip	5.25	4.84	10.09
4400	Three 12 C.Y. dump trucks, 3 mile round trip	7.20	6	13.20
4600	3/4 C.Y. pwr. shovel, six 8 C.Y. dump trucks, 2 mile round trip	6.20	7.50	13.70
4700	Nine 8 C.Y. dump trucks, 4 mile round trip	8.70	10.15	18.85
4800	Three 12 C.Y. dump trucks, 1 mile round trip	5.15	4.15	9.30
4900	Four 12 C.Y. dump trucks, 3 mile round trip	7.25	5.60	12.85
5000	Two 16 C.Y. dump trailers, 1 mile round trip	5.05	4.09	9.14
5200	Three 16 C.Y. dump trailers, 3 mile round trip	6.65	5.05	11.70

G1030 Site Earthwork

G1030 130	Excavate and Haul Clay	COST PER C.Y.		
		EQUIP.	LABOR	TOTAL
5400	1-1/2 C.Y. pwr. shovel, six 12 C.Y. dump trucks, 2 mile round trip	6.55	4.82	11.37
5500	Four 16 C.Y. dump trailers, 1 mile round trip	4.61	3.17	7.78
5600	Seven 16 C.Y. dump trailers, 4 mile round trip	6.65	4.63	11.28
5800	Five 20 C.Y. dump trailers, 3 mile round trip	5.40	3.59	8.99
6000	3 C.Y. pwr. shovel, nine 16 C.Y. dump trailers, 2 mile round trip	4.93	3.23	8.16
6100	Twelve 16 C.Y. dump trailers, 4 mile round trip	6.50	4.18	10.68
6200	Six 20 C.Y. dump trailers, 1 mile round trip	3.84	2.60	6.44
6400	Nine 20 C.Y. dump trailers, 3 mile round trip	5.20	3.40	8.60
6600	1/2 C.Y. dragline bucket, two 8 C.Y. dump trucks, 1 mile round trip	8.80	10.65	19.45
6800	Four 8 C.Y. dump trucks, 4 mile round trip	11.55	13.50	25.05
7000	Two 12 C.Y. dump trucks, 3 mile round trip	9.85	8.95	18.80
7200	3/4 C.Y. dragline bucket, four 8 C.Y. dump trucks, 2 mile round trip	7.80	9.15	16.95
7300	Six 8 C.Y. dump trucks, 4 mile round trip	10.25	12.40	22.65
7400	Two 12 C.Y. dump trucks, 2 mile round trip	8.95	8	16.95
7500	Three 12 C.Y. dump trucks, 4 mile round trip	10.10	8.55	18.65
7600	Two 16 C.Y. dump trailers, 3 mile round trip	8.30	7.20	15.50
7800	1-1/2 C.Y. dragline bucket, five 12 C.Y. dump trucks, 3 mile round trip	8.10	5.90	14
7900	Three 16 C.Y. dump trailers, 1 mile round trip	5.60	4.09	9.69
8000	Five 16 C.Y. dump trailers, 4 mile round trip	7.65	5.35	13
8100	Three 20 C.Y. dump trailers, 2 mile round trip	5.60	4.11	9.71
8400	3 C.Y. dragline bucket, eight 16 C.Y. dump trailers, 3 mile round trip	6.50	4.29	10.79
8500	Six 20 C.Y. dump trailers, 2 mile round trip	4.89	3.31	8.20
8600	Eight 20 C.Y. dump trailers, 4 mile round trip	6.20	4.11	10.31

G1030 Site Earthwork

The Loading and Hauling of Rock System balances the productivity of loading equipment to hauling equipment. It is assumed that the hauling equipment will encounter light traffic and will move up no considerable grades on the haul route.

The Expanded System Listing shows Loading and Hauling systems that use either a track or wheel front-end loader. Track loaders indicated range from 1-1/2 Cubic Yards capacity to 4-1/2 Cubic Yards capacity. Wheel loaders range from 1-1/2 Cubic Yards to 5 Cubic Yards. Trucks for hauling range from 8 Cubic Yards capacity to 20 Cubic Yards capacity. Each system lists the number of trucks involved and the distance (round trip) that each must travel.

System Components	QUANTITY	UNIT	COST PER C.Y.		
			EQUIP.	LABOR	TOTAL
SYSTEM G1030 150 1000					
LOAD & HAUL ROCK, 1-1/2 C.Y. TRACK LOADER, SIX 8 C.Y. TRUCKS, 1 MRT					
Excavating bulk, F.E. loader, track mtd., 1.5 C.Y.	1.000	B.C.Y.	1	1.47	2.47
8 C.Y. truck, cycle 2 miles	1.650	L.C.Y.	5.49	5.87	11.36
Spotter at earth fill dump or in cut	.010	Hr.		.81	.81
TOTAL			6.49	8.15	14.64

G1030 150	Load & Haul Rock	COST PER C.Y.		
		EQUIP.	LABOR	TOTAL
1000	Load & haul rock, 1-1/2 C.Y. track loader, six 8 C.Y. trucks, 1 MRT	6.50	8.15	14.65
1200	Nine 8 C.Y. dump trucks, 3 mile round trip	8.80	10.75	19.55
1400	Six 12 C.Y. dump trucks, 4 mile round trip	9.80	7.85	17.65
1600	Three 16 C.Y. dump trucks, 2 mile round trip	6.45	5.35	11.80
2000	2-1/2 C.Y. track loader, twelve 8 C.Y. dump trucks, 3 mile round trip	9.20	10.15	19.35
2200	Five 12 C.Y. dump trucks, 1 mile round trip	6.30	4.53	10.83
2400	Eight 12 C.Y. dump trucks, 4 mile round trip	10.15	7.30	17.45
2600	Four 16 C.Y. dump trailers, 2 mile round trip	6.85	4.83	11.68
3000	3-1/2 C.Y. track loader, eight 12 C.Y. dump trucks, 2 mile round trip	8.25	5.70	13.95
3200	Five 16 C.Y. dump trucks, 1 mile round trip	5.95	3.88	9.83
3400	Seven 16 C.Y. dump trailers, 3 mile round trip	7.95	5.35	13.30
3600	Seven 20 C.Y. dump trailers, 4 mile round trip	7.40	4.92	12.32
4000	4-1/2 C.Y. track loader, nine 12 C.Y. dump trucks, 1 mile round trip	6.20	4.12	10.32
4200	Eight 16 C.Y. dump trailers, 2 mile round trip	6.60	4.20	10.80
4400	Eleven 16 C.Y. dump trailers, 4 mile round trip	8.45	5.35	13.80
4600	Seven 20 C.Y. dump trailers, 2 mile round trip	5.75	3.63	9.38
5000	1-1/2 C.Y. wheel loader, nine 8 C.Y. dump trucks, 2 mile round trip	6.85	8.60	15.45
5200	Four 12 C.Y. dump trucks, 1 mile round trip	5.65	4.86	10.51
5400	Seven 12 C.Y. dump trucks, 4 mile round trip	9.40	7.55	16.95
5600	Five 16 C.Y. dump trailers, 4 mile round trip	7.90	6.05	13.95
6000	3 C.Y. wheel loader, eight 12 C.Y. dump trucks, 2 mile round trip	7.35	5.50	12.85
6200	Five 16 C.Y. dump trailers, 1 mile round trip	5.10	3.65	8.75
6400	Seven 16 C.Y. dump trailers, 3 mile round trip	6.10	4.53	10.63
6600	Seven 20 C.Y. dump trailers, 4 mile round trip	6.50	4.68	11.18
7000	5 C.Y. wheel loader, twelve 12 C.Y. dump trucks, 1 mile round trip	5.60	3.85	9.45
7200	Nine 16 C.Y. dump trailers, 1 mile round trip	5.30	3.52	8.82
7400	Eight 20 C.Y. dump trailers, 1 mile round trip	4.57	3	7.57
7600	Twelve 20 C.Y. dump trailers, 3 mile round trip	6.20	3.99	10.19

G10 Site Preparation

G1030 Site Earthwork

The Excavation of Sandy Clay/Loam System balances the productivity of the excavating equipment to the hauling equipment. It is assumed that the hauling equipment will encounter light traffic and will move up no considerable grades on the haul route. No mobilization cost is included. All costs given in these systems include a swell factor of 25% for hauling.

The Expanded System Listing shows Excavation systems using backhoes ranging from 1/2 Cubic Yard capacity to 3-1/2 Cubic Yards. Truck capacities range from 8 Cubic Yards to 20 Cubic Yards. Each system lists the number of trucks involved and the distance (round trip) that each must travel.

System Components	QUANTITY	UNIT	COST PER C.Y. EQUIP.	COST PER C.Y. LABOR	COST PER C.Y. TOTAL
SYSTEM G1030 160 1000					
EXCAVATE SANDY CLAY/LOAM, 1/2 CY BACKHOE, TWO 8 CY DUMP TRUCKS, 1 MRT					
Excavating, bulk hyd. backhoe wheel mtd., 1/2 C.Y.	1.000	B.C.Y.	.88	1.96	2.84
8 C.Y. truck, cycle 2 miles	1.000	L.C.Y.	4.33	4.63	8.96
Spotter at earth fill dump or in cut	.020	Hr.		.93	.93
TOTAL			5.21	7.52	12.73

G1030 160	Excavate and Haul Sandy Clay/Loam	COST PER C.Y. EQUIP.	COST PER C.Y. LABOR	COST PER C.Y. TOTAL
1000	Excavate sandy clay/loam, 1/2 C.Y. backhoe, two 8 C.Y. dump trucks, 1 MRT	5.20	7.50	12.70
1200	Three 8 C.Y. dump trucks, 3 mile round trip	7.05	9.65	16.70
1400	Two 12 C.Y. dump trucks, 4 mile round trip	7.80	7.30	15.10
1600	3/4 C.Y. backhoe, three 8 C.Y. dump trucks, 1 mile round trip	5.20	6.55	11.75
1700	Five 8 C.Y. dump trucks, 3 mile round trip	6.95	8.95	15.90
1800	Two 12 C.Y. dump trucks, 2 mile round trip	6.45	5.65	12.10
1900	Two 16 C.Y. dump trailers, 3 mile round trip	6	4.83	10.85
2000	Two 20 C.Y. dump trailers, 4 mile round trip	5.65	4.73	10.40
2200	1-1/2 C.Y. excavator, eight 8 C.Y. dump trucks, 3 mile round trip	6.80	7.95	14.75
2300	Four 12 C.Y. dump trucks, 2 mile round trip	6.15	4.84	11
2400	Six 12 C.Y. dump trucks, 4 mile round trip	7.50	5.60	13.10
2500	Three 16 C.Y. dump trailers, 2 mile round trip	4.87	3.55	8.40
2600	Two 20 C.Y. dump trailers, 1 mile round trip	3.83	2.88	6.70
2700	Three 20 C.Y. dump trailer, 3 mile round trip	5.10	3.65	8.75
2800	2-1/2 C.Y. excavator, six 12 C.Y. dump trucks, 1 mile round trip	4.33	3.19	7.50
2900	Eight 12 C.Y. dump trucks, 3 mile round trip	6.30	4.51	10.80
3000	Four 16 C.Y. dump trailers, 1 mile round trip	4.14	2.85	7
3100	Six 16 C.Y. dump trailers, 3 mile round trip	5.70	3.97	9.65
3200	Six 20 C.Y. dump trailers, 4 mile round trip	5.25	3.63	8.90
3400	3-1/2 C.Y. excavator, six 16 C.Y. dump trailers, 1 mile round trip	4.39	2.81	7.20
3600	Ten 16 C.Y. dump trailers, 4 mile round trip	6.40	4.03	10.45
3800	Eight 20 C.Y. dump trailers, 3 mile round trip	5.10	3.19	8.30

G10 Site Preparation

G1030 Site Earthwork

The Gravel Backfilling System includes: a bulldozer to place and level backfill in specified lifts; compaction equipment; and a water wagon for adjusting moisture content.

The Expanded System Listing shows Gravel Backfilling operations with bulldozers ranging from 75 H.P. to 300 H.P. The maximum hauling distance ranges from 50' to 300'. Lifts for the compaction range from 6" to 12". There is no waste included in the assumptions.

System Components	QUANTITY	UNIT	COST PER C.Y.		
			EQUIP.	LABOR	TOTAL
SYSTEM G1030 205 1000					
GRAVEL BACKFILL, 80 HP DOZER & COMPACTORS, 50' HAUL, 6" LIFTS, 2 PASSES					
Backfilling, dozer, 80 H.P., 50' haul, sand and gravel, from stockpile	1.000	L.C.Y.	.47	.77	1.24
Water wagon rent per day	.003	Hr.	.21	.18	.39
Compaction, vibrating roller, 6" lifts, 2 passes	1.000	Hr.	.20	2.31	2.51
TOTAL			.88	3.26	4.14

G1030 205	Gravel Backfill	COST PER C.Y.		
		EQUIP.	LABOR	TOTAL
1000	Gravel backfill, 80 HP dozer & compactors, 50' haul, 6"lifts, 2 passes	.88	3.26	4.14
1050	4 passes	1.10	4.38	5.48
1100	12" lifts, 2 passes	.63	1.66	2.29
1150	4 passes	.86	2.60	3.46
1200	150' haul, 6" lifts, 2 passes	1.35	4.03	5.38
1250	4 passes	1.57	5.15	6.72
1300	12" lifts, 2 passes	1.21	3.91	5.12
1350	4 passes	1.43	5.05	6.48
1400	300' haul, 6" lifts, 2 passes	1.81	4.77	6.58
1450	4 passes	2.03	5.90	7.93
1500	12" lifts, 2 passes	1.56	3.17	4.73
1550	4 passes	1.79	4.11	5.90
1600	105 HP dozer & vibrating compactors, 50' haul, 6" lifts, 2 passes	.90	3.12	4.02
1650	4 passes	1.12	4.24	5.36
1700	12" lifts, 2 passes	.65	1.52	2.17
1750	4 passes	.88	2.46	3.34
1800	150' haul, 6" lifts, 2 passes	1.40	3.75	5.15
1850	4 passes	1.62	4.87	6.49
1900	12" lifts, 2 passes	1.15	2.15	3.30
1950	4 passes	1.38	3.09	4.47
2000	300' haul, 6" lifts, 2 passes	1.84	4.31	6.15
2050	4 passes	2.06	5.45	7.51
2100	12" lifts, 2 passes	1.59	2.71	4.30
2150	4 passes	1.82	3.65	5.47
2200	200 HP dozer & roller compactors, 150' haul, 6" lifts, 2 passes	1.66	1.15	2.81
2250	4 passes	1.92	1.44	3.36
2300	12" lifts, 2 passes	1.44	.91	2.35
2350	4 passes	1.69	1.20	2.89
2600	300' haul, 6" lifts, 2 passes	2.31	1.51	3.82
2650	4 passes	2.57	1.80	4.37
2700	12" lifts, 2 passes	2.09	1.27	3.36
2750	4 passes	2.34	1.56	3.90

604

G1030 Site Earthwork

G1030 205	Gravel Backfill	COST PER C.Y.		
		EQUIP.	LABOR	TOTAL
3000	300 HP dozer & roller compactors, 150' haul, 6" lifts, 2 passes	1.36	.84	2.20
3050	4 passes	1.62	1.13	2.75
3100	12" lifts, 2 passes	1.14	.60	1.74
3150	4 passes	1.39	.89	2.28
3200	300' haul, 6" lifts, 2 passes	1.80	1.02	2.82
3250	4 passes	2.06	1.31	3.37
3300	12" lifts, 2 passes	1.58	.78	2.36
3350	4 passes	1.83	1.07	2.90

For customer support on your Site Work & Landscape Cost Data, call 877.737.1594.

G10 Site Preparation

G1030 Site Earthwork

The Common Earth Backfilling System includes: a bulldozer to place and level backfill in specified lifts; compaction equipment; and a water wagon for adjusting moisture content.

The Expanded System Listing shows Common Earth Backfilling with bulldozers ranging from 80 H.P. to 300 H.P. The maximum distance ranges from 50' to 300'. Lifts for the compaction range from 4" to 8". There is no waste included in the assumptions.

System Components	QUANTITY	UNIT	COST PER C.Y.		
			EQUIP.	LABOR	TOTAL
SYSTEM G1030 210 1000					
EARTH BACKFILL, 80 HP DOZER & ROLLER , 50' HAUL, 4" LIFTS, 2 PASSES					
Backfilling, dozer 80 H.P. 50' haul, common earth, from stockpile	1.000	L.C.Y.	.53	.87	1.40
Water wagon, rent per day	.004	Hr.	.28	.24	.52
Compaction, roller, 4" lifts, 2 passes	.035	Hr.	.75	3.71	4.46
TOTAL			1.56	4.82	6.38

G1030 210	Common Earth Backfill	COST PER C.Y.		
		EQUIP.	LABOR	TOTAL
1000	Earth backfill, 80 HP dozer & roller compactors, 50' haul,4" lifts,2 passes	1.56	4.82	6.38
1050	4 passes	2.32	8.55	10.87
1100	8" lifts, 2 passes	1.20	3.02	4.22
1150	4 passes	1.56	4.82	6.38
1200	150' haul, 4" lifts, 2 passes	2.09	5.70	7.79
1250	4 passes	2.85	9.40	12.25
1300	8" lifts, 2 passes	1.73	3.88	5.61
1350	4 passes	2.09	5.70	7.79
1400	300' haul, 4" lifts, 2 passes	2.60	6.50	9.10
1450	4 passes	3.36	10.20	13.56
1500	8" lifts, 2 passes	2.24	4.71	6.95
1550	4 passes	2.60	6.50	9.10
1600	105 HP dozer & roller compactors, 50' haul, 4" lifts, 2 passes	1.57	4.64	6.21
1650	4 passes	2.33	8.35	10.68
1700	8" lifts, 2 passes	1.21	2.84	4.05
1750	4 passes	1.57	4.64	6.21
1800	150' haul, 4" lifts, 2 passes	2.12	5.35	7.47
1850	4 passes	2.88	9.05	11.93
1900	8" lifts, 2 passes	1.76	3.54	5.30
1950	4 passes	2.12	5.35	7.47
2000	300' haul, 4" lifts, 2 passes	2.63	6	8.63
2050	4 passes	3.39	9.70	13.09
2100	8" lifts, 2 passes	2.27	4.19	6.46
2150	4 passes	2.63	6	8.63
2200	200 HP dozer & roller compactors, 150' haul, 4" lifts, 2 passes	2.32	3.13	5.45
2250	4 passes	2.97	5.25	8.22
2300	8" lifts, 2 passes	2	2.07	4.07
2350	4 passes	2.32	3.13	5.45
2600	300' haul, 4" lifts, 2 passes	3.01	3.51	6.52
2650	4 passes	3.66	5.65	9.31
2700	8" lifts, 2 passes	2.69	2.45	5.14
2750	4 passes	3.01	3.51	6.52

G1030 Site Earthwork

G1030 210	Common Earth Backfill	COST PER C.Y.		
		EQUIP.	LABOR	TOTAL
3000	300 HP dozer & roller compactors, 150' haul, 4" lift, 2 passes	2	2.79	4.79
3050	4 passes	2.65	4.91	7.56
3100	8" lifts, 2 passes	1.68	1.73	3.41
3150	4 passes	2	2.79	4.79
3200	300' haul, 4" lifts, 2 passes	2.48	2.99	5.47
3250	4 passes	3.13	5.10	8.23
3300	8" lifts, 2 passes	2.16	1.93	4.09
3350	4 passes	2.48	2.99	5.47

The Clay Backfilling System includes: a bulldozer to place and level backfill in specified lifts; compaction equipment; and a water wagon for adjusting moisture content.

The Expanded System Listing shows Clay Backfilling with bulldozers ranging from 80 H.P. to 300 H.P. The maximum distance ranges from 50' to 300'. Lifts for the compaction range from 4" to 8". There is no waste included in the assumptions.

System Components	QUANTITY	UNIT	COST PER C.Y.		
			EQUIP.	LABOR	TOTAL
SYSTEM G1030 215 1000					
CLAY BACKFILL, 80 HP DOZER & TAMPER, 50' HAUL, 4" LIFTS, 2 PASSES					
Backfilling, dozer 80 H.P. 50' haul, clay from stockpile	1.000	L.C.Y.	.61	.99	1.60
Water wagon rent per day	.004	Hr.	.28	.24	.52
Compaction, tamper, 4" lifts, 2 passes	1.000	Hr.	.16	1.19	1.35
TOTAL			1.05	2.42	3.47

G1030 215	Clay Backfill	COST PER C.Y.		
		EQUIP.	LABOR	TOTAL
1000	Clay backfill, 80 HP dozer & tamper compactors, 50' haul, 4" lifts, 2 passes	1.05	2.42	3.47
1050	4 passes	1.21	3.60	4.81
1100	8" lifts, 2 passes	.97	1.82	2.79
1150	4 passes	1.05	2.42	3.47
1200	150' haul, 4" lifts, 2 passes	1.66	3.42	5.08
1250	4 passes	1.82	4.60	6.42
1300	8" lifts, 2 passes	1.58	2.82	4.40
1350	4 passes	1.66	3.42	5.08
1400	300' haul, 4" lifts, 2 passes	2.23	4.35	6.58
1450	4 passes	2.39	5.55	7.94
1500	8" lifts, 2 passes	2.15	3.75	5.90
1550	4 Passes	2.23	4.35	6.58
1600	105 HP dozer & tamper compactors, 50' haul, 4" lifts, 2 passes	1.04	2.20	3.24
1650	4 passes	1.20	3.38	4.58
1700	8" lifts, 2 passes	.96	1.60	2.56
1750	4 passes	1.04	2.20	3.24
1800	150' haul, 4" lifts, 2 passes	1.65	2.97	4.62
1850	4 passes	1.81	4.15	5.96
1900	8" lifts, 2 passes	1.57	2.37	3.94
1950	4 passes	1.65	2.97	4.62
2000	300' haul, 4" lifts, 2 passes	2.23	3.71	5.94
2050	4 passes	2.39	4.89	7.28
2100	8" lifts, 2 passes	2.15	3.11	5.26
2150	4 passes	2.23	3.71	5.94
2200	200 HP dozer & sheepsfoot compactors, 150' haul, 5" lifts, 2 passes	2.40	1.46	3.86
2250	4 passes	2.87	1.76	4.63
2300	8" lifts, 2 passes	2.11	1.27	3.38
2350	4 passes	2.36	1.44	3.80
2600	300' haul, 4" lifts, 2 passes	3.14	1.87	5.01
2650	4 passes	3.61	2.17	5.78
2700	8" lifts, 2 passes	2.85	1.68	4.53
2750	4 passes	3.10	1.85	4.95

G1030 Site Earthwork

G1030 215	Clay Backfill	COST PER C.Y.		
		EQUIP.	LABOR	TOTAL
3000	300 HP dozer & sheepsfoot compactors, 150' haul, 4" lifts, 2 passes	2.06	1.09	3.15
3050	4 passes	2.53	1.39	3.92
3100	8" lifts, 2 passes	1.77	.90	2.67
3150	4 passes	2.02	1.07	3.09
3200	300' haul, 4" lifts, 2 passes	2.53	1.28	3.81
3250	4 passes	3	1.58	4.58
3300	8" lifts, 2 passes	2.24	1.09	3.33
3350	4 passes	2.49	1.26	3.75

G1030 Site Earthwork

The Sandy Clay/Loam Backfilling System includes: a bulldozer to place and level backfill in specified lifts; compaction equipment; and a water wagon for adjusting moisture content.

The Expanded System Listing shows Common Earth Backfilling with bulldozers ranging from 80 H.P. to 300 H.P. The maximum distance ranges from 50' to 300'. Lifts for the compaction range from 4" to 8". There is no waste included in the assumptions.

System Components	QUANTITY	UNIT	COST PER C.Y.		
			EQUIP.	LABOR	TOTAL
SYSTEM G1030 220 1000					
SANDY CLAY BACKFILL, 80 HP DOZER & ROLLER, 50' HAUL, 4" LIFTS, 2 PASSES					
Backfilling, dozer 80 H.P. 50' haul, common earth, from stockpile	1.000	L.C.Y.	.49	.79	1.28
Water wagon, rent per day	.004	Hr.	.28	.24	.52
Compaction, roller, 4" lifts, 2 passes	.035	Hr.	.75	3.71	4.46
TOTAL			1.52	4.74	6.26

G1030 220	Sandy Clay/Loam Backfill	COST PER C.Y.		
		EQUIP.	LABOR	TOTAL
0900	Backfill Sandy Clay/Loam using dozer and compactors			
1000	Backfill, 80 HP dozer & roller compactors, 50' haul, 4" lifts, 2 passes	1.52	4.74	6.25
1050	4 passes	2.28	8.45	10.75
1100	8" lifts, 2 passes	1.16	2.94	4.10
1150	4 passes	1.52	4.74	6.25
1200	150' haul, 4" lifts, 2 passes	2	5.55	7.55
1250	4 passes	2.76	9.25	12
1300	8" lifts, 2 passes	1.64	3.73	5.35
1350	4 passes	2	5.55	7.55
1400	300' haul, 4" lifts, 2 passes	2.47	6.30	8.75
1450	4 passes	3.23	10	13.25
1500	8" lifts, 2 passes	2.11	4.50	6.60
1550	4 passes	2.47	6.30	8.75
1600	105 HP dozer & roller compactors, 50' haul, 4" lifts, 2 passes	1.53	4.59	6.10
1650	4 passes	2.29	8.30	10.60
1700	8" lifts, 2 passes	1.17	2.79	3.96
1750	4 passes	1.53	4.59	6.10
1800	150' haul, 4" lifts, 2 passes	2.04	5.25	7.30
1850	4 passes	2.80	8.95	11.75
1900	8" lifts, 2 passes	1.68	3.44	5.10
1950	4 passes	2.04	5.25	7.30
2000	300' haul, 4" lifts, 2 passes	2.49	5.80	8.30
2050	4 passes	3.25	9.50	12.75
2100	8" lifts, 2 passes	2.13	4.01	6.15
2150	4 passes	2.49	5.80	8.30
2200	200 HP dozer & roller compactors, 150' haul, 4" lifts, 2 passes	2.20	3.06	5.25
2250	4 passes	2.85	5.20	8.05
2300	8" lifts, 2 passes	1.88	2	3.88
2350	4 passes	2.20	3.06	5.25
2600	300' haul, 4" lifts, 2 passes	2.86	3.43	6.30
2650	4 passes	3.51	5.55	9.05
2700	8" lifts, 2 passes	2.54	2.37	4.91

G10 Site Preparation

G1030 Site Earthwork

G1030 220	Sandy Clay/Loam Backfill	COST PER C.Y.		
		EQUIP.	LABOR	TOTAL
2750	4 passes	2.86	3.43	6.30
3000	300 HP dozer & roller compactors, 150' haul, 4" lift, 2 passes	1.90	2.75	4.65
3050	4 passes	2.55	4.87	7.40
3100	8" lifts, 2 passes	1.58	1.69	3.27
3150	4 passes	1.90	2.75	4.65
3200	300' haul, 4" lifts, 2 passes	2.35	2.93	5.30
3250	4 passes	3	5.05	8.05
3300	8" lifts, 2 passes	2.03	1.87	3.90
3350	4 passes	2.35	2.93	5.30

G1030 Site Earthwork

Trenching Systems are shown on a cost per linear foot basis. The systems include: excavation; backfill and removal of spoil; and compaction for various depths and trench bottom widths. The backfill has been reduced to accommodate a pipe of suitable diameter and bedding.

The slope for trench sides varies from none to 1:1.

The Expanded System Listing shows Trenching Systems that range from 2' to 12' in width. Depths range from 2' to 25'.

System Components	QUANTITY	UNIT	COST PER L.F.		
			EQUIP.	LABOR	TOTAL
SYSTEM G1030 805 1310					
TRENCHING COMMON EARTH, NO SLOPE, 2' WIDE, 2' DP, 3/8 C.Y. BUCKET					
Excavation, trench, hyd. backhoe, track mtd., 3/8 C.Y. bucket	.148	B.C.Y.	.40	1.07	1.47
Backfill and load spoil, from stockpile	.153	L.C.Y.	.13	.32	.45
Compaction by vibrating plate, 6" lifts, 4 passes	.118	E.C.Y.	.03	.39	.42
Remove excess spoil, 8 C.Y. dump truck, 2 mile roundtrip	.040	L.C.Y.	.15	.16	.31
TOTAL			.71	1.94	2.65

G1030 805	Trenching Common Earth	COST PER L.F.		
		EQUIP.	LABOR	TOTAL
1310	Trenching, common earth, no slope, 2' wide, 2' deep, 3/8 C.Y. bucket	.71	1.94	2.65
1320	3' deep, 3/8 C.Y. bucket	1	2.93	3.93
1330	4' deep, 3/8 C.Y. bucket	1.29	3.90	5.19
1340	6' deep, 3/8 C.Y. bucket	1.67	5.05	6.72
1350	8' deep, 1/2 C.Y. bucket	2.21	6.70	8.91
1360	10' deep, 1 C.Y. bucket	3.46	7.95	11.41
1400	4' wide, 2' deep, 3/8 C.Y. bucket	1.60	3.83	5.43
1410	3' deep, 3/8 C.Y. bucket	2.20	5.80	8
1420	4' deep, 1/2 C.Y. bucket	2.56	6.50	9.06
1430	6' deep, 1/2 C.Y. bucket	4.12	10.45	14.57
1440	8' deep, 1/2 C.Y. bucket	6.60	13.45	20.05
1450	10' deep, 1 C.Y. bucket	7.95	16.70	24.65
1460	12' deep, 1 C.Y. bucket	10.25	21.50	31.75
1470	15' deep, 1-1/2 C.Y. bucket	9.40	19.05	28.45
1480	18' deep, 2-1/2 C.Y. bucket	13	26.50	39.50
1520	6' wide, 6' deep, 5/8 C.Y. bucket w/trench box	8.50	15.45	23.95
1530	8' deep, 3/4 C.Y. bucket	11.30	20.50	31.80
1540	10' deep, 1 C.Y. bucket	11.50	21	32.50
1550	12' deep, 1-1/2 C.Y. bucket	12.35	22.50	34.85
1560	16' deep, 2-1/2 C.Y. bucket	16.90	28.50	45.40
1570	20' deep, 3-1/2 C.Y. bucket	22	34	56
1580	24' deep, 3-1/2 C.Y. bucket	26	40.50	66.50
1640	8' wide, 12' deep, 1-1/2 C.Y. bucket w/trench box	17.30	28.50	45.80
1650	15' deep, 1-1/2 C.Y. bucket	22.50	37.50	60
1660	18' deep, 2-1/2 C.Y. bucket	24.50	38	62.50
1680	24' deep, 3-1/2 C.Y. bucket	35.50	52.50	88
1730	10' wide, 20' deep, 3-1/2 C.Y. bucket w/trench box	28.50	50	78.50
1740	24' deep, 3-1/2 C.Y. bucket	42.50	60	102.50
1780	12' wide, 20' deep, 3-1/2 C.Y. bucket w/trench box	45	63.50	108.50
1790	25' deep, bucket	55.50	81	136.50
1800	1/2 to 1 slope, 2' wide, 2' deep, 3/8 C.Y. bucket	1	2.93	3.93
1810	3' deep, 3/8 C.Y. bucket	1.67	5.15	6.82
1820	4' deep, 3/8 C.Y. bucket	2.49	7.85	10.34
1840	6' deep, 3/8 C.Y. bucket	4	12.70	16.70

G10 Site Preparation

G1030 Site Earthwork

G1030 805	Trenching Common Earth	COST PER L.F.		
		EQUIP.	LABOR	TOTAL
1860	8' deep, 1/2 C.Y. bucket	6.35	20.50	26.85
1880	10' deep, 1 C.Y. bucket	11.90	28	39.90
2300	4' wide, 2' deep, 3/8 C.Y. bucket	1.90	4.81	6.71
2310	3' deep, 3/8 C.Y. bucket	2.87	8	10.87
2320	4' deep, 1/2 C.Y. bucket	3.61	9.90	13.51
2340	6' deep, 1/2 C.Y. bucket	6.90	18.55	25.45
2360	8' deep, 1/2 C.Y. bucket	12.75	27	39.75
2380	10' deep, 1 C.Y. bucket	17.60	38.50	56.10
2400	12' deep, 1 C.Y. bucket	24	52	76
2430	15' deep, 1-1/2 C.Y. bucket	26.50	55.50	82
2460	18' deep, 2-1/2 C.Y. bucket	46	87	133
2840	6' wide, 6' deep, 5/8 C.Y. bucket w/trench box	12.55	23	35.55
2860	8' deep, 3/4 C.Y. bucket	18.20	34.50	52.70
2880	10' deep, 1 C.Y. bucket	18.55	35	53.55
2900	12' deep, 1-1/2 C.Y. bucket	23.50	46	69.50
2940	16' deep, 2-1/2 C.Y. bucket	38.50	67.50	106
2980	20' deep, 3-1/2 C.Y. bucket	55	91	146
3020	24' deep, 3-1/2 C.Y. bucket	77.50	125	202.50
3100	8' wide, 12' deep, 1-1/2 C.Y. bucket w/trench box	29	52.50	81.50
3120	15' deep, 1-1/2 C.Y. bucket	42	76	118
3140	18' deep, 2-1/2 C.Y. bucket	53	90.50	143.50
3180	24' deep, 3-1/2 C.Y. bucket	86.50	137	223.50
3270	10' wide, 20' deep, 3-1/2 C.Y. bucket w/trench box	55.50	105	160.50
3280	24' deep, 3-1/2 C.Y. bucket	96	149	245
3370	12' wide, 20' deep, 3-1/2 C.Y. bucket w/trench box	80.50	122	202.50
3380	25' deep, 3-1/2 C.Y. bucket	112	174	286
3500	1 to 1 slope, 2' wide, 2' deep, 3/8 C.Y. bucket	1.29	3.90	5.19
3520	3' deep, 3/8 C.Y. bucket	3.70	8.80	12.50
3540	4' deep, 3/8 C.Y. bucket	3.68	11.75	15.43
3560	6' deep, 1/2 C.Y. bucket	4	12.70	16.70
3580	8' deep, 1/2 C.Y. bucket	7.90	25.50	33.40
3600	10' deep, 1 C.Y. bucket	20.50	48.50	69
3800	4' wide, 2' deep, 3/8 C.Y. bucket	2.20	5.80	8
3820	3' deep, 3/8 C.Y. bucket	3.54	10.20	13.74
3840	4' deep, 1/2 C.Y. bucket	4.64	13.30	17.94
3860	6' deep, 1/2 C.Y. bucket	9.65	26.50	36.15
3880	8' deep, 1/2 C.Y. bucket	18.95	41	59.95
3900	10' deep, 1 C.Y. bucket	27.50	60	87.50
3920	12' deep, 1 C.Y. bucket	40	86.50	126.50
3940	15' deep, 1-1/2 C.Y. bucket	43.50	92.50	136
3960	18' deep, 2-1/2 C.Y. bucket	63.50	120	183.50
4030	6' wide, 6' deep, 5/8 C.Y. bucket w/trench box	16.50	31	47.50
4040	8' deep, 3/4 C.Y. bucket	23.50	42.50	66
4050	10' deep, 1 C.Y. bucket	27	52	79
4060	12' deep, 1-1/2 C.Y. bucket	36	70.50	106.50
4070	16' deep, 2-1/2 C.Y. bucket	60.50	107	167.50
4080	20' deep, 3-1/2 C.Y. bucket	88.50	149	237.50
4090	24' deep, 3-1/2 C.Y. bucket	129	209	338
4500	8' wide, 12' deep, 1-1/2 C.Y. bucket w/trench box	41	76	117
4550	15' deep, 1-1/2 C.Y. bucket	62	114	176
4600	18' deep, 2-1/2 C.Y. bucket	80.50	140	220.50
4650	24' deep, 3-1/2 C.Y. bucket	138	221	359
4800	10' wide, 20' deep, 3-1/2 C.Y. bucket w/trench box	82.50	160	242.50
4850	24' deep, 3-1/2 C.Y. bucket	147	233	380
4950	12' wide, 20' deep, 3-1/2 C.Y. bucket w/trench box	116	180	296
4980	25' deep, 3-1/2 C.Y. bucket	167	263	430

G1030   Site Earthwork

Trenching Systems are shown on a cost per linear foot basis. The systems include: excavation; backfill and removal of spoil; and compaction for various depths and trench bottom widths. The backfill has been reduced to accommodate a pipe of suitable diameter and bedding.

The slope for trench sides varies from none to 1:1.

The Expanded System Listing shows Trenching Systems that range from 2' to 12' in width. Depths range from 2' to 25'.

System Components	QUANTITY	UNIT	COST PER L.F. EQUIP.	COST PER L.F. LABOR	COST PER L.F. TOTAL
SYSTEM G1030 806 1310					
TRENCHING LOAM & SANDY CLAY, NO SLOPE, 2' WIDE, 2' DP, 3/8 C.Y. BUCKET					
Excavation, trench, hyd. backhoe, track mtd., 3/8 C.Y. bucket	.148	B.C.Y.	.37	.98	1.35
Backfill and load spoil, from stockpile	.165	L.C.Y.	.14	.35	.49
Compaction by vibrating plate 18" wide, 6" lifts, 4 passes	.118	E.C.Y.	.03	.39	.42
Remove excess spoil, 8 C.Y. dump truck, 2 mile roundtrip	.042	L.C.Y.	.16	.17	.33
TOTAL			.70	1.89	2.59

G1030 806	Trenching Loam & Sandy Clay	COST PER L.F. EQUIP.	COST PER L.F. LABOR	COST PER L.F. TOTAL
1310	Trenching, loam & sandy clay, no slope, 2' wide, 2' deep, 3/8 C.Y. bucket	.70	1.89	2.59
1320	3' deep, 3/8 C.Y. bucket	1.08	3.13	4.21
1330	4' deep, 3/8 C.Y. bucket	1.27	3.81	5.10
1340	6' deep, 3/8 C.Y. bucket	1.80	4.51	6.30
1350	8' deep, 1/2 C.Y. bucket	2.38	5.95	8.35
1360	10' deep, 1 C.Y. bucket	2.69	6.40	9.10
1400	4' wide, 2' deep, 3/8 C.Y. bucket	1.60	3.75	5.35
1410	3' deep, 3/8 C.Y. bucket	2.18	5.65	7.85
1420	4' deep, 1/2 C.Y. bucket	2.55	6.40	8.95
1430	6' deep, 1/2 C.Y. bucket	4.39	9.35	13.75
1440	8' deep, 1/2 C.Y. bucket	6.45	13.25	19.70
1450	10' deep, 1 C.Y. bucket	6.45	13.60	20
1460	12' deep, 1 C.Y. bucket	8.10	16.90	25
1470	15' deep, 1-1/2 C.Y. bucket	9.80	19.70	29.50
1480	18' deep, 2-1/2 C.Y. bucket	11.50	21.50	33
1520	6' wide, 6' deep, 5/8 C.Y. bucket w/trench box	8.25	15.20	23.50
1530	8' deep, 3/4 C.Y. bucket	10.90	19.95	31
1540	10' deep, 1 C.Y. bucket	10.55	20.50	31
1550	12' deep, 1-1/2 C.Y. bucket	12.05	23	35
1560	16' deep, 2-1/2 C.Y. bucket	16.50	28.50	45
1570	20' deep, 3-1/2 C.Y. bucket	20	34	54
1580	24' deep, 3-1/2 C.Y. bucket	25.50	41.50	67
1640	8' wide, 12' deep, 1-1/4 C.Y. bucket w/trench box	17.05	29	46
1650	15' deep, 1-1/2 C.Y. bucket	21	36.50	57.50
1660	18' deep, 2-1/2 C.Y. bucket	25	41.50	66.50
1680	24' deep, 3-1/2 C.Y. bucket	34.50	53.50	88
1730	10' wide, 20' deep, 3-1/2 C.Y. bucket w/trench box	34.50	53.50	88
1740	24' deep, 3-1/2 C.Y. bucket	43.50	66	110
1780	12' wide, 20' deep, 3-1/2 C.Y. bucket w/trench box	42	63.50	106
1790	25' deep, 3-1/2 C.Y. bucket	54.50	82	137
1800	1/2:1 slope, 2' wide, 2' deep, 3/8 C.Y. bucket	.98	2.86	3.84
1810	3' deep, 3/8 C.Y. bucket	1.63	5	6.65
1820	4' deep, 3/8 C.Y. bucket	2.43	7.65	10.10
1840	6' deep, 3/8 C.Y. bucket	4.31	11.30	15.60

G1030 Site Earthwork

G1030 806	Trenching Loam & Sandy Clay	COST PER L.F.		
		EQUIP.	LABOR	TOTAL
1860	8' deep, 1/2 C.Y. bucket	6.85	18.10	25
1880	10' deep, 1 C.Y. bucket	9.15	22.50	31.50
2300	4' wide, 2' deep, 3/8 C.Y. bucket	1.88	4.70	6.60
2310	3' deep, 3/8 C.Y. bucket	2.83	7.80	10.65
2320	4' deep, 1/2 C.Y. bucket	3.57	9.70	13.25
2340	6' deep, 1/2 C.Y. bucket	7.35	16.65	24
2360	8' deep, 1/2 C.Y. bucket	12.40	27	39.50
2380	10' deep, 1 C.Y. bucket	14.10	31	45
2400	12' deep, 1 C.Y. bucket	23.50	51.50	75
2430	15' deep, 1-1/2 C.Y. bucket	27.50	57.50	85
2460	18' deep, 2-1/2 C.Y. bucket	45.50	88	134
2840	6' wide, 6' deep, 5/8 C.Y. bucket w/trench box	11.95	23	35
2860	8' deep, 3/4 C.Y. bucket	17.50	34	51.50
2880	10' deep, 1 C.Y. bucket	18.90	38	57
2900	12' deep, 1-1/2 C.Y. bucket	23.50	46.50	70
2940	16' deep, 2-1/2 C.Y. bucket	37.50	68.50	106
2980	20' deep, 3-1/2 C.Y. bucket	53	92.50	146
3020	24' deep, 3-1/2 C.Y. bucket	75	127	202
3100	8' wide, 12' deep, 1-1/2 C.Y. bucket w/trench box	28.50	52.50	81
3120	15' deep, 1-1/2 C.Y. bucket	39	74	113
3140	18' deep, 2-1/2 C.Y. bucket	52	91.50	144
3180	24' deep, 3-1/2 C.Y. bucket	84	139	223
3270	10' wide, 20' deep, 3-1/2 C.Y. bucket w/trench box	67.50	112	180
3280	24' deep, 3-1/2 C.Y. bucket	93	151	244
3320	12' wide, 20' deep, 3-1/2 C.Y. bucket w/trench box	75	122	197
3380	25' deep, 3-1/2 C.Y. bucket w/trench box	102	164	266
3500	1:1 slope, 2' wide, 2' deep, 3/8 C.Y. bucket	1.27	3.81	5.10
3520	3' deep, 3/8 C.Y. bucket	2.28	7.15	9.45
3540	4' deep, 3/8 C.Y. bucket	3.59	11.45	15.05
3560	6' deep, 1/2 C.Y. bucket	4.31	11.30	15.60
3580	8' deep, 1/2 C.Y. bucket	11.35	30	41.50
3600	10' deep, 1 C.Y. bucket	15.65	39	54.50
3800	4' wide, 2' deep, 3/8 C.Y. bucket	2.18	5.65	7.85
3820	3' deep, 1/2 C.Y. bucket	3.48	9.95	13.45
3840	4' deep, 1/2 C.Y. bucket	4.58	13.05	17.65
3860	6' deep, 1/2 C.Y. bucket	10.30	24	34.50
3880	8' deep, 1/2 C.Y. bucket	18.40	40.50	59
3900	10' deep, 1 C.Y. bucket	22	49	71
3920	12' deep, 1 C.Y. bucket	31.50	69	101
3940	15' deep, 1-1/2 C.Y. bucket	45.50	95.50	141
3960	18' deep, 2-1/2 C.Y. bucket	62	121	183
4030	6' wide, 6' deep, 5/8 C.Y. bucket w/trench box	15.70	31	46.50
4040	8' deep, 3/4 C.Y. bucket	24	47.50	71.50
4050	10' deep, 1 C.Y. bucket	27	56	83
4060	12' deep, 1-1/2 C.Y. bucket	35	70.50	106
4070	16' deep, 2-1/2 C.Y. bucket	59	108	167
4080	20' deep, 3-1/2 C.Y. bucket	86	151	237
4090	24' deep, 3-1/2 C.Y. bucket	125	212	335
4500	8' wide, 12' deep, 1-1/4 C.Y. bucket w/trench box	40	76.50	117
4550	15' deep, 1-1/2 C.Y. bucket	56.50	111	168
4600	18' deep, 2-1/2 C.Y. bucket	78.50	142	221
4650	24' deep, 3-1/2 C.Y. bucket	134	224	360
4800	10' wide, 20' deep, 3-1/2 C.Y. bucket w/trench box	100	171	271
4850	24' deep, 3-1/2 C.Y. bucket	143	237	380
4950	12' wide, 20' deep, 3-1/2 C.Y. bucket w/trench box	108	181	289
4980	25' deep, 3-1/2 C.Y. bucket	162	267	430

G1030 Site Earthwork

Trenching Systems are shown on a cost per linear foot basis. The systems include: excavation; backfill and removal of spoil; and compaction for various depths and trench bottom widths. The backfill has been reduced to accommodate a pipe of suitable diameter and bedding.

The slope for trench sides varies from none to 1:1.

The Expanded System Listing shows Trenching Systems that range from 2' to 12' in width. Depths range from 2' to 25'.

System Components			COST PER L.F.		
	QUANTITY	UNIT	EQUIP.	LABOR	TOTAL
SYSTEM G1030 807 1310					
TRENCHING SAND & GRAVEL, NO SLOPE, 2' WIDE, 2' DEEP, 3/8 C.Y. BUCKET					
Excavation, trench, hyd. backhoe, track mtd., 3/8 C.Y. bucket	.148	B.C.Y.	.36	.97	1.33
Backfill and load spoil, from stockpile	.140	L.C.Y.	.11	.30	.41
Compaction by vibrating plate 18" wide, 6" lifts, 4 passes	.118	E.C.Y.	.03	.39	.42
Remove excess spoil, 8 C.Y. dump truck, 2 mile roundtrip	.035	L.C.Y.	.13	.14	.27
TOTAL			.63	1.80	2.43

G1030 807	Trenching Sand & Gravel	COST PER L.F.		
		EQUIP.	LABOR	TOTAL
1310	Trenching, sand & gravel, no slope, 2' wide, 2' deep, 3/8 C.Y. bucket	.63	1.80	2.43
1320	3' deep, 3/8 C.Y. bucket	1.01	3.01	4.02
1330	4' deep, 3/8 C.Y. bucket	1.18	3.62	4.80
1340	6' deep, 3/8 C.Y. bucket	1.70	4.30	6
1350	8' deep, 1/2 C.Y. bucket	2.25	5.70	7.95
1360	10' deep, 1 C.Y. bucket	2.50	6.05	8.55
1400	4' wide, 2' deep, 3/8 C.Y. bucket	1.46	3.54	5
1410	3' deep, 3/8 C.Y. bucket	2.01	5.35	7.35
1420	4' deep, 1/2 C.Y. bucket	2.33	6.05	8.40
1430	6' deep, 1/2 C.Y. bucket	4.16	8.95	13.10
1440	8' deep, 1/2 C.Y. bucket	6.05	12.60	18.65
1450	10' deep, 1 C.Y. bucket	6.05	12.85	18.90
1460	12' deep, 1 C.Y. bucket	7.65	16	23.50
1470	15' deep, 1-1/2 C.Y. bucket	9.25	18.55	28
1480	18' deep, 2-1/2 C.Y. bucket	10.85	20.50	31.50
1520	6' wide, 6' deep, 5/8 C.Y. bucket w/trench box	7.75	14.35	22
1530	8' deep, 3/4 C.Y. bucket	10.30	18.95	29.50
1540	10' deep, 1 C.Y. bucket	9.95	19.15	29
1550	12' deep, 1-1/2 C.Y. bucket	11.40	21.50	33
1560	16' deep, 2 C.Y. bucket	15.75	27	43
1570	20' deep, 3-1/2 C.Y. bucket	19.10	32	51
1580	24' deep, 3-1/2 C.Y. bucket	24	39	63
1640	8' wide, 12' deep, 1-1/2 C.Y. bucket w/trench box	16.05	27	43
1650	15' deep, 1-1/2 C.Y. bucket	19.50	34.50	54
1660	18' deep, 2-1/2 C.Y. bucket	23.50	39	62.50
1680	24' deep, 3-1/2 C.Y. bucket	32.50	50	82.50
1730	10' wide, 20' deep, 3-1/2 C.Y. bucket w/trench box	32.50	50	82.50
1740	24' deep, 3-1/2 C.Y. bucket	41	62	103
1780	12' wide, 20' deep, 3-1/2 C.Y. bucket w/trench box	39.50	59.50	99
1790	25' deep, 3-1/2 C.Y. bucket	51	77	128
1800	1/2:1 slope, 2' wide, 2' deep, 3/8 C.Y. bucket	.91	2.72	3.63
1810	3' deep, 3/8 C.Y. bucket	1.53	4.77	6.30
1820	4' deep, 3/8 C.Y. bucket	2.27	7.30	9.55
1840	6' deep, 3/8 C.Y. bucket	4.10	10.80	14.90

G1030 Site Earthwork

G1030 807	Trenching Sand & Gravel	COST PER L.F.		
		EQUIP.	LABOR	TOTAL
1860	8' deep, 1/2 C.Y. bucket	6.55	17.30	24
1880	10' deep, 1 C.Y. bucket	8.55	21.50	30
2300	4' wide, 2' deep, 3/8 C.Y. bucket	1.74	4.45	6.20
2310	3' deep, 3/8 C.Y. bucket	2.62	7.40	10
2320	4' deep, 1/2 C.Y. bucket	3.29	9.20	12.50
2340	6' deep, 1/2 C.Y. bucket	7	15.95	23
2360	8' deep, 1/2 C.Y. bucket	11.75	25.50	37.50
2380	10' deep, 1 C.Y. bucket	13.35	29.50	43
2400	12' deep, 1 C.Y. bucket	22.50	49	71.50
2430	15' deep, 1-1/2 C.Y. bucket	26	54.50	80.50
2460	18' deep, 2-1/2 C.Y. bucket	43	83	126
2840	6' wide, 6' deep, 5/8 C.Y. bucket w/trench box	11.35	22	33.50
2860	8' deep, 3/4 C.Y. bucket	16.60	32	48.50
2880	10' deep, 1 C.Y. bucket	17.85	36	54
2900	12' deep, 1-1/2 C.Y. bucket	22.50	44	66.50
2940	16' deep, 2 C.Y. bucket	36	64.50	101
2980	20' deep, 3-1/2 C.Y. bucket	50.50	87	138
3020	24' deep, 3-1/2 C.Y. bucket	71.50	119	191
3100	8' wide, 12' deep, 1-1/4 C.Y. bucket w/trench box	27	50	77
3120	15' deep, 1-1/2 C.Y. bucket	36.50	69.50	106
3140	18' deep, 2-1/2 C.Y. bucket	49	86	135
3180	24' deep, 3-1/2 C.Y. bucket	80	130	210
3270	10' wide, 20' deep, 3-1/2 C.Y. bucket w/trench box	64	105	169
3280	24' deep, 3-1/2 C.Y. bucket	88	142	230
3370	12' wide, 20' deep, 3-1/2 C.Y. bucket w/trench box	71.50	117	189
3380	25' deep, 3-1/2 C.Y. bucket	103	164	267
3500	1:1 slope, 2' wide, 2' deep, 3/8 C.Y. bucket	2.05	4.46	6.50
3520	3' deep, 3/8 C.Y. bucket	2.14	6.85	9
3540	4' deep, 3/8 C.Y. bucket	3.36	10.95	14.30
3560	6' deep, 3/8 C.Y. bucket	4.10	10.80	14.90
3580	8' deep, 1/2 C.Y. bucket	10.80	29	40
3600	10' deep, 1 C.Y. bucket	14.65	36.50	51
3800	4' wide, 2' deep, 3/8 C.Y. bucket	2.01	5.35	7.35
3820	3' deep, 3/8 C.Y. bucket	3.24	9.50	12.75
3840	4' deep, 1/2 C.Y. bucket	4.23	12.35	16.60
3860	6' deep, 1/2 C.Y. bucket	9.85	23	33
3880	8' deep, 1/2 C.Y. bucket	17.45	38.50	56
3900	10' deep, 1 C.Y. bucket	20.50	46	66.50
3920	12' deep, 1 C.Y. bucket	30	65.50	95.50
3940	15' deep, 1-1/2 C.Y. bucket	43	90	133
3960	18' deep, 2-1/2 C.Y. bucket	59	114	173
4030	6' wide, 6' deep, 5/8 C.Y. bucket w/trench box	14.90	29.50	44.50
4040	8' deep, 3/4 C.Y. bucket	23	45.50	68.50
4050	10' deep, 1 C.Y. bucket	25.50	53	78.50
4060	12' deep, 1-1/2 C.Y. bucket	33	66.50	99.50
4070	16' deep, 2 C.Y. bucket	56.50	102	159
4080	20' deep, 3-1/2 C.Y. bucket	81.50	142	224
4090	24' deep, 3-1/2 C.Y. bucket	119	199	320
4500	8' wide, 12' deep, 1-1/2 C.Y. bucket w/trench box	38	72.50	111
4550	15' deep, 1-1/2 C.Y. bucket	53.50	105	159
4600	18' deep, 2-1/2 C.Y. bucket	74.50	134	209
4650	24' deep, 3-1/2 C.Y. bucket	127	210	335
4800	10' wide, 20' deep, 3-1/2 C.Y. bucket w/trench box	95	160	255
4850	24' deep, 3-1/2 C.Y. bucket	135	222	355
4950	12' wide, 20' deep, 3-1/2 C.Y. bucket w/trench box	102	170	272
4980	25' deep, 3-1/2 C.Y. bucket	154	251	405

617

The Pipe Bedding System is shown for various pipe diameters. Compacted bank sand is used for pipe bedding and to fill 12″ over the pipe. No backfill is included. Various side slopes are shown to accommodate different soil conditions. Pipe sizes vary from 6″ to 84″ diameter.

System Components	QUANTITY	UNIT	COST PER L.F.		
			MAT.	INST.	TOTAL
SYSTEM G1030 815 1440					
PIPE BEDDING, SIDE SLOPE 0 TO 1, 1′ WIDE, PIPE SIZE 6″ DIAMETER					
Borrow, bank sand, 2 mile haul, machine spread	.086	C.Y.	1.68	.70	2.38
Compaction, vibrating plate	.086	C.Y.		.22	.22
TOTAL			1.68	.92	2.60

G1030 815	Pipe Bedding	COST PER L.F.		
		MAT.	INST.	TOTAL
1440	Pipe bedding, side slope 0 to 1, 1′ wide, pipe size 6″ diameter	1.68	.92	2.60
1460	2′ wide, pipe size 8″ diameter	3.63	1.97	5.60
1480	Pipe size 10″ diameter	3.70	2.01	5.71
1500	Pipe size 12″ diameter	3.78	2.05	5.83
1520	3′ wide, pipe size 14″ diameter	6.15	3.33	9.48
1540	Pipe size 15″ diameter	6.20	3.35	9.55
1560	Pipe size 16″ diameter	6.25	3.39	9.64
1580	Pipe size 18″ diameter	6.35	3.46	9.81
1600	4′ wide, pipe size 20″ diameter	9.05	4.92	13.97
1620	Pipe size 21″ diameter	9.15	4.96	14.11
1640	Pipe size 24″ diameter	9.35	5.05	14.40
1660	Pipe size 30″ diameter	9.50	5.15	14.65
1680	6′ wide, pipe size 32″ diameter	16.25	8.85	25.10
1700	Pipe size 36″ diameter	16.65	9	25.65
1720	7′ wide, pipe size 48″ diameter	26.50	14.35	40.85
1740	8′ wide, pipe size 60″ diameter	32	17.45	49.45
1760	10′ wide, pipe size 72″ diameter	45	24.50	69.50
1780	12′ wide, pipe size 84″ diameter	59	32	91
2140	Side slope 1/2 to 1, 1′ wide, pipe size 6″ diameter	3.13	1.69	4.82
2160	2′ wide, pipe size 8″ diameter	5.30	2.88	8.18
2180	Pipe size 10″ diameter	5.70	3.09	8.79
2200	Pipe size 12″ diameter	6.05	3.27	9.32
2220	3′ wide, pipe size 14″ diameter	8.70	4.73	13.43
2240	Pipe size 15″ diameter	8.90	4.83	13.73
2260	Pipe size 16″ diameter	9.15	4.96	14.11
2280	Pipe size 18″ diameter	9.60	5.20	14.80
2300	4′ wide, pipe size 20″ diameter	12.70	6.90	19.60
2320	Pipe size 21″ diameter	13	7.05	20.05
2340	Pipe size 24″ diameter	13.80	7.50	21.30
2360	Pipe size 30″ diameter	15.30	8.30	23.60
2380	6′ wide, pipe size 32″ diameter	22.50	12.25	34.75
2400	Pipe size 36″ diameter	24	13.05	37.05
2420	7′ wide, pipe size 48″ diameter	37.50	20.50	58
2440	8′ wide, pipe size 60″ diameter	47.50	26	73.50
2460	10′ wide, pipe size 72″ diameter	65	35.50	100.50
2480	12′ wide, pipe size 84″ diameter	85.50	46	131.50
2620	Side slope 1 to 1, 1′ wide, pipe size 6″ diameter	4.58	2.49	7.07
2640	2′ wide, pipe size 8″ diameter	7.05	3.83	10.88

G1030 Site Earthwork

G1030 815	Pipe Bedding	COST PER L.F.		
		MAT.	INST.	TOTAL
2660	Pipe size 10" diameter	7.65	4.15	11.80
2680	Pipe size 12" diameter	8.35	4.53	12.88
2700	3' wide, pipe size 14" diameter	11.30	6.15	17.45
2720	Pipe size 15" diameter	11.65	6.30	17.95
2740	Pipe size 16" diameter	12.05	6.55	18.60
2760	Pipe size 18" diameter	12.90	7	19.90
2780	4' wide, pipe size 20" diameter	16.35	8.85	25.20
2800	Pipe size 21" diameter	16.80	9.10	25.90
2820	Pipe size 24" diameter	18.25	9.90	28.15
2840	Pipe size 30" diameter	21	11.40	32.40
2860	6' wide, pipe size 32" diameter	29	15.65	44.65
2880	Pipe size 36" diameter	31.50	17	48.50
2900	7' wide, pipe size 48" diameter	48.50	26.50	75
2920	8' wide, pipe size 60" diameter	63	34	97
2940	10' wide, pipe size 72" diameter	85.50	46.50	132
2960	12' wide, pipe size 84" diameter	112	60.50	172.50

619

G2010 Roadways

The Bituminous Roadway Systems are listed for pavement thicknesses between 3-1/2" and 7" and gravel bases from 3" to 22" in depth. Systems costs are expressed per linear foot for varying widths of two and multi-lane roads. Earth moving is not included. Granite curbs and line painting are added as required system components.

System Components	QUANTITY	UNIT	COST PER L.F.		
			MAT.	INST.	TOTAL
SYSTEM G2010 230 1050					
BITUM. ROADWAY, TWO LANES, 3-1/2" TH. PVMT., 3" TH. GRAVEL BASE, 24' WIDE					
Compact subgrade, 4 passes	2.670	E.C.Y.		.48	.48
Bank gravel, 2 mi haul, dozer spread	.250	L.C.Y.	6.13	2.04	8.17
Compaction, granular material to 98%	.259	E.C.Y.		.17	.17
Grading, fine grade, 3 passes with grader	2.670	S.Y.		15.55	15.55
Bituminous paving, binder course, 2-1/2" thick	2.670	S.Y.	27.90	4.06	31.96
Bituminous paving, wearing course, 1" thick	2.670	S.Y.	11.08	2.38	13.46
Curbs, granite, split face, straight, 5" x 16"	2.000	L.F.	25.70	27.68	53.38
Thermoplastic, white or yellow, 4" wide, less than 6000 L.F.	4.000	L.F.	1.36	1.08	2.44
TOTAL			72.17	53.44	125.61

G2010 230	Bituminous Roadways Gravel Base	COST PER L.F.		
		MAT.	INST.	TOTAL
1050	Bitum. roadway, two lanes, 3-1/2" th. pvmt., 3" th. gravel base, 24' wide	72	53.50	125.50
1100	28' wide	80	54	134
1150	32' wide	87.50	58	145.50
1200	4" th. gravel base, 24' wide	74.50	51.50	126
1210	28' wide	82.50	55.50	138
1220	32' wide	90.50	59	149.50
1222	36' wide	98.50	62.50	161
1224	40' wide	106	66.50	172.50
1230	6" th. gravel base, 24' wide	79	53.50	132.50
1240	28' wide	87.50	57	144.50
1250	32' wide	96	61.50	157.50
1252	36' wide	105	65.50	170.50
1254	40' wide	113	69.50	182.50
1256	8" th. gravel base, 24' wide	83	55	138
1258	28' wide	92.50	59.50	152
1260	32' wide	102	63.50	165.50
1262	36' wide	111	68	179
1264	40' wide	120	72.50	192.50
1300	9" th. gravel base, 24' wide	84.50	56	140.50
1350	28' wide	94.50	60.50	155
1400	32' wide	104	64.50	168.50
1410	10" th. gravel base, 24' wide	87.50	56.50	144
1412	28' wide	97.50	61	158.50
1414	32' wide	108	66	174
1416	36' wide	118	70.50	188.50
1418	40' wide	128	75.50	203.50
1420	12" thick gravel base, 24' wide	91.50	58.50	150
1422	28' wide	102	63.50	165.50
1424	32' wide	113	68.50	181.50
1426	36' wide	124	73.50	197.50

G2010 230	Bituminous Roadways Gravel Base	COST PER L.F.		
		MAT.	INST.	TOTAL
1428	40' wide	135	78	213
1430	15" thick gravel base, 24' wide	98	61	159
1432	28' wide	110	66.50	176.50
1434	32' wide	122	71.50	193.50
1436	36' wide	134	77	211
1438	40' wide	145	82.50	227.50
1440	18" thick gravel base, 24' wide	105	63.50	168.50
1442	28' wide	117	69.50	186.50
1444	32' wide	130	75.50	205.50
1446	36' wide	143	81	224
1448	40' wide	156	87	243
1550	4" th. pvmt., 4" th. gravel base, 24' wide	80	52	132
1600	28' wide	89	56	145
1650	32' wide	98	60	158
1652	36' wide	107	63.50	170.50
1654	40' wide	116	67.50	183.50
1700	6" th. gravel base, 24' wide	84.50	54	138.50
1710	28' wide	94	58	152
1720	32' wide	104	62.50	166.50
1722	36' wide	113	66	179
1724	40' wide	123	70.50	193.50
1726	8" th. gravel base, 24' wide	89	55.50	144.50
1728	28' wide	99	60	159
1730	32' wide	109	64	173
1732	36' wide	120	69	189
1734	40' wide	130	73.50	203.50
1800	10" th. gravel base, 24' wide	93	57.50	150.50
1850	28' wide	104	60.50	164.50
1900	32' wide	115	66.50	181.50
1902	36' wide	126	71.50	197.50
1904	40' wide	132	74.50	206.50
2050	4" th. pvmt., 5" th. gravel base, 24' wide	83	55.50	138.50
2100	28' wide	92.50	60	152.50
2150	32' wide	102	64.50	166.50
2200	8" th. gravel base, 24' wide	90	58	148
2210	28' wide	100	63	163
2220	32' wide	111	68	179
2300	12" th. gravel base, 24' wide	99.50	59.50	159
2350	28' wide	111	64.50	175.50
2400	32' wide	123	69.50	192.50
2410	36' wide	135	74	209
2412	40' wide	147	79.50	226.50
2420	15" th. gravel base, 24' wide	101	60	161
2422	28' wide	119	67.50	186.50
2424	32' wide	132	73	205
2426	36' wide	145	78.50	223.50
2428	40' wide	158	84	242
2430	18" th. gravel base, 24' wide	112	64.50	176.50
2432	28' wide	126	71	197
2434	32' wide	141	76.50	217.50
2436	36' wide	155	82.50	237.50
2438	40' wide	169	88	257
2550	4-1/2" th. pvmt., 5" th. gravel base, 24' wide	89	56	145
2600	28' wide	99	61	160
2650	32' wide	110	66	176
2700	6" th. gravel base, 24' wide	91	57	148
2710	28' wide	102	62	164
2720	32' wide	113	66.50	179.50

G2010 Roadways

G2010 230	Bituminous Roadways Gravel Base	COST PER L.F.		
		MAT.	INST.	TOTAL
2800	13" th. gravel base, 24' wide	105	62.50	167.50
2850	28' wide	119	67.50	186.50
2900	32' wide	132	73.50	205.50
3050	5" th. pvmt., 6" th. gravel base, 24' wide	97	58	155
3100	28' wide	109	63	172
3150	32' wide	121	67	188
3300	14" th. gravel base, 24' wide	114	63.50	177.50
3350	28' wide	129	69.50	198.50
3400	32' wide	143	75.50	218.50
3550	5-1/2" th. pvmt., 7" th. gravel base, 24' wide	105	59	164
3600	28' wide	118	64	182
3650	32' wide	131	69	200
3800	17" th. gravel base, 24' wide	126	66.50	192.50
3850	28' wide	143	73	216
3900	32' wide	160	79.50	239.50
4050	Multi lane, 5" th. pvmt., 6" th. gravel base, 48' wide	168	87	255
4100	72' wide	239	117	356
4150	96' wide	310	147	457
4300	14" th. gravel base, 48' wide	200	99.50	299.50
4350	72' wide	287	135	422
4400	96' wide	375	171	546
4550	5-1/2" th. pvmt., 7" th. gravel base, 48' wide	184	90	274
4600	72' wide	263	121	384
4650	96' wide	340	152	492
4800	17" th. gravel base, 48' wide	226	105	331
4850	72' wide	325	143	468
4900	96' wide	425	182	607
5050	6" th. pvmt., 8" th. gravel base, 48' wide	199	92	291
5100	72' wide	285	124	409
5150	96' wide	370	156	526
5200	10" th. gravel base, 48' wide	208	95	303
5210	72' wide	299	129	428
5220	96' wide	390	163	553
5300	20" th. gravel base, 48' wide	249	110	359
5350	72' wide	360	151	511
5400	96' wide	475	193	668
5550	7" th. pvmt., 9" th. gravel base, 48' wide	227	95.50	322.50
5600	72' wide	325	130	455
5650	96' wide	425	164	589
5700	10" th. gravel base, 48' wide	232	97.50	329.50
5710	72' wide	335	133	468
5720	96' wide	440	167	607
5800	22" th. gravel base, 48' wide	281	115	396
5850	72' wide	410	159	569
5900	96' wide	535	203	738

G2010 Roadways

The Bituminous Roadway Systems are listed for pavement thicknesses between 3-1/2″ and 7″ and crushed stone bases from 3″ to 22″ in depth. Systems costs are expressed per linear foot for varying widths of two and multi-lane roads. Earth moving is not included. Granite curbs and line painting are added as required system components.

System Components	QUANTITY	UNIT	COST PER L.F.		
			MAT.	INST.	TOTAL
SYSTEM G2010 232 1050					
BITUMINOUS ROADWAY, TWO LANES, 3-1/2″ PAVEMENT					
3″ THICK CRUSHED STONE BASE, 24′ WIDE					
Compact subgrade, 4 passes	.222	E.C.Y.		.48	.48
3/4″ crushed stonel, 2 mi haul, dozer spread	.266	C.Y.	6.92	2.16	9.08
Compaction, granular material to 98%	.259	E.C.Y.		.17	.17
Grading, fine grade, 3 passes with grader	3.300	S.Y.		15.55	15.55
Bituminous paving, binder course, 2-1/2″ thick	2.670	S.Y.	27.90	4.06	31.96
Bituminous paving, wearing course, 1″ thick	2.670	S.Y.	11.08	2.38	13.46
Curbs, granite, split face, straight, 5″ x 16″	2.000	L.F.	25.70	27.68	53.38
Thermoplastic, white or yellow, 4″ wide, less than 6000 L.F.	4.000	L.F.	1.36	1.08	2.44
TOTAL			72.96	53.56	126.52

G2010 232	Bituminous Roadways Crushed Stone	COST PER L.F.		
		MAT.	INST.	TOTAL
1050	Bitum. roadway, two lanes, 3-1/2″ th. pvmt., 3″ th. crushed stone, 24′ wide	73	53.50	126.50
1100	28′ wide	80.50	54	134.50
1150	32′ wide	88	62.50	150.50
1200	4″ thick crushed stone, 24′ wide	75	51.50	126.50
1210	28′ wide	83	55.50	138.50
1220	32′ wide	91	59	150
1222	36′ wide	99	62.50	161.50
1224	40′ wide	107	66.50	173.50
1230	6″ thick crushed stone, 24′ wide	79.50	53.50	133
1240	28′ wide	88.50	57	145.50
1250	32′ wide	97	61.50	158.50
1252	36′ wide	106	65.50	171.50
1254	40′ wide	115	69.50	184.50
1256	8″ thick crushed stone, 24′ wide	84	55	139
1258	28′ wide	93.50	59.50	153
1260	32′ wide	103	63.50	166.50
1262	36′ wide	113	68	181
1264	40′ wide	122	72.50	194.50
1300	9″ thick crushed stone, 24′ wide	87	56	143
1350	28′ wide	96.50	61	157.50
1400	32′ wide	107	65.50	172.50
1410	10″ thick crushed stone, 24′ wide	89	56.50	145.50
1412	28′ wide	99	61	160
1414	32′ wide	109	66	175
1416	36′ wide	120	70.50	190.50
1418	40′ wide	130	75.50	205.50

G2010 232	Bituminous Roadways Crushed Stone	COST PER L.F.		
		MAT.	INST.	TOTAL
1420	12" thick crushed stone, 24' wide	93.50	58.50	152
1422	28' wide	104	63.50	167.50
1424	32' wide	115	68.50	183.50
1426	36' wide	126	73.50	199.50
1428	40' wide	137	78	215
1430	15" thick crushed stone, 24' wide	100	61	161
1432	28' wide	112	66.50	178.50
1434	32' wide	124	71.50	195.50
1436	36' wide	137	77	214
1438	40' wide	149	82.50	231.50
1440	18" thick crushed stone, 24' wide	107	63.50	170.50
1442	28' wide	120	69.50	189.50
1444	32' wide	134	75.50	209.50
1446	36' wide	147	81	228
1448	40' wide	160	87	247
1550	4" thick pavement., 4" thick crushed stone, 24' wide	81	52	133
1600	28' wide	90	56	146
1650	32' wide	99	60	159
1652	36' wide	107	63.50	170.50
1654	40' wide	116	67.50	183.50
1700	6" thick crushed stone, 24' wide	85.50	54	139.50
1710	28' wide	95	58	153
1720	32' wide	105	62.50	167.50
1722	36' wide	114	66	180
1724	40' wide	124	70.50	194.50
1726	8" thick crushed stone, 24' wide	90	55.50	145.50
1728	28' wide	100	60	160
1730	32' wide	111	64	175
1732	36' wide	121	69	190
1734	40' wide	132	73.50	205.50
1800	10" thick crushed stone, 24' wide	94.50	57.50	152
1850	28' wide	106	61	167
1900	32' wide	117	67	184
1902	36' wide	128	71.50	199.50
1904	40' wide	133	74.50	207.50
2050	4" th. pavement, 5" thick crushed stone, 24' wide	84	55.50	139.50
2100	28' wide	94	60.50	154.50
2150	32' wide	104	65	169
2300	12" thick crushed stone, 24' wide	100	61.50	161.50
2350	28' wide	113	66.50	179.50
2400	32' wide	125	72	197
2550	4-1/2" thick pavement, 5" thick crushed stone, 24' wide	90	56	146
2600	28' wide	100	61	161
2650	32' wide	111	66	177
2800	13" thick crushed stone, 24' wide	108	62.50	170.50
2850	28' wide	122	68.50	190.50
2900	32' wide	136	74	210
3050	5" thick pavement, 6" thick crushed stone, 24' wide	97.50	57.50	155
3100	28' wide	110	62.50	172.50
3150	32' wide	122	67.50	189.50
3300	14" thick crushed stone, 24' wide	116	63.50	179.50
3350	28' wide	131	69.50	200.50
3400	32' wide	146	75.50	221.50
3550	5-1/2" thick pavement., 7" thick crushed stone, 24' wide	106	59	165
3600	28' wide	120	64	184
3650	32' wide	133	69	202
3800	17" thick crushed stone, 24' wide	129	66.50	195.50
3850	28' wide	160	77	237

G2010 Roadways

G2010 232	Bituminous Roadways Crushed Stone	COST PER L.F.		
		MAT.	INST.	TOTAL
3900	32' wide	190	87.50	277.50
4050	Multi lane, 5" thick pavement, 6" thick crushed stone, 48' wide	169	86.50	255.50
4100	72' wide	241	117	358
4150	96' wide	310	146	456
4300	14" thick crushed stone, 48' wide	206	99	305
4350	72' wide	296	135	431
4400	96' wide	385	171	556
4550	5-1/2" thick pavement, 7" thick crushed stone, 48' wide	187	89.50	276.50
4600	72' wide	267	121	388
4650	96' wide	345	152	497
4800	17" thick crushed stone, 48' wide	233	105	338
4850	72' wide	335	144	479
4900	96' wide	440	182	622
5050	6" thick pavement, 8" thick crushed stone, 48' wide	202	92.50	294.50
5100	72' wide	291	125	416
5150	96' wide	380	157	537
5300	20" thick crushed stone, 48' wide	258	111	369
5350	72' wide	375	152	527
5400	96' wide	490	194	684
5550	7" thick pavement, 9" thick crushed stone, 48' wide	230	96	326
5600	72' wide	335	130	465
5650	96' wide	435	164	599
5800	22" thick crushed stone, 48' wide	290	117	407
5850	72' wide	425	161	586
5900	96' wide	555	205	760

G20 Site Improvements

G2020 Parking Lots

The Parking Lot System includes: compacted bank-run gravel; fine grading with a grader and roller; and bituminous concrete wearing course. All Parking Lot systems are on a cost per car basis. There are three basic types of systems: 90° angle, 60° angle, and 45° angle. The gravel base is compacted to 98%. Final stall design and lay-out of the parking lot with precast bumpers, sealcoating and white paint is also included.

The Expanded System Listing shows the three basic parking lot types with various depths of both gravel base and wearing course. The gravel base depths range from 6″ to 10″. The bituminous paving wearing course varies from a depth of 3″ to 6″.

System Components	QUANTITY	UNIT	COST PER CAR		
			MAT.	INST.	TOTAL
SYSTEM G2020 210 1500					
PARKING LOT, 90° ANGLE PARKING, 3″ BITUMINOUS PAVING, 6″ GRAVEL BASE					
Surveying crew for layout, 4 man crew	.020	Day		50.20	50.20
Borrow, bank run gravel, haul 2 mi., spread w/dozer, no compaction	7.223	L.C.Y.	176.96	58.65	235.61
Grading, fine grade 3 passes with motor grader	43.333	S.Y.		103.62	103.62
Compact w/vibrating plate, 8″ lifts, granular mat'l. to 98%	7.223	E.C.Y.		48.25	48.25
Binder course paving 2″ thick	43.333	S.Y.	361.83	58.50	420.33
Wear course paving 1″ thick	43.333	S.Y.	179.83	38.56	218.39
Seal coating, petroleum resistant under 1,000 S.Y.	43.333	S.Y.	61.97	58.50	120.47
Lines on pvmt., parking stall, paint, white, 4″ wide	1.000	Ea.	4.88	3.71	8.59
Precast concrete parking bar, 6″ x 10″ x 6'-0″	1.000	Ea.	43.50	19.50	63
TOTAL			828.97	439.49	1,268.46

G2020 210	Parking Lots Gravel Base	COST PER CAR		
		MAT.	INST.	TOTAL
1500	Parking lot, 90° angle parking, 3″ bituminous paving, 6″ gravel base	830	440	1,270
1520	8″ gravel base	890	475	1,365
1540	10″ gravel base	945	510	1,455
1560	4″ bituminous paving, 6″ gravel base	1,050	465	1,515
1580	8″ gravel base	1,125	500	1,625
1600	10″ gravel base	1,175	535	1,710
1620	6″ bituminous paving, 6″ gravel base	1,425	495	1,920
1640	8″ gravel base	1,475	535	2,010
1660	10″ gravel base	1,550	570	2,120
1800	60° angle parking, 3″ bituminous paving, 6″ gravel base	830	440	1,270
1820	8″ gravel base	890	475	1,365
1840	10″ gravel base	945	510	1,455
1860	4″ bituminous paving, 6″ gravel base	1,050	465	1,515
1880	8″ gravel base	1,125	500	1,625
1900	10″ gravel base	1,175	535	1,710
1920	6″ bituminous paving, 6″ gravel base	1,425	495	1,920
1940	8″ gravel base	1,475	535	2,010
1960	10″ gravel base	1,550	570	2,120
2200	45° angle parking, 3″ bituminous paving, 6″ gravel base	850	450	1,300
2220	8″ gravel base	910	490	1,400
2240	10″ gravel base	970	525	1,495
2260	4″ bituminous paving, 6″ gravel base	1,075	480	1,555
2280	8″ gravel base	1,150	515	1,665
2300	10″ gravel base	1,200	550	1,750
2320	6″ bituminous paving, 6″ gravel base	1,450	510	1,960
2340	8″ gravel base	1,525	545	2,070
2360	10″ gravel base	1,575	585	2,160

G2020 Parking Lots

The Parking Lot System includes: compacted crushed stone; fine grading with a grader and roller; and bituminous concrete wearing course. All Parking Lot systems are on a cost per car basis. There are three basic types of systems: 90° angle, 60° angle, and 45° angle. The crushed stone is compacted to 98%. Final stall design and lay-out of the parking lot with precast bumpers, sealcoating and white paint is also included.

The Expanded System Listing shows the three basic parking lot types with various depths of both crushed stone and wearing course. The crushed stone depths range from 6" to 10". The bituminous paving wearing course varies from a depth of 3" to 6".

System Components	QUANTITY	UNIT	COST PER CAR		
			MAT.	INST.	TOTAL
SYSTEM G2020 212 1500					
PARKING LOT, 90° ANGLE PARKING, 3" BITUMINOUS PAVING, 6" CRUSHED STONE					
Surveying crew for layout, 4 man crew	.020	Day		50.20	50.20
Borrow, 3/4" crushed stone, haul 2 mi., spread w/dozer, no compaction	8.645	C.Y.	224.77	70.20	294.97
Grading, fine grade 3 passes with motor grader	43.333	S.Y.		204.10	204.10
Compact w/ vibrating plate, 8" lifts, granular mat'l. to 98%	7.222	E.C.Y.		48.25	48.25
Binder course paving, 2" thick	43.333	S.Y.	361.83	58.50	420.33
Wearing course, 1" thick	43.333	S.Y.	179.83	38.56	218.39
Seal coating, petroleum resistant under 1,000 S.Y.	43.333	S.Y.	61.97	58.50	120.47
Lines on pvmt., parking stall, paint, white, 4" wide	1.000	Ea.	4.88	3.71	8.59
Precast concrete parking bar, 6" x 10" x 6'-0"	1.000	Ea.	43.50	19.50	63
TOTAL			876.78	551.52	1,428.30

G2020 212	Parking Lots Crushed Stone	COST PER CAR		
		MAT.	INST.	TOTAL
1500	Parking lot, 90° angle parking, 3" bituminous paving, 6" crushed stone	875	550	1,425
1520	8" 3/4 inch crushed stone	950	590	1,540
1540	10" 3/4 inch crushed stone	1,025	630	1,655
1560	4" bituminous paving, 6" 3/4 inch crushed stone	1,100	575	1,675
1580	8" 3/4 inch crushed stone	1,175	615	1,790
1600	10" 3/4 inch crushed stone	1,250	655	1,905
1620	6" bituminous paving, 6" 3/4 inch crushed stone	1,475	605	2,080
1640	8" 3/4 inch crushed stone	1,550	645	2,195
1660	10" 3/4 inch crushed stone	1,625	690	2,315
1800	60° angle parking, 3" bituminous paving, 6" 3/4 inch crushed stone	875	550	1,425
1820	8" 3/4 inch crushed stone	950	590	1,540
1840	10" 3/4 inch crushed stone	1,025	630	1,655
1860	4" bituminous paving, 6" 3/4 inch crushed stone	1,100	575	1,675
1880	8" 3/4 inch crushed stone	1,175	615	1,790
1900	10" 3/4 inch crushed stone	1,250	655	1,905
1920	6" bituminous paving, 6" 3/4 inch crushed stone	1,450	605	2,055
1940	8" 3/4 inch crushed stone	1,550	645	2,195
1960	10" 3/4 inch crushed stone	1,625	690	2,315
2200	45° angle parking, 3" bituminous paving, 6" 3/4 inch crushed stone	720	525	1,245
2220	8" 3/4 inch crushed stone	970	600	1,570
2240	10" 3/4 inch crushed stone	1,050	645	1,695
2260	4" bituminous paving, 6" 3/4 inch crushed stone	1,125	590	1,715
2280	8" 3/4 inch crushed stone	1,200	630	1,830
2300	10" 3/4 inch crushed stone	1,275	670	1,945
2320	6" bituminous paving, 6" 3/4 inch crushed stone	1,500	620	2,120
2340	8" 3/4 inch crushed stone	1,575	660	2,235
2360	10" 3/4 inch crushed stone	1,650	705	2,355

For customer support on your Site Work & Landscape Cost Data, call 877.737.1594.

G2020 Parking Lots

System Components	QUANTITY	UNIT	COST PER EACH		
			MAT.	INST.	TOTAL
SYSTEM G2020 214 1500					
PARKING LOT, 10 CARS WITH HANDICAP AND LIGHTING					
90 ° ANGLE PARKING, 3″ BITUMINOUS PAVING, 6″ CRUSHED STONE					
Surveying crew for layout, 4 man crew	.210	Day		527.10	527.10
Excavate for poles	4.740	B.C.Y.		549.84	549.84
Concrete pole bases	.940	C.Y.	172.02	261.55	433.57
Light poles	2.000	Ea.	2,050	1,224	3,274
Backfill around poles	3.800	L.C.Y.		159.60	159.60
Compact around poles	3.800	E.C.Y.		21.74	21.74
Power feed excavation	228.000	L.F.		189.24	189.24
Undergound conduit	228.000	L.F.	371.64	829.92	1,201.56
Power feed backfill	228.000	L.F.		150.48	150.48
Borrow, 3/4″ crushed stone, haul 2 mi., spread w/dozer, no compaction	91.000	C.Y.	2,366	738.92	3,104.92
Grading, fine grade 3 passes with motor grader	231.000	S.Y.		1,088.01	1,088.01
Compact crushed stone	75.840	E.C.Y.		376.93	376.93
Haul asphalt to site 5 miles	101.000	L.C.Y.		805.98	805.98
Binder course paving, 2″ thick	455.000	S.Y.	3,799.25	614.25	4,413.50
Wear course paving 1″ thick	455.000	S.Y.	1,888.25	404.95	2,293.20
Seal coating pavement	455.000	S.Y.	650.65	614.25	1,264.90
Precast concrete parking bar, 6″ x 10″ x 6'-0″	10.500	Ea.	456.75	204.75	661.50
Stall parking striping	10.500	Ea.	51.24	38.96	90.20
Handicap sign	1.000	Ea.	136	139.50	275.50
400 watt HPS luminaire	2.000	Ea.	1,280	596	1,876
Safety switch for lighting feed	1.000	Ea.	80.50	205	285.50
#8 wire feed for poles	4.560	C.L.F.	168.72	373.92	542.64
TOTAL			13,471.02	10,114.89	23,585.91

G2020 214	Parking Lots With Handicap & Lighting	COST PER EACH		
		MAT.	INST.	TOTAL
1490	Parking Lot, 90° Angle Parking, 3″ Bituminous Paving, 6″ Crushed Stone			
1500	10 cars with one handicap & lighting	13,500	10,100	23,600
1510	20 cars with one handicap	24,200	17,100	41,300
1520	30 cars with 2 handicap	37,300	26,300	63,600
1530	40 cars with 2 handicap	49,900	35,200	85,100
1540	50 cars with 3 handicap	61,000	42,600	103,600
1550	60 cars with 3 handicap	73,500	51,500	125,000
1560	70 cars with 4 handicap	87,000	60,500	147,500
1570	80 cars with 4 handicap	97,500	67,500	165,000
1580	90 cars with 5 handicap	110,500	77,000	187,500

G2020 Parking Lots

G2020 214	Parking Lots With Handicap & Lighting	COST PER EACH		
		MAT.	INST.	TOTAL
1590	100 cars with 5 handicap	121,500	84,000	205,500
1600	110 cars with 6 handicap	134,500	93,500	228,000
1610	120 cars with 6 handicap	145,500	100,500	246,000
1690	Parking Lot, 90° Angle Parking, 3" Bituminous Paving, 8" Crushed Stone			
1700	10 cars with one handicap & lighting	14,300	10,500	24,800
1710	20 cars with one handicap	25,700	17,800	43,500
1720	30 cars with 2 handicap	39,600	27,400	67,000
1730	40 cars with 2 handicap	53,000	36,600	89,600
1740	50 cars with 3 handicap	65,000	44,400	109,400
1750	60 cars with 3 handicap	78,500	53,500	132,000
1760	70 cars with 4 handicap	92,000	63,000	155,000
1770	80 cars with 4 handicap	103,500	70,500	174,000
1780	90 cars with 5 handicap	117,500	80,000	197,500
1790	100 cars with 5 handicap	129,000	87,500	216,500
1800	110 cars with 6 handicap	143,000	97,500	240,500
1810	120 cars with 6 handicap	154,500	104,500	259,000
1890	Parking Lot, 90° Angle Parking, 3" Bituminous Paving, 10" Crushed Stone			
1900	10 cars with one handicap & lighting	15,100	10,900	26,000
1910	20 cars with one handicap	27,200	18,600	45,800
1920	30 cars with 2 handicap	42,000	28,600	70,600
1930	40 cars with 2 handicap	56,000	38,100	94,100
1940	50 cars with 3 handicap	69,000	46,200	115,200
1950	60 cars with 3 handicap	83,000	56,000	139,000
1960	70 cars with 4 handicap	97,500	66,000	163,500
1970	80 cars with 4 handicap	110,000	73,500	183,500
1980	90 cars with 5 handicap	124,500	83,500	208,000
1990	100 cars with 5 handicap	137,000	91,500	228,500
2000	110 cars with 6 handicap	151,500	101,500	253,000
2010	120 cars with 6 handicap	164,000	109,000	273,000
2190	Parking Lot, 90° Angle Parking, 4" Bituminous Paving, 6" Crushed Stone			
2200	10 cars with one handicap & lighting	15,900	10,400	26,300
2210	20 cars with one handicap	28,800	17,700	46,500
2220	30 cars with 2 handicap	44,400	27,200	71,600
2230	40 cars with 2 handicap	59,000	36,200	95,200
2240	50 cars with 3 handicap	73,000	43,900	116,900
2250	60 cars with 3 handicap	87,500	53,000	140,500
2260	70 cars with 4 handicap	103,000	62,500	165,500
2270	80 cars with 4 handicap	116,000	70,000	186,000
2280	90 cars with 5 handicap	131,500	79,500	211,000
2290	100 cars with 5 handicap	144,500	86,500	231,000
2300	110 cars with 6 handicap	160,500	96,500	257,000
2310	120 cars with 6 handicap	173,000	103,500	276,500
2390	Parking Lot, 90° Angle Parking, 4" Bituminous Paving, 8" Crushed Stone			
2400	10 cars with one handicap & lighting	16,600	10,800	27,400
2410	20 cars with one handicap	30,300	18,300	48,600
2420	30 cars with 2 handicap	46,600	28,200	74,800
2430	40 cars with 2 handicap	62,500	37,700	100,200
2440	50 cars with 3 handicap	76,500	45,700	122,200
2450	60 cars with 3 handicap	92,500	55,000	147,500
2460	70 cars with 4 handicap	108,500	65,000	173,500
2470	80 cars with 4 handicap	122,500	72,500	195,000
2480	90 cars with 5 handicap	138,500	82,500	221,000
2490	100 cars with 5 handicap	152,500	90,000	242,500
2500	110 cars with 6 handicap	168,500	100,500	269,000
2510	120 cars with 6 handicap	182,500	108,000	290,500
2590	Parking Lot, 90° Angle Parking, 4" Bituminous Paving, 10" Crushed Stone			
2600	10 cars with one handicap & lighting	17,400	11,200	28,600
2610	20 cars with one handicap	31,900	19,100	51,000

G2020 Parking Lots

G2020 214	Parking Lots With Handicap & Lighting	COST PER EACH		
		MAT.	INST.	TOTAL
2620	30 cars with 2 handicap	49,000	29,400	78,400
2630	40 cars with 2 handicap	65,500	39,200	104,700
2640	50 cars with 3 handicap	80,500	47,600	128,100
2650	60 cars with 3 handicap	97,000	57,500	154,500
2660	70 cars with 4 handicap	114,000	68,000	182,000
2670	80 cars with 4 handicap	128,500	75,500	204,000
2680	90 cars with 5 handicap	145,500	86,000	231,500
2690	100 cars with 5 handicap	160,000	94,000	254,000
2700	110 cars with 6 handicap	177,500	104,500	282,000
2710	120 cars with 6 handicap	192,000	112,000	304,000
2790	Parking Lot, 90° Angle Parking, 5″ Bituminous Paving, 6″ Crushed Stone			
2800	10 cars with one handicap & lighting	17,800	10,600	28,400
2810	20 cars with one handicap	32,500	18,000	50,500
2820	30 cars with 2 handicap	50,000	27,700	77,700
2830	40 cars with 2 handicap	66,500	36,900	103,400
2840	50 cars with 3 handicap	82,000	44,700	126,700
2850	60 cars with 3 handicap	99,000	54,000	153,000
2860	70 cars with 4 handicap	116,500	64,000	180,500
2870	80 cars with 4 handicap	131,000	71,500	202,500
2880	90 cars with 5 handicap	148,500	81,000	229,500
2890	100 cars with 5 handicap	163,500	88,500	252,000
2900	110 cars with 6 handicap	181,000	98,000	279,000
2910	120 cars with 6 handicap	195,500	105,500	301,000
2990	Parking Lot, 90° Angle Parking, 5″ Bituminous Paving, 8″ Crushed Stone			
3000	10 cars with one handicap & lighting	18,600	10,900	29,500
3010	20 cars with one handicap	34,100	18,700	52,800
3020	30 cars with 2 handicap	52,500	28,800	81,300
3030	40 cars with 2 handicap	69,500	38,400	107,900
3040	50 cars with 3 handicap	86,000	46,600	132,600
3050	60 cars with 3 handicap	103,500	56,000	159,500
3060	70 cars with 4 handicap	121,500	66,500	188,000
3070	80 cars with 4 handicap	137,000	74,000	211,000
3080	90 cars with 5 handicap	155,500	84,000	239,500
3090	100 cars with 5 handicap	171,000	92,000	263,000
3100	110 cars with 6 handicap	189,000	102,000	291,000
3110	120 cars with 6 handicap	205,000	109,500	314,500
3190	Parking Lot, 90° Angle Parking, 5″ Bituminous Paving, 10″ Crushed Stone			
3200	10 cars with one handicap & lighting	19,400	11,300	30,700
3210	20 cars with one handicap	35,600	19,500	55,100
3220	30 cars with 2 handicap	54,500	29,900	84,400
3230	40 cars with 2 handicap	73,000	39,800	112,800
3240	50 cars with 3 handicap	90,000	48,500	138,500
3250	60 cars with 3 handicap	108,000	58,500	166,500
3260	70 cars with 4 handicap	127,000	68,500	195,500
3270	80 cars with 4 handicap	143,500	77,000	220,500
3280	90 cars with 5 handicap	162,500	87,500	250,000
3290	100 cars with 5 handicap	179,000	95,500	274,500
3300	110 cars with 6 handicap	198,000	106,000	304,000
3310	120 cars with 6 handicap	214,000	114,500	328,500
3390	Parking Lot, 90° Angle Parking, 6″ Bituminous Paving, 6″ Crushed Stone			
3400	10 cars with one handicap & lighting	19,700	10,700	30,400
3410	20 cars with one handicap	36,300	18,300	54,600
3420	30 cars with 2 handicap	55,500	28,100	83,600
3430	40 cars with 2 handicap	74,000	37,500	111,500
3440	50 cars with 3 handicap	91,500	45,500	137,000
3450	60 cars with 3 handicap	110,000	55,000	165,000
3460	70 cars with 4 handicap	129,500	64,500	194,000
3470	80 cars with 4 handicap	146,000	72,000	218,000

G20 Site Improvements

G2020 Parking Lots

G2020 214	Parking Lots With Handicap & Lighting	COST PER EACH		
		MAT.	INST.	TOTAL
3480	90 cars with 5 handicap	165,500	82,000	247,500
3490	100 cars with 5 handicap	182,000	90,000	272,000
3500	110 cars with 6 handicap	201,500	99,500	301,000
3510	120 cars with 6 handicap	218,000	107,000	325,000
3590	Parking Lot, 90° Angle Parking, 6" Bituminous Paving, 8" Crushed Stone			
3600	10 cars with one handicap & lighting	20,500	11,100	31,600
3610	20 cars with one handicap	37,800	19,000	56,800
3620	30 cars with 2 handicap	58,000	29,300	87,300
3630	40 cars with 2 handicap	77,000	38,900	115,900
3640	50 cars with 3 handicap	95,500	47,400	142,900
3650	60 cars with 3 handicap	114,500	57,000	171,500
3660	70 cars with 4 handicap	135,000	67,500	202,500
3670	80 cars with 4 handicap	152,000	75,000	227,000
3680	90 cars with 5 handicap	172,500	85,500	258,000
3690	100 cars with 5 handicap	189,500	93,000	282,500
3700	110 cars with 6 handicap	210,000	103,500	313,500
3710	120 cars with 6 handicap	227,000	112,000	339,000
3790	Parking Lot, 90° Angle Parking, 6" Bituminous Paving, 10" Crushed Stone			
3800	10 cars with one handicap & lighting	21,300	11,500	32,800
3810	20 cars with one handicap	39,400	19,700	59,100
3820	30 cars with 2 handicap	60,500	30,300	90,800
3830	40 cars with 2 handicap	80,500	40,400	120,900
3840	50 cars with 3 handicap	99,500	49,100	148,600
3850	60 cars with 3 handicap	119,500	59,500	179,000
3860	70 cars with 4 handicap	140,500	70,000	210,500
3870	80 cars with 4 handicap	158,500	78,000	236,500
3880	90 cars with 5 handicap	179,500	88,500	268,000
3890	100 cars with 5 handicap	197,500	97,000	294,500
3900	110 cars with 6 handicap	218,500	108,000	326,500
3910	120 cars with 6 handicap	236,500	116,000	352,500

For customer support on your Site Work & Landscape Cost Data, call 877.737.1594.

G2030 Pedestrian Paving

The Bituminous Sidewalk System includes: excavation; compacted gravel base (hand graded), bituminous surface; and hand grading along the edge of the completed walk.

The Expanded System Listing shows Bituminous Sidewalk systems with wearing course depths ranging from 1" to 2-1/2" of bituminous material. The gravel base ranges from 4" to 8". Sidewalk widths are shown ranging from 3' to 5'. Costs are on a linear foot basis.

System Components	QUANTITY	UNIT	COST PER L.F.		
			MAT.	INST.	TOTAL
SYSTEM G2030 110 1580					
BITUMINOUS SIDEWALK, 1″ THICK PAVING, 4″ GRAVEL BASE, 3′ WIDTH					
Excavation, bulk, dozer, push 50′	.046	B.C.Y.		.10	.10
Borrow, bank run gravel, haul 2 mi., spread w/dozer, no compaction	.037	L.C.Y.	.91	.30	1.21
Compact w/vib. plate, 8″ lifts	.037	E.C.Y.		.10	.10
Fine grade, area to be paved, small area	.333	S.Y.		3.25	3.25
Asphaltic concrete, 2″ thick	.333	S.Y.	1.36	.72	2.08
Backfill by hand, no compaction, light soil	.006	L.C.Y.		.20	.20
TOTAL			2.27	4.67	6.94

G2030 110	Bituminous Sidewalks	COST PER L.F.		
		MAT.	INST.	TOTAL
1580	Bituminous sidewalk, 1″ thick paving, 4″ gravel base, 3′ width	2.27	4.67	6.94
1600	4′ width	3.01	5.05	8.06
1620	5′ width	3.83	5.30	9.13
1640	6″ gravel base, 3′ width	2.73	4.91	7.64
1660	4′ width	3.62	5.35	8.97
1680	5′ width	4.55	5.85	10.40
1700	8″ gravel base, 3′ width	3.17	5.15	8.32
1720	4′ width	4.24	5.70	9.94
1740	5′ width	5.30	6.25	11.55
1800	1-1/2″ thick paving, 4″ gravel base, 3′ width	3.02	4.87	7.89
1820	4′ width	3.99	5.40	9.39
1840	5′ width	4.92	6.20	11.12
1860	6″ gravel base, 3′ width	3.48	5.10	8.58
1880	4′ width	4.52	5.95	10.47
1900	5′ width	5.75	6.30	12.05
1920	8″ gravel base, 3′ width	3.85	5.60	9.45
1940	4′ width	5.20	6	11.20
1960	5′ width	6.45	7	13.45
2120	2″ thick paving, 4″ gravel base, 3′ width	3.62	5.60	9.22
2140	4′ width	4.82	6.25	11.07
2160	5′ width	6.05	6.90	12.95
2180	6″ gravel base, 3′ width	4.08	5.85	9.93
2200	4′ width	5.45	6.55	12
2240	8″ gravel base, 3′ width	4.52	6.05	10.57
2280	5′ width	7.55	7.65	15.20
2400	2-1/2″ thick paving, 4″ gravel base, 3′ width	5.25	6.25	11.50
2420	4′ width	6.95	7.05	14
2460	6″ gravel base, 3′ width	5.70	6.50	12.20
2500	5′ width	9.55	8.30	17.85
2520	8″ gravel base, 3′ width	6.15	6.70	12.85
2540	4′ width	8.15	7.65	15.80
2560	5′ width	10.30	8.70	19

G2030 Pedestrian Paving

The Concrete Sidewalk System includes: excavation; compacted gravel base (hand graded); forms; welded wire fabric; and 3,000 p.s.i. air-entrained concrete (broom finish).

The Expanded System Listing shows Concrete Sidewalk systems with wearing course depths ranging from 4" to 6". The gravel base ranges from 4" to 8". Sidewalk widths are shown ranging from 3' to 5'. Costs are on a linear foot basis.

System Components	QUANTITY	UNIT	COST PER L.F.		
			MAT.	INST.	TOTAL
SYSTEM G2030 120 1580					
CONCRETE SIDEWALK 4" THICK, 4" GRAVEL BASE, 3' WIDE					
Excavation, box out with dozer	.100	B.C.Y.		.22	.22
Gravel base, haul 2 miles, spread with dozer	.037	L.C.Y.	.91	.30	1.21
Compaction with vibrating plate	.037	E.C.Y.		.10	.10
Fine grade by hand	.333	S.Y.		3.29	3.29
Concrete in place including forms and reinforcing	.037	C.Y.	5.58	7.86	13.44
Backfill edges by hand	.010	L.C.Y.		.33	.33
TOTAL			6.49	12.10	18.59

G2030 120	Concrete Sidewalks	COST PER L.F.		
		MAT.	INST.	TOTAL
1580	Concrete sidewalk, 4" thick, 4" gravel base, 3' wide	6.50	12.10	18.60
1600	4' wide	8.65	14.90	23.55
1620	5' wide	10.80	17.70	28.50
1640	6" gravel base, 3' wide	6.95	12.30	19.25
1660	4' wide	9.25	15.20	24.45
1680	5' wide	11.60	18.05	29.65
1700	8" gravel base, 3' wide	7.40	12.55	19.95
1720	4' wide	9.85	15.55	25.40
1740	5' wide	12.30	18.45	30.75
1800	5" thick concrete, 4" gravel base, 3' wide	8.40	13.10	21.50
1820	4' wide	11.15	16.15	27.30
1840	5' wide	13.95	19.25	33.20
1860	6" gravel base, 3' wide	8.85	13.35	22.20
1880	4' wide	11.75	16.50	28.25
1900	5' wide	14.75	19	33.75
1920	8" gravel base, 3' wide	9.30	13.55	22.85
1940	4' wide	12.40	17.70	30.10
1960	5' wide	15.45	19.40	34.85
2120	6" thick concrete, 4" gravel base, 3' wide	9.60	13.85	23.45
2140	4' wide	12.80	17.10	29.90
2160	5' wide	16	20.50	36.50
2180	6" gravel base, 3' wide	10.05	14.05	24.10
2200	4' wide	13.40	17.45	30.85
2220	5' wide	16.80	21	37.80
2240	8" gravel base, 3' wide	10.50	14.30	24.80
2260	4' wide	14.05	17.75	31.80
2280	5' wide	17.50	21	38.50

633

The Plaza Systems listed include several brick and tile paving surfaces on three different bases: gravel, slab on grade and suspended slab. The system cost includes this base cost with the exception of the suspended slab. The type of bedding for the pavers depends on the base being used, and alternate bedding may be desirable. Also included in the paving costs are edging and precast grating costs and where concrete bases are involved, expansion joints.

System Components	QUANTITY	UNIT	COST PER S.F.		
			MAT.	INST.	TOTAL
SYSTEM G2030 150 2050					
PLAZA, BRICK PAVERS, 4" X 8" X 1-3/4", GRAVEL BASE, STONE DUST BED					
Compact subgrade, static roller, 4 passes	.111	S.Y.		.04	.04
Bank gravel, 2 mi haul, dozer spread	.012	L.C.Y.	.30	.10	.40
Compact gravel bedding or base, vibrating plate	.012	E.C.Y.		.04	.04
Grading fine grade, 3 passes with grader	.111	S.Y.		.52	.52
Coarse washed sand bed, 1"	.003	C.Y.	.11	.07	.18
Brick paver, 4" x 8" x 1-3/4"	4.150	Ea.	3.21	4.29	7.50
Brick edging, stood on end, 3 per L.F.	.060	L.F.	.34	.63	.97
Concrete tree grate, 5' square	.004	Ea.	1.81	.30	2.11
TOTAL			5.77	5.99	11.76

G2030 150	Brick & Tile Plazas	COST PER S.F.		
		MAT.	INST.	TOTAL
1050	Plaza, asphalt pavers, 6" x 12" x 1-1/4", gravel base, asphalt bedding	12.75	11.05	23.80
1100	Slab on grade, asphalt bedding	15	12.05	27.05
1150	Suspended slab, insulated & mastic bedding	16.75	14.70	31.45
1300	6" x 12" x 3", gravel base, asphalt, bedding	17.60	11.40	29
1350	Slab on grade, asphalt bedding	19.10	12.35	31.45
1400	Suspended slab, insulated & mastic bedding	21	15	36
2050	Brick pavers, 4" x 8" x 1-3/4", gravel base, stone dust bedding	5.75	6	11.75
2100	Slab on grade, asphalt bedding	8	8.75	16.75
2150	Suspended slab, insulated & no bedding	9.75	11.35	21.10
2300	4" x 8" x 2-1/4", gravel base, stone dust bedding	5.85	5.95	11.80
2350	Slab on grade, asphalt bedding	8.05	8.75	16.80
2400	Suspended slab, insulated & no bedding	9.80	11.35	21.15
2550	Shale pavers, 4" x 8" x 2-1/4", gravel base, stone dust bedding	6	6.85	12.85
2600	Slab on grade, asphalt bedding	8.20	9.60	17.80
2650	Suspended slab, insulated & no bedding	5.40	7.95	13.35
3050	Thin set tile, 4" x 4" x 3/8", slab on grade	8.85	9.70	18.55
3300	4" x 4" x 3/4", slab on grade	10.20	6.50	16.70
3550	Concrete paving stone, 4" x 8" x 2-1/2", gravel base, sand bedding	4.48	4.22	8.70
3600	Slab on grade, asphalt bedding	6.30	6.45	12.75
3650	Suspended slab, insulated & no bedding	3.50	4.82	8.32
3800	4" x 8" x 3-1/4", gravel base, sand bedding	4.48	4.22	8.70
3850	Slab on grade, asphalt bedding	5.60	4.98	10.58
3900	Suspended slab, insulated & no bedding	3.50	4.82	8.32
4050	Concrete patio blocks, 8" x 16" x 2", gravel base, sand bedding	4.66	5.45	10.11
4100	Slab on grade, asphalt bedding	6.70	8.15	14.85
4150	Suspended slab, insulated & no bedding	3.68	6.05	9.73

G2030 Pedestrian Paving

G2030 150	Brick & Tile Plazas	COST PER S.F.		
		MAT.	INST.	TOTAL
4300	16" x 16" x 2", gravel base, sand bedding	5.45	4.42	9.87
4350	Slab on grade, asphalt bedding	6.80	5.60	12.40
4400	Suspended slab, insulated & no bedding	4.66	5.40	10.06
4550	24" x 24" x 2", gravel base, sand bedding	6.15	3.37	9.52
4600	Slab on grade, asphalt bedding	8.15	6	14.15
4650	Suspended slab, insulated & no bedding	5.35	4.38	9.73
5050	Bluestone flagging, 3/4" thick irregular, gravel base, sand bedding	10.90	13.05	23.95
5100	Slab on grade, mastic bedding	16.55	17.90	34.45
5300	1" thick, irregular, gravel base, sand bedding	9.65	14.30	23.95
5350	Slab on grade, mastic bedding	15.30	19.15	34.45
5550	Flagstone, 3/4" thick irregular, gravel base, sand bedding	17.55	12.45	30
5600	Slab on grade, mastic bedding	23	17.30	40.30
5800	1-1/2" thick, random rectangular, gravel base, sand bedding	18.60	14.30	32.90
5850	Slab on grade, mastic bedding	24	19.15	43.15
6050	Granite pavers, 3-1/2" x 3-1/2" x 3-1/2", gravel base, sand bedding	16	13.15	29.15
6100	Slab on grade, mortar bedding	19.05	21	40.05
6300	4" x 4" x 4", gravel base, sand bedding	16.75	12.80	29.55
6350	Slab on grade, mortar bedding	18.80	17.25	36.05
6550	4" x 12" x 4", gravel base, sand bedding	13.85	12.45	26.30
6600	Slab on grade, mortar bedding	15.90	16.90	32.80
6800	6" x 15" x 4", gravel base, sand bedding	8.70	11.75	20.45
6850	Slab on grade, mortar bedding	10.75	16.20	26.95
7050	Limestone, 3" thick, gravel base, sand bedding	13.85	16.25	30.10
7100	Slab on grade, mortar bedding	15.90	20.50	36.40
7300	4" thick, gravel base, sand bedding	17.45	16.65	34.10
7350	Slab on grade, mortar bedding	19.50	21	40.50
7550	5" thick, gravel base, sand bedding	21	17.05	38.05
7600	Slab on grade, mortar bedding	23	21.50	44.50
8050	Slate flagging, 3/4" thick, gravel base, sand bedding	12.90	13.15	26.05
8100	Slab on grade, mastic bedding	25.50	18.95	44.45
8300	1" thick, gravel base, sand bedding	14.55	14.05	28.60
8350	Slab on grade, mastic bedding	20.50	19.35	39.85

G2030 Pedestrian Paving

The Step System has three basic types: railroad tie, cast-in-place concrete or brick with a concrete base. System elements include: gravel base compaction; and backfill.

Wood Step Systems use 6″ x 6″ railroad ties that produce 3′ to 6′ wide steps that range from 2-riser to 5-riser configurations. Cast in Place Concrete Step Systems are either monolithic or aggregate finish. They range from 3′ to 6′ in width. Concrete Steps Systems are either in a 2-riser or 5-riser configuration. Precast Concrete Step Systems are listed for 4′ to 7′ widths with both 2-riser and 5-riser models. Brick Step Systems are placed on a 12″ concrete base. The size range is the same as cost in place concrete. Costs are on a per unit basis. All systems are assumed to include a full landing at the top 4′ long.

System Components	QUANTITY	UNIT	COST PER EACH		
			MAT.	INST.	TOTAL
SYSTEM G2030 310 0960					
STAIRS, RAILROAD TIES, 6″ X 8″, 3′ WIDE, 2 RISERS					
Excavation, by hand, sandy soil	1.327	C.Y.		76.97	76.97
Borrow fill, bank run gravel	.664	C.Y.	14.61		14.61
Delivery charge	.664	C.Y.		19.69	19.69
Backfill compaction, 6″ layers, hand tamp	.664	C.Y.		14.94	14.94
Railroad ties, wood, creosoted, 6″ x 8″ x 8′-6″, C.L. lots	5.000	Ea.	285	184.75	469.75
Backfill by hand, no compaction, light soil	.800	C.Y.		26.40	26.40
Remove excess spoil, 12 C.Y. dump truck	1.200	L.C.Y.		8.29	8.29
TOTAL			299.61	331.04	630.65

G2030 310	Stairs	COST PER EACH		
		MAT.	INST.	TOTAL
0960	Stairs, railroad ties, 6″ x 8″, 3′ wide, 2 risers	300	330	630
0980	5 risers	705	670	1,375
1000	4′ wide, 2 risers	305	365	670
1020	5 risers	710	700	1,410
1040	5′ wide, 2 risers	360	430	790
1060	5 risers	885	860	1,745
1080	6′ wide, 2 risers	365	465	830
1100	5 risers	890	890	1,780
2520	Concrete, cast in place, 3′ wide, 2 risers	197	460	657
2540	5 risers	261	650	911
2560	4′ wide, 2 risers	243	600	843
2580	5 risers	315	840	1,155
2600	5′ wide, 2 risers	290	750	1,040
2620	5 risers	365	1,000	1,365
2640	6′ wide, 2 risers	330	870	1,200
2660	5 risers	425	1,175	1,600
2800	Exposed aggregate finish, 3′ wide, 2 risers	205	475	680
2820	5 risers	275	650	925
2840	4′ wide, 2 risers	253	600	853
2860	5 risers	335	840	1,175
2880	5′ wide, 2 risers	305	750	1,055
2900	5 risers	390	1,000	1,390
2920	6′ wide, 2 risers	345	870	1,215
2940	5 risers	450	1,175	1,625
3200	Precast, 4′ wide, 2 risers	480	350	830
3220	5 risers	740	510	1,250

G2030 Pedestrian Paving

G2030 310	Stairs	COST PER EACH		
		MAT.	INST.	TOTAL
3240	5' wide, 2 risers	545	415	960
3260	5 risers	860	555	1,415
3280	6' wide, 2 risers	605	435	1,040
3300	5 risers	950	590	1,540
3320	7' wide, 2 risers	770	465	1,235
3340	5 risers	1,275	635	1,910
4100	Brick, incl 12" conc base, 3' wide, 2 risers	330	1,150	1,480
4120	5 risers	475	1,725	2,200
4140	4' wide, 2 risers	415	1,425	1,840
4160	5 risers	590	2,150	2,740
4180	5' wide, 2 risers	495	1,700	2,195
4200	5 risers	700	2,525	3,225
4220	6' wide, 2 risers	575	1,975	2,550
4240	5 risers	815	2,900	3,715

637

G2040 Site Development

There are four basic types of Concrete Retaining Wall Systems: reinforced concrete with level backfill; reinforced concrete with sloped backfill or surcharge; unreinforced with level backfill; and unreinforced with sloped backfill or surcharge. System elements include: all necessary forms (4 uses); 3,000 p.s.i. concrete with an 8" chute; all necessary reinforcing steel; and underdrain. Exposed concrete is patched and rubbed.

The Expanded System Listing shows walls that range in thickness from 10" to 18" for reinforced concrete walls with level backfill and 12" to 24" for reinforced walls with sloped backfill. Walls range from a height of 4' to 20'. Unreinforced level and sloped backfill walls range from a height of 3' to 10'.

System Components				COST PER L.F.		
	QUANTITY	UNIT		MAT.	INST.	TOTAL
SYSTEM G2040 210 1000						
CONC. RETAIN. WALL REINFORCED, LEVEL BACKFILL, 4' HIGH						
Forms in place, cont. wall footing & keyway, 4 uses	2.000	S.F.		4.88	9.06	13.94
Forms in place, retaining wall forms, battered to 8' high, 4 uses	8.000	SFCA		5.84	69.20	75.04
Reinforcing in place, walls, #3 to #7	.004	Ton		4.30	3.50	7.80
Concrete ready mix, regular weight, 3000 psi	.204	C.Y.		22.85		22.85
Placing concrete and vibrating footing con., shallow direct chute	.074	C.Y.			1.82	1.82
Placing concrete and vibrating walls, 8" thick, direct chute	.130	C.Y.			4.26	4.26
Pipe bedding, crushed or screened bank run gravel	1.000	L.F.		3.08	1.40	4.48
Pipe, subdrainage, corrugated plastic, 4" diameter	1.000	L.F.		.55	.77	1.32
Finish walls and break ties, patch walls	4.000	S.F.		.16	3.96	4.12
TOTAL				41.66	93.97	135.63

G2040 210	Concrete Retaining Walls	COST PER L.F.		
		MAT.	INST.	TOTAL
1000	Conc. retain. wall, reinforced, level backfill, 4' high x 2'-2" base, 10" thick	41.50	94	135.50
1200	6' high x 3'-3" base, 10" thick	60	136	196
1400	8' high x 4'-3" base, 10" thick	77.50	178	255.50
1600	10' high x 5'-4" base, 13" thick	101	261	362
1800	12' high x 6'-6" base, 14" thick	124	310	434
2200	16' high x 8'-6" base, 16" thick	188	420	608
2600	20' high x 10'-5" base, 18" thick	276	550	826
3000	Sloped backfill, 4' high x 3'-2" base, 12" thick	50.50	97.50	148
3200	6' high x 4'-6" base, 12" thick	71	140	211
3400	8' high x 5'-11" base, 12" thick	94	184	278
3600	10' high x 7'-5" base, 16" thick	134	274	408
3800	12' high x 8'-10" base, 18" thick	174	330	504
4200	16' high x 11'-10" base, 21" thick	291	470	761
4600	20' high x 15'-0" base, 24" thick	450	640	1,090
5000	Unreinforced, level backfill, 3'-0" high x 1'-6" base	21.50	63	84.50
5200	4'-0" high x 2'-0" base	33.50	84	117.50
5400	6'-0" high x 3'-0" base	62.50	131	193.50
5600	8'-0" high x 4'-0" base	99.50	174	273.50
5800	10'-0" high x 5'-0" base	147	269	416
7000	Sloped backfill, 3'-0" high x 2'-0" base	26	65.50	91.50
7200	4'-0" high x 3'-0" base	43.50	87.50	131
7400	6'-0" high x 5'-0" base	90	138	228
7600	8'-0" high x 7'-0" base	153	188	341
7800	10'-0" high x 9'-0" base	234	291	525

G2040 Site Development

The Masonry Retaining Wall System includes: a reinforced concrete foundation footing for the wall with all necessary forms and 3,000 p.s.i. concrete; sand aggregate concrete blocks with steel reinforcing; solid grouting and underdrain.

The Expanded System Listing shows walls that range in thickness from 8″ to 12″ and in height from 3′-4″ to 8′.

System Components	QUANTITY	UNIT	COST PER L.F.		
			MAT.	INST.	TOTAL
SYSTEM G2040 220 1000					
REINF. CMU WALL, LEVEL FILL, 8″ THICK, 3′-4″ HIGH, 2′-4″ CONC. FTG.					
Forms in place, continuous wall footings 4 uses	1.670	S.F.	4.07	7.57	11.64
Joint reinforcing, #5 & #6 steel bars, vertical	5.590	Lb.	2.96	4.86	7.82
Concrete block, found. wall, cut joints, 8″ x 16″ x 8″ block	3.330	S.F.	12.65	20.48	33.13
Grout concrete block cores solid, 8″ thick, .258 CF/SF, pumped	3.330	S.F.	4.16	10.92	15.08
Concrete ready mix, regular wt., 3000 psi	.070	C.Y.	12.03		12.03
Pipe bedding, crushed or screened bank run gravel	1.000	L.F.	3.08	1.40	4.48
Pipe, subdrainage, corrugated plastic, 4″ diameter	1.000	L.F.	.55	.77	1.32
TOTAL			39.50	46	85.50

G2040 220	Masonry Retaining Walls	COST PER L.F.		
		MAT.	INST.	TOTAL
1000	Wall, reinforced CMU, level fill, 8″ thick, 3′-4″ high, 2′-4″ base	39.50	46	85.50
1200	4′-0″ high x 2′-9″ base	40	55.50	95.50
1400	4′-8″ high x 3′-3″ base	48	66	114
1600	5′-4″ high x 3′-8″ base	55.50	75	130.50
1800	6′-0″ high x 4′-2″ base	65.50	85.50	151
1840	10″ thick, 4′-0″ high x 2′-10″ base	41	56	97
1860	4′-8″ high x 3′-4″ base	49	66.50	115.50
1880	5′-4″ high x 3′-10″ base	56.50	75.50	132
1900	6′-0″ high x 4′-4″ base	66.50	86.50	153
1920	6′-8″ high x 4′-10″ base	73.50	95	168.50
1940	7′-4″ high x 5′-4″ base	86.50	108	194.50
2000	12″ thick, 5′-4″ high x 4′-0″ base	64	97	161
2200	6′-0″ high x 4′-6″ base	75.50	111	186.50
2400	6′-8″ high x 5′-0″ base	83	123	206
2600	7′-4″ high x 5′-6″ base	97.50	138	235.50
2800	8′-0″ high x 5′-11″ base	105	151	256

639

G2040 Site Development

Wood Post Retaining Wall Systems are either constructed of redwood, cedar, pressure-treated lumber or creosoted lumber. System elements include wood posts installed side-by-side to various heights; and underdrain.

The Expanded System Listing shows a wide variety of configurations with each type of wood. Costs are on a linear foot basis. Each grouping in the listing shows walls with either 4″ x 4″, 6″ x 6″, 8″ x 8″, or random diameter lumber.

System Components	QUANTITY	UNIT	COST PER L.F.		
			MAT.	INST.	TOTAL
SYSTEM G2040 230 1000					
WOOD POST RETAINING WALL, SIDE-BY-SIDE 4 X 4 REDWOOD, 1′ HIGH					
Redwood post, columns and girts, 4″ x 4″	8.000	B.F.	42.40	17.80	60.20
Pipe bedding, crushed or screened bank run gravel	1.000	L.F.	.84	.38	1.22
Pipe, subdrainage, corrugated plastic, 4″ diameter	1.000	L.F.	.55	.77	1.32
TOTAL			43.79	18.95	62.74

G2040 230	Wood Post Retaining Walls	COST PER L.F.		
		MAT.	INST.	TOTAL
1000	Wood post retaining wall, side by side 4 x 4, redwood, 1′ high	44	18.95	62.95
1200	2′ high	87	37	124
1400	Cedar, 1′ high	27	18.95	45.95
1600	2′ high	53.50	37	90.50
1800	Pressure treated lumber, 1′ high	10	16.55	26.55
2000	2′ high	19.30	32	51.30
2200	Creosoted lumber, 1′ high	8.90	14.65	23.55
2400	2′ high	16.05	26.50	42.55
2600	6 x 6, redwood, 2′ high	219	44	263
2800	4′ high	440	87.50	527.50
3000	Cedar, 2′ high	112	44	156
3200	4′ high	224	87.50	311.50
3400	Pressure treated lumber, 2′ high	38.50	36	74.50
3600	4′ high	77	72	149
3800	Creosoted lumber, 2′ high	31	29	60
4000	4′ high	61.50	57.50	119
4200	8 x 8, redwood, 4′ high	560	96.50	656.50
4400	6′ high	1,050	179	1,229
4600	Cedar, 4′ high	237	96.50	333.50
4800	6′ high	445	179	624
5000	Pressure treated lumber, 4′ high	108	112	220
5200	6′ high	200	208	408
5400	Creosoted lumber, 4′ high	87.50	91	178.50
5600	6′ high	162	168	330
5800	Random diameter poles, cedar, 4′ high	55	38	93
6000	6′ high	82.50	56.50	139
6200	8′ high	110	74.50	184.50
7000	Creosoted lumber, 4′ high	23.50	21	44.50
7200	6′ high	34	30.50	64.50
7400	8′ high	46.50	41	87.50

G2040 Site Development

A Post and Board Retaining Wall System is constructed of one of four types of lumber: redwood, cedar, creosoted wood or pressure-treated lumber. The system includes all the elements that must go into a wall that resists lateral pressure. System elements include: posts and boards; cap; underdrain; and deadman where required.

The Expanded System Listing shows a wide variety of wall configurations with each type of lumber. The spacing of the deadman in the wall is indicated for each wall system. Wall heights vary from 3' to 10'.

System Components			COST PER L.F.		
	QUANTITY	UNIT	MAT.	INST.	TOTAL
SYSTEM G2040 240 1000					
POST & BOARD RETAINING WALL, 2" PLANKS, 4 X 4 POSTS, 3' HIGH					
Redwood post, 4" x 4"	2.000	B.F.	10.60	4.45	15.05
Redwood joist and cap, 2" x 10"	7.000	B.F.	39.80	5.28	45.08
Pipe bedding, crushed or screened bank run gravel	1.000	L.F.	1.54	.71	2.25
Pipe, subdrainage, corrugated plastic, 4" diameter	1.000	L.F.	.55	.77	1.32
TOTAL			52.49	11.21	63.70

G2040 240	Post & Board Retaining Walls	COST PER L.F.		
		MAT.	INST.	TOTAL
1000	Post & board retaining wall, 2" planking, redwood, 4 x 4 post, 4' spacing, 3' high	52.50	11.20	63.70
1200	2' spacing, 4' high	64	19.25	83.25
1400	6 x 6 post, 4' spacing, 5' high	117	24	141
1600	3' spacing, 6' high	166	33.50	199.50
1800	6 x 6 post with deadman, 3' spacing, 8' high	219	44	263
2000	8 x 8 post, 2' spacing, 8' high	495	86.50	581.50
2200	8 x 8 post with deadman, 2' spacing, 9' high	565	96	661
2400	Cedar, 4 x 4 post, 4' spacing, 3' high	27	11.70	38.70
2600	4 x 4 post with deadman, 2' spacing, 4' high	55	21	76
2800	6 x 6 post, 4' spacing, 4' high	55	20	75
3000	3' spacing, 5' high	79	29	108
3200	2' spacing, 6' high	125	46.50	171.50
3400	6 x 6 post with deadman, 3' spacing, 6' high	97.50	36	133.50
3600	8 x 8 post with deadman, 2' spacing, 8' high	245	89.50	334.50
3800	Pressure treated, 4 x 4 post, 4' spacing, 3' high	10.15	21.50	31.65
4000	3' spacing, 4' high	15.55	31	46.55
4200	4 x 4 post with deadman, 2' spacing, 5' high	34	41.50	75.50
4400	6 x 6 post, 3' spacing, 6' high	77	71.50	148.50
4600	2' spacing, 7' high	52.50	70.50	123
4800	6 x 6 post with deadman, 3' spacing, 8' high	55.50	68	123.50
5000	8 x 8 post with deadman, 2' spacing, 10' high	147	157	304
5200	Creosoted, 4 x 4 post, 4' spacing, 3' high	10.15	21.50	31.65
5400	3' spacing, 4' high	15.55	31	46.55
5600	4 x 4 post with deadman, 2' spacing, 5' high	34	41.50	75.50
5800	6 x 6 post, 3' spacing, 6' high	35.50	52.50	88
6000	2' spacing, 7' high	52.50	70.50	123
6200	6 x 6 post with deadman, 3' spacing 8' high	55.50	68	123.50
6400	8 x 8 post with deadman, 2' spacing, 10' high	147	157	304

641

A Wood Tie Retaining Wall System is constructed of one of four types of lumber: redwood, cedar, creosoted wood or pressure-treated lumber. The system includes all the elements that must go into a wall that resists lateral pressure. System elements include: wood ties; threaded rod (1/2" diameter); underdrain; and deadman where required.

The Expanded System Listing shows a wide variety of wall configurations with each type of lumber. The spacing of the deadman in the wall is indicated for each wall system. Wall heights vary from 2' to 8'.

System Components	QUANTITY	UNIT	COST PER L.F.		
			MAT.	INST.	TOTAL
SYSTEM G2040 250 1000					
WOOD TIE WALL, ROD CONNECTOR AT 4'-0", REDWOOD, 6" X 6", 2'-0" HIGH					
Redwood post columns and girts, 6" x 6"	12.000	B.F.	108.60	21.30	129.90
Accessories, hangers, coil threaded rods, continuous, 1/2" diam.	.050	L.F.	.75		.75
Pipe bedding, crushed or screened bank run gravel	1.000	L.F.	1.54	.71	2.25
Pipe, subdrainage, corrugated plastic, 4" diameter	1.000	L.F.	.55	.77	1.32
TOTAL			111.44	22.78	134.22

G2040 250	Wood Tie Retaining Walls	COST PER L.F.		
		MAT.	INST.	TOTAL
1000	Wood tie wall, rod connector at 4'-0", redwood, 6" x 6", 2'-0" high	111	22.50	133.50
1400	Deadman at 6'-0", 4'-0" high	258	52	310
1600	6'-0" high	385	77.50	462.50
2000	8 x 8, deadman at 6'-0", 4'-0" high	385	66.50	451.50
2200	6'-0" high	585	100	685
2400	8'-0" high	770	133	903
3000	Cedar, 6 x 6, 2'-0" high	58	22.50	80.50
3400	Deadman at 6'-0", 4'-0" high	133	52	185
3600	6'-0" high	200	77.50	277.50
4000	8 x 8, deadman at 6'-0", 4'-0" high	165	66.50	231.50
4200	6'-0" high	249	100	349
4400	8'-0" high	330	133	463
7000	Pressure treated wood, 6 x 6, 2'-0" high	21	18.90	39.90
7400	Deadman at 6'-0", 4'-0" high	47.50	43	90.50
7600	6'-0" high	70.50	64	134.50
8000	8 x 8, deadman at 6'-0", 4'-0" high	76	77.50	153.50
8200	6'-0" high	114	116	230
8400	8'-0" high	151	154	305

G2040 Site Development

The Stone Retaining Wall System is constructed of one of four types of stone. Each of the four types is listed in terms of cost per ton. Construction is either dry set or mortar set. System elements include excavation; concrete base; crushed stone; underdrain; and backfill.

The Expanded System Listing shows six heights above grade for each type, ranging from 3' above grade to 12' above grade.

System Components	QUANTITY	UNIT	COST PER L.F.		
			MAT.	INST.	TOTAL
SYSTEM G2040 260 2400					
STONE RETAINING WALL, DRY SET, STONE AT $250/TON, 3' ABOVE GRADE					
Excavation, trench, hyd backhoe	.880	C.Y.		6.65	6.65
Strip footing, 36" x 12", reinforced	.111	C.Y.	16.21	14.38	30.59
Stone, wall material, type 1	6.550	C.F.	53.82		53.82
Setting stone wall, dry	6.550	C.F.		67.47	67.47
Stone borrow, delivered, 3/8", machine spread	.320	C.Y.	9.76	2.60	12.36
Piping, subdrainage, perforated PVC, 4" diameter	1.000	L.F.	1.60	4.14	5.74
Backfill with dozer, trench, up to 300' haul, no compaction	1.019	C.Y.		2.68	2.68
TOTAL			81.39	97.92	179.31

G2040 260	Stone Retaining Walls	COST PER L.F.		
		MAT.	INST.	TOTAL
2400	Stone retaining wall, dry set, stone at $250/ton, height above grade 3'	81.50	98	179.50
2420	Height above grade 4'	98	116	214
2440	Height above grade 6'	129	156	285
2460	Height above grade 8'	182	243	425
2480	Height above grade 10'	235	315	550
2500	Height above grade 12'	291	400	691
2600	$350/ton stone, height above grade 3'	103	98	201
2620	Height above grade 4'	126	116	242
2640	Height above grade 6'	170	156	326
2660	Height above grade 8'	242	243	485
2680	Height above grade 10'	315	315	630
2700	Height above grade 12'	395	400	795
2800	$450/ton stone, height above grade 3'	125	98	223
2820	Height above grade 4'	155	116	271
2840	Height above grade 6'	211	156	367
2860	Height above grade 8'	305	243	548
2880	Height above grade 10'	400	315	715
2900	Height above grade 12'	505	400	905
3000	$650/ton stone, height above grade 3'	168	98	266
3020	Height above grade 4'	211	116	327
3040	Height above grade 6'	292	156	448
3060	Height above grade 8'	425	243	668
3080	Height above grade 10'	565	315	880
3100	Height above grade 12'	710	400	1,110
5020	Mortar set, stone at $250/ton, height above grade 3'	81.50	86.50	168
5040	Height above grade 4'	98	102	200

For customer support on your Site Work & Landscape Cost Data, call 877.737.1594.

G2040 Site Development

G2040 260	Stone Retaining Walls	COST PER L.F.		
		MAT.	INST.	TOTAL
5060	Height above grade 6'	129	135	264
5080	Height above grade 8'	182	208	390
5100	Height above grade 10'	235	271	506
5120	Height above grade 12'	291	340	631
5300	$350/ton stone, height above grade 3'	103	86.50	189.50
5320	Height above grade 4'	126	102	228
5340	Height above grade 6'	170	135	305
5360	Height above grade 8'	242	208	450
5380	Height above grade 10'	315	271	586
5400	Height above grade 12'	395	340	735
5500	$450/ton stone, height above grade 3'	125	86.50	211.50
5520	Height above grade 4'	155	102	257
5540	Height above grade 6'	211	135	346
5560	Height above grade 8'	305	208	513
5580	Height above grade 10'	400	271	671
5600	Height above grade 12'	505	340	845
5700	$650/ton stone, height above grade 3'	168	86.50	254.50
5720	Height above grade 4'	211	102	313
5740	Height above grade 6'	292	135	427
5760	Height above grade 8'	425	208	633
5780	Height above grade 10'	565	271	836
5800	Height above grade 12'	710	340	1,050

G2040 Site Development

The Gabion Retaining Wall Systems list three types of surcharge conditions: level, sloped and highway, for two different facing configurations: stepped and straight with batter. Costs are expressed per L.F. for heights ranging from 6' to 18' for retaining sandy or clay soil. For protection against sloughing in wet clay materials, counterforts have been added for these systems. Drainage stone has been added behind the walls to avoid any additional lateral pressures.

System Components	QUANTITY	UNIT	COST PER L.F.		
			MAT.	INST.	TOTAL
SYSTEM G2040 270 1000					
GABION RET. WALL, LEVEL BACKFILL, STEPPED FACE, 4' BASE, 6' HIGH					
3' x 3' cross section gabion	2.000	Ea.	91.11	160	251.11
3' x 1' cross section gabion	1.000	Ea.	24.22	9.63	33.85
Crushed stone drainage	.220	C.Y.	6.50	2.04	8.54
TOTAL			121.83	171.67	293.50

G2040 270	Gabion Retaining Walls	COST PER L.F.		
		MAT.	INST.	TOTAL
1000	Gabion ret. wall, level backfill, stepped face, 4' base, 6' high, sandy soi	122	172	294
1040	Clay soil with counterforts @ 16' O.C.	184	350	534
1100	5' base, 9' high, sandy soil	218	272	490
1140	Clay soil with counterforts @ 16' O.C.	370	545	915
1200	6' base, 12' high, sandy soil	315	435	750
1240	Clay soil with counterforts @ 16' O.C.	560	1,150	1,710
1300	7'-6" base, 15' high, sandy soil	445	605	1,050
1340	Clay soil with counterforts @ 16' O.C.	1,075	1,600	2,675
1400	9' base, 18' high, sandy soil	585	850	1,435
1440	Clay soil with counterforts @ 16' O.C.	1,200	1,950	3,150
2000	Straight face w/1:6 batter, 3' base, 6' high, sandy soil	104	165	269
2040	Clay soil with counterforts @ 16' O.C.	166	345	511
2100	4'-6" base, 9' high, sandy soil	181	268	449
2140	Clay soil with counterforts @ 16' O.C.	335	540	875
2200	6' base, 12' high, sandy soil	277	430	707
2240	Clay soil with counterforts @ 16' O.C.	525	1,150	1,675
2300	7'-6" base, 15' high, sandy soil	400	615	1,015
2340	Clay soil with counterforts @ 16' O.C.	825	1,275	2,100
2400	18' high, sandy soil	520	795	1,315
2440	Clay soil with counterforts @ 16' O.C.	845	930	1,775
3000	Backfill sloped 1-1/2:1, stepped face, 4'-6" base, 6' high, sandy soil	124	185	309
3040	Clay soil with counterforts @ 16' O.C.	185	365	550
3100	6' base, 9' high, sandy soil	217	345	562
3140	Clay soil with counterforts @ 16' O.C.	370	615	985
3200	7'-6" base, 12' high, sandy soil	340	525	865
3240	Clay soil with counterforts @ 16' O.C.	585	1,250	1,835
3300	9' base, 15' high, sandy soil	475	765	1,240
3340	Clay soil with counterforts @ 16' O.C.	1,100	1,775	2,875
3400	10'-6" base, 18' high, sandy soil	645	1,025	1,670
3440	Clay soil with counterforts @ 16' O.C.	1,250	2,125	3,375
4000	Straight face with 1:6 batter, 4'-6" base, 6' high, sandy soil	130	186	316
4040	Clay soil with counterforts @ 16' O.C.	192	365	557
4100	6' base, 9' high, sandy soil	226	350	576
4140	Clay soil with counterforts @ 16' O.C.	380	620	1,000

645

G2040 Site Development

G2040 270	Gabion Retaining Walls	COST PER L.F.		
		MAT.	INST.	TOTAL
4200	7'-6" base, 12' high, sandy soil	350	535	885
4240	Clay soil with counterforts @ 16' O.C.	595	1,275	1,870
4300	9' base, 15' high, sandy soil	490	775	1,265
4340	Clay soil with counterforts @ 16' O.C.	1,125	1,800	2,925
4400	18' high, sandy soil	630	1,025	1,655
4440	Clay soil with counterforts @ 16' O.C.	1,250	2,100	3,350
5000	Highway surcharge, straight face, 6' base, 6' high, sandy soil	189	325	514
5040	Clay soil with counterforts @ 16' O.C.	251	505	756
5100	9' base, 9' high, sandy soil	330	560	890
5140	Clay soil with counterforts @ 16' O.C.	480	830	1,310
5200	12' high, sandy soil	585	840	1,425
5240	Clay soil with counterforts @ 16' O.C.	910	2,100	3,010
5300	12' base, 15' high, sandy soil	655	1,125	1,780
5340	Clay soil with counterforts @ 16' O.C.	1,075	1,775	2,850
5400	18' high, sandy soil	840	1,450	2,290
5440	Clay soil with counterforts @ 16' O.C.	1,450	2,525	3,975

G2040 Site Development

Wood Deck Systems are either constructed of pressure treated lumber or redwood lumber. The system includes: the deck, joists (16″ or 24″ on-center), girders, posts (8′ on-center) and railings. Decking is constructed of either 1″ x 4″ or 2″ x 6″ stock. Joists range from 2″ x 8″ to 2″ x 10″ depending on the size of the system. The size ranges hold true for both pressure treated lumber and redwood systems.

Costs are on a square foot basis.

System Components	QUANTITY	UNIT	COST PER S.F. MAT.	COST PER S.F. INST.	COST PER S.F. TOTAL
SYSTEM G2040 910 1000					
WOOD DECK, TREATED LUMBER, 2″ X 8″ JOISTS @ 16″ O.C., 2″ X 6″ DECKING					
Decking, planks, fir 2″ x 6″ treated	2.080	B.F.	1.76	4.78	6.54
Framing, joists, fir 2″ x 8″ treated	1.330	B.F.	1.14	2.56	3.70
Framing, beams, fir 2″ x 10″ treated	.133	B.F.	.12	.23	.35
Framing, post, 4″ x 4″, treated	.333	B.F.	.35	.64	.99
Framing, railing, 2″ x 4″ lumber, treated	.667	B.F.	.56	2.14	2.70
Excavating pits by hand, heavy soil or clay	.002	C.Y.		.35	.35
Spread footing, concrete	.002	C.Y.	.37	.55	.92
TOTAL			4.30	11.25	15.55

G2040 910	Wood Decks	COST PER S.F. MAT.	COST PER S.F. INST.	COST PER S.F. TOTAL
1000	Wood deck, treated lumber, 2″ x 8″ joists @ 16″ O.C., 2″ x 6″ decking	4.30	11.25	15.55
1004	2″ x 4″ decking	4.45	13.85	18.30
1008	1″ x 6″ decking	5.70	8.95	14.65
1012	1″ x 4″ decking	5.45	8.75	14.20
1500	2″ x 10″ joists @ 16″ O.C., 2″ x 6″ decking	4.59	11.90	16.49
1504	2″ x 4″ decking	4.74	14.50	19.24
1508	1″ x 6″ decking	6	9.60	15.60
1512	1″ x 4″ decking	5.70	9.40	15.10
1560	2″ x 10″ joists @ 24″ O.C., 2″ x 6″ decking	4.30	11.25	15.55
1564	2″ x 4″ decking	4.45	13.85	18.30
1568	1″ x 6″ decking	5.70	8.95	14.65
1572	1″ x 4″ decking	5.45	8.75	14.20
4000	Redwood lumber, 2″ x 8″ joists @ 16″ O.C., 2″ x 6″ decking	9.50	5.15	14.65
4004	2″ x 4″ decking	9.75	5.30	15.05
4008	1″ x 6″ decking	13.60	6.65	20.25
4012	1″ x 4″ decking	13.45	6.55	20
4500	2″ x 10″ joists @ 16″ O.C., 2″ x 6″ decking	13.85	5.65	19.50
4504	2″ x 4″ decking	14.90	6	20.90
4508	1″ x 6″ decking	14.90	6.95	21.85
4512	1″ x 4″ decking	14.75	6.85	21.60
4600	2″ x 10″ joists @ 24″ O.C., 2″ x 6″ decking	12.60	5.40	18
4612	2″ x 4″ decking	13.65	5.75	19.40
4616	1″ x 6″ decking	13.60	6.65	20.25
4620	1″ x 4″ decking	13.45	6.55	20

647

G2040 Site Development

- Chain Link Fence
- Concrete Sidewalk
- Pool Equipment (Building not included in price)
- 12' x 30' Swimming Pool
- Fence Gate

The Swimming Pool System is a complete package. Everything from excavation to deck hardware is included in system costs. Below are three basic types of pool systems: residential, motel, and municipal. Systems elements include: excavation, pool materials, installation, deck hardware, pumps and filters, sidewalk, and fencing.

The Expanded System Listing shows three basic types of pools with a variety of finishes and basic materials. These systems are either vinyl lined with metal sides; gunite shell with a cement plaster finish or tile finish; or concrete sided with vinyl lining. Pool sizes listed here vary from 12' x 30' to 60' x 82.5'. All costs are on a per unit basis.

System Components	QUANTITY	UNIT	COST EACH MAT.	COST EACH INST.	COST EACH TOTAL
SYSTEM G2040 920 1000					
SWIMMING POOL, RESIDENTIAL, CONC. SIDES, VINYL LINED, 12' X 30'					
Swimming pools,resi in-ground,vyl lined,conc sides,W/ equip,sand bot	360.000	S.F.	9,180	5,266.80	14,446.80
4" thick reinforced concrete sidewalk, broom finish, no base	400.000	S.F.	744	1,048	1,792
Chain link fence, residential, 3' high	124.000	L.F.	288.92	416.64	705.56
Fence gate, chain link	1.000	Ea.	89.50	140.50	230
TOTAL			10,302.42	6,871.94	17,174.36

G2040 920	Swimming Pools	COST EACH MAT.	COST EACH INST.	COST EACH TOTAL
1000	Swimming pool, residential class, concrete sides, vinyl lined, 12' x 30'	10,300	6,875	17,175
1100	16' x 32'	11,700	7,775	19,475
1200	20' x 40'	15,100	9,925	25,025
1500	Tile finish, 12' x 30'	23,800	28,800	52,600
1600	16' x 32'	24,300	30,400	54,700
1700	20' x 40'	36,400	43,000	79,400
2000	Metal sides, vinyl lined, 12' x 30'	8,850	4,525	13,375
2100	16' x 32'	10,100	5,100	15,200
2200	20' x 40'	13,000	6,450	19,450
3000	Gunite shell, cement plaster finish, 12' x 30'	18,400	12,600	31,000
3100	16' x 32'	23,300	16,300	39,600
3200	20' x 40'	32,300	16,100	48,400
4000	Motel class, concrete sides, vinyl lined, 20' x 40'	21,900	13,800	35,700
4100	28' x 60'	30,700	19,300	50,000
4500	Tile finish, 20' x 40'	42,800	49,800	92,600
4600	28' x 60'	68,500	80,500	149,000
5000	Metal sides, vinyl lined, 20' x 40'	23,000	10,200	33,200
5100	28' x 60'	30,800	13,800	44,600
6000	Gunite shell, cement plaster finish, 20' x 40'	60,500	40,300	100,800
6100	28' x 60'	90,500	60,000	150,500
7000	Municipal class, gunite shell, cement plaster finish, 42' x 75'	242,000	142,500	384,500
7100	60' x 82.5'	311,000	182,500	493,500
7500	Concrete walls, tile finish, 42' x 75'	274,000	189,000	463,000
7600	60' x 82.5'	357,500	250,000	607,500
7700	Tile finish and concrete gutter, 42' x 75'	300,500	189,000	489,500
7800	60' x 82.5'	389,500	250,000	639,500
7900	Tile finish and stainless gutter, 42' x 75'	351,500	189,000	540,500
8000	60' x 82.5'	520,000	289,500	809,500

Building

Service Driveway

Landscaping

Sidewalk

Parking

Entrance Slab

Hidden Features
Utilities and Lighting
(Features do not represent actual sizes)

G2040 990	Site Development Components for Buildings	COST EACH		
		MAT.	INST.	TOTAL
0970	Assume minimal and balanced cut & fill, no rock, no demolition, no haz mat. Lin			
0980	60,000 SF 2-Story Office Bldg on 3.3 Acres w/20% Green Space			
1000	Site Preparation	635	48,300	48,935
1002	Utilities	88,000	104,500	192,500
1004	Pavement	322,500	197,500	520,000
1006	Stormwater Management	283,500	59,500	343,000
1008	Sidewalks	14,300	18,900	33,200
1010	Exterior lighting	48,300	38,700	87,000
1014	Landscaping	73,500	51,500	125,000
1028	80,000 SF 4-Story Office Bldg on 3.5 Acres w/20% Green Space			
1030	Site preparation	650	52,000	52,650
1032	Utilities	82,000	95,000	177,000
1034	Pavement	387,000	237,000	624,000
1036	Stormwater Managmement	298,500	62,500	361,000
1038	Sidewalks	11,700	15,400	27,100
1040	Lighting	47,900	40,800	88,700
1042	Landscaping	76,000	53,500	129,500
1058	16,000 SF 1-Story Medical Office Bldg on 1.7 Acres w/25% Green Space			
1060	Site preparation	455	37,000	37,455
1062	Utilities	63,500	76,500	140,000
1064	Pavement	150,000	93,000	243,000
1066	Stormwater Management	138,000	29,100	167,100
1068	Sidewalks	10,400	13,800	24,200
1070	Lighting	29,700	22,400	52,100
1072	Landscaping	49,800	31,600	81,400
1098	36,000 SF 3-Story Apartment Bldg on 1.6 Acres w/25% Green Space			
1100	Site preparation	440	36,500	36,940
1102	Utilities	59,500	70,000	129,500

649

G2040 Site Development

G2040 990	Site Development Components for Buildings	COST EACH		
		MAT.	INST.	TOTAL
1104	Pavement	151,500	93,500	245,000
1106	Stormwater Management	128,500	27,100	155,600
1108	Sidewalks	9,025	12,000	21,025
1110	Lighting	27,700	21,300	49,000
1112	Landscaping	47,600	30,000	77,600
1128	130,000 SF 3-Story Hospital Bldg on 5.9 Acres w/17% Green Space			
1130	Site preparation	850	68,500	69,350
1132	Utilities	117,000	137,000	254,000
1134	Pavement	659,500	402,000	1,061,500
1136	Stormwater Management	530,000	111,500	641,500
1138	Sidewalks	17,200	22,600	39,800
1140	Lighting	79,000	68,500	147,500
1142	Landscaping	106,000	81,500	187,500
1158	60,000 SF 1-Story Light Manufacturing Bldg on 3.9 Acres w/18% Green Space			
1160	Site preparation	695	51,500	52,195
1162	Utilities	104,000	130,000	234,000
1164	Pavement	308,000	171,000	479,000
1166	Stormwater Management	349,000	73,500	422,500
1168	Sidewalks	20,200	26,700	46,900
1170	Lighting	58,500	44,200	102,700
1172	Landscaping	80,000	57,500	137,500
1198	8,000 SF 1-Story Restaurant Bldg on 1.4 Acres w/26% Green Space			
1200	Site preparation	415	35,700	36,115
1202	Utilities	54,000	61,000	115,000
1204	Pavement	144,000	90,000	234,000
1206	Stormwater Management	113,500	23,900	137,400
1208	Sidewalks	7,375	9,725	17,100
1210	Lighting	24,700	19,700	44,400
1212	Landscaping	44,700	27,600	72,300
1228	20,000 SF 1-Story Retail Store Bldg on 2.1 Acres w/23% Green Space			
1230	Site preparation	510	42,800	43,310
1232	Utilities	70,500	85,000	155,500
1234	Pavement	195,000	120,500	315,500
1236	Stormwater Management	177,000	37,300	214,300
1238	Sidewalks	11,700	15,400	27,100
1240	Lighting	34,000	26,000	60,000
1242	Landscaping	57,000	37,200	94,200
1258	60,000 SF 1-Story Warehouse on 3.1 Acres w/19% Green Space			
1260	Site preparation	615	47,600	48,215
1262	Utilities	93,500	122,000	215,500
1264	Pavement	186,000	96,500	282,500
1266	Stormwater Management	272,000	57,500	329,500
1268	Sidewalks	20,200	26,700	46,900
1270	Lighting	49,200	34,400	83,600
1272	Landscaping	68,500	47,600	116,100

G2050 Landscaping

The Lawn Systems listed include different types of seeding, sodding and ground covers for flat and sloped areas. Costs are given per thousand square feet for different size jobs; residential, small commercial and large commercial. The size of the job relates to the type and productivity of the equipment being used. Components include furnishing and spreading screened loam, spreading fertilizer and limestone and mulching planted and seeded surfaces. Sloped surfaces include jute mesh or staking depending on the type of cover.

System Components	QUANTITY	UNIT	COST PER M.S.F.		
			MAT.	INST.	TOTAL
SYSTEM G2050 410 1000					
LAWN, FLAT AREA, SEEDED, TURF MIX, RESIDENTIAL					
Scarify subsoil, residential, skid steer loader w/scarifiers, 50 HP	1.000	M.S.F.		27.50	27.50
Root raking and loading, residential, no boulders	1.000	M.S.F.		36	36
Spread topsoil, skid steer loader and hand dress	18.500	C.Y.	499.50	116.74	616.24
Spread ground limestone, push spreader	110.000	S.Y.	13.20	3.30	16.50
Spread fertilizer, push spreader	110.000	S.Y.	14.30	3.30	17.60
Till topsoil, 26" rototiller	110.000	S.Y.		56.10	56.10
By hand (raking)	1.000	M.S.F.		31	31
Rolling topsoil, hand push roller	18.500	C.Y.		2.59	2.59
Seeding, turf mix, push spreader	1.000	M.S.F.	12.40	58	70.40
Straw, mulch	110.000	S.Y.	72.60	106.70	179.30
TOTAL			612	441.23	1,053.23

G2050 410	Lawns & Ground Cover	COST PER M.S.F.		
		MAT.	INST.	TOTAL
1000	Lawn, flat area, seeded, turf mix, residential	610	440	1,050
1040	Small commercial	615	510	1,125
1080	Large commercial	630	420	1,050
1200	Shade mix, residential	610	440	1,050
1240	Small commercial	615	510	1,125
1280	Large commercial	625	420	1,045
1400	Utility mix, residential	610	440	1,050
1440	Small commercial	610	510	1,120
1480	Large commercial	640	420	1,060
2000	Sod, bluegrass, residential	850	470	1,320
2040	Small commercial	805	635	1,440
2080	Large commercial	795	510	1,305
2200	Bentgrass, residential	840	465	1,305
2240	Small commercial	815	630	1,445
2280	Large commercial	805	525	1,330
2400	Ground cover, English ivy, residential	2,325	1,150	3,475
2440	Small commercial	2,350	1,375	3,725
2480	Large commercial	2,350	1,275	3,625
2600	Pachysandra, residential	3,500	6,025	9,525
2640	Small commercial	3,500	6,225	9,725
2680	Large commercial	3,500	6,125	9,625
2800	Vinca minor, residential	2,725	1,800	4,525

G2050 Landscaping

G2050 410	Lawns & Ground Cover	COST PER M.S.F.		
		MAT.	INST.	TOTAL
2840	Small commercial	2,725	2,000	4,725
2880	Large commercial	2,725	1,900	4,625
3000	Sloped areas, seeded, slope mix, residential	805	580	1,385
3040	Small commercial	810	610	1,420
3080	Large commercial	825	605	1,430
3200	Birdsfoot trefoil, residential	800	585	1,385
3240	Small commercial	800	610	1,410
3280	Large commercial	805	605	1,410
3400	Clover, residential	795	580	1,375
3440	Small commercial	800	610	1,410
3480	Large commercial	810	605	1,415
3600	Crown vetch, residential	920	580	1,500
3640	Small commercial	920	610	1,530
3680	Large commercial	955	605	1,560
3800	Wildflower, residential	795	580	1,375
3840	Small commercial	795	610	1,405
3880	Large commercial	805	605	1,410
4600	Sod, bluegrass, residential	905	970	1,875
4640	Small commercial	860	1,025	1,885
4680	Large commercial	850	930	1,780
4800	Bent grass, residential	895	530	1,425
4840	Small commercial	870	695	1,565
4880	Large commercial	860	675	1,535
5000	Ground cover, English ivy, residential	2,500	1,275	3,775
5040	Small commercial	2,525	1,475	4,000
5080	Large commercial	2,525	1,450	3,975
5200	Pachysandra, residential	3,800	6,625	10,425
5240	Small commercial	3,800	6,850	10,650
5280	Large commercial	3,800	6,800	10,600
5400	Vinca minor, residential	2,925	2,000	4,925
5440	Small commercial	2,525	2,175	4,700
5480	Large commercial	2,950	2,150	5,100

G2050 Landscaping

There are three basic types of Site Irrigation Systems: pop-up, riser mounted and quick coupling. Sprinkler heads are spray, impact or gear driven. Each system includes: the hardware for spraying the water; the pipe and fittings needed to deliver the water; and all other accessory equipment such as valves, couplings, nipples, and nozzles. Excavation heads and backfill costs are also included in the system.

The Expanded System Listing shows a wide variety of Site Irrigation Systems.

System Components	QUANTITY	UNIT	COST PER S.F.		
			MAT.	INST.	TOTAL
SYSTEM G2050 710 1000					
SITE IRRIGATION, POP UP SPRAY, PLASTIC, 10' RADIUS, 1000 S.F., PVC PIPE					
Excavation, chain trencher	54.000	L.F.		44.82	44.82
Pipe, fittings & nipples, PVC Schedule 40, 1" diameter	5.000	Ea.	4.25	112.50	116.75
Fittings, bends or elbows, 4" diameter	5.000	Ea.	54	250	304
Couplings PVC plastic, high pressure, 1" diameter	5.000	Ea.	4.25	142.50	146.75
Valves, bronze, globe, 125 lb. rising stem, threaded, 1" diameter	1.000	Ea.	169	37.50	206.50
Head & nozzle, pop-up spray, PVC plastic	5.000	Ea.	17	100	117
Backfill by hand with compaction	54.000	L.F.		35.64	35.64
Total cost per 1,000 S.F.			248.50	722.96	971.46
Total cost per S.F.			.25	.72	.97

G2050 710	Site Irrigation	COST PER S.F.		
		MAT.	INST.	TOTAL
1000	Site irrigation, pop up spray, 10' radius, 1000 S.F., PVC pipe	.25	.73	.98
1100	Polyethylene pipe	.28	.62	.90
1200	14' radius, 8000 S.F., PVC pipe	.09	.31	.40
1300	Polyethylene pipe	.09	.29	.38
1400	18' square, 1000 S.F. PVC pipe	.24	.49	.73
1500	Polyethylene pipe	.25	.42	.67
1600	24' square, 8000 S.F., PVC pipe	.07	.20	.27
1700	Polyethylene pipe	.07	.19	.26
1800	4' x 30' strip, 200 S.F., PVC pipe	1.15	2.04	3.19
1900	Polyethylene pipe	1.17	1.89	3.06
2000	6' x 40' strip, 800 S.F., PVC pipe	.31	.67	.98
2200	Economy brass, 11' radius, 1000 S.F., PVC pipe	.31	.68	.99
2300	Polyethylene pipe	.32	.62	.94
2400	14' radius, 8000 S.F., PVC pipe	.11	.31	.42
2500	Polyethylene pipe	.11	.29	.40
2600	3' x 28' strip, 200 S.F., PVC pipe	1.28	2.04	3.32
2700	Polyethylene pipe	1.30	1.89	3.19
2800	7' x 36' strip, 1000 S.F., PVC pipe	.28	.54	.82
2900	Polyethylene pipe	.28	.49	.77
3000	Hd brass, 11' radius, 1000 S.F., PVC pipe	.35	.68	1.03
3100	Polyethylene pipe	.36	.62	.98
3200	14' radius, 8000 S.F., PVC pipe	.13	.31	.44
3300	Polyethylene pipe	.13	.29	.42
3400	Riser mounted spray, plastic,10'radius, 1000 S.F., PVC pipe	.27	.68	.95
3500	Polyethylene pipe	.28	.62	.90
3600	12' radius, 5000 S.F., PVC pipe	.13	.41	.54

G2050 710	Site Irrigation	COST PER S.F.		
		MAT.	INST.	TOTAL
3700	Polyethylene pipe	.13	.38	.51
3800	19' square, 2000 S.F., PVC pipe	.12	.22	.34
3900	Polyethylene pipe	.12	.20	.32
4000	24' square, 8000 S.F., PVC pipe	.07	.20	.27
4100	Polyethylene pipe	.07	.19	.26
4200	5' x 32' strip, 300 S.F., PVC pipe	.76	1.38	2.14
4300	Polyethylene pipe	.77	1.28	2.05
4400	6' x 40' strip, 800 S.F., PVC pipe	.31	.67	.98
4500	Polyethylene pipe	.32	.61	.93
4600	Brass, 11' radius, 1000 S.F., PVC pipe	.31	.68	.99
4700	Polyethylene pipe	.32	.62	.94
4800	14' radius, 8000 S.F., PVC pipe	.11	.31	.42
4900	Polythylene pipe	.11	.29	.40
5000	Pop up gear drive stream type, plastic, 30' radius, 10,000 S.F., PVC pipe	.28	.60	.88
5020	Polyethylene pipe	.12	.17	.29
5040	40,000 S.F., PVC pipe	.25	.61	.86
5060	Polyethylene pipe	.09	.18	.27
5080	Riser mounted gear drive stream type, plas., 30' rad., 10,000 S.F., PVC pipe	.27	.60	.87
5100	Polyethylene pipe	.11	.17	.28
5120	40,000 S.F., PVC pipe	.25	.61	.86
5140	Polyethylene pipe	.09	.18	.27
5200	Q.C. valve thread type w/impact head, brass, 75' rad, 20,000 S.F., PVC pipe	.12	.23	.35
5250	Polyethylene pipe	.05	.05	.10
5300	100,000 S.F., PVC pipe	.17	.37	.54
5350	Polyethylene pipe	.07	.08	.15
5400	Q.C. valve lug type w/impact head, brass, 75' rad, 20,000 S.F., PVC pipe	.12	.23	.35
5450	Polyethylene pipe	.05	.05	.10
5500	100,000 S.F. PVC pipe	.17	.37	.54
5550	Polyethylene pipe	.07	.08	.15
6000	Site irrigation, pop up impact type, plastic, 40' rad., 10,000 S.F., PVC pipe	.18	.38	.56
6100	Polyethylene pipe	.07	.10	.17
6200	45,000 S.F., PVC pipe	.17	.43	.60
6300	Polyethylene pipe	.06	.11	.17
6400	High medium volume brass, 40' radius, 10,000 S.F., PVC pipe	.19	.38	.57
6500	Polyethylene pipe	.08	.10	.18
6600	45,000 S.F. PVC pipe	.17	.43	.60
6700	Polyethylene pipe	.06	.11	.17
6800	High volume brass, 60' radius, 25,000 S.F., PVC pipe	.14	.30	.44
6900	Polyethylene pipe	.06	.08	.14
7000	100,000 S.F., PVC pipe	.14	.30	.44
7100	Polyethylene pipe	.06	.07	.13
7200	Riser mounted part/full impact type, plas., 40' rad., 10,000 S.F., PVC pipe	.17	.38	.55
7300	Polyethylene pipe	.07	.20	.27
7400	45,000 S.F., PVC pipe	.16	.43	.59
7500	Polyethylene pipe	.05	.11	.16
7600	Low medium volume brass, 40' radius, 10,000 S.F., PVC pipe	.18	.38	.56
7700	Polyethylene pipe	.07	.10	.17
7800	45,000 S.F., PVC pipe	.17	.43	.60
7900	Polyethylene pipe	.06	.11	.17
8000	Medium volume brass, 50' radius, 30,000 S.F., PVC pipe	.15	.32	.47
8100	Polyethylene pipe	.06	.08	.14
8200	70,000 S.F., PVC pipe	.21	.52	.73
8300	Polyethylene pipe	.06	.12	.18
8400	Riser mounted full only impact type, plas., 40' rad., 10,000 S.F., PVC pipe	.17	.38	.55
8500	Polyethylene pipe	.06	.10	.16
8600	45,000 S.F., PVC pipe	.16	.43	.59
8700	Polyethylene pipe	.05	.11	.16
8800	Low medium volume brass, 40' radius, 10,000 S.F., PVC pipe	.18	.38	.56

G20 Site Improvements

G2050 Landscaping

G2050 710	Site Irrigation	COST PER S.F.		
		MAT.	INST.	TOTAL
8900	Polyethylene pipe	.07	.10	.17
9000	45,000 S.F., PVC pipe	.17	.43	.60
9100	Polyethylene pipe	.06	.11	.17
9200	High volume brass, 80' radius, 75,000 S.F., PVC pipe	.10	.22	.32
9300	Polyethylene pipe	.01	.02	.03
9400	150,000 S.F., PVC pipe	.10	.20	.30
9500	Polyethylene pipe	.01	.02	.03
9600	Very high volume brass, 100' radius, 100,000 S.F., PVC pipe	.09	.17	.26
9700	Polyethylene pipe	.01	.02	.03
9800	200,000 S.F., PVC pipe	.09	.17	.26
9900	Polyethylene pipe	.01	.02	.03

G20 Site Improvements

G2050 Landscaping

Valve
Backflow Preventer
Pressure Regulator
Filter
Tubing Adapter
Drip Tubing

Drip irrigation systems can be for either lawns or individual plants. Shown below are drip irrigation systems for lawns. These drip type systems are most cost effective where there are water restrictions on use or the cost of water is very high. The supply uses PVC piping with the laterals polyethylene drip lines.

System Components	QUANTITY	UNIT	MAT.	INST.	TOTAL
SYSTEM G2050 720 1000					
SITE IRRIGATION, DRIP SYSTEM, 800 S.F. (20' X40')					
Excavate supply and header lines 4" x 18" deep	50.000	L.F.		44.50	44.50
Excavate drip lines 4" x 4" deep	5.000	L.F.		744.80	744.80
Install supply manifold (stop valve, strainer, PRV, adapters)	1.000	Ea.	24.50	150	174.50
Install 3/4" PVC supply line and risers to 4 " drip level	75.000	L.F.	24	150	174
Install 3/4" PVC fittings for supply line	33.000	Ea.	55.77	496.65	552.42
Install PVC to drip line adapters	14.000	Ea.	15.26	210.70	225.96
Install 1/4 inch drip lines with hose clamps	560.000	L.F.	123.20	280	403.20
Backfill trenches	3.180	C.Y.		133.56	133.56
Cleanup area when completed	1.000	Ea.		116	116
Total cost per 800 S.F.			242.73	2,326.21	2,568.94
Total cost per S.F.			.30	2.91	3.21

G2050 720	Site Irrigation	MAT.	INST.	TOTAL
1000	Site irrigation, drip lawn watering system, 800 S.F. (20' x 40' area)	.30	2.91	3.21
1100	1000 S.F. (20' x 50' area)	.27	2.63	2.90
1200	1600 S.F. (40' x 40' area), 2 zone	.30	2.77	3.07
1300	2000 S.F. (40' x 50' area), 2 zone	.27	2.54	2.81
1400	2400 S.F. (60' x 40' area), 3 zone	.29	2.76	3.05
1500	3000 S.F. (60' x 50' area), 3 zone	.27	2.48	2.75
1600	3200 S.F. (2 x 40' x 40'), 4 zone	.28	2.72	3
1700	4000 S.F. (2 x 40' x 50'), 4 zone	.27	2.49	2.76
1800	4800 S.F. (2 x 60' x 40'), 6 zone with control	.33	2.72	3.05
1900	6000 S.F. (2 x 60' x 50'), 6 zone with control	.28	2.46	2.74
2000	6400 S.F. (4 x 40' x 40'), 8 zone with control	.32	2.75	3.07
2100	8000 S.F. (4 x 40' x 50'), 8 zone with control	.29	2.50	2.79
2200	3200 S.F. (2 x 40' x 40'), 4 zone with control	.32	2.79	3.11
2300	4000 S.F. (2 x 40' x 50'), 4 zone with control	.29	2.54	2.83
2400	2400 S.F. (60' x 40'), 3 zone with control	.34	2.85	3.19
2500	3000 S.F. (60' x 50'), 3 zone with control	.30	2.55	2.85
2600	4800 S.F. (2 x 60' x 40'), 6 zone, manual	.29	2.69	2.98
2700	6000 S.F. (2 x 60' x 50'), 6 zone, manual	.26	2.42	2.68
2800	1000 S.F. (10' x 100' area)	.17	1.63	1.80
2900	2000 S.F. (2 x 10' x 100' area)	.17	1.58	1.75

656

For customer support on your Site Work & Landscape Cost Data, call 877.737.1594.

G2050 Landscaping

The Tree Pit Systems are listed for different heights of deciduous and evergreen trees, from 4' and above. Costs are given showing the pit size to accommodate the soil ball and the type of soil being excavated. In clay soils drainage tile has been included in addition to gravel drainage. Woven drainage fabric is applied before bark mulch is spread, assuming runoff is not harmful to roots.

System Components	QUANTITY	UNIT	COST EACH MAT.	COST EACH INST.	COST EACH TOTAL
SYSTEM G2050 910 1220					
TREE PIT, 5' TO 6' TREE, DECIDUOUS, 2' X 1-1/4' DEEP PIT, CLAY SOIL					
Heavy soil or clay	.262	C.Y.		30.39	30.39
Fill in pit, screened gravel, 3/4" to 1/2"	.050	C.Y.	1.10	2	3.10
Perforated PVC, schedule 40, 4" diameter	3.000	L.F.	4.80	31.89	36.69
Mix planting soil, by hand, incl. loam, peat & manure	.304	C.Y.	14.29	4.70	18.99
Prepared planting mix, by hand	.304	C.Y.		11.70	11.70
Fabric, laid in trench, polypropylene, ideal conditions	.500	S.Y.	.83	.20	1.03
Bark mulch, hand spread, 3"	.346	C.Y.	1.35	1.60	2.95
TOTAL			22.37	82.48	104.85

G2050 910	Tree Pits	COST EACH MAT.	COST EACH INST.	COST EACH TOTAL
1000	Tree pit, 4' to 5' tree, evergreen, 2-1/2' x 1-1/2' deep pit, sandy soil	43	70	113
1020	Clay soil	40	105	145
1200	5' to 6' tree, deciduous, 2' x 1-1/4' deep pit, sandy soil	23.50	35.50	59
1220	Clay soil	22.50	82.50	105
1300	Evergreen, 3' x 1-3/4' deep pit, sandy soil	70.50	106	176.50
1320	Clay soil	62.50	156	218.50
1360	3-1/2' x 1-3/4' deep pit, sandy soil	89.50	132	221.50
1380	Clay soil	78	181	259
1400	6' to 7' tree, evergreen, 4' x 1-3/4' deep pit, sandy soil	108	155	263
1420	Clay soil	94.50	208	302.50
1600	7' to 9' tree, deciduous, 2-1/2' x 1-1/2' deep pit, sandy soil	43	87.50	130.50
1620	Clay soil	40	105	145
1800	8' to 10' tree, deciduous, 3' x 1-3/4' deep pit, sandy soil	70.50	106	176.50
1820	Clay soil	62.50	156	218.50
1900	Evergreen, 4-1/2' x 2' deep pit, sandy soil, smaller ball	160	223	383
1910	Larger ball	155	218	373
1920	Clay soil, smaller ball	135	270	405
1930	Larger ball	131	265	396
2000	10' to 12' tree, deciduous, 3-1/2' x 1-3/4' deep pit, sandy soil	89.50	131	220.50
2020	Clay soil	78	181	259

G2050 Landscaping

G2050 910	Tree Pits	COST EACH		
		MAT.	INST.	TOTAL
2060	4' x 1-3/4' deep pit, sandy soil	113	162	275
2080	Clay soil	100	224	324
2100	Evergreen, 5' x 2-1/4' deep pit, sandy soil, smaller ball	213	294	507
2110	Larger ball	206	286	492
2120	Clay soil, smaller ball	175	335	510
2130	Larger ball	168	325	493
2200	12' to 14' tree, deciduous, 4-1/2' x 2' deep pit, sandy soil, smaller ball	160	223	383
2210	Larger ball	155	218	373
2220	Clay soil, smaller ball	135	270	405
2230	Larger ball	131	265	396
2400	13' to 15' tree, evergreen, 6' x 2-1/2' deep pit, sandy soil	305	420	725
2420	Clay soil	244	440	684
2600	14' to 16' tree, deciduous, 5' x 2-1/4' deep pit, sandy soil, smaller ball	213	294	507
2610	Larger ball	206	286	492
2620	Clay soil, smaller ball	175	335	510
2630	Larger ball	168	325	493
2800	16' to 18' tree, deciduous, 6' x 2-1/2' deep pit, sandy soil	305	420	725
2820	Clay soil	244	440	684
2900	Evergreen, 7' x 3' deep pit, sandy soil	510	695	1,205
2920	Clay soil	405	680	1,085
3000	Over 18' tree, deciduous, 7' x 3' deep pit, sandy soil	510	695	1,205
3020	Clay soil	405	680	1,085
3100	Evergreen, 8' x 3-1/4' deep pit, sandy soil	715	965	1,680
3120	Clay soil	570	920	1,490

G3010 Water Supply

The Water Service Systems are for copper service taps from 1″ to 2″ diameter into pressurized mains from 6″ to 8″ diameter. Costs are given for two offsets with depths varying from 2′ to 10′. Included in system components are excavation and backfill and required curb stops with boxes.

System Components	QUANTITY	UNIT	COST EACH		
			MAT.	INST.	TOTAL
SYSTEM G3010 121 1000					
WATER SERVICE, LEAD FREE, 6″ MAIN, 1″ COPPER SERVICE, 10′ OFFSET, 2′ DEEP					
Trench excavation, 1/2 C.Y. backhoe, 1 laborer	2.220	C.Y.		16.79	16.79
Drill & tap pressurized main, 6″, 1″ to 2″ service	1.000	Ea.		425	425
Corporation stop, 1″ diameter	1.000	Ea.	119	44.50	163.50
Saddles, 3/4″ & 1″ diameter, add	1.000	Ea.	84.50		84.50
Copper tubing, type K, 1″ diameter	12.000	L.F.	111	47.88	158.88
Piping, curb stops, no lead, 1″ diameter	1.000	Ea.	172	44.50	216.50
Curb box, cast iron, 1/2″ to 1″ curb stops	1.000	Ea.	56.50	59	115.50
Backfill by hand, no compaction, heavy soil	2.890	C.Y.		7.60	7.60
Compaction, vibrating plate	2.220	C.Y.		18.07	18.07
TOTAL			543	663.34	1,206.34

G3010 121	Water Service, Lead Free	COST EACH		
		MAT.	INST.	TOTAL
1000	Water service, Lead Free, 6″ main, 1″ copper service, 10′ offset, 2′ deep	545	665	1,210
1040	4′ deep	545	705	1,250
1060	6′ deep	425	850	1,275
1080	8′ deep	545	985	1,530
1100	10′ deep	545	1,075	1,620
1200	20′ offset, 2′ deep	545	705	1,250
1240	4′ deep	545	790	1,335
1260	6′ deep	425	1,125	1,550
1280	8′ deep	545	1,350	1,895
1300	10′ deep	545	1,525	2,070
1400	1-1/2″ copper service, 10′ offset, 2′ deep	985	720	1,705
1440	4′ deep	985	765	1,750
1460	6′ deep	985	955	1,940
1480	8′ deep	985	1,050	2,035
1500	10′ deep	985	1,125	2,110
1520	20′ offset, 2′ deep	985	765	1,750
1530	4′ deep	985	850	1,835
1540	6′ deep	985	1,225	2,210
1560	8′ deep	985	1,400	2,385
1580	10′ deep	985	1,575	2,560
1600	2″ copper service, 10′ offset, 2′ deep	1,250	750	2,000
1610	4′ deep	1,225	795	2,020
1620	6′ deep	1,225	985	2,210
1630	8′ deep	1,225	1,075	2,300
1650	10′ deep	1,225	1,175	2,400
1660	20′ offset, 2′ deep	1,225	795	2,020
1670	4′ deep	1,225	880	2,105
1680	6′ deep	1,225	1,275	2,500

659

G3010 Water Supply

G3010 121	Water Service, Lead Free	COST EACH		
		MAT.	INST.	TOTAL
1690	8' deep	1,225	1,425	2,650
1695	10' deep	1,225	1,625	2,850
1700	8" main, 1" copper service, 10' offset, 2' deep	545	705	1,250
1710	4' deep	545	745	1,290
1720	6' deep	425	890	1,315
1730	8' deep	545	1,025	1,570
1740	10' deep	545	1,125	1,670
1750	20' offset, 2' deep	545	745	1,290
1760	4' deep	545	830	1,375
1770	6' deep	425	1,175	1,600
1780	8' deep	545	1,400	1,945
1790	10' deep	545	1,575	2,120
1800	1-1/2" copper service, 10' offset, 2' deep	985	760	1,745
1810	4' deep	985	805	1,790
1820	6' deep	985	995	1,980
1830	8' deep	985	1,450	2,435
1840	10' deep	985	1,175	2,160
1850	20' offset, 2' deep	985	805	1,790
1860	4' deep	1,225	835	2,060
1870	6' deep	985	1,275	2,260
1880	8' deep	985	1,450	2,435
1890	10' deep	985	1,625	2,610
1900	2" copper service, 10' offset, 2' deep	1,250	790	2,040
1910	4' deep	1,225	835	2,060
1920	6' deep	1,225	1,025	2,250
1930	8' deep	1,225	1,100	2,325
1940	10' deep	1,225	1,225	2,450
1950	20' offset, 2' deep	1,225	835	2,060
1960	4' deep	1,225	920	2,145
1970	6' deep	1,225	1,300	2,525
1980	8' deep	1,225	1,475	2,700
1990	10' deep	1,225	1,650	2,875

G3010 Water Supply

- Ground Surface
- Backfill
- Utility Pipe
- Bedding (Crushed Stone)

System Components	QUANTITY	UNIT	COST L.F.		
			MAT.	INST.	TOTAL
SYSTEM G3010 122 1000					
WATERLINE 4″ DUCTILE IRON INCLUDING COMMON EARTH EXCAVATION,					
BEDDING, BACKFILL AND COMPACTION					
Excavate Trench	.296	B.C.Y.		1.99	1.99
Crushed stone bedding material	.203	L.C.Y.	5.28	2.59	7.87
Compact bedding	.173	E.C.Y.		.97	.97
Install 4″ MJ ductile iron pipe	1.000	L.F.	33.50	16.85	50.35
Backfill trench	.160	L.C.Y.		.47	.47
Compact fill material in trench	.123	E.C.Y.		.62	.62
Dispose of excess fill material on-site	.225	L.C.Y.		2.64	2.64
TOTAL			38.78	26.13	64.91

G3010 122	Waterline (Common Earth Excavation)	COST L.F.		
		MAT.	INST.	TOTAL
0950	Waterline including common earth excavation, bedding, backfill and compaction			
1000	4″ MJ ductile iron, 4′ deep	39	26	65
1150	6 inch	40.50	30.50	71
1200	8 inch	55	35.50	90.50
1250	10 inch	70.50	39.50	110
1300	12 inch	94	42.50	136.50
1400	4″ push joint ductile iron, 4′ deep	28.50	17.75	46.25
1450	6 ″	24.50	19.70	44.20
1500	8 ″	31.50	26.50	58
1550	10 ″	47	29	76
1600	12 ″	49.50	33	82.50
1700	4″ PVC Class 150, 4′ deep	8.60	13.45	22.05
1750	6 ″	11.90	14.55	26.45
1800	8 ″	16	15.95	31.95
1900	4″ PVC Class 200, 4′ deep	8.30	15.25	23.55
1950	6 ″	11.35	16.70	28.05
2000	8 ″	15.60	18.55	34.15
2100	6″ PVC C900, 4′ deep	11.90	16.70	28.60
2150	8 ″	16	18.45	34.45
2160	10 ″	21.50	20	41.50
2200	12 ″	29	22.50	51.50
2300	6″ HDPE SDR21 fusion, 4′ deep	12.45	18.50	30.95
2350	8 ″	15.75	20.50	36.25
2360	10 ″	22	21	43
2400	12 ″	26.50	23.50	50
2500	10″, 1/4″ wall black steel, 4′ deep	50.50	38.50	89
2550	12″	61.50	40	101.50
3000	18″ MJ ductile iron, 6′ deep with trench box	158	87.50	245.50
3050	24″	174	112	286
3100	18″ push joint ductile iron, 6′ deep with trench box	81	72	153
3200	24″	84	83.50	167.50
3300	18″ PVC C905, 6′ deep with trench box	45.50	52.50	98

G3010 122	Waterline (Common Earth Excavation)	COST L.F.		
		MAT.	INST.	TOTAL
3350	24"	67	61.50	128.50
3400	18" HDPE fusion SDR 21, 6' deep with trench box	60.50	66	126.50
3450	24"	84.50	79	163.50
3500	24" Concrete (CCP) , 6' deep with trench box	68.50	74	142.50
3600	18", 1/4" wall black steel , 6' deep with trench box	97.50	71	168.50
3650	18", 5/16" wall	117	71	188
3700	18", 3/8" wall	138	171	309
3750	24", 3/8" wall	182	197	379
3800	36" Concrete (CCP) , 8' deep with trench box	110	112	222
3900	36" PVC C905 , 8' deep with trench box	171	90	261
4000	36" 5/16" wall black steel , 8' deep with trench box	230	259	489
4050	36" 1/2" wall black steel	345	280	625
5000	4" MJ ductile iron, 5' deep	38.50	27	65.50
5005	6"	40.50	31.50	72
5010	8"	54.50	36	90.50
5015	10"	70	40.50	110.50
5020	12"	93	43	136
5100	4" push on joint ductile iron, 5' deep	28	18.55	46.55
5105	6"	24	20.50	44.50
5110	8"	31	27.50	58.50
5115	10"	46.50	29	75.50
5120	12"	48.50	32	80.50
5200	4" PVC Class 150, 5' deep	8.45	14.30	22.75
5205	6"	11.60	15.30	26.90
5210	8"	15.55	16.55	32.10
5300	4" PVC Class 200, 5' deep	8.20	16.10	24.30
5305	6"	11.05	17.45	28.50
5310	8"	15.15	19.15	34.30
5405	6" PVC C900, 5' deep	11.60	17.45	29.05
5410	8"	15.55	19.05	34.60
5415	10"	21.50	21	42.50
5420	12"	28	23	51
5505	6" HDPE SDR21 fusion, 5' deep	12.15	19.25	31.40
5510	8"	15.30	21	36.30
5515	10"	22	22	44
5520	12"	25.50	24	49.50
5615	10", 1/4" wall black steel, 5' deep	50	38.50	88.50
5620	12"	60.50	40	100.50
7000	4" MJ ductile iron, 7' deep	49	53	102
7005	6"	51.50	58	109.50
7010	8"	66.50	63.50	130
7015	10"	82.50	68.50	151
7020	12"	106	71.50	177.50
7100	4" push on joint ductile iron, 7' deep	38.50	44.50	83
7105	6"	35.50	47	82.50
7110	8"	43	54.50	97.50
7115	10"	59	57	116
7120	12"	62	61	123
7200	4" PVC Class 150, 7' deep	19	40	59
7205	6"	23	42	65
7210	8"	27.50	44	71.50
7300	4" PVC Class 200, 7' deep	18.70	42	60.70
7305	6"	22.50	44.50	67
7310	8"	27	46.50	73.50
7405	6" PVC C900, 7' deep	23	44.50	67.50
7410	8"	27.50	46.50	74
7415	10"	34.50	49	83.50
7420	12"	41.50	51.50	93

G3010 Water Supply

G3010 122	Waterline (Common Earth Excavation)	COST L.F.		
		MAT.	INST.	TOTAL
7505	6" HDPE SDR21 fusion, 7' deep	23.50	46	69.50
7510	8"	27.50	48.50	76
7515	10"	35	50	85
7520	12"	39.50	53	92.50

G30 Site Mechanical Utilities

G3010 Water Supply

Ground Surface
Backfill
Utility Pipe
Bedding (Crushed Stone)

System Components	QUANTITY	UNIT	COST L.F.		
			MAT.	INST.	TOTAL
SYSTEM G3010 124 1000					
WATERLINE 4″ DUCTILE IRON INCLUDING LOAM & SANDY CLAY EXCAVATION,					
BEDDING, BACKFILL AND COMPACTION					
Excavate Trench	.296	B.C.Y.		1.84	1.84
Crushed stone bedding material	.203	L.C.Y.	5.28	2.59	7.87
Compact bedding	.173	E.C.Y.		.97	.97
Install 4″ MJ ductile iron pipe	1.000	L.F.	33.50	16.85	50.35
Backfill trench	.173	L.C.Y.		.50	.50
Compact fill material in trench	.123	E.C.Y.		.62	.62
Dispose of excess fill material on-site	.242	L.C.Y.		2.85	2.85
TOTAL			38.78	26.22	65

G3010 124	Waterline (Loam & Sandy Clay Excavation)	COST L.F.		
		MAT.	INST.	TOTAL
0950	Waterline including loam & sandy clay excavation, bedding, backfill and compaction			
1000	4″ MJ ductile iron, 4′ deep	39	26	65
1150	6 inch	40.50	31	71.50
1200	8 inch	55	35.50	90.50
1250	10 inch	70.50	40	110.50
1300	12 inch	94	42.50	136.50
1400	4″ push joint ductile iron, 4′ deep	28.50	17.80	46.30
1450	6 ″	24.50	19.85	44.35
1500	8 ″	31.50	27	58.50
1550	10 ″	47	29	76
1600	12 ″	49.50	32	81.50
1700	4″ PVC Class 150, 4′ deep	8.30	13.50	21.80
1750	6 ″	11.60	14.60	26.20
1800	8 ″	15.70	16	31.70
1900	4″ PVC Class 200, 4′ deep	8	15.30	23.30
1950	6 ″	11.05	16.75	27.80
2000	8 ″	15.30	18.60	33.90
2100	6″ PVC C900, 4′ deep	11.60	16.75	28.35
2150	8 ″	15.70	18.50	34.20
2200	12 ″	29	22.50	51.50
2300	6″ HDPE SDR21 fusion, 4′ deep	12.15	18.55	30.70
2350	8 ″	15.45	20.50	35.95
2400	12 ″	26.50	23.50	50
2500	10″, 1/4″ wall black steel, 4′ deep	50.50	38.50	89
2550	12″	61.50	40	101.50
3000	18″ MJ ductile iron, 6′ deep with trench box	158	88	246
3050	24″	174	112	286
3100	18″ push joint ductile iron, 6′ deep with trench box	81	75.50	156.50
3200	24″	84	84	168
3300	18″ PVC C905, 6′ deep with trench box	45	53	98
3350	24″	66.50	61.50	128
3400	18″ HDPE fusion SDR 21, 6′ deep with trench box	60	66	126

For customer support on your Site Work & Landscape Cost Data, call 877.737.1594.

G3010 Water Supply

G3010 124	Waterline (Loam & Sandy Clay Excavation)	COST L.F.		
		MAT.	INST.	TOTAL
3450	24"	84	79	163
3500	24" Concrete (CCP) , 6' deep with trench box	68.50	74.50	143
3600	18", 1/4" wall black steel , 6' deep with trench box	97.50	71.50	169
3650	18", 5/16" wall	117	71.50	188.50
3700	18", 3/8" wall	138	171	309
3750	24", 3/8" wall	182	198	380
3800	36" Concrete (CCP) , 8' deep with trench box	110	113	223
3900	36" PVC C905 , 8' deep with trench box	171	91.50	262.50
4000	36" 5/16" wall black steel , 8' deep with trench box	230	260	490
4050	36" 1/2" wall black steel	345	282	627
5000	4" MJ ductile iron, 5' deep	38.50	27	65.50
5005	6"	40.50	31.50	72
5010	8"	54.50	36	90.50
5015	10"	70	40.50	110.50
5020	12"	93	43	136
5100	4" push on joint ductile iron, 5' deep	28	18.65	46.65
5105	6"	24	20.50	44.50
5110	8"	31	27.50	58.50
5115	10"	46.50	29.50	76
5120	12"	48.50	32	80.50
5200	4" PVC Class 150, 5' deep	8.45	14.35	22.80
5205	6"	11.60	15.35	26.95
5210	8"	15.55	16.60	32.15
5300	4" PVC Class 200, 5' deep	8.20	16.15	24.35
5305	6"	11.05	17.50	28.55
5310	8"	15.15	19.20	34.35
5405	6" PVC C900, 5' deep	11.60	17.50	29.10
5410	8"	15.55	19.10	34.65
5415	10"	21.50	21	42.50
5420	12"	28	23	51
5505	6" HDPE SDR21 fusion, 5' deep	12.15	19.30	31.45
5510	8"	15.30	21	36.30
5515	10"	22	22	44
5520	12"	25.50	24	49.50
5615	10", 1/4" wall black steel, 5' deep	50	38.50	88.50
5620	12"	60.50	40	100.50
6000	4" MJ ductile iron, 6' deep	49	49.50	98.50
6005	6"	51.50	54.50	106
6010	8"	66.50	59.50	126
6015	10"	82.50	64.50	147
6020	12"	106	67.50	173.50
6100	4" push on joint ductile iron, 6' deep	38.50	40.50	79
6105	6"	35.50	43.50	79
6110	8"	43	51	94
6115	10"	59	54	113
6120	12"	62	57	119
6200	4" PVC Class 150, 6' deep	19	36.50	55.50
6205	6"	23.50	38.50	62
6210	8"	27.50	40.50	68
6300	4" PVC Class 200, 6' deep	18.70	38.50	57.20
6305	6"	22.50	40.50	63
6310	8"	27	43	70
6405	6" PVC C900, 6' deep	23	40.50	63.50
6410	8"	27.50	43	70.50
6415	10"	34.50	45	79.50
6420	12"	41.50	47.50	89
6505	6" HDPE SDR21 fusion, 6' deep	23.50	42	65.50
6510	8"	27.50	44.50	72

665

For customer support on your Site Work & Landscape Cost Data, call 877.737.1594.

G30 Site Mechanical Utilities

G3010 Water Supply

G3010 124	Waterline (Loam & Sandy Clay Excavation)	COST L.F.		
		MAT.	INST.	TOTAL
6515	10"	35	47	82
6520	12"	39.50	49	88.50
6615	10", 1/4" wall black steel, 6' deep	62.50	62.50	125
6620	12"	74	64.50	138.50
7000	4" MJ ductile iron, 7' deep	49	52.50	101.50
7005	6"	51.50	57.50	109
7010	8"	66.50	62.50	129
7015	10"	82.50	67.50	150
7020	12"	106	71	177
7100	4" push on joint ductile iron, 7' deep	38.50	44	82.50
7105	6"	35.50	46.50	82
7110	8"	43	54.50	97.50
7115	10"	59	57	116
7120	12"	62	60	122
7200	4" PVC Class 150, 7' deep	19	40	59
7205	6"	23	41.50	64.50
7210	8"	27.50	43.50	71
7300	4" PVC Class 200, 7' deep	18.70	41.50	60.20
7305	6"	22.50	43.50	66
7310	8"	27	46	73
7405	6" PVC C900, 7' deep	23	43.50	66.50
7410	8"	27.50	46	73.50
7415	10"	34.50	48.50	83
7420	12"	41.50	51	92.50
7505	6" HDPE SDR21 fusion, 7' deep	23.50	45.50	69
7510	8"	27.50	48	75.50
7515	10"	35	49.50	84.50
7520	12"	39.50	52	91.50

G3010 Water Supply

The Fire Hydrant Systems include: four different hydrants with three different lengths of offsets, at several depths of trenching. Excavation and backfill is included with each system as well as thrust blocks as necessary and pipe bedding. Finally spreading of excess material and fine grading complete the components.

System Components	QUANTITY	UNIT	COST PER EACH		
			MAT.	INST.	TOTAL
SYSTEM G3010 410 1500					
HYDRANT, 4-1/2″ VALVE SIZE, TWO WAY, 10′ OFFSET, 2′ DEEP					
Excavation, trench, 1 C.Y. hydraulic backhoe	3.556	C.Y.		28.63	28.63
Sleeve, 12″ x 6″	1.000	Ea.	1,300	112.40	1,412.40
Ductile iron pipe, 6″ diameter	8.000	L.F.	280	168.88	448.88
Gate valve, 6″	1.000	Ea.	2,575	320	2,895
Hydrant valve box, 6′ long	1.000	Ea.	310	77.50	387.50
4-1/2″ valve size, depth 2′-0″	1.000	Ea.	1,825	202.15	2,027.15
Thrust blocks, at valve, shoe and sleeve	1.600	C.Y.	292.80	445.18	737.98
Borrow, crushed stone, 3/8″	4.089	C.Y.	122	32.48	154.48
Backfill and compact, dozer, air tamped	4.089	C.Y.		70.74	70.74
Spread excess excavated material	.204	C.Y.		8.57	8.57
Fine grade, hand	400.000	S.F.		269.50	269.50
TOTAL			6,704.80	1,736.03	8,440.83

G3010 410	Fire Hydrants	COST PER EACH		
		MAT.	INST.	TOTAL
1000	Hydrant, 4-1/2″ valve size, two way, 0′ offset, 2′ deep	6,425	1,200	7,625
1100	4′ deep	6,750	1,225	7,975
1200	6′ deep	6,900	1,275	8,175
1300	8′ deep	7,125	1,325	8,450
1400	10′ deep	7,300	1,400	8,700
1500	10′ offset, 2′ deep	6,700	1,750	8,450
1600	4′ deep	7,025	2,050	9,075
1700	6′ deep	7,175	2,575	9,750
1800	8′ deep	7,400	3,400	10,800
1900	10′ deep	7,575	5,075	12,650
2000	20′ offset, 2′ deep	7,050	2,300	9,350
2100	4′ deep	7,375	2,775	10,150
2200	6′ deep	7,525	3,600	11,125
2300	8′ deep	7,750	4,775	12,525
2400	10′ deep	7,925	6,375	14,300
2500	Hydrant, 4-1/2″ valve size, three way, 0′ offset, 2′ deep	6,550	1,225	7,775
2600	4′ deep	6,900	1,225	8,125
2700	6′ deep	7,050	1,300	8,350
2800	8′ deep	7,300	1,350	8,650
2900	10′ deep	7,500	1,425	8,925
3000	10′ offset, 2′ deep	6,825	1,750	8,575
3100	4′ deep	7,175	2,050	9,225
3200	6′ deep	7,350	2,600	9,950
3300	8′ deep	7,575	3,400	10,975

G3010 Water Supply

G3010 410	Fire Hydrants	COST PER EACH		
		MAT.	INST.	TOTAL
3400	10' deep	7,775	5,100	12,875
3500	20' offset, 2' deep	7,175	2,325	9,500
3600	4' deep	7,525	2,800	10,325
3700	6' deep	7,700	3,625	11,325
3800	8' deep	7,925	4,800	12,725
3900	10' deep	8,125	6,400	14,525
5000	5-1/4" valve size, two way, 0' offset, 2' deep	6,550	1,200	7,750
5100	4' deep	6,700	1,225	7,925
5200	6' deep	6,850	1,275	8,125
5300	8' deep	7,075	1,325	8,400
5400	10' deep	7,425	1,400	8,825
5500	10' offset, 2' deep	6,825	1,750	8,575
5600	4' deep	6,975	2,050	9,025
5700	6' deep	7,125	2,575	9,700
5800	8' deep	7,350	3,400	10,750
5900	10' deep	7,700	5,075	12,775
6000	20' offset, 2' deep	7,175	2,300	9,475
6100	4' deep	7,325	2,775	10,100
6200	6' deep	7,475	3,600	11,075
6300	8' deep	7,700	4,775	12,475
6400	10' deep	8,050	6,375	14,425
6500	Three way, 0' offset, 2' deep	6,675	1,225	7,900
6600	4' deep	6,850	1,225	8,075
6700	6' deep	7,000	1,300	8,300
6800	8' deep	7,250	1,350	8,600
6900	10' deep	7,625	1,425	9,050
7000	10' offset, 2' deep	6,975	1,750	8,725
7100	4' deep	7,125	2,050	9,175
7200	6' deep	7,275	2,600	9,875
7300	8' deep	7,525	3,400	10,925
7400	10' deep	7,900	5,100	13,000
7500	20' offset, 2' deep	7,325	2,325	9,650
7600	4' deep	7,475	2,525	10,000
7700	6' deep	7,625	3,625	11,250

G30 Site Mechanical Utilities

G3020 Sanitary Sewer

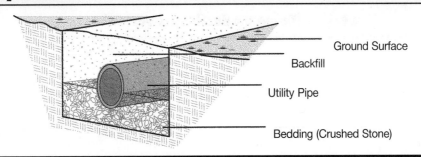

Ground Surface
Backfill
Utility Pipe
Bedding (Crushed Stone)

System Components	QUANTITY	UNIT	COST L.F.		
			MAT.	INST.	TOTAL
SYSTEM G3020 112 1000					
SEWERLINE 4″ B&S CAST IRON INCLUDING COMMON EARTH EXCAVATION,					
BEDDING, BACKFILL AND COMPACTION					
Excavate Trench	.296	B.C.Y.		1.99	1.99
Crushed stone bedding material	.203	L.C.Y.	5.28	2.59	7.87
Compact bedding	.173	E.C.Y.		.97	.97
Install 4″ B&S cast iron pipe	1.000	L.F.	17.55	19.35	36.90
Backfill trench	.160	L.C.Y.		.47	.47
Compact fill material in trench	.123	E.C.Y.		.62	.62
Dispose of excess fill material on-site	.225	L.C.Y.		2.64	2.64
TOTAL			22.83	28.63	51.46

G3020 112	Sewerline (Common Earth Excavation)	COST L.F.		
		MAT.	INST.	TOTAL
0950	Sewerline including common earth excavation, bedding, backfill and compaction			
1000	4″ B&S Cast iron, 4′ deep	23	28.50	51.50
1150	6 inch	36.50	33	69.50
1200	8 inch	56.50	48.50	105
1250	10 inch	90	51	141
1300	12 inch	127	58	185
1400	4″ HDPE type S watertight, 4′ deep	6.30	12.95	19.25
1450	6 ″	8.10	13.50	21.60
1500	8 ″	11.10	14.05	25.15
1550	10 ″	13.65	14.50	28.15
1600	12 ″	14.90	18.50	33.40
1700	4″ PVC, SDR 35, 20′ length , 4′ deep	6.90	13.40	20.30
1750	6 ″	9.30	14.05	23.35
1800	8 ″- 13′ length	13.65	14.60	28.25
1900	10″	18.95	16.45	35.40
1950	12 ″	21	16.95	37.95
2000	12 ″ Concrete w/gasket class 3	20	22.50	42.50
2100	12 ″ class 4	21	22.50	43.50
2200	12 ″ class 5	23.50	22.50	46
3000	18″ HDPE type S watertight, 6′ deep with trench box	34	46	80
3050	24″	39.50	48	87.50
3100	18″ PVC, SDR 35, 13′ length, 6′ deep with trench box	35	49	84
3150	24″	48.50	51.50	100
3200	18″ concrete w/gasket class 3, 6′ deep with trench box	40.50	52	92.50
3250	24″ class 3	55.50	55	110.50
3300	18″ class 4	41.50	52	93.50
3350	24″ class 4	54	55	109
3400	18″ class 5	44.50	52	96.50
3450	24″ class 5	59	55	114
4000	30″ HDPE type S, watertight, 8′ deep with trench box	58.50	69.50	128
4050	36″	68.50	73.50	142
5000	30″ concrete w/gaskets class 3, 8′ deep with trench box	87	109	196
5050	36″ class 3	105	123	228
5100	30″ class 4	86	109	195

G3020 Sanitary Sewer

G3020 112	Sewerline (Common Earth Excavation)	COST L.F.		
		MAT.	INST.	TOTAL
5150	36" class 4	105	123	228
5200	30" class 5	92.50	109	201.50
5250	36" class 5	114	123	237
5500	4" B&S Cast iron, 5' deep	22.50	29.50	52
5502	6"	36.50	33.50	70
5504	8"	56	49	105
5506	10"	89.50	52	141.50
5508	12"	126	58.50	184.50
5510	4" HDPE type S watertight, 5' deep	6.15	13.75	19.90
5512	6"	7.80	14.25	22.05
5514	8"	10.65	14.65	25.30
5516	10"	12.95	14.95	27.90
5518	12"	14	15.40	29.40
5520	4" PVC, SDR 35, 5' deep	6.75	14.25	21
5522	6"	9	14.80	23.80
5524	8"	13.20	15.20	28.40
5526	10"	18.25	16.85	35.10
5528	12"	19.90	17.20	37.10
5532	12" Concrete w/gasket class 3, 5' deep	19.20	23	42.20
5534	12" class 4	20	23	43
5536	12" class 5	22.50	23	45.50
6000	4" B&S Cast iron, 6' deep	33	53	86
6002	6"	47.50	59	106.50
6004	8"	68	74	142
6006	10"	102	77.50	179.50
6008	12"	139	84.50	223.50
6010	4" HDPE type S watertight, 6' deep	16.70	37.50	54.20
6012	6"	19.10	39.50	58.60
6014	8"	22.50	40	62.50
6016	10"	25.50	40.50	66
6018	12"	27.50	41.50	69
6020	4" PVC, SDR 35, 6' deep	17.30	38	55.30
6022	6"	20.50	40	60.50
6024	8"	25	40.50	65.50
6026	10"	31	42.50	73.50
6028	12"	33.50	43.50	77
6032	12" Concrete w/gasket class 3, 6' deep	32.50	49	81.50
6034	12" class 4	33.50	49	82.50
6036	12" class 5	36	49	85
6500	4" B&S Cast iron, 7' deep	33	55.50	88.50
6502	6"	47.50	62	109.50
6504	8"	68	76.50	144.50
6506	10"	102	80	182
6508	12"	139	87	226
6510	4" HDPE type S watertight, 7' deep	16.70	39.50	56.20
6512	6"	19.10	42.50	61.60
6514	8"	22.50	42	64.50
6516	10"	25.50	43	68.50
6518	12"	27.50	44	71.50
6520	4" PVC, SDR 35, 7' deep	17.30	40	57.30
6522	6"	20.50	43	63.50
6524	8"	25	42.50	67.50
6526	10"	31	45	76
6528	12"	33.50	46	79.50
6532	12" Concrete w/gasket class 3, 7' deep	32.50	52	84.50
6534	12" class 4	33.50	52	85.50
6536	12" class 5	36	52	88

G3020 Sanitary Sewer

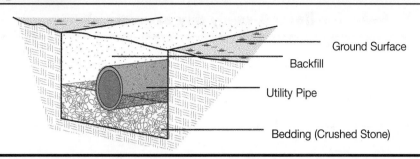

Ground Surface
Backfill
Utility Pipe
Bedding (Crushed Stone)

System Components	QUANTITY	UNIT	COST L.F.		
			MAT.	INST.	TOTAL
SYSTEM G3020 114 1000					
SEWERLINE 4″ B&S CAST IRON INCLUDING LOAM & SANDY CLAY EXCAVATION,					
BEDDING, BACKFILL AND COMPACTION					
Excavate Trench	.296	B.C.Y.		1.84	1.84
Crushed stone bedding material	.203	L.C.Y.	5.28	2.59	7.87
Compact bedding	.173	E.C.Y.		.97	.97
Install 4″ B&S cast iron pipe	1.000	L.F.	17.55	19.35	36.90
Backfill trench	.173	L.C.Y.		.50	.50
Compact fill material in trench	.123	E.C.Y.		.62	.62
Dispose of excess fill material on-site	.242	L.C.Y.		2.85	2.85
TOTAL			22.83	28.72	51.55

G3020 114	Sewerline (loam & sandy clay excavation)	COST L.F.		
		MAT.	INST.	TOTAL
0950	Sewerline incl. loam & sandy clay excavation, bedding, backfill and compaction			
1000	4″ B&S Cast iron, 4′ deep	23	29	52
1150	6 inch	36.50	33	69.50
1200	8 inch	56.50	48.50	105
1250	10 inch	90	51.50	141.50
1300	12 inch	127	58	185
1400	4″ HDPE type S watertight, 4′ deep	6.30	13	19.30
1450	6 ″	8.10	13.55	21.65
1500	8 ″	11.10	14.15	25.25
1550	10 ″	13.65	14.60	28.25
1600	12 ″	14.90	15.30	30.20
1700	4″ PVC, SDR 35, 20′ length, 4′ deep	6.90	13.50	20.40
1750	6 ″	9.30	14.10	23.40
1800	8 ″- 13′ length	13.65	14.70	28.35
1900	10″	18.95	16.55	35.50
1950	12″	21	17.10	38.10
2000	12 ″ Concrete w/gasket class 3	20	23	43
2100	12 ″ class 4	21	23	44
2200	12 ″ class 5	23.50	23	46.50
3000	18″ HDPE type S watertight, 6′ deep with trench box	34	46	80
3050	24″	39.50	48.50	88
3100	18″ PVC, SDR 35, 13′ length, 6′ deep with trench box	35	48.50	83.50
3150	24″	48.50	52	100.50
3200	18″ concrete w/gasket class 3, 6′ deep with trench box	40.50	52	92.50
3250	24″ class 3	55.50	55.50	111
3300	18″ class 4	41.50	52	93.50
3350	24″ class 4	54	55.50	109.50
3400	18″ class 5	44.50	52	96.50
3450	24″ class 5	59	55.50	114.50
4000	30″ HDPE type S, watertight, 8′ deep with trench box	58.50	71	129.50
4050	36″	68.50	74.50	143
5000	30″ concrete w/gaskets class 3, 8′ deep with trench box	87	110	197
5050	36″ class 3	105	124	229
5100	30″ class 4	86	110	196

671

G3020 Sanitary Sewer

G3020 114	Sewerline (loam & sandy clay excavation)	COST L.F.		
		MAT.	INST.	TOTAL
5150	36" class 4	105	124	229
5200	30" class 5	92.50	110	202.50
5250	36" class 5	114	124	238
5500	4" B&S Cast iron, 5' deep	22.50	29.50	52
5502	6"	36.50	34	70.50
5504	8"	56	49	105
5506	10"	89.50	52	141.50
5508	12"	126	58.50	184.50
5510	4" HDPE type S watertight, 5' deep	6.15	13.85	20
5512	6"	7.80	14.30	22.10
5514	8"	10.65	14.70	25.35
5516	10"	12.95	15	27.95
5518	12"	14	15.55	29.55
5520	4" PVC, SDR 35, 5' deep	6.75	14.30	21.05
5522	6"	9	14.85	23.85
5524	8"	13.20	15.25	28.45
5526	10"	18.25	16.90	35.15
5528	12"	19.90	17.30	37.20
5532	12" Concrete w/gasket class 3, 5' deep	19.20	23	42.20
5534	12" class 4	20	23	43
5536	12" class 5	22.50	23	45.50
6000	4" B&S Cast iron, 6' deep	33	53.50	86.50
6002	6"	47.50	59.50	107
6004	8"	68	74	142
6006	10"	102	78	180
6008	12"	139	85	224
6010	4" HDPE type S watertight, 6' deep	16.70	38	54.70
6012	6"	19.10	40	59.10
6014	8"	22.50	39.50	62
6016	10"	25.50	41	66.50
6018	12"	27.50	42	69.50
6020	4" PVC, SDR 35, 6' deep	17.30	38.50	55.80
6022	6"	20.50	40.50	61
6024	8"	25	40.50	65.50
6026	10"	31	43	74
6028	12"	33.50	44	77.50
6032	12" Concrete w/gasket class 3, 6' deep	32.50	49.50	82
6034	12" class 4	33.50	49.50	83
6036	12" class 5	36	49.50	85.50
6500	4" B&S Cast iron, 7' deep	33	55	88
6502	6"	47.50	61	108.50
6504	8"	68	76	144
6506	10"	102	79	181
6508	12"	139	86.50	225.50
6510	4" HDPE type S watertight, 7' deep	16.70	39.50	56.20
6512	6"	19.10	41.50	60.60
6514	8"	22.50	41.50	64
6516	10"	25.50	42.50	68
6518	12"	27.50	43.50	71
6520	4" PVC, SDR 35, 7' deep	17.30	39.50	56.80
6522	6"	20.50	42	62.50
6524	8"	25	42	67
6526	10"	31	44.50	75.50
6528	12"	33.50	45	78.50
6532	12" Concrete w/gasket class 3, 7' deep	32.50	51	83.50
6534	12" class 4	33.50	51	84.50
6536	12" class 5	36	51	87

G3020 Sanitary Sewer

The Septic System includes: a septic tank; leaching field; concrete distribution boxes; plus excavation and gravel backfill.

The Expanded System Listing shows systems with tanks ranging from 1000 gallons to 2000 gallons. Tanks are either concrete or fiberglass. Cost is on a complete unit basis.

System Components	QUANTITY	UNIT	COST EACH		
			MAT.	INST.	TOTAL
SYSTEM G3020 302 0300					
1000 GALLON TANK, LEACHING FIELD, 600 S.F., 50′ FROM BLDG.					
Mobilization	2.000	Ea.		1,590	1,590
Septic tank, precast, 1000 gallon	1.000	Ea.	1,100	251.95	1,351.95
Effluent filter	1.000	Ea.	46	75	121
Distribution box, precast, 5 outlets	1.000	Ea.	88.50	58	146.50
Flow leveler	3.000	Ea.	7.44	27.75	35.19
Sewer pipe, PVC, SDR 35, 4″ diameter	40.000	L.F.	256	662.40	918.40
Tee	1.000	Ea.	14.80	75	89.80
Elbow	2.000	Ea.	21.60	100	121.60
Viewport cap	1.000	Ea.	8.40	25	33.40
Filter fabric	67.000	S.Y.	110.55	26.13	136.68
Detectable marking tape	1.600	C.L.F.	11.44	4.94	16.38
Excavation	160.000	C.Y.		1,995.20	1,995.20
Backfill	133.000	L.C.Y.		389.69	389.69
Spoil	55.000	L.C.Y.		357.50	357.50
Compaction	113.000	E.C.Y.		944.68	944.68
Stone fill, 3/4″ to 1-1/2″	39.000	C.Y.	1,560	498.03	2,058.03
TOTAL			3,224.73	7,081.27	10,306

G3020 302	Septic Systems	COST EACH		
		MAT.	INST.	TOTAL
0300	1000 gal. concrete septic tank, 600 S.F. leaching field, 50 feet from bldg.	3,225	7,075	10,300
0301	200 feet from building	3,475	8,750	12,225
0305	750 S.F. leaching field, 50 feet from building	3,675	7,700	11,375
0306	200 feet from building	3,925	9,400	13,325
0400	1250 gal. concrete septic tank, 600 S.F. leaching field, 50 feet from bldg.	3,275	7,350	10,625
0401	200 feet from building	3,525	9,050	12,575
0405	750 S.F. leaching field, 50 feet from building	3,725	8,000	11,725
0406	200 feet from building	3,975	9,725	13,700
0410	1000 S.F. leaching field, 50 feet from building	4,500	9,150	13,650
0411	200 feet from building	4,750	10,900	15,650
0500	1500 gal. concrete septic tank, 600 S.F. leaching field, 50 feet from bldg.	3,625	7,625	11,250
0501	200 feet from building	3,850	9,325	13,175
0505	750 S.F. leaching field, 50 feet from building	4,050	8,275	12,325
0506	200 feet from building	4,300	10,800	15,100
0510	1000 S.F. leaching field, 50 feet from building	4,825	9,425	14,250
0511	200 feet from building	5,075	11,200	16,275
0515	1100 S.F. leaching field, 50 feet from building	5,125	9,850	14,975
0516	200 feet from building	5,375	11,700	17,075
0600	2000 gal concrete tank, 1200 S.F. leaching field, 50 feet from building	6,075	10,500	16,575
0601	200 feet from building	6,325	12,100	18,425

G3020 Sanitary Sewer

G3020 302	Septic Systems	COST EACH		
		MAT.	INST.	TOTAL
0605	1500 S.F. leaching field, 50 feet from building	6,975	11,800	18,775
0606	200 feet from building	7,225	13,500	20,725
0710	2500 gal concrete tank, 1500 S.F. leaching field, 50 feet from building	7,100	12,500	19,600
0711	200 feet from building	7,350	14,200	21,550
0715	1600 S.F. leaching field, 50 feet from building	7,450	13,000	20,450
0716	200 feet from building	7,700	14,700	22,400
0720	1800 S.F. leaching field, 50 feet from building	8,050	14,000	22,050
0721	200 feet from building	8,300	15,700	24,000
1300	1000 gal. 2 compartment tank, 600 S.F. leaching field, 50 feet from bldg.	2,875	7,075	9,950
1301	200 feet from building	3,100	8,750	11,850
1305	750 S.F. leaching field, 50 feet from building	3,300	7,700	11,000
1306	200 feet from building	3,550	9,400	12,950
1400	1250 gal. 2 compartment tank, 600 S.F. leaching field, 50 feet from bldg.	3,100	7,350	10,450
1401	200 feet from building	3,350	9,050	12,400
1405	750 S.F. leaching field, 50 feet from building	3,525	8,000	11,525
1406	200 feet from building	3,775	9,725	13,500
1410	1000 S.F. leaching field, 50 feet from building	4,325	9,150	13,475
1411	200 feet from building	4,575	10,900	15,475
1500	1500 gal. 2 compartment tank, 600 S.F. leaching field, 50 feet from bldg.	3,950	7,625	11,575
1501	200 feet from building	4,175	9,325	13,500
1505	750 S.F. leaching field, 50 feet from building	4,375	8,275	12,650
1506	200 feet from building	4,625	10,800	15,425
1510	1000 S.F. leaching field, 50 feet from building	5,150	9,425	14,575
1511	200 feet from building	5,400	11,200	16,600
1515	1100 S.F. leaching field, 50 feet from building	5,450	9,850	15,300
1516	200 feet from building	5,700	11,700	17,400
1600	2000 gal 2 compartment tank, 1200 S.F. leaching field, 50 feet from bldg.	6,200	10,500	16,700
1601	200 feet from building	6,450	12,100	18,550
1605	1500 S.F. leaching field, 50 feet from building	7,100	11,800	18,900
1606	200 feet from building	7,350	13,500	20,850
1710	2500 gal 2 compartment tank, 1500 S.F. leaching field, 50 feet from bldg.	7,800	12,500	20,300
1711	200 feet from building	8,050	14,200	22,250
1715	1600 S.F. leaching field, 50 feet from building	8,150	13,000	21,150
1716	200 feet from building	8,400	14,700	23,100
1720	1800 S.F. leaching field, 50 feet from building	8,750	14,000	22,750
1721	200 feet from building	9,000	15,700	24,700

G3020 Sanitary Sewer

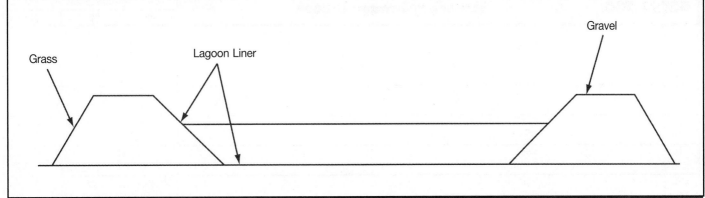

System Components	QUANTITY	UNIT	COST EACH		
			MAT.	INST.	TOTAL
SYSTEM G3020 730 1000					
500,000 GPD, SECONDARY DOMESTIC SEWAGE LAGOON, COMMON EARTH					
Supervision of lagoon construction	60.000	Day		36,000	36,000
Quality Control of Earthwork per day	30.000	Day		13,950	13,950
Excavate lagoon	10780.000	B.C.Y.		26,734.40	26,734.40
Finish grade slopes for seeding	40.000	M.S.F.		1,180	1,180
Spread & grade top of lagoon banks for compaction	753.000	M.S.F.		47,439	47,439
Compact lagoon banks	10725.000	E.C.Y.		8,258.25	8,258.25
Install pond liner	202.000	M.S.F.	126,250	227,250	353,500
Provide water for compaction and dust control	2156.000	E.C.Y.	2,889.04	4,527.60	7,416.64
Dispose of excess material on-site	72.000	L.C.Y.		262.08	262.08
Seed non-lagoon side of banks	40.000	M.S.F.	1,300	1,162	2,462
Place gravel on top of banks	2311.000	S.Y.	11,670.55	3,420.28	15,090.83
Provide 6 ' high fence around lagoon	1562.000	L.F.	32,802	10,949.62	43,751.62
Provide 12' wide fence gate	3.000	Opng.	1,515	1,566	3,081
Temporary Fencing	1562.000	L.F.	5,076.50	3,608.22	8,684.72
TOTAL			181,503.09	386,307.45	567,810.54

G3020 730	Secondary Sewage Lagoon	COST EACH		
		MAT.	INST.	TOTAL
0980	Lagoons, Secondary, 10 day retention, 5.1 foot depth, no mechanical aeration			
1000	500,000 GPD Secondary Domestic Sewage Lagoon, common earth, 10 day retention	181,500	386,500	568,000
1100	600,000 GPD	206,000	453,000	659,000
1200	700,000 GPD	229,500	601,500	831,000
1300	800,000 GPD	253,500	548,000	801,500
1400	900,000 GPD	277,000	608,000	885,000
1500	1 MGD	322,500	702,500	1,025,000
1600	2 MGD	535,000	1,231,500	1,766,500
1700	3 MGD	863,500	1,903,500	2,767,000
2000	500,000 GPD sandy clay & loam	181,500	387,500	569,000
2100	600,000 GPD	206,000	453,500	659,500
2200	700,000 GPD	229,500	491,500	721,000
2300	800,000 GPD	253,500	549,000	802,500
2400	900,000 GPD	277,000	609,000	886,000
2500	1 MGD	322,500	704,500	1,027,000
2600	2 MGD	535,000	1,231,500	1,766,500
2700	3 MGD	863,500	1,906,000	2,769,500
3000	500,000 GPD sand & gravel	181,500	378,500	560,000
3100	600,000 GPD	206,000	442,500	648,500
3200	700,000 GPD	229,500	479,500	709,000
3300	800,000 GPD	253,500	535,500	789,000
3400	900,000 GPD	277,000	593,500	870,500

675

G30 Site Mechanical Utilities

G3020 Sanitary Sewer

G3020 730	Secondary Sewage Lagoon	COST EACH		
		MAT.	INST.	TOTAL
3500	1 MGD	322,500	686,500	1,009,000
3600	2 MGD	535,000	1,198,000	1,733,000
3700	3 MGD	863,500	1,854,000	2,717,500
6000	500,000 GPD, Domestic Sewage Secondary Lagoon, common earth, 10 day, no liner	47,600	157,000	204,600
6100	600,000 GPD	59,500	188,500	248,000
6200	700,000 GPD	63,000	197,500	260,500
6300	800,000 GPD	66,500	218,500	285,000
6400	900,000 GPD	70,000	235,500	305,500
6500	1 MGD	82,500	270,500	353,000
6600	2 MGD	110,000	466,500	576,500
6700	3 MGD	193,000	696,500	889,500
7000	500,000 GPD sandy clay & loam	55,500	160,000	215,500
7100	600,000 GPD	59,500	189,000	248,500
7200	700,000 GPD	63,000	192,500	255,500
7300	800,000 GPD	66,500	212,500	279,000
7400	900,000 GPD	70,000	237,000	307,000
7500	1 MGD	82,500	272,500	355,000
7600	2 MGD	110,000	466,500	576,500
7700	3 MGD	193,000	698,500	891,500

G3020 Sanitary Sewer

System Components	QUANTITY	UNIT	COST EACH		
			MAT.	INST.	TOTAL
SYSTEM G3020 740 1000					
WASTEWATER TREATMENT, AERATION, 75 CFM PREPACKAGED BLOWER SYSTEM					
Prepacked blower, 38 CFM	3.000	Ea.	9,825	2,385	12,210
Flexible coupling-2" diameter	3.000	Ea.	111	57.15	168.15
Wafer style check valve-2" diameter	3.000	Ea.	402	237	639
Wafer style butterfly valve-2" diameter	3.000	Ea.	291	151.50	442.50
Wafer style butterfly valve-3" diameter	1.000	Ea.	108	160	268
Blower Pressure Relief Valves-adjustable-3" Diameter	1.000	Ea.	184	160	344
Silencer with polyester filter-3" Connection	1.000	Ea.	178	160	338
Pipe-2" diameter	30.000	L.F.	484.50	690	1,174.50
Pipe-3" diameter	50.000	L.F.	1,425	1,275	2,700
3 x 3 x 2 Tee	3.000	Ea.	300	276	576
Pipe cap-3" diameter	1.000	Ea.	87	42.50	129.50
Pressure gage	1.000	Ea.	11.40	22.50	33.90
Master control panel	1.000	Ea.	965	262	1,227
TOTAL			14,371.90	5,878.65	20,250.55

G3020 740	Blower System for Wastewater Aeration	COST EACH		
		MAT.	INST.	TOTAL
1000	75 CFM Prepackaged Blower System	14,400	5,875	20,275
1100	250 CFM	13,700	8,425	22,125
1200	450 CFM	25,900	8,925	34,825
1300	700 CFM	44,400	11,200	55,600
1400	1000 CFM	44,600	11,900	56,500

677

G3030 Storm Sewer

Manhole   Catch Basin

The Manhole and Catch Basin System includes: excavation with a backhoe; a formed concrete footing; frame and cover; cast iron steps and compacted backfill.

The Expanded System Listing shows manholes that have a 4', 5' and 6' inside diameter riser. Depths range from 4' to 14'. Construction material shown is either concrete, concrete block, precast concrete, or brick.

System Components	QUANTITY	UNIT	COST PER EACH		
			MAT.	INST.	TOTAL
SYSTEM G3030 210 1920					
MANHOLE/CATCH BASIN, BRICK, 4' I.D. RISER, 4' DEEP					
Excavation, hydraulic backhoe, 3/8 C.Y. bucket	14.815	B.C.Y.		119.26	119.26
Trim sides and bottom of excavation	64.000	S.F.		62.08	62.08
Forms in place, manhole base, 4 uses	20.000	SFCA	16.40	106	122.40
Reinforcing in place footings, #4 to #7	.019	Ton	20.43	23.75	44.18
Concrete, 3000 psi	.925	C.Y.	103.60		103.60
Place and vibrate concrete, footing, direct chute	.925	C.Y.		49.26	49.26
Catch basin or MH, brick, 4' ID, 4' deep	1.000	Ea.	575	1,025	1,600
Catch basin or MH steps; heavy galvanized cast iron	1.000	Ea.	21	14.10	35.10
Catch basin or MH frame and cover	1.000	Ea.	268	245.50	513.50
Fill, granular	12.954	L.C.Y.	297.94		297.94
Backfill, spread with wheeled front end loader	12.954	L.C.Y.		34.07	34.07
Backfill compaction, 12" lifts, air tamp	12.954	E.C.Y.		117.88	117.88
TOTAL			1,302.37	1,796.90	3,099.27

G3030 210	Manholes & Catch Basins	COST PER EACH		
		MAT.	INST.	TOTAL
1920	Manhole/catch basin, brick, 4' I.D. riser, 4' deep	1,300	1,775	3,075
1940	6' deep	1,850	2,500	4,350
1960	8' deep	2,450	3,425	5,875
1980	10' deep	2,900	4,200	7,100
3000	12' deep	3,625	4,575	8,200
3020	14' deep	4,450	6,425	10,875
3200	Block, 4' I.D. riser, 4' deep	1,175	1,450	2,625
3220	6' deep	1,650	2,050	3,700
3240	8' deep	2,200	2,850	5,050
3260	10' deep	2,625	3,500	6,125
3280	12' deep	3,325	4,450	7,775
3300	14' deep	4,150	5,425	9,575
4620	Concrete, cast-in-place, 4' I.D. riser, 4' deep	1,275	2,475	3,750
4640	6' deep	1,825	3,325	5,150
4660	8' deep	2,550	4,800	7,350
4680	10' deep	3,075	5,950	9,025
4700	12' deep	3,875	7,375	11,250
4720	14' deep	4,800	8,825	13,625
5820	Concrete, precast, 4' I.D. riser, 4' deep	1,525	1,325	2,850
5840	6' deep	2,050	1,775	3,825

G3030 Storm Sewer

G3030 210	Manholes & Catch Basins	COST PER EACH		
		MAT.	INST.	TOTAL
5860	8' deep	2,575	2,475	5,050
5880	10' deep	3,125	3,050	6,175
5900	12' deep	3,925	3,775	7,700
5920	14' deep	4,875	4,775	9,650
6000	5' I.D. riser, 4' deep	2,600	1,500	4,100
6020	6' deep	3,225	2,100	5,325
6040	8' deep	4,175	2,775	6,950
6060	10' deep	5,300	3,525	8,825
6080	12' deep	6,525	4,525	11,050
6100	14' deep	7,900	5,500	13,400
6200	6' I.D. riser, 4' deep	3,325	1,975	5,300
6220	6' deep	4,150	2,600	6,750
6240	8' deep	5,275	3,675	8,950
6260	10' deep	6,675	4,650	11,325
6280	12' deep	8,200	5,850	14,050
6300	14' deep	9,850	7,100	16,950

G3030 Storm Sewer

The Headwall Systems are listed in concrete and different stone wall materials for two different backfill slope conditions. The backfill slope directly affects the length of the wing walls. Walls are listed for different culvert sizes starting at 30″ diameter. Excavation and backfill are included in the system components, and are figured from an elevation 2′ below the bottom of the pipe.

System Components	QUANTITY	UNIT	COST PER EACH MAT.	COST PER EACH INST.	COST PER EACH TOTAL
SYSTEM G3030 310 2000					
HEADWALL, C.I.P. CONCRETE FOR 30″ PIPE, 3′ LONG WING WALLS					
Excavation, hydraulic backhoe, 3/8 C.Y. bucket	2.500	B.C.Y.		225.40	225.40
Formwork, 2 uses	157.000	SFCA	418.52	1,912.35	2,330.87
Reinforcing in place, A615 Gr 60, longer and heavier dowels, add	45.000	Lb.	26.55	81.45	108
Concrete, 3000 psi	2.600	C.Y.	291.20		291.20
Place concrete, spread footings, direct chute	2.600	C.Y.		138.45	138.45
Backfill, dozer	2.500	L.C.Y.		55.16	55.16
TOTAL			736.27	2,412.81	3,149.08

G3030 310	Headwalls	COST PER EACH MAT.	COST PER EACH INST.	COST PER EACH TOTAL
2000	Headwall, 1-1/2 to 1 slope soil, C.I.P. conc, 30″ pipe, 3′ long wing walls	735	2,400	3,135
2020	Pipe size 36″, 3′-6″ long wing walls	920	2,900	3,820
2040	Pipe size 42″, 4′ long wing walls	1,125	3,375	4,500
2060	Pipe size 48″, 4′-6″ long wing walls	1,325	3,950	5,275
2080	Pipe size 54″, 5′-0″ long wing walls	1,575	4,575	6,150
2100	Pipe size 60″, 5′-6″ long wing walls	1,850	5,225	7,075
2120	Pipe size 72″, 6′-6″ long wing walls	2,450	6,725	9,175
2140	Pipe size 84″, 7′-6″ long wing walls	3,125	8,300	11,425
2500	$250/ton stone, pipe size 30″, 3′ long wing walls	540	880	1,420
2520	Pipe size 36″, 3′-6″ long wing walls	695	1,050	1,745
2540	Pipe size 42″, 4′ long wing walls	870	1,250	2,120
2560	Pipe size 48″, 4′-6″ long wing walls	1,075	1,475	2,550
2580	Pipe size 54″, 5′ long wing walls	1,300	1,725	3,025
2600	Pipe size 60″, 5′-6″ long wing walls	1,550	2,000	3,550
2620	Pipe size 72″, 6′-6″ long wing walls	2,125	2,650	4,775
2640	Pipe size 84″, 7′-6″ long wing walls	2,800	3,400	6,200
3000	$350/ton stone, pipe size 30″, 3′ long wing walls	755	880	1,635
3020	Pipe size 36″, 3′-6″ long wing walls	970	1,050	2,020
3040	Pipe size 42″, 4′ long wing walls	1,225	1,250	2,475
3060	Pipe size 48″, 4′-6″ long wing walls	1,500	1,475	2,975
3080	Pipe size 54″, 5′ long wing walls	1,825	1,725	3,550
3100	Pipe size 60″, 5′-6″ long wing walls	2,150	2,000	4,150
3120	Pipe size 72″, 6′-6″ long wing walls	2,975	2,650	5,625
3140	Pipe size 84″, 7′-6″ long wing walls	3,900	3,400	7,300
3500	$450/ton stone, pipe size 30″, 3′ long wing walls	975	880	1,855
3520	Pipe size 36″, 3′-6″ long wing walls	1,250	1,050	2,300
3540	Pipe size 42″, 4′ long wing walls	1,575	1,250	2,825
3560	Pipe size 48″, 4′-6″ long wing walls	1,950	1,475	3,425
3580	Pipe size 54″, 5′ long wing walls	2,350	1,725	4,075
3600	Pipe size 60″, 5′-6″ long wing walls	2,775	2,000	4,775

G3030 Storm Sewer

G3030 310	Headwalls	COST PER EACH		
		MAT.	INST.	TOTAL
3620	Pipe size 72", 6'-6" long wing walls	3,850	2,650	6,500
3640	Pipe size 84", 7'-6" long wing walls	5,050	3,400	8,450
4000	$650/ton stone, pipe size 30", 3' long wing walls	1,400	880	2,280
4020	Pipe size 36", 3'-6" long wing walls	1,800	1,050	2,850
4040	Pipe size 42", 4' long wing walls	2,275	1,250	3,525
4060	Pipe size 48", 4'-6" long wing walls	2,800	1,475	4,275
4080	Pipe size 54", 5' long wing walls	3,375	1,725	5,100
4100	Pipe size 60", 5'-6" long wing walls	4,000	2,000	6,000
4120	Pipe size 72", 6'-6" long wing walls	5,525	2,650	8,175
4140	Pipe size 84", 7'-6" long wing walls	7,275	3,400	10,675
4500	2 to 1 slope soil, C.I.P. concrete, pipe size 30", 4'-3" long wing walls	880	2,800	3,680
4520	Pipe size 36", 5' long wing walls	1,100	3,400	4,500
4540	Pipe size 42", 5'-9" long wing walls	1,375	4,100	5,475
4560	Pipe size 48", 6'-6" long wing walls	1,650	4,725	6,375
4580	Pipe size 54", 7'-3" long wing walls	1,950	5,525	7,475
4600	Pipe size 60", 8'-0" long wing walls	2,275	6,325	8,600
4620	Pipe size 72", 9'-6" long wing walls	3,075	8,250	11,325
4640	Pipe size 84", 11'-0" long wing walls	3,950	10,200	14,150
5000	$250/ton stone, pipe size 30", 4'-3" long wing walls	655	1,000	1,655
5020	Pipe size 36", 5' long wing walls	860	1,250	2,110
5040	Pipe size 42", 5'-9" long wing walls	1,075	1,500	2,575
5060	Pipe size 48", 6'-6" long wing walls	1,350	1,775	3,125
5080	Pipe size 54", 7'-3" long wing walls	1,625	2,100	3,725
5100	Pipe size 60", 8'-0" long wing walls	1,950	2,450	4,400
5120	Pipe size 72", 9'-6" long wing walls	870	3,650	4,520
5140	Pipe size 84", 11'-0" long wing walls	1,150	4,800	5,950
5500	$350/ton stone, pipe size 30", 4'-3" long wing walls	915	1,000	1,915
5520	Pipe size 36", 5' long wing walls	1,200	1,250	2,450
5540	Pipe size 42", 5'-9" long wing walls	1,525	1,500	3,025
5560	Pipe size 48", 6'-6" long wing walls	1,875	1,775	3,650
5580	Pipe size 54", 7'-3" long wing walls	2,275	2,100	4,375
5600	Pipe size 60", 8'-0" long wing walls	2,725	2,450	5,175
5620	Pipe size 72", 9'-6" long wing walls	3,775	3,275	7,050
5640	Pipe size 84", 11'-0" long wing walls	5,025	4,275	9,300
6000	$450/ton stone, pipe size 30", 4'-3" long wing walls	1,175	1,000	2,175
6020	Pipe size 36", 5'-0" long wing walls	1,550	1,250	2,800
6040	Pipe size 42", 5'-9" long wing walls	1,975	1,500	3,475
6060	Pipe size 48", 6'-6" long wing walls	2,450	1,775	4,225
6080	Pipe size 54", 7'-3" long wing walls	2,950	2,100	5,050
6100	Pipe size 60", 8'-0" long wing walls	3,525	2,450	5,975
6120	Pipe size 72", 9'-6" long wing walls	4,875	3,275	8,150
6140	Pipe size 84", 11'-0" long wing walls	6,500	4,275	10,775
6500	$650/ton stone, pipe size 30", 4'-3" long wing walls	1,700	1,000	2,700
6520	Pipe size 36", 5' long wing walls	2,250	1,250	3,500
6540	Pipe size 42", 5'-9" long wing walls	2,825	1,500	4,325
6560	Pipe size 48", 6'-6" long wing walls	3,500	1,775	5,275
6580	Pipe size 54", 7'-3" long wing walls	4,250	2,100	6,350
6600	Pipe size 60", 8'-0" long wing walls	5,050	2,450	7,500
6620	Pipe size 72", 9'-6" long wing walls	7,025	3,275	10,300
6640	Pipe size 84", 11'-0" long wing walls	9,350	4,275	13,625

681

G3030 Storm Sewer

Most new project sites will require some degree of work to address the quantity and, sometimes, quality of the stormwater produced from that site. The extent of this work is determined by design professionals, based on local and federal guidelines. In general, the scope of stormwater work will be a function of the amount of impervious surface (roof and paved areas) to be constructed, the permeability of soil, and the sensitivity of the location to stormwater issues overall. Absent further information, an allowance of $3 per SF of impervious surface is advisable. Note that these costs rely on the inlet and piping of a traditional stormwater drainage system and are additive to that base work unless otherwise stated.

1050 Small Surface Retention

Small surface retention areas, or rain gardens, are typically 200 to 800 SF depressions that intercept surface storm run-off and retain and remediate (improve) water through filtration and absorption with specialized plants and fill material. These can be attractive if maintained and located in smaller areas to treat smaller flows.

1100 Large Surface Detention

Large surface detention areas collect stormwater in open basins and release runoff at a set rate. These basins make up about 10% of the impervious area of a site and must be protected by a fence. This option is the least expensive per volume of capacity, but the results are usually not attractive and it is not always allowed by local ordinance.

1150 Sub-Surface Detention, Gravel

Sub-Surface detention systems (gravel) are large areas (typically located under surface parking) in which existing earth is replaced by gravel and the voids within are utilized as a temporary storage area for storm water. Water access can be by pervious pavers or a traditional inlet system.

1200 Sub-Surface Detention, Gravel & Void Structure

Sub-Surface detention (gravel and void structure) is a hybrid solution consisting of the gravel solution above with the presence of structures that create additional volumes of storage. These typically employ inlets which can be supplemented to provide improved water quality.

1250 Sub-Surface Detention, Structural Vaults

Sub-Surface detention systems (structural vaults) are large precast enclosures providing high-volume water storage. It is the most expensive system but requires the least amount of space for a given volume of capacity.

G3030 610	Stormwater Management (costs per CF of stormwater)	COST PER C.F.		
		MAT.	INST.	TOTAL
1050	Small Surface Retention	6.95	2.77	9.72
1100	Large Surface Detention	.23	.39	.62
1150	Sub-Surface Detention, Gravel	4.21	3.26	7.47
1200	Sub-Surface Detention, Gravel & Void Structure	9	1.64	10.64
1250	Sub-Surface Detention, Structural Vaults	19.70	1.96	21.66

G3060 Fuel Distribution

System Components	QUANTITY	UNIT	COST L.F.		
			MAT.	INST.	TOTAL
SYSTEM G3060 112 1000					
GASLINE 1/2″ PE, 60 PSI COILS, COMPRESSION COUPLING, INCLUDING COMMON					
EARTH EXCAVATION, BEDDING, BACKFILL AND COMPACTION					
Excavate Trench	.170	B.C.Y.		1.14	1.14
Sand bedding material	.090	L.C.Y.	1.76	1.15	2.91
Compact bedding	.070	E.C.Y.		.39	.39
Install 1/2″ gas pipe	1.000	L.F.	.50	3.66	4.16
Backfill trench	.120	L.C.Y.		.35	.35
Compact fill material in trench	.100	E.C.Y.		.49	.49
Dispose of excess fill material on-site	.090	L.C.Y.		1.06	1.06
TOTAL			2.26	8.24	10.50

G3060 112	Gasline (Common Earth Excavation)	COST L.F.		
		MAT.	INST.	TOTAL
0950	Gasline, including common earth excavation, bedding, backfill and compaction			
1000	1/2″ diameter PE, 60 psi coils, compression coupling, SDR 11, 2' deep	2.26	8.25	10.51
1010	4' deep	2.26	10.55	12.81
1020	6' deep	2.26	12.85	15.11
1050	1″ diameter PE, 60 psi coils, compression coupling, SDR 11, 2' deep	2.92	8.65	11.57
1060	4' deep	2.92	10.95	13.87
1070	6' deep	2.92	13.25	16.17
1100	1 1/4″ diameter PE, 60 psi coils, compression coupling, SDR 11, 2' deep	3.54	8.65	12.19
1110	4' deep	3.54	10.95	14.49
1120	6' deep	3.54	13.25	16.79
1150	2″ diameter PE, 60 psi coils, compression coupling, SDR 11, 2' deep	4.86	9.15	14.01
1160	4' deep	4.86	11.45	16.31
1180	6' deep	4.86	13.75	18.61
1200	3″ diameter PE, 60 psi coils, compression coupling, SDR 11, 2' deep	9.85	11.15	21
1210	4' deep	9.85	13.45	23.30
1220	6' deep	9.85	15.75	25.60

683

G30 Site Mechanical Utilities

G3060 Fuel Distribution

G3060 112	Gasline (Common Earth Excavation)	COST L.F.		
		MAT.	INST.	TOTAL
1250	4" diameter PE, 60 psi 40' length, compression coupling, SDR 11, 2' deep	18.60	15.50	34.10
1260	4' deep	18.60	17.80	36.40
1270	6' deep	18.60	20	38.60
1300	6" diameter PE, 60 psi 40' length w/coupling, SDR 11, 2' deep	40	16.45	56.45
1310	4' deep	40	18.75	58.75
1320	6' deep	40	21	61
1350	8" diameter PE, 60 psi 40' length w/coupling, SDR 11, 4' deep	60	21	81
1360	6' deep	60	23.50	83.50
2000	1" diameter steel plain end, Schedule 40, 2' deep	7	13.75	20.75
2010	4' deep	7	16.10	23.10
2020	6' deep	7	18.35	25.35
2050	2" diameter, steel plain end, Schedule 40, 2' deep	9.95	14.45	24.40
2060	4' deep	9.95	16.80	26.75
2070	6' deep	9.95	19.05	29
2100	3" diameter, steel plain end, Schedule 40, 2' deep	16.35	16.35	32.70
2110	4' deep	16.35	18.65	35
2120	6' deep	16.35	21	37.35
2150	4" diameter, steel plain end, Schedule 40, 2' deep	20.50	22.50	43
2160	4' deep	20.50	25	45.50
2170	6' deep	20.50	27	47.50
2200	5" diameter, steel plain end, Schedule 40, 2' deep	28.50	25	53.50
2210	4' deep	28.50	27.50	56
2220	6' deep	28.50	29.50	58
2250	6" diameter, steel plain end, Schedule 40, 2' deep	34.50	29.50	64
2260	4' deep	34.50	32	66.50
2270	6' deep	34.50	34.50	69
2300	8" diameter, steel plain end, Schedule 40, 2' deep	53	36	89
2310	4' deep	53	38.50	91.50
2320	6' deep	53	41	94
2350	10" diameter, steel plain end, Schedule 40, 2' deep	132	48.50	180.50
2360	4' deep	132	50.50	182.50
2370	6' deep	132	53.50	185.50
2400	12" diameter, steel plain end, Schedule 40, 2' deep	146	59	205
2410	4' deep	146	61	207
2420	6' deep	146	63.50	209.50
2460	14" diameter, steel plain end, Schedule 40, 4' deep	156	66	222
2470	6' deep	156	68	224
2510	16" diameter, Schedule 40, 4' deep	171	70.50	241.50
2520	6' deep	171	73	244
2560	18" diameter, Schedule 40, 4' deep	219	76	295
2570	6' deep	219	79	298
2600	20" diameter, steel plain end, Schedule 40, 4' deep	340	82	422
2610	6' deep	340	85.50	425.50
2650	24" diameter, steel plain end, Schedule 40, 4' deep	385	97.50	482.50
2660	6' deep	385	101	486
3150	4" diameter, steel plain end, Schedule 80, 2' deep	54.50	35.50	90
3160	4' deep	54.50	37.50	92
3170	6' deep	54.50	40	94.50
3200	5" diameter, steel plain end, Schedule 80, 2' deep	78	36	114
3210	4' deep	78	38.50	116.50
3220	6' deep	78	40.50	118.50
3250	6" diameter, steel plain end, Schedule 80, 2' deep	106	40	146
3260	4' deep	106	42	148
3270	6' deep	106	44.50	150.50
3300	8" diameter, steel plain end, Schedule 80, 2' deep	140	45.50	185.50
3310	4' deep	140	47.50	187.50
3320	6' deep	140	50	190
3350	10" diameter, steel plain end, Schedule 80, 2' deep	209	53	262

684

For customer support on your Site Work & Landscape Cost Data, call 877.737.1594.

G3060 Fuel Distribution

G3060 112	Gasline (Common Earth Excavation)	COST L.F.		
		MAT.	INST.	TOTAL
3360	4' deep	209	55	264
3370	6' deep	209	57.50	266.50
3400	12" diameter, steel plain end, Schedule 80, 2' deep	278	64.50	342.50
3410	4' deep	278	66.50	344.50
3420	6' deep	278	69.50	347.50

685

For customer support on your Site Work & Landscape Cost Data, call 877.737.1594.

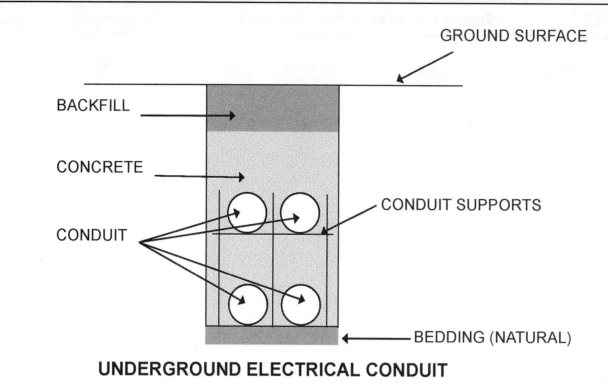

GROUND SURFACE

BACKFILL

CONCRETE

CONDUIT SUPPORTS

CONDUIT

BEDDING (NATURAL)

UNDERGROUND ELECTRICAL CONDUIT

System Components	QUANTITY	UNIT	COST EACH		
			MAT.	INST.	TOTAL
SYSTEM G4010 312 1000					
2000 AMP UNDERGROUND SERVICE INCLUDING COMMON EARTH EXCAVATION,					
CONCRETE, BACKFILL AND COMPACTION					
Excavate Trench	44.440	B.C.Y.		298.19	298.19
4 inch conduit bank	108.000	L.F.	1,085.40	2,646	3,731.40
4 inch fitting	8.000	Ea.	252	436	688
4 inch bells	4.000	Ea.	18.76	218	236.76
Concrete material	16.580	C.Y.	1,856.96		1,856.96
Concrete placement	16.580	C.Y.		407.37	407.37
Backfill trench	33.710	L.C.Y.		98.77	98.77
Compact fill material in trench	25.930	E.C.Y.		128.87	128.87
Dispose of excess fill material on-site	24.070	L.C.Y.		282.58	282.58
500 kcmil power cable	18.000	C.L.F.	22,950	7,380	30,330
Wire, 600 volt stranded copper wire, type THW, 1/0	6.000	C.L.F.	1,650	1,194	2,844
TOTAL			27,813.12	13,089.78	40,902.90

G4010 312	Underground Power Feed	COST EACH		
		MAT.	INST.	TOTAL
0950	Underground electrical including common earth excavation, concrete, backfill and compaction			
1000	2000 Amp service, 100' length, 4' depth	27,800	13,100	40,900
1100	1600 Amp service	21,800	10,100	31,900
1200	1200 Amp service	16,900	8,375	25,275
1300	1000 Amp service	14,500	7,650	22,150
1400	800 Amp service	12,500	7,200	19,700
1500	600 Amp service	8,350	6,675	15,025

G4010 Electrical Distribution

System Components	QUANTITY	UNIT	COST L.F.		
			MAT.	INST.	TOTAL
SYSTEM G4010 320 1012					
UNDERGROUND ELECTRICAL CONDUIT, 2″ DIAMETER, INCLUDING EXCAVATION,					
CONCRETE, BEDDING, BACKFILL, AND COMPACTION					
Excavate Trench	.150	B.C.Y.		1.01	1.01
Base spacer	.200	Ea.	.34	2.34	2.68
Conduit	1.000	L.F.	1.63	3.64	5.27
Concrete material	.050	C.Y.	5.60		5.60
Concrete placement	.050	C.Y.		1.23	1.23
Backfill trench	.120	L.C.Y.		.35	.35
Compact fill material in trench	.100	E.C.Y.		.49	.49
Dispose of excess fill material on-site	.120	L.C.Y.		1.40	1.40
Marking tape	.010	C.L.F.	.30	.03	.33
TOTAL			7.87	10.49	18.36

G4010 320	Underground Electrical Conduit	COST L.F.		
		MAT.	INST.	TOTAL
0950	Underground electrical conduit, including common earth excavation,			
0952	Concrete, bedding, backfill and compaction			
1012	2″ dia. Schedule 40 PVC, 2′ deep	7.85	10.50	18.35
1014	4′ deep	7.85	15	22.85
1016	6′ deep	7.85	19.35	27.20
1022	2 @ 2″ dia. Schedule 40 PVC, 2′ deep	9.85	16.45	26.30
1024	4′ deep	9.85	21	30.85
1026	6′ deep	9.85	25	34.85
1032	3 @ 2″ dia. Schedule 40 PVC, 2′ deep	11.80	22.50	34.30
1034	4′ deep	11.80	27	38.80
1036	6′ deep	11.80	31	42.80
1042	4 @ 2″ dia. Schedule 40 PVC, 2′ deep	16	28	44
1044	4′ deep	16	32.50	48.50
1046	6′ deep	16	37	53

687

For customer support on your Site Work & Landscape Cost Data, call 877.737.1594.

G4010 Electrical Distribution

G4010 320	Underground Electrical Conduit	COST L.F.		
		MAT.	INST.	TOTAL
1062	6 @ 2" dia. Schedule 40 PVC, 2' deep	19.95	40	59.95
1064	4' deep	19.95	44	63.95
1066	6' deep	19.95	49	68.95
1082	8 @ 2" dia. Schedule 40 PVC, 2' deep	24	52	76
1084	4' deep	24	56	80
1086	6' deep	24	60.50	84.50
1092	9 @ 2" dia. Schedule 40 PVC, 2' deep	26	57.50	83.50
1094	4' deep	28	62	90
1096	6' deep	28	66.50	94.50
1212	3" dia. Schedule 40 PVC, 2' deep	10.45	12.85	23.30
1214	4' deep	10.45	17.40	27.85
1216	6' deep	10.45	21.50	31.95
1222	2 @ 3" dia. Schedule 40 PVC, 2' deep	12.80	21	33.80
1224	4' deep	12.80	25.50	38.30
1226	6' deep	12.80	30	42.80
1232	3 @ 3" dia. Schedule 40 PVC, 2' deep	16.25	29.50	45.75
1234	4' deep	16.25	34	50.25
1236	6' deep	16.25	38	54.25
1242	4 @ 3" dia. Schedule 40 PVC, 2' deep	23	37.50	60.50
1244	4' deep	23	42	65
1246	6' deep	23	46.50	69.50
1262	6 @ 3" dia. Schedule 40 PVC, 2' deep	29	54	83
1264	4' deep	29	58.50	87.50
1266	6' deep	29	63	92
1282	8 @ 3" dia. Schedule 40 PVC, 2' deep	36	71	107
1284	4' deep	36	75	111
1286	6' deep	36	80	116
1292	9 @ 3" dia. Schedule 40 PVC, 2' deep	41.50	80	121.50
1294	4' deep	42.50	83.50	126
1296	6' deep	42.50	87.50	130
1312	4" dia. Schedule 40 PVC, 2' deep	11.75	15.75	27.50
1314	4' deep	11.75	20.50	32.25
1316	6' deep	11.75	24.50	36.25
1322	2 @ 4" dia. Schedule 40 PVC, 2' deep	16.45	27.50	43.95
1324	4' deep	16.45	31.50	47.95
1326	6' deep	16.45	36	52.45
1332	3 @ 4" dia. Schedule 40 PVC, 2' deep	20	38.50	58.50
1334	4' deep	20	42.50	62.50
1336	6' deep	20	47	67
1342	4 @ 4" dia. Schedule 40 PVC, 2' deep	29	50	79
1344	4' deep	29	54.50	83.50
1346	6' deep	29	59	88
1362	6 @ 4" dia. Schedule 40 PVC, 2' deep	37.50	73	110.50
1364	4' deep	37.50	77	114.50
1366	6' deep	37.50	81.50	119
1382	8 @ 4" dia. Schedule 40 PVC, 2' deep	48	96	144
1384	4' deep	48	101	149
1386	6' deep	48	107	155
1392	9 @ 4" dia. Schedule 40 PVC, 2' deep	54	108	162
1394	4' deep	54	111	165
1396	6' deep	54	115	169
1412	5" dia. Schedule 40 PVC, 2' deep	13.75	18.85	32.60
1414	4' deep	13.75	23	36.75
1416	6' deep	13.75	27.50	41.25
1422	2 @ 5" dia. Schedule 40 PVC, 2' deep	20.50	33.50	54
1424	4' deep	20.50	37.50	58
1426	6' deep	20.50	42	62.50
1432	3 @ 5" dia. Schedule 40 PVC, 2' deep	27.50	48	75.50

G4010 Electrical Distribution

G4010 320	Underground Electrical Conduit	COST L.F.		
		MAT.	INST.	TOTAL
1434	4' deep	27.50	53	80.50
1436	6' deep	27.50	57	84.50
1442	4 @ 5" dia. Schedule 40 PVC, 2' deep	37.50	62	99.50
1444	4' deep	37.50	66.50	104
1446	6' deep	37.50	70.50	108
1462	6 @ 5" dia. Schedule 40 PVC, 2' deep	49.50	90.50	140
1464	4' deep	49.50	95.50	145
1466	6' deep	49.50	100	149.50
1482	8 @ 5" dia. Schedule 40 PVC, 2' deep	65.50	121	186.50
1484	4' deep	65.50	127	192.50
1486	6' deep	65.50	132	197.50
1492	9 @ 5" dia. Schedule 40 PVC, 2' deep	73	136	209
1494	4' deep	73	139	212
1496	6' deep	73	143	216
1512	6" dia. Schedule 40 PVC, 2' deep	17.10	23	40.10
1514	4' deep	17.10	27	44.10
1516	6' deep	17.10	32	49.10
1522	2 @ 6" dia. Schedule 40 PVC, 2' deep	25	41	66
1524	4' deep	25	45	70
1526	6' deep	25	50	75
1532	3 @ 6" dia. Schedule 40 PVC, 2' deep	35	60	95
1534	4' deep	35	65.50	100.50
1536	6' deep	35	71	106
1542	4 @ 6" dia. Schedule 40 PVC, 2' deep	46	77	123
1544	4' deep	46	82	128
1546	6' deep	46	86	132
1562	6 @ 6" dia. Schedule 40 PVC, 2' deep	65	115	180
1564	4' deep	65	120	185
1566	6' deep	65	126	191
1582	8 @ 6" dia. Schedule 40 PVC, 2' deep	86.50	153	239.50
1584	4' deep	86.50	160	246.50
1586	6' deep	86.50	167	253.50
1592	9 @ 6" dia. Schedule 40 PVC, 2' deep	96.50	172	268.50
1594	4' deep	96.50	175	271.50
1596	6' deep	96.50	180	276.50

G4020 Site Lighting

The Site Lighting System includes the complete unit from foundation to electrical fixtures. Each system includes: excavation; concrete base; backfill by hand; compaction with a plate compacter; pole of specified material; all fixtures; and lamps.

The Expanded System Listing shows Site Lighting Systems that use one of two types of lamps: high pressure sodium; and metal halide. Systems are listed for 400-watt and 1000-watt lamps. Pole height varies from 20′ to 40′. There are four types of poles possibly listed: aluminum, fiberglass, steel and wood.

System Components	QUANTITY	UNIT	COST EACH MAT.	COST EACH INST.	COST EACH TOTAL
SYSTEM G4020 110 5820					
SITE LIGHTING, METAL HALIDE, 400 WATT, ALUMINUM POLE, 20′ HIGH					
Excavating, by hand, pits to 6′ deep, heavy soil	2.368	C.Y.		274.69	274.69
Concrete in place incl. forms and reinf. stl. spread footings under 1 CY	.465	C.Y.	85.10	129.39	214.49
Backfill	1.903	C.Y.		79.93	79.93
Compact, vibrating plate	1.903	C.Y.		10.88	10.88
Aluminum light pole, 20′, no concrete base	1.000	Ea.	1,025	612	1,637
Road area luminaire wire	.300	C.L.F.	11.10	24.60	35.70
Roadway area luminaire, metal halide 400 W	1.000	Ea.	610	298	908
TOTAL			1,731.20	1,429.49	3,160.69

G4020 110	Site Lighting	MAT.	INST.	TOTAL
2320	Site lighting, high pressure sodium, 400 watt, aluminum pole, 20′ high	1,750	1,425	3,175
2340	30′ high	2,700	1,750	4,450
2360	40′ high	3,200	2,250	5,450
2520	Fiberglass pole, 20′ high	1,475	1,275	2,750
2540	30′ high	1,675	1,575	3,250
2560	40′ high	2,450	2,000	4,450
2720	Steel pole, 20′ high	1,925	1,500	3,425
2740	30′ high	2,175	1,850	4,025
2760	40′ high	2,725	2,425	5,150
2920	Wood pole, 20′ high	985	1,400	2,385
2940	30′ high	1,225	1,750	2,975
2960	40′ high	1,575	2,150	3,725
3120	1000 watt, aluminum pole, 20′ high	1,850	1,450	3,300
3140	30′ high	2,800	1,775	4,575
3160	40′ high	3,300	2,300	5,600
3320	Fiberglass pole, 20′ high	1,550	1,300	2,850
3340	30′ high	1,775	1,600	3,375
3360	40′ high	2,550	2,025	4,575
3420	Steel pole, 20′ high	2,025	1,525	3,550
3440	30′ high	2,275	1,875	4,150

G4020 Site Lighting

G4020 110	Site Lighting	COST EACH		
		MAT.	INST.	TOTAL
3460	40' high	2,825	2,450	5,275
3520	Wood pole, 20' high	1,075	1,425	2,500
3540	30' high	1,325	1,775	3,100
3560	40' high	1,650	2,175	3,825
5820	Metal halide, 400 watt, aluminum pole, 20' high	1,725	1,425	3,150
5840	30' high	2,675	1,750	4,425
5860	40' high	3,175	2,250	5,425
6120	Fiberglass pole, 20' high	1,450	1,275	2,725
6140	30' high	1,650	1,575	3,225
6160	40' high	2,425	2,000	4,425
6320	Steel pole, 20' high	1,900	1,500	3,400
6340	30' high	2,150	1,850	4,000
6360	40' high	2,700	2,425	5,125
7620	1000 watt, aluminum pole, 20' high	1,800	1,450	3,250
7640	30' high	2,750	1,775	4,525
7660	40' high	3,250	2,300	5,550
7900	Fiberglass pole, 20' high	1,525	1,300	2,825
7920	30' high	1,725	1,600	3,325
7940	40' high	2,500	2,025	4,525
8120	Steel pole, 20' high	1,975	1,525	3,500
8140	30' high	2,225	1,875	4,100
8160	40' high	2,775	2,450	5,225

For customer support on your Site Work & Landscape Cost Data, call 877.737.1594.

G4020 Site Lighting

Table G4020 210 Procedure for Calculating Floodlights Required for Various Footcandles
Poles should not be spaced more than 4 times the fixture mounting height for good light distribution.

Estimating Chart
Select Lamp type.

Determine total square feet.

Chart will show quantity of fixtures to provide 1 footcandle initial, at intersection of lines. Multiply fixture quantity by desired footcandle level.

Chart based on use of wide beam luminaires in an area whose dimensions are large compared to mounting height and is approximate only.

To maintain 1 footcandle over a large area use these watts per square foot:

Incandescent	0.15
Metal Halide	0.032
Mercury Vapor	0.05
High Pressure Sodium	0.024

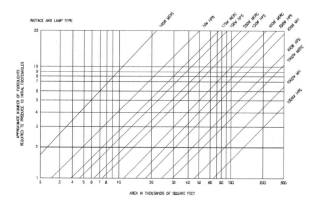

System Components		QUANTITY	UNIT	COST EACH		
				MAT.	INST.	TOTAL
SYSTEM G4020 210 0200						
LIGHT POLES, ALUMINUM, 20' HIGH, 1 ARM BRACKET						
Aluminum light pole, 20', no concrete base		1.000	Ea.	1,025	612	1,637
Bracket arm for Aluminum light pole		1.000	Ea.	133	82	215
Excavation by hand, pits to 6' deep, heavy soil or clay		2.368	C.Y.		274.69	274.69
Footing, concrete incl forms, reinforcing, spread, under 1 C.Y.		.465	C.Y.	85.10	129.39	214.49
Backfill by hand		1.903	C.Y.		79.93	79.93
Compaction vibrating plate		1.903	C.Y.		10.88	10.88
	TOTAL			1,243.10	1,188.89	2,431.99

G4020 210	Light Pole (Installed)	COST EACH		
		MAT.	INST.	TOTAL
0200	Light pole, aluminum, 20' high, 1 arm bracket	1,250	1,175	2,425
0240	2 arm brackets	1,375	1,175	2,550
0280	3 arm brackets	1,500	1,225	2,725
0320	4 arm brackets	1,650	1,225	2,875
0360	30' high, 1 arm bracket	2,200	1,500	3,700
0400	2 arm brackets	2,325	1,500	3,825
0440	3 arm brackets	2,450	1,525	3,975
0480	4 arm brackets	2,600	1,525	4,125
0680	40' high, 1 arm bracket	2,675	2,000	4,675
0720	2 arm brackets	2,825	2,000	4,825
0760	3 arm brackets	2,950	2,050	5,000
0800	4 arm brackets	3,100	2,050	5,150
0840	Steel, 20' high, 1 arm bracket	1,475	1,250	2,725
0880	2 arm brackets	1,525	1,250	2,775
0920	3 arm brackets	1,575	1,300	2,875
0960	4 arm brackets	1,625	1,300	2,925
1000	30' high, 1 arm bracket	1,725	1,600	3,325
1040	2 arm brackets	1,775	1,600	3,375
1080	3 arm brackets	1,800	1,650	3,450
1120	4 arm brackets	1,875	1,650	3,525
1320	40' high, 1 arm bracket	2,275	2,175	4,450
1360	2 arm brackets	2,325	2,175	4,500
1400	3 arm brackets	2,350	2,225	4,575
1440	4 arm brackets	2,425	2,225	4,650

G9020 Site Repair & Maintenance

G9020 100	Clean and Wrap Marine Piles	COST EACH		
		MAT.	INST.	TOTAL
1000	Clean & wrap 5 foot long, 8 inch diameter wood pile using nails from boat	92.50	106	198.50
1010	6 foot long	111	176	287
1020	7 foot long	129	184	313
1030	8 foot long	148	191	339
1040	9 foot long	166	197	363
1050	10 foot long	185	204	389
1060	11 foot long	203	262	465
1070	12 foot long	221	268	489
1075	13 foot long	240	276	516
1080	14 foot long	258	283	541
1090	15 foot long	277	290	567
1100	Clean & wrap 5 foot long, 10 inch diameter	115	132	247
1110	6 foot long	138	220	358
1120	7 foot long	161	228	389
1130	8 foot long	184	237	421
1140	9 foot long	207	245	452
1150	10 foot long	230	253	483
1160	11 foot long	253	335	588
1170	12 foot long	276	345	621
1175	13 foot long	299	355	654
1180	14 foot long	320	360	680
1190	15 foot long	345	370	715
1200	Clean & wrap 5 foot long, 12 inch diameter	138	157	295
1210	6 foot long	165	264	429
1220	7 foot long	193	275	468
1230	8 foot long	220	284	504
1240	9 foot long	248	295	543
1250	10 foot long	275	305	580
1260	11 foot long	305	395	700
1270	12 foot long	330	410	740
1275	13 foot long	360	420	780
1280	14 foot long	385	430	815
1290	15 foot long	415	440	855
1300	Clean & wrap 5 foot long, 13 inch diameter	150	172	322
1310	6 foot long	180	288	468
1320	7 foot long	210	299	509
1330	8 foot long	240	310	550
1340	9 foot long	270	320	590
1350	10 foot long	300	335	635
1360	11 foot long	330	430	760
1370	12 foot long	360	440	800
1375	13 foot long	390	450	840
1380	14 foot long	420	460	880
1390	15 foot long	450	470	920
1400	Clean & wrap 5 foot long, 14 inch diameter	163	185	348
1410	6 foot long	195	305	500
1420	7 foot long	228	315	543
1430	8 foot long	260	325	585
1440	9 foot long	293	340	633
1450	10 foot long	325	350	675
1460	11 foot long	360	455	815
1470	12 foot long	390	465	855
1475	13 foot long	425	480	905
1480	14 foot long	455	490	945
1490	15 foot long	490	500	990
1500	Clean & wrap 5 foot long, 8 inch diameter wood pile using straps from boat	143	103	246
1510	6 foot long	171	173	344
1520	7 foot long	200	179	379

693

For customer support on your Site Work & Landscape Cost Data, call 877.737.1594.

G9020 Site Repair & Maintenance

G9020 100	Clean and Wrap Marine Piles	COST EACH		
		MAT.	INST.	TOTAL
1530	8 foot long	228	185	413
1540	9 foot long	257	191	448
1550	10 foot long	285	198	483
1560	11 foot long	315	255	570
1570	12 foot long	340	261	601
1575	13 foot long	370	267	637
1580	14 foot long	400	273	673
1590	15 foot long	430	279	709
1600	Clean & wrap 5 foot long, 10 inch diameter	178	128	306
1610	6 foot long	213	215	428
1620	7 foot long	249	222	471
1630	8 foot long	284	230	514
1640	9 foot long	320	238	558
1650	10 foot long	355	246	601
1660	11 foot long	390	330	720
1670	12 foot long	425	335	760
1675	13 foot long	460	345	805
1680	14 foot long	495	350	845
1690	15 foot long	535	360	895
1700	Clean & wrap 5 foot long, 12 inch diameter	213	152	365
1710	6 foot long	255	258	513
1720	7 foot long	298	267	565
1730	8 foot long	340	277	617
1740	9 foot long	385	286	671
1750	10 foot long	425	295	720
1760	11 foot long	470	390	860
1770	12 foot long	510	395	905
1775	13 foot long	555	410	965
1780	14 foot long	595	415	1,010
1790	15 foot long	640	425	1,065
1800	Clean & wrap 5 foot long, 13 inch diameter	230	166	396
1810	6 foot long	276	281	557
1820	7 foot long	320	291	611
1830	8 foot long	370	300	670
1840	9 foot long	415	310	725
1850	10 foot long	460	320	780
1860	11 foot long	505	415	920
1870	12 foot long	550	425	975
1875	13 foot long	600	435	1,035
1880	14 foot long	645	445	1,090
1890	15 foot long	690	455	1,145
1900	Clean & wrap 5 foot long, 14 inch diameter	248	179	427
1910	6 foot long	297	296	593
1920	7 foot long	345	305	650
1930	8 foot long	395	320	715
1940	9 foot long	445	330	775
1950	10 foot long	495	340	835
1960	11 foot long	545	440	985
1970	12 foot long	595	455	1,050
1975	13 foot long	645	465	1,110
1980	14 foot long	695	475	1,170
1990	15 foot long	745	485	1,230
2000	Clean & wrap 5 foot long, 12 inch diameter concrete pile from boat w/straps	213	134	347
2010	6 foot long	255	223	478
2020	7 foot long	298	233	531
2030	8 foot long	340	242	582
2040	9 foot long	385	251	636
2050	10 foot long	425	261	686

G90 Other Site Construction

G9020 Site Repair & Maintenance

G9020 100	Clean and Wrap Marine Piles	COST EACH		
		MAT.	INST.	TOTAL
2060	11 foot long	470	345	815
2070	12 foot long	510	355	865
2080	13 foot long	555	365	920
2085	14 foot long	595	375	970
2090	15 foot long	640	380	1,020
2100	Clean & wrap 5 foot long, 14 inch diameter	248	156	404
2110	6 foot long	297	259	556
2120	7 foot long	345	270	615
2130	8 foot long	395	281	676
2140	9 foot long	445	292	737
2150	10 foot long	495	305	800
2160	11 foot long	545	390	935
2170	12 foot long	595	400	995
2180	13 foot long	645	415	1,060
2185	14 foot long	695	420	1,115
2190	15 foot long	745	430	1,175

695

Reference Section

All the reference information is in one section, making it easy to find what you need to know ... and easy to use the book on a daily basis. This section is visually identified by a vertical black bar on the page edges.

In this Reference Section, we've included Equipment Rental Costs, a listing of rental and operating costs; Crew Listings, a full listing of all crews and equipment, and their costs; Historical Cost Indexes for cost comparisons over time; City Cost Indexes and Location Factors for adjusting costs to the region you are in; Reference Tables, where you will find explanations, estimating information and procedures, or technical data; Change Orders, information on pricing changes to contract documents; Square Foot Costs that allow you to make a rough estimate for the overall cost of a project; and an explanation of all the Abbreviations in the book.

Table of Contents

Estimating Tips

- This section contains the average costs to rent and operate hundreds of pieces of construction equipment. This is useful information when estimating the time and material requirements of any particular operation in order to establish a unit or total cost. Equipment costs include not only rental, but also operating costs for equipment under normal use.

Rental Costs

- Equipment rental rates are obtained from the following industry sources throughout North America: contractors, suppliers, dealers, manufacturers, and distributors.

- Rental rates vary throughout the country, with larger cities generally having lower rates. Lease plans for new equipment are available for periods in excess of six months, with a percentage of payments applying toward purchase.

- Monthly rental rates vary from 2% to 5% of the purchase price of the equipment depending on the anticipated life of the equipment and its wearing parts.

- Weekly rental rates are about 1/3 the monthly rates, and daily rental rates are about 1/3 the weekly rate.

- Rental rates can also be treated as reimbursement costs for contractor-owned equipment. Owned equipment costs include depreciation, loan payments, interest, taxes, insurance, storage, and major repairs.

Operating Costs

- The operating costs include parts and labor for routine servicing, such as repair and replacement of pumps, filters and worn lines. Normal operating expendables, such as fuel, lubricants, tires and electricity (where applicable), are also included.

- Extraordinary operating expendables with highly variable wear patterns, such as diamond bits and blades, are excluded. These costs can be found as material costs in the Unit Price section.

- The hourly operating costs listed do not include the operator's wages.

Equipment Cost/Day

- Any power equipment required by a crew is shown in the Crew Listings with a daily cost.

- The daily cost of equipment needed by a crew is based on dividing the weekly rental rate by 5 (number of working days in the week), and then adding the hourly operating cost times 8 (the number of hours in a day). This "Equipment Cost/Day" is shown in the far right column of the Equipment Rental pages.

- If equipment is needed for only one or two days, it is best to develop your own cost by including components for daily rent and hourly operating cost. This is important when the listed Crew for a task does not contain the equipment needed, such as a crane for lifting mechanical heating/cooling equipment up onto a roof.

- If the quantity of work is less than the crew's Daily Output shown for a Unit Price line item that includes a bare unit equipment cost, it is recommended to estimate one day's rental cost and operating cost for equipment shown in the Crew Listing for that line item.

Mobilization/ Demobilization

- The cost to move construction equipment from an equipment yard or rental company to the job site and back again is not included in equipment rental costs listed in the Reference Section, nor in the bare equipment cost of any unit price line item, nor in any equipment costs shown in the Crew listings.

- Mobilization (to the site) and demobilization (from the site) costs can be found in the Unit Price Section.

- If a piece of equipment is already at the job site, it is not appropriate to utilize mobilization/demobilization costs again in an estimate.

01 54 33 | Equipment Rental

			UNIT	HOURLY OPER. COST	RENT PER DAY	RENT PER WEEK	RENT PER MONTH	EQUIPMENT COST/DAY	
10	0010	**CONCRETE EQUIPMENT RENTAL** without operators	R015433 -10						10
	0200	Bucket, concrete lightweight, 1/2 C.Y.	Ea.	.80	23.50	70	210	20.40	
	0300	1 C.Y.		.90	27.50	83	249	23.80	
	0400	1-1/2 C.Y.		1.10	36.50	110	330	30.80	
	0500	2 C.Y.		1.25	45	135	405	37	
	0580	8 C.Y.		6.10	257	770	2,300	202.80	
	0600	Cart, concrete, self-propelled, operator walking, 10 C.F.		3.25	56.50	170	510	60	
	0700	Operator riding, 18 C.F.		5.35	95	285	855	99.80	
	0800	Conveyer for concrete, portable, gas, 16" wide, 26' long		12.60	123	370	1,100	174.80	
	0900	46' long		13.00	148	445	1,325	193	
	1000	56' long		13.10	157	470	1,400	198.80	
	1100	Core drill, electric, 2-1/2 H.P., 1" to 8" bit diameter		1.77	68.50	205	615	55.15	
	1150	11 H.P., 8" to 18" cores		5.95	113	340	1,025	115.60	
	1200	Finisher, concrete floor, gas, riding trowel, 96" wide		12.75	145	435	1,300	189	
	1300	Gas, walk-behind, 3 blade, 36" trowel		2.15	20	60	180	29.20	
	1400	4 blade, 48" trowel		4.20	27.50	83	249	50.20	
	1500	Float, hand-operated (Bull float) 48" wide		.08	13.35	40	120	8.65	
	1570	Curb builder, 14 H.P., gas, single screw		14.65	248	745	2,225	266.20	
	1590	Double screw		15.35	290	870	2,600	296.80	
	1600	Floor grinder, concrete and terrazzo, electric, 22" path		2.57	158	475	1,425	115.55	
	1700	Edger, concrete, electric, 7" path		1.04	51.50	155	465	39.30	
	1750	Vacuum pick-up system for floor grinders, wet/dry		1.49	81.50	245	735	60.90	
	1800	Mixer, powered, mortar and concrete, gas, 6 C.F., 18 H.P.		8.65	118	355	1,075	140.20	
	1900	10 C.F., 25 H.P.		10.80	143	430	1,300	172.40	
	2000	16 C.F.		11.15	165	495	1,475	188.20	
	2100	Concrete, stationary, tilt drum, 2 C.Y.		6.90	232	695	2,075	194.20	
	2120	Pump, concrete, truck mounted 4" line 80' boom		25.00	865	2,600	7,800	720	
	2140	5" line, 110' boom		32.40	1,150	3,435	10,300	946.20	
	2160	Mud jack, 50 C.F. per hr.		7.30	125	375	1,125	133.40	
	2180	225 C.F. per hr.		9.50	145	435	1,300	163	
	2190	Shotcrete pump rig, 12 C.Y./hr.		14.85	220	660	1,975	250.80	
	2200	35 C.Y./hr.		17.50	235	705	2,125	281	
	2600	Saw, concrete, manual, gas, 18 H.P.		6.75	45	135	405	81	
	2650	Self-propelled, gas, 30 H.P.		13.30	102	305	915	167.40	
	2675	V-groove crack chaser, manual, gas, 6 H.P.		2.35	17.35	52	156	29.20	
	2700	Vibrators, concrete, electric, 60 cycle, 2 H.P.		.46	8.65	26	78	8.90	
	2800	3 H.P.		.60	11.65	35	105	11.80	
	2900	Gas engine, 5 H.P.		2.00	16	48	144	25.60	
	3000	8 H.P.		2.75	15.35	46	138	31.20	
	3050	Vibrating screed, gas engine, 8 H.P.		2.91	71.50	215	645	66.30	
	3120	Concrete transit mixer, 6 x 4, 250 H.P., 8 C.Y., rear discharge		61.55	570	1,715	5,150	835.40	
	3200	Front discharge		72.45	700	2,095	6,275	998.60	
	3300	6 x 6, 285 H.P., 12 C.Y., rear discharge		71.50	660	1,980	5,950	968	
	3400	Front discharge		74.00	705	2,120	6,350	1,016	
20	0010	**EARTHWORK EQUIPMENT RENTAL** without operators	R015433 -10						20
	0040	Aggregate spreader, push type 8' to 12' wide	Ea.	3.05	25.50	76	228	39.60	
	0045	Tailgate type, 8' wide		2.90	32.50	98	294	42.80	
	0055	Earth auger, truck-mounted, for fence & sign posts, utility poles		19.15	440	1,320	3,950	417.20	
	0060	For borings and monitoring wells		46.65	675	2,030	6,100	779.20	
	0070	Portable, trailer mounted		3.30	32.50	98	294	46	
	0075	Truck-mounted, for caissons, water wells		100.15	2,900	8,705	26,100	2,542	
	0080	Horizontal boring machine, 12" to 36" diameter, 45 H.P.		24.20	192	575	1,725	308.60	
	0090	12" to 48" diameter, 65 H.P.		34.35	335	1,000	3,000	474.80	
	0095	Auger, for fence posts, gas engine, hand held		.60	6	18	54	8.40	
	0100	Excavator, diesel hydraulic, crawler mounted, 1/2 C.Y. cap.		24.65	420	1,255	3,775	448.20	
	0120	5/8 C.Y. capacity		32.55	550	1,645	4,925	589.40	
	0140	3/4 C.Y. capacity		35.60	615	1,850	5,550	654.80	
	0150	1 C.Y. capacity		49.70	690	2,075	6,225	812.60	

01 54 33 | Equipment Rental

		UNIT	HOURLY OPER. COST	RENT PER DAY	RENT PER WEEK	RENT PER MONTH	EQUIPMENT COST/DAY	
20	0200	1-1/2 C.Y. capacity	Ea.	59.80	920	2,760	8,275	1,030	20
	0300	2 C.Y. capacity		67.35	1,050	3,180	9,550	1,175	
	0320	2-1/2 C.Y. capacity		102.55	1,300	3,925	11,800	1,605	
	0325	3-1/2 C.Y. capacity		144.45	2,150	6,420	19,300	2,440	
	0330	4-1/2 C.Y. capacity		173.40	2,625	7,880	23,600	2,963	
	0335	6 C.Y. capacity		219.80	2,900	8,680	26,000	3,494	
	0340	7 C.Y. capacity		222.05	3,025	9,070	27,200	3,590	
	0342	Excavator attachments, bucket thumbs		3.20	245	735	2,200	172.60	
	0345	Grapples		2.75	193	580	1,750	138	
	0346	Hydraulic hammer for boom mounting, 4000 ft lb.		12.40	350	1,045	3,125	308.20	
	0347	5000 ft lb.		14.40	425	1,280	3,850	371.20	
	0348	8000 ft lb.		21.30	625	1,875	5,625	545.40	
	0349	12,000 ft lb.		23.35	750	2,245	6,725	635.80	
	0350	Gradall type, truck mounted, 3 ton @ 15' radius, 5/8 C.Y.		43.65	890	2,665	8,000	882.20	
	0370	1 C.Y. capacity		47.85	1,025	3,095	9,275	1,002	
	0400	Backhoe-loader, 40 to 45 H.P., 5/8 C.Y. capacity		14.90	240	720	2,150	263.20	
	0450	45 H.P. to 60 H.P., 3/4 C.Y. capacity		23.40	295	885	2,650	364.20	
	0460	80 H.P., 1-1/4 C.Y. capacity		25.60	310	935	2,800	391.80	
	0470	112 H.P., 1-1/2 C.Y. capacity		40.95	645	1,930	5,800	713.60	
	0482	Backhoe-loader attachment, compactor, 20,000 lb.		5.80	142	425	1,275	131.40	
	0485	Hydraulic hammer, 750 ft lb.		3.30	96.50	290	870	84.40	
	0486	Hydraulic hammer, 1200 ft lb.		6.30	217	650	1,950	180.40	
	0500	Brush chipper, gas engine, 6" cutter head, 35 H.P.		11.10	105	315	945	151.80	
	0550	Diesel engine, 12" cutter head, 130 H.P.		27.55	285	855	2,575	391.40	
	0600	15" cutter head, 165 H.P.		33.10	335	1,005	3,025	465.80	
	0750	Bucket, clamshell, general purpose, 3/8 C.Y.		1.30	38.50	115	345	33.40	
	0800	1/2 C.Y.		1.40	45	135	405	38.20	
	0850	3/4 C.Y.		1.55	55	165	495	45.40	
	0900	1 C.Y.		1.60	58.50	175	525	47.80	
	0950	1-1/2 C.Y.		2.55	81.50	245	735	69.40	
	1000	2 C.Y.		2.70	90	270	810	75.60	
	1010	Bucket, dragline, medium duty, 1/2 C.Y.		.75	23.50	70	210	20	
	1020	3/4 C.Y.		.75	24.50	73	219	20.60	
	1030	1 C.Y.		.80	26	78	234	22	
	1040	1-1/2 C.Y.		1.20	40	120	360	33.60	
	1050	2 C.Y.		1.30	45	135	405	37.40	
	1070	3 C.Y.		1.95	61.50	185	555	52.60	
	1200	Compactor, manually guided 2-drum vibratory smooth roller, 7.5 H.P.		7.25	203	610	1,825	180	
	1250	Rammer/tamper, gas, 8"		2.75	46.50	140	420	50	
	1260	15"		3.05	53.50	160	480	56.40	
	1300	Vibratory plate, gas, 18" plate, 3000 lb. blow		2.70	24.50	73	219	36.20	
	1350	21" plate, 5000 lb. blow		3.40	32.50	98	294	46.80	
	1370	Curb builder/extruder, 14 H.P., gas, single screw		14.65	248	745	2,225	266.20	
	1390	Double screw		15.35	290	870	2,600	296.80	
	1500	Disc harrow attachment, for tractor		.44	73.50	221	665	47.70	
	1810	Feller buncher, shearing & accumulating trees, 100 H.P.		48.30	755	2,260	6,775	838.40	
	1860	Grader, self-propelled, 25,000 lb.		39.50	640	1,925	5,775	701	
	1910	30,000 lb.		43.15	650	1,955	5,875	736.20	
	1920	40,000 lb.		64.90	1,100	3,275	9,825	1,174	
	1930	55,000 lb.		84.15	1,700	5,130	15,400	1,699	
	1950	Hammer, pavement breaker, self-propelled, diesel, 1000 to 1250 lb.		29.90	350	1,055	3,175	450.20	
	2000	1300 to 1500 lb.		44.85	705	2,110	6,325	780.80	
	2050	Pile driving hammer, steam or air, 4150 ft lb. @ 225 bpm		10.40	475	1,420	4,250	367.20	
	2100	8750 ft lb. @ 145 bpm		12.40	660	1,975	5,925	494.20	
	2150	15,000 ft lb. @ 60 bpm		14.00	790	2,370	7,100	586	
	2200	24,450 ft lb. @ 111 bpm		15.00	875	2,630	7,900	646	
	2250	Leads, 60' high for pile driving hammers up to 20,000 ft lb.		3.30	80.50	242	725	74.80	
	2300	90' high for hammers over 20,000 ft lb.		4.95	141	424	1,275	124.40	

For customer support on your Site Work & Landscape Cost Data, call 877.737.1594.

701

			UNIT	HOURLY OPER. COST	RENT PER DAY	RENT PER WEEK	RENT PER MONTH	EQUIPMENT COST/DAY	
20	2350	Diesel type hammer, 22,400 ft lb.	Ea.	22.55	460	1,380	4,150	456.40	20
	2400	41,300 ft lb.		32.00	540	1,625	4,875	581	
	2450	141,000 ft lb.		51.65	960	2,875	8,625	988.20	
	2500	Vib. elec. hammer/extractor, 200 kW diesel generator, 34 H.P.		54.90	635	1,900	5,700	819.20	
	2550	80 H.P.		100.65	925	2,775	8,325	1,360	
	2600	150 H.P.		190.90	1,775	5,300	15,900	2,587	
	2800	Log chipper, up to 22" diameter, 600 H.P.		63.30	640	1,915	5,750	889.40	
	2850	Logger, for skidding & stacking logs, 150 H.P.		52.75	815	2,445	7,325	911	
	2860	Mulcher, diesel powered, trailer mounted		24.05	212	635	1,900	319.40	
	2900	Rake, spring tooth, with tractor		18.23	345	1,042	3,125	354.25	
	3000	Roller, vibratory, tandem, smooth drum, 20 H.P.		8.80	145	435	1,300	157.40	
	3050	35 H.P.		11.10	247	740	2,225	236.80	
	3100	Towed type vibratory compactor, smooth drum, 50 H.P.		26.00	315	940	2,825	396	
	3150	Sheepsfoot, 50 H.P.		27.35	345	1,035	3,100	425.80	
	3170	Landfill compactor, 220 H.P.		91.00	1,475	4,440	13,300	1,616	
	3200	Pneumatic tire roller, 80 H.P.		16.80	350	1,050	3,150	344.40	
	3250	120 H.P.		25.20	600	1,800	5,400	561.60	
	3300	Sheepsfoot vibratory roller, 240 H.P.		68.95	1,100	3,270	9,800	1,206	
	3320	340 H.P.		100.85	1,575	4,730	14,200	1,753	
	3350	Smooth drum vibratory roller, 75 H.P.		24.85	585	1,755	5,275	549.80	
	3400	125 H.P.		32.55	710	2,135	6,400	687.40	
	3410	Rotary mower, brush, 60", with tractor		22.60	315	950	2,850	370.80	
	3420	Rototiller, walk-behind, gas, 5 H.P.		1.96	51.50	155	465	46.70	
	3422	8 H.P.		3.08	80	240	720	72.65	
	3440	Scrapers, towed type, 7 C.Y. capacity		5.80	113	340	1,025	114.40	
	3450	10 C.Y. capacity		6.60	157	470	1,400	146.80	
	3500	15 C.Y. capacity		7.10	180	540	1,625	164.80	
	3525	Self-propelled, single engine, 14 C.Y. capacity		114.76	1,600	4,830	14,500	1,884	
	3550	Dual engine, 21 C.Y. capacity		173.80	2,175	6,490	19,500	2,688	
	3600	31 C.Y. capacity		231.70	3,075	9,195	27,600	3,693	
	3640	44 C.Y. capacity		287.80	3,950	11,885	35,700	4,679	
	3650	Elevating type, single engine, 11 C.Y. capacity		71.45	985	2,955	8,875	1,163	
	3700	22 C.Y. capacity		139.55	2,350	7,025	21,100	2,521	
	3710	Screening plant 110 H.P. w/5' x 10' screen		25.35	400	1,200	3,600	442.80	
	3720	5' x 16' screen		29.65	505	1,515	4,550	540.20	
	3850	Shovel, crawler-mounted, front-loading, 7 C.Y. capacity		258.85	3,200	9,610	28,800	3,993	
	3855	12 C.Y. capacity		386.45	4,400	13,220	39,700	5,736	
	3860	Shovel/backhoe bucket, 1/2 C.Y.		2.50	66.50	200	600	60	
	3870	3/4 C.Y.		2.55	75	225	675	65.40	
	3880	1 C.Y.		2.65	83.50	250	750	71.20	
	3890	1-1/2 C.Y.		2.75	96.50	290	870	80	
	3910	3 C.Y.		3.15	130	390	1,175	103.20	
	3950	Stump chipper, 18" deep, 30 H.P.		7.82	205	615	1,850	185.55	
	4110	Dozer, crawler, torque converter, diesel 80 H.P.		29.05	400	1,200	3,600	472.40	
	4150	105 H.P.		35.60	530	1,590	4,775	602.80	
	4200	140 H.P.		51.25	795	2,380	7,150	886	
	4260	200 H.P.		77.25	1,275	3,845	11,500	1,387	
	4310	300 H.P.		100.65	1,825	5,460	16,400	1,897	
	4360	410 H.P.		132.60	2,250	6,720	20,200	2,405	
	4370	500 H.P.		171.15	3,225	9,650	29,000	3,299	
	4380	700 H.P.		280.90	4,550	13,660	41,000	4,979	
	4400	Loader, crawler, torque conv., diesel, 1-1/2 C.Y., 80 H.P.		31.25	455	1,360	4,075	522	
	4450	1-1/2 to 1-3/4 C.Y., 95 H.P.		34.60	590	1,765	5,300	629.80	
	4510	1-3/4 to 2-1/4 C.Y., 130 H.P.		53.80	875	2,630	7,900	956.40	
	4530	2-1/2 to 3-1/4 C.Y., 190 H.P.		65.95	1,100	3,300	9,900	1,188	
	4560	3-1/2 to 5 C.Y., 275 H.P.		87.80	1,425	4,295	12,900	1,561	
	4610	Front end loader, 4WD, articulated frame, diesel, 1 to 1-1/4 C.Y., 70 H.P.		19.75	235	705	2,125	299	
	4620	1-1/2 to 1-3/4 C.Y., 95 H.P.		24.80	300	900	2,700	378.40	

01 54 33 | Equipment Rental

		UNIT	HOURLY OPER. COST	RENT PER DAY	RENT PER WEEK	RENT PER MONTH	EQUIPMENT COST/DAY	
20	4650	1-3/4 to 2 C.Y., 130 H.P.	Ea.	29.15	380	1,140	3,425	461.20	20
	4710	2-1/2 to 3-1/2 C.Y., 145 H.P.		33.10	425	1,275	3,825	519.80	
	4730	3 to 4-1/2 C.Y., 185 H.P.		42.40	550	1,650	4,950	669.20	
	4760	5-1/4 to 5-3/4 C.Y., 270 H.P.		67.50	905	2,710	8,125	1,082	
	4810	7 to 9 C.Y., 475 H.P.		114.05	1,700	5,125	15,400	1,937	
	4870	9 - 11 C.Y., 620 H.P.		160.55	2,775	8,290	24,900	2,942	
	4880	Skid steer loader, wheeled, 10 C.F., 30 H.P. gas		10.45	150	450	1,350	173.60	
	4890	1 C.Y., 78 H.P., diesel		20.20	262	785	2,350	318.60	
	4892	Skid-steer attachment, auger		.48	80.50	242	725	52.25	
	4893	Backhoe		.66	111	332	995	71.70	
	4894	Broom		.74	124	372	1,125	80.30	
	4895	Forks		.22	36	108	325	23.35	
	4896	Grapple		.56	92.50	278	835	60.10	
	4897	Concrete hammer		1.06	177	531	1,600	114.70	
	4898	Tree spade		1.03	172	515	1,550	111.25	
	4899	Trencher		.54	90	270	810	58.30	
	4900	Trencher, chain, boom type, gas, operator walking, 12 H.P.		5.00	46.50	140	420	68	
	4910	Operator riding, 40 H.P.		20.15	290	870	2,600	335.20	
	5000	Wheel type, diesel, 4' deep, 12" wide		85.95	845	2,535	7,600	1,195	
	5100	6' deep, 20" wide		92.75	1,925	5,740	17,200	1,890	
	5150	Chain type, diesel, 5' deep, 8" wide		38.35	560	1,675	5,025	641.80	
	5200	Diesel, 8' deep, 16" wide		155.95	3,600	10,770	32,300	3,402	
	5202	Rock trencher, wheel type, 6" wide x 18" deep		21.50	335	1,000	3,000	372	
	5206	Chain type, 18" wide x 7' deep		112.00	2,800	8,395	25,200	2,575	
	5210	Tree spade, self-propelled		14.38	267	800	2,400	275.05	
	5250	Truck, dump, 2-axle, 12 ton, 8 C.Y. payload, 220 H.P.		34.40	227	680	2,050	411.20	
	5300	Three axle dump, 16 ton, 12 C.Y. payload, 400 H.P.		61.00	340	1,015	3,050	691	
	5310	Four axle dump, 25 ton, 18 C.Y. payload, 450 H.P.		71.75	490	1,475	4,425	869	
	5350	Dump trailer only, rear dump, 16-1/2 C.Y.		5.45	138	415	1,250	126.60	
	5400	20 C.Y.		5.90	157	470	1,400	141.20	
	5450	Flatbed, single axle, 1-1/2 ton rating		25.55	68.50	205	615	245.40	
	5500	3 ton rating		30.65	96.50	290	870	303.20	
	5550	Off highway rear dump, 25 ton capacity		73.90	1,275	3,800	11,400	1,351	
	5600	35 ton capacity		82.50	1,425	4,260	12,800	1,512	
	5610	50 ton capacity		102.65	1,700	5,080	15,200	1,837	
	5620	65 ton capacity		105.65	1,700	5,090	15,300	1,863	
	5630	100 ton capacity		151.40	2,850	8,570	25,700	2,925	
	6000	Vibratory plow, 25 H.P., walking		8.45	60	180	540	103.60	
40	0010	**GENERAL EQUIPMENT RENTAL** without operators	R015433 -10						40
	0150	Aerial lift, scissor type, to 15' high, 1000 lb. cap., electric	Ea.	3.05	51.50	155	465	55.40	
	0160	To 25' high, 2000 lb. capacity		3.45	66.50	200	600	67.60	
	0170	Telescoping boom to 40' high, 500 lb. capacity, diesel		13.55	320	965	2,900	301.40	
	0180	To 45' high, 500 lb. capacity		14.75	350	1,055	3,175	329	
	0190	To 60' high, 600 lb. capacity		17.20	495	1,490	4,475	435.60	
	0195	Air compressor, portable, 6.5 CFM, electric		.67	12.65	38	114	12.95	
	0196	Gasoline		.81	19	57	171	17.90	
	0200	Towed type, gas engine, 60 CFM		13.55	48.50	145	435	137.40	
	0300	160 CFM		15.80	50	150	450	156.40	
	0400	Diesel engine, rotary screw, 250 CFM		17.05	108	325	975	201.40	
	0500	365 CFM		23.10	132	395	1,175	263.80	
	0550	450 CFM		29.35	165	495	1,475	333.80	
	0600	600 CFM		51.70	228	685	2,050	550.60	
	0700	750 CFM		51.90	237	710	2,125	557.20	
	0800	For silenced models, small sizes, add to rent		3%	5%	5%	5%		
	0900	Large sizes, add to rent		5%	7%	7%	7%		
	0930	Air tools, breaker, pavement, 60 lb.	Ea.	.50	9.65	29	87	9.80	
	0940	80 lb.		.50	10.35	31	93	10.20	
	0950	Drills, hand (jackhammer) 65 lb.		.60	17.35	52	156	15.20	

40

		UNIT	HOURLY OPER. COST	RENT PER DAY	RENT PER WEEK	RENT PER MONTH	EQUIPMENT COST/DAY	
0960	Track or wagon, swing boom, 4" drifter	Ea.	62.50	880	2,640	7,925	1,028	40
0970	5" drifter		74.45	1,075	3,235	9,700	1,243	
0975	Track mounted quarry drill, 6" diameter drill		128.10	1,600	4,765	14,300	1,978	
0980	Dust control per drill		1.02	23.50	71	213	22.35	
0990	Hammer, chipping, 12 lb.		.55	26	78	234	20	
1000	Hose, air with couplings, 50' long, 3/4" diameter		.03	5	15	45	3.25	
1100	1" diameter		.04	6.35	19	57	4.10	
1200	1-1/2" diameter		.05	9	27	81	5.80	
1300	2" diameter		.07	12	36	108	7.75	
1400	2-1/2" diameter		.11	19	57	171	12.30	
1410	3" diameter		.14	23	69	207	14.90	
1450	Drill, steel, 7/8" x 2'		.05	8.65	26	78	5.60	
1460	7/8" x 6'		.05	9	27	81	5.80	
1520	Moil points		.02	3.33	10	30	2.15	
1525	Pneumatic nailer w/accessories		.58	38.50	115	345	27.65	
1530	Sheeting driver for 60 lb. breaker		.04	6	18	54	3.90	
1540	For 90 lb. breaker		.12	8	24	72	5.75	
1550	Spade, 25 lb.		.45	6.65	20	60	7.60	
1560	Tamper, single, 35 lb.		.55	36.50	109	325	26.20	
1570	Triple, 140 lb.		.82	54.50	164	490	39.35	
1580	Wrenches, impact, air powered, up to 3/4" bolt		.40	12.65	38	114	10.80	
1590	Up to 1-1/4" bolt		.50	23.50	70	210	18	
1600	Barricades, barrels, reflectorized, 1 to 99 barrels		.03	4.60	13.80	41.50	3	
1610	100 to 200 barrels		.02	3.53	10.60	32	2.30	
1620	Barrels with flashers, 1 to 99 barrels		.03	5.25	15.80	47.50	3.40	
1630	100 to 200 barrels		.03	4.20	12.60	38	2.75	
1640	Barrels with steady burn type C lights		.04	7	21	63	4.50	
1650	Illuminated board, trailer mounted, with generator		3.50	130	390	1,175	106	
1670	Portable barricade, stock, with flashers, 1 to 6 units		.03	5.25	15.80	47.50	3.40	
1680	25 to 50 units		.03	4.90	14.70	44	3.20	
1685	Butt fusion machine, wheeled, 1.5 HP electric, 2" - 8" diameter pipe		2.63	167	500	1,500	121.05	
1690	Tracked, 20 HP diesel, 4"-12" diameter pipe		11.14	490	1,465	4,400	382.10	
1695	83 HP diesel, 8" - 24" diameter pipe		30.46	975	2,930	8,800	829.70	
1700	Carts, brick, hand powered, 1000 lb. capacity		.50	83.50	251	755	54.20	
1800	Gas engine, 1500 lb., 7-1/2' lift		4.17	115	345	1,025	102.35	
1822	Dehumidifier, medium, 6 lb./hr., 150 CFM		1.00	62	186	560	45.20	
1824	Large, 18 lb./hr., 600 CFM		2.02	126	378	1,125	91.75	
1830	Distributor, asphalt, trailer mounted, 2000 gal., 38 H.P. diesel		9.95	325	980	2,950	275.60	
1840	3000 gal., 38 H.P. diesel		11.45	355	1,070	3,200	305.60	
1850	Drill, rotary hammer, electric		1.02	26	78	234	23.75	
1860	Carbide bit, 1-1/2" diameter, add to electric rotary hammer		.02	3.61	10.84	32.50	2.35	
1865	Rotary, crawler, 250 H.P.		148.50	2,050	6,185	18,600	2,425	
1870	Emulsion sprayer, 65 gal., 5 H.P. gas engine		2.91	97	291	875	81.50	
1880	200 gal., 5 H.P. engine		7.85	162	485	1,450	159.80	
1900	Floor auto-scrubbing machine, walk-behind, 28" path		4.98	325	970	2,900	233.85	
1930	Floodlight, mercury vapor, or quartz, on tripod, 1000 watt		.44	20.50	62	186	15.90	
1940	2000 watt		.83	41	123	370	31.25	
1950	Floodlights, trailer mounted with generator, 1 - 300 watt light		3.65	71.50	215	645	72.20	
1960	2 - 1000 watt lights		4.85	96.50	290	870	96.80	
2000	4 - 300 watt lights		4.55	93.50	280	840	92.40	
2005	Foam spray rig, incl. box trailer, compressor, generator, proportioner		35.03	490	1,465	4,400	573.25	
2020	Forklift, straight mast, 12' lift, 5000 lb., 2 wheel drive, gas		26.35	202	605	1,825	331.80	
2040	21' lift, 5000 lb., 4 wheel drive, diesel		20.90	240	720	2,150	311.20	
2050	For rough terrain, 42' lift, 35' reach, 9000 lb., 110 H.P.		29.55	485	1,450	4,350	526.40	
2060	For plant, 4 ton capacity, 80 H.P., 2 wheel drive, gas		16.15	93.50	280	840	185.20	
2080	10 ton capacity, 120 H.P., 2 wheel drive, diesel		24.10	162	485	1,450	289.80	
2100	Generator, electric, gas engine, 1.5 kW to 3 kW		3.75	11.35	34	102	36.80	
2200	5 kW		4.80	15.35	46	138	47.60	

01 54 33 | Equipment Rental

		UNIT	HOURLY OPER. COST	RENT PER DAY	RENT PER WEEK	RENT PER MONTH	EQUIPMENT COST/DAY	
40	2300	10 kW	Ea.	9.10	36.50	110	330	94.80	40
	2400	25 kW		10.60	85	255	765	135.80	
	2500	Diesel engine, 20 kW		12.10	66.50	200	600	136.80	
	2600	50 kW		23.35	103	310	930	248.80	
	2700	100 kW		43.30	128	385	1,150	423.40	
	2800	250 kW		85.15	235	705	2,125	822.20	
	2850	Hammer, hydraulic, for mounting on boom, to 500 ft lb.		2.55	75	225	675	65.40	
	2860	1000 ft lb.		4.35	127	380	1,150	110.80	
	2900	Heaters, space, oil or electric, 50 MBH		2.01	7.65	23	69	20.70	
	3000	100 MBH		3.76	10.65	32	96	36.50	
	3100	300 MBH		11.03	38.50	115	345	111.25	
	3150	500 MBH		18.15	45	135	405	172.20	
	3200	Hose, water, suction with coupling, 20' long, 2" diameter		.02	3	9	27	1.95	
	3210	3" diameter		.03	4.33	13	39	2.85	
	3220	4" diameter		.03	5	15	45	3.25	
	3230	6" diameter		.11	17.65	53	159	11.50	
	3240	8" diameter		.27	44.50	133	400	28.75	
	3250	Discharge hose with coupling, 50' long, 2" diameter		.01	1.33	4	12	.90	
	3260	3" diameter		.01	2.33	7	21	1.50	
	3270	4" diameter		.02	3.67	11	33	2.35	
	3280	6" diameter		.06	9.35	28	84	6.10	
	3290	8" diameter		.18	30	90	270	19.45	
	3295	Insulation blower		.78	6	18	54	9.85	
	3300	Ladders, extension type, 16' to 36' long		.14	22.50	68	204	14.70	
	3400	40' to 60' long		.19	31	93	279	20.10	
	3405	Lance for cutting concrete		2.35	71.50	215	645	61.80	
	3407	Lawn mower, rotary, 22", 5 H.P.		1.80	49	147	440	43.80	
	3408	48" self propelled		2.98	75	225	675	68.85	
	3410	Level, electronic, automatic, with tripod and leveling rod		1.20	75.50	226	680	54.80	
	3430	Laser type, for pipe and sewer line and grade		.73	48.50	145	435	34.85	
	3440	Rotating beam for interior control		.78	52	156	470	37.45	
	3460	Builder's optical transit, with tripod and rod		.09	14.65	44	132	9.50	
	3500	Light towers, towable, with diesel generator, 2000 watt		4.55	93.50	280	840	92.40	
	3600	4000 watt		4.85	96.50	290	870	96.80	
	3700	Mixer, powered, plaster and mortar, 6 C.F., 7 H.P.		2.70	20	60	180	33.60	
	3800	10 C.F., 9 H.P.		2.80	31.50	94	282	41.20	
	3850	Nailer, pneumatic		.58	38.50	115	345	27.65	
	3900	Paint sprayers complete, 8 CFM		1.04	69.50	208	625	49.90	
	4000	17 CFM		1.90	127	380	1,150	91.20	
	4020	Pavers, bituminous, rubber tires, 8' wide, 50 H.P., diesel		31.15	490	1,465	4,400	542.20	
	4030	10' wide, 150 H.P.		106.10	1,800	5,370	16,100	1,923	
	4050	Crawler, 8' wide, 100 H.P., diesel		88.65	1,800	5,385	16,200	1,786	
	4060	10' wide, 150 H.P.		113.15	2,200	6,610	19,800	2,227	
	4070	Concrete paver, 12' to 24' wide, 250 H.P.		101.40	1,550	4,675	14,000	1,746	
	4080	Placer-spreader-trimmer, 24' wide, 300 H.P.		150.25	2,650	7,960	23,900	2,794	
	4100	Pump, centrifugal gas pump, 1-1/2" diam., 65 GPM		3.90	48.50	145	435	60.20	
	4200	2" diameter, 130 GPM		5.35	53.50	160	480	74.80	
	4300	3" diameter, 250 GPM		5.65	55	165	495	78.20	
	4400	6" diameter, 1500 GPM		30.45	172	515	1,550	346.60	
	4500	Submersible electric pump, 1-1/4" diameter, 55 GPM		.39	16.35	49	147	12.90	
	4600	1-1/2" diameter, 83 GPM		.43	18.65	56	168	14.65	
	4700	2" diameter, 120 GPM		1.50	23.50	70	210	26	
	4800	3" diameter, 300 GPM		2.69	41.50	125	375	46.50	
	4900	4" diameter, 560 GPM		12.34	158	475	1,425	193.70	
	5000	6" diameter, 1590 GPM		18.40	212	635	1,900	274.20	
	5100	Diaphragm pump, gas, single, 1-1/2" diameter		1.18	49.50	148	445	39.05	
	5200	2" diameter		4.25	61.50	185	555	71	
	5300	3" diameter		4.25	61.50	185	555	71	

For customer support on your Site Work & Landscape Cost Data, call 877.737.1594.

705

40

		UNIT	HOURLY OPER. COST	RENT PER DAY	RENT PER WEEK	RENT PER MONTH	EQUIPMENT COST/DAY	
5400	Double, 4" diameter	Ea.	6.40	105	315	945	114.20	**40**
5450	Pressure washer 5 GPM, 3000 psi		4.90	51.50	155	465	70.20	
5460	7 GPM, 3000 psi		6.45	60	180	540	87.60	
5500	Trash pump, self-priming, gas, 2" diameter		4.60	21	63	189	49.40	
5600	Diesel, 4" diameter		9.15	88.50	265	795	126.20	
5650	Diesel, 6" diameter		25.25	147	440	1,325	290	
5655	Grout Pump		26.35	268	805	2,425	371.80	
5700	Salamanders, L.P. gas fired, 100,000 Btu		3.96	13.65	41	123	39.90	
5705	50,000 Btu		2.21	10.35	31	93	23.90	
5720	Sandblaster, portable, open top, 3 C.F. capacity		.55	26.50	80	240	20.40	
5730	6 C.F. capacity		.95	40	120	360	31.60	
5740	Accessories for above		.13	21.50	65	195	14.05	
5750	Sander, floor		.70	14.35	43	129	14.20	
5760	Edger		.50	14.35	43	129	12.60	
5800	Saw, chain, gas engine, 18" long		2.30	21.50	64	192	31.20	
5900	Hydraulic powered, 36" long		.75	65	195	585	45	
5950	60" long		.75	66.50	200	600	46	
6000	Masonry, table mounted, 14" diameter, 5 H.P.		1.32	56.50	170	510	44.55	
6050	Portable cut-off, 8 H.P.		2.50	33.50	100	300	40	
6100	Circular, hand held, electric, 7-1/4" diameter		.23	4.67	14	42	4.65	
6200	12" diameter		.23	8	24	72	6.65	
6250	Wall saw, w/hydraulic power, 10 H.P.		9.70	61.50	185	555	114.60	
6275	Shot blaster, walk-behind, 20" wide		4.75	293	880	2,650	214	
6280	Sidewalk broom, walk-behind		2.52	78.50	235	705	67.15	
6300	Steam cleaner, 100 gallons per hour		3.70	76.50	230	690	75.60	
6310	200 gallons per hour		5.35	95	285	855	99.80	
6340	Tar Kettle/Pot, 400 gallons		15.60	75	225	675	169.80	
6350	Torch, cutting, acetylene-oxygen, 150' hose, excludes gases		.30	15	45	135	11.40	
6360	Hourly operating cost includes tips and gas		19.00				152	
6410	Toilet, portable chemical		.13	21	63	189	13.65	
6420	Recycle flush type		.15	25	75	225	16.20	
6430	Toilet, fresh water flush, garden hose,		.18	30.50	91	273	19.65	
6440	Hoisted, non-flush, for high rise		.15	24.50	74	222	16	
6465	Tractor, farm with attachment		21.50	297	890	2,675	350	
6480	Trailers, platform, flush deck, 2 axle, 3 ton capacity		1.45	20	60	180	23.60	
6500	25 ton capacity		5.45	117	350	1,050	113.60	
6600	40 ton capacity		7.00	163	490	1,475	154	
6700	3 axle, 50 ton capacity		7.55	180	540	1,625	168.40	
6800	75 ton capacity		9.40	235	705	2,125	216.20	
6810	Trailer mounted cable reel for high voltage line work		5.45	260	779	2,325	199.40	
6820	Trailer mounted cable tensioning rig		10.85	515	1,550	4,650	396.80	
6830	Cable pulling rig		73.05	2,900	8,680	26,000	2,320	
6900	Water tank trailer, engine driven discharge, 5000 gallons		7.00	142	425	1,275	141	
6925	10,000 gallons		9.50	197	590	1,775	194	
6950	Water truck, off highway, 6000 gallons		88.15	770	2,315	6,950	1,168	
7010	Tram car for high voltage line work, powered, 2 conductor		6.60	141	423	1,275	137.40	
7020	Transit (builder's level) with tripod		.09	14.65	44	132	9.50	
7030	Trench box, 3000 lb., 6' x 8'		.56	93.50	280	840	60.50	
7040	7200 lb., 6' x 20'		.75	125	375	1,125	81	
7050	8000 lb., 8' x 16'		1.08	180	540	1,625	116.65	
7060	9500 lb., 8' x 20'		1.21	201	603	1,800	130.30	
7065	11,000 lb., 8' x 24'		1.27	211	633	1,900	136.75	
7070	12,000 lb., 10' x 20'		1.50	249	748	2,250	161.60	
7100	Truck, pickup, 3/4 ton, 2 wheel drive		13.65	58.50	175	525	144.20	
7200	4 wheel drive		13.95	73.50	220	660	155.60	
7250	Crew carrier, 9 passenger		19.30	86.50	260	780	206.40	
7290	Flat bed truck, 20,000 lb. GVW		21.70	125	375	1,125	248.60	
7300	Tractor, 4 x 2, 220 H.P.		30.20	197	590	1,775	359.60	

			UNIT	HOURLY OPER. COST	RENT PER DAY	RENT PER WEEK	RENT PER MONTH	EQUIPMENT COST/DAY	
40	7410	330 H.P.	Ea.	44.75	270	810	2,425	520	**40**
	7500	6 x 4, 380 H.P.		51.35	315	945	2,825	599.80	
	7600	450 H.P.		62.30	380	1,145	3,425	727.40	
	7610	Tractor, with A frame, boom and winch, 225 H.P.		33.00	272	815	2,450	427	
	7620	Vacuum truck, hazardous material, 2500 gallons		12.05	290	870	2,600	270.40	
	7625	5,000 gallons		14.26	405	1,220	3,650	358.10	
	7650	Vacuum, HEPA, 16 gallon, wet/dry		.85	18	54	162	17.60	
	7655	55 gallon, wet/dry		.80	27	81	243	22.60	
	7660	Water tank, portable		.16	26.50	80	240	17.30	
	7690	Sewer/catch basin vacuum, 14 C.Y., 1500 gallons		18.53	610	1,830	5,500	514.25	
	7700	Welder, electric, 200 amp		3.88	16.35	49	147	40.85	
	7800	300 amp		5.71	20	60	180	57.70	
	7900	Gas engine, 200 amp		14.65	23.50	70	210	131.20	
	8000	300 amp		16.38	24.50	74	222	145.85	
	8100	Wheelbarrow, any size		.08	13	39	117	8.45	
	8200	Wrecking ball, 4000 lb.		2.35	68.50	205	615	59.80	
50	0010	**HIGHWAY EQUIPMENT RENTAL** without operators							**50**
	0050	Asphalt batch plant, portable drum mixer, 100 ton/hr.	Ea.	78.06	1,425	4,270	12,800	1,478	
	0060	200 ton/hr.		89.18	1,500	4,530	13,600	1,619	
	0070	300 ton/hr.		106.34	1,775	5,325	16,000	1,916	
	0100	Backhoe attachment, long stick, up to 185 H.P., 10.5' long		.35	23.50	70	210	16.80	
	0140	Up to 250 H.P., 12' long		.38	25	75	225	18.05	
	0180	Over 250 H.P., 15' long		.53	35	105	315	25.25	
	0200	Special dipper arm, up to 100 H.P., 32' long		1.08	71.50	215	645	51.65	
	0240	Over 100 H.P., 33' long		1.34	89.50	268	805	64.30	
	0280	Catch basin/sewer cleaning truck, 3 ton, 9 C.Y., 1000 gal.		42.70	385	1,160	3,475	573.60	
	0300	Concrete batch plant, portable, electric, 200 C.Y./hr.		22.87	515	1,550	4,650	492.95	
	0520	Grader/dozer attachment, ripper/scarifier, rear mounted, up to 135 H.P.		2.90	56.50	170	510	57.20	
	0540	Up to 180 H.P.		3.90	88.50	265	795	84.20	
	0580	Up to 250 H.P.		5.00	117	350	1,050	110	
	0700	Pvmt. removal bucket, for hyd. excavator, up to 90 H.P.		1.90	53.50	160	480	47.20	
	0740	Up to 200 H.P.		2.15	73.50	220	660	61.20	
	0780	Over 200 H.P.		2.25	85	255	765	69	
	0900	Aggregate spreader, self-propelled, 187 H.P.		53.00	685	2,050	6,150	834	
	1000	Chemical spreader, 3 C.Y.		3.30	43.50	130	390	52.40	
	1900	Hammermill, traveling, 250 H.P.		78.83	2,075	6,240	18,700	1,879	
	2000	Horizontal borer, 3" diameter, 13 H.P. gas driven		6.35	55	165	495	83.80	
	2150	Horizontal directional drill, 20,000 lb. thrust, 78 H.P. diesel		31.15	675	2,025	6,075	654.20	
	2160	30,000 lb. thrust, 115 H.P.		38.90	1,025	3,100	9,300	931.20	
	2170	50,000 lb. thrust, 170 H.P.		55.65	1,325	3,960	11,900	1,237	
	2190	Mud trailer for HDD, 1500 gallons, 175 H.P., gas		31.90	152	455	1,375	346.20	
	2200	Hydromulcher, diesel, 3000 gallon, for truck mounting		23.40	245	735	2,200	334.20	
	2300	Gas, 600 gallon		8.60	98.50	295	885	127.80	
	2400	Joint & crack cleaner, walk behind, 25 H.P.		3.95	50	150	450	61.60	
	2500	Filler, trailer mounted, 400 gallons, 20 H.P.		9.50	210	630	1,900	202	
	3000	Paint striper, self-propelled, 40 gallon, 22 H.P.		7.30	155	465	1,400	151.40	
	3100	120 gallon, 120 H.P.		23.00	395	1,185	3,550	421	
	3200	Post drivers, 6" I-Beam frame, for truck mounting		19.05	380	1,135	3,400	379.40	
	3400	Road sweeper, self-propelled, 8' wide, 90 H.P.		39.80	575	1,720	5,150	662.40	
	3450	Road sweeper, vacuum assisted, 4 C.Y., 220 gallons		75.75	635	1,900	5,700	986	
	4000	Road mixer, self-propelled, 130 H.P.		46.85	765	2,295	6,875	833.80	
	4100	310 H.P.		83.25	2,100	6,315	18,900	1,929	
	4220	Cold mix paver, incl. pug mill and bitumen tank, 165 H.P.		97.00	2,275	6,855	20,600	2,147	
	4240	Pavement brush, towed		3.20	93.50	280	840	81.60	
	4250	Paver, asphalt, wheel or crawler, 130 H.P., diesel		96.65	2,275	6,795	20,400	2,132	
	4300	Paver, road widener, gas 1' to 6', 67 H.P.		48.50	895	2,680	8,050	924	
	4400	Diesel, 2' to 14', 88 H.P.		62.70	1,050	3,135	9,400	1,129	
	4600	Slipform pavers, curb and gutter, 2 track, 75 H.P.		57.20	900	2,700	8,100	997.60	

R015433 -10

For customer support on your Site Work & Landscape Cost Data, call 877.737.1594.

707

01 54 33 | Equipment Rental

		UNIT	HOURLY OPER. COST	RENT PER DAY	RENT PER WEEK	RENT PER MONTH	EQUIPMENT COST/DAY	
50	4700	4 track, 165 H.P.	Ea.	41.50	740	2,220	6,650	776	**50**
	4800	Median barrier, 215 H.P.		60.50	1,050	3,150	9,450	1,114	
	4901	Trailer, low bed, 75 ton capacity		10.10	235	705	2,125	221.80	
	5000	Road planer, walk behind, 10" cutting width, 10 H.P.		3.70	33.50	100	300	49.60	
	5100	Self-propelled, 12" cutting width, 64 H.P.		10.40	113	340	1,025	151.20	
	5120	Traffic line remover, metal ball blaster, truck mounted, 115 H.P.		47.95	730	2,190	6,575	821.60	
	5140	Grinder, truck mounted, 115 H.P.		54.60	790	2,375	7,125	911.80	
	5160	Walk-behind, 11 H.P.		4.20	53.50	160	480	65.60	
	5200	Pavement profiler, 4' to 6' wide, 450 H.P.		254.50	3,325	9,960	29,900	4,028	
	5300	8' to 10' wide, 750 H.P.		399.20	4,350	13,055	39,200	5,805	
	5400	Roadway plate, steel, 1" x 8' x 20'		.08	13.35	40	120	8.65	
	5600	Stabilizer, self-propelled, 150 H.P.		49.30	600	1,795	5,375	753.40	
	5700	310 H.P.		99.05	1,675	5,030	15,100	1,798	
	5800	Striper, truck mounted, 120 gallon paint, 460 H.P.		64.20	485	1,455	4,375	804.60	
	5900	Thermal paint heating kettle, 115 gallons		8.20	25.50	77	231	81	
	6000	Tar kettle, 330 gallon, trailer mounted		12.25	56.50	170	510	132	
	7000	Tunnel locomotive, diesel, 8 to 12 ton		31.85	585	1,750	5,250	604.80	
	7005	Electric, 10 ton		26.00	665	1,995	5,975	607	
	7010	Muck cars, 1/2 C.Y. capacity		2.00	24.50	73	219	30.60	
	7020	1 C.Y. capacity		2.25	32.50	97	291	37.40	
	7030	2 C.Y. capacity		2.35	36.50	110	330	40.80	
	7040	Side dump, 2 C.Y. capacity		2.60	45	135	405	47.80	
	7050	3 C.Y. capacity		3.45	50	150	450	57.60	
	7060	5 C.Y. capacity		4.95	63.50	190	570	77.60	
	7100	Ventilating blower for tunnel, 7-1/2 H.P.		2.05	51.50	155	465	47.40	
	7110	10 H.P.		2.28	51.50	155	465	49.25	
	7120	20 H.P.		3.48	67.50	202	605	68.25	
	7140	40 H.P.		5.76	96.50	290	870	104.10	
	7160	60 H.P.		8.77	152	455	1,375	161.15	
	7175	75 H.P.		11.66	207	620	1,850	217.30	
	7180	200 H.P.		23.65	305	910	2,725	371.20	
	7800	Windrow loader, elevating		55.00	1,300	3,935	11,800	1,227	
60	0010	**LIFTING AND HOISTING EQUIPMENT RENTAL** without operators							**60**
	0120	Aerial lift truck, 2 person, to 80'	Ea.	26.30	705	2,120	6,350	634.40	
	0140	Boom work platform, 40' snorkel		12.00	275	825	2,475	261	
	0150	Crane, flatbed mounted, 3 ton capacity		16.35	188	565	1,700	243.80	
	0200	Crane, climbing, 106' jib, 6000 lb. capacity, 410 fpm		39.35	1,650	4,960	14,900	1,307	
	0300	101' jib, 10,250 lb. capacity, 270 fpm		45.95	2,100	6,280	18,800	1,624	
	0500	Tower, static, 130' high, 106' jib, 6200 lb. capacity at 400 fpm		43.20	1,900	5,730	17,200	1,492	
	0600	Crawler mounted, lattice boom, 1/2 C.Y., 15 tons at 12' radius		36.98	625	1,870	5,600	669.85	
	0700	3/4 C.Y., 20 tons at 12' radius		49.31	780	2,340	7,025	862.50	
	0800	1 C.Y., 25 tons at 12' radius		65.75	1,050	3,120	9,350	1,150	
	0900	1-1/2 C.Y., 40 tons at 12' radius		65.75	1,050	3,150	9,450	1,156	
	1000	2 C.Y., 50 tons at 12' radius		69.70	1,225	3,680	11,000	1,294	
	1100	3 C.Y., 75 tons at 12' radius		74.70	1,425	4,305	12,900	1,459	
	1200	100 ton capacity, 60' boom		84.60	1,650	4,950	14,900	1,667	
	1300	165 ton capacity, 60' boom		107.75	1,925	5,785	17,400	2,019	
	1400	200 ton capacity, 70' boom		130.55	2,400	7,210	21,600	2,486	
	1500	350 ton capacity, 80' boom		182.90	3,625	10,845	32,500	3,632	
	1600	Truck mounted, lattice boom, 6 x 4, 20 tons at 10' radius		37.11	1,075	3,260	9,775	948.90	
	1700	25 tons at 10' radius		40.09	1,175	3,550	10,700	1,031	
	1800	8 x 4, 30 tons at 10' radius		43.61	1,250	3,780	11,300	1,105	
	1900	40 tons at 12' radius		46.70	1,325	3,950	11,900	1,164	
	2000	60 tons at 15' radius		53.07	1,400	4,180	12,500	1,261	
	2050	82 tons at 15' radius		59.80	1,475	4,460	13,400	1,370	
	2100	90 tons at 15' radius		67.36	1,625	4,860	14,600	1,511	
	2200	115 tons at 15' radius		76.11	1,800	5,430	16,300	1,695	
	2300	150 tons at 18' radius		83.65	1,900	5,720	17,200	1,813	

Reference codes: R015433-10, R015433-15, R312316-45

01 54 33 | Equipment Rental

		UNIT	HOURLY OPER. COST	RENT PER DAY	RENT PER WEEK	RENT PER MONTH	EQUIPMENT COST/DAY	
60	2350	165 tons at 18' radius	Ea.	90.05	2,025	6,060	18,200	1,932	60
	2400	Truck mounted, hydraulic, 12 ton capacity		42.60	520	1,565	4,700	653.80	
	2500	25 ton capacity		44.95	630	1,885	5,650	736.60	
	2550	33 ton capacity		45.50	645	1,930	5,800	750	
	2560	40 ton capacity		58.85	750	2,250	6,750	920.80	
	2600	55 ton capacity		76.80	855	2,570	7,700	1,128	
	2700	80 ton capacity		100.45	1,375	4,105	12,300	1,625	
	2720	100 ton capacity		94.20	1,425	4,250	12,800	1,604	
	2740	120 ton capacity		100.05	1,525	4,575	13,700	1,715	
	2760	150 ton capacity		127.60	2,000	5,995	18,000	2,220	
	2800	Self-propelled, 4 x 4, with telescoping boom, 5 ton		17.55	225	675	2,025	275.40	
	2900	12-1/2 ton capacity		32.30	360	1,075	3,225	473.40	
	3000	15 ton capacity		33.00	375	1,130	3,400	490	
	3050	20 ton capacity		35.95	445	1,335	4,000	554.60	
	3100	25 ton capacity		37.55	500	1,495	4,475	599.40	
	3150	40 ton capacity		46.00	560	1,675	5,025	703	
	3200	Derricks, guy, 20 ton capacity, 60' boom, 75' mast		27.55	405	1,214	3,650	463.20	
	3300	100' boom, 115' mast		43.21	695	2,090	6,275	763.70	
	3400	Stiffleg, 20 ton capacity, 70' boom, 37' mast		30.11	525	1,580	4,750	556.90	
	3500	100' boom, 47' mast		46.29	845	2,530	7,600	876.30	
	3550	Helicopter, small, lift to 1250 lb. maximum, w/pilot		103.70	3,275	9,800	29,400	2,790	
	3600	Hoists, chain type, overhead, manual, 3/4 ton		.10	.33	1	3	1	
	3900	10 ton		.70	6	18	54	9.20	
	4000	Hoist and tower, 5000 lb. cap., portable electric, 40' high		4.95	233	699	2,100	179.40	
	4100	For each added 10' section, add		.11	18.35	55	165	11.90	
	4200	Hoist and single tubular tower, 5000 lb. electric, 100' high		6.70	325	976	2,925	248.80	
	4300	For each added 6'-6" section, add		.19	31.50	95	285	20.50	
	4400	Hoist and double tubular tower, 5000 lb., 100' high		7.19	360	1,075	3,225	272.50	
	4500	For each added 6'-6" section, add		.21	35	105	315	22.70	
	4550	Hoist and tower, mast type, 6000 lb., 100' high		7.76	370	1,115	3,350	285.10	
	4570	For each added 10' section, add		.13	21.50	65	195	14.05	
	4600	Hoist and tower, personnel, electric, 2000 lb., 100' @ 125 fpm		16.31	990	2,970	8,900	724.50	
	4700	3000 lb., 100' @ 200 fpm		18.62	1,125	3,360	10,100	820.95	
	4800	3000 lb., 150' @ 300 fpm		20.62	1,250	3,760	11,300	916.95	
	4900	4000 lb., 100' @ 300 fpm		21.38	1,275	3,840	11,500	939.05	
	5000	6000 lb., 100' @ 275 fpm		23.06	1,350	4,030	12,100	990.50	
	5100	For added heights up to 500', add	L.F.	.01	1.67	5	15	1.10	
	5200	Jacks, hydraulic, 20 ton	Ea.	.05	2	6	18	1.60	
	5500	100 ton		.40	11.65	35	105	10.20	
	6100	Jacks, hydraulic, climbing w/50' jackrods, control console, 30 ton cap.		2.01	134	402	1,200	96.50	
	6150	For each added 10' jackrod section, add		.05	3.33	10	30	2.40	
	6300	50 ton capacity		3.23	215	646	1,950	155.05	
	6350	For each added 10' jackrod section, add		.06	4	12	36	2.90	
	6500	125 ton capacity		8.45	565	1,690	5,075	405.60	
	6550	For each added 10' jackrod section, add		.58	38.50	115	345	27.65	
	6600	Cable jack, 10 ton capacity with 200' cable		1.68	112	336	1,000	80.65	
	6650	For each added 50' of cable, add		.20	13.35	40	120	9.60	
70	0010	**WELLPOINT EQUIPMENT RENTAL** without operators							70
	0020	Based on 2 months rental							
	0100	Combination jetting & wellpoint pump, 60 H.P. diesel	Ea.	18.40	330	996	3,000	346.40	
	0200	High pressure gas jet pump, 200 H.P., 300 psi	"	44.06	284	851	2,550	522.70	
	0300	Discharge pipe, 8" diameter	L.F.	.01	.54	1.62	4.86	.40	
	0350	12" diameter		.01	.79	2.38	7.15	.55	
	0400	Header pipe, flows up to 150 GPM, 4" diameter		.01	.49	1.47	4.41	.35	
	0500	400 GPM, 6" diameter		.01	.57	1.72	5.15	.40	
	0600	800 GPM, 8" diameter		.01	.79	2.38	7.15	.55	
	0700	1500 GPM, 10" diameter		.01	.84	2.51	7.55	.60	

At row 0010: R015433 -10

01 54 33	Equipment Rental	UNIT	HOURLY OPER. COST	RENT PER DAY	RENT PER WEEK	RENT PER MONTH	EQUIPMENT COST/DAY	
70	0800	2500 GPM, 12″ diameter	L.F.	.02	1.58	4.74	14.20	1.10	**70**
	0900	4500 GPM, 16″ diameter		.03	2.02	6.07	18.20	1.45	
	0950	For quick coupling aluminum and plastic pipe, add	↓	.03	2.09	6.28	18.85	1.50	
	1100	Wellpoint, 25′ long, with fittings & riser pipe, 1-1/2″ or 2″ diameter	Ea.	.06	4.18	12.54	37.50	3	
	1200	Wellpoint pump, diesel powered, 4″ suction, 20 H.P.		7.83	191	574	1,725	177.45	
	1300	6″ suction, 30 H.P.		10.70	237	712	2,125	228	
	1400	8″ suction, 40 H.P.		14.45	325	976	2,925	310.80	
	1500	10″ suction, 75 H.P.		22.27	380	1,141	3,425	406.35	
	1600	12″ suction, 100 H.P.		31.72	605	1,810	5,425	615.75	
	1700	12″ suction, 175 H.P.	↓	47.41	670	2,010	6,025	781.30	
80	0010	**MARINE EQUIPMENT RENTAL** without operators							**80**
	0200	Barge, 400 Ton, 30′ wide x 90′ long	Ea.	17.50	1,050	3,180	9,550	776	
	0240	800 Ton, 45′ wide x 90′ long		21.25	1,300	3,870	11,600	944	
	2000	Tugboat, diesel, 100 H.P.		38.20	217	650	1,950	435.60	
	2040	250 H.P.		79.25	395	1,180	3,550	870	
	2080	380 H.P.		156.80	1,175	3,535	10,600	1,961	
	3000	Small work boat, gas, 16-foot, 50 H.P.		17.15	60	180	540	173.20	
	4000	Large, diesel, 48-foot, 200 H.P.	↓	89.40	1,250	3,740	11,200	1,463	

Crew No.		Bare Costs		Incl. Subs O&P		Cost Per Labor-Hour	

Crew A-1	Hr.	Daily	Hr.	Daily	Bare Costs	Incl. O&P
1 Building Laborer	$37.60	$300.80	$57.85	$462.80	$37.60	$57.85
1 Concrete Saw, Gas Manual		81.00		89.10	10.13	11.14
8 L.H., Daily Totals		$381.80		$551.90	$47.73	$68.99

Crew A-1A	Hr.	Daily	Hr.	Daily	Bare Costs	Incl. O&P
1 Skilled Worker	$48.65	$389.20	$75.15	$601.20	$48.65	$75.15
1 Shot Blaster, 20"		214.00		235.40	26.75	29.43
8 L.H., Daily Totals		$603.20		$836.60	$75.40	$104.58

Crew A-1B	Hr.	Daily	Hr.	Daily	Bare Costs	Incl. O&P
1 Building Laborer	$37.60	$300.80	$57.85	$462.80	$37.60	$57.85
1 Concrete Saw		167.40		184.14	20.93	23.02
8 L.H., Daily Totals		$468.20		$646.94	$58.52	$80.87

Crew A-1C	Hr.	Daily	Hr.	Daily	Bare Costs	Incl. O&P
1 Building Laborer	$37.60	$300.80	$57.85	$462.80	$37.60	$57.85
1 Chain Saw, Gas, 18"		31.20		34.32	3.90	4.29
8 L.H., Daily Totals		$332.00		$497.12	$41.50	$62.14

Crew A-1D	Hr.	Daily	Hr.	Daily	Bare Costs	Incl. O&P
1 Building Laborer	$37.60	$300.80	$57.85	$462.80	$37.60	$57.85
1 Vibrating Plate, Gas, 18"		36.20		39.82	4.53	4.98
8 L.H., Daily Totals		$337.00		$502.62	$42.13	$62.83

Crew A-1E	Hr.	Daily	Hr.	Daily	Bare Costs	Incl. O&P
1 Building Laborer	$37.60	$300.80	$57.85	$462.80	$37.60	$57.85
1 Vibrating Plate, Gas, 21"		46.80		51.48	5.85	6.43
8 L.H., Daily Totals		$347.60		$514.28	$43.45	$64.28

Crew A-1F	Hr.	Daily	Hr.	Daily	Bare Costs	Incl. O&P
1 Building Laborer	$37.60	$300.80	$57.85	$462.80	$37.60	$57.85
1 Rammer/Tamper, Gas, 8"		50.00		55.00	6.25	6.88
8 L.H., Daily Totals		$350.80		$517.80	$43.85	$64.72

Crew A-1G	Hr.	Daily	Hr.	Daily	Bare Costs	Incl. O&P
1 Building Laborer	$37.60	$300.80	$57.85	$462.80	$37.60	$57.85
1 Rammer/Tamper, Gas, 15"		56.40		62.04	7.05	7.75
8 L.H., Daily Totals		$357.20		$524.84	$44.65	$65.61

Crew A-1H	Hr.	Daily	Hr.	Daily	Bare Costs	Incl. O&P
1 Building Laborer	$37.60	$300.80	$57.85	$462.80	$37.60	$57.85
1 Exterior Steam Cleaner		75.60		83.16	9.45	10.40
8 L.H., Daily Totals		$376.40		$545.96	$47.05	$68.25

Crew A-1J	Hr.	Daily	Hr.	Daily	Bare Costs	Incl. O&P
1 Building Laborer	$37.60	$300.80	$57.85	$462.80	$37.60	$57.85
1 Cultivator, Walk-Behind, 5 H.P.		46.70		51.37	5.84	6.42
8 L.H., Daily Totals		$347.50		$514.17	$43.44	$64.27

Crew A-1K	Hr.	Daily	Hr.	Daily	Bare Costs	Incl. O&P
1 Building Laborer	$37.60	$300.80	$57.85	$462.80	$37.60	$57.85
1 Cultivator, Walk-Behind, 8 H.P.		72.65		79.92	9.08	9.99
8 L.H., Daily Totals		$373.45		$542.72	$46.68	$67.84

Crew A-1M	Hr.	Daily	Hr.	Daily	Bare Costs	Incl. O&P
1 Building Laborer	$37.60	$300.80	$57.85	$462.80	$37.60	$57.85
1 Snow Blower, Walk-Behind		67.15		73.86	8.39	9.23
8 L.H., Daily Totals		$367.95		$536.66	$45.99	$67.08

Crew A-2	Hr.	Daily	Hr.	Daily	Bare Costs	Incl. O&P
2 Laborers	$37.60	$601.60	$57.85	$925.60	$38.10	$58.27
1 Truck Driver (light)	39.10	312.80	59.10	472.80		
1 Flatbed Truck, Gas, 1.5 Ton		245.40		269.94	10.23	11.25
24 L.H., Daily Totals		$1159.80		$1668.34	$48.33	$69.51

Crew A-2A	Hr.	Daily	Hr.	Daily	Bare Costs	Incl. O&P
2 Laborers	$37.60	$601.60	$57.85	$925.60	$38.10	$58.27
1 Truck Driver (light)	39.10	312.80	59.10	472.80		
1 Flatbed Truck, Gas, 1.5 Ton		245.40		269.94		
1 Concrete Saw		167.40		184.14	17.20	18.92
24 L.H., Daily Totals		$1327.20		$1852.48	$55.30	$77.19

Crew A-2B	Hr.	Daily	Hr.	Daily	Bare Costs	Incl. O&P
1 Truck Driver (light)	$39.10	$312.80	$59.10	$472.80	$39.10	$59.10
1 Flatbed Truck, Gas, 1.5 Ton		245.40		269.94	30.68	33.74
8 L.H., Daily Totals		$558.20		$742.74	$69.78	$92.84

Crew A-3A	Hr.	Daily	Hr.	Daily	Bare Costs	Incl. O&P
1 Equip. Oper. (light)	$48.60	$388.80	$73.75	$590.00	$48.60	$73.75
1 Pickup Truck, 4 x 4, 3/4 Ton		155.60		171.16	19.45	21.40
8 L.H., Daily Totals		$544.40		$761.16	$68.05	$95.14

Crew A-3B	Hr.	Daily	Hr.	Daily	Bare Costs	Incl. O&P
1 Equip. Oper. (medium)	$50.60	$404.80	$76.75	$614.00	$45.33	$68.65
1 Truck Driver (heavy)	40.05	320.40	60.55	484.40		
1 Dump Truck, 12 C.Y., 400 H.P.		691.00		760.10		
1 F.E. Loader, W.M., 2.5 C.Y.		519.80		571.78	75.67	83.24
16 L.H., Daily Totals		$1936.00		$2430.28	$121.00	$151.89

Crew A-3C	Hr.	Daily	Hr.	Daily	Bare Costs	Incl. O&P
1 Equip. Oper. (light)	$48.60	$388.80	$73.75	$590.00	$48.60	$73.75
1 Loader, Skid Steer, 78 H.P.		318.60		350.46	39.83	43.81
8 L.H., Daily Totals		$707.40		$940.46	$88.42	$117.56

Crew A-3D	Hr.	Daily	Hr.	Daily	Bare Costs	Incl. O&P
1 Truck Driver (light)	$39.10	$312.80	$59.10	$472.80	$39.10	$59.10
1 Pickup Truck, 4 x 4, 3/4 Ton		155.60		171.16		
1 Flatbed Trailer, 25 Ton		113.60		124.96	33.65	37.02
8 L.H., Daily Totals		$582.00		$768.92	$72.75	$96.11

Crew A-3E	Hr.	Daily	Hr.	Daily	Bare Costs	Incl. O&P
1 Equip. Oper. (crane)	$51.70	$413.60	$78.45	$627.60	$45.88	$69.50
1 Truck Driver (heavy)	40.05	320.40	60.55	484.40		
1 Pickup Truck, 4 x 4, 3/4 Ton		155.60		171.16	9.72	10.70
16 L.H., Daily Totals		$889.60		$1283.16	$55.60	$80.20

Crew A-3F	Hr.	Daily	Hr.	Daily	Bare Costs	Incl. O&P
1 Equip. Oper. (crane)	$51.70	$413.60	$78.45	$627.60	$45.88	$69.50
1 Truck Driver (heavy)	40.05	320.40	60.55	484.40		
1 Pickup Truck, 4 x 4, 3/4 Ton		155.60		171.16		
1 Truck Tractor, 6x4, 380 H.P.		599.80		659.78		
1 Lowbed Trailer, 75 Ton		221.80		243.98	61.08	67.18
16 L.H., Daily Totals		$1711.20		$2186.92	$106.95	$136.68

Crew A-3G

Crew A-3G	Bare Costs Hr.	Daily	Incl. Subs O&P Hr.	Daily	Cost Per Labor-Hour Bare Costs	Incl. O&P
1 Equip. Oper. (crane)	$51.70	$413.60	$78.45	$627.60	$45.88	$69.50
1 Truck Driver (heavy)	40.05	320.40	60.55	484.40		
1 Pickup Truck, 4 x 4, 3/4 Ton		155.60		171.16		
1 Truck Tractor, 6x4, 450 H.P.		727.40		800.14		
1 Lowbed Trailer, 75 Ton		221.80		243.98	69.05	75.95
16 L.H., Daily Totals		$1838.80		$2327.28	$114.93	$145.46

Crew A-3H

Crew A-3H	Bare Costs Hr.	Daily	Incl. Subs O&P Hr.	Daily	Cost Per Labor-Hour Bare Costs	Incl. O&P
1 Equip. Oper. (crane)	$51.70	$413.60	$78.45	$627.60	$51.70	$78.45
1 Hyd. Crane, 12 Ton (Daily)		860.80		946.88	107.60	118.36
8 L.H., Daily Totals		$1274.40		$1574.48	$159.30	$196.81

Crew A-3I

Crew A-3I	Bare Costs Hr.	Daily	Incl. Subs O&P Hr.	Daily	Cost Per Labor-Hour Bare Costs	Incl. O&P
1 Equip. Oper. (crane)	$51.70	$413.60	$78.45	$627.60	$51.70	$78.45
1 Hyd. Crane, 25 Ton (Daily)		989.60		1088.56	123.70	136.07
8 L.H., Daily Totals		$1403.20		$1716.16	$175.40	$214.52

Crew A-3J

Crew A-3J	Bare Costs Hr.	Daily	Incl. Subs O&P Hr.	Daily	Cost Per Labor-Hour Bare Costs	Incl. O&P
1 Equip. Oper. (crane)	$51.70	$413.60	$78.45	$627.60	$51.70	$78.45
1 Hyd. Crane, 40 Ton (Daily)		1221.00		1343.10	152.63	167.89
8 L.H., Daily Totals		$1634.60		$1970.70	$204.32	$246.34

Crew A-3K

Crew A-3K	Bare Costs Hr.	Daily	Incl. Subs O&P Hr.	Daily	Cost Per Labor-Hour Bare Costs	Incl. O&P
1 Equip. Oper. (crane)	$51.70	$413.60	$78.45	$627.60	$48.45	$73.50
1 Equip. Oper. (oiler)	45.20	361.60	68.55	548.40		
1 Hyd. Crane, 55 Ton (Daily)		1469.00		1615.90		
1 P/U Truck, 3/4 Ton (Daily)		167.20		183.92	102.26	112.49
16 L.H., Daily Totals		$2411.40		$2975.82	$150.71	$185.99

Crew A-3L

Crew A-3L	Bare Costs Hr.	Daily	Incl. Subs O&P Hr.	Daily	Cost Per Labor-Hour Bare Costs	Incl. O&P
1 Equip. Oper. (crane)	$51.70	$413.60	$78.45	$627.60	$48.45	$73.50
1 Equip. Oper. (oiler)	45.20	361.60	68.55	548.40		
1 Hyd. Crane, 80 Ton (Daily)		2174.00		2391.40		
1 P/U Truck, 3/4 Ton (Daily)		167.20		183.92	146.32	160.96
16 L.H., Daily Totals		$3116.40		$3751.32	$194.78	$234.46

Crew A-3M

Crew A-3M	Bare Costs Hr.	Daily	Incl. Subs O&P Hr.	Daily	Cost Per Labor-Hour Bare Costs	Incl. O&P
1 Equip. Oper. (crane)	$51.70	$413.60	$78.45	$627.60	$48.45	$73.50
1 Equip. Oper. (oiler)	45.20	361.60	68.55	548.40		
1 Hyd. Crane, 100 Ton (Daily)		2169.00		2385.90		
1 P/U Truck, 3/4 Ton (Daily)		167.20		183.92	146.01	160.61
16 L.H., Daily Totals		$3111.40		$3745.82	$194.46	$234.11

Crew A-3N

Crew A-3N	Bare Costs Hr.	Daily	Incl. Subs O&P Hr.	Daily	Cost Per Labor-Hour Bare Costs	Incl. O&P
1 Equip. Oper. (crane)	$51.70	$413.60	$78.45	$627.60	$51.70	$78.45
1 Tower Cane (monthly)		1128.00		1240.80	141.00	155.10
8 L.H., Daily Totals		$1541.60		$1868.40	$192.70	$233.55

Crew A-3P

Crew A-3P	Bare Costs Hr.	Daily	Incl. Subs O&P Hr.	Daily	Cost Per Labor-Hour Bare Costs	Incl. O&P
1 Equip. Oper. (light)	$48.60	$388.80	$73.75	$590.00	$48.60	$73.75
1 A.T. Forklift, 42' lift		526.40		579.04	65.80	72.38
8 L.H., Daily Totals		$915.20		$1169.04	$114.40	$146.13

Crew A-3Q

Crew A-3Q	Bare Costs Hr.	Daily	Incl. Subs O&P Hr.	Daily	Cost Per Labor-Hour Bare Costs	Incl. O&P
1 Equip. Oper. (light)	$48.60	$388.80	$73.75	$590.00	$48.60	$73.75
1 Pickup Truck, 4 x 4, 3/4 Ton		155.60		171.16		
1 Flatbed trailer, 3 Ton		23.60		25.96	22.40	24.64
8 L.H., Daily Totals		$568.00		$787.12	$71.00	$98.39

Crew A-4

Crew A-4	Bare Costs Hr.	Daily	Incl. Subs O&P Hr.	Daily	Cost Per Labor-Hour Bare Costs	Incl. O&P
2 Carpenters	$46.95	$751.20	$72.25	$1156.00	$44.75	$68.43
1 Painter, Ordinary	40.35	322.80	60.80	486.40		
24 L.H., Daily Totals		$1074.00		$1642.40	$44.75	$68.43

Crew A-5

Crew A-5	Bare Costs Hr.	Daily	Incl. Subs O&P Hr.	Daily	Cost Per Labor-Hour Bare Costs	Incl. O&P
2 Laborers	$37.60	$601.60	$57.85	$925.60	$37.77	$57.99
.25 Truck Driver (light)	39.10	78.20	59.10	118.20		
.25 Flatbed Truck, Gas, 1.5 Ton		61.35		67.48	3.41	3.75
18 L.H., Daily Totals		$741.15		$1111.29	$41.17	$61.74

Crew A-6

Crew A-6	Bare Costs Hr.	Daily	Incl. Subs O&P Hr.	Daily	Cost Per Labor-Hour Bare Costs	Incl. O&P
1 Instrument Man	$48.65	$389.20	$75.15	$601.20	$46.88	$71.92
1 Rodman/Chainman	45.10	360.80	68.70	549.60		
1 Level, Electronic		54.80		60.28	3.42	3.77
16 L.H., Daily Totals		$804.80		$1211.08	$50.30	$75.69

Crew A-7

Crew A-7	Bare Costs Hr.	Daily	Incl. Subs O&P Hr.	Daily	Cost Per Labor-Hour Bare Costs	Incl. O&P
1 Chief of Party	$60.90	$487.20	$93.20	$745.60	$51.55	$79.02
1 Instrument Man	48.65	389.20	75.15	601.20		
1 Rodman/Chainman	45.10	360.80	68.70	549.60		
1 Level, Electronic		54.80		60.28	2.28	2.51
24 L.H., Daily Totals		$1292.00		$1956.68	$53.83	$81.53

Crew A-8

Crew A-8	Bare Costs Hr.	Daily	Incl. Subs O&P Hr.	Daily	Cost Per Labor-Hour Bare Costs	Incl. O&P
1 Chief of Party	$60.90	$487.20	$93.20	$745.60	$49.94	$76.44
1 Instrument Man	48.65	389.20	75.15	601.20		
2 Rodmen/Chainmen	45.10	721.60	68.70	1099.20		
1 Level, Electronic		54.80		60.28	1.71	1.88
32 L.H., Daily Totals		$1652.80		$2506.28	$51.65	$78.32

Crew A-9

Crew A-9	Bare Costs Hr.	Daily	Incl. Subs O&P Hr.	Daily	Cost Per Labor-Hour Bare Costs	Incl. O&P
1 Asbestos Foreman	$52.85	$422.80	$82.30	$658.40	$52.41	$81.60
7 Asbestos Workers	52.35	2931.60	81.50	4564.00		
64 L.H., Daily Totals		$3354.40		$5222.40	$52.41	$81.60

Crew A-10A

Crew A-10A	Bare Costs Hr.	Daily	Incl. Subs O&P Hr.	Daily	Cost Per Labor-Hour Bare Costs	Incl. O&P
1 Asbestos Foreman	$52.85	$422.80	$82.30	$658.40	$52.52	$81.77
2 Asbestos Workers	52.35	837.60	81.50	1304.00		
24 L.H., Daily Totals		$1260.40		$1962.40	$52.52	$81.77

Crew A-10B

Crew A-10B	Bare Costs Hr.	Daily	Incl. Subs O&P Hr.	Daily	Cost Per Labor-Hour Bare Costs	Incl. O&P
1 Asbestos Foreman	$52.85	$422.80	$82.30	$658.40	$52.48	$81.70
3 Asbestos Workers	52.35	1256.40	81.50	1956.00		
32 L.H., Daily Totals		$1679.20		$2614.40	$52.48	$81.70

Crew A-10C

Crew A-10C	Bare Costs Hr.	Daily	Incl. Subs O&P Hr.	Daily	Cost Per Labor-Hour Bare Costs	Incl. O&P
3 Asbestos Workers	$52.35	$1256.40	$81.50	$1956.00	$52.35	$81.50
1 Flatbed Truck, Gas, 1.5 Ton		245.40		269.94	10.23	11.25
24 L.H., Daily Totals		$1501.80		$2225.94	$62.58	$92.75

Crew A-10D

Crew A-10D	Bare Costs Hr.	Daily	Incl. Subs O&P Hr.	Daily	Cost Per Labor-Hour Bare Costs	Incl. O&P
2 Asbestos Workers	$52.35	$837.60	$81.50	$1304.00	$50.40	$77.50
1 Equip. Oper. (crane)	51.70	413.60	78.45	627.60		
1 Equip. Oper. (oiler)	45.20	361.60	68.55	548.40		
1 Hydraulic Crane, 33 Ton		750.00		825.00	23.44	25.78
32 L.H., Daily Totals		$2362.80		$3305.00	$73.84	$103.28

Crew A-11

Crew A-11	Hr.	Daily	Hr.	Daily	Bare Costs	Incl. O&P
1 Asbestos Foreman	$52.85	$422.80	$82.30	$658.40	$52.41	$81.60
7 Asbestos Workers	52.35	2931.60	81.50	4564.00		
2 Chip. Hammers, 12 Lb., Elec.		40.00		44.00	.63	.69
64 L.H., Daily Totals		$3394.40		$5266.40	$53.04	$82.29

Crew A-12

Crew A-12	Hr.	Daily	Hr.	Daily	Bare Costs	Incl. O&P
1 Asbestos Foreman	$52.85	$422.80	$82.30	$658.40	$52.41	$81.60
7 Asbestos Workers	52.35	2931.60	81.50	4564.00		
1 Trk-Mtd Vac, 14 CY, 1500 Gal.		514.25		565.67		
1 Flatbed Truck, 20,000 GVW		248.60		273.46	11.92	13.11
64 L.H., Daily Totals		$4117.25		$6061.53	$64.33	$94.71

Crew A-13

Crew A-13	Hr.	Daily	Hr.	Daily	Bare Costs	Incl. O&P
1 Equip. Oper. (light)	$48.60	$388.80	$73.75	$590.00	$48.60	$73.75
1 Trk-Mtd Vac, 14 CY, 1500 Gal.		514.25		565.67		
1 Flatbed Truck, 20,000 GVW		248.60		273.46	95.36	104.89
8 L.H., Daily Totals		$1151.65		$1429.14	$143.96	$178.64

Crew B-1

Crew B-1	Hr.	Daily	Hr.	Daily	Bare Costs	Incl. O&P
1 Labor Foreman (outside)	$39.60	$316.80	$60.95	$487.60	$38.27	$58.88
2 Laborers	37.60	601.60	57.85	925.60		
24 L.H., Daily Totals		$918.40		$1413.20	$38.27	$58.88

Crew B-1A

Crew B-1A	Hr.	Daily	Hr.	Daily	Bare Costs	Incl. O&P
1 Labor Foreman (outside)	$39.60	$316.80	$60.95	$487.60	$38.27	$58.88
2 Laborers	37.60	601.60	57.85	925.60		
2 Cutting Torches		22.80		25.08		
2 Sets of Gases		304.00		334.40	13.62	14.98
24 L.H., Daily Totals		$1245.20		$1772.68	$51.88	$73.86

Crew B-1B

Crew B-1B	Hr.	Daily	Hr.	Daily	Bare Costs	Incl. O&P
1 Labor Foreman (outside)	$39.60	$316.80	$60.95	$487.60	$41.63	$63.77
2 Laborers	37.60	601.60	57.85	925.60		
1 Equip. Oper. (crane)	51.70	413.60	78.45	627.60		
2 Cutting Torches		22.80		25.08		
2 Sets of Gases		304.00		334.40		
1 Hyd. Crane, 12 Ton		653.80		719.18	30.64	33.71
32 L.H., Daily Totals		$2312.60		$3119.46	$72.27	$97.48

Crew B-1C

Crew B-1C	Hr.	Daily	Hr.	Daily	Bare Costs	Incl. O&P
1 Labor Foreman (outside)	$39.60	$316.80	$60.95	$487.60	$38.27	$58.88
2 Laborers	37.60	601.60	57.85	925.60		
1 Aerial Lift Truck, 60' Boom		435.60		479.16	18.15	19.97
24 L.H., Daily Totals		$1354.00		$1892.36	$56.42	$78.85

Crew B-1D

Crew B-1D	Hr.	Daily	Hr.	Daily	Bare Costs	Incl. O&P
2 Laborers	$37.60	$601.60	$57.85	$925.60	$37.60	$57.85
1 Small Work Boat, Gas, 50 H.P.		173.20		190.52		
1 Pressure Washer, 7 GPM		87.60		96.36	16.30	17.93
16 L.H., Daily Totals		$862.40		$1212.48	$53.90	$75.78

Crew B-1E

Crew B-1E	Hr.	Daily	Hr.	Daily	Bare Costs	Incl. O&P
1 Labor Foreman (outside)	$39.60	$316.80	$60.95	$487.60	$38.10	$58.63
3 Laborers	37.60	902.40	57.85	1388.40		
1 Work Boat, Diesel, 200 H.P.		1463.00		1609.30		
2 Pressure Washer, 7 GPM		175.20		192.72	51.19	56.31
32 L.H., Daily Totals		$2857.40		$3678.02	$89.29	$114.94

Crew B-1F

Crew B-1F	Hr.	Daily	Hr.	Daily	Bare Costs	Incl. O&P
2 Skilled Workers	$48.65	$778.40	$75.15	$1202.40	$44.97	$69.38
1 Laborer	37.60	300.80	57.85	462.80		
1 Small Work Boat, Gas, 50 H.P.		173.20		190.52		
1 Pressure Washer, 7 GPM		87.60		96.36	10.87	11.95
24 L.H., Daily Totals		$1340.00		$1952.08	$55.83	$81.34

Crew B-1G

Crew B-1G	Hr.	Daily	Hr.	Daily	Bare Costs	Incl. O&P
2 Laborers	$37.60	$601.60	$57.85	$925.60	$37.60	$57.85
1 Small Work Boat, Gas, 50 H.P.		173.20		190.52	10.82	11.91
16 L.H., Daily Totals		$774.80		$1116.12	$48.42	$69.76

Crew B-1H

Crew B-1H	Hr.	Daily	Hr.	Daily	Bare Costs	Incl. O&P
2 Skilled Workers	$48.65	$778.40	$75.15	$1202.40	$44.97	$69.38
1 Laborer	37.60	300.80	57.85	462.80		
1 Small Work Boat, Gas, 50 H.P.		173.20		190.52	7.22	7.94
24 L.H., Daily Totals		$1252.40		$1855.72	$52.18	$77.32

Crew B-1J

Crew B-1J	Hr.	Daily	Hr.	Daily	Bare Costs	Incl. O&P
1 Labor Foreman (inside)	$38.10	$304.80	$58.65	$469.20	$37.85	$58.25
1 Laborer	37.60	300.80	57.85	462.80		
16 L.H., Daily Totals		$605.60		$932.00	$37.85	$58.25

Crew B-1K

Crew B-1K	Hr.	Daily	Hr.	Daily	Bare Costs	Incl. O&P
1 Carpenter Foreman (inside)	$47.45	$379.60	$73.05	$584.40	$47.20	$72.65
1 Carpenter	46.95	375.60	72.25	578.00		
16 L.H., Daily Totals		$755.20		$1162.40	$47.20	$72.65

Crew B-2

Crew B-2	Hr.	Daily	Hr.	Daily	Bare Costs	Incl. O&P
1 Labor Foreman (outside)	$39.60	$316.80	$60.95	$487.60	$38.00	$58.47
4 Laborers	37.60	1203.20	57.85	1851.20		
40 L.H., Daily Totals		$1520.00		$2338.80	$38.00	$58.47

Crew B-2A

Crew B-2A	Hr.	Daily	Hr.	Daily	Bare Costs	Incl. O&P
1 Labor Foreman (outside)	$39.60	$316.80	$60.95	$487.60	$38.27	$58.88
2 Laborers	37.60	601.60	57.85	925.60		
1 Aerial Lift Truck, 60' Boom		435.60		479.16	18.15	19.97
24 L.H., Daily Totals		$1354.00		$1892.36	$56.42	$78.85

Crew B-3

Crew B-3	Hr.	Daily	Hr.	Daily	Bare Costs	Incl. O&P
1 Labor Foreman (outside)	$39.60	$316.80	$60.95	$487.60	$40.92	$62.42
2 Laborers	37.60	601.60	57.85	925.60		
1 Equip. Oper. (medium)	50.60	404.80	76.75	614.00		
2 Truck Drivers (heavy)	40.05	640.80	60.55	968.80		
1 Crawler Loader, 3 C.Y.		1188.00		1306.80		
2 Dump Trucks, 12 C.Y., 400 H.P.		1382.00		1520.20	53.54	58.90
48 L.H., Daily Totals		$4534.00		$5823.00	$94.46	$121.31

Crew B-3A

Crew B-3A	Hr.	Daily	Hr.	Daily	Bare Costs	Incl. O&P
4 Laborers	$37.60	$1203.20	$57.85	$1851.20	$40.20	$61.63
1 Equip. Oper. (medium)	50.60	404.80	76.75	614.00		
1 Hyd. Excavator, 1.5 C.Y.		1030.00		1133.00	25.75	28.32
40 L.H., Daily Totals		$2638.00		$3598.20	$65.95	$89.95

Crew B-3B

Crew B-3B	Hr.	Daily	Hr.	Daily	Bare Costs	Incl. O&P
2 Laborers	$37.60	$601.60	$57.85	$925.60	$41.46	$63.25
1 Equip. Oper. (medium)	50.60	404.80	76.75	614.00		
1 Truck Driver (heavy)	40.05	320.40	60.55	484.40		
1 Backhoe Loader, 80 H.P.		391.80		430.98		
1 Dump Truck, 12 C.Y., 400 H.P.		691.00		760.10	33.84	37.22
32 L.H., Daily Totals		$2409.60		$3215.08	$75.30	$100.47

713

For customer support on your Site Work & Landscape Cost Data, call 877.737.1594.

Crew B-3C

Crew B-3C	Hr.	Daily	Hr.	Daily	Bare Costs	Incl. O&P
3 Laborers	$37.60	$902.40	$57.85	$1388.40	$40.85	$62.58
1 Equip. Oper. (medium)	50.60	404.80	76.75	614.00		
1 Crawler Loader, 4 C.Y.		1561.00		1717.10	48.78	53.66
32 L.H., Daily Totals		$2868.20		$3719.50	$89.63	$116.23

Crew B-4

Crew B-4	Hr.	Daily	Hr.	Daily	Bare Costs	Incl. O&P
1 Labor Foreman (outside)	$39.60	$316.80	$60.95	$487.60	$38.34	$58.82
4 Laborers	37.60	1203.20	57.85	1851.20		
1 Truck Driver (heavy)	40.05	320.40	60.55	484.40		
1 Truck Tractor, 220 H.P.		359.60		395.56		
1 Flatbed Trailer, 40 Ton		154.00		169.40	10.70	11.77
48 L.H., Daily Totals		$2354.00		$3388.16	$49.04	$70.59

Crew B-5

Crew B-5	Hr.	Daily	Hr.	Daily	Bare Costs	Incl. O&P
1 Labor Foreman (outside)	$39.60	$316.80	$60.95	$487.60	$41.60	$63.69
4 Laborers	37.60	1203.20	57.85	1851.20		
2 Equip. Oper. (medium)	50.60	809.60	76.75	1228.00		
1 Air Compressor, 250 cfm		201.40		221.54		
2 Breakers, Pavement, 60 lb.		19.60		21.56		
2 -50' Air Hoses, 1.5"		11.60		12.76		
1 Crawler Loader, 3 C.Y.		1188.00		1306.80	25.37	27.90
56 L.H., Daily Totals		$3750.20		$5129.46	$66.97	$91.60

Crew B-5A

Crew B-5A	Hr.	Daily	Hr.	Daily	Bare Costs	Incl. O&P
1 Labor Foreman (outside)	$39.60	$316.80	$60.95	$487.60	$41.26	$63.03
6 Laborers	37.60	1804.80	57.85	2776.80		
2 Equip. Oper. (medium)	50.60	809.60	76.75	1228.00		
1 Equip. Oper. (light)	48.60	388.80	73.75	590.00		
2 Truck Drivers (heavy)	40.05	640.80	60.55	968.80		
1 Air Compressor, 365 cfm		263.80		290.18		
2 Breakers, Pavement, 60 lb.		19.60		21.56		
8 -50' Air Hoses, 1"		32.80		36.08		
2 Dump Trucks, 8 C.Y., 220 H.P.		822.40		904.64	11.86	13.05
96 L.H., Daily Totals		$5099.40		$7303.66	$53.12	$76.08

Crew B-5B

Crew B-5B	Hr.	Daily	Hr.	Daily	Bare Costs	Incl. O&P
1 Powderman	$48.65	$389.20	$75.15	$601.20	$45.00	$68.38
2 Equip. Oper. (medium)	50.60	809.60	76.75	1228.00		
3 Truck Drivers (heavy)	40.05	961.20	60.55	1453.20		
1 F.E. Loader, W.M., 2.5 C.Y.		519.80		571.78		
3 Dump Trucks, 12 C.Y., 400 H.P.		2073.00		2280.30		
1 Air Compressor, 365 CFM		263.80		290.18	59.51	65.46
48 L.H., Daily Totals		$5016.60		$6424.66	$104.51	$133.85

Crew B-5C

Crew B-5C	Hr.	Daily	Hr.	Daily	Bare Costs	Incl. O&P
3 Laborers	$37.60	$902.40	$57.85	$1388.40	$42.55	$64.80
1 Equip. Oper. (medium)	50.60	404.80	76.75	614.00		
2 Truck Drivers (heavy)	40.05	640.80	60.55	968.80		
1 Equip. Oper. (crane)	51.70	413.60	78.45	627.60		
1 Equip. Oper. (oiler)	45.20	361.60	68.55	548.40		
2 Dump Trucks, 12 C.Y., 400 H.P.		1382.00		1520.20		
1 Crawler Loader, 4 C.Y.		1561.00		1717.10		
1 S.P. Crane, 4x4, 25 Ton		599.40		659.34	55.35	60.88
64 L.H., Daily Totals		$6265.60		$8043.84	$97.90	$125.69

Crew B-5D

Crew B-5D	Hr.	Daily	Hr.	Daily	Bare Costs	Incl. O&P
1 Labor Foreman (outside)	$39.60	$316.80	$60.95	$487.60	$41.41	$63.30
4 Laborers	37.60	1203.20	57.85	1851.20		
2 Equip. Oper. (medium)	50.60	809.60	76.75	1228.00		
1 Truck Driver (heavy)	40.05	320.40	60.55	484.40		
1 Air Compressor, 250 cfm		201.40		221.54		
2 Breakers, Pavement, 60 lb.		19.60		21.56		
2 -50' Air Hoses, 1.5"		11.60		12.76		
1 Crawler Loader, 3 C.Y.		1188.00		1306.80		
1 Dump Truck, 12 C.Y., 400 H.P.		691.00		760.10	32.99	36.29
64 L.H., Daily Totals		$4761.60		$6373.96	$74.40	$99.59

Crew B-6

Crew B-6	Hr.	Daily	Hr.	Daily	Bare Costs	Incl. O&P
2 Laborers	$37.60	$601.60	$57.85	$925.60	$41.27	$63.15
1 Equip. Oper. (light)	48.60	388.80	73.75	590.00		
1 Backhoe Loader, 48 H.P.		364.20		400.62	15.18	16.69
24 L.H., Daily Totals		$1354.60		$1916.22	$56.44	$79.84

Crew B-6A

Crew B-6A	Hr.	Daily	Hr.	Daily	Bare Costs	Incl. O&P
.5 Labor Foreman (outside)	$39.60	$158.40	$60.95	$243.80	$43.20	$66.03
1 Laborer	37.60	300.80	57.85	462.80		
1 Equip. Oper. (medium)	50.60	404.80	76.75	614.00		
1 Vacuum Truck, 5000 Gal.		358.10		393.91	17.91	19.70
20 L.H., Daily Totals		$1222.10		$1714.51	$61.10	$85.73

Crew B-6B

Crew B-6B	Hr.	Daily	Hr.	Daily	Bare Costs	Incl. O&P
2 Labor Foremen (outside)	$39.60	$633.60	$60.95	$975.20	$38.27	$58.88
4 Laborers	37.60	1203.20	57.85	1851.20		
1 S.P. Crane, 4x4, 5 Ton		275.40		302.94		
1 Flatbed Truck, Gas, 1.5 Ton		245.40		269.94		
1 Butt Fusion Mach., 4"-12" diam.		382.10		420.31	18.81	20.69
48 L.H., Daily Totals		$2739.70		$3819.59	$57.08	$79.57

Crew B-6C

Crew B-6C	Hr.	Daily	Hr.	Daily	Bare Costs	Incl. O&P
2 Labor Foremen (outside)	$39.60	$633.60	$60.95	$975.20	$38.27	$58.88
4 Laborers	37.60	1203.20	57.85	1851.20		
1 S.P. Crane, 4x4, 12 Ton		473.40		520.74		
1 Flatbed Truck, Gas, 3 Ton		303.20		333.52		
1 Butt Fusion Mach., 8"-24" diam.		829.70		912.67	33.46	36.81
48 L.H., Daily Totals		$3443.10		$4593.33	$71.73	$95.69

Crew B-7

Crew B-7	Hr.	Daily	Hr.	Daily	Bare Costs	Incl. O&P
1 Labor Foreman (outside)	$39.60	$316.80	$60.95	$487.60	$40.10	$61.52
4 Laborers	37.60	1203.20	57.85	1851.20		
1 Equip. Oper. (medium)	50.60	404.80	76.75	614.00		
1 Brush Chipper, 12", 130 H.P.		391.40		430.54		
1 Crawler Loader, 3 C.Y.		1188.00		1306.80		
2 Chain Saws, Gas, 36" Long		90.00		99.00	34.78	38.26
48 L.H., Daily Totals		$3594.20		$4789.14	$74.88	$99.77

Crew B-7A

Crew B-7A	Hr.	Daily	Hr.	Daily	Bare Costs	Incl. O&P
2 Laborers	$37.60	$601.60	$57.85	$925.60	$41.27	$63.15
1 Equip. Oper. (light)	48.60	388.80	73.75	590.00		
1 Rake w/Tractor		354.25		389.68		
2 Chain Saw, Gas, 18"		62.40		68.64	17.36	19.10
24 L.H., Daily Totals		$1407.05		$1973.92	$58.63	$82.25

Crew B-7B

Crew No.	Hr.	Daily	Hr.	Daily	Bare Costs	Incl. O&P
1 Labor Foreman (outside)	$39.60	$316.80	$60.95	$487.60	$40.09	$61.38
4 Laborers	37.60	1203.20	57.85	1851.20		
1 Equip. Oper. (medium)	50.60	404.80	76.75	614.00		
1 Truck Driver (heavy)	40.05	320.40	60.55	484.40		
1 Brush Chipper, 12", 130 H.P.		391.40		430.54		
1 Crawler Loader, 3 C.Y.		1188.00		1306.80		
2 Chain Saws, Gas, 36" Long		90.00		99.00		
1 Dump Truck, 8 C.Y., 220 H.P.		411.20		452.32	37.15	40.87
56 L.H., Daily Totals		$4325.80		$5725.86	$77.25	$102.25

Crew B-7C

Crew No.	Hr.	Daily	Hr.	Daily	Bare Costs	Incl. O&P
1 Labor Foreman (outside)	$39.60	$316.80	$60.95	$487.60	$40.09	$61.38
4 Laborers	37.60	1203.20	57.85	1851.20		
1 Equip. Oper. (medium)	50.60	404.80	76.75	614.00		
1 Truck Driver (heavy)	40.05	320.40	60.55	484.40		
1 Brush Chipper, 12", 130 H.P.		391.40		430.54		
1 Crawler Loader, 3 C.Y.		1188.00		1306.80		
2 Chain Saws, Gas, 36" Long		90.00		99.00		
1 Dump Truck, 12 C.Y., 400 H.P.		691.00		760.10	42.15	46.37
56 L.H., Daily Totals		$4605.60		$6033.64	$82.24	$107.74

Crew B-8

Crew No.	Hr.	Daily	Hr.	Daily	Bare Costs	Incl. O&P
1 Labor Foreman (outside)	$39.60	$316.80	$60.95	$487.60	$42.66	$64.97
2 Laborers	37.60	601.60	57.85	925.60		
2 Equip. Oper. (medium)	50.60	809.60	76.75	1228.00		
1 Equip. Oper. (oiler)	45.20	361.60	68.55	548.40		
2 Truck Drivers (heavy)	40.05	640.80	60.55	968.80		
1 Hyd. Crane, 25 Ton		736.60		810.26		
1 Crawler Loader, 3 C.Y.		1188.00		1306.80		
2 Dump Trucks, 12 C.Y., 400 H.P.		1382.00		1520.20	51.67	56.83
64 L.H., Daily Totals		$6037.00		$7795.66	$94.33	$121.81

Crew B-9

Crew No.	Hr.	Daily	Hr.	Daily	Bare Costs	Incl. O&P
1 Labor Foreman (outside)	$39.60	$316.80	$60.95	$487.60	$38.00	$58.47
4 Laborers	37.60	1203.20	57.85	1851.20		
1 Air Compressor, 250 cfm		201.40		221.54		
2 Breakers, Pavement, 60 lb.		19.60		21.56		
2 -50' Air Hoses, 1.5"		11.60		12.76	5.82	6.40
40 L.H., Daily Totals		$1752.60		$2594.66	$43.81	$64.87

Crew B-9A

Crew No.	Hr.	Daily	Hr.	Daily	Bare Costs	Incl. O&P
2 Laborers	$37.60	$601.60	$57.85	$925.60	$38.42	$58.75
1 Truck Driver (heavy)	40.05	320.40	60.55	484.40		
1 Water Tank Trailer, 5000 Gal.		141.00		155.10		
1 Truck Tractor, 220 H.P.		359.60		395.56		
2 -50' Discharge Hoses, 3"		3.00		3.30	20.98	23.08
24 L.H., Daily Totals		$1425.60		$1963.96	$59.40	$81.83

Crew B-9B

Crew No.	Hr.	Daily	Hr.	Daily	Bare Costs	Incl. O&P
2 Laborers	$37.60	$601.60	$57.85	$925.60	$38.42	$58.75
1 Truck Driver (heavy)	40.05	320.40	60.55	484.40		
2 -50' Discharge Hoses, 3"		3.00		3.30		
1 Water Tank Trailer, 5000 Gal.		141.00		155.10		
1 Truck Tractor, 220 H.P.		359.60		395.56		
1 Pressure Washer		70.20		77.22	23.91	26.30
24 L.H., Daily Totals		$1495.80		$2041.18	$62.33	$85.05

Crew B-9D

Crew No.	Hr.	Daily	Hr.	Daily	Bare Costs	Incl. O&P
1 Labor Foreman (outside)	$39.60	$316.80	$60.95	$487.60	$38.00	$58.47
4 Common Laborers	37.60	1203.20	57.85	1851.20		
1 Air Compressor, 250 cfm		201.40		221.54		
2 -50' Air Hoses, 1.5"		11.60		12.76		
2 Air Powered Tampers		52.40		57.64	6.63	7.30
40 L.H., Daily Totals		$1785.40		$2630.74	$44.63	$65.77

Crew B-10

Crew No.	Hr.	Daily	Hr.	Daily	Bare Costs	Incl. O&P
1 Equip. Oper. (medium)	$50.60	$404.80	$76.75	$614.00	$46.27	$70.45
.5 Laborer	37.60	150.40	57.85	231.40		
12 L.H., Daily Totals		$555.20		$845.40	$46.27	$70.45

Crew B-10A

Crew No.	Hr.	Daily	Hr.	Daily	Bare Costs	Incl. O&P
1 Equip. Oper. (medium)	$50.60	$404.80	$76.75	$614.00	$46.27	$70.45
.5 Laborer	37.60	150.40	57.85	231.40		
1 Roller, 2-Drum, W.B., 7.5 H.P.		180.00		198.00	15.00	16.50
12 L.H., Daily Totals		$735.20		$1043.40	$61.27	$86.95

Crew B-10B

Crew No.	Hr.	Daily	Hr.	Daily	Bare Costs	Incl. O&P
1 Equip. Oper. (medium)	$50.60	$404.80	$76.75	$614.00	$46.27	$70.45
.5 Laborer	37.60	150.40	57.85	231.40		
1 Dozer, 200 H.P.		1387.00		1525.70	115.58	127.14
12 L.H., Daily Totals		$1942.20		$2371.10	$161.85	$197.59

Crew B-10C

Crew No.	Hr.	Daily	Hr.	Daily	Bare Costs	Incl. O&P
1 Equip. Oper. (medium)	$50.60	$404.80	$76.75	$614.00	$46.27	$70.45
.5 Laborer	37.60	150.40	57.85	231.40		
1 Dozer, 200 H.P.		1387.00		1525.70		
1 Vibratory Roller, Towed, 23 Ton		396.00		435.60	148.58	163.44
12 L.H., Daily Totals		$2338.20		$2806.70	$194.85	$233.89

Crew B-10D

Crew No.	Hr.	Daily	Hr.	Daily	Bare Costs	Incl. O&P
1 Equip. Oper. (medium)	$50.60	$404.80	$76.75	$614.00	$46.27	$70.45
.5 Laborer	37.60	150.40	57.85	231.40		
1 Dozer, 200 H.P.		1387.00		1525.70		
1 Sheepsft. Roller, Towed		425.80		468.38	151.07	166.17
12 L.H., Daily Totals		$2368.00		$2839.48	$197.33	$236.62

Crew B-10E

Crew No.	Hr.	Daily	Hr.	Daily	Bare Costs	Incl. O&P
1 Equip. Oper. (medium)	$50.60	$404.80	$76.75	$614.00	$46.27	$70.45
.5 Laborer	37.60	150.40	57.85	231.40		
1 Tandem Roller, 5 Ton		157.40		173.14	13.12	14.43
12 L.H., Daily Totals		$712.60		$1018.54	$59.38	$84.88

Crew B-10F

Crew No.	Hr.	Daily	Hr.	Daily	Bare Costs	Incl. O&P
1 Equip. Oper. (medium)	$50.60	$404.80	$76.75	$614.00	$46.27	$70.45
.5 Laborer	37.60	150.40	57.85	231.40		
1 Tandem Roller, 10 Ton		236.80		260.48	19.73	21.71
12 L.H., Daily Totals		$792.00		$1105.88	$66.00	$92.16

Crew B-10G

Crew No.	Hr.	Daily	Hr.	Daily	Bare Costs	Incl. O&P
1 Equip. Oper. (medium)	$50.60	$404.80	$76.75	$614.00	$46.27	$70.45
.5 Laborer	37.60	150.40	57.85	231.40		
1 Sheepsfoot Roller, 240 H.P.		1206.00		1326.60	100.50	110.55
12 L.H., Daily Totals		$1761.20		$2172.00	$146.77	$181.00

Crew B-10H

	Bare Costs		Incl. Subs O&P		Cost Per Labor-Hour	
Crew B-10H	Hr.	Daily	Hr.	Daily	Bare Costs	Incl. O&P
1 Equip. Oper. (medium)	$50.60	$404.80	$76.75	$614.00	$46.27	$70.45
.5 Laborer	37.60	150.40	57.85	231.40		
1 Diaphragm Water Pump, 2"		71.00		78.10		
1 -20' Suction Hose, 2"		1.95		2.15		
2 -50' Discharge Hoses, 2"		1.80		1.98	6.23	6.85
12 L.H., Daily Totals		$629.95		$927.63	$52.50	$77.30

Crew B-10I

	Bare Costs		Incl. Subs O&P		Cost Per Labor-Hour	
Crew B-10I	Hr.	Daily	Hr.	Daily	Bare Costs	Incl. O&P
1 Equip. Oper. (medium)	$50.60	$404.80	$76.75	$614.00	$46.27	$70.45
.5 Laborer	37.60	150.40	57.85	231.40		
1 Diaphragm Water Pump, 4"		114.20		125.62		
1 -20' Suction Hose, 4"		3.25		3.58		
2 -50' Discharge Hoses, 4"		4.70		5.17	10.18	11.20
12 L.H., Daily Totals		$677.35		$979.76	$56.45	$81.65

Crew B-10J

	Bare Costs		Incl. Subs O&P		Cost Per Labor-Hour	
Crew B-10J	Hr.	Daily	Hr.	Daily	Bare Costs	Incl. O&P
1 Equip. Oper. (medium)	$50.60	$404.80	$76.75	$614.00	$46.27	$70.45
.5 Laborer	37.60	150.40	57.85	231.40		
1 Centrifugal Water Pump, 3"		78.20		86.02		
1 -20' Suction Hose, 3"		2.85		3.13		
2 -50' Discharge Hoses, 3"		3.00		3.30	7.00	7.70
12 L.H., Daily Totals		$639.25		$937.86	$53.27	$78.15

Crew B-10K

	Bare Costs		Incl. Subs O&P		Cost Per Labor-Hour	
Crew B-10K	Hr.	Daily	Hr.	Daily	Bare Costs	Incl. O&P
1 Equip. Oper. (medium)	$50.60	$404.80	$76.75	$614.00	$46.27	$70.45
.5 Laborer	37.60	150.40	57.85	231.40		
1 Centr. Water Pump, 6"		346.60		381.26		
1 -20' Suction Hose, 6"		11.50		12.65		
2 -50' Discharge Hoses, 6"		12.20		13.42	30.86	33.94
12 L.H., Daily Totals		$925.50		$1252.73	$77.13	$104.39

Crew B-10L

	Bare Costs		Incl. Subs O&P		Cost Per Labor-Hour	
Crew B-10L	Hr.	Daily	Hr.	Daily	Bare Costs	Incl. O&P
1 Equip. Oper. (medium)	$50.60	$404.80	$76.75	$614.00	$46.27	$70.45
.5 Laborer	37.60	150.40	57.85	231.40		
1 Dozer, 80 H.P.		472.40		519.64	39.37	43.30
12 L.H., Daily Totals		$1027.60		$1365.04	$85.63	$113.75

Crew B-10M

	Bare Costs		Incl. Subs O&P		Cost Per Labor-Hour	
Crew B-10M	Hr.	Daily	Hr.	Daily	Bare Costs	Incl. O&P
1 Equip. Oper. (medium)	$50.60	$404.80	$76.75	$614.00	$46.27	$70.45
.5 Laborer	37.60	150.40	57.85	231.40		
1 Dozer, 300 H.P.		1897.00		2086.70	158.08	173.89
12 L.H., Daily Totals		$2452.20		$2932.10	$204.35	$244.34

Crew B-10N

	Bare Costs		Incl. Subs O&P		Cost Per Labor-Hour	
Crew B-10N	Hr.	Daily	Hr.	Daily	Bare Costs	Incl. O&P
1 Equip. Oper. (medium)	$50.60	$404.80	$76.75	$614.00	$46.27	$70.45
.5 Laborer	37.60	150.40	57.85	231.40		
1 F.E. Loader, T.M., 1.5 C.Y		522.00		574.20	43.50	47.85
12 L.H., Daily Totals		$1077.20		$1419.60	$89.77	$118.30

Crew B-10O

	Bare Costs		Incl. Subs O&P		Cost Per Labor-Hour	
Crew B-10O	Hr.	Daily	Hr.	Daily	Bare Costs	Incl. O&P
1 Equip. Oper. (medium)	$50.60	$404.80	$76.75	$614.00	$46.27	$70.45
.5 Laborer	37.60	150.40	57.85	231.40		
1 F.E. Loader, T.M., 2.25 C.Y.		956.40		1052.04	79.70	87.67
12 L.H., Daily Totals		$1511.60		$1897.44	$125.97	$158.12

Crew B-10P

	Bare Costs		Incl. Subs O&P		Cost Per Labor-Hour	
Crew B-10P	Hr.	Daily	Hr.	Daily	Bare Costs	Incl. O&P
1 Equip. Oper. (medium)	$50.60	$404.80	$76.75	$614.00	$46.27	$70.45
.5 Laborer	37.60	150.40	57.85	231.40		
1 Crawler Loader, 3 C.Y.		1188.00		1306.80	99.00	108.90
12 L.H., Daily Totals		$1743.20		$2152.20	$145.27	$179.35

Crew B-10Q

	Bare Costs		Incl. Subs O&P		Cost Per Labor-Hour	
Crew B-10Q	Hr.	Daily	Hr.	Daily	Bare Costs	Incl. O&P
1 Equip. Oper. (medium)	$50.60	$404.80	$76.75	$614.00	$46.27	$70.45
.5 Laborer	37.60	150.40	57.85	231.40		
1 Crawler Loader, 4 C.Y.		1561.00		1717.10	130.08	143.09
12 L.H., Daily Totals		$2116.20		$2562.50	$176.35	$213.54

Crew B-10R

	Bare Costs		Incl. Subs O&P		Cost Per Labor-Hour	
Crew B-10R	Hr.	Daily	Hr.	Daily	Bare Costs	Incl. O&P
1 Equip. Oper. (medium)	$50.60	$404.80	$76.75	$614.00	$46.27	$70.45
.5 Laborer	37.60	150.40	57.85	231.40		
1 F.E. Loader, W.M., 1 C.Y.		299.00		328.90	24.92	27.41
12 L.H., Daily Totals		$854.20		$1174.30	$71.18	$97.86

Crew B-10S

	Bare Costs		Incl. Subs O&P		Cost Per Labor-Hour	
Crew B-10S	Hr.	Daily	Hr.	Daily	Bare Costs	Incl. O&P
1 Equip. Oper. (medium)	$50.60	$404.80	$76.75	$614.00	$46.27	$70.45
.5 Laborer	37.60	150.40	57.85	231.40		
1 F.E. Loader, W.M., 1.5 C.Y.		378.40		416.24	31.53	34.69
12 L.H., Daily Totals		$933.60		$1261.64	$77.80	$105.14

Crew B-10T

	Bare Costs		Incl. Subs O&P		Cost Per Labor-Hour	
Crew B-10T	Hr.	Daily	Hr.	Daily	Bare Costs	Incl. O&P
1 Equip. Oper. (medium)	$50.60	$404.80	$76.75	$614.00	$46.27	$70.45
.5 Laborer	37.60	150.40	57.85	231.40		
1 F.E. Loader, W.M., 2.5 C.Y.		519.80		571.78	43.32	47.65
12 L.H., Daily Totals		$1075.00		$1417.18	$89.58	$118.10

Crew B-10U

	Bare Costs		Incl. Subs O&P		Cost Per Labor-Hour	
Crew B-10U	Hr.	Daily	Hr.	Daily	Bare Costs	Incl. O&P
1 Equip. Oper. (medium)	$50.60	$404.80	$76.75	$614.00	$46.27	$70.45
.5 Laborer	37.60	150.40	57.85	231.40		
1 F.E. Loader, W.M., 5.5 C.Y.		1082.00		1190.20	90.17	99.18
12 L.H., Daily Totals		$1637.20		$2035.60	$136.43	$169.63

Crew B-10V

	Bare Costs		Incl. Subs O&P		Cost Per Labor-Hour	
Crew B-10V	Hr.	Daily	Hr.	Daily	Bare Costs	Incl. O&P
1 Equip. Oper. (medium)	$50.60	$404.80	$76.75	$614.00	$46.27	$70.45
.5 Laborer	37.60	150.40	57.85	231.40		
1 Dozer, 700 H.P.		4979.00		5476.90	414.92	456.41
12 L.H., Daily Totals		$5534.20		$6322.30	$461.18	$526.86

Crew B-10W

	Bare Costs		Incl. Subs O&P		Cost Per Labor-Hour	
Crew B-10W	Hr.	Daily	Hr.	Daily	Bare Costs	Incl. O&P
1 Equip. Oper. (medium)	$50.60	$404.80	$76.75	$614.00	$46.27	$70.45
.5 Laborer	37.60	150.40	57.85	231.40		
1 Dozer, 105 H.P.		602.80		663.08	50.23	55.26
12 L.H., Daily Totals		$1158.00		$1508.48	$96.50	$125.71

Crew B-10X

	Bare Costs		Incl. Subs O&P		Cost Per Labor-Hour	
Crew B-10X	Hr.	Daily	Hr.	Daily	Bare Costs	Incl. O&P
1 Equip. Oper. (medium)	$50.60	$404.80	$76.75	$614.00	$46.27	$70.45
.5 Laborer	37.60	150.40	57.85	231.40		
1 Dozer, 410 H.P.		2405.00		2645.50	200.42	220.46
12 L.H., Daily Totals		$2960.20		$3490.90	$246.68	$290.91

Crew B-10Y

	Bare Costs		Incl. Subs O&P		Cost Per Labor-Hour	
Crew B-10Y	Hr.	Daily	Hr.	Daily	Bare Costs	Incl. O&P
1 Equip. Oper. (medium)	$50.60	$404.80	$76.75	$614.00	$46.27	$70.45
.5 Laborer	37.60	150.40	57.85	231.40		
1 Vibr. Roller, Towed, 12 Ton		549.80		604.78	45.82	50.40
12 L.H., Daily Totals		$1105.00		$1450.18	$92.08	$120.85

Crew B-11A

	Bare Costs		Incl. Subs O&P		Cost Per Labor-Hour	
Crew B-11A	Hr.	Daily	Hr.	Daily	Bare Costs	Incl. O&P
1 Equipment Oper. (med.)	$50.60	$404.80	$76.75	$614.00	$44.10	$67.30
1 Laborer	37.60	300.80	57.85	462.80		
1 Dozer, 200 H.P.		1387.00		1525.70	86.69	95.36
16 L.H., Daily Totals		$2092.60		$2602.50	$130.79	$162.66

Crews

Crew B-11B	Hr.	Daily	Hr.	Daily	Bare Costs	Incl. O&P
1 Equipment Oper. (light)	$48.60	$388.80	$73.75	$590.00	$43.10	$65.80
1 Laborer	37.60	300.80	57.85	462.80		
1 Air Powered Tamper		26.20		28.82		
1 Air Compressor, 365 cfm		263.80		290.18		
2 -50' Air Hoses, 1.5"		11.60		12.76	18.85	20.73
16 L.H., Daily Totals		$991.20		$1384.56	$61.95	$86.53

Crew B-11C	Hr.	Daily	Hr.	Daily	Bare Costs	Incl. O&P
1 Equipment Oper. (med.)	$50.60	$404.80	$76.75	$614.00	$44.10	$67.30
1 Laborer	37.60	300.80	57.85	462.80		
1 Backhoe Loader, 48 H.P.		364.20		400.62	22.76	25.04
16 L.H., Daily Totals		$1069.80		$1477.42	$66.86	$92.34

Crew B-11J	Hr.	Daily	Hr.	Daily	Bare Costs	Incl. O&P
1 Equipment Oper. (med.)	$50.60	$404.80	$76.75	$614.00	$44.10	$67.30
1 Laborer	37.60	300.80	57.85	462.80		
1 Grader, 30,000 Lbs.		736.20		809.82		
1 Ripper, Beam & 1 Shank		84.20		92.62	51.27	56.40
16 L.H., Daily Totals		$1526.00		$1979.24	$95.38	$123.70

Crew B-11K	Hr.	Daily	Hr.	Daily	Bare Costs	Incl. O&P
1 Equipment Oper. (med.)	$50.60	$404.80	$76.75	$614.00	$44.10	$67.30
1 Laborer	37.60	300.80	57.85	462.80		
1 Trencher, Chain Type, 8' D		3402.00		3742.20	212.63	233.89
16 L.H., Daily Totals		$4107.60		$4819.00	$256.73	$301.19

Crew B-11L	Hr.	Daily	Hr.	Daily	Bare Costs	Incl. O&P
1 Equipment Oper. (med.)	$50.60	$404.80	$76.75	$614.00	$44.10	$67.30
1 Laborer	37.60	300.80	57.85	462.80		
1 Grader, 30,000 Lbs.		736.20		809.82	46.01	50.61
16 L.H., Daily Totals		$1441.80		$1886.62	$90.11	$117.91

Crew B-11M	Hr.	Daily	Hr.	Daily	Bare Costs	Incl. O&P
1 Equipment Oper. (med.)	$50.60	$404.80	$76.75	$614.00	$44.10	$67.30
1 Laborer	37.60	300.80	57.85	462.80		
1 Backhoe Loader, 80 H.P.		391.80		430.98	24.49	26.94
16 L.H., Daily Totals		$1097.40		$1507.78	$68.59	$94.24

Crew B-11N	Hr.	Daily	Hr.	Daily	Bare Costs	Incl. O&P
1 Labor Foreman (outside)	$39.60	$316.80	$60.95	$487.60	$42.34	$64.19
2 Equipment Operators (med.)	50.60	809.60	76.75	1228.00		
6 Truck Drivers (heavy)	40.05	1922.40	60.55	2906.40		
1 F.E. Loader, W.M., 5.5 C.Y.		1082.00		1190.20		
1 Dozer, 410 H.P.		2405.00		2645.50		
6 Dump Trucks, Off Hwy., 50 Ton		11022.00		12124.20	201.51	221.67
72 L.H., Daily Totals		$17557.80		$20581.90	$243.86	$285.86

Crew B-11Q	Hr.	Daily	Hr.	Daily	Bare Costs	Incl. O&P
1 Equipment Operator (med.)	$50.60	$404.80	$76.75	$614.00	$46.27	$70.45
.5 Laborer	37.60	150.40	57.85	231.40		
1 Dozer, 140 H.P.		886.00		974.60	73.83	81.22
12 L.H., Daily Totals		$1441.20		$1820.00	$120.10	$151.67

Crew B-11R	Hr.	Daily	Hr.	Daily	Bare Costs	Incl. O&P
1 Equipment Operator (med.)	$50.60	$404.80	$76.75	$614.00	$46.27	$70.45
.5 Laborer	37.60	150.40	57.85	231.40		
1 Dozer, 200 H.P.		1387.00		1525.70	115.58	127.14
12 L.H., Daily Totals		$1942.20		$2371.10	$161.85	$197.59

Crew B-11S	Hr.	Daily	Hr.	Daily	Bare Costs	Incl. O&P
1 Equipment Operator (med.)	$50.60	$404.80	$76.75	$614.00	$46.27	$70.45
.5 Laborer	37.60	150.40	57.85	231.40		
1 Dozer, 300 H.P.		1897.00		2086.70		
1 Ripper, Beam & 1 Shank		84.20		92.62	165.10	181.61
12 L.H., Daily Totals		$2536.40		$3024.72	$211.37	$252.06

Crew B-11T	Hr.	Daily	Hr.	Daily	Bare Costs	Incl. O&P
1 Equipment Operator (med.)	$50.60	$404.80	$76.75	$614.00	$46.27	$70.45
.5 Laborer	37.60	150.40	57.85	231.40		
1 Dozer, 410 H.P.		2405.00		2645.50		
1 Ripper, Beam & 2 Shanks		110.00		121.00	209.58	230.54
12 L.H., Daily Totals		$3070.20		$3611.90	$255.85	$300.99

Crew B-11U	Hr.	Daily	Hr.	Daily	Bare Costs	Incl. O&P
1 Equipment Operator (med.)	$50.60	$404.80	$76.75	$614.00	$46.27	$70.45
.5 Laborer	37.60	150.40	57.85	231.40		
1 Dozer, 520 H.P.		3299.00		3628.90	274.92	302.41
12 L.H., Daily Totals		$3854.20		$4474.30	$321.18	$372.86

Crew B-11V	Hr.	Daily	Hr.	Daily	Bare Costs	Incl. O&P
3 Laborers	$37.60	$902.40	$57.85	$1388.40	$37.60	$57.85
1 Roller, 2-Drum, W.B., 7.5 H.P.		180.00		198.00	7.50	8.25
24 L.H., Daily Totals		$1082.40		$1586.40	$45.10	$66.10

Crew B-11W	Hr.	Daily	Hr.	Daily	Bare Costs	Incl. O&P
1 Equipment Operator (med.)	$50.60	$404.80	$76.75	$614.00	$40.73	$61.67
1 Common Laborer	37.60	300.80	57.85	462.80		
10 Truck Drivers (heavy)	40.05	3204.00	60.55	4844.00		
1 Dozer, 200 H.P.		1387.00		1525.70		
1 Vibratory Roller, Towed, 23 Ton		396.00		435.60		
10 Dump Trucks, 8 C.Y., 220 H.P.		4112.00		4523.20	61.41	67.55
96 L.H., Daily Totals		$9804.60		$12405.30	$102.13	$129.22

Crew B-11Y	Hr.	Daily	Hr.	Daily	Bare Costs	Incl. O&P
1 Labor Foreman (outside)	$39.60	$316.80	$60.95	$487.60	$42.16	$64.49
5 Common Laborers	37.60	1504.00	57.85	2314.00		
3 Equipment Operators (med.)	50.60	1214.40	76.75	1842.00		
1 Dozer, 80 H.P.		472.40		519.64		
2 Roller, 2-Drum, W.B., 7.5 H.P.		360.00		396.00		
4 Vibrating Plate, Gas, 21"		187.20		205.92	14.16	15.58
72 L.H., Daily Totals		$4054.80		$5765.16	$56.32	$80.07

Crew B-12A	Hr.	Daily	Hr.	Daily	Bare Costs	Incl. O&P
1 Equip. Oper. (crane)	$51.70	$413.60	$78.45	$627.60	$44.65	$68.15
1 Laborer	37.60	300.80	57.85	462.80		
1 Hyd. Excavator, 1 C.Y.		812.60		893.86	50.79	55.87
16 L.H., Daily Totals		$1527.00		$1984.26	$95.44	$124.02

Crew B-12B	Hr.	Daily	Hr.	Daily	Bare Costs	Incl. O&P
1 Equip. Oper. (crane)	$51.70	$413.60	$78.45	$627.60	$44.65	$68.15
1 Laborer	37.60	300.80	57.85	462.80		
1 Hyd. Excavator, 1.5 C.Y.		1030.00		1133.00	64.38	70.81
16 L.H., Daily Totals		$1744.40		$2223.40	$109.03	$138.96

Crew B-12C	Hr.	Daily	Hr.	Daily	Bare Costs	Incl. O&P
1 Equip. Oper. (crane)	$51.70	$413.60	$78.45	$627.60	$44.65	$68.15
1 Laborer	37.60	300.80	57.85	462.80		
1 Hyd. Excavator, 2 C.Y.		1175.00		1292.50	73.44	80.78
16 L.H., Daily Totals		$1889.40		$2382.90	$118.09	$148.93

Crew No.	Bare Costs Hr.	Daily	Incl. Subs O&P Hr.	Daily	Cost Per Labor-Hour Bare Costs	Incl. O&P
Crew B-12D	Hr.	Daily	Hr.	Daily	Bare Costs	Incl. O&P
1 Equip. Oper. (crane)	$51.70	$413.60	$78.45	$627.60	$44.65	$68.15
1 Laborer	37.60	300.80	57.85	462.80		
1 Hyd. Excavator, 3.5 C.Y.		2440.00		2684.00	152.50	167.75
16 L.H., Daily Totals		$3154.40		$3774.40	$197.15	$235.90
Crew B-12E	Hr.	Daily	Hr.	Daily	Bare Costs	Incl. O&P
1 Equip. Oper. (crane)	$51.70	$413.60	$78.45	$627.60	$44.65	$68.15
1 Laborer	37.60	300.80	57.85	462.80		
1 Hyd. Excavator, .5 C.Y.		448.20		493.02	28.01	30.81
16 L.H., Daily Totals		$1162.60		$1583.42	$72.66	$98.96
Crew B-12F	Hr.	Daily	Hr.	Daily	Bare Costs	Incl. O&P
1 Equip. Oper. (crane)	$51.70	$413.60	$78.45	$627.60	$44.65	$68.15
1 Laborer	37.60	300.80	57.85	462.80		
1 Hyd. Excavator, .75 C.Y.		654.80		720.28	40.92	45.02
16 L.H., Daily Totals		$1369.20		$1810.68	$85.58	$113.17
Crew B-12G	Hr.	Daily	Hr.	Daily	Bare Costs	Incl. O&P
1 Equip. Oper. (crane)	$51.70	$413.60	$78.45	$627.60	$44.65	$68.15
1 Laborer	37.60	300.80	57.85	462.80		
1 Crawler Crane, 15 Ton		669.85		736.84		
1 Clamshell Bucket, .5 C.Y.		38.20		42.02	44.25	48.68
16 L.H., Daily Totals		$1422.45		$1869.26	$88.90	$116.83
Crew B-12H	Hr.	Daily	Hr.	Daily	Bare Costs	Incl. O&P
1 Equip. Oper. (crane)	$51.70	$413.60	$78.45	$627.60	$44.65	$68.15
1 Laborer	37.60	300.80	57.85	462.80		
1 Crawler Crane, 25 Ton		1150.00		1265.00		
1 Clamshell Bucket, 1 C.Y.		47.80		52.58	74.86	82.35
16 L.H., Daily Totals		$1912.20		$2407.98	$119.51	$150.50
Crew B-12I	Hr.	Daily	Hr.	Daily	Bare Costs	Incl. O&P
1 Equip. Oper. (crane)	$51.70	$413.60	$78.45	$627.60	$44.65	$68.15
1 Laborer	37.60	300.80	57.85	462.80		
1 Crawler Crane, 20 Ton		862.50		948.75		
1 Dragline Bucket, .75 C.Y.		20.60		22.66	55.19	60.71
16 L.H., Daily Totals		$1597.50		$2061.81	$99.84	$128.86
Crew B-12J	Hr.	Daily	Hr.	Daily	Bare Costs	Incl. O&P
1 Equip. Oper. (crane)	$51.70	$413.60	$78.45	$627.60	$44.65	$68.15
1 Laborer	37.60	300.80	57.85	462.80		
1 Gradall, 5/8 C.Y.		882.20		970.42	55.14	60.65
16 L.H., Daily Totals		$1596.60		$2060.82	$99.79	$128.80
Crew B-12K	Hr.	Daily	Hr.	Daily	Bare Costs	Incl. O&P
1 Equip. Oper. (crane)	$51.70	$413.60	$78.45	$627.60	$44.65	$68.15
1 Laborer	37.60	300.80	57.85	462.80		
1 Gradall, 3 Ton, 1 C.Y.		1002.00		1102.20	62.63	68.89
16 L.H., Daily Totals		$1716.40		$2192.60	$107.28	$137.04
Crew B-12L	Hr.	Daily	Hr.	Daily	Bare Costs	Incl. O&P
1 Equip. Oper. (crane)	$51.70	$413.60	$78.45	$627.60	$44.65	$68.15
1 Laborer	37.60	300.80	57.85	462.80		
1 Crawler Crane, 15 Ton		669.85		736.84		
1 F.E. Attachment, .5 C.Y.		60.00		66.00	45.62	50.18
16 L.H., Daily Totals		$1444.25		$1893.23	$90.27	$118.33

Crew No.	Bare Costs Hr.	Daily	Incl. Subs O&P Hr.	Daily	Cost Per Labor-Hour Bare Costs	Incl. O&P
Crew B-12M	Hr.	Daily	Hr.	Daily	Bare Costs	Incl. O&P
1 Equip. Oper. (crane)	$51.70	$413.60	$78.45	$627.60	$44.65	$68.15
1 Laborer	37.60	300.80	57.85	462.80		
1 Crawler Crane, 20 Ton		862.50		948.75		
1 F.E. Attachment, .75 C.Y.		65.40		71.94	57.99	63.79
16 L.H., Daily Totals		$1642.30		$2111.09	$102.64	$131.94
Crew B-12N	Hr.	Daily	Hr.	Daily	Bare Costs	Incl. O&P
1 Equip. Oper. (crane)	$51.70	$413.60	$78.45	$627.60	$44.65	$68.15
1 Laborer	37.60	300.80	57.85	462.80		
1 Crawler Crane, 25 Ton		1150.00		1265.00		
1 F.E. Attachment, 1 C.Y.		71.20		78.32	76.33	83.96
16 L.H., Daily Totals		$1935.60		$2433.72	$120.97	$152.11
Crew B-12O	Hr.	Daily	Hr.	Daily	Bare Costs	Incl. O&P
1 Equip. Oper. (crane)	$51.70	$413.60	$78.45	$627.60	$44.65	$68.15
1 Laborer	37.60	300.80	57.85	462.80		
1 Crawler Crane, 40 Ton		1156.00		1271.60		
1 F.E. Attachment, 1.5 C.Y.		80.00		88.00	77.25	84.97
16 L.H., Daily Totals		$1950.40		$2450.00	$121.90	$153.13
Crew B-12P	Hr.	Daily	Hr.	Daily	Bare Costs	Incl. O&P
1 Equip. Oper. (crane)	$51.70	$413.60	$78.45	$627.60	$44.65	$68.15
1 Laborer	37.60	300.80	57.85	462.80		
1 Crawler Crane, 40 Ton		1156.00		1271.60		
1 Dragline Bucket, 1.5 C.Y.		33.60		36.96	74.35	81.78
16 L.H., Daily Totals		$1904.00		$2398.96	$119.00	$149.94
Crew B-12Q	Hr.	Daily	Hr.	Daily	Bare Costs	Incl. O&P
1 Equip. Oper. (crane)	$51.70	$413.60	$78.45	$627.60	$44.65	$68.15
1 Laborer	37.60	300.80	57.85	462.80		
1 Hyd. Excavator, 5/8 C.Y.		589.40		648.34	36.84	40.52
16 L.H., Daily Totals		$1303.80		$1738.74	$81.49	$108.67
Crew B-12S	Hr.	Daily	Hr.	Daily	Bare Costs	Incl. O&P
1 Equip. Oper. (crane)	$51.70	$413.60	$78.45	$627.60	$44.65	$68.15
1 Laborer	37.60	300.80	57.85	462.80		
1 Hyd. Excavator, 2.5 C.Y.		1605.00		1765.50	100.31	110.34
16 L.H., Daily Totals		$2319.40		$2855.90	$144.96	$178.49
Crew B-12T	Hr.	Daily	Hr.	Daily	Bare Costs	Incl. O&P
1 Equip. Oper. (crane)	$51.70	$413.60	$78.45	$627.60	$44.65	$68.15
1 Laborer	37.60	300.80	57.85	462.80		
1 Crawler Crane, 75 Ton		1459.00		1604.90		
1 F.E. Attachment, 3 C.Y.		103.20		113.52	97.64	107.40
16 L.H., Daily Totals		$2276.60		$2808.82	$142.29	$175.55
Crew B-12V	Hr.	Daily	Hr.	Daily	Bare Costs	Incl. O&P
1 Equip. Oper. (crane)	$51.70	$413.60	$78.45	$627.60	$44.65	$68.15
1 Laborer	37.60	300.80	57.85	462.80		
1 Crawler Crane, 75 Ton		1459.00		1604.90		
1 Dragline Bucket, 3 C.Y.		52.60		57.86	94.47	103.92
16 L.H., Daily Totals		$2226.00		$2753.16	$139.13	$172.07
Crew B-12Y	Hr.	Daily	Hr.	Daily	Bare Costs	Incl. O&P
1 Equip. Oper. (crane)	$51.70	$413.60	$78.45	$627.60	$42.30	$64.72
2 Laborers	37.60	601.60	57.85	925.60		
1 Hyd. Excavator, 3.5 C.Y.		2440.00		2684.00	101.67	111.83
24 L.H., Daily Totals		$3455.20		$4237.20	$143.97	$176.55

Crew B-12Z

Crew B-12Z	Bare Costs Hr.	Daily	Incl. Subs O&P Hr.	Daily	Bare Costs	Incl. O&P
1 Equip. Oper. (crane)	$51.70	$413.60	$78.45	$627.60	$42.30	$64.72
2 Laborers	37.60	601.60	57.85	925.60		
1 Hyd. Excavator, 2.5 C.Y.		1605.00		1765.50	66.88	73.56
24 L.H., Daily Totals		$2620.20		$3318.70	$109.18	$138.28

Crew B-13

Crew B-13	Hr.	Daily	Hr.	Daily	Bare Costs	Incl. O&P
1 Labor Foreman (outside)	$39.60	$316.80	$60.95	$487.60	$40.99	$62.76
4 Laborers	37.60	1203.20	57.85	1851.20		
1 Equip. Oper. (crane)	51.70	413.60	78.45	627.60		
1 Equip. Oper. (oiler)	45.20	361.60	68.55	548.40		
1 Hyd. Crane, 25 Ton		736.60		810.26	13.15	14.47
56 L.H., Daily Totals		$3031.80		$4325.06	$54.14	$77.23

Crew B-13A

Crew B-13A	Hr.	Daily	Hr.	Daily	Bare Costs	Incl. O&P
1 Labor Foreman (outside)	$39.60	$316.80	$60.95	$487.60	$42.30	$64.46
2 Laborers	37.60	601.60	57.85	925.60		
2 Equipment Operators (med.)	50.60	809.60	76.75	1228.00		
2 Truck Drivers (heavy)	40.05	640.80	60.55	968.80		
1 Crawler Crane, 75 Ton		1459.00		1604.90		
1 Crawler Loader, 4 C.Y.		1561.00		1717.10		
2 Dump Trucks, 8 C.Y., 220 H.P.		822.40		904.64	68.61	75.48
56 L.H., Daily Totals		$6211.20		$7836.64	$110.91	$139.94

Crew B-13B

Crew B-13B	Hr.	Daily	Hr.	Daily	Bare Costs	Incl. O&P
1 Labor Foreman (outside)	$39.60	$316.80	$60.95	$487.60	$40.99	$62.76
4 Laborers	37.60	1203.20	57.85	1851.20		
1 Equip. Oper. (crane)	51.70	413.60	78.45	627.60		
1 Equip. Oper. (oiler)	45.20	361.60	68.55	548.40		
1 Hyd. Crane, 55 Ton		1128.00		1240.80	20.14	22.16
56 L.H., Daily Totals		$3423.20		$4755.60	$61.13	$84.92

Crew B-13C

Crew B-13C	Hr.	Daily	Hr.	Daily	Bare Costs	Incl. O&P
1 Labor Foreman (outside)	$39.60	$316.80	$60.95	$487.60	$40.99	$62.76
4 Laborers	37.60	1203.20	57.85	1851.20		
1 Equip. Oper. (crane)	51.70	413.60	78.45	627.60		
1 Equip. Oper. (oiler)	45.20	361.60	68.55	548.40		
1 Crawler Crane, 100 Ton		1667.00		1833.70	29.77	32.74
56 L.H., Daily Totals		$3962.20		$5348.50	$70.75	$95.51

Crew B-13D

Crew B-13D	Hr.	Daily	Hr.	Daily	Bare Costs	Incl. O&P
1 Laborer	$37.60	$300.80	$57.85	$462.80	$44.65	$68.15
1 Equip. Oper. (crane)	51.70	413.60	78.45	627.60		
1 Hyd. Excavator, 1 C.Y.		812.60		893.86		
1 Trench Box		81.00		89.10	55.85	61.44
16 L.H., Daily Totals		$1608.00		$2073.36	$100.50	$129.59

Crew B-13E

Crew B-13E	Hr.	Daily	Hr.	Daily	Bare Costs	Incl. O&P
1 Laborer	$37.60	$300.80	$57.85	$462.80	$44.65	$68.15
1 Equip. Oper. (crane)	51.70	413.60	78.45	627.60		
1 Hyd. Excavator, 1.5 C.Y.		1030.00		1133.00		
1 Trench Box		81.00		89.10	69.44	76.38
16 L.H., Daily Totals		$1825.40		$2312.50	$114.09	$144.53

Crew B-13F

Crew B-13F	Hr.	Daily	Hr.	Daily	Bare Costs	Incl. O&P
1 Laborer	$37.60	$300.80	$57.85	$462.80	$44.65	$68.15
1 Equip. Oper. (crane)	51.70	413.60	78.45	627.60		
1 Hyd. Excavator, 3.5 C.Y.		2440.00		2684.00		
1 Trench Box		81.00		89.10	157.56	173.32
16 L.H., Daily Totals		$3235.40		$3863.50	$202.21	$241.47

Crew B-13G

Crew B-13G	Hr.	Daily	Hr.	Daily	Bare Costs	Incl. O&P
1 Laborer	$37.60	$300.80	$57.85	$462.80	$44.65	$68.15
1 Equip. Oper. (crane)	51.70	413.60	78.45	627.60		
1 Hyd. Excavator, .75 C.Y.		654.80		720.28		
1 Trench Box		81.00		89.10	45.99	50.59
16 L.H., Daily Totals		$1450.20		$1899.78	$90.64	$118.74

Crew B-13H

Crew B-13H	Hr.	Daily	Hr.	Daily	Bare Costs	Incl. O&P
1 Laborer	$37.60	$300.80	$57.85	$462.80	$44.65	$68.15
1 Equip. Oper. (crane)	51.70	413.60	78.45	627.60		
1 Gradall, 5/8 C.Y.		882.20		970.42		
1 Trench Box		81.00		89.10	60.20	66.22
16 L.H., Daily Totals		$1677.60		$2149.92	$104.85	$134.37

Crew B-13I

Crew B-13I	Hr.	Daily	Hr.	Daily	Bare Costs	Incl. O&P
1 Laborer	$37.60	$300.80	$57.85	$462.80	$44.65	$68.15
1 Equip. Oper. (crane)	51.70	413.60	78.45	627.60		
1 Gradall, 3 Ton, 1 C.Y.		1002.00		1102.20		
1 Trench Box		81.00		89.10	67.69	74.46
16 L.H., Daily Totals		$1797.40		$2281.70	$112.34	$142.61

Crew B-13J

Crew B-13J	Hr.	Daily	Hr.	Daily	Bare Costs	Incl. O&P
1 Laborer	$37.60	$300.80	$57.85	$462.80	$44.65	$68.15
1 Equip. Oper. (crane)	51.70	413.60	78.45	627.60		
1 Hyd. Excavator, 2.5 C.Y.		1605.00		1765.50		
1 Trench Box		81.00		89.10	105.38	115.91
16 L.H., Daily Totals		$2400.40		$2945.00	$150.03	$184.06

Crew B-13K

Crew B-13K	Hr.	Daily	Hr.	Daily	Bare Costs	Incl. O&P
2 Equip. Opers. (crane)	$51.70	$827.20	$78.45	$1255.20	$51.70	$78.45
1 Hyd. Excavator, .75 C.Y.		654.80		720.28		
1 Hyd. Hammer, 4000 ft-lb		308.20		339.02		
1 Hyd. Excavator, .75 C.Y.		654.80		720.28	101.11	111.22
16 L.H., Daily Totals		$2445.00		$3034.78	$152.81	$189.67

Crew B-13L

Crew B-13L	Hr.	Daily	Hr.	Daily	Bare Costs	Incl. O&P
2 Equip. Opers. (crane)	$51.70	$827.20	$78.45	$1255.20	$51.70	$78.45
1 Hyd. Excavator, 1.5 C.Y.		1030.00		1133.00		
1 Hyd. Hammer, 5000 ft-lb		371.20		408.32		
1 Hyd. Excavator, .75 C.Y.		654.80		720.28	128.50	141.35
16 L.H., Daily Totals		$2883.20		$3516.80	$180.20	$219.80

Crew B-13M

Crew B-13M	Hr.	Daily	Hr.	Daily	Bare Costs	Incl. O&P
2 Equip. Opers. (crane)	$51.70	$827.20	$78.45	$1255.20	$51.70	$78.45
1 Hyd. Excavator, 2.5 C.Y.		1605.00		1765.50		
1 Hyd. Hammer, 8000 ft-lb		545.40		599.94		
1 Hyd. Excavator, 1.5 C.Y.		1030.00		1133.00	198.78	218.65
16 L.H., Daily Totals		$4007.60		$4753.64	$250.47	$297.10

Crew B-13N

Crew B-13N	Hr.	Daily	Hr.	Daily	Bare Costs	Incl. O&P
2 Equip. Opers. (crane)	$51.70	$827.20	$78.45	$1255.20	$51.70	$78.45
1 Hyd. Excavator, 3.5 C.Y.		2440.00		2684.00		
1 Hyd. Hammer, 12,000 ft-lb		635.80		699.38		
1 Hyd. Excavator, 1.5 C.Y.		1030.00		1133.00	256.61	282.27
16 L.H., Daily Totals		$4933.00		$5771.58	$308.31	$360.72

For customer support on your Site Work & Landscape Cost Data, call 877.737.1594.

Crews

Crew No.	Bare Costs Hr.	Daily	Incl. Subs O&P Hr.	Daily	Bare Costs	Incl. O&P
Crew B-14	Hr.	Daily	Hr.	Daily	Bare Costs	Incl. O&P
1 Labor Foreman (outside)	$39.60	$316.80	$60.95	$487.60	$39.77	$61.02
4 Laborers	37.60	1203.20	57.85	1851.20		
1 Equip. Oper. (light)	48.60	388.80	73.75	590.00		
1 Backhoe Loader, 48 H.P.		364.20		400.62	7.59	8.35
48 L.H., Daily Totals		$2273.00		$3329.42	$47.35	$69.36
Crew B-14A	Hr.	Daily	Hr.	Daily	Bare Costs	Incl. O&P
1 Equip. Oper. (crane)	$51.70	$413.60	$78.45	$627.60	$47.00	$71.58
.5 Laborer	37.60	150.40	57.85	231.40		
1 Hyd. Excavator, 4.5 C.Y.		2963.00		3259.30	246.92	271.61
12 L.H., Daily Totals		$3527.00		$4118.30	$293.92	$343.19
Crew B-14B	Hr.	Daily	Hr.	Daily	Bare Costs	Incl. O&P
1 Equip. Oper. (crane)	$51.70	$413.60	$78.45	$627.60	$47.00	$71.58
.5 Laborer	37.60	150.40	57.85	231.40		
1 Hyd. Excavator, 6 C.Y.		3494.00		3843.40	291.17	320.28
12 L.H., Daily Totals		$4058.00		$4702.40	$338.17	$391.87
Crew B-14C	Hr.	Daily	Hr.	Daily	Bare Costs	Incl. O&P
1 Equip. Oper. (crane)	$51.70	$413.60	$78.45	$627.60	$47.00	$71.58
.5 Laborer	37.60	150.40	57.85	231.40		
1 Hyd. Excavator, 7 C.Y.		3590.00		3949.00	299.17	329.08
12 L.H., Daily Totals		$4154.00		$4808.00	$346.17	$400.67
Crew B-14F	Hr.	Daily	Hr.	Daily	Bare Costs	Incl. O&P
1 Equip. Oper. (crane)	$51.70	$413.60	$78.45	$627.60	$47.00	$71.58
.5 Laborer	37.60	150.40	57.85	231.40		
1 Hyd. Shovel, 7 C.Y.		3993.00		4392.30	332.75	366.02
12 L.H., Daily Totals		$4557.00		$5251.30	$379.75	$437.61
Crew B-14G	Hr.	Daily	Hr.	Daily	Bare Costs	Incl. O&P
1 Equip. Oper. (crane)	$51.70	$413.60	$78.45	$627.60	$47.00	$71.58
.5 Laborer	37.60	150.40	57.85	231.40		
1 Hyd. Shovel, 12 C.Y.		5736.00		6309.60	478.00	525.80
12 L.H., Daily Totals		$6300.00		$7168.60	$525.00	$597.38
Crew B-14J	Hr.	Daily	Hr.	Daily	Bare Costs	Incl. O&P
1 Equip. Oper. (medium)	$50.60	$404.80	$76.75	$614.00	$46.27	$70.45
.5 Laborer	37.60	150.40	57.85	231.40		
1 F.E. Loader, 8 C.Y.		1937.00		2130.70	161.42	177.56
12 L.H., Daily Totals		$2492.20		$2976.10	$207.68	$248.01
Crew B-14K	Hr.	Daily	Hr.	Daily	Bare Costs	Incl. O&P
1 Equip. Oper. (medium)	$50.60	$404.80	$76.75	$614.00	$46.27	$70.45
.5 Laborer	37.60	150.40	57.85	231.40		
1 F.E. Loader, 10 C.Y.		2942.00		3236.20	245.17	269.68
12 L.H., Daily Totals		$3497.20		$4081.60	$291.43	$340.13
Crew B-15	Hr.	Daily	Hr.	Daily	Bare Costs	Incl. O&P
1 Equipment Oper. (med.)	$50.60	$404.80	$76.75	$614.00	$42.71	$64.79
.5 Laborer	37.60	150.40	57.85	231.40		
2 Truck Drivers (heavy)	40.05	640.80	60.55	968.80		
2 Dump Trucks, 12 C.Y., 400 H.P.		1382.00		1520.20		
1 Dozer, 200 H.P.		1387.00		1525.70	98.89	108.78
28 L.H., Daily Totals		$3965.00		$4860.10	$141.61	$173.57

Crew No.	Bare Costs Hr.	Daily	Incl. Subs O&P Hr.	Daily	Bare Costs	Incl. O&P
Crew B-16	Hr.	Daily	Hr.	Daily	Bare Costs	Incl. O&P
1 Labor Foreman (outside)	$39.60	$316.80	$60.95	$487.60	$38.71	$59.30
2 Laborers	37.60	601.60	57.85	925.60		
1 Truck Driver (heavy)	40.05	320.40	60.55	484.40		
1 Dump Truck, 12 C.Y., 400 H.P.		691.00		760.10	21.59	23.75
32 L.H., Daily Totals		$1929.80		$2657.70	$60.31	$83.05
Crew B-17	Hr.	Daily	Hr.	Daily	Bare Costs	Incl. O&P
2 Laborers	$37.60	$601.60	$57.85	$925.60	$40.96	$62.50
1 Equip. Oper. (light)	48.60	388.80	73.75	590.00		
1 Truck Driver (heavy)	40.05	320.40	60.55	484.40		
1 Backhoe Loader, 48 H.P.		364.20		400.62		
1 Dump Truck, 8 C.Y., 220 H.P.		411.20		452.32	24.23	26.65
32 L.H., Daily Totals		$2086.20		$2852.94	$65.19	$89.15
Crew B-17A	Hr.	Daily	Hr.	Daily	Bare Costs	Incl. O&P
2 Labor Foremen (outside)	$39.60	$633.60	$60.95	$975.20	$40.41	$62.24
6 Laborers	37.60	1804.80	57.85	2776.80		
1 Skilled Worker Foreman (out)	50.65	405.20	78.25	626.00		
1 Skilled Worker	48.65	389.20	75.15	601.20		
80 L.H., Daily Totals		$3232.80		$4979.20	$40.41	$62.24
Crew B-17B	Hr.	Daily	Hr.	Daily	Bare Costs	Incl. O&P
2 Laborers	$37.60	$601.60	$57.85	$925.60	$40.96	$62.50
1 Equip. Oper. (light)	48.60	388.80	73.75	590.00		
1 Truck Driver (heavy)	40.05	320.40	60.55	484.40		
1 Backhoe Loader, 48 H.P.		364.20		400.62		
1 Dump Truck, 12 C.Y., 400 H.P.		691.00		760.10	32.98	36.27
32 L.H., Daily Totals		$2366.00		$3160.72	$73.94	$98.77
Crew B-18	Hr.	Daily	Hr.	Daily	Bare Costs	Incl. O&P
1 Labor Foreman (outside)	$39.60	$316.80	$60.95	$487.60	$38.27	$58.88
2 Laborers	37.60	601.60	57.85	925.60		
1 Vibrating Plate, Gas, 21"		46.80		51.48	1.95	2.15
24 L.H., Daily Totals		$965.20		$1464.68	$40.22	$61.03
Crew B-19	Hr.	Daily	Hr.	Daily	Bare Costs	Incl. O&P
1 Pile Driver Foreman (outside)	$48.10	$384.80	$76.15	$609.20	$47.64	$74.20
4 Pile Drivers	46.10	1475.20	73.00	2336.00		
2 Equip. Oper. (crane)	51.70	827.20	78.45	1255.20		
1 Equip. Oper. (oiler)	45.20	361.60	68.55	548.40		
1 Crawler Crane, 40 Ton		1156.00		1271.60		
1 Lead, 90' High		124.40		136.84		
1 Hammer, Diesel, 22k ft-lb		456.40		502.04	27.14	29.85
64 L.H., Daily Totals		$4785.60		$6659.28	$74.78	$104.05
Crew B-19A	Hr.	Daily	Hr.	Daily	Bare Costs	Incl. O&P
1 Pile Driver Foreman (outside)	$48.10	$384.80	$76.15	$609.20	$47.64	$74.20
4 Pile Drivers	46.10	1475.20	73.00	2336.00		
2 Equip. Oper. (crane)	51.70	827.20	78.45	1255.20		
1 Equip. Oper. (oiler)	45.20	361.60	68.55	548.40		
1 Crawler Crane, 75 Ton		1459.00		1604.90		
1 Lead, 90' high		124.40		136.84		
1 Hammer, Diesel, 41k ft-lb		581.00		639.10	33.82	37.20
64 L.H., Daily Totals		$5213.20		$7129.64	$81.46	$111.40

Crews

Crew B-19B

Crew No.	Bare Costs Hr.	Bare Costs Daily	Incl. Subs O&P Hr.	Incl. Subs O&P Daily	Cost Per Labor-Hour Bare Costs	Cost Per Labor-Hour Incl. O&P
1 Pile Driver Foreman (outside)	$48.10	$384.80	$76.15	$609.20	$47.64	$74.20
4 Pile Drivers	46.10	1475.20	73.00	2336.00		
2 Equip. Oper. (crane)	51.70	827.20	78.45	1255.20		
1 Equip. Oper. (oiler)	45.20	361.60	68.55	548.40		
1 Crawler Crane, 40 Ton		1156.00		1271.60		
1 Lead, 90' High		124.40		136.84		
1 Hammer, Diesel, 22k ft-lb		456.40		502.04		
1 Barge, 400 Ton		776.00		853.60	39.26	43.19
64 L.H., Daily Totals		$5561.60		$7512.88	$86.90	$117.39

Crew B-19C

Crew No.	Bare Costs Hr.	Bare Costs Daily	Incl. Subs O&P Hr.	Incl. Subs O&P Daily	Cost Per Labor-Hour Bare Costs	Cost Per Labor-Hour Incl. O&P
1 Pile Driver Foreman (outside)	$48.10	$384.80	$76.15	$609.20	$47.64	$74.20
4 Pile Drivers	46.10	1475.20	73.00	2336.00		
2 Equip. Oper. (crane)	51.70	827.20	78.45	1255.20		
1 Equip. Oper. (oiler)	45.20	361.60	68.55	548.40		
1 Crawler Crane, 75 Ton		1459.00		1604.90		
1 Lead, 90' High		124.40		136.84		
1 Hammer, Diesel, 41k ft-lb		581.00		639.10		
1 Barge, 400 Ton		776.00		853.60	45.94	50.54
64 L.H., Daily Totals		$5989.20		$7983.24	$93.58	$124.74

Crew B-20

Crew No.	Bare Costs Hr.	Bare Costs Daily	Incl. Subs O&P Hr.	Incl. Subs O&P Daily	Cost Per Labor-Hour Bare Costs	Cost Per Labor-Hour Incl. O&P
1 Labor Foreman (outside)	$39.60	$316.80	$60.95	$487.60	$41.95	$64.65
1 Skilled Worker	48.65	389.20	75.15	601.20		
1 Laborer	37.60	300.80	57.85	462.80		
24 L.H., Daily Totals		$1006.80		$1551.60	$41.95	$64.65

Crew B-20A

Crew No.	Bare Costs Hr.	Bare Costs Daily	Incl. Subs O&P Hr.	Incl. Subs O&P Daily	Cost Per Labor-Hour Bare Costs	Cost Per Labor-Hour Incl. O&P
1 Labor Foreman (outside)	$39.60	$316.80	$60.95	$487.60	$45.71	$69.59
1 Laborer	37.60	300.80	57.85	462.80		
1 Plumber	58.70	469.60	88.65	709.20		
1 Plumber Apprentice	46.95	375.60	70.90	567.20		
32 L.H., Daily Totals		$1462.80		$2226.80	$45.71	$69.59

Crew B-21

Crew No.	Bare Costs Hr.	Bare Costs Daily	Incl. Subs O&P Hr.	Incl. Subs O&P Daily	Cost Per Labor-Hour Bare Costs	Cost Per Labor-Hour Incl. O&P
1 Labor Foreman (outside)	$39.60	$316.80	$60.95	$487.60	$43.34	$66.62
1 Skilled Worker	48.65	389.20	75.15	601.20		
1 Laborer	37.60	300.80	57.85	462.80		
.5 Equip. Oper. (crane)	51.70	206.80	78.45	313.80		
.5 S.P. Crane, 4x4, 5 Ton		137.70		151.47	4.92	5.41
28 L.H., Daily Totals		$1351.30		$2016.87	$48.26	$72.03

Crew B-21A

Crew No.	Bare Costs Hr.	Bare Costs Daily	Incl. Subs O&P Hr.	Incl. Subs O&P Daily	Cost Per Labor-Hour Bare Costs	Cost Per Labor-Hour Incl. O&P
1 Labor Foreman (outside)	$39.60	$316.80	$60.95	$487.60	$46.91	$71.36
1 Laborer	37.60	300.80	57.85	462.80		
1 Plumber	58.70	469.60	88.65	709.20		
1 Plumber Apprentice	46.95	375.60	70.90	567.20		
1 Equip. Oper. (crane)	51.70	413.60	78.45	627.60		
1 S.P. Crane, 4x4, 12 Ton		473.40		520.74	11.84	13.02
40 L.H., Daily Totals		$2349.80		$3375.14	$58.74	$84.38

Crew B-21B

Crew No.	Bare Costs Hr.	Bare Costs Daily	Incl. Subs O&P Hr.	Incl. Subs O&P Daily	Cost Per Labor-Hour Bare Costs	Cost Per Labor-Hour Incl. O&P
1 Labor Foreman (outside)	$39.60	$316.80	$60.95	$487.60	$40.82	$62.59
3 Laborers	37.60	902.40	57.85	1388.40		
1 Equip. Oper. (crane)	51.70	413.60	78.45	627.60		
1 Hyd. Crane, 12 Ton		653.80		719.18	16.34	17.98
40 L.H., Daily Totals		$2286.60		$3222.78	$57.16	$80.57

Crew B-21C

Crew No.	Bare Costs Hr.	Bare Costs Daily	Incl. Subs O&P Hr.	Incl. Subs O&P Daily	Cost Per Labor-Hour Bare Costs	Cost Per Labor-Hour Incl. O&P
1 Labor Foreman (outside)	$39.60	$316.80	$60.95	$487.60	$40.99	$62.76
4 Laborers	37.60	1203.20	57.85	1851.20		
1 Equip. Oper. (crane)	51.70	413.60	78.45	627.60		
1 Equip. Oper. (oiler)	45.20	361.60	68.55	548.40		
2 Cutting Torches		22.80		25.08		
2 Sets of Gases		304.00		334.40		
1 Lattice Boom Crane, 90 Ton		1511.00		1662.10	32.82	36.10
56 L.H., Daily Totals		$4133.00		$5536.38	$73.80	$98.86

Crew B-22

Crew No.	Bare Costs Hr.	Bare Costs Daily	Incl. Subs O&P Hr.	Incl. Subs O&P Daily	Cost Per Labor-Hour Bare Costs	Cost Per Labor-Hour Incl. O&P
1 Labor Foreman (outside)	$39.60	$316.80	$60.95	$487.60	$43.90	$67.41
1 Skilled Worker	48.65	389.20	75.15	601.20		
1 Laborer	37.60	300.80	57.85	462.80		
.75 Equip. Oper. (crane)	51.70	310.20	78.45	470.70		
.75 S.P. Crane, 4x4, 5 Ton		206.55		227.21	6.88	7.57
30 L.H., Daily Totals		$1523.55		$2249.51	$50.78	$74.98

Crew B-22A

Crew No.	Bare Costs Hr.	Bare Costs Daily	Incl. Subs O&P Hr.	Incl. Subs O&P Daily	Cost Per Labor-Hour Bare Costs	Cost Per Labor-Hour Incl. O&P
1 Labor Foreman (outside)	$39.60	$316.80	$60.95	$487.60	$43.03	$66.05
1 Skilled Worker	48.65	389.20	75.15	601.20		
2 Laborers	37.60	601.60	57.85	925.60		
1 Equipment Operator, Crane	51.70	413.60	78.45	627.60		
1 S.P. Crane, 4x4, 5 Ton		275.40		302.94		
1 Butt Fusion Mach., 4"-12" diam.		382.10		420.31	16.44	18.08
40 L.H., Daily Totals		$2378.70		$3365.25	$59.47	$84.13

Crew B-22B

Crew No.	Bare Costs Hr.	Bare Costs Daily	Incl. Subs O&P Hr.	Incl. Subs O&P Daily	Cost Per Labor-Hour Bare Costs	Cost Per Labor-Hour Incl. O&P
1 Labor Foreman (outside)	$39.60	$316.80	$60.95	$487.60	$43.03	$66.05
1 Skilled Worker	48.65	389.20	75.15	601.20		
2 Laborers	37.60	601.60	57.85	925.60		
1 Equip. Oper. (crane)	51.70	413.60	78.45	627.60		
1 S.P. Crane, 4x4, 5 Ton		275.40		302.94		
1 Butt Fusion Mach., 8"-24" diam.		829.70		912.67	27.63	30.39
40 L.H., Daily Totals		$2826.30		$3857.61	$70.66	$96.44

Crew B-22C

Crew No.	Bare Costs Hr.	Bare Costs Daily	Incl. Subs O&P Hr.	Incl. Subs O&P Daily	Cost Per Labor-Hour Bare Costs	Cost Per Labor-Hour Incl. O&P
1 Skilled Worker	$48.65	$389.20	$75.15	$601.20	$43.13	$66.50
1 Laborer	37.60	300.80	57.85	462.80		
1 Butt Fusion Mach., 2"-8" diam.		121.05		133.16	7.57	8.32
16 L.H., Daily Totals		$811.05		$1197.16	$50.69	$74.82

Crew B-23

Crew No.	Bare Costs Hr.	Bare Costs Daily	Incl. Subs O&P Hr.	Incl. Subs O&P Daily	Cost Per Labor-Hour Bare Costs	Cost Per Labor-Hour Incl. O&P
1 Labor Foreman (outside)	$39.60	$316.80	$60.95	$487.60	$38.00	$58.47
4 Laborers	37.60	1203.20	57.85	1851.20		
1 Drill Rig, Truck-Mounted		2542.00		2796.20		
1 Flatbed Truck, Gas, 3 Ton		303.20		333.52	71.13	78.24
40 L.H., Daily Totals		$4365.20		$5468.52	$109.13	$136.71

Crew B-23A

Crew No.	Bare Costs Hr.	Bare Costs Daily	Incl. Subs O&P Hr.	Incl. Subs O&P Daily	Cost Per Labor-Hour Bare Costs	Cost Per Labor-Hour Incl. O&P
1 Labor Foreman (outside)	$39.60	$316.80	$60.95	$487.60	$42.60	$65.18
1 Laborer	37.60	300.80	57.85	462.80		
1 Equip. Oper. (medium)	50.60	404.80	76.75	614.00		
1 Drill Rig, Truck-Mounted		2542.00		2796.20		
1 Pickup Truck, 3/4 Ton		144.20		158.62	111.93	123.12
24 L.H., Daily Totals		$3708.60		$4519.22	$154.53	$188.30

Crew B-23B

	Bare Costs Hr.	Daily	Incl. Subs O&P Hr.	Daily	Cost Per Labor-Hour Bare Costs	Incl. O&P
1 Labor Foreman (outside)	$39.60	$316.80	$60.95	$487.60	$42.60	$65.18
1 Laborer	37.60	300.80	57.85	462.80		
1 Equip. Oper. (medium)	50.60	404.80	76.75	614.00		
1 Drill Rig, Truck-Mounted		2542.00		2796.20		
1 Pickup Truck, 3/4 Ton		144.20		158.62		
1 Centr. Water Pump, 6"		346.60		381.26	126.37	139.00
24 L.H., Daily Totals		$4055.20		$4900.48	$168.97	$204.19

Crew B-24

	Bare Costs Hr.	Daily	Incl. Subs O&P Hr.	Daily	Cost Per Labor-Hour Bare Costs	Incl. O&P
1 Cement Finisher	$45.00	$360.00	$66.65	$533.20	$43.18	$65.58
1 Laborer	37.60	300.80	57.85	462.80		
1 Carpenter	46.95	375.60	72.25	578.00		
24 L.H., Daily Totals		$1036.40		$1574.00	$43.18	$65.58

Crew B-25

	Bare Costs Hr.	Daily	Incl. Subs O&P Hr.	Daily	Cost Per Labor-Hour Bare Costs	Incl. O&P
1 Labor Foreman (outside)	$39.60	$316.80	$60.95	$487.60	$41.33	$63.29
7 Laborers	37.60	2105.60	57.85	3239.60		
3 Equip. Oper. (medium)	50.60	1214.40	76.75	1842.00		
1 Asphalt Paver, 130 H.P.		2132.00		2345.20		
1 Tandem Roller, 10 Ton		236.80		260.48		
1 Roller, Pneum. Whl., 12 Ton		344.40		378.84	30.83	33.91
88 L.H., Daily Totals		$6350.00		$8553.72	$72.16	$97.20

Crew B-25B

	Bare Costs Hr.	Daily	Incl. Subs O&P Hr.	Daily	Cost Per Labor-Hour Bare Costs	Incl. O&P
1 Labor Foreman (outside)	$39.60	$316.80	$60.95	$487.60	$42.10	$64.41
7 Laborers	37.60	2105.60	57.85	3239.60		
4 Equip. Oper. (medium)	50.60	1619.20	76.75	2456.00		
1 Asphalt Paver, 130 H.P.		2132.00		2345.20		
2 Tandem Rollers, 10 Ton		473.60		520.96		
1 Roller, Pneum. Whl., 12 Ton		344.40		378.84	30.73	33.80
96 L.H., Daily Totals		$6991.60		$9428.20	$72.83	$98.21

Crew B-25C

	Bare Costs Hr.	Daily	Incl. Subs O&P Hr.	Daily	Cost Per Labor-Hour Bare Costs	Incl. O&P
1 Labor Foreman (outside)	$39.60	$316.80	$60.95	$487.60	$42.27	$64.67
3 Laborers	37.60	902.40	57.85	1388.40		
2 Equip. Oper. (medium)	50.60	809.60	76.75	1228.00		
1 Asphalt Paver, 130 H.P.		2132.00		2345.20		
1 Tandem Roller, 10 Ton		236.80		260.48	49.35	54.28
48 L.H., Daily Totals		$4397.60		$5709.68	$91.62	$118.95

Crew B-25D

	Bare Costs Hr.	Daily	Incl. Subs O&P Hr.	Daily	Cost Per Labor-Hour Bare Costs	Incl. O&P
1 Labor Foreman (outside)	$39.60	$316.80	$60.95	$487.60	$42.39	$64.83
3 Laborers	37.60	902.40	57.85	1388.40		
2.125 Equip. Oper. (medium)	50.60	860.20	76.75	1304.75		
.125 Truck Driver (heavy)	40.05	40.05	60.55	60.55		
.125 Truck Tractor, 6x4, 380 H.P.		74.97		82.47		
.125 Dist. Tanker, 3000 Gallon		38.20		42.02		
1 Asphalt Paver, 130 H.P.		2132.00		2345.20		
1 Tandem Roller, 10 Ton		236.80		260.48	49.64	54.60
50 L.H., Daily Totals		$4601.43		$5971.47	$92.03	$119.43

Crew B-25E

	Bare Costs Hr.	Daily	Incl. Subs O&P Hr.	Daily	Cost Per Labor-Hour Bare Costs	Incl. O&P
1 Labor Foreman (outside)	$39.60	$316.80	$60.95	$487.60	$42.50	$64.97
3 Laborers	37.60	902.40	57.85	1388.40		
2.250 Equip. Oper. (medium)	50.60	910.80	76.75	1381.50		
.25 Truck Driver (heavy)	40.05	80.10	60.55	121.10		
.25 Truck Tractor, 6x4, 380 H.P.		149.95		164.94		
.25 Dist. Tanker, 3000 Gallon		76.40		84.04		
1 Asphalt Paver, 130 H.P.		2132.00		2345.20		
1 Tandem Roller, 10 Ton		236.80		260.48	49.91	54.90
52 L.H., Daily Totals		$4805.25		$6233.27	$92.41	$119.87

Crew B-26

	Bare Costs Hr.	Daily	Incl. Subs O&P Hr.	Daily	Cost Per Labor-Hour Bare Costs	Incl. O&P
1 Labor Foreman (outside)	$39.60	$316.80	$60.95	$487.60	$42.18	$64.57
6 Laborers	37.60	1804.80	57.85	2776.80		
2 Equip. Oper. (medium)	50.60	809.60	76.75	1228.00		
1 Rodman (reinf.)	52.55	420.40	82.10	656.80		
1 Cement Finisher	45.00	360.00	66.65	533.20		
1 Grader, 30,000 Lbs.		736.20		809.82		
1 Paving Mach. & Equip.		2794.00		3073.40	40.12	44.13
88 L.H., Daily Totals		$7241.80		$9565.62	$82.29	$108.70

Crew B-26A

	Bare Costs Hr.	Daily	Incl. Subs O&P Hr.	Daily	Cost Per Labor-Hour Bare Costs	Incl. O&P
1 Labor Foreman (outside)	$39.60	$316.80	$60.95	$487.60	$42.18	$64.57
6 Laborers	37.60	1804.80	57.85	2776.80		
2 Equip. Oper. (medium)	50.60	809.60	76.75	1228.00		
1 Rodman (reinf.)	52.55	420.40	82.10	656.80		
1 Cement Finisher	45.00	360.00	66.65	533.20		
1 Grader, 30,000 Lbs.		736.20		809.82		
1 Paving Mach. & Equip.		2794.00		3073.40		
1 Concrete Saw		167.40		184.14	42.02	46.22
88 L.H., Daily Totals		$7409.20		$9749.76	$84.20	$110.79

Crew B-26B

	Bare Costs Hr.	Daily	Incl. Subs O&P Hr.	Daily	Cost Per Labor-Hour Bare Costs	Incl. O&P
1 Labor Foreman (outside)	$39.60	$316.80	$60.95	$487.60	$42.88	$65.59
6 Laborers	37.60	1804.80	57.85	2776.80		
3 Equip. Oper. (medium)	50.60	1214.40	76.75	1842.00		
1 Rodman (reinf.)	52.55	420.40	82.10	656.80		
1 Cement Finisher	45.00	360.00	66.65	533.20		
1 Grader, 30,000 Lbs.		736.20		809.82		
1 Paving Mach. & Equip.		2794.00		3073.40		
1 Concrete Pump, 110' Boom		946.20		1040.82	46.63	51.29
96 L.H., Daily Totals		$8592.80		$11220.44	$89.51	$116.88

Crew B-26C

	Bare Costs Hr.	Daily	Incl. Subs O&P Hr.	Daily	Cost Per Labor-Hour Bare Costs	Incl. O&P
1 Labor Foreman (outside)	$39.60	$316.80	$60.95	$487.60	$41.34	$63.35
6 Laborers	37.60	1804.80	57.85	2776.80		
1 Equip. Oper. (medium)	50.60	404.80	76.75	614.00		
1 Rodman (reinf.)	52.55	420.40	82.10	656.80		
1 Cement Finisher	45.00	360.00	66.65	533.20		
1 Paving Mach. & Equip.		2794.00		3073.40		
1 Concrete Saw		167.40		184.14	37.02	40.72
80 L.H., Daily Totals		$6268.20		$8325.94	$78.35	$104.07

Crew B-27

	Bare Costs Hr.	Daily	Incl. Subs O&P Hr.	Daily	Cost Per Labor-Hour Bare Costs	Incl. O&P
1 Labor Foreman (outside)	$39.60	$316.80	$60.95	$487.60	$38.10	$58.63
3 Laborers	37.60	902.40	57.85	1388.40		
1 Berm Machine		296.80		326.48	9.28	10.20
32 L.H., Daily Totals		$1516.00		$2202.48	$47.38	$68.83

Crew B-28

	Bare Costs Hr.	Daily	Incl. Subs O&P Hr.	Daily	Cost Per Labor-Hour Bare Costs	Incl. O&P
2 Carpenters	$46.95	$751.20	$72.25	$1156.00	$43.83	$67.45
1 Laborer	37.60	300.80	57.85	462.80		
24 L.H., Daily Totals		$1052.00		$1618.80	$43.83	$67.45

Crew B-29

	Bare Costs Hr.	Daily	Incl. Subs O&P Hr.	Daily	Cost Per Labor-Hour Bare Costs	Incl. O&P
1 Labor Foreman (outside)	$39.60	$316.80	$60.95	$487.60	$40.99	$62.76
4 Laborers	37.60	1203.20	57.85	1851.20		
1 Equip. Oper. (crane)	51.70	413.60	78.45	627.60		
1 Equip. Oper. (oiler)	45.20	361.60	68.55	548.40		
1 Gradall, 5/8 C.Y.		882.20		970.42	15.75	17.33
56 L.H., Daily Totals		$3177.40		$4485.22	$56.74	$80.09

Crews

Crew No.	Bare Costs Hr.	Daily	Incl. Subs O&P Hr.	Daily	Cost Per Labor-Hour Bare Costs	Incl. O&P
Crew B-30	Hr.	Daily	Hr.	Daily	Bare Costs	Incl. O&P
1 Equip. Oper. (medium)	$50.60	$404.80	$76.75	$614.00	$43.57	$65.95
2 Truck Drivers (heavy)	40.05	640.80	60.55	968.80		
1 Hyd. Excavator, 1.5 C.Y.		1030.00		1133.00		
2 Dump Trucks, 12 C.Y., 400 H.P.		1382.00		1520.20	100.50	110.55
24 L.H., Daily Totals		$3457.60		$4236.00	$144.07	$176.50

Crew No.	Bare Costs Hr.	Daily	Incl. Subs O&P Hr.	Daily	Cost Per Labor-Hour Bare Costs	Incl. O&P
Crew B-31	Hr.	Daily	Hr.	Daily	Bare Costs	Incl. O&P
1 Labor Foreman (outside)	$39.60	$316.80	$60.95	$487.60	$39.87	$61.35
3 Laborers	37.60	902.40	57.85	1388.40		
1 Carpenter	46.95	375.60	72.25	578.00		
1 Air Compressor, 250 cfm		201.40		221.54		
1 Sheeting Driver		5.75		6.33		
2 -50' Air Hoses, 1.5"		11.60		12.76	5.47	6.02
40 L.H., Daily Totals		$1813.55		$2694.63	$45.34	$67.37

Crew No.	Bare Costs Hr.	Daily	Incl. Subs O&P Hr.	Daily	Cost Per Labor-Hour Bare Costs	Incl. O&P
Crew B-32	Hr.	Daily	Hr.	Daily	Bare Costs	Incl. O&P
1 Laborer	$37.60	$300.80	$57.85	$462.80	$47.35	$72.03
3 Equip. Oper. (medium)	50.60	1214.40	76.75	1842.00		
1 Grader, 30,000 Lbs.		736.20		809.82		
1 Tandem Roller, 10 Ton		236.80		260.48		
1 Dozer, 200 H.P.		1387.00		1525.70	73.75	81.13
32 L.H., Daily Totals		$3875.20		$4900.80	$121.10	$153.15

Crew No.	Bare Costs Hr.	Daily	Incl. Subs O&P Hr.	Daily	Cost Per Labor-Hour Bare Costs	Incl. O&P
Crew B-32A	Hr.	Daily	Hr.	Daily	Bare Costs	Incl. O&P
1 Laborer	$37.60	$300.80	$57.85	$462.80	$46.27	$70.45
2 Equip. Oper. (medium)	50.60	809.60	76.75	1228.00		
1 Grader, 30,000 Lbs.		736.20		809.82		
1 Roller, Vibratory, 25 Ton		687.40		756.14	59.32	65.25
24 L.H., Daily Totals		$2534.00		$3256.76	$105.58	$135.70

Crew No.	Bare Costs Hr.	Daily	Incl. Subs O&P Hr.	Daily	Cost Per Labor-Hour Bare Costs	Incl. O&P
Crew B-32B	Hr.	Daily	Hr.	Daily	Bare Costs	Incl. O&P
1 Laborer	$37.60	$300.80	$57.85	$462.80	$46.27	$70.45
2 Equip. Oper. (medium)	50.60	809.60	76.75	1228.00		
1 Dozer, 200 H.P.		1387.00		1525.70		
1 Roller, Vibratory, 25 Ton		687.40		756.14	86.43	95.08
24 L.H., Daily Totals		$3184.80		$3972.64	$132.70	$165.53

Crew No.	Bare Costs Hr.	Daily	Incl. Subs O&P Hr.	Daily	Cost Per Labor-Hour Bare Costs	Incl. O&P
Crew B-32C	Hr.	Daily	Hr.	Daily	Bare Costs	Incl. O&P
1 Labor Foreman (outside)	$39.60	$316.80	$60.95	$487.60	$44.43	$67.82
2 Laborers	37.60	601.60	57.85	925.60		
3 Equip. Oper. (medium)	50.60	1214.40	76.75	1842.00		
1 Grader, 30,000 Lbs.		736.20		809.82		
1 Tandem Roller, 10 Ton		236.80		260.48		
1 Dozer, 200 H.P.		1387.00		1525.70	49.17	54.08
48 L.H., Daily Totals		$4492.80		$5851.20	$93.60	$121.90

Crew No.	Bare Costs Hr.	Daily	Incl. Subs O&P Hr.	Daily	Cost Per Labor-Hour Bare Costs	Incl. O&P
Crew B-33A	Hr.	Daily	Hr.	Daily	Bare Costs	Incl. O&P
1 Equip. Oper. (medium)	$50.60	$404.80	$76.75	$614.00	$46.89	$71.35
.5 Laborer	37.60	150.40	57.85	231.40		
.25 Equip. Oper. (medium)	50.60	101.20	76.75	153.50		
1 Scraper, Towed, 7 C.Y.		114.40		125.84		
1.25 Dozers, 300 H.P.		2371.25		2608.38	177.55	195.30
14 L.H., Daily Totals		$3142.05		$3733.11	$224.43	$266.65

Crew No.	Bare Costs Hr.	Daily	Incl. Subs O&P Hr.	Daily	Cost Per Labor-Hour Bare Costs	Incl. O&P
Crew B-33B	Hr.	Daily	Hr.	Daily	Bare Costs	Incl. O&P
1 Equip. Oper. (medium)	$50.60	$404.80	$76.75	$614.00	$46.89	$71.35
.5 Laborer	37.60	150.40	57.85	231.40		
.25 Equip. Oper. (medium)	50.60	101.20	76.75	153.50		
1 Scraper, Towed, 10 C.Y.		146.80		161.48		
1.25 Dozers, 300 H.P.		2371.25		2608.38	179.86	197.85
14 L.H., Daily Totals		$3174.45		$3768.76	$226.75	$269.20

Crew No.	Bare Costs Hr.	Daily	Incl. Subs O&P Hr.	Daily	Cost Per Labor-Hour Bare Costs	Incl. O&P
Crew B-33C	Hr.	Daily	Hr.	Daily	Bare Costs	Incl. O&P
1 Equip. Oper. (medium)	$50.60	$404.80	$76.75	$614.00	$46.89	$71.35
.5 Laborer	37.60	150.40	57.85	231.40		
.25 Equip. Oper. (medium)	50.60	101.20	76.75	153.50		
1 Scraper, Towed, 15 C.Y.		164.80		181.28		
1.25 Dozers, 300 H.P.		2371.25		2608.38	181.15	199.26
14 L.H., Daily Totals		$3192.45		$3788.55	$228.03	$270.61

Crew No.	Bare Costs Hr.	Daily	Incl. Subs O&P Hr.	Daily	Cost Per Labor-Hour Bare Costs	Incl. O&P
Crew B-33D	Hr.	Daily	Hr.	Daily	Bare Costs	Incl. O&P
1 Equip. Oper. (medium)	$50.60	$404.80	$76.75	$614.00	$46.89	$71.35
.5 Laborer	37.60	150.40	57.85	231.40		
.25 Equip. Oper. (medium)	50.60	101.20	76.75	153.50		
1 S.P. Scraper, 14 C.Y.		1884.00		2072.40		
.25 Dozer, 300 H.P.		474.25		521.67	168.45	185.29
14 L.H., Daily Totals		$3014.65		$3592.97	$215.33	$256.64

Crew No.	Bare Costs Hr.	Daily	Incl. Subs O&P Hr.	Daily	Cost Per Labor-Hour Bare Costs	Incl. O&P
Crew B-33E	Hr.	Daily	Hr.	Daily	Bare Costs	Incl. O&P
1 Equip. Oper. (medium)	$50.60	$404.80	$76.75	$614.00	$46.89	$71.35
.5 Laborer	37.60	150.40	57.85	231.40		
.25 Equip. Oper. (medium)	50.60	101.20	76.75	153.50		
1 S.P. Scraper, 21 C.Y.		2688.00		2956.80		
.25 Dozer, 300 H.P.		474.25		521.67	225.88	248.46
14 L.H., Daily Totals		$3818.65		$4477.38	$272.76	$319.81

Crew No.	Bare Costs Hr.	Daily	Incl. Subs O&P Hr.	Daily	Cost Per Labor-Hour Bare Costs	Incl. O&P
Crew B-33F	Hr.	Daily	Hr.	Daily	Bare Costs	Incl. O&P
1 Equip. Oper. (medium)	$50.60	$404.80	$76.75	$614.00	$46.89	$71.35
.5 Laborer	37.60	150.40	57.85	231.40		
.25 Equip. Oper. (medium)	50.60	101.20	76.75	153.50		
1 Elev. Scraper, 11 C.Y.		1163.00		1279.30		
.25 Dozer, 300 H.P.		474.25		521.67	116.95	128.64
14 L.H., Daily Totals		$2293.65		$2799.88	$163.83	$199.99

Crew No.	Bare Costs Hr.	Daily	Incl. Subs O&P Hr.	Daily	Cost Per Labor-Hour Bare Costs	Incl. O&P
Crew B-33G	Hr.	Daily	Hr.	Daily	Bare Costs	Incl. O&P
1 Equip. Oper. (medium)	$50.60	$404.80	$76.75	$614.00	$46.89	$71.35
.5 Laborer	37.60	150.40	57.85	231.40		
.25 Equip. Oper. (medium)	50.60	101.20	76.75	153.50		
1 Elev. Scraper, 22 C.Y.		2521.00		2773.10		
.25 Dozer, 300 H.P.		474.25		521.67	213.95	235.34
14 L.H., Daily Totals		$3651.65		$4293.68	$260.83	$306.69

Crew No.	Bare Costs Hr.	Daily	Incl. Subs O&P Hr.	Daily	Cost Per Labor-Hour Bare Costs	Incl. O&P
Crew B-33H	Hr.	Daily	Hr.	Daily	Bare Costs	Incl. O&P
.5 Laborer	$37.60	$150.40	$57.85	$231.40	$46.89	$71.35
1 Equipment Operator (med.)	50.60	404.80	76.75	614.00		
.25 Equipment Operator (med.)	50.60	101.20	76.75	153.50		
1 S.P. Scraper, 44 C.Y.		4679.00		5146.90		
.25 Dozer, 410 H.P.		601.25		661.38	377.16	414.88
14 L.H., Daily Totals		$5936.65		$6807.18	$424.05	$486.23

Crew No.	Bare Costs Hr.	Daily	Incl. Subs O&P Hr.	Daily	Cost Per Labor-Hour Bare Costs	Incl. O&P
Crew B-33J	Hr.	Daily	Hr.	Daily	Bare Costs	Incl. O&P
1 Equipment Operator (med.)	$50.60	$404.80	$76.75	$614.00	$50.60	$76.75
1 S.P. Scraper, 14 C.Y.		1884.00		2072.40	235.50	259.05
8 L.H., Daily Totals		$2288.80		$2686.40	$286.10	$335.80

Crew No.	Bare Costs Hr.	Daily	Incl. Subs O&P Hr.	Daily	Cost Per Labor-Hour Bare Costs	Incl. O&P
Crew B-33K	Hr.	Daily	Hr.	Daily	Bare Costs	Incl. O&P
1 Equipment Operator (med.)	$50.60	$404.80	$76.75	$614.00	$46.89	$71.35
.25 Equipment Operator (med.)	50.60	101.20	76.75	153.50		
.5 Laborer	37.60	150.40	57.85	231.40		
1 S.P. Scraper, 31 C.Y.		3693.00		4062.30		
.25 Dozer, 410 H.P.		601.25		661.38	306.73	337.41
14 L.H., Daily Totals		$4950.65		$5722.57	$353.62	$408.76

Crew No.	Bare Costs		Incl. Subs O&P		Cost Per Labor-Hour	
Crew B-34A	**Hr.**	**Daily**	**Hr.**	**Daily**	**Bare Costs**	**Incl. O&P**
1 Truck Driver (heavy)	$40.05	$320.40	$60.55	$484.40	$40.05	$60.55
1 Dump Truck, 8 C.Y., 220 H.P.		411.20		452.32	51.40	56.54
8 L.H., Daily Totals		$731.60		$936.72	$91.45	$117.09
Crew B-34B	**Hr.**	**Daily**	**Hr.**	**Daily**	**Bare Costs**	**Incl. O&P**
1 Truck Driver (heavy)	$40.05	$320.40	$60.55	$484.40	$40.05	$60.55
1 Dump Truck, 12 C.Y., 400 H.P.		691.00		760.10	86.38	95.01
8 L.H., Daily Totals		$1011.40		$1244.50	$126.43	$155.56
Crew B-34C	**Hr.**	**Daily**	**Hr.**	**Daily**	**Bare Costs**	**Incl. O&P**
1 Truck Driver (heavy)	$40.05	$320.40	$60.55	$484.40	$40.05	$60.55
1 Truck Tractor, 6x4, 380 H.P.		599.80		659.78		
1 Dump Trailer, 16.5 C.Y.		126.60		139.26	90.80	99.88
8 L.H., Daily Totals		$1046.80		$1283.44	$130.85	$160.43
Crew B-34D	**Hr.**	**Daily**	**Hr.**	**Daily**	**Bare Costs**	**Incl. O&P**
1 Truck Driver (heavy)	$40.05	$320.40	$60.55	$484.40	$40.05	$60.55
1 Truck Tractor, 6x4, 380 H.P.		599.80		659.78		
1 Dump Trailer, 20 C.Y.		141.20		155.32	92.63	101.89
8 L.H., Daily Totals		$1061.40		$1299.50	$132.68	$162.44
Crew B-34E	**Hr.**	**Daily**	**Hr.**	**Daily**	**Bare Costs**	**Incl. O&P**
1 Truck Driver (heavy)	$40.05	$320.40	$60.55	$484.40	$40.05	$60.55
1 Dump Truck, Off Hwy., 25 Ton		1351.00		1486.10	168.88	185.76
8 L.H., Daily Totals		$1671.40		$1970.50	$208.93	$246.31
Crew B-34F	**Hr.**	**Daily**	**Hr.**	**Daily**	**Bare Costs**	**Incl. O&P**
1 Truck Driver (heavy)	$40.05	$320.40	$60.55	$484.40	$40.05	$60.55
1 Dump Truck, Off Hwy., 35 Ton		1512.00		1663.20	189.00	207.90
8 L.H., Daily Totals		$1832.40		$2147.60	$229.05	$268.45
Crew B-34G	**Hr.**	**Daily**	**Hr.**	**Daily**	**Bare Costs**	**Incl. O&P**
1 Truck Driver (heavy)	$40.05	$320.40	$60.55	$484.40	$40.05	$60.55
1 Dump Truck, Off Hwy., 50 Ton		1837.00		2020.70	229.63	252.59
8 L.H., Daily Totals		$2157.40		$2505.10	$269.68	$313.14
Crew B-34H	**Hr.**	**Daily**	**Hr.**	**Daily**	**Bare Costs**	**Incl. O&P**
1 Truck Driver (heavy)	$40.05	$320.40	$60.55	$484.40	$40.05	$60.55
1 Dump Truck, Off Hwy., 65 Ton		1863.00		2049.30	232.88	256.16
8 L.H., Daily Totals		$2183.40		$2533.70	$272.93	$316.71
Crew B-34I	**Hr.**	**Daily**	**Hr.**	**Daily**	**Bare Costs**	**Incl. O&P**
1 Truck Driver (heavy)	$40.05	$320.40	$60.55	$484.40	$40.05	$60.55
1 Dump Truck, 18 C.Y., 450 H.P.		869.00		955.90	108.63	119.49
8 L.H., Daily Totals		$1189.40		$1440.30	$148.68	$180.04
Crew B-34J	**Hr.**	**Daily**	**Hr.**	**Daily**	**Bare Costs**	**Incl. O&P**
1 Truck Driver (heavy)	$40.05	$320.40	$60.55	$484.40	$40.05	$60.55
1 Dump Truck, Off Hwy., 100 Ton		2925.00		3217.50	365.63	402.19
8 L.H., Daily Totals		$3245.40		$3701.90	$405.68	$462.74
Crew B-34K	**Hr.**	**Daily**	**Hr.**	**Daily**	**Bare Costs**	**Incl. O&P**
1 Truck Driver (heavy)	$40.05	$320.40	$60.55	$484.40	$40.05	$60.55
1 Truck Tractor, 6x4, 450 H.P.		727.40		800.14		
1 Lowbed Trailer, 75 Ton		221.80		243.98	118.65	130.51
8 L.H., Daily Totals		$1269.60		$1528.52	$158.70	$191.07

Crew No.	Bare Costs		Incl. Subs O&P		Cost Per Labor-Hour	
Crew B-34L	**Hr.**	**Daily**	**Hr.**	**Daily**	**Bare Costs**	**Incl. O&P**
1 Equip. Oper. (light)	$48.60	$388.80	$73.75	$590.00	$48.60	$73.75
1 Flatbed Truck, Gas, 1.5 Ton		245.40		269.94	30.68	33.74
8 L.H., Daily Totals		$634.20		$859.94	$79.28	$107.49
Crew B-34M	**Hr.**	**Daily**	**Hr.**	**Daily**	**Bare Costs**	**Incl. O&P**
1 Equip. Oper. (light)	$48.60	$388.80	$73.75	$590.00	$48.60	$73.75
1 Flatbed Truck, Gas, 3 Ton		303.20		333.52	37.90	41.69
8 L.H., Daily Totals		$692.00		$923.52	$86.50	$115.44
Crew B-34N	**Hr.**	**Daily**	**Hr.**	**Daily**	**Bare Costs**	**Incl. O&P**
1 Truck Driver (heavy)	$40.05	$320.40	$60.55	$484.40	$45.33	$68.65
1 Equip. Oper. (medium)	50.60	404.80	76.75	614.00		
1 Truck Tractor, 6x4, 380 H.P.		599.80		659.78		
1 Flatbed Trailer, 40 Ton		154.00		169.40	47.11	51.82
16 L.H., Daily Totals		$1479.00		$1927.58	$92.44	$120.47
Crew B-34P	**Hr.**	**Daily**	**Hr.**	**Daily**	**Bare Costs**	**Incl. O&P**
1 Pipe Fitter	$59.75	$478.00	$90.20	$721.60	$49.82	$75.35
1 Truck Driver (light)	39.10	312.80	59.10	472.80		
1 Equip. Oper. (medium)	50.60	404.80	76.75	614.00		
1 Flatbed Truck, Gas, 3 Ton		303.20		333.52		
1 Backhoe Loader, 48 H.P.		364.20		400.62	27.81	30.59
24 L.H., Daily Totals		$1863.00		$2542.54	$77.63	$105.94
Crew B-34Q	**Hr.**	**Daily**	**Hr.**	**Daily**	**Bare Costs**	**Incl. O&P**
1 Pipe Fitter	$59.75	$478.00	$90.20	$721.60	$50.18	$75.92
1 Truck Driver (light)	39.10	312.80	59.10	472.80		
1 Equip. Oper. (crane)	51.70	413.60	78.45	627.60		
1 Flatbed Trailer, 25 Ton		113.60		124.96		
1 Dump Truck, 8 C.Y., 220 H.P.		411.20		452.32		
1 Hyd. Crane, 25 Ton		736.60		810.26	52.56	57.81
24 L.H., Daily Totals		$2465.80		$3209.54	$102.74	$133.73
Crew B-34R	**Hr.**	**Daily**	**Hr.**	**Daily**	**Bare Costs**	**Incl. O&P**
1 Pipe Fitter	$59.75	$478.00	$90.20	$721.60	$50.18	$75.92
1 Truck Driver (light)	39.10	312.80	59.10	472.80		
1 Equip. Oper. (crane)	51.70	413.60	78.45	627.60		
1 Flatbed Trailer, 25 Ton		113.60		124.96		
1 Dump Truck, 8 C.Y., 220 H.P.		411.20		452.32		
1 Hyd. Crane, 25 Ton		736.60		810.26		
1 Hyd. Excavator, 1 C.Y.		812.60		893.86	86.42	95.06
24 L.H., Daily Totals		$3278.40		$4103.40	$136.60	$170.97
Crew B-34S	**Hr.**	**Daily**	**Hr.**	**Daily**	**Bare Costs**	**Incl. O&P**
2 Pipe Fitters	$59.75	$956.00	$90.20	$1443.20	$52.81	$79.85
1 Truck Driver (heavy)	40.05	320.40	60.55	484.40		
1 Equip. Oper. (crane)	51.70	413.60	78.45	627.60		
1 Flatbed Trailer, 40 Ton		154.00		169.40		
1 Truck Tractor, 6x4, 380 H.P.		599.80		659.78		
1 Hyd. Crane, 80 Ton		1625.00		1787.50		
1 Hyd. Excavator, 2 C.Y.		1175.00		1292.50	111.06	122.16
32 L.H., Daily Totals		$5243.80		$6464.38	$163.87	$202.01
Crew B-34T	**Hr.**	**Daily**	**Hr.**	**Daily**	**Bare Costs**	**Incl. O&P**
2 Pipe Fitters	$59.75	$956.00	$90.20	$1443.20	$52.81	$79.85
1 Truck Driver (heavy)	40.05	320.40	60.55	484.40		
1 Equip. Oper. (crane)	51.70	413.60	78.45	627.60		
1 Flatbed Trailer, 40 Ton		154.00		169.40		
1 Truck Tractor, 6x4, 380 H.P.		599.80		659.78		
1 Hyd. Crane, 80 Ton		1625.00		1787.50	74.34	81.77
32 L.H., Daily Totals		$4068.80		$5171.88	$127.15	$161.62

724

Crew B-34U

Crew No.	Hr.	Daily	Hr.	Daily	Bare Costs	Incl. O&P
1 Truck Driver (heavy)	$40.05	$320.40	$60.55	$484.40	$44.33	$67.15
1 Equip. Oper. (light)	48.60	388.80	73.75	590.00		
1 Truck Tractor, 220 H.P.		359.60		395.56		
1 Flatbed Trailer, 25 Ton		113.60		124.96	29.57	32.53
16 L.H., Daily Totals		$1182.40		$1594.92	$73.90	$99.68

Crew B-34V

Crew No.	Hr.	Daily	Hr.	Daily	Bare Costs	Incl. O&P
1 Truck Driver (heavy)	$40.05	$320.40	$60.55	$484.40	$46.78	$70.92
1 Equip. Oper. (crane)	51.70	413.60	78.45	627.60		
1 Equip. Oper. (light)	48.60	388.80	73.75	590.00		
1 Truck Tractor, 6x4, 450 H.P.		727.40		800.14		
1 Equipment Trailer, 50 Ton		168.40		185.24		
1 Pickup Truck, 4 x 4, 3/4 Ton		155.60		171.16	43.81	48.19
24 L.H., Daily Totals		$2174.20		$2858.54	$90.59	$119.11

Crew B-34W

Crew No.	Hr.	Daily	Hr.	Daily	Bare Costs	Incl. O&P
5 Truck Drivers (heavy)	$40.05	$1602.00	$60.55	$2422.00	$43.66	$66.21
2 Equip. Opers. (crane)	51.70	827.20	78.45	1255.20		
1 Equip. Oper. (mechanic)	51.65	413.20	78.35	626.80		
1 Laborer	37.60	300.80	57.85	462.80		
4 Truck Tractor, 6x4, 380 H.P.		2399.20		2639.12		
2 Equipment Trailer, 50 Ton		336.80		370.48		
2 Flatbed Trailer, 40 Ton		308.00		338.80		
1 Pickup Truck, 4 x 4, 3/4 Ton		155.60		171.16		
1 S.P. Crane, 4x4, 20 Ton		554.60		610.06	52.14	57.36
72 L.H., Daily Totals		$6897.40		$8896.42	$95.80	$123.56

Crew B-35

Crew No.	Hr.	Daily	Hr.	Daily	Bare Costs	Incl. O&P
1 Labor Foreman (outside)	$39.60	$316.80	$60.95	$487.60	$46.91	$71.60
1 Skilled Worker	48.65	389.20	75.15	601.20		
1 Welder (plumber)	58.70	469.60	88.65	709.20		
1 Laborer	37.60	300.80	57.85	462.80		
1 Equip. Oper. (crane)	51.70	413.60	78.45	627.60		
1 Equip. Oper. (oiler)	45.20	361.60	68.55	548.40		
1 Welder, Electric, 300 amp		57.70		63.47		
1 Hyd. Excavator, .75 C.Y.		654.80		720.28	14.84	16.33
48 L.H., Daily Totals		$2964.10		$4220.55	$61.75	$87.93

Crew B-35A

Crew No.	Hr.	Daily	Hr.	Daily	Bare Costs	Incl. O&P
1 Labor Foreman (outside)	$39.60	$316.80	$60.95	$487.60	$45.58	$69.64
2 Laborers	37.60	601.60	57.85	925.60		
1 Skilled Worker	48.65	389.20	75.15	601.20		
1 Welder (plumber)	58.70	469.60	88.65	709.20		
1 Equip. Oper. (crane)	51.70	413.60	78.45	627.60		
1 Equip. Oper. (oiler)	45.20	361.60	68.55	548.40		
1 Welder, Gas Engine, 300 amp		145.85		160.44		
1 Crawler Crane, 75 Ton		1459.00		1604.90	28.66	31.52
56 L.H., Daily Totals		$4157.25		$5664.94	$74.24	$101.16

Crew B-36

Crew No.	Hr.	Daily	Hr.	Daily	Bare Costs	Incl. O&P
1 Labor Foreman (outside)	$39.60	$316.80	$60.95	$487.60	$43.20	$66.03
2 Laborers	37.60	601.60	57.85	925.60		
2 Equip. Oper. (medium)	50.60	809.60	76.75	1228.00		
1 Dozer, 200 H.P.		1387.00		1525.70		
1 Aggregate Spreader		39.60		43.56		
1 Tandem Roller, 10 Ton		236.80		260.48	41.59	45.74
40 L.H., Daily Totals		$3391.40		$4470.94	$84.78	$111.77

Crew B-36A

Crew No.	Hr.	Daily	Hr.	Daily	Bare Costs	Incl. O&P
1 Labor Foreman (outside)	$39.60	$316.80	$60.95	$487.60	$45.31	$69.09
2 Laborers	37.60	601.60	57.85	925.60		
4 Equip. Oper. (medium)	50.60	1619.20	76.75	2456.00		
1 Dozer, 200 H.P.		1387.00		1525.70		
1 Aggregate Spreader		39.60		43.56		
1 Tandem Roller, 10 Ton		236.80		260.48		
1 Roller, Pneum. Whl., 12 Ton		344.40		378.84	35.85	39.44
56 L.H., Daily Totals		$4545.40		$6077.78	$81.17	$108.53

Crew B-36B

Crew No.	Hr.	Daily	Hr.	Daily	Bare Costs	Incl. O&P
1 Labor Foreman (outside)	$39.60	$316.80	$60.95	$487.60	$44.66	$68.03
2 Laborers	37.60	601.60	57.85	925.60		
4 Equip. Oper. (medium)	50.60	1619.20	76.75	2456.00		
1 Truck Driver (heavy)	40.05	320.40	60.55	484.40		
1 Grader, 30,000 Lbs.		736.20		809.82		
1 F.E. Loader, Crl. 1.5 C.Y.		629.80		692.78		
1 Dozer, 300 H.P.		1897.00		2086.70		
1 Roller, Vibratory, 25 Ton		687.40		756.14		
1 Truck Tractor, 6x4, 450 H.P.		727.40		800.14		
1 Water Tank Trailer, 5000 Gal.		141.00		155.10	75.29	82.82
64 L.H., Daily Totals		$7676.80		$9654.28	$119.95	$150.85

Crew B-36C

Crew No.	Hr.	Daily	Hr.	Daily	Bare Costs	Incl. O&P
1 Labor Foreman (outside)	$39.60	$316.80	$60.95	$487.60	$46.29	$70.35
3 Equip. Oper. (medium)	50.60	1214.40	76.75	1842.00		
1 Truck Driver (heavy)	40.05	320.40	60.55	484.40		
1 Grader, 30,000 Lbs.		736.20		809.82		
1 Dozer, 300 H.P.		1897.00		2086.70		
1 Roller, Vibratory, 25 Ton		687.40		756.14		
1 Truck Tractor, 6x4, 450 H.P.		727.40		800.14		
1 Water Tank Trailer, 5000 Gal.		141.00		155.10	104.72	115.20
40 L.H., Daily Totals		$6040.60		$7421.90	$151.01	$185.55

Crew B-36D

Crew No.	Hr.	Daily	Hr.	Daily	Bare Costs	Incl. O&P
1 Labor Foreman (outside)	$39.60	$316.80	$60.95	$487.60	$47.85	$72.80
3 Equip. Oper. (medium)	50.60	1214.40	76.75	1842.00		
1 Grader, 30,000 Lbs.		736.20		809.82		
1 Dozer, 300 H.P.		1897.00		2086.70		
1 Roller, Vibratory, 25 Ton		687.40		756.14	103.77	114.15
32 L.H., Daily Totals		$4851.80		$5982.26	$151.62	$186.95

Crew B-37

Crew No.	Hr.	Daily	Hr.	Daily	Bare Costs	Incl. O&P
1 Labor Foreman (outside)	$39.60	$316.80	$60.95	$487.60	$39.77	$61.02
4 Laborers	37.60	1203.20	57.85	1851.20		
1 Equip. Oper. (light)	48.60	388.80	73.75	590.00		
1 Tandem Roller, 5 Ton		157.40		173.14	3.28	3.61
48 L.H., Daily Totals		$2066.20		$3101.94	$43.05	$64.62

Crew B-37A

Crew No.	Hr.	Daily	Hr.	Daily	Bare Costs	Incl. O&P
2 Laborers	$37.60	$601.60	$57.85	$925.60	$38.10	$58.27
1 Truck Driver (light)	39.10	312.80	59.10	472.80		
1 Flatbed Truck, Gas, 1.5 Ton		245.40		269.94		
1 Tar Kettle, T.M.		132.00		145.20	15.73	17.30
24 L.H., Daily Totals		$1291.80		$1813.54	$53.83	$75.56

Crew B-37B

Crew No.	Hr.	Daily	Hr.	Daily	Bare Costs	Incl. O&P
3 Laborers	$37.60	$902.40	$57.85	$1388.40	$37.98	$58.16
1 Truck Driver (light)	39.10	312.80	59.10	472.80		
1 Flatbed Truck, Gas, 1.5 Ton		245.40		269.94		
1 Tar Kettle, T.M.		132.00		145.20	11.79	12.97
32 L.H., Daily Totals		$1592.60		$2276.34	$49.77	$71.14

Crew No.	Bare Costs Hr.	Daily	Incl. Subs O&P Hr.	Daily	Bare Costs	Incl. O&P
Crew B-37C	Hr.	Daily	Hr.	Daily	Bare Costs	Incl. O&P
2 Laborers	$37.60	$601.60	$57.85	$925.60	$38.35	$58.48
2 Truck Drivers (light)	39.10	625.60	59.10	945.60		
2 Flatbed Trucks, Gas, 1.5 Ton		490.80		539.88		
1 Tar Kettle, T.M.		132.00		145.20	19.46	21.41
32 L.H., Daily Totals		$1850.00		$2556.28	$57.81	$79.88
Crew B-37D	Hr.	Daily	Hr.	Daily	Bare Costs	Incl. O&P
1 Laborer	$37.60	$300.80	$57.85	$462.80	$38.35	$58.48
1 Truck Driver (light)	39.10	312.80	59.10	472.80		
1 Pickup Truck, 3/4 Ton		144.20		158.62	9.01	9.91
16 L.H., Daily Totals		$757.80		$1094.22	$47.36	$68.39
Crew B-37E	Hr.	Daily	Hr.	Daily	Bare Costs	Incl. O&P
3 Laborers	$37.60	$902.40	$57.85	$1388.40	$41.46	$63.18
1 Equip. Oper. (light)	48.60	388.80	73.75	590.00		
1 Equip. Oper. (medium)	50.60	404.80	76.75	614.00		
2 Truck Drivers (light)	39.10	625.60	59.10	945.60		
4 Barrels w/ Flasher		13.60		14.96		
1 Concrete Saw		167.40		184.14		
1 Rotary Hammer Drill		23.75		26.13		
1 Hammer Drill Bit		2.35		2.59		
1 Loader, Skid Steer, 30 H.P.		173.60		190.96		
1 Conc. Hammer Attach.		114.70		126.17		
1 Vibrating Plate, Gas, 18"		36.20		39.82		
2 Flatbed Trucks, Gas, 1.5 Ton		490.80		539.88	18.26	20.08
56 L.H., Daily Totals		$3344.00		$4662.64	$59.71	$83.26
Crew B-37F	Hr.	Daily	Hr.	Daily	Bare Costs	Incl. O&P
3 Laborers	$37.60	$902.40	$57.85	$1388.40	$37.98	$58.16
1 Truck Driver (light)	39.10	312.80	59.10	472.80		
4 Barrels w/ Flasher		13.60		14.96		
1 Concrete Mixer, 10 C.F.		172.40		189.64		
1 Air Compressor, 60 cfm		137.40		151.14		
1 -50' Air Hose, 3/4"		3.25		3.58		
1 Spade (Chipper)		7.60		8.36		
1 Flatbed Truck, Gas, 1.5 Ton		245.40		269.94	18.11	19.93
32 L.H., Daily Totals		$1794.85		$2498.82	$56.09	$78.09
Crew B-37G	Hr.	Daily	Hr.	Daily	Bare Costs	Incl. O&P
1 Labor Foreman (outside)	$39.60	$316.80	$60.95	$487.60	$39.77	$61.02
4 Laborers	37.60	1203.20	57.85	1851.20		
1 Equip. Oper. (light)	48.60	388.80	73.75	590.00		
1 Berm Machine		296.80		326.48		
1 Tandem Roller, 5 Ton		157.40		173.14	9.46	10.41
48 L.H., Daily Totals		$2363.00		$3428.42	$49.23	$71.43
Crew B-37H	Hr.	Daily	Hr.	Daily	Bare Costs	Incl. O&P
1 Labor Foreman (outside)	$39.60	$316.80	$60.95	$487.60	$39.77	$61.02
4 Laborers	37.60	1203.20	57.85	1851.20		
1 Equip. Oper. (light)	48.60	388.80	73.75	590.00		
1 Tandem Roller, 5 Ton		157.40		173.14		
1 Flatbed Trucks, Gas, 1.5 Ton		245.40		269.94		
1 Tar Kettle, T.M.		132.00		145.20	11.14	12.26
48 L.H., Daily Totals		$2443.60		$3517.08	$50.91	$73.27

Crew No.	Bare Costs Hr.	Daily	Incl. Subs O&P Hr.	Daily	Bare Costs	Incl. O&P
Crew B-37I	Hr.	Daily	Hr.	Daily	Bare Costs	Incl. O&P
3 Laborers	$37.60	$902.40	$57.85	$1388.40	$41.46	$63.18
1 Equip. Oper. (light)	48.60	388.80	73.75	590.00		
1 Equip. Oper. (medium)	50.60	404.80	76.75	614.00		
2 Truck Drivers (light)	39.10	625.60	59.10	945.60		
4 Barrels w/ Flasher		13.60		14.96		
1 Concrete Saw		167.40		184.14		
1 Rotary Hammer Drill		23.75		26.13		
1 Hammer Drill Bit		2.35		2.59		
1 Air Compressor, 60 cfm		137.40		151.14		
1 -50' Air Hose, 3/4"		3.25		3.58		
1 Spade (Chipper)		7.60		8.36		
1 Loader, Skid Steer, 30 H.P.		173.60		190.96		
1 Conc. Hammer Attach.		114.70		126.17		
1 Concrete Mixer, 10 C.F.		172.40		189.64		
1 Vibrating Plate, Gas, 18"		36.20		39.82		
2 Flatbed Trucks, Gas, 1.5 Ton		490.80		539.88	23.98	26.38
56 L.H., Daily Totals		$3664.65		$5015.35	$65.44	$89.56
Crew B-37J	Hr.	Daily	Hr.	Daily	Bare Costs	Incl. O&P
1 Labor Foreman (outside)	$39.60	$316.80	$60.95	$487.60	$39.77	$61.02
4 Laborers	37.60	1203.20	57.85	1851.20		
1 Equip. Oper. (light)	48.60	388.80	73.75	590.00		
1 Air Compressor, 60 cfm		137.40		151.14		
1 -50' Air Hose, 3/4"		3.25		3.58		
2 Concrete Mixer, 10 C.F.		344.80		379.28		
2 Flatbed Trucks, Gas, 1.5 Ton		490.80		539.88		
1 Shot Blaster, 20"		214.00		235.40	24.80	27.28
48 L.H., Daily Totals		$3099.05		$4238.07	$64.56	$88.29
Crew B-37K	Hr.	Daily	Hr.	Daily	Bare Costs	Incl. O&P
1 Labor Foreman (outside)	$39.60	$316.80	$60.95	$487.60	$39.77	$61.02
4 Laborers	37.60	1203.20	57.85	1851.20		
1 Equip. Oper. (light)	48.60	388.80	73.75	590.00		
1 Air Compressor, 60 cfm		137.40		151.14		
1 -50' Air Hose, 3/4"		3.25		3.58		
2 Flatbed Trucks, Gas, 1.5 Ton		490.80		539.88		
1 Shot Blaster, 20"		214.00		235.40	17.61	19.37
48 L.H., Daily Totals		$2754.25		$3858.80	$57.38	$80.39
Crew B-38	Hr.	Daily	Hr.	Daily	Bare Costs	Incl. O&P
1 Labor Foreman (outside)	$39.60	$316.80	$60.95	$487.60	$42.80	$65.43
2 Laborers	37.60	601.60	57.85	925.60		
1 Equip. Oper. (light)	48.60	388.80	73.75	590.00		
1 Equip. Oper. (medium)	50.60	404.80	76.75	614.00		
1 Backhoe Loader, 48 H.P.		364.20		400.62		
1 Hyd. Hammer, (1200 lb.)		180.40		198.44		
1 F.E. Loader, W.M., 4 C.Y.		669.20		736.12		
1 Pvmt. Rem. Bucket		61.20		67.32	31.88	35.06
40 L.H., Daily Totals		$2987.00		$4019.70	$74.67	$100.49
Crew B-39	Hr.	Daily	Hr.	Daily	Bare Costs	Incl. O&P
1 Labor Foreman (outside)	$39.60	$316.80	$60.95	$487.60	$39.77	$61.02
4 Laborers	37.60	1203.20	57.85	1851.20		
1 Equip. Oper. (light)	48.60	388.80	73.75	590.00		
1 Air Compressor, 250 cfm		201.40		221.54		
2 Breakers, Pavement, 60 lb.		19.60		21.56		
2 -50' Air Hoses, 1.5"		11.60		12.76	4.85	5.33
48 L.H., Daily Totals		$2141.40		$3184.66	$44.61	$66.35

Crew No.	Bare Costs		Incl. Subs O&P		Cost Per Labor-Hour	
Crew B-40	Hr.	Daily	Hr.	Daily	Bare Costs	Incl. O&P
1 Pile Driver Foreman (outside)	$48.10	$384.80	$76.15	$609.20	$47.64	$74.20
4 Pile Drivers	46.10	1475.20	73.00	2336.00		
2 Equip. Oper. (crane)	51.70	827.20	78.45	1255.20		
1 Equip. Oper. (oiler)	45.20	361.60	68.55	548.40		
1 Crawler Crane, 40 Ton		1156.00		1271.60		
1 Vibratory Hammer & Gen.		2587.00		2845.70	58.48	64.33
64 L.H., Daily Totals		$6791.80		$8866.10	$106.12	$138.53
Crew B-40B	Hr.	Daily	Hr.	Daily	Bare Costs	Incl. O&P
1 Labor Foreman (outside)	$39.60	$316.80	$60.95	$487.60	$41.55	$63.58
3 Laborers	37.60	902.40	57.85	1388.40		
1 Equip. Oper. (crane)	51.70	413.60	78.45	627.60		
1 Equip. Oper. (oiler)	45.20	361.60	68.55	548.40		
1 Lattice Boom Crane, 40 Ton		1164.00		1280.40	24.25	26.68
48 L.H., Daily Totals		$3158.40		$4332.40	$65.80	$90.26
Crew B-41	Hr.	Daily	Hr.	Daily	Bare Costs	Incl. O&P
1 Labor Foreman (outside)	$39.60	$316.80	$60.95	$487.60	$38.95	$59.84
4 Laborers	37.60	1203.20	57.85	1851.20		
.25 Equip. Oper. (crane)	51.70	103.40	78.45	156.90		
.25 Equip. Oper. (oiler)	45.20	90.40	68.55	137.10		
.25 Crawler Crane, 40 Ton		289.00		317.90	6.57	7.22
44 L.H., Daily Totals		$2002.80		$2950.70	$45.52	$67.06
Crew B-42	Hr.	Daily	Hr.	Daily	Bare Costs	Incl. O&P
1 Labor Foreman (outside)	$39.60	$316.80	$60.95	$487.60	$42.44	$66.35
4 Laborers	37.60	1203.20	57.85	1851.20		
1 Equip. Oper. (crane)	51.70	413.60	78.45	627.60		
1 Equip. Oper. (oiler)	45.20	361.60	68.55	548.40		
1 Welder	52.65	421.20	91.45	731.60		
1 Hyd. Crane, 25 Ton		736.60		810.26		
1 Welder, Gas Engine, 300 amp		145.85		160.44		
1 Horz. Boring Csg. Mch.		474.80		522.28	21.21	23.33
64 L.H., Daily Totals		$4073.65		$5739.38	$63.65	$89.68
Crew B-43	Hr.	Daily	Hr.	Daily	Bare Costs	Incl. O&P
1 Labor Foreman (outside)	$39.60	$316.80	$60.95	$487.60	$41.55	$63.58
3 Laborers	37.60	902.40	57.85	1388.40		
1 Equip. Oper. (crane)	51.70	413.60	78.45	627.60		
1 Equip. Oper. (oiler)	45.20	361.60	68.55	548.40		
1 Drill Rig, Truck-Mounted		2542.00		2796.20	52.96	58.25
48 L.H., Daily Totals		$4536.40		$5848.20	$94.51	$121.84
Crew B-44	Hr.	Daily	Hr.	Daily	Bare Costs	Incl. O&P
1 Pile Driver Foreman (outside)	$48.10	$384.80	$76.15	$609.20	$46.69	$72.86
4 Pile Drivers	46.10	1475.20	73.00	2336.00		
2 Equip. Oper. (crane)	51.70	827.20	78.45	1255.20		
1 Laborer	37.60	300.80	57.85	462.80		
1 Crawler Crane, 40 Ton		1156.00		1271.60		
1 Lead, 60' High		74.80		82.28		
1 Hammer, Diesel, 15K ft.-lbs.		586.00		644.60	28.39	31.23
64 L.H., Daily Totals		$4804.80		$6661.68	$75.08	$104.09
Crew B-45	Hr.	Daily	Hr.	Daily	Bare Costs	Incl. O&P
1 Equip. Oper. (medium)	$50.60	$404.80	$76.75	$614.00	$45.33	$68.65
1 Truck Driver (heavy)	40.05	320.40	60.55	484.40		
1 Dist. Tanker, 3000 Gallon		305.60		336.16		
1 Truck Tractor, 6x4, 380 H.P.		599.80		659.78	56.59	62.25
16 L.H., Daily Totals		$1630.60		$2094.34	$101.91	$130.90

Crew No.	Bare Costs		Incl. Subs O&P		Cost Per Labor-Hour	
Crew B-46	Hr.	Daily	Hr.	Daily	Bare Costs	Incl. O&P
1 Pile Driver Foreman (outside)	$48.10	$384.80	$76.15	$609.20	$42.18	$65.95
2 Pile Drivers	46.10	737.60	73.00	1168.00		
3 Laborers	37.60	902.40	57.85	1388.40		
1 Chain Saw, Gas, 36" Long		45.00		49.50	.94	1.03
48 L.H., Daily Totals		$2069.80		$3215.10	$43.12	$66.98
Crew B-47	Hr.	Daily	Hr.	Daily	Bare Costs	Incl. O&P
1 Blast Foreman (outside)	$39.60	$316.80	$60.95	$487.60	$41.93	$64.18
1 Driller	37.60	300.80	57.85	462.80		
1 Equip. Oper. (light)	48.60	388.80	73.75	590.00		
1 Air Track Drill, 4"		1028.00		1130.80		
1 Air Compressor, 600 cfm		550.60		605.66		
2 -50' Air Hoses, 3"		29.80		32.78	67.02	73.72
24 L.H., Daily Totals		$2614.80		$3309.64	$108.95	$137.90
Crew B-47A	Hr.	Daily	Hr.	Daily	Bare Costs	Incl. O&P
1 Drilling Foreman (outside)	$39.60	$316.80	$60.95	$487.60	$45.50	$69.32
1 Equip. Oper. (heavy)	51.70	413.60	78.45	627.60		
1 Equip. Oper. (oiler)	45.20	361.60	68.55	548.40		
1 Air Track Drill, 5"		1243.00		1367.30	51.79	56.97
24 L.H., Daily Totals		$2335.00		$3030.90	$97.29	$126.29
Crew B-47C	Hr.	Daily	Hr.	Daily	Bare Costs	Incl. O&P
1 Laborer	$37.60	$300.80	$57.85	$462.80	$43.10	$65.80
1 Equip. Oper. (light)	48.60	388.80	73.75	590.00		
1 Air Compressor, 750 cfm		557.20		612.92		
2 -50' Air Hoses, 3"		29.80		32.78		
1 Air Track Drill, 4"		1028.00		1130.80	100.94	111.03
16 L.H., Daily Totals		$2304.60		$2829.30	$144.04	$176.83
Crew B-47E	Hr.	Daily	Hr.	Daily	Bare Costs	Incl. O&P
1 Labor Foreman (outside)	$39.60	$316.80	$60.95	$487.60	$38.10	$58.63
3 Laborers	37.60	902.40	57.85	1388.40		
1 Flatbed Truck, Gas, 3 Ton		303.20		333.52	9.47	10.42
32 L.H., Daily Totals		$1522.40		$2209.52	$47.58	$69.05
Crew B-47G	Hr.	Daily	Hr.	Daily	Bare Costs	Incl. O&P
1 Labor Foreman (outside)	$39.60	$316.80	$60.95	$487.60	$40.85	$62.60
2 Laborers	37.60	601.60	57.85	925.60		
1 Equip. Oper. (light)	48.60	388.80	73.75	590.00		
1 Air Track Drill, 4"		1028.00		1130.80		
1 Air Compressor, 600 cfm		550.60		605.66		
2 -50' Air Hoses, 3"		29.80		32.78		
1 Gunite Pump Rig		371.80		408.98	61.88	68.07
32 L.H., Daily Totals		$3287.40		$4181.42	$102.73	$130.67
Crew B-47H	Hr.	Daily	Hr.	Daily	Bare Costs	Incl. O&P
1 Skilled Worker Foreman (out)	$50.65	$405.20	$78.25	$626.00	$49.15	$75.92
3 Skilled Workers	48.65	1167.60	75.15	1803.60		
1 Flatbed Truck, Gas, 3 Ton		303.20		333.52	9.47	10.42
32 L.H., Daily Totals		$1876.00		$2763.12	$58.63	$86.35

For customer support on your Site Work & Landscape Cost Data, call 877.737.1594.

727

Crew No.	Bare Costs		Incl. Subs O&P		Cost Per Labor-Hour	

Crew B-48

Crew B-48	Hr.	Daily	Hr.	Daily	Bare Costs	Incl. O&P
1 Labor Foreman (outside)	$39.60	$316.80	$60.95	$487.60	$42.56	$65.04
3 Laborers	37.60	902.40	57.85	1388.40		
1 Equip. Oper. (crane)	51.70	413.60	78.45	627.60		
1 Equip. Oper. (oiler)	45.20	361.60	68.55	548.40		
1 Equip. Oper. (light)	48.60	388.80	73.75	590.00		
1 Centr. Water Pump, 6"		346.60		381.26		
1 -20' Suction Hose, 6"		11.50		12.65		
1 -50' Discharge Hose, 6"		6.10		6.71		
1 Drill Rig, Truck-Mounted		2542.00		2796.20	51.90	57.09
56 L.H., Daily Totals		$5289.40		$6838.82	$94.45	$122.12

Crew B-49

Crew B-49	Hr.	Daily	Hr.	Daily	Bare Costs	Incl. O&P
1 Labor Foreman (outside)	$39.60	$316.80	$60.95	$487.60	$44.27	$68.02
3 Laborers	37.60	902.40	57.85	1388.40		
2 Equip. Oper. (crane)	51.70	827.20	78.45	1255.20		
2 Equip. Oper. (oilers)	45.20	723.20	68.55	1096.80		
1 Equip. Oper. (light)	48.60	388.80	73.75	590.00		
2 Pile Drivers	46.10	737.60	73.00	1168.00		
1 Hyd. Crane, 25 Ton		736.60		810.26		
1 Centr. Water Pump, 6"		346.60		381.26		
1 -20' Suction Hose, 6"		11.50		12.65		
1 -50' Discharge Hose, 6"		6.10		6.71		
1 Drill Rig, Truck-Mounted		2542.00		2796.20	41.40	45.53
88 L.H., Daily Totals		$7538.80		$9993.08	$85.67	$113.56

Crew B-50

Crew B-50	Hr.	Daily	Hr.	Daily	Bare Costs	Incl. O&P
2 Pile Driver Foremen (outside)	$48.10	$769.60	$76.15	$1218.40	$45.30	$70.66
6 Pile Drivers	46.10	2212.80	73.00	3504.00		
2 Equip. Oper. (crane)	51.70	827.20	78.45	1255.20		
1 Equip. Oper. (oiler)	45.20	361.60	68.55	548.40		
3 Laborers	37.60	902.40	57.85	1388.40		
1 Crawler Crane, 40 Ton		1156.00		1271.60		
1 Lead, 60' High		74.80		82.28		
1 Hammer, Diesel, 15K ft.-lbs.		586.00		644.60		
1 Air Compressor, 600 cfm		550.60		605.66		
2 -50' Air Hoses, 3"		29.80		32.78		
1 Chain Saw, Gas, 36" Long		45.00		49.50	21.81	23.99
112 L.H., Daily Totals		$7515.80		$10600.82	$67.11	$94.65

Crew B-51

Crew B-51	Hr.	Daily	Hr.	Daily	Bare Costs	Incl. O&P
1 Labor Foreman (outside)	$39.60	$316.80	$60.95	$487.60	$38.18	$58.58
4 Laborers	37.60	1203.20	57.85	1851.20		
1 Truck Driver (light)	39.10	312.80	59.10	472.80		
1 Flatbed Truck, Gas, 1.5 Ton		245.40		269.94	5.11	5.62
48 L.H., Daily Totals		$2078.20		$3081.54	$43.30	$64.20

Crew B-52

Crew B-52	Hr.	Daily	Hr.	Daily	Bare Costs	Incl. O&P
1 Carpenter Foreman (outside)	$48.95	$391.60	$75.35	$602.80	$43.61	$66.75
1 Carpenter	46.95	375.60	72.25	578.00		
3 Laborers	37.60	902.40	57.85	1388.40		
1 Cement Finisher	45.00	360.00	66.65	533.20		
.5 Rodman (reinf.)	52.55	210.20	82.10	328.40		
.5 Equip. Oper. (medium)	50.60	202.40	76.75	307.00		
.5 Crawler Loader, 3 C.Y.		594.00		653.40	10.61	11.67
56 L.H., Daily Totals		$3036.20		$4391.20	$54.22	$78.41

Crew B-53

Crew B-53	Hr.	Daily	Hr.	Daily	Bare Costs	Incl. O&P
1 Equip. Oper. (light)	$48.60	$388.80	$73.75	$590.00	$48.60	$73.75
1 Trencher, Chain, 12 H.P.		68.00		74.80	8.50	9.35
8 L.H., Daily Totals		$456.80		$664.80	$57.10	$83.10

Crew B-54

Crew B-54	Hr.	Daily	Hr.	Daily	Bare Costs	Incl. O&P
1 Equip. Oper. (light)	$48.60	$388.80	$73.75	$590.00	$48.60	$73.75
1 Trencher, Chain, 40 H.P.		335.20		368.72	41.90	46.09
8 L.H., Daily Totals		$724.00		$958.72	$90.50	$119.84

Crew B-54A

Crew B-54A	Hr.	Daily	Hr.	Daily	Bare Costs	Incl. O&P
.17 Labor Foreman (outside)	$39.60	$53.86	$60.95	$82.89	$49.00	$74.45
1 Equipment Operator (med.)	50.60	404.80	76.75	614.00		
1 Wheel Trencher, 67 H.P.		1195.00		1314.50	127.67	140.44
9.36 L.H., Daily Totals		$1653.66		$2011.39	$176.67	$214.89

Crew B-54B

Crew B-54B	Hr.	Daily	Hr.	Daily	Bare Costs	Incl. O&P
.25 Labor Foreman (outside)	$39.60	$79.20	$60.95	$121.90	$48.40	$73.59
1 Equipment Operator (med.)	50.60	404.80	76.75	614.00		
1 Wheel Trencher, 150 H.P.		1890.00		2079.00	.189.00	207.90
10 L.H., Daily Totals		$2374.00		$2814.90	$237.40	$281.49

Crew B-54C

Crew B-54C	Hr.	Daily	Hr.	Daily	Bare Costs	Incl. O&P
1 Laborer	$37.60	$300.80	$57.85	$462.80	$44.10	$67.30
1 Equipment Operator (med.)	50.60	404.80	76.75	614.00		
1 Wheel Trencher, 67 H.P.		1195.00		1314.50	74.69	82.16
16 L.H., Daily Totals		$1900.60		$2391.30	$118.79	$149.46

Crew B-54D

Crew B-54D	Hr.	Daily	Hr.	Daily	Bare Costs	Incl. O&P
1 Laborer	$37.60	$300.80	$57.85	$462.80	$44.10	$67.30
1 Equipment Operator (med.)	50.60	404.80	76.75	614.00		
1 Rock Trencher, 6" Width		372.00		409.20	23.25	25.57
16 L.H., Daily Totals		$1077.60		$1486.00	$67.35	$92.88

Crew B-54E

Crew B-54E	Hr.	Daily	Hr.	Daily	Bare Costs	Incl. O&P
1 Laborer	$37.60	$300.80	$57.85	$462.80	$44.10	$67.30
1 Equipment Operator (med.)	50.60	404.80	76.75	614.00		
1 Rock Trencher, 18" Width		2575.00		2832.50	160.94	177.03
16 L.H., Daily Totals		$3280.60		$3909.30	$205.04	$244.33

Crew B-55

Crew B-55	Hr.	Daily	Hr.	Daily	Bare Costs	Incl. O&P
2 Laborers	$37.60	$601.60	$57.85	$925.60	$38.10	$58.27
1 Truck Driver (light)	39.10	312.80	59.10	472.80		
1 Truck-Mounted Earth Auger		779.20		857.12		
1 Flatbed Truck, Gas, 3 Ton		303.20		333.52	45.10	49.61
24 L.H., Daily Totals		$1996.80		$2589.04	$83.20	$107.88

Crew B-56

Crew B-56	Hr.	Daily	Hr.	Daily	Bare Costs	Incl. O&P
1 Laborer	$37.60	$300.80	$57.85	$462.80	$43.10	$65.80
1 Equip. Oper. (light)	48.60	388.80	73.75	590.00		
1 Air Track Drill, 4"		1028.00		1130.80		
1 Air Compressor, 600 cfm		550.60		605.66		
1 -50' Air Hose, 3"		14.90		16.39	99.59	109.55
16 L.H., Daily Totals		$2283.10		$2805.65	$142.69	$175.35

For customer support on your Site Work & Landscape Cost Data, call 877.737.1594.

Crew B-57	Hr.	Daily	Hr.	Daily	Bare Costs	Incl. O&P
1 Labor Foreman (outside)	$39.60	$316.80	$60.95	$487.60	$43.38	$66.23
2 Laborers	37.60	601.60	57.85	925.60		
1 Equip. Oper. (crane)	51.70	413.60	78.45	627.60		
1 Equip. Oper. (light)	48.60	388.80	73.75	590.00		
1 Equip. Oper. (oiler)	45.20	361.60	68.55	548.40		
1 Crawler Crane, 25 Ton		1150.00		1265.00		
1 Clamshell Bucket, 1 C.Y.		47.80		52.58		
1 Centr. Water Pump, 6"		346.60		381.26		
1 -20' Suction Hose, 6"		11.50		12.65		
20 -50' Discharge Hoses, 6"		122.00		134.20	34.96	38.45
48 L.H., Daily Totals		$3760.30		$5024.89	$78.34	$104.69

Crew B-58	Hr.	Daily	Hr.	Daily	Bare Costs	Incl. O&P
2 Laborers	$37.60	$601.60	$57.85	$925.60	$41.27	$63.15
1 Equip. Oper. (light)	48.60	388.80	73.75	590.00		
1 Backhoe Loader, 48 H.P.		364.20		400.62		
1 Small Helicopter, w/ Pilot		2790.00		3069.00	131.43	144.57
24 L.H., Daily Totals		$4144.60		$4985.22	$172.69	$207.72

Crew B-59	Hr.	Daily	Hr.	Daily	Bare Costs	Incl. O&P
1 Truck Driver (heavy)	$40.05	$320.40	$60.55	$484.40	$40.05	$60.55
1 Truck Tractor, 220 H.P.		359.60		395.56		
1 Water Tank Trailer, 5000 Gal.		141.00		155.10	62.58	68.83
8 L.H., Daily Totals		$821.00		$1035.06	$102.63	$129.38

Crew B-59A	Hr.	Daily	Hr.	Daily	Bare Costs	Incl. O&P
2 Laborers	$37.60	$601.60	$57.85	$925.60	$38.42	$58.75
1 Truck Driver (heavy)	40.05	320.40	60.55	484.40		
1 Water Tank Trailer, 5000 Gal.		141.00		155.10		
1 Truck Tractor, 220 H.P.		359.60		395.56	20.86	22.94
24 L.H., Daily Totals		$1422.60		$1960.66	$59.27	$81.69

Crew B-60	Hr.	Daily	Hr.	Daily	Bare Costs	Incl. O&P
1 Labor Foreman (outside)	$39.60	$316.80	$60.95	$487.60	$44.13	$67.31
2 Laborers	37.60	601.60	57.85	925.60		
1 Equip. Oper. (crane)	51.70	413.60	78.45	627.60		
2 Equip. Oper. (light)	48.60	777.60	73.75	1180.00		
1 Equip. Oper. (oiler)	45.20	361.60	68.55	548.40		
1 Crawler Crane, 40 Ton		1156.00		1271.60		
1 Lead, 60' High		74.80		82.28		
1 Hammer, Diesel, 15K ft.-lbs.		586.00		644.60		
1 Backhoe Loader, 48 H.P.		364.20		400.62	38.95	42.84
56 L.H., Daily Totals		$4652.20		$6168.30	$83.08	$110.15

Crew B-61	Hr.	Daily	Hr.	Daily	Bare Costs	Incl. O&P
1 Labor Foreman (outside)	$39.60	$316.80	$60.95	$487.60	$40.20	$61.65
3 Laborers	37.60	902.40	57.85	1388.40		
1 Equip. Oper. (light)	48.60	388.80	73.75	590.00		
1 Cement Mixer, 2 C.Y.		194.20		213.62		
1 Air Compressor, 160 cfm		156.40		172.04	8.77	9.64
40 L.H., Daily Totals		$1958.60		$2851.66	$48.97	$71.29

Crew B-62	Hr.	Daily	Hr.	Daily	Bare Costs	Incl. O&P
2 Laborers	$37.60	$601.60	$57.85	$925.60	$41.27	$63.15
1 Equip. Oper. (light)	48.60	388.80	73.75	590.00		
1 Loader, Skid Steer, 30 H.P.		173.60		190.96	7.23	7.96
24 L.H., Daily Totals		$1164.00		$1706.56	$48.50	$71.11

Crew B-62A	Hr.	Daily	Hr.	Daily	Bare Costs	Incl. O&P
2 Laborers	$37.60	$601.60	$57.85	$925.60	$41.27	$63.15
1 Equip. Oper. (light)	48.60	388.80	73.75	590.00		
1 Loader, Skid Steer, 30 H.P.		173.60		190.96		
1 Trencher Attachment		58.30		64.13	9.66	10.63
24 L.H., Daily Totals		$1222.30		$1770.69	$50.93	$73.78

Crew B-63	Hr.	Daily	Hr.	Daily	Bare Costs	Incl. O&P
4 Laborers	$37.60	$1203.20	$57.85	$1851.20	$39.80	$61.03
1 Equip. Oper. (light)	48.60	388.80	73.75	590.00		
1 Loader, Skid Steer, 30 H.P.		173.60		190.96	4.34	4.77
40 L.H., Daily Totals		$1765.60		$2632.16	$44.14	$65.80

Crew B-63B	Hr.	Daily	Hr.	Daily	Bare Costs	Incl. O&P
1 Labor Foreman (inside)	$38.10	$304.80	$58.65	$469.20	$40.48	$62.02
2 Laborers	37.60	601.60	57.85	925.60		
1 Equip. Oper. (light)	48.60	388.80	73.75	590.00		
1 Loader, Skid Steer, 78 H.P.		318.60		350.46	9.96	10.95
32 L.H., Daily Totals		$1613.80		$2335.26	$50.43	$72.98

Crew B-64	Hr.	Daily	Hr.	Daily	Bare Costs	Incl. O&P
1 Laborer	$37.60	$300.80	$57.85	$462.80	$38.35	$58.48
1 Truck Driver (light)	39.10	312.80	59.10	472.80		
1 Power Mulcher (small)		151.80		166.98		
1 Flatbed Truck, Gas, 1.5 Ton		245.40		269.94	24.82	27.31
16 L.H., Daily Totals		$1010.80		$1372.52	$63.17	$85.78

Crew B-65	Hr.	Daily	Hr.	Daily	Bare Costs	Incl. O&P
1 Laborer	$37.60	$300.80	$57.85	$462.80	$38.35	$58.48
1 Truck Driver (light)	39.10	312.80	59.10	472.80		
1 Power Mulcher (Large)		319.40		351.34		
1 Flatbed Truck, Gas, 1.5 Ton		245.40		269.94	35.30	38.83
16 L.H., Daily Totals		$1178.40		$1556.88	$73.65	$97.31

Crew B-66	Hr.	Daily	Hr.	Daily	Bare Costs	Incl. O&P
1 Equip. Oper. (light)	$48.60	$388.80	$73.75	$590.00	$48.60	$73.75
1 Loader-Backhoe, 40 H.P.		263.20		289.52	32.90	36.19
8 L.H., Daily Totals		$652.00		$879.52	$81.50	$109.94

Crew B-67	Hr.	Daily	Hr.	Daily	Bare Costs	Incl. O&P
1 Millwright	$49.15	$393.20	$72.35	$578.80	$48.88	$73.05
1 Equip. Oper. (light)	48.60	388.80	73.75	590.00		
1 Forklift, R/T, 4,000 Lb.		311.20		342.32	19.45	21.40
16 L.H., Daily Totals		$1093.20		$1511.12	$68.33	$94.44

Crew B-67B	Hr.	Daily	Hr.	Daily	Bare Costs	Incl. O&P
1 Millwright Foreman (inside)	$49.65	$397.20	$73.10	$584.80	$49.40	$72.72
1 Millwright	49.15	393.20	72.35	578.80		
16 L.H., Daily Totals		$790.40		$1163.60	$49.40	$72.72

Crew B-68	Hr.	Daily	Hr.	Daily	Bare Costs	Incl. O&P
2 Millwrights	$49.15	$786.40	$72.35	$1157.60	$48.97	$72.82
1 Equip. Oper. (light)	48.60	388.80	73.75	590.00		
1 Forklift, R/T, 4,000 Lb.		311.20		342.32	12.97	14.26
24 L.H., Daily Totals		$1486.40		$2089.92	$61.93	$87.08

Crew B-68A	Hr.	Daily	Hr.	Daily	Bare Costs	Incl. O&P
1 Millwright Foreman (inside)	$49.65	$397.20	$73.10	$584.80	$49.32	$72.60
2 Millwrights	49.15	786.40	72.35	1157.60		
1 Forklift, 8,000 Lb.		185.20		203.72	7.72	8.49
24 L.H., Daily Totals		$1368.80		$1946.12	$57.03	$81.09

Crew No.	Bare Costs		Incl. Subs O&P		Cost Per Labor-Hour	

Crew B-68B	Hr.	Daily	Hr.	Daily	Bare Costs	Incl. O&P
1 Millwright Foreman (inside)	$49.65	$397.20	$73.10	$584.80	$53.54	$79.86
2 Millwrights	49.15	786.40	72.35	1157.60		
2 Electricians	54.70	875.20	81.95	1311.20		
2 Plumbers	58.70	939.20	88.65	1418.40		
1 Forklift, 5,000 Lb.		331.80		364.98	5.92	6.52
56 L.H., Daily Totals		$3329.80		$4836.98	$59.46	$86.37

Crew B-68C	Hr.	Daily	Hr.	Daily	Bare Costs	Incl. O&P
1 Millwright Foreman (inside)	$49.65	$397.20	$73.10	$584.80	$53.05	$79.01
1 Millwright	49.15	393.20	72.35	578.80		
1 Electrician	54.70	437.60	81.95	655.60		
1 Plumber	58.70	469.60	88.65	709.20		
1 Forklift, 5,000 Lb.		331.80		364.98	10.37	11.41
32 L.H., Daily Totals		$2029.40		$2893.38	$63.42	$90.42

Crew B-68D	Hr.	Daily	Hr.	Daily	Bare Costs	Incl. O&P
1 Labor Foreman (inside)	$38.10	$304.80	$58.65	$469.20	$41.43	$63.42
1 Laborer	37.60	300.80	57.85	462.80		
1 Equip. Oper. (light)	48.60	388.80	73.75	590.00		
1 Forklift, 5,000 Lb.		331.80		364.98	13.82	15.21
24 L.H., Daily Totals		$1326.20		$1886.98	$55.26	$78.62

Crew B-68E	Hr.	Daily	Hr.	Daily	Bare Costs	Incl. O&P
1 Struc. Steel Foreman (inside)	$53.15	$425.20	$92.30	$738.40	$52.75	$91.62
3 Struc. Steel Workers	52.65	1263.60	91.45	2194.80		
1 Welder	52.65	421.20	91.45	731.60		
1 Forklift, 8,000 Lb.		185.20		203.72	4.63	5.09
40 L.H., Daily Totals		$2295.20		$3868.52	$57.38	$96.71

Crew B-68F	Hr.	Daily	Hr.	Daily	Bare Costs	Incl. O&P
1 Skilled Worker Foreman (out)	$50.65	$405.20	$78.25	$626.00	$49.32	$76.18
2 Skilled Workers	48.65	778.40	75.15	1202.40		
1 Forklift, 5,000 Lb.		331.80		364.98	13.82	15.21
24 L.H., Daily Totals		$1515.40		$2193.38	$63.14	$91.39

Crew B-68G	Hr.	Daily	Hr.	Daily	Bare Costs	Incl. O&P
2 Structural Steel Workers	$52.65	$842.40	$91.45	$1463.20	$52.65	$91.45
1 Forklift, 5,000 Lb.		331.80		364.98	20.74	22.81
16 L.H., Daily Totals		$1174.20		$1828.18	$73.39	$114.26

Crew B-69	Hr.	Daily	Hr.	Daily	Bare Costs	Incl. O&P
1 Labor Foreman (outside)	$39.60	$316.80	$60.95	$487.60	$41.55	$63.58
3 Laborers	37.60	902.40	57.85	1388.40		
1 Equip. Oper. (crane)	51.70	413.60	78.45	627.60		
1 Equip. Oper. (oiler)	45.20	361.60	68.55	548.40		
1 Hyd. Crane, 80 Ton		1625.00		1787.50	33.85	37.24
48 L.H., Daily Totals		$3619.40		$4839.50	$75.40	$100.82

Crew B-69A	Hr.	Daily	Hr.	Daily	Bare Costs	Incl. O&P
1 Labor Foreman (outside)	$39.60	$316.80	$60.95	$487.60	$41.33	$62.98
3 Laborers	37.60	902.40	57.85	1388.40		
1 Equip. Oper. (medium)	50.60	404.80	76.75	614.00		
1 Concrete Finisher	45.00	360.00	66.65	533.20		
1 Curb/Gutter Paver, 2-Track		997.60		1097.36	20.78	22.86
48 L.H., Daily Totals		$2981.60		$4120.56	$62.12	$85.84

Crew B-69B	Hr.	Daily	Hr.	Daily	Bare Costs	Incl. O&P
1 Labor Foreman (outside)	$39.60	$316.80	$60.95	$487.60	$41.33	$62.98
3 Laborers	37.60	902.40	57.85	1388.40		
1 Equip. Oper. (medium)	50.60	404.80	76.75	614.00		
1 Cement Finisher	45.00	360.00	66.65	533.20		
1 Curb/Gutter Paver, 4-Track		776.00		853.60	16.17	17.78
48 L.H., Daily Totals		$2760.00		$3876.80	$57.50	$80.77

Crew B-70	Hr.	Daily	Hr.	Daily	Bare Costs	Incl. O&P
1 Labor Foreman (outside)	$39.60	$316.80	$60.95	$487.60	$43.46	$66.39
3 Laborers	37.60	902.40	57.85	1388.40		
3 Equip. Oper. (medium)	50.60	1214.40	76.75	1842.00		
1 Grader, 30,000 Lbs.		736.20		809.82		
1 Ripper, Beam & 1 Shank		84.20		92.62		
1 Road Sweeper, S.P., 8' wide		662.40		728.64		
1 F.E. Loader, W.M., 1.5 C.Y.		378.40		416.24	33.24	36.56
56 L.H., Daily Totals		$4294.80		$5765.32	$76.69	$102.95

Crew B-70A	Hr.	Daily	Hr.	Daily	Bare Costs	Incl. O&P
1 Laborer	$37.60	$300.80	$57.85	$462.80	$48.00	$72.97
4 Equip. Oper. (medium)	50.60	1619.20	76.75	2456.00		
1 Grader, 40,000 Lbs.		1174.00		1291.40		
1 F.E. Loader, W.M., 2.5 C.Y.		519.80		571.78		
1 Dozer, 80 H.P.		472.40		519.64		
1 Roller, Pneum. Whl., 12 Ton		344.40		378.84	62.77	69.04
40 L.H., Daily Totals		$4430.60		$5680.46	$110.77	$142.01

Crew B-71	Hr.	Daily	Hr.	Daily	Bare Costs	Incl. O&P
1 Labor Foreman (outside)	$39.60	$316.80	$60.95	$487.60	$43.46	$66.39
3 Laborers	37.60	902.40	57.85	1388.40		
3 Equip. Oper. (medium)	50.60	1214.40	76.75	1842.00		
1 Pvmt. Profiler, 750 H.P.		5805.00		6385.50		
1 Road Sweeper, S.P., 8' wide		662.40		728.64		
1 F.E. Loader, W.M., 1.5 C.Y.		378.40		416.24	122.25	134.47
56 L.H., Daily Totals		$9279.40		$11248.38	$165.70	$200.86

Crew B-72	Hr.	Daily	Hr.	Daily	Bare Costs	Incl. O&P
1 Labor Foreman (outside)	$39.60	$316.80	$60.95	$487.60	$44.35	$67.69
3 Laborers	37.60	902.40	57.85	1388.40		
4 Equip. Oper. (medium)	50.60	1619.20	76.75	2456.00		
1 Pvmt. Profiler, 750 H.P.		5805.00		6385.50		
1 Hammermill, 250 H.P.		1879.00		2066.90		
1 Windrow Loader		1227.00		1349.70		
1 Mix Paver 165 H.P.		2147.00		2361.70		
1 Roller, Pneum. Whl., 12 Ton		344.40		378.84	178.16	195.98
64 L.H., Daily Totals		$14240.80		$16874.64	$222.51	$263.67

Crew B-73	Hr.	Daily	Hr.	Daily	Bare Costs	Incl. O&P
1 Labor Foreman (outside)	$39.60	$316.80	$60.95	$487.60	$45.98	$70.05
2 Laborers	37.60	601.60	57.85	925.60		
5 Equip. Oper. (medium)	50.60	2024.00	76.75	3070.00		
1 Road Mixer, 310 H.P.		1929.00		2121.90		
1 Tandem Roller, 10 Ton		236.80		260.48		
1 Hammermill, 250 H.P.		1879.00		2066.90		
1 Grader, 30,000 Lbs.		736.20		809.82		
.5 F.E. Loader, W.M., 1.5 C.Y.		189.20		208.12		
.5 Truck Tractor, 220 H.P.		179.80		197.78		
.5 Water Tank Trailer, 5000 Gal.		70.50		77.55	81.57	89.73
64 L.H., Daily Totals		$8162.90		$10225.75	$127.55	$159.78

For customer support on your Site Work & Landscape Cost Data, call 877.737.1594.

Crew No.	Bare Costs		Incl. Subs O&P		Cost Per Labor-Hour	

Crew B-74

Crew B-74	Hr.	Daily	Hr.	Daily	Bare Costs	Incl. O&P
1 Labor Foreman (outside)	$39.60	$316.80	$60.95	$487.60	$44.96	$68.36
1 Laborer	37.60	300.80	57.85	462.80		
4 Equip. Oper. (medium)	50.60	1619.20	76.75	2456.00		
2 Truck Drivers (heavy)	40.05	640.80	60.55	968.80		
1 Grader, 30,000 Lbs.		736.20		809.82		
1 Ripper, Beam & 1 Shank		84.20		92.62		
2 Stabilizers, 310 H.P.		3596.00		3955.60		
1 Flatbed Truck, Gas, 3 Ton		303.20		333.52		
1 Chem. Spreader, Towed		52.40		57.64		
1 Roller, Vibratory, 25 Ton		687.40		756.14		
1 Water Tank Trailer, 5000 Gal.		141.00		155.10		
1 Truck Tractor, 220 H.P.		359.60		395.56	93.13	102.44
64 L.H., Daily Totals		$8837.60		$10931.20	$138.09	$170.80

Crew B-75

Crew B-75	Hr.	Daily	Hr.	Daily	Bare Costs	Incl. O&P
1 Labor Foreman (outside)	$39.60	$316.80	$60.95	$487.60	$45.66	$69.48
1 Laborer	37.60	300.80	57.85	462.80		
4 Equip. Oper. (medium)	50.60	1619.20	76.75	2456.00		
1 Truck Driver (heavy)	40.05	320.40	60.55	484.40		
1 Grader, 30,000 Lbs.		736.20		809.82		
1 Ripper, Beam & 1 Shank		84.20		92.62		
2 Stabilizers, 310 H.P.		3596.00		3955.60		
1 Dist. Tanker, 3000 Gallon		305.60		336.16		
1 Truck Tractor, 6x4, 380 H.P.		599.80		659.78		
1 Roller, Vibratory, 25 Ton		687.40		756.14	107.31	118.04
56 L.H., Daily Totals		$8566.40		$10500.92	$152.97	$187.52

Crew B-76

Crew B-76	Hr.	Daily	Hr.	Daily	Bare Costs	Incl. O&P
1 Dock Builder Foreman (outside)	$48.10	$384.80	$76.15	$609.20	$47.47	$74.07
5 Dock Builders	46.10	1844.00	73.00	2920.00		
2 Equip. Oper. (crane)	51.70	827.20	78.45	1255.20		
1 Equip. Oper. (oiler)	45.20	361.60	68.55	548.40		
1 Crawler Crane, 50 Ton		1294.00		1423.40		
1 Barge, 400 Ton		776.00		853.60		
1 Hammer, Diesel, 15K ft.-lbs.		586.00		644.60		
1 Lead, 60' High		74.80		82.28		
1 Air Compressor, 600 cfm		550.60		605.66		
2 -50' Air Hoses, 3"		29.80		32.78	45.99	50.59
72 L.H., Daily Totals		$6728.80		$8975.12	$93.46	$124.65

Crew B-76A

Crew B-76A	Hr.	Daily	Hr.	Daily	Bare Costs	Incl. O&P
1 Labor Foreman (outside)	$39.60	$316.80	$60.95	$487.60	$40.56	$62.15
5 Laborers	37.60	1504.00	57.85	2314.00		
1 Equip. Oper. (crane)	51.70	413.60	78.45	627.60		
1 Equip. Oper. (oiler)	45.20	361.60	68.55	548.40		
1 Crawler Crane, 50 Ton		1294.00		1423.40		
1 Barge, 400 Ton		776.00		853.60	32.34	35.58
64 L.H., Daily Totals		$4666.00		$6254.60	$72.91	$97.73

Crew B-77

Crew B-77	Hr.	Daily	Hr.	Daily	Bare Costs	Incl. O&P
1 Labor Foreman (outside)	$39.60	$316.80	$60.95	$487.60	$38.30	$58.72
3 Laborers	37.60	902.40	57.85	1388.40		
1 Truck Driver (light)	39.10	312.80	59.10	472.80		
1 Crack Cleaner, 25 H.P.		61.60		67.76		
1 Crack Filler, Trailer Mtd.		202.00		222.20		
1 Flatbed Truck, Gas, 3 Ton		303.20		333.52	14.17	15.59
40 L.H., Daily Totals		$2098.80		$2972.28	$52.47	$74.31

Crew No.	Bare Costs		Incl. Subs O&P		Cost Per Labor-Hour	

Crew B-78

Crew B-78	Hr.	Daily	Hr.	Daily	Bare Costs	Incl. O&P
1 Labor Foreman (outside)	$39.60	$316.80	$60.95	$487.60	$38.18	$58.58
4 Laborers	37.60	1203.20	57.85	1851.20		
1 Truck Driver (light)	39.10	312.80	59.10	472.80		
1 Paint Striper, S.P., 40 Gallon		151.40		166.54		
1 Flatbed Truck, Gas, 3 Ton		303.20		333.52		
1 Pickup Truck, 3/4 Ton		144.20		158.62	12.48	13.72
48 L.H., Daily Totals		$2431.60		$3470.28	$50.66	$72.30

Crew B-78A

Crew B-78A	Hr.	Daily	Hr.	Daily	Bare Costs	Incl. O&P
1 Equip. Oper. (light)	$48.60	$388.80	$73.75	$590.00	$48.60	$73.75
1 Line Rem. (Metal Balls) 115 H.P.		821.60		903.76	102.70	112.97
8 L.H., Daily Totals		$1210.40		$1493.76	$151.30	$186.72

Crew B-78B

Crew B-78B	Hr.	Daily	Hr.	Daily	Bare Costs	Incl. O&P
2 Laborers	$37.60	$601.60	$57.85	$925.60	$38.82	$59.62
.25 Equip. Oper. (light)	48.60	97.20	73.75	147.50		
1 Pickup Truck, 3/4 Ton		144.20		158.62		
1 Line Rem.,11 H.P.,Walk Behind		65.60		72.16		
.25 Road Sweeper, S.P., 8' wide		165.60		182.16	20.86	22.94
18 L.H., Daily Totals		$1074.20		$1486.04	$59.68	$82.56

Crew B-78C

Crew B-78C	Hr.	Daily	Hr.	Daily	Bare Costs	Incl. O&P
1 Labor Foreman (outside)	$39.60	$316.80	$60.95	$487.60	$38.18	$58.58
4 Laborers	37.60	1203.20	57.85	1851.20		
1 Truck Driver (light)	39.10	312.80	59.10	472.80		
1 Paint Striper, T.M., 120 Gal.		804.60		885.06		
1 Flatbed Truck, Gas, 3 Ton		303.20		333.52		
1 Pickup Truck, 3/4 Ton		144.20		158.62	26.08	28.69
48 L.H., Daily Totals		$3084.80		$4188.80	$64.27	$87.27

Crew B-78D

Crew B-78D	Hr.	Daily	Hr.	Daily	Bare Costs	Incl. O&P
2 Labor Foremen (outside)	$39.60	$633.60	$60.95	$975.20	$38.15	$58.59
7 Laborers	37.60	2105.60	57.85	3239.60		
1 Truck Driver (light)	39.10	312.80	59.10	472.80		
1 Paint Striper, T.M., 120 Gal.		804.60		885.06		
1 Flatbed Truck, Gas, 3 Ton		303.20		333.52		
3 Pickup Trucks, 3/4 Ton		432.60		475.86		
1 Air Compressor, 60 cfm		137.40		151.14		
1 -50' Air Hose, 3/4"		3.25		3.58		
1 Breakers, Pavement, 60 lb.		9.80		10.78	21.14	23.25
80 L.H., Daily Totals		$4742.85		$6547.53	$59.29	$81.84

Crew B-78E

Crew B-78E	Hr.	Daily	Hr.	Daily	Bare Costs	Incl. O&P
2 Labor Foremen (outside)	$39.60	$633.60	$60.95	$975.20	$38.06	$58.47
9 Laborers	37.60	2707.20	57.85	4165.20		
1 Truck Driver (light)	39.10	312.80	59.10	472.80		
1 Paint Striper, T.M., 120 Gal.		804.60		885.06		
1 Flatbed Truck, Gas, 3 Ton		303.20		333.52		
4 Pickup Trucks, 3/4 Ton		576.80		634.48		
2 Air Compressor, 60 cfm		274.80		302.28		
2 -50' Air Hose, 3/4"		6.50		7.15		
2 Breakers, Pavement, 60 lb.		19.60		21.56	20.68	22.75
96 L.H., Daily Totals		$5639.10		$7797.25	$58.74	$81.22

Crew B-78F

Crew No.	Bare Costs Hr.	Bare Costs Daily	Incl. Subs O&P Hr.	Incl. Subs O&P Daily	Cost Per Labor-Hour Bare Costs	Cost Per Labor-Hour Incl. O&P
2 Labor Foremen (outside)	$39.60	$633.60	$60.95	$975.20	$37.99	$58.38
11 Laborers	37.60	3308.80	57.85	5090.80		
1 Truck Driver (light)	39.10	312.80	59.10	472.80		
1 Paint Striper, T.M., 120 Gal.		804.60		885.06		
1 Flatbed Truck, Gas, 3 Ton		303.20		333.52		
7 Pickup Trucks, 3/4 Ton		1009.40		1110.34		
3 Air Compressor, 60 cfm		412.20		453.42		
3 -50' Air Hose, 3/4"		9.75		10.73		
3 Breakers, Pavement, 60 lb.		29.40		32.34	22.93	25.23
112 L.H., Daily Totals		$6823.75		$9364.20	$60.93	$83.61

Crew B-79

Crew No.	Bare Costs Hr.	Bare Costs Daily	Incl. Subs O&P Hr.	Incl. Subs O&P Daily	Cost Per Labor-Hour Bare Costs	Cost Per Labor-Hour Incl. O&P
1 Labor Foreman (outside)	$39.60	$316.80	$60.95	$487.60	$38.30	$58.72
3 Laborers	37.60	902.40	57.85	1388.40		
1 Truck Driver (light)	39.10	312.80	59.10	472.80		
1 Paint Striper, T.M., 120 Gal.		804.60		885.06		
1 Heating Kettle, 115 Gallon		81.00		89.10		
1 Flatbed Truck, Gas, 3 Ton		303.20		333.52		
2 Pickup Trucks, 3/4 Ton		288.40		317.24	36.93	40.62
40 L.H., Daily Totals		$3009.20		$3973.72	$75.23	$99.34

Crew B-79A

Crew No.	Bare Costs Hr.	Bare Costs Daily	Incl. Subs O&P Hr.	Incl. Subs O&P Daily	Cost Per Labor-Hour Bare Costs	Cost Per Labor-Hour Incl. O&P
1.5 Equip. Oper. (light)	$48.60	$583.20	$73.75	$885.00	$48.60	$73.75
.5 Line Remov. (Grinder) 115 H.P.		455.90		501.49		
1 Line Rem. (Metal Balls) 115 H.P.		821.60		903.76	106.46	117.10
12 L.H., Daily Totals		$1860.70		$2290.25	$155.06	$190.85

Crew B-79B

Crew No.	Bare Costs Hr.	Bare Costs Daily	Incl. Subs O&P Hr.	Incl. Subs O&P Daily	Cost Per Labor-Hour Bare Costs	Cost Per Labor-Hour Incl. O&P
1 Laborer	$37.60	$300.80	$57.85	$462.80	$37.60	$57.85
1 Set of Gases		152.00		167.20	19.00	20.90
8 L.H., Daily Totals		$452.80		$630.00	$56.60	$78.75

Crew B-79C

Crew No.	Bare Costs Hr.	Bare Costs Daily	Incl. Subs O&P Hr.	Incl. Subs O&P Daily	Cost Per Labor-Hour Bare Costs	Cost Per Labor-Hour Incl. O&P
1 Labor Foreman (outside)	$39.60	$316.80	$60.95	$487.60	$38.10	$58.47
5 Laborers	37.60	1504.00	57.85	2314.00		
1 Truck Driver (light)	39.10	312.80	59.10	472.80		
1 Paint Striper, T.M., 120 Gal.		804.60		885.06		
1 Heating Kettle, 115 Gallon		81.00		89.10		
1 Flatbed Truck, Gas, 3 Ton		303.20		333.52		
3 Pickup Trucks, 3/4 Ton		432.60		475.86		
1 Air Compressor, 60 cfm		137.40		151.14		
1 -50' Air Hose, 3/4"		3.25		3.58		
1 Breakers, Pavement, 60 lb.		9.80		10.78	31.64	34.80
56 L.H., Daily Totals		$3905.45		$5223.44	$69.74	$93.28

Crew B-79D

Crew No.	Bare Costs Hr.	Bare Costs Daily	Incl. Subs O&P Hr.	Incl. Subs O&P Daily	Cost Per Labor-Hour Bare Costs	Cost Per Labor-Hour Incl. O&P
2 Labor Foremen (outside)	$39.60	$633.60	$60.95	$975.20	$38.29	$58.78
5 Laborers	37.60	1504.00	57.85	2314.00		
1 Truck Driver (light)	39.10	312.80	59.10	472.80		
1 Paint Striper, T.M., 120 Gal.		804.60		885.06		
1 Heating Kettle, 115 Gallon		81.00		89.10		
1 Flatbed Truck, Gas, 3 Ton		303.20		333.52		
4 Pickup Trucks, 3/4 Ton		576.80		634.48		
1 Air Compressor, 60 cfm		137.40		151.14		
1 -50' Air Hose, 3/4"		3.25		3.58		
1 Breakers, Pavement, 60 lb.		9.80		10.78	29.94	32.93
64 L.H., Daily Totals		$4366.45		$5869.65	$68.23	$91.71

Crew B-79E

Crew No.	Bare Costs Hr.	Bare Costs Daily	Incl. Subs O&P Hr.	Incl. Subs O&P Daily	Cost Per Labor-Hour Bare Costs	Cost Per Labor-Hour Incl. O&P
2 Labor Foremen (outside)	$39.60	$633.60	$60.95	$975.20	$38.15	$58.59
7 Laborers	37.60	2105.60	57.85	3239.60		
1 Truck Driver (light)	39.10	312.80	59.10	472.80		
1 Paint Striper, T.M., 120 Gal.		804.60		885.06		
1 Heating Kettle, 115 Gallon		81.00		89.10		
1 Flatbed Truck, Gas, 3 Ton		303.20		333.52		
5 Pickup Trucks, 3/4 Ton		721.00		793.10		
2 Air Compressors, 60 cfm		274.80		302.28		
2 -50' Air Hoses, 3/4"		6.50		7.15		
2 Breakers, Pavement, 60 lb.		19.60		21.56	27.63	30.40
80 L.H., Daily Totals		$5262.70		$7119.37	$65.78	$88.99

Crew B-80

Crew No.	Bare Costs Hr.	Bare Costs Daily	Incl. Subs O&P Hr.	Incl. Subs O&P Daily	Cost Per Labor-Hour Bare Costs	Cost Per Labor-Hour Incl. O&P
1 Labor Foreman (outside)	$39.60	$316.80	$60.95	$487.60	$41.23	$62.91
1 Laborer	37.60	300.80	57.85	462.80		
1 Truck Driver (light)	39.10	312.80	59.10	472.80		
1 Equip. Oper. (light)	48.60	388.80	73.75	590.00		
1 Flatbed Truck, Gas, 3 Ton		303.20		333.52		
1 Earth Auger, Truck-Mtd.		417.20		458.92	22.51	24.76
32 L.H., Daily Totals		$2039.60		$2805.64	$63.74	$87.68

Crew B-80A

Crew No.	Bare Costs Hr.	Bare Costs Daily	Incl. Subs O&P Hr.	Incl. Subs O&P Daily	Cost Per Labor-Hour Bare Costs	Cost Per Labor-Hour Incl. O&P
3 Laborers	$37.60	$902.40	$57.85	$1388.40	$37.60	$57.85
1 Flatbed Truck, Gas, 3 Ton		303.20		333.52	12.63	13.90
24 L.H., Daily Totals		$1205.60		$1721.92	$50.23	$71.75

Crew B-80B

Crew No.	Bare Costs Hr.	Bare Costs Daily	Incl. Subs O&P Hr.	Incl. Subs O&P Daily	Cost Per Labor-Hour Bare Costs	Cost Per Labor-Hour Incl. O&P
3 Laborers	$37.60	$902.40	$57.85	$1388.40	$40.35	$61.83
1 Equip. Oper. (light)	48.60	388.80	73.75	590.00		
1 Crane, Flatbed Mounted, 3 Ton		243.80		268.18	7.62	8.38
32 L.H., Daily Totals		$1535.00		$2246.58	$47.97	$70.21

Crew B-80C

Crew No.	Bare Costs Hr.	Bare Costs Daily	Incl. Subs O&P Hr.	Incl. Subs O&P Daily	Cost Per Labor-Hour Bare Costs	Cost Per Labor-Hour Incl. O&P
2 Laborers	$37.60	$601.60	$57.85	$925.60	$38.10	$58.27
1 Truck Driver (light)	39.10	312.80	59.10	472.80		
1 Flatbed Truck, Gas, 1.5 Ton		245.40		269.94		
1 Manual Fence Post Auger, Gas		8.40		9.24	10.57	11.63
24 L.H., Daily Totals		$1168.20		$1677.58	$48.67	$69.90

Crew B-81

Crew No.	Bare Costs Hr.	Bare Costs Daily	Incl. Subs O&P Hr.	Incl. Subs O&P Daily	Cost Per Labor-Hour Bare Costs	Cost Per Labor-Hour Incl. O&P
1 Laborer	$37.60	$300.80	$57.85	$462.80	$42.75	$65.05
1 Equip. Oper. (medium)	50.60	404.80	76.75	614.00		
1 Truck Driver (heavy)	40.05	320.40	60.55	484.40		
1 Hydromulcher, T.M., 3000 Gal.		334.20		367.62		
1 Truck Tractor, 220 H.P.		359.60		395.56	28.91	31.80
24 L.H., Daily Totals		$1719.80		$2324.38	$71.66	$96.85

Crew B-81A

Crew No.	Bare Costs Hr.	Bare Costs Daily	Incl. Subs O&P Hr.	Incl. Subs O&P Daily	Cost Per Labor-Hour Bare Costs	Cost Per Labor-Hour Incl. O&P
1 Laborer	$37.60	$300.80	$57.85	$462.80	$38.35	$58.48
1 Truck Driver (light)	39.10	312.80	59.10	472.80		
1 Hydromulcher, T.M., 600 Gal.		127.80		140.58		
1 Flatbed Truck, Gas, 3 Ton		303.20		333.52	26.94	29.63
16 L.H., Daily Totals		$1044.60		$1409.70	$65.29	$88.11

Crew B-82

Crew No.	Bare Costs Hr.	Bare Costs Daily	Incl. Subs O&P Hr.	Incl. Subs O&P Daily	Cost Per Labor-Hour Bare Costs	Cost Per Labor-Hour Incl. O&P
1 Laborer	$37.60	$300.80	$57.85	$462.80	$43.10	$65.80
1 Equip. Oper. (light)	48.60	388.80	73.75	590.00		
1 Horiz. Borer, 6 H.P.		83.80		92.18	5.24	5.76
16 L.H., Daily Totals		$773.40		$1144.98	$48.34	$71.56

Crew No.	Bare Costs		Incl. Subs O&P		Cost Per Labor-Hour	
Crew B-82A	Hr.	Daily	Hr.	Daily	Bare Costs	Incl. O&P
2 Laborers	$37.60	$601.60	$57.85	$925.60	$43.10	$65.80
2 Equip. Opers. (light)	48.60	777.60	73.75	1180.00		
2 Dump Truck, 8 C.Y., 220 H.P.		822.40		904.64		
1 Flatbed Trailer, 25 Ton		113.60		124.96		
1 Horiz. Dir. Drill, 20k lb. Thrust		654.20		719.62		
1 Mud Trailer for HDD, 1500 Gal.		346.20		380.82		
1 Pickup Truck, 4 x 4, 3/4 Ton		155.60		171.16		
1 Flatbed trailer, 3 Ton		23.60		25.96		
1 Loader, Skid Steer, 78 H.P.		318.60		350.46	76.07	83.68
32 L.H., Daily Totals		$3813.40		$4783.22	$119.17	$149.48
Crew B-82B	Hr.	Daily	Hr.	Daily	Bare Costs	Incl. O&P
2 Laborers	$37.60	$601.60	$57.85	$925.60	$43.10	$65.80
2 Equip. Opers. (light)	48.60	777.60	73.75	1180.00		
2 Dump Truck, 8 C.Y., 220 H.P.		822.40		904.64		
1 Flatbed Trailer, 25 Ton		113.60		124.96		
1 Horiz. Dir. Drill, 30k lb. Thrust		931.20		1024.32		
1 Mud Trailer for HDD, 1500 Gal.		346.20		380.82		
1 Pickup Truck, 4 x 4, 3/4 Ton		155.60		171.16		
1 Flatbed trailer, 3 Ton		23.60		25.96		
1 Loader, Skid Steer, 78 H.P.		318.60		350.46	84.72	93.20
32 L.H., Daily Totals		$4090.40		$5087.92	$127.83	$159.00
Crew B-82C	Hr.	Daily	Hr.	Daily	Bare Costs	Incl. O&P
2 Laborers	$37.60	$601.60	$57.85	$925.60	$43.10	$65.80
2 Equip. Opers. (light)	48.60	777.60	73.75	1180.00		
2 Dump Truck, 8 C.Y., 220 H.P.		822.40		904.64		
1 Flatbed Trailer, 25 Ton		113.60		124.96		
1 Horiz. Dir. Drill, 50k lb. Thrust		1237.00		1360.70		
1 Mud Trailer for HDD, 1500 Gal.		346.20		380.82		
1 Pickup Truck, 4 x 4, 3/4 Ton		155.60		171.16		
1 Flatbed trailer, 3 Ton		23.60		25.96		
1 Loader, Skid Steer, 78 H.P.		318.60		350.46	94.28	103.71
32 L.H., Daily Totals		$4396.20		$5424.30	$137.38	$169.51
Crew B-82D	Hr.	Daily	Hr.	Daily	Bare Costs	Incl. O&P
1 Equip. Oper. (light)	$48.60	$388.80	$73.75	$590.00	$48.60	$73.75
1 Mud Trailer for HDD, 1500 Gal.		346.20		380.82	43.27	47.60
8 L.H., Daily Totals		$735.00		$970.82	$91.88	$121.35
Crew B-83	Hr.	Daily	Hr.	Daily	Bare Costs	Incl. O&P
1 Tugboat Captain	$50.60	$404.80	$76.75	$614.00	$44.10	$67.30
1 Tugboat Hand	37.60	300.80	57.85	462.80		
1 Tugboat, 250 H.P.		870.00		957.00	54.38	59.81
16 L.H., Daily Totals		$1575.60		$2033.80	$98.47	$127.11
Crew B-84	Hr.	Daily	Hr.	Daily	Bare Costs	Incl. O&P
1 Equip. Oper. (medium)	$50.60	$404.80	$76.75	$614.00	$50.60	$76.75
1 Rotary Mower/Tractor		370.80		407.88	46.35	50.98
8 L.H., Daily Totals		$775.60		$1021.88	$96.95	$127.74
Crew B-85	Hr.	Daily	Hr.	Daily	Bare Costs	Incl. O&P
3 Laborers	$37.60	$902.40	$57.85	$1388.40	$40.69	$62.17
1 Equip. Oper. (medium)	50.60	404.80	76.75	614.00		
1 Truck Driver (heavy)	40.05	320.40	60.55	484.40		
1 Aerial Lift Truck, 80'		634.40		697.84		
1 Brush Chipper, 12", 130 H.P.		391.40		430.54		
1 Pruning Saw, Rotary		6.65		7.32	25.81	28.39
40 L.H., Daily Totals		$2660.05		$3622.49	$66.50	$90.56

Crew No.	Bare Costs		Incl. Subs O&P		Cost Per Labor-Hour	
Crew B-86	Hr.	Daily	Hr.	Daily	Bare Costs	Incl. O&P
1 Equip. Oper. (medium)	$50.60	$404.80	$76.75	$614.00	$50.60	$76.75
1 Stump Chipper, S.P.		185.55		204.10	23.19	25.51
8 L.H., Daily Totals		$590.35		$818.11	$73.79	$102.26
Crew B-86A	Hr.	Daily	Hr.	Daily	Bare Costs	Incl. O&P
1 Equip. Oper. (medium)	$50.60	$404.80	$76.75	$614.00	$50.60	$76.75
1 Grader, 30,000 Lbs.		736.20		809.82	92.03	101.23
8 L.H., Daily Totals		$1141.00		$1423.82	$142.63	$177.98
Crew B-86B	Hr.	Daily	Hr.	Daily	Bare Costs	Incl. O&P
1 Equip. Oper. (medium)	$50.60	$404.80	$76.75	$614.00	$50.60	$76.75
1 Dozer, 200 H.P.		1387.00		1525.70	173.38	190.71
8 L.H., Daily Totals		$1791.80		$2139.70	$223.97	$267.46
Crew B-87	Hr.	Daily	Hr.	Daily	Bare Costs	Incl. O&P
1 Laborer	$37.60	$300.80	$57.85	$462.80	$48.00	$72.97
4 Equip. Oper. (medium)	50.60	1619.20	76.75	2456.00		
2 Feller Bunchers, 100 H.P.		1676.80		1844.48		
1 Log Chipper, 22" Tree		889.40		978.34		
1 Dozer, 105 H.P.		602.80		663.08		
1 Chain Saw, Gas, 36" Long		45.00		49.50	80.35	88.39
40 L.H., Daily Totals		$5134.00		$6454.20	$128.35	$161.35
Crew B-88	Hr.	Daily	Hr.	Daily	Bare Costs	Incl. O&P
1 Laborer	$37.60	$300.80	$57.85	$462.80	$48.74	$74.05
6 Equip. Oper. (medium)	50.60	2428.80	76.75	3684.00		
2 Feller Bunchers, 100 H.P.		1676.80		1844.48		
1 Log Chipper, 22" Tree		889.40		978.34		
2 Log Skidders, 50 H.P.		1822.00		2004.20		
1 Dozer, 105 H.P.		602.80		663.08		
1 Chain Saw, Gas, 36" Long		45.00		49.50	89.93	98.92
56 L.H., Daily Totals		$7765.60		$9686.40	$138.67	$172.97
Crew B-89	Hr.	Daily	Hr.	Daily	Bare Costs	Incl. O&P
1 Equip. Oper. (light)	$48.60	$388.80	$73.75	$590.00	$43.85	$66.42
1 Truck Driver (light)	39.10	312.80	59.10	472.80		
1 Flatbed Truck, Gas, 3 Ton		303.20		333.52		
1 Concrete Saw		167.40		184.14		
1 Water Tank, 65 Gal.		17.30		19.03	30.49	33.54
16 L.H., Daily Totals		$1189.50		$1599.49	$74.34	$99.97
Crew B-89A	Hr.	Daily	Hr.	Daily	Bare Costs	Incl. O&P
1 Skilled Worker	$48.65	$389.20	$75.15	$601.20	$43.13	$66.50
1 Laborer	37.60	300.80	57.85	462.80		
1 Core Drill (Large)		115.60		127.16	7.22	7.95
16 L.H., Daily Totals		$805.60		$1191.16	$50.35	$74.45
Crew B-89B	Hr.	Daily	Hr.	Daily	Bare Costs	Incl. O&P
1 Equip. Oper. (light)	$48.60	$388.80	$73.75	$590.00	$43.85	$66.42
1 Truck Driver (light)	39.10	312.80	59.10	472.80		
1 Wall Saw, Hydraulic, 10 H.P.		114.60		126.06		
1 Generator, Diesel, 100 kW		423.40		465.74		
1 Water Tank, 65 Gal.		17.30		19.03		
1 Flatbed Truck, Gas, 3 Ton		303.20		333.52	53.66	59.02
16 L.H., Daily Totals		$1560.10		$2007.15	$97.51	$125.45

For customer support on your Site Work & Landscape Cost Data, call 877.737.1594.

733

Crew No.	Bare Costs Hr.	Daily	Incl. Subs O&P Hr.	Daily	Cost Per L-H Bare Costs	Incl. O&P
Crew B-90	Hr.	Daily	Hr.	Daily	Bare Costs	Incl. O&P
1 Labor Foreman (outside)	$39.60	$316.80	$60.95	$487.60	$41.21	$62.89
3 Laborers	37.60	902.40	57.85	1388.40		
2 Equip. Oper. (light)	48.60	777.60	73.75	1180.00		
2 Truck Drivers (heavy)	40.05	640.80	60.55	968.80		
1 Road Mixer, 310 H.P.		1929.00		2121.90		
1 Dist. Truck, 2000 Gal.		275.60		303.16	34.45	37.89
64 L.H., Daily Totals		$4842.20		$6449.86	$75.66	$100.78

Crew No.	Hr.	Daily	Hr.	Daily	Bare Costs	Incl. O&P
Crew B-90A						
1 Labor Foreman (outside)	$39.60	$316.80	$60.95	$487.60	$45.31	$69.09
2 Laborers	37.60	601.60	57.85	925.60		
4 Equip. Oper. (medium)	50.60	1619.20	76.75	2456.00		
2 Graders, 30,000 Lbs.		1472.40		1619.64		
1 Tandem Roller, 10 Ton		236.80		260.48		
1 Roller, Pneum. Whl., 12 Ton		344.40		378.84	36.67	40.34
56 L.H., Daily Totals		$4591.20		$6128.16	$81.99	$109.43

Crew No.	Hr.	Daily	Hr.	Daily	Bare Costs	Incl. O&P
Crew B-90B						
1 Labor Foreman (outside)	$39.60	$316.80	$60.95	$487.60	$44.43	$67.82
2 Laborers	37.60	601.60	57.85	925.60		
3 Equip. Oper. (medium)	50.60	1214.40	76.75	1842.00		
1 Roller, Pneum. Whl., 12 Ton		344.40		378.84		
1 Road Mixer, 310 H.P.		1929.00		2121.90	47.36	52.10
48 L.H., Daily Totals		$4406.20		$5755.94	$91.80	$119.92

Crew No.	Hr.	Daily	Hr.	Daily	Bare Costs	Incl. O&P
Crew B-90C						
1 Labor Foreman (outside)	$39.60	$316.80	$60.95	$487.60	$42.00	$64.02
4 Laborers	37.60	1203.20	57.85	1851.20		
3 Equip. Oper. (medium)	50.60	1214.40	76.75	1842.00		
3 Truck Drivers (heavy)	40.05	961.20	60.55	1453.20		
3 Road Mixers, 310 H.P.		5787.00		6365.70	65.76	72.34
88 L.H., Daily Totals		$9482.60		$11999.70	$107.76	$136.36

Crew No.	Hr.	Daily	Hr.	Daily	Bare Costs	Incl. O&P
Crew B-90D						
1 Labor Foreman (outside)	$39.60	$316.80	$60.95	$487.60	$41.32	$63.07
6 Laborers	37.60	1804.80	57.85	2776.80		
3 Equip. Oper. (medium)	50.60	1214.40	76.75	1842.00		
3 Truck Drivers (heavy)	40.05	961.20	60.55	1453.20		
3 Road Mixers, 310 H.P.		5787.00		6365.70	55.64	61.21
104 L.H., Daily Totals		$10084.20		$12925.30	$96.96	$124.28

Crew No.	Hr.	Daily	Hr.	Daily	Bare Costs	Incl. O&P
Crew B-90E						
1 Labor Foreman (outside)	$39.60	$316.80	$60.95	$487.60	$42.43	$64.79
4 Laborers	37.60	1203.20	57.85	1851.20		
3 Equip. Oper. (medium)	50.60	1214.40	76.75	1842.00		
1 Truck Driver (heavy)	40.05	320.40	60.55	484.40		
1 Road Mixers, 310 H.P.		1929.00		2121.90	26.79	29.47
72 L.H., Daily Totals		$4983.80		$6787.10	$69.22	$94.27

Crew No.	Hr.	Daily	Hr.	Daily	Bare Costs	Incl. O&P
Crew B-91						
1 Labor Foreman (outside)	$39.60	$316.80	$60.95	$487.60	$44.66	$68.03
2 Laborers	37.60	601.60	57.85	925.60		
4 Equip. Oper. (medium)	50.60	1619.20	76.75	2456.00		
1 Truck Driver (heavy)	40.05	320.40	60.55	484.40		
1 Dist. Tanker, 3000 Gallon		305.60		336.16		
1 Truck Tractor, 6x4, 380 H.P.		599.80		659.78		
1 Aggreg. Spreader, S.P.		834.00		917.40		
1 Roller, Pneum. Whl., 12 Ton		344.40		378.84		
1 Tandem Roller, 10 Ton		236.80		260.48	36.26	39.89
64 L.H., Daily Totals		$5178.60		$6906.26	$80.92	$107.91

Crew No.	Bare Costs Hr.	Daily	Incl. Subs O&P Hr.	Daily	Cost Per L-H Bare Costs	Incl. O&P
Crew B-91B	Hr.	Daily	Hr.	Daily	Bare Costs	Incl. O&P
1 Laborer	$37.60	$300.80	$57.85	$462.80	$44.10	$67.30
1 Equipment Oper. (med.)	50.60	404.80	76.75	614.00		
1 Road Sweeper, Vac. Assist.		986.00		1084.60	61.63	67.79
16 L.H., Daily Totals		$1691.60		$2161.40	$105.72	$135.09

Crew No.	Hr.	Daily	Hr.	Daily	Bare Costs	Incl. O&P
Crew B-91C						
1 Laborer	$37.60	$300.80	$57.85	$462.80	$38.35	$58.48
1 Truck Driver (light)	39.10	312.80	59.10	472.80		
1 Catch Basin Cleaning Truck		573.60		630.96	35.85	39.44
16 L.H., Daily Totals		$1187.20		$1566.56	$74.20	$97.91

Crew No.	Hr.	Daily	Hr.	Daily	Bare Costs	Incl. O&P
Crew B-91D						
1 Labor Foreman (outside)	$39.60	$316.80	$60.95	$487.60	$43.13	$65.77
5 Laborers	37.60	1504.00	57.85	2314.00		
5 Equip. Oper. (medium)	50.60	2024.00	76.75	3070.00		
2 Truck Drivers (heavy)	40.05	640.80	60.55	968.80		
1 Aggreg. Spreader, S.P.		834.00		917.40		
2 Truck Tractor, 6x4, 380 H.P.		1199.60		1319.56		
2 Dist. Tanker, 3000 Gallon		611.20		672.32		
2 Pavement Brush, Towed		163.20		179.52		
2 Roller, Pneum. Whl., 12 Ton		688.80		757.68	33.62	36.99
104 L.H., Daily Totals		$7982.40		$10686.88	$76.75	$102.76

Crew No.	Hr.	Daily	Hr.	Daily	Bare Costs	Incl. O&P
Crew B-92						
1 Labor Foreman (outside)	$39.60	$316.80	$60.95	$487.60	$38.10	$58.63
3 Laborers	37.60	902.40	57.85	1388.40		
1 Crack Cleaner, 25 H.P.		61.60		67.76		
1 Air Compressor, 60 cfm		137.40		151.14		
1 Tar Kettle, T.M.		132.00		145.20		
1 Flatbed Truck, Gas, 3 Ton		303.20		333.52	19.82	21.80
32 L.H., Daily Totals		$1853.40		$2573.62	$57.92	$80.43

Crew No.	Hr.	Daily	Hr.	Daily	Bare Costs	Incl. O&P
Crew B-93						
1 Equip. Oper. (medium)	$50.60	$404.80	$76.75	$614.00	$50.60	$76.75
1 Feller Buncher, 100 H.P.		838.40		922.24	104.80	115.28
8 L.H., Daily Totals		$1243.20		$1536.24	$155.40	$192.03

Crew No.	Hr.	Daily	Hr.	Daily	Bare Costs	Incl. O&P
Crew B-94A						
1 Laborer	$37.60	$300.80	$57.85	$462.80	$37.60	$57.85
1 Diaphragm Water Pump, 2"		71.00		78.10		
1 -20' Suction Hose, 2"		1.95		2.15		
2 -50' Discharge Hoses, 2"		1.80		1.98	9.34	10.28
8 L.H., Daily Totals		$375.55		$545.02	$46.94	$68.13

Crew No.	Hr.	Daily	Hr.	Daily	Bare Costs	Incl. O&P
Crew B-94B						
1 Laborer	$37.60	$300.80	$57.85	$462.80	$37.60	$57.85
1 Diaphragm Water Pump, 4"		114.20		125.62		
1 -20' Suction Hose, 4"		3.25		3.58		
2 -50' Discharge Hoses, 4"		4.70		5.17	15.27	16.80
8 L.H., Daily Totals		$422.95		$597.16	$52.87	$74.65

Crew No.	Hr.	Daily	Hr.	Daily	Bare Costs	Incl. O&P
Crew B-94C						
1 Laborer	$37.60	$300.80	$57.85	$462.80	$37.60	$57.85
1 Centrifugal Water Pump, 3"		78.20		86.02		
1 -20' Suction Hose, 3"		2.85		3.13		
2 -50' Discharge Hoses, 3"		3.00		3.30	10.51	11.56
8 L.H., Daily Totals		$384.85		$555.26	$48.11	$69.41

For customer support on your Site Work & Landscape Cost Data, call 877.737.1594.

Crews

Crew No.	Bare Costs		Incl. Subs O&P		Cost Per Labor-Hour	
Crew B-94D	Hr.	Daily	Hr.	Daily	Bare Costs	Incl. O&P
1 Laborer	$37.60	$300.80	$57.85	$462.80	$37.60	$57.85
1 Centr. Water Pump, 6"		346.60		381.26		
1 -20' Suction Hose, 6"		11.50		12.65		
2 -50' Discharge Hoses, 6"		12.20		13.42	46.29	50.92
8 L.H., Daily Totals		$671.10		$870.13	$83.89	$108.77
Crew C-1	Hr.	Daily	Hr.	Daily	Bare Costs	Incl. O&P
3 Carpenters	$46.95	$1126.80	$72.25	$1734.00	$44.61	$68.65
1 Laborer	37.60	300.80	57.85	462.80		
32 L.H., Daily Totals		$1427.60		$2196.80	$44.61	$68.65
Crew C-2	Hr.	Daily	Hr.	Daily	Bare Costs	Incl. O&P
1 Carpenter Foreman (outside)	$48.95	$391.60	$75.35	$602.80	$45.73	$70.37
4 Carpenters	46.95	1502.40	72.25	2312.00		
1 Laborer	37.60	300.80	57.85	462.80		
48 L.H., Daily Totals		$2194.80		$3377.60	$45.73	$70.37
Crew C-2A	Hr.	Daily	Hr.	Daily	Bare Costs	Incl. O&P
1 Carpenter Foreman (outside)	$48.95	$391.60	$75.35	$602.80	$45.40	$69.43
3 Carpenters	46.95	1126.80	72.25	1734.00		
1 Cement Finisher	45.00	360.00	66.65	533.20		
1 Laborer	37.60	300.80	57.85	462.80		
48 L.H., Daily Totals		$2179.20		$3332.80	$45.40	$69.43
Crew C-3	Hr.	Daily	Hr.	Daily	Bare Costs	Incl. O&P
1 Rodman Foreman (outside)	$54.55	$436.40	$85.20	$681.60	$48.57	$75.38
4 Rodmen (reinf.)	52.55	1681.60	82.10	2627.20		
1 Equip. Oper. (light)	48.60	388.80	73.75	590.00		
2 Laborers	37.60	601.60	57.85	925.60		
3 Stressing Equipment		30.60		33.66		
.5 Grouting Equipment		81.50		89.65	1.75	1.93
64 L.H., Daily Totals		$3220.50		$4947.71	$50.32	$77.31
Crew C-4	Hr.	Daily	Hr.	Daily	Bare Costs	Incl. O&P
1 Rodman Foreman (outside)	$54.55	$436.40	$85.20	$681.60	$53.05	$82.88
3 Rodmen (reinf.)	52.55	1261.20	82.10	1970.40		
3 Stressing Equipment		30.60		33.66	.96	1.05
32 L.H., Daily Totals		$1728.20		$2685.66	$54.01	$83.93
Crew C-4A	Hr.	Daily	Hr.	Daily	Bare Costs	Incl. O&P
2 Rodmen (reinf.)	$52.55	$840.80	$82.10	$1313.60	$52.55	$82.10
4 Stressing Equipment		40.80		44.88	2.55	2.81
16 L.H., Daily Totals		$881.60		$1358.48	$55.10	$84.91
Crew C-5	Hr.	Daily	Hr.	Daily	Bare Costs	Incl. O&P
1 Rodman Foreman (outside)	$54.55	$436.40	$85.20	$681.60	$51.66	$80.09
4 Rodmen (reinf.)	52.55	1681.60	82.10	2627.20		
1 Equip. Oper. (crane)	51.70	413.60	78.45	627.60		
1 Equip. Oper. (oiler)	45.20	361.60	68.55	548.40		
1 Hyd. Crane, 25 Ton		736.60		810.26	13.15	14.47
56 L.H., Daily Totals		$3629.80		$5295.06	$64.82	$94.55
Crew C-6	Hr.	Daily	Hr.	Daily	Bare Costs	Incl. O&P
1 Labor Foreman (outside)	$39.60	$316.80	$60.95	$487.60	$39.17	$59.83
4 Laborers	37.60	1203.20	57.85	1851.20		
1 Cement Finisher	45.00	360.00	66.65	533.20		
2 Gas Engine Vibrators		62.40		68.64	1.30	1.43
48 L.H., Daily Totals		$1942.40		$2940.64	$40.47	$61.26

Crew No.	Bare Costs		Incl. Subs O&P		Cost Per Labor-Hour	
Crew C-7	Hr.	Daily	Hr.	Daily	Bare Costs	Incl. O&P
1 Labor Foreman (outside)	$39.60	$316.80	$60.95	$487.60	$40.93	$62.46
5 Laborers	37.60	1504.00	57.85	2314.00		
1 Cement Finisher	45.00	360.00	66.65	533.20		
1 Equip. Oper. (medium)	50.60	404.80	76.75	614.00		
1 Equip. Oper. (oiler)	45.20	361.60	68.55	548.40		
2 Gas Engine Vibrators		62.40		68.64		
1 Concrete Bucket, 1 C.Y.		23.80		26.18		
1 Hyd. Crane, 55 Ton		1128.00		1240.80	16.86	18.55
72 L.H., Daily Totals		$4161.40		$5832.82	$57.80	$81.01
Crew C-7A	Hr.	Daily	Hr.	Daily	Bare Costs	Incl. O&P
1 Labor Foreman (outside)	$39.60	$316.80	$60.95	$487.60	$38.46	$58.91
5 Laborers	37.60	1504.00	57.85	2314.00		
2 Truck Drivers (heavy)	40.05	640.80	60.55	968.80		
2 Conc. Transit Mixers		2032.00		2235.20	31.75	34.92
64 L.H., Daily Totals		$4493.60		$6005.60	$70.21	$93.84
Crew C-7B	Hr.	Daily	Hr.	Daily	Bare Costs	Incl. O&P
1 Labor Foreman (outside)	$39.60	$316.80	$60.95	$487.60	$40.56	$62.15
5 Laborers	37.60	1504.00	57.85	2314.00		
1 Equipment Operator, Crane	51.70	413.60	78.45	627.60		
1 Equipment Oiler	45.20	361.60	68.55	548.40		
1 Conc. Bucket, 2 C.Y.		37.00		40.70		
1 Lattice Boom Crane, 165 Ton		1932.00		2125.20	30.77	33.84
64 L.H., Daily Totals		$4565.00		$6143.50	$71.33	$95.99
Crew C-7C	Hr.	Daily	Hr.	Daily	Bare Costs	Incl. O&P
1 Labor Foreman (outside)	$39.60	$316.80	$60.95	$487.60	$41.10	$62.96
5 Laborers	37.60	1504.00	57.85	2314.00		
2 Equipment Operators (med.)	50.60	809.60	76.75	1228.00		
2 F.E. Loaders, W.M. 4 C.Y.		1338.40		1472.24	20.91	23.00
64 L.H., Daily Totals		$3968.80		$5501.84	$62.01	$85.97
Crew C-7D	Hr.	Daily	Hr.	Daily	Bare Costs	Incl. O&P
1 Labor Foreman (outside)	$39.60	$316.80	$60.95	$487.60	$39.74	$60.99
5 Laborers	37.60	1504.00	57.85	2314.00		
1 Equip. Oper. (medium)	50.60	404.80	76.75	614.00		
1 Concrete Conveyer		198.80		218.68	3.55	3.90
56 L.H., Daily Totals		$2424.40		$3634.28	$43.29	$64.90
Crew C-8	Hr.	Daily	Hr.	Daily	Bare Costs	Incl. O&P
1 Labor Foreman (outside)	$39.60	$316.80	$60.95	$487.60	$41.86	$63.51
3 Laborers	37.60	902.40	57.85	1388.40		
2 Cement Finishers	45.00	720.00	66.65	1066.40		
1 Equip. Oper. (medium)	50.60	404.80	76.75	614.00		
1 Concrete Pump (Small)		720.00		792.00	12.86	14.14
56 L.H., Daily Totals		$3064.00		$4348.40	$54.71	$77.65
Crew C-8A	Hr.	Daily	Hr.	Daily	Bare Costs	Incl. O&P
1 Labor Foreman (outside)	$39.60	$316.80	$60.95	$487.60	$40.40	$61.30
3 Laborers	37.60	902.40	57.85	1388.40		
2 Cement Finishers	45.00	720.00	66.65	1066.40		
48 L.H., Daily Totals		$1939.20		$2942.40	$40.40	$61.30

735

Crew C-8B	Hr.	Daily	Hr.	Daily	Bare Costs	Incl. O&P
1 Labor Foreman (outside)	$39.60	$316.80	$60.95	$487.60	$40.60	$62.25
3 Laborers	37.60	902.40	57.85	1388.40		
1 Equip. Oper. (medium)	50.60	404.80	76.75	614.00		
1 Vibrating Power Screed		66.30		72.93		
1 Roller, Vibratory, 25 Ton		687.40		756.14		
1 Dozer, 200 H.P.		1387.00		1525.70	53.52	58.87
40 L.H., Daily Totals		$3764.70		$4844.77	$94.12	$121.12

Crew C-8C	Hr.	Daily	Hr.	Daily	Bare Costs	Incl. O&P
1 Labor Foreman (outside)	$39.60	$316.80	$60.95	$487.60	$41.33	$62.98
3 Laborers	37.60	902.40	57.85	1388.40		
1 Cement Finisher	45.00	360.00	66.65	533.20		
1 Equip. Oper. (medium)	50.60	404.80	76.75	614.00		
1 Shotcrete Rig, 12 C.Y./hr		250.80		275.88		
1 Air Compressor, 160 cfm		156.40		172.04		
4 -50' Air Hoses, 1"		16.40		18.04		
4 -50' Air Hoses, 2"		31.00		34.10	9.47	10.42
48 L.H., Daily Totals		$2438.60		$3523.26	$50.80	$73.40

Crew C-8D	Hr.	Daily	Hr.	Daily	Bare Costs	Incl. O&P
1 Labor Foreman (outside)	$39.60	$316.80	$60.95	$487.60	$42.70	$64.80
1 Laborer	37.60	300.80	57.85	462.80		
1 Cement Finisher	45.00	360.00	66.65	533.20		
1 Equipment Oper. (light)	48.60	388.80	73.75	590.00		
1 Air Compressor, 250 cfm		201.40		221.54		
2 -50' Air Hoses, 1"		8.20		9.02	6.55	7.21
32 L.H., Daily Totals		$1576.00		$2304.16	$49.25	$72.00

Crew C-8E	Hr.	Daily	Hr.	Daily	Bare Costs	Incl. O&P
1 Labor Foreman (outside)	$39.60	$316.80	$60.95	$487.60	$41.00	$62.48
3 Laborers	37.60	902.40	57.85	1388.40		
1 Cement Finisher	45.00	360.00	66.65	533.20		
1 Equipment Oper. (light)	48.60	388.80	73.75	590.00		
1 Shotcrete Rig, 35 C.Y./hr		281.00		309.10		
1 Air Compressor, 250 cfm		201.40		221.54		
4 -50' Air Hoses, 1"		16.40		18.04		
4 -50' Air Hoses, 2"		31.00		34.10	11.04	12.14
48 L.H., Daily Totals		$2497.80		$3581.98	$52.04	$74.62

Crew C-10	Hr.	Daily	Hr.	Daily	Bare Costs	Incl. O&P
1 Laborer	$37.60	$300.80	$57.85	$462.80	$42.53	$63.72
2 Cement Finishers	45.00	720.00	66.65	1066.40		
24 L.H., Daily Totals		$1020.80		$1529.20	$42.53	$63.72

Crew C-10B	Hr.	Daily	Hr.	Daily	Bare Costs	Incl. O&P
3 Laborers	$37.60	$902.40	$57.85	$1388.40	$40.56	$61.37
2 Cement Finishers	45.00	720.00	66.65	1066.40		
1 Concrete Mixer, 10 C.F.		172.40		189.64		
2 Trowels, 48" Walk-Behind		100.40		110.44	6.82	7.50
40 L.H., Daily Totals		$1895.20		$2754.88	$47.38	$68.87

Crew C-10C	Hr.	Daily	Hr.	Daily	Bare Costs	Incl. O&P
1 Laborer	$37.60	$300.80	$57.85	$462.80	$42.53	$63.72
2 Cement Finishers	45.00	720.00	66.65	1066.40		
1 Trowel, 48" Walk-Behind		50.20		55.22	2.09	2.30
24 L.H., Daily Totals		$1071.00		$1584.42	$44.63	$66.02

Crew C-10D	Hr.	Daily	Hr.	Daily	Bare Costs	Incl. O&P
1 Laborer	$37.60	$300.80	$57.85	$462.80	$42.53	$63.72
2 Cement Finishers	45.00	720.00	66.65	1066.40		
1 Vibrating Power Screed		66.30		72.93		
1 Trowel, 48" Walk-Behind		50.20		55.22	4.85	5.34
24 L.H., Daily Totals		$1137.30		$1657.35	$47.39	$69.06

Crew C-10E	Hr.	Daily	Hr.	Daily	Bare Costs	Incl. O&P
1 Laborer	$37.60	$300.80	$57.85	$462.80	$42.53	$63.72
2 Cement Finishers	45.00	720.00	66.65	1066.40		
1 Vibrating Power Screed		66.30		72.93		
1 Cement Trowel, 96" Ride-On		189.00		207.90	10.64	11.70
24 L.H., Daily Totals		$1276.10		$1810.03	$53.17	$75.42

Crew C-10F	Hr.	Daily	Hr.	Daily	Bare Costs	Incl. O&P
1 Laborer	$37.60	$300.80	$57.85	$462.80	$42.53	$63.72
2 Cement Finishers	45.00	720.00	66.65	1066.40		
1 Aerial Lift Truck, 60' Boom		435.60		479.16	18.15	19.97
24 L.H., Daily Totals		$1456.40		$2008.36	$60.68	$83.68

Crew C-11	Hr.	Daily	Hr.	Daily	Bare Costs	Incl. O&P
1 Struc. Steel Foreman (outside)	$54.65	$437.20	$94.95	$759.60	$51.94	$87.85
6 Struc. Steel Workers	52.65	2527.20	91.45	4389.60		
1 Equip. Oper. (crane)	51.70	413.60	78.45	627.60		
1 Equip. Oper. (oiler)	45.20	361.60	68.55	548.40		
1 Lattice Boom Crane, 150 Ton		1813.00		1994.30	25.18	27.70
72 L.H., Daily Totals		$5552.60		$8319.50	$77.12	$115.55

Crew C-12	Hr.	Daily	Hr.	Daily	Bare Costs	Incl. O&P
1 Carpenter Foreman (outside)	$48.95	$391.60	$75.35	$602.80	$46.52	$71.40
3 Carpenters	46.95	1126.80	72.25	1734.00		
1 Laborer	37.60	300.80	57.85	462.80		
1 Equip. Oper. (crane)	51.70	413.60	78.45	627.60		
1 Hyd. Crane, 12 Ton		653.80		719.18	13.62	14.98
48 L.H., Daily Totals		$2886.60		$4146.38	$60.14	$86.38

Crew C-13	Hr.	Daily	Hr.	Daily	Bare Costs	Incl. O&P
1 Struc. Steel Worker	$52.65	$421.20	$91.45	$731.60	$50.75	$85.05
1 Welder	52.65	421.20	91.45	731.60		
1 Carpenter	46.95	375.60	72.25	578.00		
1 Welder, Gas Engine, 300 amp		145.85		160.44	6.08	6.68
24 L.H., Daily Totals		$1363.85		$2201.64	$56.83	$91.73

Crew C-14	Hr.	Daily	Hr.	Daily	Bare Costs	Incl. O&P
1 Carpenter Foreman (outside)	$48.95	$391.60	$75.35	$602.80	$46.18	$70.93
5 Carpenters	46.95	1878.00	72.25	2890.00		
4 Laborers	37.60	1203.20	57.85	1851.20		
4 Rodmen (reinf.)	52.55	1681.60	82.10	2627.20		
2 Cement Finishers	45.00	720.00	66.65	1066.40		
1 Equip. Oper. (crane)	51.70	413.60	78.45	627.60		
1 Equip. Oper. (oiler)	45.20	361.60	68.55	548.40		
1 Hyd. Crane, 80 Ton		1625.00		1787.50	11.28	12.41
144 L.H., Daily Totals		$8274.60		$12001.10	$57.46	$83.34

Crew No.	Bare Costs		Incl. Subs O&P		Cost Per Labor-Hour	
Crew C-14A	**Hr.**	**Daily**	**Hr.**	**Daily**	**Bare Costs**	**Incl. O&P**
1 Carpenter Foreman (outside)	$48.95	$391.60	$75.35	$602.80	$47.25	$72.75
16 Carpenters	46.95	6009.60	72.25	9248.00		
4 Rodmen (reinf.)	52.55	1681.60	82.10	2627.20		
2 Laborers	37.60	601.60	57.85	925.60		
1 Cement Finisher	45.00	360.00	66.65	533.20		
1 Equip. Oper. (medium)	50.60	404.80	76.75	614.00		
1 Gas Engine Vibrator		31.20		34.32		
1 Concrete Pump (Small)		720.00		792.00	3.76	4.13
200 L.H., Daily Totals		$10200.40		$15377.12	$51.00	$76.89

Crew C-14B	Hr.	Daily	Hr.	Daily	Bare Costs	Incl. O&P
1 Carpenter Foreman (outside)	$48.95	$391.60	$75.35	$602.80	$47.16	$72.52
16 Carpenters	46.95	6009.60	72.25	9248.00		
4 Rodmen (reinf.)	52.55	1681.60	82.10	2627.20		
2 Laborers	37.60	601.60	57.85	925.60		
2 Cement Finishers	45.00	720.00	66.65	1066.40		
1 Equip. Oper. (medium)	50.60	404.80	76.75	614.00		
1 Gas Engine Vibrator		31.20		34.32		
1 Concrete Pump (Small)		720.00		792.00	3.61	3.97
208 L.H., Daily Totals		$10560.40		$15910.32	$50.77	$76.49

Crew C-14C	Hr.	Daily	Hr.	Daily	Bare Costs	Incl. O&P
1 Carpenter Foreman (outside)	$48.95	$391.60	$75.35	$602.80	$45.08	$69.36
6 Carpenters	46.95	2253.60	72.25	3468.00		
2 Rodmen (reinf.)	52.55	840.80	82.10	1313.60		
4 Laborers	37.60	1203.20	57.85	1851.20		
1 Cement Finisher	45.00	360.00	66.65	533.20		
1 Gas Engine Vibrator		31.20		34.32	.28	.31
112 L.H., Daily Totals		$5080.40		$7803.12	$45.36	$69.67

Crew C-14D	Hr.	Daily	Hr.	Daily	Bare Costs	Incl. O&P
1 Carpenter Foreman (outside)	$48.95	$391.60	$75.35	$602.80	$46.80	$71.97
18 Carpenters	46.95	6760.80	72.25	10404.00		
2 Rodmen (reinf.)	52.55	840.80	82.10	1313.60		
2 Laborers	37.60	601.60	57.85	925.60		
1 Cement Finisher	45.00	360.00	66.65	533.20		
1 Equip. Oper. (medium)	50.60	404.80	76.75	614.00		
1 Gas Engine Vibrator		31.20		34.32		
1 Concrete Pump (Small)		720.00		792.00	3.76	4.13
200 L.H., Daily Totals		$10110.80		$15219.52	$50.55	$76.10

Crew C-14E	Hr.	Daily	Hr.	Daily	Bare Costs	Incl. O&P
1 Carpenter Foreman (outside)	$48.95	$391.60	$75.35	$602.80	$46.44	$71.68
2 Carpenters	46.95	751.20	72.25	1156.00		
4 Rodmen (reinf.)	52.55	1681.60	82.10	2627.20		
3 Laborers	37.60	902.40	57.85	1388.40		
1 Cement Finisher	45.00	360.00	66.65	533.20		
1 Gas Engine Vibrator		31.20		34.32	.35	.39
88 L.H., Daily Totals		$4118.00		$6341.92	$46.80	$72.07

Crew C-14F	Hr.	Daily	Hr.	Daily	Bare Costs	Incl. O&P
1 Labor Foreman (outside)	$39.60	$316.80	$60.95	$487.60	$42.76	$64.06
2 Laborers	37.60	601.60	57.85	925.60		
6 Cement Finishers	45.00	2160.00	66.65	3199.20		
1 Gas Engine Vibrator		31.20		34.32	.43	.48
72 L.H., Daily Totals		$3109.60		$4646.72	$43.19	$64.54

Crew C-14G	Hr.	Daily	Hr.	Daily	Bare Costs	Incl. O&P
1 Labor Foreman (outside)	$39.60	$316.80	$60.95	$487.60	$42.11	$63.32
2 Laborers	37.60	601.60	57.85	925.60		
4 Cement Finishers	45.00	1440.00	66.65	2132.80		
1 Gas Engine Vibrator		31.20		34.32	.56	.61
56 L.H., Daily Totals		$2389.60		$3580.32	$42.67	$63.93

Crew C-14H	Hr.	Daily	Hr.	Daily	Bare Costs	Incl. O&P
1 Carpenter Foreman (outside)	$48.95	$391.60	$75.35	$602.80	$46.33	$71.08
2 Carpenters	46.95	751.20	72.25	1156.00		
1 Rodman (reinf.)	52.55	420.40	82.10	656.80		
1 Laborer	37.60	300.80	57.85	462.80		
1 Cement Finisher	45.00	360.00	66.65	533.20		
1 Gas Engine Vibrator		31.20		34.32	.65	.71
48 L.H., Daily Totals		$2255.20		$3445.92	$46.98	$71.79

Crew C-14L	Hr.	Daily	Hr.	Daily	Bare Costs	Incl. O&P
1 Carpenter Foreman (outside)	$48.95	$391.60	$75.35	$602.80	$43.84	$67.24
6 Carpenters	46.95	2253.60	72.25	3468.00		
4 Laborers	37.60	1203.20	57.85	1851.20		
1 Cement Finisher	45.00	360.00	66.65	533.20		
1 Gas Engine Vibrator		31.20		34.32	.33	.36
96 L.H., Daily Totals		$4239.60		$6489.52	$44.16	$67.60

Crew C-14M	Hr.	Daily	Hr.	Daily	Bare Costs	Incl. O&P
1 Carpenter Foreman (outside)	$48.95	$391.60	$75.35	$602.80	$45.77	$70.13
2 Carpenters	46.95	751.20	72.25	1156.00		
1 Rodman (reinf.)	52.55	420.40	82.10	656.80		
2 Laborers	37.60	601.60	57.85	925.60		
1 Cement Finisher	45.00	360.00	66.65	533.20		
1 Equip. Oper. (medium)	50.60	404.80	76.75	614.00		
1 Gas Engine Vibrator		31.20		34.32		
1 Concrete Pump (Small)		720.00		792.00	11.74	12.91
64 L.H., Daily Totals		$3680.80		$5314.72	$57.51	$83.04

Crew C-15	Hr.	Daily	Hr.	Daily	Bare Costs	Incl. O&P
1 Carpenter Foreman (outside)	$48.95	$391.60	$75.35	$602.80	$44.24	$67.64
2 Carpenters	46.95	751.20	72.25	1156.00		
3 Laborers	37.60	902.40	57.85	1388.40		
2 Cement Finishers	45.00	720.00	66.65	1066.40		
1 Rodman (reinf.)	52.55	420.40	82.10	656.80		
72 L.H., Daily Totals		$3185.60		$4870.40	$44.24	$67.64

Crew C-16	Hr.	Daily	Hr.	Daily	Bare Costs	Incl. O&P
1 Labor Foreman (outside)	$39.60	$316.80	$60.95	$487.60	$41.86	$63.51
3 Laborers	37.60	902.40	57.85	1388.40		
2 Cement Finishers	45.00	720.00	66.65	1066.40		
1 Equip. Oper. (medium)	50.60	404.80	76.75	614.00		
1 Gunite Pump Rig		371.80		408.98		
2 -50' Air Hoses, 3/4"		6.50		7.15		
2 -50' Air Hoses, 2"		15.50		17.05	7.03	7.74
56 L.H., Daily Totals		$2737.80		$3989.58	$48.89	$71.24

Crew C-16A	Hr.	Daily	Hr.	Daily	Bare Costs	Incl. O&P
1 Laborer	$37.60	$300.80	$57.85	$462.80	$44.55	$66.97
2 Cement Finishers	45.00	720.00	66.65	1066.40		
1 Equip. Oper. (medium)	50.60	404.80	76.75	614.00		
1 Gunite Pump Rig		371.80		408.98		
2 -50' Air Hoses, 3/4"		6.50		7.15		
2 -50' Air Hoses, 2"		15.50		17.05		
1 Aerial Lift Truck, 60' Boom		435.60		479.16	25.92	28.51
32 L.H., Daily Totals		$2255.00		$3055.54	$70.47	$95.49

737

Crew C-17

Crew No.	Bare Costs Hr.	Daily	Incl. Subs O&P Hr.	Daily	Cost Per L-H Bare Costs	Incl. O&P
2 Skilled Worker Foremen (out)	$50.65	$810.40	$78.25	$1252.00	$49.05	$75.77
8 Skilled Workers	48.65	3113.60	75.15	4809.60		
80 L.H., Daily Totals		$3924.00		$6061.60	$49.05	$75.77

Crew C-17A

Crew No.	Bare Costs Hr.	Daily	Incl. Subs O&P Hr.	Daily	Cost Per L-H Bare Costs	Incl. O&P
2 Skilled Worker Foremen (out)	$50.65	$810.40	$78.25	$1252.00	$49.08	$75.80
8 Skilled Workers	48.65	3113.60	75.15	4809.60		
.125 Equip. Oper. (crane)	51.70	51.70	78.45	78.45		
.125 Hyd. Crane, 80 Ton		203.13		223.44	2.51	2.76
81 L.H., Daily Totals		$4178.82		$6363.49	$51.59	$78.56

Crew C-17B

Crew No.	Bare Costs Hr.	Daily	Incl. Subs O&P Hr.	Daily	Cost Per L-H Bare Costs	Incl. O&P
2 Skilled Worker Foremen (out)	$50.65	$810.40	$78.25	$1252.00	$49.11	$75.84
8 Skilled Workers	48.65	3113.60	75.15	4809.60		
.25 Equip. Oper. (crane)	51.70	103.40	78.45	156.90		
.25 Hyd. Crane, 80 Ton		406.25		446.88		
.25 Trowel, 48" Walk-Behind		12.55		13.81	5.11	5.62
82 L.H., Daily Totals		$4446.20		$6679.18	$54.22	$81.45

Crew C-17C

Crew No.	Bare Costs Hr.	Daily	Incl. Subs O&P Hr.	Daily	Cost Per L-H Bare Costs	Incl. O&P
2 Skilled Worker Foremen (out)	$50.65	$810.40	$78.25	$1252.00	$49.15	$75.87
8 Skilled Workers	48.65	3113.60	75.15	4809.60		
.375 Equip. Oper. (crane)	51.70	155.10	78.45	235.35		
.375 Hyd. Crane, 80 Ton		609.38		670.31	7.34	8.08
83 L.H., Daily Totals		$4688.48		$6967.26	$56.49	$83.94

Crew C-17D

Crew No.	Bare Costs Hr.	Daily	Incl. Subs O&P Hr.	Daily	Cost Per L-H Bare Costs	Incl. O&P
2 Skilled Worker Foremen (out)	$50.65	$810.40	$78.25	$1252.00	$49.18	$75.90
8 Skilled Workers	48.65	3113.60	75.15	4809.60		
.5 Equip. Oper. (crane)	51.70	206.80	78.45	313.80		
.5 Hyd. Crane, 80 Ton		812.50		893.75	9.67	10.64
84 L.H., Daily Totals		$4943.30		$7269.15	$58.85	$86.54

Crew C-17E

Crew No.	Bare Costs Hr.	Daily	Incl. Subs O&P Hr.	Daily	Cost Per L-H Bare Costs	Incl. O&P
2 Skilled Worker Foremen (out)	$50.65	$810.40	$78.25	$1252.00	$49.05	$75.77
8 Skilled Workers	48.65	3113.60	75.15	4809.60		
1 Hyd. Jack with Rods		96.50		106.15	1.21	1.33
80 L.H., Daily Totals		$4020.50		$6167.75	$50.26	$77.10

Crew C-18

Crew No.	Bare Costs Hr.	Daily	Incl. Subs O&P Hr.	Daily	Cost Per L-H Bare Costs	Incl. O&P
.125 Labor Foreman (outside)	$39.60	$39.60	$60.95	$60.95	$37.82	$58.19
1 Laborer	37.60	300.80	57.85	462.80		
1 Concrete Cart, 10 C.F.		60.00		66.00	6.67	7.33
9 L.H., Daily Totals		$400.40		$589.75	$44.49	$65.53

Crew C-19

Crew No.	Bare Costs Hr.	Daily	Incl. Subs O&P Hr.	Daily	Cost Per L-H Bare Costs	Incl. O&P
.125 Labor Foreman (outside)	$39.60	$39.60	$60.95	$60.95	$37.82	$58.19
1 Laborer	37.60	300.80	57.85	462.80		
1 Concrete Cart, 18 C.F.		99.80		109.78	11.09	12.20
9 L.H., Daily Totals		$440.20		$633.53	$48.91	$70.39

Crew C-20

Crew No.	Bare Costs Hr.	Daily	Incl. Subs O&P Hr.	Daily	Cost Per L-H Bare Costs	Incl. O&P
1 Labor Foreman (outside)	$39.60	$316.80	$60.95	$487.60	$40.40	$61.70
5 Laborers	37.60	1504.00	57.85	2314.00		
1 Cement Finisher	45.00	360.00	66.65	533.20		
1 Equip. Oper. (medium)	50.60	404.80	76.75	614.00		
2 Gas Engine Vibrators		62.40		68.64		
1 Concrete Pump (Small)		720.00		792.00	12.23	13.45
64 L.H., Daily Totals		$3368.00		$4809.44	$52.63	$75.15

Crew C-21

Crew No.	Bare Costs Hr.	Daily	Incl. Subs O&P Hr.	Daily	Cost Per L-H Bare Costs	Incl. O&P
1 Labor Foreman (outside)	$39.60	$316.80	$60.95	$487.60	$40.40	$61.70
5 Laborers	37.60	1504.00	57.85	2314.00		
1 Cement Finisher	45.00	360.00	66.65	533.20		
1 Equip. Oper. (medium)	50.60	404.80	76.75	614.00		
2 Gas Engine Vibrators		62.40		68.64		
1 Concrete Conveyer		198.80		218.68	4.08	4.49
64 L.H., Daily Totals		$2846.80		$4236.12	$44.48	$66.19

Crew C-22

Crew No.	Bare Costs Hr.	Daily	Incl. Subs O&P Hr.	Daily	Cost Per L-H Bare Costs	Incl. O&P
1 Rodman Foreman (outside)	$54.55	$436.40	$85.20	$681.60	$52.74	$82.28
4 Rodmen (reinf.)	52.55	1681.60	82.10	2627.20		
.125 Equip. Oper. (crane)	51.70	51.70	78.45	78.45		
.125 Equip. Oper. (oiler)	45.20	45.20	68.55	68.55		
.125 Hyd. Crane, 25 Ton		92.08		101.28	2.19	2.41
42 L.H., Daily Totals		$2306.97		$3557.08	$54.93	$84.69

Crew C-23

Crew No.	Bare Costs Hr.	Daily	Incl. Subs O&P Hr.	Daily	Cost Per L-H Bare Costs	Incl. O&P
2 Skilled Worker Foremen (out)	$50.65	$810.40	$78.25	$1252.00	$49.01	$75.44
6 Skilled Workers	48.65	2335.20	75.15	3607.20		
1 Equip. Oper. (crane)	51.70	413.60	78.45	627.60		
1 Equip. Oper. (oiler)	45.20	361.60	68.55	548.40		
1 Lattice Boom Crane, 90 Ton		1511.00		1662.10	18.89	20.78
80 L.H., Daily Totals		$5431.80		$7697.30	$67.90	$96.22

Crew C-23A

Crew No.	Bare Costs Hr.	Daily	Incl. Subs O&P Hr.	Daily	Cost Per L-H Bare Costs	Incl. O&P
1 Labor Foreman (outside)	$39.60	$316.80	$60.95	$487.60	$42.34	$64.73
2 Laborers	37.60	601.60	57.85	925.60		
1 Equip. Oper. (crane)	51.70	413.60	78.45	627.60		
1 Equip. Oper. (oiler)	45.20	361.60	68.55	548.40		
1 Crawler Crane, 100 Ton		1667.00		1833.70		
3 Conc. Buckets, 8 C.Y.		608.40		669.24	56.88	62.57
40 L.H., Daily Totals		$3969.00		$5092.14	$99.22	$127.30

Crew C-24

Crew No.	Bare Costs Hr.	Daily	Incl. Subs O&P Hr.	Daily	Cost Per L-H Bare Costs	Incl. O&P
2 Skilled Worker Foremen (out)	$50.65	$810.40	$78.25	$1252.00	$49.01	$75.44
6 Skilled Workers	48.65	2335.20	75.15	3607.20		
1 Equip. Oper. (crane)	51.70	413.60	78.45	627.60		
1 Equip. Oper. (oiler)	45.20	361.60	68.55	548.40		
1 Lattice Boom Crane, 150 Ton		1813.00		1994.30	22.66	24.93
80 L.H., Daily Totals		$5733.80		$8029.50	$71.67	$100.37

Crew C-25

Crew No.	Bare Costs Hr.	Daily	Incl. Subs O&P Hr.	Daily	Cost Per L-H Bare Costs	Incl. O&P
2 Rodmen (reinf.)	$52.55	$840.80	$82.10	$1313.60	$41.30	$66.70
2 Rodmen Helpers	30.05	480.80	51.30	820.80		
32 L.H., Daily Totals		$1321.60		$2134.40	$41.30	$66.70

Crew C-27

Crew No.	Bare Costs Hr.	Daily	Incl. Subs O&P Hr.	Daily	Cost Per L-H Bare Costs	Incl. O&P
2 Cement Finishers	$45.00	$720.00	$66.65	$1066.40	$45.00	$66.65
1 Concrete Saw		167.40		184.14	10.46	11.51
16 L.H., Daily Totals		$887.40		$1250.54	$55.46	$78.16

Crew C-28

Crew No.	Bare Costs Hr.	Daily	Incl. Subs O&P Hr.	Daily	Cost Per L-H Bare Costs	Incl. O&P
1 Cement Finisher	$45.00	$360.00	$66.65	$533.20	$45.00	$66.65
1 Portable Air Compressor, Gas		17.90		19.69	2.24	2.46
8 L.H., Daily Totals		$377.90		$552.89	$47.24	$69.11

Crew C-29

Crew No.	Bare Costs Hr.	Daily	Incl. Subs O&P Hr.	Daily	Cost Per L-H Bare Costs	Incl. O&P
1 Laborer	$37.60	$300.80	$57.85	$462.80	$37.60	$57.85
1 Pressure Washer		70.20		77.22	8.78	9.65
8 L.H., Daily Totals		$371.00		$540.02	$46.38	$67.50

For customer support on your Site Work & Landscape Cost Data, call 877.737.1594.

Crews

Crew No.	Bare Costs Hr.	Daily	Incl. Subs O&P Hr.	Daily	Cost Per Labor-Hour Bare Costs	Incl. O&P
Crew C-30	Hr.	Daily	Hr.	Daily	Bare Costs	Incl. O&P
1 Laborer	$37.60	$300.80	$57.85	$462.80	$37.60	$57.85
1 Concrete Mixer, 10 C.F.		172.40		189.64	21.55	23.70
8 L.H., Daily Totals		$473.20		$652.44	$59.15	$81.56
Crew C-31	Hr.	Daily	Hr.	Daily	Bare Costs	Incl. O&P
1 Cement Finisher	$45.00	$360.00	$66.65	$533.20	$45.00	$66.65
1 Grout Pump		371.80		408.98	46.48	51.12
8 L.H., Daily Totals		$731.80		$942.18	$91.47	$117.77
Crew C-32	Hr.	Daily	Hr.	Daily	Bare Costs	Incl. O&P
1 Cement Finisher	$45.00	$360.00	$66.65	$533.20	$41.30	$62.25
1 Laborer	37.60	300.80	57.85	462.80		
1 Crack Chaser Saw, Gas, 6 H.P.		29.20		32.12		
1 Vacuum Pick-Up System		60.90		66.99	5.63	6.19
16 L.H., Daily Totals		$750.90		$1095.11	$46.93	$68.44
Crew D-1	Hr.	Daily	Hr.	Daily	Bare Costs	Incl. O&P
1 Bricklayer	$46.15	$369.20	$70.45	$563.60	$42.10	$64.28
1 Bricklayer Helper	38.05	304.40	58.10	464.80		
16 L.H., Daily Totals		$673.60		$1028.40	$42.10	$64.28
Crew D-2	Hr.	Daily	Hr.	Daily	Bare Costs	Incl. O&P
3 Bricklayers	$46.15	$1107.60	$70.45	$1690.80	$43.28	$66.12
2 Bricklayer Helpers	38.05	608.80	58.10	929.60		
.5 Carpenter	46.95	187.80	72.25	289.00		
44 L.H., Daily Totals		$1904.20		$2909.40	$43.28	$66.12
Crew D-3	Hr.	Daily	Hr.	Daily	Bare Costs	Incl. O&P
3 Bricklayers	$46.15	$1107.60	$70.45	$1690.80	$43.10	$65.83
2 Bricklayer Helpers	38.05	608.80	58.10	929.60		
.25 Carpenter	46.95	93.90	72.25	144.50		
42 L.H., Daily Totals		$1810.30		$2764.90	$43.10	$65.83
Crew D-4	Hr.	Daily	Hr.	Daily	Bare Costs	Incl. O&P
1 Bricklayer	$46.15	$369.20	$70.45	$563.60	$42.71	$65.10
2 Bricklayer Helpers	38.05	608.80	58.10	929.60		
1 Equip. Oper. (light)	48.60	388.80	73.75	590.00		
1 Grout Pump, 50 C.F./hr.		133.40		146.74	4.17	4.59
32 L.H., Daily Totals		$1500.20		$2229.94	$46.88	$69.69
Crew D-5	Hr.	Daily	Hr.	Daily	Bare Costs	Incl. O&P
1 Bricklayer	46.15	369.20	70.45	563.60	46.15	70.45
8 L.H., Daily Totals		$369.20		$563.60	$46.15	$70.45
Crew D-6	Hr.	Daily	Hr.	Daily	Bare Costs	Incl. O&P
3 Bricklayers	$46.15	$1107.60	$70.45	$1690.80	$42.29	$64.59
3 Bricklayer Helpers	38.05	913.20	58.10	1394.40		
.25 Carpenter	46.95	93.90	72.25	144.50		
50 L.H., Daily Totals		$2114.70		$3229.70	$42.29	$64.59
Crew D-7	Hr.	Daily	Hr.	Daily	Bare Costs	Incl. O&P
1 Tile Layer	$42.80	$342.40	$63.30	$506.40	$38.17	$56.45
1 Tile Layer Helper	33.55	268.40	49.60	396.80		
16 L.H., Daily Totals		$610.80		$903.20	$38.17	$56.45
Crew D-8	Hr.	Daily	Hr.	Daily	Bare Costs	Incl. O&P
3 Bricklayers	$46.15	$1107.60	$70.45	$1690.80	$42.91	$65.51
2 Bricklayer Helpers	38.05	608.80	58.10	929.60		
40 L.H., Daily Totals		$1716.40		$2620.40	$42.91	$65.51

Crew No.	Bare Costs Hr.	Daily	Incl. Subs O&P Hr.	Daily	Cost Per Labor-Hour Bare Costs	Incl. O&P
Crew D-9	Hr.	Daily	Hr.	Daily	Bare Costs	Incl. O&P
3 Bricklayers	$46.15	$1107.60	$70.45	$1690.80	$42.10	$64.28
3 Bricklayer Helpers	38.05	913.20	58.10	1394.40		
48 L.H., Daily Totals		$2020.80		$3085.20	$42.10	$64.28
Crew D-10	Hr.	Daily	Hr.	Daily	Bare Costs	Incl. O&P
1 Bricklayer Foreman (outside)	$48.15	$385.20	$73.55	$588.40	$46.01	$70.14
1 Bricklayer	46.15	369.20	70.45	563.60		
1 Bricklayer Helper	38.05	304.40	58.10	464.80		
1 Equip. Oper. (crane)	51.70	413.60	78.45	627.60		
1 S.P. Crane, 4x4, 12 Ton		473.40		520.74	14.79	16.27
32 L.H., Daily Totals		$1945.80		$2765.14	$60.81	$86.41
Crew D-11	Hr.	Daily	Hr.	Daily	Bare Costs	Incl. O&P
1 Bricklayer Foreman (outside)	$48.15	$385.20	$73.55	$588.40	$44.12	$67.37
1 Bricklayer	46.15	369.20	70.45	563.60		
1 Bricklayer Helper	38.05	304.40	58.10	464.80		
24 L.H., Daily Totals		$1058.80		$1616.80	$44.12	$67.37
Crew D-12	Hr.	Daily	Hr.	Daily	Bare Costs	Incl. O&P
1 Bricklayer Foreman (outside)	$48.15	$385.20	$73.55	$588.40	$42.60	$65.05
1 Bricklayer	46.15	369.20	70.45	563.60		
2 Bricklayer Helpers	38.05	608.80	58.10	929.60		
32 L.H., Daily Totals		$1363.20		$2081.60	$42.60	$65.05
Crew D-13	Hr.	Daily	Hr.	Daily	Bare Costs	Incl. O&P
1 Bricklayer Foreman (outside)	$48.15	$385.20	$73.55	$588.40	$44.84	$68.48
1 Bricklayer	46.15	369.20	70.45	563.60		
2 Bricklayer Helpers	38.05	608.80	58.10	929.60		
1 Carpenter	46.95	375.60	72.25	578.00		
1 Equip. Oper. (crane)	51.70	413.60	78.45	627.60		
1 S.P. Crane, 4x4, 12 Ton		473.40		520.74	9.86	10.85
48 L.H., Daily Totals		$2625.80		$3807.94	$54.70	$79.33
Crew E-1	Hr.	Daily	Hr.	Daily	Bare Costs	Incl. O&P
1 Welder Foreman (outside)	$54.65	$437.20	$94.95	$759.60	$51.97	$86.72
1 Welder	52.65	421.20	91.45	731.60		
1 Equip. Oper. (light)	48.60	388.80	73.75	590.00		
1 Welder, Gas Engine, 300 amp		145.85		160.44	6.08	6.68
24 L.H., Daily Totals		$1393.05		$2241.64	$58.04	$93.40
Crew E-2	Hr.	Daily	Hr.	Daily	Bare Costs	Incl. O&P
1 Struc. Steel Foreman (outside)	$54.65	$437.20	$94.95	$759.60	$51.74	$86.82
4 Struc. Steel Workers	52.65	1684.80	91.45	2926.40		
1 Equip. Oper. (crane)	51.70	413.60	78.45	627.60		
1 Equip. Oper. (oiler)	45.20	361.60	68.55	548.40		
1 Lattice Boom Crane, 90 Ton		1511.00		1662.10	26.98	29.68
56 L.H., Daily Totals		$4408.20		$6524.10	$78.72	$116.50
Crew E-3	Hr.	Daily	Hr.	Daily	Bare Costs	Incl. O&P
1 Struc. Steel Foreman (outside)	$54.65	$437.20	$94.95	$759.60	$53.32	$92.62
1 Struc. Steel Worker	52.65	421.20	91.45	731.60		
1 Welder	52.65	421.20	91.45	731.60		
1 Welder, Gas Engine, 300 amp		145.85		160.44	6.08	6.68
24 L.H., Daily Totals		$1425.45		$2383.24	$59.39	$99.30

For customer support on your Site Work & Landscape Cost Data, call 877.737.1594.

739

Crew No.	Bare Costs Hr.	Daily	Incl. Subs O&P Hr.	Daily	Cost Per Labor-Hour Bare Costs	Incl. O&P
Crew E-3A						
1 Struc. Steel Foreman (outside)	$54.65	$437.20	$94.95	$759.60	$53.32	$92.62
1 Struc. Steel Worker	52.65	421.20	91.45	731.60		
1 Welder	52.65	421.20	91.45	731.60		
1 Welder, Gas Engine, 300 amp		145.85		160.44		
1 Aerial Lift Truck, 40' Boom		301.40		331.54	18.64	20.50
24 L.H., Daily Totals		$1726.85		$2714.78	$71.95	$113.12
Crew E-4						
1 Struc. Steel Foreman (outside)	$54.65	$437.20	$94.95	$759.60	$53.15	$92.33
3 Struc. Steel Workers	52.65	1263.60	91.45	2194.80		
1 Welder, Gas Engine, 300 amp		145.85		160.44	4.56	5.01
32 L.H., Daily Totals		$1846.65		$3114.84	$57.71	$97.34
Crew E-5						
2 Struc. Steel Foremen (outside)	$54.65	$874.40	$94.95	$1519.20	$52.21	$88.56
5 Struc. Steel Workers	52.65	2106.00	91.45	3658.00		
1 Equip. Oper. (crane)	51.70	413.60	78.45	627.60		
1 Welder	52.65	421.20	91.45	731.60		
1 Equip. Oper. (oiler)	45.20	361.60	68.55	548.40		
1 Lattice Boom Crane, 90 Ton		1511.00		1662.10		
1 Welder, Gas Engine, 300 amp		145.85		160.44	20.71	22.78
80 L.H., Daily Totals		$5833.65		$8907.33	$72.92	$111.34
Crew E-6						
3 Struc. Steel Foremen (outside)	$54.65	$1311.60	$94.95	$2278.80	$52.25	$88.76
9 Struc. Steel Workers	52.65	3790.80	91.45	6584.40		
1 Equip. Oper. (crane)	51.70	413.60	78.45	627.60		
1 Welder	52.65	421.20	91.45	731.60		
1 Equip. Oper. (oiler)	45.20	361.60	68.55	548.40		
1 Equip. Oper. (light)	48.60	388.80	73.75	590.00		
1 Lattice Boom Crane, 90 Ton		1511.00		1662.10		
1 Welder, Gas Engine, 300 amp		145.85		160.44		
1 Air Compressor, 160 cfm		156.40		172.04		
2 Impact Wrenches		36.00		39.60	14.45	15.89
128 L.H., Daily Totals		$8536.85		$13394.98	$66.69	$104.65
Crew E-7						
1 Struc. Steel Foreman (outside)	$54.65	$437.20	$94.95	$759.60	$52.21	$88.56
4 Struc. Steel Workers	52.65	1684.80	91.45	2926.40		
1 Equip. Oper. (crane)	51.70	413.60	78.45	627.60		
1 Equip. Oper. (oiler)	45.20	361.60	68.55	548.40		
1 Welder Foreman (outside)	54.65	437.20	94.95	759.60		
2 Welders	52.65	842.40	91.45	1463.20		
1 Lattice Boom Crane, 90 Ton		1511.00		1662.10		
2 Welder, Gas Engine, 300 amp		291.70		320.87	22.53	24.79
80 L.H., Daily Totals		$5979.50		$9067.77	$74.74	$113.35
Crew E-8						
1 Struc. Steel Foreman (outside)	$54.65	$437.20	$94.95	$759.60	$52.00	$87.87
4 Struc. Steel Workers	52.65	1684.80	91.45	2926.40		
1 Welder Foreman (outside)	54.65	437.20	94.95	759.60		
4 Welders	52.65	1684.80	91.45	2926.40		
1 Equip. Oper. (crane)	51.70	413.60	78.45	627.60		
1 Equip. Oper. (oiler)	45.20	361.60	68.55	548.40		
1 Equip. Oper. (light)	48.60	388.80	73.75	590.00		
1 Lattice Boom Crane, 90 Ton		1511.00		1662.10		
4 Welder, Gas Engine, 300 amp		583.40		641.74	20.14	22.15
104 L.H., Daily Totals		$7502.40		$11441.84	$72.14	$110.02

Crew No.	Bare Costs Hr.	Daily	Incl. Subs O&P Hr.	Daily	Cost Per Labor-Hour Bare Costs	Incl. O&P
Crew E-9						
2 Struc. Steel Foremen (outside)	$54.65	$874.40	$94.95	$1519.20	$52.25	$88.76
5 Struc. Steel Workers	52.65	2106.00	91.45	3658.00		
1 Welder Foreman (outside)	54.65	437.20	94.95	759.60		
5 Welders	52.65	2106.00	91.45	3658.00		
1 Equip. Oper. (crane)	51.70	413.60	78.45	627.60		
1 Equip. Oper. (oiler)	45.20	361.60	68.55	548.40		
1 Equip. Oper. (light)	48.60	388.80	73.75	590.00		
1 Lattice Boom Crane, 90 Ton		1511.00		1662.10		
5 Welder, Gas Engine, 300 amp		729.25		802.17	17.50	19.25
128 L.H., Daily Totals		$8927.85		$13825.08	$69.75	$108.01
Crew E-10						
1 Welder Foreman (outside)	$54.65	$437.20	$94.95	$759.60	$53.65	$93.20
1 Welder	52.65	421.20	91.45	731.60		
1 Welder, Gas Engine, 300 amp		145.85		160.44		
1 Flatbed Truck, Gas, 3 Ton		303.20		333.52	28.07	30.87
16 L.H., Daily Totals		$1307.45		$1985.16	$81.72	$124.07
Crew E-11						
2 Painters, Struc. Steel	$41.45	$663.20	$72.95	$1167.20	$42.27	$69.38
1 Building Laborer	37.60	300.80	57.85	462.80		
1 Equip. Oper. (light)	48.60	388.80	73.75	590.00		
1 Air Compressor, 250 cfm		201.40		221.54		
1 Sandblaster, Portable, 3 C.F.		20.40		22.44		
1 Set Sand Blasting Accessories		14.05		15.46	7.37	8.11
32 L.H., Daily Totals		$1588.65		$2479.43	$49.65	$77.48
Crew E-11A						
2 Painters, Struc. Steel	$41.45	$663.20	$72.95	$1167.20	$42.27	$69.38
1 Building Laborer	37.60	300.80	57.85	462.80		
1 Equip. Oper. (light)	48.60	388.80	73.75	590.00		
1 Air Compressor, 250 cfm		201.40		221.54		
1 Sandblaster, Portable, 3 C.F.		20.40		22.44		
1 Set Sand Blasting Accessories		14.05		15.46		
1 Aerial Lift Truck, 60' Boom		435.60		479.16	20.98	23.08
32 L.H., Daily Totals		$2024.25		$2958.59	$63.26	$92.46
Crew E-11B						
2 Painters, Struc. Steel	$41.45	$663.20	$72.95	$1167.20	$40.17	$67.92
1 Building Laborer	37.60	300.80	57.85	462.80		
2 Paint Sprayer, 8 C.F.M.		99.80		109.78		
1 Aerial Lift Truck, 60' Boom		435.60		479.16	22.31	24.54
24 L.H., Daily Totals		$1499.40		$2218.94	$62.48	$92.46
Crew E-12						
1 Welder Foreman (outside)	$54.65	$437.20	$94.95	$759.60	$51.63	$84.35
1 Equip. Oper. (light)	48.60	388.80	73.75	590.00		
1 Welder, Gas Engine, 300 amp		145.85		160.44	9.12	10.03
16 L.H., Daily Totals		$971.85		$1510.04	$60.74	$94.38
Crew E-13						
1 Welder Foreman (outside)	$54.65	$437.20	$94.95	$759.60	$52.63	$87.88
.5 Equip. Oper. (light)	48.60	194.40	73.75	295.00		
1 Welder, Gas Engine, 300 amp		145.85		160.44	12.15	13.37
12 L.H., Daily Totals		$777.45		$1215.04	$64.79	$101.25
Crew E-14						
1 Welder Foreman (outside)	$54.65	$437.20	$94.95	$759.60	$54.65	$94.95
1 Welder, Gas Engine, 300 amp		145.85		160.44	18.23	20.05
8 L.H., Daily Totals		$583.05		$920.03	$72.88	$115.00

Crew No.	Bare Costs		Incl. Subs O&P		Cost Per Labor-Hour	

Crew E-16	Hr.	Daily	Hr.	Daily	Bare Costs	Incl. O&P
1 Welder Foreman (outside)	$54.65	$437.20	$94.95	$759.60	$53.65	$93.20
1 Welder	52.65	421.20	91.45	731.60		
1 Welder, Gas Engine, 300 amp		145.85		160.44	9.12	10.03
16 L.H., Daily Totals		$1004.25		$1651.64	$62.77	$103.23

Crew E-17	Hr.	Daily	Hr.	Daily	Bare Costs	Incl. O&P
1 Struc. Steel Foreman (outside)	$54.65	$437.20	$94.95	$759.60	$53.65	$93.20
1 Structural Steel Worker	52.65	421.20	91.45	731.60		
16 L.H., Daily Totals		$858.40		$1491.20	$53.65	$93.20

Crew E-18	Hr.	Daily	Hr.	Daily	Bare Costs	Incl. O&P
1 Struc. Steel Foreman (outside)	$54.65	$437.20	$94.95	$759.60	$52.64	$89.21
3 Structural Steel Workers	52.65	1263.60	91.45	2194.80		
1 Equipment Operator (med.)	50.60	404.80	76.75	614.00		
1 Lattice Boom Crane, 20 Ton		948.90		1043.79	23.72	26.09
40 L.H., Daily Totals		$3054.50		$4612.19	$76.36	$115.30

Crew E-19	Hr.	Daily	Hr.	Daily	Bare Costs	Incl. O&P
1 Struc. Steel Foreman (outside)	$54.65	$437.20	$94.95	$759.60	$51.97	$86.72
1 Structural Steel Worker	52.65	421.20	91.45	731.60		
1 Equip. Oper. (light)	48.60	388.80	73.75	590.00		
1 Lattice Boom Crane, 20 Ton		948.90		1043.79	39.54	43.49
24 L.H., Daily Totals		$2196.10		$3124.99	$91.50	$130.21

Crew E-20	Hr.	Daily	Hr.	Daily	Bare Costs	Incl. O&P
1 Struc. Steel Foreman (outside)	$54.65	$437.20	$94.95	$759.60	$51.85	$87.40
5 Structural Steel Workers	52.65	2106.00	91.45	3658.00		
1 Equip. Oper. (crane)	51.70	413.60	78.45	627.60		
1 Equip. Oper. (oiler)	45.20	361.60	68.55	548.40		
1 Lattice Boom Crane, 40 Ton		1164.00		1280.40	18.19	20.01
64 L.H., Daily Totals		$4482.40		$6874.00	$70.04	$107.41

Crew E-22	Hr.	Daily	Hr.	Daily	Bare Costs	Incl. O&P
1 Skilled Worker Foreman (out)	$50.65	$405.20	$78.25	$626.00	$49.32	$76.18
2 Skilled Workers	48.65	778.40	75.15	1202.40		
24 L.H., Daily Totals		$1183.60		$1828.40	$49.32	$76.18

Crew E-24	Hr.	Daily	Hr.	Daily	Bare Costs	Incl. O&P
3 Structural Steel Workers	$52.65	$1263.60	$91.45	$2194.80	$52.14	$87.78
1 Equipment Operator (med.)	50.60	404.80	76.75	614.00		
1 Hyd. Crane, 25 Ton		736.60		810.26	23.02	25.32
32 L.H., Daily Totals		$2405.00		$3619.06	$75.16	$113.10

Crew E-25	Hr.	Daily	Hr.	Daily	Bare Costs	Incl. O&P
1 Welder Foreman (outside)	$54.65	$437.20	$94.95	$759.60	$54.65	$94.95
1 Cutting Torch		11.40		12.54	1.43	1.57
8 L.H., Daily Totals		$448.60		$772.14	$56.08	$96.52

Crew F-3	Hr.	Daily	Hr.	Daily	Bare Costs	Incl. O&P
4 Carpenters	$46.95	$1502.40	$72.25	$2312.00	$47.90	$73.49
1 Equip. Oper. (crane)	51.70	413.60	78.45	627.60		
1 Hyd. Crane, 12 Ton		653.80		719.18	16.34	17.98
40 L.H., Daily Totals		$2569.80		$3658.78	$64.25	$91.47

Crew F-4	Hr.	Daily	Hr.	Daily	Bare Costs	Incl. O&P
4 Carpenters	$46.95	$1502.40	$72.25	$2312.00	$47.45	$72.67
1 Equip. Oper. (crane)	51.70	413.60	78.45	627.60		
1 Equip. Oper. (oiler)	45.20	361.60	68.55	548.40		
1 Hyd. Crane, 55 Ton		1128.00		1240.80	23.50	25.85
48 L.H., Daily Totals		$3405.60		$4728.80	$70.95	$98.52

Crew F-5	Hr.	Daily	Hr.	Daily	Bare Costs	Incl. O&P
1 Carpenter Foreman (outside)	$48.95	$391.60	$75.35	$602.80	$47.45	$73.03
3 Carpenters	46.95	1126.80	72.25	1734.00		
32 L.H., Daily Totals		$1518.40		$2336.80	$47.45	$73.03

Crew F-6	Hr.	Daily	Hr.	Daily	Bare Costs	Incl. O&P
2 Carpenters	$46.95	$751.20	$72.25	$1156.00	$44.16	$67.73
2 Building Laborers	37.60	601.60	57.85	925.60		
1 Equip. Oper. (crane)	51.70	413.60	78.45	627.60		
1 Hyd. Crane, 12 Ton		653.80		719.18	16.34	17.98
40 L.H., Daily Totals		$2420.20		$3428.38	$60.51	$85.71

Crew F-7	Hr.	Daily	Hr.	Daily	Bare Costs	Incl. O&P
2 Carpenters	$46.95	$751.20	$72.25	$1156.00	$42.27	$65.05
2 Building Laborers	37.60	601.60	57.85	925.60		
32 L.H., Daily Totals		$1352.80		$2081.60	$42.27	$65.05

Crew G-1	Hr.	Daily	Hr.	Daily	Bare Costs	Incl. O&P
1 Roofer Foreman (outside)	$42.10	$336.80	$71.85	$574.80	$37.51	$64.04
4 Roofers Composition	40.10	1283.20	68.45	2190.40		
2 Roofer Helpers	30.05	480.80	51.30	820.80		
1 Application Equipment		193.00		212.30		
1 Tar Kettle/Pot		169.80		186.78		
1 Crew Truck		206.40		227.04	10.16	11.18
56 L.H., Daily Totals		$2670.00		$4212.12	$47.68	$75.22

Crew G-2	Hr.	Daily	Hr.	Daily	Bare Costs	Incl. O&P
1 Plasterer	$42.95	$343.60	$64.40	$515.20	$39.55	$59.78
1 Plasterer Helper	38.10	304.80	57.10	456.80		
1 Building Laborer	37.60	300.80	57.85	462.80		
1 Grout Pump, 50 C.F./hr.		133.40		146.74	5.56	6.11
24 L.H., Daily Totals		$1082.60		$1581.54	$45.11	$65.90

Crew G-2A	Hr.	Daily	Hr.	Daily	Bare Costs	Incl. O&P
1 Roofer Composition	$40.10	$320.80	$68.45	$547.60	$35.92	$59.20
1 Roofer Helper	30.05	240.40	51.30	410.40		
1 Building Laborer	37.60	300.80	57.85	462.80		
1 Foam Spray Rig, Trailer-Mtd.		573.25		630.58		
1 Pickup Truck, 3/4 Ton		144.20		158.62	29.89	32.88
24 L.H., Daily Totals		$1579.45		$2209.99	$65.81	$92.08

Crew G-3	Hr.	Daily	Hr.	Daily	Bare Costs	Incl. O&P
2 Sheet Metal Workers	$55.95	$895.20	$85.50	$1368.00	$46.77	$71.67
2 Building Laborers	37.60	601.60	57.85	925.60		
32 L.H., Daily Totals		$1496.80		$2293.60	$46.77	$71.67

Crew G-4	Hr.	Daily	Hr.	Daily	Bare Costs	Incl. O&P
1 Labor Foreman (outside)	$39.60	$316.80	$60.95	$487.60	$38.27	$58.88
2 Building Laborers	37.60	601.60	57.85	925.60		
1 Flatbed Truck, Gas, 1.5 Ton		245.40		269.94		
1 Air Compressor, 160 cfm		156.40		172.04	16.74	18.42
24 L.H., Daily Totals		$1320.20		$1855.18	$55.01	$77.30

Crew G-5	Hr.	Daily	Hr.	Daily	Bare Costs	Incl. O&P
1 Roofer Foreman (outside)	$42.10	$336.80	$71.85	$574.80	$36.48	$62.27
2 Roofers Composition	40.10	641.60	68.45	1095.20		
2 Roofer Helpers	30.05	480.80	51.30	820.80		
1 Application Equipment		193.00		212.30	4.83	5.31
40 L.H., Daily Totals		$1652.20		$2703.10	$41.31	$67.58

Crew G-6A

Crew No.	Bare Costs Hr.	Daily	Incl. Subs O&P Hr.	Daily	Cost Per Labor-Hour Bare Costs	Incl. O&P
2 Roofers Composition	$40.10	$641.60	$68.45	$1095.20	$40.10	$68.45
1 Small Compressor, Electric		12.95		14.24		
2 Pneumatic Nailers		55.30		60.83	4.27	4.69
16 L.H., Daily Totals		$709.85		$1170.28	$44.37	$73.14

Crew G-7

Crew No.	Bare Costs Hr.	Daily	Incl. Subs O&P Hr.	Daily	Cost Per Labor-Hour Bare Costs	Incl. O&P
1 Carpenter	$46.95	$375.60	$72.25	$578.00	$46.95	$72.25
1 Small Compressor, Electric		12.95		14.24		
1 Pneumatic Nailer		27.65		30.41	5.08	5.58
8 L.H., Daily Totals		$416.20		$622.66	$52.02	$77.83

Crew H-1

Crew No.	Bare Costs Hr.	Daily	Incl. Subs O&P Hr.	Daily	Cost Per Labor-Hour Bare Costs	Incl. O&P
2 Glaziers	$45.10	$721.60	$68.70	$1099.20	$48.88	$80.08
2 Struc. Steel Workers	52.65	842.40	91.45	1463.20		
32 L.H., Daily Totals		$1564.00		$2562.40	$48.88	$80.08

Crew H-2

Crew No.	Bare Costs Hr.	Daily	Incl. Subs O&P Hr.	Daily	Cost Per Labor-Hour Bare Costs	Incl. O&P
2 Glaziers	$45.10	$721.60	$68.70	$1099.20	$42.60	$65.08
1 Building Laborer	37.60	300.80	57.85	462.80		
24 L.H., Daily Totals		$1022.40		$1562.00	$42.60	$65.08

Crew H-3

Crew No.	Bare Costs Hr.	Daily	Incl. Subs O&P Hr.	Daily	Cost Per Labor-Hour Bare Costs	Incl. O&P
1 Glazier	$45.10	$360.80	$68.70	$549.60	$40.27	$61.83
1 Helper	35.45	283.60	54.95	439.60		
16 L.H., Daily Totals		$644.40		$989.20	$40.27	$61.83

Crew H-4

Crew No.	Bare Costs Hr.	Daily	Incl. Subs O&P Hr.	Daily	Cost Per Labor-Hour Bare Costs	Incl. O&P
1 Carpenter	$46.95	$375.60	$72.25	$578.00	$43.90	$67.27
1 Carpenter Helper	35.45	283.60	54.95	439.60		
.5 Electrician	54.70	218.80	81.95	327.80		
20 L.H., Daily Totals		$878.00		$1345.40	$43.90	$67.27

Crew J-1

Crew No.	Bare Costs Hr.	Daily	Incl. Subs O&P Hr.	Daily	Cost Per Labor-Hour Bare Costs	Incl. O&P
3 Plasterers	$42.95	$1030.80	$64.40	$1545.60	$41.01	$61.48
2 Plasterer Helpers	38.10	609.60	57.10	913.60		
1 Mixing Machine, 6 C.F.		140.20		154.22	3.50	3.86
40 L.H., Daily Totals		$1780.60		$2613.42	$44.52	$65.34

Crew J-2

Crew No.	Bare Costs Hr.	Daily	Incl. Subs O&P Hr.	Daily	Cost Per Labor-Hour Bare Costs	Incl. O&P
3 Plasterers	$42.95	$1030.80	$64.40	$1545.60	$41.34	$61.80
2 Plasterer Helpers	38.10	609.60	57.10	913.60		
1 Lather	43.00	344.00	63.40	507.20		
1 Mixing Machine, 6 C.F.		140.20		154.22	2.92	3.21
48 L.H., Daily Totals		$2124.60		$3120.62	$44.26	$65.01

Crew J-3

Crew No.	Bare Costs Hr.	Daily	Incl. Subs O&P Hr.	Daily	Cost Per Labor-Hour Bare Costs	Incl. O&P
1 Terrazzo Worker	$42.95	$343.60	$63.50	$508.00	$39.23	$58.00
1 Terrazzo Helper	35.50	284.00	52.50	420.00		
1 Floor Grinder, 22" Path		115.55		127.11		
1 Terrazzo Mixer		188.20		207.02	18.98	20.88
16 L.H., Daily Totals		$931.35		$1262.13	$58.21	$78.88

Crew J-4

Crew No.	Bare Costs Hr.	Daily	Incl. Subs O&P Hr.	Daily	Cost Per Labor-Hour Bare Costs	Incl. O&P
2 Cement Finishers	$45.00	$720.00	$66.65	$1066.40	$42.53	$63.72
1 Laborer	37.60	300.80	57.85	462.80		
1 Floor Grinder, 22" Path		115.55		127.11		
1 Floor Edger, 7" Path		39.30		43.23		
1 Vacuum Pick-Up System		60.90		66.99	8.99	9.89
24 L.H., Daily Totals		$1236.55		$1766.53	$51.52	$73.61

Crew J-4A

Crew No.	Bare Costs Hr.	Daily	Incl. Subs O&P Hr.	Daily	Cost Per Labor-Hour Bare Costs	Incl. O&P
2 Cement Finishers	$45.00	$720.00	$66.65	$1066.40	$41.30	$62.25
2 Laborers	37.60	601.60	57.85	925.60		
1 Floor Grinder, 22" Path		115.55		127.11		
1 Floor Edger, 7" Path		39.30		43.23		
1 Vacuum Pick-Up System		60.90		66.99		
1 Floor Auto Scrubber		233.85		257.24	14.05	15.46
32 L.H., Daily Totals		$1771.20		$2486.56	$55.35	$77.70

Crew J-4B

Crew No.	Bare Costs Hr.	Daily	Incl. Subs O&P Hr.	Daily	Cost Per Labor-Hour Bare Costs	Incl. O&P
1 Laborer	$37.60	$300.80	$57.85	$462.80	$37.60	$57.85
1 Floor Auto Scrubber		233.85		257.24	29.23	32.15
8 L.H., Daily Totals		$534.65		$720.03	$66.83	$90.00

Crew J-6

Crew No.	Bare Costs Hr.	Daily	Incl. Subs O&P Hr.	Daily	Cost Per Labor-Hour Bare Costs	Incl. O&P
2 Painters	$40.35	$645.60	$60.80	$972.80	$41.73	$63.30
1 Building Laborer	37.60	300.80	57.85	462.80		
1 Equip. Oper. (light)	48.60	388.80	73.75	590.00		
1 Air Compressor, 250 cfm		201.40		221.54		
1 Sandblaster, Portable, 3 C.F.		20.40		22.44		
1 Set Sand Blasting Accessories		14.05		15.46	7.37	8.11
32 L.H., Daily Totals		$1571.05		$2285.03	$49.10	$71.41

Crew J-7

Crew No.	Bare Costs Hr.	Daily	Incl. Subs O&P Hr.	Daily	Cost Per Labor-Hour Bare Costs	Incl. O&P
2 Painters	$40.35	$645.60	$60.80	$972.80	$40.35	$60.80
1 Floor Belt Sander		14.20		15.62		
1 Floor Sanding Edger		12.60		13.86	1.68	1.84
16 L.H., Daily Totals		$672.40		$1002.28	$42.02	$62.64

Crew K-1

Crew No.	Bare Costs Hr.	Daily	Incl. Subs O&P Hr.	Daily	Cost Per Labor-Hour Bare Costs	Incl. O&P
1 Carpenter	$46.95	$375.60	$72.25	$578.00	$43.02	$65.67
1 Truck Driver (light)	39.10	312.80	59.10	472.80		
1 Flatbed Truck, Gas, 3 Ton		303.20		333.52	18.95	20.84
16 L.H., Daily Totals		$991.60		$1384.32	$61.98	$86.52

Crew K-2

Crew No.	Bare Costs Hr.	Daily	Incl. Subs O&P Hr.	Daily	Cost Per Labor-Hour Bare Costs	Incl. O&P
1 Struc. Steel Foreman (outside)	$54.65	$437.20	$94.95	$759.60	$48.80	$81.83
1 Struc. Steel Worker	52.65	421.20	91.45	731.60		
1 Truck Driver (light)	39.10	312.80	59.10	472.80		
1 Flatbed Truck, Gas, 3 Ton		303.20		333.52	12.63	13.90
24 L.H., Daily Totals		$1474.40		$2297.52	$61.43	$95.73

Crew L-1

Crew No.	Bare Costs Hr.	Daily	Incl. Subs O&P Hr.	Daily	Cost Per Labor-Hour Bare Costs	Incl. O&P
1 Electrician	$54.70	$437.60	$81.95	$655.60	$56.70	$85.30
1 Plumber	58.70	469.60	88.65	709.20		
16 L.H., Daily Totals		$907.20		$1364.80	$56.70	$85.30

Crew L-2

Crew No.	Bare Costs Hr.	Daily	Incl. Subs O&P Hr.	Daily	Cost Per Labor-Hour Bare Costs	Incl. O&P
1 Carpenter	$46.95	$375.60	$72.25	$578.00	$41.20	$63.60
1 Carpenter Helper	35.45	283.60	54.95	439.60		
16 L.H., Daily Totals		$659.20		$1017.60	$41.20	$63.60

Crew L-3

Crew No.	Bare Costs Hr.	Daily	Incl. Subs O&P Hr.	Daily	Cost Per Labor-Hour Bare Costs	Incl. O&P
1 Carpenter	$46.95	$375.60	$72.25	$578.00	$51.14	$77.99
.5 Electrician	54.70	218.80	81.95	327.80		
.5 Sheet Metal Worker	55.95	223.80	85.50	342.00		
16 L.H., Daily Totals		$818.20		$1247.80	$51.14	$77.99

Crew L-3A

	Bare Costs Hr.	Daily	Incl. Subs O&P Hr.	Daily	Cost Per Labor-Hour Bare Costs	Incl. O&P
1 Carpenter Foreman (outside)	$48.95	$391.60	$75.35	$602.80	$51.28	$78.73
.5 Sheet Metal Worker	55.95	223.80	85.50	342.00		
12 L.H., Daily Totals		$615.40		$944.80	$51.28	$78.73

Crew L-4

	Hr.	Daily	Hr.	Daily	Bare Costs	Incl. O&P
2 Skilled Workers	$48.65	$778.40	$75.15	$1202.40	$44.25	$68.42
1 Helper	35.45	283.60	54.95	439.60		
24 L.H., Daily Totals		$1062.00		$1642.00	$44.25	$68.42

Crew L-5

	Hr.	Daily	Hr.	Daily	Bare Costs	Incl. O&P
1 Struc. Steel Foreman (outside)	$54.65	$437.20	$94.95	$759.60	$52.80	$90.09
5 Struc. Steel Workers	52.65	2106.00	91.45	3658.00		
1 Equip. Oper. (crane)	51.70	413.60	78.45	627.60		
1 Hyd. Crane, 25 Ton		736.60		810.26	13.15	14.47
56 L.H., Daily Totals		$3693.40		$5855.46	$65.95	$104.56

Crew L-5A

	Hr.	Daily	Hr.	Daily	Bare Costs	Incl. O&P
1 Struc. Steel Foreman (outside)	$54.65	$437.20	$94.95	$759.60	$52.91	$89.08
2 Structural Steel Workers	52.65	842.40	91.45	1463.20		
1 Equip. Oper. (crane)	51.70	413.60	78.45	627.60		
1 S.P. Crane, 4x4, 25 Ton		599.40		659.34	18.73	20.60
32 L.H., Daily Totals		$2292.60		$3509.74	$71.64	$109.68

Crew L-5B

	Hr.	Daily	Hr.	Daily	Bare Costs	Incl. O&P
1 Struc. Steel Foreman (outside)	$54.65	$437.20	$94.95	$759.60	$53.97	$85.46
2 Structural Steel Workers	52.65	842.40	91.45	1463.20		
2 Electricians	54.70	875.20	81.95	1311.20		
2 Steamfitters/Pipefitters	59.75	956.00	90.20	1443.20		
1 Equip. Oper. (crane)	51.70	413.60	78.45	627.60		
1 Equip. Oper. (oiler)	45.20	361.60	68.55	548.40		
1 Hyd. Crane, 80 Ton		1625.00		1787.50	22.57	24.83
72 L.H., Daily Totals		$5511.00		$7940.70	$76.54	$110.29

Crew L-6

	Hr.	Daily	Hr.	Daily	Bare Costs	Incl. O&P
1 Plumber	$58.70	$469.60	$88.65	$709.20	$57.37	$86.42
.5 Electrician	54.70	218.80	81.95	327.80		
12 L.H., Daily Totals		$688.40		$1037.00	$57.37	$86.42

Crew L-7

	Hr.	Daily	Hr.	Daily	Bare Costs	Incl. O&P
2 Carpenters	$46.95	$751.20	$72.25	$1156.00	$45.39	$69.52
1 Building Laborer	37.60	300.80	57.85	462.80		
.5 Electrician	54.70	218.80	81.95	327.80		
28 L.H., Daily Totals		$1270.80		$1946.60	$45.39	$69.52

Crew L-8

	Hr.	Daily	Hr.	Daily	Bare Costs	Incl. O&P
2 Carpenters	$46.95	$751.20	$72.25	$1156.00	$49.30	$75.53
.5 Plumber	58.70	234.80	88.65	354.60		
20 L.H., Daily Totals		$986.00		$1510.60	$49.30	$75.53

Crew L-9

	Hr.	Daily	Hr.	Daily	Bare Costs	Incl. O&P
1 Labor Foreman (inside)	$38.10	$304.80	$58.65	$469.20	$42.96	$68.17
2 Building Laborers	37.60	601.60	57.85	925.60		
1 Struc. Steel Worker	52.65	421.20	91.45	731.60		
.5 Electrician	54.70	218.80	81.95	327.80		
36 L.H., Daily Totals		$1546.40		$2454.20	$42.96	$68.17

Crew L-10

	Hr.	Daily	Hr.	Daily	Bare Costs	Incl. O&P
1 Struc. Steel Foreman (outside)	$54.65	$437.20	$94.95	$759.60	$53.00	$88.28
1 Structural Steel Worker	52.65	421.20	91.45	731.60		
1 Equip. Oper. (crane)	51.70	413.60	78.45	627.60		
1 Hyd. Crane, 12 Ton		653.80		719.18	27.24	29.97
24 L.H., Daily Totals		$1925.80		$2837.98	$80.24	$118.25

Crew L-11

	Hr.	Daily	Hr.	Daily	Bare Costs	Incl. O&P
2 Wreckers	$37.60	$601.60	$62.10	$993.60	$43.88	$69.10
1 Equip. Oper. (crane)	51.70	413.60	78.45	627.60		
1 Equip. Oper. (light)	48.60	388.80	73.75	590.00		
1 Hyd. Excavator, 2.5 C.Y.		1605.00		1765.50		
1 Loader, Skid Steer, 78 H.P.		318.60		350.46	60.11	66.12
32 L.H., Daily Totals		$3327.60		$4327.16	$103.99	$135.22

Crew M-1

	Hr.	Daily	Hr.	Daily	Bare Costs	Incl. O&P
3 Elevator Constructors	$76.50	$1836.00	$114.20	$2740.80	$72.67	$108.49
1 Elevator Apprentice	61.20	489.60	91.35	730.80		
5 Hand Tools		46.00		50.60	1.44	1.58
32 L.H., Daily Totals		$2371.60		$3522.20	$74.11	$110.07

Crew M-3

	Hr.	Daily	Hr.	Daily	Bare Costs	Incl. O&P
1 Electrician Foreman (outside)	$56.70	$453.60	$84.95	$679.60	$57.56	$86.48
1 Common Laborer	37.60	300.80	57.85	462.80		
.25 Equipment Operator (med.)	50.60	101.20	76.75	153.50		
1 Elevator Constructor	76.50	612.00	114.20	913.60		
1 Elevator Apprentice	61.20	489.60	91.35	730.80		
.25 S.P. Crane, 4x4, 20 Ton		138.65		152.51	4.08	4.49
34 L.H., Daily Totals		$2095.85		$3092.82	$61.64	$90.97

Crew M-4

	Hr.	Daily	Hr.	Daily	Bare Costs	Incl. O&P
1 Electrician Foreman (outside)	$56.70	$453.60	$84.95	$679.60	$56.94	$85.58
1 Common Laborer	37.60	300.80	57.85	462.80		
.25 Equipment Operator, Crane	51.70	103.40	78.45	156.90		
.25 Equip. Oper. (oiler)	45.20	90.40	68.55	137.10		
1 Elevator Constructor	76.50	612.00	114.20	913.60		
1 Elevator Apprentice	61.20	489.60	91.35	730.80		
.25 S.P. Crane, 4x4, 40 Ton		175.75		193.32	4.88	5.37
36 L.H., Daily Totals		$2225.55		$3274.13	$61.82	$90.95

Crew Q-1

	Hr.	Daily	Hr.	Daily	Bare Costs	Incl. O&P
1 Plumber	$58.70	$469.60	$88.65	$709.20	$52.83	$79.78
1 Plumber Apprentice	46.95	375.60	70.90	567.20		
16 L.H., Daily Totals		$845.20		$1276.40	$52.83	$79.78

Crew Q-1A

	Hr.	Daily	Hr.	Daily	Bare Costs	Incl. O&P
.25 Plumber Foreman (outside)	$60.70	$121.40	$91.65	$183.30	$59.10	$89.25
1 Plumber	58.70	469.60	88.65	709.20		
10 L.H., Daily Totals		$591.00		$892.50	$59.10	$89.25

Crew Q-1C

	Hr.	Daily	Hr.	Daily	Bare Costs	Incl. O&P
1 Plumber	$58.70	$469.60	$88.65	$709.20	$52.08	$78.77
1 Plumber Apprentice	46.95	375.60	70.90	567.20		
1 Equip. Oper. (medium)	50.60	404.80	76.75	614.00		
1 Trencher, Chain Type, 8' D		3402.00		3742.20	141.75	155.93
24 L.H., Daily Totals		$4652.00		$5632.60	$193.83	$234.69

Crew Q-2

	Hr.	Daily	Hr.	Daily	Bare Costs	Incl. O&P
2 Plumbers	$58.70	$939.20	$88.65	$1418.40	$54.78	$82.73
1 Plumber Apprentice	46.95	375.60	70.90	567.20		
24 L.H., Daily Totals		$1314.80		$1985.60	$54.78	$82.73

For customer support on your Site Work & Landscape Cost Data, call 877.737.1594.

743

Crew Q-3

Crew No.	Bare Costs Hr.	Bare Costs Daily	Incl. Subs O&P Hr.	Incl. Subs O&P Daily	Cost Per Labor-Hour Bare Costs	Cost Per Labor-Hour Incl. O&P
1 Plumber Foreman (inside)	$59.20	$473.60	$89.40	$715.20	$55.89	$84.40
2 Plumbers	58.70	939.20	88.65	1418.40		
1 Plumber Apprentice	46.95	375.60	70.90	567.20		
32 L.H., Daily Totals		$1788.40		$2700.80	$55.89	$84.40

Crew Q-4

Crew No.	Bare Costs Hr.	Bare Costs Daily	Incl. Subs O&P Hr.	Incl. Subs O&P Daily	Cost Per Labor-Hour Bare Costs	Cost Per Labor-Hour Incl. O&P
1 Plumber Foreman (inside)	$59.20	$473.60	$89.40	$715.20	$55.89	$84.40
1 Plumber	58.70	469.60	88.65	709.20		
1 Welder (plumber)	58.70	469.60	88.65	709.20		
1 Plumber Apprentice	46.95	375.60	70.90	567.20		
1 Welder, Electric, 300 amp		57.70		63.47	1.80	1.98
32 L.H., Daily Totals		$1846.10		$2764.27	$57.69	$86.38

Crew Q-5

Crew No.	Bare Costs Hr.	Bare Costs Daily	Incl. Subs O&P Hr.	Incl. Subs O&P Daily	Cost Per Labor-Hour Bare Costs	Cost Per Labor-Hour Incl. O&P
1 Steamfitter	$59.75	$478.00	$90.20	$721.60	$53.77	$81.20
1 Steamfitter Apprentice	47.80	382.40	72.20	577.60		
16 L.H., Daily Totals		$860.40		$1299.20	$53.77	$81.20

Crew Q-6

Crew No.	Bare Costs Hr.	Bare Costs Daily	Incl. Subs O&P Hr.	Incl. Subs O&P Daily	Cost Per Labor-Hour Bare Costs	Cost Per Labor-Hour Incl. O&P
2 Steamfitters	$59.75	$956.00	$90.20	$1443.20	$55.77	$84.20
1 Steamfitter Apprentice	47.80	382.40	72.20	577.60		
24 L.H., Daily Totals		$1338.40		$2020.80	$55.77	$84.20

Crew Q-7

Crew No.	Bare Costs Hr.	Bare Costs Daily	Incl. Subs O&P Hr.	Incl. Subs O&P Daily	Cost Per Labor-Hour Bare Costs	Cost Per Labor-Hour Incl. O&P
1 Steamfitter Foreman (inside)	$60.25	$482.00	$91.00	$728.00	$56.89	$85.90
2 Steamfitters	59.75	956.00	90.20	1443.20		
1 Steamfitter Apprentice	47.80	382.40	72.20	577.60		
32 L.H., Daily Totals		$1820.40		$2748.80	$56.89	$85.90

Crew Q-8

Crew No.	Bare Costs Hr.	Bare Costs Daily	Incl. Subs O&P Hr.	Incl. Subs O&P Daily	Cost Per Labor-Hour Bare Costs	Cost Per Labor-Hour Incl. O&P
1 Steamfitter Foreman (inside)	$60.25	$482.00	$91.00	$728.00	$56.89	$85.90
1 Steamfitter	59.75	478.00	90.20	721.60		
1 Welder (steamfitter)	59.75	478.00	90.20	721.60		
1 Steamfitter Apprentice	47.80	382.40	72.20	577.60		
1 Welder, Electric, 300 amp		57.70		63.47	1.80	1.98
32 L.H., Daily Totals		$1878.10		$2812.27	$58.69	$87.88

Crew Q-9

Crew No.	Bare Costs Hr.	Bare Costs Daily	Incl. Subs O&P Hr.	Incl. Subs O&P Daily	Cost Per Labor-Hour Bare Costs	Cost Per Labor-Hour Incl. O&P
1 Sheet Metal Worker	$55.95	$447.60	$85.50	$684.00	$50.35	$76.95
1 Sheet Metal Apprentice	44.75	358.00	68.40	547.20		
16 L.H., Daily Totals		$805.60		$1231.20	$50.35	$76.95

Crew Q-10

Crew No.	Bare Costs Hr.	Bare Costs Daily	Incl. Subs O&P Hr.	Incl. Subs O&P Daily	Cost Per Labor-Hour Bare Costs	Cost Per Labor-Hour Incl. O&P
2 Sheet Metal Workers	$55.95	$895.20	$85.50	$1368.00	$52.22	$79.80
1 Sheet Metal Apprentice	44.75	358.00	68.40	547.20		
24 L.H., Daily Totals		$1253.20		$1915.20	$52.22	$79.80

Crew Q-11

Crew No.	Bare Costs Hr.	Bare Costs Daily	Incl. Subs O&P Hr.	Incl. Subs O&P Daily	Cost Per Labor-Hour Bare Costs	Cost Per Labor-Hour Incl. O&P
1 Sheet Metal Foreman (inside)	$56.45	$451.60	$86.25	$690.00	$53.27	$81.41
2 Sheet Metal Workers	55.95	895.20	85.50	1368.00		
1 Sheet Metal Apprentice	44.75	358.00	68.40	547.20		
32 L.H., Daily Totals		$1704.80		$2605.20	$53.27	$81.41

Crew Q-12

Crew No.	Bare Costs Hr.	Bare Costs Daily	Incl. Subs O&P Hr.	Incl. Subs O&P Daily	Cost Per Labor-Hour Bare Costs	Cost Per Labor-Hour Incl. O&P
1 Sprinkler Installer	$56.15	$449.20	$84.95	$679.60	$50.52	$76.45
1 Sprinkler Apprentice	44.90	359.20	67.95	543.60		
16 L.H., Daily Totals		$808.40		$1223.20	$50.52	$76.45

Crew Q-13

Crew No.	Bare Costs Hr.	Bare Costs Daily	Incl. Subs O&P Hr.	Incl. Subs O&P Daily	Cost Per Labor-Hour Bare Costs	Cost Per Labor-Hour Incl. O&P
1 Sprinkler Foreman (inside)	$56.65	$453.20	$85.70	$685.60	$53.46	$80.89
2 Sprinkler Installers	56.15	898.40	84.95	1359.20		
1 Sprinkler Apprentice	44.90	359.20	67.95	543.60		
32 L.H., Daily Totals		$1710.80		$2588.40	$53.46	$80.89

Crew Q-14

Crew No.	Bare Costs Hr.	Bare Costs Daily	Incl. Subs O&P Hr.	Incl. Subs O&P Daily	Cost Per Labor-Hour Bare Costs	Cost Per Labor-Hour Incl. O&P
1 Asbestos Worker	$52.35	$418.80	$81.50	$652.00	$47.13	$73.38
1 Asbestos Apprentice	41.90	335.20	65.25	522.00		
16 L.H., Daily Totals		$754.00		$1174.00	$47.13	$73.38

Crew Q-15

Crew No.	Bare Costs Hr.	Bare Costs Daily	Incl. Subs O&P Hr.	Incl. Subs O&P Daily	Cost Per Labor-Hour Bare Costs	Cost Per Labor-Hour Incl. O&P
1 Plumber	$58.70	$469.60	$88.65	$709.20	$52.83	$79.78
1 Plumber Apprentice	46.95	375.60	70.90	567.20		
1 Welder, Electric, 300 amp		57.70		63.47	3.61	3.97
16 L.H., Daily Totals		$902.90		$1339.87	$56.43	$83.74

Crew Q-16

Crew No.	Bare Costs Hr.	Bare Costs Daily	Incl. Subs O&P Hr.	Incl. Subs O&P Daily	Cost Per Labor-Hour Bare Costs	Cost Per Labor-Hour Incl. O&P
2 Plumbers	$58.70	$939.20	$88.65	$1418.40	$54.78	$82.73
1 Plumber Apprentice	46.95	375.60	70.90	567.20		
1 Welder, Electric, 300 amp		57.70		63.47	2.40	2.64
24 L.H., Daily Totals		$1372.50		$2049.07	$57.19	$85.38

Crew Q-17

Crew No.	Bare Costs Hr.	Bare Costs Daily	Incl. Subs O&P Hr.	Incl. Subs O&P Daily	Cost Per Labor-Hour Bare Costs	Cost Per Labor-Hour Incl. O&P
1 Steamfitter	$59.75	$478.00	$90.20	$721.60	$53.77	$81.20
1 Steamfitter Apprentice	47.80	382.40	72.20	577.60		
1 Welder, Electric, 300 amp		57.70		63.47	3.61	3.97
16 L.H., Daily Totals		$918.10		$1362.67	$57.38	$85.17

Crew Q-17A

Crew No.	Bare Costs Hr.	Bare Costs Daily	Incl. Subs O&P Hr.	Incl. Subs O&P Daily	Cost Per Labor-Hour Bare Costs	Cost Per Labor-Hour Incl. O&P
1 Steamfitter	$59.75	$478.00	$90.20	$721.60	$53.08	$80.28
1 Steamfitter Apprentice	47.80	382.40	72.20	577.60		
1 Equip. Oper. (crane)	51.70	413.60	78.45	627.60		
1 Hyd. Crane, 12 Ton		653.80		719.18		
1 Welder, Electric, 300 amp		57.70		63.47	29.65	32.61
24 L.H., Daily Totals		$1985.50		$2709.45	$82.73	$112.89

Crew Q-18

Crew No.	Bare Costs Hr.	Bare Costs Daily	Incl. Subs O&P Hr.	Incl. Subs O&P Daily	Cost Per Labor-Hour Bare Costs	Cost Per Labor-Hour Incl. O&P
2 Steamfitters	$59.75	$956.00	$90.20	$1443.20	$55.77	$84.20
1 Steamfitter Apprentice	47.80	382.40	72.20	577.60		
1 Welder, Electric, 300 amp		57.70		63.47	2.40	2.64
24 L.H., Daily Totals		$1396.10		$2084.27	$58.17	$86.84

Crew Q-19

Crew No.	Bare Costs Hr.	Bare Costs Daily	Incl. Subs O&P Hr.	Incl. Subs O&P Daily	Cost Per Labor-Hour Bare Costs	Cost Per Labor-Hour Incl. O&P
1 Steamfitter	$59.75	$478.00	$90.20	$721.60	$54.08	$81.45
1 Steamfitter Apprentice	47.80	382.40	72.20	577.60		
1 Electrician	54.70	437.60	81.95	655.60		
24 L.H., Daily Totals		$1298.00		$1954.80	$54.08	$81.45

Crew Q-20

Crew No.	Bare Costs Hr.	Bare Costs Daily	Incl. Subs O&P Hr.	Incl. Subs O&P Daily	Cost Per Labor-Hour Bare Costs	Cost Per Labor-Hour Incl. O&P
1 Sheet Metal Worker	$55.95	$447.60	$85.50	$684.00	$51.22	$77.95
1 Sheet Metal Apprentice	44.75	358.00	68.40	547.20		
.5 Electrician	54.70	218.80	81.95	327.80		
20 L.H., Daily Totals		$1024.40		$1559.00	$51.22	$77.95

Crew Q-21

Crew No.	Bare Costs Hr.	Bare Costs Daily	Incl. Subs O&P Hr.	Incl. Subs O&P Daily	Cost Per Labor-Hour Bare Costs	Cost Per Labor-Hour Incl. O&P
2 Steamfitters	$59.75	$956.00	$90.20	$1443.20	$55.50	$83.64
1 Steamfitter Apprentice	47.80	382.40	72.20	577.60		
1 Electrician	54.70	437.60	81.95	655.60		
32 L.H., Daily Totals		$1776.00		$2676.40	$55.50	$83.64

Crew No.	Bare Costs Hr.	Daily	Incl. Subs O&P Hr.	Daily	Cost Per Labor-Hour Bare Costs	Incl. O&P
Crew Q-22	Hr.	Daily	Hr.	Daily	Bare Costs	Incl. O&P
1 Plumber	$58.70	$469.60	$88.65	$709.20	$52.83	$79.78
1 Plumber Apprentice	46.95	375.60	70.90	567.20		
1 Hyd. Crane, 12 Ton		653.80		719.18	40.86	44.95
16 L.H., Daily Totals		$1499.00		$1995.58	$93.69	$124.72

Crew Q-22A	Hr.	Daily	Hr.	Daily	Bare Costs	Incl. O&P
1 Plumber	$58.70	$469.60	$88.65	$709.20	$48.74	$73.96
1 Plumber Apprentice	46.95	375.60	70.90	567.20		
1 Laborer	37.60	300.80	57.85	462.80		
1 Equip. Oper. (crane)	51.70	413.60	78.45	627.60		
1 Hyd. Crane, 12 Ton		653.80		719.18	20.43	22.47
32 L.H., Daily Totals		$2213.40		$3085.98	$69.17	$96.44

Crew Q-23	Hr.	Daily	Hr.	Daily	Bare Costs	Incl. O&P
1 Plumber Foreman (outside)	$60.70	$485.60	$91.65	$733.20	$56.67	$85.68
1 Plumber	58.70	469.60	88.65	709.20		
1 Equip. Oper. (medium)	50.60	404.80	76.75	614.00		
1 Lattice Boom Crane, 20 Ton		948.90		1043.79	39.54	43.49
24 L.H., Daily Totals		$2308.90		$3100.19	$96.20	$129.17

Crew R-1	Hr.	Daily	Hr.	Daily	Bare Costs	Incl. O&P
1 Electrician Foreman	$55.20	$441.60	$82.70	$661.60	$48.37	$73.08
3 Electricians	54.70	1312.80	81.95	1966.80		
2 Helpers	35.45	567.20	54.95	879.20		
48 L.H., Daily Totals		$2321.60		$3507.60	$48.37	$73.08

Crew R-1A	Hr.	Daily	Hr.	Daily	Bare Costs	Incl. O&P
1 Electrician	$54.70	$437.60	$81.95	$655.60	$45.08	$68.45
1 Helper	35.45	283.60	54.95	439.60		
16 L.H., Daily Totals		$721.20		$1095.20	$45.08	$68.45

Crew R-2	Hr.	Daily	Hr.	Daily	Bare Costs	Incl. O&P
1 Electrician Foreman	$55.20	$441.60	$82.70	$661.60	$48.84	$73.84
3 Electricians	54.70	1312.80	81.95	1966.80		
2 Helpers	35.45	567.20	54.95	879.20		
1 Equip. Oper. (crane)	51.70	413.60	78.45	627.60		
1 S.P. Crane, 4x4, 5 Ton		275.40		302.94	4.92	5.41
56 L.H., Daily Totals		$3010.60		$4438.14	$53.76	$79.25

Crew R-3	Hr.	Daily	Hr.	Daily	Bare Costs	Incl. O&P
1 Electrician Foreman	$55.20	$441.60	$82.70	$661.60	$54.30	$81.55
1 Electrician	54.70	437.60	81.95	655.60		
.5 Equip. Oper. (crane)	51.70	206.80	78.45	313.80		
.5 S.P. Crane, 4x4, 5 Ton		137.70		151.47	6.88	7.57
20 L.H., Daily Totals		$1223.70		$1782.47	$61.19	$89.12

Crew R-4	Hr.	Daily	Hr.	Daily	Bare Costs	Incl. O&P
1 Struc. Steel Foreman (outside)	$54.65	$437.20	$94.95	$759.60	$53.46	$90.25
3 Struc. Steel Workers	52.65	1263.60	91.45	2194.80		
1 Electrician	54.70	437.60	81.95	655.60		
1 Welder, Gas Engine, 300 amp		145.85		160.44	3.65	4.01
40 L.H., Daily Totals		$2284.25		$3770.43	$57.11	$94.26

Crew R-5	Hr.	Daily	Hr.	Daily	Bare Costs	Incl. O&P
1 Electrician Foreman	$55.20	$441.60	$82.70	$661.60	$47.75	$72.20
4 Electrician Linemen	54.70	1750.40	81.95	2622.40		
2 Electrician Operators	54.70	875.20	81.95	1311.20		
4 Electrician Groundmen	35.45	1134.40	54.95	1758.40		
1 Crew Truck		206.40		227.04		
1 Flatbed Truck, 20,000 GVW		248.60		273.46		
1 Pickup Truck, 3/4 Ton		144.20		158.62		
.2 Hyd. Crane, 55 Ton		225.60		248.16		
.2 Hyd. Crane, 12 Ton		130.76		143.84		
.2 Earth Auger, Truck-Mtd.		83.44		91.78		
1 Tractor w/Winch		427.00		469.70	16.66	18.32
88 L.H., Daily Totals		$5667.60		$7966.20	$64.40	$90.53

Crew R-6	Hr.	Daily	Hr.	Daily	Bare Costs	Incl. O&P
1 Electrician Foreman	$55.20	$441.60	$82.70	$661.60	$47.75	$72.20
4 Electrician Linemen	54.70	1750.40	81.95	2622.40		
2 Electrician Operators	54.70	875.20	81.95	1311.20		
4 Electrician Groundmen	35.45	1134.40	54.95	1758.40		
1 Crew Truck		206.40		227.04		
1 Flatbed Truck, 20,000 GVW		248.60		273.46		
1 Pickup Truck, 3/4 Ton		144.20		158.62		
.2 Hyd. Crane, 55 Ton		225.60		248.16		
.2 Hyd. Crane, 12 Ton		130.76		143.84		
.2 Earth Auger, Truck-Mtd.		83.44		91.78		
1 Tractor w/Winch		427.00		469.70		
3 Cable Trailers		598.20		658.02		
.5 Tensioning Rig		198.40		218.24		
.5 Cable Pulling Rig		1160.00		1276.00	38.89	42.78
88 L.H., Daily Totals		$7624.20		$10118.46	$86.64	$114.98

Crew R-7	Hr.	Daily	Hr.	Daily	Bare Costs	Incl. O&P
1 Electrician Foreman	$55.20	$441.60	$82.70	$661.60	$38.74	$59.58
5 Electrician Groundmen	35.45	1418.00	54.95	2198.00		
1 Crew Truck		206.40		227.04	4.30	4.73
48 L.H., Daily Totals		$2066.00		$3086.64	$43.04	$64.31

Crew R-8	Hr.	Daily	Hr.	Daily	Bare Costs	Incl. O&P
1 Electrician Foreman	$55.20	$441.60	$82.70	$661.60	$48.37	$73.08
3 Electrician Linemen	54.70	1312.80	81.95	1966.80		
2 Electrician Groundmen	35.45	567.20	54.95	879.20		
1 Pickup Truck, 3/4 Ton		144.20		158.62		
1 Crew Truck		206.40		227.04	7.30	8.03
48 L.H., Daily Totals		$2672.20		$3893.26	$55.67	$81.11

Crew R-9	Hr.	Daily	Hr.	Daily	Bare Costs	Incl. O&P
1 Electrician Foreman	$55.20	$441.60	$82.70	$661.60	$45.14	$68.54
1 Electrician Lineman	54.70	437.60	81.95	655.60		
2 Electrician Operators	54.70	875.20	81.95	1311.20		
4 Electrician Groundmen	35.45	1134.40	54.95	1758.40		
1 Pickup Truck, 3/4 Ton		144.20		158.62		
1 Crew Truck		206.40		227.04	5.48	6.03
64 L.H., Daily Totals		$3239.40		$4772.46	$50.62	$74.57

Crew R-10	Hr.	Daily	Hr.	Daily	Bare Costs	Incl. O&P
1 Electrician Foreman	$55.20	$441.60	$82.70	$661.60	$51.58	$77.58
4 Electrician Linemen	54.70	1750.40	81.95	2622.40		
1 Electrician Groundman	35.45	283.60	54.95	439.60		
1 Crew Truck		206.40		227.04		
3 Tram Cars		412.20		453.42	12.89	14.18
48 L.H., Daily Totals		$3094.20		$4404.06	$64.46	$91.75

745

For customer support on your Site Work & Landscape Cost Data, call 877.737.1594.

Crew No.	Bare Costs		Incl. Subs O&P		Cost Per Labor-Hour	
Crew R-11	Hr.	Daily	Hr.	Daily	Bare Costs	Incl. O&P
1 Electrician Foreman	$55.20	$441.60	$82.70	$661.60	$51.90	$78.11
4 Electricians	54.70	1750.40	81.95	2622.40		
1 Equip. Oper. (crane)	51.70	413.60	78.45	627.60		
1 Common Laborer	37.60	300.80	57.85	462.80		
1 Crew Truck		206.40		227.04		
1 Hyd. Crane, 12 Ton		653.80		719.18	15.36	16.90
56 L.H., Daily Totals		$3766.60		$5320.62	$67.26	$95.01
Crew R-12	Hr.	Daily	Hr.	Daily	Bare Costs	Incl. O&P
1 Carpenter Foreman (inside)	$47.45	$379.60	$73.05	$584.40	$44.45	$69.24
4 Carpenters	46.95	1502.40	72.25	2312.00		
4 Common Laborers	37.60	1203.20	57.85	1851.20		
1 Equip. Oper. (medium)	50.60	404.80	76.75	614.00		
1 Steel Worker	52.65	421.20	91.45	731.60		
1 Dozer, 200 H.P.		1387.00		1525.70		
1 Pickup Truck, 3/4 Ton		144.20		158.62	17.40	19.14
88 L.H., Daily Totals		$5442.40		$7777.52	$61.85	$88.38
Crew R-13	Hr.	Daily	Hr.	Daily	Bare Costs	Incl. O&P
1 Electrician Foreman	$55.20	$441.60	$82.70	$661.60	$52.84	$79.37
3 Electricians	54.70	1312.80	81.95	1966.80		
.25 Equip. Oper. (crane)	51.70	103.40	78.45	156.90		
1 Equipment Oiler	45.20	361.60	68.55	548.40		
.25 Hydraulic Crane, 33 Ton		187.50		206.25	4.46	4.91
42 L.H., Daily Totals		$2406.90		$3539.95	$57.31	$84.28
Crew R-15	Hr.	Daily	Hr.	Daily	Bare Costs	Incl. O&P
1 Electrician Foreman	$55.20	$441.60	$82.70	$661.60	$53.77	$80.71
4 Electricians	54.70	1750.40	81.95	2622.40		
1 Equipment Oper. (light)	48.60	388.80	73.75	590.00		
1 Aerial Lift Truck, 40' Boom		301.40		331.54	6.28	6.91
48 L.H., Daily Totals		$2882.20		$4205.54	$60.05	$87.62
Crew R-18	Hr.	Daily	Hr.	Daily	Bare Costs	Incl. O&P
.25 Electrician Foreman	$55.20	$110.40	$82.70	$165.40	$42.89	$65.39
1 Electrician	54.70	437.60	81.95	655.60		
2 Helpers	35.45	567.20	54.95	879.20		
26 L.H., Daily Totals		$1115.20		$1700.20	$42.89	$65.39
Crew R-19	Hr.	Daily	Hr.	Daily	Bare Costs	Incl. O&P
.5 Electrician Foreman	$55.20	$220.80	$82.70	$330.80	$54.80	$82.10
2 Electricians	54.70	875.20	81.95	1311.20		
20 L.H., Daily Totals		$1096.00		$1642.00	$54.80	$82.10
Crew R-21	Hr.	Daily	Hr.	Daily	Bare Costs	Incl. O&P
1 Electrician Foreman	$55.20	$441.60	$82.70	$661.60	$54.72	$82.01
3 Electricians	54.70	1312.80	81.95	1966.80		
.1 Equip. Oper. (medium)	50.60	40.48	76.75	61.40		
.1 S.P. Crane, 4x4, 25 Ton		59.94		65.93	1.83	2.01
32.8 L.H., Daily Totals		$1854.82		$2755.73	$56.55	$84.02
Crew R-22	Hr.	Daily	Hr.	Daily	Bare Costs	Incl. O&P
.66 Electrician Foreman	$55.20	$291.46	$82.70	$436.66	$46.51	$70.47
2 Electricians	54.70	875.20	81.95	1311.20		
2 Helpers	35.45	567.20	54.95	879.20		
37.28 L.H., Daily Totals		$1733.86		$2627.06	$46.51	$70.47

Crew No.	Bare Costs		Incl. Subs O&P		Cost Per Labor-Hour	
Crew R-30	Hr.	Daily	Hr.	Daily	Bare Costs	Incl. O&P
.25 Electrician Foreman (outside)	$56.70	$113.40	$84.95	$169.90	$44.33	$67.35
1 Electrician	54.70	437.60	81.95	655.60		
2 Laborers, (Semi-Skilled)	37.60	601.60	57.85	925.60		
26 L.H., Daily Totals		$1152.60		$1751.10	$44.33	$67.35
Crew R-31	Hr.	Daily	Hr.	Daily	Bare Costs	Incl. O&P
1 Electrician	$54.70	$437.60	$81.95	$655.60	$54.70	$81.95
1 Core Drill, Electric, 2.5 H.P.		55.15		60.66	6.89	7.58
8 L.H., Daily Totals		$492.75		$716.26	$61.59	$89.53
Crew W-41E	Hr.	Daily	Hr.	Daily	Bare Costs	Incl. O&P
.5 Plumber Foreman (outside)	$60.70	$242.80	$91.65	$366.60	$50.66	$76.93
1 Plumber	58.70	469.60	88.65	709.20		
1 Laborer	37.60	300.80	57.85	462.80		
20 L.H., Daily Totals		$1013.20		$1538.60	$50.66	$76.93

Historical Cost Indexes

The table below lists both the RSMeans® historical cost index based on Jan. 1, 1993 = 100 as well as the computed value of an index based on Jan. 1, 2015 costs. Since the Jan. 1, 2015 figure is estimated, space is left to write in the actual index figures as they become available through either the quarterly *RSMeans Construction Cost Indexes* or as printed in the *Engineering News-Record*. To compute the actual index based on Jan. 1, 2015 = 100, divide the historical cost index for a particular year by the actual Jan. 1, 2015 construction cost index. Space has been left to advance the index figures as the year progresses.

Year	Historical Cost Index Jan. 1, 1993 = 100		Current Index Based on Jan. 1, 2015 = 100		Year	Historical Cost Index Jan. 1, 1993 = 100	Current Index Based on Jan. 1, 2015 = 100		Year	Historical Cost Index Jan. 1, 1993 = 100	Current Index Based on Jan. 1, 2015 = 100	
	Est.	Actual	Est.	Actual		Actual	Est.	Actual		Actual	Est.	Actual
Oct 2015*					July 2000	120.9	58.5		July 1982	76.1	36.8	
July 2015*					1999	117.6	56.9		1981	70.0	33.9	
April 2015*					1998	115.1	55.7		1980	62.9	30.4	
Jan 2015*	206.7		100.0	100.0	1997	112.8	54.6		1979	57.8	28.0	
July 2014		204.9	99.1		1996	110.2	53.3		1978	53.5	25.9	
2013		201.2	97.3		1995	107.6	52.1		1977	49.5	23.9	
2012		194.6	94.1		1994	104.4	50.5		1976	46.9	22.7	
2011		191.2	92.5		1993	101.7	49.2		1975	44.8	21.7	
2010		183.5	88.8		1992	99.4	48.1		1974	41.4	20.0	
2009		180.1	87.1		1991	96.8	46.8		1973	37.7	18.2	
2008		180.4	87.3		1990	94.3	45.6		1972	34.8	16.8	
2007		169.4	82.0		1989	92.1	44.6		1971	32.1	15.5	
2006		162.0	78.4		1988	89.9	43.5		1970	28.7	13.9	
2005		151.6	73.3		1987	87.7	42.4		1969	26.9	13.0	
2004		143.7	69.5		1986	84.2	40.7		1968	24.9	12.0	
2003		132.0	63.9		1985	82.6	40.0		1967	23.5	11.4	
2002		128.7	62.3		1984	82.0	39.7		1966	22.7	11.0	
2001		125.1	60.5		1983	80.2	38.8		1965	21.7	10.5	

Adjustments to Costs

The "Historical Cost Index" can be used to convert national average building costs at a particular time to the approximate building costs for some other time.

Example:

Estimate and compare construction costs for different years in the same city.

To estimate the national average construction cost of a building in 1970, knowing that it cost $900,000 in 2015:

INDEX in 1970 = 28.7

INDEX in 2015 = 206.7

Note: The city cost indexes for Canada can be used to convert U.S. national averages to local costs in Canadian dollars.

Example:

To estimate and compare the cost of a building in Toronto, ON in 2015 with the known cost of $600,000 (US$) in New York, NY in 2015:

INDEX Toronto = 110.9

INDEX New York = 131.8

$$\frac{\text{INDEX Toronto}}{\text{INDEX New York}} \times \text{Cost New York} = \text{Cost Toronto}$$

$$\frac{110.9}{131.8} \times \$600,000 = .841 \times \$600,000 = \$504,600$$

The construction cost of the building in Toronto is $504,600 (CN$).

Time Adjustment Using the Historical Cost Indexes:

$$\frac{\text{Index for Year A}}{\text{Index for Year B}} \times \text{Cost in Year B} = \text{Cost in Year A}$$

$$\frac{\text{INDEX 1970}}{\text{INDEX 2015}} \times \text{Cost 2015} = \text{Cost 1970}$$

$$\frac{28.7}{206.7} \times \$900,000 = .139 \times \$900,000 = \$125,100$$

The construction cost of the building in 1970 is $125,100.

*Historical Cost Index updates and other resources are provided on the following website.
http://info.thegordiangroup.com/RSMeans.html

How to Use the City Cost Indexes

What you should know before you begin

RSMeans City Cost Indexes (CCI) are an extremely useful tool to use when you want to compare costs from city to city and region to region.

This publication contains average construction cost indexes for 731 U.S. and Canadian cities covering over 930 three-digit zip code locations, as listed directly under each city.

Keep in mind that a City Cost Index number is a percentage ratio of a specific city's cost to the national average cost of the same item at a stated time period.

In other words, these index figures represent relative construction factors (or, if you prefer, multipliers) for Material and Installation costs, as well as the weighted average for Total In Place costs for each CSI MasterFormat division. Installation costs include both labor and equipment rental costs. When estimating equipment rental rates only, for a specific location, use 01 54 33 EQUIPMENT RENTAL COSTS in the Reference Section at the back of the book.

The 30 City Average Index is the average of 30 major U.S. cities and serves as a National Average.

Index figures for both material and installation are based on the 30 major city average of 100 and represent the cost relationship as of July 1, 2014. The index for each division is computed from representative material and labor quantities for that division. The weighted average for each city is a weighted total of the components listed above it, but does not include relative productivity between trades or cities.

As changes occur in local material prices, labor rates, and equipment rental rates (including fuel costs), the impact of these changes should be accurately measured by the change in the City Cost Index for each particular city (as compared to the 30 City Average).

Therefore, if you know (or have estimated) building costs in one city today, you can easily convert those costs to expected building costs in another city.

In addition, by using the Historical Cost Index, you can easily convert National Average building costs at a particular time to the approximate building costs for some other time. The City Cost Indexes can then be applied to calculate the costs for a particular city.

Quick Calculations

Location Adjustment Using the City Cost Indexes:

$$\frac{\text{Index for City A}}{\text{Index for City B}} \times \text{Cost in City B} = \text{Cost in City A}$$

Time Adjustment for the National Average Using the Historical Cost Index:

$$\frac{\text{Index for Year A}}{\text{Index for Year B}} \times \text{Cost in Year B} = \text{Cost in Year A}$$

Adjustment from the National Average:

$$\frac{\text{Index for City A}}{100} \times \text{National Average Cost} = \text{Cost in City A}$$

Since each of the other RSMeans publications contains many different items, any *one* item multiplied by the particular city index may give incorrect results. However, the larger the number of items compiled, the closer the results should be to actual costs for that particular city.

The City Cost Indexes for Canadian cities are calculated using Canadian material and equipment prices and labor rates, in Canadian dollars. Therefore, indexes for Canadian cities can be used to convert U.S. National Average prices to local costs in Canadian dollars.

How to use this section

1. Compare costs from city to city.

In using the RSMeans Indexes, remember that an index number is not a fixed number but a ratio: It's a percentage ratio of a building component's cost at any stated time to the National Average cost of that same component at the same time period. Put in the form of an equation:

$$\frac{\text{Specific City Cost}}{\text{National Average Cost}} \times 100 = \text{City Index Number}$$

Therefore, when making cost comparisons between cities, do not subtract one city's index number from the index number of another city and read the result as a percentage difference. Instead, divide one city's index number by that of the other city. The resulting number may then be used as a multiplier to calculate cost differences from city to city.

The formula used to find cost differences between cities for the purpose of comparison is as follows:

$$\frac{\text{City A Index}}{\text{City B Index}} \times \text{City B Cost (Known)} = \text{City A Cost (Unknown)}$$

In addition, you can use RSMeans CCI to calculate and compare costs division by division between cities using the same basic formula. (Just be sure that you're comparing similar divisions.)

2. Compare a specific city's construction costs with the National Average.

When you're studying construction location feasibility, it's advisable to compare a prospective project's cost index with an index of the National Average cost.

For example, divide the weighted average index of construction costs of a specific city by that of the 30 City Average, which = 100.

$$\frac{\text{City Index}}{100} = \% \text{ of National Average}$$

As a result, you get a ratio that indicates the relative cost of construction in that city in comparison with the National Average.

3. Convert U.S. National Average to actual costs in Canadian City.

$$\frac{\text{Index for Canadian City}}{100} \times \text{National Average Cost} = \text{Cost in Canadian City in \$ CAN}$$

4. Adjust construction cost data based on a National Average.

When you use a source of construction cost data which is based on a National Average (such as RSMeans cost data publications), it is necessary to adjust those costs to a specific location.

$$\frac{\text{City Index}}{100} \times \frac{\text{"Book" Cost Based on}}{\text{National Average Costs}} = \frac{\text{City Cost}}{\text{(Unknown)}}$$

5. When applying the City Cost Indexes to demolition projects, use the appropriate division installation index. For example, for removal of existing doors and windows, use Division 8 (Openings) index.

What you might like to know about how we developed the Indexes

The information presented in the CCI is organized according to the Construction Specifications Institute (CSI) MasterFormat 2014 classification system.

To create a reliable index, RSMeans researched the building type most often constructed in the United States and Canada. Because it was concluded that no one type of building completely represented the building construction industry, nine different types of buildings were combined to create a composite model.

The exact material, labor, and equipment quantities are based on detailed analyses of these nine building types, and then each quantity is weighted in proportion to expected usage. These various material items, labor hours, and equipment rental rates are thus combined to form a composite building representing as closely as possible the actual usage of materials, labor, and equipment used in the North American building construction industry.

The following structures were chosen to make up that composite model:

1. Factory, 1 story
2. Office, 2–4 story
3. Store, Retail
4. Town Hall, 2–3 story
5. High School, 2–3 story
6. Hospital, 4–8 story
7. Garage, Parking
8. Apartment, 1–3 story
9. Hotel/Motel, 2–3 story

For the purposes of ensuring the timeliness of the data, the components of the index for the composite model have been streamlined. They currently consist of:

- specific quantities of 66 commonly used construction materials;
- specific labor-hours for 21 building construction trades; and
- specific days of equipment rental for 6 types of construction equipment (normally used to install the 66 material items by the 21 trades.) Fuel costs and routine maintenance costs are included in the equipment cost.

A sophisticated computer program handles the updating of all costs for each city on a quarterly basis. Material and equipment price quotations are gathered quarterly from cities in the United States and Canada. These prices and the latest negotiated labor wage rates for 21 different building trades are used to compile the quarterly update of the City Cost Index.

The 30 major U.S. cities used to calculate the National Average are:

Atlanta, GA	Memphis, TN
Baltimore, MD	Milwaukee, WI
Boston, MA	Minneapolis, MN
Buffalo, NY	Nashville, TN
Chicago, IL	New Orleans, LA
Cincinnati, OH	New York, NY
Cleveland, OH	Philadelphia, PA
Columbus, OH	Phoenix, AZ
Dallas, TX	Pittsburgh, PA
Denver, CO	St. Louis, MO
Detroit, MI	San Antonio, TX
Houston, TX	San Diego, CA
Indianapolis, IN	San Francisco, CA
Kansas City, MO	Seattle, WA
Los Angeles, CA	Washington, DC

What the CCI does not indicate

The weighted average for each city is a total of the divisional components weighted to reflect typical usage, but it does not include the productivity variations between trades or cities.

In addition, the CCI does not take into consideration factors such as the following:

- managerial efficiency
- competitive conditions
- automation
- restrictive union practices
- unique local requirements
- regional variations due to specific building codes

City Cost Indexes

Table 1

DIVISION		UNITED STATES 30 CITY AVERAGE			ALABAMA — ANNISTON 362			BIRMINGHAM 350-352			BUTLER 369			DECATUR 356			DOTHAN 363		
		MAT.	INST.	TOTAL	MAT.	INST.	TOTAL	MAT.	INST.	TOTAL	MAT.	INST.	TOTAL	MAT.	INST.	TOTAL	MAT.	INST.	TOTAL
015433	CONTRACTOR EQUIPMENT		100.0	100.0		101.0	101.0		101.1	101.1		98.2	98.2		101.0	101.0		98.2	98.2
0241, 31-34	SITE & INFRASTRUCTURE, DEMOLITION	100.0	100.0	100.0	90.2	93.1	92.3	97.4	93.8	94.8	103.5	87.1	91.8	88.8	91.5	90.7	101.2	87.1	91.1
0310	Concrete Forming & Accessories	100.0	100.0	100.0	90.1	47.1	53.0	93.1	75.9	78.2	86.4	42.6	48.6	94.6	45.4	52.1	95.5	42.0	49.4
0320	Concrete Reinforcing	100.0	100.0	100.0	87.8	86.3	87.1	94.7	86.9	90.7	92.8	45.9	68.9	88.6	77.0	82.7	92.8	45.4	68.7
0330	Cast-in-Place Concrete	100.0	100.0	100.0	101.8	49.7	80.4	110.0	74.6	95.4	99.3	54.8	81.0	103.4	64.1	87.2	99.3	46.3	77.5
03	CONCRETE	100.0	100.0	100.0	102.1	57.0	79.9	102.2	78.4	90.5	103.0	49.3	76.6	98.3	59.3	79.1	102.3	46.0	74.7
04	MASONRY	100.0	100.0	100.0	100.1	66.8	79.3	98.8	76.0	84.6	105.9	48.6	70.2	97.3	51.3	68.6	107.1	39.7	65.1
05	METALS	100.0	100.0	100.0	104.0	91.5	100.1	104.0	94.1	101.0	102.8	76.6	94.8	106.2	86.1	100.0	102.9	75.3	94.4
06	WOOD, PLASTICS & COMPOSITES	100.0	100.0	100.0	90.5	42.7	63.7	97.4	76.1	85.4	85.0	42.4	61.1	98.9	42.9	67.6	97.4	42.4	66.6
07	THERMAL & MOISTURE PROTECTION	100.0	100.0	100.0	97.9	52.9	79.5	99.7	81.5	92.2	98.0	56.7	81.0	96.7	58.3	81.0	98.0	49.1	77.9
08	OPENINGS	100.0	100.0	100.0	98.6	50.1	87.3	103.2	76.0	96.8	98.6	44.2	85.9	106.5	50.4	93.5	98.6	44.2	86.0
0920	Plaster & Gypsum Board	100.0	100.0	100.0	90.8	41.4	57.4	94.8	75.8	81.9	87.9	41.0	56.2	95.8	41.6	59.2	98.6	41.0	59.7
0950, 0980	Ceilings & Acoustic Treatment	100.0	100.0	100.0	80.4	41.4	54.7	89.8	75.8	80.6	80.4	41.0	54.5	87.2	41.6	57.2	80.4	41.0	54.5
0960	Flooring	100.0	100.0	100.0	91.5	64.3	75.1	102.5	76.7	95.1	95.8	56.0	84.4	99.7	50.6	85.6	100.6	27.5	79.7
0970, 0990	Wall Finishes & Painting/Coating	100.0	100.0	100.0	103.7	31.5	60.1	103.9	66.5	81.3	103.7	53.3	73.3	99.6	66.8	79.8	103.7	53.3	73.3
09	FINISHES	100.0	100.0	100.0	87.0	43.0	62.8	95.4	74.8	84.1	89.9	45.7	65.5	91.9	47.7	67.6	92.5	40.1	63.6
COVERS	DIVS. 10 - 14, 25, 28, 41, 43, 44, 46	100.0	100.0	100.0	100.0	68.3	93.6	100.0	88.4	97.7	100.0	41.4	88.2	100.0	43.2	88.5	100.0	41.5	88.2
21, 22, 23	FIRE SUPPRESSION, PLUMBING & HVAC	100.0	100.0	100.0	100.0	55.4	82.0	100.0	70.4	88.1	97.3	33.3	71.5	100.0	40.8	76.1	97.3	33.2	71.5
26, 27, 3370	ELECTRICAL, COMMUNICATIONS & UTIL.	100.0	100.0	100.0	93.1	57.3	74.2	99.0	61.6	79.3	95.0	40.2	66.0	94.2	64.9	78.7	93.8	57.4	74.6
MF2014	WEIGHTED AVERAGE	100.0	100.0	100.0	98.6	61.8	82.6	100.6	76.7	90.2	98.9	49.4	77.3	99.8	57.9	81.5	99.0	49.4	77.4

Table 2 — ALABAMA

DIVISION		EVERGREEN 364			GADSDEN 359			HUNTSVILLE 357-358			JASPER 355			MOBILE 365-366			MONTGOMERY 360-361		
		MAT.	INST.	TOTAL	MAT.	INST.	TOTAL	MAT.	INST.	TOTAL	MAT.	INST.	TOTAL	MAT.	INST.	TOTAL	MAT.	INST.	TOTAL
015433	CONTRACTOR EQUIPMENT		98.2	98.2		101.0	101.0		101.0	101.0		101.0	101.0		98.2	98.2		98.2	98.2
0241, 31-34	SITE & INFRASTRUCTURE, DEMOLITION	104.0	87.4	92.2	94.9	92.7	93.3	88.6	92.7	91.5	94.6	92.4	93.1	96.4	88.1	90.5	96.5	88.1	90.5
0310	Concrete Forming & Accessories	83.0	44.2	49.5	86.9	42.5	48.6	94.6	69.9	73.3	92.1	34.6	42.5	94.5	54.0	59.6	94.1	44.1	51.0
0320	Concrete Reinforcing	92.9	45.9	69.0	94.0	86.8	90.3	88.6	81.6	85.1	88.6	85.6	87.1	90.6	83.6	87.0	95.8	86.1	90.9
0330	Cast-in-Place Concrete	99.3	57.3	82.1	103.4	66.7	88.3	100.7	69.5	87.9	114.5	44.1	85.6	104.1	66.4	88.6	105.2	56.5	85.2
03	CONCRETE	103.3	50.9	77.5	102.9	60.8	82.2	97.0	72.9	85.2	106.6	49.4	78.5	98.9	65.3	82.4	100.2	57.9	79.4
04	MASONRY	105.9	53.2	73.0	95.6	62.4	74.9	98.8	67.7	79.4	92.9	41.2	60.7	103.7	54.2	72.9	100.0	49.7	68.6
05	METALS	102.9	76.5	94.7	104.0	93.2	100.7	106.2	90.6	101.4	104.0	90.2	99.7	105.0	91.6	100.9	104.0	91.9	100.3
06	WOOD, PLASTICS & COMPOSITES	81.3	42.4	59.5	89.3	38.7	61.0	98.9	72.6	84.2	95.9	31.6	59.9	95.9	52.8	71.8	95.3	42.4	65.6
07	THERMAL & MOISTURE PROTECTION	97.9	56.9	81.1	96.8	71.7	86.5	96.6	77.6	88.8	96.8	45.4	75.7	97.6	70.1	86.3	97.9	66.6	85.0
08	OPENINGS	98.6	44.2	85.9	102.8	49.0	90.3	106.5	67.4	97.4	102.8	48.0	90.0	102.2	58.8	92.1	103.3	53.1	91.7
0920	Plaster & Gypsum Board	87.2	41.0	56.0	88.2	37.3	53.8	95.8	72.2	79.9	92.1	30.0	50.1	95.2	51.8	65.9	94.6	41.0	58.4
0950, 0980	Ceilings & Acoustic Treatment	80.4	41.0	54.5	83.8	37.3	53.2	89.0	72.2	78.0	83.8	30.0	48.4	85.6	51.8	63.4	88.0	41.0	57.1
0960	Flooring	93.9	56.0	83.1	95.5	76.7	90.1	99.7	76.7	93.1	97.8	40.2	81.3	100.5	58.5	88.5	97.3	58.5	86.2
0970, 0990	Wall Finishes & Painting/Coating	103.7	53.3	73.3	99.6	60.7	76.1	99.6	65.9	79.3	99.6	38.6	62.8	107.3	54.3	75.3	103.3	53.3	73.1
09	FINISHES	89.2	46.8	65.9	89.4	48.7	67.0	92.3	70.7	80.4	90.5	34.4	59.6	92.7	53.5	71.1	92.8	46.1	67.0
COVERS	DIVS. 10 - 14, 25, 28, 41, 43, 44, 46	100.0	79.2	88.5	100.0	79.8	95.9	100.0	85.3	97.0	100.0	39.8	87.8	100.0	83.1	96.6	100.0	79.6	95.9
21, 22, 23	FIRE SUPPRESSION, PLUMBING & HVAC	97.3	35.6	72.4	102.0	36.3	75.5	100.0	61.6	84.5	102.0	61.4	85.6	99.9	60.7	84.1	100.0	34.2	73.4
26, 27, 3370	ELECTRICAL, COMMUNICATIONS & UTIL.	92.5	40.2	64.8	94.3	61.6	77.0	95.3	64.9	79.3	93.8	61.3	76.6	95.7	59.1	76.3	96.3	60.9	77.6
MF2014	WEIGHTED AVERAGE	98.6	50.7	77.7	99.9	60.0	82.5	99.8	72.1	87.8	100.2	57.5	81.6	99.9	65.4	84.9	99.9	57.1	81.2

Table 3 — ALABAMA / ALASKA

DIVISION		PHENIX CITY 368			SELMA 367			TUSCALOOSA 354			ANCHORAGE 995-996			FAIRBANKS 997			JUNEAU 998		
		MAT.	INST.	TOTAL	MAT.	INST.	TOTAL	MAT.	INST.	TOTAL	MAT.	INST.	TOTAL	MAT.	INST.	TOTAL	MAT.	INST.	TOTAL
015433	CONTRACTOR EQUIPMENT		98.2	98.2		98.2	98.2		101.0	101.0		114.7	114.7		114.7	114.7		114.7	114.7
0241, 31-34	SITE & INFRASTRUCTURE, DEMOLITION	107.8	88.2	93.9	101.0	88.1	91.8	89.1	92.9	91.8	127.2	129.6	128.9	119.2	129.6	126.6	135.6	129.6	131.3
0310	Concrete Forming & Accessories	90.1	39.1	46.1	87.6	42.6	48.8	94.5	47.9	54.3	123.7	119.8	120.3	131.6	119.9	121.5	130.1	119.8	121.2
0320	Concrete Reinforcing	92.8	61.4	76.8	92.8	85.2	89.0	88.6	86.8	87.7	149.7	110.7	129.9	150.9	110.7	130.5	135.7	110.7	123.0
0330	Cast-in-Place Concrete	99.3	57.0	81.9	99.3	46.5	77.6	104.9	68.4	89.9	132.0	117.8	126.2	128.3	118.2	124.1	133.2	117.8	126.9
03	CONCRETE	106.2	51.3	79.2	101.7	53.7	78.1	99.0	63.8	81.7	138.6	116.7	127.9	123.8	116.9	120.4	136.0	116.7	126.5
04	MASONRY	105.9	41.1	65.5	109.6	38.7	65.4	97.6	65.5	77.6	184.6	125.3	147.6	189.5	125.3	149.5	176.6	125.3	144.6
05	METALS	102.8	81.9	96.4	102.8	89.3	98.7	105.3	93.2	101.6	113.6	103.4	110.5	117.6	103.5	113.3	116.3	103.4	112.3
06	WOOD, PLASTICS & COMPOSITES	90.2	35.4	59.5	87.0	42.4	62.0	98.9	44.4	68.4	129.2	118.7	123.4	136.1	118.7	126.4	129.4	118.7	123.4
07	THERMAL & MOISTURE PROTECTION	98.3	63.8	84.1	97.8	52.1	79.1	96.7	73.7	87.3	159.5	118.0	142.5	166.5	119.1	147.1	168.0	118.0	147.5
08	OPENINGS	98.6	43.5	85.8	98.6	53.1	88.0	106.5	58.8	95.4	132.7	115.6	128.7	128.9	115.7	125.8	129.8	115.6	126.5
0920	Plaster & Gypsum Board	92.2	33.9	52.8	90.1	41.0	56.9	95.8	43.1	60.2	140.9	119.1	126.2	164.8	119.1	133.9	148.1	119.1	128.5
0950, 0980	Ceilings & Acoustic Treatment	80.4	33.9	49.8	80.4	41.0	54.5	89.0	43.1	54.5	119.6	119.1	119.3	119.2	119.1	119.2	125.9	119.1	121.4
0960	Flooring	97.6	58.5	86.4	96.2	28.5	76.8	99.7	76.7	93.1	134.6	133.0	134.1	127.2	133.0	128.9	131.0	133.0	131.6
0970, 0990	Wall Finishes & Painting/Coating	103.7	53.3	73.3	103.7	53.3	73.3	99.6	45.9	67.2	136.8	116.3	124.4	133.5	121.2	126.1	132.1	116.3	122.6
09	FINISHES	91.4	42.2	64.3	90.0	40.2	62.6	92.3	51.2	69.7	134.3	122.2	127.7	132.4	122.8	127.1	134.4	122.2	127.7
COVERS	DIVS. 10 - 14, 25, 28, 41, 43, 44, 46	100.0	79.3	95.8	100.0	41.4	88.2	100.0	81.4	96.2	100.0	112.8	102.6	100.0	112.8	102.6	100.0	112.8	102.6
21, 22, 23	FIRE SUPPRESSION, PLUMBING & HVAC	97.3	34.5	72.0	97.3	33.6	71.6	100.0	34.0	73.4	100.3	105.0	102.2	100.2	108.0	103.4	100.3	105.0	102.2
26, 27, 3370	ELECTRICAL, COMMUNICATIONS & UTIL.	94.4	69.5	81.3	93.6	40.2	65.4	94.8	61.6	77.3	117.7	117.8	117.7	130.0	117.8	123.5	119.9	117.8	118.8
MF2014	WEIGHTED AVERAGE	99.5	54.6	79.9	98.7	49.9	77.4	99.8	61.2	83.0	121.1	115.6	118.7	121.0	116.4	119.0	121.3	115.6	118.8

750

DIVISION		ALASKA			ARIZONA												
		KETCHIKAN			CHAMBERS			FLAGSTAFF			GLOBE			KINGMAN			MESA/TEMPE		
		999			865			860			855			864			852		
		MAT.	INST.	TOTAL	MAT.	INST.	TOTAL	MAT.	INST.	TOTAL	MAT.	INST.	TOTAL	MAT.	INST.	TOTAL	MAT.	INST.	TOTAL
015433	CONTRACTOR EQUIPMENT		114.7	114.7		93.0	93.0		93.0	93.0		92.2	92.2		93.0	93.0		92.2	92.2
0241, 31 - 34	SITE & INFRASTRUCTURE, DEMOLITION	173.8	129.6	142.4	69.6	96.1	88.4	87.3	96.3	93.7	97.3	95.6	96.1	69.6	96.3	88.6	89.0	95.8	93.8
0310	Concrete Forming & Accessories	122.9	119.8	120.2	98.8	58.1	63.7	104.4	65.1	70.5	99.0	58.1	63.7	97.0	65.1	69.5	102.2	69.3	73.9
0320	Concrete Reinforcing	117.4	110.7	114.0	97.1	85.2	91.1	97.0	85.3	91.0	108.0	85.2	96.4	97.2	85.3	91.1	108.7	85.3	96.8
0330	Cast-in-Place Concrete	259.2	117.8	201.2	90.7	73.2	83.5	90.8	73.4	83.7	94.3	72.0	85.1	90.4	73.4	83.4	95.0	72.3	85.7
03	CONCRETE	208.7	116.7	163.5	95.0	68.6	82.0	114.1	71.8	93.3	110.0	68.2	89.5	94.6	71.8	83.4	101.8	73.3	87.8
04	MASONRY	198.4	125.3	152.8	92.5	62.3	73.7	92.6	62.4	73.8	109.9	62.2	80.1	92.5	62.4	73.7	110.1	62.2	80.3
05	METALS	117.8	103.4	113.4	96.2	75.6	89.8	96.7	76.3	90.4	93.3	76.0	88.0	96.8	76.3	90.5	93.6	76.8	88.4
06	WOOD, PLASTICS & COMPOSITES	126.3	118.7	122.1	101.0	55.0	75.2	107.3	64.2	83.1	97.6	55.0	73.8	96.1	64.2	78.2	101.1	69.8	83.6
07	THERMAL & MOISTURE PROTECTION	169.3	118.0	148.3	94.6	65.0	82.5	96.2	68.1	84.7	101.9	63.0	85.9	94.6	65.6	82.7	101.2	65.1	86.4
08	OPENINGS	130.8	115.6	127.3	108.1	65.3	98.2	108.3	70.3	99.4	100.0	65.3	91.9	108.3	70.3	99.5	100.1	73.3	93.8
0920	Plaster & Gypsum Board	152.7	119.1	130.0	90.2	53.7	65.5	93.6	63.2	73.0	96.6	53.7	67.6	82.9	63.2	69.6	98.7	68.9	78.6
0950, 0980	Ceilings & Acoustic Treatment	112.7	119.1	116.9	99.7	53.7	69.5	100.5	63.2	76.0	88.9	53.7	65.8	100.5	63.2	76.0	88.9	68.9	75.8
0960	Flooring	127.2	133.0	128.9	93.3	39.5	77.9	95.4	39.7	79.5	103.5	39.5	85.2	92.1	53.7	81.1	104.7	49.5	88.9
0970, 0990	Wall Finishes & Painting/Coating	133.5	116.3	123.1	98.3	55.1	72.2	98.3	55.1	72.2	103.4	55.1	74.3	98.3	55.1	72.2	103.4	55.1	74.3
09	FINISHES	133.4	122.2	127.2	93.7	52.9	71.2	96.6	58.4	75.6	97.1	53.0	72.8	92.5	60.7	75.0	96.8	63.6	78.5
COVERS	DIVS. 10 - 14, 25, 28, 41, 43, 44, 46	100.0	112.8	102.6	100.0	82.3	96.4	100.0	83.3	96.6	100.0	82.4	96.4	100.0	83.3	96.6	100.0	84.0	96.8
21, 22, 23	FIRE SUPPRESSION, PLUMBING & HVAC	98.4	105.0	101.1	97.0	78.9	89.7	100.2	79.0	91.6	95.2	78.9	88.7	97.0	79.0	89.7	100.0	79.0	91.5
26, 27, 3370	ELECTRICAL, COMMUNICATIONS & UTIL.	129.9	117.8	123.5	104.5	70.9	86.7	103.4	61.3	81.1	97.5	61.2	78.3	104.5	61.3	81.7	94.2	61.3	76.8
MF2014	WEIGHTED AVERAGE	132.0	115.6	124.8	97.6	71.5	86.2	101.3	71.8	88.4	98.8	70.0	86.3	97.6	72.0	86.4	98.6	72.8	87.4

DIVISION		ARIZONA												ARKANSAS				
		PHOENIX			PRESCOTT			SHOW LOW			TUCSON			BATESVILLE			CAMDEN		
		850,853			863			859			856 - 857			725			717		
		MAT.	INST.	TOTAL	MAT.	INST.	TOTAL	MAT.	INST.	TOTAL	MAT.	INST.	TOTAL	MAT.	INST.	TOTAL	MAT.	INST.	TOTAL
015433	CONTRACTOR EQUIPMENT		92.7	92.7		93.0	93.0		92.2	92.2		92.2	92.2		89.1	89.1		89.1	89.1
0241, 31 - 34	SITE & INFRASTRUCTURE, DEMOLITION	89.4	96.0	94.1	76.0	96.0	90.2	99.2	95.6	96.6	85.2	95.8	92.7	77.1	84.9	82.6	78.3	84.4	82.7
0310	Concrete Forming & Accessories	103.1	68.3	73.1	100.4	52.5	59.1	106.3	69.1	74.2	102.5	68.1	72.9	85.9	44.9	50.5	83.7	30.7	38.0
0320	Concrete Reinforcing	107.0	85.4	96.0	97.1	85.2	91.0	108.7	85.2	96.8	89.9	85.3	87.5	87.4	67.5	77.3	93.6	67.4	80.3
0330	Cast-in-Place Concrete	95.1	72.4	85.8	90.7	73.1	83.5	94.3	72.1	85.2	97.8	72.3	87.3	77.4	45.3	64.2	82.6	38.3	64.4
03	CONCRETE	101.4	73.0	87.4	100.1	66.1	83.4	112.4	73.1	93.1	100.0	72.8	86.6	83.5	50.1	67.1	87.5	41.3	64.8
04	MASONRY	97.5	64.1	76.7	92.6	62.3	73.7	109.9	62.2	80.1	95.5	62.2	74.8	99.8	40.7	63.0	116.6	31.4	63.5
05	METALS	95.1	77.6	89.7	96.7	75.3	90.1	93.1	76.1	87.8	94.3	76.7	88.9	99.5	66.9	89.4	103.9	66.5	92.4
06	WOOD, PLASTICS & COMPOSITES	102.1	68.3	83.2	102.4	47.4	71.6	105.8	69.8	85.6	101.4	68.3	82.8	88.9	45.5	65.0	90.3	29.7	56.4
07	THERMAL & MOISTURE PROTECTION	100.9	67.0	87.0	95.1	64.2	82.4	102.1	65.0	86.9	102.4	64.2	86.7	98.2	43.9	76.0	94.2	35.7	70.2
08	OPENINGS	102.0	72.5	95.2	108.3	61.1	97.3	99.2	73.3	93.2	96.3	72.5	90.7	97.7	45.8	85.6	102.1	40.6	87.8
0920	Plaster & Gypsum Board	101.0	67.4	78.2	90.3	45.9	60.3	100.9	68.9	79.3	104.0	67.4	79.2	83.3	44.3	56.9	85.0	28.0	46.5
0950, 0980	Ceilings & Acoustic Treatment	96.5	67.4	77.3	98.8	45.9	64.0	88.9	68.9	75.8	89.8	67.4	75.0	83.2	44.3	57.6	83.3	28.0	47.0
0960	Flooring	104.9	51.7	89.7	94.1	39.5	78.5	106.2	45.0	88.7	95.2	44.2	80.6	96.7	59.1	85.9	99.6	39.6	82.4
0970, 0990	Wall Finishes & Painting/Coating	103.4	61.7	78.3	98.3	55.1	72.2	103.4	55.1	74.3	104.5	55.1	74.7	107.4	41.2	67.4	104.4	50.4	71.8
09	FINISHES	98.9	63.8	79.6	94.2	48.5	69.0	98.7	62.7	78.8	94.9	61.6	76.5	86.6	46.7	64.6	88.5	33.5	58.2
COVERS	DIVS. 10 - 14, 25, 28, 41, 43, 44, 46	100.0	83.9	96.7	100.0	81.4	96.3	100.0	84.0	96.8	100.0	83.9	96.7	100.0	39.5	87.8	100.0	35.6	87.0
21, 22, 23	FIRE SUPPRESSION, PLUMBING & HVAC	99.9	79.0	91.5	100.2	78.9	91.6	95.2	79.0	88.7	100.0	79.0	91.5	95.3	51.6	77.7	95.3	53.1	78.3
26, 27, 3370	ELECTRICAL, COMMUNICATIONS & UTIL.	101.0	66.7	82.9	103.0	61.2	80.9	94.6	61.2	77.0	96.5	61.3	77.9	96.5	63.5	79.0	96.8	62.1	78.5
MF2014	WEIGHTED AVERAGE	99.2	73.8	88.1	99.2	68.9	86.0	98.9	72.5	87.4	97.4	72.4	86.5	94.6	54.6	77.1	97.1	50.1	76.6

DIVISION		ARKANSAS																
		FAYETTEVILLE			FORT SMITH			HARRISON			HOT SPRINGS			JONESBORO			LITTLE ROCK		
		727			729			726			719			724			720 - 722		
		MAT.	INST.	TOTAL	MAT.	INST.	TOTAL	MAT.	INST.	TOTAL	MAT.	INST.	TOTAL	MAT.	INST.	TOTAL	MAT.	INST.	TOTAL
015433	CONTRACTOR EQUIPMENT		89.1	89.1		89.1	89.1		89.1	89.1		89.1	89.1		108.3	108.3		89.1	89.1
0241, 31 - 34	SITE & INFRASTRUCTURE, DEMOLITION	76.4	86.3	83.5	81.8	86.7	85.3	82.1	84.9	84.1	81.4	85.8	84.5	103.2	101.1	101.7	93.1	86.8	88.6
0310	Concrete Forming & Accessories	81.2	38.5	44.4	101.3	57.3	63.4	90.6	44.8	51.1	81.1	35.7	41.9	89.6	48.2	53.9	96.4	60.0	65.0
0320	Concrete Reinforcing	87.4	71.3	79.2	88.4	72.0	80.1	87.0	63.7	75.1	91.8	67.5	79.4	84.5	70.1	77.2	93.4	68.3	80.6
0330	Cast-in-Place Concrete	77.4	49.4	65.9	88.5	70.3	81.0	85.8	43.4	68.4	84.5	38.8	65.7	84.3	55.0	72.2	87.3	70.3	80.3
03	CONCRETE	83.2	49.3	66.5	91.3	65.0	78.4	90.8	48.7	70.1	91.2	43.7	67.9	88.1	56.0	72.3	92.8	65.5	79.4
04	MASONRY	90.5	41.4	59.9	96.9	50.9	68.3	100.1	39.0	62.0	87.6	33.5	53.9	91.9	41.9	60.7	96.8	50.9	68.2
05	METALS	99.5	67.8	89.7	101.8	70.6	92.2	100.6	66.5	90.1	103.8	66.9	92.5	95.9	80.0	91.0	102.0	69.4	92.0
06	WOOD, PLASTICS & COMPOSITES	85.8	35.5	57.6	107.6	59.0	80.4	96.0	45.5	67.7	87.5	35.7	58.5	93.9	48.3	68.4	99.9	62.5	78.9
07	THERMAL & MOISTURE PROTECTION	99.0	45.3	77.0	99.4	57.5	82.2	98.5	42.6	75.6	94.4	37.9	71.2	103.3	49.1	81.1	95.7	57.8	80.2
08	OPENINGS	97.7	44.7	85.4	98.5	56.2	88.7	98.5	46.5	86.4	102.1	42.3	88.2	100.6	54.0	89.7	99.5	58.4	89.9
0920	Plaster & Gypsum Board	81.8	34.0	49.5	89.4	58.3	68.4	88.3	44.3	58.6	84.0	34.2	50.4	97.7	46.9	63.4	94.6	61.8	72.5
0950, 0980	Ceilings & Acoustic Treatment	83.2	34.0	50.9	84.8	58.3	67.4	84.8	44.3	58.2	83.3	34.2	51.0	86.2	46.9	60.3	88.0	61.8	70.8
0960	Flooring	94.0	59.1	84.0	102.9	60.8	90.9	98.8	59.1	87.5	98.5	59.1	87.2	68.9	53.4	64.5	101.0	60.8	89.5
0970, 0990	Wall Finishes & Painting/Coating	107.4	29.4	60.3	107.4	53.8	75.1	107.4	41.2	67.4	104.4	55.2	74.7	94.9	48.4	66.8	108.8	55.2	76.5
09	FINISHES	85.7	40.0	60.5	89.9	57.6	72.1	88.6	46.8	65.6	88.4	41.0	62.3	83.7	48.5	64.3	92.7	59.8	74.6
COVERS	DIVS. 10 - 14, 25, 28, 41, 43, 44, 46	100.0	48.7	89.6	100.0	78.8	95.7	100.0	49.1	89.7	100.0	36.5	87.2	100.0	45.2	88.9	100.0	79.2	95.8
21, 22, 23	FIRE SUPPRESSION, PLUMBING & HVAC	95.3	50.2	77.1	100.1	50.6	80.1	95.3	49.4	76.8	95.3	48.7	76.5	100.3	52.5	81.0	99.9	56.2	82.3
26, 27, 3370	ELECTRICAL, COMMUNICATIONS & UTIL.	90.1	51.2	69.5	93.7	64.5	78.3	95.0	37.1	64.4	99.0	67.8	82.5	100.2	63.5	80.8	100.7	70.2	84.6
MF2014	WEIGHTED AVERAGE	93.4	52.0	75.4	97.2	61.6	81.7	95.9	50.4	76.0	96.4	51.8	76.9	96.7	59.1	80.3	98.5	64.0	83.4

For customer support on your Site Work & Landscape Cost Data, call 877.737.1594.

751

City Cost Indexes

ARKANSAS / CALIFORNIA

DIVISION		PINE BLUFF 716 MAT.	INST.	TOTAL	RUSSELLVILLE 728 MAT.	INST.	TOTAL	TEXARKANA 718 MAT.	INST.	TOTAL	WEST MEMPHIS 723 MAT.	INST.	TOTAL	ALHAMBRA 917-918 MAT.	INST.	TOTAL	ANAHEIM 928 MAT.	INST.	TOTAL
015433	CONTRACTOR EQUIPMENT		89.1	89.1		89.1	89.1		89.9	89.9		108.3	108.3		100.1	100.1		100.8	100.8
0241, 31 - 34	SITE & INFRASTRUCTURE, DEMOLITION	83.7	86.8	85.9	78.3	84.9	83.0	94.9	87.1	89.3	110.5	101.1	103.8	97.9	110.9	107.1	99.4	108.3	105.7
0310	Concrete Forming & Accessories	80.7	60.0	62.8	86.6	54.7	59.1	87.3	40.1	46.6	95.5	48.5	54.9	117.1	116.4	116.5	105.4	124.2	121.6
0320	Concrete Reinforcing	93.5	68.2	80.7	88.0	67.3	77.5	93.1	67.5	80.1	84.5	70.1	77.2	106.6	113.3	110.0	93.8	113.2	103.7
0330	Cast-in-Place Concrete	84.5	70.3	78.7	81.1	45.3	66.4	92.1	43.3	72.0	88.4	55.1	74.7	95.1	120.8	105.6	92.9	123.3	105.4
03	CONCRETE	92.1	65.5	79.0	86.7	54.4	70.8	89.8	47.2	68.9	95.5	56.2	76.2	101.1	116.5	108.7	101.8	120.8	111.2
04	MASONRY	125.0	50.9	78.8	96.1	37.3	59.5	102.4	33.1	59.2	79.4	41.9	56.0	122.7	121.1	121.7	80.0	118.8	104.2
05	METALS	104.6	69.4	93.8	99.5	66.5	89.3	96.8	66.9	87.6	95.0	80.3	90.5	85.3	100.9	90.1	102.7	101.1	102.2
06	WOOD, PLASTICS & COMPOSITES	87.0	62.5	73.3	91.3	59.0	73.2	95.5	42.0	65.5	100.1	48.3	71.1	100.0	122.1	106.7	101.9	122.6	113.5
07	THERMAL & MOISTURE PROTECTION	94.5	57.8	79.5	99.2	43.9	76.5	95.2	44.5	74.4	103.7	49.1	81.3	95.1	118.1	104.5	99.4	122.0	108.7
08	OPENINGS	102.1	58.4	91.9	97.7	55.7	87.9	107.3	46.5	93.2	100.6	54.0	89.7	91.8	114.8	97.2	104.2	120.6	108.0
0920	Plaster & Gypsum Board	83.6	61.8	68.9	83.3	58.3	66.4	86.6	40.7	55.6	100.2	46.9	64.2	97.4	112.5	107.6	107.1	123.2	118.0
0950, 0980	Ceilings & Acoustic Treatment	83.3	61.8	69.2	83.2	58.3	66.8	86.6	40.7	56.4	84.3	46.9	59.7	100.2	112.5	108.3	105.0	123.2	117.0
0960	Flooring	98.2	60.8	87.5	96.2	59.1	85.6	100.4	51.0	86.3	71.0	53.4	66.0	95.4	110.2	99.6	101.9	112.0	104.8
0970, 0990	Wall Finishes & Painting/Coating	104.4	55.2	74.7	107.4	35.0	63.7	104.4	30.3	59.7	94.9	50.4	68.0	100.5	111.5	107.1	98.9	106.8	103.7
09	FINISHES	88.3	59.8	72.6	86.7	54.1	68.7	90.7	40.4	62.9	85.0	48.8	65.0	99.8	114.0	107.6	100.5	120.1	111.3
COVERS	DIVS. 10 - 14, 25, 28, 41, 43, 44, 46	100.0	79.2	95.8	100.0	41.0	88.1	100.0	32.6	86.4	100.0	45.2	88.9	100.0	110.5	102.1	100.0	112.0	102.4
21, 22, 23	FIRE SUPPRESSION, PLUMBING & HVAC	100.1	52.9	81.1	95.3	51.5	77.6	100.1	53.5	81.3	95.6	65.8	83.6	95.2	115.6	103.4	100.0	118.6	107.5
26, 27, 3370	ELECTRICAL, COMMUNICATIONS & UTIL.	97.0	70.2	82.8	93.7	44.7	67.8	98.9	36.0	65.7	101.9	65.7	82.8	118.4	120.5	119.5	92.2	105.7	99.3
MF2014	WEIGHTED AVERAGE	99.4	63.3	83.6	94.6	53.7	76.8	98.2	49.2	76.8	96.1	62.4	81.4	98.3	114.8	105.5	99.4	114.9	106.2

CALIFORNIA

DIVISION		BAKERSFIELD 932-933 MAT.	INST.	TOTAL	BERKELEY 947 MAT.	INST.	TOTAL	EUREKA 955 MAT.	INST.	TOTAL	FRESNO 936-938 MAT.	INST.	TOTAL	INGLEWOOD 903-905 MAT.	INST.	TOTAL	LONG BEACH 906-908 MAT.	INST.	TOTAL
015433	CONTRACTOR EQUIPMENT		98.8	98.8		100.3	100.3		98.5	98.5		98.8	98.8		96.5	96.5		96.5	96.5
0241, 31 - 34	SITE & INFRASTRUCTURE, DEMOLITION	100.4	106.0	104.4	118.4	107.6	110.7	110.8	103.9	105.9	103.1	105.4	104.7	89.3	103.5	99.4	95.9	103.5	101.3
0310	Concrete Forming & Accessories	104.0	124.3	121.5	115.9	149.9	145.2	114.8	133.6	131.0	104.3	134.2	130.1	111.8	115.4	114.9	106.5	115.4	114.1
0320	Concrete Reinforcing	103.4	113.2	108.4	94.5	114.4	104.6	102.5	114.1	108.4	80.6	113.7	97.5	102.7	113.3	108.1	101.9	113.3	107.7
0330	Cast-in-Place Concrete	94.0	122.6	105.7	123.4	124.8	124.0	100.8	118.0	107.9	99.4	118.9	107.4	84.5	121.4	99.7	96.2	121.4	106.5
03	CONCRETE	97.9	120.6	109.1	107.3	132.7	119.8	112.8	123.2	117.9	98.6	123.8	111.0	90.9	116.3	103.4	99.8	116.3	107.9
04	MASONRY	100.2	118.3	111.5	113.4	134.3	126.5	104.0	132.6	121.8	103.6	122.0	115.1	76.3	121.2	104.3	85.3	121.2	107.7
05	METALS	105.3	100.9	104.0	106.9	100.5	104.9	102.6	98.9	101.4	105.6	100.5	104.1	94.4	101.5	96.6	94.3	101.5	96.5
06	WOOD, PLASTICS & COMPOSITES	96.0	122.7	111.0	111.4	154.9	135.8	114.8	128.9	122.7	108.1	138.5	125.1	103.8	110.7	107.6	96.9	110.7	104.6
07	THERMAL & MOISTURE PROTECTION	98.1	116.1	105.5	105.2	137.2	118.3	103.4	119.8	110.1	88.7	116.0	99.9	98.3	118.0	106.4	98.5	118.0	106.5
08	OPENINGS	97.8	116.1	102.0	93.0	140.6	104.1	103.5	113.5	105.8	98.1	124.7	104.3	88.8	114.1	94.7	88.8	114.1	94.7
0920	Plaster & Gypsum Board	101.9	123.2	116.3	111.6	156.0	141.6	113.4	139.5	131.0	100.6	139.5	126.9	103.8	111.0	108.7	99.9	111.0	107.4
0950, 0980	Ceilings & Acoustic Treatment	96.3	123.2	114.0	106.2	156.0	139.0	110.1	139.5	129.4	92.8	139.5	123.5	100.3	111.0	107.4	100.3	111.0	107.4
0960	Flooring	106.8	110.2	107.7	108.2	127.6	113.8	106.0	116.5	109.0	113.3	133.5	119.1	104.4	110.2	106.0	101.8	110.2	104.2
0970, 0990	Wall Finishes & Painting/Coating	111.4	102.0	105.7	102.5	143.9	127.5	100.5	46.2	67.7	129.0	107.2	115.8	100.9	111.5	107.3	100.9	111.5	107.3
09	FINISHES	100.0	120.5	111.3	105.4	147.2	128.4	106.1	123.6	115.8	102.1	133.2	119.2	102.7	113.2	108.5	101.8	113.2	108.1
COVERS	DIVS. 10 - 14, 25, 28, 41, 43, 44, 46	100.0	111.9	102.4	100.0	126.4	105.3	100.0	122.2	104.5	100.0	122.2	104.5	100.0	110.4	102.1	100.0	110.4	102.1
21, 22, 23	FIRE SUPPRESSION, PLUMBING & HVAC	100.1	117.1	107.0	95.3	147.8	116.5	95.2	110.6	101.4	100.2	111.3	104.7	94.8	115.6	103.2	94.8	115.6	103.2
26, 27, 3370	ELECTRICAL, COMMUNICATIONS & UTIL.	103.6	102.5	103.1	109.4	145.0	128.2	99.1	116.7	108.4	93.8	100.8	97.5	103.8	120.5	112.6	103.5	120.5	112.5
MF2014	WEIGHTED AVERAGE	100.7	113.6	106.3	102.7	135.1	116.8	102.1	116.4	108.4	100.1	115.3	106.7	94.8	114.1	103.2	96.2	114.1	104.0

CALIFORNIA

DIVISION		LOS ANGELES 900-902 MAT.	INST.	TOTAL	MARYSVILLE 959 MAT.	INST.	TOTAL	MODESTO 953 MAT.	INST.	TOTAL	MOJAVE 935 MAT.	INST.	TOTAL	OAKLAND 946 MAT.	INST.	TOTAL	OXNARD 930 MAT.	INST.	TOTAL
015433	CONTRACTOR EQUIPMENT		100.1	100.1		98.5	98.5		98.5	98.5		98.8	98.8		100.3	100.3		97.7	97.7
0241, 31 - 34	SITE & INFRASTRUCTURE, DEMOLITION	96.6	107.1	104.1	107.2	105.0	105.7	102.2	105.1	104.3	96.4	106.0	103.2	124.7	107.6	112.5	103.3	104.0	103.8
0310	Concrete Forming & Accessories	108.6	124.3	122.2	104.6	134.4	130.3	100.7	134.3	129.7	116.1	112.1	112.6	104.9	149.9	143.7	107.5	124.3	122.0
0320	Concrete Reinforcing	103.6	113.4	108.6	102.5	113.8	108.2	106.2	113.8	110.0	97.3	113.1	105.3	96.7	114.4	105.7	95.5	113.1	104.4
0330	Cast-in-Place Concrete	91.2	122.0	103.9	112.6	119.2	115.3	100.8	119.2	108.4	86.0	122.4	101.0	117.0	124.8	120.2	100.1	122.7	109.4
03	CONCRETE	95.9	120.6	108.0	113.9	124.0	118.9	104.7	124.0	114.2	91.0	115.1	102.8	106.8	132.7	119.5	99.2	120.6	109.7
04	MASONRY	90.5	122.6	110.5	104.9	123.1	116.2	102.9	123.1	115.5	101.9	118.3	112.1	120.6	134.3	129.2	104.8	116.5	112.1
05	METALS	101.1	102.9	101.7	102.0	101.8	102.0	99.1	101.7	99.9	102.8	100.3	102.0	101.4	100.4	101.1	100.7	100.7	100.7
06	WOOD, PLASTICS & COMPOSITES	103.0	122.6	113.9	103.0	138.5	122.9	98.5	138.5	120.9	107.4	106.8	107.1	98.8	154.9	130.2	102.1	122.7	113.6
07	THERMAL & MOISTURE PROTECTION	97.6	121.2	107.3	102.9	121.5	110.5	102.5	118.7	109.1	94.4	110.9	101.2	103.1	137.2	117.1	97.4	119.8	106.6
08	OPENINGS	95.4	120.7	101.3	102.8	125.3	108.0	101.6	125.4	107.1	93.2	107.5	96.5	93.1	140.6	104.1	95.7	120.6	101.5
0920	Plaster & Gypsum Board	103.6	123.2	116.9	105.0	139.5	128.3	107.5	139.5	129.1	110.8	106.8	108.1	105.7	156.0	139.7	104.7	123.2	117.2
0950, 0980	Ceilings & Acoustic Treatment	110.5	123.2	118.8	109.2	139.5	129.1	105.0	139.5	127.7	94.2	106.8	102.5	108.9	156.0	139.9	96.6	123.2	114.1
0960	Flooring	102.0	112.0	104.9	102.0	117.6	106.4	102.4	112.8	105.3	112.6	110.2	111.9	103.4	127.6	110.3	104.8	112.0	106.9
0970, 0990	Wall Finishes & Painting/Coating	100.0	111.5	106.9	100.5	115.8	109.7	100.5	117.0	110.5	111.1	102.0	105.6	102.5	143.9	127.5	111.1	101.1	105.1
09	FINISHES	104.2	120.6	113.3	103.1	131.5	118.8	102.2	130.9	118.0	101.8	109.9	106.2	104.3	147.2	127.9	99.4	119.6	110.5
COVERS	DIVS. 10 - 14, 25, 28, 41, 43, 44, 46	100.0	111.9	102.4	100.0	122.2	104.5	100.0	122.2	104.5	100.0	107.8	101.6	100.0	126.3	105.3	100.0	112.2	102.5
21, 22, 23	FIRE SUPPRESSION, PLUMBING & HVAC	99.9	118.6	107.5	95.2	109.0	100.8	100.0	111.3	104.6	95.3	115.1	103.3	100.1	147.8	119.4	100.1	118.6	107.6
26, 27, 3370	ELECTRICAL, COMMUNICATIONS & UTIL.	102.0	121.3	112.2	95.7	107.4	101.9	98.2	104.0	101.3	92.0	99.9	96.2	108.5	139.3	124.8	97.7	107.3	102.8
MF2014	WEIGHTED AVERAGE	99.2	117.5	107.2	101.3	115.9	107.7	100.8	115.7	107.3	96.8	109.8	102.5	103.1	134.3	116.7	99.6	114.4	106.0

752

City Cost Indexes

CALIFORNIA

DIVISION		PALM SPRINGS 922			PALO ALTO 943			PASADENA 910-912			REDDING 960			RICHMOND 948			RIVERSIDE 925		
		MAT.	INST.	TOTAL	MAT.	INST.	TOTAL	MAT.	INST.	TOTAL	MAT.	INST.	TOTAL	MAT.	INST.	TOTAL	MAT.	INST.	TOTAL
015433	CONTRACTOR EQUIPMENT		99.6	99.6		100.3	100.3		100.1	100.1		98.5	98.5		100.3	100.3		99.6	99.6
0241, 31-34	SITE & INFRASTRUCTURE, DEMOLITION	90.9	106.3	101.8	114.4	107.6	109.6	94.9	110.9	106.3	125.1	105.0	110.8	123.8	107.6	112.3	97.9	106.3	103.9
0310	Concrete Forming & Accessories	101.9	115.3	113.4	103.0	146.3	140.3	106.2	115.3	114.1	107.8	142.7	137.9	118.7	149.7	145.5	105.8	124.2	121.7
0320	Concrete Reinforcing	107.8	113.1	110.5	94.5	114.4	104.6	107.5	113.3	110.5	118.7	113.8	116.2	94.5	114.3	104.6	104.7	113.1	109.0
0330	Cast-in-Place Concrete	88.6	123.2	102.8	104.4	124.8	112.8	90.2	120.8	102.8	118.0	119.2	118.5	120.0	124.8	122.0	96.3	123.3	107.4
03	CONCRETE	96.6	116.8	106.5	96.5	131.1	113.5	96.6	116.0	106.2	122.7	127.7	125.2	108.8	132.6	120.5	102.6	120.8	111.6
04	MASONRY	77.6	118.5	103.1	97.4	134.3	120.4	106.5	121.1	115.6	130.0	123.1	125.7	113.2	132.8	125.4	78.6	118.1	103.2
05	METALS	103.3	100.8	102.5	98.9	100.3	99.3	85.3	100.8	90.1	101.6	101.8	101.7	98.9	100.2	99.3	102.8	101.0	102.3
06	WOOD, PLASTICS & COMPOSITES	96.6	110.8	104.5	96.1	150.2	126.4	86.5	110.6	100.0	110.6	149.8	132.6	115.3	154.9	137.5	101.9	122.6	113.5
07	THERMAL & MOISTURE PROTECTION	99.1	118.7	107.2	102.7	137.5	117.0	94.9	117.4	104.1	121.6	122.1	121.8	103.3	135.9	116.7	99.6	121.1	108.4
08	OPENINGS	100.1	114.1	103.4	93.1	136.9	103.3	91.8	114.0	97.0	114.1	131.5	118.1	93.1	139.4	103.9	102.8	120.6	107.0
0920	Plaster & Gypsum Board	102.0	111.0	108.1	103.9	151.1	135.9	90.2	111.0	104.3	106.2	151.1	136.6	113.6	156.0	142.3	106.3	123.2	117.7
0950, 0980	Ceilings & Acoustic Treatment	101.7	111.0	107.8	107.1	151.1	136.0	100.2	111.0	107.3	131.5	151.1	144.4	107.1	156.0	139.3	109.2	123.2	118.4
0960	Flooring	104.6	107.2	105.3	102.4	127.6	109.6	90.8	110.2	96.3	98.0	117.6	103.6	109.9	127.6	115.0	106.0	112.0	107.7
0970, 0990	Wall Finishes & Painting/Coating	97.2	111.3	105.7	102.5	143.9	127.5	100.5	111.5	107.1	115.9	115.8	115.8	102.5	143.9	127.5	97.2	106.8	103.0
09	FINISHES	99.1	112.8	106.6	102.7	144.4	125.6	97.3	113.2	106.0	109.3	138.2	125.3	106.9	147.2	129.1	102.1	120.1	112.0
COVERS	DIVS. 10-14, 25, 28, 41, 43, 44, 46	100.0	110.7	102.2	100.0	125.9	105.2	100.0	110.3	102.1	100.0	123.4	104.7	100.0	126.3	105.3	100.0	112.0	102.4
21, 22, 23	FIRE SUPPRESSION, PLUMBING & HVAC	95.2	115.5	103.4	95.3	145.5	115.6	95.2	115.6	103.4	100.2	109.0	103.7	95.3	147.8	116.5	100.0	118.6	107.5
26, 27, 3370	ELECTRICAL, COMMUNICATIONS & UTIL.	95.3	105.4	100.7	108.4	150.2	130.5	115.1	120.5	118.0	99.2	107.4	103.5	109.0	132.7	121.5	91.9	105.4	99.1
MF2014	WEIGHTED AVERAGE	97.2	112.0	103.6	98.9	134.5	114.4	96.4	114.6	104.3	107.8	117.7	112.1	101.8	133.1	115.4	99.4	114.6	106.0

CALIFORNIA

DIVISION		SACRAMENTO 942,956-958			SALINAS 939			SAN BERNARDINO 923-924			SAN DIEGO 919-921			SAN FRANCISCO 940-941			SAN JOSE 951		
		MAT.	INST.	TOTAL	MAT.	INST.	TOTAL	MAT.	INST.	TOTAL	MAT.	INST.	TOTAL	MAT.	INST.	TOTAL	MAT.	INST.	TOTAL
015433	CONTRACTOR EQUIPMENT		99.9	99.9		98.8	98.8		99.6	99.6		100.1	100.1		110.7	110.7		99.3	99.3
0241, 31-34	SITE & INFRASTRUCTURE, DEMOLITION	100.6	113.3	109.6	116.3	105.7	108.8	77.7	106.3	98.0	101.7	104.0	103.4	127.0	113.6	117.5	133.5	100.4	109.9
0310	Concrete Forming & Accessories	103.3	137.0	132.4	111.0	137.4	133.7	109.6	115.2	114.4	105.4	113.3	112.2	104.6	150.9	144.6	107.0	149.8	143.9
0320	Concrete Reinforcing	89.4	113.8	101.8	96.0	114.2	105.2	104.7	113.0	108.9	104.2	113.1	108.7	110.1	115.0	112.6	93.5	114.5	104.1
0330	Cast-in-Place Concrete	99.0	120.3	107.7	98.9	119.6	107.4	66.6	123.2	89.8	98.9	107.8	102.6	120.0	126.4	122.6	117.1	124.2	120.0
03	CONCRETE	97.0	125.2	110.9	108.5	125.6	116.9	76.8	116.8	96.4	101.8	110.7	106.2	110.3	134.4	122.1	110.8	132.9	121.7
04	MASONRY	98.4	123.1	113.8	101.6	128.1	118.1	84.9	115.9	104.2	97.4	115.6	108.7	121.1	141.5	133.8	131.4	134.4	133.3
05	METALS	97.0	96.1	96.7	105.5	102.9	104.7	102.8	100.5	102.1	101.1	101.4	101.2	107.6	110.8	108.6	97.5	107.5	100.6
06	WOOD, PLASTICS & COMPOSITES	92.9	141.7	120.2	107.3	141.5	126.4	105.8	110.8	108.6	100.6	110.2	106.0	98.8	155.1	130.3	111.3	154.7	135.6
07	THERMAL & MOISTURE PROTECTION	110.8	121.3	115.1	95.0	126.1	107.7	98.3	117.7	106.3	99.3	107.1	102.5	104.9	141.9	120.1	98.9	139.3	115.4
08	OPENINGS	106.3	127.2	111.1	96.9	133.3	105.4	100.2	114.1	103.4	99.1	111.8	102.1	97.3	140.7	107.4	92.8	140.5	103.9
0920	Plaster & Gypsum Board	101.0	142.6	129.1	105.8	142.6	130.6	108.2	111.0	110.1	97.8	110.3	106.3	108.3	156.0	140.6	102.7	156.0	138.7
0950, 0980	Ceilings & Acoustic Treatment	107.1	142.6	130.4	94.2	142.6	126.0	105.0	111.0	109.0	107.7	110.3	109.4	117.1	156.0	142.7	103.3	156.0	138.0
0960	Flooring	102.6	117.6	106.9	107.1	121.1	111.1	107.8	110.2	108.5	98.5	112.0	102.4	103.4	127.6	110.3	95.4	127.6	104.6
0970, 0990	Wall Finishes & Painting/Coating	100.2	116.7	110.1	112.3	143.9	131.4	97.2	104.0	101.3	97.1	111.5	105.8	102.5	153.2	133.1	100.8	143.9	126.8
09	FINISHES	101.4	133.6	119.1	101.4	137.0	121.0	100.5	112.5	107.1	102.9	112.9	108.4	106.5	148.3	129.6	100.7	147.0	126.2
COVERS	DIVS. 10-14, 25, 28, 41, 43, 44, 46	100.0	123.0	104.6	100.0	122.6	104.6	100.0	108.1	101.6	100.0	109.7	102.0	100.0	126.8	105.4	100.0	125.9	105.2
21, 22, 23	FIRE SUPPRESSION, PLUMBING & HVAC	100.0	120.8	108.4	95.3	117.7	104.4	95.2	115.6	103.4	99.9	116.9	106.8	100.1	175.0	130.3	100.0	147.3	119.1
26, 27, 3370	ELECTRICAL, COMMUNICATIONS & UTIL.	103.5	108.7	106.2	93.2	120.9	107.8	95.3	103.4	99.6	101.2	98.5	99.8	108.6	157.8	134.6	101.1	155.9	130.1
MF2014	WEIGHTED AVERAGE	100.5	119.3	108.7	100.2	121.6	109.5	95.1	111.3	102.1	100.5	109.6	104.5	105.2	145.4	122.7	102.5	136.6	117.4

CALIFORNIA

DIVISION		SAN LUIS OBISPO 934			SAN MATEO 944			SAN RAFAEL 949			SANTA ANA 926-927			SANTA BARBARA 931			SANTA CRUZ 950		
		MAT.	INST.	TOTAL	MAT.	INST.	TOTAL	MAT.	INST.	TOTAL	MAT.	INST.	TOTAL	MAT.	INST.	TOTAL	MAT.	INST.	TOTAL
015433	CONTRACTOR EQUIPMENT		98.8	98.8		100.3	100.3		100.3	100.3		99.6	99.6		98.8	98.8		99.3	99.3
0241, 31-34	SITE & INFRASTRUCTURE, DEMOLITION	108.4	106.0	106.7	121.3	107.6	111.6	113.2	113.4	113.4	89.4	106.3	101.4	103.3	106.0	105.2	133.1	100.0	109.6
0310	Concrete Forming & Accessories	117.9	115.4	115.8	109.0	149.8	144.2	112.9	149.9	144.9	109.9	115.3	114.5	108.3	124.2	122.1	107.0	137.6	133.4
0320	Concrete Reinforcing	97.3	113.1	105.0	94.5	114.6	104.7	95.1	114.6	105.1	108.3	113.1	110.8	95.5	113.2	104.5	115.7	114.2	114.9
0330	Cast-in-Place Concrete	106.3	122.5	112.9	116.2	124.8	119.7	135.2	124.1	130.7	85.0	123.2	100.7	99.8	122.6	109.1	116.3	121.4	118.4
03	CONCRETE	106.9	116.6	111.7	105.4	132.7	118.8	126.0	132.4	129.1	94.2	116.8	105.3	99.0	120.6	109.6	113.9	126.5	120.1
04	MASONRY	103.5	118.3	112.7	112.9	137.3	128.1	93.2	137.4	120.7	74.6	118.8	102.1	102.2	119.1	112.7	135.3	128.2	130.9
05	METALS	103.5	100.6	102.6	98.7	100.6	99.3	100.1	98.8	99.7	102.9	100.8	102.2	101.2	100.9	101.1	104.5	106.3	105.0
06	WOOD, PLASTICS & COMPOSITES	109.9	110.9	110.5	104.0	154.9	132.5	101.8	154.7	131.4	107.8	110.8	109.5	102.1	122.7	113.6	111.3	141.6	128.3
07	THERMAL & MOISTURE PROTECTION	95.1	116.9	104.0	103.1	138.8	117.7	107.2	138.9	120.2	99.4	118.3	107.2	94.6	118.9	104.5	98.8	129.2	111.3
08	OPENINGS	95.1	109.7	98.5	93.1	139.4	103.8	103.8	139.3	112.1	99.5	114.1	102.9	96.6	120.6	102.2	94.0	133.4	103.2
0920	Plaster & Gypsum Board	112.2	111.0	111.4	108.9	156.0	140.8	111.5	156.0	141.6	109.6	111.0	110.6	104.7	123.2	117.2	110.1	142.6	132.0
0950, 0980	Ceilings & Acoustic Treatment	94.2	111.0	105.3	107.1	156.0	139.3	115.4	156.0	142.1	105.0	111.0	109.0	96.6	123.2	114.1	106.7	142.6	130.3
0960	Flooring	113.5	110.2	112.6	105.1	127.6	111.5	115.0	121.1	116.8	108.3	110.2	108.8	106.2	108.6	106.9	99.6	121.1	105.7
0970, 0990	Wall Finishes & Painting/Coating	111.1	101.7	105.5	102.5	143.9	127.5	98.9	142.6	125.3	97.2	106.8	103.0	111.1	101.1	105.1	101.0	143.9	126.9
09	FINISHES	103.2	112.3	108.2	104.7	147.2	128.1	107.6	145.8	128.6	102.0	112.8	107.9	100.0	119.0	110.5	103.7	137.1	122.1
COVERS	DIVS. 10-14, 25, 28, 41, 43, 44, 46	100.0	120.6	104.2	100.0	126.4	105.3	100.0	125.7	105.2	100.0	110.7	102.2	100.0	112.2	102.5	100.0	122.9	104.6
21, 22, 23	FIRE SUPPRESSION, PLUMBING & HVAC	95.3	115.6	103.5	95.3	142.2	114.2	95.3	169.5	125.2	95.2	114.3	102.9	100.1	118.6	107.6	100.0	117.8	107.2
26, 27, 3370	ELECTRICAL, COMMUNICATIONS & UTIL.	92.0	106.4	99.6	108.4	148.0	129.3	105.4	120.0	113.1	95.4	105.7	100.8	91.0	110.5	101.3	100.3	120.9	111.2
MF2014	WEIGHTED AVERAGE	99.4	112.0	104.9	100.9	134.6	115.6	103.5	136.7	118.0	96.9	111.8	103.4	98.9	115.1	106.0	104.5	121.8	112.0

DIVISION — CALIFORNIA / COLORADO

DIVISION		SANTA ROSA 954 MAT.	INST.	TOTAL	STOCKTON 952 MAT.	INST.	TOTAL	SUSANVILLE 961 MAT.	INST.	TOTAL	VALLEJO 945 MAT.	INST.	TOTAL	VAN NUYS 913-916 MAT.	INST.	TOTAL	ALAMOSA 811 MAT.	INST.	TOTAL
015433	CONTRACTOR EQUIPMENT		99.0	99.0		98.5	98.5		98.5	98.5		100.3	100.3		100.1	100.1		93.8	93.8
0241, 31 - 34	SITE & INFRASTRUCTURE, DEMOLITION	103.0	105.1	104.5	102.0	105.1	104.2	131.8	105.0	112.8	100.5	113.2	109.5	111.4	110.9	111.0	134.7	88.0	101.5
0310	Concrete Forming & Accessories	102.9	148.1	141.9	104.8	136.6	132.2	109.1	142.8	138.1	103.4	147.7	141.6	112.7	115.3	115.0	105.0	67.5	72.7
0320	Concrete Reinforcing	103.4	114.8	109.2	106.2	113.8	110.1	118.7	113.2	115.9	96.3	114.5	105.6	107.5	113.3	110.5	105.1	76.4	90.5
0330	Cast-in-Place Concrete	110.6	120.8	114.8	98.2	119.2	106.9	107.4	119.3	112.3	107.7	121.5	113.4	95.1	120.8	105.7	101.1	78.4	91.8
03	CONCRETE	113.7	130.9	122.1	103.7	125.0	114.2	125.2	127.7	126.4	102.2	130.5	116.1	110.2	116.0	113.0	113.5	73.3	93.8
04	MASONRY	103.1	137.2	124.3	102.8	123.1	115.5	127.9	112.7	118.4	71.6	133.1	109.9	122.7	121.1	121.7	126.0	71.9	92.3
05	METALS	103.2	105.0	103.8	99.3	101.8	100.0	100.6	101.1	100.7	100.1	98.1	99.5	84.4	100.8	89.5	98.2	80.2	92.7
06	WOOD, PLASTICS & COMPOSITES	98.0	154.5	129.6	104.3	141.5	125.1	112.5	149.8	133.4	90.6	154.7	126.5	95.0	110.6	103.7	98.0	67.5	80.9
07	THERMAL & MOISTURE PROTECTION	99.8	136.2	114.7	102.6	119.9	109.7	122.2	120.4	121.4	105.0	135.3	117.4	95.7	117.4	104.6	104.9	78.1	93.9
08	OPENINGS	101.0	140.4	110.2	101.6	127.1	107.5	113.9	131.5	118.0	105.6	140.5	113.7	91.6	114.0	96.8	98.3	74.1	92.7
0920	Plaster & Gypsum Board	103.9	156.0	139.2	107.5	142.6	131.2	107.1	151.1	136.9	105.8	156.0	139.8	95.3	111.0	105.9	79.0	66.3	70.4
0950, 0980	Ceilings & Acoustic Treatment	105.0	156.0	138.6	112.5	142.6	132.3	124.1	151.1	141.9	117.3	156.0	142.8	97.7	111.0	106.5	96.3	66.3	76.6
0960	Flooring	105.0	115.2	107.9	102.4	112.8	105.3	98.4	122.1	105.2	110.6	127.6	115.4	93.2	110.2	98.0	113.5	54.8	96.7
0970, 0990	Wall Finishes & Painting/Coating	97.2	142.6	124.6	100.5	117.0	110.5	115.9	115.8	115.8	99.8	142.6	125.6	100.5	111.5	107.1	114.1	39.8	69.3
09	FINISHES	101.1	143.6	124.5	103.8	132.7	119.7	108.9	139.0	125.5	104.6	145.8	127.3	99.3	113.2	107.0	102.5	61.7	80.0
COVERS	DIVS. 10 - 14, 25, 28, 41, 43, 44, 46	100.0	123.8	104.8	100.0	122.5	104.6	100.0	123.5	104.7	100.0	124.3	104.9	100.0	110.3	102.1	100.0	88.5	97.7
21, 22, 23	FIRE SUPPRESSION, PLUMBING & HVAC	95.2	167.3	124.3	100.0	111.3	104.6	95.4	109.0	100.9	100.1	127.5	111.1	95.2	115.6	103.4	95.2	72.0	85.9
26, 27, 3370	ELECTRICAL, COMMUNICATIONS & UTIL.	95.7	114.3	105.5	98.2	110.6	104.8	99.6	118.4	109.5	100.9	122.4	112.3	115.1	120.5	118.0	99.1	72.5	85.0
MF2014	WEIGHTED AVERAGE	100.8	134.7	115.6	100.9	117.2	108.0	106.8	118.1	111.7	100.1	127.2	111.9	99.1	114.6	105.9	102.2	73.7	89.8

DIVISION — COLORADO

DIVISION		BOULDER 803 MAT.	INST.	TOTAL	COLORADO SPRINGS 808-809 MAT.	INST.	TOTAL	DENVER 800-802 MAT.	INST.	TOTAL	DURANGO 813 MAT.	INST.	TOTAL	FORT COLLINS 805 MAT.	INST.	TOTAL	FORT MORGAN 807 MAT.	INST.	TOTAL
015433	CONTRACTOR EQUIPMENT		97.5	97.5		95.8	95.8		100.4	100.4		93.8	93.8		97.5	97.5		97.5	97.5
0241, 31 - 34	SITE & INFRASTRUCTURE, DEMOLITION	94.8	96.4	95.9	96.9	94.7	95.3	96.1	102.6	100.7	128.5	88.0	99.7	107.1	96.0	99.2	97.7	95.9	96.4
0310	Concrete Forming & Accessories	103.1	79.9	83.1	93.6	79.4	81.3	100.0	76.0	79.3	111.4	67.7	73.7	100.7	74.7	78.3	103.6	74.9	78.9
0320	Concrete Reinforcing	98.9	76.6	87.5	98.1	80.2	89.0	98.1	80.2	89.0	105.1	76.5	90.5	99.0	76.6	87.6	99.1	76.5	87.6
0330	Cast-in-Place Concrete	101.8	80.0	92.9	104.6	88.3	97.9	99.0	82.8	92.4	116.3	78.5	100.8	114.9	78.9	100.1	99.9	78.9	91.3
03	CONCRETE	103.1	79.6	91.5	106.3	82.9	94.8	100.7	79.5	90.3	116.1	73.4	95.1	113.5	76.7	95.4	101.5	76.8	89.4
04	MASONRY	91.0	72.1	79.2	91.3	81.9	85.4	93.3	72.2	80.1	113.6	71.9	87.6	108.5	75.7	88.1	104.9	72.2	84.5
05	METALS	96.0	83.5	92.2	99.1	85.7	95.0	101.6	85.6	96.7	98.2	80.4	92.7	97.2	80.4	92.0	95.7	80.3	91.0
06	WOOD, PLASTICS & COMPOSITES	102.2	83.0	91.4	91.7	77.3	83.6	99.8	77.2	87.2	107.6	67.5	85.1	99.6	77.2	87.0	102.2	77.2	88.2
07	THERMAL & MOISTURE PROTECTION	103.1	81.7	94.3	103.9	85.6	96.4	102.4	75.8	91.5	104.9	78.1	93.9	103.5	73.5	91.2	103.0	81.2	94.1
08	OPENINGS	98.2	82.5	94.5	102.4	80.5	97.3	103.0	80.4	97.8	105.3	74.1	98.0	98.2	79.4	93.8	98.1	79.4	93.8
0920	Plaster & Gypsum Board	105.1	82.7	89.9	87.9	76.7	80.3	100.7	76.8	84.5	92.5	66.3	74.8	99.1	76.7	84.0	105.1	76.7	85.9
0950, 0980	Ceilings & Acoustic Treatment	96.9	82.7	87.5	104.4	76.7	86.2	107.3	76.8	87.2	96.3	66.3	76.6	96.9	76.7	83.6	96.9	76.7	83.6
0960	Flooring	99.7	83.8	95.2	92.0	68.2	85.2	96.7	84.8	93.3	118.2	54.8	100.0	96.6	54.8	84.6	100.1	54.8	87.1
0970, 0990	Wall Finishes & Painting/Coating	101.7	66.6	80.5	101.4	40.5	64.7	101.7	75.7	86.0	114.1	39.8	69.3	101.7	40.2	64.6	101.7	53.6	72.6
09	FINISHES	101.7	79.4	89.4	98.8	72.8	84.5	102.4	77.3	88.6	105.0	61.7	81.1	100.5	67.4	82.3	101.8	68.9	83.7
COVERS	DIVS. 10 - 14, 25, 28, 41, 43, 44, 46	100.0	89.4	97.9	100.0	92.2	98.4	100.0	88.8	97.7	100.0	88.4	97.7	100.0	88.8	97.7	100.0	88.8	97.7
21, 22, 23	FIRE SUPPRESSION, PLUMBING & HVAC	95.3	77.3	88.1	100.2	88.2	95.4	100.0	79.9	91.9	95.2	83.1	90.3	100.1	77.2	90.9	95.3	77.2	88.0
26, 27, 3370	ELECTRICAL, COMMUNICATIONS & UTIL.	97.4	84.5	90.6	100.8	82.1	90.9	102.6	83.2	92.4	98.5	69.4	83.1	97.4	84.5	90.6	97.8	84.5	90.7
MF2014	WEIGHTED AVERAGE	97.8	81.3	90.6	100.4	84.0	93.2	100.8	81.7	92.5	102.7	75.7	90.9	101.3	79.0	91.6	98.3	79.0	89.9

DIVISION — COLORADO

DIVISION		GLENWOOD SPRINGS 816 MAT.	INST.	TOTAL	GOLDEN 804 MAT.	INST.	TOTAL	GRAND JUNCTION 815 MAT.	INST.	TOTAL	GREELEY 806 MAT.	INST.	TOTAL	MONTROSE 814 MAT.	INST.	TOTAL	PUEBLO 810 MAT.	INST.	TOTAL
015433	CONTRACTOR EQUIPMENT		96.7	96.7		97.5	97.5		96.7	96.7		97.5	97.5		95.2	95.2		93.8	93.8
0241, 31 - 34	SITE & INFRASTRUCTURE, DEMOLITION	143.2	95.1	109.0	107.3	96.2	99.4	128.4	94.7	104.5	94.0	95.4	95.0	137.1	91.2	104.5	120.6	91.0	99.6
0310	Concrete Forming & Accessories	102.0	75.0	78.7	96.1	74.8	77.8	110.2	74.4	79.3	98.6	78.4	81.2	101.4	74.8	78.4	107.3	79.4	83.3
0320	Concrete Reinforcing	104.0	76.5	90.0	99.1	76.4	87.6	104.3	76.3	90.1	98.9	75.1	86.8	103.9	76.4	89.9	100.6	80.2	90.2
0330	Cast-in-Place Concrete	101.1	77.9	91.6	100.0	78.9	91.3	111.9	77.1	97.6	96.1	59.1	80.9	101.7	77.8	91.5	100.4	87.8	95.2
03	CONCRETE	118.5	76.5	97.9	111.9	76.7	94.6	112.5	75.9	94.5	98.3	71.3	85.0	109.7	76.3	93.3	102.7	82.7	92.9
04	MASONRY	98.9	72.1	82.2	107.7	71.8	85.3	132.6	71.5	94.5	102.6	49.0	69.2	106.2	71.9	84.9	95.4	81.7	86.9
05	METALS	97.9	80.9	92.6	95.9	80.1	91.0	99.5	79.2	93.2	97.2	77.5	91.1	97.1	80.0	91.8	101.1	86.2	96.5
06	WOOD, PLASTICS & COMPOSITES	93.2	77.3	84.3	94.3	77.2	84.7	105.3	77.3	89.6	96.8	83.0	89.1	94.3	77.4	84.8	100.9	77.6	87.8
07	THERMAL & MOISTURE PROTECTION	104.8	79.2	94.3	103.9	75.4	92.2	104.0	68.5	89.5	102.9	66.4	87.9	105.0	79.2	94.4	103.5	83.6	95.3
08	OPENINGS	104.2	79.4	98.5	98.2	78.8	93.7	105.0	78.8	98.9	98.1	82.4	94.5	105.5	79.5	99.4	100.2	80.6	95.6
0920	Plaster & Gypsum Board	117.8	76.7	90.0	96.9	76.7	83.3	131.0	76.7	94.3	97.6	82.7	87.5	78.3	76.7	77.2	83.9	76.7	79.1
0950, 0980	Ceilings & Acoustic Treatment	95.5	76.7	83.2	96.9	76.7	83.6	95.5	76.7	83.2	96.9	82.7	87.5	96.3	76.7	83.4	104.7	76.7	86.3
0960	Flooring	112.8	50.4	95.0	94.7	54.8	83.3	117.5	54.8	99.6	95.7	54.8	84.0	115.8	45.4	95.7	114.6	84.8	106.1
0970, 0990	Wall Finishes & Painting/Coating	114.1	66.5	85.4	101.7	66.6	80.5	114.1	66.6	85.4	101.7	25.0	55.4	114.1	39.8	69.3	114.1	37.5	67.9
09	FINISHES	107.9	69.6	86.8	100.4	71.0	84.2	109.3	70.4	87.9	99.3	69.2	82.7	103.2	65.7	82.5	103.7	75.6	88.2
COVERS	DIVS. 10 - 14, 25, 28, 41, 43, 44, 46	100.0	88.8	97.7	100.0	88.8	97.7	100.0	88.8	97.7	100.0	89.4	97.9	100.0	89.1	97.8	100.0	92.7	98.5
21, 22, 23	FIRE SUPPRESSION, PLUMBING & HVAC	95.2	83.0	90.3	95.3	76.7	87.8	99.9	82.5	92.9	100.1	77.2	90.8	95.2	83.0	90.3	99.9	76.8	90.6
26, 27, 3370	ELECTRICAL, COMMUNICATIONS & UTIL.	95.7	69.4	81.8	97.8	84.5	90.7	98.2	53.8	74.7	97.4	84.5	90.6	98.2	56.4	76.1	99.1	73.0	85.3
MF2014	WEIGHTED AVERAGE	102.3	78.1	91.8	99.8	78.9	90.7	104.8	75.3	91.9	98.9	75.5	88.7	101.4	75.4	90.1	101.1	80.3	92.0

COLORADO / CONNECTICUT

DIVISION		SALIDA 812 MAT.	INST.	TOTAL	BRIDGEPORT 066 MAT.	INST.	TOTAL	BRISTOL 060 MAT.	INST.	TOTAL	HARTFORD 061 MAT.	INST.	TOTAL	MERIDEN 064 MAT.	INST.	TOTAL	NEW BRITAIN 060 MAT.	INST.	TOTAL
015433	CONTRACTOR EQUIPMENT		95.2	95.2		100.9	100.9		100.9	100.9		100.9	100.9		101.3	101.3		100.9	100.9
0241, 31 - 34	SITE & INFRASTRUCTURE, DEMOLITION	128.2	91.5	102.1	109.8	105.1	106.4	108.9	105.0	106.2	104.4	105.0	104.9	106.7	105.8	106.0	109.1	105.0	106.2
0310	Concrete Forming & Accessories	110.1	74.7	79.6	98.9	124.5	121.0	98.9	124.3	120.8	95.7	124.3	120.4	98.6	124.3	120.8	99.2	124.3	120.9
0320	Concrete Reinforcing	103.7	76.4	89.8	105.1	127.3	116.4	105.1	127.3	116.4	104.6	127.3	116.2	105.1	127.3	116.4	105.1	127.3	116.4
0330	Cast-in-Place Concrete	115.8	77.8	100.2	107.9	127.1	115.8	101.1	127.1	111.8	103.0	127.1	112.9	97.3	127.1	109.5	102.8	127.1	112.7
03	CONCRETE	111.2	76.3	94.1	106.6	125.7	116.0	103.4	125.6	114.3	104.0	125.6	114.6	101.6	125.6	113.4	104.2	125.6	114.7
04	MASONRY	133.9	71.9	95.3	111.8	134.0	125.6	102.9	134.0	122.3	107.7	134.0	124.1	102.5	134.0	122.1	105.2	134.0	123.1
05	METALS	96.7	79.9	91.6	100.5	125.5	108.2	100.5	125.4	108.1	105.6	125.4	111.7	97.4	125.4	106.0	96.5	125.4	105.4
06	WOOD, PLASTICS & COMPOSITES	101.9	77.4	88.2	98.8	123.4	112.6	98.8	123.4	112.6	92.3	123.4	109.7	98.8	123.4	112.6	98.8	123.4	112.6
07	THERMAL & MOISTURE PROTECTION	104.0	79.2	93.8	98.6	129.1	111.1	98.7	126.0	109.9	102.8	126.0	112.3	98.7	126.0	109.9	98.7	126.0	109.9
08	OPENINGS	98.4	79.5	94.0	101.2	132.1	108.4	101.2	132.1	108.4	100.3	132.1	107.7	103.6	132.1	110.2	101.2	132.1	108.4
0920	Plaster & Gypsum Board	78.6	76.7	77.3	101.7	123.5	116.4	101.7	123.5	116.4	97.4	123.5	115.0	103.2	123.5	116.9	101.7	123.5	116.4
0950, 0980	Ceilings & Acoustic Treatment	96.3	76.7	83.4	86.4	123.5	110.8	86.4	123.5	110.8	89.7	123.5	111.9	90.4	123.5	112.2	86.4	123.5	110.8
0960	Flooring	120.6	45.4	99.1	101.9	131.2	110.3	101.9	131.2	110.3	100.5	131.2	109.2	101.9	131.2	110.3	101.9	131.2	110.3
0970, 0990	Wall Finishes & Painting/Coating	114.1	41.7	70.4	104.9	122.9	115.8	104.9	122.9	115.8	105.9	122.9	116.2	104.9	122.9	115.8	104.9	122.9	115.8
09	FINISHES	103.6	65.9	82.8	97.2	125.0	112.6	97.3	125.0	112.6	96.3	125.0	112.1	98.4	125.0	113.1	97.3	125.0	112.6
COVERS	DIVS. 10 - 14, 25, 28, 41, 43, 44, 46	100.0	89.2	97.8	100.0	112.4	102.5	100.0	112.4	102.5	100.0	112.4	102.5	100.0	112.4	102.5	100.0	112.4	102.5
21, 22, 23	FIRE SUPPRESSION, PLUMBING & HVAC	95.2	72.0	85.8	100.0	116.4	106.6	100.0	116.4	106.6	100.0	116.4	106.6	95.2	116.4	103.8	100.0	116.4	106.6
26, 27, 3370	ELECTRICAL, COMMUNICATIONS & UTIL.	98.4	72.5	84.7	98.5	112.2	105.7	98.5	111.8	105.6	97.9	112.8	105.8	98.4	111.8	105.5	98.6	111.8	105.6
MF2014	WEIGHTED AVERAGE	101.9	75.3	90.3	101.3	120.8	109.8	100.5	120.6	109.3	101.4	120.8	109.8	98.9	120.7	108.4	100.1	120.6	109.1

CONNECTICUT

DIVISION		NEW HAVEN 065 MAT.	INST.	TOTAL	NEW LONDON 063 MAT.	INST.	TOTAL	NORWALK 068 MAT.	INST.	TOTAL	STAMFORD 069 MAT.	INST.	TOTAL	WATERBURY 067 MAT.	INST.	TOTAL	WILLIMANTIC 062 MAT.	INST.	TOTAL
015433	CONTRACTOR EQUIPMENT		101.3	101.3		101.3	101.3		100.9	100.9		100.9	100.9		100.9	100.9		100.9	100.9
0241, 31 - 34	SITE & INFRASTRUCTURE, DEMOLITION	108.9	105.8	106.7	101.1	105.8	104.4	109.5	105.1	106.4	110.2	105.1	106.6	109.5	105.0	106.3	109.5	105.0	106.3
0310	Concrete Forming & Accessories	98.6	124.3	120.8	98.6	124.3	120.8	98.9	124.9	121.3	98.9	124.9	121.3	98.9	124.3	120.8	98.9	124.1	120.6
0320	Concrete Reinforcing	105.1	127.3	116.4	82.4	127.3	105.2	105.1	127.4	116.5	105.1	127.4	116.5	105.1	127.3	116.4	105.1	127.2	116.4
0330	Cast-in-Place Concrete	104.5	127.1	113.8	89.1	127.1	104.7	106.2	128.6	115.4	107.9	128.6	116.4	107.9	127.1	115.8	100.8	125.8	111.0
03	CONCRETE	118.7	125.6	122.1	91.4	125.6	108.2	105.8	126.4	115.9	106.6	126.4	116.3	106.6	125.6	115.9	103.3	125.0	114.0
04	MASONRY	103.2	134.0	122.4	101.5	134.0	121.7	102.7	135.4	123.1	103.4	135.4	123.3	103.4	134.0	122.5	102.7	134.0	122.2
05	METALS	96.8	125.4	105.6	96.5	125.4	105.4	100.5	126.1	108.3	100.5	126.1	108.3	100.5	125.4	108.1	100.2	125.2	107.9
06	WOOD, PLASTICS & COMPOSITES	98.8	123.4	112.6	98.8	123.4	112.6	98.8	123.4	112.6	98.8	123.4	112.6	98.8	123.4	112.6	98.8	123.4	112.6
07	THERMAL & MOISTURE PROTECTION	98.8	126.1	110.0	98.7	126.0	109.9	98.8	129.6	111.4	98.7	129.6	111.4	98.7	126.1	110.0	98.8	124.6	109.5
08	OPENINGS	101.2	132.1	108.4	104.0	132.1	110.6	101.2	132.1	108.4	101.2	132.1	108.4	101.2	132.1	108.4	104.0	132.1	110.6
0920	Plaster & Gypsum Board	101.7	123.5	116.4	101.7	123.5	116.4	101.7	123.5	116.4	101.7	123.5	116.4	101.7	123.5	116.4	101.7	123.5	116.4
0950, 0980	Ceilings & Acoustic Treatment	86.4	123.5	110.8	84.5	123.5	110.2	86.4	123.5	110.8	86.4	123.5	110.8	86.4	123.5	110.8	84.5	123.5	110.2
0960	Flooring	101.9	131.2	110.3	101.9	131.2	110.3	101.9	131.2	110.3	101.9	131.2	110.3	101.9	131.2	110.3	101.9	133.2	110.9
0970, 0990	Wall Finishes & Painting/Coating	104.9	122.9	115.8	104.9	122.9	115.8	104.9	122.9	115.8	104.9	122.9	115.8	104.9	122.9	115.8	104.9	122.9	115.8
09	FINISHES	97.3	125.0	112.6	96.4	125.0	112.2	97.3	125.0	112.6	97.4	125.0	112.6	97.2	125.0	112.5	97.0	125.4	112.6
COVERS	DIVS. 10 - 14, 25, 28, 41, 43, 44, 46	100.0	112.4	102.5	100.0	112.4	102.5	100.0	112.6	102.6	100.0	112.6	102.6	100.0	112.4	102.5	100.0	112.4	102.5
21, 22, 23	FIRE SUPPRESSION, PLUMBING & HVAC	100.0	116.4	106.6	95.2	116.4	103.8	100.0	116.4	106.6	100.0	116.4	106.6	100.0	116.4	106.6	100.0	116.4	106.5
26, 27, 3370	ELECTRICAL, COMMUNICATIONS & UTIL.	98.4	111.8	105.5	95.3	111.8	104.0	98.5	167.2	134.8	98.5	167.2	134.8	98.0	112.2	105.5	98.5	109.6	104.4
MF2014	WEIGHTED AVERAGE	101.6	120.7	109.9	97.1	120.7	107.4	100.8	128.7	113.0	100.9	128.7	113.0	100.9	120.7	109.5	100.8	120.2	109.2

D.C. / DELAWARE / FLORIDA

DIVISION		WASHINGTON 200 - 205 MAT.	INST.	TOTAL	DOVER 199 MAT.	INST.	TOTAL	NEWARK 197 MAT.	INST.	TOTAL	WILMINGTON 198 MAT.	INST.	TOTAL	DAYTONA BEACH 321 MAT.	INST.	TOTAL	FORT LAUDERDALE 333 MAT.	INST.	TOTAL
015433	CONTRACTOR EQUIPMENT		105.5	105.5		118.0	118.0		118.0	118.0		118.2	118.2		98.2	98.2		91.0	91.0
0241, 31 - 34	SITE & INFRASTRUCTURE, DEMOLITION	103.8	94.5	97.2	102.3	113.3	110.1	102.6	113.3	110.2	99.5	113.6	109.5	105.9	89.2	94.0	96.4	77.1	82.7
0310	Concrete Forming & Accessories	97.4	78.3	80.9	96.3	102.2	101.4	97.0	102.2	101.5	98.1	102.2	101.6	97.6	68.1	72.1	95.7	68.4	72.1
0320	Concrete Reinforcing	105.4	93.8	99.5	94.0	102.9	98.5	91.5	102.9	97.3	93.4	102.9	98.2	91.2	76.6	83.8	88.2	72.1	80.0
0330	Cast-in-Place Concrete	115.4	88.0	104.2	104.6	104.6	104.6	90.0	104.6	96.0	99.2	104.6	101.4	90.2	70.8	82.2	94.6	77.1	87.4
03	CONCRETE	107.7	85.9	97.0	102.2	104.0	103.1	94.6	104.0	99.2	99.6	104.0	101.8	91.6	71.8	81.9	94.5	73.3	84.0
04	MASONRY	98.2	80.0	86.9	107.5	98.1	101.6	103.2	98.1	100.0	108.5	98.1	102.0	99.1	65.7	78.3	102.8	68.3	81.3
05	METALS	99.9	108.6	102.6	102.0	116.7	106.5	103.5	116.7	107.5	102.0	116.7	106.5	104.7	91.1	100.5	102.0	89.6	98.2
06	WOOD, PLASTICS & COMPOSITES	95.3	76.2	84.6	94.0	101.9	98.4	95.8	101.9	99.2	92.0	101.9	97.6	96.3	69.2	81.1	84.3	67.2	74.7
07	THERMAL & MOISTURE PROTECTION	101.7	85.8	95.2	98.8	110.0	103.4	101.7	110.0	105.1	97.9	110.0	102.9	96.2	73.6	86.9	100.3	77.2	90.8
08	OPENINGS	99.9	87.9	97.1	91.3	110.9	95.9	91.6	110.9	96.1	89.9	110.9	94.8	98.6	67.4	91.3	97.5	65.5	90.1
0920	Plaster & Gypsum Board	108.0	75.5	86.0	97.1	101.8	100.3	99.5	101.8	101.1	101.7	101.8	101.8	95.6	68.7	77.4	105.4	66.6	79.2
0950, 0980	Ceilings & Acoustic Treatment	112.2	75.5	88.1	91.3	101.8	98.2	88.7	101.8	97.3	92.4	101.8	98.6	84.9	68.7	74.2	87.9	66.6	74.2
0960	Flooring	104.7	93.6	101.5	99.8	109.7	102.7	96.8	109.7	100.5	104.3	109.7	105.9	110.5	73.6	100.0	105.1	69.3	94.9
0970, 0990	Wall Finishes & Painting/Coating	108.0	82.2	92.4	97.2	106.4	102.8	97.3	106.4	102.8	95.0	106.4	101.9	104.5	74.1	86.2	98.9	70.2	81.6
09	FINISHES	100.8	80.5	89.6	96.2	103.6	100.3	95.0	103.6	99.7	98.7	103.6	101.4	96.9	69.3	81.7	94.9	68.1	80.1
COVERS	DIVS. 10 - 14, 25, 28, 41, 43, 44, 46	100.0	98.6	99.7	100.0	88.0	97.6	100.0	88.0	97.6	100.0	88.0	97.6	100.0	84.4	96.9	100.0	87.4	97.5
21, 22, 23	FIRE SUPPRESSION, PLUMBING & HVAC	100.1	92.1	96.9	100.0	117.4	107.0	100.1	117.4	107.1	100.1	117.4	107.1	99.9	76.1	90.3	100.0	66.5	86.5
26, 27, 3370	ELECTRICAL, COMMUNICATIONS & UTIL.	101.5	105.8	103.8	96.6	111.9	104.7	98.7	111.9	105.7	99.8	111.9	106.2	95.8	54.9	74.2	96.0	72.7	83.7
MF2014	WEIGHTED AVERAGE	101.1	91.9	97.1	99.3	109.2	103.6	98.8	109.2	103.3	99.3	109.2	103.6	99.0	72.9	87.6	98.6	72.6	87.2

FLORIDA

DIVISION		FORT MYERS 339,341			GAINESVILLE 326,344			JACKSONVILLE 320,322			LAKELAND 338			MELBOURNE 329			MIAMI 330 - 332,340		
		MAT.	INST.	TOTAL	MAT.	INST.	TOTAL	MAT.	INST.	TOTAL	MAT.	INST.	TOTAL	MAT.	INST.	TOTAL	MAT.	INST.	TOTAL
015433	CONTRACTOR EQUIPMENT		98.2	98.2		98.2	98.2		98.2	98.2		98.2	98.2		98.2	98.2		91.0	91.0
0241, 31 - 34	SITE & INFRASTRUCTURE, DEMOLITION	107.3	88.3	93.8	113.9	88.3	95.7	106.0	88.6	93.6	109.2	88.7	94.6	112.7	88.5	95.5	99.5	76.9	83.4
0310	Concrete Forming & Accessories	91.5	74.8	77.1	92.7	54.3	59.6	97.4	54.7	60.5	88.0	75.3	77.1	93.8	69.8	73.1	100.7	68.7	73.1
0320	Concrete Reinforcing	89.3	92.7	91.0	96.8	64.8	80.5	91.2	64.9	77.8	91.5	93.6	92.5	92.3	76.6	84.3	94.3	72.2	83.0
0330	Cast-in-Place Concrete	98.7	68.2	86.2	103.6	62.6	86.7	91.1	68.3	81.8	100.9	69.6	88.1	108.7	73.1	94.1	95.5	78.1	88.3
03	CONCRETE	95.1	76.9	86.2	102.6	60.7	82.0	92.1	62.8	77.7	96.8	77.8	87.5	103.0	73.3	88.4	96.1	73.7	85.1
04	MASONRY	95.8	61.9	74.7	114.0	61.2	81.1	99.1	61.2	75.5	114.1	75.8	90.2	97.5	69.8	80.2	103.1	71.9	83.7
05	METALS	104.2	96.8	102.0	103.6	85.0	97.9	103.2	85.4	97.7	104.1	97.8	102.2	113.4	91.3	106.6	102.4	88.5	98.1
06	WOOD, PLASTICS & COMPOSITES	81.1	77.4	79.0	89.9	51.8	68.5	96.3	51.8	71.4	76.5	77.4	77.0	91.5	69.2	79.0	90.6	67.2	77.5
07	THERMAL & MOISTURE PROTECTION	100.1	80.0	91.9	96.5	61.7	82.2	96.4	62.3	82.4	100.1	84.6	93.7	96.6	76.0	88.2	101.6	71.6	89.3
08	OPENINGS	98.4	74.4	92.8	96.9	52.7	86.6	98.6	55.8	88.6	98.4	75.1	93.0	97.8	70.7	91.5	99.7	65.5	91.7
0920	Plaster & Gypsum Board	101.0	77.1	84.9	91.3	50.7	63.9	95.6	50.7	65.3	97.4	77.1	83.7	91.3	68.7	76.0	103.2	66.6	78.4
0950, 0980	Ceilings & Acoustic Treatment	82.7	77.1	79.0	79.5	50.7	60.6	84.9	50.7	62.5	82.7	77.1	79.0	83.3	68.7	73.7	92.2	66.6	75.4
0960	Flooring	102.3	55.1	88.8	108.1	43.1	89.5	110.5	64.5	97.4	100.3	56.5	87.8	108.3	73.6	98.4	107.3	73.0	97.5
0970, 0990	Wall Finishes & Painting/Coating	103.7	67.6	81.9	104.5	67.6	82.3	104.5	67.6	82.3	103.7	67.6	81.9	104.5	91.9	96.9	96.0	70.2	80.5
09	FINISHES	94.4	70.7	81.3	95.3	52.5	71.7	94.5	56.7	74.8	93.5	71.0	81.1	95.9	72.3	82.9	97.1	69.2	81.7
COVERS	DIVS. 10 - 14, 25, 28, 41, 43, 44, 46	100.0	72.6	94.5	100.0	82.8	96.5	100.0	81.0	96.2	100.0	72.6	94.5	100.0	85.8	97.1	100.0	88.0	97.6
21, 22, 23	FIRE SUPPRESSION, PLUMBING & HVAC	97.4	64.3	84.1	98.8	64.1	84.8	99.9	64.2	85.5	97.4	80.8	90.7	99.9	78.2	91.2	100.0	66.4	86.4
26, 27, 3370	ELECTRICAL, COMMUNICATIONS & UTIL.	98.1	62.8	79.5	96.1	71.8	83.3	95.5	62.2	77.9	96.3	61.6	77.9	97.0	67.8	81.6	100.1	74.9	86.8
MF2014	WEIGHTED AVERAGE	98.6	72.6	87.3	100.3	66.7	85.7	98.8	66.4	84.7	99.4	77.8	90.0	101.7	76.3	90.6	99.8	73.1	88.2

FLORIDA

DIVISION		ORLANDO 327 - 328,347			PANAMA CITY 324			PENSACOLA 325			SARASOTA 342			ST. PETERSBURG 337			TALLAHASSEE 323		
		MAT.	INST.	TOTAL	MAT.	INST.	TOTAL	MAT.	INST.	TOTAL	MAT.	INST.	TOTAL	MAT.	INST.	TOTAL	MAT.	INST.	TOTAL
015433	CONTRACTOR EQUIPMENT		98.2	98.2		98.2	98.2		98.2	98.2		98.2	98.2		98.2	98.2		98.2	98.2
0241, 31 - 34	SITE & INFRASTRUCTURE, DEMOLITION	107.6	88.4	93.9	117.6	87.4	96.1	117.6	87.9	96.5	114.0	88.4	95.8	110.9	88.1	94.7	105.1	87.7	92.7
0310	Concrete Forming & Accessories	101.4	72.0	76.1	96.7	43.9	51.1	94.6	51.8	57.7	96.0	75.0	77.9	94.9	51.0	57.1	99.9	44.1	51.8
0320	Concrete Reinforcing	96.6	73.9	85.0	95.3	72.5	83.7	97.7	73.0	85.1	92.5	93.5	93.0	91.5	86.1	88.7	98.3	64.7	81.2
0330	Cast-in-Place Concrete	112.1	70.6	95.1	95.7	56.7	79.7	118.2	65.9	96.8	106.6	69.5	91.4	102.0	64.5	86.6	97.2	56.4	80.5
03	CONCRETE	103.4	73.0	88.4	100.8	55.4	78.5	110.7	62.2	86.9	100.2	77.5	89.1	98.5	63.8	81.4	97.3	54.0	76.0
04	MASONRY	100.6	65.7	78.8	103.9	47.3	68.6	124.7	54.5	80.9	99.8	75.8	84.8	157.9	49.0	90.0	103.6	53.8	72.6
05	METALS	102.4	89.6	98.5	104.4	86.5	98.9	105.6	87.9	100.2	105.2	97.5	102.8	105.0	92.9	101.3	102.2	84.6	96.8
06	WOOD, PLASTICS & COMPOSITES	95.8	75.2	84.2	95.1	41.8	65.2	92.7	51.5	69.7	95.7	77.4	85.4	85.5	50.1	65.7	95.0	41.3	64.9
07	THERMAL & MOISTURE PROTECTION	94.9	74.3	86.4	96.6	62.3	82.5	96.6	62.3	82.5	98.1	84.6	92.5	100.3	57.8	82.8	102.6	71.5	89.9
08	OPENINGS	101.4	69.2	93.9	96.5	46.5	84.9	96.5	56.9	87.3	99.7	74.2	93.8	98.4	60.9	89.6	100.2	47.3	87.9
0920	Plaster & Gypsum Board	99.7	74.9	82.9	94.5	40.4	57.9	97.4	50.5	65.7	97.8	77.1	83.8	103.5	49.0	66.7	108.1	40.0	62.0
0950, 0980	Ceilings & Acoustic Treatment	91.4	74.9	80.5	83.3	40.4	55.1	83.3	50.5	61.7	86.2	77.1	80.3	84.5	49.0	61.2	94.1	40.0	58.5
0960	Flooring	104.1	73.6	95.4	110.1	43.0	90.9	106.1	63.0	93.7	111.1	57.9	95.9	104.1	55.2	90.1	111.1	62.0	97.0
0970, 0990	Wall Finishes & Painting/Coating	103.4	70.2	83.4	104.5	64.9	80.6	104.5	67.6	82.3	109.5	67.6	84.2	103.7	60.8	77.8	99.5	67.6	80.3
09	FINISHES	98.2	72.4	84.0	97.5	44.8	68.5	96.4	54.8	73.5	99.9	71.2	84.1	95.9	51.7	71.6	100.7	48.5	72.0
COVERS	DIVS. 10 - 14, 25, 28, 41, 43, 44, 46	100.0	85.1	97.0	100.0	46.2	89.1	100.0	46.3	89.1	100.0	72.6	94.5	100.0	55.8	91.1	100.0	65.8	93.1
21, 22, 23	FIRE SUPPRESSION, PLUMBING & HVAC	99.9	66.5	82.4	99.9	52.3	80.7	99.9	52.5	80.8	99.9	64.8	85.7	100.0	58.4	83.2	100.0	38.9	75.4
26, 27, 3370	ELECTRICAL, COMMUNICATIONS & UTIL.	97.6	60.0	77.7	94.5	59.3	75.9	98.5	53.8	75.9	97.2	61.6	78.4	96.3	61.6	77.9	103.3	60.0	80.4
MF2014	WEIGHTED AVERAGE	100.5	70.0	87.2	100.2	57.8	81.7	102.7	61.2	84.6	100.8	74.3	89.2	102.6	63.3	85.5	100.8	56.9	81.7

FLORIDA / GEORGIA

DIVISION		TAMPA 335 - 336,346			WEST PALM BEACH 334,349			ALBANY 317,398			ATHENS 306			ATLANTA 300 - 303,399			AUGUSTA 308 - 309		
		MAT.	INST.	TOTAL	MAT.	INST.	TOTAL	MAT.	INST.	TOTAL	MAT.	INST.	TOTAL	MAT.	INST.	TOTAL	MAT.	INST.	TOTAL
015433	CONTRACTOR EQUIPMENT		98.2	98.2		91.0	91.0		91.9	91.9		94.2	94.2		94.7	94.7		94.2	94.2
0241, 31 - 34	SITE & INFRASTRUCTURE, DEMOLITION	111.4	88.6	95.2	93.2	77.1	81.8	98.8	78.7	84.5	100.9	93.4	95.6	97.6	94.8	95.7	94.5	93.2	93.6
0310	Concrete Forming & Accessories	97.7	75.6	78.6	99.2	68.1	72.4	90.4	43.6	50.0	92.9	45.9	52.4	96.7	73.5	76.7	94.2	65.5	69.4
0320	Concrete Reinforcing	88.2	93.6	91.0	90.7	71.8	81.1	90.6	80.2	85.3	95.3	77.9	86.5	94.6	81.2	87.8	95.7	71.8	83.6
0330	Cast-in-Place Concrete	99.7	69.7	87.4	90.0	74.3	83.5	92.4	54.5	76.8	107.8	55.6	86.4	107.8	70.8	92.6	101.9	49.9	80.5
03	CONCRETE	97.0	77.9	87.6	91.3	72.1	81.9	93.1	55.8	74.8	104.8	56.0	80.8	102.2	74.1	88.4	97.5	61.7	79.9
04	MASONRY	103.9	75.8	86.4	102.3	66.6	80.0	102.2	49.1	69.2	81.5	53.8	64.2	95.2	66.2	77.1	95.5	43.3	63.0
05	METALS	104.0	98.1	102.2	101.1	89.3	97.4	105.0	85.5	99.0	91.9	73.3	86.2	92.8	77.0	88.0	91.6	71.6	85.5
06	WOOD, PLASTICS & COMPOSITES	89.3	77.4	82.6	89.2	67.2	76.9	85.0	38.0	58.7	91.8	40.9	63.3	96.1	75.8	84.7	93.3	70.9	80.8
07	THERMAL & MOISTURE PROTECTION	100.5	84.6	94.0	100.1	70.2	87.8	95.9	60.3	81.3	94.1	52.8	77.2	94.0	72.0	85.0	93.7	57.0	78.7
08	OPENINGS	99.7	79.2	94.9	96.8	65.5	89.5	91.1	44.2	80.2	89.5	45.7	79.3	94.7	71.9	89.4	89.5	62.2	83.1
0920	Plaster & Gypsum Board	106.1	77.1	86.5	110.2	66.6	80.7	97.5	36.5	56.3	98.7	39.4	58.7	100.9	75.4	83.6	99.8	70.4	79.9
0950, 0980	Ceilings & Acoustic Treatment	87.9	77.1	80.8	82.7	66.6	72.1	84.0	36.5	52.8	97.2	39.4	59.2	97.2	75.4	82.9	98.1	70.4	79.3
0960	Flooring	105.1	56.5	91.2	106.8	66.4	95.3	110.9	47.8	92.9	96.4	53.9	84.2	97.7	65.2	88.4	96.6	46.6	82.3
0970, 0990	Wall Finishes & Painting/Coating	103.7	67.6	81.9	98.9	70.2	81.6	105.3	52.8	73.6	106.0	46.0	69.8	106.0	85.1	93.4	106.0	46.0	69.8
09	FINISHES	97.4	71.0	82.8	94.7	67.5	79.7	98.1	43.2	67.9	95.4	45.7	68.0	95.7	73.4	83.4	95.2	60.5	76.1
COVERS	DIVS. 10 - 14, 25, 28, 41, 43, 44, 46	100.0	85.1	97.0	100.0	87.4	97.5	100.0	80.2	96.0	100.0	77.3	95.4	100.0	85.6	97.1	100.0	78.5	95.7
21, 22, 23	FIRE SUPPRESSION, PLUMBING & HVAC	100.0	80.8	92.2	97.4	62.7	83.4	99.9	68.0	87.0	95.2	69.6	84.9	99.9	70.6	88.1	100.0	61.2	84.4
26, 27, 3370	ELECTRICAL, COMMUNICATIONS & UTIL.	96.0	61.6	77.8	97.2	72.7	84.3	96.9	58.7	76.7	99.7	69.5	83.8	99.0	71.9	84.7	100.4	61.8	80.0
MF2014	WEIGHTED AVERAGE	100.1	78.4	90.6	97.4	71.1	85.9	98.5	61.3	82.3	95.5	63.9	81.7	97.6	74.4	87.5	96.3	63.6	82.1

For customer support on your Site Work & Landscape Cost Data, call 877.737.1594.

City Cost Indexes

DIVISION		GEORGIA																	
		COLUMBUS 318 - 319			DALTON 307			GAINESVILLE 305			MACON 310 - 312			SAVANNAH 313 - 314			STATESBORO 304		
		MAT.	INST.	TOTAL	MAT.	INST.	TOTAL	MAT.	INST.	TOTAL	MAT.	INST.	TOTAL	MAT.	INST.	TOTAL	MAT.	INST.	TOTAL
015433	CONTRACTOR EQUIPMENT		91.9	91.9		106.1	106.1		94.2	94.2		102.3	102.3		92.8	92.8		93.4	93.4
0241, 31 - 34	SITE & INFRASTRUCTURE, DEMOLITION	98.7	78.7	84.5	101.1	97.8	98.8	100.8	93.3	95.5	99.8	93.5	95.3	100.6	80.1	86.1	102.0	77.5	84.6
0310	Concrete Forming & Accessories	90.3	54.3	59.3	85.7	46.7	52.1	96.4	42.9	50.2	89.9	51.9	57.1	92.1	50.0	55.8	80.3	51.4	55.4
0320	Concrete Reinforcing	90.9	80.6	85.7	94.8	73.9	84.2	95.1	77.8	86.3	92.1	80.3	86.1	98.1	71.9	84.7	94.4	41.8	67.6
0330	Cast-in-Place Concrete	92.1	53.9	76.4	104.7	50.2	82.3	113.3	52.9	88.5	90.9	65.6	80.5	100.2	55.2	81.7	107.6	59.7	87.9
03	CONCRETE	93.0	60.4	77.0	103.9	54.6	79.7	106.7	53.7	80.6	92.6	63.3	78.2	98.0	57.3	78.0	104.2	54.0	79.6
04	MASONRY	102.6	55.2	73.1	83.8	36.7	54.4	89.5	54.2	67.5	115.9	44.5	71.4	98.8	50.9	69.0	84.7	40.6	57.2
05	METALS	104.5	86.3	98.9	92.8	82.8	89.7	91.2	72.5	85.4	100.1	85.9	95.7	101.3	82.4	95.5	96.3	72.6	89.0
06	WOOD, PLASTICS & COMPOSITES	85.0	52.1	66.6	75.2	47.5	59.7	95.9	37.9	63.4	91.8	51.2	69.0	96.0	45.9	68.0	68.5	53.9	60.3
07	THERMAL & MOISTURE PROTECTION	95.9	63.5	82.6	96.1	51.5	77.8	94.1	54.8	78.0	94.4	62.2	81.2	95.0	56.6	79.2	94.7	51.1	76.8
08	OPENINGS	91.1	59.0	83.7	90.1	49.5	80.6	89.5	40.0	77.9	90.0	52.8	81.3	94.9	48.4	84.1	91.1	40.6	79.4
0920	Plaster & Gypsum Board	97.5	51.1	66.1	86.2	46.2	59.2	100.9	36.3	57.3	103.0	50.1	67.2	95.6	44.7	61.2	86.9	52.8	63.9
0950, 0980	Ceilings & Acoustic Treatment	84.0	51.1	62.4	109.3	46.2	67.8	97.2	36.3	57.2	79.2	50.1	60.1	91.5	44.7	60.8	105.7	52.8	71.0
0960	Flooring	110.9	50.4	93.6	96.8	46.9	82.5	97.6	46.6	83.0	87.9	47.8	76.5	108.6	46.4	90.8	115.6	44.9	95.4
0970, 0990	Wall Finishes & Painting/Coating	105.3	66.5	81.9	96.3	59.8	74.2	106.0	46.0	69.8	107.7	52.8	74.6	103.8	58.3	76.3	103.5	39.2	64.7
09	FINISHES	98.0	53.5	73.5	103.0	47.1	72.2	95.9	41.6	66.0	86.7	49.9	66.4	98.2	48.9	71.0	106.9	49.0	75.0
COVERS	DIVS. 10 - 14, 25, 28, 41, 43, 44, 46	100.0	81.8	96.3	100.0	22.8	84.4	100.0	39.4	87.8	100.0	80.2	96.0	100.0	78.0	95.6	100.0	43.5	88.6
21, 22, 23	FIRE SUPPRESSION, PLUMBING & HVAC	99.9	63.4	85.2	95.2	57.0	79.8	95.2	69.5	84.8	99.9	66.7	86.6	100.0	61.8	84.6	95.7	56.7	80.0
26, 27, 3370	ELECTRICAL, COMMUNICATIONS & UTIL.	97.1	69.6	82.5	109.7	67.7	87.5	99.7	69.5	83.8	96.1	61.2	77.7	101.7	57.4	78.3	99.9	57.4	77.4
MF2014	WEIGHTED AVERAGE	98.4	65.4	84.0	97.2	59.0	80.5	96.0	61.6	81.0	97.2	64.7	83.0	99.2	60.9	82.5	97.3	55.8	79.2

DIVISION		GEORGIA						HAWAII									IDAHO		
		VALDOSTA 316			WAYCROSS 315			HILO 967			HONOLULU 968			STATES & POSS., GUAM 969			BOISE 836 - 837		
		MAT.	INST.	TOTAL	MAT.	INST.	TOTAL	MAT.	INST.	TOTAL	MAT.	INST.	TOTAL	MAT.	INST.	TOTAL	MAT.	INST.	TOTAL
015433	CONTRACTOR EQUIPMENT		91.9	91.9		91.9	91.9		99.5	99.5		99.5	99.5		164.5	164.5		98.2	98.2
0241, 31 - 34	SITE & INFRASTRUCTURE, DEMOLITION	107.9	78.8	85.3	104.7	77.4	85.3	144.8	106.5	117.6	155.4	106.5	120.6	184.9	103.7	127.2	85.5	96.3	93.2
0310	Concrete Forming & Accessories	81.0	44.1	49.2	82.8	64.7	67.2	111.2	135.6	132.2	123.6	135.6	134.0	113.7	63.6	70.5	100.8	77.4	80.7
0320	Concrete Reinforcing	92.8	76.4	84.4	92.8	72.7	82.5	123.5	117.9	120.7	132.5	117.9	125.1	214.4	30.2	120.7	99.2	80.4	89.6
0330	Cast-in-Place Concrete	90.5	55.9	76.3	102.2	48.2	80.0	198.3	125.7	168.5	163.7	125.7	148.1	171.9	105.5	144.7	91.6	88.4	90.3
03	CONCRETE	98.1	55.8	77.3	101.2	61.4	81.6	158.1	127.7	143.2	150.8	127.7	139.5	159.9	72.3	116.9	99.1	81.9	90.7
04	MASONRY	108.9	50.5	72.5	109.7	39.3	65.8	150.5	128.3	136.7	150.6	128.3	136.7	213.9	43.5	107.7	121.4	84.2	98.2
05	METALS	104.1	84.0	97.9	103.1	77.7	95.3	108.1	107.3	107.8	120.7	107.3	116.5	139.2	76.2	119.8	102.2	80.9	95.6
06	WOOD, PLASTICS & COMPOSITES	73.4	37.6	53.4	75.0	72.4	73.5	114.5	139.2	128.3	134.4	139.2	137.1	127.1	67.4	93.7	93.1	75.9	83.4
07	THERMAL & MOISTURE PROTECTION	96.1	62.4	82.3	95.9	50.3	77.2	120.8	124.6	122.4	138.4	124.6	132.7	140.4	65.2	109.6	94.6	81.4	89.2
08	OPENINGS	87.3	42.5	76.9	87.4	57.8	80.5	111.3	132.8	116.3	121.8	132.8	124.4	116.6	54.1	102.1	99.1	71.2	92.6
0920	Plaster & Gypsum Board	90.4	36.2	53.8	90.4	72.0	78.0	109.7	140.1	130.3	151.3	140.1	143.7	219.9	55.5	108.8	92.4	75.1	80.7
0950, 0980	Ceilings & Acoustic Treatment	81.5	36.2	51.7	79.6	72.0	74.6	121.5	140.1	133.8	132.0	140.1	137.3	237.3	55.5	117.8	99.1	75.1	83.3
0960	Flooring	104.7	47.8	88.4	105.9	29.9	84.1	116.0	139.9	122.8	132.2	139.9	134.4	135.5	46.4	110.0	96.3	83.7	92.7
0970, 0990	Wall Finishes & Painting/Coating	105.3	52.2	73.2	105.3	46.0	69.5	110.4	143.8	130.6	119.4	143.8	134.2	115.9	35.9	67.6	103.2	39.5	64.7
09	FINISHES	95.6	43.6	67.0	95.2	57.4	74.4	113.7	138.6	127.4	128.4	138.6	134.0	188.8	58.9	117.2	96.0	74.8	84.3
COVERS	DIVS. 10 - 14, 25, 28, 41, 43, 44, 46	100.0	77.1	95.4	100.0	51.5	90.2	100.0	116.0	103.2	100.0	116.0	103.2	100.0	75.2	95.0	100.0	87.4	97.5
21, 22, 23	FIRE SUPPRESSION, PLUMBING & HVAC	99.9	70.0	87.9	96.9	57.1	80.8	100.2	107.7	103.2	100.3	107.7	103.3	102.6	37.4	76.3	100.0	71.8	88.6
26, 27, 3370	ELECTRICAL, COMMUNICATIONS & UTIL.	95.0	56.2	74.5	99.6	57.4	77.3	106.5	121.1	114.2	107.9	121.1	114.9	153.5	41.2	94.1	98.5	72.8	84.9
MF2014	WEIGHTED AVERAGE	98.5	61.4	82.3	98.3	59.4	81.4	114.8	120.2	117.2	119.5	120.2	119.8	136.2	58.0	102.1	100.1	78.6	90.7

DIVISION		IDAHO															ILLINOIS		
		COEUR D'ALENE 838			IDAHO FALLS 834			LEWISTON 835			POCATELLO 832			TWIN FALLS 833			BLOOMINGTON 617		
		MAT.	INST.	TOTAL	MAT.	INST.	TOTAL	MAT.	INST.	TOTAL	MAT.	INST.	TOTAL	MAT.	INST.	TOTAL	MAT.	INST.	TOTAL
015433	CONTRACTOR EQUIPMENT		92.8	92.8		98.2	98.2		92.8	92.8		98.2	98.2		98.2	98.2		101.6	101.6
0241, 31 - 34	SITE & INFRASTRUCTURE, DEMOLITION	83.1	91.7	89.2	83.1	96.1	92.4	89.9	92.5	91.7	85.8	96.3	93.3	92.1	97.2	95.8	97.4	98.4	98.1
0310	Concrete Forming & Accessories	112.6	81.1	85.5	94.7	78.1	80.4	117.9	82.2	87.1	101.0	77.1	80.4	102.0	54.7	61.2	84.3	117.2	112.7
0320	Concrete Reinforcing	106.2	96.5	101.3	101.0	80.0	90.3	106.2	96.8	101.4	99.6	80.2	89.7	101.3	79.9	90.4	94.6	110.7	102.8
0330	Cast-in-Place Concrete	99.0	87.2	94.1	87.2	74.3	81.9	102.9	86.0	95.9	94.1	88.3	91.7	96.6	63.9	83.1	102.8	114.8	107.7
03	CONCRETE	105.7	86.1	96.1	91.3	77.2	84.4	109.3	86.2	98.0	98.3	81.7	90.1	105.8	63.3	84.9	100.1	115.2	107.5
04	MASONRY	122.9	83.9	98.6	116.5	81.0	94.4	123.4	85.9	100.0	118.8	81.1	95.3	121.6	81.1	96.4	120.3	118.3	119.1
05	METALS	96.3	86.9	93.4	110.0	79.1	100.5	95.7	88.0	93.4	110.1	80.3	100.9	110.1	78.9	100.5	97.6	113.6	102.5
06	WOOD, PLASTICS & COMPOSITES	96.8	81.0	88.0	86.8	78.8	82.3	102.4	81.0	90.4	93.1	75.9	83.4	94.2	47.2	67.9	86.4	115.4	102.6
07	THERMAL & MOISTURE PROTECTION	148.3	80.8	120.6	94.3	71.7	85.0	148.5	81.4	121.0	94.7	73.7	86.1	95.4	74.7	86.9	98.4	112.8	104.3
08	OPENINGS	117.8	73.0	107.4	102.8	68.0	94.7	117.8	75.6	108.0	99.8	66.3	92.0	102.8	48.8	90.2	94.9	104.9	97.2
0920	Plaster & Gypsum Board	161.4	80.5	106.7	78.5	78.1	78.2	162.5	80.5	107.0	80.7	75.1	76.9	82.3	45.6	57.5	91.3	115.8	107.9
0950, 0980	Ceilings & Acoustic Treatment	129.0	80.5	97.1	97.2	78.1	84.6	129.0	80.5	97.1	104.7	75.1	85.2	99.7	45.6	64.1	88.0	115.8	106.3
0960	Flooring	138.3	45.9	111.9	96.4	43.1	81.2	141.2	93.8	127.7	99.6	83.7	95.1	100.7	43.1	84.3	93.8	118.7	100.9
0970, 0990	Wall Finishes & Painting/Coating	123.8	67.8	90.0	103.3	40.3	65.3	123.8	67.8	90.0	103.1	41.1	65.7	103.3	37.3	63.4	93.8	126.4	113.5
09	FINISHES	161.8	73.3	113.0	93.3	68.7	79.7	162.9	82.8	118.8	96.6	75.0	84.7	96.7	49.7	70.8	93.3	118.9	107.4
COVERS	DIVS. 10 - 14, 25, 28, 41, 43, 44, 46	100.0	87.4	97.5	100.0	47.7	89.4	100.0	87.6	97.5	100.0	87.4	97.5	100.0	44.2	88.7	100.0	105.2	101.0
21, 22, 23	FIRE SUPPRESSION, PLUMBING & HVAC	99.5	82.6	92.7	100.9	71.7	89.1	100.7	85.6	94.6	99.9	71.8	88.6	99.9	69.3	87.6	95.1	108.8	100.7
26, 27, 3370	ELECTRICAL, COMMUNICATIONS & UTIL.	91.0	77.6	83.9	90.8	70.4	80.0	88.9	80.7	84.5	96.2	70.4	82.6	92.3	60.1	75.3	94.2	94.6	94.4
MF2014	WEIGHTED AVERAGE	107.9	82.2	96.7	99.8	74.7	88.9	108.7	84.9	98.3	101.1	77.4	90.8	102.2	67.3	87.0	97.5	109.4	102.7

ILLINOIS

DIVISION		CARBONDALE 629			CENTRALIA 628			CHAMPAIGN 618 - 619			CHICAGO 606 - 608			DECATUR 625			EAST ST. LOUIS 620 - 622		
		MAT.	INST.	TOTAL	MAT.	INST.	TOTAL	MAT.	INST.	TOTAL	MAT.	INST.	TOTAL	MAT.	INST.	TOTAL	MAT.	INST.	TOTAL
015433	CONTRACTOR EQUIPMENT		108.0	108.0		108.0	108.0		102.4	102.4		94.3	94.3		102.4	102.4		108.0	108.0
0241, 31 - 34	SITE & INFRASTRUCTURE, DEMOLITION	98.7	99.5	99.2	99.0	100.1	99.8	106.4	99.0	101.2	107.0	95.7	99.0	93.2	99.1	97.4	101.2	99.8	100.2
0310	Concrete Forming & Accessories	90.0	109.0	106.4	91.6	112.8	109.9	90.7	115.2	111.8	96.6	156.7	148.4	91.8	114.9	111.8	87.6	114.8	111.1
0320	Concrete Reinforcing	91.2	111.6	101.6	91.2	111.8	101.7	94.6	105.1	99.9	99.0	158.1	129.1	89.3	102.7	96.1	91.1	109.9	100.6
0330	Cast-in-Place Concrete	97.2	102.5	99.4	97.7	117.3	105.7	119.2	109.5	115.2	107.5	149.4	124.7	106.1	110.5	107.9	99.3	117.0	106.6
03	CONCRETE	90.1	107.9	98.9	90.6	114.8	102.5	113.1	111.3	112.2	102.6	153.2	127.5	101.3	111.1	106.1	91.7	115.2	103.2
04	MASONRY	83.6	108.6	99.2	83.6	116.7	104.2	145.3	117.7	128.1	101.1	156.6	135.7	79.6	114.7	101.5	83.9	116.6	104.3
05	METALS	96.2	119.6	103.4	96.2	120.8	103.8	97.6	108.7	101.0	94.3	134.3	106.6	99.9	108.1	102.4	97.3	119.4	104.1
06	WOOD, PLASTICS & COMPOSITES	91.7	106.1	99.8	94.1	109.7	102.8	93.5	113.9	104.9	104.0	155.9	133.1	91.9	113.9	104.2	89.2	112.1	102.0
07	THERMAL & MOISTURE PROTECTION	97.1	101.5	98.9	97.2	111.7	103.1	99.0	113.2	104.9	98.0	145.1	117.3	103.2	109.3	105.7	97.2	110.2	102.5
08	OPENINGS	89.4	114.2	95.2	89.4	116.2	95.7	95.5	111.2	99.2	105.3	158.7	117.8	100.9	110.6	103.2	89.5	116.9	95.9
0920	Plaster & Gypsum Board	97.2	106.2	103.3	98.3	110.0	106.2	93.7	114.2	107.6	92.7	157.6	136.6	100.0	114.2	109.6	96.1	112.4	107.2
0950, 0980	Ceilings & Acoustic Treatment	91.4	106.2	101.2	91.4	110.0	103.6	88.0	114.2	105.2	99.2	157.6	137.6	98.1	114.2	108.7	91.4	112.4	105.2
0960	Flooring	122.2	120.2	121.6	123.2	115.7	121.0	96.7	120.2	103.4	96.9	148.0	111.5	109.1	116.7	111.3	121.2	115.7	119.6
0970, 0990	Wall Finishes & Painting/Coating	112.6	97.4	103.5	112.6	106.6	109.0	93.8	110.0	103.6	91.9	153.0	128.8	102.5	106.5	104.9	112.6	103.5	107.1
09	FINISHES	101.8	108.6	105.5	102.2	112.6	107.9	95.2	115.9	106.6	98.0	155.6	129.7	101.8	115.0	109.1	101.4	113.8	108.2
COVERS	DIVS. 10 - 14, 25, 28, 41, 43, 44, 46	100.0	102.6	100.5	100.0	104.1	100.8	100.0	104.4	100.9	100.0	124.5	105.0	100.0	104.3	100.9	100.0	104.4	100.9
21, 22, 23	FIRE SUPPRESSION, PLUMBING & HVAC	95.1	106.1	99.5	95.1	95.3	95.2	95.1	105.5	99.3	99.8	133.9	113.6	99.9	98.5	99.4	99.9	98.8	99.4
26, 27, 3370	ELECTRICAL, COMMUNICATIONS & UTIL.	95.4	107.7	101.9	96.8	107.7	102.6	97.4	94.9	96.1	98.3	133.9	117.1	99.5	90.4	94.7	96.4	103.5	100.1
MF2014	WEIGHTED AVERAGE	94.7	107.9	100.5	95.0	108.5	100.9	101.0	107.6	103.9	99.8	139.7	117.2	99.2	104.9	101.7	96.4	108.7	101.8

ILLINOIS

DIVISION		EFFINGHAM 624			GALESBURG 614			JOLIET 604			KANKAKEE 609			LA SALLE 613			NORTH SUBURBAN 600 - 603		
		MAT.	INST.	TOTAL	MAT.	INST.	TOTAL	MAT.	INST.	TOTAL	MAT.	INST.	TOTAL	MAT.	INST.	TOTAL	MAT.	INST.	TOTAL
015433	CONTRACTOR EQUIPMENT		102.4	102.4		101.6	101.6		92.5	92.5		92.5	92.5		101.6	101.6		92.5	92.5
0241, 31 - 34	SITE & INFRASTRUCTURE, DEMOLITION	97.6	98.9	98.5	99.9	98.3	98.8	106.9	94.9	98.4	100.5	94.6	96.3	99.2	99.2	99.2	106.1	94.9	98.1
0310	Concrete Forming & Accessories	96.3	114.0	111.6	90.6	116.6	113.1	98.4	159.6	151.2	91.8	143.2	136.2	104.6	125.3	122.4	97.8	154.0	146.3
0320	Concrete Reinforcing	92.2	99.9	96.1	94.1	110.6	102.5	99.0	150.8	125.4	99.8	147.4	124.0	94.3	144.7	119.9	99.0	156.5	128.3
0330	Cast-in-Place Concrete	105.7	108.4	106.8	105.9	106.2	106.0	107.4	146.5	123.5	100.1	132.5	113.4	105.7	122.5	112.6	107.5	141.2	121.3
03	CONCRETE	102.1	109.4	105.7	103.2	112.0	107.5	102.7	152.1	126.9	96.7	139.3	117.7	104.1	127.9	115.8	102.7	148.8	125.4
04	MASONRY	88.2	108.5	100.8	120.5	118.0	118.9	104.3	148.5	131.8	100.6	141.2	125.9	120.5	125.1	123.4	101.1	144.1	127.9
05	METALS	97.0	105.6	99.7	97.6	113.0	102.4	92.2	129.1	103.6	92.2	126.6	102.8	97.7	131.6	108.1	93.4	131.4	105.1
06	WOOD, PLASTICS & COMPOSITES	94.2	113.5	105.2	93.3	115.5	105.7	105.7	161.0	136.7	97.8	142.2	122.7	108.8	123.7	117.1	104.0	155.7	132.9
07	THERMAL & MOISTURE PROTECTION	102.7	106.6	104.3	98.5	107.6	102.2	97.8	141.6	115.8	97.0	135.7	112.9	98.7	117.8	106.5	98.2	139.3	115.1
08	OPENINGS	94.9	109.9	98.4	94.9	111.0	98.6	102.8	159.6	116.0	95.4	148.4	107.7	94.9	129.5	102.9	102.9	158.2	115.8
0920	Plaster & Gypsum Board	99.7	114.2	109.5	93.7	115.9	108.7	89.9	162.9	139.2	86.7	143.4	125.0	100.1	124.3	116.5	92.7	157.3	136.4
0950, 0980	Ceilings & Acoustic Treatment	91.4	114.2	106.4	88.0	115.9	106.3	99.2	162.9	141.0	99.2	143.4	128.3	88.0	124.3	111.9	99.2	157.3	137.4
0960	Flooring	110.1	120.2	113.0	96.6	118.7	102.9	96.5	140.3	109.1	93.7	131.9	104.6	102.8	122.6	108.5	96.9	140.3	109.3
0970, 0990	Wall Finishes & Painting/Coating	102.5	104.2	103.5	93.8	95.1	94.5	90.1	152.5	127.8	90.1	126.4	112.0	93.8	126.4	113.5	91.9	152.5	128.4
09	FINISHES	100.6	115.2	108.7	94.6	115.4	106.1	97.4	156.9	130.2	95.7	137.9	119.0	97.3	124.3	112.2	97.9	152.7	128.1
COVERS	DIVS. 10 - 14, 25, 28, 41, 43, 44, 46	100.0	70.8	94.1	100.0	105.1	101.0	100.0	124.5	105.0	100.0	120.8	104.2	100.0	102.5	100.5	100.0	122.3	104.5
21, 22, 23	FIRE SUPPRESSION, PLUMBING & HVAC	95.2	102.8	98.2	95.1	105.3	99.2	99.9	131.2	112.5	95.1	129.0	108.7	95.1	123.4	106.6	99.8	128.6	111.4
26, 27, 3370	ELECTRICAL, COMMUNICATIONS & UTIL.	97.3	107.6	102.8	95.1	86.6	90.6	97.5	137.9	118.9	92.3	137.1	116.0	92.2	137.1	116.0	97.2	128.5	113.8
MF2014	WEIGHTED AVERAGE	97.3	106.0	101.1	98.2	106.7	101.9	99.2	138.4	116.3	95.6	131.7	111.3	98.4	124.4	109.7	99.3	135.1	114.9

ILLINOIS

DIVISION		PEORIA 615 - 616			QUINCY 623			ROCK ISLAND 612			ROCKFORD 610 - 611			SOUTH SUBURBAN 605			SPRINGFIELD 626 - 627		
		MAT.	INST.	TOTAL	MAT.	INST.	TOTAL	MAT.	INST.	TOTAL	MAT.	INST.	TOTAL	MAT.	INST.	TOTAL	MAT.	INST.	TOTAL
015433	CONTRACTOR EQUIPMENT		101.6	101.6		102.4	102.4		101.6	101.6		101.6	101.6		92.5	92.5		102.4	102.4
0241, 31 - 34	SITE & INFRASTRUCTURE, DEMOLITION	100.4	98.3	98.9	96.5	98.7	98.0	98.0	97.4	97.5	99.8	99.7	99.7	106.1	94.9	98.1	99.0	99.1	99.1
0310	Concrete Forming & Accessories	93.7	117.4	114.2	94.2	111.8	109.4	92.3	104.2	102.5	98.1	131.3	126.7	97.8	154.0	146.3	92.6	115.3	112.1
0320	Concrete Reinforcing	91.7	110.8	101.4	91.8	105.3	98.7	94.1	103.7	99.0	86.7	136.9	112.2	99.0	156.5	128.3	94.2	105.1	99.7
0330	Cast-in-Place Concrete	102.7	114.1	107.3	105.9	102.9	104.7	103.6	97.3	101.0	105.1	126.4	113.8	107.5	141.2	121.3	100.8	109.2	104.2
03	CONCRETE	100.2	115.0	107.5	101.7	107.6	104.6	101.0	102.0	101.5	100.9	130.4	115.4	102.7	148.8	125.4	99.1	111.3	105.1
04	MASONRY	120.1	118.1	118.8	111.7	104.1	106.9	120.3	97.0	105.8	94.1	135.8	120.0	101.1	144.1	127.9	91.0	117.8	107.7
05	METALS	100.4	113.8	104.5	97.1	108.0	100.5	97.7	108.4	101.0	100.4	128.2	108.9	93.4	131.4	105.1	97.5	109.3	101.1
06	WOOD, PLASTICS & COMPOSITES	101.2	115.5	109.2	91.8	113.9	104.2	95.0	104.4	100.3	101.1	128.3	116.4	104.0	155.7	132.9	89.2	113.9	103.0
07	THERMAL & MOISTURE PROTECTION	99.3	112.4	104.7	102.7	103.5	103.0	98.5	98.3	98.4	101.8	129.0	113.0	98.2	139.3	115.1	104.4	112.2	107.6
08	OPENINGS	101.3	116.0	104.7	95.8	111.4	99.4	94.9	103.2	96.8	101.3	132.1	108.5	102.9	158.2	115.8	103.0	111.2	104.9
0920	Plaster & Gypsum Board	97.1	115.9	109.8	98.3	114.2	109.0	93.7	104.5	101.0	97.1	129.1	118.8	92.7	157.3	136.4	98.7	114.2	109.2
0950, 0980	Ceilings & Acoustic Treatment	93.0	115.9	108.1	91.4	114.2	106.4	88.0	104.5	98.8	93.0	129.1	116.7	99.2	157.3	137.4	102.1	114.2	110.1
0960	Flooring	99.9	118.7	105.3	109.1	108.1	108.8	97.7	105.6	100.0	99.9	122.6	106.4	96.9	140.3	109.3	113.5	107.8	111.9
0970, 0990	Wall Finishes & Painting/Coating	93.8	126.4	113.5	102.5	106.5	104.9	93.8	95.1	94.5	93.8	133.1	117.5	91.9	152.5	128.4	101.1	106.5	104.3
09	FINISHES	97.2	118.9	109.2	100.1	111.8	106.6	94.9	103.7	99.7	97.2	130.0	115.3	97.9	152.7	128.1	104.9	113.5	109.6
COVERS	DIVS. 10 - 14, 25, 28, 41, 43, 44, 46	100.0	105.2	101.0	100.0	71.2	94.2	100.0	99.0	99.8	100.0	114.3	102.9	100.0	122.3	104.5	100.0	104.5	100.9
21, 22, 23	FIRE SUPPRESSION, PLUMBING & HVAC	99.9	104.9	101.9	95.2	101.0	97.5	95.1	99.9	97.1	100.0	116.5	106.7	99.8	128.6	111.4	99.9	103.3	101.3
26, 27, 3370	ELECTRICAL, COMMUNICATIONS & UTIL.	96.1	96.7	96.4	94.7	80.8	87.3	87.3	95.5	91.6	96.4	131.1	114.7	97.3	128.5	113.8	102.4	92.0	96.9
MF2014	WEIGHTED AVERAGE	100.5	109.3	104.4	98.1	101.0	99.3	97.2	100.5	98.6	99.5	124.8	110.5	99.3	135.1	114.9	100.0	106.5	102.8

City Cost Indexes

INDIANA

DIVISION		ANDERSON 460			BLOOMINGTON 474			COLUMBUS 472			EVANSVILLE 476 - 477			FORT WAYNE 467 - 468			GARY 463 - 464		
		MAT.	INST.	TOTAL	MAT.	INST.	TOTAL	MAT.	INST.	TOTAL	MAT.	INST.	TOTAL	MAT.	INST.	TOTAL	MAT.	INST.	TOTAL
015433	CONTRACTOR EQUIPMENT		97.0	97.0		86.5	86.5		86.5	86.5		116.0	116.0		97.0	97.0		97.0	97.0
0241, 31 - 34	SITE & INFRASTRUCTURE, DEMOLITION	93.9	96.1	95.5	85.8	94.4	91.9	82.2	94.3	90.8	91.0	123.9	114.4	94.8	96.0	95.7	94.5	99.6	98.1
0310	Concrete Forming & Accessories	97.8	81.5	83.7	101.0	80.7	83.5	95.0	78.6	80.8	94.4	82.7	84.3	96.1	75.2	78.1	97.9	116.3	113.8
0320	Concrete Reinforcing	95.8	82.8	89.2	86.8	80.9	83.8	87.2	80.9	84.0	95.1	78.1	86.4	95.8	75.5	85.5	95.8	110.8	103.5
0330	Cast-in-Place Concrete	109.4	80.2	97.4	103.6	78.2	93.1	103.1	71.2	90.0	99.0	87.9	94.4	116.3	82.8	102.5	114.3	113.9	114.1
03	CONCRETE	100.8	81.7	91.5	105.0	79.7	92.6	104.2	76.3	90.5	105.3	83.8	94.7	104.0	78.4	91.4	103.2	114.2	108.6
04	MASONRY	94.1	80.1	85.4	95.6	76.5	83.7	95.4	76.5	83.6	91.2	82.5	85.8	98.5	77.9	85.6	95.6	114.6	107.5
05	METALS	92.8	89.3	91.7	95.8	77.6	90.2	95.9	77.0	90.0	89.3	85.0	87.9	92.8	85.9	90.7	92.8	108.7	97.7
06	WOOD, PLASTICS & COMPOSITES	100.2	81.9	89.9	112.9	80.9	95.0	107.7	78.2	91.2	93.5	82.0	87.0	99.9	74.7	85.8	97.7	115.7	107.8
07	THERMAL & MOISTURE PROTECTION	107.7	75.9	94.7	95.1	78.3	88.2	94.7	78.1	87.9	99.4	83.7	93.0	107.5	77.7	95.3	106.3	108.6	107.2
08	OPENINGS	98.5	82.1	94.7	105.8	81.1	100.1	101.5	79.6	96.4	99.1	80.8	94.9	98.5	74.2	92.9	98.5	120.3	103.6
0920	Plaster & Gypsum Board	102.5	81.6	88.4	97.5	81.0	86.4	95.0	78.2	83.6	93.4	80.8	84.9	101.8	74.2	83.1	96.1	116.4	109.8
0950, 0980	Ceilings & Acoustic Treatment	87.9	81.6	83.7	80.9	81.0	81.0	80.9	78.2	79.1	85.5	80.8	82.4	87.9	74.2	78.9	87.9	116.4	106.6
0960	Flooring	100.6	85.0	96.2	105.5	75.0	96.8	100.8	75.0	93.4	100.3	80.7	94.7	100.6	78.8	94.4	100.6	123.4	107.1
0970, 0990	Wall Finishes & Painting/Coating	105.6	69.4	83.7	95.3	82.4	87.5	95.3	82.4	87.5	101.2	84.9	91.4	105.6	73.9	86.5	105.6	123.9	116.7
09	FINISHES	95.6	81.0	87.6	94.8	79.8	86.5	93.0	78.2	84.9	93.8	82.6	87.6	95.4	75.7	84.5	94.7	118.7	107.9
COVERS	DIVS. 10 - 14, 25, 28, 41, 43, 44, 46	100.0	91.8	98.3	100.0	90.8	98.1	100.0	90.5	98.1	100.0	95.9	99.2	100.0	91.7	98.3	100.0	106.1	101.2
21, 22, 23	FIRE SUPPRESSION, PLUMBING & HVAC	100.0	78.8	91.5	99.7	78.9	91.3	94.9	78.8	88.4	99.9	79.6	91.7	100.0	72.1	88.7	100.0	106.6	102.7
26, 27, 3370	ELECTRICAL, COMMUNICATIONS & UTIL.	87.0	88.4	87.7	98.9	88.0	93.2	98.1	87.9	92.7	95.1	88.3	91.5	87.7	79.2	83.2	98.7	107.6	103.4
MF2014	WEIGHTED AVERAGE	97.0	83.8	91.3	99.3	81.8	91.6	97.2	80.9	90.1	97.1	86.9	92.6	97.6	79.1	89.5	98.3	110.4	103.6

INDIANA

DIVISION		INDIANAPOLIS 461 - 462			KOKOMO 469			LAFAYETTE 479			LAWRENCEBURG 470			MUNCIE 473			NEW ALBANY 471		
		MAT.	INST.	TOTAL	MAT.	INST.	TOTAL	MAT.	INST.	TOTAL	MAT.	INST.	TOTAL	MAT.	INST.	TOTAL	MAT.	INST.	TOTAL
015433	CONTRACTOR EQUIPMENT		93.7	93.7		97.0	97.0		86.5	86.5		104.4	104.4		95.0	95.0		94.5	94.5
0241, 31 - 34	SITE & INFRASTRUCTURE, DEMOLITION	93.5	99.3	97.7	90.3	96.0	94.4	83.1	94.3	91.0	81.2	110.4	102.0	85.6	94.6	92.0	78.2	96.8	91.4
0310	Concrete Forming & Accessories	98.6	85.6	87.4	101.2	76.6	80.0	92.6	82.6	84.0	91.5	75.4	77.6	92.6	81.0	82.6	89.5	73.3	75.5
0320	Concrete Reinforcing	99.4	83.0	91.1	86.7	81.1	83.9	86.8	82.7	84.7	86.1	74.2	80.1	96.0	82.7	89.3	87.4	77.1	82.2
0330	Cast-in-Place Concrete	101.9	86.4	95.5	108.3	82.7	97.8	103.7	81.8	94.7	97.0	74.8	87.9	108.8	78.6	96.4	100.1	74.0	89.4
03	CONCRETE	100.9	85.1	93.1	97.5	80.1	89.0	104.5	82.1	93.5	97.4	75.5	86.6	103.5	81.0	92.4	102.8	74.6	89.0
04	MASONRY	95.8	80.3	86.2	93.7	79.1	84.6	101.2	80.3	88.2	79.9	74.7	76.7	97.7	80.1	86.7	86.9	68.3	75.3
05	METALS	93.5	80.5	89.5	89.3	88.3	89.0	94.3	78.4	89.4	91.0	83.5	88.7	97.6	89.2	95.0	92.9	81.0	89.3
06	WOOD, PLASTICS & COMPOSITES	99.7	86.2	92.2	103.4	75.0	87.5	104.7	83.1	92.6	91.9	75.2	82.6	106.3	81.5	92.4	94.1	74.3	83.0
07	THERMAL & MOISTURE PROTECTION	100.7	80.8	92.5	107.3	75.7	94.3	94.7	80.6	88.9	100.1	76.7	90.5	97.7	76.8	89.2	86.8	69.6	79.7
08	OPENINGS	105.7	84.5	100.8	93.3	77.9	89.8	99.9	82.8	95.9	101.4	75.3	95.3	99.0	81.9	95.0	98.7	76.3	93.5
0920	Plaster & Gypsum Board	97.0	85.8	89.5	107.5	74.5	85.2	92.2	83.3	86.1	71.5	75.0	73.9	93.4	81.6	85.4	91.6	73.8	79.6
0950, 0980	Ceilings & Acoustic Treatment	93.8	85.8	88.6	87.9	74.5	79.1	76.7	83.3	81.0	89.7	75.0	80.0	81.7	81.6	81.6	85.5	73.8	77.8
0960	Flooring	101.4	85.0	96.7	104.6	93.3	101.3	99.7	88.8	96.6	74.1	85.0	77.2	99.9	85.0	95.6	97.9	62.8	87.9
0970, 0990	Wall Finishes & Painting/Coating	103.6	82.4	90.8	105.6	71.7	85.2	95.3	93.1	94.0	96.2	71.6	81.4	95.3	69.4	79.7	101.2	82.7	90.0
09	FINISHES	96.1	85.4	90.2	97.3	78.8	87.1	91.4	85.0	87.9	83.7	77.2	80.1	92.4	80.6	85.9	93.1	72.7	81.8
COVERS	DIVS. 10 - 14, 25, 28, 41, 43, 44, 46	100.0	93.3	98.7	100.0	91.1	98.2	100.0	91.1	98.2	100.0	43.6	88.6	100.0	90.8	98.1	100.0	43.1	88.5
21, 22, 23	FIRE SUPPRESSION, PLUMBING & HVAC	99.9	79.4	91.6	95.2	79.0	88.7	94.9	79.4	88.6	95.8	74.1	87.1	99.7	78.7	91.2	95.2	75.2	87.1
26, 27, 3370	ELECTRICAL, COMMUNICATIONS & UTIL.	101.0	88.4	94.4	91.4	78.7	84.7	97.6	82.5	89.6	93.0	73.5	82.7	90.9	79.6	84.9	93.6	75.8	84.2
MF2014	WEIGHTED AVERAGE	99.1	84.8	92.9	94.8	81.5	89.0	96.9	82.7	90.7	94.0	77.7	86.9	97.9	82.3	91.1	95.1	75.4	86.5

INDIANA / IOWA

DIVISION		SOUTH BEND 465 - 466			TERRE HAUTE 478			WASHINGTON 475			BURLINGTON 526			CARROLL 514			CEDAR RAPIDS 522 - 524		
		MAT.	INST.	TOTAL	MAT.	INST.	TOTAL	MAT.	INST.	TOTAL	MAT.	INST.	TOTAL	MAT.	INST.	TOTAL	MAT.	INST.	TOTAL
015433	CONTRACTOR EQUIPMENT		105.3	105.3		116.0	116.0		116.0	116.0		99.4	99.4		99.4	99.4		96.1	96.1
0241, 31 - 34	SITE & INFRASTRUCTURE, DEMOLITION	96.7	96.2	96.3	92.9	124.1	115.1	92.4	121.3	113.0	98.3	96.5	97.0	87.5	96.5	93.9	100.0	95.1	96.5
0310	Concrete Forming & Accessories	99.5	81.4	83.9	95.4	82.2	84.0	96.2	78.8	81.2	94.8	75.5	78.2	82.6	50.4	54.8	100.5	82.3	84.8
0320	Concrete Reinforcing	97.3	79.9	88.4	95.1	82.9	88.9	87.9	48.8	68.0	91.0	82.7	86.8	91.8	78.7	85.1	91.7	84.2	87.9
0330	Cast-in-Place Concrete	106.6	79.8	95.6	95.9	85.6	91.6	104.3	84.8	96.3	111.7	55.1	88.4	111.7	59.7	90.3	111.9	79.7	98.7
03	CONCRETE	98.3	81.8	90.2	108.4	83.7	96.2	114.3	75.3	95.1	102.6	70.8	86.9	101.3	60.2	81.1	102.7	82.3	92.7
04	MASONRY	105.7	77.8	88.3	98.9	79.6	86.9	91.3	80.8	84.8	102.3	64.9	79.0	104.2	74.1	85.4	108.2	78.0	89.4
05	METALS	92.8	99.9	95.0	90.0	87.4	89.2	84.6	68.2	79.5	88.8	93.0	90.1	88.9	88.7	88.8	91.3	92.2	91.5
06	WOOD, PLASTICS & COMPOSITES	94.8	81.6	87.4	95.7	82.1	88.1	96.1	78.9	86.5	95.1	76.6	84.8	81.6	44.9	61.1	101.9	82.6	91.1
07	THERMAL & MOISTURE PROTECTION	101.9	80.6	93.2	99.5	80.8	91.8	99.6	82.2	92.5	102.9	73.9	91.0	103.2	69.4	89.3	103.9	80.9	94.5
08	OPENINGS	96.0	80.5	92.4	99.7	82.2	95.6	96.4	67.6	89.7	94.8	70.4	89.1	99.3	53.4	88.6	100.3	81.9	96.0
0920	Plaster & Gypsum Board	90.8	81.3	84.4	93.4	81.0	85.0	93.4	77.7	82.8	102.3	75.9	84.5	97.7	43.2	60.9	106.9	82.3	90.3
0950, 0980	Ceilings & Acoustic Treatment	88.9	81.3	83.9	85.5	81.0	82.6	79.6	77.7	78.3	98.7	75.9	83.7	98.7	43.2	62.3	101.2	82.3	88.8
0960	Flooring	99.3	91.1	96.9	100.3	85.0	95.9	101.2	76.4	94.1	107.9	37.8	87.8	102.2	33.2	82.5	124.0	78.3	110.9
0970, 0990	Wall Finishes & Painting/Coating	99.2	87.1	91.9	101.2	83.1	90.3	101.2	83.4	90.5	106.3	78.5	89.5	106.3	78.7	89.6	107.6	72.2	86.3
09	FINISHES	95.4	83.9	89.1	93.8	82.8	87.7	93.1	79.6	85.6	102.5	68.9	84.0	98.7	48.3	71.0	108.4	80.6	93.1
COVERS	DIVS. 10 - 14, 25, 28, 41, 43, 44, 46	100.0	92.8	98.5	100.0	93.7	98.7	100.0	95.3	99.0	100.0	86.8	97.3	100.0	65.1	92.9	100.0	91.8	98.3
21, 22, 23	FIRE SUPPRESSION, PLUMBING & HVAC	99.9	77.1	90.7	99.9	79.6	91.7	95.2	77.6	88.1	95.4	75.2	87.3	95.4	72.6	86.2	100.2	80.5	92.2
26, 27, 3370	ELECTRICAL, COMMUNICATIONS & UTIL.	99.6	86.6	92.7	93.3	86.7	89.8	93.8	84.2	88.8	100.6	67.7	83.2	101.3	81.3	90.7	98.1	80.6	88.8
MF2014	WEIGHTED AVERAGE	98.0	84.4	92.1	97.9	86.5	92.9	95.8	81.8	89.7	97.2	75.3	87.6	97.0	71.2	85.8	100.0	83.2	92.7

For customer support on your Site Work & Landscape Cost Data, call 877.737.1594.

759

IOWA

DIVISION		COUNCIL BLUFFS 515			CRESTON 508			DAVENPORT 527 - 528			DECORAH 521			DES MOINES 500 - 503,509			DUBUQUE 520		
		MAT.	INST.	TOTAL	MAT.	INST.	TOTAL	MAT.	INST.	TOTAL	MAT.	INST.	TOTAL	MAT.	INST.	TOTAL	MAT.	INST.	TOTAL
015433	CONTRACTOR EQUIPMENT		95.5	95.5		99.4	99.4		99.4	99.4		99.4	99.4		101.1	101.1		94.9	94.9
0241, 31 - 34	SITE & INFRASTRUCTURE, DEMOLITION	103.8	91.5	95.0	93.9	95.5	95.1	98.7	98.6	98.6	96.9	95.5	95.9	102.9	99.8	100.7	97.9	92.4	94.0
0310	Concrete Forming & Accessories	82.0	71.2	72.7	78.4	65.8	67.5	100.0	91.3	92.5	92.3	45.4	51.8	95.4	81.8	83.6	83.3	74.9	76.1
0320	Concrete Reinforcing	93.6	79.0	86.1	89.3	82.4	85.8	91.7	97.0	94.4	91.0	76.5	83.6	98.2	86.7	92.3	90.4	84.1	87.2
0330	Cast-in-Place Concrete	116.4	73.6	98.8	115.2	64.1	94.2	107.8	90.1	100.5	108.6	58.0	87.8	101.4	87.5	95.7	109.6	98.6	105.1
03	CONCRETE	105.0	74.3	89.9	102.9	69.3	86.4	100.7	92.5	96.7	100.5	57.0	79.1	100.0	85.4	92.8	99.4	85.5	92.6
04	MASONRY	109.8	75.0	88.1	108.1	81.9	91.7	105.3	86.8	93.7	124.0	71.4	91.2	101.0	81.2	88.7	109.2	73.9	87.2
05	METALS	96.3	89.3	94.1	93.8	90.5	92.8	91.3	102.7	94.8	89.0	85.8	88.0	99.9	96.5	98.8	89.8	92.0	90.5
06	WOOD, PLASTICS & COMPOSITES	80.4	70.9	75.1	74.1	61.6	67.1	101.9	91.0	95.8	92.2	37.1	61.3	91.8	81.1	85.8	82.1	73.5	77.3
07	THERMAL & MOISTURE PROTECTION	103.3	67.1	88.5	104.2	77.6	93.3	103.4	87.5	96.8	103.1	53.4	82.7	98.5	79.4	90.6	103.6	73.9	91.4
08	OPENINGS	99.3	75.9	93.9	108.4	63.9	98.1	100.3	90.8	98.1	97.8	48.6	86.4	102.7	86.5	98.9	99.3	79.3	94.7
0920	Plaster & Gypsum Board	97.7	70.3	79.2	93.6	60.5	71.2	106.9	90.8	96.0	101.2	35.2	56.6	90.4	80.6	83.8	97.7	72.9	81.0
0950, 0980	Ceilings & Acoustic Treatment	98.7	70.3	80.0	90.8	60.5	70.9	101.2	90.8	94.4	98.7	35.2	57.0	94.2	80.6	85.2	98.7	72.9	81.8
0960	Flooring	100.8	80.7	95.0	97.4	33.2	79.1	110.3	97.0	106.5	107.6	47.2	90.3	102.5	89.6	98.8	114.9	77.0	104.1
0970, 0990	Wall Finishes & Painting/Coating	102.2	65.8	80.2	101.0	78.7	87.5	106.3	95.5	99.8	106.3	32.9	62.0	96.2	88.6	91.6	106.7	63.8	80.8
09	FINISHES	99.4	72.1	84.4	94.2	60.2	75.4	104.3	92.7	97.9	102.2	42.6	69.4	97.1	83.7	89.7	103.7	73.5	87.1
COVERS	DIVS. 10 - 14, 25, 28, 41, 43, 44, 46	100.0	88.6	97.7	100.0	69.5	93.8	100.0	94.5	98.9	100.0	82.9	96.5	100.0	92.1	98.4	100.0	90.2	98.0
21, 22, 23	FIRE SUPPRESSION, PLUMBING & HVAC	100.2	74.2	89.7	95.2	79.7	89.0	100.2	92.8	97.2	95.4	72.9	86.3	99.9	79.7	91.7	100.2	75.3	90.1
26, 27, 3370	ELECTRICAL, COMMUNICATIONS & UTIL.	103.6	81.5	91.9	93.8	81.3	87.2	95.6	91.0	93.2	98.1	44.3	69.7	105.4	81.3	92.7	102.1	78.2	89.4
MF2014	WEIGHTED AVERAGE	100.7	78.1	90.9	98.2	77.3	89.1	99.0	93.1	96.4	98.0	64.2	83.3	100.5	85.2	93.8	99.1	80.2	90.9

IOWA

DIVISION		FORT DODGE 505			MASON CITY 504			OTTUMWA 525			SHENANDOAH 516			SIBLEY 512			SIOUX CITY 510 - 511		
		MAT.	INST.	TOTAL	MAT.	INST.	TOTAL	MAT.	INST.	TOTAL	MAT.	INST.	TOTAL	MAT.	INST.	TOTAL	MAT.	INST.	TOTAL
015433	CONTRACTOR EQUIPMENT		99.4	99.4		99.4	99.4		94.9	94.9		95.5	95.5		99.4	99.4		99.4	99.4
0241, 31 - 34	SITE & INFRASTRUCTURE, DEMOLITION	102.2	94.4	96.6	102.3	95.4	97.4	98.1	90.5	92.7	102.2	90.5	93.9	108.1	94.2	98.2	109.9	95.0	99.3
0310	Concrete Forming & Accessories	78.9	45.1	49.7	83.1	45.5	50.6	90.3	73.7	75.9	83.6	56.5	60.2	84.0	37.9	44.2	100.5	66.4	71.1
0320	Concrete Reinforcing	89.3	67.2	78.1	89.2	81.8	85.4	91.0	86.1	88.5	93.6	68.4	80.7	93.6	65.3	79.2	91.7	77.9	84.7
0330	Cast-in-Place Concrete	108.2	44.2	81.9	108.2	57.5	87.4	112.4	53.7	88.3	112.5	59.8	90.9	110.3	44.7	83.4	111.0	55.5	88.2
03	CONCRETE	98.2	50.4	74.7	98.5	57.9	78.5	102.1	69.9	86.3	102.4	61.0	82.1	101.4	47.0	74.6	102.0	65.8	84.2
04	MASONRY	106.9	37.9	63.9	120.5	69.8	88.9	105.8	57.8	75.9	109.4	75.0	88.0	128.6	38.1	72.2	102.2	54.6	72.6
05	METALS	93.9	81.3	90.1	94.0	88.7	92.4	88.8	91.7	89.7	95.3	83.3	91.6	89.1	79.7	86.2	91.3	87.4	90.1
06	WOOD, PLASTICS & COMPOSITES	74.5	45.2	58.1	78.4	37.1	55.3	89.3	80.9	84.6	82.1	52.8	65.7	82.9	35.9	56.6	101.9	66.6	82.1
07	THERMAL & MOISTURE PROTECTION	103.5	57.1	84.5	103.0	63.5	86.8	103.7	64.6	87.7	102.6	65.2	87.2	102.9	48.3	80.5	103.4	64.3	87.4
08	OPENINGS	101.9	49.5	89.7	93.5	50.1	83.4	99.3	77.7	94.3	90.3	54.7	82.0	95.9	43.8	83.8	100.3	65.9	92.3
0920	Plaster & Gypsum Board	93.6	43.5	59.8	93.6	35.2	54.1	98.8	80.6	86.5	97.7	51.6	66.5	97.7	33.9	54.6	106.9	65.7	79.0
0950, 0980	Ceilings & Acoustic Treatment	90.8	43.5	59.7	90.8	35.2	54.2	98.7	80.6	86.8	98.7	51.6	67.7	98.7	33.9	56.1	101.2	65.7	77.9
0960	Flooring	98.9	47.2	84.1	100.9	47.2	85.6	117.9	50.2	98.5	101.5	34.3	82.3	103.1	34.0	83.3	110.3	53.7	94.1
0970, 0990	Wall Finishes & Painting/Coating	101.0	61.7	77.3	101.0	30.1	58.2	106.7	78.7	89.8	102.2	65.8	80.2	106.3	61.7	79.4	106.3	63.5	80.5
09	FINISHES	96.1	46.1	68.5	96.7	42.0	66.5	104.9	70.4	85.9	99.5	52.3	73.4	101.9	38.0	66.7	105.8	63.6	82.5
COVERS	DIVS. 10 - 14, 25, 28, 41, 43, 44, 46	100.0	81.7	96.3	100.0	86.5	97.3	100.0	82.4	96.4	100.0	66.1	93.2	100.0	80.8	96.1	100.0	88.2	97.6
21, 22, 23	FIRE SUPPRESSION, PLUMBING & HVAC	95.2	65.5	83.3	95.2	70.5	85.2	95.4	70.9	85.5	95.4	73.5	86.6	95.4	68.0	84.3	100.2	75.8	90.4
26, 27, 3370	ELECTRICAL, COMMUNICATIONS & UTIL.	100.3	41.9	69.4	99.4	55.6	76.3	100.4	72.0	85.4	98.1	81.5	89.3	98.1	41.4	68.1	98.1	73.0	84.8
MF2014	WEIGHTED AVERAGE	97.9	58.2	80.6	97.6	65.8	83.8	97.9	73.7	87.3	97.6	71.2	86.1	98.3	56.4	80.0	99.7	72.6	87.9

DIVISION		IOWA SPENCER 513			IOWA WATERLOO 506 - 507			KANSAS BELLEVILLE 669			KANSAS COLBY 677			KANSAS DODGE CITY 678			KANSAS EMPORIA 668		
		MAT.	INST.	TOTAL	MAT.	INST.	TOTAL	MAT.	INST.	TOTAL	MAT.	INST.	TOTAL	MAT.	INST.	TOTAL	MAT.	INST.	TOTAL
015433	CONTRACTOR EQUIPMENT		99.4	99.4		99.4	99.4		103.4	103.4		103.4	103.4		103.4	103.4		101.6	101.6
0241, 31 - 34	SITE & INFRASTRUCTURE, DEMOLITION	108.1	94.2	98.2	107.6	95.3	98.8	111.0	95.0	99.7	112.3	95.2	100.1	114.9	94.9	100.7	103.0	92.5	95.5
0310	Concrete Forming & Accessories	90.2	37.9	45.1	94.1	55.1	60.5	96.2	54.1	59.8	99.5	58.3	64.0	93.1	58.2	63.0	87.2	65.3	68.3
0320	Concrete Reinforcing	93.6	67.1	80.1	89.9	83.9	86.8	96.6	55.1	75.5	98.9	55.2	76.7	96.5	55.1	75.4	95.3	55.7	75.2
0330	Cast-in-Place Concrete	110.3	44.7	83.4	115.8	59.2	92.6	124.2	55.7	96.1	127.1	55.8	97.8	129.3	55.5	99.3	120.1	53.6	92.8
03	CONCRETE	101.8	47.3	75.0	104.4	63.1	84.1	119.3	56.2	88.3	119.9	58.1	89.5	121.3	57.9	90.2	111.5	60.5	86.5
04	MASONRY	128.6	38.1	72.2	107.7	73.1	86.1	99.2	58.7	73.9	108.1	59.9	78.1	118.9	58.9	81.5	105.5	68.5	82.4
05	METALS	89.0	80.5	86.4	96.4	91.1	94.7	95.6	77.3	90.0	96.0	77.7	90.4	97.4	76.7	91.1	95.3	78.9	90.3
06	WOOD, PLASTICS & COMPOSITES	89.2	35.9	59.3	91.6	48.0	67.2	97.9	52.1	72.3	103.6	57.9	78.0	95.8	57.9	74.5	88.7	66.6	76.3
07	THERMAL & MOISTURE PROTECTION	103.8	48.2	81.0	103.3	71.3	90.2	94.8	60.7	80.8	99.1	61.6	83.7	99.1	60.7	83.4	93.1	75.9	86.0
08	OPENINGS	107.5	44.4	92.9	94.4	58.2	86.0	98.6	48.4	86.9	103.2	51.5	91.2	103.1	51.5	91.1	96.3	56.3	87.0
0920	Plaster & Gypsum Board	98.8	33.9	54.9	101.9	46.5	64.4	97.2	50.6	65.7	99.7	56.5	70.5	94.0	56.5	68.7	94.4	65.5	74.9
0950, 0980	Ceilings & Acoustic Treatment	98.7	33.9	56.1	94.2	46.5	62.8	86.3	50.6	62.8	84.0	56.5	65.9	84.0	56.5	65.9	86.3	65.5	72.7
0960	Flooring	105.7	34.0	85.2	106.2	64.9	94.4	103.0	39.2	84.8	103.1	39.2	84.9	99.6	39.2	82.3	98.0	36.4	80.4
0970, 0990	Wall Finishes & Painting/Coating	106.3	61.7	79.4	101.0	77.8	87.0	100.0	38.9	63.1	104.7	38.9	65.0	104.7	38.9	65.0	100.0	38.9	63.1
09	FINISHES	102.8	38.0	67.1	100.3	57.6	76.8	96.9	49.3	70.6	96.6	52.7	72.4	94.9	52.7	71.6	94.0	57.3	73.8
COVERS	DIVS. 10 - 14, 25, 28, 41, 43, 44, 46	100.0	80.8	96.1	100.0	87.8	97.5	100.0	40.8	88.0	100.0	41.4	88.2	100.0	41.4	88.2	100.0	40.5	88.0
21, 22, 23	FIRE SUPPRESSION, PLUMBING & HVAC	95.4	68.0	84.3	100.0	79.8	91.9	95.2	71.6	85.7	95.2	69.0	84.6	100.0	69.0	87.5	95.2	73.4	86.4
26, 27, 3370	ELECTRICAL, COMMUNICATIONS & UTIL.	99.9	41.4	69.0	95.8	55.7	74.6	96.5	67.7	81.3	100.0	64.5	81.2	96.8	73.8	84.6	93.9	71.4	82.0
MF2014	WEIGHTED AVERAGE	99.9	56.6	81.0	99.5	71.8	87.4	99.6	64.9	84.4	101.1	65.0	85.4	102.7	66.0	86.7	97.9	69.2	85.4

City Cost Indexes

KANSAS

DIVISION		FORT SCOTT 667 MAT.	INST.	TOTAL	HAYS 676 MAT.	INST.	TOTAL	HUTCHINSON 675 MAT.	INST.	TOTAL	INDEPENDENCE 673 MAT.	INST.	TOTAL	KANSAS CITY 660-662 MAT.	INST.	TOTAL	LIBERAL 679 MAT.	INST.	TOTAL
015433	CONTRACTOR EQUIPMENT		102.5	102.5		103.4	103.4		103.4	103.4		103.4	103.4		99.9	99.9		103.4	103.4
0241, 31 - 34	SITE & INFRASTRUCTURE, DEMOLITION	99.8	93.4	95.2	117.7	95.2	101.7	96.2	95.0	95.4	116.0	95.1	101.1	94.4	93.1	93.5	117.3	95.0	101.5
0310	Concrete Forming & Accessories	104.2	76.8	80.6	97.2	58.3	63.7	87.9	58.2	62.2	107.9	66.3	72.0	100.9	94.2	95.1	93.5	58.2	63.0
0320	Concrete Reinforcing	94.6	93.3	94.0	96.5	55.2	75.5	96.5	55.1	75.4	95.9	62.7	79.0	91.8	97.2	94.6	97.8	55.1	76.1
0330	Cast-in-Place Concrete	111.4	54.5	88.0	100.3	55.8	82.0	92.9	53.1	76.6	129.5	53.4	98.5	95.4	97.4	96.3	100.3	53.1	80.9
03	CONCRETE	106.6	72.9	90.1	110.4	58.1	84.7	92.4	57.1	75.0	122.6	62.2	92.9	98.4	96.2	97.3	112.5	57.1	85.2
04	MASONRY	106.7	60.3	77.8	118.0	59.9	81.8	107.9	58.6	77.2	105.3	64.5	79.9	107.8	99.4	102.6	116.6	58.6	80.4
05	METALS	95.3	92.8	94.5	95.6	77.7	90.1	95.4	76.7	89.6	95.3	80.5	90.8	102.9	100.1	102.1	95.9	76.7	90.0
06	WOOD, PLASTICS & COMPOSITES	108.7	83.5	94.6	100.6	57.9	76.7	90.9	57.9	72.4	113.7	68.0	88.1	104.4	94.5	98.8	96.4	57.9	74.8
07	THERMAL & MOISTURE PROTECTION	94.0	80.8	88.6	99.4	61.6	83.9	98.0	60.6	82.7	99.1	80.5	91.5	93.7	98.0	95.5	99.5	60.6	83.6
08	OPENINGS	96.3	78.2	92.1	103.1	51.5	91.1	103.0	51.5	91.0	100.7	58.8	90.9	97.7	89.0	95.7	103.1	51.5	91.1
0920	Plaster & Gypsum Board	99.7	82.9	88.4	97.3	56.5	69.7	93.0	56.5	68.3	106.9	67.0	79.9	92.9	94.2	93.8	94.8	56.5	68.9
0950, 0980	Ceilings & Acoustic Treatment	86.3	82.9	84.1	84.0	56.5	65.9	84.0	56.5	65.9	84.0	67.0	72.8	86.3	94.2	91.5	84.0	56.5	65.9
0960	Flooring	113.7	39.4	92.5	100.2	39.2	84.0	96.8	39.2	80.3	107.3	39.2	87.8	91.4	98.7	93.5	99.8	39.2	82.5
0970, 0990	Wall Finishes & Painting/Coating	101.8	38.9	63.8	104.7	38.9	65.0	104.7	38.9	65.0	104.7	38.9	65.0	108.5	67.7	83.9	104.7	38.9	65.0
09	FINISHES	99.6	66.9	81.6	96.4	52.7	72.3	92.4	52.7	70.5	98.9	58.7	76.8	94.3	91.0	92.5	95.7	52.7	72.0
COVERS	DIVS. 10 - 14, 25, 28, 41, 43, 44, 46	100.0	46.2	89.1	100.0	41.4	88.2	100.0	41.4	88.2	100.0	42.5	88.4	100.0	61.9	92.3	100.0	41.4	88.2
21, 22, 23	FIRE SUPPRESSION, PLUMBING & HVAC	95.2	68.3	84.3	95.2	69.0	84.6	95.2	69.0	84.6	95.2	70.1	85.1	99.9	96.4	98.5	95.2	67.2	83.9
26, 27, 3370	ELECTRICAL, COMMUNICATIONS & UTIL.	93.2	71.4	81.6	98.9	67.7	82.4	93.9	67.7	80.0	96.1	71.4	83.0	98.7	97.2	97.9	96.8	73.8	84.6
MF2014	WEIGHTED AVERAGE	97.9	73.0	87.0	100.5	65.4	85.2	96.5	65.0	82.8	100.9	69.2	87.1	99.5	94.8	97.5	100.4	65.5	85.2

KANSAS / KENTUCKY

DIVISION		SALINA 674 MAT.	INST.	TOTAL	TOPEKA 664-666 MAT.	INST.	TOTAL	WICHITA 670-672 MAT.	INST.	TOTAL	ASHLAND 411-412 MAT.	INST.	TOTAL	BOWLING GREEN 421-422 MAT.	INST.	TOTAL	CAMPTON 413-414 MAT.	INST.	TOTAL
015433	CONTRACTOR EQUIPMENT		103.4	103.4		101.6	101.6		103.4	103.4		97.3	97.3		94.5	94.5		101.1	101.1
0241, 31 - 34	SITE & INFRASTRUCTURE, DEMOLITION	105.2	95.2	98.1	98.2	91.5	93.4	101.8	93.8	96.1	112.3	86.3	93.8	78.6	97.1	91.8	87.0	98.3	95.0
0310	Concrete Forming & Accessories	89.7	54.9	59.7	98.4	40.9	48.8	95.3	51.0	57.1	87.9	105.2	102.8	85.7	83.0	83.4	89.4	82.6	83.6
0320	Concrete Reinforcing	95.9	59.4	77.3	94.9	99.5	97.2	95.3	77.3	86.1	88.8	108.7	98.9	86.2	91.3	88.8	87.0	101.8	94.5
0330	Cast-in-Place Concrete	112.3	53.7	88.2	100.4	45.5	77.9	105.3	51.7	83.3	91.1	101.1	95.2	90.4	95.5	92.5	100.8	73.6	89.6
03	CONCRETE	107.3	56.7	82.5	99.4	55.1	77.7	101.6	57.4	79.9	98.6	104.8	101.6	96.8	88.9	92.9	100.7	83.2	92.1
04	MASONRY	134.8	59.9	88.2	102.5	55.9	73.4	106.3	50.2	71.4	97.8	103.7	101.5	99.7	80.2	87.5	96.9	69.0	79.5
05	METALS	97.3	80.6	92.1	99.4	96.9	98.6	99.4	84.2	94.7	92.1	110.3	97.7	93.6	87.3	91.7	92.9	92.0	92.6
06	WOOD, PLASTICS & COMPOSITES	92.4	52.1	69.8	97.1	37.3	63.6	95.1	51.3	70.6	76.0	105.2	92.3	88.6	83.1	85.5	87.1	89.0	88.2
07	THERMAL & MOISTURE PROTECTION	98.6	61.4	83.3	96.7	67.4	84.7	97.2	56.1	80.4	91.0	97.5	93.7	86.6	80.2	84.0	99.7	67.5	86.5
08	OPENINGS	103.1	48.5	90.4	100.8	55.4	90.2	105.3	56.2	93.9	97.9	99.6	98.3	98.7	79.3	94.2	100.2	87.6	97.3
0920	Plaster & Gypsum Board	93.0	50.6	64.3	96.8	35.3	55.2	91.8	49.8	63.4	60.9	105.4	91.0	87.4	82.9	84.3	87.4	88.1	87.9
0950, 0980	Ceilings & Acoustic Treatment	84.0	50.6	62.0	92.0	35.3	54.7	88.8	49.8	63.2	80.8	105.4	97.0	85.5	82.9	83.8	85.5	88.1	87.2
0960	Flooring	98.2	61.9	87.8	103.4	73.7	94.9	105.4	63.0	93.3	79.4	102.4	86.0	95.8	86.0	93.0	98.0	41.2	81.7
0970, 0990	Wall Finishes & Painting/Coating	104.7	38.9	65.0	101.8	52.5	72.1	103.6	48.0	70.0	103.1	101.2	102.0	101.2	72.7	84.0	101.2	65.4	79.6
09	FINISHES	93.6	53.6	71.6	98.5	45.9	69.5	97.7	52.3	72.7	80.9	104.8	94.1	91.8	82.8	86.8	92.6	74.0	82.4
COVERS	DIVS. 10 - 14, 25, 28, 41, 43, 44, 46	100.0	86.0	97.2	100.0	47.2	89.3	100.0	83.0	96.6	100.0	94.1	98.8	100.0	62.3	92.4	100.0	55.8	91.1
21, 22, 23	FIRE SUPPRESSION, PLUMBING & HVAC	100.0	69.1	87.5	100.0	69.1	87.5	99.8	64.8	85.7	95.0	92.5	94.0	99.9	82.7	93.0	95.2	79.8	89.0
26, 27, 3370	ELECTRICAL, COMMUNICATIONS & UTIL.	96.6	73.8	84.5	97.5	71.8	83.9	100.9	73.8	86.5	91.4	97.3	94.5	94.0	81.5	87.4	91.4	66.1	78.0
MF2014	WEIGHTED AVERAGE	101.5	67.6	86.7	99.5	66.0	84.9	100.7	66.0	85.6	94.6	99.3	96.6	96.2	83.9	90.8	95.8	78.6	88.3

KENTUCKY

DIVISION		CORBIN 407-409 MAT.	INST.	TOTAL	COVINGTON 410 MAT.	INST.	TOTAL	ELIZABETHTOWN 427 MAT.	INST.	TOTAL	FRANKFORT 406 MAT.	INST.	TOTAL	HAZARD 417-418 MAT.	INST.	TOTAL	HENDERSON 424 MAT.	INST.	TOTAL
015433	CONTRACTOR EQUIPMENT		101.1	101.1		104.4	104.4		94.5	94.5		101.1	101.1		101.1	101.1		116.0	116.0
0241, 31 - 34	SITE & INFRASTRUCTURE, DEMOLITION	87.9	98.1	95.1	82.6	112.3	103.7	73.1	97.2	90.2	88.9	99.2	96.2	84.8	99.6	95.3	81.1	124.0	111.6
0310	Concrete Forming & Accessories	84.5	70.6	72.5	85.0	82.0	82.4	80.7	80.5	80.5	94.2	71.8	74.8	86.1	83.5	83.8	92.5	81.5	83.0
0320	Concrete Reinforcing	86.0	68.9	77.7	85.7	91.1	88.5	86.6	90.8	88.8	97.7	90.8	94.2	87.4	107.6	97.7	86.3	84.8	85.6
0330	Cast-in-Place Concrete	93.6	58.6	79.2	96.5	97.6	96.9	81.8	73.0	78.2	89.4	69.1	81.1	97.0	82.5	91.0	79.9	90.6	84.3
03	CONCRETE	93.3	66.8	80.3	98.9	89.7	94.4	88.6	80.0	84.4	93.8	74.8	84.5	97.3	87.7	92.6	93.9	85.4	89.7
04	MASONRY	94.4	61.9	74.1	111.8	101.5	105.4	83.5	75.4	78.5	94.6	79.4	85.1	94.8	71.5	80.3	103.6	92.9	96.9
05	METALS	90.4	78.2	86.6	91.0	96.9	92.8	92.8	87.2	91.1	93.0	87.8	91.4	92.9	94.2	93.3	84.4	86.9	85.1
06	WOOD, PLASTICS & COMPOSITES	76.9	75.9	76.4	85.0	71.7	77.6	83.7	82.0	82.7	91.4	68.7	78.7	84.1	89.0	86.8	91.3	79.0	84.4
07	THERMAL & MOISTURE PROTECTION	99.3	63.8	84.7	100.3	92.3	97.0	86.3	76.9	82.5	101.0	75.1	90.4	99.7	69.5	87.3	99.0	91.3	95.9
08	OPENINGS	97.9	65.6	90.4	102.4	81.7	97.6	98.7	83.2	95.1	104.5	76.7	98.0	100.6	79.9	95.8	96.8	79.9	92.9
0920	Plaster & Gypsum Board	92.3	74.6	80.3	68.8	71.4	70.6	86.7	81.7	83.3	96.5	67.2	76.7	86.7	88.1	87.6	90.2	77.8	81.8
0950, 0980	Ceilings & Acoustic Treatment	80.4	74.6	76.6	88.8	71.4	77.4	85.5	81.7	83.0	89.6	67.2	74.8	85.5	88.1	87.2	79.6	77.8	78.4
0960	Flooring	97.2	41.2	81.2	71.8	88.6	76.6	93.4	86.0	91.3	106.0	54.4	91.2	96.4	42.0	80.9	99.5	86.0	95.6
0970, 0990	Wall Finishes & Painting/Coating	107.2	49.4	72.3	96.2	83.2	88.3	101.2	76.2	86.1	109.1	79.8	91.4	101.2	65.4	79.6	101.2	96.0	98.1
09	FINISHES	90.7	63.6	75.8	82.7	82.0	82.4	90.6	80.7	85.1	97.6	68.8	81.7	91.9	74.8	82.5	91.4	83.8	87.2
COVERS	DIVS. 10 - 14, 25, 28, 41, 43, 44, 46	100.0	48.4	89.6	100.0	98.7	99.7	100.0	84.2	96.8	100.0	65.5	93.0	100.0	56.6	91.2	100.0	65.4	93.0
21, 22, 23	FIRE SUPPRESSION, PLUMBING & HVAC	95.2	71.4	85.6	95.9	92.4	94.5	95.5	80.1	89.3	100.1	82.3	92.9	95.2	80.7	89.4	95.5	77.6	88.3
26, 27, 3370	ELECTRICAL, COMMUNICATIONS & UTIL.	91.4	80.1	85.4	95.2	79.3	86.8	91.2	80.2	85.4	101.3	87.1	93.8	91.4	58.4	73.9	93.4	80.3	86.5
MF2014	WEIGHTED AVERAGE	94.0	71.8	84.3	95.9	91.4	93.9	92.8	82.0	88.1	98.1	80.7	90.5	95.2	78.7	88.0	93.7	86.1	90.4

For customer support on your Site Work & Landscape Cost Data, call 877.737.1594.

761

KENTUCKY

DIVISION		LEXINGTON 403 - 405			LOUISVILLE 400 - 402			OWENSBORO 423			PADUCAH 420			PIKEVILLE 415 - 416			SOMERSET 425 - 426		
		MAT.	INST.	TOTAL	MAT.	INST.	TOTAL	MAT.	INST.	TOTAL	MAT.	INST.	TOTAL	MAT.	INST.	TOTAL	MAT.	INST.	TOTAL
015433	CONTRACTOR EQUIPMENT		101.1	101.1		94.5	94.5		116.0	116.0		116.0	116.0		97.3	97.3		101.1	101.1
0241, 31 - 34	SITE & INFRASTRUCTURE, DEMOLITION	90.1	100.6	97.5	84.8	97.3	93.7	91.0	124.5	114.8	83.7	123.4	111.9	123.2	85.3	96.3	77.9	98.8	92.8
0310	Concrete Forming & Accessories	96.4	73.0	76.2	95.8	82.0	83.9	90.9	85.1	85.9	88.9	79.9	81.1	96.8	88.9	90.0	87.0	75.9	77.4
0320	Concrete Reinforcing	94.4	92.2	93.3	96.8	92.6	94.7	86.3	91.8	89.1	86.8	86.2	86.5	89.3	108.4	99.0	86.6	90.8	88.7
0330	Cast-in-Place Concrete	95.8	92.7	94.5	96.4	73.9	87.2	93.2	91.1	92.4	85.2	86.5	85.7	100.1	96.7	98.7	79.9	98.3	87.5
03	CONCRETE	96.5	83.7	90.2	97.1	81.3	89.4	106.3	88.5	97.5	98.6	83.5	91.2	112.7	96.0	104.5	83.6	86.6	85.1
04	MASONRY	93.7	73.3	81.0	91.6	78.8	83.6	95.9	91.5	93.2	98.8	88.4	92.3	95.3	96.8	96.2	89.8	76.7	81.6
05	METALS	92.8	89.0	91.6	93.9	88.2	92.1	85.8	90.6	87.3	82.9	86.7	84.1	92.0	108.8	97.2	92.8	87.6	91.2
06	WOOD, PLASTICS & COMPOSITES	92.0	68.7	79.0	90.9	83.1	86.5	89.2	83.3	85.9	86.8	79.1	82.5	85.5	88.3	87.1	84.6	75.9	79.7
07	THERMAL & MOISTURE PROTECTION	99.5	84.1	93.2	96.3	78.2	88.9	99.4	92.8	96.7	99.1	78.8	90.8	91.7	79.5	86.7	99.0	71.2	87.6
08	OPENINGS	98.1	73.9	92.5	93.5	84.3	91.4	96.8	85.7	94.2	96.0	77.5	91.7	98.6	87.8	96.1	99.5	77.7	94.4
0920	Plaster & Gypsum Board	101.9	67.2	78.4	98.0	82.9	87.8	88.7	82.2	84.3	87.7	77.9	81.1	63.8	88.1	80.2	86.7	74.6	78.5
0950, 0980	Ceilings & Acoustic Treatment	84.5	67.2	73.1	88.9	82.9	84.9	79.6	82.2	81.3	79.6	77.9	78.5	80.8	88.1	85.6	85.5	74.6	78.3
0960	Flooring	101.9	70.3	92.9	98.6	86.0	95.0	98.9	86.0	95.2	97.8	59.4	86.8	83.4	102.4	88.8	96.7	41.2	80.8
0970, 0990	Wall Finishes & Painting/Coating	107.2	81.0	91.4	104.7	76.2	87.5	101.2	96.0	98.1	101.2	79.7	88.2	103.1	81.2	89.9	101.2	76.2	86.1
09	FINISHES	94.4	72.3	82.2	94.9	82.3	88.0	91.5	86.0	88.5	90.7	76.1	82.7	83.3	90.9	87.5	91.2	69.4	79.2
COVERS	DIVS. 10 - 14, 25, 28, 41, 43, 44, 46	100.0	86.5	97.3	100.0	84.9	96.9	100.0	102.9	100.6	100.0	61.8	92.3	100.0	56.3	91.2	100.0	58.5	91.6
21, 22, 23	FIRE SUPPRESSION, PLUMBING & HVAC	100.0	79.5	91.7	100.0	80.9	92.3	99.9	78.6	91.4	95.5	81.1	89.7	95.0	87.2	91.8	95.5	77.4	88.2
26, 27, 3370	ELECTRICAL, COMMUNICATIONS & UTIL.	94.2	81.5	87.5	99.4	81.5	89.9	93.5	81.4	87.1	95.8	79.9	87.4	94.4	73.4	83.3	91.8	80.2	85.6
MF2014	WEIGHTED AVERAGE	96.6	81.4	90.0	96.6	83.3	90.8	96.3	88.9	93.1	93.9	84.5	89.8	96.9	88.6	93.3	93.2	79.9	87.4

LOUISIANA

DIVISION		ALEXANDRIA 713 - 714			BATON ROUGE 707 - 708			HAMMOND 704			LAFAYETTE 705			LAKE CHARLES 706			MONROE 712		
		MAT.	INST.	TOTAL	MAT.	INST.	TOTAL	MAT.	INST.	TOTAL	MAT.	INST.	TOTAL	MAT.	INST.	TOTAL	MAT.	INST.	TOTAL
015433	CONTRACTOR EQUIPMENT		89.9	89.9		89.5	89.5		90.1	90.1		90.1	90.1		89.5	89.5		89.9	89.9
0241, 31 - 34	SITE & INFRASTRUCTURE, DEMOLITION	101.2	87.1	91.1	104.0	87.2	92.0	102.1	87.8	91.9	103.2	88.1	92.5	103.9	87.0	91.9	101.2	87.0	91.1
0310	Concrete Forming & Accessories	82.9	43.4	48.9	97.6	60.8	65.8	78.4	46.2	50.7	96.0	54.1	59.9	96.8	56.7	62.2	82.4	43.3	48.7
0320	Concrete Reinforcing	94.9	54.3	74.2	101.1	58.9	79.6	97.9	59.3	78.3	99.3	58.9	78.7	99.3	59.1	78.9	93.8	54.0	73.6
0330	Cast-in-Place Concrete	96.2	49.9	77.2	97.2	58.8	81.4	95.8	44.0	74.5	95.3	47.9	75.8	100.3	67.3	86.8	96.2	56.8	80.0
03	CONCRETE	95.5	48.8	72.6	98.9	60.4	80.0	95.2	48.9	72.5	96.4	53.7	75.4	98.8	61.5	80.5	95.3	51.1	73.6
04	MASONRY	121.3	53.4	79.0	94.9	54.1	69.5	95.7	51.2	68.0	95.7	52.4	68.7	95.0	58.8	72.5	115.6	47.9	73.4
05	METALS	95.4	70.4	87.7	100.6	72.1	91.8	95.7	71.2	88.1	94.8	72.1	87.8	94.8	72.6	87.9	95.4	69.9	87.6
06	WOOD, PLASTICS & COMPOSITES	90.5	41.7	63.2	99.0	63.8	79.3	84.2	47.0	63.3	105.1	55.7	77.7	103.8	57.7	78.0	89.8	42.2	63.1
07	THERMAL & MOISTURE PROTECTION	95.6	62.9	82.2	96.2	65.4	83.5	96.5	61.4	82.1	97.1	63.8	83.4	96.1	66.8	84.1	95.6	60.8	81.3
08	OPENINGS	109.1	44.7	94.1	97.9	59.1	88.9	93.0	51.7	83.4	96.7	53.2	86.6	96.7	54.9	87.0	109.1	47.6	94.8
0920	Plaster & Gypsum Board	84.2	40.4	54.6	96.7	63.0	74.0	97.5	45.7	62.5	105.7	54.7	71.2	105.7	56.8	72.6	83.8	40.9	54.8
0950, 0980	Ceilings & Acoustic Treatment	84.1	40.4	55.4	91.3	63.0	72.7	94.1	45.7	62.3	92.4	54.7	67.6	93.3	56.8	69.3	84.1	40.9	55.7
0960	Flooring	98.5	65.7	89.1	101.8	65.7	91.5	96.3	65.7	87.5	104.9	65.7	93.7	104.9	72.9	95.7	98.1	57.1	86.4
0970, 0990	Wall Finishes & Painting/Coating	104.4	64.4	80.3	94.7	46.3	65.5	99.4	48.3	68.6	99.4	57.9	74.4	99.4	50.0	69.6	104.4	48.1	70.4
09	FINISHES	89.8	48.9	67.2	94.7	60.2	75.7	94.8	49.7	70.0	98.1	56.3	75.0	98.3	58.6	76.4	89.6	45.5	65.3
COVERS	DIVS. 10 - 14, 25, 28, 41, 43, 44, 46	100.0	50.0	89.9	100.0	80.8	96.1	100.0	45.4	89.0	100.0	79.4	95.8	100.0	80.3	96.0	100.0	45.7	89.0
21, 22, 23	FIRE SUPPRESSION, PLUMBING & HVAC	100.1	55.3	82.1	100.0	59.5	83.7	95.3	42.8	74.1	100.1	61.1	84.4	100.1	62.0	84.7	100.1	54.3	81.6
26, 27, 3370	ELECTRICAL, COMMUNICATIONS & UTIL.	95.7	57.9	75.7	100.8	61.6	80.1	96.7	56.0	75.2	97.9	67.4	81.8	97.4	65.0	80.3	97.7	59.6	77.6
MF2014	WEIGHTED AVERAGE	99.4	57.2	81.0	99.1	63.7	83.7	95.8	54.5	77.8	97.9	63.0	82.7	98.1	65.0	83.7	99.3	56.5	80.6

LOUISIANA / MAINE

DIVISION		NEW ORLEANS 700 - 701			SHREVEPORT 710 - 711			THIBODAUX 703			AUGUSTA 043			BANGOR 044			BATH 045		
		MAT.	INST.	TOTAL	MAT.	INST.	TOTAL	MAT.	INST.	TOTAL	MAT.	INST.	TOTAL	MAT.	INST.	TOTAL	MAT.	INST.	TOTAL
015433	CONTRACTOR EQUIPMENT		90.4	90.4		89.9	89.9		90.1	90.1		100.9	100.9		100.9	100.9		100.9	100.9
0241, 31 - 34	SITE & INFRASTRUCTURE, DEMOLITION	103.4	91.1	94.7	105.5	87.1	92.4	104.4	88.1	92.8	91.6	101.1	98.4	93.3	101.3	99.0	91.0	101.1	98.2
0310	Concrete Forming & Accessories	95.1	65.5	69.5	98.5	44.2	51.7	90.4	64.6	68.1	95.9	94.8	94.9	93.1	96.6	96.1	88.9	94.9	94.1
0320	Concrete Reinforcing	100.2	60.1	79.8	98.3	54.4	76.0	97.9	59.1	78.2	96.1	106.7	101.5	87.7	108.1	98.1	86.8	107.9	97.5
0330	Cast-in-Place Concrete	98.0	69.4	86.3	101.1	53.6	81.6	102.9	51.6	81.8	101.5	58.8	84.0	82.2	110.6	93.9	82.2	58.9	72.7
03	CONCRETE	99.0	66.3	82.9	100.4	50.5	75.9	100.5	59.7	80.4	103.1	84.1	93.8	94.1	102.9	98.4	94.1	84.4	89.4
04	MASONRY	97.7	59.8	74.1	107.1	50.5	71.8	120.5	48.8	75.8	107.4	63.6	80.1	118.0	103.9	109.2	125.6	86.1	101.0
05	METALS	110.3	73.3	98.9	99.5	70.6	90.6	95.6	71.6	88.2	106.0	86.6	100.1	96.1	89.3	94.0	94.6	88.4	92.7
06	WOOD, PLASTICS & COMPOSITES	97.9	66.3	80.2	101.7	42.7	68.7	92.3	69.7	79.6	91.1	105.3	99.0	90.1	96.4	93.6	84.6	105.3	96.2
07	THERMAL & MOISTURE PROTECTION	94.9	68.8	84.2	95.3	59.8	80.8	96.4	61.8	82.2	100.1	65.0	85.7	97.8	84.4	92.3	97.8	71.8	87.1
08	OPENINGS	97.8	65.4	90.2	108.0	45.3	93.4	97.6	64.1	89.8	106.3	87.9	102.0	102.8	83.0	98.2	102.8	87.8	99.3
0920	Plaster & Gypsum Board	101.4	65.7	77.2	94.0	41.5	58.5	99.7	69.2	79.0	100.6	104.8	103.5	99.4	95.7	96.9	95.5	104.8	101.8
0950, 0980	Ceilings & Acoustic Treatment	98.2	65.7	76.8	88.1	41.5	57.4	94.1	69.2	77.7	97.4	104.8	102.3	86.2	95.7	92.5	84.3	104.8	97.8
0960	Flooring	105.7	65.7	94.2	101.9	61.3	90.3	102.3	44.1	85.7	103.9	55.3	90.0	97.1	114.3	102.0	95.3	55.3	83.9
0970, 0990	Wall Finishes & Painting/Coating	101.9	64.1	79.1	100.4	44.6	66.7	100.7	49.6	69.9	112.7	63.3	82.9	105.0	44.1	68.3	105.0	44.1	68.3
09	FINISHES	101.2	65.1	81.3	94.5	46.3	67.9	97.2	59.8	76.6	100.2	85.8	92.3	95.7	94.8	95.2	94.2	83.7	88.4
COVERS	DIVS. 10 - 14, 25, 28, 41, 43, 44, 46	100.0	83.1	96.6	100.0	78.1	95.6	100.0	81.4	96.2	100.0	100.5	100.1	100.0	109.8	102.0	100.0	100.5	100.1
21, 22, 23	FIRE SUPPRESSION, PLUMBING & HVAC	100.0	65.1	85.9	99.9	58.6	83.3	95.3	61.7	81.8	99.9	64.2	85.5	100.1	74.3	89.7	95.4	64.3	82.8
26, 27, 3370	ELECTRICAL, COMMUNICATIONS & UTIL.	102.1	73.3	86.9	103.5	66.6	84.0	95.3	73.3	83.7	100.9	80.1	89.9	97.2	75.8	85.9	95.2	80.1	87.2
MF2014	WEIGHTED AVERAGE	101.4	69.5	87.5	101.0	59.6	83.0	98.2	65.4	83.9	102.1	79.5	92.3	99.0	89.5	94.9	97.5	81.9	90.7

		MAINE																
		HOULTON			KITTERY			LEWISTON			MACHIAS			PORTLAND			ROCKLAND		
	DIVISION	047			039			042			046			040 - 041			048		
		MAT.	INST.	TOTAL	MAT.	INST.	TOTAL	MAT.	INST.	TOTAL	MAT.	INST.	TOTAL	MAT.	INST.	TOTAL	MAT.	INST.	TOTAL
015433	CONTRACTOR EQUIPMENT		100.9	100.9		100.9	100.9		100.9	100.9		100.9	100.9		100.9	100.9		100.9	100.9
0241, 31 - 34	SITE & INFRASTRUCTURE, DEMOLITION	93.0	102.2	99.5	84.8	101.2	96.5	90.9	101.3	98.3	92.3	102.2	99.4	90.1	101.3	98.1	88.7	102.2	98.3
0310	Concrete Forming & Accessories	96.7	101.6	101.0	89.2	95.5	94.6	98.5	96.7	96.9	93.9	101.6	100.5	98.5	96.7	96.9	94.9	101.6	100.7
0320	Concrete Reinforcing	87.7	106.5	97.2	84.1	107.9	96.2	107.8	108.1	107.9	87.7	106.5	97.2	102.2	108.1	105.2	87.7	106.5	97.2
0330	Cast-in-Place Concrete	82.3	71.7	77.9	81.2	59.8	72.4	83.9	110.7	94.9	82.2	71.1	77.7	96.7	110.7	102.4	83.9	71.1	78.7
03	CONCRETE	95.1	91.5	93.4	89.7	85.0	87.4	94.7	102.9	98.7	94.6	91.3	93.0	101.9	102.9	102.4	92.0	91.3	91.6
04	MASONRY	101.3	76.3	85.7	113.3	87.1	97.0	101.9	103.9	103.2	101.3	76.3	85.7	112.8	103.9	107.2	95.2	76.3	83.4
05	METALS	94.8	86.6	92.3	85.5	88.6	86.4	99.5	89.3	96.4	94.8	86.5	92.3	107.9	89.3	102.2	94.7	86.5	92.2
06	WOOD, PLASTICS & COMPOSITES	94.0	105.3	100.3	89.2	105.3	98.2	96.0	96.4	96.2	91.0	105.3	99.0	93.7	96.4	95.2	91.9	105.3	99.4
07	THERMAL & MOISTURE PROTECTION	97.9	72.6	87.5	99.2	71.1	87.7	97.6	84.4	92.2	97.8	71.6	87.1	100.1	84.4	93.7	97.5	71.7	86.9
08	OPENINGS	102.9	86.1	99.0	102.0	87.8	98.7	106.2	83.0	100.8	102.9	86.1	99.0	104.5	83.0	99.5	102.8	86.1	98.9
0920	Plaster & Gypsum Board	101.6	104.8	103.8	100.0	104.8	103.3	104.9	95.7	98.7	100.1	104.8	103.3	102.5	95.7	97.9	100.1	104.8	103.3
0950, 0980	Ceilings & Acoustic Treatment	84.3	104.8	97.8	94.2	104.8	101.2	95.4	95.7	95.6	84.3	104.8	97.8	99.1	95.7	96.9	84.3	104.8	97.8
0960	Flooring	98.3	51.7	85.0	99.8	57.7	87.7	100.0	114.3	104.1	97.5	51.7	84.4	98.6	114.3	103.1	97.9	51.7	84.7
0970, 0990	Wall Finishes & Painting/Coating	105.0	137.1	124.4	96.4	38.4	61.4	105.0	44.1	68.3	105.0	137.1	124.4	102.0	44.1	67.1	105.0	137.1	124.4
09	FINISHES	95.9	97.8	97.0	96.5	83.7	89.5	98.9	94.8	96.6	95.4	97.8	96.7	98.8	94.8	96.6	95.2	97.8	96.6
COVERS	DIVS. 10 - 14, 25, 28, 41, 43, 44, 46	100.0	106.4	101.3	100.0	100.8	100.2	100.0	109.8	102.0	100.0	106.4	101.3	100.0	109.8	102.0	100.0	106.4	101.3
21, 22, 23	FIRE SUPPRESSION, PLUMBING & HVAC	95.4	73.2	86.4	95.3	76.6	87.8	100.1	74.3	89.7	95.4	73.2	86.4	100.0	74.3	89.6	95.4	73.2	86.4
26, 27, 3370	ELECTRICAL, COMMUNICATIONS & UTIL.	99.2	80.1	89.1	97.0	80.1	88.1	99.3	80.1	89.1	99.2	80.1	89.1	98.9	80.1	89.0	99.1	80.1	89.1
MF2014	WEIGHTED AVERAGE	97.2	85.6	92.1	95.2	84.7	90.6	99.6	90.1	95.5	97.1	85.5	92.0	102.0	90.1	96.8	96.3	85.5	91.6

		MAINE			MARYLAND														
		WATERVILLE			ANNAPOLIS			BALTIMORE			COLLEGE PARK			CUMBERLAND			EASTON		
	DIVISION	049			214			210 - 212			207 - 208			215			216		
		MAT.	INST.	TOTAL	MAT.	INST.	TOTAL	MAT.	INST.	TOTAL	MAT.	INST.	TOTAL	MAT.	INST.	TOTAL	MAT.	INST.	TOTAL
015433	CONTRACTOR EQUIPMENT		100.9	100.9		99.8	99.8		103.4	103.4		105.5	105.5		99.8	99.8		99.8	99.8
0241, 31 - 34	SITE & INFRASTRUCTURE, DEMOLITION	92.8	101.1	98.7	103.0	91.5	94.9	101.5	95.6	97.3	100.5	94.5	96.2	94.3	91.8	92.5	101.4	88.6	92.3
0310	Concrete Forming & Accessories	88.4	94.8	93.9	97.2	73.6	76.8	101.4	71.1	75.3	84.3	70.2	72.2	91.4	81.0	82.4	89.2	70.2	72.8
0320	Concrete Reinforcing	87.7	106.7	97.3	100.3	80.7	90.3	105.6	80.7	92.9	105.4	78.1	91.5	86.6	72.3	79.3	86.0	79.0	82.4
0330	Cast-in-Place Concrete	82.3	58.8	72.6	110.0	75.7	95.9	107.5	76.4	94.7	116.5	77.5	100.4	91.7	85.6	89.2	101.8	48.1	79.8
03	CONCRETE	95.6	84.1	90.0	104.8	76.6	90.9	104.8	75.8	90.6	107.5	75.5	91.8	90.2	81.8	86.1	98.0	65.2	81.9
04	MASONRY	112.2	63.6	81.9	103.5	71.6	83.6	100.1	71.7	82.4	111.8	69.0	85.1	99.1	83.8	89.5	113.4	42.9	69.4
05	METALS	94.8	86.6	92.3	104.0	93.4	100.8	100.6	93.9	98.5	86.8	97.4	90.0	98.5	90.5	96.1	98.8	87.2	95.2
06	WOOD, PLASTICS & COMPOSITES	84.0	105.3	95.9	92.9	75.4	83.1	99.6	72.1	84.2	80.0	70.0	74.4	84.9	80.1	82.2	82.7	77.4	79.7
07	THERMAL & MOISTURE PROTECTION	97.9	65.0	84.4	100.2	78.8	91.4	101.9	78.6	92.3	101.9	78.7	92.4	100.2	78.9	91.5	100.3	59.0	83.4
08	OPENINGS	102.9	87.9	99.4	105.8	80.3	99.9	99.0	78.5	94.2	94.3	74.8	89.7	99.7	78.0	94.7	98.0	71.4	91.8
0920	Plaster & Gypsum Board	95.5	104.8	101.8	100.5	74.9	83.2	102.3	71.3	81.4	99.0	69.0	78.8	102.3	79.8	87.1	102.3	77.0	85.2
0950, 0980	Ceilings & Acoustic Treatment	84.3	104.8	97.8	91.3	74.9	80.6	94.0	71.3	79.1	102.2	69.0	80.4	93.3	79.8	84.4	93.3	77.0	82.6
0960	Flooring	95.0	55.3	83.6	99.8	77.2	93.3	100.7	77.2	94.0	97.8	79.7	92.6	95.5	90.8	94.2	94.7	51.7	82.4
0970, 0990	Wall Finishes & Painting/Coating	105.0	63.3	79.8	92.1	79.2	84.3	97.9	79.2	86.6	108.0	77.6	89.7	96.5	73.4	82.5	96.5	77.6	85.1
09	FINISHES	94.3	85.8	89.6	94.8	74.3	83.5	100.1	72.3	84.8	95.3	71.9	82.4	96.5	81.9	88.5	96.7	69.1	81.5
COVERS	DIVS. 10 - 14, 25, 28, 41, 43, 44, 46	100.0	100.5	100.1	100.0	86.2	97.2	100.0	86.2	97.2	100.0	85.5	97.1	100.0	90.5	98.1	100.0	75.3	95.0
21, 22, 23	FIRE SUPPRESSION, PLUMBING & HVAC	95.4	64.2	82.8	100.1	80.5	92.2	100.0	80.6	92.2	95.4	83.6	90.7	95.2	73.0	86.3	95.2	68.3	84.4
26, 27, 3370	ELECTRICAL, COMMUNICATIONS & UTIL.	99.2	80.1	89.1	99.5	91.9	95.5	102.0	91.9	96.6	101.1	99.7	100.4	98.3	81.8	89.6	97.8	65.2	80.5
MF2014	WEIGHTED AVERAGE	97.5	79.5	89.7	101.5	82.0	93.0	100.8	81.9	92.6	97.2	83.4	91.2	96.8	81.8	90.2	98.3	68.6	85.3

		MARYLAND														MASSACHUSETTS		
		ELKTON			HAGERSTOWN			SALISBURY			SILVER SPRING			WALDORF			BOSTON		
	DIVISION	219			217			218			209			206			020 - 022, 024		
		MAT.	INST.	TOTAL	MAT.	INST.	TOTAL	MAT.	INST.	TOTAL	MAT.	INST.	TOTAL	MAT.	INST.	TOTAL	MAT.	INST.	TOTAL
015433	CONTRACTOR EQUIPMENT		99.8	99.8		99.8	99.8		99.8	99.8		98.1	98.1		98.1	98.1		106.5	106.5
0241, 31 - 34	SITE & INFRASTRUCTURE, DEMOLITION	88.4	89.5	89.2	92.6	92.3	92.4	101.3	88.6	92.3	89.0	87.6	88.0	95.4	87.3	89.7	98.9	109.1	106.2
0310	Concrete Forming & Accessories	95.4	81.0	82.9	90.3	75.1	77.2	103.9	51.7	58.9	92.8	70.4	73.5	100.2	68.7	73.0	102.7	143.8	138.1
0320	Concrete Reinforcing	86.0	105.3	95.8	86.6	72.3	79.3	86.0	63.5	74.6	104.1	77.9	90.8	104.8	78.0	91.1	108.9	155.8	132.8
0330	Cast-in-Place Concrete	82.5	75.2	79.5	87.4	85.7	86.7	101.8	46.7	79.2	119.3	79.3	102.8	133.6	76.5	110.2	104.0	151.2	123.4
03	CONCRETE	83.3	84.3	83.8	86.8	79.2	83.0	99.0	53.7	76.8	105.9	76.1	91.2	116.5	74.4	95.8	105.7	147.5	126.2
04	MASONRY	98.3	58.9	73.8	105.3	83.8	91.9	113.1	47.3	72.1	110.9	72.3	86.8	95.4	67.2	77.9	106.6	164.2	142.5
05	METALS	98.8	101.3	99.6	98.7	90.7	96.2	98.8	81.2	93.4	91.0	93.8	91.9	91.0	93.9	91.9	100.2	132.4	110.1
06	WOOD, PLASTICS & COMPOSITES	90.0	86.8	88.3	84.0	71.9	77.2	100.6	55.1	75.1	86.5	69.2	76.8	94.0	69.2	80.1	98.6	143.3	123.6
07	THERMAL & MOISTURE PROTECTION	99.9	73.5	89.1	100.0	76.8	90.5	100.6	63.7	85.4	105.4	84.9	97.0	105.8	82.7	96.4	103.4	151.9	123.3
08	OPENINGS	98.0	81.3	94.1	98.0	73.0	92.2	98.2	61.7	89.7	85.7	74.3	83.0	86.2	74.3	83.5	101.4	146.2	111.8
0920	Plaster & Gypsum Board	105.2	86.7	92.7	102.3	71.3	81.4	111.6	54.0	72.6	105.1	69.0	80.7	108.3	69.0	81.8	107.5	144.1	132.2
0950, 0980	Ceilings & Acoustic Treatment	93.3	86.7	89.0	94.3	71.3	79.2	93.3	54.0	67.5	112.2	69.0	80.4	112.2	69.0	83.8	106.1	144.1	131.1
0960	Flooring	97.0	58.5	86.0	95.2	90.8	93.9	94.0	64.7	90.4	104.1	79.7	97.2	107.7	79.0	99.5	97.9	182.7	122.2
0970, 0990	Wall Finishes & Painting/Coating	96.5	77.6	85.1	96.5	77.6	85.1	96.5	77.6	85.1	115.8	77.6	92.8	115.8	77.6	92.8	104.4	155.9	135.4
09	FINISHES	96.9	76.9	85.9	96.4	77.5	86.0	99.8	56.3	75.8	96.9	71.4	82.8	98.6	70.7	83.2	104.2	152.7	130.9
COVERS	DIVS. 10 - 14, 25, 28, 41, 43, 44, 46	100.0	59.9	91.9	100.0	89.6	97.9	100.0	38.7	87.6	100.0	84.7	96.9	100.0	83.0	96.6	100.0	119.4	103.9
21, 22, 23	FIRE SUPPRESSION, PLUMBING & HVAC	95.2	80.5	89.3	100.0	86.2	94.4	95.2	59.9	81.0	95.4	84.8	91.2	95.4	82.3	90.1	100.1	132.4	113.1
26, 27, 3370	ELECTRICAL, COMMUNICATIONS & UTIL.	99.6	91.9	95.5	98.1	81.8	89.5	96.5	67.1	81.0	98.4	99.7	99.1	95.7	99.7	97.8	100.8	135.4	119.1
MF2014	WEIGHTED AVERAGE	95.9	81.9	89.8	97.6	83.3	91.4	98.7	62.1	82.7	96.5	83.2	90.7	97.1	81.7	90.4	101.6	139.5	118.1

For customer support on your Site Work & Landscape Cost Data, call 877.737.1594.

763

MASSACHUSETTS

DIVISION		BROCKTON 023			BUZZARDS BAY 025			FALL RIVER 027			FITCHBURG 014			FRAMINGHAM 017			GREENFIELD 013		
		MAT.	INST.	TOTAL	MAT.	INST.	TOTAL	MAT.	INST.	TOTAL	MAT.	INST.	TOTAL	MAT.	INST.	TOTAL	MAT.	INST.	TOTAL
015433	CONTRACTOR EQUIPMENT		102.7	102.7		102.7	102.7		103.7	103.7		100.9	100.9		101.9	101.9		100.9	100.9
0241, 31 - 34	SITE & INFRASTRUCTURE, DEMOLITION	94.5	105.7	102.4	84.8	105.6	99.6	93.5	105.8	102.2	86.3	105.6	100.0	83.0	105.3	98.9	90.0	104.3	100.1
0310	Concrete Forming & Accessories	101.6	138.7	133.6	99.2	138.5	133.1	101.6	138.8	133.6	93.8	130.8	125.7	101.2	138.8	133.6	92.1	113.2	110.3
0320	Concrete Reinforcing	106.4	155.6	131.4	85.3	160.1	123.4	106.4	160.2	133.7	83.9	151.4	118.3	83.9	155.6	120.4	87.3	124.4	106.2
0330	Cast-in-Place Concrete	97.7	151.5	119.8	81.2	151.5	110.1	94.5	152.0	118.1	85.9	150.5	112.4	85.9	148.3	111.5	88.3	131.2	105.9
03	CONCRETE	101.8	145.2	123.1	86.2	145.9	115.5	100.3	146.2	122.9	85.9	140.4	112.7	88.7	144.1	116.0	89.6	120.9	104.9
04	MASONRY	101.7	160.0	138.0	94.4	160.0	135.3	102.6	159.9	138.3	101.0	159.0	137.2	107.2	160.1	140.1	105.4	136.0	124.4
05	METALS	97.4	130.0	107.5	92.3	131.7	104.4	97.4	132.1	108.1	95.5	125.5	104.7	95.5	130.0	106.2	97.8	110.4	101.7
06	WOOD, PLASTICS & COMPOSITES	99.1	138.4	121.1	96.1	138.4	119.8	99.1	138.7	121.3	93.7	128.3	113.1	100.1	138.2	121.4	91.5	110.9	102.4
07	THERMAL & MOISTURE PROTECTION	100.9	148.7	120.5	100.1	147.0	119.4	100.8	146.3	119.5	99.2	141.5	116.5	99.3	149.1	119.7	99.2	121.9	108.5
08	OPENINGS	102.2	143.5	111.9	97.9	139.2	107.5	102.2	139.3	110.9	104.6	137.0	112.2	94.9	143.4	106.2	104.7	115.0	107.1
0920	Plaster & Gypsum Board	93.7	139.0	124.3	89.5	139.0	123.0	93.7	139.0	124.3	100.3	128.6	119.4	102.8	139.0	127.3	101.0	110.7	107.5
0950, 0980	Ceilings & Acoustic Treatment	102.2	139.0	126.4	88.2	139.0	121.6	102.2	139.0	126.4	89.0	128.6	115.0	89.0	139.0	121.9	97.4	110.7	106.1
0960	Flooring	98.6	182.7	122.7	96.7	182.7	121.3	97.7	182.7	122.0	98.1	182.7	122.3	99.7	182.7	123.5	97.3	154.0	113.5
0970, 0990	Wall Finishes & Painting/Coating	99.9	155.1	133.2	99.9	155.1	133.2	99.9	155.1	133.2	99.5	155.1	133.1	100.5	155.1	133.5	99.5	115.8	109.4
09	FINISHES	98.9	149.1	126.6	94.2	149.1	124.4	98.7	149.3	126.6	94.6	143.1	121.3	95.3	148.9	124.8	96.7	121.0	110.0
COVERS	DIVS. 10 - 14, 25, 28, 41, 43, 44, 46	100.0	117.9	103.6	100.0	117.9	103.6	100.0	118.5	103.7	100.0	109.0	101.8	100.0	117.5	103.5	100.0	104.6	100.9
21, 22, 23	FIRE SUPPRESSION, PLUMBING & HVAC	100.1	111.1	104.6	95.4	111.1	101.7	100.1	111.2	104.6	96.0	113.6	103.1	96.0	126.1	108.1	96.0	102.8	98.7
26, 27, 3370	ELECTRICAL, COMMUNICATIONS & UTIL.	99.3	100.1	99.7	96.3	100.1	98.3	99.2	100.1	99.7	100.1	105.1	102.8	96.6	128.9	113.7	100.1	98.9	99.5
MF2014	WEIGHTED AVERAGE	99.9	128.1	112.2	94.4	128.1	109.1	99.7	128.3	112.2	96.5	126.5	109.6	95.7	135.1	112.9	97.7	112.3	104.1

MASSACHUSETTS

DIVISION		HYANNIS 026			LAWRENCE 019			LOWELL 018			NEW BEDFORD 027			PITTSFIELD 012			SPRINGFIELD 010 - 011		
		MAT.	INST.	TOTAL	MAT.	INST.	TOTAL	MAT.	INST.	TOTAL	MAT.	INST.	TOTAL	MAT.	INST.	TOTAL	MAT.	INST.	TOTAL
015433	CONTRACTOR EQUIPMENT		102.7	102.7		102.7	102.7		100.9	100.9		103.7	103.7		100.9	100.9		100.9	100.9
0241, 31 - 34	SITE & INFRASTRUCTURE, DEMOLITION	90.9	105.6	101.3	95.2	105.7	102.7	94.2	105.7	102.3	92.1	105.8	101.8	95.2	104.2	101.6	94.6	104.4	101.6
0310	Concrete Forming & Accessories	93.5	138.5	132.3	102.4	139.0	134.0	99.0	139.0	133.5	101.6	138.8	133.6	99.0	112.2	110.4	99.3	113.6	111.6
0320	Concrete Reinforcing	85.3	160.1	123.4	103.8	150.4	127.5	104.6	150.4	127.9	106.4	160.2	133.7	86.6	122.3	104.8	104.6	124.4	114.7
0330	Cast-in-Place Concrete	89.1	151.5	114.7	99.4	148.9	119.7	90.3	148.9	114.4	83.3	152.0	111.5	98.5	129.7	111.3	94.0	131.7	109.5
03	CONCRETE	92.4	145.9	118.7	103.7	143.5	123.2	95.1	143.3	118.8	95.0	146.2	120.2	96.2	119.5	107.6	96.9	121.2	108.8
04	MASONRY	100.6	160.0	137.6	112.3	160.7	142.5	100.2	160.0	137.5	100.6	159.9	137.6	100.9	133.2	121.0	100.5	136.9	123.2
05	METALS	93.7	131.7	105.4	98.2	128.3	107.5	98.2	126.0	106.7	97.4	132.1	108.1	98.0	109.5	101.5	100.9	110.4	103.8
06	WOOD, PLASTICS & COMPOSITES	89.3	138.4	116.8	100.6	138.4	121.8	99.8	138.4	121.4	99.1	138.7	121.3	99.8	110.9	106.0	99.8	110.9	106.0
07	THERMAL & MOISTURE PROTECTION	100.4	147.0	119.5	99.7	148.5	119.7	99.5	148.6	119.7	100.7	146.3	119.4	99.6	120.7	108.2	99.5	122.2	108.8
08	OPENINGS	98.5	139.2	108.0	99.0	142.1	109.0	105.9	142.1	114.4	102.2	139.3	110.9	105.9	114.4	107.9	105.9	115.0	108.0
0920	Plaster & Gypsum Board	85.2	139.0	121.6	105.6	139.0	128.2	105.6	139.0	128.2	93.7	139.0	124.3	105.6	110.7	109.0	105.6	110.7	109.0
0950, 0980	Ceilings & Acoustic Treatment	93.8	139.0	123.5	99.3	139.0	125.4	99.3	139.0	125.4	102.2	139.0	126.4	99.3	110.7	106.8	99.3	110.7	106.8
0960	Flooring	94.4	182.7	119.6	100.2	182.7	123.8	100.2	182.7	123.8	97.7	182.7	122.0	100.6	154.0	115.9	99.7	154.0	115.3
0970, 0990	Wall Finishes & Painting/Coating	99.9	155.1	133.2	99.6	155.1	133.1	99.5	155.1	133.1	99.9	155.1	133.2	99.5	115.8	109.4	100.9	115.8	109.9
09	FINISHES	94.4	149.1	124.6	98.8	149.1	126.5	98.7	149.1	126.5	98.6	149.3	126.5	98.8	120.3	110.6	98.7	121.2	111.1
COVERS	DIVS. 10 - 14, 25, 28, 41, 43, 44, 46	100.0	117.9	103.6	100.0	118.1	103.6	100.0	118.1	103.6	100.0	118.5	103.7	100.0	103.7	100.7	100.0	104.9	101.0
21, 22, 23	FIRE SUPPRESSION, PLUMBING & HVAC	100.1	111.1	104.6	100.1	124.8	110.0	100.1	125.7	110.4	100.1	111.2	104.6	100.1	101.4	100.6	100.1	103.3	101.4
26, 27, 3370	ELECTRICAL, COMMUNICATIONS & UTIL.	96.8	100.1	98.5	99.1	128.9	114.9	99.6	128.9	115.1	100.0	100.1	100.1	99.6	98.9	99.2	99.7	98.9	99.2
MF2014	WEIGHTED AVERAGE	97.0	128.1	110.6	100.3	134.6	115.3	99.5	134.5	114.8	99.1	128.3	111.8	99.7	111.3	104.8	100.2	112.6	105.6

MASSACHUSETTS / MICHIGAN

DIVISION		WORCESTER 015 - 016			ANN ARBOR 481			BATTLE CREEK 490			BAY CITY 487			DEARBORN 481			DETROIT 482		
		MAT.	INST.	TOTAL	MAT.	INST.	TOTAL	MAT.	INST.	TOTAL	MAT.	INST.	TOTAL	MAT.	INST.	TOTAL	MAT.	INST.	TOTAL
015433	CONTRACTOR EQUIPMENT		100.9	100.9		110.7	110.7		102.8	102.8		110.7	110.7		110.7	110.7		98.8	98.8
0241, 31 - 34	SITE & INFRASTRUCTURE, DEMOLITION	94.6	105.6	102.4	82.3	98.8	94.0	93.3	87.5	89.2	73.9	97.8	90.9	82.1	98.9	94.1	94.7	100.6	98.9
0310	Concrete Forming & Accessories	99.6	130.7	126.5	98.3	111.6	109.8	97.6	87.6	89.0	98.4	87.1	88.6	98.2	115.8	113.3	100.8	115.8	113.7
0320	Concrete Reinforcing	104.6	150.6	128.0	92.3	120.1	106.5	91.4	93.3	92.4	92.3	119.2	106.0	92.3	120.2	106.5	94.9	120.1	107.8
0330	Cast-in-Place Concrete	93.5	150.5	116.9	88.8	107.4	96.4	99.0	100.4	99.6	85.0	90.6	87.3	86.8	109.9	96.3	94.1	109.9	100.6
03	CONCRETE	96.6	140.2	118.0	93.5	112.0	102.6	98.1	92.5	95.4	91.7	95.2	93.4	92.6	114.7	103.5	96.6	113.6	105.0
04	MASONRY	100.0	159.0	136.8	104.4	108.4	106.9	105.2	87.0	94.0	104.0	87.0	93.4	104.3	111.6	108.9	97.9	111.6	106.5
05	METALS	101.0	125.2	108.4	94.2	118.8	101.8	98.3	87.6	95.0	94.8	115.4	101.2	94.3	119.1	101.9	94.9	102.1	97.1
06	WOOD, PLASTICS & COMPOSITES	100.3	128.3	116.0	97.5	112.8	106.0	96.5	87.2	91.3	97.5	86.5	91.3	97.5	116.8	108.3	103.0	116.8	110.7
07	THERMAL & MOISTURE PROTECTION	99.5	141.5	116.7	100.4	108.2	103.6	94.6	84.8	90.6	98.2	92.4	95.8	98.9	115.7	105.8	97.7	115.7	105.1
08	OPENINGS	105.9	136.7	113.1	100.1	110.4	101.9	96.6	82.3	93.3	99.4	93.9	98.1	99.4	112.6	102.5	99.2	112.9	102.4
0920	Plaster & Gypsum Board	105.6	128.6	121.2	103.8	112.4	109.6	93.7	82.9	86.4	103.8	85.3	91.3	103.8	116.6	112.4	100.5	116.6	111.3
0950, 0980	Ceilings & Acoustic Treatment	99.3	128.6	118.5	88.7	112.4	104.3	96.3	82.9	87.5	89.7	85.3	86.8	88.7	116.6	107.0	91.2	116.6	107.9
0960	Flooring	100.2	179.8	123.0	97.5	117.6	103.2	105.7	91.9	101.7	97.5	81.5	92.9	96.9	113.9	101.8	95.9	113.9	101.1
0970, 0990	Wall Finishes & Painting/Coating	99.5	155.1	133.1	96.2	98.7	97.7	107.9	81.9	92.2	96.2	82.0	87.6	96.2	100.8	99.0	97.3	100.8	99.4
09	FINISHES	98.7	142.5	122.9	92.8	111.6	103.1	98.0	87.6	92.3	92.6	84.8	88.3	92.6	114.3	104.5	93.9	114.3	105.1
COVERS	DIVS. 10 - 14, 25, 28, 41, 43, 44, 46	100.0	109.0	101.8	100.0	105.8	101.2	100.0	96.4	99.3	100.0	94.1	98.8	100.0	107.1	101.4	100.0	107.1	101.4
21, 22, 23	FIRE SUPPRESSION, PLUMBING & HVAC	100.1	113.6	105.5	100.0	98.8	99.5	100.0	87.4	94.9	100.0	83.6	93.4	100.0	109.2	103.7	100.0	110.2	104.1
26, 27, 3370	ELECTRICAL, COMMUNICATIONS & UTIL.	99.7	105.1	102.5	96.3	108.8	102.9	94.4	83.7	88.8	95.2	90.3	92.6	96.3	107.0	101.9	98.2	107.0	102.9
MF2014	WEIGHTED AVERAGE	100.2	126.4	111.6	97.1	107.5	101.7	98.3	87.6	93.7	96.6	91.7	94.5	97.0	111.0	103.1	97.8	109.6	102.9

MICHIGAN

DIVISION		FLINT 484 - 485			GAYLORD 497			GRAND RAPIDS 493,495			IRON MOUNTAIN 498 - 499			JACKSON 492			KALAMAZOO 491		
		MAT.	INST.	TOTAL	MAT.	INST.	TOTAL	MAT.	INST.	TOTAL	MAT.	INST.	TOTAL	MAT.	INST.	TOTAL	MAT.	INST.	TOTAL
015433	CONTRACTOR EQUIPMENT		110.7	110.7		104.7	104.7		102.8	102.8		93.7	93.7		104.7	104.7		102.8	102.8
0241, 31 - 34	SITE & INFRASTRUCTURE, DEMOLITION	71.7	98.0	90.4	88.5	85.0	86.0	93.2	87.6	89.2	96.1	93.7	94.4	109.4	87.3	93.7	93.6	87.5	89.3
0310	Concrete Forming & Accessories	101.3	89.9	91.5	95.5	77.3	79.8	97.1	84.6	86.3	87.8	85.0	85.4	92.5	86.7	87.5	97.6	87.3	88.7
0320	Concrete Reinforcing	92.3	119.6	106.2	85.2	118.6	102.2	97.8	93.2	95.5	85.0	99.8	92.5	82.8	119.4	101.4	91.4	93.4	92.4
0330	Cast-in-Place Concrete	89.4	92.4	90.6	98.7	86.1	93.5	104.1	97.6	101.4	116.8	85.4	103.9	98.6	92.2	96.0	101.0	98.8	100.1
03	CONCRETE	94.0	97.1	95.5	94.6	88.9	91.8	101.6	90.2	96.0	104.3	87.9	96.2	89.3	95.4	92.3	101.6	91.8	96.8
04	MASONRY	104.5	96.5	99.5	116.2	79.1	93.1	102.0	87.4	92.9	101.2	86.1	91.8	95.1	91.6	92.9	103.8	89.1	94.6
05	METALS	94.3	116.3	101.0	99.7	109.9	102.8	95.3	87.1	92.8	99.0	89.6	96.1	99.9	114.1	104.2	98.3	86.5	94.7
06	WOOD, PLASTICS & COMPOSITES	100.9	88.2	93.8	89.4	76.8	82.4	97.7	83.2	89.6	85.0	85.1	85.0	88.1	84.7	86.2	96.5	87.2	91.3
07	THERMAL & MOISTURE PROTECTION	98.2	96.3	97.4	93.2	74.5	85.5	97.4	76.6	88.9	96.7	81.4	90.4	92.5	92.6	92.5	94.6	85.1	90.7
08	OPENINGS	99.4	95.6	98.5	97.5	75.1	92.3	103.4	84.7	99.0	104.6	76.0	98.0	96.5	93.1	95.7	96.6	81.7	93.1
0920	Plaster & Gypsum Board	105.2	87.1	93.0	93.4	74.9	80.9	95.4	78.8	84.2	51.7	85.2	74.3	91.7	82.9	85.8	93.7	82.9	86.4
0950, 0980	Ceilings & Acoustic Treatment	88.7	87.1	87.6	95.4	74.9	81.9	104.3	78.8	87.5	94.4	85.2	88.3	95.4	82.9	87.2	96.3	82.9	87.5
0960	Flooring	97.5	95.8	97.0	97.8	92.4	96.2	105.5	85.7	99.8	122.4	93.8	114.2	96.5	82.7	92.6	105.7	82.7	99.1
0970, 0990	Wall Finishes & Painting/Coating	96.2	85.4	89.7	103.8	82.0	90.6	109.7	80.8	92.3	126.1	72.1	93.5	103.8	96.8	99.6	107.9	81.9	92.2
09	FINISHES	92.1	89.8	90.9	97.4	79.1	87.3	101.6	84.2	92.0	100.0	85.3	91.9	98.3	86.2	91.6	98.0	85.6	91.2
COVERS	DIVS. 10 - 14, 25, 28, 41, 43, 44, 46	100.0	95.5	99.1	100.0	88.6	97.7	100.0	96.4	99.3	100.0	87.2	97.4	100.0	100.9	100.2	100.0	96.4	99.3
21, 22, 23	FIRE SUPPRESSION, PLUMBING & HVAC	100.0	89.6	95.8	95.6	78.4	88.6	100.0	83.0	93.1	95.5	85.3	91.4	95.6	88.4	92.7	100.0	80.8	92.3
26, 27, 3370	ELECTRICAL, COMMUNICATIONS & UTIL.	96.3	96.0	96.1	92.4	79.1	85.4	99.7	79.1	88.8	98.7	84.3	91.1	96.3	108.8	102.9	94.3	81.8	87.7
MF2014	WEIGHTED AVERAGE	96.8	96.0	96.4	97.2	83.6	91.3	99.7	85.1	93.3	99.3	86.2	93.6	96.5	95.1	95.9	98.7	85.7	93.0

MICHIGAN / MINNESOTA

DIVISION		LANSING 488 - 489			MUSKEGON 494			ROYAL OAK 480,483			SAGINAW 486			TRAVERSE CITY 496			BEMIDJI 566		
		MAT.	INST.	TOTAL	MAT.	INST.	TOTAL	MAT.	INST.	TOTAL	MAT.	INST.	TOTAL	MAT.	INST.	TOTAL	MAT.	INST.	TOTAL
015433	CONTRACTOR EQUIPMENT		110.7	110.7		102.8	102.8		96.2	96.2		110.7	110.7		93.7	93.7		98.2	98.2
0241, 31 - 34	SITE & INFRASTRUCTURE, DEMOLITION	95.6	98.0	97.3	91.2	87.5	88.5	86.5	98.4	95.0	74.9	97.8	91.2	82.4	93.2	90.0	95.4	97.5	96.9
0310	Concrete Forming & Accessories	98.2	89.7	90.9	98.0	84.1	86.0	94.1	112.6	110.1	98.3	87.6	89.1	87.8	75.2	76.9	86.1	89.6	89.1
0320	Concrete Reinforcing	94.3	119.4	107.1	92.1	93.3	92.7	83.7	119.9	102.1	92.3	119.2	106.0	86.3	92.5	89.5	93.7	106.6	100.2
0330	Cast-in-Place Concrete	103.5	92.1	98.8	98.6	94.8	97.1	77.8	106.3	89.5	87.7	90.5	88.9	91.2	78.2	85.9	106.0	103.0	104.8
03	CONCRETE	100.8	96.9	98.9	96.4	89.1	92.8	80.5	110.8	95.4	93.0	95.4	94.2	85.8	79.8	82.9	97.6	98.5	98.1
04	MASONRY	106.6	94.2	98.9	102.2	88.5	93.7	98.2	112.0	106.8	106.0	87.0	94.1	99.2	82.4	88.7	102.5	103.7	103.3
05	METALS	93.9	115.6	100.6	96.0	87.2	93.3	97.3	98.0	97.5	94.3	115.2	100.7	99.0	88.2	95.7	92.1	120.0	100.7
06	WOOD, PLASTICS & COMPOSITES	96.3	88.8	92.1	93.2	83.4	87.7	93.0	113.1	104.3	93.8	87.6	90.3	85.0	75.1	79.4	71.3	85.5	79.3
07	THERMAL & MOISTURE PROTECTION	98.6	89.6	94.9	93.6	78.9	87.6	96.8	111.2	102.7	99.0	92.6	96.4	95.8	71.7	85.9	104.7	95.4	100.9
08	OPENINGS	103.2	95.1	101.3	95.8	84.5	93.2	99.3	109.4	101.7	97.4	94.5	96.7	104.6	70.6	96.7	100.2	107.2	101.8
0920	Plaster & Gypsum Board	96.9	87.7	90.7	75.7	79.0	77.9	101.3	112.7	109.0	103.8	86.4	92.1	51.7	74.9	67.3	102.2	85.3	90.8
0950, 0980	Ceilings & Acoustic Treatment	94.0	87.7	89.8	97.1	79.0	85.2	88.0	112.7	104.3	88.7	86.4	87.2	94.4	74.9	81.6	122.8	85.3	98.2
0960	Flooring	106.6	85.7	100.6	104.5	85.7	99.1	94.8	113.9	100.3	97.5	81.5	92.9	122.4	94.9	114.5	104.4	120.8	109.1
0970, 0990	Wall Finishes & Painting/Coating	108.0	80.8	91.6	106.3	80.8	90.9	97.6	96.8	97.1	96.2	82.0	87.6	126.1	44.7	76.9	102.2	95.9	98.4
09	FINISHES	98.3	87.6	92.4	94.7	83.2	88.4	91.7	111.5	102.6	92.4	85.5	88.6	99.0	74.1	85.3	106.2	95.2	100.1
COVERS	DIVS. 10 - 14, 25, 28, 41, 43, 44, 46	100.0	100.6	100.1	100.0	96.0	99.2	100.0	103.0	100.6	100.0	94.3	98.8	100.0	84.6	96.9	100.0	96.9	99.4
21, 22, 23	FIRE SUPPRESSION, PLUMBING & HVAC	99.9	88.6	95.3	99.9	82.3	92.8	95.6	107.2	100.3	100.0	83.1	93.2	95.5	77.7	88.3	95.6	83.4	90.6
26, 27, 3370	ELECTRICAL, COMMUNICATIONS & UTIL.	98.6	93.3	95.8	94.8	79.1	86.5	98.4	104.4	101.6	93.9	90.5	92.1	94.0	79.1	86.1	104.3	104.6	104.5
MF2014	WEIGHTED AVERAGE	99.3	94.7	97.3	97.2	84.8	91.8	94.9	106.9	100.1	96.4	91.8	94.4	96.3	80.1	89.3	98.2	98.2	98.2

MINNESOTA

DIVISION		BRAINERD 564			DETROIT LAKES 565			DULUTH 556 - 558			MANKATO 560			MINNEAPOLIS 553 - 555			ROCHESTER 559		
		MAT.	INST.	TOTAL	MAT.	INST.	TOTAL	MAT.	INST.	TOTAL	MAT.	INST.	TOTAL	MAT.	INST.	TOTAL	MAT.	INST.	TOTAL
015433	CONTRACTOR EQUIPMENT		100.8	100.8		98.2	98.2		99.1	99.1		100.8	100.8		102.6	102.6		99.1	99.1
0241, 31 - 34	SITE & INFRASTRUCTURE, DEMOLITION	96.9	102.2	100.7	93.6	97.9	96.6	100.6	99.4	99.7	93.8	102.9	100.3	97.9	104.7	102.8	97.4	99.0	98.5
0310	Concrete Forming & Accessories	87.7	91.6	91.1	83.1	91.6	90.4	98.7	109.9	108.4	95.6	109.1	107.3	100.7	128.6	124.8	99.3	106.5	105.5
0320	Concrete Reinforcing	92.5	106.7	99.7	93.7	106.6	100.2	97.4	107.1	102.3	92.4	116.2	104.5	92.2	116.6	104.6	91.7	116.4	104.3
0330	Cast-in-Place Concrete	115.2	106.7	111.7	102.9	106.1	104.2	114.8	106.0	111.2	106.2	107.3	106.6	109.6	117.4	112.8	112.3	99.4	107.0
03	CONCRETE	101.7	100.7	101.2	95.2	100.4	97.8	106.5	108.7	107.6	97.2	106.1	101.5	103.4	122.8	112.9	102.5	106.8	104.6
04	MASONRY	126.4	112.0	117.4	126.3	110.1	116.2	107.6	117.6	113.9	114.5	110.4	112.0	109.0	126.7	120.1	104.5	114.1	110.5
05	METALS	93.2	120.0	101.5	92.1	120.0	100.6	101.7	122.4	108.0	93.1	125.5	103.0	99.1	128.9	108.3	100.4	127.3	108.7
06	WOOD, PLASTICS & COMPOSITES	89.4	85.3	87.1	68.4	85.5	78.0	98.2	109.3	104.4	98.8	96.4	97.5	106.7	127.4	118.3	103.2	105.3	104.4
07	THERMAL & MOISTURE PROTECTION	103.4	107.7	105.2	104.6	108.3	106.1	101.6	114.9	107.1	103.8	99.0	101.8	102.8	127.4	112.9	104.9	100.9	103.2
08	OPENINGS	86.9	107.1	91.6	100.2	107.2	101.8	102.5	116.5	105.8	91.5	115.5	97.1	97.1	133.6	105.6	96.4	121.5	102.2
0920	Plaster & Gypsum Board	86.9	85.3	85.8	101.1	85.3	90.5	90.2	110.0	103.6	91.5	96.8	95.1	95.8	128.6	117.9	97.6	105.8	103.2
0950, 0980	Ceilings & Acoustic Treatment	59.3	85.3	76.4	122.8	85.3	98.2	96.1	110.0	105.3	59.3	96.8	84.0	98.2	128.6	118.2	93.2	105.8	101.5
0960	Flooring	103.3	120.8	108.3	103.2	120.8	108.2	101.9	122.1	107.6	105.0	120.8	109.5	97.9	120.8	104.4	102.9	120.8	108.0
0970, 0990	Wall Finishes & Painting/Coating	96.0	95.9	95.9	102.2	95.9	98.4	101.9	110.3	107.0	108.3	104.9	106.3	98.2	126.1	115.1	97.2	104.9	101.9
09	FINISHES	89.4	96.4	93.2	105.5	96.5	100.6	98.3	112.5	106.1	91.1	103.4	97.9	98.6	127.6	114.6	97.4	109.1	103.8
COVERS	DIVS. 10 - 14, 25, 28, 41, 43, 44, 46	100.0	98.3	99.7	100.0	98.6	99.7	100.0	97.6	99.5	100.0	98.6	99.7	100.0	109.7	102.0	100.0	102.8	100.6
21, 22, 23	FIRE SUPPRESSION, PLUMBING & HVAC	94.8	86.1	91.3	95.6	86.0	91.7	99.8	96.5	98.5	94.8	87.7	91.9	99.9	115.6	106.2	99.9	96.2	98.4
26, 27, 3370	ELECTRICAL, COMMUNICATIONS & UTIL.	101.8	102.4	102.1	104.0	67.5	84.7	98.4	102.4	100.6	108.6	89.2	98.3	101.2	111.4	106.6	98.6	89.2	93.6
MF2014	WEIGHTED AVERAGE	96.9	100.5	98.5	98.9	95.1	97.3	101.3	107.3	103.9	97.2	101.3	99.0	100.4	120.0	108.9	99.9	104.7	102.0

For customer support on your Site Work & Landscape Cost Data, call 877.737.1594.

765

		MINNESOTA															MISSISSIPPI		
	DIVISION	SAINT PAUL			ST. CLOUD			THIEF RIVER FALLS			WILLMAR			WINDOM			BILOXI		
		550 - 551			563			567			562			561			395		
		MAT.	INST.	TOTAL	MAT.	INST.	TOTAL	MAT.	INST.	TOTAL	MAT.	INST.	TOTAL	MAT.	INST.	TOTAL	MAT.	INST.	TOTAL
015433	CONTRACTOR EQUIPMENT		99.1	99.1		100.8	100.8		98.2	98.2		100.8	100.8		100.8	100.8		98.8	98.8
0241, 31 - 34	SITE & INFRASTRUCTURE, DEMOLITION	95.2	100.1	98.7	92.5	104.3	100.9	94.4	97.5	96.6	91.8	102.0	99.1	86.0	101.0	96.6	100.6	88.4	91.9
0310	Concrete Forming & Accessories	93.9	123.0	119.0	84.9	117.7	113.2	86.8	89.0	88.7	84.7	91.1	90.2	89.1	84.8	85.4	94.7	52.9	58.7
0320	Concrete Reinforcing	98.9	116.6	107.9	92.6	116.4	104.7	94.0	106.5	100.4	92.2	116.0	104.3	92.2	115.3	104.0	95.0	58.3	76.4
0330	Cast-in-Place Concrete	124.0	116.7	121.0	101.7	114.8	107.1	105.1	88.1	98.1	103.3	85.3	95.9	89.4	66.3	79.9	108.4	54.0	86.0
03	CONCRETE	111.2	120.1	115.5	92.9	116.9	104.7	96.3	93.1	94.7	92.9	94.9	93.9	83.6	85.5	84.5	101.6	55.9	79.2
04	MASONRY	111.7	126.7	121.1	111.1	119.9	116.6	102.4	104.5	103.7	115.4	112.0	113.3	125.8	92.1	104.8	102.7	44.3	66.3
05	METALS	101.1	128.6	109.6	93.9	126.8	104.0	92.2	119.4	100.6	93.0	124.5	102.7	92.9	122.4	102.0	94.9	81.7	90.8
06	WOOD, PLASTICS & COMPOSITES	93.4	119.9	108.2	86.7	114.9	102.5	72.3	85.5	79.7	86.4	85.5	85.9	90.7	82.8	86.3	99.1	56.1	75.0
07	THERMAL & MOISTURE PROTECTION	104.1	126.4	113.3	103.6	117.5	109.3	105.6	98.4	102.7	103.4	108.6	105.5	103.4	89.6	97.7	97.4	56.1	80.4
08	OPENINGS	99.8	129.5	106.7	91.5	126.7	99.7	100.2	107.2	101.8	89.0	91.9	89.7	92.7	90.4	92.2	99.6	57.7	89.8
0920	Plaster & Gypsum Board	88.9	120.9	110.6	86.9	115.8	106.4	101.8	85.3	90.7	86.9	85.6	86.0	86.9	82.8	84.1	101.7	55.2	70.3
0950, 0980	Ceilings & Acoustic Treatment	95.6	120.9	112.3	59.3	115.8	96.4	122.8	85.3	98.2	59.3	85.6	76.6	59.3	82.8	74.7	87.3	55.2	66.2
0960	Flooring	103.7	120.8	108.6	100.0	120.8	105.9	104.1	120.8	108.8	101.6	120.8	107.1	103.9	120.8	108.8	101.4	55.1	88.1
0970, 0990	Wall Finishes & Painting/Coating	105.3	126.1	117.8	108.3	126.1	119.1	102.2	95.9	98.4	102.2	95.9	98.4	102.2	104.9	103.8	99.5	43.5	65.7
09	FINISHES	97.9	123.1	111.8	88.9	119.2	105.6	106.0	95.2	100.0	88.9	94.2	91.8	89.1	91.3	90.3	93.3	52.4	70.8
COVERS	DIVS. 10 - 14, 25, 28, 41, 43, 44, 46	100.0	108.6	101.7	100.0	104.3	100.9	100.0	96.8	99.3	100.0	98.2	99.6	100.0	93.7	98.7	100.0	55.4	91.0
21, 22, 23	FIRE SUPPRESSION, PLUMBING & HVAC	99.9	113.8	105.5	99.6	113.8	105.3	95.6	83.1	90.5	94.8	106.8	99.6	94.8	84.1	90.5	100.0	49.1	79.5
26, 27, 3370	ELECTRICAL, COMMUNICATIONS & UTIL.	97.1	111.4	104.7	101.8	111.4	106.9	101.3	67.5	83.5	101.8	85.2	93.0	108.6	89.2	98.3	103.8	56.9	79.0
MF2014	WEIGHTED AVERAGE	101.4	117.9	108.6	96.9	116.0	105.2	97.8	92.4	95.4	95.5	101.3	98.0	95.9	92.3	94.3	99.2	58.1	81.3

		MISSISSIPPI																	
	DIVISION	CLARKSDALE			COLUMBUS			GREENVILLE			GREENWOOD			JACKSON			LAUREL		
		386			397			387			389			390 - 392			394		
		MAT.	INST.	TOTAL	MAT.	INST.	TOTAL	MAT.	INST.	TOTAL	MAT.	INST.	TOTAL	MAT.	INST.	TOTAL	MAT.	INST.	TOTAL
015433	CONTRACTOR EQUIPMENT		98.8	98.8		98.8	98.8		98.8	98.8		98.8	98.8		98.8	98.8		98.8	98.8
0241, 31 - 34	SITE & INFRASTRUCTURE, DEMOLITION	98.3	88.2	91.1	98.9	88.4	91.5	103.9	88.4	92.9	101.0	87.9	91.7	97.6	88.4	91.1	104.4	88.3	92.9
0310	Concrete Forming & Accessories	85.0	49.2	54.2	83.3	51.2	55.6	81.7	63.7	66.1	94.2	49.2	55.4	93.6	57.5	62.5	83.3	52.9	57.1
0320	Concrete Reinforcing	99.8	41.6	70.1	101.8	42.5	71.6	100.3	60.3	79.9	99.8	52.5	75.7	100.2	56.1	77.7	102.4	39.1	70.2
0330	Cast-in-Place Concrete	105.6	53.5	84.2	110.5	58.6	89.2	108.7	55.6	86.9	113.5	53.2	88.7	98.7	56.8	81.5	108.1	55.2	86.4
03	CONCRETE	98.7	50.9	75.2	103.2	53.7	78.9	104.2	61.6	83.3	105.2	52.7	79.4	97.7	58.5	78.5	106.0	52.7	79.8
04	MASONRY	100.6	45.0	66.0	131.6	51.6	81.7	149.8	49.5	87.3	101.3	44.9	66.1	109.2	49.5	72.0	127.1	48.1	77.9
05	METALS	95.4	73.4	88.6	91.9	74.2	86.5	96.4	82.5	92.1	95.4	74.8	89.0	101.8	80.8	95.4	92.0	73.3	86.3
06	WOOD, PLASTICS & COMPOSITES	82.1	51.2	64.8	83.9	52.2	66.1	78.7	68.1	72.8	95.0	51.2	70.5	96.3	59.6	75.8	85.1	54.6	68.0
07	THERMAL & MOISTURE PROTECTION	95.7	47.2	75.8	97.3	51.5	78.5	96.0	60.0	81.2	96.1	47.1	76.0	97.5	59.2	81.8	97.4	53.1	79.3
08	OPENINGS	97.0	49.4	85.9	98.9	49.5	87.4	97.0	61.4	88.7	97.0	50.7	86.2	103.7	55.6	92.5	95.6	50.3	85.0
0920	Plaster & Gypsum Board	90.2	50.2	63.1	91.3	51.2	64.2	89.8	67.6	74.8	100.9	50.2	66.6	95.0	58.8	70.5	91.3	53.7	65.8
0950, 0980	Ceilings & Acoustic Treatment	82.9	50.2	61.4	82.0	51.2	61.8	85.7	67.6	73.8	82.9	50.2	61.4	89.7	58.8	69.4	82.0	53.7	63.4
0960	Flooring	105.7	52.8	90.6	95.5	59.3	85.1	104.1	52.8	89.4	111.1	52.8	94.4	99.3	55.1	86.7	94.2	52.8	82.4
0970, 0990	Wall Finishes & Painting/Coating	104.4	46.1	69.2	99.5	53.0	71.4	104.4	65.9	81.2	104.4	46.1	69.2	96.5	65.9	78.0	99.5	60.9	76.2
09	FINISHES	94.0	49.9	66.7	89.1	53.2	69.3	94.6	62.9	77.1	97.4	49.9	71.2	93.2	58.3	74.0	89.2	54.3	70.0
COVERS	DIVS. 10 - 14, 25, 28, 41, 43, 44, 46	100.0	55.7	91.1	100.0	56.8	91.3	100.0	58.5	91.6	100.0	55.7	91.1	100.0	57.5	91.4	100.0	37.5	87.4
21, 22, 23	FIRE SUPPRESSION, PLUMBING & HVAC	97.9	41.3	75.1	97.4	37.5	73.3	100.0	47.6	78.8	97.9	39.3	74.3	100.1	57.0	82.7	97.5	45.8	76.6
26, 27, 3370	ELECTRICAL, COMMUNICATIONS & UTIL.	97.1	46.4	70.3	100.8	49.1	73.5	97.1	62.7	78.9	97.1	43.4	68.8	105.4	62.7	82.8	102.6	56.9	78.5
MF2014	WEIGHTED AVERAGE	97.3	52.6	77.8	98.8	53.9	79.2	101.0	61.7	83.9	98.4	52.2	78.3	100.7	62.2	83.9	98.9	55.8	80.1

		MISSISSIPPI									MISSOURI								
	DIVISION	MCCOMB			MERIDIAN			TUPELO			BOWLING GREEN			CAPE GIRARDEAU			CHILLICOTHE		
		396			393			388			633			637			646		
		MAT.	INST.	TOTAL	MAT.	INST.	TOTAL	MAT.	INST.	TOTAL	MAT.	INST.	TOTAL	MAT.	INST.	TOTAL	MAT.	INST.	TOTAL
015433	CONTRACTOR EQUIPMENT		98.8	98.8		98.8	98.8		98.8	98.8		106.9	106.9		106.9	106.9		101.9	101.9
0241, 31 - 34	SITE & INFRASTRUCTURE, DEMOLITION	92.2	88.0	89.2	96.2	88.7	90.8	95.6	88.1	90.3	89.6	95.6	93.9	91.3	95.4	94.2	105.2	94.6	97.7
0310	Concrete Forming & Accessories	83.3	50.9	55.4	80.4	63.3	65.7	82.2	51.2	55.5	92.3	87.3	88.0	85.2	85.1	85.1	89.0	93.0	92.5
0320	Concrete Reinforcing	103.0	41.0	71.4	101.8	56.1	78.5	97.6	52.5	74.7	101.4	102.8	102.1	102.7	88.7	95.5	96.8	106.5	101.8
0330	Cast-in-Place Concrete	96.0	53.0	78.3	102.7	59.2	84.8	105.6	54.9	84.8	91.2	84.7	88.5	90.2	86.0	88.5	103.0	85.8	95.9
03	CONCRETE	92.9	51.3	72.5	97.2	61.9	79.8	98.2	54.2	76.6	95.8	90.5	93.2	94.9	87.3	91.2	105.6	93.6	99.7
04	MASONRY	133.0	44.4	77.7	102.4	53.5	71.9	138.4	47.9	82.0	117.6	98.7	105.8	113.9	80.0	92.8	102.9	98.8	100.3
05	METALS	92.2	71.6	85.8	93.0	81.0	89.3	95.3	75.1	89.1	94.6	114.4	100.7	95.6	107.0	99.1	95.1	108.5	99.2
06	WOOD, PLASTICS & COMPOSITES	83.9	54.0	67.2	81.2	65.1	72.2	79.3	52.2	64.1	90.8	86.0	88.1	83.5	85.5	84.6	93.6	93.3	93.4
07	THERMAL & MOISTURE PROTECTION	96.9	46.4	76.2	97.0	61.6	82.5	95.7	52.9	78.2	100.3	98.9	99.7	100.2	84.2	93.6	98.3	94.5	96.8
08	OPENINGS	99.0	51.0	87.8	98.9	64.1	90.8	97.0	50.6	86.2	97.7	97.5	97.6	97.7	82.9	94.2	95.0	95.7	95.2
0920	Plaster & Gypsum Board	91.3	53.0	65.4	91.3	64.5	73.2	89.8	51.2	63.7	95.2	85.6	88.7	94.2	85.1	88.0	102.0	92.9	95.8
0950, 0980	Ceilings & Acoustic Treatment	82.0	53.0	63.0	83.9	64.5	71.2	82.9	51.2	62.0	92.6	85.6	88.0	92.6	85.1	87.6	89.1	92.9	91.6
0960	Flooring	95.5	52.8	83.3	94.2	55.1	83.0	104.4	52.8	89.6	96.4	96.8	96.5	93.3	84.0	90.6	97.3	102.5	98.8
0970, 0990	Wall Finishes & Painting/Coating	99.5	42.3	65.0	99.5	76.1	85.4	104.4	58.7	76.8	97.1	102.8	100.5	97.1	73.2	82.7	87.9	106.3	99.0
09	FINISHES	88.5	51.0	67.8	88.8	63.7	75.0	93.5	52.6	71.0	97.8	89.7	93.4	96.7	83.0	89.2	100.2	96.1	97.9
COVERS	DIVS. 10 - 14, 25, 28, 41, 43, 44, 46	100.0	59.1	91.7	100.0	59.5	91.8	100.0	56.8	91.3	100.0	88.2	97.6	100.0	93.5	98.7	100.0	88.5	97.7
21, 22, 23	FIRE SUPPRESSION, PLUMBING & HVAC	97.4	34.6	72.1	100.0	59.1	83.5	98.1	43.2	76.0	95.2	96.2	95.6	99.9	96.8	98.7	95.3	97.0	96.0
26, 27, 3370	ELECTRICAL, COMMUNICATIONS & UTIL.	99.2	49.4	72.9	102.6	57.8	78.9	96.9	49.3	71.7	96.9	82.6	89.3	96.9	101.5	99.3	92.4	78.6	85.1
MF2014	WEIGHTED AVERAGE	97.4	51.7	77.5	97.6	64.1	83.0	98.8	54.9	79.7	97.3	94.4	96.0	98.2	92.4	95.7	97.6	94.5	96.3

City Cost Indexes

MISSOURI

DIVISION		COLUMBIA 652 MAT.	INST.	TOTAL	FLAT RIVER 636 MAT.	INST.	TOTAL	HANNIBAL 634 MAT.	INST.	TOTAL	HARRISONVILLE 647 MAT.	INST.	TOTAL	JEFFERSON CITY 650-651 MAT.	INST.	TOTAL	JOPLIN 648 MAT.	INST.	TOTAL
015433	CONTRACTOR EQUIPMENT		108.0	108.0		106.9	106.9		106.9	106.9		101.9	101.9		108.0	108.0		105.7	105.7
0241, 31-34	SITE & INFRASTRUCTURE, DEMOLITION	102.8	97.2	98.8	92.2	95.6	94.6	87.6	95.7	93.4	96.6	95.7	95.9	102.3	97.2	98.6	105.6	99.7	101.4
0310	Concrete Forming & Accessories	86.9	81.8	82.5	98.3	84.3	86.2	90.5	79.0	80.6	86.2	98.7	97.0	98.3	81.8	84.1	101.3	75.3	78.9
0320	Concrete Reinforcing	96.3	119.0	107.9	102.7	107.7	105.3	100.9	97.7	99.3	96.4	115.3	106.0	98.5	111.9	105.3	99.9	98.5	99.2
0330	Cast-in-Place Concrete	96.1	87.8	92.7	94.2	93.8	94.0	86.3	86.0	86.2	105.5	103.9	104.8	102.0	87.0	95.9	111.5	77.9	97.1
03	CONCRETE	93.2	92.2	92.7	98.8	93.2	96.0	92.1	86.3	89.2	101.8	104.0	102.9	98.9	90.6	94.8	105.2	81.4	93.5
04	MASONRY	154.1	90.0	114.2	114.5	81.4	93.9	109.0	101.3	104.2	97.4	103.4	101.2	112.0	90.0	98.3	96.5	85.9	89.9
05	METALS	98.4	121.2	105.4	94.5	115.6	101.0	94.6	111.9	99.9	95.6	113.2	101.0	98.0	118.3	104.2	98.2	100.5	98.9
06	WOOD, PLASTICS & COMPOSITES	91.7	78.7	84.4	99.1	82.6	89.9	88.9	73.8	80.4	89.9	97.5	94.2	100.0	78.7	88.1	106.0	74.2	88.2
07	THERMAL & MOISTURE PROTECTION	96.2	87.5	92.6	100.5	93.8	97.7	100.1	97.0	98.8	97.6	103.2	99.9	101.8	87.6	96.0	97.7	78.9	90.0
08	OPENINGS	99.5	95.0	98.4	97.7	97.2	97.6	97.7	82.3	94.1	95.1	102.8	96.9	99.1	93.1	97.7	96.2	78.5	92.1
0920	Plaster & Gypsum Board	87.2	78.0	81.0	101.3	82.1	88.3	94.5	73.0	79.9	97.3	97.3	97.3	91.3	78.0	82.3	108.2	73.2	84.5
0950, 0980	Ceilings & Acoustic Treatment	93.2	78.0	83.2	92.6	82.1	85.7	92.6	73.0	79.7	89.1	97.3	94.5	97.2	78.0	84.6	90.0	73.2	78.9
0960	Flooring	97.6	98.6	97.9	99.4	84.0	95.0	95.8	96.8	96.1	92.6	102.5	95.4	104.4	98.6	102.7	123.8	74.9	109.8
0970, 0990	Wall Finishes & Painting/Coating	105.2	77.1	88.2	97.1	78.4	85.8	97.1	102.8	100.5	92.5	103.8	99.3	102.3	77.1	87.1	87.5	74.9	79.9
09	FINISHES	92.8	83.0	87.4	99.7	82.2	90.1	97.4	83.1	89.5	97.8	99.5	98.7	97.2	83.0	89.4	107.0	75.3	89.6
COVERS	DIVS. 10-14, 25, 28, 41, 43, 44, 46	100.0	96.2	99.2	100.0	91.8	98.3	100.0	87.8	97.5	100.0	90.6	98.1	100.0	96.2	99.2	100.0	87.9	97.6
21, 22, 23	FIRE SUPPRESSION, PLUMBING & HVAC	99.8	96.4	98.4	95.2	97.8	96.2	95.2	97.5	96.1	95.2	100.0	97.2	99.8	98.1	99.1	100.1	72.1	88.8
26, 27, 3370	ELECTRICAL, COMMUNICATIONS & UTIL.	94.8	86.5	90.4	101.1	101.5	101.3	95.7	82.6	88.8	98.8	99.6	99.2	100.4	86.5	93.0	90.4	77.5	83.6
MF2014	WEIGHTED AVERAGE	100.2	93.9	97.5	98.1	95.0	96.8	96.2	92.4	94.6	97.1	101.5	99.1	99.9	93.7	97.2	99.5	81.7	91.8

MISSOURI

DIVISION		KANSAS CITY 640-641 MAT.	INST.	TOTAL	KIRKSVILLE 635 MAT.	INST.	TOTAL	POPLAR BLUFF 639 MAT.	INST.	TOTAL	ROLLA 654-655 MAT.	INST.	TOTAL	SEDALIA 653 MAT.	INST.	TOTAL	SIKESTON 638 MAT.	INST.	TOTAL
015433	CONTRACTOR EQUIPMENT		103.3	103.3		99.1	99.1		101.5	101.5		108.0	108.0		99.9	99.9		101.5	101.5
0241, 31-34	SITE & INFRASTRUCTURE, DEMOLITION	98.9	98.2	98.4	91.8	91.4	91.5	79.1	95.4	90.7	101.5	97.1	98.3	99.0	92.8	94.6	82.4	95.4	91.7
0310	Concrete Forming & Accessories	100.1	105.4	104.6	83.2	80.6	81.0	83.3	85.0	84.7	95.0	91.9	92.3	92.4	81.4	82.9	84.3	84.9	84.9
0320	Concrete Reinforcing	94.9	119.8	107.6	101.6	98.8	100.2	104.7	94.7	99.6	96.7	94.7	95.7	95.3	106.2	100.8	104.0	98.4	101.2
0330	Cast-in-Place Concrete	103.7	106.6	104.9	94.1	83.8	89.9	72.4	86.5	78.2	98.3	96.2	97.5	102.7	83.8	94.9	77.4	86.5	81.1
03	CONCRETE	101.1	108.7	104.8	110.8	86.0	98.6	85.9	88.1	86.9	95.2	95.0	95.1	109.8	87.7	99.0	89.5	88.7	89.1
04	MASONRY	99.5	107.5	104.5	121.0	88.9	101.0	112.5	80.1	92.3	126.3	87.9	102.4	132.9	88.3	105.1	112.2	80.1	92.2
05	METALS	105.9	115.8	108.9	94.2	103.8	97.2	94.8	101.7	96.9	97.8	110.5	101.7	96.5	108.0	100.1	95.1	103.2	97.4
06	WOOD, PLASTICS & COMPOSITES	105.3	105.0	105.1	77.0	78.7	77.9	76.1	85.5	81.4	100.3	92.8	96.1	93.1	78.7	85.1	77.7	85.5	82.1
07	THERMAL & MOISTURE PROTECTION	97.8	106.8	101.5	106.8	88.2	99.2	105.2	85.9	97.3	96.4	93.4	95.1	102.5	93.1	98.7	105.3	84.5	96.8
08	OPENINGS	102.5	109.2	104.0	102.7	85.8	98.8	103.7	84.5	99.2	99.5	88.3	96.9	104.5	87.4	100.5	103.7	85.5	99.5
0920	Plaster & Gypsum Board	105.2	105.0	105.0	89.8	78.0	81.8	90.2	85.1	86.7	89.3	92.5	91.5	82.5	78.0	79.5	92.0	85.1	87.3
0950, 0980	Ceilings & Acoustic Treatment	96.7	105.0	102.1	90.9	78.0	82.4	92.6	85.1	87.6	93.2	92.5	92.7	93.2	78.0	83.2	92.6	85.1	87.6
0960	Flooring	98.0	109.0	101.2	74.4	95.8	80.5	88.3	82.0	86.5	101.2	95.8	99.6	78.8	95.8	83.7	88.7	82.0	86.8
0970, 0990	Wall Finishes & Painting/Coating	92.5	112.2	104.4	92.5	82.1	86.2	92.0	73.2	80.7	105.2	100.6	102.5	105.2	106.3	105.9	92.0	73.2	80.7
09	FINISHES	102.0	106.6	104.5	96.5	82.7	88.9	96.5	82.7	88.9	94.3	93.4	93.8	91.9	85.4	88.3	97.1	82.7	89.2
COVERS	DIVS. 10-14, 25, 28, 41, 43, 44, 46	100.0	100.6	100.1	100.0	87.1	97.4	100.0	93.6	98.7	100.0	89.0	97.8	100.0	90.2	98.0	100.0	94.2	98.8
21, 22, 23	FIRE SUPPRESSION, PLUMBING & HVAC	100.0	104.3	101.7	95.2	97.3	96.1	95.2	96.3	95.6	95.0	98.2	96.3	95.0	95.9	95.4	95.2	96.3	95.6
26, 27, 3370	ELECTRICAL, COMMUNICATIONS & UTIL.	100.3	100.1	100.2	95.8	82.5	88.8	96.1	101.5	99.0	93.2	86.5	89.6	94.7	128.8	112.7	95.3	101.5	98.6
MF2014	WEIGHTED AVERAGE	101.4	105.7	103.3	99.5	89.9	95.3	96.2	92.0	94.4	97.9	94.6	96.5	100.2	97.3	98.9	96.7	92.2	94.8

MISSOURI / MONTANA

DIVISION		SPRINGFIELD 656-658 MAT.	INST.	TOTAL	ST. JOSEPH 644-645 MAT.	INST.	TOTAL	ST. LOUIS 630-631 MAT.	INST.	TOTAL	BILLINGS 590-591 MAT.	INST.	TOTAL	BUTTE 597 MAT.	INST.	TOTAL	GREAT FALLS 594 MAT.	INST.	TOTAL
015433	CONTRACTOR EQUIPMENT		102.5	102.5		101.9	101.9		107.9	107.9		98.5	98.5		98.2	98.2		98.2	98.2
0241, 31-34	SITE & INFRASTRUCTURE, DEMOLITION	101.6	95.1	97.0	100.5	93.9	95.8	91.7	98.9	96.8	95.0	96.3	95.9	102.0	96.1	97.8	105.7	96.2	98.9
0310	Concrete Forming & Accessories	101.4	79.1	82.2	100.0	89.6	91.0	98.4	104.8	103.9	98.4	71.5	75.2	85.5	71.8	73.7	98.4	71.5	75.2
0320	Concrete Reinforcing	92.7	118.7	105.9	93.8	115.0	104.6	93.9	112.7	103.4	90.2	81.7	85.9	97.8	81.9	89.7	90.2	81.8	85.9
0330	Cast-in-Place Concrete	104.3	79.6	94.2	103.6	103.3	103.5	90.2	105.0	96.3	129.3	67.6	103.9	142.3	69.0	112.2	150.4	63.7	114.8
03	CONCRETE	105.8	87.4	96.8	100.9	99.7	100.3	94.4	107.1	100.7	109.8	72.9	91.7	113.8	73.5	94.0	119.5	71.5	96.0
04	MASONRY	102.9	89.8	94.8	99.3	96.1	97.3	95.4	111.9	105.7	128.0	73.7	94.2	123.5	76.6	94.3	128.0	75.4	95.2
05	METALS	102.8	108.8	104.7	101.9	112.4	105.2	100.3	120.2	106.4	105.8	90.0	100.9	100.1	90.1	97.1	103.2	90.0	99.2
06	WOOD, PLASTICS & COMPOSITES	101.8	77.1	88.0	106.0	87.6	95.7	99.0	103.0	101.2	98.6	70.5	82.8	85.7	70.8	77.4	99.9	70.5	83.4
07	THERMAL & MOISTURE PROTECTION	100.7	82.2	93.2	98.2	95.6	97.1	100.2	106.9	103.0	106.5	69.9	91.5	106.3	71.0	91.8	106.9	68.5	91.2
08	OPENINGS	107.2	84.3	101.9	100.6	98.6	100.1	97.6	110.9	100.7	97.3	68.7	90.6	95.6	70.0	89.6	98.5	68.0	91.4
0920	Plaster & Gypsum Board	90.4	76.3	80.9	109.7	87.0	94.4	102.2	103.1	102.8	98.0	69.8	78.9	98.7	70.2	79.4	107.3	69.8	82.0
0950, 0980	Ceilings & Acoustic Treatment	93.2	76.3	82.1	95.8	87.0	90.0	97.6	103.1	101.2	81.5	69.8	73.8	88.3	70.2	76.4	90.0	69.8	76.7
0960	Flooring	99.9	74.9	92.8	101.5	107.3	103.2	99.2	97.6	98.7	106.6	70.2	96.2	104.4	74.2	95.7	111.5	74.2	100.8
0970, 0990	Wall Finishes & Painting/Coating	99.0	74.9	84.4	87.9	86.7	87.2	97.1	106.0	102.5	105.2	86.6	94.0	103.4	51.2	71.9	103.4	86.6	93.3
09	FINISHES	96.7	78.0	86.4	103.2	91.7	96.9	100.8	103.1	102.1	96.6	72.6	83.4	97.2	69.7	82.0	101.1	73.3	85.8
COVERS	DIVS. 10-14, 25, 28, 41, 43, 44, 46	100.0	94.8	99.0	100.0	96.9	99.4	100.0	102.4	100.5	100.0	94.7	98.9	100.0	94.8	98.9	100.0	94.7	98.9
21, 22, 23	FIRE SUPPRESSION, PLUMBING & HVAC	99.8	74.6	89.6	100.1	89.0	95.6	100.0	107.4	103.0	100.1	74.7	89.9	100.2	75.6	90.3	100.2	70.7	88.3
26, 27, 3370	ELECTRICAL, COMMUNICATIONS & UTIL.	99.2	69.7	83.6	98.8	78.6	88.2	99.2	108.3	104.0	98.5	72.2	84.6	105.5	71.7	87.7	97.7	71.9	84.1
MF2014	WEIGHTED AVERAGE	101.7	83.7	93.8	100.6	93.5	97.5	98.7	107.8	102.7	102.7	77.1	91.5	102.6	77.3	91.6	104.1	76.2	91.9

For customer support on your Site Work & Landscape Cost Data, call 877.737.1594.

City Cost Indexes

MONTANA

DIVISION		HAVRE 595 MAT.	INST.	TOTAL	HELENA 596 MAT.	INST.	TOTAL	KALISPELL 599 MAT.	INST.	TOTAL	MILES CITY 593 MAT.	INST.	TOTAL	MISSOULA 598 MAT.	INST.	TOTAL	WOLF POINT 592 MAT.	INST.	TOTAL
015433	CONTRACTOR EQUIPMENT		98.2	98.2		98.2	98.2		98.2	98.2		98.2	98.2		98.2	98.2		98.2	98.2
0241, 31 - 34	SITE & INFRASTRUCTURE, DEMOLITION	109.2	95.8	99.7	98.5	95.8	96.6	92.2	96.0	94.9	98.5	95.4	96.3	85.1	95.8	92.7	115.5	95.6	101.3
0310	Concrete Forming & Accessories	78.4	69.0	70.3	101.5	65.2	70.2	88.7	71.4	73.8	96.8	67.6	71.6	88.7	71.4	73.8	89.2	67.9	70.8
0320	Concrete Reinforcing	98.6	81.7	90.0	102.5	81.7	91.9	98.8	83.4	91.8	98.2	81.8	89.8	99.5	83.4	91.3	99.6	81.8	90.5
0330	Cast-in-Place Concrete	153.3	60.4	115.1	115.0	62.9	93.6	123.6	62.7	98.6	135.3	60.3	104.5	104.9	64.9	88.4	151.5	60.6	114.2
03	CONCRETE	122.7	69.3	96.5	106.7	68.4	87.9	102.6	71.5	87.3	110.4	68.6	89.9	90.0	72.2	81.3	126.5	68.9	98.2
04	MASONRY	124.5	69.8	90.4	120.1	75.7	92.4	122.2	77.0	94.0	129.7	65.3	89.6	147.9	76.6	103.4	131.0	66.0	90.5
05	METALS	96.3	89.6	94.2	102.1	88.8	98.0	96.1	90.6	94.4	95.4	89.9	93.7	96.6	90.7	94.8	95.5	89.2	93.6
06	WOOD, PLASTICS & COMPOSITES	77.4	70.5	73.5	102.9	62.3	80.2	89.1	70.5	78.7	96.9	70.5	82.1	89.1	70.5	78.7	88.5	70.5	78.4
07	THERMAL & MOISTURE PROTECTION	106.6	68.0	90.8	103.9	70.7	90.3	105.9	72.8	92.3	106.2	65.7	89.6	105.5	79.1	94.7	107.1	66.0	90.3
08	OPENINGS	95.6	68.0	89.2	99.8	65.2	91.7	95.6	68.5	89.3	95.1	68.0	88.8	95.6	68.3	89.2	95.1	67.4	88.7
0920	Plaster & Gypsum Board	94.8	69.8	77.9	96.0	61.4	72.6	98.7	69.8	79.2	106.7	69.8	81.8	98.7	69.8	79.2	102.1	69.8	80.3
0950, 0980	Ceilings & Acoustic Treatment	88.3	69.8	76.2	90.8	61.4	71.5	88.3	69.8	76.2	87.5	69.8	75.9	88.3	69.8	76.2	87.5	69.8	75.9
0960	Flooring	101.8	74.2	93.9	106.7	59.1	93.1	106.2	74.2	97.1	111.3	70.2	99.5	106.2	74.2	97.1	107.6	70.2	96.9
0970, 0990	Wall Finishes & Painting/Coating	103.4	48.6	70.4	99.7	47.2	68.0	103.4	47.2	69.5	103.4	47.2	69.5	103.4	62.0	78.4	103.4	48.6	70.4
09	FINISHES	96.5	67.7	80.6	98.6	61.6	78.2	97.2	69.1	81.7	100.0	65.7	81.1	96.7	70.7	82.3	99.6	66.0	81.1
COVERS	DIVS. 10 - 14, 25, 28, 41, 43, 44, 46	100.0	70.8	94.1	100.0	94.0	98.8	100.0	93.9	98.8	100.0	90.4	98.1	100.0	93.7	98.7	100.0	90.6	98.1
21, 22, 23	FIRE SUPPRESSION, PLUMBING & HVAC	95.4	67.8	84.3	100.1	70.1	88.0	95.4	69.2	84.8	95.4	69.6	85.0	100.2	69.2	87.7	95.4	70.0	85.1
26, 27, 3370	ELECTRICAL, COMMUNICATIONS & UTIL.	97.7	71.2	83.7	104.6	71.3	87.0	102.2	69.3	84.8	97.7	76.9	86.7	103.2	67.7	84.5	97.7	76.9	86.7
MF2014	WEIGHTED AVERAGE	101.2	73.1	89.0	102.4	73.8	89.9	99.0	75.3	88.7	100.1	74.0	88.7	99.9	75.5	89.3	102.3	74.2	90.0

NEBRASKA

DIVISION		ALLIANCE 693 MAT.	INST.	TOTAL	COLUMBUS 686 MAT.	INST.	TOTAL	GRAND ISLAND 688 MAT.	INST.	TOTAL	HASTINGS 689 MAT.	INST.	TOTAL	LINCOLN 683-685 MAT.	INST.	TOTAL	MCCOOK 690 MAT.	INST.	TOTAL
015433	CONTRACTOR EQUIPMENT		97.8	97.8		101.6	101.6		101.6	101.6		101.6	101.6		101.6	101.6		101.6	101.6
0241, 31 - 34	SITE & INFRASTRUCTURE, DEMOLITION	100.5	98.8	99.3	100.2	92.3	94.6	105.0	93.1	96.5	103.7	92.3	95.6	92.7	93.0	92.9	103.8	92.2	95.6
0310	Concrete Forming & Accessories	87.3	56.4	60.7	95.5	67.4	71.2	95.1	72.4	75.5	98.2	71.9	75.5	95.7	68.2	71.9	93.0	56.1	61.2
0320	Concrete Reinforcing	108.8	85.1	96.7	98.3	76.5	87.2	97.7	76.4	86.9	97.7	77.1	87.2	96.7	76.0	86.1	101.8	76.2	88.8
0330	Cast-in-Place Concrete	113.7	60.0	91.6	115.7	60.0	92.8	122.5	67.2	99.8	122.5	63.2	98.2	92.4	69.6	83.1	122.6	59.3	96.6
03	CONCRETE	123.9	63.5	94.2	108.8	67.3	88.4	113.7	72.1	93.3	113.9	70.6	92.6	95.6	71.0	83.5	112.9	62.0	87.9
04	MASONRY	115.6	74.1	89.7	122.7	77.8	94.7	115.4	76.1	90.9	124.9	88.0	101.9	104.8	67.2	81.4	110.7	73.9	87.8
05	METALS	101.5	78.7	94.5	96.1	84.6	92.6	97.8	86.3	94.3	98.7	85.8	94.7	99.9	85.5	95.5	96.3	83.6	92.4
06	WOOD, PLASTICS & COMPOSITES	87.0	52.2	67.5	101.2	66.7	81.9	100.4	72.2	84.6	104.1	72.2	86.3	98.4	66.7	80.7	95.7	52.2	71.4
07	THERMAL & MOISTURE PROTECTION	104.3	67.8	89.4	100.8	69.8	88.1	100.9	72.8	89.4	100.9	83.4	93.8	98.1	69.9	86.5	98.9	66.6	85.6
08	OPENINGS	94.5	58.6	86.1	95.4	66.1	88.6	95.5	69.7	89.5	95.5	69.1	89.3	107.8	63.0	97.4	95.0	56.6	86.1
0920	Plaster & Gypsum Board	82.7	50.7	61.1	90.9	65.6	73.8	90.1	71.3	77.4	91.9	71.3	78.0	96.2	65.6	75.5	93.7	50.7	64.7
0950, 0980	Ceilings & Acoustic Treatment	91.9	50.7	64.8	80.2	65.6	70.6	80.2	71.3	74.3	80.2	71.3	74.3	90.4	65.6	74.1	88.0	50.7	63.5
0960	Flooring	99.9	82.1	94.8	92.9	100.4	95.0	92.7	107.2	96.8	93.9	100.4	95.7	101.0	83.6	96.0	97.6	82.1	93.1
0970, 0990	Wall Finishes & Painting/Coating	168.5	54.8	99.9	85.5	63.7	72.4	85.5	63.7	74.7	85.5	63.7	72.4	103.8	77.9	88.1	93.8	47.7	66.0
09	FINISHES	98.4	59.5	77.0	89.9	71.9	80.0	90.0	77.1	82.9	90.6	75.2	82.1	96.9	71.7	83.0	95.6	58.6	75.2
COVERS	DIVS. 10 - 14, 25, 28, 41, 43, 44, 46	100.0	65.3	93.0	100.0	86.1	97.2	100.0	88.7	97.7	100.0	86.7	97.3	100.0	88.1	97.6	100.0	64.5	92.8
21, 22, 23	FIRE SUPPRESSION, PLUMBING & HVAC	95.3	70.5	85.3	95.2	76.0	87.4	100.0	78.0	91.1	95.2	76.0	87.5	99.9	78.0	91.0	95.1	75.9	87.4
26, 27, 3370	ELECTRICAL, COMMUNICATIONS & UTIL.	92.3	69.4	80.2	93.6	82.3	87.6	92.2	67.0	78.9	91.6	83.6	87.4	105.4	67.0	85.1	94.4	69.4	81.2
MF2014	WEIGHTED AVERAGE	101.0	70.5	87.7	98.4	77.1	89.1	100.0	77.1	90.0	99.4	79.8	90.9	100.5	74.9	89.4	98.7	71.1	86.7

NEBRASKA / NEVADA

DIVISION		NORFOLK 687 MAT.	INST.	TOTAL	NORTH PLATTE 691 MAT.	INST.	TOTAL	OMAHA 680-681 MAT.	INST.	TOTAL	VALENTINE 692 MAT.	INST.	TOTAL	CARSON CITY 897 MAT.	INST.	TOTAL	ELKO 898 MAT.	INST.	TOTAL
015433	CONTRACTOR EQUIPMENT		92.8	92.8		101.6	101.6		92.8	92.8		95.9	95.9		98.2	98.2		98.2	98.2
0241, 31 - 34	SITE & INFRASTRUCTURE, DEMOLITION	83.6	91.5	89.2	105.2	92.3	94.6	90.0	92.1	91.5	88.6	96.5	94.2	84.5	99.0	94.8	66.9	97.6	88.8
0310	Concrete Forming & Accessories	81.7	71.1	72.5	95.4	71.5	74.8	94.3	72.4	75.4	83.7	55.5	59.6	103.3	92.8	94.2	109.2	81.3	85.2
0320	Concrete Reinforcing	98.4	66.5	82.2	101.2	77.1	88.9	99.7	76.6	87.9	101.8	66.1	83.7	103.2	118.4	111.0	102.7	113.2	108.1
0330	Cast-in-Place Concrete	116.7	62.4	94.4	122.6	64.5	98.7	101.1	75.5	90.6	108.4	57.2	87.4	100.4	85.7	94.4	95.1	80.2	89.0
03	CONCRETE	107.3	67.5	87.8	113.0	70.8	92.3	100.1	74.5	87.5	110.2	58.9	85.0	100.9	95.2	98.1	95.4	87.2	91.4
04	MASONRY	129.4	79.1	98.0	98.6	87.9	92.0	106.8	79.0	89.4	110.9	73.9	87.8	117.3	94.6	103.2	115.0	71.9	88.1
05	METALS	99.6	73.5	91.6	95.5	85.4	92.4	99.9	78.9	93.4	107.6	73.4	97.1	94.0	104.7	97.3	96.9	99.4	97.7
06	WOOD, PLASTICS & COMPOSITES	84.0	71.7	77.1	97.8	72.2	83.5	94.1	72.0	81.7	81.7	51.7	64.9	92.1	94.4	93.4	100.6	81.8	90.1
07	THERMAL & MOISTURE PROTECTION	100.8	73.6	89.4	98.9	82.8	92.3	99.5	75.5	88.7	99.6	67.6	86.5	103.5	92.3	99.0	99.9	76.1	90.1
08	OPENINGS	97.2	66.5	90.0	94.3	69.1	88.4	100.0	71.5	93.3	96.9	55.6	87.3	99.5	107.9	101.4	100.9	85.9	97.4
0920	Plaster & Gypsum Board	90.8	71.3	77.6	93.7	71.3	78.6	100.5	71.6	81.0	95.6	50.7	65.3	100.9	94.1	96.3	105.3	81.2	89.0
0950, 0980	Ceilings & Acoustic Treatment	92.0	71.3	78.4	88.0	71.3	77.0	93.0	71.6	78.9	104.9	50.7	69.3	94.0	94.1	94.1	94.4	81.2	85.7
0960	Flooring	117.4	100.4	112.5	98.5	100.4	99.1	113.4	81.9	104.4	127.4	79.8	113.8	101.9	107.9	103.6	105.4	51.1	89.9
0970, 0990	Wall Finishes & Painting/Coating	151.7	63.7	98.6	93.8	63.7	75.6	126.2	67.2	90.6	167.2	66.1	106.1	101.2	80.8	88.9	102.6	95.9	98.5
09	FINISHES	108.8	75.2	90.3	95.9	75.2	84.5	106.0	73.3	88.0	118.2	59.7	86.0	97.9	94.3	95.9	97.6	77.2	86.3
COVERS	DIVS. 10 - 14, 25, 28, 41, 43, 44, 46	100.0	85.5	97.1	100.0	66.8	93.3	100.0	87.6	97.5	100.0	62.5	92.4	100.0	89.8	97.9	100.0	62.8	92.5
21, 22, 23	FIRE SUPPRESSION, PLUMBING & HVAC	95.0	75.8	87.1	99.9	76.0	90.2	99.9	76.8	90.6	94.8	75.7	87.1	100.0	80.1	92.0	97.7	79.6	90.4
26, 27, 3370	ELECTRICAL, COMMUNICATIONS & UTIL.	92.4	82.3	87.1	92.6	77.1	84.4	99.1	82.3	90.2	89.7	86.6	88.0	103.2	96.7	99.7	100.7	96.6	98.6
MF2014	WEIGHTED AVERAGE	100.0	76.7	89.8	99.0	78.3	90.0	100.2	78.6	90.8	101.2	72.5	88.7	99.7	93.5	97.0	98.3	84.9	92.4

NEVADA / NEW HAMPSHIRE

DIVISION		ELY 893 MAT.	INST.	TOTAL	LAS VEGAS 889-891 MAT.	INST.	TOTAL	RENO 894-895 MAT.	INST.	TOTAL	CHARLESTON 036 MAT.	INST.	TOTAL	CLAREMONT 037 MAT.	INST.	TOTAL	CONCORD 032-033 MAT.	INST.	TOTAL
015433	CONTRACTOR EQUIPMENT		98.2	98.2		98.2	98.2		98.2	98.2		100.9	100.9		100.9	100.9		100.9	100.9
0241, 31 - 34	SITE & INFRASTRUCTURE, DEMOLITION	72.2	99.1	91.3	75.4	101.0	93.6	72.2	99.0	91.3	86.9	99.6	96.0	80.9	99.6	94.2	93.7	103.9	100.9
0310	Concrete Forming & Accessories	102.3	105.7	105.2	103.5	109.6	108.8	98.7	92.7	93.5	86.8	81.1	81.9	92.6	81.1	82.7	95.5	93.6	93.8
0320	Concrete Reinforcing	101.5	111.6	106.7	93.7	119.9	107.1	96.0	119.9	108.1	84.1	93.5	88.9	84.1	93.5	88.9	95.3	94.1	94.7
0330	Cast-in-Place Concrete	102.1	105.4	103.4	98.9	107.8	102.5	108.0	85.7	98.8	97.1	70.5	86.2	89.2	70.5	81.6	112.2	90.5	103.3
03	CONCRETE	103.4	106.4	104.9	98.7	110.6	104.6	103.1	95.4	99.3	99.1	80.0	89.7	91.1	80.0	85.6	106.6	92.5	99.6
04	MASONRY	119.7	102.5	109.0	108.3	104.0	105.6	114.3	94.6	102.0	97.5	84.7	89.5	96.9	84.7	89.3	110.9	104.2	106.7
05	METALS	96.9	103.3	98.9	104.5	108.6	105.8	98.4	105.1	100.5	92.8	90.1	92.0	92.8	90.1	92.0	98.8	93.8	97.3
06	WOOD, PLASTICS & COMPOSITES	91.3	106.8	100.0	89.8	107.9	99.9	85.9	94.4	90.6	87.4	90.2	89.0	93.6	90.2	91.7	95.4	92.4	93.7
07	THERMAL & MOISTURE PROTECTION	100.3	95.7	98.4	113.8	102.6	109.2	99.9	92.3	96.8	98.8	72.3	88.0	98.7	72.3	87.9	101.9	91.5	97.6
08	OPENINGS	100.8	98.8	100.3	99.9	115.6	103.5	98.7	102.3	99.6	102.0	76.4	96.0	103.3	76.4	97.0	104.9	87.2	100.8
0920	Plaster & Gypsum Board	101.0	107.0	105.1	97.5	108.1	104.7	92.0	94.1	93.4	100.0	89.3	92.8	101.0	89.3	93.1	103.9	91.6	95.6
0950, 0980	Ceilings & Acoustic Treatment	94.4	107.0	102.7	102.7	108.1	106.3	99.4	94.1	95.9	94.2	89.3	91.0	94.2	89.3	91.0	99.9	91.6	94.4
0960	Flooring	103.0	57.2	89.9	94.6	107.9	98.4	99.9	107.9	102.2	98.4	32.1	79.4	100.6	32.1	81.0	102.7	116.9	106.8
0970, 0990	Wall Finishes & Painting/Coating	102.6	121.0	113.7	102.6	121.0	114.8	102.6	80.8	89.4	96.4	45.7	65.8	96.4	46.0	65.9	95.8	95.4	95.6
09	FINISHES	96.8	98.9	98.0	95.8	110.4	103.9	95.6	94.3	94.9	95.3	69.7	81.2	95.6	69.8	81.4	97.4	97.9	97.7
COVERS	DIVS. 10 - 14, 25, 28, 41, 43, 44, 46	100.0	63.6	92.6	100.0	104.4	100.9	100.0	89.8	97.9	100.0	92.2	98.4	100.0	92.2	98.4	100.0	104.3	100.9
21, 22, 23	FIRE SUPPRESSION, PLUMBING & HVAC	97.7	104.5	100.5	100.1	104.4	101.8	100.0	80.1	92.0	95.3	39.6	72.8	95.3	39.7	72.9	99.9	84.4	93.7
26, 27, 3370	ELECTRICAL, COMMUNICATIONS & UTIL.	101.0	109.1	105.3	105.4	119.9	113.1	101.4	96.7	98.9	98.5	52.9	74.4	98.5	52.9	74.4	99.5	83.6	91.1
MF2014	WEIGHTED AVERAGE	99.4	102.2	100.6	100.9	108.7	104.3	99.6	93.3	96.8	96.7	69.5	84.8	95.9	69.5	84.4	101.1	92.5	97.4

NEW HAMPSHIRE / NEW JERSEY

DIVISION		KEENE 034 MAT.	INST.	TOTAL	LITTLETON 035 MAT.	INST.	TOTAL	MANCHESTER 031 MAT.	INST.	TOTAL	NASHUA 030 MAT.	INST.	TOTAL	PORTSMOUTH 038 MAT.	INST.	TOTAL	ATLANTIC CITY 082,084 MAT.	INST.	TOTAL
015433	CONTRACTOR EQUIPMENT		100.9	100.9		100.9	100.9		100.9	100.9		100.9	100.9		100.9	100.9		99.1	99.1
0241, 31 - 34	SITE & INFRASTRUCTURE, DEMOLITION	94.0	99.9	98.2	81.0	99.9	94.4	93.6	103.9	100.9	95.7	103.9	101.5	89.2	104.0	99.7	96.4	105.2	102.7
0310	Concrete Forming & Accessories	91.3	83.0	84.2	102.9	83.0	85.8	96.9	94.0	94.4	99.3	94.0	94.8	88.2	94.3	93.4	109.0	127.5	125.0
0320	Concrete Reinforcing	84.1	93.6	88.9	84.8	93.6	89.3	103.7	94.1	98.8	105.1	94.1	99.5	84.1	94.2	89.2	76.3	118.1	97.6
0330	Cast-in-Place Concrete	97.6	72.8	87.4	87.6	72.7	81.5	110.6	113.1	111.7	92.4	113.1	100.9	87.6	113.2	98.1	86.1	133.0	105.3
03	CONCRETE	98.7	81.6	90.3	90.5	81.6	86.1	107.2	100.4	103.9	98.9	100.4	99.7	90.6	100.6	95.5	93.1	126.5	109.5
04	MASONRY	101.3	88.3	93.2	107.9	88.3	95.7	102.9	104.2	103.7	101.4	104.2	103.1	97.2	104.2	101.5	111.8	132.0	124.4
05	METALS	93.5	90.7	92.6	93.5	90.7	92.6	101.3	94.3	99.2	98.8	94.3	97.5	95.0	94.9	94.9	95.6	106.1	98.8
06	WOOD, PLASTICS & COMPOSITES	92.0	90.2	91.0	103.5	90.2	96.0	95.3	92.4	93.7	101.9	92.4	96.6	88.7	92.4	90.8	109.6	127.2	119.4
07	THERMAL & MOISTURE PROTECTION	99.2	75.3	89.4	98.8	73.8	88.5	101.5	95.0	98.8	99.6	95.0	97.7	99.3	115.0	105.7	105.9	124.2	113.4
08	OPENINGS	100.4	81.2	96.0	104.4	77.1	98.0	105.2	87.2	101.0	105.4	87.2	101.2	106.2	84.0	101.0	101.7	124.4	107.0
0920	Plaster & Gypsum Board	100.3	89.3	92.9	114.6	89.3	97.5	104.7	91.6	95.8	110.0	91.6	97.5	100.0	91.6	94.3	105.4	127.5	120.3
0950, 0980	Ceilings & Acoustic Treatment	94.2	89.3	91.0	94.2	89.3	91.0	101.7	91.6	95.0	105.1	91.6	96.2	95.1	91.6	92.8	81.3	127.5	111.6
0960	Flooring	100.2	52.6	86.6	109.9	32.1	87.6	98.6	116.9	103.8	103.7	116.9	107.4	98.5	116.9	103.8	105.4	159.9	121.0
0970, 0990	Wall Finishes & Painting/Coating	96.4	45.7	65.8	96.4	59.9	74.4	100.7	95.4	97.5	96.4	95.4	95.8	96.4	95.4	95.8	93.9	130.2	115.8
09	FINISHES	97.0	74.5	84.6	100.2	72.2	84.8	98.6	97.9	98.2	101.7	97.9	99.6	96.2	97.9	97.1	96.0	134.5	117.2
COVERS	DIVS. 10 - 14, 25, 28, 41, 43, 44, 46	100.0	93.4	98.7	100.0	98.6	99.7	100.0	104.3	100.9	100.0	104.3	100.9	100.0	104.3	100.9	100.0	111.5	102.3
21, 22, 23	FIRE SUPPRESSION, PLUMBING & HVAC	95.3	43.3	74.3	95.3	63.8	82.6	99.9	84.4	93.7	100.1	84.4	93.8	100.1	84.4	93.8	99.7	123.6	109.3
26, 27, 3370	ELECTRICAL, COMMUNICATIONS & UTIL.	98.5	63.2	79.9	99.8	55.9	76.6	99.8	83.6	91.2	101.2	83.6	91.9	99.1	83.6	90.9	91.1	138.1	116.0
MF2014	WEIGHTED AVERAGE	97.2	73.3	86.7	97.1	76.3	88.0	101.4	93.8	98.1	100.5	93.8	97.6	97.9	94.3	96.4	98.2	124.8	109.8

NEW JERSEY

DIVISION		CAMDEN 081 MAT.	INST.	TOTAL	DOVER 078 MAT.	INST.	TOTAL	ELIZABETH 072 MAT.	INST.	TOTAL	HACKENSACK 076 MAT.	INST.	TOTAL	JERSEY CITY 073 MAT.	INST.	TOTAL	LONG BRANCH 077 MAT.	INST.	TOTAL
015433	CONTRACTOR EQUIPMENT		99.1	99.1		100.9	100.9		100.9	100.9		100.9	100.9		99.1	99.1		98.7	98.7
0241, 31 - 34	SITE & INFRASTRUCTURE, DEMOLITION	97.8	105.5	103.3	102.0	106.3	105.1	106.1	106.3	106.3	103.0	106.3	105.3	93.4	106.3	102.5	97.5	106.0	103.6
0310	Concrete Forming & Accessories	100.2	127.5	123.8	97.8	128.3	124.1	110.2	128.4	125.9	97.8	128.3	124.1	101.8	128.3	124.7	102.4	128.0	124.5
0320	Concrete Reinforcing	100.1	118.3	109.4	77.2	137.2	107.7	77.2	137.2	107.7	77.2	137.2	107.7	100.1	137.2	119.0	77.2	137.1	107.7
0330	Cast-in-Place Concrete	83.5	132.9	103.8	101.5	127.7	112.2	87.1	131.4	105.3	99.2	131.4	112.4	79.2	127.7	99.1	88.0	132.9	106.4
03	CONCRETE	94.0	126.5	110.0	98.8	128.7	113.5	94.5	130.1	112.0	97.0	130.0	113.2	92.1	128.6	110.0	96.2	130.2	112.9
04	MASONRY	101.3	132.0	120.4	93.0	132.5	117.6	108.7	132.5	123.5	96.9	132.5	119.1	87.0	132.5	115.4	101.3	132.0	120.5
05	METALS	101.1	106.1	102.6	93.3	116.2	100.4	94.8	116.2	101.4	93.4	116.1	100.4	98.9	113.9	103.5	93.4	113.7	99.7
06	WOOD, PLASTICS & COMPOSITES	98.4	127.2	114.5	96.2	127.2	113.5	111.7	127.2	120.4	96.2	127.2	113.5	97.1	127.2	114.0	98.2	127.1	114.4
07	THERMAL & MOISTURE PROTECTION	105.8	123.3	113.0	100.6	132.8	113.8	100.8	133.3	114.1	100.4	125.5	110.7	100.2	132.8	113.5	100.3	124.4	110.2
08	OPENINGS	104.1	124.5	108.8	105.5	127.7	110.6	103.6	127.7	109.2	102.9	127.7	108.7	101.6	127.7	107.7	97.8	127.6	104.7
0920	Plaster & Gypsum Board	101.5	127.5	118.9	100.9	127.5	118.9	107.7	127.5	121.0	100.9	127.5	118.9	104.3	127.5	120.0	102.7	127.5	119.4
0950, 0980	Ceilings & Acoustic Treatment	91.5	127.5	115.1	83.8	127.5	112.5	85.7	127.5	113.1	83.8	127.5	112.5	94.9	127.5	116.3	83.8	127.5	112.5
0960	Flooring	101.5	159.9	118.2	93.6	178.1	117.8	98.5	178.1	121.3	93.6	178.1	117.8	94.6	178.1	118.5	94.8	178.1	118.6
0970, 0990	Wall Finishes & Painting/Coating	93.9	130.2	115.8	98.4	132.5	119.0	98.4	132.5	119.0	98.4	132.5	119.0	98.5	132.5	119.0	98.5	130.2	117.6
09	FINISHES	96.4	134.5	117.4	93.7	136.9	117.5	96.9	136.9	118.9	93.5	136.9	117.4	96.6	136.9	118.8	94.5	137.5	118.2
COVERS	DIVS. 10 - 14, 25, 28, 41, 43, 44, 46	100.0	111.5	102.3	100.0	118.1	103.7	100.0	118.1	103.7	100.0	118.1	103.7	100.0	118.1	103.7	100.0	111.3	102.3
21, 22, 23	FIRE SUPPRESSION, PLUMBING & HVAC	100.0	123.6	109.5	99.7	127.4	110.9	100.1	125.5	110.3	99.7	127.4	110.9	100.1	127.4	111.1	99.7	127.1	110.8
26, 27, 3370	ELECTRICAL, COMMUNICATIONS & UTIL.	96.0	138.1	118.2	92.8	137.7	116.5	93.4	137.7	116.8	92.8	140.1	117.8	97.6	140.1	120.1	92.5	130.8	112.7
MF2014	WEIGHTED AVERAGE	99.5	124.8	110.5	97.9	127.8	110.9	98.8	127.6	111.3	97.6	128.1	110.9	97.9	127.9	111.0	97.1	126.3	109.8

NEW JERSEY

DIVISION	NEW BRUNSWICK 088-089			NEWARK 070-071			PATERSON 074-075			POINT PLEASANT 087			SUMMIT 079			TRENTON 085-086		
	MAT.	INST.	TOTAL	MAT.	INST.	TOTAL	MAT.	INST.	TOTAL	MAT.	INST.	TOTAL	MAT.	INST.	TOTAL	MAT.	INST.	TOTAL
015433 CONTRACTOR EQUIPMENT		98.7	98.7		100.9	100.9		100.9	100.9		98.7	98.7		100.9	100.9		98.7	98.7
0241,31-34 SITE & INFRASTRUCTURE, DEMOLITION	109.2	106.0	107.0	107.8	106.3	106.8	105.0	106.3	105.9	110.9	106.0	107.4	103.7	106.3	105.6	95.8	106.0	103.0
0310 Concrete Forming & Accessories	103.3	128.3	124.8	97.6	128.4	124.2	99.9	128.2	124.3	97.7	127.9	123.7	100.6	128.4	124.5	98.6	127.7	123.7
0320 Concrete Reinforcing	77.2	137.2	107.7	99.8	137.2	118.8	100.1	137.2	119.0	77.2	137.1	107.7	77.2	137.2	107.7	99.8	112.4	106.2
0330 Cast-in-Place Concrete	106.3	133.2	117.4	108.8	131.5	118.1	102.8	131.4	113.4	106.3	132.8	117.2	84.3	131.4	103.6	101.8	132.8	114.5
03 CONCRETE	110.4	130.5	120.3	105.8	130.1	117.7	102.2	130.0	115.3	110.1	130.1	119.9	91.5	130.1	110.5	102.5	125.5	113.8
04 MASONRY	109.3	132.5	123.7	99.6	132.5	120.1	93.6	132.5	117.9	97.0	132.0	118.8	95.5	132.5	118.6	103.9	132.0	121.4
05 METALS	95.6	113.8	101.2	100.8	116.3	105.5	94.2	116.1	100.9	95.6	113.5	101.1	93.3	116.2	100.4	100.8	105.2	102.1
06 WOOD, PLASTICS & COMPOSITES	103.0	127.1	116.5	93.9	127.2	112.5	98.8	127.2	114.7	95.9	127.1	113.4	100.1	127.2	115.3	95.6	127.1	113.3
07 THERMAL & MOISTURE PROTECTION	106.1	132.0	116.7	101.1	133.3	114.3	100.7	125.5	110.9	106.2	124.4	113.7	101.0	133.3	114.2	105.5	124.3	113.2
08 OPENINGS	96.1	127.6	103.5	104.4	127.7	109.8	108.3	127.7	112.8	98.2	129.2	105.4	110.2	127.7	114.2	106.1	122.2	109.8
0920 Plaster & Gypsum Board	102.6	127.5	119.4	101.1	127.5	118.9	104.3	127.5	120.0	98.3	127.5	118.0	102.7	127.5	119.4	98.7	127.5	118.1
0950, 0980 Ceilings & Acoustic Treatment	81.3	127.5	111.6	97.6	127.5	117.2	94.9	127.5	116.3	81.3	127.5	111.6	83.8	127.5	112.5	93.1	127.5	115.7
0960 Flooring	103.0	178.1	124.5	95.7	178.1	119.2	94.6	178.1	118.5	100.5	159.9	117.5	94.9	178.1	118.7	102.1	172.2	122.1
0970, 0990 Wall Finishes & Painting/Coating	93.9	132.5	117.2	99.8	132.5	119.5	98.4	132.5	119.0	93.9	130.2	115.8	98.4	132.5	119.0	99.1	130.2	117.8
09 FINISHES	96.0	136.8	118.5	95.6	136.9	118.3	96.7	136.9	118.9	94.7	134.5	116.6	94.6	136.9	117.9	96.6	136.5	118.6
COVERS DIVS. 10-14, 25, 28, 41, 43, 44, 46	100.0	118.0	103.6	100.0	118.1	103.7	100.0	118.1	103.7	100.0	108.8	101.8	100.0	118.1	103.7	100.0	111.3	102.3
21, 22, 23 FIRE SUPPRESSION, PLUMBING & HVAC	99.7	127.4	110.8	100.1	127.4	111.1	100.1	127.4	111.1	99.7	127.0	110.7	99.7	125.5	110.1	100.1	126.9	110.9
26, 27, 3370 ELECTRICAL, COMMUNICATIONS & UTIL.	91.8	136.8	115.6	101.2	140.1	121.8	97.6	137.7	118.8	91.1	130.7	112.1	93.4	137.7	116.8	99.3	135.4	118.4
MF2014 WEIGHTED AVERAGE	99.7	127.6	111.9	101.2	128.4	113.0	99.6	127.8	111.9	99.2	125.9	110.8	97.9	127.6	110.8	100.9	125.1	111.5

NEW JERSEY / NEW MEXICO

DIVISION	VINELAND 080,083			ALBUQUERQUE 870-872			CARRIZOZO 883			CLOVIS 881			FARMINGTON 874			GALLUP 873		
	MAT.	INST.	TOTAL	MAT.	INST.	TOTAL	MAT.	INST.	TOTAL	MAT.	INST.	TOTAL	MAT.	INST.	TOTAL	MAT.	INST.	TOTAL
015433 CONTRACTOR EQUIPMENT		99.1	99.1		110.1	110.1		110.1	110.1		110.1	110.1		110.1	110.1		110.1	110.1
0241,31-34 SITE & INFRASTRUCTURE, DEMOLITION	100.7	105.5	104.1	87.6	103.3	98.7	105.8	103.3	104.0	94.1	103.3	100.6	94.1	103.3	100.6	102.1	103.3	102.9
0310 Concrete Forming & Accessories	95.2	127.6	123.1	101.7	64.6	69.7	99.2	64.6	69.3	99.2	64.5	69.2	101.7	64.6	69.7	101.7	64.6	69.7
0320 Concrete Reinforcing	76.3	116.1	96.6	98.4	68.9	83.4	107.0	68.9	87.6	108.2	68.9	88.2	107.6	68.9	87.9	103.0	68.9	85.6
0330 Cast-in-Place Concrete	92.8	133.0	109.3	98.9	70.4	87.2	95.8	70.4	85.4	95.7	70.3	85.3	99.8	70.4	87.7	93.9	70.4	84.3
03 CONCRETE	97.9	126.2	111.8	100.2	68.5	84.6	117.0	68.5	93.2	105.8	68.4	87.4	103.9	68.5	86.5	110.0	68.5	89.6
04 MASONRY	99.4	132.0	119.7	105.0	58.7	76.1	103.4	58.7	75.5	103.4	58.7	75.5	113.7	58.7	79.4	99.4	58.7	74.0
05 METALS	95.5	105.5	98.6	105.2	86.8	99.5	99.5	86.8	95.6	99.2	86.7	95.3	102.9	86.8	97.9	102.0	86.8	97.3
06 WOOD, PLASTICS & COMPOSITES	92.8	127.2	112.1	97.5	65.5	79.6	93.1	65.5	77.6	93.1	65.5	77.6	97.7	65.5	79.7	97.7	65.5	79.7
07 THERMAL & MOISTURE PROTECTION	105.7	124.2	113.3	94.8	73.5	86.0	100.3	73.5	89.3	99.2	73.5	88.7	94.9	73.5	86.2	95.9	73.5	86.7
08 OPENINGS	97.7	124.1	103.8	101.2	67.7	93.4	98.6	67.7	91.4	98.7	67.7	91.5	103.6	67.7	95.3	103.6	67.7	95.3
0920 Plaster & Gypsum Board	96.9	127.5	117.5	95.8	64.2	74.4	78.6	64.2	68.8	78.6	64.2	68.8	89.4	64.2	72.3	89.4	64.2	72.3
0950, 0980 Ceilings & Acoustic Treatment	81.3	127.5	111.6	95.5	64.2	74.9	96.3	64.2	75.2	96.3	64.2	75.2	92.6	64.2	73.9	92.6	64.2	73.9
0960 Flooring	99.6	159.9	116.8	101.9	66.0	91.6	101.2	66.0	91.2	101.2	66.0	91.2	103.7	66.0	92.9	103.7	66.0	92.9
0970, 0990 Wall Finishes & Painting/Coating	93.9	130.2	115.8	113.2	66.6	85.1	103.3	66.6	81.1	103.3	66.6	81.1	107.1	66.6	82.7	107.1	66.6	82.7
09 FINISHES	93.5	134.5	116.1	95.9	64.8	78.8	96.6	64.8	79.1	95.4	64.8	78.5	94.8	64.8	78.3	96.0	64.8	78.8
COVERS DIVS. 10-14, 25, 28, 41, 43, 44, 46	100.0	111.5	102.3	100.0	82.9	96.5	100.0	82.9	96.5	100.0	82.9	96.5	100.0	82.9	96.5	100.0	82.9	96.5
21, 22, 23 FIRE SUPPRESSION, PLUMBING & HVAC	99.7	123.6	109.3	100.1	69.0	87.6	97.2	69.0	85.8	97.2	68.7	85.7	100.0	69.0	87.5	97.1	69.0	85.8
26, 27, 3370 ELECTRICAL, COMMUNICATIONS & UTIL.	91.1	138.1	116.0	91.2	71.2	80.6	92.8	71.2	81.4	90.2	71.2	80.2	88.8	71.2	79.5	88.0	71.2	79.1
MF2014 WEIGHTED AVERAGE	97.5	124.7	109.4	99.6	72.6	87.8	100.3	72.6	88.2	98.3	72.5	87.1	100.1	72.6	88.1	99.5	72.6	87.8

NEW MEXICO

DIVISION	LAS CRUCES 880			LAS VEGAS 877			ROSWELL 882			SANTA FE 875			SOCORRO 878			TRUTH/CONSEQUENCES 879		
	MAT.	INST.	TOTAL	MAT.	INST.	TOTAL	MAT.	INST.	TOTAL	MAT.	INST.	TOTAL	MAT.	INST.	TOTAL	MAT.	INST.	TOTAL
015433 CONTRACTOR EQUIPMENT		86.0	86.0		110.1	110.1		110.1	110.1		110.1	110.1		110.1	110.1		86.0	86.0
0241,31-34 SITE & INFRASTRUCTURE, DEMOLITION	94.0	82.9	86.1	93.6	103.3	100.5	96.3	103.3	101.3	98.8	103.3	102.0	89.8	103.3	99.4	108.3	82.9	90.3
0310 Concrete Forming & Accessories	95.7	63.4	67.8	101.7	64.6	69.7	99.2	64.6	69.3	100.4	64.6	69.5	101.7	64.6	69.7	99.3	63.4	68.3
0320 Concrete Reinforcing	104.6	68.7	86.4	104.7	68.9	86.5	108.2	68.9	88.2	103.8	68.9	86.1	106.8	68.9	87.5	100.8	68.7	84.5
0330 Cast-in-Place Concrete	90.4	62.7	79.0	97.1	70.4	86.1	95.8	70.4	85.3	105.3	70.4	91.0	95.1	70.4	85.0	104.2	62.7	87.1
03 CONCRETE	84.9	65.0	75.1	101.2	68.5	85.1	106.5	68.5	87.8	104.0	68.5	86.5	100.2	68.5	84.6	94.1	65.0	79.8
04 MASONRY	99.2	58.3	73.7	99.7	58.7	74.1	114.3	58.7	79.6	104.1	58.7	75.8	99.6	58.7	74.1	97.2	58.3	73.0
05 METALS	98.1	80.3	92.6	101.7	86.8	97.1	100.4	86.8	96.2	99.0	86.8	95.2	102.0	86.8	97.3	101.6	80.3	95.0
06 WOOD, PLASTICS & COMPOSITES	82.5	64.4	72.4	97.7	65.5	79.7	93.1	65.5	77.6	99.3	65.5	80.4	97.7	65.5	79.7	89.1	64.4	75.3
07 THERMAL & MOISTURE PROTECTION	86.0	68.6	78.8	94.5	73.5	85.9	99.3	73.5	88.7	96.9	73.5	87.3	94.5	73.5	85.9	83.3	68.6	77.2
08 OPENINGS	91.5	67.1	85.8	99.9	67.7	92.4	98.5	67.7	91.4	102.0	67.7	94.0	99.8	67.7	92.3	93.1	67.1	87.0
0920 Plaster & Gypsum Board	77.5	64.2	68.5	89.4	64.2	72.3	78.6	64.2	68.8	98.9	64.2	75.4	89.4	64.2	72.3	91.1	64.2	72.9
0950, 0980 Ceilings & Acoustic Treatment	84.2	64.2	71.0	92.6	64.2	73.9	96.3	64.2	75.2	93.0	64.2	74.0	92.6	64.2	73.9	82.4	64.2	70.4
0960 Flooring	131.2	66.0	112.5	103.7	66.0	92.9	101.2	66.0	91.2	110.8	66.0	98.0	103.7	66.0	92.9	135.3	66.0	115.4
0970, 0990 Wall Finishes & Painting/Coating	90.7	66.6	76.2	107.1	66.6	82.7	103.3	66.6	81.1	111.8	66.6	84.5	107.1	66.6	82.7	97.7	66.6	79.0
09 FINISHES	105.2	63.9	82.5	94.7	64.8	78.2	95.5	64.8	78.6	99.7	64.8	80.5	94.6	64.8	78.2	107.5	63.9	83.5
COVERS DIVS. 10-14, 25, 28, 41, 43, 44, 46	100.0	80.2	96.0	100.0	82.9	96.5	100.0	82.9	96.5	100.0	82.9	96.5	100.0	82.9	96.5	100.0	80.2	96.0
21, 22, 23 FIRE SUPPRESSION, PLUMBING & HVAC	100.3	68.7	87.6	97.1	69.0	85.8	99.9	69.0	87.5	100.0	69.0	87.5	97.1	69.0	85.8	97.1	68.7	85.6
26, 27, 3370 ELECTRICAL, COMMUNICATIONS & UTIL.	92.1	71.2	81.0	90.6	71.2	80.4	91.7	71.2	80.9	102.9	71.2	86.2	88.5	71.2	79.4	92.3	71.2	81.2
MF2014 WEIGHTED AVERAGE	96.1	69.4	84.4	98.0	72.6	86.9	100.0	72.6	88.0	100.8	72.6	88.5	97.6	72.6	86.7	97.5	69.4	85.2

NEW MEXICO / NEW YORK

DIVISION		NEW MEXICO TUCUMCARI 884			NEW YORK ALBANY 120-122			BINGHAMTON 137-139			BRONX 104			BROOKLYN 112			BUFFALO 140-142		
		MAT.	INST.	TOTAL	MAT.	INST.	TOTAL	MAT.	INST.	TOTAL	MAT.	INST.	TOTAL	MAT.	INST.	TOTAL	MAT.	INST.	TOTAL
015433	CONTRACTOR EQUIPMENT		110.1	110.1		112.9	112.9		114.1	114.1		110.6	110.6		113.3	113.3		97.1	97.1
0241, 31 - 34	SITE & INFRASTRUCTURE, DEMOLITION	93.8	103.3	100.5	83.8	106.3	99.8	95.9	94.1	94.6	108.8	120.8	117.3	120.3	127.6	125.5	98.3	98.2	98.2
0310	Concrete Forming & Accessories	99.2	64.5	69.2	100.1	100.6	100.5	100.8	88.5	90.2	98.4	175.3	164.8	107.2	182.9	172.5	97.3	116.5	113.9
0320	Concrete Reinforcing	106.0	68.9	87.1	104.0	103.8	103.9	93.7	97.8	95.8	103.9	184.4	144.9	95.1	205.9	151.5	97.8	102.1	100.0
0330	Cast-in-Place Concrete	95.7	70.3	85.3	91.9	111.3	99.9	102.7	127.9	113.1	95.9	173.4	127.7	104.8	172.1	132.4	106.7	119.7	112.0
03	CONCRETE	105.0	68.4	87.0	99.0	105.4	102.1	95.8	105.2	100.4	96.1	174.8	134.8	107.5	181.3	143.7	103.0	114.1	108.4
04	MASONRY	114.6	58.7	79.8	101.0	112.6	108.2	109.7	127.8	121.0	92.7	177.5	145.5	120.2	177.4	155.9	105.1	121.0	115.0
05	METALS	99.2	86.7	95.3	104.1	110.3	106.0	96.3	118.9	103.3	99.9	151.6	115.8	104.4	150.1	118.4	99.6	95.4	98.3
06	WOOD, PLASTICS & COMPOSITES	93.1	65.5	77.6	98.7	97.9	98.3	104.9	84.7	93.6	94.4	174.9	139.5	106.9	185.1	150.6	99.4	116.4	108.9
07	THERMAL & MOISTURE PROTECTION	99.1	73.5	88.6	105.9	105.8	105.9	107.3	103.6	105.8	108.5	163.2	131.0	108.4	164.1	131.2	101.8	110.6	105.4
08	OPENINGS	98.5	67.7	91.3	102.6	94.0	100.6	93.0	85.0	91.1	87.9	175.5	108.3	90.4	180.0	111.2	97.7	103.9	99.1
0920	Plaster & Gypsum Board	78.6	64.2	68.8	97.2	97.6	97.5	107.4	83.8	91.4	99.2	176.9	151.7	102.8	187.6	160.2	98.3	116.7	110.7
0950, 0980	Ceilings & Acoustic Treatment	96.3	64.2	75.2	92.4	97.6	95.8	91.1	83.8	86.3	83.8	176.9	145.0	87.1	187.6	153.2	102.0	116.7	111.6
0960	Flooring	101.2	66.0	91.2	97.1	113.7	101.9	106.8	103.6	105.9	98.3	186.8	123.6	113.9	186.8	134.8	101.3	121.2	107.0
0970, 0990	Wall Finishes & Painting/Coating	103.3	66.6	81.1	103.8	94.3	98.0	93.3	98.8	96.6	102.9	157.4	135.8	123.4	157.4	143.9	98.8	112.4	107.0
09	FINISHES	95.4	64.8	78.5	94.7	101.9	98.7	94.9	91.1	92.8	94.0	175.9	139.1	108.4	181.9	148.9	100.6	117.9	110.2
COVERS	DIVS. 10 - 14, 25, 28, 41, 43, 44, 46	100.0	82.9	96.5	100.0	99.0	99.8	100.0	96.2	99.2	100.0	135.0	107.1	100.0	135.4	107.1	100.0	105.6	101.1
21, 22, 23	FIRE SUPPRESSION, PLUMBING & HVAC	97.2	68.7	85.7	100.0	102.8	101.1	100.5	90.2	96.3	100.2	165.5	126.6	99.7	165.4	126.2	100.0	96.7	98.7
26, 27, 3370	ELECTRICAL, COMMUNICATIONS & UTIL.	92.8	71.2	81.4	98.7	104.1	101.6	99.9	105.4	102.8	97.0	181.9	141.9	99.7	181.9	143.1	100.2	102.7	101.5
MF2014	WEIGHTED AVERAGE	99.0	72.5	87.4	100.1	104.7	102.1	98.5	101.4	99.8	97.7	166.1	127.5	102.8	168.5	131.4	100.3	106.2	102.9

NEW YORK

DIVISION		ELMIRA 148-149			FAR ROCKAWAY 116			FLUSHING 113			GLENS FALLS 128			HICKSVILLE 115,117,118			JAMAICA 114		
		MAT.	INST.	TOTAL	MAT.	INST.	TOTAL	MAT.	INST.	TOTAL	MAT.	INST.	TOTAL	MAT.	INST.	TOTAL	MAT.	INST.	TOTAL
015433	CONTRACTOR EQUIPMENT		116.0	116.0		113.3	113.3		113.3	113.3		112.9	112.9		113.3	113.3		113.3	113.3
0241, 31 - 34	SITE & INFRASTRUCTURE, DEMOLITION	97.1	94.1	95.0	123.4	127.6	126.4	123.4	127.6	126.4	73.6	105.8	96.5	113.3	126.3	122.6	117.7	127.6	124.7
0310	Concrete Forming & Accessories	81.3	93.2	91.6	93.5	175.1	163.9	97.3	175.1	164.4	85.7	90.3	89.7	90.0	154.5	145.6	97.3	175.1	164.4
0320	Concrete Reinforcing	97.4	95.7	96.5	95.1	205.9	151.5	96.7	205.9	152.3	95.4	94.4	94.9	95.1	210.2	153.7	95.1	205.9	151.5
0330	Cast-in-Place Concrete	93.7	103.2	97.6	113.3	172.1	137.5	113.3	172.1	137.5	85.3	106.7	94.1	96.3	165.5	124.7	104.8	172.1	132.4
03	CONCRETE	90.8	98.6	94.6	113.6	177.8	145.1	114.1	177.8	145.4	88.3	97.5	92.9	99.4	167.1	132.6	106.8	177.8	141.7
04	MASONRY	103.5	102.1	102.6	124.1	177.4	157.4	118.1	177.4	155.1	100.7	105.6	103.7	114.6	166.8	147.1	122.2	177.4	156.6
05	METALS	96.7	117.3	103.0	104.4	150.1	118.4	104.4	150.1	118.4	97.7	106.1	100.3	105.8	149.1	119.2	104.4	150.1	118.4
06	WOOD, PLASTICS & COMPOSITES	85.0	92.2	89.0	90.1	174.6	137.4	94.8	174.6	139.5	87.1	87.6	87.3	86.6	152.6	123.6	94.8	174.6	139.5
07	THERMAL & MOISTURE PROTECTION	103.9	94.1	99.9	108.3	163.0	130.7	108.3	163.0	130.7	98.8	97.2	98.2	107.9	156.3	127.8	108.1	163.0	130.6
08	OPENINGS	99.4	88.9	97.0	89.0	174.4	108.8	89.0	174.4	108.8	93.3	86.2	91.7	89.0	163.4	106.3	89.0	174.4	108.8
0920	Plaster & Gypsum Board	97.8	91.7	93.7	91.6	176.9	149.2	94.1	176.9	150.0	89.1	87.0	87.7	91.2	154.2	133.8	94.1	176.9	150.0
0950, 0980	Ceilings & Acoustic Treatment	95.4	91.7	93.0	76.2	176.9	142.4	76.2	176.9	142.4	82.1	87.0	85.3	75.2	154.2	127.2	76.2	176.9	142.4
0960	Flooring	94.6	103.6	97.1	109.2	186.8	131.4	110.6	186.8	132.4	86.2	111.3	93.3	108.3	185.1	130.2	110.6	186.8	132.4
0970, 0990	Wall Finishes & Painting/Coating	98.9	90.0	93.5	123.4	157.4	143.9	123.4	157.4	143.9	101.1	87.4	92.8	123.4	157.4	143.9	123.4	157.4	143.9
09	FINISHES	95.5	94.7	95.0	103.5	175.7	143.3	104.3	175.7	143.6	86.1	93.1	90.0	102.1	159.7	133.8	103.8	175.7	143.4
COVERS	DIVS. 10 - 14, 25, 28, 41, 43, 44, 46	100.0	99.4	99.9	100.0	134.2	106.9	100.0	134.2	106.9	100.0	96.2	99.2	100.0	128.2	105.7	100.0	134.2	106.9
21, 22, 23	FIRE SUPPRESSION, PLUMBING & HVAC	95.5	91.5	93.9	95.0	165.3	123.4	95.0	165.3	123.4	95.5	95.7	95.6	99.7	154.4	121.8	95.0	165.3	123.4
26, 27, 3370	ELECTRICAL, COMMUNICATIONS & UTIL.	96.5	96.2	96.3	107.0	181.9	146.6	107.0	181.9	146.6	93.6	100.5	97.3	99.0	143.4	122.5	97.9	181.9	142.3
MF2014	WEIGHTED AVERAGE	96.7	97.4	97.0	102.6	166.8	130.6	102.5	166.8	130.5	94.0	98.6	96.0	100.9	153.3	123.7	100.8	166.8	129.6

NEW YORK

DIVISION		JAMESTOWN 147			KINGSTON 124			LONG ISLAND CITY 111			MONTICELLO 127			MOUNT VERNON 105			NEW ROCHELLE 108		
		MAT.	INST.	TOTAL	MAT.	INST.	TOTAL	MAT.	INST.	TOTAL	MAT.	INST.	TOTAL	MAT.	INST.	TOTAL	MAT.	INST.	TOTAL
015433	CONTRACTOR EQUIPMENT		93.9	93.9		113.3	113.3		113.3	113.3		113.3	113.3		110.6	110.6		110.6	110.6
0241, 31 - 34	SITE & INFRASTRUCTURE, DEMOLITION	98.4	94.2	95.4	140.6	122.9	128.0	121.3	127.6	125.8	135.5	122.7	126.4	115.2	118.5	117.6	114.6	118.5	117.4
0310	Concrete Forming & Accessories	81.3	86.9	86.1	87.1	104.4	102.0	101.6	175.1	165.0	94.7	102.9	101.8	88.8	139.1	132.1	103.6	139.0	134.2
0320	Concrete Reinforcing	97.6	98.9	98.2	95.8	140.6	118.6	95.1	205.9	151.5	95.1	140.1	118.0	102.9	183.3	143.8	103.0	183.3	143.9
0330	Cast-in-Place Concrete	97.2	102.1	99.2	115.2	135.1	123.4	108.1	172.1	134.4	107.8	124.8	114.8	107.1	141.3	121.1	107.0	141.3	121.1
03	CONCRETE	93.8	94.3	94.0	110.8	121.5	116.0	109.9	177.8	143.3	105.5	117.2	111.2	105.4	146.9	125.8	105.0	146.9	125.6
04	MASONRY	111.8	99.9	104.4	116.0	141.3	131.8	116.9	177.4	154.6	108.6	128.7	121.1	98.1	147.3	128.8	98.1	147.3	128.8
05	METALS	94.0	92.1	93.5	106.1	117.2	109.5	104.4	150.1	118.4	106.0	116.2	109.2	99.6	135.6	110.7	99.9	135.6	110.9
06	WOOD, PLASTICS & COMPOSITES	83.5	84.0	83.8	88.4	96.4	92.9	100.9	174.6	142.2	96.1	96.4	96.3	84.6	136.2	113.5	101.4	136.2	120.9
07	THERMAL & MOISTURE PROTECTION	103.4	93.5	99.3	122.3	137.2	128.4	108.3	163.0	130.7	122.0	132.1	126.1	109.4	144.1	123.6	109.5	144.1	123.7
08	OPENINGS	99.2	85.6	96.1	95.9	117.3	100.9	89.0	174.4	108.8	91.1	117.3	97.2	87.9	148.6	102.0	88.0	148.6	102.1
0920	Plaster & Gypsum Board	88.5	83.2	84.9	91.4	96.3	94.7	98.7	176.9	151.5	92.1	96.3	94.9	94.9	137.0	123.3	106.3	137.0	127.0
0950, 0980	Ceilings & Acoustic Treatment	92.0	83.2	86.2	72.9	96.3	88.3	76.2	176.9	142.4	72.9	96.3	88.3	82.1	137.0	118.2	82.1	137.0	118.2
0960	Flooring	97.7	103.6	99.4	103.8	72.5	94.9	112.1	186.8	133.5	106.1	72.5	96.5	90.2	186.8	117.8	97.1	186.8	122.8
0970, 0990	Wall Finishes & Painting/Coating	100.2	94.2	96.6	134.4	116.8	123.8	123.4	157.4	143.9	134.4	116.8	123.8	101.1	157.4	135.1	101.1	157.4	135.1
09	FINISHES	94.6	89.9	92.0	101.0	97.1	98.8	105.1	175.7	144.0	101.4	96.3	98.6	91.2	149.2	123.2	94.6	149.2	124.7
COVERS	DIVS. 10 - 14, 25, 28, 41, 43, 44, 46	100.0	98.9	99.7	100.0	111.9	102.4	100.0	134.2	106.9	100.0	110.8	102.2	100.0	125.2	105.1	100.0	121.9	104.4
21, 22, 23	FIRE SUPPRESSION, PLUMBING & HVAC	95.4	87.2	92.1	95.4	122.3	106.3	99.7	165.3	126.2	95.4	116.7	104.0	95.5	134.1	111.1	95.5	134.1	111.1
26, 27, 3370	ELECTRICAL, COMMUNICATIONS & UTIL.	95.4	96.3	95.9	95.1	111.0	103.5	98.5	181.9	142.6	95.1	111.0	103.5	95.2	155.2	126.9	95.2	155.2	126.9
MF2014	WEIGHTED AVERAGE	96.8	92.5	94.9	102.6	118.5	109.6	102.4	166.8	130.5	101.1	115.1	107.2	97.5	141.4	116.6	97.9	141.3	116.8

City Cost Indexes

NEW YORK

DIVISION		NEW YORK 100-102 MAT.	INST.	TOTAL	NIAGARA FALLS 143 MAT.	INST.	TOTAL	PLATTSBURGH 129 MAT.	INST.	TOTAL	POUGHKEEPSIE 125-126 MAT.	INST.	TOTAL	QUEENS 110 MAT.	INST.	TOTAL	RIVERHEAD 119 MAT.	INST.	TOTAL
015433	CONTRACTOR EQUIPMENT		111.1	111.1		93.9	93.9		98.9	98.9		113.3	113.3		113.3	113.3		113.3	113.3
0241, 31-34	SITE & INFRASTRUCTURE, DEMOLITION	117.3	121.5	120.2	100.5	95.5	97.0	106.1	103.0	103.9	136.5	123.5	127.2	116.6	127.6	124.4	114.5	125.9	122.6
0310	Concrete Forming & Accessories	102.6	183.3	172.2	81.3	114.4	109.8	91.1	95.4	94.9	87.1	165.0	154.3	90.1	175.1	163.4	94.6	153.4	145.3
0320	Concrete Reinforcing	109.9	210.4	161.0	96.3	102.5	99.5	99.9	102.7	101.3	95.8	141.0	118.8	96.7	205.9	152.3	96.9	184.2	141.3
0330	Cast-in-Place Concrete	107.8	177.7	136.5	100.6	120.3	108.7	104.4	104.4	104.4	111.5	137.9	122.4	99.6	172.1	129.4	97.9	164.5	125.3
03	CONCRETE	106.2	184.2	144.5	95.9	113.3	104.4	102.5	99.3	101.0	107.9	149.5	128.3	102.6	177.8	139.6	100.1	161.4	130.2
04	MASONRY	102.5	177.5	149.2	119.9	127.5	124.6	95.0	101.6	99.1	108.6	144.5	131.0	111.1	177.4	152.4	119.9	166.3	148.8
05	METALS	113.1	151.9	125.0	96.7	93.8	95.8	102.0	91.2	98.7	106.1	119.8	110.3	104.4	150.1	118.4	106.3	138.4	116.2
06	WOOD, PLASTICS & COMPOSITES	98.5	185.4	147.2	83.4	110.3	98.5	93.8	93.5	93.6	88.4	174.6	136.7	86.7	174.6	135.9	91.8	152.6	125.9
07	THERMAL & MOISTURE PROTECTION	108.6	164.5	131.5	103.5	112.9	107.4	116.3	100.5	109.8	122.3	146.8	132.3	107.9	163.0	130.5	108.8	156.1	128.2
08	OPENINGS	93.7	180.9	114.0	99.2	100.7	99.6	101.6	90.8	99.1	95.9	159.5	110.7	89.0	174.4	108.8	89.0	157.5	104.9
0920	Plaster & Gypsum Board	106.0	187.6	161.2	88.5	110.3	103.3	109.4	92.6	98.0	91.4	176.9	149.2	91.2	176.9	149.1	92.5	154.2	134.2
0950, 0980	Ceilings & Acoustic Treatment	102.2	187.6	158.4	92.0	110.3	104.1	98.1	92.6	94.5	72.9	176.9	141.2	76.2	176.9	142.4	76.1	154.2	127.5
0960	Flooring	99.5	186.8	124.5	97.7	121.2	104.4	108.9	113.7	110.3	103.8	167.2	122.0	108.3	186.8	130.7	109.2	142.7	118.8
0970, 0990	Wall Finishes & Painting/Coating	102.9	157.4	135.8	100.2	112.4	107.6	130.0	91.4	106.7	134.4	117.2	124.0	123.4	157.4	143.9	123.4	157.4	143.9
09	FINISHES	99.9	182.1	145.2	94.7	115.9	106.4	97.9	98.0	98.0	100.8	163.0	135.1	102.5	175.7	142.8	102.7	151.3	129.5
COVERS	DIVS. 10-14, 25, 28, 41, 43, 44, 46	100.0	136.1	107.3	100.0	107.1	101.4	100.0	98.0	99.6	100.0	121.6	104.4	100.0	134.2	106.9	100.0	127.6	105.6
21, 22, 23	FIRE SUPPRESSION, PLUMBING & HVAC	100.1	165.5	126.5	95.4	100.0	97.2	95.4	96.6	95.9	95.4	127.0	108.1	99.7	165.3	126.2	99.9	151.4	120.7
26, 27, 3370	ELECTRICAL, COMMUNICATIONS & UTIL.	104.7	181.9	145.5	94.0	100.3	97.3	91.6	90.3	90.9	95.1	119.9	108.2	99.0	181.9	142.8	100.6	133.6	118.1
MF2014	WEIGHTED AVERAGE	103.4	168.7	131.8	97.8	106.4	101.5	99.1	96.7	98.0	101.8	136.7	117.0	100.9	166.8	129.6	101.6	148.2	121.9

NEW YORK

DIVISION		ROCHESTER 144-146 MAT.	INST.	TOTAL	SCHENECTADY 123 MAT.	INST.	TOTAL	STATEN ISLAND 103 MAT.	INST.	TOTAL	SUFFERN 109 MAT.	INST.	TOTAL	SYRACUSE 130-132 MAT.	INST.	TOTAL	UTICA 133-135 MAT.	INST.	TOTAL
015433	CONTRACTOR EQUIPMENT		116.7	116.7		112.9	112.9		110.6	110.6		110.6	110.6		112.9	112.9		112.9	112.9
0241, 31-34	SITE & INFRASTRUCTURE, DEMOLITION	85.9	109.9	102.9	84.2	106.3	99.9	119.9	120.8	120.6	111.4	116.3	114.9	94.8	105.6	102.4	73.5	104.3	95.4
0310	Concrete Forming & Accessories	98.7	98.2	98.3	103.0	100.6	100.9	88.3	183.3	170.2	96.9	135.2	129.9	99.8	91.0	92.2	101.0	87.9	89.7
0320	Concrete Reinforcing	100.1	95.7	97.9	94.4	103.8	99.2	103.9	210.4	158.1	103.0	140.9	122.3	94.7	96.4	95.6	94.7	95.7	95.2
0330	Cast-in-Place Concrete	94.2	104.4	98.4	102.9	111.3	106.4	107.1	173.5	134.4	103.8	138.2	117.9	95.4	105.9	99.7	87.3	104.7	94.4
03	CONCRETE	99.3	100.6	99.9	102.9	105.4	104.1	107.1	182.7	144.2	102.0	136.3	118.9	98.9	97.8	98.4	96.9	95.9	96.4
04	MASONRY	107.0	104.9	105.7	97.7	112.6	107.0	104.7	177.5	150.1	97.6	142.6	125.7	101.5	105.2	103.8	93.1	103.9	99.8
05	METALS	104.1	107.3	105.1	101.9	110.3	104.5	97.8	151.8	114.4	97.8	119.4	104.5	99.8	105.6	101.6	97.7	105.1	100.0
06	WOOD, PLASTICS & COMPOSITES	97.6	97.6	97.6	107.4	97.9	102.1	83.3	185.4	140.4	94.0	136.2	117.6	101.3	88.5	94.2	101.3	84.7	92.0
07	THERMAL & MOISTURE PROTECTION	103.5	101.7	102.7	100.3	105.8	102.6	108.9	164.3	131.6	109.3	142.1	122.8	102.3	97.6	100.4	90.6	97.6	93.5
08	OPENINGS	105.3	92.2	102.2	99.4	94.0	98.1	87.9	181.2	109.6	88.0	139.0	99.8	95.0	85.6	92.8	98.0	83.4	94.6
0920	Plaster & Gypsum Board	107.2	97.4	100.6	98.8	97.6	98.0	95.0	187.6	157.6	98.5	137.0	124.5	98.0	88.0	91.2	98.0	84.0	88.5
0950, 0980	Ceilings & Acoustic Treatment	100.4	97.4	98.5	88.7	97.6	94.6	83.8	187.6	152.0	82.1	137.0	118.2	91.1	88.0	89.0	91.1	84.0	86.4
0960	Flooring	93.8	113.3	99.4	92.9	113.7	98.9	94.2	186.8	120.7	93.5	185.1	119.7	94.6	102.1	96.8	92.1	102.2	95.0
0970, 0990	Wall Finishes & Painting/Coating	100.3	99.1	99.6	101.1	94.3	97.0	102.9	157.4	135.8	101.1	124.9	115.5	98.5	99.8	99.3	91.3	99.8	96.4
09	FINISHES	100.4	101.3	100.9	91.6	101.9	97.3	93.2	182.1	142.2	92.3	140.0	118.6	94.0	93.5	93.7	92.1	91.1	91.6
COVERS	DIVS. 10-14, 25, 28, 41, 43, 44, 46	100.0	99.8	100.0	100.0	99.0	99.8	100.0	136.1	107.3	100.0	123.6	104.8	100.0	96.5	99.3	100.0	96.2	99.2
21, 22, 23	FIRE SUPPRESSION, PLUMBING & HVAC	100.1	90.3	96.1	100.2	102.8	101.2	100.2	165.5	126.5	95.5	123.3	106.7	100.2	91.9	96.9	100.2	92.2	97.0
26, 27, 3370	ELECTRICAL, COMMUNICATIONS & UTIL.	98.7	94.6	96.6	98.1	104.1	101.3	97.0	181.9	141.9	102.8	119.9	111.8	100.0	102.2	101.1	98.1	102.2	100.3
MF2014	WEIGHTED AVERAGE	101.1	99.1	100.2	99.3	104.7	101.7	99.2	168.4	129.4	97.6	129.0	111.3	98.9	98.0	98.5	97.1	97.1	97.1

NEW YORK / NORTH CAROLINA

DIVISION		WATERTOWN 136 MAT.	INST.	TOTAL	WHITE PLAINS 106 MAT.	INST.	TOTAL	YONKERS 107 MAT.	INST.	TOTAL	ASHEVILLE 287-288 MAT.	INST.	TOTAL	CHARLOTTE 281-282 MAT.	INST.	TOTAL	DURHAM 277 MAT.	INST.	TOTAL
015433	CONTRACTOR EQUIPMENT		112.9	112.9		110.6	110.6		110.6	110.6		96.3	96.3		96.3	96.3		101.7	101.7
0241, 31-34	SITE & INFRASTRUCTURE, DEMOLITION	80.9	105.7	98.5	108.5	118.5	115.6	116.7	118.5	118.0	102.4	76.9	84.3	105.6	76.9	85.2	100.4	85.7	89.9
0310	Concrete Forming & Accessories	85.9	94.3	93.1	101.9	139.1	134.0	102.2	143.9	138.2	96.0	41.3	48.8	99.7	42.8	50.6	100.2	44.3	52.0
0320	Concrete Reinforcing	95.3	96.5	95.9	103.0	183.3	143.9	107.1	183.3	145.9	93.0	63.0	77.7	98.8	58.5	78.3	91.2	57.9	74.2
0330	Cast-in-Place Concrete	101.5	107.6	104.1	95.1	141.3	114.1	106.3	141.4	120.7	115.4	51.3	89.1	120.2	49.8	91.3	101.6	47.1	79.2
03	CONCRETE	109.3	99.9	104.7	95.7	146.9	120.9	105.2	149.1	126.7	106.0	50.6	78.8	108.6	49.9	79.8	98.7	49.5	74.5
04	MASONRY	94.2	107.9	102.8	97.1	147.3	128.4	102.1	147.3	130.3	93.6	43.7	62.5	101.9	51.2	70.3	86.4	37.9	56.2
05	METALS	97.8	105.6	100.2	99.3	135.6	110.5	108.9	135.7	117.1	103.1	82.3	96.7	104.0	80.9	96.9	121.4	79.9	108.6
06	WOOD, PLASTICS & COMPOSITES	83.0	92.2	88.1	99.5	136.2	120.0	99.3	142.7	123.6	97.9	40.3	65.6	103.0	41.9	68.8	96.7	44.7	67.6
07	THERMAL & MOISTURE PROTECTION	90.9	100.1	94.7	109.2	144.1	123.5	109.5	144.8	124.0	106.7	43.7	80.8	100.8	46.6	78.6	106.9	45.7	81.8
08	OPENINGS	98.0	89.4	96.0	88.0	148.6	102.1	91.1	151.7	105.2	97.1	44.1	84.8	102.5	45.0	89.1	105.8	47.1	92.2
0920	Plaster & Gypsum Board	88.7	91.7	90.8	101.3	137.0	125.4	105.6	143.6	131.3	100.1	38.3	58.3	100.0	39.9	59.4	105.9	42.8	63.3
0950, 0980	Ceilings & Acoustic Treatment	91.1	91.7	91.5	82.1	137.0	118.2	100.5	143.6	128.9	85.7	38.3	54.5	88.8	39.9	56.7	88.1	42.8	58.3
0960	Flooring	86.0	102.2	90.6	95.6	186.8	121.7	95.2	186.8	121.4	102.2	42.7	85.2	101.6	43.4	84.9	103.9	42.7	86.4
0970, 0990	Wall Finishes & Painting/Coating	91.3	96.2	94.3	101.1	157.4	135.1	101.1	157.4	135.1	113.6	40.3	69.3	113.8	49.4	74.9	105.4	37.4	64.3
09	FINISHES	89.7	95.7	93.0	92.9	149.2	123.9	98.0	153.0	128.3	95.6	40.7	65.3	95.5	42.9	66.5	96.0	42.9	66.7
COVERS	DIVS. 10-14, 25, 28, 41, 43, 44, 46	100.0	97.5	99.5	100.0	125.2	105.1	100.0	126.3	105.3	100.0	77.7	95.5	100.0	78.1	95.6	100.0	72.1	94.4
21, 22, 23	FIRE SUPPRESSION, PLUMBING & HVAC	100.2	85.9	94.4	100.3	134.1	114.0	100.3	134.1	114.0	100.4	53.4	81.4	100.0	54.1	81.5	100.5	52.9	81.3
26, 27, 3370	ELECTRICAL, COMMUNICATIONS & UTIL.	100.0	90.4	94.9	95.2	155.1	126.9	102.9	163.8	135.1	102.2	55.7	77.6	101.2	58.5	78.6	96.1	55.6	74.7
MF2014	WEIGHTED AVERAGE	98.5	96.3	97.5	97.6	141.4	116.7	102.1	143.7	120.2	100.8	55.3	80.9	101.9	56.8	82.2	102.9	55.3	82.1

For customer support on your Site Work & Landscape Cost Data, call 877.737.1594.

NORTH CAROLINA

DIVISION		ELIZABETH CITY 279			FAYETTEVILLE 283			GASTONIA 280			GREENSBORO 270,272-274			HICKORY 286			KINSTON 285		
		MAT.	INST.	TOTAL	MAT.	INST.	TOTAL	MAT.	INST.	TOTAL	MAT.	INST.	TOTAL	MAT.	INST.	TOTAL	MAT.	INST.	TOTAL
015433	CONTRACTOR EQUIPMENT		106.0	106.0		101.7	101.7		96.3	96.3		101.7	101.7		101.7	101.7		101.7	101.7
0241,31-34	SITE & INFRASTRUCTURE, DEMOLITION	104.6	87.4	92.4	101.7	85.6	90.3	102.3	76.9	84.2	100.3	85.7	89.9	101.2	85.5	90.1	100.3	85.6	89.8
0310	Concrete Forming & Accessories	85.3	42.5	48.4	95.6	60.3	65.2	103.1	38.7	47.5	99.9	44.4	52.1	92.0	37.1	44.6	88.2	42.1	48.4
0320	Concrete Reinforcing	89.2	45.9	67.2	96.8	58.0	77.0	93.5	56.5	74.7	90.1	58.0	73.8	93.0	56.1	74.2	92.5	45.8	68.7
0330	Cast-in-Place Concrete	101.8	47.0	79.3	121.0	48.3	91.2	112.8	52.7	88.1	100.8	47.6	79.0	115.4	48.1	87.7	111.4	44.8	84.0
03	CONCRETE	98.7	46.4	73.0	108.1	57.1	83.1	104.5	48.7	77.1	98.1	49.8	74.4	105.7	46.3	76.5	102.4	45.5	74.4
04	MASONRY	98.6	48.0	67.1	97.3	38.9	60.9	98.3	50.9	68.7	82.5	41.4	56.9	82.3	43.7	58.2	89.1	48.1	63.6
05	METALS	107.1	75.8	97.5	124.2	80.0	110.6	103.9	80.0	96.5	113.7	80.0	103.4	103.2	78.7	95.7	102.0	74.8	93.6
06	WOOD, PLASTICS & COMPOSITES	80.1	43.6	59.7	97.1	66.8	80.1	107.0	36.6	67.6	96.4	44.9	67.6	92.1	35.2	60.2	88.6	42.9	63.0
07	THERMAL & MOISTURE PROTECTION	106.2	43.3	80.4	106.3	45.9	81.5	106.9	45.2	81.6	106.7	42.8	80.5	107.0	41.7	80.2	106.8	42.8	80.6
08	OPENINGS	102.6	38.4	87.7	97.2	59.1	88.4	100.9	41.0	87.0	105.8	47.2	92.2	97.2	36.8	83.1	97.3	43.1	84.7
0920	Plaster & Gypsum Board	98.6	41.0	59.7	104.7	65.6	78.3	107.0	34.5	58.0	107.5	43.0	63.9	100.1	33.1	54.8	99.8	41.0	60.1
0950,0980	Ceilings & Acoustic Treatment	88.1	41.0	57.1	86.5	65.6	72.7	89.0	34.5	53.2	88.1	43.0	58.4	85.7	33.1	51.1	89.0	41.0	57.4
0960	Flooring	95.7	23.2	75.0	102.4	42.7	85.3	105.4	42.7	87.4	103.9	39.7	85.6	102.1	32.8	82.3	99.6	22.6	77.6
0970,0990	Wall Finishes & Painting/Coating	105.4	42.0	67.1	113.6	33.2	65.0	113.6	40.3	69.3	105.4	31.6	60.9	113.6	40.3	69.3	113.6	39.2	68.7
09	FINISHES	93.0	38.7	63.0	96.5	55.3	73.8	98.1	38.6	65.3	96.3	41.9	66.3	95.8	35.4	62.5	95.5	38.0	63.8
COVERS	DIVS. 10-14, 25, 28, 41, 43, 44, 46	100.0	79.4	95.8	100.0	74.3	94.8	100.0	77.3	95.4	100.0	75.9	95.1	100.0	77.1	95.4	100.0	71.6	94.3
21,22,23	FIRE SUPPRESSION, PLUMBING & HVAC	95.6	51.1	77.7	100.2	52.7	81.0	100.4	52.4	81.0	100.4	53.1	81.3	95.6	52.2	78.1	95.6	51.2	77.7
26,27,3370	ELECTRICAL, COMMUNICATIONS & UTIL.	95.9	34.5	63.4	101.4	50.7	74.6	101.6	57.4	78.2	95.2	55.7	74.3	99.6	57.4	77.3	99.4	46.1	71.2
MF2014	WEIGHTED AVERAGE	99.3	51.6	78.5	104.5	58.1	84.2	101.6	55.1	81.3	101.3	55.7	81.4	98.8	53.9	79.2	98.4	52.7	78.5

NORTH CAROLINA / NORTH DAKOTA

DIVISION		MURPHY 289			RALEIGH 275-276			ROCKY MOUNT 278			WILMINGTON 284			WINSTON-SALEM 271			BISMARCK 585		
		MAT.	INST.	TOTAL	MAT.	INST.	TOTAL	MAT.	INST.	TOTAL	MAT.	INST.	TOTAL	MAT.	INST.	TOTAL	MAT.	INST.	TOTAL
015433	CONTRACTOR EQUIPMENT		96.3	96.3		101.7	101.7		101.7	101.7		96.3	96.3		101.7	101.7		98.2	98.2
0241,31-34	SITE & INFRASTRUCTURE, DEMOLITION	103.5	76.7	84.5	101.3	85.7	90.2	102.6	85.7	90.6	103.7	77.1	84.8	100.6	85.7	90.0	101.4	96.9	98.2
0310	Concrete Forming & Accessories	103.7	39.3	48.2	98.9	46.6	53.8	91.9	44.2	50.8	97.5	48.8	55.5	101.9	48.0	55.4	104.9	40.8	49.6
0320	Concrete Reinforcing	92.6	45.4	68.6	96.2	56.0	75.7	89.2	55.8	72.2	93.7	57.9	75.5	90.1	57.9	73.7	99.9	92.7	96.2
0330	Cast-in-Place Concrete	119.4	44.4	88.6	106.7	51.4	84.0	99.6	47.7	78.3	115.0	49.5	88.1	103.4	50.0	81.4	102.6	47.5	79.9
03	CONCRETE	109.2	44.1	77.2	101.7	51.7	77.1	99.5	49.3	74.9	105.9	52.4	79.6	99.4	52.2	76.2	101.5	54.2	78.3
04	MASONRY	85.3	41.2	57.8	86.6	42.2	58.9	76.7	39.5	53.5	82.8	41.7	57.2	82.7	38.6	55.2	114.6	56.4	78.3
05	METALS	100.9	74.2	92.7	105.7	79.2	97.5	106.3	78.4	97.7	102.7	79.9	95.7	110.8	79.9	101.3	103.4	88.4	98.8
06	WOOD, PLASTICS & COMPOSITES	107.8	39.7	69.7	95.1	47.5	68.5	87.4	44.7	63.5	100.1	49.0	71.5	96.4	49.4	70.1	95.3	34.7	61.4
07	THERMAL & MOISTURE PROTECTION	106.9	40.8	79.8	100.5	47.0	78.5	106.6	40.8	79.7	106.7	46.9	82.2	106.7	43.5	80.8	112.4	51.3	87.4
08	OPENINGS	97.1	38.9	83.5	104.8	47.4	91.4	101.8	41.9	87.9	97.3	51.0	86.5	105.8	49.7	92.8	108.0	50.1	94.5
0920	Plaster & Gypsum Board	106.1	37.6	59.8	99.8	45.7	63.3	100.5	42.8	61.5	102.4	47.2	65.1	107.5	47.6	67.0	98.8	33.0	54.3
0950,0980	Ceilings & Acoustic Treatment	85.7	37.6	54.1	88.8	45.7	60.5	85.6	42.8	57.5	86.5	47.2	60.7	88.1	47.6	61.5	112.9	33.0	60.4
0960	Flooring	105.7	24.1	82.4	101.2	42.7	84.5	99.4	21.8	77.2	102.9	44.4	86.2	103.9	42.7	86.4	99.4	72.1	91.6
0970,0990	Wall Finishes & Painting/Coating	113.6	39.4	68.8	104.2	36.9	63.5	105.4	38.5	65.0	113.6	38.7	68.4	105.4	36.7	64.0	101.9	29.4	58.1
09	FINISHES	97.7	36.1	63.7	95.5	44.7	67.5	93.9	39.3	63.8	96.3	46.8	69.0	96.3	45.7	68.4	102.7	42.8	69.7
COVERS	DIVS. 10-14, 25, 28, 41, 43, 44, 46	100.0	76.9	95.3	100.0	72.6	94.5	100.0	72.5	94.5	100.0	73.8	94.7	100.0	78.7	95.7	100.0	82.5	96.5
21,22,23	FIRE SUPPRESSION, PLUMBING & HVAC	95.6	50.9	77.6	100.0	52.5	80.8	95.6	52.7	78.3	100.4	54.9	82.0	100.4	53.3	81.4	100.1	71.9	88.7
26,27,3370	ELECTRICAL, COMMUNICATIONS & UTIL.	103.2	29.3	64.1	98.3	40.4	67.7	97.9	39.7	67.1	102.4	50.7	75.1	95.2	55.7	74.3	102.5	71.6	86.2
MF2014	WEIGHTED AVERAGE	99.6	48.3	77.2	100.5	54.1	80.3	98.5	52.3	78.3	100.3	55.9	81.0	101.0	56.5	81.6	103.1	66.2	87.0

NORTH DAKOTA

DIVISION		DEVILS LAKE 583			DICKINSON 586			FARGO 580-581			GRAND FORKS 582			JAMESTOWN 584			MINOT 587		
		MAT.	INST.	TOTAL	MAT.	INST.	TOTAL	MAT.	INST.	TOTAL	MAT.	INST.	TOTAL	MAT.	INST.	TOTAL	MAT.	INST.	TOTAL
015433	CONTRACTOR EQUIPMENT		98.2	98.2		98.2	98.2		98.2	98.2		98.2	98.2		98.2	98.2		98.2	98.2
0241,31-34	SITE & INFRASTRUCTURE, DEMOLITION	105.7	94.4	97.7	113.6	92.9	99.9	102.6	96.9	98.5	109.6	92.9	97.7	104.7	92.9	96.3	107.1	96.9	99.8
0310	Concrete Forming & Accessories	101.2	35.4	44.4	90.8	34.9	42.5	99.3	41.5	49.4	94.5	34.2	42.5	92.3	34.1	42.1	90.5	67.0	70.2
0320	Concrete Reinforcing	100.2	93.1	96.6	101.1	92.8	96.9	96.9	92.8	94.8	98.7	92.9	95.7	100.8	91.3	95.9	102.1	93.2	97.6
0330	Cast-in-Place Concrete	126.3	46.0	93.3	114.3	44.4	85.6	113.6	49.2	87.2	114.3	44.1	85.5	124.7	44.1	91.6	114.3	46.5	86.4
03	CONCRETE	110.6	51.3	81.5	109.6	50.2	80.4	105.9	55.1	80.9	106.8	49.8	78.8	109.1	48.7	79.5	105.5	65.6	85.9
04	MASONRY	121.7	64.9	86.3	124.3	60.4	84.5	114.2	56.4	78.2	115.9	64.4	83.8	135.1	32.8	71.3	114.2	65.4	83.8
05	METALS	99.9	87.4	96.0	99.8	82.5	94.5	103.0	88.7	98.6	99.8	82.1	94.4	99.8	63.7	88.7	100.1	89.3	96.8
06	WOOD, PLASTICS & COMPOSITES	95.2	32.0	59.8	83.1	32.0	54.5	92.9	35.2	60.6	87.4	32.0	56.4	85.0	32.0	55.3	82.8	70.1	75.7
07	THERMAL & MOISTURE PROTECTION	107.6	49.8	83.9	108.1	48.5	83.7	107.4	51.6	84.5	107.8	49.8	84.0	107.4	41.5	80.4	107.5	57.4	87.0
08	OPENINGS	100.7	42.7	87.2	100.7	42.7	87.2	100.5	50.3	88.9	100.7	42.7	87.2	100.7	32.2	84.8	100.9	69.3	93.5
0920	Plaster & Gypsum Board	118.4	30.2	58.8	109.1	30.2	55.8	96.6	33.5	54.0	110.5	30.2	56.2	110.2	30.2	56.1	109.1	69.4	82.3
0950,0980	Ceilings & Acoustic Treatment	114.3	30.2	59.0	114.3	30.2	59.0	112.1	33.5	60.5	114.3	30.2	59.0	114.3	30.2	59.0	114.3	69.4	84.8
0960	Flooring	107.9	35.9	87.3	101.4	35.9	82.7	102.8	72.1	94.0	103.3	35.9	84.0	102.1	35.9	83.2	101.1	89.3	97.8
0970,0990	Wall Finishes & Painting/Coating	104.4	22.5	54.9	104.4	31.5	60.4	101.2	70.7	82.8	104.4	28.2	58.4	104.4	22.5	54.9	104.4	27.9	58.2
09	FINISHES	108.2	32.2	66.3	105.9	33.2	65.8	103.8	47.7	72.9	106.1	32.8	65.7	105.3	32.2	65.0	105.0	67.0	84.1
COVERS	DIVS. 10-14, 25, 28, 41, 43, 44, 46	100.0	32.4	86.3	100.0	32.6	86.4	100.0	82.6	96.5	100.0	32.5	86.4	100.0	80.6	96.1	100.0	86.4	97.3
21,22,23	FIRE SUPPRESSION, PLUMBING & HVAC	95.6	74.0	86.9	95.6	66.2	83.7	100.1	77.0	90.8	100.4	33.3	73.3	95.6	35.0	71.2	100.4	60.2	84.2
26,27,3370	ELECTRICAL, COMMUNICATIONS & UTIL.	98.3	35.8	65.3	107.7	72.5	89.1	102.4	68.4	84.4	102.1	53.5	76.4	98.3	35.7	65.2	105.5	75.7	89.8
MF2014	WEIGHTED AVERAGE	102.0	58.6	83.1	102.8	60.9	84.6	102.7	67.6	87.4	102.7	51.6	80.4	102.1	45.2	77.3	102.7	71.3	89.0

773

For customer support on your Site Work & Landscape Cost Data, call 877.737.1594.

City Cost Indexes

DIVISION		NORTH DAKOTA WILLISTON 588 MAT.	INST.	TOTAL	AKRON 442-443 MAT.	INST.	TOTAL	OHIO ATHENS 457 MAT.	INST.	TOTAL	CANTON 446-447 MAT.	INST.	TOTAL	CHILLICOTHE 456 MAT.	INST.	TOTAL	CINCINNATI 451-452 MAT.	INST.	TOTAL
015433	CONTRACTOR EQUIPMENT		98.2	98.2		94.4	94.4		90.4	90.4		94.4	94.4		99.7	99.7		99.5	99.5
0241, 31 - 34	SITE & INFRASTRUCTURE, DEMOLITION	107.5	92.9	97.1	98.1	101.6	100.6	111.0	91.6	97.2	98.2	101.0	100.2	97.0	102.6	101.0	94.1	102.4	100.0
0310	Concrete Forming & Accessories	96.3	34.9	43.3	99.0	94.3	95.0	95.0	84.3	85.8	99.0	83.7	85.8	97.4	92.3	93.0	99.3	79.2	82.0
0320	Concrete Reinforcing	103.1	92.8	97.9	99.5	92.1	95.7	93.1	87.0	90.0	99.5	75.8	87.5	90.1	80.4	85.1	95.5	79.2	87.2
0330	Cast-in-Place Concrete	114.3	44.4	85.6	94.0	98.0	95.7	111.5	96.5	105.4	94.9	95.0	95.0	101.2	99.3	100.4	93.2	92.4	92.9
03	CONCRETE	106.9	50.2	79.1	97.3	94.4	95.9	107.6	88.6	98.3	97.7	85.7	91.8	101.9	92.4	97.2	96.3	84.0	90.3
04	MASONRY	108.8	60.4	78.7	93.3	96.2	95.1	86.4	90.4	88.9	94.0	84.3	87.9	94.0	100.5	98.1	93.7	85.0	88.2
05	METALS	100.0	82.5	94.6	95.4	81.6	91.1	103.0	80.0	95.9	95.4	74.5	88.9	94.9	85.7	92.1	97.2	84.6	93.3
06	WOOD, PLASTICS & COMPOSITES	88.8	32.0	57.0	99.1	93.6	96.0	85.7	84.9	85.3	99.5	82.8	90.2	98.4	89.6	93.5	100.9	76.8	87.4
07	THERMAL & MOISTURE PROTECTION	107.7	48.5	83.5	110.8	96.5	104.9	99.4	94.8	97.5	112.0	91.4	103.5	101.2	97.4	99.7	99.2	88.7	94.9
08	OPENINGS	100.8	42.7	87.3	110.7	93.3	106.7	101.7	82.3	97.2	104.3	77.9	98.2	93.8	83.5	91.4	102.0	77.4	96.3
0920	Plaster & Gypsum Board	110.5	30.2	56.2	96.9	93.2	94.4	91.4	84.1	86.5	98.0	82.1	87.2	93.3	89.5	90.7	94.9	76.3	82.3
0950, 0980	Ceilings & Acoustic Treatment	114.3	30.2	59.0	93.0	93.2	93.1	103.3	84.1	90.7	93.0	82.1	85.8	97.9	89.5	92.4	98.7	76.3	84.0
0960	Flooring	104.1	35.9	84.6	96.9	93.4	95.9	121.3	99.0	114.9	97.1	81.7	92.7	98.3	97.7	98.1	99.3	90.7	96.8
0970, 0990	Wall Finishes & Painting/Coating	104.4	31.5	60.4	96.3	106.3	102.3	100.5	99.1	99.6	96.3	83.2	88.4	97.8	92.9	94.9	97.8	83.9	89.4
09	FINISHES	106.2	33.2	66.0	98.0	95.3	96.5	101.8	89.0	94.8	98.2	82.9	89.8	98.8	93.3	95.8	99.2	81.1	89.3
COVERS	DIVS. 10 - 14, 25, 28, 41, 43, 44, 46	100.0	32.6	86.4	100.0	98.2	99.6	100.0	52.0	90.3	100.0	95.4	99.1	100.0	92.6	98.5	100.0	99.3	97.8
21, 22, 23	FIRE SUPPRESSION, PLUMBING & HVAC	95.6	66.2	83.7	100.1	94.6	97.9	95.3	51.3	77.6	100.1	81.4	92.5	95.8	95.2	95.6	100.0	83.3	93.3
26, 27, 3370	ELECTRICAL, COMMUNICATIONS & UTIL.	102.5	72.5	86.6	99.3	93.9	96.5	95.5	98.1	96.9	98.5	92.7	95.5	95.0	85.6	90.0	93.9	79.4	86.3
MF2014	WEIGHTED AVERAGE	101.2	60.9	83.7	99.9	94.2	97.4	99.6	80.4	91.2	99.3	85.6	93.3	96.8	93.0	95.1	98.3	84.5	92.2

DIVISION		OHIO CLEVELAND 441 MAT.	INST.	TOTAL	COLUMBUS 430-432 MAT.	INST.	TOTAL	DAYTON 453-454 MAT.	INST.	TOTAL	HAMILTON 450 MAT.	INST.	TOTAL	LIMA 458 MAT.	INST.	TOTAL	LORAIN 440 MAT.	INST.	TOTAL
015433	CONTRACTOR EQUIPMENT		94.7	94.7		93.6	93.6		94.7	94.7		99.7	99.7		92.9	92.9		94.4	94.4
0241, 31 - 34	SITE & INFRASTRUCTURE, DEMOLITION	98.0	102.2	101.0	95.5	98.3	97.5	92.9	101.8	99.2	92.8	102.1	99.4	104.6	91.6	95.4	97.5	102.9	101.4
0310	Concrete Forming & Accessories	99.1	99.6	99.5	100.3	84.5	86.7	99.3	79.0	81.8	99.4	79.4	82.1	95.0	86.9	88.1	99.1	86.8	88.5
0320	Concrete Reinforcing	100.0	92.5	96.2	102.7	82.6	92.5	95.5	81.3	88.3	95.5	79.2	87.2	93.1	81.5	87.2	99.5	92.4	95.9
0330	Cast-in-Place Concrete	92.2	106.5	98.1	94.1	93.7	93.9	86.7	86.4	86.6	92.9	92.7	92.8	102.4	97.5	100.4	89.5	104.1	95.5
03	CONCRETE	96.5	99.8	98.2	97.9	87.1	92.6	93.3	81.8	87.6	96.2	84.2	90.3	100.4	89.3	94.9	95.2	93.2	94.2
04	MASONRY	97.8	105.6	102.7	96.6	94.0	95.0	93.2	83.5	87.1	93.5	85.5	88.5	117.7	86.4	98.2	89.9	104.6	99.1
05	METALS	96.9	84.4	93.1	96.9	80.7	91.9	96.4	78.6	91.0	96.5	84.5	92.8	103.0	81.5	96.4	96.0	82.8	91.9
06	WOOD, PLASTICS & COMPOSITES	98.2	97.1	97.6	97.1	82.3	88.8	102.2	77.1	88.1	100.9	76.8	87.4	85.6	86.3	86.0	99.1	80.9	88.9
07	THERMAL & MOISTURE PROTECTION	109.5	108.6	109.1	100.9	94.9	98.4	104.7	87.6	97.7	101.4	88.8	96.2	99.0	95.0	97.3	111.9	103.0	108.2
08	OPENINGS	100.6	95.2	99.3	102.4	80.0	97.2	101.3	78.1	95.9	98.9	77.4	93.9	101.7	79.8	96.6	104.3	86.4	100.2
0920	Plaster & Gypsum Board	96.2	96.8	96.6	93.5	81.8	85.6	94.9	76.6	82.6	94.9	76.3	82.3	91.4	85.5	87.4	96.9	80.1	85.5
0950, 0980	Ceilings & Acoustic Treatment	91.3	96.8	94.9	97.7	81.8	87.3	99.7	76.6	84.5	98.7	76.3	84.0	102.4	85.5	91.3	93.0	80.1	84.5
0960	Flooring	96.7	105.0	99.3	92.0	90.3	91.5	102.0	80.7	95.9	99.3	90.7	96.8	120.3	92.2	112.3	97.1	105.0	99.3
0970, 0990	Wall Finishes & Painting/Coating	96.3	105.1	101.6	95.5	92.9	94.0	97.8	85.0	90.1	97.8	84.7	89.9	100.5	82.7	89.8	96.3	105.1	101.6
09	FINISHES	97.5	100.9	99.4	94.1	85.9	89.6	100.2	79.3	88.7	99.1	81.4	89.3	100.8	87.2	93.3	98.0	91.1	94.2
COVERS	DIVS. 10 - 14, 25, 28, 41, 43, 44, 46	100.0	102.5	100.5	100.0	93.3	98.6	100.0	89.1	97.8	100.0	89.5	97.9	100.0	95.2	99.0	100.0	100.3	100.1
21, 22, 23	FIRE SUPPRESSION, PLUMBING & HVAC	100.0	100.5	100.2	100.1	92.0	96.8	100.9	86.6	95.2	100.6	83.6	93.7	95.3	89.0	92.8	100.1	92.1	96.9
26, 27, 3370	ELECTRICAL, COMMUNICATIONS & UTIL.	98.8	105.0	102.1	97.6	87.8	92.4	92.6	83.0	87.5	93.0	83.3	87.9	95.8	80.3	87.6	98.7	88.0	93.0
MF2014	WEIGHTED AVERAGE	99.0	100.3	99.6	98.6	89.2	94.5	98.0	84.4	92.1	97.9	85.1	92.3	100.0	86.8	94.3	98.9	93.0	96.3

DIVISION		OHIO MANSFIELD 448-449 MAT.	INST.	TOTAL	MARION 433 MAT.	INST.	TOTAL	SPRINGFIELD 455 MAT.	INST.	TOTAL	STEUBENVILLE 439 MAT.	INST.	TOTAL	TOLEDO 434-436 MAT.	INST.	TOTAL	YOUNGSTOWN 444-445 MAT.	INST.	TOTAL
015433	CONTRACTOR EQUIPMENT		94.4	94.4		93.2	93.2		94.7	94.7		98.1	98.1		96.0	96.0		94.4	94.4
0241, 31 - 34	SITE & INFRASTRUCTURE, DEMOLITION	93.9	101.5	99.3	91.8	97.1	95.6	93.2	100.5	98.4	133.1	106.9	114.5	94.8	99.0	97.8	98.0	102.0	100.8
0310	Concrete Forming & Accessories	89.1	83.7	84.5	96.7	81.2	83.3	99.3	83.5	85.7	98.3	89.4	90.7	100.3	97.1	97.6	99.0	87.5	89.1
0320	Concrete Reinforcing	90.6	76.4	83.4	94.7	82.5	88.5	95.5	81.3	88.3	92.3	85.5	88.8	102.7	85.4	93.9	99.5	85.6	92.4
0330	Cast-in-Place Concrete	87.1	94.7	90.2	85.9	92.7	88.7	89.1	86.3	87.9	93.3	94.1	93.6	94.1	100.0	96.5	93.1	96.9	94.7
03	CONCRETE	89.7	85.7	87.7	89.9	85.1	87.6	94.4	83.8	89.2	93.8	89.7	91.8	97.9	95.5	96.7	96.9	89.8	93.4
04	MASONRY	92.4	97.0	95.3	98.8	95.5	96.7	93.4	83.5	87.2	86.2	94.2	91.2	104.8	99.9	101.7	93.6	93.6	93.6
05	METALS	96.2	75.5	89.8	96.0	78.7	90.6	96.4	78.4	90.9	92.5	79.5	88.5	96.7	85.5	93.3	95.4	78.7	90.3
06	WOOD, PLASTICS & COMPOSITES	86.7	83.7	84.9	92.8	79.8	85.5	103.6	83.6	92.4	88.4	88.3	88.3	97.1	96.9	97.0	99.1	86.1	91.8
07	THERMAL & MOISTURE PROTECTION	111.3	94.4	104.4	100.5	85.2	94.2	104.6	88.2	97.9	112.8	96.4	106.1	102.5	102.7	102.6	112.1	94.3	104.8
08	OPENINGS	104.9	76.0	98.2	96.6	76.5	91.9	99.3	79.0	94.6	97.8	83.7	94.0	99.7	91.3	97.7	104.3	85.1	99.8
0920	Plaster & Gypsum Board	90.7	80.1	83.5	91.4	79.3	83.2	94.9	83.3	87.1	90.7	87.5	88.6	93.5	96.9	95.8	96.9	85.5	89.2
0950, 0980	Ceilings & Acoustic Treatment	93.9	80.1	84.8	97.7	79.3	85.6	99.7	83.3	88.9	94.8	87.5	90.0	97.7	96.9	97.2	93.0	85.5	88.1
0960	Flooring	92.5	107.5	96.8	90.9	107.5	95.6	102.0	80.7	95.9	118.6	100.4	113.4	91.2	99.7	93.6	97.1	93.9	96.2
0970, 0990	Wall Finishes & Painting/Coating	96.3	88.5	91.6	95.5	47.5	66.5	97.8	85.0	90.1	107.8	103.1	104.9	95.6	102.0	99.4	96.3	92.6	94.1
09	FINISHES	95.8	88.2	91.6	93.1	82.6	87.3	100.2	83.2	90.8	110.0	92.6	100.4	93.8	98.1	96.2	98.1	88.8	93.0
COVERS	DIVS. 10 - 14, 25, 28, 41, 43, 44, 46	100.0	96.2	99.2	100.0	54.4	90.8	100.0	89.8	97.9	100.0	95.0	99.0	100.0	98.7	99.7	100.0	96.4	99.3
21, 22, 23	FIRE SUPPRESSION, PLUMBING & HVAC	95.3	88.9	92.7	95.3	91.0	93.4	100.9	81.3	93.0	95.7	92.0	94.2	100.1	100.4	100.2	100.1	87.1	94.8
26, 27, 3370	ELECTRICAL, COMMUNICATIONS & UTIL.	96.2	79.0	87.1	91.9	79.0	85.1	92.6	87.8	90.1	86.9	114.1	101.3	97.6	104.7	101.4	98.7	86.0	92.0
MF2014	WEIGHTED AVERAGE	96.7	87.3	92.6	95.1	85.3	90.8	98.0	84.7	92.2	96.8	94.9	96.0	98.7	98.1	98.4	99.2	89.0	94.7

For customer support on your Site Work & Landscape Cost Data, call 877.737.1594.

Section 1

DIVISION		OHIO			OKLAHOMA													
		ZANESVILLE 437 - 438			ARDMORE 734			CLINTON 736			DURANT 747			ENID 737			GUYMON 739		
		MAT.	INST.	TOTAL	MAT.	INST.	TOTAL	MAT.	INST.	TOTAL	MAT.	INST.	TOTAL	MAT.	INST.	TOTAL	MAT.	INST.	TOTAL
015433	CONTRACTOR EQUIPMENT		93.2	93.2		82.7	82.7		81.8	81.8		81.8	81.8		81.8	81.8		81.8	81.8
0241, 31 - 34	SITE & INFRASTRUCTURE, DEMOLITION	94.5	98.7	97.5	96.2	91.6	92.9	97.6	90.2	92.3	95.5	89.9	91.5	99.3	90.2	92.8	101.6	90.0	93.3
0310	Concrete Forming & Accessories	93.7	81.3	83.0	94.0	40.4	47.8	92.5	46.6	53.0	85.5	44.1	49.8	96.2	34.1	42.7	99.8	44.9	52.4
0320	Concrete Reinforcing	94.1	85.1	89.5	90.8	79.8	85.2	91.3	79.8	85.5	95.8	80.2	87.9	90.7	79.8	85.2	91.3	79.8	85.5
0330	Cast-in-Place Concrete	90.5	91.7	91.0	97.5	43.4	75.3	94.3	45.1	74.1	91.7	42.8	71.6	94.3	46.4	74.6	94.3	43.1	73.3
03	CONCRETE	93.5	85.3	89.5	95.2	49.3	72.7	94.7	52.7	74.1	92.3	50.8	71.9	95.3	47.6	71.8	98.2	51.2	75.1
04	MASONRY	95.5	85.9	89.5	103.4	57.1	74.5	129.7	57.1	84.4	95.6	62.3	74.9	110.1	57.1	77.0	105.9	53.7	73.3
05	METALS	97.4	80.4	92.1	102.5	70.1	92.5	102.6	70.1	92.6	93.5	70.7	86.5	104.0	70.0	93.6	103.2	69.8	92.9
06	WOOD, PLASTICS & COMPOSITES	88.5	79.8	83.6	97.4	37.9	64.0	96.4	46.2	68.3	88.1	43.0	62.9	100.1	29.3	60.5	104.0	46.0	71.5
07	THERMAL & MOISTURE PROTECTION	100.6	92.6	97.3	108.9	60.6	89.1	109.1	61.5	89.6	99.7	61.8	84.2	109.2	59.9	89.0	109.5	57.3	88.1
08	OPENINGS	96.6	79.3	92.5	102.9	49.0	90.3	102.9	53.3	91.4	96.3	52.0	86.0	102.9	43.9	89.1	103.0	49.2	90.5
0920	Plaster & Gypsum Board	88.2	79.3	82.2	89.8	36.6	53.8	89.4	45.2	59.6	79.4	41.9	54.1	90.5	27.8	48.1	90.7	44.9	59.8
0950, 0980	Ceilings & Acoustic Treatment	97.7	79.3	85.6	85.7	36.6	53.4	85.7	45.2	59.1	82.4	41.9	55.8	85.7	27.8	47.6	86.5	44.9	59.2
0960	Flooring	89.3	90.3	89.6	107.0	43.2	88.7	105.8	41.1	87.3	102.8	61.9	91.1	107.4	41.1	88.6	109.3	24.4	85.0
0970, 0990	Wall Finishes & Painting/Coating	95.5	92.9	94.0	104.7	51.3	72.5	104.7	51.3	72.5	103.9	51.3	72.1	104.7	51.3	72.5	104.7	33.0	61.5
09	FINISHES	92.4	83.6	87.5	92.9	40.1	63.8	92.7	44.7	66.3	90.2	46.6	66.2	93.5	34.6	61.1	94.5	38.9	63.9
COVERS	DIVS. 10 - 14, 25, 28, 41, 43, 44, 46	100.0	88.5	97.7	100.0	77.6	95.5	100.0	78.6	95.7	100.0	77.9	95.5	100.0	76.7	95.3	100.0	77.4	95.4
21, 22, 23	FIRE SUPPRESSION, PLUMBING & HVAC	95.3	89.9	93.1	95.6	65.8	83.6	95.6	65.9	83.6	95.5	65.4	83.4	100.3	65.8	86.4	95.6	63.8	82.7
26, 27, 3370	ELECTRICAL, COMMUNICATIONS & UTIL.	92.3	83.4	87.5	93.6	70.9	81.6	94.6	70.9	82.1	96.5	70.9	83.0	94.6	70.9	82.1	96.2	61.5	77.9
MF2014	WEIGHTED AVERAGE	95.6	86.5	91.6	98.3	61.9	82.4	99.6	63.1	83.7	95.1	63.5	81.3	100.2	60.5	82.9	99.4	59.7	82.1

Section 2

DIVISION		OKLAHOMA																
		LAWTON 735			MCALESTER 745			MIAMI 743			MUSKOGEE 744			OKLAHOMA CITY 730 - 731			PONCA CITY 746		
		MAT.	INST.	TOTAL	MAT.	INST.	TOTAL	MAT.	INST.	TOTAL	MAT.	INST.	TOTAL	MAT.	INST.	TOTAL	MAT.	INST.	TOTAL
015433	CONTRACTOR EQUIPMENT		82.7	82.7		81.8	81.8		89.9	89.9		89.9	89.9		83.0	83.0		81.8	81.8
0241, 31 - 34	SITE & INFRASTRUCTURE, DEMOLITION	95.7	91.6	92.8	89.1	90.1	89.9	90.5	87.3	88.2	90.8	87.1	88.2	95.1	92.0	92.9	95.9	90.1	91.8
0310	Concrete Forming & Accessories	99.8	44.3	52.0	83.5	43.6	49.1	96.9	66.2	70.4	101.4	33.4	42.7	97.7	57.9	63.4	92.2	46.3	52.6
0320	Concrete Reinforcing	91.0	79.8	85.3	95.5	79.8	87.5	94.0	79.9	86.8	94.9	79.3	87.0	96.2	79.9	87.9	94.9	79.9	87.2
0330	Cast-in-Place Concrete	91.2	46.4	72.8	80.4	45.2	65.9	84.3	47.5	69.2	85.3	45.8	69.1	92.9	46.9	74.0	94.2	44.7	73.8
03	CONCRETE	91.5	52.1	72.1	82.9	51.3	67.4	87.6	63.0	75.5	89.4	47.7	68.9	94.9	58.3	76.9	94.4	52.4	73.8
04	MASONRY	105.8	57.1	75.4	114.3	56.1	78.1	98.4	56.3	72.1	116.9	45.2	72.2	109.8	56.4	76.5	90.9	56.1	69.2
05	METALS	108.0	70.1	96.4	93.4	70.0	86.2	93.4	82.1	89.9	94.8	80.4	90.4	100.7	70.2	91.3	93.4	70.3	86.3
06	WOOD, PLASTICS & COMPOSITES	103.0	43.1	69.5	86.5	43.0	61.7	101.0	72.9	85.3	105.6	30.7	63.6	97.0	61.8	77.3	96.3	46.0	68.1
07	THERMAL & MOISTURE PROTECTION	108.9	61.3	89.4	99.4	60.6	83.5	99.8	64.3	85.2	99.9	48.6	78.8	101.1	62.9	85.4	99.9	66.2	86.1
08	OPENINGS	104.6	51.4	92.2	96.2	51.8	85.9	96.2	68.3	89.7	96.2	42.4	83.7	104.0	61.6	94.2	96.2	53.1	86.2
0920	Plaster & Gypsum Board	92.4	42.0	58.3	78.4	41.9	53.7	84.8	72.6	76.5	86.9	29.0	47.8	98.0	61.2	73.1	83.7	44.9	57.5
0950, 0980	Ceilings & Acoustic Treatment	93.2	42.0	59.6	82.4	41.9	55.8	82.4	72.6	75.9	90.8	29.0	50.2	96.4	61.2	73.3	82.4	44.9	57.8
0960	Flooring	109.7	41.1	90.1	101.8	41.1	84.4	108.8	61.9	95.4	111.3	39.8	90.8	106.2	41.1	87.6	105.9	41.1	87.4
0970, 0990	Wall Finishes & Painting/Coating	104.7	51.3	72.5	103.9	37.8	64.0	103.9	77.5	87.9	103.9	34.2	61.8	106.4	51.3	73.2	103.9	51.3	72.1
09	FINISHES	95.5	42.8	66.5	89.2	41.0	62.6	92.0	67.3	78.4	94.2	33.0	60.8	97.6	53.7	73.4	91.8	44.3	65.6
COVERS	DIVS. 10 - 14, 25, 28, 41, 43, 44, 46	100.0	78.2	95.6	100.0	77.9	95.5	100.0	81.6	96.3	100.0	76.1	95.2	100.0	80.0	96.0	100.0	78.2	95.6
21, 22, 23	FIRE SUPPRESSION, PLUMBING & HVAC	100.3	65.9	86.4	95.5	61.6	81.8	95.5	61.9	81.9	100.3	60.6	84.3	100.1	65.5	86.2	95.5	61.8	81.9
26, 27, 3370	ELECTRICAL, COMMUNICATIONS & UTIL.	96.2	70.9	82.8	94.9	64.5	78.8	96.3	64.6	79.5	94.5	52.4	72.2	101.7	70.9	85.4	94.5	70.4	81.7
MF2014	WEIGHTED AVERAGE	100.7	62.8	84.2	94.5	60.4	79.7	94.8	67.5	82.9	97.4	55.7	79.2	100.3	65.7	85.2	95.1	62.1	80.7

Section 3

DIVISION		OKLAHOMA												OREGON				
		POTEAU 749			SHAWNEE 748			TULSA 740 - 741			WOODWARD 738			BEND 977			EUGENE 974		
		MAT.	INST.	TOTAL	MAT.	INST.	TOTAL	MAT.	INST.	TOTAL	MAT.	INST.	TOTAL	MAT.	INST.	TOTAL	MAT.	INST.	TOTAL
015433	CONTRACTOR EQUIPMENT		89.1	89.1		81.8	81.8		89.9	89.9		81.8	81.8		98.8	98.8		98.8	98.8
0241, 31 - 34	SITE & INFRASTRUCTURE, DEMOLITION	77.2	85.8	83.3	99.0	90.1	92.7	97.1	87.5	90.3	97.9	90.2	92.4	105.4	102.9	103.6	96.1	102.9	100.9
0310	Concrete Forming & Accessories	90.1	41.0	47.8	85.4	43.7	49.5	101.5	40.3	48.7	92.6	46.8	53.1	110.1	98.8	100.4	106.5	98.7	99.8
0320	Concrete Reinforcing	95.9	79.8	87.7	94.9	79.8	87.3	95.1	79.8	87.3	90.7	79.9	85.2	93.3	99.6	96.5	97.4	99.6	98.5
0330	Cast-in-Place Concrete	84.3	44.9	68.1	97.2	42.9	74.9	92.9	46.2	73.7	94.3	45.3	74.2	104.4	102.7	103.7	101.1	102.6	101.7
03	CONCRETE	89.9	50.9	70.7	96.0	50.6	73.7	94.7	51.0	73.2	95.0	52.8	74.3	107.1	100.0	103.6	98.8	100.0	99.4
04	MASONRY	98.7	56.2	72.2	115.6	56.1	78.5	99.3	60.0	74.8	98.6	57.1	72.7	104.1	103.3	103.6	101.1	103.3	102.5
05	METALS	93.4	81.7	89.8	93.3	69.9	86.1	98.1	81.4	93.0	102.7	70.5	92.8	91.9	96.4	93.3	92.6	96.2	93.7
06	WOOD, PLASTICS & COMPOSITES	93.0	39.1	62.8	88.0	43.0	62.8	104.8	36.6	66.6	96.5	46.0	68.2	101.7	98.4	99.9	97.6	98.4	98.1
07	THERMAL & MOISTURE PROTECTION	99.9	60.5	83.7	99.9	59.3	83.2	99.8	62.2	84.4	109.1	66.6	91.7	107.9	94.9	102.6	107.2	91.6	100.8
08	OPENINGS	96.2	49.9	85.5	96.2	51.8	85.9	97.8	47.5	86.1	102.9	53.1	91.3	96.9	102.3	98.1	97.1	102.3	98.4
0920	Plaster & Gypsum Board	82.3	37.8	52.2	79.4	41.9	54.1	86.9	35.2	51.9	89.6	44.9	59.4	107.4	98.2	101.2	106.0	98.2	100.7
0950, 0980	Ceilings & Acoustic Treatment	82.4	37.8	53.1	82.4	41.9	55.8	90.8	35.2	54.3	86.5	44.9	59.2	91.3	98.2	95.8	92.3	98.2	96.1
0960	Flooring	105.2	61.9	92.8	102.8	32.7	82.8	110.0	42.8	90.8	105.8	43.2	87.9	110.5	103.4	108.5	108.9	103.4	107.3
0970, 0990	Wall Finishes & Painting/Coating	103.9	51.3	72.1	103.9	34.1	61.8	103.9	40.5	65.6	104.7	51.3	72.5	106.4	74.8	87.3	106.4	74.8	87.3
09	FINISHES	89.9	44.3	64.8	90.4	39.2	62.2	94.7	38.9	63.9	93.0	44.9	66.5	102.7	96.8	99.5	101.2	96.8	98.8
COVERS	DIVS. 10 - 14, 25, 28, 41, 43, 44, 46	100.0	77.7	95.5	100.0	77.9	95.5	100.0	78.8	95.7	100.0	78.5	95.7	100.0	99.6	99.9	100.0	99.6	99.9
21, 22, 23	FIRE SUPPRESSION, PLUMBING & HVAC	95.5	61.8	81.9	95.5	65.4	83.4	100.3	63.5	85.4	95.6	65.9	83.6	95.1	100.8	97.4	99.9	100.8	100.2
26, 27, 3370	ELECTRICAL, COMMUNICATIONS & UTIL.	94.6	64.6	78.7	96.6	70.9	83.0	96.5	64.6	79.6	96.1	70.9	82.8	101.6	96.1	98.7	100.1	96.1	98.0
MF2014	WEIGHTED AVERAGE	94.3	61.4	80.0	96.5	61.8	81.4	98.1	61.6	82.2	98.3	63.4	83.1	98.9	99.4	99.1	98.6	99.3	98.9

For customer support on your Site Work & Landscape Cost Data, call 877.737.1594.

775

City Cost Indexes

OREGON

DIVISION		KLAMATH FALLS 976			MEDFORD 975			PENDLETON 978			PORTLAND 970-972			SALEM 973			VALE 979		
		MAT.	INST.	TOTAL	MAT.	INST.	TOTAL	MAT.	INST.	TOTAL	MAT.	INST.	TOTAL	MAT.	INST.	TOTAL	MAT.	INST.	TOTAL
015433	CONTRACTOR EQUIPMENT		98.8	98.8		98.8	98.8		96.2	96.2		98.8	98.8		98.8	98.8		96.2	96.2
0241, 31 - 34	SITE & INFRASTRUCTURE, DEMOLITION	109.2	102.9	104.7	103.4	102.9	103.0	102.5	96.4	98.2	98.5	102.9	101.6	91.9	102.9	99.7	90.5	96.4	94.7
0310	Concrete Forming & Accessories	102.9	98.6	99.2	102.0	98.6	99.1	103.3	99.0	99.6	107.7	98.9	100.1	106.0	98.8	99.8	109.9	98.7	100.2
0320	Concrete Reinforcing	93.3	99.6	96.5	94.9	99.6	97.3	92.6	99.7	96.2	98.1	99.7	98.9	103.6	99.6	101.6	90.4	99.6	95.1
0330	Cast-in-Place Concrete	104.4	102.6	103.7	104.4	102.6	103.7	105.2	103.9	104.7	103.9	102.7	103.4	97.9	102.7	99.9	82.9	103.8	91.5
03	CONCRETE	109.7	99.9	104.9	104.6	99.9	102.3	91.4	100.6	95.9	100.3	100.1	100.2	98.2	100.0	99.1	76.9	100.4	88.5
04	MASONRY	117.5	103.3	108.6	98.2	103.3	101.4	107.8	103.4	105.0	102.5	103.3	103.0	109.3	103.3	105.6	106.1	103.4	104.4
05	METALS	91.9	96.2	93.2	92.2	96.2	93.4	98.1	96.9	97.7	93.5	96.5	94.4	98.7	96.4	98.0	98.0	96.6	97.5
06	WOOD, PLASTICS & COMPOSITES	92.6	98.4	95.9	91.5	98.4	95.3	94.7	98.5	96.8	98.6	98.4	98.5	95.5	98.4	97.1	103.2	98.5	100.6
07	THERMAL & MOISTURE PROTECTION	108.2	92.9	101.9	107.8	92.9	101.7	101.1	93.5	98.0	107.1	96.7	102.9	104.9	94.9	100.8	100.5	94.4	98.0
08	OPENINGS	96.9	102.3	98.1	99.7	102.3	100.3	93.2	102.4	95.4	95.0	102.3	96.7	98.7	102.3	99.5	93.2	94.1	93.4
0920	Plaster & Gypsum Board	102.9	98.2	99.7	102.2	98.2	99.5	90.2	98.2	95.6	105.5	98.2	100.5	102.1	98.2	99.4	95.9	98.2	97.4
0950, 0980	Ceilings & Acoustic Treatment	98.9	98.2	98.4	105.4	98.2	100.7	64.4	98.2	86.6	94.2	98.2	96.8	99.3	98.2	98.5	64.4	98.2	82.6
0960	Flooring	107.6	103.4	106.4	107.1	103.4	106.1	74.7	103.4	82.9	106.4	103.4	105.5	107.2	103.4	106.1	76.7	103.4	84.4
0970, 0990	Wall Finishes & Painting/Coating	106.4	70.4	84.6	106.4	70.4	84.6	96.6	72.8	82.2	106.2	72.8	86.0	104.6	74.8	86.6	96.6	74.8	83.4
09	FINISHES	103.4	96.3	99.5	103.8	96.3	99.6	72.3	96.7	85.7	100.8	96.6	98.5	100.0	96.8	98.2	72.7	96.9	86.0
COVERS	DIVS. 10 - 14, 25, 28, 41, 43, 44, 46	100.0	99.5	99.9	100.0	99.5	99.9	100.0	90.1	98.0	100.0	99.6	99.9	100.0	99.6	99.9	100.0	99.9	100.0
21, 22, 23	FIRE SUPPRESSION, PLUMBING & HVAC	95.1	100.7	97.4	99.9	100.7	100.2	97.0	113.2	103.5	99.9	100.8	100.2	99.9	100.8	100.2	97.0	98.0	97.4
26, 27, 3370	ELECTRICAL, COMMUNICATIONS & UTIL.	100.2	80.8	89.9	103.9	80.8	91.6	92.3	97.1	94.8	100.4	103.2	101.9	108.0	96.1	101.7	92.3	97.0	94.8
MF2014	WEIGHTED AVERAGE	99.8	97.1	98.6	100.0	97.1	98.8	94.8	101.4	97.7	98.8	100.4	99.5	100.5	99.4	100.0	92.9	98.1	95.2

PENNSYLVANIA

DIVISION		ALLENTOWN 181			ALTOONA 166			BEDFORD 155			BRADFORD 167			BUTLER 160			CHAMBERSBURG 172		
		MAT.	INST.	TOTAL	MAT.	INST.	TOTAL	MAT.	INST.	TOTAL	MAT.	INST.	TOTAL	MAT.	INST.	TOTAL	MAT.	INST.	TOTAL
015433	CONTRACTOR EQUIPMENT		112.9	112.9		112.9	112.9		109.6	109.6		112.9	112.9		112.9	112.9		112.1	112.1
0241, 31 - 34	SITE & INFRASTRUCTURE, DEMOLITION	93.6	104.5	101.3	96.8	104.4	102.2	101.4	100.1	100.5	92.4	103.5	100.3	88.1	105.8	100.7	89.2	101.2	97.8
0310	Concrete Forming & Accessories	99.2	113.0	111.1	84.2	80.4	80.9	84.1	80.8	81.3	86.4	81.9	82.5	85.7	96.0	94.6	90.2	80.0	81.4
0320	Concrete Reinforcing	94.7	108.1	101.5	91.8	102.7	97.3	93.1	80.9	86.9	93.7	103.2	98.5	92.4	109.1	100.9	91.7	103.0	97.4
0330	Cast-in-Place Concrete	86.5	104.9	94.0	96.3	86.1	92.1	106.7	70.1	91.6	92.0	92.6	92.3	85.1	96.7	89.9	91.1	69.8	82.3
03	CONCRETE	93.6	110.1	101.7	89.1	88.1	88.6	102.1	78.5	90.5	95.4	91.0	93.2	81.3	99.9	90.4	101.9	82.2	92.3
04	MASONRY	97.4	101.0	99.7	100.5	64.5	78.0	114.1	87.0	97.2	97.6	88.4	91.9	102.6	98.9	100.3	102.6	87.4	93.1
05	METALS	100.0	123.0	107.1	93.9	116.8	101.0	97.6	104.0	99.6	97.9	116.5	103.6	93.6	121.9	102.3	97.5	114.6	102.7
06	WOOD, PLASTICS & COMPOSITES	100.7	115.8	109.1	79.2	83.2	81.4	84.0	80.7	82.2	85.5	80.1	82.5	80.6	95.5	89.0	88.0	80.8	84.0
07	THERMAL & MOISTURE PROTECTION	102.3	119.1	109.2	101.4	91.0	97.1	103.0	87.7	96.7	102.3	91.7	97.9	101.1	100.7	100.9	99.3	72.5	88.3
08	OPENINGS	95.0	115.0	99.6	88.7	89.3	88.8	98.0	81.6	94.2	95.2	91.0	94.2	88.7	104.8	92.4	94.1	82.8	91.4
0920	Plaster & Gypsum Board	95.9	116.0	109.5	87.7	82.5	84.2	92.3	80.0	84.0	88.5	79.2	82.2	87.7	95.2	92.7	96.7	80.0	85.4
0950, 0980	Ceilings & Acoustic Treatment	82.8	116.0	104.6	87.0	82.5	84.0	95.0	80.0	85.1	85.4	79.2	81.3	87.9	95.2	92.7	84.0	80.0	81.4
0960	Flooring	94.6	95.9	95.0	88.2	97.5	90.9	93.1	88.2	91.7	89.4	105.3	94.0	89.0	81.0	86.7	97.9	46.2	83.1
0970, 0990	Wall Finishes & Painting/Coating	98.5	70.5	81.6	94.0	109.2	103.2	100.2	81.6	89.0	98.5	94.6	96.1	94.0	109.2	103.2	105.9	81.6	91.2
09	FINISHES	91.8	105.5	99.4	90.0	85.8	87.7	95.0	80.8	87.2	89.9	85.5	87.5	89.9	93.6	91.9	92.1	73.7	82.0
COVERS	DIVS. 10 - 14, 25, 28, 41, 43, 44, 46	100.0	105.6	101.1	100.0	95.4	99.1	100.0	98.3	99.7	100.0	99.2	99.8	100.0	102.4	100.5	100.0	96.1	99.2
21, 22, 23	FIRE SUPPRESSION, PLUMBING & HVAC	100.2	112.1	105.0	99.7	82.5	92.8	95.2	87.3	92.0	95.5	90.7	93.6	95.0	93.9	94.6	95.5	87.1	92.1
26, 27, 3370	ELECTRICAL, COMMUNICATIONS & UTIL.	99.1	98.4	98.8	89.3	112.2	101.4	94.3	112.2	103.8	92.7	112.2	103.0	89.9	111.2	101.1	89.6	86.3	87.8
MF2014	WEIGHTED AVERAGE	97.9	108.6	102.5	94.6	91.9	93.4	98.2	91.3	95.2	95.7	96.4	96.0	92.5	102.0	96.6	96.2	88.0	92.6

PENNSYLVANIA

DIVISION		DOYLESTOWN 189			DUBOIS 158			ERIE 164 - 165			GREENSBURG 156			HARRISBURG 170 - 171			HAZLETON 182		
		MAT.	INST.	TOTAL	MAT.	INST.	TOTAL	MAT.	INST.	TOTAL	MAT.	INST.	TOTAL	MAT.	INST.	TOTAL	MAT.	INST.	TOTAL
015433	CONTRACTOR EQUIPMENT		93.9	93.9		109.6	109.6		112.9	112.9		109.6	109.6		112.1	112.1		112.9	112.9
0241, 31 - 34	SITE & INFRASTRUCTURE, DEMOLITION	106.9	90.2	96.5	106.1	100.5	102.1	93.7	105.2	101.9	97.8	102.9	101.4	89.6	103.5	99.5	86.9	104.7	99.6
0310	Concrete Forming & Accessories	83.2	128.2	122.0	83.5	84.6	84.4	98.5	88.1	89.5	90.7	95.9	95.2	100.4	87.9	89.6	80.8	88.7	87.6
0320	Concrete Reinforcing	91.6	130.9	111.6	92.6	103.5	98.1	93.7	103.3	98.6	92.6	109.1	101.0	101.4	106.2	103.9	91.9	107.1	99.6
0330	Cast-in-Place Concrete	81.7	86.7	83.8	102.9	92.9	98.8	94.7	81.8	89.4	99.0	96.3	97.9	93.2	95.8	94.3	81.7	93.1	86.4
03	CONCRETE	89.2	114.2	101.5	103.6	92.2	98.0	88.2	90.0	89.1	97.2	99.6	98.4	97.7	95.4	96.6	86.3	95.0	90.6
04	MASONRY	100.7	128.1	117.7	114.4	91.1	99.9	89.6	92.5	91.4	124.8	98.9	108.7	102.5	89.6	94.5	110.2	95.7	101.2
05	METALS	97.5	123.8	105.6	97.6	116.1	103.3	94.1	117.0	101.2	97.5	120.6	104.6	104.0	121.4	109.4	99.7	120.6	106.1
06	WOOD, PLASTICS & COMPOSITES	81.0	130.7	108.8	82.9	83.1	83.0	96.9	86.6	91.1	90.9	95.4	93.4	95.8	86.7	90.7	79.6	86.6	83.5
07	THERMAL & MOISTURE PROTECTION	100.1	131.4	112.9	103.2	96.5	100.5	101.9	92.6	98.1	102.8	100.7	102.0	102.5	110.2	105.7	101.8	106.6	103.8
08	OPENINGS	97.2	137.9	106.7	98.0	92.7	96.7	88.8	92.2	89.6	97.9	104.7	99.5	100.6	94.0	99.0	95.6	92.3	94.8
0920	Plaster & Gypsum Board	86.2	131.4	116.7	91.2	82.5	85.3	95.9	86.0	89.2	93.5	95.2	94.6	100.6	86.0	90.7	86.6	86.0	86.2
0950, 0980	Ceilings & Acoustic Treatment	82.0	131.4	114.5	95.0	82.5	86.7	82.8	86.0	84.9	94.2	95.2	94.8	92.6	86.0	88.3	83.7	86.0	85.2
0960	Flooring	79.4	134.3	95.1	92.9	105.3	96.4	93.2	91.8	92.8	96.2	68.0	88.2	103.2	91.7	99.9	87.0	94.6	89.2
0970, 0990	Wall Finishes & Painting/Coating	98.0	69.0	80.5	100.2	106.6	104.1	103.5	94.6	98.1	100.2	106.6	104.1	106.4	89.6	96.3	98.5	106.4	103.2
09	FINISHES	83.2	122.4	104.8	95.2	89.5	92.1	92.2	88.8	90.4	95.6	91.7	93.4	96.9	88.0	92.0	88.1	89.5	88.9
COVERS	DIVS. 10 - 14, 25, 28, 41, 43, 44, 46	100.0	70.6	94.1	100.0	99.1	99.8	100.0	100.8	100.2	100.0	102.2	100.4	100.0	97.4	99.5	100.0	101.0	100.2
21, 22, 23	FIRE SUPPRESSION, PLUMBING & HVAC	95.0	127.4	108.1	95.2	88.4	92.4	99.7	92.9	97.0	95.2	91.1	93.5	100.1	92.1	96.9	95.5	99.2	97.0
26, 27, 3370	ELECTRICAL, COMMUNICATIONS & UTIL.	92.1	128.1	111.1	94.9	112.2	104.0	91.1	96.7	94.0	94.9	112.2	104.1	96.8	88.3	92.3	93.6	91.7	92.6
MF2014	WEIGHTED AVERAGE	94.9	120.6	106.1	98.5	96.8	97.8	94.5	95.8	95.1	98.2	100.9	99.4	99.8	95.6	98.0	95.4	98.3	96.6

For customer support on your Site Work & Landscape Cost Data, call 877.737.1594.

		PENNSYLVANIA																
DIVISION		INDIANA 157			JOHNSTOWN 159			KITTANNING 162			LANCASTER 175-176			LEHIGH VALLEY 180			MONTROSE 188		
		MAT.	INST.	TOTAL	MAT.	INST.	TOTAL	MAT.	INST.	TOTAL	MAT.	INST.	TOTAL	MAT.	INST.	TOTAL	MAT.	INST.	TOTAL
015433	CONTRACTOR EQUIPMENT		109.6	109.6		109.6	109.6		112.9	112.9		112.1	112.1		112.9	112.9		112.9	112.9
0241, 31 - 34	SITE & INFRASTRUCTURE, DEMOLITION	95.9	101.2	99.7	101.9	102.2	102.1	90.7	105.7	101.4	81.6	103.5	97.2	90.7	104.3	100.4	89.4	102.1	98.4
0310	Concrete Forming & Accessories	84.7	86.3	86.1	83.5	84.8	84.6	85.7	95.9	94.5	92.3	87.5	88.2	92.8	112.7	110.0	81.8	88.5	87.6
0320	Concrete Reinforcing	91.8	109.2	100.6	93.1	108.9	101.2	92.4	109.2	101.0	91.4	106.1	98.9	91.9	108.1	100.4	96.3	106.3	101.4
0330	Cast-in-Place Concrete	97.1	95.9	96.6	107.6	92.4	101.4	88.4	96.5	91.7	77.5	97.9	85.9	88.4	104.7	95.1	86.7	90.9	88.4
03	CONCRETE	94.7	95.2	94.9	102.9	93.2	98.2	83.8	99.7	91.6	89.8	96.0	92.8	92.6	109.8	101.1	91.3	93.7	92.5
04	MASONRY	110.1	100.1	103.9	110.9	90.6	98.3	105.4	100.1	102.1	108.2	90.1	97.0	97.3	101.0	99.6	97.3	95.1	95.9
05	METALS	97.7	120.1	104.6	97.6	118.9	104.2	93.7	121.9	102.4	97.5	120.8	104.7	99.7	122.0	106.5	98.0	114.1	102.9
06	WOOD, PLASTICS & COMPOSITES	84.8	83.1	83.8	82.9	83.1	83.0	80.6	95.5	89.0	90.8	86.7	88.5	92.2	115.8	105.4	80.4	88.4	84.9
07	THERMAL & MOISTURE PROTECTION	102.7	98.2	100.9	103.0	95.1	99.7	101.1	101.0	101.1	98.8	97.1	98.1	102.2	102.8	102.4	101.8	91.7	97.7
08	OPENINGS	98.0	94.4	97.1	98.0	90.9	96.3	88.7	101.2	91.6	94.1	98.6	95.1	95.6	115.0	100.1	92.2	93.1	92.4
0920	Plaster & Gypsum Board	92.7	82.5	85.8	91.0	82.5	85.2	87.7	95.2	92.7	98.5	86.0	90.1	89.5	116.0	107.4	87.1	87.8	87.6
0950, 0980	Ceilings & Acoustic Treatment	95.0	82.5	86.7	94.2	82.5	86.5	87.9	95.2	92.7	84.0	86.0	85.3	83.7	116.0	105.0	85.4	87.8	87.0
0960	Flooring	93.7	105.3	97.0	92.9	98.2	94.4	89.0	105.3	93.6	98.8	91.7	96.8	91.9	95.9	93.0	87.6	57.9	79.1
0970, 0990	Wall Finishes & Painting/Coating	100.2	106.6	104.1	100.2	109.2	105.6	94.0	106.6	101.6	105.9	57.1	76.5	98.5	66.4	79.1	98.5	106.4	103.2
09	FINISHES	94.8	90.0	92.1	94.6	88.8	91.4	90.1	97.4	94.1	92.0	84.5	87.9	90.2	104.1	97.9	88.9	84.7	86.6
COVERS	DIVS. 10 - 14, 25, 28, 41, 43, 44, 46	100.0	100.6	100.1	100.0	99.3	99.9	100.0	102.2	100.5	100.0	97.4	99.5	100.0	106.0	101.2	100.0	101.2	100.2
21, 22, 23	FIRE SUPPRESSION, PLUMBING & HVAC	95.2	90.8	93.4	95.2	88.7	92.5	95.0	96.9	95.8	95.5	92.3	94.2	95.5	112.0	102.2	95.5	98.4	96.7
26, 27, 3370	ELECTRICAL, COMMUNICATIONS & UTIL.	94.9	112.2	104.1	94.9	112.2	104.0	89.3	112.2	101.4	91.0	44.0	66.2	93.6	143.4	119.90	92.7	97.6	95.3
MF2014	WEIGHTED AVERAGE	97.1	99.3	98.0	98.1	97.2	97.7	92.9	103.3	97.4	95.1	89.0	92.4	95.8	114.0	103.7	94.7	96.9	95.7

		PENNSYLVANIA																	
DIVISION		NEW CASTLE 161			NORRISTOWN 194			OIL CITY 163			PHILADELPHIA 190-191			PITTSBURGH 150-152			POTTSVILLE 179		
		MAT.	INST.	TOTAL	MAT.	INST.	TOTAL	MAT.	INST.	TOTAL	MAT.	INST.	TOTAL	MAT.	INST.	TOTAL	MAT.	INST.	TOTAL
015433	CONTRACTOR EQUIPMENT		112.9	112.9		98.8	98.8		112.9	112.9		98.2	98.2		110.8	110.8		112.1	112.1
0241, 31 - 34	SITE & INFRASTRUCTURE, DEMOLITION	88.5	105.8	100.8	95.8	100.6	99.2	87.1	103.7	98.9	101.6	100.0	100.5	101.3	104.9	103.8	84.4	103.4	97.9
0310	Concrete Forming & Accessories	85.7	95.6	94.3	83.2	129.7	123.3	85.7	83.4	83.7	98.9	140.1	134.4	98.5	96.7	97.0	83.3	89.7	88.8
0320	Concrete Reinforcing	91.3	92.5	91.9	90.2	137.9	114.5	92.4	92.3	92.4	100.6	137.9	119.6	93.6	109.4	101.6	90.7	102.7	96.8
0330	Cast-in-Place Concrete	85.9	96.5	90.2	85.0	127.1	102.3	83.4	95.5	88.4	98.0	132.2	112.1	102.9	96.5	100.3	82.6	100.9	90.1
03	CONCRETE	81.6	96.4	88.9	89.2	130.1	109.3	80.1	90.5	85.2	99.4	136.4	117.6	100.5	100.1	100.3	93.3	97.3	95.3
04	MASONRY	101.9	97.7	99.3	110.4	124.9	119.4	101.8	95.8	98.0	96.7	130.7	117.9	103.0	102.1	102.4	102.1	102.2	102.2
05	METALS	93.7	113.6	99.8	99.2	130.0	108.7	93.7	111.5	99.2	102.0	130.2	110.7	99.0	121.3	105.9	97.7	118.8	104.2
06	WOOD, PLASTICS & COMPOSITES	80.6	95.9	89.2	79.9	130.6	108.3	80.6	80.1	80.3	98.6	141.9	122.9	100.6	95.8	97.9	80.2	88.1	84.6
07	THERMAL & MOISTURE PROTECTION	101.1	98.0	99.8	101.4	131.1	113.5	101.0	94.4	98.3	102.8	135.2	116.1	103.1	101.6	102.4	98.9	106.7	102.1
08	OPENINGS	88.7	96.6	90.5	86.9	140.1	99.2	88.7	80.3	86.7	98.6	146.2	109.7	101.8	105.0	102.5	94.1	91.8	93.6
0920	Plaster & Gypsum Board	87.7	95.6	93.0	85.6	131.4	116.5	87.7	79.2	82.0	96.6	143.1	128.0	99.8	95.6	96.9	93.5	87.5	89.5
0950, 0980	Ceilings & Acoustic Treatment	87.9	95.6	92.9	84.5	131.4	115.3	87.9	79.2	82.2	94.0	143.1	126.2	95.0	95.6	95.4	84.0	87.5	86.3
0960	Flooring	89.0	57.5	80.0	92.9	139.2	106.1	89.0	105.3	93.6	98.4	139.2	110.1	99.5	106.6	101.5	95.2	91.7	94.2
0970, 0990	Wall Finishes & Painting/Coating	94.0	109.2	103.2	98.6	147.8	128.3	94.0	106.6	101.6	99.8	154.7	133.0	100.2	119.2	111.7	105.9	106.4	106.2
09	FINISHES	90.0	89.6	89.8	90.7	133.0	114.0	89.8	87.8	88.7	98.9	141.8	122.5	97.7	100.2	99.1	90.5	91.3	90.9
COVERS	DIVS. 10 - 14, 25, 28, 41, 43, 44, 46	100.0	102.4	100.5	100.0	117.5	103.5	100.0	100.6	100.1	100.0	120.8	104.2	100.0	102.2	100.4	100.0	98.7	99.7
21, 22, 23	FIRE SUPPRESSION, PLUMBING & HVAC	95.0	93.6	94.4	95.2	127.3	108.2	95.0	92.9	94.2	100.0	131.8	112.9	99.9	100.4	100.1	95.5	98.6	96.8
26, 27, 3370	ELECTRICAL, COMMUNICATIONS & UTIL.	89.9	98.1	94.2	93.0	148.4	122.3	91.8	111.1	102.0	97.1	148.4	124.2	97.2	112.2	105.1	89.2	95.5	92.5
MF2014	WEIGHTED AVERAGE	92.5	97.9	94.8	95.0	129.5	110.0	92.4	96.9	94.4	99.7	133.6	114.5	99.9	104.6	102.0	94.9	98.5	96.5

		PENNSYLVANIA																	
DIVISION		READING 195-196			SCRANTON 184-185			STATE COLLEGE 168			STROUDSBURG 183			SUNBURY 178			UNIONTOWN 154		
		MAT.	INST.	TOTAL	MAT.	INST.	TOTAL	MAT.	INST.	TOTAL	MAT.	INST.	TOTAL	MAT.	INST.	TOTAL	MAT.	INST.	TOTAL
015433	CONTRACTOR EQUIPMENT		118.0	118.0		112.9	112.9		112.1	112.1		112.9	112.9		112.9	112.9		109.6	109.6
0241, 31 - 34	SITE & INFRASTRUCTURE, DEMOLITION	100.3	112.7	109.1	94.1	104.8	101.7	84.4	103.1	97.7	88.5	102.2	98.2	96.6	104.5	102.2	96.5	102.9	101.0
0310	Concrete Forming & Accessories	98.8	90.2	91.4	99.3	88.6	90.0	84.4	80.3	80.8	87.2	89.4	89.1	96.1	88.5	89.6	77.6	96.0	93.5
0320	Concrete Reinforcing	91.5	104.7	98.2	94.7	106.6	100.8	93.0	103.4	98.3	95.0	111.6	103.4	93.2	106.2	99.8	92.6	109.1	101.0
0330	Cast-in-Place Concrete	76.2	97.3	84.9	90.3	93.1	91.5	87.1	65.6	78.2	85.1	72.6	80.0	90.2	95.5	92.4	97.1	96.4	96.8
03	CONCRETE	88.2	96.7	92.4	95.4	94.9	95.1	95.5	81.0	88.4	90.1	88.9	89.5	96.7	95.5	96.1	94.4	99.7	97.0
04	MASONRY	99.5	93.0	95.4	97.7	95.7	96.4	103.1	77.9	87.4	95.1	100.4	98.4	102.3	89.7	94.5	127.0	98.9	109.4
05	METALS	99.5	121.2	106.2	102.1	120.5	107.8	97.7	117.6	103.8	99.7	115.9	104.7	97.4	120.0	104.4	97.4	120.6	104.5
06	WOOD, PLASTICS & COMPOSITES	98.5	88.1	92.6	100.7	86.2	92.6	87.6	83.2	85.1	86.4	88.4	87.5	88.9	88.1	88.5	76.7	95.4	87.2
07	THERMAL & MOISTURE PROTECTION	101.8	112.1	106.0	102.2	95.6	99.5	101.5	90.6	97.4	102.0	85.3	95.2	100.0	104.9	102.0	102.6	100.7	101.8
08	OPENINGS	91.3	98.9	93.1	95.0	91.9	94.3	92.0	89.3	91.4	95.6	88.2	93.9	94.2	92.8	93.9	97.9	104.7	99.5
0920	Plaster & Gypsum Board	96.8	87.5	90.5	98.0	85.6	89.6	89.6	82.5	84.8	88.0	87.8	87.9	92.7	87.5	89.2	89.2	95.2	93.2
0950, 0980	Ceilings & Acoustic Treatment	76.9	87.5	83.9	91.1	85.6	87.5	82.9	82.5	82.6	82.0	87.8	85.8	80.7	87.5	85.2	94.2	95.2	94.8
0960	Flooring	96.8	91.7	95.4	94.6	107.0	98.2	92.3	97.5	93.8	89.9	51.3	78.9	95.9	87.7	93.5	90.4	105.3	94.7
0970, 0990	Wall Finishes & Painting/Coating	97.3	106.4	102.8	98.5	106.4	103.2	98.5	109.2	105.0	98.5	64.6	78.0	105.9	94.3	98.9	100.2	109.2	105.6
09	FINISHES	92.0	90.8	91.3	93.9	93.1	93.4	89.4	85.8	87.4	88.9	80.0	84.0	91.3	88.7	89.9	93.2	97.5	95.6
COVERS	DIVS. 10 - 14, 25, 28, 41, 43, 44, 46	100.0	100.3	100.1	100.0	101.0	100.2	100.0	93.1	98.6	100.0	62.4	92.4	100.0	97.9	99.6	100.0	102.2	100.4
21, 22, 23	FIRE SUPPRESSION, PLUMBING & HVAC	100.1	108.8	103.7	100.2	99.1	99.8	95.5	85.9	91.6	95.5	100.0	97.4	95.5	92.9	94.1	95.2	91.1	93.6
26, 27, 3370	ELECTRICAL, COMMUNICATIONS & UTIL.	99.6	95.5	97.5	99.2	97.7	98.4	91.9	112.2	102.6	93.6	143.3	119.9	89.5	90.8	90.2	92.0	112.2	102.7
MF2014	WEIGHTED AVERAGE	97.1	102.1	99.3	98.6	99.2	98.9	95.3	92.8	94.2	95.3	101.4	97.9	95.8	95.8	95.8	97.3	101.7	99.2

For customer support on your Site Work & Landscape Cost Data, call 877.737.1594.

777

PENNSYLVANIA

DIVISION		WASHINGTON 153			WELLSBORO 169			WESTCHESTER 193			WILKES-BARRE 186 - 187			WILLIAMSPORT 177			YORK 173 - 174		
		MAT.	INST.	TOTAL	MAT.	INST.	TOTAL	MAT.	INST.	TOTAL	MAT.	INST.	TOTAL	MAT.	INST.	TOTAL	MAT.	INST.	TOTAL
015433	CONTRACTOR EQUIPMENT		109.6	109.6		112.9	112.9		98.8	98.8		112.9	112.9		112.9	112.9		112.1	112.1
0241, 31 - 34	SITE & INFRASTRUCTURE, DEMOLITION	96.6	102.9	101.1	95.9	102.0	100.3	101.6	97.8	98.9	86.5	104.7	99.5	87.9	103.4	98.9	85.2	103.5	98.2
0310	Concrete Forming & Accessories	84.8	96.2	94.6	85.8	86.7	86.6	89.8	128.2	122.9	89.9	88.9	89.1	92.5	61.0	65.3	86.9	88.1	87.9
0320	Concrete Reinforcing	92.6	109.3	101.1	93.0	106.2	99.7	89.3	113.6	101.7	93.7	107.1	100.6	92.5	64.6	78.3	93.2	106.2	99.8
0330	Cast-in-Place Concrete	97.1	96.4	96.8	91.2	88.9	90.3	94.1	126.4	107.4	81.7	93.0	86.4	76.4	74.2	75.5	83.0	98.1	89.2
03	CONCRETE	94.9	99.8	97.3	97.8	92.2	95.1	96.9	124.5	110.5	87.2	95.1	91.1	84.7	68.2	76.6	94.5	96.3	95.4
04	MASONRY	109.4	100.5	103.9	103.6	89.7	94.9	104.7	124.9	117.3	110.6	95.3	101.0	93.9	93.7	93.8	103.6	90.1	95.2
05	METALS	97.3	120.9	104.6	97.8	114.2	102.9	99.2	117.2	104.8	97.9	121.0	105.0	97.5	100.4	98.4	99.1	121.4	105.9
06	WOOD, PLASTICS & COMPOSITES	84.9	95.4	90.8	84.9	88.1	86.7	87.1	130.6	111.5	88.9	86.6	87.6	85.2	51.0	66.1	84.1	86.7	85.5
07	THERMAL & MOISTURE PROTECTION	102.7	101.1	102.1	102.5	89.6	97.2	101.7	129.9	113.3	101.8	106.4	103.7	99.4	102.4	100.6	99.0	110.4	103.7
08	OPENINGS	97.9	104.7	99.5	95.1	93.0	94.6	86.9	126.1	96.0	92.2	98.8	93.8	94.2	53.5	84.7	94.1	94.0	94.1
0920	Plaster & Gypsum Board	92.4	95.2	94.3	87.9	87.5	87.6	87.0	131.4	117.0	88.8	86.0	86.9	93.5	49.3	63.6	94.3	86.0	88.7
0950, 0980	Ceilings & Acoustic Treatment	94.2	95.2	94.8	82.9	87.5	85.9	84.5	131.4	115.3	85.4	86.0	85.8	84.0	49.3	61.2	83.1	86.0	85.0
0960	Flooring	93.8	105.3	97.1	89.1	50.8	78.2	95.7	139.2	108.1	90.7	94.6	91.8	94.8	49.7	81.9	96.4	91.7	95.1
0970, 0990	Wall Finishes & Painting/Coating	100.2	109.2	105.6	98.5	106.4	103.2	98.6	147.8	128.3	98.5	106.4	103.2	105.9	106.4	106.2	105.9	89.6	96.1
09	FINISHES	94.6	97.8	96.4	89.5	82.2	85.5	92.1	131.0	113.6	89.9	90.8	90.4	91.1	62.3	75.2	90.8	88.1	89.3
COVERS	DIVS. 10 - 14, 25, 28, 41, 43, 44, 46	100.0	102.2	100.4	100.0	97.9	99.6	100.0	117.3	103.5	100.0	100.8	100.2	100.0	94.6	98.9	100.0	97.6	99.5
21, 22, 23	FIRE SUPPRESSION, PLUMBING & HVAC	95.2	97.2	96.0	95.5	91.1	93.7	95.2	125.8	107.6	95.5	99.0	96.9	95.5	93.1	94.5	100.2	92.4	97.1
26, 27, 3370	ELECTRICAL, COMMUNICATIONS & UTIL.	94.3	112.2	103.8	92.7	86.5	89.5	92.9	114.9	104.5	93.6	91.7	92.6	90.0	74.6	81.8	91.0	88.3	89.5
MF2014	WEIGHTED AVERAGE	97.0	103.2	99.7	96.3	92.6	94.7	95.9	121.5	107.1	95.1	98.7	96.6	93.8	83.0	89.1	96.7	95.9	96.3

DIVISION		PUERTO RICO SAN JUAN 009			RHODE ISLAND NEWPORT 028			RHODE ISLAND PROVIDENCE 029			SOUTH CAROLINA AIKEN 298			SOUTH CAROLINA BEAUFORT 299			SOUTH CAROLINA CHARLESTON 294		
		MAT.	INST.	TOTAL	MAT.	INST.	TOTAL	MAT.	INST.	TOTAL	MAT.	INST.	TOTAL	MAT.	INST.	TOTAL	MAT.	INST.	TOTAL
015433	CONTRACTOR EQUIPMENT		90.5	90.5		102.4	102.4		102.4	102.4		101.3	101.3		101.3	101.3		101.3	101.3
0241, 31 - 34	SITE & INFRASTRUCTURE, DEMOLITION	133.8	91.2	103.5	89.2	105.0	100.4	91.4	105.0	101.1	118.9	87.4	96.5	114.3	85.6	93.9	99.7	86.3	90.2
0310	Concrete Forming & Accessories	92.4	17.8	28.1	101.5	122.4	119.5	99.8	122.4	119.3	97.5	67.4	71.5	96.4	37.9	46.0	95.4	63.0	67.5
0320	Concrete Reinforcing	188.3	12.7	98.9	106.4	149.2	128.2	102.3	149.2	126.2	93.7	65.2	79.2	92.8	25.8	58.7	92.7	59.3	75.7
0330	Cast-in-Place Concrete	103.8	30.4	73.7	79.5	124.1	97.8	95.5	124.1	107.2	79.2	69.8	75.4	79.2	47.2	66.1	92.9	49.5	75.1
03	CONCRETE	108.7	22.2	66.2	93.2	127.5	110.0	100.4	127.5	113.7	102.7	68.9	86.1	99.9	40.9	70.9	94.4	58.9	77.0
04	MASONRY	90.1	16.9	44.5	95.4	132.5	118.5	101.3	132.5	120.7	79.6	61.4	68.3	93.9	33.3	56.1	95.1	40.9	61.4
05	METALS	118.4	34.6	92.6	97.4	125.6	106.1	103.1	125.6	110.0	101.8	83.8	96.3	101.8	68.2	91.5	103.8	80.4	96.6
06	WOOD, PLASTICS & COMPOSITES	94.4	17.5	51.3	99.0	120.9	111.3	100.1	120.9	111.7	97.0	68.6	81.1	95.3	37.8	63.1	94.0	68.4	79.7
07	THERMAL & MOISTURE PROTECTION	129.1	21.6	85.0	100.6	121.5	109.2	100.5	121.5	109.1	102.7	66.4	87.8	102.4	38.8	76.3	101.6	47.3	79.3
08	OPENINGS	152.0	15.4	120.2	102.2	128.2	108.3	107.3	128.2	112.2	99.0	64.8	91.1	99.0	36.7	84.5	102.9	63.3	93.7
0920	Plaster & Gypsum Board	159.8	14.9	61.9	92.9	120.9	111.9	94.5	120.9	112.4	104.0	67.4	79.3	107.4	35.7	59.0	109.0	67.3	80.8
0950, 0980	Ceilings & Acoustic Treatment	225.7	14.9	87.2	93.2	120.9	111.4	90.1	120.9	110.4	86.4	67.4	73.9	89.8	35.7	54.3	89.8	67.3	75.0
0960	Flooring	224.3	16.6	164.9	97.7	141.5	110.2	98.0	141.5	110.4	105.4	68.4	94.8	106.8	51.2	90.9	106.5	58.2	92.7
0970, 0990	Wall Finishes & Painting/Coating	213.5	16.8	94.8	99.9	129.2	117.6	97.7	129.2	116.7	109.5	70.3	85.8	109.5	34.7	64.3	109.5	66.9	83.8
09	FINISHES	210.6	17.6	104.2	96.6	126.9	113.3	93.7	126.9	112.0	98.3	68.0	81.6	99.5	39.8	66.6	97.8	63.5	78.9
COVERS	DIVS. 10 - 14, 25, 28, 41, 43, 44, 46	100.0	17.5	83.3	100.0	108.6	101.7	100.0	108.6	101.7	100.0	71.8	94.3	100.0	70.4	94.0	100.0	69.0	93.7
21, 22, 23	FIRE SUPPRESSION, PLUMBING & HVAC	103.3	14.0	67.3	100.1	110.6	104.3	99.9	110.6	104.2	95.7	63.1	82.5	95.7	36.5	71.8	100.5	53.7	81.6
26, 27, 3370	ELECTRICAL, COMMUNICATIONS & UTIL.	125.9	13.2	66.3	100.0	99.0	99.5	99.6	99.0	99.2	96.9	65.9	80.5	100.7	33.6	65.2	99.0	88.8	93.6
MF2014	WEIGHTED AVERAGE	122.7	24.4	79.8	98.4	117.5	106.7	100.6	117.5	108.0	98.6	69.1	85.7	99.3	44.9	75.6	99.9	65.2	84.8

DIVISION		SOUTH CAROLINA COLUMBIA 290 - 292			SOUTH CAROLINA FLORENCE 295			SOUTH CAROLINA GREENVILLE 296			SOUTH CAROLINA ROCK HILL 297			SOUTH CAROLINA SPARTANBURG 293			SOUTH DAKOTA ABERDEEN 574		
		MAT.	INST.	TOTAL	MAT.	INST.	TOTAL	MAT.	INST.	TOTAL	MAT.	INST.	TOTAL	MAT.	INST.	TOTAL	MAT.	INST.	TOTAL
015433	CONTRACTOR EQUIPMENT		101.3	101.3		101.3	101.3		101.3	101.3		101.3	101.3		101.3	101.3		98.2	98.2
0241, 31 - 34	SITE & INFRASTRUCTURE, DEMOLITION	99.8	86.3	90.2	108.8	86.3	92.8	104.1	85.9	91.2	101.7	85.9	90.5	103.9	86.0	91.1	99.2	93.7	95.3
0310	Concrete Forming & Accessories	94.4	45.1	51.9	83.2	45.3	50.5	95.0	45.1	52.0	93.2	38.7	46.2	98.0	45.3	52.5	94.8	36.6	44.6
0320	Concrete Reinforcing	95.8	59.1	77.1	92.3	59.3	75.5	92.2	44.5	67.9	93.0	44.1	68.1	92.2	57.0	74.3	96.1	38.1	66.6
0330	Cast-in-Place Concrete	95.8	50.1	77.0	79.2	49.4	66.9	79.2	49.3	66.9	79.2	43.9	64.7	79.2	49.4	66.9	105.6	43.5	80.1
03	CONCRETE	96.2	51.1	74.1	94.2	51.0	73.0	93.0	48.2	71.0	90.9	43.3	67.5	93.2	50.6	72.3	102.8	40.7	72.3
04	MASONRY	91.5	37.6	57.9	79.8	40.9	55.6	77.4	40.9	54.7	101.6	34.6	59.8	79.8	40.9	55.6	115.9	55.4	78.2
05	METALS	100.9	79.6	94.3	102.6	80.0	95.6	102.6	74.5	93.9	101.8	71.2	92.4	102.6	79.1	95.4	95.9	63.6	86.0
06	WOOD, PLASTICS & COMPOSITES	98.0	44.8	68.2	79.7	44.8	60.2	93.7	44.8	66.4	92.0	38.9	62.3	98.0	44.8	68.2	99.6	36.0	64.0
07	THERMAL & MOISTURE PROTECTION	97.2	43.3	75.1	101.9	44.8	78.5	101.8	44.8	78.5	101.6	39.7	76.3	101.8	44.8	78.5	99.2	47.7	78.1
08	OPENINGS	104.6	50.5	92.0	99.1	50.5	87.8	99.0	47.0	86.9	99.0	39.4	85.2	99.0	50.0	87.6	99.1	36.7	84.6
0920	Plaster & Gypsum Board	102.3	42.9	62.2	97.1	42.9	60.5	102.6	42.9	62.3	101.9	36.8	57.9	105.5	42.9	63.2	103.7	34.3	56.8
0950, 0980	Ceilings & Acoustic Treatment	91.3	42.9	59.5	87.3	42.9	58.1	86.4	42.9	57.8	86.4	36.8	53.8	86.4	42.9	57.8	93.2	34.3	54.5
0960	Flooring	100.5	43.6	84.2	98.4	43.6	82.7	104.3	57.2	90.8	103.3	44.4	86.5	105.6	57.2	91.8	108.4	50.3	91.8
0970, 0990	Wall Finishes & Painting/Coating	106.2	66.9	82.5	109.5	66.9	83.8	109.5	66.9	83.8	109.5	39.2	67.0	109.5	66.9	83.8	102.6	37.1	63.1
09	FINISHES	95.9	46.6	68.7	94.4	47.1	68.3	96.3	49.3	70.4	95.7	39.4	64.6	97.1	49.3	70.8	100.3	38.8	66.4
COVERS	DIVS. 10 - 14, 25, 28, 41, 43, 44, 46	100.0	66.3	93.2	100.0	66.3	93.2	100.0	66.3	93.2	100.0	64.6	92.9	100.0	66.3	93.2	100.0	40.5	88.0
21, 22, 23	FIRE SUPPRESSION, PLUMBING & HVAC	100.0	53.0	81.1	100.0	53.1	81.4	100.0	53.0	81.3	95.7	44.2	74.9	100.5	53.1	81.3	100.1	39.8	75.8
26, 27, 3370	ELECTRICAL, COMMUNICATIONS & UTIL.	99.0	59.7	78.3	96.8	59.7	77.2	99.1	57.4	77.0	99.1	56.6	76.6	99.1	57.4	77.1	101.7	51.1	75.0
MF2014	WEIGHTED AVERAGE	99.3	56.5	80.6	98.2	56.9	80.2	98.3	55.8	79.8	97.8	50.3	77.1	98.6	56.7	80.3	100.5	49.6	78.3

City Cost Indexes

SOUTH DAKOTA

DIVISION		MITCHELL 573 MAT.	INST.	TOTAL	MOBRIDGE 576 MAT.	INST.	TOTAL	PIERRE 575 MAT.	INST.	TOTAL	RAPID CITY 577 MAT.	INST.	TOTAL	SIOUX FALLS 570-571 MAT.	INST.	TOTAL	WATERTOWN 572 MAT.	INST.	TOTAL
015433	CONTRACTOR EQUIPMENT		98.2	98.2		98.2	98.2		98.2	98.2		98.2	98.2		99.2	99.2		98.2	98.2
0241, 31-34	SITE & INFRASTRUCTURE, DEMOLITION	96.0	93.7	94.3	95.9	93.7	94.3	100.5	93.7	95.7	97.7	93.8	94.9	94.3	95.4	95.0	95.8	93.7	94.3
0310	Concrete Forming & Accessories	94.0	37.0	44.8	84.9	36.8	43.4	97.7	38.4	46.6	102.2	36.7	45.7	98.8	40.5	48.5	81.6	36.6	42.8
0320	Concrete Reinforcing	95.5	46.3	70.5	98.0	38.1	67.5	99.0	71.1	84.8	89.9	71.3	80.4	98.0	71.2	84.3	92.9	38.2	65.1
0330	Cast-in-Place Concrete	102.6	42.3	77.8	102.6	43.5	78.3	98.5	42.2	75.4	101.8	42.8	77.6	92.3	42.9	72.0	102.6	45.9	79.3
03	CONCRETE	100.5	41.8	71.7	100.3	40.7	71.0	99.0	47.3	73.6	99.8	46.7	73.7	95.9	48.4	72.6	99.2	41.5	70.9
04	MASONRY	103.9	53.3	72.4	113.4	55.4	77.2	117.4	53.5	77.6	113.5	56.4	77.9	105.1	53.6	73.0	141.1	57.4	88.9
05	METALS	95.0	63.8	85.4	95.0	63.6	85.3	98.4	79.1	92.4	97.8	79.7	92.2	98.2	79.3	92.4	95.0	64.1	85.5
06	WOOD, PLASTICS & COMPOSITES	98.5	36.5	63.8	87.6	36.2	58.8	104.5	36.8	66.6	103.5	33.3	64.2	96.8	39.3	64.6	83.8	36.0	57.0
07	THERMAL & MOISTURE PROTECTION	98.9	45.6	77.1	99.0	47.8	78.0	101.8	45.9	78.9	99.6	47.8	78.3	101.9	48.2	79.9	98.8	48.3	78.1
08	OPENINGS	97.7	37.3	83.6	100.4	36.3	85.5	105.7	46.7	92.0	103.1	44.8	89.6	106.5	48.1	92.9	97.7	36.5	83.4
0920	Plaster & Gypsum Board	102.1	34.8	56.7	96.2	34.6	54.5	100.1	35.1	56.2	103.2	31.6	54.8	90.7	37.7	54.9	93.9	34.3	53.6
0950, 0980	Ceilings & Acoustic Treatment	89.9	34.8	53.7	93.2	34.6	54.7	93.3	35.1	55.0	95.7	31.6	53.6	90.6	37.7	55.8	89.9	34.3	53.3
0960	Flooring	107.9	50.3	91.4	103.5	50.3	88.3	107.4	35.8	86.9	107.6	78.6	99.3	103.8	74.9	95.5	102.1	50.3	87.3
0970, 0990	Wall Finishes & Painting/Coating	102.6	40.6	65.2	102.6	41.7	65.8	105.7	44.6	68.8	102.6	44.6	67.6	101.7	44.6	67.2	102.6	37.1	63.1
09	FINISHES	99.1	39.5	66.2	97.7	39.4	65.6	100.8	37.3	65.8	100.5	43.9	69.3	97.1	46.5	69.2	96.2	38.8	64.6
COVERS	DIVS. 10-14, 25, 28, 41, 43, 44, 46	100.0	37.6	87.4	100.0	40.5	88.0	100.0	75.8	95.1	100.0	75.7	95.1	100.0	76.2	95.2	100.0	40.5	88.0
21, 22, 23	FIRE SUPPRESSION, PLUMBING & HVAC	95.3	39.4	72.8	95.3	39.9	73.0	100.0	64.5	85.7	100.1	65.0	85.9	100.0	38.6	75.2	95.3	39.9	73.0
26, 27, 3370	ELECTRICAL, COMMUNICATIONS & UTIL.	99.9	44.0	70.3	101.7	44.8	71.7	104.8	51.8	76.8	98.0	51.8	73.6	101.3	75.1	87.5	99.0	44.8	70.4
MF2014	WEIGHTED AVERAGE	97.8	48.4	76.3	98.5	48.8	76.8	101.7	58.4	82.8	100.4	59.5	82.6	100.0	57.7	81.5	99.0	49.1	77.2

TENNESSEE

DIVISION		CHATTANOOGA 373-374 MAT.	INST.	TOTAL	COLUMBIA 384 MAT.	INST.	TOTAL	COOKEVILLE 385 MAT.	INST.	TOTAL	JACKSON 383 MAT.	INST.	TOTAL	JOHNSON CITY 376 MAT.	INST.	TOTAL	KNOXVILLE 377-379 MAT.	INST.	TOTAL
015433	CONTRACTOR EQUIPMENT		103.8	103.8		98.2	98.2		98.2	98.2		104.5	104.5		97.7	97.7		97.7	97.7
0241, 31-34	SITE & INFRASTRUCTURE, DEMOLITION	104.5	97.9	99.8	89.1	86.9	87.5	94.5	86.4	88.8	97.7	96.8	97.1	111.1	86.6	93.7	90.7	87.3	88.3
0310	Concrete Forming & Accessories	97.1	56.4	62.0	82.1	62.0	64.8	82.2	35.4	41.8	89.0	44.9	51.0	83.7	38.9	45.1	95.6	61.0	65.7
0320	Concrete Reinforcing	91.2	67.4	79.1	87.4	61.2	74.1	87.4	61.2	74.1	87.4	62.0	74.4	91.7	60.3	75.7	91.2	62.3	76.5
0330	Cast-in-Place Concrete	101.3	62.7	85.5	94.2	51.6	76.7	106.7	43.5	80.7	104.2	49.3	81.6	81.6	60.2	72.8	95.2	65.7	83.1
03	CONCRETE	96.0	62.3	79.4	96.7	59.8	78.6	106.9	45.2	76.6	97.7	51.6	75.1	103.3	52.3	78.3	93.4	64.4	79.1
04	MASONRY	109.7	51.7	73.5	127.7	54.6	82.1	121.9	43.8	73.2	127.9	47.2	77.6	125.7	44.8	75.3	86.6	55.3	67.1
05	METALS	98.7	89.2	95.8	96.4	86.0	93.2	96.5	85.9	93.2	98.8	85.9	94.8	95.9	85.2	92.6	99.3	87.0	95.5
06	WOOD, PLASTICS & COMPOSITES	104.0	57.3	77.8	70.1	64.4	66.9	70.3	33.7	49.8	85.4	45.4	63.0	76.9	36.9	54.5	91.0	60.6	73.9
07	THERMAL & MOISTURE PROTECTION	99.4	59.9	83.2	93.6	59.2	79.5	94.0	45.7	74.2	96.0	54.1	78.8	94.5	52.6	77.3	92.5	61.6	79.8
08	OPENINGS	99.7	57.6	89.9	92.6	57.9	84.6	92.7	42.2	80.9	100.3	51.6	89.0	96.2	45.1	84.3	93.3	58.6	85.2
0920	Plaster & Gypsum Board	82.8	56.5	65.0	87.7	63.7	71.5	87.7	32.1	50.1	89.3	44.1	58.8	102.4	35.5	57.2	109.0	59.8	75.8
0950, 0980	Ceilings & Acoustic Treatment	96.6	56.5	70.2	77.0	63.7	68.3	77.0	32.1	47.5	86.2	44.1	58.5	93.0	35.5	55.2	93.8	59.8	71.5
0960	Flooring	99.1	58.9	87.7	89.3	20.5	69.7	89.4	58.6	80.6	87.1	40.8	73.9	96.7	40.6	80.7	101.3	55.8	88.3
0970, 0990	Wall Finishes & Painting/Coating	102.5	70.7	83.3	94.0	33.4	57.4	94.0	36.5	59.3	95.8	49.6	67.9	99.6	42.1	64.9	99.6	81.2	88.5
09	FINISHES	97.2	58.2	75.7	89.8	52.0	69.0	90.3	38.4	61.7	89.7	43.7	64.4	101.9	38.1	66.7	94.5	62.0	76.6
COVERS	DIVS. 10-14, 25, 28, 41, 43, 44, 46	100.0	41.8	88.3	100.0	47.9	89.5	100.0	41.0	88.1	100.0	43.0	88.5	100.0	75.5	95.1	100.0	81.7	96.3
21, 22, 23	FIRE SUPPRESSION, PLUMBING & HVAC	100.2	62.6	85.0	97.4	78.1	89.6	97.4	72.6	87.4	100.1	68.0	87.1	99.9	59.1	83.4	99.9	67.9	87.0
26, 27, 3370	ELECTRICAL, COMMUNICATIONS & UTIL.	102.3	69.2	84.8	94.2	57.4	74.7	95.9	61.6	77.8	101.0	58.5	78.5	92.5	46.3	68.1	98.1	56.0	75.8
MF2014	WEIGHTED AVERAGE	100.0	66.2	85.2	96.9	66.1	83.5	98.1	59.1	81.1	99.9	61.2	83.0	99.8	56.5	80.9	96.6	66.9	83.7

TENNESSEE / TEXAS

DIVISION		MCKENZIE 382 MAT.	INST.	TOTAL	MEMPHIS 375,380-381 MAT.	INST.	TOTAL	NASHVILLE 370-372 MAT.	INST.	TOTAL	ABILENE 795-796 MAT.	INST.	TOTAL	AMARILLO 790-791 MAT.	INST.	TOTAL	AUSTIN 786-787 MAT.	INST.	TOTAL
015433	CONTRACTOR EQUIPMENT		98.2	98.2		102.8	102.8		103.7	103.7		89.9	89.9		89.9	89.9		89.4	89.4
0241, 31-34	SITE & INFRASTRUCTURE, DEMOLITION	94.3	86.5	88.7	94.1	93.7	93.8	98.9	97.5	97.9	99.4	88.7	91.8	97.3	88.6	91.1	102.4	88.4	92.4
0310	Concrete Forming & Accessories	90.0	38.1	45.2	94.3	64.9	69.0	98.9	65.8	70.3	99.0	65.5	70.1	97.9	57.1	62.7	98.6	59.1	64.5
0320	Concrete Reinforcing	87.5	61.9	74.5	99.7	68.7	83.9	96.0	67.7	81.6	92.9	52.5	72.3	99.0	51.3	74.7	96.5	48.5	72.1
0330	Cast-in-Place Concrete	104.4	57.3	85.1	94.1	61.3	80.6	90.3	65.9	80.3	96.6	63.7	83.1	94.1	63.7	81.6	93.4	66.3	82.3
03	CONCRETE	105.5	51.3	78.9	94.1	65.8	80.2	92.4	67.6	80.2	95.0	63.0	79.3	96.7	59.0	78.2	95.7	60.2	78.3
04	MASONRY	126.2	46.2	76.3	99.8	62.7	76.7	93.8	59.0	72.1	104.2	63.6	78.9	109.7	63.6	81.0	107.6	56.5	75.7
05	METALS	96.5	86.1	93.3	100.1	90.6	97.2	100.4	89.9	97.2	105.3	69.8	94.4	101.6	69.2	91.7	100.5	66.3	90.0
06	WOOD, PLASTICS & COMPOSITES	79.1	36.3	55.1	95.4	67.0	79.5	101.6	66.6	82.0	101.1	68.5	82.8	100.8	57.1	76.4	94.4	59.9	75.0
07	THERMAL & MOISTURE PROTECTION	94.0	48.7	75.4	100.5	63.4	82.4	95.7	61.5	81.7	100.0	67.7	86.7	97.9	65.3	84.5	104.2	64.8	88.1
08	OPENINGS	92.7	44.1	81.4	100.1	66.0	92.2	98.5	65.9	90.9	97.1	63.3	89.2	101.1	56.8	90.8	104.3	55.6	92.9
0920	Plaster & Gypsum Board	90.5	34.8	52.8	95.6	66.3	75.8	95.8	66.0	75.6	84.0	68.0	73.2	92.1	56.3	67.9	86.7	59.2	68.1
0950, 0980	Ceilings & Acoustic Treatment	77.0	34.8	49.2	93.9	66.3	75.8	95.5	66.0	76.1	88.9	68.0	75.2	98.0	56.3	70.6	87.9	59.2	69.0
0960	Flooring	92.1	39.3	77.0	99.4	36.1	81.3	97.7	64.2	88.2	110.9	76.5	101.1	106.5	76.5	97.9	105.7	64.1	93.8
0970, 0990	Wall Finishes & Painting/Coating	94.0	49.6	67.2	97.0	55.7	72.1	100.5	72.0	83.3	106.6	56.1	76.1	100.8	56.1	73.8	104.3	48.8	70.8
09	FINISHES	91.3	38.2	62.1	97.3	58.5	75.9	100.2	66.0	81.4	93.7	67.1	79.0	96.8	60.3	76.7	95.6	58.7	75.2
COVERS	DIVS. 10-14, 25, 28, 41, 43, 44, 46	100.0	27.4	85.3	100.0	82.4	96.4	100.0	82.9	96.5	100.0	82.2	96.4	100.0	68.6	93.7	100.0	80.5	96.1
21, 22, 23	FIRE SUPPRESSION, PLUMBING & HVAC	97.4	68.3	85.6	100.0	73.9	89.5	100.0	84.0	93.5	100.3	49.0	79.6	100.0	54.9	81.8	100.1	60.1	84.0
26, 27, 3370	ELECTRICAL, COMMUNICATIONS & UTIL.	95.6	62.9	78.3	101.7	65.3	82.4	97.6	63.1	79.4	99.3	48.7	72.5	101.1	64.1	81.6	96.8	63.9	79.4
MF2014	WEIGHTED AVERAGE	98.2	59.2	81.2	99.0	71.3	86.9	98.4	74.1	87.8	99.7	62.2	83.3	100.2	63.2	84.1	100.0	63.6	84.1

TEXAS

DIVISION		BEAUMONT 776 - 777			BROWNWOOD 768			BRYAN 778			CHILDRESS 792			CORPUS CHRISTI 783 - 784			DALLAS 752 - 753		
		MAT.	INST.	TOTAL	MAT.	INST.	TOTAL	MAT.	INST.	TOTAL	MAT.	INST.	TOTAL	MAT.	INST.	TOTAL	MAT.	INST.	TOTAL
015433	CONTRACTOR EQUIPMENT		91.5	91.5		89.9	89.9		91.5	91.5		89.9	89.9		96.6	96.6		99.1	99.1
0241, 31 - 34	SITE & INFRASTRUCTURE, DEMOLITION	90.0	89.9	89.9	105.2	89.6	94.1	81.8	90.5	88.0	109.7	88.0	94.3	140.1	84.4	100.5	104.3	89.8	94.0
0310	Concrete Forming & Accessories	101.8	61.9	67.4	99.0	60.5	65.8	81.0	67.1	69.0	97.3	65.5	69.8	100.2	58.1	63.9	101.2	65.8	70.7
0320	Concrete Reinforcing	95.9	65.2	80.3	92.9	52.1	72.1	98.3	48.6	73.0	93.0	52.1	72.2	88.0	48.5	67.9	100.2	52.5	75.9
0330	Cast-in-Place Concrete	89.5	64.7	79.3	101.4	63.6	85.9	71.7	65.4	69.1	99.1	63.7	84.5	109.8	64.4	91.2	98.0	64.6	84.3
03	CONCRETE	96.3	64.2	80.5	101.2	60.7	81.3	80.9	63.7	72.5	104.0	62.9	83.8	100.1	59.9	80.4	99.0	64.1	81.9
04	MASONRY	106.8	63.9	80.0	141.8	56.6	88.7	146.3	60.4	92.7	108.5	56.6	76.2	91.0	56.6	69.6	102.4	56.7	73.9
05	METALS	95.2	75.5	89.1	99.9	69.1	90.5	94.8	70.1	87.2	102.7	69.2	92.4	94.7	77.9	89.5	100.4	80.0	94.1
06	WOOD, PLASTICS & COMPOSITES	106.1	61.8	81.3	99.5	61.9	78.4	73.5	68.5	70.7	100.4	68.5	82.6	116.0	58.4	83.7	104.1	68.6	84.2
07	THERMAL & MOISTURE PROTECTION	101.9	66.7	87.5	98.2	65.2	84.7	93.9	66.3	82.5	100.5	64.8	85.9	104.5	66.2	88.8	93.0	66.4	82.1
08	OPENINGS	94.0	62.3	86.7	94.7	59.7	86.6	97.2	61.6	88.9	94.2	63.3	87.1	109.1	54.7	96.5	99.5	63.5	91.1
0920	Plaster & Gypsum Board	102.3	61.2	74.5	87.8	61.2	69.8	90.3	68.0	75.2	83.6	68.0	73.1	98.4	57.5	70.7	96.7	68.0	77.3
0950, 0980	Ceilings & Acoustic Treatment	98.2	61.2	73.9	80.6	61.2	67.8	91.2	68.0	76.0	87.3	68.0	74.6	92.7	57.5	69.6	97.8	68.0	78.2
0960	Flooring	112.4	73.0	101.1	95.3	64.1	86.3	85.8	64.1	79.6	109.1	64.1	96.2	118.7	64.1	103.1	102.8	64.1	91.7
0970, 0990	Wall Finishes & Painting/Coating	95.1	59.4	73.6	104.2	56.1	75.1	92.5	62.2	74.2	106.6	56.1	76.1	120.1	56.5	81.7	107.0	56.1	76.3
09	FINISHES	93.7	63.4	77.0	87.7	60.7	72.8	82.3	66.2	73.4	94.0	64.6	77.8	105.9	58.7	79.9	100.0	64.7	80.5
COVERS	DIVS. 10 - 14, 25, 28, 41, 43, 44, 46	100.0	83.4	96.7	100.0	81.4	96.3	100.0	82.7	96.5	100.0	82.2	96.4	100.0	82.6	96.5	100.0	82.5	96.5
21, 22, 23	FIRE SUPPRESSION, PLUMBING & HVAC	100.2	64.1	85.6	95.4	50.0	77.1	95.4	66.5	83.8	95.5	54.9	79.1	100.2	58.9	83.5	100.0	62.4	84.9
26, 27, 3370	ELECTRICAL, COMMUNICATIONS & UTIL.	95.2	70.6	82.2	93.4	42.8	66.7	93.4	67.4	79.7	99.2	64.1	80.7	92.8	60.0	75.5	95.2	64.6	79.0
MF2014	WEIGHTED AVERAGE	97.4	68.6	84.9	98.9	59.4	81.7	94.9	68.2	83.3	99.3	64.3	84.0	100.9	63.5	84.6	99.5	67.4	85.5

TEXAS

DIVISION		DEL RIO 788			DENTON 762			EASTLAND 764			EL PASO 798 - 799,885			FORT WORTH 760 - 761			GALVESTON 775		
		MAT.	INST.	TOTAL	MAT.	INST.	TOTAL	MAT.	INST.	TOTAL	MAT.	INST.	TOTAL	MAT.	INST.	TOTAL	MAT.	INST.	TOTAL
015433	CONTRACTOR EQUIPMENT		89.4	89.4		95.8	95.8		89.9	89.9		89.9	89.9		89.9	89.9		100.5	100.5
0241, 31 - 34	SITE & INFRASTRUCTURE, DEMOLITION	121.8	88.4	98.0	105.5	81.3	88.3	108.0	87.6	93.5	101.7	87.6	91.7	102.1	88.7	92.6	107.2	88.4	93.8
0310	Concrete Forming & Accessories	96.5	57.8	63.1	106.2	65.3	70.9	99.8	65.3	70.0	97.8	63.4	68.1	98.0	65.6	70.1	89.8	64.6	68.1
0320	Concrete Reinforcing	88.7	48.4	68.2	94.3	52.1	72.8	93.1	50.9	71.6	99.2	52.0	75.2	98.4	52.4	75.0	97.8	62.4	79.8
0330	Cast-in-Place Concrete	118.2	63.2	95.6	78.5	64.6	72.8	107.2	63.6	89.3	88.4	63.7	78.3	95.0	63.7	82.1	95.2	66.4	83.4
03	CONCRETE	121.3	58.6	90.5	80.0	63.9	72.1	105.9	62.6	84.6	94.0	61.9	78.3	97.0	63.1	80.4	97.5	66.4	82.2
04	MASONRY	106.9	56.5	75.5	152.1	56.7	92.6	106.8	56.6	75.5	99.0	57.7	73.3	104.7	56.6	74.7	102.5	60.4	76.3
05	METALS	94.4	66.2	85.7	99.5	80.6	93.7	99.7	68.5	90.1	98.5	67.4	89.0	101.5	69.5	91.7	96.3	88.3	93.9
06	WOOD, PLASTICS & COMPOSITES	96.5	58.3	75.1	111.3	68.6	87.4	106.1	68.5	85.1	91.3	65.7	76.9	97.3	68.5	81.2	89.4	64.7	75.6
07	THERMAL & MOISTURE PROTECTION	101.3	65.3	86.5	96.0	66.7	84.0	98.6	65.9	85.1	99.8	64.4	85.3	96.0	65.9	83.6	93.0	67.1	82.4
08	OPENINGS	101.8	54.7	90.8	112.2	63.4	100.8	70.4	63.0	68.7	93.3	58.1	85.1	99.4	63.4	91.0	101.6	63.2	92.7
0920	Plaster & Gypsum Board	94.7	57.5	69.6	92.1	68.0	75.8	87.8	68.0	74.4	95.9	65.1	75.1	91.8	68.0	75.7	96.8	64.0	74.7
0950, 0980	Ceilings & Acoustic Treatment	89.1	57.5	68.3	84.7	68.0	73.8	80.6	68.0	72.3	91.4	65.1	74.1	90.5	68.0	75.7	94.6	64.0	74.5
0960	Flooring	100.7	64.1	90.2	90.4	64.1	82.9	121.4	64.1	105.0	110.4	64.1	97.1	117.9	64.1	102.5	100.1	64.1	89.8
0970, 0990	Wall Finishes & Painting/Coating	106.4	48.8	71.6	115.6	56.1	79.7	105.8	56.1	75.8	106.2	53.7	74.5	103.2	56.1	74.7	103.4	60.0	77.2
09	FINISHES	98.2	57.7	75.9	85.8	64.7	74.2	95.8	64.6	78.6	97.3	63.0	78.4	98.4	64.6	79.8	91.4	63.7	76.2
COVERS	DIVS. 10 - 14, 25, 28, 41, 43, 44, 46	100.0	80.5	96.1	100.0	82.5	96.5	100.0	82.2	96.4	100.0	81.0	96.2	100.0	82.3	96.4	100.0	84.5	96.9
21, 22, 23	FIRE SUPPRESSION, PLUMBING & HVAC	95.4	57.3	80.0	95.4	42.6	74.1	95.4	49.9	77.1	100.0	50.3	80.0	100.0	58.4	83.2	95.4	66.7	83.8
26, 27, 3370	ELECTRICAL, COMMUNICATIONS & UTIL.	94.9	68.8	81.1	95.9	64.6	79.3	93.3	64.5	78.1	99.1	57.4	77.0	94.7	64.5	78.8	95.0	67.9	80.7
MF2014	WEIGHTED AVERAGE	100.8	63.2	84.4	98.9	62.5	83.0	95.9	63.2	81.6	98.0	61.7	82.2	99.3	65.3	84.5	97.0	70.0	85.2

TEXAS

DIVISION		GIDDINGS 789			GREENVILLE 754			HOUSTON 770 - 772			HUNTSVILLE 773			LAREDO 780			LONGVIEW 756		
		MAT.	INST.	TOTAL	MAT.	INST.	TOTAL	MAT.	INST.	TOTAL	MAT.	INST.	TOTAL	MAT.	INST.	TOTAL	MAT.	INST.	TOTAL
015433	CONTRACTOR EQUIPMENT		89.4	89.4		96.7	96.7		100.4	100.4		91.5	91.5		89.4	89.4		91.4	91.4
0241, 31 - 34	SITE & INFRASTRUCTURE, DEMOLITION	107.8	88.4	94.0	97.9	85.4	89.0	106.0	88.2	93.4	96.6	89.9	91.8	102.1	88.4	92.5	95.8	92.3	93.3
0310	Concrete Forming & Accessories	94.1	57.9	62.9	92.3	65.3	69.0	91.8	64.6	68.4	87.8	61.6	65.2	96.6	58.0	63.3	88.4	64.9	68.1
0320	Concrete Reinforcing	89.2	45.9	67.2	100.7	52.1	76.0	97.5	61.4	79.1	98.5	50.6	74.1	88.7	48.8	68.4	99.6	52.0	75.4
0330	Cast-in-Place Concrete	100.2	63.2	85.0	89.3	63.9	78.9	92.3	66.4	81.7	98.6	64.6	84.6	84.6	63.3	75.8	103.8	62.8	86.9
03	CONCRETE	97.6	58.2	78.2	91.6	63.6	77.8	95.2	66.2	80.9	103.9	61.3	83.0	92.5	58.8	75.9	107.5	62.3	85.3
04	MASONRY	115.7	56.5	78.8	160.0	56.6	95.6	102.3	66.5	80.0	145.1	58.9	91.4	100.2	63.5	77.3	155.7	56.6	93.9
05	METALS	93.9	65.3	85.1	97.7	79.3	92.1	99.2	88.2	95.8	94.7	69.2	86.8	97.0	66.9	87.8	91.1	67.8	83.9
06	WOOD, PLASTICS & COMPOSITES	95.6	58.3	74.7	93.5	68.6	79.5	91.7	64.7	76.6	82.0	61.8	70.7	96.5	58.3	75.1	87.2	68.4	76.7
07	THERMAL & MOISTURE PROTECTION	102.0	64.5	86.6	93.0	66.0	81.9	92.6	67.8	82.4	94.9	65.9	83.0	100.2	66.5	86.4	94.5	65.2	82.5
08	OPENINGS	100.8	54.0	89.9	97.7	63.4	89.7	104.3	62.8	94.6	97.2	58.5	88.2	101.6	54.7	90.7	87.8	63.3	82.1
0920	Plaster & Gypsum Board	93.7	57.5	69.2	90.3	68.0	75.3	99.1	64.0	75.4	94.2	61.2	71.9	95.8	57.5	69.9	89.1	68.0	74.9
0950, 0980	Ceilings & Acoustic Treatment	89.1	57.5	68.3	93.6	68.0	76.8	99.6	64.0	76.2	91.2	61.2	71.5	93.3	57.5	69.8	90.3	68.0	75.7
0960	Flooring	101.1	64.1	90.5	98.6	64.1	88.7	101.2	64.1	90.6	89.4	64.1	82.1	100.5	64.1	90.1	103.5	64.1	92.2
0970, 0990	Wall Finishes & Painting/Coating	106.4	48.8	71.6	107.0	56.1	76.3	103.4	62.2	78.5	92.5	59.4	72.5	106.4	53.2	74.3	96.8	56.1	72.2
09	FINISHES	97.1	57.7	75.4	96.6	64.6	79.0	98.9	64.0	79.7	84.7	61.6	72.0	97.7	58.2	75.9	101.7	64.5	81.2
COVERS	DIVS. 10 - 14, 25, 28, 41, 43, 44, 46	100.0	80.8	96.1	100.0	82.3	96.4	100.0	84.5	96.9	100.0	81.0	96.2	100.0	80.5	96.1	100.0	82.0	96.4
21, 22, 23	FIRE SUPPRESSION, PLUMBING & HVAC	95.4	64.6	83.0	95.3	49.0	76.6	100.1	66.7	86.6	95.4	65.9	83.5	100.2	64.1	85.6	95.3	33.6	70.4
26, 27, 3370	ELECTRICAL, COMMUNICATIONS & UTIL.	91.8	63.9	77.1	92.0	64.6	77.5	96.9	67.5	81.4	93.4	68.0	80.0	95.1	60.9	77.0	92.2	55.6	72.9
MF2014	WEIGHTED AVERAGE	97.7	64.0	83.0	98.8	64.0	83.6	99.4	70.5	86.8	98.0	66.7	84.4	98.3	64.5	83.6	98.5	58.7	81.2

TEXAS

DIVISION		LUBBOCK 793 - 794			LUFKIN 759			MCALLEN 785			MCKINNEY 750			MIDLAND 797			ODESSA 797		
		MAT.	INST.	TOTAL	MAT.	INST.	TOTAL	MAT.	INST.	TOTAL	MAT.	INST.	TOTAL	MAT.	INST.	TOTAL	MAT.	INST.	TOTAL
015433	CONTRACTOR EQUIPMENT		98.5	98.5		91.4	91.4		96.8	96.8		96.7	96.7		98.5	98.5		89.9	89.9
0241, 31 - 34	SITE & INFRASTRUCTURE, DEMOLITION	123.8	86.1	97.0	91.2	94.0	93.1	144.1	84.4	101.7	94.6	85.3	88.0	126.7	86.1	97.8	99.7	88.0	91.4
0310	Concrete Forming & Accessories	97.9	57.2	62.8	91.7	61.7	65.9	101.2	57.5	63.5	91.3	65.3	68.8	101.9	65.4	70.5	98.9	65.4	70.0
0320	Concrete Reinforcing	94.1	52.5	72.9	101.3	64.9	82.8	88.2	48.4	67.9	100.7	50.9	75.3	95.1	52.1	73.2	92.9	52.1	72.1
0330	Cast-in-Place Concrete	96.8	64.7	83.6	92.9	64.0	81.0	119.3	64.1	96.6	83.8	63.8	75.6	102.9	64.6	87.2	96.6	63.6	83.1
03	CONCRETE	93.7	60.4	77.4	99.8	63.6	82.0	107.9	59.5	84.1	87.0	63.3	75.3	98.2	64.0	81.4	95.0	62.8	79.2
04	MASONRY	103.6	64.0	78.9	119.4	58.8	81.6	106.8	56.4	75.4	172.2	56.6	100.2	121.5	56.7	81.1	104.2	56.6	74.6
05	METALS	109.0	81.3	100.5	97.9	72.4	90.0	94.3	77.5	89.2	97.6	78.8	91.8	107.2	80.7	99.0	104.6	69.1	93.7
06	WOOD, PLASTICS & COMPOSITES	101.1	57.3	76.5	95.3	61.8	76.5	114.6	58.4	83.1	92.3	68.6	79.0	106.0	68.6	85.1	101.1	68.5	82.8
07	THERMAL & MOISTURE PROTECTION	89.3	66.2	79.8	94.3	65.6	82.5	104.8	59.8	86.3	92.8	66.0	81.8	89.5	65.4	79.7	100.0	65.9	86.0
08	OPENINGS	108.5	57.2	96.6	66.7	63.0	65.9	105.7	54.7	93.9	97.7	63.0	89.6	107.5	63.4	97.2	97.1	63.3	89.2
0920	Plaster & Gypsum Board	84.4	56.3	65.4	88.0	61.2	69.9	99.4	57.5	71.1	90.0	68.0	75.1	85.9	68.0	73.8	84.0	68.0	73.2
0950, 0980	Ceilings & Acoustic Treatment	90.6	56.3	68.1	84.4	61.2	69.1	93.3	57.5	69.8	93.6	68.0	76.8	88.1	68.0	74.9	88.9	68.0	75.2
0960	Flooring	104.4	64.1	92.8	138.2	64.1	117.0	118.1	63.8	102.6	98.2	64.1	88.4	105.7	64.1	93.8	110.9	64.1	97.5
0970, 0990	Wall Finishes & Painting/Coating	119.0	56.1	81.0	96.8	56.1	72.2	120.1	48.8	77.1	107.0	56.1	76.3	119.0	56.1	81.0	106.6	56.1	76.1
09	FINISHES	96.4	58.0	75.2	110.2	61.2	83.2	106.4	57.8	79.6	96.2	64.6	78.8	96.8	64.7	79.1	93.7	64.6	77.7
COVERS	DIVS. 10 - 14, 25, 28, 41, 43, 44, 46	100.0	81.3	96.2	100.0	80.9	96.1	100.0	80.7	96.1	100.0	82.3	96.4	100.0	81.2	96.2	100.0	80.9	96.1
21, 22, 23	FIRE SUPPRESSION, PLUMBING & HVAC	99.8	50.7	80.0	95.3	64.4	82.8	95.4	58.7	80.6	95.3	45.4	75.2	95.0	49.1	76.5	100.3	49.1	79.6
26, 27, 3370	ELECTRICAL, COMMUNICATIONS & UTIL.	97.9	64.2	80.1	93.5	70.6	81.4	92.6	36.3	62.8	92.1	64.6	77.5	97.9	64.2	80.1	99.4	64.1	80.7
MF2014	WEIGHTED AVERAGE	101.6	63.6	85.0	95.6	67.8	83.5	101.0	59.8	83.0	98.7	63.1	83.2	101.5	64.2	85.2	99.6	63.1	83.7

TEXAS

DIVISION		PALESTINE 758			SAN ANGELO 769			SAN ANTONIO 781 - 782			TEMPLE 765			TEXARKANA 755			TYLER 757		
		MAT.	INST.	TOTAL	MAT.	INST.	TOTAL	MAT.	INST.	TOTAL	MAT.	INST.	TOTAL	MAT.	INST.	TOTAL	MAT.	INST.	TOTAL
015433	CONTRACTOR EQUIPMENT		91.4	91.4		89.9	89.9		91.9	91.9		89.9	89.9		91.4	91.4		91.4	91.4
0241, 31 - 34	SITE & INFRASTRUCTURE, DEMOLITION	96.6	92.6	93.8	101.5	89.7	93.1	100.9	92.0	94.5	89.8	89.1	89.3	85.9	92.0	90.2	95.1	92.4	93.2
0310	Concrete Forming & Accessories	82.7	65.4	67.8	99.3	58.7	64.3	95.0	58.1	63.2	102.8	57.8	64.0	99.0	57.4	63.1	93.6	65.4	69.3
0320	Concrete Reinforcing	98.8	52.1	75.1	92.7	52.1	72.1	93.6	49.8	71.3	92.9	49.1	70.6	98.7	52.3	75.1	99.6	52.4	75.6
0330	Cast-in-Place Concrete	84.9	63.0	75.9	95.7	64.8	83.0	85.6	65.2	77.2	78.5	63.1	72.2	85.5	62.7	76.2	101.9	63.0	85.9
03	CONCRETE	101.6	62.6	82.4	96.7	60.3	78.8	91.7	59.7	76.0	82.9	58.7	71.0	92.8	59.0	76.2	107.1	62.7	85.3
04	MASONRY	113.8	56.6	78.2	138.0	58.7	88.5	96.8	65.3	77.2	151.0	56.4	92.1	176.5	56.6	101.8	166.0	56.6	97.8
05	METALS	97.6	68.3	88.6	100.1	69.1	90.6	96.9	68.6	88.2	99.8	66.5	89.6	91.0	67.8	83.9	97.5	68.4	88.5
06	WOOD, PLASTICS & COMPOSITES	85.3	68.4	75.8	99.8	58.3	76.5	94.7	57.4	73.8	108.9	58.3	80.6	99.7	58.2	76.5	97.0	68.4	81.0
07	THERMAL & MOISTURE PROTECTION	94.8	65.3	82.7	98.0	66.0	84.9	96.4	68.2	84.8	97.7	64.8	84.2	94.1	64.2	81.9	94.6	65.3	82.6
08	OPENINGS	66.7	63.3	65.9	94.7	57.8	86.1	102.7	54.4	91.5	67.1	57.0	64.7	87.7	57.8	80.8	66.6	63.4	65.9
0920	Plaster & Gypsum Board	85.2	68.0	73.6	87.8	57.5	67.3	98.0	56.5	70.0	87.8	57.5	67.3	93.4	57.5	69.1	88.0	68.0	74.5
0950, 0980	Ceilings & Acoustic Treatment	84.4	68.0	73.6	80.6	57.5	65.4	102.7	56.5	72.3	80.6	57.5	65.4	90.3	57.5	68.7	84.4	68.0	73.6
0960	Flooring	129.9	64.1	111.1	95.3	64.1	86.4	104.1	64.1	92.6	123.2	64.1	106.3	111.1	64.1	97.6	140.1	64.1	118.4
0970, 0990	Wall Finishes & Painting/Coating	96.8	56.1	72.2	104.2	56.1	75.1	106.3	53.2	74.2	105.8	48.8	71.4	96.8	56.1	72.2	96.8	56.1	72.2
09	FINISHES	108.0	64.5	84.0	87.5	59.1	71.8	103.4	58.1	78.4	95.1	57.7	74.5	104.0	58.5	78.9	111.1	64.5	85.4
COVERS	DIVS. 10 - 14, 25, 28, 41, 43, 44, 46	100.0	82.0	96.4	100.0	81.0	96.2	100.0	81.2	96.2	100.0	81.1	96.2	100.0	80.9	96.1	100.0	82.0	96.4
21, 22, 23	FIRE SUPPRESSION, PLUMBING & HVAC	95.3	59.6	80.9	95.4	50.1	77.1	100.0	63.2	85.1	95.4	54.7	79.0	95.3	37.0	71.8	95.3	62.4	82.0
26, 27, 3370	ELECTRICAL, COMMUNICATIONS & UTIL.	89.8	55.6	71.7	97.4	44.8	69.6	96.4	60.9	77.6	94.5	59.8	76.2	93.4	60.1	75.8	92.2	55.5	72.8
MF2014	WEIGHTED AVERAGE	95.0	64.4	81.7	98.5	59.6	81.5	98.5	65.1	84.0	94.7	61.7	80.3	98.0	58.4	80.7	98.5	65.0	83.9

TEXAS / UTAH

DIVISION		VICTORIA 779			WACO 766 - 767			WAXAHACHIE 751			WHARTON 774			WICHITA FALLS 763			LOGAN 843		
		MAT.	INST.	TOTAL	MAT.	INST.	TOTAL	MAT.	INST.	TOTAL	MAT.	INST.	TOTAL	MAT.	INST.	TOTAL	MAT.	INST.	TOTAL
015433	CONTRACTOR EQUIPMENT		99.3	99.3		89.9	89.9		96.7	96.7		100.5	100.5		89.9	89.9		97.5	97.5
0241, 31 - 34	SITE & INFRASTRUCTURE, DEMOLITION	111.8	85.7	93.2	98.6	88.7	91.6	96.0	85.4	88.4	117.1	87.8	96.2	99.3	88.7	91.8	96.0	95.7	95.8
0310	Concrete Forming & Accessories	90.0	59.0	63.3	101.2	65.5	70.4	91.3	65.5	69.0	84.9	61.7	64.9	101.2	65.5	70.4	104.7	58.1	64.5
0320	Concrete Reinforcing	93.9	48.5	70.8	92.5	48.5	70.1	100.7	50.9	75.4	97.7	50.6	73.7	92.5	51.3	71.5	99.6	81.3	90.3
0330	Cast-in-Place Concrete	106.9	65.6	89.9	84.9	66.8	77.4	88.4	63.9	78.3	109.8	65.5	91.6	90.7	63.7	79.6	87.3	73.4	81.6
03	CONCRETE	104.9	60.9	83.3	89.7	63.3	76.7	90.6	63.4	77.2	109.1	62.5	86.2	92.4	62.8	77.9	106.0	68.3	87.5
04	MASONRY	120.0	58.9	81.9	105.2	56.6	74.9	160.7	56.6	95.8	103.6	58.9	75.8	105.7	63.6	79.5	105.8	63.2	79.3
05	METALS	94.9	80.7	90.5	102.2	67.8	91.6	97.7	79.0	92.0	96.3	81.6	91.8	102.2	69.8	92.2	102.2	79.0	95.0
06	WOOD, PLASTICS & COMPOSITES	92.5	58.4	73.4	107.1	68.5	85.5	92.3	68.6	79.0	83.1	62.0	71.3	107.1	68.5	85.5	85.3	54.9	68.3
07	THERMAL & MOISTURE PROTECTION	96.8	66.9	84.6	98.5	65.8	85.1	92.9	66.0	81.9	93.4	66.6	82.4	98.5	67.7	85.9	97.4	67.9	85.3
08	OPENINGS	101.4	56.1	90.8	77.7	62.4	74.1	97.7	63.0	89.6	101.6	58.6	91.6	77.7	63.3	74.4	94.3	56.5	85.5
0920	Plaster & Gypsum Board	93.8	57.5	69.3	88.2	68.0	74.6	90.4	68.0	75.3	92.5	61.2	71.3	88.2	68.0	74.6	78.9	53.5	61.7
0950, 0980	Ceilings & Acoustic Treatment	95.4	57.5	70.5	82.2	68.0	72.9	95.3	68.0	77.4	94.6	61.2	72.6	82.2	68.0	72.9	97.2	53.5	68.5
0960	Flooring	99.5	64.1	89.4	122.4	64.1	105.8	98.2	64.1	88.4	97.7	64.1	88.1	123.4	76.5	110.0	101.2	47.7	85.9
0970, 0990	Wall Finishes & Painting/Coating	103.6	59.4	76.9	105.8	48.8	71.4	107.0	56.1	76.3	103.4	59.4	76.8	108.5	56.1	76.8	103.3	60.7	77.5
09	FINISHES	89.4	59.6	73.0	95.8	63.8	78.1	96.8	64.6	79.1	90.8	61.7	74.8	96.3	67.1	80.2	96.2	55.3	73.6
COVERS	DIVS. 10 - 14, 25, 28, 41, 43, 44, 46	100.0	80.8	96.1	100.0	82.3	96.4	100.0	82.3	96.4	100.0	81.3	96.2	100.0	69.8	93.9	100.0	85.1	97.0
21, 22, 23	FIRE SUPPRESSION, PLUMBING & HVAC	95.4	65.9	83.5	100.2	54.7	81.8	95.3	58.5	80.5	95.4	65.0	83.1	100.2	54.2	81.6	99.9	69.5	87.6
26, 27, 3370	ELECTRICAL, COMMUNICATIONS & UTIL.	99.8	57.6	77.5	97.6	63.6	79.6	92.1	64.6	77.5	98.6	68.0	82.4	99.3	60.1	78.6	97.5	73.0	84.6
MF2014	WEIGHTED AVERAGE	99.0	65.6	84.4	96.5	64.1	82.4	98.6	65.9	84.4	98.9	67.7	85.3	97.1	64.4	82.8	99.8	70.1	86.9

For customer support on your Site Work & Landscape Cost Data, call 877.737.1594.

781

City Cost Indexes

UTAH / VERMONT

DIVISION		OGDEN 842,844 MAT.	INST.	TOTAL	PRICE 845 MAT.	INST.	TOTAL	PROVO 846-847 MAT.	INST.	TOTAL	SALT LAKE CITY 840-841 MAT.	INST.	TOTAL	BELLOWS FALLS 051 MAT.	INST.	TOTAL	BENNINGTON 052 MAT.	INST.	TOTAL
015433	CONTRACTOR EQUIPMENT		97.5	97.5		96.6	96.6		96.6	96.6		97.5	97.5		100.9	100.9		100.9	100.9
0241, 31 - 34	SITE & INFRASTRUCTURE, DEMOLITION	84.9	95.7	92.6	93.3	93.8	93.7	92.3	94.1	93.6	84.5	95.6	92.4	88.2	100.5	96.9	87.5	100.5	96.7
0310	Concrete Forming & Accessories	104.7	58.1	64.5	107.1	48.3	56.4	106.3	58.0	64.7	107.1	58.0	64.8	98.3	85.5	87.3	95.9	106.6	105.2
0320	Concrete Reinforcing	99.2	81.3	90.1	106.8	81.1	93.7	107.7	81.3	94.3	101.5	81.3	91.2	83.2	85.7	84.5	83.2	85.7	84.5
0330	Cast-in-Place Concrete	88.7	73.4	82.4	87.4	59.5	75.9	87.4	73.3	81.6	96.9	73.3	87.2	87.0	110.7	96.7	87.0	110.7	96.7
03	CONCRETE	95.9	68.3	82.3	107.3	59.0	83.6	105.9	68.2	87.4	114.8	68.2	91.9	91.0	94.2	92.6	90.8	103.6	97.1
04	MASONRY	99.7	63.2	77.0	110.9	61.3	80.0	111.1	63.2	81.2	113.1	63.2	82.0	103.6	95.2	98.4	112.4	95.2	101.6
05	METALS	102.7	79.0	95.4	99.4	76.6	92.4	100.3	78.9	93.7	106.2	78.9	97.8	94.8	88.3	92.8	94.7	88.2	92.7
06	WOOD, PLASTICS & COMPOSITES	85.3	54.9	68.3	88.6	44.3	63.8	86.8	54.9	68.9	87.2	54.9	69.1	103.7	83.5	92.4	100.6	112.4	107.2
07	THERMAL & MOISTURE PROTECTION	96.4	67.9	84.7	99.0	59.9	82.9	99.0	67.9	86.2	103.4	67.9	88.9	97.0	82.7	91.1	97.0	81.1	90.4
08	OPENINGS	94.3	56.5	85.5	98.2	48.9	86.7	98.2	56.5	88.5	96.2	56.5	86.9	105.0	86.5	100.7	105.0	102.3	104.3
0920	Plaster & Gypsum Board	78.9	53.5	61.7	81.7	42.5	55.2	79.2	53.5	61.8	90.5	53.5	65.5	106.0	82.4	90.1	104.2	112.2	109.6
0950, 0980	Ceilings & Acoustic Treatment	97.2	53.5	68.5	97.2	42.5	61.3	97.2	53.5	68.5	91.5	53.5	66.5	91.5	82.4	85.6	91.5	112.2	105.1
0960	Flooring	99.0	47.7	84.3	102.3	35.5	83.2	102.0	47.7	86.5	103.2	47.7	87.3	100.6	104.6	101.8	99.7	104.6	101.1
0970, 0990	Wall Finishes & Painting/Coating	103.3	60.7	77.5	103.3	37.5	63.6	103.3	62.6	78.7	106.7	62.6	80.1	97.4	105.8	102.5	97.4	105.8	102.5
09	FINISHES	94.3	55.3	72.8	97.3	43.5	67.7	96.8	55.5	74.0	96.6	55.5	74.0	95.9	90.7	93.0	95.4	107.8	102.2
COVERS	DIVS. 10 - 14, 25, 28, 41, 43, 44, 46	100.0	85.1	97.0	100.0	45.8	89.0	100.0	85.0	97.0	100.0	85.0	97.0	100.0	97.6	99.5	100.0	100.7	100.1
21, 22, 23	FIRE SUPPRESSION, PLUMBING & HVAC	99.9	69.5	87.6	97.5	67.7	85.5	99.9	69.4	87.6	100.1	69.4	87.7	95.3	96.4	95.7	95.3	96.4	95.7
26, 27, 3370	ELECTRICAL, COMMUNICATIONS & UTIL.	97.9	73.0	84.7	103.5	73.0	87.4	98.4	59.8	78.0	100.5	59.8	79.0	101.5	89.3	95.1	101.5	61.2	80.2
MF2014	WEIGHTED AVERAGE	98.1	70.1	85.9	100.2	64.6	84.7	100.3	68.2	86.3	102.2	68.3	87.4	97.2	93.0	95.3	97.5	93.5	95.8

VERMONT

DIVISION		BRATTLEBORO 053 MAT.	INST.	TOTAL	BURLINGTON 054 MAT.	INST.	TOTAL	GUILDHALL 059 MAT.	INST.	TOTAL	MONTPELIER 056 MAT.	INST.	TOTAL	RUTLAND 057 MAT.	INST.	TOTAL	ST. JOHNSBURY 058 MAT.	INST.	TOTAL
015433	CONTRACTOR EQUIPMENT		100.9	100.9		100.9	100.9		100.9	100.9		100.9	100.9		100.9	100.9		100.9	100.9
0241, 31 - 34	SITE & INFRASTRUCTURE, DEMOLITION	88.9	100.5	97.1	93.0	100.4	98.2	87.2	99.0	95.6	91.5	100.1	97.6	91.7	100.1	97.7	87.3	99.0	95.6
0310	Concrete Forming & Accessories	98.6	85.4	87.2	98.0	87.6	89.0	96.1	78.3	80.7	97.9	84.1	86.0	98.9	87.6	89.1	94.4	78.3	80.5
0320	Concrete Reinforcing	82.3	85.7	84.0	101.1	85.6	93.2	83.9	85.6	84.8	94.1	85.6	89.8	103.9	85.6	94.6	82.3	85.6	84.0
0330	Cast-in-Place Concrete	89.7	110.7	98.3	100.9	109.6	104.5	84.3	101.0	91.2	100.9	109.6	104.5	85.2	109.6	95.2	84.3	101.0	91.2
03	CONCRETE	93.0	94.1	93.6	101.2	94.7	98.0	88.6	87.6	88.1	100.1	93.1	96.7	94.3	94.7	94.5	88.2	87.6	87.9
04	MASONRY	111.5	95.2	101.3	115.7	93.7	102.0	111.8	78.2	90.8	109.6	93.7	99.7	93.9	93.7	93.8	138.8	78.2	101.0
05	METALS	94.7	88.2	92.7	103.5	87.5	98.6	94.8	87.3	92.5	99.6	87.4	95.9	100.6	87.4	96.5	94.8	87.3	92.5
06	WOOD, PLASTICS & COMPOSITES	104.0	83.5	92.5	99.9	88.2	93.3	100.0	83.5	90.8	97.7	83.5	89.7	104.2	88.2	95.2	94.8	83.5	88.5
07	THERMAL & MOISTURE PROTECTION	97.1	78.0	89.3	103.8	80.4	94.2	96.8	70.7	86.1	103.3	79.9	93.7	97.2	80.4	90.3	96.7	70.7	86.1
08	OPENINGS	105.0	86.5	100.7	108.4	85.0	103.0	105.0	82.4	99.7	105.8	82.4	100.3	108.4	85.0	102.9	105.0	82.4	99.7
0920	Plaster & Gypsum Board	106.0	82.4	90.1	109.7	87.2	94.5	112.4	82.4	92.2	108.9	82.4	91.0	106.6	87.2	93.5	113.8	82.4	92.6
0950, 0980	Ceilings & Acoustic Treatment	91.5	82.4	85.6	101.0	87.2	91.9	91.5	82.4	85.6	95.1	82.4	86.8	95.9	87.2	90.2	91.5	82.4	85.6
0960	Flooring	100.7	104.6	101.8	102.4	104.6	103.1	103.6	104.6	103.9	103.2	104.6	103.6	100.6	104.6	101.8	106.9	104.6	106.3
0970, 0990	Wall Finishes & Painting/Coating	97.4	105.8	102.5	102.9	85.2	92.2	97.4	85.2	90.0	101.7	85.2	91.7	97.4	85.2	90.0	97.4	85.2	90.0
09	FINISHES	96.0	90.7	93.1	99.7	90.8	94.8	97.5	84.2	90.2	97.9	88.0	92.5	97.1	90.8	93.6	98.7	84.2	90.7
COVERS	DIVS. 10 - 14, 25, 28, 41, 43, 44, 46	100.0	97.6	99.5	100.0	97.5	99.5	100.0	91.8	98.3	100.0	97.0	99.4	100.0	97.5	99.5	100.0	91.8	98.3
21, 22, 23	FIRE SUPPRESSION, PLUMBING & HVAC	95.3	96.4	95.7	99.9	71.8	88.6	95.3	64.0	82.7	95.1	71.8	85.7	100.1	71.8	88.7	95.3	64.0	82.7
26, 27, 3370	ELECTRICAL, COMMUNICATIONS & UTIL.	101.5	89.3	95.1	102.2	61.2	80.5	101.5	61.2	80.2	99.7	61.2	79.3	101.6	61.2	80.2	101.5	61.2	80.2
MF2014	WEIGHTED AVERAGE	97.8	92.8	95.6	102.4	83.6	94.2	97.4	77.8	88.8	99.5	82.8	92.2	99.7	83.6	92.7	98.6	77.8	89.6

VERMONT / VIRGINIA

DIVISION		WHITE RIVER JCT. 050 MAT.	INST.	TOTAL	ALEXANDRIA 223 MAT.	INST.	TOTAL	ARLINGTON 222 MAT.	INST.	TOTAL	BRISTOL 242 MAT.	INST.	TOTAL	CHARLOTTESVILLE 229 MAT.	INST.	TOTAL	CULPEPER 227 MAT.	INST.	TOTAL
015433	CONTRACTOR EQUIPMENT		100.9	100.9		103.0	103.0		101.7	101.7		101.7	101.7		106.1	106.1		101.7	101.7
0241, 31 - 34	SITE & INFRASTRUCTURE, DEMOLITION	91.5	99.2	97.0	114.3	89.8	96.9	124.5	87.7	98.3	108.8	86.1	92.6	113.5	88.1	95.4	111.8	87.6	94.6
0310	Concrete Forming & Accessories	93.1	78.9	80.8	92.2	72.8	75.5	91.2	72.0	74.7	87.1	42.5	48.6	85.4	48.7	53.7	82.5	71.4	72.9
0320	Concrete Reinforcing	83.2	85.6	84.4	83.0	87.0	85.1	93.7	84.4	88.9	93.7	68.4	80.8	93.1	72.8	82.7	93.7	84.2	88.9
0330	Cast-in-Place Concrete	89.7	101.9	94.7	105.1	81.8	95.6	102.3	80.3	93.3	101.8	48.5	79.9	105.9	55.5	85.2	104.8	69.2	90.2
03	CONCRETE	94.7	88.2	91.5	102.0	79.6	91.0	106.7	78.3	92.8	102.9	51.2	77.5	103.5	57.2	80.8	100.6	74.1	87.6
04	MASONRY	124.5	79.7	96.6	91.3	72.8	79.8	106.3	70.7	84.1	95.4	51.4	68.0	120.3	53.2	78.5	107.5	70.7	84.6
05	METALS	94.8	87.3	92.5	105.7	97.0	103.0	104.3	97.2	102.1	103.1	85.7	97.8	103.4	90.2	99.3	103.5	95.3	101.0
06	WOOD, PLASTICS & COMPOSITES	97.4	83.5	89.6	95.0	71.0	81.6	91.5	71.0	80.0	83.7	40.0	59.2	82.2	45.6	61.7	80.8	71.0	75.3
07	THERMAL & MOISTURE PROTECTION	97.1	71.4	86.6	102.7	81.5	94.0	104.7	80.6	94.8	104.2	60.1	86.1	103.8	67.7	89.0	104.0	78.1	93.4
08	OPENINGS	105.0	82.4	99.7	100.9	75.2	94.9	99.0	75.2	93.5	102.0	46.5	89.1	100.2	52.0	89.0	100.5	75.2	94.6
0920	Plaster & Gypsum Board	102.8	82.4	89.0	107.4	69.9	82.1	104.2	69.9	81.0	99.7	38.0	58.0	99.7	43.0	61.4	99.9	69.9	79.6
0950, 0980	Ceilings & Acoustic Treatment	91.5	82.4	85.6	91.4	69.9	77.3	89.8	69.9	76.7	88.9	38.0	55.4	88.9	43.0	58.8	89.8	69.9	76.7
0960	Flooring	98.6	104.6	100.4	106.0	82.9	99.4	104.5	81.9	98.0	101.0	66.5	91.1	99.7	66.5	90.2	99.7	81.9	94.6
0970, 0990	Wall Finishes & Painting/Coating	97.4	85.2	90.0	124.0	80.0	97.5	124.0	80.0	97.5	109.6	54.3	76.2	109.6	76.1	89.3	124.0	76.1	95.1
09	FINISHES	95.2	84.6	89.3	100.1	74.6	86.0	100.0	73.8	85.6	96.5	47.2	69.3	96.2	53.5	72.6	96.9	73.2	83.9
COVERS	DIVS. 10 - 14, 25, 28, 41, 43, 44, 46	100.0	92.3	98.4	100.0	88.6	97.7	100.0	87.6	97.5	100.0	67.8	93.5	100.0	79.3	95.8	100.0	87.6	97.5
21, 22, 23	FIRE SUPPRESSION, PLUMBING & HVAC	95.3	64.8	83.0	100.3	86.9	94.9	100.3	85.4	94.3	95.6	50.5	77.4	95.6	69.3	85.0	95.6	72.9	86.4
26, 27, 3370	ELECTRICAL, COMMUNICATIONS & UTIL.	101.5	61.2	80.2	97.1	102.4	99.9	94.7	99.2	97.1	96.8	35.4	64.3	96.7	71.9	83.6	99.3	99.2	99.2
MF2014	WEIGHTED AVERAGE	98.5	78.3	89.7	101.1	85.5	94.3	101.9	84.0	94.1	99.4	54.9	80.0	100.5	67.1	86.0	99.9	80.5	91.4

782

City Cost Indexes

VIRGINIA

DIVISION		FAIRFAX 220-221 MAT.	INST.	TOTAL	FARMVILLE 239 MAT.	INST.	TOTAL	FREDERICKSBURG 224-225 MAT.	INST.	TOTAL	GRUNDY 246 MAT.	INST.	TOTAL	HARRISONBURG 228 MAT.	INST.	TOTAL	LYNCHBURG 245 MAT.	INST.	TOTAL
015433	CONTRACTOR EQUIPMENT		101.7	101.7		106.1	106.1		101.7	101.7		101.7	101.7		101.7	101.7		101.7	101.7
0241, 31-34	SITE & INFRASTRUCTURE, DEMOLITION	123.1	87.8	98.0	109.2	87.6	93.8	111.4	87.7	94.5	106.6	84.8	91.1	120.1	86.3	96.1	107.5	86.3	92.4
0310	Concrete Forming & Accessories	85.4	72.0	73.9	98.0	43.7	51.2	85.4	69.4	71.6	90.3	36.4	43.8	81.4	42.6	47.9	87.1	60.3	64.0
0320	Concrete Reinforcing	93.7	87.0	90.3	90.9	49.9	70.0	94.4	87.0	90.6	92.4	50.4	71.0	93.7	64.9	79.0	93.1	68.5	80.5
0330	Cast-in-Place Concrete	102.3	80.6	93.4	103.1	53.5	82.7	103.9	69.3	89.7	101.8	47.5	79.5	102.3	58.0	84.1	101.8	57.7	83.7
03	CONCRETE	106.3	78.8	92.8	101.2	49.9	76.0	100.3	73.8	87.3	101.6	44.4	73.5	104.1	53.8	79.4	101.5	62.3	82.3
04	MASONRY	106.2	71.4	84.5	103.5	44.9	66.9	106.6	70.7	84.2	96.5	47.3	65.8	104.2	50.3	70.6	112.0	53.2	75.4
05	METALS	103.6	97.0	101.5	101.0	77.1	93.6	103.5	96.2	101.3	103.1	69.9	92.9	103.4	83.9	97.4	103.3	86.3	98.1
06	WOOD, PLASTICS & COMPOSITES	83.7	71.0	76.6	96.4	44.1	67.1	83.7	68.1	75.0	86.7	35.1	57.8	79.8	39.0	56.9	83.7	62.6	71.9
07	THERMAL & MOISTURE PROTECTION	104.6	73.7	91.9	104.3	49.3	81.8	104.0	78.5	93.6	104.2	45.3	80.0	104.4	63.9	87.8	104.0	63.9	87.6
08	OPENINGS	99.0	75.2	93.5	100.7	43.0	87.3	100.2	73.6	94.0	102.0	34.4	86.3	100.5	49.4	88.6	100.5	58.8	90.8
0920	Plaster & Gypsum Board	99.9	69.9	79.6	108.6	41.5	63.2	99.9	66.9	77.6	99.7	32.9	54.5	99.7	36.9	57.3	99.7	61.3	73.7
0950, 0980	Ceilings & Acoustic Treatment	89.8	69.9	76.7	84.8	41.5	56.3	89.8	66.9	74.8	88.9	32.9	52.1	88.9	36.9	54.8	88.9	61.3	70.8
0960	Flooring	101.4	81.9	95.8	106.5	60.3	93.3	101.4	81.9	95.8	102.3	33.7	82.6	99.4	74.0	92.1	101.0	66.5	91.1
0970, 0990	Wall Finishes & Painting/Coating	124.0	80.0	97.5	112.8	38.7	68.1	124.0	76.1	95.1	109.6	35.1	64.6	124.0	54.3	81.9	109.6	54.3	76.2
09	FINISHES	98.5	74.0	85.0	98.0	46.0	69.4	97.4	71.5	83.1	96.7	35.1	62.8	97.3	47.8	70.1	96.3	60.2	76.4
COVERS	DIVS. 10-14, 25, 28, 41, 43, 44, 46	100.0	87.8	97.5	100.0	45.7	89.0	100.0	83.4	96.6	100.0	43.7	88.6	100.0	67.6	93.5	100.0	70.9	94.1
21, 22, 23	FIRE SUPPRESSION, PLUMBING & HVAC	95.6	85.7	91.6	95.5	43.4	74.5	95.6	85.1	91.3	95.6	62.1	82.1	95.6	66.9	84.0	95.6	69.0	84.8
26, 27, 3370	ELECTRICAL, COMMUNICATIONS & UTIL.	97.9	99.2	98.6	90.1	48.2	68.0	94.9	99.2	97.2	96.8	44.6	69.2	96.9	96.4	96.7	97.9	52.7	74.0
MF2014	WEIGHTED AVERAGE	100.7	84.0	93.4	98.7	52.4	78.5	99.5	82.7	92.1	99.3	52.5	78.9	100.2	67.2	85.8	99.9	65.6	85.0

VIRGINIA

DIVISION		NEWPORT NEWS 236 MAT.	INST.	TOTAL	NORFOLK 233-235 MAT.	INST.	TOTAL	PETERSBURG 238 MAT.	INST.	TOTAL	PORTSMOUTH 237 MAT.	INST.	TOTAL	PULASKI 243 MAT.	INST.	TOTAL	RICHMOND 230-232 MAT.	INST.	TOTAL
015433	CONTRACTOR EQUIPMENT		106.1	106.1		106.7	106.7		106.1	106.1		106.0	106.0		101.7	101.7		106.1	106.1
0241, 31-34	SITE & INFRASTRUCTURE, DEMOLITION	108.2	88.8	94.4	108.9	89.8	95.3	111.7	89.0	95.6	106.7	88.6	93.8	105.9	85.5	91.4	103.6	89.0	93.2
0310	Concrete Forming & Accessories	97.3	64.1	68.7	97.9	64.3	68.9	90.6	57.2	61.8	86.4	53.1	57.7	90.3	38.7	45.8	97.6	57.2	62.8
0320	Concrete Reinforcing	90.6	72.0	81.2	94.7	72.1	83.2	90.3	73.0	81.5	90.3	72.0	81.0	92.4	64.6	78.3	97.5	73.0	85.0
0330	Cast-in-Place Concrete	100.2	66.1	86.2	105.2	66.1	89.1	106.3	53.7	84.7	99.2	66.0	85.6	101.8	48.2	79.8	98.1	53.7	79.8
03	CONCRETE	98.4	67.6	83.3	101.5	67.7	84.9	103.6	60.4	82.4	97.1	62.6	80.2	101.6	48.7	75.6	98.5	60.4	79.8
04	MASONRY	97.8	53.9	70.5	103.8	53.9	72.7	111.9	52.6	75.0	103.8	53.9	72.7	91.5	48.2	64.5	102.5	52.6	71.4
05	METALS	103.3	89.8	99.2	103.1	89.9	99.1	101.1	90.7	97.9	102.2	89.1	98.2	103.2	82.5	96.8	107.1	90.7	102.0
06	WOOD, PLASTICS & COMPOSITES	95.3	66.2	79.0	93.2	66.2	78.1	86.4	58.6	70.8	82.9	51.5	65.3	86.7	36.8	58.7	95.0	58.6	74.6
07	THERMAL & MOISTURE PROTECTION	104.3	68.4	89.6	100.9	68.4	87.5	104.3	68.3	89.5	104.3	66.8	88.9	104.2	51.1	82.4	102.2	68.3	88.3
08	OPENINGS	101.1	62.2	92.1	100.4	62.2	91.5	100.4	59.0	90.8	101.2	54.1	90.2	102.0	42.2	88.1	104.8	59.0	94.1
0920	Plaster & Gypsum Board	109.4	64.3	78.9	105.5	64.3	77.6	101.3	56.4	71.0	101.6	49.1	66.1	99.7	34.7	55.7	104.2	56.4	71.9
0950, 0980	Ceilings & Acoustic Treatment	88.2	64.3	72.5	88.9	64.3	72.7	85.7	56.4	66.4	88.2	49.1	62.5	88.9	34.7	53.3	90.6	56.4	68.1
0960	Flooring	106.5	66.5	95.1	105.6	66.5	94.4	102.5	71.2	93.6	99.5	66.5	90.0	102.3	66.5	92.0	103.4	71.2	94.2
0970, 0990	Wall Finishes & Painting/Coating	112.8	42.0	70.1	113.0	76.1	90.7	112.8	76.1	90.6	112.8	76.1	90.6	109.6	54.3	76.2	110.0	76.1	89.5
09	FINISHES	98.7	62.2	78.6	98.2	66.0	80.5	96.3	61.2	76.9	95.6	56.7	74.2	96.7	43.7	67.5	98.5	61.2	77.9
COVERS	DIVS. 10-14, 25, 28, 41, 43, 44, 46	100.0	82.2	96.4	100.0	82.2	96.4	100.0	79.6	95.9	100.0	72.0	94.3	100.0	44.0	88.7	100.0	79.6	95.9
21, 22, 23	FIRE SUPPRESSION, PLUMBING & HVAC	100.3	63.6	85.5	100.0	64.3	85.6	95.5	67.5	84.2	100.3	64.3	85.8	95.6	62.2	82.1	99.9	67.5	86.8
26, 27, 3370	ELECTRICAL, COMMUNICATIONS & UTIL.	92.8	63.5	77.3	95.5	58.3	75.8	93.0	71.9	81.8	91.2	58.3	73.8	96.8	54.4	74.4	96.8	71.9	83.6
MF2014	WEIGHTED AVERAGE	100.0	68.2	86.1	100.5	68.2	86.4	99.4	68.7	86.0	99.4	65.3	84.5	99.0	57.3	80.9	101.3	68.7	87.1

VIRGINIA / WASHINGTON

DIVISION		ROANOKE 240-241 MAT.	INST.	TOTAL	STAUNTON 244 MAT.	INST.	TOTAL	WINCHESTER 226 MAT.	INST.	TOTAL	CLARKSTON 994 MAT.	INST.	TOTAL	EVERETT 982 MAT.	INST.	TOTAL	OLYMPIA 985 MAT.	INST.	TOTAL
015433	CONTRACTOR EQUIPMENT		101.7	101.7		106.1	106.1		101.7	101.7		91.2	91.2		101.6	101.6		101.6	101.6
0241, 31-34	SITE & INFRASTRUCTURE, DEMOLITION	106.4	86.3	94.1	109.9	87.7	96.6	118.7	87.6	96.6	99.2	90.1	92.7	91.5	108.4	103.5	93.4	108.4	104.1
0310	Concrete Forming & Accessories	96.8	60.5	65.5	89.9	50.0	55.5	83.8	69.5	71.4	112.7	67.4	73.6	113.4	100.4	102.2	99.0	100.3	100.1
0320	Concrete Reinforcing	93.4	68.5	80.7	93.1	48.9	70.6	93.1	86.4	89.7	112.0	87.2	99.4	104.2	98.8	101.5	110.8	98.7	104.6
0330	Cast-in-Place Concrete	115.7	57.7	91.9	105.9	51.5	83.6	102.3	69.3	88.7	96.3	81.9	90.4	103.5	106.2	104.6	98.9	106.2	101.9
03	CONCRETE	105.9	62.4	84.5	102.9	52.0	77.9	103.5	73.7	88.9	107.2	76.3	92.0	98.7	101.6	100.1	98.9	101.6	100.2
04	MASONRY	97.7	53.2	70.0	106.9	51.4	72.3	101.7	59.7	75.5	102.3	81.5	89.3	110.6	100.8	104.5	103.0	99.1	100.6
05	METALS	105.5	86.5	99.7	103.4	80.5	96.3	103.5	94.7	100.8	88.3	81.6	86.2	101.8	92.4	98.9	101.2	92.1	98.4
06	WOOD, PLASTICS & COMPOSITES	95.9	62.6	77.3	86.7	49.9	66.1	82.2	68.1	74.3	113.2	63.8	85.5	111.7	100.0	105.2	91.1	100.0	96.1
07	THERMAL & MOISTURE PROTECTION	103.8	66.8	88.7	103.8	52.0	82.6	104.5	75.6	92.7	143.8	77.2	116.5	103.7	101.7	102.9	103.5	96.8	100.7
08	OPENINGS	100.9	58.8	91.1	100.5	48.1	88.3	102.1	73.7	95.5	119.0	68.7	107.3	101.3	99.8	101.0	106.9	99.9	105.3
0920	Plaster & Gypsum Board	107.4	61.3	76.2	99.7	47.5	64.4	99.9	66.9	77.6	145.7	62.5	89.5	109.4	99.9	103.0	101.3	99.9	100.4
0950, 0980	Ceilings & Acoustic Treatment	91.4	61.3	71.6	88.9	47.5	61.7	89.8	66.9	74.8	97.6	62.5	74.5	99.8	99.9	99.9	98.1	99.9	99.3
0960	Flooring	106.0	66.5	94.7	101.9	39.5	84.0	100.7	81.9	95.4	91.6	47.1	78.9	113.8	91.6	107.4	103.8	91.7	100.3
0970, 0990	Wall Finishes & Painting/Coating	109.6	54.3	76.2	109.6	34.5	64.3	124.0	87.2	101.8	100.0	58.5	75.0	95.4	91.5	93.0	99.0	91.5	94.5
09	FINISHES	99.0	61.1	78.1	96.6	46.6	69.0	97.9	72.7	84.0	110.3	61.3	83.3	104.7	97.6	100.8	98.9	97.6	98.2
COVERS	DIVS. 10-14, 25, 28, 41, 43, 44, 46	100.0	70.9	94.1	100.0	70.9	94.1	100.0	87.3	97.4	100.0	75.4	95.0	100.0	99.0	99.8	100.0	100.5	100.1
21, 22, 23	FIRE SUPPRESSION, PLUMBING & HVAC	100.3	64.8	86.0	95.6	58.9	80.8	95.6	87.7	92.4	95.6	83.4	90.7	100.1	99.1	99.7	100.0	99.1	99.7
26, 27, 3370	ELECTRICAL, COMMUNICATIONS & UTIL.	96.8	54.4	74.4	95.6	74.9	84.7	95.3	99.2	97.4	92.4	94.8	93.7	104.9	98.5	101.5	104.4	99.1	101.6
MF2014	WEIGHTED AVERAGE	101.5	65.1	85.6	99.7	61.8	83.2	100.0	82.2	92.2	101.5	80.2	92.2	101.6	99.6	100.7	101.2	99.4	100.4

City Cost Indexes

WASHINGTON

DIVISION		RICHLAND 993			SEATTLE 980-981,987			SPOKANE 990-992			TACOMA 983-984			VANCOUVER 986			WENATCHEE 988		
		MAT.	INST.	TOTAL	MAT.	INST.	TOTAL	MAT.	INST.	TOTAL	MAT.	INST.	TOTAL	MAT.	INST.	TOTAL	MAT.	INST.	TOTAL
015433	CONTRACTOR EQUIPMENT		91.2	91.2		101.6	101.6		91.2	91.2		101.6	101.6		96.7	96.7		101.6	101.6
0241, 31 - 34	SITE & INFRASTRUCTURE, DEMOLITION	101.8	91.0	94.1	95.1	106.7	103.4	101.1	91.0	93.9	94.5	108.4	104.4	104.2	96.1	98.4	103.2	107.1	106.0
0310	Concrete Forming & Accessories	112.8	78.5	83.2	108.3	100.9	102.0	118.2	78.1	83.6	104.2	100.4	100.9	104.9	90.5	92.5	105.8	77.6	81.5
0320	Concrete Reinforcing	107.4	87.4	97.2	105.1	98.9	101.9	108.2	87.3	97.6	103.1	98.8	100.9	103.9	98.4	101.1	103.9	87.7	95.6
0330	Cast-in-Place Concrete	96.5	84.4	91.5	100.9	106.4	103.2	100.3	84.2	93.7	106.4	106.2	106.3	118.8	98.4	110.4	108.6	77.3	95.7
03	CONCRETE	106.8	82.2	94.7	99.6	102.1	100.8	109.1	82.0	95.8	100.4	101.6	101.0	110.7	94.6	102.8	108.4	79.6	94.2
04	MASONRY	104.3	84.3	91.8	108.2	100.9	103.6	104.9	84.3	92.0	106.2	100.9	102.9	106.7	95.6	99.8	108.6	91.4	97.9
05	METALS	88.7	84.9	87.5	102.5	94.2	99.9	90.9	84.5	89.0	103.6	92.3	100.1	101.0	91.8	98.2	101.0	86.2	96.4
06	WOOD, PLASTICS & COMPOSITES	113.4	76.1	92.5	104.9	100.0	102.2	122.4	76.1	96.5	101.0	100.0	100.4	92.9	90.2	91.4	102.5	75.8	87.5
07	THERMAL & MOISTURE PROTECTION	145.0	78.8	117.8	102.1	101.8	102.0	141.4	79.5	116.0	103.5	98.5	101.4	104.0	91.6	98.9	104.1	81.5	94.8
08	OPENINGS	121.4	71.3	109.7	100.1	99.9	100.0	121.9	71.8	110.3	102.0	99.9	101.5	98.3	92.8	97.0	101.5	71.0	94.4
0920	Plaster & Gypsum Board	145.7	75.2	98.1	103.6	99.9	101.1	137.7	75.2	95.5	107.8	99.9	102.5	105.7	90.1	95.1	110.2	74.9	86.4
0950, 0980	Ceilings & Acoustic Treatment	104.2	75.2	85.1	110.2	99.9	103.5	99.5	75.2	83.5	103.1	99.9	101.0	100.2	90.1	93.5	95.4	74.9	82.0
0960	Flooring	92.0	80.1	88.6	108.3	106.8	107.8	91.2	85.3	89.5	107.2	91.7	102.8	113.5	102.2	110.2	109.9	62.6	96.4
0970, 0990	Wall Finishes & Painting/Coating	100.0	67.6	80.4	96.3	91.5	93.4	100.2	70.9	82.5	95.4	91.5	93.0	97.6	70.8	81.4	95.4	72.6	81.6
09	FINISHES	112.0	76.7	92.6	105.0	100.6	102.6	109.8	78.1	92.3	103.4	97.6	100.2	101.5	90.6	95.5	103.8	73.5	87.1
COVERS	DIVS. 10 - 14, 25, 28, 41, 43, 44, 46	100.0	85.4	97.0	100.0	100.5	100.1	100.0	85.3	97.0	100.0	100.5	100.1	100.0	60.7	92.1	100.0	77.2	95.4
21, 22, 23	FIRE SUPPRESSION, PLUMBING & HVAC	100.5	107.6	103.3	100.0	115.1	106.1	100.4	84.3	93.9	100.2	99.2	99.8	100.3	87.0	94.9	95.4	86.7	91.9
26, 27, 3370	ELECTRICAL, COMMUNICATIONS & UTIL.	89.7	94.8	92.4	102.6	107.0	104.9	88.0	79.0	83.3	104.7	99.1	101.7	109.7	101.0	105.1	105.5	98.4	101.8
MF2014	WEIGHTED AVERAGE	103.1	89.3	97.1	101.4	104.7	102.8	103.4	82.3	94.2	101.8	99.7	100.9	102.7	92.1	98.1	101.6	86.6	95.0

WASHINGTON / WEST VIRGINIA

DIVISION		YAKIMA 989			BECKLEY 258-259			BLUEFIELD 247-248			BUCKHANNON 262			CHARLESTON 250-253			CLARKSBURG 263-264		
		MAT.	INST.	TOTAL	MAT.	INST.	TOTAL	MAT.	INST.	TOTAL	MAT.	INST.	TOTAL	MAT.	INST.	TOTAL	MAT.	INST.	TOTAL
015433	CONTRACTOR EQUIPMENT		101.6	101.6		101.7	101.7		101.7	101.7		101.7	101.7		101.7	101.7		101.7	101.7
0241, 31 - 34	SITE & INFRASTRUCTURE, DEMOLITION	96.8	107.8	104.7	100.5	89.9	92.9	100.6	89.9	92.9	106.8	89.9	94.8	101.5	90.7	93.8	107.4	89.9	95.0
0310	Concrete Forming & Accessories	104.6	95.8	97.0	83.5	93.6	92.2	87.0	93.6	92.7	86.4	94.3	93.2	96.7	94.1	94.4	83.8	94.2	92.8
0320	Concrete Reinforcing	103.5	87.4	95.3	92.7	89.0	90.8	92.0	84.1	88.0	92.6	84.2	88.3	101.0	89.1	94.9	92.6	84.1	88.3
0330	Cast-in-Place Concrete	113.6	83.9	101.4	98.1	103.0	100.1	99.6	102.9	101.0	99.3	101.8	100.3	96.8	103.0	99.3	108.8	100.0	105.2
03	CONCRETE	105.3	89.9	97.7	97.6	96.4	97.0	97.4	95.5	96.5	100.4	95.4	98.0	99.1	96.7	97.9	104.4	94.8	99.7
04	MASONRY	99.8	83.1	89.4	98.9	98.9	98.9	93.3	98.9	96.8	104.5	98.9	101.0	95.8	97.9	97.1	108.4	98.9	102.4
05	METALS	101.6	86.3	96.9	100.9	98.1	100.0	103.4	96.3	101.2	103.6	97.1	101.6	99.6	98.9	99.4	103.6	96.9	101.5
06	WOOD, PLASTICS & COMPOSITES	101.4	100.0	100.6	83.5	93.4	89.1	85.6	93.4	90.0	84.9	93.4	89.7	98.4	93.4	95.6	81.5	93.4	88.2
07	THERMAL & MOISTURE PROTECTION	103.6	82.7	95.0	102.9	90.6	97.9	104.0	90.6	98.5	104.2	91.7	99.1	99.4	90.4	95.7	104.1	90.6	98.6
08	OPENINGS	101.5	81.0	96.7	101.3	85.8	97.7	102.5	84.6	98.3	102.5	84.6	98.4	103.6	85.8	99.4	102.5	85.1	98.5
0920	Plaster & Gypsum Board	107.4	99.9	102.4	97.0	93.0	94.3	98.9	93.0	94.9	99.3	93.0	95.1	100.3	93.0	95.4	97.2	93.0	94.4
0950, 0980	Ceilings & Acoustic Treatment	97.3	99.9	99.0	83.9	93.0	89.9	87.3	93.0	91.1	88.9	93.0	91.6	92.2	93.0	92.7	88.9	93.0	91.6
0960	Flooring	108.1	58.0	93.8	102.4	118.0	106.8	98.9	118.0	104.3	98.6	118.0	104.1	106.4	118.0	109.7	97.6	118.0	103.4
0970, 0990	Wall Finishes & Painting/Coating	95.4	70.9	80.6	107.4	91.5	97.8	109.6	94.6	100.6	109.6	94.3	100.3	106.9	95.9	100.2	109.6	94.3	100.3
09	FINISHES	102.5	86.6	93.7	94.7	98.6	96.9	94.8	98.9	97.1	95.7	98.9	97.5	99.1	98.8	99.0	95.0	98.9	97.2
COVERS	DIVS. 10 - 14, 25, 28, 41, 43, 44, 46	100.0	97.6	99.5	100.0	56.9	91.3	100.0	56.9	91.3	100.0	101.5	100.3	100.0	101.2	100.2	100.0	101.5	100.3
21, 22, 23	FIRE SUPPRESSION, PLUMBING & HVAC	100.2	107.2	103.0	95.5	93.5	94.7	95.6	92.8	94.4	95.6	95.1	95.4	100.0	93.4	97.4	95.6	95.0	95.3
26, 27, 3370	ELECTRICAL, COMMUNICATIONS & UTIL.	107.8	94.9	101.0	93.9	91.1	92.4	95.7	91.1	93.3	97.1	96.1	96.6	99.1	91.1	94.8	97.1	96.1	96.6
MF2014	WEIGHTED AVERAGE	102.0	94.1	98.6	97.9	93.3	95.9	98.3	92.9	96.0	99.6	95.5	97.8	99.9	94.8	97.6	100.1	95.4	98.1

WEST VIRGINIA

DIVISION		GASSAWAY 266			HUNTINGTON 255-257			LEWISBURG 249			MARTINSBURG 254			MORGANTOWN 265			PARKERSBURG 261		
		MAT.	INST.	TOTAL	MAT.	INST.	TOTAL	MAT.	INST.	TOTAL	MAT.	INST.	TOTAL	MAT.	INST.	TOTAL	MAT.	INST.	TOTAL
015433	CONTRACTOR EQUIPMENT		101.7	101.7		101.7	101.7		101.7	101.7		101.7	101.7		101.7	101.7		101.7	101.7
0241, 31 - 34	SITE & INFRASTRUCTURE, DEMOLITION	104.2	89.9	94.0	105.1	90.9	95.0	116.3	89.8	97.5	104.2	90.2	94.3	101.6	90.5	93.7	109.8	90.6	96.2
0310	Concrete Forming & Accessories	85.8	92.2	91.4	95.3	95.9	95.8	84.2	93.5	92.2	83.6	82.8	82.9	84.2	93.9	92.6	88.6	90.3	90.1
0320	Concrete Reinforcing	92.6	84.0	88.3	94.1	92.9	93.5	92.6	83.9	88.2	92.7	80.6	86.6	92.6	84.1	88.3	92.0	83.9	87.9
0330	Cast-in-Place Concrete	104.0	103.5	103.7	106.9	102.5	105.1	99.7	102.9	101.0	102.8	96.7	100.3	99.3	101.6	100.2	101.5	96.4	99.4
03	CONCRETE	100.8	95.1	98.0	102.8	98.0	100.4	107.1	95.4	101.4	101.2	87.9	94.7	97.2	95.2	96.2	102.5	91.8	97.2
04	MASONRY	109.2	95.9	100.9	96.4	100.8	99.1	95.9	95.9	95.9	99.7	89.5	93.3	126.5	98.9	109.3	82.9	91.7	88.4
05	METALS	103.5	96.8	101.4	103.3	100.4	102.4	103.4	96.0	101.2	101.3	94.2	99.1	103.6	96.6	101.5	104.2	96.6	101.9
06	WOOD, PLASTICS & COMPOSITES	84.0	90.7	87.8	94.7	95.3	95.1	81.8	93.4	88.3	83.5	81.6	82.5	81.8	93.4	88.3	85.0	89.1	87.3
07	THERMAL & MOISTURE PROTECTION	104.0	90.6	98.5	103.0	90.8	98.0	104.8	90.8	99.0	103.1	79.3	93.4	104.0	90.6	98.5	103.9	89.0	97.8
08	OPENINGS	100.7	83.2	96.6	100.5	87.6	97.5	102.5	84.6	98.4	103.3	73.4	96.3	103.8	85.1	99.4	101.4	82.3	96.9
0920	Plaster & Gypsum Board	98.6	90.2	92.9	104.8	95.0	98.1	97.2	93.0	94.4	97.6	80.9	86.3	97.2	93.0	94.4	99.7	88.5	92.1
0950, 0980	Ceilings & Acoustic Treatment	88.9	90.2	89.8	86.4	95.0	92.0	88.9	93.0	91.6	86.4	80.9	82.8	88.9	93.0	91.6	88.9	88.5	88.7
0960	Flooring	98.4	118.0	104.0	109.8	121.7	113.2	97.7	118.0	103.5	102.4	118.0	106.8	97.7	118.0	103.5	101.5	118.0	106.2
0970, 0990	Wall Finishes & Painting/Coating	109.6	95.9	101.3	107.4	94.6	99.7	109.6	75.4	88.9	107.4	41.4	67.5	109.6	94.3	100.3	109.6	94.6	100.6
09	FINISHES	95.2	97.5	96.5	98.5	100.8	99.8	96.1	96.8	96.5	95.6	83.1	88.7	94.6	98.9	97.0	96.6	95.9	96.2
COVERS	DIVS. 10 - 14, 25, 28, 41, 43, 44, 46	100.0	101.2	100.2	100.0	101.8	100.4	100.0	56.9	91.3	100.0	97.7	99.5	100.0	65.8	93.1	100.0	100.5	100.1
21, 22, 23	FIRE SUPPRESSION, PLUMBING & HVAC	95.6	92.3	93.9	100.3	90.5	96.4	95.6	93.5	94.7	95.5	86.0	91.7	95.6	95.0	95.3	100.3	88.3	95.4
26, 27, 3370	ELECTRICAL, COMMUNICATIONS & UTIL.	97.1	91.1	93.9	97.8	95.3	96.5	93.0	91.1	92.0	100.1	81.8	90.4	97.3	96.1	96.7	97.2	92.7	94.8
MF2014	WEIGHTED AVERAGE	99.5	93.9	97.1	100.7	95.7	98.5	99.8	92.4	96.6	99.3	86.4	93.7	100.2	94.4	97.6	100.1	91.8	96.5

WEST VIRGINIA / WISCONSIN

DIVISION		PETERSBURG 268			ROMNEY 267			WHEELING 260			BELOIT 535			EAU CLAIRE 547			GREEN BAY 541-543		
		MAT.	INST.	TOTAL	MAT.	INST.	TOTAL	MAT.	INST.	TOTAL	MAT.	INST.	TOTAL	MAT.	INST.	TOTAL	MAT.	INST.	TOTAL
015433	CONTRACTOR EQUIPMENT		101.7	101.7		101.7	101.7		101.7	101.7		102.3	102.3		100.4	100.4		98.2	98.2
0241, 31 - 34	SITE & INFRASTRUCTURE, DEMOLITION	100.9	90.5	93.5	103.6	90.5	94.3	110.6	90.4	96.2	94.7	108.3	104.3	96.1	102.9	101.0	99.7	98.9	99.2
0310	Concrete Forming & Accessories	87.4	91.6	91.0	83.4	91.8	90.6	90.3	93.2	92.8	100.2	100.3	100.3	97.1	99.4	99.1	105.5	98.7	99.7
0320	Concrete Reinforcing	92.0	82.5	87.2	92.6	81.0	86.7	91.4	84.0	87.7	92.3	116.0	104.3	90.4	99.2	94.9	88.7	92.4	90.6
0330	Cast-in-Place Concrete	99.3	99.1	99.2	104.0	99.1	102.0	101.5	100.1	100.9	100.6	100.9	100.7	104.0	99.2	102.0	107.6	99.7	104.3
03	CONCRETE	97.3	93.0	95.2	100.6	92.8	96.8	102.5	94.4	98.5	98.8	103.5	101.1	99.7	99.4	99.6	102.8	98.0	100.5
04	MASONRY	99.5	98.9	99.1	96.2	98.9	97.9	107.6	93.9	99.1	100.6	104.3	102.9	94.7	102.1	99.3	126.7	101.4	110.9
05	METALS	103.7	95.8	101.2	103.7	95.5	101.2	104.4	96.8	102.1	93.1	107.7	97.6	95.0	101.4	97.0	97.4	98.2	97.6
06	WOOD, PLASTICS & COMPOSITES	85.9	90.7	88.6	80.9	90.7	86.4	86.7	93.4	90.5	99.9	99.2	99.5	105.1	99.3	101.9	110.0	99.3	104.0
07	THERMAL & MOISTURE PROTECTION	104.0	86.0	96.6	104.1	83.4	95.6	104.3	90.0	98.4	102.1	96.8	99.9	102.4	86.7	95.9	104.3	86.0	96.8
08	OPENINGS	103.8	82.8	98.9	103.7	82.4	98.8	102.2	85.1	98.2	102.5	108.8	103.9	103.7	96.2	102.0	100.1	96.0	99.2
0920	Plaster & Gypsum Board	99.3	90.2	93.2	96.8	90.2	92.4	99.7	93.0	95.2	94.5	99.6	97.9	102.9	99.6	100.6	98.7	99.6	99.3
0950, 0980	Ceilings & Acoustic Treatment	88.9	90.2	89.8	88.9	90.2	89.8	88.9	93.0	91.6	88.1	99.6	95.6	90.4	99.6	96.4	81.9	99.6	93.5
0960	Flooring	99.4	118.0	104.7	97.5	118.0	103.4	102.3	118.0	106.8	99.8	118.1	105.1	91.4	114.1	97.9	110.2	114.1	111.3
0970, 0990	Wall Finishes & Painting/Coating	109.6	94.3	100.3	109.6	94.3	100.3	109.6	94.3	100.3	98.3	97.2	97.7	94.5	86.4	89.6	105.4	83.2	92.0
09	FINISHES	95.4	97.3	96.4	94.7	97.3	96.1	96.9	98.2	97.6	97.4	103.1	100.5	94.6	101.2	98.3	99.0	100.7	99.9
COVERS	DIVS. 10 - 14, 25, 28, 41, 43, 44, 46	100.0	65.5	93.0	100.0	101.2	100.2	100.0	95.4	99.1	100.0	96.6	99.3	100.0	96.8	99.3	100.0	96.5	99.3
21, 22, 23	FIRE SUPPRESSION, PLUMBING & HVAC	95.6	93.7	94.8	95.6	93.4	94.7	100.3	93.6	97.6	100.1	98.6	99.5	100.1	87.6	95.0	100.3	85.1	94.2
26, 27, 3370	ELECTRICAL, COMMUNICATIONS & UTIL.	100.5	81.8	90.6	99.8	81.8	90.3	94.4	96.1	95.3	101.0	86.7	93.4	103.8	84.9	93.8	98.2	82.0	89.6
MF2014	WEIGHTED AVERAGE	99.3	91.3	95.8	99.4	92.2	96.3	101.2	94.3	98.2	98.9	100.7	99.7	99.3	95.3	97.5	101.2	93.4	97.8

WISCONSIN

DIVISION		KENOSHA 531			LA CROSSE 546			LANCASTER 538			MADISON 537			MILWAUKEE 530,532			NEW RICHMOND 540		
		MAT.	INST.	TOTAL	MAT.	INST.	TOTAL	MAT.	INST.	TOTAL	MAT.	INST.	TOTAL	MAT.	INST.	TOTAL	MAT.	INST.	TOTAL
015433	CONTRACTOR EQUIPMENT		100.2	100.2		100.4	100.4		102.3	102.3		102.3	102.3		90.5	90.5		100.8	100.8
0241, 31 - 34	SITE & INFRASTRUCTURE, DEMOLITION	100.3	105.2	103.8	90.1	102.8	99.1	93.9	108.2	104.1	92.4	108.3	103.7	94.6	98.5	97.4	94.4	103.3	100.8
0310	Concrete Forming & Accessories	108.0	100.5	101.6	84.1	99.1	97.1	99.5	97.9	98.2	102.0	100.1	100.4	104.1	118.0	116.1	92.4	100.9	99.7
0320	Concrete Reinforcing	92.1	97.9	95.0	90.1	91.5	90.9	93.5	91.3	92.3	97.9	91.6	94.7	95.7	98.2	97.0	87.8	99.0	93.5
0330	Cast-in-Place Concrete	109.4	107.3	108.5	93.5	95.9	94.5	100.0	100.9	100.4	91.1	100.8	95.1	99.8	109.6	103.8	108.3	82.5	97.7
03	CONCRETE	103.5	102.4	103.0	90.8	96.8	93.7	98.5	97.8	98.1	95.7	98.8	97.2	99.7	110.5	105.0	97.5	94.3	95.9
04	MASONRY	97.9	114.1	108.0	93.8	105.9	101.4	100.7	104.3	102.9	101.5	104.3	103.2	104.9	120.6	114.7	121.6	102.3	109.6
05	METALS	93.9	101.2	96.2	94.9	98.2	95.9	90.6	95.0	92.0	91.9	97.2	93.6	97.5	94.8	96.7	95.1	99.7	96.5
06	WOOD, PLASTICS & COMPOSITES	105.0	96.4	100.2	90.1	99.3	95.3	99.1	99.2	99.2	96.7	99.2	98.1	104.7	118.5	112.5	94.0	102.5	98.7
07	THERMAL & MOISTURE PROTECTION	102.2	108.7	104.9	101.8	90.2	97.1	101.9	82.5	93.9	102.8	105.1	103.8	100.8	114.0	106.2	103.6	92.2	98.9
08	OPENINGS	96.9	101.1	97.9	103.7	85.0	99.4	97.9	85.8	95.1	107.9	100.5	106.2	101.0	113.2	103.8	89.1	97.5	91.1
0920	Plaster & Gypsum Board	85.3	96.7	93.0	97.7	99.6	99.0	93.3	99.6	97.5	99.6	99.6	99.6	101.0	119.3	113.4	87.7	103.0	98.1
0950, 0980	Ceilings & Acoustic Treatment	88.1	96.7	93.7	89.5	99.6	96.1	83.1	99.6	93.9	94.0	99.6	97.6	95.9	119.3	111.3	58.5	103.0	87.8
0960	Flooring	118.8	110.4	116.4	85.6	114.1	93.7	99.5	110.5	102.7	103.2	110.5	105.3	98.2	114.0	102.7	103.2	114.1	106.3
0970, 0990	Wall Finishes & Painting/Coating	108.3	115.5	112.6	94.5	77.9	84.5	98.3	66.4	79.1	102.4	97.2	99.3	94.4	122.9	111.6	108.3	86.4	95.1
09	FINISHES	102.5	103.6	103.1	91.6	100.3	96.4	96.0	96.5	96.3	98.6	101.9	100.4	100.9	118.6	110.7	90.0	101.3	96.2
COVERS	DIVS. 10 - 14, 25, 28, 41, 43, 44, 46	100.0	101.1	100.2	100.0	96.7	99.3	100.0	49.7	89.8	100.0	99.7	99.9	100.0	104.6	100.9	100.0	96.1	99.2
21, 22, 23	FIRE SUPPRESSION, PLUMBING & HVAC	100.3	97.0	98.9	100.1	87.5	95.0	95.3	87.3	92.1	100.0	95.6	98.2	100.0	103.5	101.4	94.8	86.9	91.6
26, 27, 3370	ELECTRICAL, COMMUNICATIONS & UTIL.	101.5	98.7	100.1	104.2	85.1	94.1	100.8	85.1	92.5	102.1	92.1	96.8	100.8	99.5	100.1	101.9	85.1	93.0
MF2014	WEIGHTED AVERAGE	99.5	102.2	100.7	97.8	94.5	96.3	96.7	92.5	94.8	99.1	99.0	99.1	100.0	107.2	103.1	96.8	94.6	95.9

WISCONSIN

DIVISION		OSHKOSH 549			PORTAGE 539			RACINE 534			RHINELANDER 545			SUPERIOR 548			WAUSAU 544		
		MAT.	INST.	TOTAL	MAT.	INST.	TOTAL	MAT.	INST.	TOTAL	MAT.	INST.	TOTAL	MAT.	INST.	TOTAL	MAT.	INST.	TOTAL
015433	CONTRACTOR EQUIPMENT		98.2	98.2		102.3	102.3		102.3	102.3		98.2	98.2		100.8	100.8		98.2	98.2
0241, 31 - 34	SITE & INFRASTRUCTURE, DEMOLITION	91.5	98.9	96.8	85.0	108.0	101.4	94.5	109.0	104.8	103.3	98.8	100.1	91.3	103.3	99.9	87.4	98.9	95.6
0310	Concrete Forming & Accessories	88.6	98.1	96.8	91.7	98.9	97.9	100.5	100.5	100.5	86.2	97.8	96.2	90.5	91.9	91.7	88.1	98.7	97.2
0320	Concrete Reinforcing	88.8	92.3	90.6	93.5	91.4	92.5	92.3	97.9	95.1	89.0	90.9	90.0	87.8	91.4	89.6	89.0	91.3	90.2
0330	Cast-in-Place Concrete	99.7	99.4	99.6	85.9	101.8	92.4	98.7	107.0	102.1	113.1	99.3	107.4	102.0	97.9	100.3	93.0	99.6	95.7
03	CONCRETE	92.4	97.6	94.9	86.4	98.5	92.4	97.9	102.3	100.1	104.7	97.2	101.0	91.8	94.2	93.0	87.3	97.8	92.5
04	MASONRY	107.9	101.4	103.8	99.6	104.3	102.5	100.6	114.0	109.0	125.3	101.4	110.4	120.8	104.5	110.6	107.4	101.4	103.6
05	METALS	95.4	96.7	95.8	91.3	96.0	92.7	94.8	101.2	96.8	95.3	96.7	95.7	96.1	98.2	96.8	95.1	97.7	95.9
06	WOOD, PLASTICS & COMPOSITES	89.8	99.3	95.1	89.2	99.2	94.8	100.2	96.4	98.1	87.3	99.3	94.0	92.3	90.1	91.0	89.2	99.3	94.9
07	THERMAL & MOISTURE PROTECTION	103.4	85.7	96.1	101.4	92.6	97.7	102.1	108.3	104.7	104.2	83.5	95.7	103.3	92.2	98.7	103.3	84.4	95.5
08	OPENINGS	95.9	94.5	95.8	98.1	92.3	96.8	102.5	101.1	102.2	96.0	87.1	93.9	88.6	91.1	89.2	96.1	95.7	96.0
0920	Plaster & Gypsum Board	86.2	99.6	95.2	86.4	99.6	95.3	94.5	96.7	96.0	86.2	99.6	95.2	87.6	90.2	89.4	86.2	99.6	95.2
0950, 0980	Ceilings & Acoustic Treatment	81.9	99.6	93.5	85.6	99.6	94.8	88.1	99.6	93.7	81.9	99.6	93.5	59.3	90.2	79.6	81.9	99.6	93.5
0960	Flooring	101.6	114.1	105.2	96.2	118.1	102.5	99.8	110.4	102.8	100.9	114.1	104.7	104.4	122.4	109.6	101.5	114.1	105.1
0970, 0990	Wall Finishes & Painting/Coating	102.2	101.4	101.7	98.3	66.4	79.1	98.3	115.5	108.7	102.2	60.4	76.9	96.0	102.8	100.1	102.2	83.2	90.7
09	FINISHES	94.0	100.9	97.8	94.1	98.6	96.6	97.4	103.6	100.8	94.8	97.0	96.0	89.3	98.6	94.4	93.7	100.7	97.5
COVERS	DIVS. 10 - 14, 25, 28, 41, 43, 44, 46	100.0	64.6	92.8	100.0	63.4	92.6	100.0	101.1	100.2	100.0	55.0	90.9	100.0	94.1	98.8	100.0	96.5	99.3
21, 22, 23	FIRE SUPPRESSION, PLUMBING & HVAC	95.6	85.0	91.3	95.3	95.3	95.3	100.1	97.0	98.8	95.6	86.7	92.0	94.8	89.4	92.6	95.6	86.4	91.9
26, 27, 3370	ELECTRICAL, COMMUNICATIONS & UTIL.	102.5	80.4	90.9	104.8	92.1	98.1	100.8	98.6	99.6	101.8	81.8	91.3	107.1	99.0	102.8	103.7	81.8	92.1
MF2014	WEIGHTED AVERAGE	96.9	91.9	94.7	95.3	96.6	95.9	99.1	102.4	100.5	99.3	91.2	95.8	96.6	96.3	96.5	96.2	93.5	95.0

For customer support on your Site Work & Landscape Cost Data, call 877.737.1594.

785

WYOMING

DIVISION		CASPER 826			CHEYENNE 820			NEWCASTLE 827			RAWLINS 823			RIVERTON 825			ROCK SPRINGS 829 - 831		
		MAT.	INST.	TOTAL	MAT.	INST.	TOTAL	MAT.	INST.	TOTAL	MAT.	INST.	TOTAL	MAT.	INST.	TOTAL	MAT.	INST.	TOTAL
015433	CONTRACTOR EQUIPMENT		98.2	98.2		98.2	98.2		98.2	98.2		98.2	98.2		98.2	98.2		98.2	98.2
0241, 31 - 34	SITE & INFRASTRUCTURE, DEMOLITION	98.6	94.4	95.6	92.5	94.4	93.8	85.1	94.0	91.5	98.4	94.0	95.3	92.1	94.0	93.5	89.2	94.0	92.6
0310	Concrete Forming & Accessories	102.5	50.1	57.3	104.4	53.5	60.5	94.8	62.2	66.7	99.2	62.2	67.3	93.7	62.1	66.5	101.5	62.1	67.5
0320	Concrete Reinforcing	105.7	70.6	87.8	98.0	70.6	84.1	105.5	70.8	87.9	105.2	70.8	87.7	106.1	70.6	88.0	106.1	70.6	88.0
0330	Cast-in-Place Concrete	102.8	72.0	90.2	95.0	72.1	85.6	95.9	61.6	81.8	96.0	61.6	81.9	96.0	60.0	81.2	95.9	59.9	81.1
03	CONCRETE	101.7	62.1	82.3	98.6	63.7	81.4	99.0	63.9	81.8	111.8	63.9	88.3	106.7	63.3	85.4	99.5	63.2	81.7
04	MASONRY	108.2	51.9	73.1	103.7	51.9	71.4	100.3	54.8	71.9	100.3	54.8	71.9	100.3	50.5	69.3	160.4	50.4	91.8
05	METALS	99.3	72.1	90.9	101.7	72.1	92.6	97.8	72.0	89.9	97.9	72.0	89.9	98.0	71.6	89.8	98.7	71.1	90.2
06	WOOD, PLASTICS & COMPOSITES	97.2	49.7	70.6	96.5	54.3	72.9	86.4	66.9	75.5	90.4	66.9	77.2	85.3	66.9	75.0	95.4	66.9	79.4
07	THERMAL & MOISTURE PROTECTION	105.9	55.1	85.1	100.1	55.6	81.8	101.8	55.8	82.9	103.2	55.8	83.7	102.7	59.9	85.1	101.9	59.9	84.7
08	OPENINGS	108.0	53.3	95.3	108.3	55.8	96.1	112.6	61.7	100.8	112.3	61.7	100.5	112.5	61.7	100.7	113.0	61.3	101.0
0920	Plaster & Gypsum Board	97.4	48.1	64.1	89.3	52.9	64.7	85.2	65.8	72.1	85.5	65.8	72.2	85.2	65.8	72.1	97.3	65.8	76.0
0950, 0980	Ceilings & Acoustic Treatment	99.2	48.1	65.6	91.0	52.9	66.0	92.9	65.8	75.1	92.9	65.8	75.1	92.9	65.8	75.1	92.9	65.8	75.1
0960	Flooring	112.0	56.4	96.1	109.9	56.4	94.6	103.5	56.4	90.0	106.2	56.4	92.0	103.0	56.4	89.7	108.4	56.4	93.5
0970, 0990	Wall Finishes & Painting/Coating	104.7	43.1	67.5	111.2	43.1	70.0	107.1	55.4	75.9	107.1	55.4	75.9	107.1	55.4	75.9	107.1	55.4	75.9
09	FINISHES	103.2	49.6	73.6	100.0	52.3	73.7	95.0	60.8	76.1	97.2	60.8	77.1	95.7	60.8	76.5	98.1	60.8	77.5
COVERS	DIVS. 10 - 14, 25, 28, 41, 43, 44, 46	100.0	87.6	97.5	100.0	88.2	97.6	100.0	89.1	97.8	100.0	89.1	97.8	100.0	81.4	96.2	100.0	80.8	96.1
21, 22, 23	FIRE SUPPRESSION, PLUMBING & HVAC	99.9	64.1	85.4	99.9	64.1	85.4	97.4	63.4	83.7	97.4	63.4	83.7	97.4	63.4	83.7	99.8	63.3	85.1
26, 27, 3370	ELECTRICAL, COMMUNICATIONS & UTIL.	103.3	64.1	82.6	105.8	68.6	86.1	104.5	69.0	85.7	104.5	69.0	85.7	104.5	62.9	82.5	102.4	62.9	81.5
MF2014	WEIGHTED AVERAGE	102.0	63.9	85.4	101.5	65.2	85.7	99.9	66.9	85.5	101.8	66.9	86.6	101.0	65.4	85.5	103.7	65.3	87.0

WYOMING / CANADA

DIVISION		SHERIDAN 828			WHEATLAND 822			WORLAND 824			YELLOWSTONE NAT'L PA 821			BARRIE, ONTARIO			BATHURST, NEW BRUNSWICK		
		MAT.	INST.	TOTAL	MAT.	INST.	TOTAL	MAT.	INST.	TOTAL	MAT.	INST.	TOTAL	MAT.	INST.	TOTAL	MAT.	INST.	TOTAL
015433	CONTRACTOR EQUIPMENT		98.2	98.2		98.2	98.2		98.2	98.2		98.2	98.2		102.1	102.1		102.2	102.2
0241, 31 - 34	SITE & INFRASTRUCTURE, DEMOLITION	92.4	94.4	93.8	89.6	94.0	92.8	87.1	94.0	92.0	87.2	94.2	92.2	118.5	100.4	105.6	103.4	96.6	98.6
0310	Concrete Forming & Accessories	102.2	50.6	57.7	96.8	52.7	58.8	96.9	62.0	66.8	96.9	63.1	67.8	124.4	89.4	94.2	104.4	63.7	69.3
0320	Concrete Reinforcing	106.1	70.9	88.2	105.5	70.8	87.8	106.1	70.6	88.0	107.9	70.6	88.9	173.2	83.8	127.7	137.0	56.5	96.0
0330	Cast-in-Place Concrete	99.2	72.0	88.1	100.2	61.5	84.3	95.9	59.9	81.1	95.9	61.6	81.8	165.6	89.0	134.2	131.6	61.9	103.0
03	CONCRETE	106.9	62.4	85.0	103.7	59.7	82.1	99.2	63.2	81.6	99.5	64.3	82.2	150.3	88.4	119.9	124.6	62.4	94.1
04	MASONRY	100.6	56.3	73.0	100.7	54.7	72.0	100.3	50.4	69.2	100.4	53.4	71.1	171.5	98.0	125.7	160.8	64.9	101.1
05	METALS	101.6	72.4	92.6	97.8	71.7	89.8	98.0	71.5	89.8	98.6	71.5	90.3	110.2	90.2	104.0	109.0	71.5	97.5
06	WOOD, PLASTICS & COMPOSITES	97.9	50.4	71.3	88.3	54.3	69.2	88.3	66.9	76.3	88.3	66.9	76.3	119.8	88.2	102.1	101.8	64.0	80.7
07	THERMAL & MOISTURE PROTECTION	102.9	56.3	83.8	102.1	55.8	83.1	101.9	57.5	83.7	101.4	58.8	83.9	111.8	89.1	102.5	106.0	62.2	88.1
08	OPENINGS	113.2	52.7	99.1	111.1	55.8	98.3	112.8	61.7	100.9	105.6	61.7	95.4	93.9	86.5	92.2	87.9	55.9	80.5
0920	Plaster & Gypsum Board	109.4	48.8	68.5	85.2	52.8	63.3	85.2	65.8	72.1	85.4	65.8	72.1	151.1	87.7	108.2	137.6	62.7	87.0
0950, 0980	Ceilings & Acoustic Treatment	95.7	48.8	64.9	92.9	52.8	66.6	92.9	65.8	75.1	93.7	65.8	75.4	91.5	87.7	89.0	106.4	62.7	77.7
0960	Flooring	107.5	56.4	92.9	105.0	56.4	91.1	105.0	56.4	91.1	105.0	56.4	91.1	127.2	98.9	119.1	107.9	47.2	90.6
0970, 0990	Wall Finishes & Painting/Coating	109.4	43.1	69.4	107.1	34.4	63.3	107.1	55.4	75.9	107.1	55.4	75.9	116.2	89.9	100.3	117.6	51.6	77.8
09	FINISHES	102.8	50.0	73.7	95.8	51.0	71.1	95.5	60.8	76.3	95.7	61.5	76.8	115.0	91.5	102.1	111.3	59.7	82.8
COVERS	DIVS. 10 - 14, 25, 28, 41, 43, 44, 46	100.0	87.7	97.5	100.0	80.3	96.0	100.0	81.4	96.2	100.0	82.4	96.4	139.2	74.4	126.1	131.1	65.3	117.8
21, 22, 23	FIRE SUPPRESSION, PLUMBING & HVAC	97.4	64.1	83.9	97.4	63.3	83.6	97.4	63.3	83.6	97.4	64.9	84.3	101.8	99.3	100.8	102.0	69.8	89.0
26, 27, 3370	ELECTRICAL, COMMUNICATIONS & UTIL.	107.4	63.0	83.9	104.5	68.6	85.5	104.5	62.9	82.5	103.2	62.9	81.9	116.8	90.5	102.9	112.7	61.8	85.8
MF2014	WEIGHTED AVERAGE	102.6	64.3	85.9	100.4	64.3	84.7	100.0	65.3	84.9	99.3	66.3	84.9	117.7	93.0	106.9	111.5	67.3	92.2

CANADA

DIVISION		BRANDON, MANITOBA			BRANTFORD, ONTARIO			BRIDGEWATER, NOVA SCOTIA			CALGARY, ALBERTA			CAP-DE-LA-MADELEINE, QUEBEC			CHARLESBOURG, QUEBEC		
		MAT.	INST.	TOTAL	MAT.	INST.	TOTAL	MAT.	INST.	TOTAL	MAT.	INST.	TOTAL	MAT.	INST.	TOTAL	MAT.	INST.	TOTAL
015433	CONTRACTOR EQUIPMENT		104.5	104.5		102.1	102.1		101.9	101.9		107.1	107.1		102.8	102.8		102.8	102.8
0241, 31 - 34	SITE & INFRASTRUCTURE, DEMOLITION	133.0	99.3	109.1	118.0	100.7	105.7	102.6	98.2	99.5	124.0	105.4	110.7	98.4	99.9	99.4	98.4	99.9	99.4
0310	Concrete Forming & Accessories	146.5	72.5	82.7	124.9	96.9	100.7	97.1	71.6	75.1	124.4	97.4	101.1	130.7	88.0	93.8	130.7	88.0	93.8
0320	Concrete Reinforcing	185.9	53.2	118.4	165.4	82.5	123.2	140.6	46.7	92.8	135.6	71.9	103.2	140.6	78.8	109.2	140.6	78.8	109.2
0330	Cast-in-Place Concrete	133.4	76.7	110.1	153.6	110.3	135.8	157.8	72.2	122.7	189.0	107.3	155.5	124.0	97.8	113.2	124.0	97.8	113.2
03	CONCRETE	145.6	71.0	109.0	141.8	98.8	120.7	139.4	67.9	104.3	159.1	96.1	128.2	124.3	89.8	107.4	124.3	89.8	107.4
04	MASONRY	233.5	67.6	130.1	168.0	102.6	127.2	163.4	71.9	106.4	196.3	91.4	130.9	163.9	87.1	116.0	163.9	87.1	116.0
05	METALS	125.6	76.8	110.6	109.1	90.9	103.5	108.2	74.2	97.7	137.0	89.3	122.3	107.4	87.6	101.3	107.4	87.6	101.3
06	WOOD, PLASTICS & COMPOSITES	154.2	73.5	109.0	123.7	95.7	108.1	92.9	71.1	80.7	102.3	97.2	99.4	135.3	88.0	108.8	135.3	88.0	108.8
07	THERMAL & MOISTURE PROTECTION	135.0	71.8	109.1	113.8	94.7	106.0	108.6	69.9	92.8	117.8	94.6	108.3	107.4	89.9	100.3	107.4	89.9	100.3
08	OPENINGS	105.5	64.8	96.1	92.4	92.7	92.5	86.1	64.9	81.1	89.9	86.2	89.1	93.6	81.1	90.7	93.6	81.1	90.7
0920	Plaster & Gypsum Board	119.3	72.2	87.4	130.1	95.5	106.7	130.7	70.0	89.7	139.4	96.6	110.5	157.0	87.4	109.9	157.0	87.4	109.9
0950, 0980	Ceilings & Acoustic Treatment	109.6	72.2	85.0	96.5	95.5	95.8	130.7	70.0	79.1	138.8	96.6	111.0	96.5	87.4	90.5	96.5	87.4	90.5
0960	Flooring	138.6	70.2	119.1	120.5	98.9	114.3	102.7	67.2	92.5	122.3	92.6	113.8	120.5	99.5	114.5	120.5	99.5	114.5
0970, 0990	Wall Finishes & Painting/Coating	126.5	58.7	85.6	118.3	98.6	106.4	118.3	64.1	85.6	127.4	112.4	118.3	118.3	91.7	102.2	118.3	91.7	102.2
09	FINISHES	122.5	71.0	94.1	112.4	97.9	104.4	106.2	70.3	86.6	125.5	98.7	110.7	115.3	90.8	101.8	115.3	90.8	101.8
COVERS	DIVS. 10 - 14, 25, 28, 41, 43, 44, 46	131.1	67.6	118.3	131.1	76.6	120.1	131.1	66.6	118.1	131.1	96.9	124.2	131.1	85.2	121.9	131.1	85.2	121.9
21, 22, 23	FIRE SUPPRESSION, PLUMBING & HVAC	102.1	84.1	94.9	102.0	102.3	102.1	102.0	84.4	94.9	101.2	92.9	97.8	102.3	91.0	97.8	102.3	91.0	97.8
26, 27, 3370	ELECTRICAL, COMMUNICATIONS & UTIL.	118.6	69.6	92.7	111.5	89.9	100.1	117.1	64.4	89.2	113.5	101.3	107.1	111.2	72.6	90.8	111.2	72.6	90.8
MF2014	WEIGHTED AVERAGE	125.2	75.8	103.7	114.9	96.9	107.1	112.9	74.6	96.2	123.5	95.7	111.4	112.4	87.6	101.6	112.4	87.6	101.6

City Cost Indexes

CANADA

	DIVISION	CHARLOTTETOWN, PRINCE EDWARD ISLAND			CHICOUTIMI, QUEBEC			CORNER BROOK, NEWFOUNDLAND			CORNWALL, ONTARIO			DALHOUSIE, NEW BRUNSWICK			DARTMOUTH, NOVA SCOTIA		
		MAT.	INST.	TOTAL	MAT.	INST.	TOTAL	MAT.	INST.	TOTAL	MAT.	INST.	TOTAL	MAT.	INST.	TOTAL	MAT.	INST.	TOTAL
015433	CONTRACTOR EQUIPMENT		101.8	101.8		102.8	102.8		103.3	103.3		102.1	102.1		102.2	102.2		101.9	101.9
0241, 31 - 34	SITE & INFRASTRUCTURE, DEMOLITION	121.3	95.7	103.1	100.7	99.1	99.6	137.7	97.1	108.9	116.1	100.2	104.8	100.9	96.6	97.8	124.8	98.2	105.9
0310	Concrete Forming & Accessories	110.4	58.2	65.4	133.2	93.1	98.6	121.8	61.7	69.9	122.6	89.6	94.1	103.5	63.9	69.3	111.8	71.6	77.2
0320	Concrete Reinforcing	141.5	46.8	93.3	103.3	95.9	99.5	170.3	48.6	108.4	165.4	82.2	123.1	142.7	56.6	98.9	178.2	46.7	111.3
0330	Cast-in-Place Concrete	166.8	61.2	123.4	124.0	99.8	114.0	155.3	70.6	120.5	138.2	100.6	122.7	131.8	62.0	103.2	149.8	72.2	118.0
03	CONCRETE	147.1	57.9	103.3	114.6	95.9	105.4	182.2	63.2	123.7	134.3	92.2	113.6	132.5	62.5	98.1	162.1	67.9	115.8
04	MASONRY	178.4	62.6	106.3	162.7	95.0	120.5	229.3	64.1	126.4	166.8	94.0	121.4	160.2	64.9	100.8	244.8	71.9	137.1
05	METALS	133.9	67.6	113.5	108.8	92.2	103.7	126.0	72.9	109.7	109.1	89.6	103.1	104.4	71.8	94.3	125.9	74.2	110.0
06	WOOD, PLASTICS & COMPOSITES	97.8	57.8	75.4	137.4	93.6	112.9	128.3	60.8	90.5	122.1	89.0	103.6	100.2	64.0	80.0	116.1	71.1	90.9
07	THERMAL & MOISTURE PROTECTION	121.3	60.4	96.3	106.5	96.4	102.3	139.8	61.8	107.8	113.6	89.3	103.6	110.8	62.2	90.9	136.8	69.9	109.4
08	OPENINGS	88.2	50.0	79.3	92.2	80.6	89.5	112.4	57.1	99.5	93.6	86.2	91.9	89.1	55.9	81.4	95.3	64.9	88.2
0920	Plaster & Gypsum Board	131.6	56.3	80.7	159.4	93.2	114.6	149.0	59.3	88.4	189.4	88.6	121.3	141.2	62.7	88.2	144.6	70.0	94.2
0950, 0980	Ceilings & Acoustic Treatment	120.2	56.3	78.2	105.6	93.2	97.4	110.5	59.3	76.9	99.0	88.6	92.2	98.9	62.7	75.1	117.2	70.0	86.2
0960	Flooring	111.7	62.9	97.8	123.6	99.5	116.8	121.0	57.2	102.8	120.5	97.5	113.9	106.5	72.1	96.7	116.1	67.2	102.1
0970, 0990	Wall Finishes & Painting/Coating	125.6	42.9	75.7	117.2	106.4	110.8	126.4	61.8	87.4	118.3	91.9	102.4	120.7	51.6	79.0	126.4	64.1	88.8
09	FINISHES	117.1	57.8	84.4	118.4	96.5	106.4	122.0	60.9	88.4	121.0	91.6	104.8	110.6	64.5	85.2	120.1	70.3	92.6
COVERS	DIVS. 10 - 14, 25, 28, 41, 43, 44, 46	131.1	64.8	117.7	131.1	86.5	122.1	131.1	65.6	117.9	131.1	74.0	119.6	131.1	65.3	117.8	131.1	66.6	118.1
21, 22, 23	FIRE SUPPRESSION, PLUMBING & HVAC	102.3	63.8	86.8	102.0	92.3	98.1	102.1	71.8	89.9	102.3	100.1	101.4	102.0	69.8	89.0	102.1	84.4	95.0
26, 27, 3370	ELECTRICAL, COMMUNICATIONS & UTIL.	110.6	52.3	79.8	109.7	86.8	97.6	116.0	58.3	85.5	112.4	90.9	101.0	114.5	58.4	84.8	120.7	64.4	90.9
MF2014	WEIGHTED AVERAGE	120.0	62.8	95.1	111.4	92.9	103.3	129.6	67.6	102.6	115.0	93.3	105.5	111.9	67.5	92.5	126.1	74.6	103.7

CANADA

	DIVISION	EDMONTON, ALBERTA			FORT MCMURRAY, ALBERTA			FREDERICTON, NEW BRUNSWICK			GATINEAU, QUEBEC			GRANBY, QUEBEC			HALIFAX, NOVA SCOTIA		
		MAT.	INST.	TOTAL	MAT.	INST.	TOTAL	MAT.	INST.	TOTAL	MAT.	INST.	TOTAL	MAT.	INST.	TOTAL	MAT.	INST.	TOTAL
015433	CONTRACTOR EQUIPMENT		107.1	107.1		104.4	104.4		102.2	102.2		102.8	102.8		102.8	102.8		101.9	101.9
0241, 31 - 34	SITE & INFRASTRUCTURE, DEMOLITION	144.1	105.4	116.6	123.1	101.3	107.6	105.0	96.6	99.1	98.2	99.8	99.4	98.7	99.8	99.5	109.2	98.3	101.5
0310	Concrete Forming & Accessories	123.2	97.4	100.9	122.8	92.3	96.5	120.3	64.2	71.9	130.7	87.8	93.7	130.7	87.8	93.7	108.4	78.8	82.9
0320	Concrete Reinforcing	134.2	71.9	102.5	152.9	71.8	111.7	132.8	56.7	94.1	148.7	78.8	113.2	148.7	78.8	113.2	144.3	62.7	102.7
0330	Cast-in-Place Concrete	183.9	107.3	152.4	203.9	105.1	163.3	128.3	62.0	101.1	122.3	97.8	112.2	126.4	97.7	114.6	149.4	81.9	121.7
03	CONCRETE	156.4	96.1	126.8	163.6	93.1	129.0	126.6	62.7	95.2	124.8	89.8	107.6	126.7	89.7	108.5	136.4	77.3	107.4
04	MASONRY	187.2	91.4	127.5	207.9	89.1	133.8	182.6	66.5	110.2	163.7	87.1	116.0	164.1	87.1	116.1	185.9	84.7	122.8
05	METALS	136.9	89.3	122.3	135.4	88.9	121.1	129.1	72.3	111.6	107.4	87.4	101.2	107.4	87.4	101.2	134.9	81.5	118.5
06	WOOD, PLASTICS & COMPOSITES	105.2	97.2	100.7	117.6	91.8	103.2	116.7	64.0	87.2	135.3	88.0	108.8	135.3	88.0	108.8	97.1	77.8	86.3
07	THERMAL & MOISTURE PROTECTION	122.7	94.6	111.2	121.9	91.9	109.6	116.0	63.2	94.4	107.4	89.9	100.3	107.4	88.3	99.6	119.0	79.4	102.8
08	OPENINGS	89.2	86.2	88.5	93.6	83.3	91.2	89.3	54.8	81.2	93.6	76.3	89.6	93.6	76.3	89.6	93.5	72.0	88.5
0920	Plaster & Gypsum Board	134.3	96.6	108.8	128.2	91.1	103.1	137.4	62.7	86.9	126.6	87.4	100.1	129.0	87.4	100.8	127.0	77.0	93.2
0950, 0980	Ceilings & Acoustic Treatment	139.5	96.6	111.3	104.9	91.1	95.8	116.1	62.7	81.0	96.5	87.4	90.5	96.5	87.4	90.5	118.7	77.0	91.3
0960	Flooring	122.5	92.6	114.0	120.5	92.6	112.5	116.8	75.3	104.9	120.5	99.5	114.5	120.5	99.5	114.5	109.2	88.3	103.3
0970, 0990	Wall Finishes & Painting/Coating	122.4	112.4	116.3	118.4	95.5	104.5	123.1	65.8	88.5	118.3	91.7	102.2	118.3	91.7	102.2	124.9	87.4	102.2
09	FINISHES	126.6	98.7	111.2	115.3	93.0	103.0	117.7	66.7	89.6	111.2	90.8	100.0	111.5	90.8	100.1	115.6	81.8	97.0
COVERS	DIVS. 10 - 14, 25, 28, 41, 43, 44, 46	131.1	96.9	124.2	131.1	95.2	123.9	131.1	65.3	117.8	131.1	85.2	121.9	131.1	85.2	121.9	131.1	68.5	118.5
21, 22, 23	FIRE SUPPRESSION, PLUMBING & HVAC	101.1	92.9	97.8	102.4	99.0	101.0	102.3	79.3	93.0	102.3	91.0	97.8	102.0	91.0	97.6	100.6	77.6	91.3
26, 27, 3370	ELECTRICAL, COMMUNICATIONS & UTIL.	110.6	101.3	105.7	105.8	85.4	95.1	116.1	77.1	95.5	111.2	72.6	90.8	111.8	72.6	91.1	117.0	81.2	98.1
MF2014	WEIGHTED AVERAGE	123.1	95.7	111.2	123.6	92.8	110.2	117.4	72.5	97.9	112.1	87.4	101.3	112.3	87.4	101.4	119.6	80.9	102.7

CANADA

	DIVISION	HAMILTON, ONTARIO			HULL, QUEBEC			JOLIETTE, QUEBEC			KAMLOOPS, BRITISH COLUMBIA			KINGSTON, ONTARIO			KITCHENER, ONTARIO		
		MAT.	INST.	TOTAL	MAT.	INST.	TOTAL	MAT.	INST.	TOTAL	MAT.	INST.	TOTAL	MAT.	INST.	TOTAL	MAT.	INST.	TOTAL
015433	CONTRACTOR EQUIPMENT		108.9	108.9		102.8	102.8		102.8	102.8		106.1	106.1		104.4	104.4		104.3	104.3
0241, 31 - 34	SITE & INFRASTRUCTURE, DEMOLITION	115.5	112.4	113.3	98.2	99.8	99.4	98.8	99.9	99.6	120.5	103.3	108.3	116.1	104.0	107.5	99.6	104.8	103.3
0310	Concrete Forming & Accessories	120.9	94.7	98.3	130.7	87.8	93.7	130.7	88.0	93.8	123.4	90.8	95.3	122.8	89.6	94.2	113.0	87.2	90.8
0320	Concrete Reinforcing	146.4	92.0	118.7	148.7	78.8	113.2	140.6	78.8	109.2	110.3	76.8	93.2	165.4	82.2	123.1	100.8	91.9	96.3
0330	Cast-in-Place Concrete	143.5	101.0	126.1	122.3	97.8	112.2	127.4	97.8	115.2	110.3	101.6	106.7	138.2	100.6	122.7	129.0	93.6	114.4
03	CONCRETE	132.8	96.3	114.8	124.8	89.8	107.6	125.9	89.8	108.2	132.9	92.0	112.8	136.2	92.2	114.6	110.8	90.4	100.8
04	MASONRY	183.0	101.2	132.0	163.7	87.1	116.0	164.1	87.1	116.1	170.7	95.0	123.5	173.5	94.1	124.0	150.8	97.6	117.6
05	METALS	123.4	92.5	113.9	107.4	87.4	101.2	107.4	87.6	101.3	109.8	87.5	102.9	118.0	89.5	104.3	117.4	92.2	109.6
06	WOOD, PLASTICS & COMPOSITES	100.4	93.9	96.8	135.3	88.0	108.8	135.3	88.0	108.8	105.2	89.4	96.4	122.1	89.2	103.7	109.7	85.5	96.1
07	THERMAL & MOISTURE PROTECTION	118.2	95.7	109.0	107.4	89.9	100.2	107.4	89.9	100.2	123.3	86.8	108.3	113.6	90.4	104.1	108.6	92.8	102.1
08	OPENINGS	91.3	91.6	91.4	93.6	76.3	89.6	93.6	81.1	90.7	90.2	85.7	89.2	93.6	85.9	91.8	84.7	85.3	84.8
0920	Plaster & Gypsum Board	149.5	93.6	111.7	126.6	87.4	100.1	157.0	87.4	109.9	113.6	88.5	96.6	192.8	88.7	122.4	120.2	84.9	96.3
0950, 0980	Ceilings & Acoustic Treatment	122.1	93.6	103.4	96.5	87.4	90.5	96.5	87.4	90.5	96.5	88.5	91.2	112.4	88.7	96.8	98.6	84.9	89.6
0960	Flooring	123.1	102.3	117.2	120.5	99.5	114.5	120.5	99.5	114.5	119.6	55.6	101.3	120.5	97.5	113.9	110.5	102.3	108.1
0970, 0990	Wall Finishes & Painting/Coating	121.6	102.6	110.2	118.3	91.7	102.2	118.3	91.7	102.2	118.3	84.0	97.6	118.3	84.9	98.1	115.3	92.6	101.6
09	FINISHES	122.0	97.0	108.2	111.2	90.8	100.0	115.3	90.8	101.8	111.7	84.2	96.6	124.4	90.9	105.9	106.4	90.2	97.5
COVERS	DIVS. 10 - 14, 25, 28, 41, 43, 44, 46	131.1	99.8	124.6	131.1	85.2	121.9	131.1	85.2	121.9	131.1	95.6	124.0	131.1	74.0	119.6	131.1	97.0	124.2
21, 22, 23	FIRE SUPPRESSION, PLUMBING & HVAC	101.3	89.2	96.4	102.0	91.0	97.6	102.0	91.0	97.6	102.0	94.4	98.9	102.3	100.3	101.5	100.4	87.7	95.3
26, 27, 3370	ELECTRICAL, COMMUNICATIONS & UTIL.	108.3	100.5	104.2	112.9	72.6	91.6	111.8	72.6	91.1	115.1	81.9	97.6	112.4	89.6	100.3	111.5	98.0	104.4
MF2014	WEIGHTED AVERAGE	117.0	96.7	108.2	112.2	87.4	101.4	112.5	87.6	101.7	114.5	90.6	104.1	116.0	93.4	106.2	109.6	92.9	102.3

City Cost Indexes

CANADA

DIVISION		LAVAL, QUEBEC			LETHBRIDGE, ALBERTA			LLOYDMINSTER, ALBERTA			LONDON, ONTARIO			MEDICINE HAT, ALBERTA			MONCTON, NEW BRUNSWICK		
		MAT.	INST.	TOTAL	MAT.	INST.	TOTAL	MAT.	INST.	TOTAL	MAT.	INST.	TOTAL	MAT.	INST.	TOTAL	MAT.	INST.	TOTAL
015433	CONTRACTOR EQUIPMENT		102.8	102.8		104.4	104.4		104.4	104.4		104.4	104.4		104.4	104.4		102.2	102.2
0241, 31 - 34	SITE & INFRASTRUCTURE, DEMOLITION	98.7	99.8	99.5	115.6	101.9	105.9	115.4	101.3	105.4	113.1	104.9	107.3	114.2	101.4	105.1	102.8	96.8	98.5
0310	Concrete Forming & Accessories	130.8	87.8	93.8	124.1	92.4	96.8	122.3	82.6	88.1	119.1	88.5	92.7	124.1	82.6	88.3	104.4	64.5	69.9
0320	Concrete Reinforcing	148.7	78.8	113.2	152.9	71.8	111.7	152.9	71.8	111.7	132.8	91.9	112.0	152.9	71.8	111.7	137.0	61.5	98.6
0330	Cast-in-Place Concrete	126.4	97.8	114.6	153.0	105.1	133.3	141.9	101.4	125.3	147.4	98.6	127.4	141.9	101.4	125.3	126.8	78.7	107.0
03	CONCRETE	126.7	89.8	108.6	139.5	93.2	116.7	134.1	87.5	111.3	132.4	92.7	112.9	134.3	87.5	111.3	122.3	69.7	96.5
04	MASONRY	164.0	87.1	116.1	181.7	89.1	124.0	163.4	82.5	113.0	182.6	98.7	130.3	163.4	82.5	113.0	160.5	65.0	101.0
05	METALS	107.4	87.4	101.3	128.8	88.9	116.5	110.0	88.8	103.4	124.9	91.8	114.7	110.0	88.7	103.4	109.0	80.4	100.2
06	WOOD, PLASTICS & COMPOSITES	135.5	88.0	108.9	121.3	91.8	104.8	117.6	82.0	97.7	108.2	86.6	96.1	121.3	82.0	99.3	101.8	64.0	80.7
07	THERMAL & MOISTURE PROTECTION	107.9	89.9	100.5	119.1	91.9	108.0	116.0	87.5	104.3	119.1	93.5	108.6	122.3	87.5	108.0	110.2	65.3	91.8
08	OPENINGS	93.6	76.3	89.6	93.6	83.3	91.2	93.6	77.9	89.9	86.4	86.6	86.4	93.6	77.9	89.9	87.9	61.0	81.6
0920	Plaster & Gypsum Board	129.3	87.4	100.9	119.1	91.1	100.2	114.4	81.0	91.8	152.4	86.1	107.6	117.2	81.0	92.8	137.6	62.7	87.0
0950, 0980	Ceilings & Acoustic Treatment	96.5	87.4	90.5	104.1	91.1	95.5	96.5	81.0	86.3	121.1	86.1	98.1	96.5	81.0	86.3	106.4	62.7	77.7
0960	Flooring	120.5	99.5	114.5	120.5	92.6	112.5	120.5	92.6	112.5	117.2	102.3	113.0	120.5	92.6	112.5	107.9	72.1	97.7
0970, 0990	Wall Finishes & Painting/Coating	118.3	91.7	102.2	118.2	104.2	109.8	118.4	81.2	96.0	122.0	99.4	108.3	118.2	81.2	95.9	117.6	51.6	77.8
09	FINISHES	111.5	90.8	100.1	112.9	94.0	102.5	110.7	84.0	96.0	120.5	91.9	104.7	110.9	84.0	96.1	111.3	64.5	85.5
COVERS	DIVS. 10 - 14, 25, 28, 41, 43, 44, 46	131.1	85.2	121.9	131.1	95.2	123.9	131.1	91.9	123.2	131.1	97.5	124.3	131.1	91.9	123.2	131.1	65.3	117.8
21, 22, 23	FIRE SUPPRESSION, PLUMBING & HVAC	100.4	91.0	96.6	102.2	95.6	99.6	102.3	95.6	99.6	101.4	86.6	95.4	102.0	92.3	98.1	102.0	70.1	89.1
26, 27, 3370	ELECTRICAL, COMMUNICATIONS & UTIL.	112.9	72.6	91.6	107.1	85.4	95.7	104.9	85.4	94.6	107.0	97.5	102.0	104.9	85.4	94.6	117.2	61.8	88.0
MF2014	WEIGHTED AVERAGE	112.1	87.4	101.3	118.4	92.2	107.0	113.4	88.9	102.8	116.4	93.3	106.3	113.6	88.2	102.5	111.8	70.1	93.6

CANADA

DIVISION		MONTREAL, QUEBEC			MOOSE JAW, SASKATCHEWAN			NEW GLASGOW, NOVA SCOTIA			NEWCASTLE, NEW BRUNSWICK			NORTH BAY, ONTARIO			OSHAWA, ONTARIO		
		MAT.	INST.	TOTAL	MAT.	INST.	TOTAL	MAT.	INST.	TOTAL	MAT.	INST.	TOTAL	MAT.	INST.	TOTAL	MAT.	INST.	TOTAL
015433	CONTRACTOR EQUIPMENT		104.5	104.5		100.6	100.6		101.9	101.9		102.2	102.2		102.1	102.1		104.3	104.3
0241, 31 - 34	SITE & INFRASTRUCTURE, DEMOLITION	112.1	99.4	103.1	115.5	95.9	101.6	118.5	98.2	104.1	103.4	96.6	98.6	133.9	99.8	109.7	110.7	103.9	105.9
0310	Concrete Forming & Accessories	124.3	93.4	97.7	107.1	60.5	66.9	111.7	71.6	77.1	104.4	63.9	69.5	147.4	87.0	95.3	118.4	89.1	93.1
0320	Concrete Reinforcing	134.0	96.0	114.7	107.9	61.9	84.5	170.3	46.7	107.4	137.0	56.6	96.1	201.7	81.8	140.7	159.6	84.4	121.3
0330	Cast-in-Place Concrete	161.7	101.2	136.8	137.7	71.1	110.4	149.8	72.2	118.0	131.6	62.0	103.0	144.3	87.1	120.8	149.1	87.9	124.0
03	CONCRETE	139.7	96.5	118.4	117.9	65.1	92.0	160.9	67.9	115.2	124.6	62.5	94.1	163.4	86.3	125.5	135.6	88.0	112.2
04	MASONRY	167.9	95.1	122.5	162.0	64.4	101.1	228.9	71.9	131.1	160.8	64.9	101.1	235.3	89.9	144.7	153.8	94.4	116.8
05	METALS	128.0	92.7	117.1	106.3	73.9	96.3	123.6	74.2	108.4	109.0	71.8	97.5	124.6	89.2	113.7	108.6	91.4	103.3
06	WOOD, PLASTICS & COMPOSITES	114.4	93.9	102.9	102.7	59.1	78.3	116.1	71.1	90.9	101.8	64.0	80.7	157.4	87.6	118.3	116.7	88.2	100.7
07	THERMAL & MOISTURE PROTECTION	116.5	96.9	108.5	106.8	64.1	89.3	136.8	69.9	109.4	110.2	62.2	90.5	143.5	85.6	119.8	109.4	87.4	100.4
08	OPENINGS	90.1	82.4	88.3	89.3	56.8	81.7	95.3	64.9	88.2	87.9	55.9	80.5	104.2	83.7	99.4	90.4	87.9	89.8
0920	Plaster & Gypsum Board	135.1	93.2	106.8	110.7	57.8	74.9	142.7	70.0	93.6	137.6	62.7	87.0	140.3	87.1	104.4	124.7	87.7	99.7
0950, 0980	Ceilings & Acoustic Treatment	126.1	93.2	104.4	96.5	57.8	71.0	109.6	70.0	83.6	106.4	62.7	77.7	109.6	87.1	94.8	95.3	87.7	90.3
0960	Flooring	122.0	99.5	115.6	110.6	63.3	97.1	116.1	67.2	102.1	107.9	72.1	97.7	138.6	97.5	126.9	113.7	104.9	111.2
0970, 0990	Wall Finishes & Painting/Coating	120.8	106.4	112.1	118.3	66.8	87.2	126.4	64.1	88.8	117.6	51.6	77.8	126.4	91.2	105.1	115.3	106.7	110.1
09	FINISHES	119.9	96.7	107.1	107.1	61.4	81.9	118.2	70.3	91.8	111.3	64.5	85.5	125.1	89.8	105.7	107.9	93.9	100.2
COVERS	DIVS. 10 - 14, 25, 28, 41, 43, 44, 46	131.1	87.1	122.3	131.1	64.6	117.7	131.1	66.6	118.1	131.1	65.3	117.8	131.1	72.7	119.3	131.1	97.2	124.3
21, 22, 23	FIRE SUPPRESSION, PLUMBING & HVAC	101.2	92.4	97.7	102.3	76.1	91.8	102.1	84.4	95.0	102.0	69.8	89.0	102.1	98.1	100.5	100.4	100.7	100.5
26, 27, 3370	ELECTRICAL, COMMUNICATIONS & UTIL.	112.6	86.8	99.0	113.9	62.8	86.9	116.3	64.4	88.9	112.0	61.8	85.5	116.4	90.8	102.9	112.6	90.5	100.9
MF2014	WEIGHTED AVERAGE	117.8	93.2	107.1	110.7	69.5	92.7	124.1	74.6	102.5	111.6	67.9	92.5	127.3	91.1	111.5	112.3	94.3	104.4

CANADA

DIVISION		OTTAWA, ONTARIO			OWEN SOUND, ONTARIO			PETERBOROUGH, ONTARIO			PORTAGE LA PRAIRIE, MANITOBA			PRINCE ALBERT, SASKATCHEWAN			PRINCE GEORGE, BRITISH COLUMBIA		
		MAT.	INST.	TOTAL	MAT.	INST.	TOTAL	MAT.	INST.	TOTAL	MAT.	INST.	TOTAL	MAT.	INST.	TOTAL	MAT.	INST.	TOTAL
015433	CONTRACTOR EQUIPMENT		104.3	104.3		102.1	102.1		102.1	102.1		104.5	104.5		100.6	100.6		106.1	106.1
0241, 31 - 34	SITE & INFRASTRUCTURE, DEMOLITION	108.2	104.6	105.7	118.5	100.3	105.5	118.0	100.2	105.3	116.6	99.3	104.3	110.9	96.1	100.3	124.0	103.3	109.3
0310	Concrete Forming & Accessories	121.2	91.4	95.5	124.4	85.5	90.9	124.9	88.1	93.1	124.3	72.0	79.2	107.1	60.3	66.8	112.7	85.5	89.3
0320	Concrete Reinforcing	138.9	91.9	115.0	173.2	83.8	127.7	165.4	82.3	123.1	152.9	53.2	102.2	112.7	61.8	86.8	110.3	76.8	93.2
0330	Cast-in-Place Concrete	145.6	99.9	126.8	165.6	83.1	131.7	153.6	88.7	127.0	141.9	76.1	114.9	124.8	71.0	102.7	138.2	101.6	123.2
03	CONCRETE	132.6	94.4	113.8	150.3	84.6	118.1	141.8	87.4	115.1	127.8	70.6	99.7	112.6	65.0	89.2	145.4	89.7	118.0
04	MASONRY	168.0	98.8	124.9	171.5	95.6	124.2	168.0	96.7	123.5	166.5	66.6	104.2	161.1	64.4	100.8	172.9	95.0	124.3
05	METALS	127.9	91.7	116.8	110.2	90.0	104.0	109.1	89.7	103.1	110.0	76.7	99.7	106.3	73.7	96.3	109.8	87.6	102.9
06	WOOD, PLASTICS & COMPOSITES	109.4	90.6	98.9	119.8	84.3	99.9	123.7	86.3	102.8	121.1	73.5	94.4	107.2	59.1	78.3	105.2	82.1	92.3
07	THERMAL & MOISTURE PROTECTION	124.4	93.8	111.8	111.8	86.4	101.4	113.8	91.2	104.5	107.3	71.3	92.5	106.7	63.0	88.8	117.2	86.1	104.4
08	OPENINGS	93.9	88.7	92.7	93.9	83.1	91.4	92.4	85.5	90.8	93.6	64.8	86.9	88.2	56.8	80.9	90.2	81.8	88.2
0920	Plaster & Gypsum Board	168.3	90.2	115.5	151.1	83.7	105.6	130.1	85.8	100.1	114.2	72.2	85.8	110.7	57.8	74.9	113.6	81.0	91.6
0950, 0980	Ceilings & Acoustic Treatment	125.6	90.2	102.4	91.5	83.7	86.4	96.5	85.8	89.4	96.5	72.2	80.5	96.5	57.8	71.0	96.5	81.0	86.3
0960	Flooring	112.3	97.5	108.1	127.2	98.9	119.1	120.5	97.5	113.9	120.5	70.2	106.1	110.6	63.3	97.1	116.0	76.2	104.6
0970, 0990	Wall Finishes & Painting/Coating	123.2	94.2	105.7	116.2	89.9	100.3	118.3	93.5	103.3	118.4	58.7	82.4	118.3	57.0	81.3	118.3	84.0	97.6
09	FINISHES	122.6	92.9	105.7	115.0	88.6	100.5	112.4	90.5	100.3	110.5	70.8	88.6	110.5	60.3	81.3	110.6	83.4	95.6
COVERS	DIVS. 10 - 14, 25, 28, 41, 43, 44, 46	131.1	95.7	124.0	139.2	73.2	125.9	131.1	74.2	119.6	131.1	67.2	118.2	131.1	64.6	117.7	131.1	94.8	123.8
21, 22, 23	FIRE SUPPRESSION, PLUMBING & HVAC	101.4	87.2	95.7	101.8	98.1	100.3	102.0	101.7	101.9	102.0	83.6	94.5	102.3	68.6	88.7	102.0	94.4	98.9
26, 27, 3370	ELECTRICAL, COMMUNICATIONS & UTIL.	107.3	98.7	102.8	118.2	89.6	103.1	111.5	90.4	100.4	113.6	60.1	85.3	113.9	62.8	86.9	111.7	81.9	96.0
MF2014	WEIGHTED AVERAGE	117.3	94.0	107.2	117.8	91.2	106.2	114.9	93.1	105.4	113.4	74.2	96.3	109.9	67.7	91.5	115.4	89.9	104.3

For customer support on your Site Work & Landscape Cost Data, call 877.737.1594.

City Cost Indexes

CANADA

DIVISION		QUEBEC, QUEBEC			RED DEER, ALBERTA			REGINA, SASKATCHEWAN			RIMOUSKI, QUEBEC			ROUYN-NORANDA, QUEBEC			SAINT HYACINTHE, QUEBEC		
		MAT.	INST.	TOTAL	MAT.	INST.	TOTAL	MAT.	INST.	TOTAL	MAT.	INST.	TOTAL	MAT.	INST.	TOTAL	MAT.	INST.	TOTAL
015433	CONTRACTOR EQUIPMENT		104.9	104.9		104.4	104.4		100.6	100.6		102.8	102.8		102.8	102.8		102.8	102.8
0241, 31 - 34	SITE & INFRASTRUCTURE, DEMOLITION	110.8	99.5	102.8	114.2	101.4	105.1	124.4	98.0	105.6	98.7	99.1	99.0	98.2	99.8	99.4	98.7	99.8	99.5
0310	Concrete Forming & Accessories	125.6	93.7	98.1	139.6	82.6	90.4	117.6	90.9	94.6	130.7	93.1	98.3	130.7	87.8	93.7	130.7	87.8	93.7
0320	Concrete Reinforcing	138.3	96.0	116.8	152.9	71.8	111.7	138.0	84.8	111.0	106.0	95.9	100.9	148.7	78.8	113.2	148.7	78.8	113.2
0330	Cast-in-Place Concrete	141.8	101.6	125.2	141.9	101.4	125.3	171.5	95.7	140.4	128.6	99.8	116.8	122.3	97.8	112.2	126.4	97.8	114.6
03	CONCRETE	131.0	96.7	114.1	135.3	87.5	111.8	148.9	91.4	120.6	121.1	95.9	108.7	124.8	89.8	107.6	126.7	89.8	108.5
04	MASONRY	163.0	95.1	120.7	163.4	82.5	113.0	183.5	96.7	129.4	163.6	95.0	120.9	163.7	87.1	116.0	164.0	87.1	116.1
05	METALS	128.0	93.0	117.2	110.0	88.7	103.4	129.3	86.4	116.1	106.9	92.2	102.4	107.4	87.4	101.2	107.4	87.4	101.2
06	WOOD, PLASTICS & COMPOSITES	115.8	93.9	103.6	121.3	82.0	99.3	101.9	91.9	96.3	135.3	93.6	112.0	135.3	88.0	108.8	135.3	88.0	108.8
07	THERMAL & MOISTURE PROTECTION	118.4	97.0	109.6	132.2	87.5	113.9	123.2	86.0	107.9	107.4	96.4	102.9	107.4	89.9	100.2	107.7	89.9	100.4
08	OPENINGS	93.0	90.1	92.3	93.6	77.9	89.9	91.9	80.7	89.3	93.2	80.6	90.2	93.6	76.3	89.6	93.6	76.3	89.6
0920	Plaster & Gypsum Board	142.1	93.2	109.0	117.2	81.0	92.8	130.5	91.6	104.2	156.8	93.2	113.8	126.4	87.4	100.8	128.7	87.4	100.8
0950, 0980	Ceilings & Acoustic Treatment	126.1	93.2	104.4	96.5	81.0	86.3	125.4	91.6	103.2	95.7	93.2	94.0	95.7	87.4	90.2	95.7	87.4	90.2
0960	Flooring	125.8	99.5	118.3	123.0	92.6	114.3	120.0	65.5	104.4	120.5	99.5	114.5	120.5	99.5	114.5	120.5	99.5	114.5
0970, 0990	Wall Finishes & Painting/Coating	127.8	106.4	114.9	118.2	81.2	95.9	123.9	92.9	105.2	118.3	106.4	111.1	118.3	91.7	102.2	118.3	91.7	102.2
09	FINISHES	122.2	96.8	108.2	111.7	84.0	96.4	122.7	87.2	103.1	115.1	96.5	104.9	111.0	90.8	99.9	111.3	90.8	100.0
COVERS	DIVS. 10 - 14, 25, 28, 41, 43, 44, 46	131.1	87.3	122.3	131.1	91.9	123.2	131.1	72.4	119.3	131.1	86.5	122.1	131.1	85.2	121.9	131.1	85.2	121.9
21, 22, 23	FIRE SUPPRESSION, PLUMBING & HVAC	101.2	92.4	97.7	102.0	92.3	98.1	100.7	84.8	94.3	102.0	92.3	98.1	102.0	91.0	97.6	98.8	91.0	95.7
26, 27, 3370	ELECTRICAL, COMMUNICATIONS & UTIL.	111.4	86.8	98.4	104.9	85.4	94.6	114.4	92.4	102.8	111.8	86.8	98.6	111.8	72.6	91.1	112.5	72.6	91.4
MF2014	WEIGHTED AVERAGE	117.1	93.6	106.8	114.1	88.2	102.8	120.7	89.0	106.9	111.8	92.9	103.6	112.0	87.4	101.3	111.6	87.4	101.1

CANADA

DIVISION		SAINT JOHN, NEW BRUNSWICK			SARNIA, ONTARIO			SASKATOON, SASKATCHEWAN			SAULT STE MARIE, ONTARIO			SHERBROOKE, QUEBEC			SOREL, QUEBEC		
		MAT.	INST.	TOTAL	MAT.	INST.	TOTAL	MAT.	INST.	TOTAL	MAT.	INST.	TOTAL	MAT.	INST.	TOTAL	MAT.	INST.	TOTAL
015433	CONTRACTOR EQUIPMENT		102.2	102.2		102.1	102.1		100.6	100.6		102.1	102.1		102.8	102.8		102.8	102.8
0241, 31 - 34	SITE & INFRASTRUCTURE, DEMOLITION	103.5	98.0	99.6	116.5	100.3	105.0	111.7	98.0	102.0	106.7	99.8	101.8	98.7	99.8	99.5	98.8	99.9	99.6
0310	Concrete Forming & Accessories	124.6	67.0	74.9	123.6	95.3	99.1	107.4	90.9	93.2	112.8	87.9	91.3	130.7	87.8	93.7	130.7	88.0	93.8
0320	Concrete Reinforcing	137.0	62.0	98.8	117.4	83.6	100.2	114.5	84.8	99.4	106.1	82.1	93.9	148.7	78.8	113.2	140.6	78.8	109.2
0330	Cast-in-Place Concrete	129.7	80.1	109.3	141.7	102.1	125.5	135.4	95.7	119.1	127.4	87.2	110.9	126.4	97.8	114.6	127.4	97.8	115.2
03	CONCRETE	125.2	71.4	98.8	128.6	95.4	112.3	119.6	91.4	105.7	113.1	86.8	100.2	126.7	89.8	108.5	125.9	89.8	108.2
04	MASONRY	180.8	73.7	114.0	179.1	99.5	129.5	168.8	96.7	123.8	164.5	94.4	120.8	164.1	87.1	116.1	164.1	87.1	116.1
05	METALS	108.9	81.7	100.5	109.1	90.1	103.2	104.5	86.4	99.0	108.3	90.2	102.7	107.4	87.4	101.2	107.4	87.6	101.3
06	WOOD, PLASTICS & COMPOSITES	125.7	65.4	91.9	122.6	94.7	107.0	100.5	91.9	95.7	109.6	88.3	97.6	135.3	88.0	108.8	135.3	88.0	108.8
07	THERMAL & MOISTURE PROTECTION	110.5	70.9	94.3	113.9	94.7	106.0	107.1	86.0	98.4	112.7	88.4	102.7	107.4	89.9	100.3	107.4	89.9	100.2
08	OPENINGS	87.8	60.6	81.5	94.7	89.4	93.4	88.9	80.7	87.0	86.5	85.6	86.3	93.6	76.3	89.6	93.6	81.1	90.7
0920	Plaster & Gypsum Board	152.7	64.2	92.9	150.6	94.4	112.6	123.5	91.6	101.9	119.6	87.8	98.1	128.7	87.4	100.8	156.8	87.4	109.9
0950, 0980	Ceilings & Acoustic Treatment	111.5	64.2	80.4	100.7	94.4	96.6	117.4	91.6	100.4	96.5	87.8	90.8	95.7	87.4	90.2	95.7	87.4	90.2
0960	Flooring	119.5	72.1	105.9	120.5	106.6	116.5	111.0	65.5	98.0	113.4	100.8	109.8	120.5	99.5	114.5	120.5	99.5	114.5
0970, 0990	Wall Finishes & Painting/Coating	117.6	80.2	95.0	118.3	105.7	110.7	120.7	92.9	103.9	118.3	97.9	106.0	118.3	91.7	102.2	118.3	91.7	102.2
09	FINISHES	117.9	69.0	91.0	116.1	98.9	106.6	114.3	87.2	99.3	108.1	91.5	99.0	111.3	90.8	100.0	115.1	90.8	101.7
COVERS	DIVS. 10 - 14, 25, 28, 41, 43, 44, 46	131.1	66.3	118.0	131.1	75.7	119.9	131.1	74.1	119.6	131.1	96.4	124.1	131.1	85.2	121.9	131.1	85.2	121.9
21, 22, 23	FIRE SUPPRESSION, PLUMBING & HVAC	102.0	79.8	93.0	102.0	107.8	104.3	100.5	84.8	94.2	102.0	94.8	99.1	102.3	91.0	97.8	102.0	91.0	97.6
26, 27, 3370	ELECTRICAL, COMMUNICATIONS & UTIL.	120.3	88.2	103.3	114.2	92.7	102.8	116.2	92.4	103.6	113.0	90.8	101.3	111.8	72.6	91.1	111.8	72.6	91.1
MF2014	WEIGHTED AVERAGE	114.0	77.9	98.3	114.8	97.5	107.3	111.1	89.1	101.5	110.3	92.1	102.3	112.4	87.4	101.5	112.5	87.6	101.7

CANADA

DIVISION		ST CATHARINES, ONTARIO			ST JEROME, QUEBEC			ST JOHNS, NEWFOUNDLAND			SUDBURY, ONTARIO			SUMMERSIDE, PRINCE EDWARD ISLAND			SYDNEY, NOVA SCOTIA		
		MAT.	INST.	TOTAL	MAT.	INST.	TOTAL	MAT.	INST.	TOTAL	MAT.	INST.	TOTAL	MAT.	INST.	TOTAL	MAT.	INST.	TOTAL
015433	CONTRACTOR EQUIPMENT		102.1	102.1		102.8	102.8		103.3	103.3		102.1	102.1		101.8	101.8		101.9	101.9
0241, 31 - 34	SITE & INFRASTRUCTURE, DEMOLITION	100.0	101.4	101.0	98.2	99.8	99.4	123.4	99.9	106.7	100.1	100.9	100.7	128.4	95.7	105.2	114.3	98.2	102.8
0310	Concrete Forming & Accessories	110.9	94.2	96.5	130.7	87.8	93.7	123.9	84.8	90.1	107.0	89.0	91.5	112.0	58.3	65.7	111.7	71.6	77.1
0320	Concrete Reinforcing	101.7	92.0	96.7	148.7	78.8	113.2	158.9	75.5	116.4	102.5	91.3	96.8	168.1	46.8	106.4	170.3	46.7	107.4
0330	Cast-in-Place Concrete	123.2	100.6	113.9	122.3	97.8	112.2	167.5	96.4	138.3	124.2	97.0	113.0	142.3	61.2	109.0	115.6	72.2	97.8
03	CONCRETE	108.0	95.9	102.1	124.8	89.8	107.6	152.6	87.2	120.5	108.4	92.2	100.4	170.1	57.9	115.0	144.7	67.9	106.9
04	MASONRY	150.3	100.7	119.4	163.7	87.1	116.0	187.7	92.4	128.3	150.4	96.6	116.8	228.1	62.6	125.0	226.2	71.9	130.1
05	METALS	107.7	92.2	102.9	107.4	87.4	101.2	136.3	84.3	120.3	107.7	91.5	102.7	123.6	67.6	106.4	123.6	74.2	108.4
06	WOOD, PLASTICS & COMPOSITES	107.4	93.9	99.8	135.3	88.0	108.8	114.7	82.8	96.8	103.6	88.3	95.0	116.4	57.8	83.6	116.1	71.1	90.9
07	THERMAL & MOISTURE PROTECTION	108.6	96.5	103.6	107.4	89.9	100.2	127.1	91.4	112.5	108.0	91.7	101.3	136.1	61.1	105.4	136.8	69.9	109.4
08	OPENINGS	84.1	90.2	85.5	93.6	76.3	89.6	93.7	74.5	89.2	84.8	85.6	85.0	108.0	50.0	94.5	95.3	64.9	88.2
0920	Plaster & Gypsum Board	108.5	93.6	98.4	126.4	87.4	100.0	143.9	82.1	102.1	112.9	87.8	95.9	143.1	56.3	84.4	142.7	70.0	93.6
0950, 0980	Ceilings & Acoustic Treatment	95.3	93.6	94.1	95.7	87.4	90.2	120.6	82.1	95.3	90.3	87.8	88.6	109.6	56.3	74.6	109.6	70.0	83.6
0960	Flooring	109.3	98.9	106.3	120.5	99.5	114.5	116.0	59.3	99.8	107.3	100.8	105.5	116.2	62.9	100.9	116.1	67.2	102.1
0970, 0990	Wall Finishes & Painting/Coating	115.3	116.0	115.7	118.3	91.7	102.2	120.4	95.9	105.6	115.3	93.6	102.2	126.4	42.9	76.0	126.4	64.1	88.8
09	FINISHES	103.8	97.8	100.4	111.0	90.8	99.9	122.0	81.4	99.6	102.7	91.6	96.5	119.2	57.8	85.4	118.2	70.3	91.8
COVERS	DIVS. 10 - 14, 25, 28, 41, 43, 44, 46	131.1	75.2	119.8	131.1	85.2	121.9	131.1	72.6	119.3	131.1	97.1	124.3	131.1	64.8	117.7	131.1	66.6	118.1
21, 22, 23	FIRE SUPPRESSION, PLUMBING & HVAC	100.4	87.8	95.3	102.0	91.0	97.6	100.8	82.1	93.3	101.9	87.8	96.2	102.1	63.8	86.7	102.1	84.4	95.0
26, 27, 3370	ELECTRICAL, COMMUNICATIONS & UTIL.	112.9	98.8	105.5	112.4	72.6	91.3	114.4	83.2	97.9	110.3	99.2	104.4	115.4	52.3	82.0	116.3	64.4	88.9
MF2014	WEIGHTED AVERAGE	107.6	94.5	101.9	112.1	87.4	101.3	122.7	85.2	106.4	107.7	93.0	101.3	126.7	62.8	98.8	122.1	74.6	101.4

For customer support on your Site Work & Landscape Cost Data, call 877.737.1594.

City Cost Indexes

		CANADA															
	DIVISION	THUNDER BAY, ONTARIO			TIMMINS, ONTARIO			TORONTO, ONTARIO			TROIS RIVIERES, QUEBEC			TRURO, NOVA SCOTIA			VANCOUVER, BRITISH COLUMBIA		
		MAT.	INST.	TOTAL	MAT.	INST.	TOTAL	MAT.	INST.	TOTAL	MAT.	INST.	TOTAL	MAT.	INST.	TOTAL	MAT.	INST.	TOTAL
015433	CONTRACTOR EQUIPMENT		102.1	102.1		102.1	102.1		104.4	104.4		102.8	102.8		101.9	101.9		112.7	112.7
0241, 31 - 34	SITE & INFRASTRUCTURE, DEMOLITION	104.8	101.3	102.3	118.0	99.8	105.1	133.8	105.6	113.7	114.8	99.9	104.2	102.8	98.2	99.5	118.2	107.6	110.6
0310	Concrete Forming & Accessories	118.3	92.2	95.8	124.9	87.0	92.2	124.3	100.8	104.0	155.5	88.0	97.3	97.1	71.6	75.1	121.1	91.0	95.1
0320	Concrete Reinforcing	90.9	90.8	90.9	165.4	81.8	122.9	146.0	94.4	119.7	170.3	78.8	123.8	140.6	46.7	92.8	134.1	79.2	106.2
0330	Cast-in-Place Concrete	135.6	99.7	120.8	153.6	87.1	126.3	136.8	111.8	126.5	119.7	97.8	110.7	159.5	72.2	123.7	143.5	97.9	124.8
03	CONCRETE	115.8	94.5	105.3	141.8	86.3	114.5	129.7	103.1	116.7	147.4	89.8	119.1	140.2	67.9	104.7	137.1	91.4	114.6
04	MASONRY	151.0	100.6	119.6	168.0	89.9	119.3	182.0	110.9	137.7	230.7	87.1	141.2	163.6	71.9	106.5	166.7	91.4	119.7
05	METALS	107.5	91.1	102.5	109.1	89.2	103.0	132.5	93.9	120.7	122.7	87.6	111.9	108.2	74.2	97.7	139.3	90.3	124.2
06	WOOD, PLASTICS & COMPOSITES	116.7	90.9	102.2	123.7	87.6	103.5	115.1	98.9	106.0	173.0	88.0	125.4	92.9	71.1	80.7	104.8	91.5	97.4
07	THERMAL & MOISTURE PROTECTION	108.8	93.8	102.7	113.8	85.6	102.2	123.9	102.8	115.2	135.2	89.9	116.6	108.6	69.9	92.8	125.2	86.9	109.5
08	OPENINGS	83.3	88.0	84.4	92.4	83.7	90.4	90.5	96.8	92.0	105.5	81.1	99.8	86.1	64.9	81.1	88.9	86.9	88.4
0920	Plaster & Gypsum Board	139.8	90.5	106.5	130.1	87.1	101.1	133.0	98.8	109.9	173.4	87.4	115.3	130.7	70.0	89.7	129.6	90.6	103.3
0950, 0980	Ceilings & Acoustic Treatment	90.3	90.5	90.4	96.5	87.1	90.3	114.9	98.8	104.3	108.8	87.4	94.7	96.5	70.0	79.1	132.2	90.6	104.8
0960	Flooring	113.7	105.9	111.4	120.5	97.5	113.9	117.0	108.4	114.6	138.6	99.5	127.5	102.7	67.2	92.5	124.6	96.0	116.4
0970, 0990	Wall Finishes & Painting/Coating	115.3	94.6	102.8	118.3	91.2	101.9	120.4	106.7	112.1	126.4	91.7	105.4	118.3	64.1	85.6	121.7	95.6	106.0
09	FINISHES	108.5	95.1	101.1	112.4	89.8	99.9	116.9	103.0	109.2	128.7	90.8	107.8	106.6	70.3	86.6	123.8	92.7	106.6
COVERS	DIVS. 10 - 14, 25, 28, 41, 43, 44, 46	131.1	75.2	119.8	131.1	72.7	119.3	131.1	101.2	125.1	131.1	85.2	121.9	131.1	66.6	118.1	131.1	94.9	123.8
21, 22, 23	FIRE SUPPRESSION, PLUMBING & HVAC	100.4	88.0	95.4	102.0	98.1	100.4	101.0	97.3	99.5	102.1	91.0	97.7	102.0	84.4	94.9	101.2	80.5	92.8
26, 27, 3370	ELECTRICAL, COMMUNICATIONS & UTIL.	111.5	97.0	103.8	113.0	90.8	101.3	108.8	101.0	104.7	116.6	72.6	93.4	111.5	64.4	86.6	109.0	83.3	95.4
MF2014	WEIGHTED AVERAGE	108.8	93.4	102.1	115.1	91.1	104.6	118.3	101.3	110.9	124.8	87.6	108.6	112.5	74.6	96.0	119.5	89.1	106.2

		CANADA															
	DIVISION	VICTORIA, BRITISH COLUMBIA			WHITEHORSE, YUKON			WINDSOR, ONTARIO			WINNIPEG, MANITOBA			YARMOUTH, NOVA SCOTIA			YELLOWKNIFE, NWT		
		MAT.	INST.	TOTAL	MAT.	INST.	TOTAL	MAT.	INST.	TOTAL	MAT.	INST.	TOTAL	MAT.	INST.	TOTAL	MAT.	INST.	TOTAL
015433	CONTRACTOR EQUIPMENT		109.3	109.3		102.1	102.1		102.1	102.1		106.5	106.5		101.9	101.9		101.9	101.9
0241, 31 - 34	SITE & INFRASTRUCTURE, DEMOLITION	123.0	107.1	111.7	142.3	96.7	109.9	95.9	101.3	99.7	118.2	100.9	105.9	118.3	98.2	104.0	154.1	101.0	116.4
0310	Concrete Forming & Accessories	112.7	90.4	93.5	129.4	59.6	69.2	118.3	90.5	94.3	128.5	69.3	77.4	111.7	71.6	77.1	132.7	80.2	87.4
0320	Concrete Reinforcing	112.0	79.1	95.2	160.8	60.0	109.5	99.6	91.9	95.7	132.9	57.9	94.7	170.3	46.7	107.4	151.4	62.7	106.2
0330	Cast-in-Place Concrete	140.3	97.2	122.6	209.3	70.3	152.2	126.2	101.9	116.2	163.9	75.0	127.4	148.3	72.2	117.0	211.2	88.1	160.6
03	CONCRETE	150.1	90.7	120.9	182.4	64.1	124.3	109.6	94.7	102.3	144.4	69.7	107.7	160.1	67.9	114.8	182.0	80.0	131.9
04	MASONRY	171.7	91.3	121.6	260.3	62.8	137.2	150.5	99.9	119.0	176.6	70.8	110.7	228.8	71.9	131.0	260.3	74.8	144.7
05	METALS	107.0	86.3	100.6	135.3	73.6	116.3	107.6	91.7	102.7	141.7	75.0	121.2	123.6	74.2	108.4	137.9	78.7	119.7
06	WOOD, PLASTICS & COMPOSITES	104.4	91.4	97.1	117.6	58.3	84.4	116.7	89.0	101.2	113.6	70.2	89.3	116.1	71.1	90.9	124.0	81.9	100.4
07	THERMAL & MOISTURE PROTECTION	116.9	86.7	104.5	139.1	62.0	107.5	108.6	93.9	102.6	120.8	71.8	100.7	136.8	69.9	109.4	151.5	78.4	121.5
08	OPENINGS	90.5	83.2	88.8	107.6	55.5	95.4	83.1	87.5	84.1	85.5	62.6	80.2	95.3	64.9	88.2	102.2	68.9	94.4
0920	Plaster & Gypsum Board	115.8	90.6	98.8	150.5	56.8	87.2	125.7	88.6	100.6	129.5	68.6	88.3	142.7	70.0	93.6	163.7	81.1	107.9
0950, 0980	Ceilings & Acoustic Treatment	98.1	90.6	93.2	144.6	56.8	86.9	90.3	88.6	89.2	136.2	68.6	91.8	109.6	70.0	83.6	138.9	81.1	100.9
0960	Flooring	116.4	76.2	104.9	141.0	61.3	118.2	113.7	103.1	110.6	117.0	75.6	105.2	116.1	67.2	102.1	135.5	92.5	123.2
0970, 0990	Wall Finishes & Painting/Coating	120.7	95.6	105.5	143.1	56.0	90.5	115.3	95.5	103.3	124.5	56.5	83.4	126.4	64.1	88.8	135.3	80.3	102.1
09	FINISHES	112.1	89.3	99.5	140.9	59.3	95.9	106.3	93.4	99.2	122.3	69.5	93.2	118.2	70.3	91.8	137.5	82.0	106.9
COVERS	DIVS. 10 - 14, 25, 28, 41, 43, 44, 46	131.1	71.5	119.1	131.1	63.9	117.6	131.1	74.7	119.7	131.1	68.7	118.5	131.1	66.6	118.1	131.1	67.1	118.2
21, 22, 23	FIRE SUPPRESSION, PLUMBING & HVAC	102.0	80.5	93.3	102.5	74.8	91.3	100.4	88.0	95.4	101.1	66.9	87.3	102.1	84.4	95.0	102.7	94.0	99.2
26, 27, 3370	ELECTRICAL, COMMUNICATIONS & UTIL.	113.1	82.7	97.0	133.5	62.2	95.8	116.0	99.0	107.0	113.3	68.0	89.4	116.3	64.4	88.9	130.5	85.2	106.5
MF2014	WEIGHTED AVERAGE	115.7	87.2	103.3	135.3	68.5	106.2	108.2	93.4	101.7	121.0	71.8	99.5	124.0	74.6	102.5	135.3	84.2	113.0

Location Factors

Costs shown in RSMeans cost data publications are based on national averages for materials and installation. To adjust these costs to a specific location, simply multiply the base cost by the factor and divide by 100 for that city. The data is arranged alphabetically by state and postal zip code numbers. For a city not listed, use the factor for a nearby city with similar economic characteristics.

STATE/ZIP	CITY	MAT.	INST.	TOTAL
ALABAMA				
350-352	Birmingham	100.6	76.7	90.2
354	Tuscaloosa	99.8	61.2	83.0
355	Jasper	100.2	57.5	81.6
356	Decatur	99.8	57.9	81.5
357-358	Huntsville	99.8	72.1	87.8
359	Gadsden	99.9	60.0	82.5
360-361	Montgomery	99.9	57.1	81.2
362	Anniston	98.6	61.8	82.6
363	Dothan	99.0	49.4	77.4
364	Evergreen	98.6	50.7	77.7
365-366	Mobile	99.9	65.4	84.9
367	Selma	98.7	49.9	77.4
368	Phenix City	99.5	54.6	79.9
369	Butler	98.9	49.4	77.3
ALASKA				
995-996	Anchorage	121.1	115.6	118.7
997	Fairbanks	121.0	116.4	119.0
998	Juneau	121.3	115.6	118.8
999	Ketchikan	132.0	115.6	124.8
ARIZONA				
850,853	Phoenix	99.2	73.8	88.1
851,852	Mesa/Tempe	98.6	72.8	87.4
855	Globe	98.8	70.0	86.3
856-857	Tucson	97.4	72.4	86.5
859	Show Low	98.9	72.5	87.4
860	Flagstaff	101.3	71.8	88.4
863	Prescott	99.2	68.9	86.0
864	Kingman	97.6	72.0	86.4
865	Chambers	97.6	71.5	86.2
ARKANSAS				
716	Pine Bluff	99.4	63.3	83.6
717	Camden	97.1	50.1	76.6
718	Texarkana	98.2	49.2	76.8
719	Hot Springs	96.4	51.8	76.9
720-722	Little Rock	98.5	64.0	83.4
723	West Memphis	96.1	62.4	81.4
724	Jonesboro	96.7	59.1	80.3
725	Batesville	94.6	54.6	77.1
726	Harrison	95.9	50.4	76.0
727	Fayetteville	93.4	52.0	75.4
728	Russellville	94.6	53.7	76.8
729	Fort Smith	97.2	61.6	81.7
CALIFORNIA				
900-902	Los Angeles	99.2	117.5	107.2
903-905	Inglewood	94.8	114.1	103.2
906-908	Long Beach	96.2	114.1	104.0
910-912	Pasadena	96.4	114.6	104.3
913-916	Van Nuys	99.1	114.6	105.9
917-918	Alhambra	98.3	114.8	105.5
919-921	San Diego	100.5	109.6	104.5
922	Palm Springs	97.2	112.0	103.6
923-924	San Bernardino	95.1	111.3	102.1
925	Riverside	99.4	114.6	106.0
926-927	Santa Ana	96.9	111.8	103.4
928	Anaheim	99.4	114.9	106.2
930	Oxnard	99.6	114.4	106.0
931	Santa Barbara	98.9	115.1	106.0
932-933	Bakersfield	100.7	113.6	106.3
934	San Luis Obispo	99.4	112.0	104.9
935	Mojave	96.8	109.8	102.5
936-938	Fresno	100.1	115.3	106.7
939	Salinas	100.2	121.6	109.5
940-941	San Francisco	105.2	145.4	122.7
942,956-958	Sacramento	100.5	119.3	108.7
943	Palo Alto	98.9	134.5	114.4
944	San Mateo	100.9	134.6	115.6
945	Vallejo	100.1	127.2	111.9
946	Oakland	103.1	134.3	116.7
947	Berkeley	102.7	135.1	116.8
948	Richmond	101.8	133.1	115.4
949	San Rafael	103.5	136.7	118.0
950	Santa Cruz	104.5	121.8	112.0

STATE/ZIP	CITY	MAT.	INST.	TOTAL
CALIFORNIA (CONT'D)				
951	San Jose	102.5	136.6	117.4
952	Stockton	100.9	117.2	108.0
953	Modesto	100.8	115.7	107.3
954	Santa Rosa	100.8	134.7	115.6
955	Eureka	102.1	116.4	108.4
959	Marysville	101.3	115.9	107.7
960	Redding	107.8	117.7	112.1
961	Susanville	106.8	118.1	111.7
COLORADO				
800-802	Denver	100.8	81.7	92.5
803	Boulder	97.8	81.3	90.6
804	Golden	99.8	78.9	90.7
805	Fort Collins	101.3	79.0	91.6
806	Greeley	98.9	75.5	88.7
807	Fort Morgan	98.3	79.0	89.9
808-809	Colorado Springs	100.4	84.0	93.2
810	Pueblo	101.1	80.3	92.0
811	Alamosa	102.2	73.7	89.8
812	Salida	101.9	75.3	90.3
813	Durango	102.7	75.7	90.9
814	Montrose	101.4	75.4	90.1
815	Grand Junction	104.8	75.3	91.9
816	Glenwood Springs	102.3	78.1	91.8
CONNECTICUT				
060	New Britain	100.1	120.6	109.1
061	Hartford	101.4	120.8	109.8
062	Willimantic	100.8	120.2	109.2
063	New London	97.1	120.7	107.4
064	Meriden	98.9	120.7	108.4
065	New Haven	101.6	120.7	109.9
066	Bridgeport	101.3	120.8	109.8
067	Waterbury	100.9	120.7	109.5
068	Norwalk	100.8	128.7	113.0
069	Stamford	100.9	128.7	113.0
D.C.				
200-205	Washington	101.1	91.9	97.1
DELAWARE				
197	Newark	98.8	109.2	103.3
198	Wilmington	99.3	109.2	103.6
199	Dover	99.3	109.2	103.6
FLORIDA				
320,322	Jacksonville	98.8	66.4	84.7
321	Daytona Beach	99.0	72.9	87.6
323	Tallahassee	100.8	56.9	81.7
324	Panama City	100.2	57.8	81.7
325	Pensacola	102.7	61.2	84.6
326,344	Gainesville	100.3	66.7	85.7
327-328,347	Orlando	100.5	70.0	87.2
329	Melbourne	101.7	76.3	90.6
330-332,340	Miami	99.8	73.1	88.2
333	Fort Lauderdale	98.6	72.6	87.2
334,349	West Palm Beach	97.4	71.1	85.9
335-336,346	Tampa	100.1	78.4	90.6
337	St. Petersburg	102.6	63.3	85.5
338	Lakeland	99.4	77.8	90.0
339,341	Fort Myers	98.6	72.6	87.3
342	Sarasota	100.8	74.3	89.2
GEORGIA				
300-303,399	Atlanta	97.6	74.4	87.5
304	Statesboro	97.3	55.8	79.2
305	Gainesville	96.0	61.6	81.0
306	Athens	95.5	63.9	81.7
307	Dalton	97.2	59.0	80.5
308-309	Augusta	96.3	63.6	82.1
310-312	Macon	97.2	64.7	83.0
313-314	Savannah	99.2	60.9	82.5
315	Waycross	98.3	59.4	81.4
316	Valdosta	98.5	61.4	82.3
317,398	Albany	98.5	61.3	82.3
318-319	Columbus	98.4	65.4	84.0

791

Location Factors

STATE/ZIP	CITY	MAT.	INST.	TOTAL
HAWAII				
967	Hilo	114.8	120.2	117.2
968	Honolulu	119.5	120.2	119.8
STATES & POSS.				
969	Guam	136.2	58.0	102.1
IDAHO				
832	Pocatello	101.1	77.4	90.8
833	Twin Falls	102.2	67.3	87.0
834	Idaho Falls	99.8	74.7	88.9
835	Lewiston	108.7	84.9	98.3
836-837	Boise	100.1	78.6	90.7
838	Coeur d'Alene	107.9	82.2	96.7
ILLINOIS				
600-603	North Suburban	99.3	135.1	114.9
604	Joliet	99.2	138.4	116.3
605	South Suburban	99.3	135.1	114.9
606-608	Chicago	99.8	139.7	117.2
609	Kankakee	95.6	131.7	111.3
610-611	Rockford	99.5	124.8	110.5
612	Rock Island	97.2	100.5	98.6
613	La Salle	98.4	124.4	109.7
614	Galesburg	98.2	106.7	101.9
615-616	Peoria	100.5	109.3	104.4
617	Bloomington	97.5	109.4	102.7
618-619	Champaign	101.0	107.6	103.9
620-622	East St. Louis	96.4	108.7	101.8
623	Quincy	98.1	101.0	99.3
624	Effingham	97.3	106.0	101.1
625	Decatur	99.2	104.9	101.7
626-627	Springfield	100.0	106.5	102.8
628	Centralia	95.0	108.5	100.9
629	Carbondale	94.7	107.9	100.5
INDIANA				
460	Anderson	97.0	83.8	91.3
461-462	Indianapolis	99.1	84.8	92.9
463-464	Gary	98.3	110.4	103.6
465-466	South Bend	98.0	84.4	92.1
467-468	Fort Wayne	97.6	79.1	89.5
469	Kokomo	94.8	81.5	89.0
470	Lawrenceburg	94.0	77.7	86.9
471	New Albany	95.1	75.4	86.5
472	Columbus	97.2	80.9	90.1
473	Muncie	97.9	82.3	91.1
474	Bloomington	99.3	81.8	91.6
475	Washington	95.8	81.8	89.7
476-477	Evansville	97.1	86.9	92.6
478	Terre Haute	97.9	86.5	92.9
479	Lafayette	96.9	82.7	90.7
IOWA				
500-503,509	Des Moines	100.5	85.2	93.8
504	Mason City	97.6	65.8	83.8
505	Fort Dodge	97.9	58.2	80.6
506-507	Waterloo	99.5	71.8	87.4
508	Creston	98.2	77.3	89.1
510-511	Sioux City	99.7	72.6	87.9
512	Sibley	98.3	56.4	80.0
513	Spencer	99.9	56.6	81.0
514	Carroll	97.0	71.2	85.8
515	Council Bluffs	100.7	78.1	90.9
516	Shenandoah	97.6	71.2	86.1
520	Dubuque	99.1	80.2	90.9
521	Decorah	98.0	64.2	83.3
522-524	Cedar Rapids	100.0	83.2	92.7
525	Ottumwa	97.9	73.7	87.3
526	Burlington	97.2	75.3	87.6
527-528	Davenport	99.0	93.1	96.4
KANSAS				
660-662	Kansas City	99.5	94.8	97.5
664-666	Topeka	99.5	66.0	84.9
667	Fort Scott	97.9	73.0	87.0
668	Emporia	97.9	69.2	85.4
669	Belleville	99.6	64.9	84.4
670-672	Wichita	100.7	66.0	85.6
673	Independence	100.9	69.2	87.1
674	Salina	101.5	67.6	86.7
675	Hutchinson	96.5	65.0	82.8
676	Hays	100.5	65.4	85.2
677	Colby	101.1	65.0	85.4

STATE/ZIP	CITY	MAT.	INST.	TOTAL
KANSAS (CONT'D)				
678	Dodge City	102.7	66.0	86.7
679	Liberal	100.4	65.5	85.2
KENTUCKY				
400-402	Louisville	96.6	83.3	90.8
403-405	Lexington	96.6	81.4	90.0
406	Frankfort	98.1	80.7	90.5
407-409	Corbin	94.0	71.8	84.3
410	Covington	95.9	91.4	93.9
411-412	Ashland	94.6	99.3	96.6
413-414	Campton	95.8	78.6	88.3
415-416	Pikeville	96.9	88.6	93.3
417-418	Hazard	95.2	78.7	88.0
420	Paducah	93.9	84.5	89.8
421-422	Bowling Green	96.2	83.9	90.8
423	Owensboro	96.3	88.9	93.1
424	Henderson	93.7	86.1	90.4
425-426	Somerset	93.2	79.9	87.4
427	Elizabethtown	92.8	82.0	88.1
LOUISIANA				
700-701	New Orleans	101.4	69.5	87.5
703	Thibodaux	98.2	65.4	83.9
704	Hammond	95.8	54.5	77.8
705	Lafayette	97.9	63.0	82.7
706	Lake Charles	98.1	65.0	83.7
707-708	Baton Rouge	99.1	63.7	83.7
710-711	Shreveport	101.0	59.6	83.0
712	Monroe	99.3	56.5	80.6
713-714	Alexandria	99.4	57.2	81.0
MAINE				
039	Kittery	95.2	84.7	90.6
040-041	Portland	102.0	90.1	96.8
042	Lewiston	99.6	90.1	95.5
043	Augusta	102.1	79.5	92.3
044	Bangor	99.0	89.5	94.9
045	Bath	97.5	81.9	90.7
046	Machias	97.1	85.5	92.0
047	Houlton	97.2	85.6	92.1
048	Rockland	96.3	85.5	91.6
049	Waterville	97.5	79.5	89.7
MARYLAND				
206	Waldorf	97.1	81.7	90.4
207-208	College Park	97.2	83.4	91.2
209	Silver Spring	96.5	83.2	90.7
210-212	Baltimore	100.8	81.9	92.6
214	Annapolis	101.5	82.0	93.0
215	Cumberland	96.8	81.8	90.2
216	Easton	98.3	68.6	85.3
217	Hagerstown	97.6	83.3	91.4
218	Salisbury	98.7	62.1	82.7
219	Elkton	95.9	81.9	89.8
MASSACHUSETTS				
010-011	Springfield	100.2	112.6	105.6
012	Pittsfield	99.7	111.3	104.8
013	Greenfield	97.7	112.3	104.1
014	Fitchburg	96.5	126.5	109.6
015-016	Worcester	100.2	126.4	111.6
017	Framingham	95.7	135.1	112.9
018	Lowell	99.5	134.5	114.8
019	Lawrence	100.3	134.6	115.3
020-022, 024	Boston	101.6	139.5	118.1
023	Brockton	99.9	128.1	112.2
025	Buzzards Bay	94.4	128.1	109.1
026	Hyannis	97.0	128.1	110.6
027	New Bedford	99.1	128.3	111.8
MICHIGAN				
480,483	Royal Oak	94.9	106.9	100.1
481	Ann Arbor	97.1	107.5	101.7
482	Detroit	97.8	109.6	102.9
484-485	Flint	96.8	96.0	96.4
486	Saginaw	96.4	91.8	94.4
487	Bay City	96.6	91.7	94.5
488-489	Lansing	99.3	94.7	97.3
490	Battle Creek	98.3	87.6	93.7
491	Kalamazoo	98.7	85.7	93.0
492	Jackson	96.5	95.1	95.9
493,495	Grand Rapids	99.7	85.1	93.3
494	Muskegon	97.2	84.8	91.8

For customer support on your Site Work & Landscape Cost Data, call 877.737.1594.

Location Factors

STATE/ZIP	CITY	MAT.	INST.	TOTAL	STATE/ZIP	CITY	MAT.	INST.	TOTAL
MICHIGAN (CONT'D)					**NEW HAMPSHIRE (CONT'D)**				
496	Traverse City	96.3	80.1	89.3	032-033	Concord	101.1	92.5	97.4
497	Gaylord	97.2	83.6	91.3	034	Keene	97.2	73.3	86.7
498-499	Iron mountain	99.3	86.2	93.6	035	Littleton	97.1	76.3	88.0
					036	Charleston	96.7	69.5	84.8
MINNESOTA					037	Claremont	95.9	69.5	84.4
550-551	Saint Paul	101.4	117.9	108.6	038	Portsmouth	97.9	94.3	96.4
553-555	Minneapolis	100.4	120.0	108.9					
556-558	Duluth	101.3	107.3	103.9	**NEW JERSEY**				
559	Rochester	99.9	104.7	102.0	070-071	Newark	101.2	128.4	113.0
560	Mankato	97.2	101.3	99.0	072	Elizabeth	98.8	127.6	111.3
561	Windom	95.9	92.3	94.3	073	Jersey City	97.9	127.9	111.0
562	Willmar	95.5	101.3	98.0	074-075	Paterson	99.6	127.8	111.9
563	St. Cloud	96.9	116.0	105.2	076	Hackensack	97.6	128.1	110.9
564	Brainerd	96.9	100.5	98.5	077	Long Branch	97.1	126.3	109.8
565	Detroit Lakes	98.9	95.1	97.3	078	Dover	97.9	127.8	110.9
566	Bemidji	98.2	98.2	98.2	079	Summit	97.9	127.6	110.8
567	Thief River Falls	97.8	92.4	95.4	080,083	Vineland	97.5	124.7	109.4
					081	Camden	99.5	124.8	110.5
MISSISSIPPI					082,084	Atlantic City	98.2	124.8	109.8
386	Clarksdale	97.3	52.6	77.8	085-086	Trenton	100.9	125.1	111.5
387	Greenville	101.0	61.7	83.9	087	Point Pleasant	99.2	125.9	110.8
388	Tupelo	98.8	54.9	79.7	088-089	New Brunswick	99.7	127.6	111.9
389	Greenwood	98.4	52.2	78.3					
390-392	Jackson	100.7	62.2	83.9	**NEW MEXICO**				
393	Meridian	97.6	64.1	83.0	870-872	Albuquerque	99.6	72.6	87.8
394	Laurel	98.9	55.8	80.1	873	Gallup	99.5	72.6	87.8
395	Biloxi	99.2	58.1	81.3	874	Farmington	100.1	72.6	88.1
396	Mccomb	97.4	51.7	77.5	875	Santa Fe	100.8	72.6	88.5
397	Columbus	98.8	53.9	79.2	877	Las Vegas	98.0	72.6	86.9
					878	Socorro	97.6	72.6	86.7
MISSOURI					879	Truth/Consequences	97.5	69.4	85.2
630-631	St. Louis	98.7	107.8	102.7	880	Las Cruces	96.1	69.4	84.4
633	Bowling Green	97.3	94.4	96.0	881	Clovis	98.3	72.5	87.1
634	Hannibal	96.2	92.4	94.6	882	Roswell	100.0	72.6	88.0
635	Kirksville	99.5	89.9	95.3	883	Carrizozo	100.3	72.6	88.2
636	Flat River	98.1	95.0	96.8	884	Tucumcari	99.0	72.5	87.4
637	Cape Girardeau	98.2	92.4	95.7					
638	Sikeston	96.7	92.2	94.8	**NEW YORK**				
639	Poplar Bluff	96.2	92.0	94.4	100-102	New York	103.4	168.7	131.8
640-641	Kansas City	101.4	105.7	103.3	103	Staten Island	99.2	168.4	129.4
644-645	St. Joseph	100.6	93.5	97.5	104	Bronx	97.7	166.1	127.5
646	Chillicothe	97.6	94.5	96.3	105	Mount Vernon	97.5	141.4	116.6
647	Harrisonville	97.1	101.5	99.1	106	White Plains	97.6	141.4	116.7
648	Joplin	99.5	81.7	91.8	107	Yonkers	102.1	143.7	120.2
650-651	Jefferson City	99.9	93.7	97.2	108	New Rochelle	97.9	141.3	116.8
652	Columbia	100.2	93.9	97.5	109	Suffern	97.6	129.0	111.3
653	Sedalia	100.2	97.3	98.9	110	Queens	100.9	166.8	129.6
654-655	Rolla	97.9	94.6	96.5	111	Long Island City	102.4	166.8	130.5
656-658	Springfield	101.7	83.7	93.8	112	Brooklyn	102.8	168.5	131.4
					113	Flushing	102.5	166.8	130.5
MONTANA					114	Jamaica	100.8	166.8	129.6
590-591	Billings	102.7	77.1	91.5	115,117,118	Hicksville	100.9	153.3	123.7
592	Wolf Point	102.3	74.2	90.0	116	Far Rockaway	102.6	166.8	130.6
593	Miles City	100.1	74.0	88.7	119	Riverhead	101.6	148.2	121.9
594	Great Falls	104.1	76.2	91.9	120-122	Albany	100.1	104.7	102.1
595	Havre	101.2	73.1	89.0	123	Schenectady	99.3	104.7	101.7
596	Helena	102.4	73.8	89.9	124	Kingston	102.6	118.5	109.6
597	Butte	102.6	77.3	91.6	125-126	Poughkeepsie	101.8	136.7	117.0
598	Missoula	99.9	75.5	89.3	127	Monticello	101.1	115.1	107.2
599	Kalispell	99.0	75.3	88.7	128	Glens Falls	94.0	98.6	96.0
					129	Plattsburgh	99.1	96.7	98.0
NEBRASKA					130-132	Syracuse	98.9	98.0	98.5
680-681	Omaha	100.2	78.6	90.8	133-135	Utica	97.1	97.1	97.1
683-685	Lincoln	100.5	74.9	89.4	136	Watertown	98.5	96.3	97.5
686	Columbus	98.4	77.1	89.1	137-139	Binghamton	98.5	101.4	99.8
687	Norfolk	100.0	76.7	89.8	140-142	Buffalo	100.3	106.2	102.9
688	Grand Island	100.0	77.1	90.0	143	Niagara Falls	97.8	106.4	101.5
689	Hastings	99.4	79.8	90.9	144-146	Rochester	101.1	99.1	100.2
690	Mccook	98.7	71.1	86.7	147	Jamestown	96.8	92.5	94.9
691	North Platte	99.0	78.3	90.0	148-149	Elmira	96.7	97.4	97.0
692	Valentine	101.2	72.5	88.7					
693	Alliance	101.0	70.5	87.7	**NORTH CAROLINA**				
					270,272-274	Greensboro	101.3	55.7	81.4
NEVADA					271	Winston-Salem	101.0	56.5	81.6
889-891	Las Vegas	100.9	108.7	104.3	275-276	Raleigh	100.5	54.1	80.3
893	Ely	99.4	102.0	100.6	277	Durham	102.9	55.3	82.1
894-895	Reno	99.6	93.3	96.8	278	Rocky Mount	98.5	52.3	78.3
897	Carson City	99.7	93.5	97.0	279	Elizabeth City	99.3	51.6	78.5
898	Elko	98.3	84.9	92.4	280	Gastonia	101.6	55.1	81.3
					281-282	Charlotte	101.9	56.8	82.2
NEW HAMPSHIRE					283	Fayetteville	104.5	58.1	84.2
030	Nashua	100.5	93.8	97.6	284	Wilmington	100.3	55.9	81.0
031	Manchester	101.4	93.8	98.1	285	Kinston	98.4	52.7	78.5

Location Factors

STATE/ZIP	CITY	MAT.	INST.	TOTAL	STATE/ZIP	CITY	MAT.	INST.	TOTAL
NORTH CAROLINA (CONT'D)					**PENNSYLVANIA (CONT'D)**				
286	Hickory	98.8	53.9	79.2	177	Williamsport	93.8	83.0	89.1
287-288	Asheville	100.8	55.3	80.9	178	Sunbury	95.8	95.8	95.8
289	Murphy	99.6	48.3	77.2	179	Pottsville	94.9	98.5	96.5
					180	Lehigh Valley	95.8	114.0	103.7
NORTH DAKOTA					181	Allentown	97.9	108.6	102.5
580-581	Fargo	102.7	67.6	87.4	182	Hazleton	95.4	98.3	96.6
582	Grand Forks	102.7	51.6	80.4	183	Stroudsburg	95.3	101.4	97.9
583	Devils Lake	102.0	58.6	83.1	184-185	Scranton	98.6	99.2	98.9
584	Jamestown	102.1	45.2	77.3	186-187	Wilkes-Barre	95.1	98.7	96.6
585	Bismarck	103.1	66.2	87.0	188	Montrose	94.7	96.9	95.7
586	Dickinson	102.8	60.9	84.6	189	Doylestown	94.9	120.6	106.1
587	Minot	102.7	71.3	89.0	190-191	Philadelphia	99.7	133.6	114.5
588	Williston	101.2	60.9	83.7	193	Westchester	95.9	121.5	107.1
					194	Norristown	95.0	129.5	110.0
OHIO					195-196	Reading	97.1	102.1	99.3
430-432	Columbus	98.6	89.2	94.5					
433	Marion	95.1	85.3	90.8	**PUERTO RICO**				
434-436	Toledo	98.7	98.1	98.4	009	San Juan	122.7	24.4	79.8
437-438	Zanesville	95.6	86.5	91.6					
439	Steubenville	96.8	94.9	96.0	**RHODE ISLAND**				
440	Lorain	98.9	93.0	96.3	028	Newport	98.4	117.5	106.7
441	Cleveland	99.0	100.3	99.6	029	Providence	100.6	117.5	108.0
442-443	Akron	99.9	94.2	97.4					
444-445	Youngstown	99.2	89.0	94.7	**SOUTH CAROLINA**				
446-447	Canton	99.3	85.6	93.3	290-292	Columbia	99.3	56.5	80.6
448-449	Mansfield	96.7	87.3	92.6	293	Spartanburg	98.6	56.7	80.3
450	Hamilton	97.9	85.1	92.3	294	Charleston	99.9	65.2	84.8
451-452	Cincinnati	98.3	84.5	92.2	295	Florence	98.2	56.9	80.2
453-454	Dayton	98.0	84.4	92.1	296	Greenville	98.3	55.8	79.8
455	Springfield	98.0	84.7	92.2	297	Rock Hill	97.8	50.3	77.1
456	Chillicothe	96.8	93.0	95.1	298	Aiken	98.6	69.1	85.7
457	Athens	99.6	80.4	91.2	299	Beaufort	99.3	44.9	75.6
458	Lima	100.0	86.8	94.3					
					SOUTH DAKOTA				
OKLAHOMA					570-571	Sioux Falls	100.0	57.7	81.5
730-731	Oklahoma City	100.3	65.7	85.2	572	Watertown	99.0	49.1	77.2
734	Ardmore	98.3	61.9	82.4	573	Mitchell	97.8	48.4	76.3
735	Lawton	100.7	62.8	84.2	574	Aberdeen	100.5	49.6	78.3
736	Clinton	99.6	63.1	83.7	575	Pierre	101.7	58.4	82.8
737	Enid	100.2	60.5	82.9	576	Mobridge	98.5	48.8	76.8
738	Woodward	98.3	63.4	83.1	577	Rapid City	100.4	59.5	82.6
739	Guymon	99.4	59.7	82.1					
740-741	Tulsa	98.1	61.6	82.2	**TENNESSEE**				
743	Miami	94.8	67.5	82.9	370-372	Nashville	98.4	74.1	87.8
744	Muskogee	97.4	55.7	79.2	373-374	Chattanooga	100.0	66.2	85.2
745	Mcalester	94.5	60.4	79.7	375,380-381	Memphis	99.0	71.3	86.9
746	Ponca City	95.1	62.1	80.7	376	Johnson City	99.8	56.5	80.9
747	Durant	95.1	63.5	81.3	377-379	Knoxville	96.6	66.9	83.7
748	Shawnee	96.5	61.8	81.4	382	Mckenzie	98.2	59.2	81.2
749	Poteau	94.3	61.4	80.0	383	Jackson	99.9	61.2	83.0
					384	Columbia	96.9	66.1	83.5
OREGON					385	Cookeville	98.1	59.1	81.1
970-972	Portland	98.8	100.4	99.5					
973	Salem	100.5	99.4	100.0	**TEXAS**				
974	Eugene	98.6	99.3	98.9	750	Mckinney	98.7	63.1	83.2
975	Medford	100.0	97.1	98.8	751	Waxahackie	98.6	65.9	84.4
976	Klamath Falls	99.8	97.1	98.6	752-753	Dallas	99.5	67.4	85.5
977	Bend	98.9	99.4	99.1	754	Greenville	98.8	64.0	83.6
978	Pendleton	94.8	101.4	97.7	755	Texarkana	98.0	58.4	80.7
979	Vale	92.9	98.1	95.2	756	Longview	98.5	58.7	81.2
					757	Tyler	98.5	65.0	83.9
PENNSYLVANIA					758	Palestine	95.0	64.4	81.7
150-152	Pittsburgh	99.9	104.6	102.0	759	Lufkin	95.6	67.8	83.5
153	Washington	97.0	103.2	99.7	760-761	Fort Worth	99.3	65.3	84.5
154	Uniontown	97.3	101.7	99.2	762	Denton	98.9	62.5	83.0
155	Bedford	98.2	91.3	95.2	763	Wichita Falls	97.1	64.4	82.8
156	Greensburg	98.2	100.9	99.4	764	Eastland	95.9	63.2	81.6
157	Indiana	97.1	99.3	98.0	765	Temple	94.7	61.7	80.3
158	Dubois	98.5	96.8	97.8	766-767	Waco	96.5	64.1	82.4
159	Johnstown	98.1	97.2	97.7	768	Brownwood	98.9	59.4	81.7
160	Butler	92.5	102.0	96.6	769	San Angelo	98.5	59.6	81.5
161	New Castle	92.5	97.9	94.8	770-772	Houston	99.4	70.5	86.8
162	Kittanning	92.9	103.3	97.4	773	Huntsville	98.0	66.7	84.4
163	Oil City	92.4	96.9	94.4	774	Wharton	98.9	67.7	85.3
164-165	Erie	94.5	95.8	95.1	775	Galveston	97.0	70.0	85.2
166	Altoona	94.6	91.9	93.4	776-777	Beaumont	97.4	68.6	84.9
167	Bradford	95.7	96.4	96.0	778	Bryan	94.9	68.2	83.3
168	State College	95.3	92.8	94.2	779	Victoria	99.0	65.6	84.4
169	Wellsboro	96.3	92.6	94.7	780	Laredo	98.3	64.5	83.6
170-171	Harrisburg	99.8	95.6	98.0	781-782	San Antonio	98.5	65.1	84.0
172	Chambersburg	96.2	88.0	92.6	783-784	Corpus Christi	100.9	63.5	84.6
173-174	York	96.7	95.9	96.3	785	Mc Allen	101.0	59.8	83.0
175-176	Lancaster	95.1	89.0	92.4	786-787	Austin	100.0	63.6	84.1

For customer support on your Site Work & Landscape Cost Data, call 877.737.1594.

Location Factors

STATE/ZIP	CITY	MAT.	INST.	TOTAL
TEXAS (CONT'D)				
788	Del Rio	100.8	63.2	84.4
789	Giddings	97.7	64.0	83.0
790-791	Amarillo	100.2	63.2	84.1
792	Childress	99.3	64.3	84.0
793-794	Lubbock	101.6	63.6	85.0
795-796	Abilene	99.7	62.2	83.3
797	Midland	101.5	64.2	85.2
798-799,885	El Paso	98.0	61.7	82.2
UTAH				
840-841	Salt Lake City	102.2	68.3	87.4
842,844	Ogden	98.1	70.1	85.9
843	Logan	99.8	70.1	86.9
845	Price	100.2	64.6	84.7
846-847	Provo	100.3	68.2	86.3
VERMONT				
050	White River Jct.	98.5	78.3	89.7
051	Bellows Falls	97.2	93.0	95.3
052	Bennington	97.5	93.5	95.8
053	Brattleboro	97.8	92.8	95.6
054	Burlington	102.4	83.6	94.2
056	Montpelier	99.5	82.8	92.2
057	Rutland	99.7	83.6	92.7
058	St. Johnsbury	98.6	77.8	89.6
059	Guildhall	97.4	77.8	88.8
VIRGINIA				
220-221	Fairfax	100.7	84.0	93.4
222	Arlington	101.9	84.0	94.1
223	Alexandria	101.1	85.5	94.3
224-225	Fredericksburg	99.5	82.7	92.1
226	Winchester	100.0	82.2	92.2
227	Culpeper	99.9	80.5	91.4
228	Harrisonburg	100.2	67.2	85.8
229	Charlottesville	100.5	67.1	86.0
230-232	Richmond	101.3	68.7	87.1
233-235	Norfolk	100.5	68.2	86.4
236	Newport News	100.0	68.2	86.1
237	Portsmouth	99.4	65.3	84.5
238	Petersburg	99.4	68.7	86.0
239	Farmville	98.7	52.4	78.5
240-241	Roanoke	101.5	65.1	85.6
242	Bristol	99.4	54.9	80.0
243	Pulaski	99.0	57.3	80.9
244	Staunton	99.7	61.8	83.2
245	Lynchburg	99.9	65.6	85.0
246	Grundy	99.3	52.5	78.9
WASHINGTON				
980-981,987	Seattle	101.4	104.7	102.8
982	Everett	101.6	99.6	100.7
983-984	Tacoma	101.8	99.7	100.9
985	Olympia	101.2	99.4	100.4
986	Vancouver	102.7	92.1	98.1
988	Wenatchee	101.6	86.6	95.0
989	Yakima	102.0	94.1	98.6
990-992	Spokane	103.4	82.3	94.2
993	Richland	103.1	89.3	97.1
994	Clarkston	101.5	80.2	92.2
WEST VIRGINIA				
247-248	Bluefield	98.3	92.9	96.0
249	Lewisburg	99.8	92.4	96.6
250-253	Charleston	99.9	94.8	97.6
254	Martinsburg	99.3	86.4	93.7
255-257	Huntington	100.7	95.7	98.5
258-259	Beckley	97.9	93.3	95.9
260	Wheeling	101.2	94.3	98.2
261	Parkersburg	100.1	91.8	96.5
262	Buckhannon	99.6	95.5	97.8
263-264	Clarksburg	100.1	95.4	98.1
265	Morgantown	100.2	94.4	97.6
266	Gassaway	99.5	93.9	97.1
267	Romney	99.4	92.2	96.3
268	Petersburg	99.3	91.3	95.8
WISCONSIN				
530,532	Milwaukee	100.0	107.2	103.1
531	Kenosha	99.5	102.2	100.7
534	Racine	99.1	102.4	100.5
535	Beloit	98.9	100.7	99.7
537	Madison	99.1	99.0	99.1

STATE/ZIP	CITY	MAT.	INST.	TOTAL
WISCONSIN (CONT'D)				
538	Lancaster	96.7	92.5	94.8
539	Portage	95.3	96.6	95.9
540	New Richmond	96.8	94.6	95.9
541-543	Green Bay	101.2	93.4	97.8
544	Wausau	96.2	93.5	95.0
545	Rhinelander	99.3	91.2	95.8
546	La Crosse	97.8	94.5	96.3
547	Eau Claire	99.3	95.3	97.5
548	Superior	96.6	96.3	96.5
549	Oshkosh	96.9	91.9	94.7
WYOMING				
820	Cheyenne	101.5	65.2	85.7
821	Yellowstone Nat'l Park	99.3	66.3	84.9
822	Wheatland	100.4	64.3	84.7
823	Rawlins	101.8	66.9	86.6
824	Worland	100.0	65.3	84.9
825	Riverton	101.0	65.4	85.5
826	Casper	102.0	63.9	85.4
827	Newcastle	99.9	66.9	85.5
828	Sheridan	102.6	64.3	85.9
829-831	Rock Springs	103.7	65.3	87.0
CANADIAN FACTORS (reflect Canadian currency)				
ALBERTA				
	Calgary	123.5	95.7	111.4
	Edmonton	123.1	95.7	111.2
	Fort McMurray	123.6	92.8	110.2
	Lethbridge	118.4	92.2	107.0
	Lloydminster	113.4	88.9	102.8
	Medicine Hat	113.6	88.2	102.5
	Red Deer	114.1	88.2	102.8
BRITISH COLUMBIA				
	Kamloops	114.5	90.6	104.1
	Prince George	115.4	89.9	104.3
	Vancouver	119.5	89.1	106.2
	Victoria	115.7	87.2	103.3
MANITOBA				
	Brandon	125.2	75.8	103.7
	Portage la Prairie	113.4	74.2	96.3
	Winnipeg	121.0	71.8	99.5
NEW BRUNSWICK				
	Bathurst	111.5	67.3	92.2
	Dalhousie	111.9	67.5	92.5
	Fredericton	117.4	72.5	97.9
	Moncton	111.8	70.1	93.6
	Newcastle	111.6	67.9	92.5
	St. John	114.0	77.9	98.3
NEWFOUNDLAND				
	Corner Brook	129.6	67.6	102.6
	St Johns	122.7	85.2	106.4
NORTHWEST TERRITORIES				
	Yellowknife	135.3	84.2	113.0
NOVA SCOTIA				
	Bridgewater	112.9	74.6	96.2
	Dartmouth	126.1	74.6	103.7
	Halifax	119.6	80.9	102.7
	New Glasgow	124.1	74.6	102.5
	Sydney	122.1	74.6	101.4
	Truro	112.5	74.6	96.0
	Yarmouth	124.0	74.6	102.5
ONTARIO				
	Barrie	117.7	93.0	106.9
	Brantford	114.9	96.9	107.1
	Cornwall	115.0	93.3	105.5
	Hamilton	117.0	96.7	108.2
	Kingston	116.0	93.4	106.2
	Kitchener	109.6	92.9	102.3
	London	116.4	93.3	106.3
	North Bay	127.3	91.1	111.5
	Oshawa	112.3	94.3	104.4
	Ottawa	117.3	94.0	107.2
	Owen Sound	117.8	91.2	106.2
	Peterborough	114.9	93.1	105.4
	Sarnia	114.8	97.5	107.3
	Sault Ste Marie	110.3	92.1	102.3

795

Location Factors

STATE/ZIP	CITY	MAT.	INST.	TOTAL
ONTARIO (CONT'D)				
	St. Catharines	107.6	94.5	101.9
	Sudbury	107.7	93.0	101.3
	Thunder Bay	108.8	93.4	102.1
	Timmins	115.1	91.1	104.6
	Toronto	118.3	101.3	110.9
	Windsor	108.2	93.4	101.7
PRINCE EDWARD ISLAND				
	Charlottetown	120.0	62.8	95.1
	Summerside	126.7	62.8	98.8
QUEBEC				
	Cap-de-la-Madeleine	112.4	87.6	101.6
	Charlesbourg	112.4	87.6	101.6
	Chicoutimi	111.4	92.9	103.3
	Gatineau	112.1	87.4	101.3
	Granby	112.3	87.4	101.4
	Hull	112.2	87.4	101.4
	Joliette	112.5	87.6	101.7
	Laval	112.1	87.4	101.3
	Montreal	117.8	93.2	107.1
	Quebec	117.1	93.6	106.8
	Rimouski	111.8	92.9	103.6
	Rouyn-Noranda	112.0	87.4	101.3
	Saint Hyacinthe	111.6	87.4	101.1
	Sherbrooke	112.4	87.4	101.5
	Sorel	112.5	87.6	101.7
	St Jerome	112.1	87.4	101.3
	Trois Rivieres	124.8	87.6	108.6
SASKATCHEWAN				
	Moose Jaw	110.7	69.5	92.7
	Prince Albert	109.9	67.7	91.5
	Regina	120.7	89.0	106.9
	Saskatoon	111.1	89.1	101.5
YUKON				
	Whitehorse	135.3	68.5	106.2

R011105-05   Tips for Accurate Estimating

1. Use pre-printed or columnar forms for orderly sequence of dimensions and locations and for recording telephone quotations.

2. Use only the front side of each paper or form except for certain pre-printed summary forms.

3. Be consistent in listing dimensions: For example, length x width x height. This helps in rechecking to ensure that, the total length of partitions is appropriate for the building area.

4. Use printed (rather than measured) dimensions where given.

5. Add up multiple printed dimensions for a single entry where possible.

6. Measure all other dimensions carefully.

7. Use each set of dimensions to calculate multiple related quantities.

8. Convert foot and inch measurements to decimal feet when listing. Memorize decimal equivalents to .01 parts of a foot (1/8″ equals approximately .01′).

9. Do not "round off" quantities until the final summary.

10. Mark drawings with different colors as items are taken off.

11. Keep similar items together, different items separate.

12. Identify location and drawing numbers to aid in future checking for completeness.

13. Measure or list everything on the drawings or mentioned in the specifications.

14. It may be necessary to list items not called for to make the job complete.

15. Be alert for: Notes on plans such as N.T.S. (not to scale); changes in scale throughout the drawings; reduced size drawings; discrepancies between the specifications and the drawings.

16. Develop a consistent pattern of performing an estimate. For example:
    a. Start the quantity takeoff at the lower floor and move to the next higher floor.
    b. Proceed from the main section of the building to the wings.
    c. Proceed from south to north or vice versa, clockwise or counterclockwise.
    d. Take off floor plan quantities first, elevations next, then detail drawings.

17. List all gross dimensions that can be either used again for different quantities, or used as a rough check of other quantities for verification (exterior perimeter, gross floor area, individual floor areas, etc.).

18. Utilize design symmetry or repetition (repetitive floors, repetitive wings, symmetrical design around a center line, similar room layouts, etc.). Note: Extreme caution is needed here so as not to omit or duplicate an area.

19. Do not convert units until the final total is obtained. For instance, when estimating concrete work, keep all units to the nearest cubic foot, then summarize and convert to cubic yards.

20. When figuring alternatives, it is best to total all items involved in the basic system, then total all items involved in the alternates. Therefore you work with positive numbers in all cases. When adds and deducts are used, it is often confusing whether to add or subtract a portion of an item; especially on a complicated or involved alternate.

R011105-50 Metric Conversion Factors

Description: This table is primarily for converting customary U.S. units in the left hand column to SI metric units in the right hand column. In addition, conversion factors for some commonly encountered Canadian and non-SI metric units are included.

If You Know		Multiply By		To Find
Length				
Inches	x	25.4[a]	=	Millimeters
Feet	x	0.3048[a]	=	Meters
Yards	x	0.9144[a]	=	Meters
Miles (statute)	x	1.609	=	Kilometers
Area				
Square inches	x	645.2	=	Square millimeters
Square feet	x	0.0929	=	Square meters
Square yards	x	0.8361	=	Square meters
Volume (Capacity)				
Cubic inches	x	16,387	=	Cubic millimeters
Cubic feet	x	0.02832	=	Cubic meters
Cubic yards	x	0.7646	=	Cubic meters
Gallons (U.S. liquids)[b]	x	0.003785	=	Cubic meters[c]
Gallons (Canadian liquid)[b]	x	0.004546	=	Cubic meters[c]
Ounces (U.S. liquid)[b]	x	29.57	=	Milliliters[c, d]
Quarts (U.S. liquid)[b]	x	0.9464	=	Liters[c, d]
Gallons (U.S. liquid)[b]	x	3.785	=	Liters[c, d]
Force				
Kilograms force[d]	x	9.807	=	Newtons
Pounds force	x	4.448	=	Newtons
Pounds force	x	0.4536	=	Kilograms force[d]
Kips	x	4448	=	Newtons
Kips	x	453.6	=	Kilograms force[d]
Pressure, Stress, Strength (Force per unit area)				
Kilograms force per square centimeter[d]	x	0.09807	=	Megapascals
Pounds force per square inch (psi)	x	0.006895	=	Megapascals
Kips per square inch	x	6.895	=	Megapascals
Pounds force per square inch (psi)	x	0.07031	=	Kilograms force per square centimeter[d]
Pounds force per square foot	x	47.88	=	Pascals
Pounds force per square foot	x	4.882	=	Kilograms force per square meter[d]
Bending Moment Or Torque				
Inch-pounds force	x	0.01152	=	Meter-kilograms force[d]
Inch-pounds force	x	0.1130	=	Newton-meters
Foot-pounds force	x	0.1383	=	Meter-kilograms force[d]
Foot-pounds force	x	1.356	=	Newton-meters
Meter-kilograms force[d]	x	9.807	=	Newton-meters
Mass				
Ounces (avoirdupois)	x	28.35	=	Grams
Pounds (avoirdupois)	x	0.4536	=	Kilograms
Tons (metric)	x	1000	=	Kilograms
Tons, short (2000 pounds)	x	907.2	=	Kilograms
Tons, short (2000 pounds)	x	0.9072	=	Megagrams[e]
Mass per Unit Volume				
Pounds mass per cubic foot	x	16.02	=	Kilograms per cubic meter
Pounds mass per cubic yard	x	0.5933	=	Kilograms per cubic meter
Pounds mass per gallon (U.S. liquid)[b]	x	119.8	=	Kilograms per cubic meter
Pounds mass per gallon (Canadian liquid)[b]	x	99.78	=	Kilograms per cubic meter
Temperature				
Degrees Fahrenheit	(F-32)/1.8		=	Degrees Celsius
Degrees Fahrenheit	(F+459.67)/1.8		=	Degrees Kelvin
Degrees Celsius	C+273.15		=	Degrees Kelvin

[a]The factor given is exact
[b]One U.S. gallon = 0.8327 Canadian gallon
[c]1 liter = 1000 milliliters = 1000 cubic centimeters
  1 cubic decimeter = 0.001 cubic meter

[d]Metric but not SI unit
[e]Called "tonne" in England and "metric ton" in other metric countries

For customer support on your Site Work & Landscape Cost Data, call 877.737.1594.

R011105-60 Weights and Measures

Measures of Length
1 Mile = 1760 Yards = 5280 Feet
1 Yard = 3 Feet = 36 inches
1 Foot = 12 Inches
1 Mil = 0.001 Inch
1 Fathom = 2 Yards = 6 Feet
1 Rod = 5.5 Yards = 16.5 Feet
1 Hand = 4 Inches
1 Span = 9 Inches
1 Micro-inch = One Millionth Inch or 0.000001 Inch
1 Micron = One Millionth Meter + 0.00003937 Inch

Surveyor's Measure
1 Mile = 8 Furlongs = 80 Chains
1 Furlong = 10 Chains = 220 Yards
1 Chain = 4 Rods = 22 Yards = 66 Feet = 100 Links
1 Link = 7.92 Inches

Square Measure
1 Square Mile = 640 Acres = 6400 Square Chains
1 Acre = 10 Square Chains = 4840 Square Yards = 43,560 Sq. Ft.
1 Square Chain = 16 Square Rods = 484 Square Yards = 4356 Sq. Ft.
1 Square Rod = 30.25 Square Yards = 272.25 Square Feet = 625 Square Lines
1 Square Yard = 9 Square Feet
1 Square Foot = 144 Square Inches
An Acre equals a Square 208.7 Feet per Side

Cubic Measure
1 Cubic Yard = 27 Cubic Feet
1 Cubic Foot = 1728 Cubic Inches
1 Cord of Wood = 4 x 4 x 8 Feet = 128 Cubic Feet
1 Perch of Masonry = 16½ x 1½ x 1 Foot = 24.75 Cubic Feet

Avoirdupois or Commercial Weight
1 Gross or Long Ton = 2240 Pounds
1 Net or Short ton = 2000 Pounds
1 Pound = 16 Ounces = 7000 Grains
1 Ounce = 16 Drachms = 437.5 Grains
1 Stone = 14 Pounds

Shipping Measure
For Measuring Internal Capacity of a Vessel:
 1 Register Ton = 100 Cubic Feet

For Measurement of Cargo:
 Approximately 40 Cubic Feet of Merchandise is considered a Shipping Ton, unless that bulk would weigh more than 2000 Pounds, in which case Freight Charge may be based upon weight.

40 Cubic Feet = 32.143 U.S. Bushels = 31.16 Imp. Bushels

Liquid Measure
1 Imperial Gallon = 1.2009 U.S. Gallon = 277.42 Cu. In.
1 Cubic Foot = 7.48 U.S. Gallons

R011110-10 Architectural Fees

Tabulated below are typical percentage fees by project size, for good professional architectural service. Fees may vary from those listed depending upon degree of design difficulty and economic conditions in any particular area.

Rates can be interpolated horizontally and vertically. Various portions of the same project requiring different rates should be adjusted proportionately. For alterations, add 50% to the fee for the first $500,000 of project cost and add 25% to the fee for project cost over $500,000.

Architectural fees tabulated below include Structural, Mechanical and Electrical Engineering Fees. They do not include the fees for special consultants such as kitchen planning, security, acoustical, interior design, etc.

Civil Engineering fees are included in the Architectural fee for project sites requiring minimal design such as city sites. However, separate Civil Engineering fees must be added when utility connections require design, drainage calculations are needed, stepped foundations are required, or provisions are required to protect adjacent wetlands.

Building Types	Total Project Size in Thousands of Dollars						
	100	250	500	1,000	5,000	10,000	50,000
Factories, garages, warehouses, repetitive housing	9.0%	8.0%	7.0%	6.2%	5.3%	4.9%	4.5%
Apartments, banks, schools, libraries, offices, municipal buildings	12.2	12.3	9.2	8.0	7.0	6.6	6.2
Churches, hospitals, homes, laboratories, museums, research	15.0	13.6	12.7	11.9	9.5	8.8	8.0
Memorials, monumental work, decorative furnishings	—	16.0	14.5	13.1	10.0	9.0	8.3

Reference Tables

R011110-30 Engineering Fees

Typical **Structural Engineering Fees** based on type of construction and total project size. These fees are included in Architectural Fees.

Type of Construction	Total Project Size (in thousands of dollars)			
	$500	$500-$1,000	$1,000-$5,000	Over $5000
Industrial buildings, factories & warehouses	Technical payroll times 2.0 to 2.5	1.60%	1.25%	1.00%
Hotels, apartments, offices, dormitories, hospitals, public buildings, food stores		2.00%	1.70%	1.20%
Museums, banks, churches and cathedrals		2.00%	1.75%	1.25%
Thin shells, prestressed concrete, earthquake resistive		2.00%	1.75%	1.50%
Parking ramps, auditoriums, stadiums, convention halls, hangars & boiler houses		2.50%	2.00%	1.75%
Special buildings, major alterations, underpinning & future expansion		Add to above 0.5%	Add to above 0.5%	Add to above 0.5%

For complex reinforced concrete or unusually complicated structures, add 20% to 50%.

Typical **Mechanical and Electrical Engineering Fees** are based on the size of the subcontract. The fee structure for both are shown below. These fees are included in Architectural Fees.

Type of Construction	Subcontract Size							
	$25,000	$50,000	$100,000	$225,000	$350,000	$500,000	$750,000	$1,000,000
Simple structures	6.4%	5.7%	4.8%	4.5%	4.4%	4.3%	4.2%	4.1%
Intermediate structures	8.0	7.3	6.5	5.6	5.1	5.0	4.9	4.8
Complex structures	10.1	9.0	9.0	8.0	7.5	7.5	7.0	7.0

For renovations, add 15% to 25% to applicable fee.

R012909-80   Sales Tax by State

State sales tax on materials is tabulated below (5 states have no sales tax). Many states allow local jurisdictions, such as a county or city, to levy additional sales tax.

Some projects may be sales tax exempt, particularly those constructed with public funds.

State	Tax (%)	State	Tax (%)	State	Tax (%)	State	Tax (%)
Alabama	4	Illinois	6.25	Montana	0	Rhode Island	7
Alaska	0	Indiana	7	Nebraska	5.5	South Carolina	6
Arizona	5.6	Iowa	6	Nevada	6.85	South Dakota	4
Arkansas	6	Kansas	6.3	New Hampshire	0	Tennessee	7
California	7.5	Kentucky	6	New Jersey	7	Texas	6.25
Colorado	2.9	Louisiana	4	New Mexico	5.13	Utah	4.7
Connecticut	6.35	Maine	5	New York	4	Vermont	6
Delaware	0	Maryland	6	North Carolina	4.75	Virginia	5
District of Columbia	6	Massachusetts	6.25	North Dakota	5	Washington	6.5
Florida	6	Michigan	6	Ohio	5.5	West Virginia	6
Georgia	4	Minnesota	6.88	Oklahoma	4.5	Wisconsin	5
Hawaii	4	Mississippi	7	Oregon	0	Wyoming	4
Idaho	6	Missouri	4.23	Pennsylvania	6	Average	5.04 %

Sales Tax by Province (Canada)

GST - a value-added tax, which the government imposes on most goods and services provided in or imported into Canada. PST - a retail sales tax, which three of the provinces impose on the price of most goods and some

services. QST - a value-added tax, similar to the federal GST, which Quebec imposes. HST - Five provinces have combined their retail sales tax with the federal GST into one harmonized tax.

Province	PST (%)	QST (%)	GST(%)	HST(%)
Alberta	0	0	5	0
British Columbia	7	0	5	0
Manitoba	8	0	5	0
New Brunswick	0	0	0	13
Newfoundland	0	0	0	13
Northwest Territories	0	0	5	0
Nova Scotia	0	0	0	15
Ontario	0	0	0	13
Prince Edward Island	0	0	0	14
Quebec	0	9.975	5	0
Saskatchewan	5	0	5	0
Yukon	0	0	5	0

R012909-85   Unemployment Taxes and Social Security Taxes

State unemployment tax rates vary not only from state to state, but also with the experience rating of the contractor. The federal unemployment tax rate is 6.0% of the first $7,000 of wages. This is reduced by a credit of up to 5.4% for timely payment to the state. The minimum federal unemployment tax is 0.6% after all credits.

Social security (FICA) for 2015 is estimated at time of publication to be 7.65% of wages up to $117,000.

801

General Requirements — R0129 Payment Procedures

R012909-90   Overtime

One way to improve the completion date of a project or eliminate negative float from a schedule is to compress activity duration times. This can be achieved by increasing the crew size or working overtime with the proposed crew.

To determine the costs of working overtime to compress activity duration times, consider the following examples. Below is an overtime efficiency and cost chart based on a five, six, or seven day week with an eight through twelve hour day. Payroll percentage increases for time and one half and double time are shown for the various working days.

Days per Week	Hours per Day	Production Efficiency					Payroll Cost Factors	
		1st Week	2nd Week	3rd Week	4th Week	Average 4 Weeks	@ 1-1/2 Times	@ 2 Times
5	8	100%	100%	100%	100%	100 %	1.000	1.000
	9	100	100	95	90	96	1.056	1.111
	10	100	95	90	85	93	1.100	1.200
	11	95	90	75	65	81	1.136	1.273
	12	90	85	70	60	76	1.167	1.333
6	8	100	100	95	90	96	1.083	1.167
	9	100	95	90	85	93	1.130	1.259
	10	95	90	85	80	88	1.167	1.333
	11	95	85	70	65	79	1.197	1.394
	12	90	80	65	60	74	1.222	1.444
7	8	100	95	85	75	89	1.143	1.286
	9	95	90	80	70	84	1.183	1.365
	10	90	85	75	65	79	1.214	1.429
	11	85	80	65	60	73	1.240	1.481
	12	85	75	60	55	69	1.262	1.524

General Requirements — R0131 Project Management & Coordination

R013113-40   Builder's Risk Insurance

Builder's Risk Insurance is insurance on a building during construction. Premiums are paid by the owner or the contractor. Blasting, collapse and underground insurance would raise total insurance costs above those listed. Floater policy for materials delivered to the job runs $.75 to $1.25 per $100 value. Contractor equipment insurance runs $.50 to $1.50 per $100 value. Insurance for miscellaneous tools to $1,500 value runs from $3.00 to $7.50 per $100 value.

Tabulated below are New England Builder's Risk insurance rates in dollars per $100 value for $1,000 deductible. For $25,000 deductible, rates can be reduced 13% to 34%. On contracts over $1,000,000, rates may be lower than those tabulated. Policies are written annually for the total completed value in place. For "all risk" insurance (excluding flood, earthquake and certain other perils) add $.025 to total rates below.

Coverage	Frame Construction (Class 1)		Average	Brick Construction (Class 4)		Average	Fire Resistive (Class 6)		Average
	Range			Range			Range		
Fire Insurance	$.350 to	$ .850	$.600	$.158 to	$.189	$.174	$.052 to	$.080	$.070
Extended Coverage	.115 to	.200	.158	.080 to	.105	.101	.081 to	.105	.100
Vandalism	.012 to	.016	.014	.008 to	.011	.011	.008 to	.011	.010
Total Annual Rate	$.477 to	$1.066	$.772	$.246 to	$.305	$.286	$.141 to	$.196	$.180

R013113-50   General Contractor's Overhead

There are two distinct types of overhead on a construction project: Project Overhead and Main Office Overhead. Project Overhead includes those costs at a construction site not directly associated with the installation of construction materials. Examples of Project Overhead costs include the following:

1. Superintendent
2. Construction office and storage trailers
3. Temporary sanitary facilities
4. Temporary utilities
5. Security fencing
6. Photographs
7. Clean up
8. Performance and payment bonds

The above Project Overhead items are also referred to as General Requirements and therefore are estimated in Division 1. Division 1 is the first division listed in the CSI MasterFormat but it is usually the last division estimated. The sum of the costs in Divisions 1 through 49 is referred to as the sum of the direct costs.

All construction projects also include indirect costs. The primary components of indirect costs are the contractor's Main Office Overhead and profit. The amount of the Main Office Overhead expense varies depending on the following:

1. Owner's compensation
2. Project managers and estimator's wages
3. Clerical support wages
4. Office rent and utilities
5. Corporate legal and accounting costs
6. Advertising
7. Automobile expenses
8. Association dues
9. Travel and entertainment expenses

These costs are usually calculated as a percentage of annual sales volume. This percentage can range from 35% for a small contractor doing less than $500,000 to 5% for a large contractor with sales in excess of $100 million.

R013113-60   Workers' Compensation Insurance Rates by Trade

The table below tabulates the national averages for workers' compensation insurance rates by trade and type of building. The average "Insurance Rate" is multiplied by the "% of Building Cost" for each trade. This produces the "Workers' Compensation" cost by % of total labor cost, to be added for each trade by building type to determine the weighted average workers' compensation rate for the building types analyzed.

Trade	Insurance Rate (% Labor Cost) Range		Average	% of Building Cost Office Bldgs.	Schools & Apts.	Mfg.	Workers' Compensation Office Bldgs.	Schools & Apts.	Mfg.
Excavation, Grading, etc.	3.4 % to	21.2%	9.7%	4.8%	4.9%	4.5%	0.47%	0.48%	0.44%
Piles & Foundations	6.1 to	28.3	14.3	7.1	5.2	8.7	1.02	0.74	1.24
Concrete	4.2 to	35.8	12.9	5.0	14.8	3.7	0.65	1.91	0.48
Masonry	4.9 to	36.4	13.7	6.9	7.5	1.9	0.95	1.03	0.26
Structural Steel	6.1 to	101.1	31.7	10.7	3.9	17.6	3.39	1.24	5.58
Miscellaneous & Ornamental Metals	4.3 to	31.5	12.2	2.8	4.0	3.6	0.34	0.49	0.44
Carpentry & Millwork	5.0 to	36.8	14.9	3.7	4.0	0.5	0.55	0.60	0.07
Metal or Composition Siding	6.1 to	69.2	18.4	2.3	0.3	4.3	0.42	0.06	0.79
Roofing	6.1 to	100.3	31.7	2.3	2.6	3.1	0.73	0.82	0.98
Doors & Hardware	4.1 to	36.8	11.3	0.9	1.4	0.4	0.10	0.16	0.05
Sash & Glazing	4.8 to	30.7	13.3	3.5	4.0	1.0	0.47	0.53	0.13
Lath & Plaster	3.1 to	36.2	10.9	3.3	6.9	0.8	0.36	0.75	0.09
Tile, Marble & Floors	3 to	24.8	8.9	2.6	3.0	0.5	0.23	0.27	0.04
Acoustical Ceilings	3.8 to	33.8	8.4	2.4	0.2	0.3	0.20	0.02	0.03
Painting	4.5 to	36.1	11.7	1.5	1.6	1.6	0.18	0.19	0.19
Interior Partitions	5.0 to	36.8	14.9	3.9	4.3	4.4	0.58	0.64	0.66
Miscellaneous Items	2.5 to	132.3	13.4	5.2	3.7	9.7	0.70	0.50	1.30
Elevators	1.3 to	12.8	5.3	2.1	1.1	2.2	0.11	0.06	0.12
Sprinklers	2.9 to	18.5	7.3	0.5	—	2.0	0.04	—	0.15
Plumbing	2.2 to	19.3	7.0	4.9	7.2	5.2	0.34	0.50	0.36
Heat., Vent., Air Conditioning	3.8 to	18.1	8.8	13.5	11.0	12.9	1.19	0.97	1.14
Electrical	2.4 to	13.5	5.8	10.1	8.4	11.1	0.59	0.49	0.64
Total	1.3 % to	132.3%	—	100.0%	100.0%	100.0%	13.61%	12.45%	15.18%
				Overall Weighted Average	13.75%				

Workers' Compensation Insurance Rates by States

The table below lists the weighted average workers' compensation base rate for each state with a factor comparing this with the national average of 13.5%.

State	Weighted Average	Factor	State	Weighted Average	Factor	State	Weighted Average	Factor
Alabama	20.6%	153	Kentucky	12.5%	93	North Dakota	8.1%	60
Alaska	12.5	93	Louisiana	19.6	145	Ohio	8.1	60
Arizona	13.8	102	Maine	11.4	84	Oklahoma	10.3	76
Arkansas	7.7	57	Maryland	13.5	100	Oregon	11.3	84
California	27.1	201	Massachusetts	11.5	85	Pennsylvania	18.3	136
Colorado	7.3	54	Michigan	13.5	100	Rhode Island	14.7	109
Connecticut	25.9	192	Minnesota	22.8	169	South Carolina	16.9	125
Delaware	14.0	104	Mississippi	14.0	104	South Dakota	14.1	104
District of Columbia	10.4	77	Missouri	13.9	103	Tennessee	12.2	90
Florida	10.8	80	Montana	8.3	61	Texas	9.3	69
Georgia	29.5	219	Nebraska	17.0	126	Utah	8.8	65
Hawaii	8.7	64	Nevada	9.2	68	Vermont	13.3	99
Idaho	10.5	78	New Hampshire	18.8	139	Virginia	8.7	64
Illinois	26.9	199	New Jersey	15.7	116	Washington	9.5	70
Indiana	5.0	37	New Mexico	15.3	113	West Virginia	7.4	55
Iowa	15.5	115	New York	19.0	141	Wisconsin	13.2	98
Kansas	9.2	68	North Carolina	17.3	128	Wyoming	6.5	48
			Weighted Average for U.S. is	13.7% of payroll = 100%				

The weighted average skilled worker rate for 35 trades is 13.5%. For bidding purposes, apply the full value of workers' compensation directly to total labor costs, or if labor is 38%, materials 42% and overhead and profit 20% of total cost, carry 38/80 × 13.5% =6.4% of cost (before overhead and profit)

into overhead. Rates vary not only from state to state but also with the experience rating of the contractor.

Rates are the most current available at the time of publication.

R015423-10   Steel Tubular Scaffolding

On new construction, tubular scaffolding is efficient up to 60' high or five stories. Above this it is usually better to use a hung scaffolding if construction permits. Swing scaffolding operations may interfere with tenants. In this case, the tubular is more practical at all heights.

In repairing or cleaning the front of an existing building the cost of tubular scaffolding per S.F. of building front increases as the height increases above the first tier. The first tier cost is relatively high due to leveling and alignment.

The minimum efficient crew for erecting and dismantling is three workers. They can set up and remove 18 frame sections per day up to 5 stories high. For 6 to 12 stories high, a crew of four is most efficient. Use two or more on top and two on the bottom for handing up or hoisting. They can

also set up and remove 18 frame sections per day. At 7' horizontal spacing, this will run about 800 S.F. per day of erecting and dismantling. Time for placing and removing planks must be added to the above. A crew of three can place and remove 72 planks per day up to 5 stories. For over 5 stories, a crew of four can place and remove 80 planks per day.

The table below shows the number of pieces required to erect tubular steel scaffolding for 1000 S.F. of building frontage. This area is made up of a scaffolding system that is 12 frames (11 bays) long by 2 frames high.

For jobs under twenty-five frames, add 50% to rental cost. Rental rates will be lower for jobs over three months duration. Large quantities for long periods can reduce rental rates by 20%.

Description of Component	Number of Pieces for 1000 S.F. of Building Front	Unit
5' Wide Standard Frame, 6'-4" High	24	Ea.
Leveling Jack & Plate	24	
Cross Brace	44	
Side Arm Bracket, 21"	12	
Guardrail Post	12	
Guardrail, 7' section	22	
Stairway Section	2	
Stairway Starter Bar	1	
Stairway Inside Handrail	2	
Stairway Outside Handrail	2	
Walk-Thru Frame Guardrail	2	↓

Scaffolding is often used as falsework over 15' high during construction of cast-in-place concrete beams and slabs. Two foot wide scaffolding is generally used for heavy beam construction. The span between frames depends upon the load to be carried with a maximum span of 5'.

Heavy duty shoring frames with a capacity of 10,000#/leg can be spaced up to 10' O.C. depending upon form support design and loading.

Scaffolding used as horizontal shoring requires less than half the material required with conventional shoring.

On new construction, erection is done by carpenters.

Rolling towers supporting horizontal shores can reduce labor and speed the job. For maintenance work, catwalks with spans up to 70' can be supported by the rolling towers.

805

R015433-10   Contractor Equipment

Rental Rates shown elsewhere in the book pertain to late model high quality machines in excellent working condition, rented from equipment dealers. Rental rates from contractors may be substantially lower than the rental rates from equipment dealers depending upon economic conditions; for older, less productive machines, reduce rates by a maximum of 15%. Any overtime must be added to the base rates. For shift work, rates are lower. Usual rule of thumb is 150% of one shift rate for two shifts; 200% for three shifts.

For periods of less than one week, operated equipment is usually more economical to rent than renting bare equipment and hiring an operator.

Costs to move equipment to a job site (mobilization) or from a job site (demobilization) are not included in rental rates, nor in any Equipment costs on any Unit Price line items or crew listings. These costs can be found elsewhere. If a piece of equipment is already at a job site, it is not appropriate to utilize mob/demob costs in an estimate again.

Rental rates vary throughout the country with larger cities generally having lower rates. Lease plans for new equipment are available for periods in excess of six months with a percentage of payments applying toward purchase.

Rental rates can also be treated as reimbursement costs for contractor-owned equipment. Owned equipment costs include depreciation, loan payments, interest, taxes, insurance, storage, and major repairs.

Monthly rental rates vary from 2% to 5% of the cost of the equipment depending on the anticipated life of the equipment and its wearing parts. Weekly rates are about 1/3 the monthly rates and daily rental rates about 1/3 the weekly rate.

The hourly operating costs for each piece of equipment include costs to the user such as fuel, oil, lubrication, normal expendables for the equipment, and a percentage of mechanic's wages chargeable to maintenance. The hourly operating costs listed do not include the operator's wages.

The daily cost for equipment used in the standard crews is figured by dividing the weekly rate by five, then adding eight times the hourly operating cost to give the total daily equipment cost, not including the operator. This figure is in the right hand column of the Equipment listings under Equipment Cost/Day.

Pile Driving rates shown for pile hammer and extractor do not include leads, crane, boiler or compressor. Vibratory pile driving requires an added field specialist during set-up and pile driving operation for the electric model. The hydraulic model requires a field specialist for set-up only. Up to 125 reuses of sheet piling are possible using vibratory drivers. For normal conditions, crane capacity for hammer type and size are as follows.

Crane Capacity	Hammer Type and Size		
	Air or Steam	Diesel	Vibratory
25 ton	to 8,750 ft.-lb.		70 H.P.
40 ton	15,000 ft.-lb.	to 32,000 ft.-lb.	170 H.P.
60 ton	25,000 ft.-lb.		300 H.P.
100 ton		112,000 ft.-lb.	

Cranes should be specified for the job by size, building and site characteristics, availability, performance characteristics, and duration of time required.

Backhoes & Shovels rent for about the same as equivalent size cranes but maintenance and operating expense is higher. Crane operators rate must be adjusted for high boom heights. Average adjustments: for 150' boom add 2% per hour; over 185', add 4% per hour; over 210', add 6% per hour; over 250', add 8% per hour and over 295', add 12% per hour.

Tower Cranes of the climbing or static type have jibs from 50' to 200' and capacities at maximum reach range from 4,000 to 14,000 pounds. Lifting capacities increase up to maximum load as the hook radius decreases.

Typical rental rates, based on purchase price are about 2% to 3% per month.

Erection and dismantling runs between 500 and 2000 labor hours. Climbing operation takes 10 labor hours per 20' climb. Crane dead time is about 5 hours per 40' climb. If crane is bolted to side of the building add cost of ties and extra mast sections. Climbing cranes have from 80' to 180' of mast while static cranes have 80' to 800' of mast.

Truck Cranes can be converted to tower cranes by using tower attachments. Mast heights over 400' have been used.

A single 100' high material **Hoist and Tower** can be erected and dismantled in about 400 labor hours; a double 100' high hoist and tower in about 600 labor hours. Erection times for additional heights are 3 and 4 labor hours per vertical foot respectively up to 150', and 4 to 5 labor hours per vertical foot over 150' high. A 40' high portable Buck hoist takes about 160 labor hours to erect and dismantle. Additional heights take 2 labor hours per vertical foot to 80' and 3 labor hours per vertical foot for the next 100'. Most material hoists do not meet local code requirements for carrying personnel.

A 150' high **Personnel Hoist** requires about 500 to 800 labor hours to erect and dismantle. Budget erection time at 5 labor hours per vertical foot for all trades. Local code requirements or labor scarcity requiring overtime can add up to 50% to any of the above erection costs.

Earthmoving Equipment: The selection of earthmoving equipment depends upon the type and quantity of material, moisture content, haul distance, haul road, time available, and equipment available. Short haul cut and fill operations may require dozers only, while another operation may require excavators, a fleet of trucks, and spreading and compaction equipment. Stockpiled material and granular material are easily excavated with front end loaders. Scrapers are most economically used with hauls between 300' and 1-1/2 miles if adequate haul roads can be maintained. Shovels are often used for blasted rock and any material where a vertical face of 8' or more can be excavated. Special conditions may dictate the use of draglines, clamshells, or backhoes. Spreading and compaction equipment must be matched to the soil characteristics, the compaction required and the rate the fill is being supplied.

R015433-15   Heavy Lifting

Hydraulic Climbing Jacks

The use of hydraulic heavy lift systems is an alternative to conventional type crane equipment. The lifting, lowering, pushing, or pulling mechanism is a hydraulic climbing jack moving on a square steel jackrod from 1-5/8" to 4" square, or a steel cable. The jackrod or cable can be vertical or horizontal, stationary or movable, depending on the individual application. When the jackrod is stationary, the climbing jack will climb the rod and push or pull the load along with itself. When the climbing jack is stationary, the jackrod is movable with the load attached to the end and the climbing jack will lift or lower the jackrod with the attached load. The heavy lift system is normally operated by a single control lever located at the hydraulic pump.

The system is flexible in that one or more climbing jacks can be applied wherever a load support point is required, and the rate of lift synchronized.

Economic benefits have been demonstrated on projects such as: erection of ground assembled roofs and floors, complete bridge spans, girders and trusses, towers, chimney liners and steel vessels, storage tanks, and heavy machinery. Other uses are raising and lowering offshore work platforms, caissons, tunnel sections and pipelines.

R015436-50   Mobilization

Costs to move rented construction equipment to a job site from an equipment dealer's or contractor's yard (mobilization), or to move the equipment off the job site (demobilization), are not included in the rental or operating rates, nor in the equipment cost on a unit price line or in a crew listing. These costs can be found consolidated in the Mobilization section of the data and elsewhere in particular site work sections. If a piece of

equipment is already on the job site, it is not appropriate to include mob/demob costs in a new estimate that requires use of that equipment. The following table identifies approximate sizes of rented construction equipment that would be hauled on a towed trailer. Because this listing is not all-encompassing, the user can infer as to what size trailer might be required for a piece of equipment not listed.

3-ton Trailer	20-ton Trailer	40-ton Trailer	50-ton Trailer
20 H.P. Excavator	110 H.P. Excavator	200 H.P. Excavator	270 H.P. Excavator
50 H.P. Skid Steer	165 H.P. Dozer	300 H.P. Dozer	Small Crawler Crane
35 H.P. Roller	150 H.P. Roller	400 H.P. Scraper	500 H.P. Scraper
40 H.P. Trencher	Backhoe	450 H.P. Art. Dump Truck	500 H.P. Art. Dump Truck

R024119-10   Demolition Defined

Whole Building Demolition - Demolition of the whole building with no concern for any particular building element, component, or material type being demolished. This type of demolition is accomplished with large pieces of construction equipment that break up the structure, load it into trucks and haul it to a disposal site, but disposal or dump fees are not included. Demolition of below-grade foundation elements, such as footings, foundation walls, grade beams, slabs on grade, etc., is not included. Certain mechanical equipment containing flammable liquids or ozone-depleting refrigerants, electric lighting elements, communication equipment components, and other building elements may contain hazardous waste, and must be removed, either selectively or carefully, as hazardous waste before the building can be demolished.

Foundation Demolition - Demolition of below-grade foundation footings, foundation walls, grade beams, and slabs on grade. This type of demolition is accomplished by hand or pneumatic hand tools, and does not include saw cutting, or handling, loading, hauling, or disposal of the debris.

Gutting - Removal of building interior finishes and electrical/mechanical systems down to the load-bearing and sub-floor elements of the rough building frame, with no concern for any particular building element, component, or material type being demolished. This type of demolition is accomplished by hand or pneumatic hand tools, and includes loading into trucks, but not hauling, disposal or dump fees, scaffolding, or shoring. Certain mechanical equipment containing flammable liquids or ozone-depleting refrigerants, electric lighting elements, communication equipment components, and other building elements may contain hazardous waste, and must be removed, either selectively or carefully, as hazardous waste, before the building is gutted.

Selective Demolition - Demolition of a selected building element, component, or finish, with some concern for surrounding or adjacent elements, components, or finishes (see the first Subdivision (s) at the beginning of appropriate Divisions). This type of demolition is accomplished by hand or pneumatic hand tools, and does not include handling, loading,

storing, hauling, or disposal of the debris, scaffolding, or shoring. "Gutting" methods may be used in order to save time, but damage that is caused to surrounding or adjacent elements, components, or finishes may have to be repaired at a later time.

Careful Removal - Removal of a piece of service equipment, building element or component, or material type, with great concern for both the removed item and surrounding or adjacent elements, components or finishes. The purpose of careful removal may be to protect the removed item for later re-use, preserve a higher salvage value of the removed item, or replace an item while taking care to protect surrounding or adjacent elements, components, connections, or finishes from cosmetic and/or structural damage. An approximation of the time required to perform this type of removal is 1/3 to 1/2 the time it would take to install a new item of like kind. This type of removal is accomplished by hand or pneumatic hand tools, and does not include loading, hauling, or storing the removed item, scaffolding, shoring, or lifting equipment.

Cutout Demolition - Demolition of a small quantity of floor, wall, roof, or other assembly, with concern for the appearance and structural integrity of the surrounding materials. This type of demolition is accomplished by hand or pneumatic hand tools, and does not include saw cutting, handling, loading, hauling, or disposal of debris, scaffolding, or shoring.

Rubbish Handling - Work activities that involve handling, loading or hauling of debris. Generally, the cost of rubbish handling must be added to the cost of all types of demolition, with the exception of whole building demolition.

Minor Site Demolition - Demolition of site elements outside the footprint of a building. This type of demolition is accomplished by hand or pneumatic hand tools, or with larger pieces of construction equipment, and may include loading a removed item onto a truck (check the Crew for equipment used). It does not include saw cutting, hauling or disposal of debris, and, sometimes, handling or loading.

R024119-20   Dumpsters

Dumpster rental costs on construction sites are presented in two ways.

The cost per week rental includes the delivery of the dumpster; its pulling or emptying once per week, and its final removal. The assumption is made that the dumpster contractor could choose to empty a dumpster by simply bringing in an empty unit and removing the full one. These costs also include the disposal of the materials in the dumpster.

The Alternate Pricing can be used when actual planned conditions are not approximated by the weekly numbers. For example, these lines can be used when a dumpster is needed for 4 weeks and will need to be emptied 2 or 3 times per week. Conversely the Alternate Pricing lines can be used when a dumpster will be rented for several weeks or months but needs to be emptied only a few times over this period.

R024119-30   Rubbish Handling Chutes

To correctly estimate the cost of rubbish handling chute systems, the individual components must be priced separately. First choose the size of the system; a 30-inch diameter chute is quite common, but the sizes range from 18 to 36 inches in diameter. The 30-inch chute comes in a standard weight and two thinner weights. The thinner weight chutes are sometimes chosen for cost savings, but they are more easily damaged.

There are several types of major chute pieces that make up the chute system. The first component to consider is the top chute section (top intake hopper) where the material is dropped into the chute at the highest point. After determining the top chute, the intermediate chute pieces called the regular chute sections are priced. Next, the number of chute control door sections (intermediate intake hoppers) must be determined. In the more complex systems, a chute control door section is provided at each floor level. The last major component to consider is bolt down frames; these are usually provided at every other floor level.

There are a number of accessories to consider for safe operation and control. There are covers for the top chute and the chute door sections. The top

chute can have a trough that allows for better loading of the chute. For the safest operation, a chute warning light system can be added that will warn the other chute intake locations not to load while another is being used. There are dust control devices that spray a water mist to keep down the dust as the debris is loaded into a Dumpster. There are special breakaway cords that are used to prevent damage to the chute if the Dumpster is removed without disconnecting from the chute. There are chute liners that can be installed to protect the chute structure from physical damage from rough abrasive materials. Warning signs can be posted at each floor level that is provided with a chute control door section.

In summary, a complete rubbish handling chute system will include one top section, several intermediate regular sections, several intermediate control door (intake hopper) sections and bolt down frames at every other floor level starting with the top floor. If so desired, the system can also include covers and a light warning system for a safer operation. The bottom of the chute should always be above the Dumpster and should be tied off with a breakaway cord to the Dumpster.

R026510-20   Underground Storage Tank Removal

Underground Storage Tank Removal can be divided into two categories: Non-Leaking and Leaking. Prior to removing an underground storage tank, tests should be made, with the proper authorities present, to determine whether a tank has been leaking or the surrounding soil has been contaminated.

To safely remove Liquid Underground Storage Tanks:
1. Excavate to the top of the tank.
2. Disconnect all piping.
3. Open all tank vents and access ports.
4. Remove all liquids and/or sludge.
5. Purge the tank with an inert gas.
6. Provide access to the inside of the tank and clean out the interior using proper personal protective equipment (PPE).
7. Excavate soil surrounding the tank using proper PPE for on-site personnel.
8. Pull and properly dispose of the tank.
9. Clean up the site of all contaminated material.
10. Install new tanks or close the excavation.

R031113-10   Wall Form Materials

Aluminum Forms

Approximate weight is 3 lbs. per S.F.C.A. Standard widths are available from 4″ to 36″ with 36″ most common. Standard lengths of 2′, 4′, 6′ to 8′ are available. Forms are lightweight and fewer ties are needed with the wider widths. The form face is either smooth or textured.

Metal Framed Plywood Forms

Manufacturers claim over 75 reuses of plywood and over 300 reuses of steel frames. Many specials such as corners, fillers, pilasters, etc. are available. Monthly rental is generally about 15% of purchase price for first month and 9% per month thereafter with 90% of rental applied to purchase for the first month and decreasing percentages thereafter. Aluminum framed forms cost 25% to 30% more than steel framed.

After the first month, extra days may be prorated from the monthly charge. Rental rates do not include ties, accessories, cleaning, loss of hardware or freight in and out. Approximate weight is 5 lbs. per S.F. for steel; 3 lbs. per S.F. for aluminum.

Forms can be rented with option to buy.

Plywood Forms, Job Fabricated

There are two types of plywood used for concrete forms.

1. Exterior plyform which is completely waterproof. This is face oiled to facilitate stripping. Ten reuses can be expected with this type with 25 reuses possible.
2. An overlaid type consists of a resin fiber fused to exterior plyform. No oiling is required except to facilitate cleaning. This is available in both high density (HDO) and medium density overlaid (MDO). Using HDO, 50 reuses can be expected with 200 possible.

Plyform is available in 5/8″ and 3/4″ thickness. High density overlaid is available in 3/8″, 1/2″, 5/8″ and 3/4″ thickness.

5/8″ thick is sufficient for most building forms, while 3/4″ is best on heavy construction.

Plywood Forms, Modular, Prefabricated

There are many plywood forming systems without frames. Most of these are manufactured from 1-1/8″ (HDO) plywood and have some hardware attached. These are used principally for foundation walls 8′ or less high. With care and maintenance, 100 reuses can be attained with decreasing quality of surface finish.

Steel Forms

Approximate weight is 6-1/2 lbs. per S.F.C.A. including accessories. Standard widths are available from 2″ to 24″, with 24″ most common. Standard lengths are from 2′ to 8′, with 4′ the most common. Forms are easily ganged into modular units.

Forms are usually leased for 15% of the purchase price per month prorated daily over 30 days.

Rental may be applied to sale price, and usually rental forms are bought. With careful handling and cleaning 200 to 400 reuses are possible.

Straight wall gang forms up to 12′ x 20′ or 8′ x 30′ can be fabricated. These crane handled forms usually lease for approx. 9% per month.

Individual job analysis is available from the manufacturer at no charge.

R031113-30   Slipforms

The slipform method of forming may be used for forming circular silo and multi-celled storage bin type structures over 30′ high, and building core shear walls over eight stories high. The shear walls, usually enclose elevator shafts, stairwells, mechanical spaces, and toilet rooms. Reuse of the form on duplicate structures will reduce the height necessary and spread the cost of building the form. Slipform systems can be used to cast chimneys, towers, piers, dams, underground shafts or other structures capable of being extruded.

Slipforms are usually 4′ high and are raised semi-continuously by jacks climbing on rods which are embedded in the concrete. The jacks are powered by a hydraulic, pneumatic, or electric source and are available in 3, 6, and 22 ton capacities. Interior work decks and exterior scaffolds must be provided for placing inserts, embedded items, reinforcing steel, and

concrete. Scaffolds below the form for finishers may be required. The interior work decks are often used as roof slab forms on silos and bin work. Form raising rates will range from 6″ to 20″ per hour for silos; 6″ to 30″ per hour for buildings; and 6″ to 48″ per hour for shaft work.

Reinforcing bars and stressing strands are usually hoisted by crane or gin pole, and the concrete material can be hoisted by crane, winch-powered skip, or pumps. The slipform system is operated on a continuous 24-hour day when a monolithic structure is desired. For least cost, the system is operated only during normal working hours.

Placing concrete will range from 0.5 to 1.5 labor-hours per C.Y. Bucks, blockouts, keyways, weldplates, etc. are extra.

R031113-40   Forms for Reinforced Concrete

Design Economy

Avoid many sizes in proportioning beams and columns.

From story to story avoid changing column dimensions. Gain strength by adding steel or using a richer mix. If a change in size of column is necessary, vary one dimension only to minimize form alterations. Keep beams and columns the same width.

From floor to floor in a multi-story building vary beam depth, not width, as that will leave slab panel form unchanged. It is cheaper to vary the strength of a beam from floor to floor by means of steel area than by 2" changes in either width or depth.

Cost Factors

Material includes the cost of lumber, cost of rent for metal pans or forms if used, nails, form ties, form oil, bolts and accessories.

Labor includes the cost of carpenters to make up, erect, remove and repair, plus common labor to clean and move. Having carpenters remove forms minimizes repairs.

Improper alignment and condition of forms will increase finishing cost. When forms are heavily oiled, concrete surfaces must be neutralized before finishing. Special curing compounds will cause spillages to spall off in first frost. Gang forming methods will reduce costs on large projects.

Materials Used

Boards are seldom used unless their architectural finish is required. Generally, steel, fiberglass and plywood are used for contact surfaces. Labor on plywood is 10% less than with boards. The plywood is backed up with 2 x 4's at 12" to 32" O.C. Walers are generally 2 - 2 x 4's. Column forms are held together with steel yokes or bands. Shoring is with adjustable shoring or scaffolding for high ceilings.

Reuse

Floor and column forms can be reused four or possibly five times without excessive repair. Remember to allow for 10% waste on each reuse.

When modular sized wall forms are made, up to twenty uses can be expected with exterior plyform.

When forms are reused, the cost to erect, strip, clean and move will not be affected. 10% replacement of lumber should be included and about one hour of carpenter time for repairs on each reuse per 100 S.F.

The reuse cost for certain accessory items normally rented on a monthly basis will be lower than the cost for the first use.

After fifth use, new material required plus time needed for repair prevent form cost from dropping further and it may go up. Much depends on care in stripping, the number of special bays, changes in beam or column sizes and other factors.

Costs for multiple use of formwork may be developed as follows:

2 Uses	3 Uses	4 Uses
$\dfrac{\text{(1st Use + Reuse)}}{2} = \text{avg. cost/2 uses}$	$\dfrac{\text{(1st Use + 2 Reuse)}}{3} = \text{avg. cost/3 uses}$	$\dfrac{\text{(1st use + 3 Reuse)}}{4} = \text{avg. cost/4 uses}$

811

Reference Tables

Concrete | R0311 Concrete Forming

R031113-60   Formwork Labor-Hours

Item	Unit	Hours Required			Total Hours	Multiple Use		
		Fabricate	Erect & Strip	Clean & Move	1 Use	2 Use	3 Use	4 Use
Beam and Girder, interior beams, 12" wide	100 S.F.	6.4	8.3	1.3	16.0	13.3	12.4	12.0
Hung from steel beams		5.8	7.7	1.3	14.8	12.4	11.6	11.2
Beam sides only, 36" high		5.8	7.2	1.3	14.3	11.9	11.1	10.7
Beam bottoms only, 24" wide		6.6	13.0	1.3	20.9	18.1	17.2	16.7
Box out for openings		9.9	10.0	1.1	21.0	16.6	15.1	14.3
Buttress forms, to 8' high		6.0	6.5	1.2	13.7	11.2	10.4	10.0
Centering, steel, 3/4" rib lath			1.0		1.0			
3/8" rib lath or slab form	▼		0.9		0.9			
Chamfer strip or keyway	100 L.F.		1.5		1.5	1.5	1.5	1.5
Columns, fiber tube 8" diameter			20.6		20.6			
12"			21.3		21.3			
16"			22.9		22.9			
20"			23.7		23.7			
24"			24.6		24.6			
30"	▼		25.6		25.6			
Columns, round steel, 12" diameter			22.0		22.0	22.0	22.0	22.0
16"			25.6		25.6	25.6	25.6	25.6
20"			30.5		30.5	30.5	30.5	30.5
24"	▼		37.7		37.7	37.7	37.7	37.7
Columns, plywood 8" x 8"	100 S.F.	7.0	11.0	1.2	19.2	16.2	15.2	14.7
12" x 12"		6.0	10.5	1.2	17.7	15.2	14.4	14.0
16" x 16"		5.9	10.0	1.2	17.1	14.7	13.8	13.4
24" x 24"		5.8	9.8	1.2	16.8	14.4	13.6	13.2
Columns, steel framed plywood 8" x 8"			10.0	1.0	11.0	11.0	11.0	11.0
12" x 12"			9.3	1.0	10.3	10.3	10.3	10.3
16" x 16"			8.5	1.0	9.5	9.5	9.5	9.5
24" x 24"			7.8	1.0	8.8	8.8	8.8	8.8
Drop head forms, plywood		9.0	12.5	1.5	23.0	19.0	17.7	17.0
Coping forms		8.5	15.0	1.5	25.0	21.3	20.0	19.4
Culvert, box			14.5	4.3	18.8	18.8	18.8	18.8
Curb forms, 6" to 12" high, on grade		5.0	8.5	1.2	14.7	12.7	12.1	11.7
On elevated slabs	▼	6.0	10.8	1.2	18.0	15.5	14.7	14.3
Edge forms to 6" high, on grade	100 L.F.	2.0	3.5	0.6	6.1	5.6	5.4	5.3
7" to 12" high	100 S.F.	2.5	5.0	1.0	8.5	7.8	7.5	7.4
Equipment foundations		10.0	18.0	2.0	30.0	25.5	24.0	23.3
Flat slabs, including drops		3.5	6.0	1.2	10.7	9.5	9.0	8.8
Hung from steel		3.0	5.5	1.2	9.7	8.7	8.4	8.2
Closed deck for domes		3.0	5.8	1.2	10.0	9.0	8.7	8.5
Open deck for pans		2.2	5.3	1.0	8.5	7.9	7.7	7.6
Footings, continuous, 12" high		3.5	3.5	1.5	8.5	7.3	6.8	6.6
Spread, 12" high		4.7	4.2	1.6	10.5	8.7	8.0	7.7
Pile caps, square or rectangular		4.5	5.0	1.5	11.0	9.3	8.7	8.4
Grade beams, 24" deep		2.5	5.3	1.2	9.0	8.3	8.0	7.9
Lintel or Sill forms		8.0	17.0	2.0	27.0	23.5	22.3	21.8
Spandrel beams, 12" wide		9.0	11.2	1.3	21.5	17.5	16.2	15.5
Stairs			25.0	4.0	29.0	29.0	29.0	29.0
Trench forms in floor		4.5	14.0	1.5	20.0	18.3	17.7	17.4
Walls, Plywood, at grade, to 8' high		5.0	6.5	1.5	13.0	11.0	9.7	9.5
8' to 16'		7.5	8.0	1.5	17.0	13.8	12.7	12.1
16' to 20'		9.0	10.0	1.5	20.5	16.5	15.2	14.5
Foundation walls, to 8' high		4.5	6.5	1.0	12.0	10.3	9.7	9.4
8' to 16' high		5.5	7.5	1.0	14.0	11.8	11.0	10.6
Retaining wall to 12' high, battered		6.0	8.5	1.5	16.0	13.5	12.7	12.3
Radial walls to 12' high, smooth		8.0	9.5	2.0	19.5	16.0	14.8	14.3
2' chords		7.0	8.0	1.5	16.5	13.5	12.5	12.0
Prefabricated modular, to 8' high		—	4.3	1.0	5.3	5.3	5.3	5.3
Steel, to 8' high		—	6.8	1.2	8.0	8.0	8.0	8.0
8' to 16' high		—	9.1	1.5	10.6	10.3	10.2	10.2
Steel framed plywood to 8' high		—	6.8	1.2	8.0	7.5	7.3	7.2
8' to 16' high	▼	—	9.3	1.2	10.5	9.5	9.2	9.0

R032110-10 Reinforcing Steel Weights and Measures

Bar Designation No.**	Nominal Weight Lb./Ft.	U.S. Customary Units			SI Units			
		Nominal Dimensions*			Nominal Dimensions*			
		Diameter in.	Cross Sectional Area, in.²	Perimeter in.	Nominal Weight kg/m	Diameter mm	Cross Sectional Area, cm²	Perimeter mm
3	.376	.375	.11	1.178	.560	9.52	.71	29.9
4	.668	.500	.20	1.571	.994	12.70	1.29	39.9
5	1.043	.625	.31	1.963	1.552	15.88	2.00	49.9
6	1.502	.750	.44	2.356	2.235	19.05	2.84	59.8
7	2.044	.875	.60	2.749	3.042	22.22	3.87	69.8
8	2.670	1.000	.79	3.142	3.973	25.40	5.10	79.8
9	3.400	1.128	1.00	3.544	5.059	28.65	6.45	90.0
10	4.303	1.270	1.27	3.990	6.403	32.26	8.19	101.4
11	5.313	1.410	1.56	4.430	7.906	35.81	10.06	112.5
14	7.650	1.693	2.25	5.320	11.384	43.00	14.52	135.1
18	13.600	2.257	4.00	7.090	20.238	57.33	25.81	180.1

* The nominal dimensions of a deformed bar are equivalent to those of a plain round bar having the same weight per foot as the deformed bar.
** Bar numbers are based on the number of eighths of an inch included in the nominal diameter of the bars.

R032110-70 Bend, Place and Tie Reinforcing

Placing and tying by rodmen for footings and slabs runs from nine hrs. per ton for heavy bars to fifteen hrs. per ton for light bars. For beams, columns, and walls, production runs from eight hrs. per ton for heavy bars to twenty hrs. per ton for light bars. Overall average for typical reinforced concrete buildings is about fourteen hrs. per ton. These production figures include the time for placing of accessories and usual inserts, but not their material cost (allow 15% of the cost of delivered bent rods). Equipment handling is necessary for the larger-sized bars so that installation costs for the very heavy bars will not decrease proportionately.

Installation costs for splicing reinforcing bars include allowance for equipment to hold the bars in place while splicing as well as necessary scaffolding for iron workers.

R032110-80 Shop-Fabricated Reinforcing Steel

The material prices for reinforcing, shown in the unit cost sections of the book, are for 50 tons or more of shop-fabricated reinforcing steel and include:
1. Mill base price of reinforcing steel
2. Mill grade/size/length extras
3. Mill delivery to the fabrication shop
4. Shop storage and handling
5. Shop drafting/detailing
6. Shop shearing and bending
7. Shop listing
8. Shop delivery to the job site

Both material and installation costs can be considerably higher for small jobs consisting primarily of smaller bars, while material costs may be slightly lower for larger jobs.

813

For customer support on your Site Work & Landscape Cost Data, call 877.737.1594.

Reference Tables

R032205-30   Common Stock Styles of Welded Wire Fabric

This table provides some of the basic specifications, sizes, and weights of welded wire fabric used for reinforcing concrete.

New Designation		Old Designation		Steel Area per Foot				Approximate Weight per 100 S.F.	
Spacing — Cross Sectional Area (in.) — (Sq. in. 100)		Spacing — Wire Gauge (in.) — (AS & W)		Longitudinal		Transverse			
				in.	cm	in.	cm	lbs	kg
Rolls	6 x 6 — W1.4 x W1.4	6 x 6 — 10 x 10		.028	.071	.028	.071	21	9.53
	6 x 6 — W2.0 x W2.0	6 x 6 — 8 x 8	1	.040	.102	.040	.102	29	13.15
	6 x 6 — W2.9 x W2.9	6 x 6 — 6 x 6		.058	.147	.058	.147	42	19.05
	6 x 6 — W4.0 x W4.0	6 x 6 — 4 x 4		.080	.203	.080	.203	58	26.91
	4 x 4 — W1.4 x W1.4	4 x 4 — 10 x 10		.042	.107	.042	.107	31	14.06
	4 x 4 — W2.0 x W2.0	4 x 4 — 8 x 8	1	.060	.152	.060	.152	43	19.50
	4 x 4 — W2.9 x W2.9	4 x 4 — 6 x 6		.087	.227	.087	.227	62	28.12
	4 x 4 — W4.0 x W4.0	4 x 4 — 4 x 4		.120	.305	.120	.305	85	38.56
Sheets	6 x 6 — W2.9 x W2.9	6 x 6 — 6 x 6		.058	.147	.058	.147	42	19.05
	6 x 6 — W4.0 x W4.0	6 x 6 — 4 x 4		.080	.203	.080	.203	58	26.31
	6 x 6 — W5.5 x W5.5	6 x 6 — 2 x 2	2	.110	.279	.110	.279	80	36.29
	4 x 4 — W1.4 x W1.4	4 x 4 — 4 x 4		.120	.305	.120	.305	85	38.56

NOTES: 1. Exact W—number size for 8 gauge is W2.1
2. Exact W—number size for 2 gauge is W5.4

The above table was compiled with the following excerpts from the WRI Manual of Standard Practices, 7th Edition, Copyright 2006. Reproduced with permission of the Wire Reinforcement Institute, Inc.:

1. Chapter 3, page 7, Table 1 Common Styles of Metric Wire Reinforcement (WWR) With Equivalent US Customary Units
2. Chapter 6, page 19, Table 5 Customary Units
3. Chapter 6, Page 23, Table 7 Customary Units (in.) Welded Plain Wire Reinforcement
4. Chapter 6, Page 25 Table 8 Wire Size Comparison
5. Chapter 9, Page 30, Table 9 Weight of Longitudinal Wires Weight (Mass) Estimating Tables
6. Chapter 9, Page 31, Table 9M Weight of Longitudinal Wires Weight (Mass) Estimating Tables
7. Chapter 9, Page 32, Table 10 Weight of Transverse Wires Based on 62" lengths of transverse wire (60" width plus 1" overhand each side)
8. Chapter 9, Page 33, Table 10M Weight of Transverse Wires

R033053-60   Maximum Depth of Frost Penetration in Inches

THIS MAP IS REASONABLY ACCURATE FOR MOST PARTS OF THE UNITED STATES BUT IS NECESSARILY HIGHLY GENERALIZED, AND CONSEQUENTLY NOT TOO ACCURATE IN MOUNTAINOUS REGIONS, PARTICULARLY IN THE ROCKIES.

R033105-20 Materials for One C.Y. of Concrete

This is an approximate method of figuring quantities of cement, sand and coarse aggregate for a field mix with waste allowance included.

With crushed gravel as coarse aggregate, to determine barrels of cement required, divide 10 by total mix; that is, for 1:2:4 mix, 10 divided by 7 = 1-3/7 barrels.

If the coarse aggregate is crushed stone, use 10-1/2 instead of 10 as given for gravel.

To determine tons of sand required, multiply barrels of cement by parts of sand and then by 0.2; that is, for the 1:2:4 mix, as above, 1-3/7 x 2 x .2 = .57 tons.

Tons of crushed gravel are in the same ratio to tons of sand as parts in the mix, or 4/2 x .57 = 1.14 tons.

1 bag cement = 94#
4 bags = 1 barrel

1 C.Y. sand or crushed gravel = 2700#
1 ton sand or crushed gravel = 20 C.F.

1 C.Y. crushed stone = 2575#
1 ton crushed stone = 21 C.F.

Average carload of cement is 692 bags; of sand or gravel is 56 tons.

Do not stack stored cement over 10 bags high.

R033105-65 Field-Mix Concrete

Presently most building jobs are built with ready-mixed concrete except at isolated locations and some larger jobs requiring over 10,000 C.Y. where land is readily available for setting up a temporary batch plant.

The most economical mix is a controlled mix using local aggregate proportioned by trial to give the required strength with the least cost of material.

R033105-70 Placing Ready-Mixed Concrete

For ground pours allow for 5% waste when figuring quantities.

Prices in the front of the book assume normal deliveries. If deliveries are made before 8 A.M. or after 5 P.M. or on Saturday afternoons add 30%. Negotiated discounts for large volumes are not included in prices in front of book.

For the lower floors without truck access, concrete may be wheeled in rubber-tired buggies, conveyer handled, crane handled or pumped. Pumping is economical if there is top steel. Conveyers are more efficient for thick slabs.

At higher floors the rubber-tired buggies may be hoisted by a hoisting tower and wheeled to location. Placement by a conveyer is limited to three floors and is best for high-volume pours. Pumped concrete is best when building has no crane access. Concrete may be pumped directly as high as thirty-six stories using special pumping techniques. Normal maximum height is about fifteen stories.

Best pumping aggregate is screened and graded bank gravel rather than crushed stone.

Pumping downward is more difficult than pumping upward. Horizontal distance from pump to pour may increase preparation time prior to pour. Placing by cranes, either mobile, climbing or tower types, continues as the most efficient method for high-rise concrete buildings.

R040513-10   Cement Mortar (material only)

Type N - 1:1:6 mix by volume. Use everywhere above grade except as noted below. - 1:3 mix using conventional masonry cement which saves handling two separate bagged materials.

Type M - 1:1/4:3 mix by volume, or 1 part cement, 1/4 (10% by wt.) lime, 3 parts sand. Use for heavy loads and where earthquakes or hurricanes may occur. Also for reinforced brick, sewers, manholes and everywhere below grade.

Mix Proportions by Volume and Compressive Strength of Mortar

Where Used	Mortar Type	Portland Cement	Masonry Cement	Hydrated Lime	Masonry Sand	Compressive Strength @ 28 days
Plain Masonry	M	1	1	—	6	
		1	—	1/4	3	2500 psi
	S	1/2	1	—	4	
		1	—	1/4 to 1/2	4	1800 psi
	N	—	1	—	3	
		1	—	1/2 to 1-1/4	6	750 psi
	O	—	1	—	3	
		1	—	1-1/4 to 2-1/2	9	350 psi
	K	1	—	2-1/2 to 4	12	75 psi
Reinforced Masonry	PM	1	1	—	6	2500 psi
	PL	1	—	1/4 to 1/2	4	2500 psi

Note: The total aggregate should be between 2.25 to 3 times the sum of the cement and lime used.

The labor cost to mix the mortar is included in the productivity and labor cost of unit price lines in unit cost sections for brickwork, blockwork and stonework.

The material cost of mixed mortar is included in the material cost of those same unit price lines and includes the cost of renting and operating a 10 C.F. mixer at the rate of 200 C.F. per day.

There are two types of mortar color used. One type is the inert additive type with about 100 lbs. per M brick as the typical quantity required. These colors are also available in smaller-batch-sized bags (1 lb. to 15 lb.) which can be placed directly into the mixer without measuring. The other type is premixed and replaces the masonry cement. Dark green color has the highest cost.

R040519-50   Masonry Reinforcing

Horizontal joint reinforcing helps prevent wall cracks where wall movement may occur and in many locations is required by code. Horizontal joint reinforcing is generally not considered to be structural reinforcing and an unreinforced wall may still contain joint reinforcing.

Reinforcing strips come in 10' and 12' lengths and in truss and ladder shapes, with and without drips. Field labor runs between 2.7 to 5.3 hours per 1000 L.F. for wall thicknesses up to 12".

The wire meets ASTM A82 for cold drawn steel wire and the typical size is 9 ga. sides and ties with 3/16" diameter also available. Typical finish is mill galvanized with zinc coating at .10 oz. per S.F. Class I (.40 oz. per S.F.) and Class III (.80 oz per S.F.) are also available, as is hot dipped galvanizing at 1.50 oz. per S.F.

817

R042110-10   Economy in Bricklaying

Have adequate supervision. Be sure bricklayers are always supplied with materials so there is no waiting. Place best bricklayers at corners and openings.

Use only screened sand for mortar. Otherwise, labor time will be wasted picking out pebbles. Use seamless metal tubs for mortar as they do not leak or catch the trowel. Locate stack and mortar for easy wheeling.

Have brick delivered for stacking. This makes for faster handling, reduces chipping and breakage, and requires less storage space. Many dealers will deliver select common in 2' x 3' x 4' pallets or face brick packaged. This affords quick handling with a crane or forklift and easy tonging in units of ten, which reduces waste.

Use wider bricks for one wythe wall construction. Keep scaffolding away from wall to allow mortar to fall clear and not stain wall.

On large jobs develop specialized crews for each type of masonry unit.

Consider designing for prefabricated panel construction on high rise projects.

Avoid excessive corners or openings. Each opening adds about 50% to labor cost for area of opening.

Bolting stone panels and using window frames as stops reduces labor costs and speeds up erection.

R042110-20   Common and Face Brick

Common building brick manufactured according to ASTM C62 and facing brick manufactured according to ASTM C216 are the two standard bricks available for general building use.

Building brick is made in three grades; SW, where high resistance to damage caused by cyclic freezing is required; MW, where moderate resistance to cyclic freezing is needed; and NW, where little resistance to cyclic freezing is needed. Facing brick is made in only the two grades SW and MW. Additionally, facing brick is available in three types; FBS, for general use; FBX, for general use where a higher degree of precision and lower permissible variation in size than FBS is needed; and FBA, for general use to produce characteristic architectural effects resulting from non-uniformity in size and texture of the units.

In figuring the material cost of brickwork, an allowance of 25% mortar waste and 3% brick breakage was included. If bricks are delivered palletized

with 280 to 300 per pallet, or packaged, allow only 1-1/2% for breakage. Packaged or palletized delivery is practical when a job is big enough to have a crane or other equipment available to handle a package of brick. This is so on all industrial work but not always true on small commercial buildings.

The use of buff and gray face is increasing, and there is a continuing trend to the Norman, Roman, Jumbo and SCR brick.

Common red clay brick for backup is not used that often. Concrete block is the most usual backup material with occasional use of sand lime or cement brick. Building brick is commonly used in solid walls for strength and as a fire stop.

Brick panels built on the ground and then crane erected to the upper floors have proven to be economical. This allows the work to be done under cover and without scaffolding.

R042110-50   Brick, Block & Mortar Quantities

Running Bond					C.F. of Mortar per M Bricks, Waste Included		For Other Bonds Standard Size Add to S.F. Quantities in Table to Left		
Number of Brick per S.F. of Wall - Single Wythe with 3/8″ Joints									
Type Brick	Nominal Size (incl. mortar) L H W		Modular Coursing	Number of Brick per S.F.	3/8″ Joint	1/2″ Joint	Bond Type	Description	Factor
Standard	8 x 2-2/3 x 4		3C=8″	6.75	8.1	10.3	Common	full header every fifth course	+20%
Economy	8 x 4 x 4		1C=4″	4.50	9.1	11.6		full header every sixth course	+16.7%
Engineer	8 x 3-1/5 x 4		5C=16″	5.63	8.5	10.8	English	full header every second course	+50%
Fire	9 x 2-1/2 x 4-1/2		2C=5″	6.40	550 # Fireclay	—	Flemish	alternate headers every course	+33.3%
Jumbo	12 x 4 x 6 or 8		1C=4″	3.00	22.5	29.2		every sixth course	+5.6%
Norman	12 x 2-2/3 x 4		3C=8″	4.50	11.2	14.3	Header = W x H exposed		+100%
Norwegian	12 x 3-1/5 x 4		5C=16″	3.75	11.7	14.9	Rowlock = H x W exposed		+100%
Roman	12 x 2 x 4		2C=4″	6.00	10.7	13.7	Rowlock stretcher = L x W exposed		+33.3%
SCR	12 x 2-2/3 x 6		3C=8″	4.50	21.8	28.0	Soldier = H x L exposed		—
Utility	12 x 4 x 4		1C=4″	3.00	12.3	15.7	Sailor = W x L exposed		-33.3%

Concrete Blocks Nominal Size		Approximate Weight per S.F.		Blocks per 100 S.F.	Mortar per M block, waste included	
		Standard	Lightweight		Partitions	Back up
2″	x 8″ x 16″	20 PSF	15 PSF	113	27 C.F.	36 C.F.
4″		30	20		41	51
6″		42	30		56	66
8″		55	38		72	82
10″		70	47		87	97
12″		85	55		102	112

Brick & Mortar Quantities
©Brick Industry Association. 2009 Feb. Technical Notes on Brick Construction 10:
Dimensioning and Estimating Brick Masonry. Reston (VA): BIA. Table 1 Modular Brick Sizes and Table 4 Quantity Estimates for Brick Masonry.

R042210-20   Concrete Block

The material cost of special block such as corner, jamb and head block can be figured at the same price as ordinary block of same size. Labor on specials is about the same as equal-sized regular block.

Bond beam and 16″ high lintel blocks are more expensive than regular units of equal size. Lintel blocks are 8″ long and either 8″ or 16″ high.

Use of motorized mortar spreader box will speed construction of continuous walls.

Hollow non-load-bearing units are made according to ASTM C129 and hollow load-bearing units according to ASTM C90.

R050516-30   Coating Structural Steel

On field-welded jobs, the shop-applied primer coat is necessarily omitted. All painting must be done in the field and usually consists of red oxide rust inhibitive paint or an aluminum paint. The table below shows paint coverage and daily production for field painting.

See Division 09 97 13.23 for hot-dipped galvanizing and for field-applied cold galvanizing and other paints and protective coatings.

See Division 05 01 10.51 for steel surface preparation treatments such as wire brushing, pressure washing and sand blasting.

Type Construction	Surface Area per Ton	Coat	One Gallon Covers		In 8 Hrs. Person Covers		Average per Ton Spray	
			Brush	Spray	Brush	Spray	Gallons	Labor-hours
Light Structural	300 S.F. to 500 S.F.	1st	500 S.F.	455 S.F.	640 S.F.	2000 S.F.	0.9 gals.	1.6 L.H.
		2nd	450	410	800	2400	1.0	1.3
		3rd	450	410	960	3200	1.0	1.0
Medium	150 S.F. to 300 S.F.	All	400	365	1600	3200	0.6	0.6
Heavy Structural	50 S.F. to 150 S.F.	1st	400	365	1920	4000	0.2	0.2
		2nd	400	365	2000	4000	0.2	0.2
		3rd	400	365	2000	4000	0.2	0.2
Weighted Average	225 S.F.	All	400	365	1350	3000	0.6	0.6

R050521-20   Welded Structural Steel

Usual weight reductions with welded design run 10% to 20% compared with bolted or riveted connections. This amounts to about the same total cost compared with bolted structures since field welding is more expensive than bolts. For normal spans of 18' to 24' figure 6 to 7 connections per ton.

Trusses — For welded trusses add 4% to weight of main members for connections. Up to 15% less steel can be expected in a welded truss compared to one that is shop bolted. Cost of erection is the same whether shop bolted or welded.

General — Typical electrodes for structural steel welding are E6010, E6011, E60T and E70T. Typical buildings vary between 2# to 8# of weld rod per

ton of steel. Buildings utilizing continuous design require about three times as much welding as conventional welded structures. In estimating field erection by welding, it is best to use the average linear feet of weld per ton to arrive at the welding cost per ton. The type, size and position of the weld will have a direct bearing on the cost per linear foot. A typical field welder will deposit 1.8# to 2# of weld rod per hour manually. Using semiautomatic methods can increase production by as much as 50% to 75%.

R050523-10   High Strength Bolts

Common bolts (A307) are usually used in secondary connections (see Division 05 05 23.10).

High strength bolts (A325 and A490) are usually specified for primary connections such as column splices, beam and girder connections to columns, column bracing, connections for supports of operating equipment or of other live loads which produce impact or reversal of stress, and in structures carrying cranes of over 5-ton capacity.

Allow 20 field bolts per ton of steel for a 6 story office building, apartment house or light industrial building. For 6 to 12 stories allow 25 bolts per ton, and above 12 stories, 30 bolts per ton. On power stations, 20 to 25 bolts per ton are needed.

R051223-10   Structural Steel

The bare material prices for structural steel, shown in the unit cost sections of the book, are for 100 tons of shop-fabricated structural steel and include:
1. Mill base price of structural steel
2. Mill scrap/grade/size/length extras
3. Mill delivery to a metals service center (warehouse)
4. Service center storage and handling
5. Service center delivery to a fabrication shop
6. Shop storage and handling
7. Shop drafting/detailing
8. Shop fabrication
9. Shop coat of primer paint
10. Shop listing
11. Shop delivery to the job site

In unit cost sections of the book that contain items for field fabrication of steel components, the bare material cost of steel includes:
1. Mill base price of structural steel
2. Mill scrap/grade/size/length extras
3. Mill delivery to a metals service center (warehouse)
4. Service center storage and handling
5. Service center delivery to the job site

R051223-20   Steel Estimating Quantities

One estimate on erection is that a crane can handle 35 to 60 pieces per day. Say the average is 45. With usual sizes of beams, girders, and columns, this would amount to about 20 tons per day. The type of connection greatly affects the speed of erection. Moment connections for continuous design slow down production and increase erection costs.

Short open web bar joists can be set at the rate of 75 to 80 per day, with 50 per day being the average for setting long span joists.

After main members are calculated, add the following for usual allowances: base plates 2% to 3%; column splices 4% to 5%; and miscellaneous details 4% to 5%, for a total of 10% to 13% in addition to main members.

The ratio of column to beam tonnage varies depending on type of steels used, typical spans, story heights and live loads.

It is more economical to keep the column size constant and to vary the strength of the column by using high strength steels. This also saves floor space. Buildings have recently gone as high as ten stories with 8" high strength columns. For light columns under W8X31 lb. sections, concrete filled steel columns are economical.

High strength steels may be used in columns and beams to save floor space and to meet head room requirements. High strength steels in some sizes sometimes require long lead times.

Round, square and rectangular columns, both plain and concrete filled, are readily available and save floor area, but are higher in cost per pound than rolled columns. For high unbraced columns, tube columns may be less expensive.

Below are average minimum figures for the weights of the structural steel frame for different types of buildings using A36 steel, rolled shapes and simple joints. For economy in domes, rise to span ratio = .13. Open web joist framing systems will reduce weights by 10% to 40%. Composite design can reduce steel weight by up to 25% but additional concrete floor slab thickness may be required. Continuous design can reduce the weights up to 20%. There are many building codes with different live load requirements and different structural requirements, such as hurricane and earthquake loadings which can alter the figures.

Structural Steel Weights per S.F. of Floor Area

Type of Building	No. of Stories	Avg. Spans	L.L. #/S.F.	Lbs. Per S.F.	Type of Building	No. of Stories	Avg. Spans	L.L. #/S.F.	Lbs. Per S.F.
Steel Frame Mfg.	1	20'x20'	40	8	Apartments	2-8	20'x20'	40	8
		30'x30'		13		9-25			14
		40'x40'		18	Office	to 10	Various	80	10
Parking garage	4	Various	80	8.5		20			18
Domes (Schwedler)*	1	200'	30	10		30			26
		300'		15		over 50			35

821

For customer support on your Site Work & Landscape Cost Data, call 877.737.1594.

R051223-25   Common Structural Steel Specifications

ASTM A992 (formerly A36, then A572 Grade 50) is the all-purpose carbon grade steel widely used in building and bridge construction.

The other high-strength steels listed below may each have certain advantages over ASTM A992 stuctural carbon steel, depending on the application. They have proven to be economical choices where, due to lighter members, the reduction of dead load and the associated savings in shipping cost can be significant.

ASTM A588 atmospheric weathering, high-strength low-alloy steels can be used in the bare (uncoated) condition, where exposure to normal atmosphere causes a tightly adherant oxide to form on the surface protecting the steel from further oxidation. ASTM A242 corrosion-resistant, high-strength low-alloy steels have enhanced atmospheric corrosion resistance of at least two times that of carbon structural steels with copper, or four times that of carbon structural steels without copper. The reduction or elimination of maintenance resulting from the use of these steels often offsets their higher initial cost.

Steel Type	ASTM Designation	Minimum Yield Stress in KSI	Shapes Available
Carbon	A36	36	All structural shape groups, and plates & bars up thru 8″ thick
	A529	50	Structural shape group 1, and plates & bars up thru 2″ thick
High-Strength Low-Alloy Quenched & Self-Tempered	A913	50	All structural shape groups
		60	
		65	
		70	
High-Strength Low-Alloy Columbium-Vanadium	A572	42	All structural shape groups, and plates & bars up thru 6″ thick
		50	All structural shape groups, and plates & bars up thru 4″ thick
		55	Structural shape groups 1 & 2, and plates & bars up thru 2″ thick
		60	Structural shape groups 1 & 2, and plates & bars up thru 1-1/4″ thick
		65	Structural shape group 1, and plates & bars up thru 1-1/4″ thick
High-Strength Low-Alloy Columbium-Vanadium	A992	50	All structural shape groups
Weathering High-Strength Low-Alloy	A242	42	Structural shape groups 4 & 5, and plates & bars over 1-1/2″ up thru 4″ thick
		46	Structural shape group 3, and plates & bars over 3/4″ up thru 1-1/2″ thick
		50	Structural shape groups 1 & 2, and plates & bars up thru 3/4″ thick
Weathering High-Strength Low-Alloy	A588	42	Plates & bars over 5″ up thru 8″ thick
		46	Plates & bars over 4″ up thru 5″ thick
		50	All structural shape groups, and plates & bars up thru 4″ thick
Quenched and Tempered	A852	70	Plates & bars up thru 4″ thick
Low-Alloy Quenched and Tempered	A514	90	Plates & bars over 2-1/2″ up thru 6″ thick
Alloy		100	Plates & bars up thru 2-1/2″ thick

R051223-30   High Strength Steels

The mill price of high strength steels may be higher than A992 carbon steel but their proper use can achieve overall savings thru total reduced weights. For columns with L/r over 100, A992 steel is best; under 100, high strength steels are economical. For heavy columns, high strength steels are economical when cover plates are eliminated. There is no economy using high strength steels for clip angles or supports or for beams where deflection governs. Thinner members are more economical than thick.

The per ton erection and fabricating costs of the high strength steels will be higher than for A992 since the same number of pieces, but less weight, will be installed.

R051223-35 Common Steel Sections

The upper portion of this table shows the name, shape, common designation and basic characteristics of commonly used steel sections. The lower portion explains how to read the designations used for the above illustrated common sections.

Shape & Designation	Name & Characteristics	Shape & Designation	Name & Characteristics
W	W Shape — Parallel flange surfaces	MC	Miscellaneous Channel — Infrequently rolled by some producers
S	American Standard Beam (I Beam) — Sloped inner flange	L	Angle — Equal or unequal legs, constant thickness
M	Miscellaneous Beams — Cannot be classified as W, HP or S; infrequently rolled by some producers	T	Structural Tee — Cut from W, M or S on center of web
C	American Standard Channel — Sloped inner flange	HP	Bearing Pile — Parallel flanges and equal flange and web thickness

Common drawing designations follow:

W Shape
W 18 x 35
— Weight in Pounds per Foot
— Nominal Depth in Inches (Actual 17-3/4")

American Standard Beam
S 12 x 31.8
— Weight in Pounds per Foot
— Depth in Inches

Miscellaneous Beam
M 8 x 6.5
— Weight in Pounds per Foot
— Depth in Inches

American Standard Channel
C 8 x 11.5
— Weight in Pounds per Foot
— Depth in Inches

Miscellaneous Channel
MC 8 x 22.8
— Weight in Pounds per Foot
— Depth in Inches

Angle
L 6 x 3-1/2 x 3/8
— Length of Long Leg in Inches
— Thickness of Each Leg in Inches
— Length of Other Leg in Inches

Tee Cut from W16 x 100
WT 8 x 50
— Weight in Pounds per Foot
— Nominal Depth in Inches (Actual 8-1/2")

Tee Cut from S12 x 35
ST 6 x 17.5
— Weight in Pounds per Foot
— Depth in Inches (Actual 6-1/4")

Tee Cut from M10 x 9
MT 5 x 4.5
— Weight in Pounds per Foot
— Depth in Inches

Bearing Pile
HP 12 x 84
— Weight in Pounds per Foot
— Nominal Depth in Inches (Actual 12-1/4")

823

R051223-45   Installation Time for Structural Steel Building Components

The following tables show the expected average installation times for various structural steel shapes. Table A presents installation times for columns, Table B for beams, Table C for light framing and bolts, and Table D for structural steel for various project types.

Table A

Description	Labor-Hours	Unit
Columns		
Steel, Concrete Filled		
3-1/2" Diameter	.933	Ea.
6-5/8" Diameter	1.120	Ea.
Steel Pipe		
3" Diameter	.933	Ea.
8" Diameter	1.120	Ea.
12" Diameter	1.244	Ea.
Structural Tubing		
4" x 4"	.966	Ea.
8" x 8"	1.120	Ea.
12" x 8"	1.167	Ea.
W Shape 2 Tier		
W8 x 31	.052	L.F.
W8 x 67	.057	L.F.
W10 x 45	.054	L.F.
W10 x 112	.058	L.F.
W12 x 50	.054	L.F.
W12 x 190	.061	L.F.
W14 x 74	.057	L.F.
W14 x 176	.061	L.F.

Table B

Description	Labor-Hours	Unit	Labor-Hours	Unit
Beams, W Shape				
W6 x 9	.949	Ea.	.093	L.F.
W10 x 22	1.037	Ea.	.085	L.F.
W12 x 26	1.037	Ea.	.064	L.F.
W14 x 34	1.333	Ea.	.069	L.F.
W16 x 31	1.333	Ea.	.062	L.F.
W18 x 50	2.162	Ea.	.088	L.F.
W21 x 62	2.222	Ea.	.077	L.F.
W24 x 76	2.353	Ea.	.072	L.F.
W27 x 94	2.581	Ea.	.067	L.F.
W30 x 108	2.857	Ea.	.067	L.F.
W33 x 130	3.200	Ea.	.071	L.F.
W36 x 300	3.810	Ea.	.077	L.F.

Table C

Description	Labor-Hours	Unit
Light Framing		
Angles 4" and Larger	.055	lbs.
Less than 4"	.091	lbs.
Channels 8" and Larger	.048	lbs.
Less than 8"	.072	lbs.
Cross Bracing Angles	.055	lbs.
Rods	.034	lbs.
Hanging Lintels	.069	lbs.
High Strength Bolts in Place		
3/4" Bolts	.070	Ea.
7/8" Bolts	.076	Ea.

Table D

Description	Labor-Hours	Unit	Labor-Hours	Unit
Apartments, Nursing Homes, etc.				
1-2 Stories	4.211	Piece	7.767	Ton
3-6 Stories	4.444	Piece	7.921	Ton
7-15 Stories	4.923	Piece	9.014	Ton
Over 15 Stories	5.333	Piece	9.209	Ton
Offices, Hospitals, etc.				
1-2 Stories	4.211	Piece	7.767	Ton
3-6 Stories	4.741	Piece	8.889	Ton
7-15 Stories	4.923	Piece	9.014	Ton
Over 15 Stories	5.120	Piece	9.209	Ton
Industrial Buildings				
1 Story	3.478	Piece	6.202	Ton

R051223-80 Dimensions and Weights of Sheet Steel

Gauge No.	Approximate Thickness					Weight		
	Inches (in fractions)	Inches (in decimal parts)		Millimeters				per Square
	Wrought Iron	Wrought Iron	Steel	Steel		per S.F. in Ounces	per S.F. in Lbs.	Meter in Kg.
0000000	1/2"	.5	.4782	12.146		320	20.000	97.650
000000	15/32"	.46875	.4484	11.389		300	18.750	91.550
00000	7/16"	.4375	.4185	10.630		280	17.500	85.440
0000	13/32"	.40625	.3886	9.870		260	16.250	79.330
000	3/8"	.375	.3587	9.111		240	15.000	73.240
00	11/32"	.34375	.3288	8.352		220	13.750	67.130
0	5/16"	.3125	.2989	7.592		200	12.500	61.030
1	9/32"	.28125	.2690	6.833		180	11.250	54.930
2	17/64"	.265625	.2541	6.454		170	10.625	51.880
3	1/4"	.25	.2391	6.073		160	10.000	48.820
4	15/64"	.234375	.2242	5.695		150	9.375	45.770
5	7/32"	.21875	.2092	5.314		140	8.750	42.720
6	13/64"	.203125	.1943	4.935		130	8.125	39.670
7	3/16"	.1875	.1793	4.554		120	7.500	36.320
8	11/64"	.171875	.1644	4.176		110	6.875	33.570
9	5/32"	.15625	.1495	3.797		100	6.250	30.520
10	9/64"	.140625	.1345	3.416		90	5.625	27.460
11	1/8"	.125	.1196	3.038		80	5.000	24.410
12	7/64"	.109375	.1046	2.657		70	4.375	21.360
13	3/32"	.09375	.0897	2.278		60	3.750	18.310
14	5/64"	.078125	.0747	1.897		50	3.125	15.260
15	9/128"	.0713125	.0673	1.709		45	2.813	13.730
16	1/16"	.0625	.0598	1.519		40	2.500	12.210
17	9/160"	.05625	.0538	1.367		36	2.250	10.990
18	1/20"	.05	.0478	1.214		32	2.000	9.765
19	7/160"	.04375	.0418	1.062		28	1.750	8.544
20	3/80"	.0375	.0359	.912		24	1.500	7.324
21	11/320"	.034375	.0329	.836		22	1.375	6.713
22	1/32"	.03125	.0299	.759		20	1.250	6.103
23	9/320"	.028125	.0269	.683		18	1.125	5.490
24	1/40"	.025	.0239	.607		16	1.000	4.882
25	7/320"	.021875	.0209	.531		14	.875	4.272
26	3/160"	.01875	.0179	.455		12	.750	3.662
27	11/640"	.0171875	.0164	.417		11	.688	3.357
28	1/64"	.015625	.0149	.378		10	.625	3.052

Reference Tables

R053100-10   Decking Descriptions

General - All Deck Products

Steel deck is made by cold forming structural grade sheet steel into a repeating pattern of parallel ribs. The strength and stiffness of the panels are the result of the ribs and the material properties of the steel. Deck lengths can be varied to suit job conditions, but because of shipping considerations, are usually less than 40 feet. Standard deck width varies with the product used but full sheets are usually 12″, 18″, 24″, 30″, or 36″. Deck is typically furnished in a standard width with the ends cut square. Any cutting for width, such as at openings or for angular fit, is done at the job site.

Deck is typically attached to the building frame with arc puddle welds, self-drilling screws, or powder or pneumatically driven pins. Sheet to sheet fastening is done with screws, button punching (crimping), or welds.

Composite Floor Deck

After installation and adequate fastening, floor deck serves several purposes. It (a) acts as a working platform, (b) stabilizes the frame, (c) serves as a concrete form for the slab, and (d) reinforces the slab to carry the design loads applied during the life of the building. Composite decks are distinguished by the presence of shear connector devices as part of the deck. These devices are designed to mechanically lock the concrete and deck together so that the concrete and the deck work together to carry subsequent floor loads. These shear connector devices can be rolled-in embossments, lugs, holes, or wires welded to the panels. The deck profile can also be used to interlock concrete and steel.

Composite deck finishes are either galvanized (zinc coated) or phosphatized/painted. Galvanized deck has a zinc coating on both the top and bottom surfaces. The phosphatized/painted deck has a bare (phosphatized) top surface that will come into contact with the concrete. This bare top surface can be expected to develop rust before the concrete is placed. The bottom side of the deck has a primer coat of paint.

Composite floor deck is normally installed so the panel ends do not overlap on the supporting beams. Shear lugs or panel profile shape often prevent a tight metal to metal fit if the panel ends overlap; the air gap caused by overlapping will prevent proper fusion with the structural steel supports when the panel end laps are shear stud welded.

Adequate end bearing of the deck must be obtained as shown on the drawings. If bearing is actually less in the field than shown on the drawings, further investigation is required.

Roof Deck

Roof deck is not designed to act compositely with other materials. Roof deck acts alone in transferring horizontal and vertical loads into the building frame. Roof deck rib openings are usually narrower than floor deck rib openings. This provides adequate support of rigid thermal insulation board.

Roof deck is typically installed to endlap approximately 2″ over supports. However, it can be butted (or lapped more than 2″) to solve field fit problems. Since designers frequently use the installed deck system as part of the horizontal bracing system (the deck as a diaphragm), any fastening substitution or change should be approved by the designer. Continuous perimeter support of the deck is necessary to limit edge deflection in the finished roof and may be required for diaphragm shear transfer.

Standard roof deck finishes are galvanized or primer painted. The standard factory applied paint for roof deck is a primer paint and is not intended to weather for extended periods of time. Field painting or touching up of abrasions and deterioration of the primer coat or other protective finishes is the responsibility of the contractor.

Cellular Deck

Cellular deck is made by attaching a bottom steel sheet to a roof deck or composite floor deck panel. Cellular deck can be used in the same manner as floor deck. Electrical, telephone, and data wires are easily run through the chase created between the deck panel and the bottom sheet.

When used as part of the electrical distribution system, the cellular deck must be installed so that the ribs line up and create a smooth cell transition at abutting ends. The joint that occurs at butting cell ends must be taped or otherwise sealed to prevent wet concrete from seeping into the cell. Cell interiors must be free of welding burrs, or other sharp intrusions, to prevent damage to wires.

When used as a roof deck, the bottom flat plate is usually left exposed to view. Care must be maintained during erection to keep good alignment and prevent damage.

Cellular deck is sometimes used with the flat plate on the top side to provide a flat working surface. Installation of the deck for this purpose requires special methods for attachment to the frame because the flat plate, now on the top, can prevent direct access to the deck material that is bearing on the structural steel. It may be advisable to treat the flat top surface to prevent slipping.

Cellular deck is always furnished galvanized or painted over galvanized.

Form Deck

Form deck can be any floor or roof deck product used as a concrete form. Connections to the frame are by the same methods used to anchor floor and roof deck. Welding washers are recommended when welding deck that is less than 20 gauge thickness.

Form deck is furnished galvanized, prime painted, or uncoated. Galvanized deck must be used for those roof deck systems where form deck is used to carry a lightweight insulating concrete fill.

Wood, Plastics & Comp. — R0611 Wood Framing

R061110-30   Lumber Product Material Prices

The price of forest products fluctuates widely from location to location and from season to season depending upon economic conditions. The bare material prices in the unit cost sections of the book show the National Average material prices in effect Jan. 1 of this book year. It must be noted that lumber prices in general may change significantly during the year.

Availability of certain items depends upon geographic location and must be checked prior to firm-price bidding.

Wood, Plastics & Comp. — R0616 Sheathing

R061636-20   Plywood

There are two types of plywood used in construction: interior, which is moisture-resistant but not waterproofed, and exterior, which is waterproofed.

The grade of the exterior surface of the plywood sheets is designated by the first letter: A, for smooth surface with patches allowed; B, for solid surface with patches and plugs allowed; C, which may be surface plugged or may have knot holes up to 1″ wide; and D, which is used only for interior type plywood and may have knot holes up to 2-1/2″ wide. "Structural Grade" is specifically designed for engineered applications such as box beams. All CC & DD grades have roof and floor spans marked on them.

Underlayment-grade plywood runs from 1/4″ to 1-1/4″ thick. Thicknesses 5/8″ and over have optional tongue and groove joints which eliminate the need for blocking the edges. Underlayment 19/32″ and over may be referred to as Sturd-i-Floor.

The price of plywood can fluctuate widely due to geographic and economic conditions.

Typical uses for various plywood grades are as follows:

AA-AD Interior — cupboards, shelving, paneling, furniture

BB Plyform — concrete form plywood

CDX — wall and roof sheathing

Structural — box beams, girders, stressed skin panels

AA-AC Exterior — fences, signs, siding, soffits, etc.

Underlayment — base for resilient floor coverings

Overlaid HDO — high density for concrete forms & highway signs

Overlaid MDO — medium density for painting, siding, soffits & signs

303 Siding — exterior siding, textured, striated, embossed, etc.

Openings — R0813 Metal Doors

R081313-20   Steel Door Selection Guide

Standard steel doors are classified into four levels, as recommended by the Steel Door Institute in the chart below. Each of the four levels offers a range of construction models and designs, to meet architectural requirements for preference and appearance, including full flush, seamless, and stile & rail. Recommended minimum gauge requirements are also included.

For complete standard steel door construction specifications and available sizes, refer to the Steel Door Institute Technical Data Series, ANSI A250.8-98 (SDI-100), and ANSI A250.4-94 Test Procedure and Acceptance Criteria for Physical Endurance of Steel Door and Hardware Reinforcements.

Level		Model	Construction	For Full Flush or Seamless		
				Min. Gauge	Thickness (in)	Thickness (mm)
I	Standard Duty	1	Full Flush			
		2	Seamless	20	0.032	0.8
II	Heavy Duty	1	Full Flush			
		2	Seamless	18	0.042	1.0
III	Extra Heavy Duty	1	Full Flush			
		2	Seamless			
		3	*Stile & Rail	16	0.053	1.3
IV	Maximum Duty	1	Full Flush			
		2	Seamless	14	0.067	1.6

*Stiles & rails are 16 gauge; flush panels, when specified, are 18 gauge

Reference Tables

R092910-10   Levels of Gypsum Drywall Finish

In the past, contract documents often used phrases such as "industry standard" and "workmanlike finish" to specify the expected quality of gypsum board wall and ceiling installations. The vagueness of these descriptions led to unacceptable work and disputes.

In order to resolve this problem, four major trade associations concerned with the manufacture, erection, finish, and decoration of gypsum board wall and ceiling systems have developed an industry-wide *Recommended Levels of Gypsum Board Finish*.

The finish of gypsum board walls and ceilings for specific final decoration is dependent on a number of factors. A primary consideration is the location of the surface and the degree of decorative treatment desired. Painted and unpainted surfaces in warehouses and other areas where appearance is normally not critical may simply require the taping of wallboard joints and 'spotting' of fastener heads. Blemish-free, smooth, monolithic surfaces often intended for painted and decorated walls and ceilings in habitated structures, ranging from single-family dwellings through monumental buildings, require additional finishing prior to the application of the final decoration.

Other factors to be considered in determining the level of finish of the gypsum board surface are (1) the type of angle of surface illumination (both natural and artificial lighting), and (2) the paint and method of application or the type and finish of wallcovering specified as the final decoration. Critical lighting conditions, gloss paints, and thin wall coverings require a higher level of gypsum board finish than do heavily textured surfaces which are subsequently painted or surfaces which are to be decorated with heavy grade wall coverings.

The following descriptions were developed jointly by the Association of the Wall and Ceiling Industries-International (AWCI), Ceiling & Interior Systems Construction Association (CISCA), Gypsum Association (GA), and Painting and Decorating Contractors of America (PDCA) as a guide.

Level 0: Used in temporary construction or wherever the final decoration has not been determined. Unfinished. No taping, finishing or corner beads are required. Also could be used where non-predecorated panels will be used in demountable-type partitions that are to be painted as a final finish.

Level 1: Frequently used in plenum areas above ceilings, in attics, in areas where the assembly would generally be concealed, or in building service corridors and other areas not normally open to public view. Some degree of sound and smoke control is provided; in some geographic areas, this level is referred to as "fire-taping," although this level of finish does not typically meet fire-resistant assembly requirements. Where a fire resistance rating is required for the gypsum board assembly, details of construction should be in accordance with reports of fire tests of assemblies that have met the requirements of the fire rating acceptable.

All joints and interior angles shall have tape embedded in joint compound. Accessories are optional at specifier discretion in corridors and other areas with pedestrian traffic. Tape and fastener heads need not be covered with joint compound. Surface shall be free of excess joint compound. Tool marks and ridges are acceptable.

Level 2: It may be specified for standard gypsum board surfaces in garages, warehouse storage, or other similar areas where surface appearance is not of primary importance.

All joints and interior angles shall have tape embedded in joint compound and shall be immediately wiped with a joint knife or trowel, leaving a thin coating of joint compound over all joints and interior angles. Fastener heads and accessories shall be covered with a coat of joint compound. Surface shall be free of excess joint compound. Tool marks and ridges are acceptable.

Level 3: Typically used in areas that are to receive heavy texture (spray or hand applied) finishes before final painting, or where commercial-grade (heavy duty) wall coverings are to be applied as the final decoration. This level of finish should not be used where smooth painted surfaces or where lighter weight wall coverings are specified. The prepared surface shall be coated with a drywall primer prior to the application of final finishes.

All joints and interior angles shall have tape embedded in joint compound and shall be immediately wiped with a joint knife or trowel, leaving a thin coating of joint compound over all joints and interior angles. One additional coat of joint compound shall be applied over all joints and interior angles. Fastener heads and accessories shall be covered with two separate coats of joint compound. All joint compounds shall be smooth and free of tool marks and ridges. The prepared surface shall be covered with a drywall primer prior to the application of the final decoration.

Level 4: This level should be used where residential grade (light duty) wall coverings, flat paints, or light textures are to be applied. The prepared surface shall be coated with a drywall primer prior to the application of final finishes. Release agents for wall coverings are specifically formulated to minimize damage if coverings are subsequently removed.

The weight, texture, and sheen level of the wall covering material selected should be taken into consideration when specifying wall coverings over this level of drywall treatment. Joints and fasteners must be sufficiently concealed if the wall covering material is lightweight, contains limited pattern, has a glossy finish, or has any combination of these features. In critical lighting areas, flat paints applied over light textures tend to reduce joint photographing. Gloss, semi-gloss, and enamel paints are not recommended over this level of finish.

All joints and interior angles shall have tape embedded in joint compound and shall be immediately wiped with a joint knife or trowel, leaving a thin coating of joint compound over all joints and interior angles. In addition, two separate coats of joint compound shall be applied over all flat joints and one separate coat of joint compound applied over interior angles. Fastener heads and accessories shall be covered with three separate coats of joint compound. All joint compounds shall be smooth and free of tool marks and ridges. The prepared surface shall be covered with a drywall primer like Sheetrock® First Coat prior to the application of the final decoration.

Level 5: The highest quality finish is the most effective method to provide a uniform surface and minimize the possibility of joint photographing and of fasteners showing through the final decoration. This level of finish is required where gloss, semi-gloss, or enamel is specified; when flat joints are specified over an untextured surface; or where critical lighting conditions occur. The prepared surface shall be coated with a drywall primer prior to the application of final decoration.

All joints and interior angles shall have tape embedded in joint compound and be immediately wiped with a joint knife or trowel, leaving a thin coating of joint compound over all joints and interior angles. Two separate coats of joint compound shall be applied over all flat joints and one separate coat of joint compound applied over interior angles. Fastener heads and accessories shall be covered with three separate coats of joint compound.

A thin skim coat of joint compound shall be trowel applied to the entire surface. Excess compound is immediately troweled off, leaving a film or skim coating of compound completely covering the paper. As an alternative to a skim coat, a material manufactured especially for this purpose may be applied such as Sheetrock® Tuff-Hide primer surfacer. The surface must be smooth and free of tool marks and ridges. The prepared surface shall be covered with a drywall primer prior to the application of the final decoration.

Special Construction   R1311 Swimming Pools

R131113-20   Swimming Pools

Pool prices given per square foot of surface area include pool structure, filter and chlorination equipment, pumps, related piping, ladders/steps, maintenance kit, skimmer and vacuum system. Decks and electrical service to equipment are not included.

Residential in-ground pool construction can be divided into two categories: vinyl lined and gunite. Vinyl lined pool walls are constructed of different materials including wood, concrete, plastic or metal. The bottom is often graded with sand over which the vinyl liner is installed. Vermiculite or soil cement bottoms may be substituted for an added cost.

Gunite pool construction is used both in residential and municipal installations. These structures are steel reinforced for strength and finished with a white cement limestone plaster.

Municipal pools will have a higher cost because plumbing codes require more expensive materials, chlorination equipment and higher filtration rates.

Municipal pools greater than 1,800 S.F. require gutter systems to control waves. This gutter may be formed into the concrete wall. Often a vinyl/stainless steel gutter or gutter/wall system is specified, which will raise the pool cost.

Competition pools usually require tile bottoms and sides with contrasting lane striping, which will also raise the pool cost.

Special Construction   R1331 Fabric Structures

R133113-10   Air Supported Structures

Air supported structures are made from fabrics that can be classified into two groups: temporary and permanent. Temporary fabrics include nylon, woven polyethylene, vinyl film, and vinyl coated dacron. These have lifespans that range from five to fifteen plus years. The cost per square foot includes a fabric shell, tension cables, primary and back-up inflation systems and doors. The lower cost structures are used for construction shelters, bulk storage and pond covers. The more expensive are used for recreational structures and warehouses.

Permanent fabrics are teflon coated fiberglass. The life of this structure is twenty plus years. The high cost limits its application to architectural designed structures which call for a clear span covered area, such as stadiums and convention centers. Both temporary and permanent structures are available in translucent fabrics which eliminates the need for daytime lighting.

Areas to be covered vary from 10,000 S.F. to any area up to 1000 foot wide by any length. Height restrictions range from a maximum of 1/2 of

width to a minimum of 1/6 of the width. Erection of even the largest of the temporary structures requires no more than a week.

Centrifugal fans provide the inflation necessary to support the structure during application of live loads. Airlocks are usually used at large entrances to prevent loss of static pressure. Some manufacturers employ propeller fans which generate sufficient airflow (30,000 CFM) to eliminate the need for airlocks. These fans may also be automatically controlled to resist high wind conditions, regulate humidity (air changes), and provide cooling and heat.

Insulation can be provided with the addition of a second or even third interior liner, creating a dead air space with an "R" value of four to nine. Some structures allow for the liner to be collapsed into the outer shell to enable the internal heat to melt accumulated snow. For cooling or air conditioning, the exterior face of the liner can be aluminized to reflect the sun's heat.

Special Construction   R1334 Fabricated Engineered Structures

R133419-10   Pre-Engineered Steel Buildings

These buildings are manufactured by many companies and normally erected by franchised dealers throughout the U.S. The four basic types are: Rigid Frames, Truss type, Post and Beam and the Sloped Beam type. Most popular roof slope is low pitch of 1" in 12". The minimum economical area of these buildings is about 3000 S.F. of floor area. Bay sizes are usually 20' to 24' but can go as high as 30' with heavier girts and purlins. Eave heights are usually 12' to 24' with 18' to 20' most typical.

Material prices shown in the Unit Price section are bare costs for the building shell only and do not include floors, foundations, anchor bolts, interior finishes or utilities. Costs assume at least three bays of 24' each, a 1" in 12" roof slope, and they are based on 30 psf roof load and 20 psf wind load

(wind load is a function of wind speed, building height, and terrain characteristics; this should be determined by a Registered Structural Engineer) and no unusual requirements. Costs include the structural frame, 26 ga. non-insulated colored corrugated or ribbed roofing and siding panels, fasteners, closures, trim and flashing but no allowance for insulation, doors, windows, skylights, gutters or downspouts. Very large projects would generally cost less for materials than the prices shown. For roof panel substitutions and wall panel substitutions, see appropriate Unit Price sections.

Conditions at the site, weather, shape and size of the building, and labor availability will affect the erection cost of the building.

R133423-30   Dome Structures

Steel — The four types are Lamella, Schwedler, Arch and Geodesic. For maximum economy, rise should be about 15 to 20% of diameter. Most common diameters are in the 200' to 300' range. Lamella domes weigh about 5 P.S.F. of floor area less than Schwedler domes. Schwedler dome weight in lbs. per S.F. approaches .046 times the diameter. Domes below 125' diameter weigh .07 times diameter and the cost per ton of steel is higher. See R051223-20 for estimating weight.

Wood — Small domes are of sawn lumber, larger ones are laminated. In larger sizes, triaxial and triangular cost about the same; radial domes cost more. Radial domes are economical in the 60' to 70' diameter range. Most economical range of all types is 80' to 200' diameters. Diameters can

run over 400'. All costs are quoted above the foundation. Prices include 2" decking and a tension tie ring in place.

Plywood — Stock prefab geodesic domes are available with diameters from 24' to 60'.

Fiberglass — Aluminum framed translucent sandwich panels with spans from 5' to 45' are commercially available.

Aluminum — Stressed skin aluminum panels form geodesic domes with spans ranging from 82' to 232'. An aluminum space truss, triangulated or nontriangulated, with aluminum or clear acrylic closure panels can be used for clear spans of 40' to 415'.

R220102-20 Labor Adjustment Factors

Labor Adjustment Factors are provided for Divisions 21, 22, and 23 to assist the mechanical estimator account for the various complexities and special conditions of any particular project. While a single percentage has been entered on each line of Division 22 01 02.20, it should be understood that these are just suggested midpoints of ranges of values commonly used by mechanical estimators. They may be increased or decreased depending on the severity of the special conditions.

The group for "existing occupied buildings", has been the subject of requests for explanation. Actually there are two stages to this group: buildings that are existing and "finished" but unoccupied, and those that also are occupied. Buildings that are "finished" may result in higher labor costs due to the

workers having to be more careful not to damage finished walls, ceilings, floors, etc. and may necessitate special protective coverings and barriers. Also corridor bends and doorways may not accommodate long pieces of pipe or larger pieces of equipment. Work above an already hung ceiling can be very time consuming. The addition of occupants may force the work to be done on premium time (nights and/or weekends), eliminate the possible use of some preferred tools such as pneumatic drivers, powder charged drivers etc. The estimator should evaluate the access to the work area and just how the work is going to be accomplished to arrive at an increase in labor costs over "normal" new construction productivity.

R220523-80 Valve Materials

VALVE MATERIALS

Bronze:
Bronze is one of the oldest materials used to make valves. It is most commonly used in hot and cold water systems and other non-corrosive services. It is often used as a seating surface in larger iron body valves to ensure tight closure.

Carbon Steel:
Carbon steel is a high strength material. Therefore, valves made from this metal are used in higher pressure services, such as steam lines up to 600 psi at 850° F. Many steel valves are available with butt-weld ends for economy and are generally used in high pressure steam service as well as other higher pressure non-corrosive services.

Forged Steel:
Valves from tough carbon steel are used in service up to 2000 psi and temperatures up to 1000° F in Gate, Globe and Check valves.

Iron:
Valves are normally used in medium to large pipe lines to control non-corrosive fluid and gases, where pressures do not exceed 250 psi at 450° F or 500 psi cold water, oil or gas.

Stainless Steel:
Developed steel alloys can be used in over 90% corrosive services.

Plastic PVC:
This is used in a great variety of valves generally in high corrosive service with lower temperatures and pressures.

VALVE SERVICE PRESSURES

Pressure ratings on valves provide an indication of the safe operating pressure for a valve at some elevated temperature. This temperature is dependent upon the materials used and the fabrication of the valve. When specific data is not available, a good "rule-of-thumb" to follow is the temperature of saturated steam on the primary rating indicated on the valve body. Example: The valve has the number 150S printed on the side indicating 150 psi and hence, a maximum operating temperature of 367° F (temperature of saturated steam and 150 psi).

DEFINITIONS
1. "WOG" – Water, oil, gas (cold working pressures).
2. "SWP" – Steam working pressure.
3. "100% area (full port) – means the area through the valve is equal to or greater than the area of standard pipe.
4. "Standard Opening" – means that the area through the valve is less than the area of standard pipe and therefore these valves should be used only where restriction of flow is unimportant.
5. "Round Port" – means the valve has a full round opening through the plug and body, of the same size and area as standard pipe.
6. "Rectangular Port" – valves have rectangular shaped ports through the plug body. The area of the port is either equal to 100% of the area of standard pipe, or restricted (standard opening). In either case it is clearly marked.
7. "ANSI" – American National Standards Institute.

R220523-90 Valve Selection Considerations

INTRODUCTION: In any piping application, valve performance is critical. Valves should be selected to give the best performance at the lowest cost.

The following is a list of performance characteristics generally expected of valves.
1. Stopping flow or starting it.
2. Throttling flow (Modulation).
3. Flow direction changing.
4. Checking backflow (Permitting flow in only one direction).
5. Relieving or regulating pressure.

In order to properly select the right valve, some facts must be determined.

A. What liquid or gas will flow through the valve?

B. Does the fluid contain suspended particles?

C. Does the fluid remain in liquid form at all times?

D. Which metals does fluid corrode?

E. What are the pressure and temperature limits? (As temperature and pressure rise, so will the price of the valve.)

F. Is there constant line pressure?

G. Is the valve merely an on-off valve?

H. Will checking of backflow be required?

I. Will the valve operate frequently or infrequently?

Valves are classified by design type into such classifications as Gate, Globe, Angle, Check, Ball, Butterfly and Plug. They are also classified by end connection, stem, pressure restrictions and material such as bronze, cast iron, etc. Each valve has a specific use. A quality valve used correctly will provide a lifetime of trouble-free service, but a high quality valve installed in the wrong service may require frequent attention.

STEM TYPES
(OS & Y)—Rising Stem-Outside Screw and Yoke

Offers a visual indication of whether the valve is open or closed. Recommended where high temperatures, corrosives, and solids in the line might cause damage to inside-valve stem threads. The stem threads are engaged by the yoke bushing so the stem rises through the hand wheel as it is turned.

(R.S.)—Rising Stem-Inside Screw

Adequate clearance for operation must be provided because both the hand wheel and the stem rise.
The valve wedge position is indicated by the position of the stem and hand wheel.

(N.R.S.)—Non-Rising Stem-Inside Screw

A minimum clearance is required for operating this type of valve. Excessive wear or damage to stem threads inside the valve may be caused by heat, corrosion, and solids. Because the hand wheel and stem do not rise, wedge position cannot be visually determined.

VALVE TYPES
Gate Valves

Provide full flow, minute pressure drop, minimum turbulence and minimum fluid trapped in the line.
They are normally used where operation is infrequent.

Globe Valves

Globe valves are designed for throttling and/or frequent operation with positive shut-off. Particular attention must be paid to the several types of seating materials available to avoid unnecessary wear. The seats must be compatible with the fluid in service and may be composition or metal. The configuration of the Globe valve opening causes turbulence which results in increased resistance. Most bronze Globe valves are rising stem-inside screw, but they are also available on O.S. & Y.

Angle Valves

The fundamental difference between the Angle valve and the Globe valve is the fluid flow through the Angle valve. It makes a 90° turn and offers less resistance to flow than the Globe valve while replacing an elbow. An Angle valve thus reduces the number of joints and installation time.

831

Check Valves

Check valves are designed to prevent backflow by automatically seating when the direction of fluid is reversed.
Swing Check valves are generally installed with Gate-valves, as they provide comparable full flow. Usually recommended for lines where flow velocities are low and should not be used on lines with pulsating flow. Recommended for horizontal installation, or in vertical lines only where flow is upward.

Lift Check Valves

These are commonly used with Globe and Angle valves since they have similar diaphragm seating arrangements and are recommended for preventing backflow of steam, air, gas and water, and on vapor lines with high flow velocities. For horizontal lines, horizontal lift checks should be used and vertical lift checks for vertical lines.

Ball Valves

Ball valves are light and easily installed, yet because of modern elastomeric seats, provide tight closure. Flow is controlled by rotating up to 90° a drilled ball which fits tightly against resilient seals. This ball seats with flow in either direction, and valve handle indicates the degree of opening. Recommended for frequent operation readily adaptable to automation, ideal for installation where space is limited.

Butterfly Valves

Butterfly valves provide bubble-tight closure with excellent throttling characteristics. They can be used for full-open, closed and for throttling applications.

The Butterfly valve consists of a disc within the valve body which is controlled by a shaft. In its closed position, the valve disc seals against a resilient seat. The disc position throughout the full 90° rotation is visually indicated by the position of the operator.

A Butterfly valve is only a fraction of the weight of a Gate valve and requires no gaskets between flanges in most cases. Recommended for frequent operation and adaptable to automation where space is limited.

Wafer and Lug type bodies when installed between two pipe flanges, can be easily removed from the line. The pressure of the bolted flanges holds the valve in place.
Locating lugs makes installation easier.

Plug Valves

Lubricated plug valves, because of the wide range of service to which they are adapted, may be classified as all purpose valves. They can be safely used at all pressure and vacuums, and at all temperatures up to the limits of available lubricants. They are the most satisfactory valves for the handling of gritty suspensions and many other destructive, erosive, corrosive and chemical solutions.

R221113-50   Pipe Material Considerations

1. Malleable fittings should be used for gas service.
2. Malleable fittings are used where there are stresses/strains due to expansion and vibration.
3. Cast fittings may be broken as an aid to disassembling of heating lines frozen by long use, temperature and minerals.
4. Cast iron pipe is extensively used for underground and submerged service.
5. Type M (light wall) copper tubing is available in hard temper only and is used for nonpressure and less severe applications than K and L.

6. Type L (medium wall) copper tubing, available hard or soft for interior service.
7. Type K (heavy wall) copper tubing, available in hard or soft temper for use where conditions are severe. For underground and interior service.
8. Hard drawn tubing requires fewer hangers or supports but should not be bent. Silver brazed fittings are recommended, however soft solder is normally used.
9. Type DMV (very light wall) copper tubing designed for drainage, waste and vent plus other non-critical pressure services.

Domestic/Imported Pipe and Fittings Cost

The prices shown in this publication for steel/cast iron pipe and steel, cast iron, malleable iron fittings are based on domestic production sold at the normal trade discounts. The above listed items of foreign manufacture may be available at prices of 1/3 to 1/2 those shown. Some imported items after minor machining or finishing operations are being sold as domestic to further complicate the system.

Caution: Most pipe prices in this book also include a coupling and pipe hangers which for the larger sizes can add significantly to the per foot cost and should be taken into account when comparing "book cost" with quoted supplier's cost.

833

Fig. R238313-11

R238313-10   Heat Trace Systems

Before you can determine the cost of a HEAT TRACE installation
the method of attachment must be established. There are (4) common
methods:

1. Cable is simply attached to the pipe with polyester tape
   every 12'.
2. Cable is attached with a continuous cover of 2" wide
   aluminum tape.
3. Cable is attached with factory extruded heat transfer cement
   and covered with metallic raceway with clips every 10'.
4. Cable is attached between layers of pipe insulation using either clips or
   polyester tape.

Example: Components for method 3 must include:

   A. Heat trace cable by voltage and watts per linear foot.
   B. Heat transfer cement, 1 gallon per 60 linear feet of cover.
   C. Metallic raceway by size and type.
   D. Raceway clips by size of pipe.

When taking off linear foot lengths of cable add the following for each valve
in the system. (E)

In all of the above methods each component of the system must be priced
individually.

SCREWED OR WELDED VALVE:			FLANGED VALVE:			BUTTERFLY VALVES:		
1/2"	=	6"	1/2"	=	1' -0"	1/2"	=	0'
3/4"	=	9"	3/4"	=	1' -6"	3/4"	=	0'
1"	=	1' -0"	1"	=	2' -0"	1"	=	1' -0"
1-1/2"	=	1' -6"	1-1/2"	=	2' -6"	1-1/2"	=	1' -6"
2"	=	2'	2"	=	2' -6"	2"	=	2' -0"
2-1/2"	=	2' -6"	2-1/2"	=	3' -0"	2-1/2"	=	2' -6"
3"	=	2' -6"	3"	=	3' -6"	3"	=	2' -6"
4"	=	4' -0"	4"	=	4' -0"	4"	=	3' -0"
6"	=	7' -0"	6"	=	8' -0"	6"	=	3' -6"
8"	=	9' -6"	8"	=	11' -0"	8"	=	4' -0"
10"	=	12' -6"	10"	=	14' -0"	10"	=	4' -0"
12"	=	15' -0"	12"	=	16' -6"	12"	=	5' -0"
14"	=	18' -0"	14"	=	19' -6"	14"	=	5' -6"
16"	=	21' -6"	16"	=	23' -0"	16"	=	6' -0"
18"	=	25' -6"	18"	=	27' -0"	18"	=	6' -6"
20"	=	28' -6"	20"	=	30' -0"	20"	=	7' -0"
24"	=	34' -0"	24"	=	36' -0"	24"	=	8' -0"
30"	=	40' -0"	30"	=	42' -0"	30"	=	10' -0"

R238313-10 Heat Trace Systems (cont.)

Add the following quantities of heat transfer cement to linear foot totals for each valve:

Nominal Valve Size	Gallons of Cement per Valve
1/2"	0.14
3/4"	0.21
1"	0.29
1-1/2"	0.36
2"	0.43
2-1/2"	0.70
3"	0.71
4"	1.00
6"	1.43
8"	1.48
10"	1.50
12"	1.60
14"	1.75
16"	2.00
18"	2.25
20"	2.50
24"	3.00
30"	3.75

The following must be added to the list of components to accurately price HEAT TRACE systems:

1. Expediter fitting and clamp fasteners (F)
2. Junction box and nipple connected to expediter fitting (G)
3. Field installed terminal blocks within junction box
4. Ground lugs
5. Piping from power source to expediter fitting
6. Controls
7. Thermostats
8. Branch wiring
9. Cable splices
10. End of cable terminations
11. Branch piping fittings and boxes

Deduct the following percentages from labor if cable lengths in the same area exceed:

150' to 250'	10%	351' to 500'	20%
251' to 350'	15%	Over 500'	25%

Add the following percentages to labor for elevated installations:

15' to 20' high	10%	31' to 35' high	40%
21' to 25' high	20%	36' to 40' high	50%
26' to 30' high	30%	Over 40' high	60%

R238313-20 Spiral-Wrapped Heat Trace Cable (Pitch Table)

In order to increase the amount of heat, occasionally heat trace cable is wrapped in a spiral fashion around a pipe; increasing the number of feet of heater cable per linear foot of pipe.

Engineers first determine the heat loss per foot of pipe (based on the insulating material, its thickness, and the temperature differential across it). A ratio is then calculated by the formula:

$$\text{Feet of Heat Trace per Foot of Pipe} = \frac{\text{Watts/Foot of Heat Loss}}{\text{Watts/Foot of the Cable}}$$

The linear distance between wraps (pitch) is then taken from a chart or table. Generally, the pitch is listed on a drawing leaving the estimator to calculate the total length of heat tape required. An approximation may be taken from this table.

Feet of Heat Trace Per Foot of Pipe

Pitch In Inches	Nominal Pipe Size in Inches															
	1	1¼	1½	2	2½	3	4	6	8	10	12	14	16	18	20	24
3.5	1.80															
4	1.65															
5	1.46	1.60	1.80													
6	1.34	1.45	1.55	1.75												
7	1.25	1.35	1.43	1.57	1.75											
8	1.20	1.28	1.34	1.45	1.60	1.80										
9	1.16	1.23	1.28	1.37	1.51	1.68										
10	1.13	1.19	1.24	1.32	1.44	1.57	1.82									
15	1.06	1.08	1.10	1.15	1.21	1.29	1.42	1.78								
20	1.04	1.05	1.06	1.08	1.13	1.17	1.25	1.49	1.73							
25		1.04	1.04	1.06	1.08	1.11	1.17	1.33	1.51	1.72						
30				1.04	1.05	1.07	1.12	1.24	1.37	1.54	1.70					
35					1.06	1.06	1.09	1.17	1.28	1.42	1.54	1.64	1.78			
40						1.05	1.07	1.14	1.22	1.33	1.44	1.52	1.64	1.75		
50							1.05	1.09	1.15	1.22	1.29	1.35	1.44	1.53	1.64	1.83
60								1.06	1.11	1.16	1.21	1.25	1.31	1.39	1.46	1.62
70								1.05	1.08	1.12	1.17	1.19	1.24	1.30	1.35	1.47
80									1.06	1.09	1.13	1.15	1.19	1.24	1.28	1.38
90									1.04	1.06	1.10	1.13	1.16	1.19	1.23	1.32
100										1.05	1.08	1.10	1.13	1.15	1.19	1.23

Note: Common practice would normally limit the lower end of the table to 5% of additional heat and above 80% an engineer would likely opt for two (2) parallel cables.

R260519-93 Metric Equivalent, Wire

United States		European	
Size AWG or kcmil	Area Cir. Mils.(cmil) mm²	Size mm²	Area Cir. Mils.
18	1620/.82	.75	1480
16	2580/1.30	1.0	1974
14	4110/2.08	1.5	2961
12	6530/3.30	2.5	4935
10	10,380/5.25	4	7896
8	16,510/8.36	6	11,844
6	26,240/13.29	10	19,740
4	41,740/21.14	16	31,584
3	52,620/26.65	25	49,350
2	66,360/33.61	–	–
1	83,690/42.39	35	69,090
1/0	105,600/53.49	50	98,700
2/0	133,100/67.42	–	–
3/0	167,800/85.00	70	138,180
4/0	211,600/107.19	95	187,530
250	250,000/126.64	120	236,880
300	300,000/151.97	150	296,100
350	350,000/177.30	–	–
400	400,000/202.63	185	365,190
500	500,000/253.29	240	473,760
600	600,000/303.95	300	592,200
700	700,000/354.60	–	–
750	750,000/379.93	–	–

U.S. vs. European Wire – Approximate Equivalents

R260533-22 Conductors in Conduit

Table below lists maximum number of conductors for various sized conduit using THW, TW or THWN insulations.

Copper Wire Size	1/2" TW	1/2" THW	1/2" THWN	3/4" TW	3/4" THW	3/4" THWN	1" TW	1" THW	1" THWN	1-1/4" TW	1-1/4" THW	1-1/4" THWN	1-1/2" TW	1-1/2" THW	1-1/2" THWN	2" TW	2" THW	2" THWN	2-1/2" TW	2-1/2" THW	2-1/2" THWN	3" THW	3" THWN	3-1/2" THW	3-1/2" THWN	4" THW	4" THWN
#14	9	6	13	15	10	24	25	16	39	44	29	69	60	40	94	99	65	154	142	93		143		192			
#12	7	4	10	12	8	18	19	13	29	35	24	51	47	32	70	78	53	114	111	76	164	117		157			
#10	5	4	6	9	6	11	15	11	18	26	19	32	36	26	44	60	43	73	85	61	104	95	160	127		163	
#8	2	1	3	4	3	5	7	5	9	12	10	16	17	13	22	28	22	36	40	32	51	49	79	66	106	85	136
#6		1	1		2	4		4	6		7	11		10	15		16	26		23	37	36	57	48	76	62	98
#4		1	1		1	2		3	4		5	7		7	9		12	16		17	22	27	35	36	47	47	60
#3		1	1		1	1		2	3		4	6		6	8		10	13		15	19	23	29	31	39	40	51
#2		1	1		1	1		2	3		4	5		5	7		9	11		13	16	20	25	27	33	34	43
#1					1	1		1	1		3	3		4	5		6	8		9	12	14	18	19	25	25	32
1/0					1	1		1	1		2	3		3	4		5	7		8	10	12	15	16	21	21	27
2/0					1	1		1	1		1	2		3	3		5	6		7	8	10	13	14	17	18	22
3/0					1	1		1	1		1	1		2	3		4	5		6	7	9	11	12	14	15	18
4/0						1		1	1		1	1		1	2		3	4		5	6	7	9	10	12	13	15
250 kcmil								1	1		1	1		1	1		2	3		4	4	6	7	8	10	10	12
300								1	1		1	1		1	1		2	3		3	4	5	6	7	8	9	11
350									1		1	1		1	1		1	2		3	3	4	5	6	7	8	9
400											1	1		1	1		1	1		2	3	4	5	5	6	7	8
500											1	1		1	1		1	1		1	2	3	4	4	5	6	7
600												1		1	1		1	1		1	1	3	3	4	4	5	5
700														1	1		1	1		1	1	2	3	3	4	4	5
750														1	1		1	1		1	1	2	2	3	3	4	4

R260590-05 Typical Overhead Service Entrance

Utility Pole

Service Entrance Cap 3"

Galvanized Conduit 3"

Two Hole Pipe Clip 3"

Coupling

Grade Line

Building Wall

Elbow

3" PVC Conduit

3" Galv. Conduit

3" Locknut

Pullbox

3" Locknut & Bushing Insulated In Pullbox

3" PVC To Galv. Adapter

Adapter

4 - 250 MCM XHHW In Above Conduit

3" Galv. Conduit Used For Safety On Pole And Through Foundation

3" Galv. Conduit To 500 AMP. Circuit Breaker Below

2 Locknuts And 1 Insulating Bushing Required Where #4 Or Larger Wire Used

837

For customer support on your Site Work & Landscape Cost Data, call 877.737.1594.

R262716-40   Standard Electrical Enclosure Types

NEMA Enclosures

Electrical enclosures serve two basic purposes; they protect people from accidental contact with enclosed electrical devices and connections, and they protect the enclosed devices and connections from specified external conditions. The National Electrical Manufacturers Association (NEMA) has established the following standards. Because these descriptions are not intended to be complete representations of NEMA listings, consultation of NEMA literature is advised for detailed information.

The following definitions and descriptions pertain to NONHAZARDOUS locations.

NEMA   Type 1: General purpose enclosures intended for use indoors, primarily to prevent accidental contact of personnel with the enclosed equipment in areas that do not involve unusual conditions.

NEMA   Type 2: Dripproof indoor enclosures intended to protect the enclosed equipment against dripping noncorrosive liquids and falling dirt.

NEMA   Type 3: Dustproof, raintight and sleet-resistant (ice-resistant) enclosures intended for use outdoors to protect the enclosed equipment against wind-blown dust, rain, sleet, and external ice formation.

NEMA   Type 3R: Rainproof and sleet-resistant (ice-resistant) enclosures which are intended for use outdoors to protect the enclosed equipment against rain. These enclosures are constructed so that the accumulation and melting of sleet (ice) will not damage the enclosure and its internal mechanisms.

NEMA   Type 3S: Enclosures intended for outdoor use to provide limited protection against wind-blown dust, rain, and sleet (ice) and to allow operation of external mechanisms when ice-laden.

NEMA   Type 4: Watertight and dust-tight enclosures intended for use indoors and out – to protect the enclosed equipment against splashing water, see page of water, falling or hose-directed water, and severe external condensation.

NEMA   Type 4X: Watertight, dust-tight, and corrosion-resistant indoor and outdoor enclosures featuring the same provisions as Type 4 enclosures, plus corrosion resistance.

NEMA   Type 5: Indoor enclosures intended primarily to provide limited protection against dust and falling dirt.

NEMA   Type 6: Enclosures intended for indoor and outdoor use – primarily to provide limited protection against the entry of water during occasional temporary submersion at a limited depth.

NEMA   Type 6R: Enclosures intended for indoor and outdoor use – primarily to provide limited protection against the entry of water during prolonged submersion at a limited depth.

NEMA   Type 11: Enclosures intended for indoor use – primarily to provide, by means of oil immersion, limited protection to enclosed equipment against the corrosive effects of liquids and gases.

NEMA   Type 12: Dust-tight and driptight indoor enclosures intended for use indoors in industrial locations to protect the enclosed equipment against fibers, flyings, lint, dust, and dirt, as well as light splashing, see page, dripping, and external condensation of noncorrosive liquids.

NEMA   Type 13: Oil-tight and dust-tight indoor enclosures intended primarily to house pilot devices, such as limit switches, foot switches, push buttons, selector switches, and pilot lights, and to protect these devices against lint and dust, see page, external condensation, and sprayed water, oil, and noncorrosive coolant.

The following definitions and descriptions pertain to HAZARDOUS, or CLASSIFIED, locations:

NEMA   Type 7: Enclosures intended to use in indoor locations classified as Class 1, Groups A, B, C, or D, as defined in the National Electrical Code.

NEMA   Type 9: Enclosures intended for use in indoor locations classified as Class 2, Groups E, F, or G, as defined in the National Electrical Code.

R312316-40   Excavating

The selection of equipment used for structural excavation and bulk excavation or for grading is determined by the following factors.

1. Quantity of material
2. Type of material
3. Depth or height of cut
4. Length of haul
5. Condition of haul road
6. Accessibility of site
7. Moisture content and dewatering requirements
8. Availability of excavating and hauling equipment

Some additional costs must be allowed for hand trimming the sides and bottom of concrete pours and other excavation below the general excavation.

Number of B.C.Y. per truck = 1.5 C.Y. bucket x 8 passes = 12 loose C.Y.

$$= 12 \times \frac{100}{118} = 10.2 \text{ B.C.Y. per truck}$$

Truck Haul Cycle:

Load truck, 8 passes	=	4 minutes
Haul distance, 1 mile	=	9 minutes
Dump time	=	2 minutes
Return, 1 mile	=	7 minutes
Spot under machine	=	1 minute
		23 minute cycle

Add the mobilization and demobilization costs to the total excavation costs. When equipment is rented for more than three days, there is often no mobilization charge by the equipment dealer. On larger jobs outside of urban areas, scrapers can move earth economically provided a dump site or fill area and adequate haul roads are available. Excavation within sheeting bracing or cofferdam bracing is usually done with a clamshell and production

When planning excavation and fill, the following should also be considered.

1. Swell factor
2. Compaction factor
3. Moisture content
4. Density requirements

A typical example for scheduling and estimating the cost of excavation of a 15' deep basement on a dry site when the material must be hauled off the site is outlined below.

Assumptions:

1. Swell factor, 18%
2. No mobilization or demobilization
3. Allowance included for idle time and moving on job
4. No dewatering, sheeting, or bracing
5. No truck spotter or hand trimming

Fleet Haul Production per day in B.C.Y.

$$4 \text{ trucks} \times \frac{50 \text{ min. hour}}{23 \text{ min. haul cycle}} \times 8 \text{ hrs.} \times 10.2 \text{ B.C.Y.}$$

$$= 4 \times 2.2 \times 8 \times 10.2 = 718 \text{ B.C.Y./day}$$

is low, since the clamshell may have to be guided by hand between the bracing. When excavating or filling an area enclosed with a wellpoint system, add 10% to 15% to the cost to allow for restricted access. When estimating earth excavation quantities for structures, allow work space outside the building footprint for construction of the foundation and a slope of 1:1 unless sheeting is used.

839

R312316-45　　Excavating Equipment

The table below lists THEORETICAL hourly production in C.Y./hr. bank measure for some typical excavation equipment. Figures assume 50 minute hours, 83% job efficiency, 100% operator efficiency, 90° swing and properly sized hauling units, which must be modified for adverse digging and loading conditions. Actual production costs in the front of the book average about 50% of the theoretical values listed here.

Equipment	Soil Type	B.C.Y. Weight	% Swell	1 C.Y.	1-1/2 C.Y.	2 C.Y.	2-1/2 C.Y.	3 C.Y.	3-1/2 C.Y.	4 C.Y.
Hydraulic Excavator	Moist loam, sandy clay	3400 lb.	40%	85	125	175	220	275	330	380
"Backhoe"	Sand and gravel	3100	18	80	120	160	205	260	310	365
15' Deep Cut	Common earth	2800	30	70	105	150	190	240	280	330
	Clay, hard, dense	3000	33	65	100	130	170	210	255	300
	Moist loam, sandy clay	3400	40	170 (6.0)	245 (7.0)	295 (7.8)	335 (8.4)	385 (8.8)	435 (9.1)	475 (9.4)
Power Shovel	Sand and gravel	3100	18	165 (6.0)	225 (7.0)	275 (7.8)	325 (8.4)	375 (8.8)	420 (9.1)	460 (9.4)
Optimum Cut (Ft.)	Common earth	2800	30	145 (7.8)	200 (9.2)	250 (10.2)	295 (11.2)	335 (12.1)	375 (13.0)	425 (13.8)
	Clay, hard, dense	3000	33	120 (9.0)	175 (10.7)	220 (12.2)	255 (13.3)	300 (14.2)	335 (15.1)	375 (16.0)
	Moist loam, sandy clay	3400	40	130 (6.6)	180 (7.4)	220 (8.0)	250 (8.5)	290 (9.0)	325 (9.5)	385 (10.0)
Drag Line	Sand and gravel	3100	18	130 (6.6)	175 (7.4)	210 (8.0)	245 (8.5)	280 (9.0)	315 (9.5)	375 (10.0)
Optimum Cut (Ft.)	Common earth	2800	30	110 (8.0)	160 (9.0)	190 (9.9)	220 (10.5)	250 (11.0)	280 (11.5)	310 (12.0)
	Clay, hard, dense	3000	33	90 (9.3)	130 (10.7)	160 (11.8)	190 (12.3)	225 (12.8)	250 (13.3)	280 (12.0)

Equipment	Soil Type	B.C.Y. Weight	% Swell	Wheel Loaders				Track Loaders		
				3 C.Y.	4 C.Y.	6 C.Y.	8 C.Y.	2-1/4 C.Y.	3 C.Y.	4 C.Y.
	Moist loam, sandy clay	3400	40	260	340	510	690	135	180	250
	Sand and gravel	3100	18	245	320	480	650	130	170	235
Loading Tractors	Common earth	2800	30	230	300	460	620	120	155	220
	Clay, hard, dense	3000	33	200	270	415	560	110	145	200
	Rock, well-blasted	4000	50	180	245	380	520	100	130	180

R312319-90   Wellpoints

A single stage wellpoint system is usually limited to dewatering an average 15′ depth below normal ground water level. Multi-stage systems are employed for greater depth with the pumping equipment installed only at the lowest header level. Ejectors with unlimited lift capacity can be economical when two or more stages of wellpoints can be replaced or when horizontal clearance is restricted, such as in deep trenches or tunneling projects, and where low water flows are expected. Wellpoints are usually spaced on 2-1/2′ to 10′ centers along a header pipe. Wellpoint spacing, header size, and pump size are all determined by the expected flow as dictated by soil conditions.

In almost all soils encountered in wellpoint dewatering, the wellpoints may be jetted into place. Cemented soils and stiff clays may require sand wicks about 12″ in diameter around each wellpoint to increase efficiency and eliminate weeping into the excavation. These sand wicks require 1/2 to 3 C.Y. of washed filter sand and are installed by using a 12″ diameter steel casing and hole puncher jetted into the ground 2′ deeper than the wellpoint. Rock may require predrilled holes.

Labor required for the complete installation and removal of a single stage wellpoint system is in the range of 3/4 to 2 labor-hours per linear foot of header, depending upon jetting conditions, wellpoint spacing, etc.

Continuous pumping is necessary except in some free draining soil where temporary flooding is permissible (as in trenches which are backfilled after each day's work). Good practice requires provision of a stand-by pump during the continuous pumping operation.

Systems for continuous trenching below the water table should be installed three to four times the length of expected daily progress to ensure uninterrupted digging, and header pipe size should not be changed during the job.

For pervious free draining soils, deep wells in place of wellpoints may be economical because of lower installation and maintenance costs. Daily production ranges between two to three wells per day, for 25′ to 40′ depths, to one well per day for depths over 50′.

Detailed analysis and estimating for any dewatering problem is available at no cost from wellpoint manufacturers. Major firms will quote "sufficient equipment" quotes or their affiliates offer lump sum proposals to cover complete dewatering responsibility.

Description for 200′ System with 8″ Header		Quantities
Equipment & Material	Wellpoints 25′ long, 2″ diameter @ 5′ O.C.	40 Each
	Header pipe, 8″ diameter	200 L.F.
	Discharge pipe, 8″ diameter	100 L.F.
	8″ valves	3 Each
	Combination jetting & wellpoint pump (standby)	1 Each
	Wellpoint pump, 8″ diameter	1 Each
	Transportation to and from site	1 Day
	Fuel for 30 days x 60 gal./day	1800 Gallons
	Lubricants for 30 days x 16 lbs./day	480 Lbs.
	Sand for points	40 C.Y.
Labor	Technician to supervise installation	1 Week
	Labor for installation and removal of system	300 Labor-hours
	4 Operators straight time 40 hrs./wk. for 4.33 wks.	693 Hrs.
	4 Operators overtime 2 hrs./wk. for 4.33 wks.	35 Hrs.

R312323-30   Compacting Backfill

Compaction of fill in embankments, around structures, in trenches, and under slabs is important to control settlement. Factors affecting compaction are:
1. Soil gradation
2. Moisture content
3. Equipment used
4. Depth of fill per lift
5. Density required

Production Rate:

$$\frac{1.75' \text{ plate width x 50 F.P.M. x 50 min./hr. x .67' lift}}{27 \text{ C.F. per C.Y.}} = 108.5 \text{ C.Y./hr.}$$

Production Rate for 4 Passes:

$$\frac{108.5 \text{ C.Y.}}{4 \text{ passes}} = 27.125 \text{ C.Y./hr. x 8 hrs.} = 217 \text{ C.Y./day}$$

Example:

Compact granular fill around a building foundation using a 21″ wide x 24″ vibratory plate in 8″ lifts. Operator moves at 50 F.P.M. working a 50 minute hour to develop 95% Modified Proctor Density with 4 passes.

R314116-40   Wood Sheet Piling

Wood sheet piling may be used for depths to 20′ where there is no ground water. If moderate ground water is encountered Tongue & Groove sheeting will help to keep it out. When considerable ground water is present, steel sheeting must be used.

For estimating purposes on trench excavation, sizes are as follows:

Depth	Sheeting	Wales	Braces	B.F. per S.F.
To 8′	3 x 12′s	6 x 8′s, 2 line	6 x 8′s, @ 10′	4.0 @ 8′
8′ x 12′	3 x 12′s	10 x 10′s, 2 line	10 x 10′s, @ 9′	5.0 average
12′ to 20′	3 x 12′s	12 x 12′s, 3 line	12 x 12′s, @ 8′	7.0 average

Sheeting to be toed in at least 2′ depending upon soil conditions. A five person crew with an air compressor and sheeting driver can drive and brace 440 SF/day at 8′ deep, 360 SF/day at 12′ deep, and 320 SF/day at 16′ deep.

For normal soils, piling can be pulled in 1/3 the time to install. Pulling difficulty increases with the time in the ground. Production can be increased by high pressure jetting.

R314116-45   Steel Sheet Piling

Limiting weights are 22 to 38#/S.F. of wall surface with 27#/S.F. average for usual types and sizes. (Weights of piles themselves are from 30.7#/L.F. to 57#/L.F. but they are 15″ to 21″ wide.) Lightweight sections 12″ to 28″ wide from 3 ga. to 12 ga. thick are also available for shallow excavations. Piles may be driven two at a time with an impact or vibratory hammer (use vibratory to pull) hung from a crane without leads. A reasonable estimate of the life of steel sheet piling is 10 uses with up to 125 uses possible if a vibratory hammer is used. Used piling costs from 50% to 80% of new piling depending on location and market conditions. Sheet piling and H piles can be rented for about 30% of the delivered mill price for the first month and 5% per month thereafter. Allow 1 labor-hour per pile for cleaning and trimming after driving. These costs increase with depth and hydrostatic head. Vibratory drivers are faster in wet granular soils and are excellent for pile extraction. Pulling difficulty increases with the time in the ground and may cost more than driving. It is often economical to abandon the sheet piling, especially if it can be used as the outer wall form. Allow about 1/3 additional length or more for toeing into ground. Add bracing, waler and strut costs. Waler costs can equal the cost per ton of sheeting.

Earthwork | **R3145 Vibroflotation & Densification**

R314513-90   Vibroflotation and Vibro Replacement Soil Compaction

Vibroflotation is a proprietary system of compacting sandy soils in place to increase relative density to about 70%. Typical bearing capacities attained will be 6000 psf for saturated sand and 12,000 psf for dry sand. Usual range is 4000 to 8000 psf capacity. Costs in the front of the book are for a vertical foot of compacted cylinder 6′ to 10′ in diameter.

Vibro replacement is a proprietary system of improving cohesive soils in place to increase bearing capacity. Most silts and clays above or below the water table can be strengthened by installation of stone columns.

The process consists of radial displacement of the soil by vibration. The created hole is then backfilled in stages with coarse granular fill which is thoroughly compacted and displaced into the surrounding soil in the form of a column.

The total project cost would depend on the number and depth of the compacted cylinders. The installing company guarantees relative soil density of the sand cylinders after compaction and the bearing capacity of the soil after the replacement process. Detailed estimating information is available from the installer at no cost.

R316326-60 Caissons

The three principal types of cassions are:

(1) Belled Caissons, which except for shallow depths and poor soil conditions, are generally recommended. They provide more bearing than shaft area. Because of its conical shape, no horizontal reinforcement of the bell is required.

(2) Straight Shaft Caissons are used where relatively light loads are to be supported by caissons that rest on high value bearing strata. While the shaft is larger in diameter than for belled types this is more than offset by the saving in time and labor.

(3) Keyed Caissons are used when extremely heavy loads are to be carried. A keyed or socketed caisson transfers its load into rock by a combination of end-bearing and shear reinforcing of the shaft. The most economical shaft often consists of a steel casing, a steel wide flange core and concrete. Allowable compressive stresses of .225 f'c for concrete, 16,000 psi for the wide flange core, and 9,000 psi for the steel casing are commonly used. The usual range of shaft diameter is 18″ to 84″. The number of sizes specified for any one project should be limited due to the problems of casing and auger storage. When hand work is to be performed, shaft diameters should not be less than 32″. When inspection of borings is required a minimum shaft diameter of 30″ is recommended. Concrete caissons are intended to be poured against earth excavation so permanent forms which add to cost should not be used if the excavation is clean and the earth sufficiently impervious to prevent excessive loss of concrete.

Soil Conditions for Belling		
Good	Requires Handwork	Not Recommended
Clay	Hard Shale	Silt
Sandy Clay	Limestone	Sand
Silty Clay	Sandstone	Gravel
Clayey Silt	Weathered Mica	Igneous Rock
Hard-pan		
Soft Shale		
Decomposed Rock		

Exterior Improvements R3292 Turf & Grasses

R329219-50 Seeding

The type of grass is determined by light, shade and moisture content of soil plus intended use. Fertilizer should be disked 4″ before seeding. For steep slopes disk five tons of mulch and lay two tons of hay or straw on surface per acre after seeding. Surface mulch can be staked, lightly disked or tar emulsion sprayed. Material for mulch can be wood chips, peat moss, partially rotted hay or straw, wood fibers and sprayed emulsions. Hemp seed blankets with fertilizer are also available. For spring seeding, watering is necessary. Late fall seeding may have to be reseeded in the spring. Hydraulic seeding, power mulching, and aerial seeding can be used on large areas.

843

Exterior Improvements   R3293 Plants

R329343-10   Plant Spacing Chart

This chart may be used when plants are to be placed equidistant from each other, staggering their position in each row.

Plant Spacing (Inches)	Row Spacing (Inches)	Plants Per (CSF)	Plant Spacing (Feet)	Row Spacing (Feet)	Plants Per (MSF)
			4	3.46	72
6	5.20	462	5	4.33	46
8	6.93	260	6	5.20	32
10	8.66	166	8	6.93	18
12	10.39	115	10	8.66	12
15	12.99	74	12	10.39	8
18	15.59	51.32	15	12.99	5.13
21	18.19	37.70	20	17.32	2.89
24	20.78	28.87	25	21.65	1.85
30	25.98	18.48	30	25.98	1.28
36	31.18	12.83	40	34.64	0.72

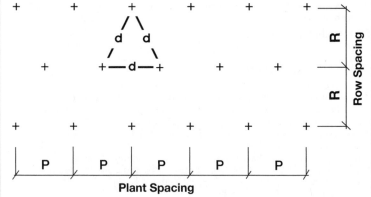

Plant Spacing

R329343-20   Trees and Plants by Environment and Purposes

Dry, Windy, Exposed Areas
Barberry
Junipers, all varieties
Locust
Maple
Oak
Pines, all varieties
Poplar, Hybrid
Privet
Spruce, all varieties
Sumac, Staghorn

Lightly Wooded Areas
Dogwood
Hemlock
Larch
Pine, White
Rhododendron
Spruce, Norway
Redbud

Total Shade Areas
Hemlock
Ivy, English
Myrtle
Pachysandra
Privet
Spice Bush
Yews, Japanese

Cold Temperatures of Northern U.S. and Canada
Arborvitae, American
Birch, White
Dogwood, Silky
Fir, Balsam
Fir, Douglas
Hemlock
Juniper, Andorra
Juniper, Blue Rug
Linden, Little Leaf
Maple, Sugar
Mountain Ash
Myrtle
Olive, Russian

Pine, Mugho
Pine, Ponderosa
Pine, Red
Pine, Scotch
Poplar, Hybrid
Privet
Rosa Rugosa
Spruce, Dwarf Alberta
Spruce, Black Hills
Spruce, Blue
Spruce, Norway
Spruce, White, Engelman
Yellow Wood

Wet, Swampy Areas
American Arborvitae
Birch, White
Black Gum
Hemlock
Maple, Red
Pine, White
Willow

Poor, Dry, Rocky Soil
Barberry
Crownvetch
Eastern Red Cedar
Juniper, Virginiana
Locust, Black
Locust, Bristly
Locust, Honey
Olive, Russian
Pines, all varieties
Privet
Rosa Rugosa
Sumac, Staghorn

Seashore Planting
Arborvitae, American
Juniper, Tamarix
Locust, Black
Oak, White
Olive, Russian
Pine, Austrian
Pine, Japanese Black

Pine, Mugho
Pine, Scotch
Privet, Amur River
Rosa Rugosa
Yew, Japanese

City Planting
Barberry
Fir, Concolor
Forsythia
Hemlock
Holly, Japanese
Ivy, English
Juniper, Andorra
Linden, Little Leaf
Locust, Honey
Maple, Norway, Silver
Oak, Pin, Red
Olive, Russian
Pachysandra
Pine, Austrian
Pine, White
Privet
Rosa Rugosa
Sumac, Staghorn
Yew, Japanese

Bonsai Planting
Azaleas
Birch, White
Ginkgo
Junipers
Pine, Bristlecone
Pine, Mugho
Spruce,k Engleman
Spruce, Dwarf Alberta

Street Planting
Linden, Little Leaf
Oak, Pin
Ginkgo

Fast Growth
Birch, White
Crownvetch
Dogwood, Silky

Fir, Douglas
Juniper, Blue Pfitzer
Juniper, Blue Rug
Maple, Silver
Olive, Autumn
Pines, Austrian, Ponderosa, Red
   Scotch and White
Poplar, Hybrid
Privet
Spruce, Norway
Spruce, Serbian
Texus, Cuspidata, Hicksi
Willow

Dense, Impenetrable Hedges
Field Plantings:
   Locust, Bristly,
   Olive, Autumn
   Sumac
Residential Area:
   Barberry, Red or Green
   Juniper, Blue Pfitzer
   Rosa Rugosa

Food for Birds
Ash, Mountain
Barberry
Bittersweet
Cherry, Manchu
Dogwood, Silky
Honesuckle, Rem Red
Hawthorn
Oaks
Olive, Autumn, Russian
Privet
Rosa Rugosa
Sumac

Erosion Control
Crownvetch
Locust, Bristly
Willow

R331113-80   Piping Designations

There are several systems currently in use to describe pipe and fittings. The following paragraphs will help to identify and clarify classifications of piping systems used for water distribution.

Piping may be classified by schedule. Piping schedules include 5S, 10S, 10, 20, 30, Standard, 40, 60, Extra Strong, 80, 100, 120, 140, 160 and Double Extra Strong. These schedules are dependent upon the pipe wall thickness. The wall thickness of a particular schedule may vary with pipe size.

Ductile iron pipe for water distribution is classified by Pressure Classes such as Class 150, 200, 250, 300 and 350. These classes are actually the rated water working pressure of the pipe in pounds per square inch (psi). The pipe in these pressure classes is designed to withstand the rated water working pressure plus a surge allowance of 100 psi.

The American Water Works Association (AWWA) provides standards for various types of **plastic pipe**. C-900 is the specification for polyvinyl chloride (PVC) piping used for water distribution in sizes ranging from 4″ through 12″. C-901 is the specification for polyethylene (PE) pressure pipe, tubing and fittings used for water distribution in sizes ranging from 1/2″ through 3″. C-905 is the specification for PVC piping sizes 14″ and greater.

PVC pressure-rated pipe is identified using the standard dimensional ratio (SDR) method. This method is defined by the American Society for Testing and Materials (ASTM) Standard D 2241. This pipe is available in SDR numbers 64, 41, 32.5, 26, 21, 17, and 13.5. Pipe with an SDR of 64 will have the thinnest wall while pipe with an SDR of 13.5 will have the thickest wall. When the pressure rating (PR) of a pipe is given in psi, it is based on a line supplying water at 73 degrees F.

The National Sanitation Foundation (NSF) seal of approval is applied to products that can be used with potable water. These products have been tested to ANSI/NSF Standard 14.

Valves and strainers are classified by American National Standards Institute (ANSI) Classes. These Classes are 125, 150, 200, 250, 300, 400, 600, 900, 1500 and 2500. Within each class there is an operating pressure range dependent upon temperature. Design parameters should be compared to the appropriate material dependent, pressure-temperature rating chart for accurate valve selection.

Utilities   **R3371 Elec. Utility Transmission & Distribution**

R337119-30   Concrete for Conduit Encasement

Table below lists C.Y. of concrete for 100 L.F. of trench. Conduits separation center to center should meet 7.5″ (N.E.C.).

Number of Conduits	1	2	3	4	6	8	9	Number of Conduits
Trench Dimension	11.5″ x 11.5″	11.5″ x 19″	11.5″ x 27″	19″ x 19″	19″ x 27″	19″ x 38″	27″ x 27″	Trench Dimension
Conduit Diameter 2.0″	3.29	5.39	7.64	8.83	12.51	17.66	17.72	Conduit Diameter 2.0″
2.5″	3.23	5.29	7.49	8.62	12.19	17.23	17.25	2.5″
3.0″	3.15	5.13	7.24	8.29	11.71	16.59	16.52	3.0″
3.5″	3.08	4.97	7.02	7.99	11.26	15.98	15.84	3.5″
4.0″	2.99	4.80	6.76	7.65	10.74	15.30	15.07	4.0″
5.0″	2.78	4.37	6.11	6.78	9.44	13.57	13.12	5.0″
6.0″	2.52	3.84	5.33	5.74	7.87	11.48	10.77	6.0″

R347216-10 Single Track R.R. Siding

The costs for a single track RR siding in the Unit Price section include the components shown in the table below.

Description of Component	Qty. per L.F. of Track	Unit
Ballast, 1-1/2″ crushed stone	.667	C.Y.
6″ x 8″ x 8′-6″ Treated timber ties, 22″ O.C.	.545	Ea.
Tie plates, 2 per tie	1.091	Ea.
Track rail	2.000	L.F.
Spikes, 6″, 4 per tie	2.182	Ea.
Splice bars w/ bolts, lock washers & nuts, @ 33′ O.C.	.061	Pair
Crew B-14 @ 57 L.F./Day	.018	Day

R347216-20 Single Track, Steel Ties, Concrete Bed

The costs for a R.R. siding with steel ties and a concrete bed in the Unit Price section include the components shown in the table below.

Description of Component	Qty. per L.F. of Track	Unit
Concrete bed, 9′ wide, 10″ thick	.278	C.Y.
Ties, W6x16 x 6′-6″ long, @ 30″ O.C.	.400	Ea.
Tie plates, 4 per tie	1.600	Ea.
Track rail	2.000	L.F.
Tie plate bolts, 1″, 8 per tie	3.200	Ea.
Splice bars w/bolts, lock washers & nuts, @ 33′ O.C.	.061	Pair
Crew B-14 @ 22 L.F./Day	.045	Day

Change Orders

Change Order Considerations

A change order is a written document, usually prepared by the design professional, and signed by the owner, the architect/engineer, and the contractor. A change order states the agreement of the parties to: an addition, deletion, or revision in the work; an adjustment in the contract sum, if any; or an adjustment in the contract time, if any. Change orders, or "extras" in the construction process occur after execution of the construction contract and impact architects/engineers, contractors, and owners.

Change orders that are properly recognized and managed can ensure orderly, professional, and profitable progress for all who are involved in the project. There are many causes for change orders and change order requests. In all cases, change orders or change order requests should be addressed promptly and in a precise and prescribed manner. The following paragraphs include information regarding change order pricing and procedures.

The Causes of Change Orders

Reasons for issuing change orders include:

- Unforeseen field conditions that require a change in the work
- Correction of design discrepancies, errors, or omissions in the contract documents
- Owner-requested changes, either by design criteria, scope of work, or project objectives
- Completion date changes for reasons unrelated to the construction process
- Changes in building code interpretations, or other public authority requirements that require a change in the work
- Changes in availability of existing or new materials and products

Procedures

Properly written contract documents must include the correct change order procedures for all parties—owners, design professionals and contractors—to follow in order to avoid costly delays and litigation.

Being "in the right" is not always a sufficient or acceptable defense. The contract provisions requiring notification and documentation must be adhered to within a defined or reasonable time frame.

The appropriate method of handling change orders is by a written proposal and acceptance by all parties involved. Prior to starting work on a project, all parties should identify their

authorized agents who may sign and accept change orders, as well as any limits placed on their authority.

Time may be a critical factor when the need for a change arises. For such cases, the contractor might be directed to proceed on a "time and materials" basis, rather than wait for all paperwork to be processed—a delay that could impede progress. In this situation, the contractor must still follow the prescribed change order procedures including, but not limited to, notification and documentation.

Lack of documentation can be very costly, especially if legal judgments are to be made, and if certain field personnel are no longer available. For time and material change orders, the contractor should keep accurate daily records of all labor and material allocated to the change.

Owners or awarding authorities who do considerable and continual building construction (such as the federal government) realize the inevitability of change orders for numerous reasons, both predictable and unpredictable. As a result, the federal government, the American Institute of Architects (AIA), the Engineers Joint Contract Documents Committee (EJCDC) and other contractor, legal, and technical organizations have developed standards and procedures to be followed by all parties to achieve contract continuance and timely completion, while being financially fair to all concerned.

Pricing Change Orders

When pricing change orders, regardless of their cause, the most significant factor is when the change occurs. The need for a change may be perceived in the field or requested by the architect/engineer *before* any of the actual installation has begun, or may evolve or appear *during* construction when the item of work in question is partially installed. In the latter cases, the original sequence of construction is disrupted, along with all contiguous and supporting systems. Change orders cause the greatest impact when they occur *after* the installation has been completed and must be uncovered, or even replaced. Post-completion changes may be caused by necessary design changes, product failure, or changes in the owner's requirements that are not discovered until the building or the systems begin to function.

Specified procedures of notification and record keeping must be adhered to and enforced regardless of the stage of construction: *before, during,* or *after* installation. Some bidding documents anticipate change orders by requiring that unit prices including overhead and profit percentages—for additional as well as deductible changes—be listed. Generally these unit prices do not fully take into account the ripple effect, or impact on other trades, and should be used for general guidance only.

When pricing change orders, it is important to classify the time frame in which the change occurs. There are two basic time frames for change orders: *pre-installation change orders,* which occur before the start of construction, and *post-installation change orders,* which involve reworking after the original installation. Change orders that occur between these stages may be priced according to the extent of work completed using a combination of techniques developed for pricing *pre-* and *post-installation* changes.

Factors To Consider When Pricing Change Orders

As an estimator begins to prepare a change order, the following questions should be reviewed to determine their impact on the final price.

General

- *Is the change order work* pre-installation *or* post-installation?

  Change order work costs vary according to how much of the installation has been completed. Once workers have the project scoped in their minds, even though they have not started, it can be difficult to refocus. Consequently they may spend more than the normal amount of time understanding the change. Also, modifications to work in place, such as trimming or refitting, usually take more time than was initially estimated. The greater the amount of work in place, the more reluctant workers are to change it. Psychologically they may resent the change and as a result the rework takes longer than normal. Post-installation change order estimates must include demolition of existing work as required to accomplish the change. If the work is performed at a later time, additional obstacles, such as building finishes, may be present which must be protected. Regardless of whether the change occurs pre-installation or post-installation, attempt to isolate the identifiable factors and price them separately. For example, add shipping costs that may be required pre-installation or any demolition required post-installation. Then analyze the potential impact on productivity of psychological and/or learning curve factors and adjust the output rates accordingly. One approach is to break down the typical workday into segments and quantify the impact on each segment.

Change Order Installation Efficiency

The labor-hours expressed (for new construction) are based on average installation time, using an efficiency level. For change order situations, adjustments to this efficiency level should reflect the daily labor-hour allocation for that particular occurrence.

- *Will the change substantially delay the original completion date?*

A significant change in the project may cause the original completion date to be extended. The extended schedule may subject the contractor to new wage rates dictated by relevant labor contracts. Project supervision and other project overhead must also be extended beyond the original completion date. The schedule extension may also put installation into a new weather season. For example, underground piping scheduled for October installation was delayed until January. As a result, frost penetrated the trench area, thereby changing the degree of difficulty of the task. Changes and delays may have a ripple effect throughout the project. This effect must be analyzed and negotiated with the owner.

- *What is the net effect of a deduct change order?*

In most cases, change orders resulting in a deduction or credit reflect only bare costs. The contractor may retain the overhead and profit based on the original bid.

Materials

- *Will you have to pay more or less for the new material, required by the change order, than you paid for the original purchase?*

The same material prices or discounts will usually apply to materials purchased for change orders as new construction. In some

instances, however, the contractor may forfeit the advantages of competitive pricing for change orders. Consider the following example:

A contractor purchased over $20,000 worth of fan coil units for an installation, and obtained the maximum discount. Some time later it was determined the project required an additional matching unit. The contractor has to purchase this unit from the original supplier to ensure a match. The supplier at this time may not discount the unit because of the small quantity, and the fact that he is no longer in a competitive situation. The impact of quantity on purchase can add between 0% and 25% to material prices and/or subcontractor quotes.

- *If materials have been ordered or delivered to the job site, will they be subject to a cancellation charge or restocking fee?*

Check with the supplier to determine if ordered materials are subject to a cancellation charge. Delivered materials not used as result of a change order may be subject to a restocking fee if returned to the supplier. Common restocking charges run between 20% and 40%. Also, delivery charges to return the goods to the supplier must be added.

Labor

- *How efficient is the existing crew at the actual installation?*

Is the same crew that performed the initial work going to do the change order? Possibly the change consists of the installation of a unit identical to one already installed; therefore, the change should take less time. Be sure to consider this potential productivity increase and modify the productivity rates accordingly.

- *If the crew size is increased, what impact will that have on supervision requirements?*

Under most bargaining agreements or management practices, there is a point at which a working foreman is replaced by a nonworking foreman. This replacement increases project overhead by adding a nonproductive worker. If additional workers are added to accelerate the project or to perform changes while maintaining the schedule, be sure to add additional supervision time if warranted. Calculate the

hours involved and the additional cost directly if possible.

- *What are the other impacts of increased crew size?*

The larger the crew, the greater the potential for productivity to decrease. Some of the factors that cause this productivity loss are: overcrowding (producing restrictive conditions in the working space), and possibly a shortage of any special tools and equipment required. Such factors affect not only the crew working on the elements directly involved in the change order, but other crews whose movement may also be hampered. As the crew increases, check its basic composition for changes by the addition or deletion of apprentices or nonworking foreman, and quantify the potential effects of equipment shortages or other logistical factors.

- *As new crews, unfamiliar with the project, are brought onto the site, how long will it take them to become oriented to the project requirements?*

The orientation time for a new crew to become 100% effective varies with the site and type of project. Orientation is easiest at a new construction site, and most difficult at existing, very restrictive renovation sites. The type of work also affects orientation time. When all elements of the work are exposed, such as concrete or masonry work, orientation is decreased. When the work is concealed or less visible, such as existing electrical systems, orientation takes longer. Usually orientation can be accomplished in one day or less. Costs for added orientation should be itemized and added to the total estimated cost.

- *How much actual production can be gained by working overtime?*

Short term overtime can be used effectively to accomplish more work in a day. However, as overtime is scheduled to run beyond several weeks, studies have shown marked decreases in output. The following chart shows the effect of long term overtime on worker efficiency. If the anticipated change requires extended overtime to keep the job on schedule, these factors can be used as a guide to predict the impact on time and cost. Add project overhead, particularly supervision, that may also be incurred.

For customer support on your Site Work & Landscape Cost Data, call 877.737.1594.

849

Days per Week	Hours per Day	Production Efficiency					Payroll Cost Factors	
		1 Week	2 Weeks	3 Weeks	4 Weeks	Average 4 Weeks	@ 1-1/2 Times	@ 2 Times
5	8	100%	100%	100%	100%	100%	100%	100%
	9	100	100	95	90	96.25	105.6	111.1
	10	100	95	90	85	91.25	110.0	120.0
	11	95	90	75	65	81.25	113.6	127.3
	12	90	85	70	60	76.25	116.7	133.3
6	8	100	100	95	90	96.25	108.3	116.7
	9	100	95	90	85	92.50	113.0	125.9
	10	95	90	85	80	87.50	116.7	133.3
	11	95	85	70	65	78.75	119.7	139.4
	12	90	80	65	60	73.75	122.2	144.4
7	8	100	95	85	75	88.75	114.3	128.6
	9	95	90	80	70	83.75	118.3	136.5
	10	90	85	75	65	78.75	121.4	142.9
	11	85	80	65	60	72.50	124.0	148.1
	12	85	75	60	55	68.75	126.2	152.4

Effects of Overtime

Caution: Under many labor agreements, Sundays and holidays are paid at a higher premium than the normal overtime rate.

The use of long-term overtime is counterproductive on almost any construction job; that is, the longer the period of overtime, the lower the actual production rate. Numerous studies have been conducted, and while they have resulted in slightly different numbers, all reach the same conclusion. The figure above tabulates the effects of overtime work on efficiency.

As illustrated, there can be a difference between the *actual* payroll cost per hour and the *effective* cost per hour for overtime work. This is due to the reduced production efficiency with the increase in weekly hours beyond 40. This difference between actual and effective cost results from overtime work over a prolonged period. Short-term overtime work does not result in as great a reduction in efficiency and, in such cases, effective cost may not vary significantly from the actual payroll cost. As the total hours per week are increased on a regular basis, more time is lost due to fatigue, lowered morale, and an increased accident rate.

As an example, assume a project where workers are working 6 days a week, 10 hours per day. From the figure above (based on productivity studies), the average effective productive hours over a 4-week period are:

$$0.875 \times 60 = 52.5$$

Depending upon the locale and day of week, overtime hours may be paid at time and a half or double time. For time and a half, the overall (average) *actual* payroll cost (including regular and overtime hours) is determined as follows:

$$\frac{40 \text{ reg. hrs.} + (20 \text{ overtime hrs.} \times 1.5)}{60 \text{ hrs.}} = 1.167$$

Based on 60 hours, the payroll cost per hour will be 116.7% of the normal rate at 40 hours per week. However, because the effective production (efficiency) for 60 hours is reduced to the equivalent of 52.5 hours, the effective cost of overtime is calculated as follows:

For time and a half:

$$\frac{40 \text{ reg. hrs.} + (20 \text{ overtime hrs.} \times 1.5)}{52.5 \text{ hrs.}} = 1.33$$

Installed cost will be 133% of the normal rate (for labor).

Thus, when figuring overtime, the actual cost per unit of work will be higher than the apparent overtime payroll dollar increase, due to the reduced productivity of the longer workweek. These efficiency calculations are true only for those cost factors determined by hours worked. Costs that are applied weekly or monthly, such as equipment rentals, will not be similarly affected.

Equipment

- *What equipment is required to complete the change order?*

Change orders may require extending the rental period of equipment already on the job site, or the addition of special equipment brought in to accomplish the change work. In either case, the additional rental charges and operator labor charges must be added.

Summary

The preceding considerations and others you deem appropriate should be analyzed and applied to a change order estimate. The impact of each should be quantified and listed on the estimate to form an audit trail.

Change orders that are properly identified, documented, and managed help to ensure the orderly, professional and profitable progress of the work. They also minimize potential claims or disputes at the end of the project.

Estimating Tips

- The cost figures in this section were derived from approximately 11,000 projects contained in the RSMeans database of completed construction projects. They include the contractor's overhead and profit, but do not generally include architectural fees or land costs. The figures have been adjusted to January of the current year. New projects are added to our files each year, and outdated projects are discarded. For this reason, certain costs may not show a uniform annual progression. In no case are all subdivisions of a project listed.

- These projects were located throughout the U.S. and reflect a tremendous variation in square foot (S.F.) and cubic foot (C.F.) costs. This is due to differences, not only in labor and material costs, but also in individual owners' requirements. For instance, a bank in a large city would have different features than one in a rural area. This is true of all the different types of buildings analyzed. Therefore, caution should be exercised when using these square foot costs. For example, for courthouses, costs in the database are local courthouse costs and will not apply to the larger, more elaborate federal courthouses. As a general rule, the projects in the 1/4 column do not include any site work or equipment, while the projects in the 3/4 column may include both equipment and site work.

The median figures do not generally include site work.

- None of the figures "go with" any others. All individual cost items were computed and tabulated separately. Thus, the sum of the median figures for plumbing, HVAC, and electrical will not normally total up to the total mechanical and electrical costs arrived at by separate analysis and tabulation of the projects.

- Each building was analyzed as to total and component costs and percentages. The figures were arranged in ascending order with the results tabulated as shown. The 1/4 column shows that 25% of the projects had lower costs and 75% had higher. The 3/4 column shows that 75% of the projects had lower costs and 25% had higher. The median column shows that 50% of the projects had lower costs and 50% had higher.

- There are two times when square foot costs are useful. The first is in the conceptual stage when no details are available. Then, square foot costs make a useful starting point. The second is after the bids are in and the costs can be worked back into their appropriate categories for information purposes. As soon as details become available in the project design, the square foot approach should be discontinued and the project priced as to its particular components. When more precision is required, or

for estimating the replacement cost of specific buildings, the current edition of *RSMeans Square Foot Costs* should be used.

- In using the figures in this section, it is recommended that the median column be used for preliminary figures if no additional information is available. The median figures, when multiplied by the total city construction cost index figures (see City Cost Indexes) and then multiplied by the project size modifier at the end of this section, should present a fairly accurate base figure, which would then have to be adjusted in view of the estimator's experience, local economic conditions, code requirements, and the owner's particular requirements. There is no need to factor the percentage figures, as these should remain constant from city to city. All tabulations mentioning air conditioning had at least partial air conditioning.

- The editors of this book would greatly appreciate receiving cost figures on one or more of your recent projects, which would then be included in the averages for next year. All cost figures received will be kept confidential, except that they will be averaged with other similar projects to arrive at square foot cost figures for next year's book. See the last page of the book for details and the discount available for submitting one or more of your projects. ■

50 17 | Square Foot Costs

50 17 00 | S.F. Costs

		UNIT	UNIT COSTS			% OF TOTAL		
			1/4	MEDIAN	3/4	1/4	MEDIAN	3/4
01	**0010**	**APARTMENTS Low Rise (1 to 3 story)**	S.F.	74.50	94	125				**01**
	0020	Total project cost	C.F.	6.70	8.85	10.95			
	0100	Site work	S.F.	5.45	8.70	15.30	6.05%	10.55%	13.95%
	0500	Masonry		1.47	3.62	5.95	1.54%	3.92%	6.50%
	1500	Finishes		7.90	10.85	13.45	9.05%	10.75%	12.85%
	1800	Equipment		2.44	3.70	5.50	2.71%	3.99%	5.95%
	2720	Plumbing		5.80	7.45	9.50	6.65%	8.95%	10.05%
	2770	Heating, ventilating, air conditioning		3.70	4.56	6.70	4.20%	5.60%	7.60%
	2900	Electrical		4.33	5.75	7.80	5.20%	6.65%	8.35%
	3100	Total: Mechanical & Electrical	↓	15.40	19.95	24.50	16.05%	18.20%	23%
	9000	Per apartment unit, total cost	Apt.	69,500	106,000	156,500			
	9500	Total: Mechanical & Electrical	"	13,100	20,700	27,000			
02	**0010**	**APARTMENTS Mid Rise (4 to 7 story)**	S.F.	99	119	147				**02**
	0020	Total project costs	C.F.	7.70	10.65	14.55			
	0100	Site work	S.F.	3.95	8	15.45	5.25%	6.70%	9.20%
	0500	Masonry		4.13	9.05	12.40	5.10%	7.25%	10.50%
	1500	Finishes		12.95	17.35	20.50	10.70%	13.50%	17.70%
	1800	Equipment		2.77	4.30	5.65	2.54%	3.47%	4.31%
	2500	Conveying equipment		2.24	2.76	3.33	2.05%	2.27%	2.69%
	2720	Plumbing		5.80	9.30	9.85	5.70%	7.20%	8.95%
	2900	Electrical		6.50	8.85	10.75	6.35%	7.20%	8.95%
	3100	Total: Mechanical & Electrical	↓	21	26	31.50	18.25%	21%	23%
	9000	Per apartment unit, total cost	Apt.	112,000	132,000	218,500			
	9500	Total: Mechanical & Electrical	"	21,100	24,400	25,600			
03	**0010**	**APARTMENTS High Rise (8 to 24 story)**	S.F.	112	129	155				**03**
	0020	Total project costs	C.F.	10.90	12.65	14.95			
	0100	Site work	S.F.	4.07	6.60	9.20	2.58%	4.84%	6.15%
	0500	Masonry		6.50	11.80	14.65	4.74%	9.65%	11.05%
	1500	Finishes		12.45	15.55	18.35	9.75%	11.80%	13.70%
	1800	Equipment		3.61	4.44	5.85	2.78%	3.49%	4.35%
	2500	Conveying equipment		2.55	3.87	5.25	2.23%	2.78%	3.37%
	2720	Plumbing		7.15	9.75	11.95	6.80%	7.20%	10.45%
	2900	Electrical		7.70	9.75	13.15	6.45%	7.65%	8.80%
	3100	Total: Mechanical & Electrical	↓	23	29.50	35.50	17.95%	22.50%	24.50%
	9000	Per apartment unit, total cost	Apt.	116,500	128,500	178,000			
	9500	Total: Mechanical & Electrical	"	23,200	28,800	30,500			
04	**0010**	**AUDITORIUMS**	S.F.	117	161	234				**04**
	0020	Total project costs	C.F.	7.30	10.15	14.55			
	2720	Plumbing	S.F.	6.90	10.20	12.20	5.85%	7.20%	8.70%
	2900	Electrical		9.40	13.55	22.50	6.85%	9.50%	11.40%
	3100	Total: Mechanical & Electrical	↓	62.50	83	101	24.50%	27.50%	31%
05	**0010**	**AUTOMOTIVE SALES**	S.F.	86.50	119	146				**05**
	0020	Total project costs	C.F.	5.70	6.80	8.85			
	2720	Plumbing	S.F.	3.93	6.85	7.45	2.89%	6.05%	6.50%
	2770	Heating, ventilating, air conditioning		6.05	9.25	10	4.61%	10%	10.35%
	2900	Electrical		6.95	10.90	16	7.25%	8.80%	12.15%
	3100	Total: Mechanical & Electrical	↓	19.35	31	37.50	17.30%	20.50%	22%
06	**0010**	**BANKS**	S.F.	170	211	268				**06**
	0020	Total project costs	C.F.	12.10	16.45	21.50			
	0100	Site work	S.F.	19.40	30.50	43	7.90%	12.95%	17%
	0500	Masonry		7.70	16.50	29.50	3.36%	6.90%	10.05%
	1500	Finishes		15.15	23	28.50	5.85%	8.65%	11.70%
	1800	Equipment		6.35	14	28.50	1.34%	5.55%	10.50%
	2720	Plumbing		5.30	7.55	11.05	2.82%	3.90%	4.93%
	2770	Heating, ventilating, air conditioning		10.05	13.45	17.90	4.86%	7.15%	8.50%
	2900	Electrical		16.05	21.50	28	8.25%	10.20%	12.20%
	3100	Total: Mechanical & Electrical	↓	38.50	51.50	62	16.55%	19.45%	24%
	3500	See also division 11 22 00							

50 17 00 | S.F. Costs

			UNIT	UNIT COSTS			% OF TOTAL			
				1/4	MEDIAN	3/4	1/4	MEDIAN	3/4	
13	0010	**CHURCHES**	S.F.	114	145	190				13
	0020	Total project costs	C.F.	7.05	8.90	11.75				
	1800	Equipment	S.F.	1.22	3.19	6.80	.83%	2.04%	4.30%	
	2720	Plumbing		4.43	6.20	9.15	3.51%	4.96%	6.25%	
	2770	Heating, ventilating, air conditioning		10.35	13.50	19.15	7.50%	10%	12%	
	2900	Electrical		9.60	13.20	18	7.30%	8.80%	10.95%	
	3100	Total: Mechanical & Electrical		29.50	39.50	53	18.30%	22%	25%	
	3500	See also division 11 91 00								
15	0010	**CLUBS, COUNTRY**	S.F.	122	147	185				15
	0020	Total project costs	C.F.	9.85	12	16.55				
	2720	Plumbing	S.F.	7.40	10.95	25	5.60%	7.90%	10%	
	2900	Electrical		9.60	13.15	17.15	7%	8.95%	11%	
	3100	Total: Mechanical & Electrical		51	64	67.50	19%	26.50%	29.50%	
17	0010	**CLUBS, SOCIAL Fraternal**	S.F.	103	141	188				17
	0020	Total project costs	C.F.	6.10	9.25	11				
	2720	Plumbing	S.F.	6.15	7.65	11.55	5.60%	6.90%	8.55%	
	2770	Heating, ventilating, air conditioning		7.15	10.70	13.75	8.20%	9.25%	14.40%	
	2900	Electrical		7.15	12.05	13.75	5.95%	9.30%	10.55%	
	3100	Total: Mechanical & Electrical		38	41	52	21%	23%	23.50%	
18	0010	**CLUBS, Y.M.C.A.**	S.F.	134	167	252				18
	0020	Total project costs	C.F.	5.65	9.45	14.05				
	2720	Plumbing	S.F.	7.75	15.40	17.25	5.65%	7.60%	10.85%	
	2900	Electrical		10.05	13	22.50	6.45%	7.95%	8.90%	
	3100	Total: Mechanical & Electrical		41	46.50	76	20.50%	21.50%	28.50%	
19	0010	**COLLEGES Classrooms & Administration**	S.F.	118	167	216				19
	0020	Total project costs	C.F.	7.10	12.50	20				
	0500	Masonry	S.F.	9.30	17.15	21	5.10%	8.05%	10.50%	
	2720	Plumbing		5.30	12.90	24	5.10%	6.60%	8.95%	
	2900	Electrical		10.05	15.85	22	7.70%	9.85%	12%	
	3100	Total: Mechanical & Electrical		42.50	58.50	77.50	23%	28%	31.50%	
21	0010	**COLLEGES Science, Engineering, Laboratories**	S.F.	230	269	310				21
	0020	Total project costs	C.F.	13.20	19.25	22				
	1800	Equipment	S.F.	6.25	29	31.50	2%	6.45%	12.65%	
	2900	Electrical		18.95	27	41.50	7.10%	9.40%	12.10%	
	3100	Total: Mechanical & Electrical		70.50	83.50	129	28.50%	31.50%	41%	
	3500	See also division 11 53 00								
23	0010	**COLLEGES Student Unions**	S.F.	147	199	241				23
	0020	Total project costs	C.F.	8.20	10.70	13.25				
	3100	Total: Mechanical & Electrical	S.F.	55	59.50	70.50	23.50%	26%	29%	
25	0010	**COMMUNITY CENTERS**	S.F.	122	150	203				25
	0020	Total project costs	C.F.	7.90	11.30	14.65				
	1800	Equipment	S.F.	2.45	4.80	7.90	1.47%	3.01%	5.30%	
	2720	Plumbing		5.75	10.05	13.70	4.85%	7%	8.95%	
	2770	Heating, ventilating, air conditioning		8.65	13.35	19.15	6.80%	10.35%	12.90%	
	2900	Electrical		10.25	13.55	19.90	7.15%	8.90%	10.40%	
	3100	Total: Mechanical & Electrical		34	43	61.50	18.80%	23%	30%	
28	0010	**COURT HOUSES**	S.F.	175	206	284				28
	0020	Total project costs	C.F.	13.40	16	20				
	2720	Plumbing	S.F.	8.30	11.60	13.15	5.95%	7.45%	8.20%	
	2900	Electrical		18.55	21	30.50	9.05%	10.65%	12.15%	
	3100	Total: Mechanical & Electrical		52	68	74.50	22.50%	26.50%	30%	
30	0010	**DEPARTMENT STORES**	S.F.	64.50	87.50	110				30
	0020	Total project costs	C.F.	3.46	4.48	6.10				
	2720	Plumbing	S.F.	2.01	2.54	3.85	1.82%	4.21%	5.90%	
	2770	Heating, ventilating, air conditioning		4.88	9.05	13.65	8.20%	9.10%	14.80%	

For customer support on your Site Work & Landscape Cost Data, call 877.737.1594.

853

50 17 00	S.F. Costs		UNIT	UNIT COSTS			% OF TOTAL			
				1/4	MEDIAN	3/4	1/4	MEDIAN	3/4	
30	2900	Electrical	S.F.	7.40	10.15	12	9.05%	12.15%	14.95%	**30**
	3100	Total: Mechanical & Electrical	↓	13.05	16.65	29	13.20%	21.50%	50%	
31	0010	**DORMITORIES Low Rise (1 to 3 story)**	S.F.	122	170	212				**31**
	0020	Total project costs	C.F.	6.90	11.20	16.75				
	2720	Plumbing	S.F.	7.35	9.85	12.45	8.05%	9%	9.65%	
	2770	Heating, ventilating, air conditioning		7.80	9.35	12.45	4.61%	8.05%	10%	
	2900	Electrical		8.10	12.35	16.90	6.40%	8.65%	9.50%	
	3100	Total: Mechanical & Electrical	↓	42	45	70.50	22%	25%	27%	
	9000	Per bed, total cost	Bed	52,000	57,500	123,500				
32	0010	**DORMITORIES Mid Rise (4 to 8 story)**	S.F.	150	196	242				**32**
	0020	Total project costs	C.F.	16.55	18.20	22				
	2900	Electrical	S.F.	15.95	18.15	24.50	8.20%	10.20%	11.95%	
	3100	Total: Mechanical & Electrical	"	44.50	89	90.50	25%	30.50%	35.50%	
	9000	Per bed, total cost	Bed	21,400	48,800	282,500				
34	0010	**FACTORIES**	S.F.	57	85	131				**34**
	0020	Total project costs	C.F.	3.65	5.45	9.05				
	0100	Site work	S.F.	6.50	11.85	18.75	6.95%	11.45%	17.95%	
	2720	Plumbing		3.07	5.70	9.45	3.73%	6.05%	8.10%	
	2770	Heating, ventilating, air conditioning		5.95	8.55	11.55	5.25%	8.45%	11.35%	
	2900	Electrical		7.05	11.20	17.05	8.10%	10.50%	14.20%	
	3100	Total: Mechanical & Electrical	↓	20	32.50	41	21%	28.50%	35.50%	
36	0010	**FIRE STATIONS**	S.F.	113	156	213				**36**
	0020	Total project costs	C.F.	6.60	9.05	12.05				
	0500	Masonry	S.F.	15.40	30	38	7.50%	10.95%	15.55%	
	1140	Roofing		3.68	9.95	11.35	1.90%	4.94%	5.05%	
	1580	Painting		2.86	4.27	4.37	1.37%	1.57%	2.07%	
	1800	Equipment		1.40	2.69	4.97	.62%	1.63%	3.42%	
	2720	Plumbing		6.30	10.05	14.25	5.85%	7.35%	9.45%	
	2770	Heating, ventilating, air conditioning		6.25	10.15	15.65	5.15%	7.40%	9.40%	
	2900	Electrical		8.15	14.35	19.35	6.90%	8.60%	10.60%	
	3100	Total: Mechanical & Electrical	↓	41.50	53	60	18.40%	23%	27%	
37	0010	**FRATERNITY HOUSES & Sorority Houses**	S.F.	113	145	199				**37**
	0020	Total project costs	C.F.	11.25	11.70	14.10				
	2720	Plumbing	S.F.	8.55	9.75	17.90	6.80%	8%	10.85%	
	2900	Electrical	↓	7.45	16.10	19.70	6.60%	9.90%	10.65%	
38	0010	**FUNERAL HOMES**	S.F.	119	162	295				**38**
	0020	Total project costs	C.F.	12.15	13.55	26				
	2900	Electrical	S.F.	5.25	9.65	10.55	3.58%	4.44%	5.95%	
39	0010	**GARAGES, COMMERCIAL (Service)**	S.F.	67.50	104	144				**39**
	0020	Total project costs	C.F.	4.43	6.55	9.50				
	1800	Equipment	S.F.	3.80	8.55	13.30	2.21%	4.62%	6.80%	
	2720	Plumbing		4.67	7.20	13.10	5.45%	7.85%	10.65%	
	2730	Heating & ventilating		4.60	7.95	10.15	5.25%	6.85%	8.20%	
	2900	Electrical		6.40	9.75	14.10	7.15%	9.25%	10.85%	
	3100	Total: Mechanical & Electrical	↓	12.10	27	40	12.35%	17.40%	26%	
40	0010	**GARAGES, MUNICIPAL (Repair)**	S.F.	105	135	192				**40**
	0020	Total project costs	C.F.	6.20	7.85	13.50				
	0500	Masonry	S.F.	5.20	18.20	28	4.03%	9.15%	12.50%	
	2720	Plumbing		4.44	8.55	16.05	3.59%	6.70%	7.95%	
	2730	Heating & ventilating		7.60	11	21	6.15%	7.45%	13.50%	
	2900	Electrical		7.65	12.35	22.50	6.90%	9.40%	13%	
	3100	Total: Mechanical & Electrical	↓	34.50	56.50	68	21.50%	25.50%	35.50%	
41	0010	**GARAGES, PARKING**	S.F.	39.50	56	96.50				**41**
	0020	Total project costs	C.F.	3.62	4.92	7.15				

		50 17 00 | S.F. Costs	UNIT	UNIT COSTS			% OF TOTAL			
				1/4	MEDIAN	3/4	1/4	MEDIAN	3/4	
41	2720	Plumbing	S.F.	.66	1.69	2.61	1.72%	2.70%	3.85%	**41**
	2900	Electrical		2.12	2.80	4.08	4.52%	5.40%	6.35%	
	3100	Total: Mechanical & Electrical	↓	4.11	6.05	7.50	7%	8.90%	11.05%	
	3200									
	9000	Per car, total cost	Car	16,300	20,400	26,000				
43	0010	**GYMNASIUMS**	S.F.	108	143	196				**43**
	0020	Total project costs	C.F.	5.35	7.25	8.90				
	1800	Equipment	S.F.	2.55	4.78	8.60	1.76%	3.26%	6.70%	
	2720	Plumbing		5.90	7.90	10.40	4.65%	6.40%	7.75%	
	2770	Heating, ventilating, air conditioning		6.40	11.10	22.50	5.15%	9.05%	11.10%	
	2900	Electrical		8.50	11.25	14.95	6.75%	8.50%	10.30%	
	3100	Total: Mechanical & Electrical	↓	29	40.50	49.50	19.75%	23.50%	29%	
	3500	See also division 11 66 00								
46	0010	**HOSPITALS**	S.F.	206	258	355				**46**
	0020	Total project costs	C.F.	15.60	19.40	28				
	1800	Equipment	S.F.	5.20	10.05	17.30	.80%	2.53%	4.80%	
	2720	Plumbing		17.70	25	32	7.60%	9.10%	10.85%	
	2770	Heating, ventilating, air conditioning		26	33.50	46.50	7.80%	12.95%	16.65%	
	2900	Electrical		22.50	30.50	45.50	10%	11.75%	14.10%	
	3100	Total: Mechanical & Electrical	↓	66.50	92.50	137	28%	33.50%	37%	
	9000	Per bed or person, total cost	Bed	238,000	328,500	378,500				
	9900	See also division 11 71 00								
48	0010	**HOUSING For the Elderly**	S.F.	101	128	157				**48**
	0020	Total project costs	C.F.	7.20	10	12.80				
	0100	Site work	S.F.	7.05	10.95	16.05	5.05%	7.90%	12.10%	
	0500	Masonry		1.91	11.55	16.85	1.30%	6.05%	11%	
	1800	Equipment		2.45	3.37	5.35	1.88%	3.23%	4.43%	
	2510	Conveying systems		2.29	3.31	4.49	1.78%	2.20%	2.81%	
	2720	Plumbing		7.50	9.60	12.10	8.15%	9.55%	10.50%	
	2730	Heating, ventilating, air conditioning		3.86	5.45	8.15	3.30%	5.60%	7.25%	
	2900	Electrical		7.55	10.25	13.10	7.30%	8.50%	10.25%	
	3100	Total: Mechanical & Electrical	↓	26	32	41	18.10%	22.50%	29%	
	9000	Per rental unit, total cost	Unit	94,000	110,000	122,500				
	9500	Total: Mechanical & Electrical	"	21,000	24,100	28,100				
50	0010	**HOUSING Public (Low Rise)**	S.F.	85	118	154				**50**
	0020	Total project costs	C.F.	6.75	9.45	11.75				
	0100	Site work	S.F.	10.85	15.60	25.50	8.35%	11.75%	16.50%	
	1800	Equipment		2.31	3.77	5.75	2.26%	3.03%	4.24%	
	2720	Plumbing		6.15	8.10	10.25	7.15%	9.05%	11.60%	
	2730	Heating, ventilating, air conditioning		3.08	6	6.55	4.26%	6.05%	6.45%	
	2900	Electrical		5.15	7.65	10.65	5.10%	6.55%	8.25%	
	3100	Total: Mechanical & Electrical	↓	24.50	31.50	35	14.50%	17.55%	26.50%	
	9000	Per apartment, total cost	Apt.	93,500	106,500	133,500				
	9500	Total: Mechanical & Electrical	"	19,900	24,600	27,200				
51	0010	**ICE SKATING RINKS**	S.F.	72.50	170	187				**51**
	0020	Total project costs	C.F.	5.35	5.45	6.30				
	2720	Plumbing	S.F.	2.72	5.10	5.20	3.12%	3.23%	5.65%	
	2900	Electrical	↓	7.80	11.95	12.65	6.30%	10.15%	15.05%	
52	0010	**JAILS**	S.F.	189	286	370				**52**
	0020	Total project costs	C.F.	19.95	28	32.50				
	1800	Equipment	S.F.	8.65	25.50	43.50	2.80%	6.95%	9.80%	
	2720	Plumbing		21.50	28.50	37.50	7%	8.90%	13.35%	
	2770	Heating, ventilating, air conditioning		19.95	26.50	51.50	7.50%	9.45%	17.75%	
	2900	Electrical		23.50	31.50	40	9.40%	11.70%	15.25%	
	3100	Total: Mechanical & Electrical	↓	62	110	131	28%	31%	36%	
53	0010	**LIBRARIES**	S.F.	143	190	248				**53**
	0020	Total project costs	C.F.	9.55	12	15.30				

50 17 00	S.F. Costs	UNIT	UNIT COSTS			% OF TOTAL			
			1/4	MEDIAN	3/4	1/4	MEDIAN	3/4	
53 0500	Masonry	S.F.	9.50	19.35	32.50	5.60%	7.15%	10.95%	**53**
1800	Equipment		1.91	5.15	7.75	.28%	1.39%	4.07%	
2720	Plumbing		5.15	7.30	10.20	3.38%	4.60%	5.70%	
2770	Heating, ventilating, air conditioning		11.45	19.35	23.50	7.80%	10.95%	12.80%	
2900	Electrical		14.40	19	25.50	8.40%	10.55%	12%	
3100	Total: Mechanical & Electrical	↓	47	57	67	21%	24%	28%	
54 0010	**LIVING, ASSISTED**	S.F.	129	154	180				**54**
0020	Total project costs	C.F.	10.90	12.70	14.45				
0500	Masonry	S.F.	3.75	4.53	5.55	2.36%	3.16%	3.86%	
1800	Equipment		2.87	3.42	4.38	2.12%	2.45%	2.87%	
2720	Plumbing		10.85	14.50	15.05	6.05%	8.15%	10.60%	
2770	Heating, ventilating, air conditioning		12.85	13.45	14.75	7.95%	9.35%	9.70%	
2900	Electrical		12.70	14.25	16.50	9%	9.95%	10.65%	
3100	Total: Mechanical & Electrical	↓	35	41	48	24%	28.50%	31.50%	
55 0010	**MEDICAL CLINICS**	S.F.	132	162	207				**55**
0020	Total project costs	C.F.	9.65	12.50	16.60				
1800	Equipment	S.F.	1.68	7.50	11.65	1.05%	2.94%	6.35%	
2720	Plumbing		8.75	12.30	16.50	6.15%	8.40%	10.10%	
2770	Heating, ventilating, air conditioning		10.45	13.70	20	6.65%	8.85%	11.35%	
2900	Electrical		11.30	16.10	21	8.10%	10%	12.20%	
3100	Total: Mechanical & Electrical	↓	36	49	67.50	22%	27%	33.50%	
3500	See also division 11 71 00								
57 0010	**MEDICAL OFFICES**	S.F.	124	154	190				**57**
0020	Total project costs	C.F.	9.25	12.50	16.95				
1800	Equipment	S.F.	4.09	8.10	11.35	.66%	4.87%	6.50%	
2720	Plumbing		6.85	10.55	14.25	5.60%	6.80%	8.50%	
2770	Heating, ventilating, air conditioning		8.25	11.95	15.75	6.10%	8%	9.70%	
2900	Electrical		9.90	14.50	20.50	7.50%	9.80%	11.70%	
3100	Total: Mechanical & Electrical	↓	27	39.50	56	19.30%	22.50%	27.50%	
59 0010	**MOTELS**	S.F.	78	113	148				**59**
0020	Total project costs	C.F.	6.95	9.30	15.25				
2720	Plumbing	S.F.	7.90	10.10	12.05	9.45%	10.60%	12.55%	
2770	Heating, ventilating, air conditioning		4.83	7.20	12.90	5.60%	5.60%	10%	
2900	Electrical		7.40	9.35	11.65	7.45%	9.05%	10.45%	
3100	Total: Mechanical & Electrical	↓	22.50	31.50	54	18.50%	24%	25.50%	
5000									
9000	Per rental unit, total cost	Unit	39,800	75,500	82,000				
9500	Total: Mechanical & Electrical	"	7,750	11,700	13,600				
60 0010	**NURSING HOMES**	S.F.	123	158	197				**60**
0020	Total project costs	C.F.	9.65	12.05	16.45				
1800	Equipment	S.F.	3.34	5.10	8.55	2%	3.62%	4.99%	
2720	Plumbing		10.50	15.90	19.20	8.75%	10.10%	12.70%	
2770	Heating, ventilating, air conditioning		11.05	16.80	22.50	9.70%	11.45%	11.80%	
2900	Electrical		12.15	15.20	21	9.40%	10.60%	12.50%	
3100	Total: Mechanical & Electrical	↓	29	40.50	68	26%	28%	30%	
9000	Per bed or person, total cost	Bed	54,500	68,000	88,000				
61 0010	**OFFICES Low Rise (1 to 4 story)**	S.F.	103	135	175				**61**
0020	Total project costs	C.F.	7.35	10.15	13.40				
0100	Site work	S.F.	8.30	14.45	21.50	5.95%	9.70%	13.55%	
0500	Masonry		4	8.05	14.70	2.61%	5.40%	8.45%	
1800	Equipment		.93	2.15	5.85	.57%	1.50%	3.42%	
2720	Plumbing		3.69	5.70	8.35	3.66%	4.50%	6.10%	
2770	Heating, ventilating, air conditioning		8.15	11.40	16.65	7.20%	10.30%	11.70%	
2900	Electrical		8.45	12.10	17.20	7.45%	9.65%	11.40%	
3100	Total: Mechanical & Electrical	↓	23.50	32.50	48.50	18.20%	22%	27%	
62 0010	**OFFICES Mid Rise (5 to 10 story)**	S.F.	109	132	180				**62**
0020	Total project costs	C.F.	7.75	9.90	14				

		50 17 00	S.F. Costs	UNIT	UNIT COSTS			% OF TOTAL			
				1/4	MEDIAN	3/4	1/4	MEDIAN	3/4	
62	2720	Plumbing	S.F.	3.30	5.10	7.35	2.83%	3.74%	4.50%	62
	2770	Heating, ventilating, air conditioning		8.30	11.85	18.95	7.65%	9.40%	11%	
	2900	Electrical		8.10	10.40	15.70	6.35%	7.80%	10%	
	3100	Total: Mechanical & Electrical	↓	21	27	51.50	18.95%	21%	27.50%	
63	0010	**OFFICES High Rise (11 to 20 story)**	S.F.	134	169	208				63
	0020	Total project costs	C.F.	9.40	11.75	16.85				
	2900	Electrical	S.F.	8.15	9.95	14.80	5.80%	7.85%	10.50%	
	3100	Total: Mechanical & Electrical	↓	26.50	35.50	59.50	16.90%	23.50%	34%	
64	0010	**POLICE STATIONS**	S.F.	161	212	270				64
	0020	Total project costs	C.F.	12.85	15.70	21.50				
	0500	Masonry	S.F.	16.10	26.50	33.50	7.80%	9.10%	11.35%	
	1800	Equipment		2.31	11.25	17.80	.98%	3.35%	6.70%	
	2720	Plumbing		9	17.95	22.50	5.65%	6.90%	10.75%	
	2770	Heating, ventilating, air conditioning		13.20	18.70	26.50	5.85%	10.55%	11.70%	
	2900	Electrical		17.60	25.50	33	9.80%	11.70%	14.50%	
	3100	Total: Mechanical & Electrical	↓	67	70.50	94	28.50%	31.50%	32.50%	
65	0010	**POST OFFICES**	S.F.	127	157	200				65
	0020	Total project costs	C.F.	7.65	9.70	11				
	2720	Plumbing	S.F.	5.15	7.10	8.95	4.24%	5.30%	5.60%	
	2770	Heating, ventilating, air conditioning		8	11.05	12.30	6.65%	7.15%	9.35%	
	2900	Electrical		10.50	14.75	17.50	7.25%	9%	11%	
	3100	Total: Mechanical & Electrical	↓	30.50	39.50	45	16.25%	18.80%	22%	
66	0010	**POWER PLANTS**	S.F.	880	1,175	2,150				66
	0020	Total project costs	C.F.	24.50	53	113				
	2900	Electrical	S.F.	62.50	132	197	9.30%	12.75%	21.50%	
	8100	Total: Mechanical & Electrical	↓	155	505	1,125	32.50%	32.50%	52.50%	
67	0010	**RELIGIOUS EDUCATION**	S.F.	103	137	170				67
	0020	Total project costs	C.F.	5.70	8.15	10.20				
	2720	Plumbing	S.F.	4.28	6.05	8.60	4.40%	5.30%	7.10%	
	2770	Heating, ventilating, air conditioning		10.80	12.25	17.30	10.05%	11.45%	12.35%	
	2900	Electrical		8.15	11.65	17.10	7.70%	9.05%	10.35%	
	3100	Total: Mechanical & Electrical	↓	35.50	45	53	22%	23.50%	26%	
69	0010	**RESEARCH Laboratories & Facilities**	S.F.	157	222	325				69
	0020	Total project costs	C.F.	11.40	22.50	27				
	1800	Equipment	S.F.	6.80	13.40	32.50	1.22%	4.80%	9.35%	
	2720	Plumbing		11.20	19.70	31.50	6.15%	8.30%	10.80%	
	2770	Heating, ventilating, air conditioning		13.80	46.50	55	7.25%	16.50%	17.50%	
	2900	Electrical		18.45	29.50	48.50	9.45%	11.15%	14.60%	
	3100	Total: Mechanical & Electrical	↓	59	104	147	29.50%	36%	41%	
70	0010	**RESTAURANTS**	S.F.	149	192	249				70
	0020	Total project costs	C.F.	12.50	16.40	21.50				
	1800	Equipment	S.F.	8.80	23.50	35.50	6.10%	13%	15.65%	
	2720	Plumbing		11.80	14.30	18.75	6.10%	8.15%	9%	
	2770	Heating, ventilating, air conditioning		14.95	21	25	9.20%	12%	12.40%	
	2900	Electrical		15.70	19.40	25	8.35%	10.55%	11.55%	
	3100	Total: Mechanical & Electrical	↓	48.50	52	67.50	21%	25%	29.50%	
	9000	Per seat unit, total cost	Seat	5,450	7,275	8,600				
	9500	Total: Mechanical & Electrical	"	1,375	1,825	2,150				
72	0010	**RETAIL STORES**	S.F.	69.50	93.50	124				72
	0020	Total project costs	C.F.	4.71	6.70	9.35				
	2720	Plumbing	S.F.	2.52	4.20	7.15	3.26%	4.60%	6.80%	
	2770	Heating, ventilating, air conditioning		5.45	7.45	11.20	6.75%	8.75%	10.15%	
	2900	Electrical		6.25	8.55	12.35	7.25%	9.90%	11.60%	
	3100	Total: Mechanical & Electrical	↓	16.65	21.50	28.50	17.05%	21%	23.50%	
74	0010	**SCHOOLS Elementary**	S.F.	114	141	172				74
	0020	Total project costs	C.F.	7.40	9.50	12.25				
	0500	Masonry	S.F.	8	17.30	25.50	4.89%	10.50%	14%	
	1800	Equipment	↓	2.63	4.96	9.40	1.83%	3.13%	4.61%	

For customer support on your Site Work & Landscape Cost Data, call 877.737.1594.

857

50 17 | Square Foot Costs

			UNIT	UNIT COSTS			% OF TOTAL		
				1/4	MEDIAN	3/4	1/4	MEDIAN	3/4
74	2720	Plumbing	S.F.	6.50	9.20	12.30	5.70%	7.15%	9.35%	74
	2730	Heating, ventilating, air conditioning		9.80	15.55	22.50	8.15%	10.80%	14.90%
	2900	Electrical		10.70	14.25	18.20	8.45%	10.05%	11.85%
	3100	Total: Mechanical & Electrical	↓	39	47.50	60	25%	27.50%	30%
	9000	Per pupil, total cost	Ea.	13,000	19,300	43,300			
	9500	Total: Mechanical & Electrical	"	3,675	4,650	11,700			
76	0010	**SCHOOLS Junior High & Middle**	S.F.	117	145	177				76
	0020	Total project costs	C.F.	7.40	9.60	10.75			
	0500	Masonry	S.F.	12.55	18.80	23	7.55%	11.10%	14.30%
	1800	Equipment		3.20	6	8.80	1.80%	3.03%	4.80%
	2720	Plumbing		6.80	8.40	10.40	5.30%	6.80%	7.25%
	2770	Heating, ventilating, air conditioning		13.60	16.55	29	8.90%	11.55%	14.20%
	2900	Electrical		11.90	14.70	18.60	8.05%	9.55%	10.60%
	3100	Total: Mechanical & Electrical	↓	37.50	48	59.50	23%	25.50%	29.50%
	9000	Per pupil, total cost	Ea.	14,800	19,400	26,100			
78	0010	**SCHOOLS Senior High**	S.F.	123	150	188				78
	0020	Total project costs	C.F.	7.35	10.30	17.40			
	1800	Equipment	S.F.	3.24	7.55	10.45	1.88%	2.67%	4.30%
	2720	Plumbing		6.80	10.25	18.70	5.60%	6.90%	8.30%
	2770	Heating, ventilating, air conditioning		11.75	15.95	24.50	8.95%	11.60%	15%
	2900	Electrical		12.30	16.40	24	8.70%	10.35%	12.50%
	3100	Total: Mechanical & Electrical	↓	40.50	48	77.50	24%	26.50%	28.50%
	9000	Per pupil, total cost	Ea.	11,500	23,300	29,200			
80	0010	**SCHOOLS Vocational**	S.F.	98.50	143	177				80
	0020	Total project costs	C.F.	6.10	8.80	12.15			
	0500	Masonry	S.F.	4.33	14.25	22	3.20%	4.61%	10.95%
	1800	Equipment		3.08	7.65	10.60	1.24%	3.10%	4.26%
	2720	Plumbing		6.30	9.35	13.80	5.40%	6.90%	8.55%
	2770	Heating, ventilating, air conditioning		8.80	16.40	27.50	8.60%	11.90%	14.65%
	2900	Electrical		10.25	14	19.15	8.45%	11%	13.20%
	3100	Total: Mechanical & Electrical	↓	38.50	67.50	86.50	27.50%	29.50%	31%
	9000	Per pupil, total cost	Ea.	13,700	36,700	54,500			
83	0010	**SPORTS ARENAS**	S.F.	86	115	177				83
	0020	Total project costs	C.F.	4.67	8.35	10.80			
	2720	Plumbing	S.F.	4.31	7.55	15.95	4.35%	6.35%	9.40%
	2770	Heating, ventilating, air conditioning		10.75	12.70	17.60	8.80%	10.20%	13.55%
	2900	Electrical	↓	7.95	12.15	15.70	7.65%	9.75%	11.90%
85	0010	**SUPERMARKETS**	S.F.	79.50	92	108				85
	0020	Total project costs	C.F.	4.42	5.35	8.10			
	2720	Plumbing	S.F.	4.44	5.60	6.50	5.40%	6%	7.45%
	2770	Heating, ventilating, air conditioning		6.55	8.65	10.55	8.60%	8.65%	9.60%
	2900	Electrical		9.30	11.35	13.50	10.40%	12.45%	13.60%
	3100	Total: Mechanical & Electrical	↓	25.50	27	36.50	23.50%	27.50%	28.50%
86	0010	**SWIMMING POOLS**	S.F.	129	300	460				86
	0020	Total project costs	C.F.	10.30	12.85	14			
	2720	Plumbing	S.F.	11.90	13.60	18.25	4.80%	9.70%	20.50%
	2900	Electrical		9.75	15.65	34.50	6.05%	6.95%	7.60%
	3100	Total: Mechanical & Electrical	↓	61	80.50	106	11.15%	14.10%	23.50%
87	0010	**TELEPHONE EXCHANGES**	S.F.	160	243	315				87
	0020	Total project costs	C.F.	10.65	17.05	23.50			
	2720	Plumbing	S.F.	7.20	11.15	16.30	4.52%	5.80%	6.90%
	2770	Heating, ventilating, air conditioning		16.75	33.50	42	11.80%	16.05%	18.40%
	2900	Electrical		17.40	27.50	49	10.90%	14%	17.85%
	3100	Total: Mechanical & Electrical		51.50	97.50	138	29.50%	33.50%	44.50%
91	0010	**THEATERS**	S.F.	102	138	203				91
	0020	Total project costs	C.F.	4.96	7.35	10.80			

50 17 00 | S.F. Costs		UNIT	UNIT COSTS			% OF TOTAL		
			1/4	MEDIAN	3/4	1/4	MEDIAN	3/4
91 2720	Plumbing	S.F.	3.34	3.88	15.85	2.92%	4.70%	6.80% **91**
2770	Heating, ventilating, air conditioning		10.45	12.65	15.65	8%	12.25%	13.40%
2900	Electrical		9.40	12.70	26	8.05%	9.35%	12.25%
3100	Total: Mechanical & Electrical	↓	24	32.50	38.50	21.50%	25.50%	27.50%
94 0010	**TOWN HALLS City Halls & Municipal Buildings**	S.F.	112	152	199			**94**
0020	Total project costs	C.F.	8.10	12.60	18.45			
2720	Plumbing	S.F.	5	9.35	16.45	4.31%	5.95%	7.95%
2770	Heating, ventilating, air conditioning		9.05	17.95	26.50	7.05%	9.05%	13.45%
2900	Electrical		11.40	15.70	21.50	8.05%	9.45%	11.65%
3100	Total: Mechanical & Electrical	↓	39.50	50	76.50	22%	26.50%	31%
97 0010	**WAREHOUSES & Storage Buildings**	S.F.	44.50	63.50	95			**97**
0020	Total project costs	C.F.	2.34	3.67	6.05			
0100	Site work	S.F.	4.62	9.15	13.80	6.05%	12.95%	19.55%
0500	Masonry		2.54	6.35	13.70	3.60%	7.35%	12%
1800	Equipment		.68	1.55	8.70	.72%	1.69%	5.55%
2720	Plumbing		1.49	2.68	5	2.90%	4.80%	6.55%
2730	Heating, ventilating, air conditioning		1.70	4.80	6.45	2.41%	5%	8.90%
2900	Electrical		2.65	4.98	8.20	5.15%	7.20%	10.05%
3100	Total: Mechanical & Electrical	↓	7.40	11.35	22.50	13.30%	18.90%	26%
99 0010	**WAREHOUSE & OFFICES Combination**	S.F.	55	73.50	101			**99**
0020	Total project costs	C.F.	2.82	4.09	6.05			
1800	Equipment	S.F.	.95	1.84	2.74	.42%	1.19%	2.40%
2720	Plumbing		2.13	3.70	5.50	3.74%	4.76%	6.30%
2770	Heating, ventilating, air conditioning		3.36	5.25	7.35	5%	5.65%	10.05%
2900	Electrical		3.75	5.55	8.65	5.85%	8%	10%
3100	Total: Mechanical & Electrical	↓	10.45	15.85	25	14.55%	19.95%	24.50%

Square Foot Project Size Modifier

One factor that affects the S.F. cost of a particular building is the size. In general, for buildings built to the same specifications in the same locality, the larger building will have the lower S.F. cost. This is due mainly to the decreasing contribution of the exterior walls, plus the economy of scale usually achievable in larger buildings. The area conversion scale shown below will give a factor to convert costs for the typical size building to an adjusted cost for the particular project.

The square foot base size table lists the median costs, most typical project size in our accumulated data, and the range in size of the projects.

The size factor for your project is determined by dividing your project area in S.F. by the typical project size for the particular building type. With this factor, enter the area conversion scale at the appropriate size factor and determine the appropriate cost multiplier for your building size.

Example: Determine the cost per S.F. for a 100,000 S.F. Mid-rise apartment building.

$$\frac{\text{Proposed building area} = 100,000 \text{ S.F.}}{\text{Typical size from below} = 50,000 \text{ S.F.}} = 2.00$$

Enter area conversion scale at 2.0, intersect curve, read horizontally the appropriate cost multiplier of .94. Size adjusted cost becomes .94 × $119.00 = $112.00 based on national average costs.

Note: For size factors less than .50, the cost multiplier is 1.1
For size factors greater than 3.5, the cost multiplier is .90

Square Foot Base Size							
Building Type	Median Cost per S.F.	Typical Size Gross S.F.	Typical Range Gross S.F.	Building Type	Median Cost per S.F.	Typical Size Gross S.F.	Typical Range Gross S.F.
Apartments, Low Rise	$ 94.00	21,000	9,700 - 37,200	Jails	$ 286.00	40,000	5,500 - 145,000
Apartments, Mid Rise	119.00	50,000	32,000 - 100,000	Libraries	190.00	12,000	7,000 - 31,000
Apartments, High Rise	129.00	145,000	95,000 - 600,000	Living, Assisted	154.00	32,300	23,500 - 50,300
Auditoriums	161.00	25,000	7,600 - 39,000	Medical Clinics	162.00	7,200	4,200 - 15,700
Auto Sales	119.00	20,000	10,800 - 28,600	Medical Offices	154.00	6,000	4,000 - 15,000
Banks	211.00	4,200	2,500 - 7,500	Motels	113.00	40,000	15,800 - 120,000
Churches	145.00	17,000	2,000 - 42,000	Nursing Homes	158.00	23,000	15,000 - 37,000
Clubs, Country	147.00	6,500	4,500 - 15,000	Offices, Low Rise	135.00	20,000	5,000 - 80,000
Clubs, Social	141.00	10,000	6,000 - 13,500	Offices, Mid Rise	132.00	120,000	20,000 - 300,000
Clubs, YMCA	167.00	28,300	12,800 - 39,400	Offices, High Rise	169.00	260,000	120,000 - 800,000
Colleges (Class)	167.00	50,000	15,000 - 150,000	Police Stations	212.00	10,500	4,000 - 19,000
Colleges (Science Lab)	269.00	45,600	16,600 - 80,000	Post Offices	157.00	12,400	6,800 - 30,000
College (Student Union)	199.00	33,400	16,000 - 85,000	Power Plants	1175.00	7,500	1,000 - 20,000
Community Center	150.00	9,400	5,300 - 16,700	Religious Education	137.00	9,000	6,000 - 12,000
Court Houses	206.00	32,400	17,800 - 106,000	Research	222.00	19,000	6,300 - 45,000
Dept. Stores	87.50	90,000	44,000 - 122,000	Restaurants	192.00	4,400	2,800 - 6,000
Dormitories, Low Rise	170.00	25,000	10,000 - 95,000	Retail Stores	93.50	7,200	4,000 - 17,600
Dormitories, Mid Rise	196.00	85,000	20,000 - 200,000	Schools, Elementary	141.00	41,000	24,500 - 55,000
Factories	85.00	26,400	12,900 - 50,000	Schools, Jr. High	145.00	92,000	52,000 - 119,000
Fire Stations	156.00	5,800	4,000 - 8,700	Schools, Sr. High	150.00	101,000	50,500 - 175,000
Fraternity Houses	145.00	12,500	8,200 - 14,800	Schools, Vocational	143.00	37,000	20,500 - 82,000
Funeral Homes	162.00	10,000	4,000 - 20,000	Sports Arenas	115.00	15,000	5,000 - 40,000
Garages, Commercial	104.00	9,300	5,000 - 13,600	Supermarkets	92.00	44,000	12,000 - 60,000
Garages, Municipal	135.00	8,300	4,500 - 12,600	Swimming Pools	300.00	20,000	10,000 - 32,000
Garages, Parking	56.00	163,000	76,400 - 225,300	Telephone Exchange	243.00	4,500	1,200 - 10,600
Gymnasiums	143.00	19,200	11,600 - 41,000	Theaters	138.00	10,500	8,800 - 17,500
Hospitals	258.00	55,000	27,200 - 125,000	Town Halls	152.00	10,800	4,800 - 23,400
House (Elderly)	128.00	37,000	21,000 - 66,000	Warehouses	63.50	25,000	8,000 - 72,000
Housing (Public)	118.00	36,000	14,400 - 74,400	Warehouse & Office	73.50	25,000	8,000 - 72,000
Ice Rinks	170.00	29,000	27,200 - 33,600				

A	Area Square Feet; Ampere	Brk., brk	Brick
AAFES	Army and Air Force Exchange Service	brkt	Bracket
		Brng.	Bearing
ABS	Acrylonitrile Butadiene Stryrene; Asbestos Bonded Steel	Brs.	Brass
		Brz.	Bronze
A.C., AC	Alternating Current; Air-Conditioning; Asbestos Cement; Plywood Grade A & C	Bsn.	Basin
		Btr.	Better
		Btu	British Thermal Unit
		BTUH	BTU per Hour
ACI	American Concrete Institute	Bu.	bushels
ACR	Air Conditioning Refrigeration	BUR	Built-up Roofing
ADA	Americans with Disabilities Act	BX	Interlocked Armored Cable
AD	Plywood, Grade A & D	°C	degree centegrade
Addit.	Additional	c	Conductivity, Copper Sweat
Adj.	Adjustable	C	Hundred; Centigrade
af	Audio-frequency	C/C	Center to Center, Cedar on Cedar
AFUE	Annual Fuel Utilization Efficiency	C-C	Center to Center
AGA	American Gas Association	Cab	Cabinet
Agg.	Aggregate	Cair.	Air Tool Laborer
A.H., Ah	Ampere Hours	Cal.	caliper
A hr.	Ampere-hour	Calc	Calculated
A.H.U., AHU	Air Handling Unit	Cap.	Capacity
A.I.A.	American Institute of Architects	Carp.	Carpenter
AIC	Ampere Interrupting Capacity	C.B.	Circuit Breaker
Allow.	Allowance	C.C.A.	Chromate Copper Arsenate
alt., alt	Alternate	C.C.F.	Hundred Cubic Feet
Alum.	Aluminum	cd	Candela
a.m.	Ante Meridiem	cd/sf	Candela per Square Foot
Amp.	Ampere	CD	Grade of Plywood Face & Back
Anod.	Anodized	CDX	Plywood, Grade C & D, exterior glue
ANSI	American National Standards Institute	Cefi.	Cement Finisher
		Cem.	Cement
APA	American Plywood Association	CF	Hundred Feet
Approx.	Approximate	C.F.	Cubic Feet
Apt.	Apartment	CFM	Cubic Feet per Minute
Asb.	Asbestos	CFRP	Carbon Fiber Reinforced Plastic
A.S.B.C.	American Standard Building Code	c.g.	Center of Gravity
Asbe.	Asbestos Worker	CHW	Chilled Water; Commercial Hot Water
ASCE.	American Society of Civil Engineers		
A.S.H.R.A.E.	American Society of Heating, Refrig. & AC Engineers	C.I., CI	Cast Iron
		C.I.P., CIP	Cast in Place
ASME	American Society of Mechanical Engineers	Circ.	Circuit
		C.L.	Carload Lot
ASTM	American Society for Testing and Materials	CL	Chain Link
		Clab.	Common Laborer
Attchmt.	Attachment	Clam	Common maintenance laborer
Avg., Ave.	Average	C.L.F.	Hundred Linear Feet
AWG	American Wire Gauge	CLF	Current Limiting Fuse
AWWA	American Water Works Assoc.	CLP	Cross Linked Polyethylene
Bbl.	Barrel	cm	Centimeter
B&B, BB	Grade B and Better; Balled & Burlapped	CMP	Corr. Metal Pipe
		CMU	Concrete Masonry Unit
B&S	Bell and Spigot	CN	Change Notice
B.&W.	Black and White	Col.	Column
b.c.c.	Body-centered Cubic	CO₂	Carbon Dioxide
B.C.Y.	Bank Cubic Yards	Comb.	Combination
BE	Bevel End	comm.	Commercial, Communication
B.F.	Board Feet	Compr.	Compressor
Bg. cem.	Bag of Cement	Conc.	Concrete
BHP	Boiler Horsepower; Brake Horsepower	Cont., cont	Continuous; Continued, Container
		Corr.	Corrugated
B.I.	Black Iron	Cos	Cosine
bidir.	bidirectional	Cot	Cotangent
Bit., Bitum.	Bituminous	Cov.	Cover
Bit., Conc.	Bituminous Concrete	C/P	Cedar on Paneling
Bk.	Backed	CPA	Control Point Adjustment
Bkrs.	Breakers	Cplg.	Coupling
Bldg., bldg	Building	CPM	Critical Path Method
Blk.	Block	CPVC	Chlorinated Polyvinyl Chloride
Bm.	Beam	C.Pr.	Hundred Pair
Boil.	Boilermaker	CRC	Cold Rolled Channel
bpm	Blows per Minute	Creos.	Creosote
BR	Bedroom	Crpt.	Carpet & Linoleum Layer
Brg.	Bearing	CRT	Cathode-ray Tube
Brhe.	Bricklayer Helper	CS	Carbon Steel, Constant Shear Bar Joist
Bric.	Bricklayer		

Csc	Cosecant
C.S.F.	Hundred Square Feet
CSI	Construction Specifications Institute
CT	Current Transformer
CTS	Copper Tube Size
Cu	Copper, Cubic
Cu. Ft.	Cubic Foot
cw	Continuous Wave
C.W.	Cool White; Cold Water
Cwt.	100 Pounds
C.W.X.	Cool White Deluxe
C.Y.	Cubic Yard (27 cubic feet)
C.Y./Hr.	Cubic Yard per Hour
Cyl.	Cylinder
d	Penny (nail size)
D	Deep; Depth; Discharge
Dis., Disch.	Discharge
Db	Decibel
Dbl.	Double
DC	Direct Current
DDC	Direct Digital Control
Demob.	Demobilization
d.f.t.	Dry Film Thickness
d.f.u.	Drainage Fixture Units
D.H.	Double Hung
DHW	Domestic Hot Water
DI	Ductile Iron
Diag.	Diagonal
Diam., Dia	Diameter
Distrib.	Distribution
Div.	Division
Dk.	Deck
D.L.	Dead Load; Diesel
DLH	Deep Long Span Bar Joist
dlx	Deluxe
Do.	Ditto
DOP	Dioctyl Phthalate Penetration Test (Air Filters)
Dp., dp	Depth
D.P.S.T.	Double Pole, Single Throw
Dr.	Drive
DR	Dimension Ratio
Drink.	Drinking
D.S.	Double Strength
D.S.A.	Double Strength A Grade
D.S.B.	Double Strength B Grade
Dty.	Duty
DWV	Drain Waste Vent
DX	Deluxe White, Direct Expansion
dyn	Dyne
e	Eccentricity
E	Equipment Only; East; emissivity
Ea.	Each
EB	Encased Burial
Econ.	Economy
E.C.Y	Embankment Cubic Yards
EDP	Electronic Data Processing
EIFS	Exterior Insulation Finish System
E.D.R.	Equiv. Direct Radiation
Eq.	Equation
EL	elevation
Elec.	Electrician; Electrical
Elev.	Elevator; Elevating
EMT	Electrical Metallic Conduit; Thin Wall Conduit
Eng.	Engine, Engineered
EPDM	Ethylene Propylene Diene Monomer
EPS	Expanded Polystyrene
Eqhv.	Equip. Oper., Heavy
Eqlt.	Equip. Oper., Light
Eqmd.	Equip. Oper., Medium
Eqmm.	Equip. Oper., Master Mechanic
Eqol.	Equip. Oper., Oilers
Equip.	Equipment
ERW	Electric Resistance Welded

861

E.S.	Energy Saver	H	High Henry	Lath.	Lather
Est.	Estimated	HC	High Capacity	Lav.	Lavatory
esu	Electrostatic Units	H.D., HD	Heavy Duty; High Density	lb.; #	Pound
E.W.	Each Way	H.D.O.	High Density Overlaid	L.B., LB	Load Bearing; L Conduit Body
EWT	Entering Water Temperature	HDPE	High density polyethelene plastic	L. & E.	Labor & Equipment
Excav.	Excavation	Hdr.	Header	lb./hr.	Pounds per Hour
excl	Excluding	Hdwe.	Hardware	lb./L.F.	Pounds per Linear Foot
Exp., exp	Expansion, Exposure	H.I.D., HID	High Intensity Discharge	lbf/sq.in.	Pound-force per Square Inch
Ext., ext	Exterior; Extension	Help.	Helper Average	L.C.L.	Less than Carload Lot
Extru.	Extrusion	HEPA	High Efficiency Particulate Air	L.C.Y.	Loose Cubic Yard
f.	Fiber stress		Filter	Ld.	Load
F	Fahrenheit; Female; Fill	Hg	Mercury	LE	Lead Equivalent
Fab., fab	Fabricated; fabric	HIC	High Interrupting Capacity	LED	Light Emitting Diode
FBGS	Fiberglass	HM	Hollow Metal	L.F.	Linear Foot
F.C.	Footcandles	HMWPE	high molecular weight	L.F. Nose	Linear Foot of Stair Nosing
f.c.c.	Face-centered Cubic		polyethylene	L.F. Rsr	Linear Foot of Stair Riser
f'c.	Compressive Stress in Concrete;	HO	High Output	Lg.	Long; Length; Large
	Extreme Compressive Stress	Horiz.	Horizontal	L & H	Light and Heat
F.E.	Front End	H.P., HP	Horsepower; High Pressure	LH	Long Span Bar Joist
FEP	Fluorinated Ethylene Propylene	H.P.F.	High Power Factor	L.H.	Labor Hours
	(Teflon)	Hr.	Hour	L.L., LL	Live Load
F.G.	Flat Grain	Hrs./Day	Hours per Day	L.L.D.	Lamp Lumen Depreciation
F.H.A.	Federal Housing Administration	HSC	High Short Circuit	lm	Lumen
Fig.	Figure	Ht.	Height	lm/sf	Lumen per Square Foot
Fin.	Finished	Htg.	Heating	lm/W	Lumen per Watt
FIPS	Female Iron Pipe Size	Htrs.	Heaters	LOA	Length Over All
Fixt.	Fixture	HVAC	Heating, Ventilation & Air-	log	Logarithm
FJP	Finger jointed and primed		Conditioning	L-O-L	Lateralolet
Fl. Oz.	Fluid Ounces	Hvy.	Heavy	long.	longitude
Flr.	Floor	HW	Hot Water	L.P., LP	Liquefied Petroleum; Low Pressure
FM	Frequency Modulation;	Hyd.; Hydr.	Hydraulic	L.P.F.	Low Power Factor
	Factory Mutual	Hz	Hertz (cycles)	LR	Long Radius
Fmg.	Framing	I.	Moment of Inertia	L.S.	Lump Sum
FM/UL	Factory Mutual/Underwriters Labs	IBC	International Building Code	Lt.	Light
Fdn.	Foundation	I.C.	Interrupting Capacity	Lt. Ga.	Light Gauge
FNPT	Female National Pipe Thread	ID	Inside Diameter	L.T.L.	Less than Truckload Lot
Fori.	Foreman, Inside	I.D.	Inside Dimension; Identification	Lt. Wt.	Lightweight
Foro.	Foreman, Outside	I.F.	Inside Frosted	L.V.	Low Voltage
Fount.	Fountain	I.M.C.	Intermediate Metal Conduit	M	Thousand; Material; Male;
fpm	Feet per Minute	In.	Inch		Light Wall Copper Tubing
FPT	Female Pipe Thread	Incan.	Incandescent	M²CA	Meters Squared Contact Area
Fr	Frame	Incl.	Included; Including	m/hr.; M.H.	Man-hour
F.R.	Fire Rating	Int.	Interior	mA	Milliampere
FRK	Foil Reinforced Kraft	Inst.	Installation	Mach.	Machine
FSK	Foil/scrim/kraft	Insul., insul	Insulation/Insulated	Mag. Str.	Magnetic Starter
FRP	Fiberglass Reinforced Plastic	I.P.	Iron Pipe	Maint.	Maintenance
FS	Forged Steel	I.P.S., IPS	Iron Pipe Size	Marb.	Marble Setter
FSC	Cast Body; Cast Switch Box	IPT	Iron Pipe Threaded	Mat; Mat'l.	Material
Ft., ft	Foot; Feet	I.W.	Indirect Waste	Max.	Maximum
Ftng.	Fitting	J	Joule	MBF	Thousand Board Feet
Ftg.	Footing	J.I.C.	Joint Industrial Council	MBH	Thousand BTU's per hr.
Ft lb.	Foot Pound	K	Thousand; Thousand Pounds;	MC	Metal Clad Cable
Furn.	Furniture		Heavy Wall Copper Tubing, Kelvin	MCC	Motor Control Center
FVNR	Full Voltage Non-Reversing	K.A.H.	Thousand Amp. Hours	M.C.F.	Thousand Cubic Feet
FVR	Full Voltage Reversing	kcmil	Thousand Circular Mils	MCFM	Thousand Cubic Feet per Minute
FXM	Female by Male	KD	Knock Down	M.C.M.	Thousand Circular Mils
Fy.	Minimum Yield Stress of Steel	K.D.A.T.	Kiln Dried After Treatment	MCP	Motor Circuit Protector
g	Gram	kg	Kilogram	MD	Medium Duty
G	Gauss	kG	Kilogauss	MDF	Medium-density fibreboard
Ga.	Gauge	kgf	Kilogram Force	M.D.O.	Medium Density Overlaid
Gal., gal.	Gallon	kHz	Kilohertz	Med.	Medium
gpm, GPM	Gallon per Minute	Kip	1000 Pounds	MF	Thousand Feet
Galv., galv	Galvanized	KJ	Kiljoule	M.F.B.M.	Thousand Feet Board Measure
GC/MS	Gas Chromatograph/Mass	K.L.	Effective Length Factor	Mfg.	Manufacturing
	Spectrometer	K.L.F.	Kips per Linear Foot	Mfrs.	Manufacturers
Gen.	General	Km	Kilometer	mg	Milligram
GFI	Ground Fault Interrupter	KO	Knock Out	MGD	Million Gallons per Day
GFRC	Glass Fiber Reinforced Concrete	K.S.F.	Kips per Square Foot	MGPH	Thousand Gallons per Hour
Glaz.	Glazier	K.S.I.	Kips per Square Inch	MH, M.H.	Manhole; Metal Halide; Man-Hour
GPD	Gallons per Day	kV	Kilovolt	MHz	Megahertz
gpf	Gallon per flush	kVA	Kilovolt Ampere	Mi.	Mile
GPH	Gallons per Hour	kVAR	Kilovar (Reactance)	MI	Malleable Iron; Mineral Insulated
GPM	Gallons per Minute	KW	Kilowatt	MIPS	Male Iron Pipe Size
GR	Grade	KWh	Kilowatt-hour	mj	Mechanical Joint
Gran.	Granular	L	Labor Only; Length; Long;	m	Meter
Grnd.	Ground		Medium Wall Copper Tubing	mm	Millimeter
GVW	Gross Vehicle Weight	Lab.	Labor	Mill.	Millwright
GWB	Gypsum wall board	lat	Latitude	Min., min.	Minimum, minute

Misc.	Miscellaneous	PDCA	Painting and Decorating
ml	Milliliter, Mainline		Contractors of America
M.L.F.	Thousand Linear Feet	P.E., PE	Professional Engineer;
Mo.	Month		Porcelain Enamel;
Mobil.	Mobilization		Polyethylene; Plain End
Mog.	Mogul Base	P.E.C.I.	Porcelain Enamel on Cast Iron
MPH	Miles per Hour	Perf.	Perforated
MPT	Male Pipe Thread	PEX	Cross linked polyethylene
MRGWB	Moisture Resistant Gypsum	Ph.	Phase
	Wallboard	P.I.	Pressure Injected
MRT	Mile Round Trip	Pile.	Pile Driver
ms	Millisecond	Pkg.	Package
M.S.F.	Thousand Square Feet	Pl.	Plate
Mstz.	Mosaic & Terrazzo Worker	Plah.	Plasterer Helper
M.S.Y.	Thousand Square Yards	Plas.	Plasterer
Mtd., mtd., mtd	Mounted	plf	Pounds Per Linear Foot
Mthe.	Mosaic & Terrazzo Helper	Pluh.	Plumbers Helper
Mtng.	Mounting	Plum.	Plumber
Mult.	Multi; Multiply	Ply.	Plywood
M.V.A.	Million Volt Amperes	p.m.	Post Meridiem
M.V.A.R.	Million Volt Amperes Reactance	Pntd.	Painted
MV	Megavolt	Pord.	Painter, Ordinary
MW	Megawatt	pp	Pages
MXM	Male by Male	PP, PPL	Polypropylene
MYD	Thousand Yards	P.P.M.	Parts per Million
N	Natural; North	Pr.	Pair
nA	Nanoampere	P.E.S.B.	Pre-engineered Steel Building
NA	Not Available; Not Applicable	Prefab.	Prefabricated
N.B.C.	National Building Code	Prefin.	Prefinished
NC	Normally Closed	Prop.	Propelled
NEMA	National Electrical Manufacturers	PSF, psf	Pounds per Square Foot
	Assoc.	PSI, psi	Pounds per Square Inch
NEHB	Bolted Circuit Breaker to 600V.	PSIG	Pounds per Square Inch Gauge
NFPA	National Fire Protection Association	PSP	Plastic Sewer Pipe
NLB	Non-Load-Bearing	Pspr.	Painter, Spray
NM	Non-Metallic Cable	Psst.	Painter, Structural Steel
nm	Nanometer	P.T.	Potential Transformer
No.	Number	P. & T.	Pressure & Temperature
NO	Normally Open	Ptd.	Painted
N.O.C.	Not Otherwise Classified	Ptns.	Partitions
Nose.	Nosing	Pu	Ultimate Load
NPT	National Pipe Thread	PVC	Polyvinyl Chloride
NQOD	Combination Plug-on/Bolt on	Pvmt.	Pavement
	Circuit Breaker to 240V.	PRV	Pressure Relief Valve
N.R.C., NRC	Noise Reduction Coefficient/	Pwr.	Power
	Nuclear Regulator Commission	Q	Quantity Heat Flow
N.R.S.	Non Rising Stem	Qt.	Quart
ns	Nanosecond	Quan., Qty.	Quantity
nW	Nanowatt	Q.C.	Quick Coupling
OB	Opposing Blade	r	Radius of Gyration
OC	On Center	R	Resistance
OD	Outside Diameter	R.C.P.	Reinforced Concrete Pipe
O.D.	Outside Dimension	Rect.	Rectangle
ODS	Overhead Distribution System	recpt.	receptacle
O.G.	Ogee	Reg.	Regular
O.H.	Overhead	Reinf.	Reinforced
O&P	Overhead and Profit	Req'd.	Required
Oper.	Operator	Res.	Resistant
Opng.	Opening	Resi.	Residential
Orna.	Ornamental	RF	Radio Frequency
OSB	Oriented Strand Board	RFID	Radio-frequency identification
OS&Y	Outside Screw and Yoke	Rgh.	Rough
OSHA	Occupational Safety and Health	RGS	Rigid Galvanized Steel
	Act	RHW	Rubber, Heat & Water Resistant;
Ovhd.	Overhead		Residential Hot Water
OWG	Oil, Water or Gas	rms	Root Mean Square
Oz.	Ounce	Rnd.	Round
P.	Pole; Applied Load; Projection	Rodm.	Rodman
p.	Page	Rofc.	Roofer, Composition
Pape.	Paperhanger	Rofp.	Roofer, Precast
P.A.P.R.	Powered Air Purifying Respirator	Rohe.	Roofer Helpers (Composition)
PAR	Parabolic Reflector	Rots.	Roofer, Tile & Slate
P.B., PB	Push Button	R.O.W.	Right of Way
Pc., Pcs.	Piece, Pieces	RPM	Revolutions per Minute
P.C.	Portland Cement; Power Connector	R.S.	Rapid Start
P.C.F.	Pounds per Cubic Foot	Rsr	Riser
PCM	Phase Contrast Microscopy	RT	Round Trip
		S.	Suction; Single Entrance; South
		SBS	Styrene Butadiere Styrene

SC	Screw Cover
SCFM	Standard Cubic Feet per Minute
Scaf.	Scaffold
Sch., Sched.	Schedule
S.C.R.	Modular Brick
S.D.	Sound Deadening
SDR	Standard Dimension Ratio
S.E.	Surfaced Edge
Sel.	Select
SER, SEU	Service Entrance Cable
S.F.	Square Foot
S.F.C.A.	Square Foot Contact Area
S.F. Flr.	Square Foot of Floor
S.F.G.	Square Foot of Ground
S.F. Hor.	Square Foot Horizontal
SFR	Square Feet of Radiation
S.F. Shlf.	Square Foot of Shelf
S4S	Surface 4 Sides
Shee.	Sheet Metal Worker
Sin.	Sine
Skwk.	Skilled Worker
SL	Saran Lined
S.L.	Slimline
Sldr.	Solder
SLH	Super Long Span Bar Joist
S.N.	Solid Neutral
SO	Stranded with oil resistant inside
	insulation
S-O-L	Socketolet
sp	Standpipe
S.P.	Static Pressure; Single Pole; Self-Propelled
Spri.	Sprinkler Installer
spwg	Static Pressure Water Gauge
S.P.D.T.	Single Pole, Double Throw
SPF	Spruce Pine Fir; Sprayed
	Polyurethane Foam
S.P.S.T.	Single Pole, Single Throw
SPT	Standard Pipe Thread
Sq.	Square; 100 Square Feet
Sq. Hd.	Square Head
Sq. In.	Square Inch
S.S.	Single Strength; Stainless Steel
S.S.B.	Single Strength B Grade
sst, ss	Stainless Steel
Sswk.	Structural Steel Worker
Sswl.	Structural Steel Welder
St.; Stl.	Steel
STC	Sound Transmission Coefficient
Std.	Standard
Stg.	Staging
STK	Select Tight Knot
STP	Standard Temperature & Pressure
Stpi.	Steamfitter, Pipefitter
Str.	Strength; Starter; Straight
Strd.	Stranded
Struct.	Structural
Sty.	Story
Subj.	Subject
Subs.	Subcontractors
Surf.	Surface
Sw.	Switch
Swbd.	Switchboard
S.Y.	Square Yard
Syn.	Synthetic
S.Y.P.	Southern Yellow Pine
Sys.	System
t.	Thickness
T	Temperature; Ton
Tan	Tangent
T.C.	Terra Cotta
T & C	Threaded and Coupled
T.D.	Temperature Difference
Tdd	Telecommunications Device for
	the Deaf
T.E.M.	Transmission Electron Microscopy
temp	Temperature, Tempered, Temporary
TFFN	Nylon Jacketed Wire

Abbreviations

TFE	Tetrafluoroethylene (Teflon)	U.L., UL	Underwriters Laboratory	w/	With
T. & G.	Tongue & Groove;	Uld.	unloading	W.C., WC	Water Column; Water Closet
	Tar & Gravel	Unfin.	Unfinished	W.F.	Wide Flange
Th., Thk.	Thick	UPS	Uninterruptible Power Supply	W.G.	Water Gauge
Thn.	Thin	URD	Underground Residential	Wldg.	Welding
Thrded	Threaded		Distribution	W. Mile	Wire Mile
Tilf.	Tile Layer, Floor	US	United States	W-O-L	Weldolet
Tilh.	Tile Layer, Helper	USGBC	U.S. Green Building Council	W.R.	Water Resistant
THHN	Nylon Jacketed Wire	USP	United States Primed	Wrck.	Wrecker
THW.	Insulated Strand Wire	UTMCD	Uniform Traffic Manual For Control	W.S.P.	Water, Steam, Petroleum
THWN	Nylon Jacketed Wire		Devices	WT., Wt.	Weight
T.L., TL	Truckload	UTP	Unshielded Twisted Pair	WWF	Welded Wire Fabric
T.M.	Track Mounted	V	Volt	XFER	Transfer
Tot.	Total	VA	Volt Amperes	XFMR	Transformer
T-O-L	Threadolet	VAT	Vinyl Asbestos Tile	XHD	Extra Heavy Duty
tmpd	Tempered	V.C.T.	Vinyl Composition Tile	XHHW,	Cross-Linked Polyethylene Wire
TPO	Thermoplastic Polyolefin	VAV	Variable Air Volume	XLPE	Insulation
T.S.	Trigger Start	VC	Veneer Core	XLP	Cross-linked Polyethylene
Tr.	Trade	VDC	Volts Direct Current	Xport	Transport
Transf.	Transformer	Vent.	Ventilation	Y	Wye
Trhv.	Truck Driver, Heavy	Vert.	Vertical	yd	Yard
Trlr	Trailer	V.F.	Vinyl Faced	yr	Year
Trlt.	Truck Driver, Light	V.G.	Vertical Grain	Δ	Delta
TTY	Teletypewriter	VHF	Very High Frequency	%	Percent
TV	Television	VHO	Very High Output	~	Approximately
T.W.	Thermoplastic Water Resistant	Vib.	Vibrating	Ø	Phase; diameter
	Wire	VLF	Vertical Linear Foot	@	At
UCI	Uniform Construction Index	VOC	Volitile Organic Compound	#	Pound; Number
UF	Underground Feeder	Vol.	Volume	<	Less Than
UGND	Underground Feeder	VRP	Vinyl Reinforced Polyester	>	Greater Than
UHF	Ultra High Frequency	W	Wire; Watt; Wide; West	Z	zone
U.I.	United Inch				

869

870

873

877

878

Index

Index

Other RSMeans Products & Services

RSMeans—
a tradition of excellence in construction cost information and services since 1942

Annual Cost Guides
RSMeans Online and *CostWorks* CD Comparison Matrix
Seminars
Reference Books
Order Form

For more information visit the RSMeans website at **www.rsmeans.com**

Unit prices according to the latest MasterFormat!

Book Selection Guide

The following table provides definitive information on the content of each cost data publication. The number of lines of data provided in each unit price or assemblies division, as well as the number of crews, is listed for each book. The presence of other elements such as reference tables, square foot models, equipment rental costs, historical cost indexes, and city cost indexes, is also indicated. You can use the table to help select the RSMeans book that has the quantity and type of information you most need in your work.

Unit Cost Divisions	Building Construction	Mechanical	Electrical	Commercial Renovation	Square Foot	Site Work Landsc.	Green Building	Interior	Concrete Masonry	Open Shop	Heavy Construction	Light Commercial	Facilities Construction	Plumbing	Residential
1	573	393	410	506		509	191	312	456	572	501	246	1042	403	178
2	777	279	85	733		993	178	399	213	776	734	481	1221	286	257
3	1690	340	230	1085		1471	987	355	2032	1689	1685	481	1788	316	388
4	957	21	0	922		720	179	612	1155	925	612	529	1172	0	441
5	1893	158	155	1090		841	1799	1095	720	1893	1037	979	1909	204	721
6	2452	18	18	2110		110	589	1528	281	2448	123	2140	2124	22	2660
7	1584	215	128	1623		581	757	532	524	1581	26	1317	1685	227	1037
8	2082	81	45	2609		265	1123	1753	105	2077	0	2193	2879	0	1526
9	1971	72	26	1767		313	449	2056	390	1911	15	1659	2220	54	1435
10	1026	17	10	642		215	27	842	158	1026	29	511	1118	235	224
11	1087	208	165	546		124	54	932	28	1071	0	230	1107	169	110
12	544	0	2	319		217	137	1654	14	532	0	352	1704	23	310
13	719	140	137	242		343	111	248	66	695	244	83	746	94	79
14	273	36	0	221		0	0	257	0	273	0	12	293	16	6
21	90	0	16	37		0	0	250	0	87	0	68	426	431	220
22	1157	7544	150	1190		1568	1067	838	20	1121	1677	857	7440	9347	712
23	1177	6971	580	928		158	902	776	38	1101	111	878	5187	1918	469
26	1354	454	10081	1021		793	611	1136	55	1349	562	1298	10030	399	617
27	72	0	297	34		13	0	71	0	72	39	52	279	0	22
28	96	58	136	71		0	21	78	0	99	0	40	151	44	25
31	1498	735	610	803		3217	289	7	1208	1443	3256	600	1560	660	611
32	822	53	8	886		4426	356	405	291	793	1841	420	1701	165	468
33	530	1079	538	252		2178	41	0	237	522	2159	128	1699	1286	154
34	107	0	47	4		190	0	0	31	62	193	0	128	0	0
35	18	0	0	0		327	0	0	0	18	442	0	84	0	0
41	60	0	0	32		7	0	22	0	60	30	0	67	14	0
44	75	79	0	0		0	0	0	0	0	0	0	75	75	0
46	23	16	0	0		274	261	0	0	23	264	0	33	33	0
48	12	0	25	0		0	25	0	0	12	17	12	12	0	12
Totals	**24719**	**18967**	**13899**	**19673**		**19853**	**10154**	**16158**	**8022**	**24231**	**15597**	**15566**	**49880**	**16421**	**12682**

Assem Div	Building Construction	Mechanical	Electrical	Commercial Renovation	Square Foot	Site Work Landscape	Assemblies	Green Building	Interior	Concrete Masonry	Heavy Construction	Light Commercial	Facilities Construction	Plumbing	Asm Div	Residential
A		15	0	188	150	577	598	0	0	536	571	154	24	0	1	376
B		0	0	848	2498	0	5658	56	329	1975	368	2089	174	0	2	211
C		0	0	647	926	0	1304	0	1629	146	0	816	250	0	3	588
D		1067	941	712	1859	72	2538	330	825	0	0	1345	1105	1088	4	851
E		0	0	86	260	0	300	0	5	0	0	257	5	0	5	392
F		0	0	0	114	0	114	0	0	0	0	0	114	3	0	6	357
G		527	447	318	249	3365	729	0	0	535	1350	205	293	677	7	307
															8	760
															9	80
															10	0
															11	0
															12	0
Totals		**1609**	**1388**	**2799**	**6056**	**4014**	**11241**	**386**	**2788**	**3192**	**2289**	**4980**	**1854**	**1765**		**3922**

Reference Section	Building Construction Costs	Mechanical	Electrical	Commercial Renovation	Square Foot	Site Work Landscape	Assem.	Green Building	Interior	Concrete Masonry	Open Shop	Heavy Construction	Light Commercial	Facilities Construction	Plumbing	Resi.
Reference Tables	yes	yes	yes	yes	no	yes	yes	yes	yes	yes	yes	yes	yes	yes	yes	yes
Models					111			25					50			28
Crews	571	571	571	550		571		571	571	571	548	571	548	550	571	548
Equipment Rental Costs	yes	yes	yes	yes		yes		yes	yes	yes	yes	yes	yes	yes	yes	yes
Historical Cost Indexes	yes	yes	yes	yes		yes	yes	yes	yes	yes	yes	yes	yes	yes	yes	no
City Cost Indexes	yes	yes	yes	yes		yes	yes	yes	yes	yes	yes	yes	yes	yes	yes	yes

888

For more information visit the RSMeans website at **www.rsmeans.com**

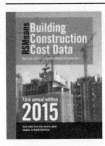

RSMeans Building Construction Cost Data 2015

Offers you unchallenged unit price reliability in an easy-to-use format. Whether used for verifying complete, finished estimates or for periodic checks, it supplies more cost facts better and faster than any comparable source. More than 24,700 unit prices have been updated for 2015. The City Cost Indexes and Location Factors cover more than 930 areas, for indexing to any project location in North America. Order and get *RSMeans Quarterly Update Service* FREE.

$206.95 | Available Sept. 2014 | Catalog no. 60015

RSMeans Mechanical Cost Data 2015

Total unit and systems price guidance for mechanical construction . . . materials, parts, fittings, and complete labor cost information. Includes prices for piping, heating, air conditioning, ventilation, and all related construction.

Plus new 2015 unit costs for:

- Thousands of installed HVAC/controls, sub-assemblies and assemblies
- "On-site" Location Factors for more than 930 cities and towns in the U.S. and Canada
- Crews, labor, and equipment

$203.95 | Available Oct. 2014 | Catalog no. 60025

RSMeans Square Foot Costs 2015
Accurate and Easy-to-Use

- **Updated price information** based on nationwide figures from suppliers, estimators, labor experts, and contractors.
- Green building models
- Realistic graphics, offering true-to-life illustrations of building projects
- Extensive information on using square foot cost data, including sample estimates and alternate pricing methods

$218.95 | Available Oct. 2014 | Catalog no. 60055

RSMeans Electrical Cost Data 2015

Pricing information for every part of electrical cost planning. More than 13,800 unit and systems costs with design tables; clear specifications and drawings; engineering guides; illustrated estimating procedures; complete labor-hour and materials costs for better scheduling and procurement; and the latest electrical products and construction methods.

- A variety of special electrical systems, including cathodic protection
- Costs for maintenance, demolition, HVAC/mechanical, specialties, equipment, and more

$208.95 | Available Oct. 2014 | Catalog no. 60035

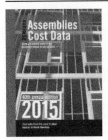

RSMeans Assemblies Cost Data 2015

RSMeans Assemblies Cost Data takes the guesswork out of preliminary or conceptual estimates. Now you don't have to try to calculate the assembled cost by working up individual component costs. We've done all the work for you.

Presents detailed illustrations, descriptions, specifications, and costs for every conceivable building assembly—over 350 types in all—arranged in the easy-to-use UNIFORMAT II system. Each illustrated "assembled" cost includes a complete grouping of materials and associated installation costs, including the installing contractor's overhead and profit.

$334.95 | Available Sept. 2014 | Catalog no. 60065

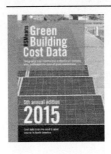

RSMeans Green Building Cost Data 2015

Estimate, plan, and budget the costs of green building for both new commercial construction and renovation work with this fifth edition of *RSMeans Green Building Cost Data*. More than 10,000 unit costs for a wide array of green building products plus assemblies costs. Easily identified cross references to LEED and Green Globes building rating systems criteria.

$170.95 | Available Nov. 2014 | Catalog no. 60555

RSMeans Facilities Construction Cost Data 2015

For the maintenance and construction of commercial, industrial, municipal, and institutional properties. Costs are shown for new and remodeling construction and are broken down into materials, labor, equipment, and overhead and profit. Special emphasis is given to sections on mechanical, electrical, furnishings, site work, building maintenance, finish work, and demolition.

More than 49,800 unit costs, plus assemblies costs and a comprehensive Reference Section are included.

$524.95 | Available Nov. 2014 | Catalog no. 60205

RSMeans Commercial Renovation Cost Data 2015
Commercial/Multi-family Residential

Use this valuable tool to estimate commercial and multi-family residential renovation and remodeling.

Includes: Updated costs for hundreds of unique methods, materials, and conditions that only come up in repair and remodeling, PLUS:

- Unit costs for more than 19,600 construction components
- Installed costs for more than 2,700 assemblies
- More than 930 "on-site" localization factors for the U.S. and Canada

$166.95 | Available Oct. 2014 | Catalog no. 60045

RSMeans Electrical Change Order Cost Data 2015

RSMeans Electrical Change Order Cost Data provides you with electrical unit prices exclusively for pricing change orders—based on the recent, direct experience of contractors and suppliers. Analyze and check your own change order estimates against the experience others have had doing the same work. It also covers productivity analysis, and change order cost justifications. With useful information for calculating the effects of change orders and dealing with their administration.

$199.95 | Available Dec. 2014 | Catalog no. 60235

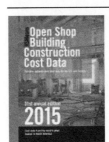

RSMeans Open Shop Building Construction Cost Data 2015

The latest costs for accurate budgeting and estimating of new commercial and residential construction . . . renovation work . . . change orders . . . cost engineering.

RSMeans Open Shop "BCCD" will assist you to:

- Develop benchmark prices for change orders.
- Plug gaps in preliminary estimates and budgets.
- Estimate complex projects.
- Substantiate invoices on contracts.
- Price ADA-related renovations.

$175.95 | Available Dec. 2014 | Catalog no. 60155

Annual Cost Guides

Unit prices according to the latest MasterFormat!

889

RSMeans Residential
Cost Data 2015

Contains square foot costs for 28 basic home models with the look of today, plus hundreds of custom additions and modifications you can quote right off the page. Includes more than 3,900 costs for 89 residential systems. Complete with blank estimating forms, sample estimates, and step-by-step instructions.

Contains line items for cultured stone and brick, PVC trim, lumber, and TPO roofing.

$148.95 | Available Oct. 2014 | Catalog no. 60175

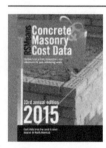

RSMeans Facilities Maintenance & Repair
Cost Data 2015

RSMeans Facilities Maintenance & Repair Cost Data gives you a complete system to manage and plan your facility repair and maintenance costs and budget efficiently. Guidelines for auditing a facility and developing an annual maintenance plan. Budgeting is included, along with reference tables on cost and management, and information on frequency and productivity of maintenance operations.

The only nationally recognized source of maintenance and repair costs. Developed in cooperation with the Civil Engineering Research Laboratory (CERL) of the Army Corps of Engineers.

$461.95 | Available Nov. 2014 | Catalog no. 60305

RSMeans Concrete & Masonry
Cost Data 2015

Provides you with cost facts for virtually all concrete/masonry estimating needs, from complicated formwork to various sizes and face finishes of brick and block—all in great detail. The comprehensive Unit Price Section contains more than 8,000 selected entries. Also contains an Assemblies [Cost] Section, and a detailed Reference Section that supplements the cost data.

$188.95 | Available Dec. 2014 | Catalog no. 60115

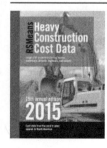

RSMeans Construction
Cost Indexes 2015

What materials and labor costs will change unexpectedly this year? By how much?

- Breakdowns for 318 major cities
- National averages for 30 key cities
- Expanded five major city indexes
- Historical construction cost indexes

$359.95 per year (subscription) | Catalog no. 50145
$94.95 individual quarters | Catalog no. 60145 A,B,C,D

RSMeans Heavy Construction
Cost Data 2015

A comprehensive guide to heavy construction costs. Includes costs for highly specialized projects such as tunnels, dams, highways, airports, and waterways. Information on labor rates, equipment, and materials costs is included. Features unit price costs, systems costs, and numerous reference tables for costs and design.

$204.95 | Available Dec. 2014 | Catalog no. 60165

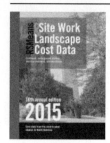

RSMeans Site Work & Landscape
Cost Data 2015

Includes unit and assemblies costs for earthwork, sewerage, piped utilities, site improvements, drainage, paving, trees and shrubs, street openings/repairs, underground tanks, and more. Contains more than 60 types of assemblies costs for accurate conceptual estimates.

Includes:

- Estimating for infrastructure improvements
- Environmentally-oriented construction
- ADA-mandated handicapped access
- Hazardous waste line items

$199.95 | Available Dec. 2014 | Catalog no. 60285

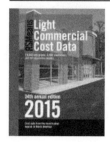

RSMeans Light Commercial
Cost Data 2015

Specifically addresses the light commercial market, which is a specialized niche in the construction industry. Aids you, the owner/designer/contractor, in preparing all types of estimates—from budgets to detailed bids. Includes new advances in methods and materials.

Assemblies Section allows you to evaluate alternatives in the early stages of design/planning.

More than 15,500 unit costs ensure that you have the prices you need, when you need them.

$153.95 | Available Nov. 2014 | Catalog no. 60185

RSMeans Labor Rates for the
Construction Industry 2015

Complete information for estimating labor costs, making comparisons, and negotiating wage rates by trade for more than 300 U.S. and Canadian cities. With 46 construction trades in each city, and historical wage rates included for comparison. Each city chart lists the county and is alphabetically arranged with handy visual flip tabs for quick reference.

$450.95 | Available Dec. 2014 | Catalog no. 60125

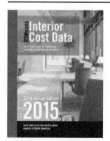

RSMeans Interior
Cost Data 2015

Provides you with prices and guidance needed to make accurate interior work estimates. Contains costs on materials, equipment, hardware, custom installations, furnishings, and labor for new and remodel commercial and industrial interior construction, including updated information on office furnishings, and reference information.

$208.95 | Available Nov. 2014 | Catalog no. 60095

RSMeans Plumbing
Cost Data 2015

Comprehensive unit prices and assemblies for plumbing, irrigation systems, commercial and residential fire protection, point-of-use water heaters, and the latest approved materials. This publication and its companion, *RSMeans Mechanical Cost Data*, provide full-range cost estimating coverage for all the mechanical trades.

Contains updated costs for potable water, radiant heat systems, and high efficiency fixtures.

$206.95 | Available Oct. 2014 | Catalog no. 60215

Annual Cost Guides

Unit prices according to the latest MasterFormat!

For more information visit the RSMeans website at **www.rsmeans.com**

RSMeans Online and RSMeans CostWorks CD Comparison Matrix

Both the RSMeans CostWorks CD package and the RSMeans Online estimating tool provide the same comprehensive, up-to-date, and localized cost information to improve planning, estimating, and budgeting with RSMeans—the industry's most-trusted source of construction cost data.

In addition to key differences noted in the comparison matrix below, both products let you do the following:

• Quickly locate costs in the searchable RSMeans database.

• Instantly adjust the data to your specific location for accurate costs anywhere in the U.S. and Canada.

• Create reliable, updated cost estimates in minutes.

• Manage, share, and export your estimates to MS Excel® with ease.

• Access a wide range of reference materials, including crew rates and national average labor rates.

Both the CD and Online options are available in a convenient one-year subscription!

Use the handy comparison matrix below to help you decide the best product for your cost estimating needs!

Why us?

For more than 70 years, RSMeans has provided the quality cost data construction professionals everywhere depend on to estimate with confidence, save time, improve decision-making, and increase profits.

Improve planning and decision-making

Back your estimates with complete, accurate, and up-to-date cost data for informed business decisions.
• Verify construction costs from third parties.
• Check validity of subcontractor proposals.
• Evaluate material and assembly alternatives.

Increase profits

Use RSMeans to estimate projects quickly and accurately, so you can gain an edge over your competition.
• Create accurate and competitive bids.
• Minimize the risk of cost overruns.
• Reduce variability.
• Gain control over costs.

The following matrix summarizes the key comparison points between RSMeans' two electronic cost data products.

	Question	CostWorks CD	RSMeans Online.com
1	How is the data presented?	• The data is organized by book title and sold at comparable book cost. • Several packaged bundles of five titles are available at a cost savings. • Available in a convenient one-year subscription	• The data is organized by book title and sold at comparable book cost. • Several packaged bundles of five titles are available at a cost savings. • RSMeans Online also offers a Complete Library title with all online data at a cost savings. • Available in a convenient one-year subscription
2	Where is the data stored?	With a typical install, the data is read off of your hard drive or off of the CD.	All data is stored on our secure server.
3	How are updates delivered?	Updates are available on a quarterly basis for download from the Costworks HomePort website.	Data is updated automatically on a quarterly basis, and users are notified when updates occur.
4	Where are my projects and estimates stored?	Upon installation, a "My CostWorks Projects" folder is created within the "My Documents" directory. All projects are defaulted to save here unless otherwise specified.	Estimates are stored on our secure server.
5	Does my IT team need to assist me in installing and running the program?	Yes, depending on the level of your permission. See #11 for system requirements.	While the product is entirely Web-based, you may need IT support with permissions for certain tasks. See #11 for system requirements.
6	Can users collaborate on projects/estimates?	Yes, you can copy project folders between computers.	You can create shared folders that can be viewed, copied, and edited by anyone within your account workgroup.

Unit prices according to the latest MasterFormat!

RSMeans Online

For more information visit the RSMeans website at www.rsmeans.com

Comparison matrix continued

7	Can I create and use my own data with the RSMeans database?	Custom lines cannot be added to the CD database. With the Estimator tool, however, you can create and add custom cost lines to any estimate. You can also save custom lines as an Estimator template for use in creating new estimates.	You can create • a custom line within an estimate • a custom cost book consisting of custom unit (not assembly) cost lines, no more than once per quarter **Note** that custom data is searchable using the Include My Custom Data feature.
8	Can I enter my own trade/labor rates and markups?	Although you cannot adjust the trade labor rates, you can add custom markups for each report template using the Estimator tool.	For each quarterly update, you can create one custom unit cost book. You can edit the labor rates by individual trade and the crew equipment costs, and also edit the associated material and equipment markups.
9	What are my reporting options?	The Estimator tool lets you create editable custom reports and report templates. Reports can also be exported to MS Excel®.	You can generate pre-formatted estimate summaries and cost lists in both PDF and Excel formats.
10	How do I find specific cost data?	You can search by CSI line number and by keyword within a division.	You can search by CSI line number and by keyword within a division. There are several additional search options, including keyword and advanced search using special characters.
11	What are the system requirements?	• Operating system – Windows XP or later • PC requirements - 256 MB RAM (recommended), 1024 x 768 High Color Monitor, 800MHz Computer (recommended), 24X CD-ROM, 250 MB Hard Disk Space	• Resolution – Recommended resolution is 1024 x 768 or higher • Compatibility - Internet Explorer version 8.x, 9.x and Mozilla Firefox version 10 and higher • iPad - iOS 5 and higher

2015 RSMeans Seminar Schedule

Note: call for exact dates and details.

Location	Dates	Location	Dates
Seattle, WA	January and August	Jacksonville FL	September
Dallas/Ft. Worth, TX	January	Dallas, TX	September
Austin, TX	February	Charleston, SC	October
Anchorage, AK	March and September	Houston, TX	October
Las Vegas, NV	March and October	Atlanta, GA	November
Washington, DC	April and September	Baltimore, MD	November
Phoenix, AZ	April	Orlando, FL	November
Kansas City, MO	April	San Diego, CA	December
Toronto	May	San Antonio, TX	December
Denver, CO	May	Raleigh, NC	December
San Francisco, CA	June		
Bethesda, MD	June		
Columbus, GA	June		
El Segundo, CA	August		

1-800-334-3509, Press 1

Professional Development

For more information visit the RSMeans website at www.rsmeans.com

eLearning Training Sessions

Learn how to use *RSMeans Online®* or *RSMeans CostWorks®* CD from the convenience of your home or office. Our eLearning training sessions let you join a training conference call and share the instructors' desktops, so you can view the presentation and step-by-step instructions on your own computer screen. The live webinars are held from 9 a.m. to 4 p.m. eastern standard time, with a one-hour break for lunch.

For these sessions, you must have a computer with high speed Internet access and a compatible Web browser. Learn more at www.rsmeansonline.com or call for a schedule: 1-800-334-3509 and press 1. Webinars are generally held on selected Wednesdays each month.

RSMeans Online®	RSMeans CostWorks® CD
$299 per person	**$299 per person**

Seminar Schedule and Professional Development

RSMeans data titles are also available in online format! Go to RSMeansOnline.com for more details.

For more information visit the RSMeans website at **www.rsmeans.com**

RSMeans Online™ Training

Construction estimating is vital to the decision-making process at each state of every project. RSMeansOnline works the way you do. It's systematic, flexible and intuitive. In this one day class you will see how you can estimate any phase of any project faster and better.

Some of what you'll learn:
• Customizing RSMeansOnline
• Making the most of RSMeans "Circle Reference" numbers
• How to integrate your cost data
• Generate reports, exporting estimates to MS Excel, sharing, collaborating and more

Also available: RSMeans Online® training webinar

Facilities Construction Estimating

In this *two-day* course, professionals working in facilities management can get help with their daily challenges to establish budgets for all phases of a project.

Some of what you'll learn:
• Determining the full scope of a project
• Identifying the scope of risks and opportunities
• Creative solutions to estimating issues
• Organizing estimates for presentation and discussion
• Special techniques for repair/remodel and maintenance projects
• Negotiating project change orders

Who should attend: facility managers, engineers, contractors, facility tradespeople, planners, and project managers.

Construction Cost Estimating: Concepts and Practice

This *one-day* introductory course to improve estimating skills and effectiveness starts with the details of interpreting bid documents, ending with the summary of the estimate and bid submission.

Some of what you'll learn:
• Using the plans and specifications for creating estimates
• The takeoff process—deriving all tasks with correct quantities
• Developing pricing, using various sources; how subcontractor pricing fits in
• Summarizing the estimate to arrive at the final number
• Formulas for area and cubic measure, adding waste and adjusting productivity to specific projects
• Evaluating subcontractors' proposals and prices
• Adding Insurance and bonds
• Understanding how labor costs are calculated
• Submitting bids and proposals

Who should attend: project managers, architects, engineers, owner's representatives, contractors, and anyone who's responsible for budgeting or estimating construction projects.

Maintenance & Repair Estimating for Facilities

This *two-day* course teaches attendees how to plan, budget, and estimate the cost of ongoing and preventive maintenance and repair for existing buildings and grounds.

Some of what you'll learn:
• The most financially favorable maintenance, repair, and replacement scheduling and estimating
• Auditing and value engineering facilities
• Preventive planning and facilities upgrading
• Determining both in-house and contract-out service costs
• Annual, asset-protecting M&R plan

Who should attend: facility managers, maintenance supervisors, buildings and grounds superintendents, plant managers, planners, estimators, and others involved in facilities planning and budgeting.

Practical Project Management for Construction Professionals

In this *two-day* course, acquire the essential knowledge and develop the skills to effectively and efficiently execute the day-to-day responsibilities of the construction project manager.

Covers:
• General conditions of the construction contract
• Contract modifications: change orders and construction change directives
• Negotiations with subcontractors and vendors
• Effective writing: notification and communications
• Dispute resolution: claims and liens

Who should attend: architects, engineers, owner's representatives, project managers.

Mechanical & Electrical Estimating

This *two-day* course teaches attendees how to prepare more accurate and complete mechanical/electrical estimates, avoiding the pitfalls of omission and double-counting, while understanding the composition and rationale within the RSMeans mechanical/electrical database.

Some of what you'll learn:
• The unique way mechanical and electrical systems are interrelated
• M&E estimates—conceptual, planning, budgeting, and bidding stages
• Order of magnitude, square foot, assemblies, and unit price estimating
• Comparative cost analysis of equipment and design alternatives

Who should attend: architects, engineers, facilities managers, mechanical and electrical contractors, and others who need a highly reliable method for developing, understanding, and evaluating mechanical and electrical contracts.

Professional Development

RSMeans data titles are also available in online format! Go to RSMeansOnline.com for more details.

For more information visit the RSMeans website at **www.rsmeans.com**

Unit Price Estimating

This interactive *two-day* seminar teaches attendees how to interpret project information and process it into final, detailed estimates with the greatest accuracy level.

The most important credential an estimator can take to the job is the ability to visualize construction and estimate accurately.

Some of what you'll learn:
- Interpreting the design in terms of cost
- The most detailed, time-tested methodology for accurate pricing
- Key cost drivers—material, labor, equipment, staging, and subcontracts
- Understanding direct and indirect costs for accurate job cost accounting and change order management

Who should attend: corporate and government estimators and purchasers, architects, engineers, and others who need to produce accurate project estimates.

RSMeans CostWorks® CD Training

This one-day course helps users become more familiar with the functionality of *RSMeans CostWorks* program. Each menu, icon, screen, and function found in the program is explained in depth. Time is devoted to hands-on estimating exercises.

Some of what you'll learn:
- Searching the database using all navigation methods
- Exporting RSMeans data to your preferred spreadsheet format
- Viewing crews, assembly components, and much more
- Automatically regionalizing the database

This training session requires you to bring a laptop computer to class.

When you register for this course you will receive an outline for your laptop requirements.

Also offering web training for RSMeans CostWorks CD!

Facilities Estimating Using RSMeans CostWorks® CD

Combines hands-on skill building with best estimating practices and real-life problems. Brings you up-to-date with key concepts, and provides tips, pointers, and guidelines to save time and avoid cost oversights and errors.

Some of what you'll learn:
- Estimating process concepts
- Customizing and adapting RSMeans cost data
- Establishing scope of work to account for all known variables
- Budget estimating: when, why, and how
- Site visits: what to look for—what you can't afford to overlook
- How to estimate repair and remodeling variables

This training session requires you to bring a laptop computer to class.

Who should attend: facility managers, architects, engineers, contractors, facility tradespeople, planners, project managers and anyone involved with JOC, SABRE, or IDIQ.

Conceptual Estimating Using RSMeans CostWorks® CD

This *two-day* class uses the leading industry data and a powerful software package to develop highly accurate conceptual estimates for your construction projects. All attendees must bring a laptop computer loaded with the current year *Square Foot Costs* and the *Assemblies Cost Data* CostWorks titles.

Some of what you'll learn:
- Introduction to conceptual estimating
- Types of conceptual estimates
- Helpful hints
- Order of magnitude estimating
- Square foot estimating
- Assemblies estimating

Who should attend: architects, engineers, contractors, construction estimators, owner's representatives, and anyone looking for an electronic method for performing square foot estimating.

Assessing Scope of Work for Facility Construction Estimating

This *two-day* practical training program addresses the vital importance of understanding the SCOPE of projects in order to produce accurate cost estimates for facility repair and remodeling.

Some of what you'll learn:
- Discussions of site visits, plans/specs, record drawings of facilities, and site-specific lists
- Review of CSI divisions, including means, methods, materials, and the challenges of scoping each topic
- Exercises in SCOPE identification and SCOPE writing for accurate estimating of projects
- Hands-on exercises that require SCOPE, take-off, and pricing

Who should attend: corporate and government estimators, planners, facility managers, and others who need to produce accurate project estimates.

Unit Price Estimating Using RSMeans CostWorks® CD

Step-by-step instruction and practice problems to identify and track key cost drivers—material, labor, equipment, staging, and subcontractors—for each specific task. Learn the most detailed, time-tested methodology for accurately "pricing" these variables, their impact on each other and on total cost.

Some of what you'll learn:
- Unit price cost estimating
- Order of magnitude, square foot, and assemblies estimating
- Quantity takeoff
- Direct and indirect construction costs
- Development of contractor's bill rates
- How to use *RSMeans Building Construction Cost Data*

This training session requires you to bring a laptop computer to class.

Who should attend: architects, engineers, corporate and government estimators, facility managers, and government procurement staff.

Professional Development

For more information visit the RSMeans website at **www.rsmeans.com**

Registration Information

Register early . . . Save up to $100! Register 30 days before the start date of a seminar and save $100 off your total fee. *Note: This discount can be applied only once per order. It cannot be applied to team discount registrations or any other special offer.*

How to register Register by phone today! The RSMeans toll-free number for making reservations is **1-800-334-3509, Press 1.**

Two-day seminar registration fee - $935. One-day *RSMeans CostWorks*® training registration fee - $375. To register by mail, complete the registration form and return, with your full fee, to: RSMeans Seminars, 700 Longwater Drive, Norwell, MA 02061.

Government pricing All federal government employees save off the regular seminar price. Other promotional discounts cannot be combined with the government discount.

Team discount program for two to four seminar registrations. Call for pricing: 1-800-334-3509, Press 1

Multiple course discounts When signing up for two or more courses, call for pricing.

Refund policy Cancellations will be accepted up to ten business days prior to the seminar start. There are no refunds for cancellations received later than ten working days prior to the first day of the seminar. A $150 processing fee will be applied for all cancellations. Written notice of cancellation is required. Substitutions can be made at any time before the session starts. **No-shows are subject to the full seminar fee.**

AACE approved courses Many seminars described and offered here have been approved for 14 hours (1.4 recertification credits) of credit by the AACE International Certification Board toward meeting the continuing education requirements for recertification as a Certified Cost Engineer/Certified Cost Consultant.

AIA Continuing Education We are registered with the AIA Continuing Education System (AIA/CES) and are committed to developing quality learning activities in accordance with the CES criteria. Many seminars meet the AIA/CES criteria for Quality Level 2. AIA members may receive (14) learning units (LUs) for each two-day RSMeans course.

Daily course schedule The first day of each seminar session begins at 8:30 a.m. and ends at 4:30 p.m. The second day begins at 8:00 a.m. and ends at 4:00 p.m. Participants are urged to bring a hand-held calculator, since many actual problems will be worked out in each session.

Continental breakfast Your registration includes the cost of a continental breakfast, and a morning and afternoon refreshment break. These informal segments allow you to discuss topics of mutual interest with other seminar attendees. (You are free to make your own lunch and dinner arrangements.)

Hotel/transportation arrangements RSMeans arranges to hold a block of rooms at most host hotels. To take advantage of special group rates when making your reservation, be sure to mention that you are attending the RSMeans seminar. You are, of course, free to stay at the lodging place of your choice. (**Hotel reservations and transportation arrangements should be made directly by seminar attendees.**)

Important Class sizes are limited, so please register as soon as possible.

Note: Pricing subject to change.

Registration Form

ADDS-1000

Call 1-800-334-3509, Press 1 to register or FAX this form 1-800-632-6732. Visit our website: www.rsmeans.com

Please register the following people for the RSMeans construction seminars as shown here. We understand that we must make our own hotel reservations if overnight stays are necessary.

☐ Full payment of $_____enclosed.

☐ Bill me.

Please print name of registrant(s).

(To appear on certificate of completion)

_____

_____

_____

_____

P.O. #: _____
GOVERNMENT AGENCIES MUST SUPPLY PURCHASE ORDER NUMBER OR TRAINING FORM.

Firm name_____

Address_____

City/State/Zip_____

Telephone no._____ Fax no._____

E-mail address_____

Charge registration(s) to: ☐ MasterCard ☐ VISA ☐ American Express

Account no._____Exp. date_____

Cardholder's signature_____

Seminar name_____

Seminar City _____

Please mail check to: RSMeans Seminars, 700 Longwater Drive, Norwell, MA 02061 USA

Professional Development

For more information visit the RSMeans website at **www.rsmeans.com**

Managing the Profitable Construction Business: The Contractor's Guide to Success and Survival Strategies, 2nd Ed.

by Thomas C. Scheifler, Ph.D.

Learn from a team of construction business veterans led by Thomas C. Schleifer, who is commonly referred to as a construction business "turnaround" expert due to the number of construction companies he has rescued from financial distress. His financial acumen, combined with his practical, hands-on experience, has made him a sought-after private consultant.

$60.00 | 288 pages, hardover | Catalog no. 67370

Construction Project Safety

by John Schaufelberger, Ken-Yu Lin

This essential introduction to construction safety for construction management personnel takes a project-based approach to present potential hazards in construction and their mitigation or prevention.

Beginning with an introduction to Accident Prevention Programs and OSHA compliance requirements, the book integrates safety instruction into the building process by following a building project from site construction through interior finish. Reinforcing this applied approach are photographs, drawings, contract documentation, and an online 3D BIM model to help visualize the on-site scenarios.

$85.00 | 320 pages, hardover | Catalog no. 67368

Project Control: Integrating Cost & Schedule in Construction

by Wayne J. Del Pico

Written by a seasoned professional in the field, *Project Control: Integrating Cost and Schedule in Construction* fills a void in the area of project control as applied in the construction industry today. It demonstrates how productivity models for an individual project are created, monitored, and controlled, and how corrective actions are implemented as deviations from the baseline occur.

$65.00 | 240 pages, softcover | Catalog no. 67366

Project Scheduling and Management for Construction, 4th Edition

by David R. Pierce

First published in 1988 by RSMeans, the new edition of *Project Scheduling and Management for Construction* has been substantially revised for both professionals and students enrolled in construction management and civil engineering programs. While retaining its emphasis on developing practical, professional-level scheduling skills, the new edition is a relatable, real world case study.

$95.00 | 272 pages, softcover | Catalog no. 67367

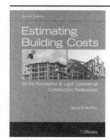

Estimating Building Costs, 2nd Edition
For the Residential & Light Commercial Construction Professional

by Wayne J. Del Pico

Explains, in detail, how to put together a reliable estimate that can be used not only for budgeting, but also for developing a schedule, managing a project, dealing with contingencies, and, ultimately, making a profit.

Completely revised and updated to reflect the CSI MasterFormat 2010 system.

$75.00 | 528 pages, softcover | Catalog no. 67343A

The Gypsum Construction Handbook, 7th Edition

by USG

The tried-and-true Gypsum Construction Handbook is a systematic guide to selecting and using gypsum drywall, veneer plaster, tile backers, ceilings, and conventional plaster building materials. A widely respected training text for aspiring architects and engineers, the book provides detailed product information and efficient installation methodology.

The 7th edition features updates in gypsum products, including ultralight panels, glass-mat panels, paper-faced plastic bead, and ultralightweight joint compound, and modern specialty acoustical and ceiling product guidelines. This comprehensive reference also incorporates the latest in sustainable products.

$40.00 | 576 pages, softcover | Catalog no. 67357B

Solar Energy: Technologies & Project Delivery for Buildings

by Andy Walker

An authoritative reference on the design of solar energy systems in building projects, with applications, operating principles, and simple tools for the construction, engineering, and design professionals, the book simplifies the solar design and engineering process and provides sample documentation for the complete design of a solar energy system for buildings.

$85.00 | 320 pages, hardover | Catalog no. 67365

RSMeans Cost Data, Student Edition

Provides a thorough introduction to cost estimating in a print and online package. Clear explanations and example-driven. The ideal reference for students and new professionals. Features include:

- Commercial and residential construction cost data in print and online formats
- Complete how-to guidance on the essentials of cost estimating
- A supplemental website with plans, problem sets, and a full sample estimate

$110.00 | 512 pages, softcover | Catalog no. 67363

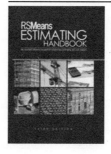

How to Estimate with Means Data & CostWorks, 4th Edition

by RSMeans and Saleh A. Mubarak, Ph.D.

This step-by-step guide takes you through all the major construction items with extensive coverage of site work, concrete and masonry, wood and metal framing, doors and windows, and other divisions. The only construction cost estimating handbook that uses the most popular source of construction data, RSMeans, this indispensible guide features access to the instructional version of *CostWorks* in electronic form, enabling you to practice techniques to solve real-world estimating problems.

$75.00 | 320 pages, softcover | Includes CostWorks CD | Catalog no. 67324C

RSMeans Estimating Handbook, 3rd Edition

Widely used in the industry for tasks ranging from routine estimates to special cost analysis projects. This handbook will help construction professionals:

- Evaluate architectural plans and specifications
- Prepare accurate quantity takeoffs
- Compare design alternatives and costs
- Perform value engineering
- Double-check estimates and quotes
- Estimate change orders

$110.00 | Over 976 pages, hardcover | Catalog No. 67276B

Reference Books

RSMeans data titles are also available in online format! Go to RSMeansOnline.com for more details.

For more information visit the RSMeans website at **www.rsmeans.com**

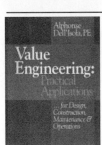

Value Engineering: Practical Applications

For Design, Construction, Maintenance & Operations

by Alphonse Dell'Isola, PE

A tool for immediate application—for engineers, architects, facility managers, owners, and contractors. Includes making the case for VE—the management briefing; integrating VE into planning, budgeting, and design; conducting life cycle costing; using VE methodology in design review and consultant selection; and case studies.

$90.00 | Over 427 pages, illustrated, softcover | Catalog no. 67319A

Risk Management for Design and Construction

Introduces risk as a central pillar of project management and shows how a project manager can prepare to deal with uncertainty. Includes:

- Integrated cost and schedule risk analysis
- An introduction to a ready-to-use system of analyzing a project's risks and tools to proactively manage risks
- A methodology that was developed and used by the Washington State Department of Transportation
- Case studies and examples on the proper application of principles
- Combining value analysis with risk analysis

$125.00 | Over 288 pages, softcover | Catalog no. 67359

How Your House Works, 2nd Edition

by Charlie Wing

Knowledge of your home's systems helps you control repair and construction costs and makes sure the correct elements are being installed or replaced. This book uncovers the mysteries behind just about every major appliance and building element in your house. See-through, cross-section drawings in full color show you exactly how these things should be put together and how they function, including what to check if they don't work. It just might save you having to call in a professional.

$22.95 | 208 pages, softcover | Catalog no. 67351A

Construction Business Management

by Nick Ganaway

Only 43% of construction firms stay in business after four years. Make sure your company thrives with valuable guidance from a pro with 25 years of success as a commercial contractor. Find out what it takes to build all aspects of a business that is profitable, enjoyable, and enduring. With a bonus chapter on retail construction.

$60.00 | 201 pages, softcover | Catalog no. 67352

The Practice of Cost Segregation Analysis

by Bruce A. Desrosiers and Wayne J. Del Pico

This expert guide walks you through the practice of cost segregation analysis, which enables property owners to defer taxes and benefit from "accelerated cost recovery" through depreciation deductions on assets that are properly identified and classified.

With a glossary of terms, sample cost segregation estimates for various building types, key information resources, and updates via a dedicated website, this book is a critical resource for anyone involved in cost segregation analysis.

$105.00 | Over 240 pages | Catalog no. 67345

Complete Book of Framing, 2nd Edition

by Scot Simpson

This updated, easy-to-learn guide to rough carpentry and framing is written by an expert with more than thirty years of framing experience. Starting with the basics, this book begins with types of lumber, nails, and what tools are needed, followed by detailed, fully illustrated steps for framing each building element. Framer-Friendly Tips throughout the book show how to get a task done right—and more easily.

$29.95 | 368 pages, softcover | Catalog no. 67353A

Green Home Improvement

by Daniel D. Chiras, PhD

With energy costs rising and environmental awareness increasing, people are looking to make their homes greener. This book, with 65 projects and actual costs and projected savings, helps homeowners prioritize their green improvements.

Projects range from simple water savers that cost only a few dollars, to bigger-ticket items such as HVAC systems. With color photos and cost estimates, each project compares options and describes the work involved, the benefits, and the savings.

$34.95 | 320 pages, illustrated, softcover | Catalog no. 67355

Life Cycle Costing for Facilities

by Alphonse Dell'Isola and Dr. Stephen Kirk

Guidance for achieving higher quality design and construction projects at lower costs! Cost-cutting efforts often sacrifice quality to yield the cheapest product. Life cycle costing enables building designers and owners to achieve both. The authors of this book show how LCC can work for a variety of projects—from roads to HVAC upgrades to different types of buildings.

$110.00 | 396 pages, hardcover | Catalog no. 67341

Project Scheduling and Management for Construction, 3rd Edition

by David R. Pierce, Jr.

A comprehensive, yet easy-to-follow guide to construction project scheduling and control—from vital project management principles through the latest scheduling, tracking, and controlling techniques. The author is a leading authority on scheduling, with years of field and teaching experience at leading academic institutions. Spend a few hours with this book and come away with a solid understanding of this essential management topic.

$64.95 | Over 286 pages, illustrated, hardcover | Catalog no. 67247B

Preventive Maintenance for Multi-Family Housing

by John C. Maciha

Prepared by one of the nation's leading experts on multi-family housing.

This complete PM system for apartment and condominium communities features expert guidance, checklists for buildings and grounds maintenance tasks and their frequencies, and a dedicated website featuring customizable electronic forms. A must-have for anyone involved with multi-family housing maintenance and upkeep.

$95.00 | 290 pages | Catalog no. 67346

Reference Books

For more information visit the RSMeans website at www.rsmeans.com

Green Building: Project Planning & Cost Estimating, 3rd Edition

Since the widely read first edition of this book, green building has gone from a growing trend to a major force in design and construction.

This new edition has been updated with the latest in green building technologies, design concepts, standards, and costs. Full-color with all new case studies—plus a new chapter on commercial real estate.

$110.00 | 480 pages, softcover | Catalog no. 67338B

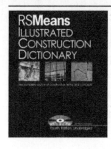

RSMeans Illustrated Construction Dictionary Unabridged 4th Edition, with CD-ROM

Long regarded as the industry's finest, *Means Illustrated Construction Dictionary* is now even better. With nearly 20,000 terms and more than 1,400 illustrations and photos, it is the clear choice for the most comprehensive and current information. The companion CD-ROM that comes with this new edition adds extra features, such as larger graphics and expanded definitions.

$110.00 | Over 880 pages, illust., hardcover | Catalog no. 67292B

Construction Supervision

Inspires excellence with proven tactics and techniques applied by thousands of construction supervisors. Leadership guidelines carve out a practical blueprint for motivating work performance and increasing productivity through effective communication. Features:

• A unique focus on field supervision and crew management

• Coverage of supervision from the foreman to the superintendent level

• An overview of technical skills whose mastery will build confidence and success for the supervisor

• A detailed view of "soft" management and communication skills

$95.00 | 464 pages, softcover | Catalog no. 67358

Building & Renovating Schools

This all-inclusive guide covers every step of the school construction process—from initial planning, needs assessment, and design, right through moving into the new facility. A must-have resource for anyone concerned with new school construction or renovation. With square foot cost models for elementary, middle, and high school facilities, and real-life case studies of recently completed school projects.

The contributors to this book—architects, construction project managers, contractors, and estimators who specialize in school construction—provide start-to-finish, expert guidance on the process.

$110.00 | Over 412 pages, hardcover | Catalog no. 67342

The Homeowner's Guide to Mold

By Michael Pugliese

Mold, whether caused by leaks, humidity or flooding, is a real health and financial issue—for homeowners and contractors. This full-color book explains:

• Construction and maintenance practices to prevent mold

• How to inspect for and remove mold

• Mold remediation procedures and costs

• What to do after a flood

• How to deal with insurance companies

$21.95 | 144 pages, softcover | Catalog no. 67344

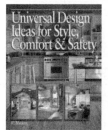

Universal Design Ideas for Style, Comfort & Safety

by RSMeans and Lexicon Consulting, Inc.

Incorporating universal design when building or remodeling helps people of any age and physical ability more fully and safely enjoy their living spaces. This book shows how universal design can be artfully blended into the most attractive homes. It discusses specialized products like adjustable countertops and chair lifts, as well as simple ways to enhance a home's safety and comfort. With color photos and expert guidance, every area of the home is covered. Includes budget estimates that give an idea how much projects will cost.

$21.95 | 160 pages, illustrated, softcover | Catalog no. 67354

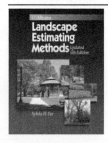

Landscape Estimating Methods, 5th Edition

Answers questions about preparing competitive landscape construction estimates, with up-to-date cost estimates and the new MasterFormat classification system. Expanded and revised to address the latest materials and methods, including new coverage on approaches to green building. Includes:

• Step-by-step explanation of the estimating process

• Sample forms and worksheets that save time and prevent errors

$75.00 | 336 pages, softcover | Catalog no. 67295C

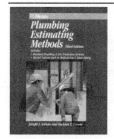

Plumbing Estimating Methods, 3rd Edition

by Joseph J. Galeno and Sheldon T. Greene

Updated and revised! This practical guide walks you through a plumbing estimate, from basic materials and installation methods through change order analysis. *Plumbing Estimating Methods* covers residential, commercial, industrial, and medical systems, and features sample takeoff and estimate forms and detailed illustrations of systems and components.

$65.00 | 381+ pages, softcover | Catalog no. 67283B

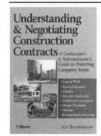

Understanding & Negotiating Construction Contracts

by Kit Werremeyer

Take advantage of the author's 30 years' experience in small-to-large (including international) construction projects. Learn how to identify, understand, and evaluate high risk terms and conditions typically found in all construction contracts—then, negotiate to lower or eliminate the risk, improve terms of payment, and reduce exposure to claims and disputes. The author avoids "legalese" and gives real-life examples from actual projects.

$80.00 | 320 pages, softcover | Catalog no. 67350

Reference Books

For more information visit the RSMeans website at www.rsmeans.com

Qty.	Book no.	COST ESTIMATING BOOKS	Unit Price	Total
	60065	Assemblies Cost Data 2015	$334.95	
	60015	Building Construction Cost Data 2015	206.95	
	60045	Commercial Renovaion Cost Data 2015	166.95	
	60115	Concrete & Masonry Cost Data 2015	188.95	
	50145	Construction Cost Indexes 2015 (subscription)	359.95	
	60145A	Construction Cost Index–January 2015	94.95	
	60145B	Construction Cost Index–April 2015	94.95	
	60145C	Construction Cost Index–July 2015	94.95	
	60145D	Construction Cost Index–October 2015	94.95	
	60345	Contr. Pricing Guide: Resid. R & R Costs 2015	39.95	
	60235	Electrical Change Order Cost Data 2015	199.95	
	60035	Electrical Cost Data 2015	208.95	
	60205	Facilities Construction Cost Data 2015	524.95	
	60305	Facilities Maintenance & Repair Cost Data 2015	461.95	
	60555	Green Building Cost Data 2015	170.95	
	60165	Heavy Construction Cost Data 2015	204.95	
	60095	Interior Cost Data 2015	208.95	
	60125	Labor Rates for the Const. Industry 2015	450.95	
	60185	Light Commercial Cost Data 2015	153.95	
	60025	Mechanical Cost Data 2015	203.95	
	60155	Open Shop Building Const. Cost Data 2015	175.95	
	60215	Plumbing Cost Data 2015	206.95	
	60175	Residential Cost Data 2015	148.95	
	60285	Site Work & Landscape Cost Data 2015	199.95	
	60055	Square Foot Costs 2015	218.95	
	62014	Yardsticks for Costing (2014)	189.95	
	62015	Yardsticks for Costing (2015)	201.95	
		REFERENCE BOOKS		
	67329	Bldrs Essentials: Best Bus. Practices for Bldrs	45.00	
	67307	Bldrs Essentials: Plan Reading & Takeoff	50.00	
	67342	Building & Renovating Schools	110.00	
	67261A	The Building Prof. Guide to Contract Documents	75.00	
	67353A	Complete Book of Framing, 2nd Ed.	29.95	
	67146	Concrete Repair & Maintenance Illustrated	75.00	
	67352	Construction Business Management	60.00	
	67364	Construction Law	115.00	
	67358	Construction Supervision	95.00	
	67363	Cost Data Student Edition	110.00	
	67314	Cost Planning & Est. for Facil. Maint.	95.00	
	67230B	Electrical Estimating Methods, 3rd Ed.	75.00	
	67343A	Est. Bldg. Costs for Resi. & Lt. Comm., 2nd Ed.	75.00	
	67276B	Estimating Handbook, 3rd Ed.	110.00	
	67318	Facilities Operations & Engineering Reference	115.00	
	67338B	Green Building: Proj. Planning & Cost Est., 3rd Ed.	110.00	
	67355	Green Home Improvement	34.95	
	67357B	The Gypsum Construction Handbook	40.00	
	67148	Heavy Construction Handbook	110.00	
	67308E	Home Improvement Costs–Int. Projects, 9th Ed.	24.95	
	67309E	Home Improvement Costs–Ext. Projects, 9th Ed.	24.95	
	67344	Homeowner's Guide to Mold	21.95	
	67324C	How to Est.w/Means Data & CostWorks, 4th Ed.	75.00	

Qty.	Book no.	REFERENCE BOOKS (Cont.)	Unit Price	Total
	67351A	How Your House Works, 2nd Ed.	22.95	
	67282A	Illustrated Const. Dictionary, Condensed, 2nd Ed.	65.00	
	67292B	Illustrated Const. Dictionary, w/CD-ROM, 4th Ed.	110.00	
	67362	Illustrated Const. Dictionary, Student Ed.	60.00	
	67348	Job Order Contracting	130.00	
	67295C	Landscape Estimating Methods, 5th Ed.	75.00	
	67341	Life Cycle Costing for Facilities	110.00	
	67370	Managing the Profitable Construction Business	60.00	
	67294B	Mechanical Estimating Methods, 4th Ed.	75.00	
	67345	Practice of Cost Segregation Analysis	105.00	
	67366	Project Control: Integrating Cost & Sched.	95.00	
	67346	Preventive Maint. for Multi-Family Housing	95.00	
	67367	Project Sched. and Manag. for Constr., 4th Ed.	95.00	
	67322B	Resi. & Light Commercial Const. Stds., 3rd Ed.	65.00	
	67359	Risk Management for Design and Construction	125.00	
	67365	Solar Energy: Technology & Project Delivery	85.00	
	67145B	Sq. Ft. & Assem. Estimating Methods, 3rd Ed.	75.00	
	67321	Total Productive Facilities Management	85.00	
	67350	Understanding and Negotiating Const. Contracts	80.00	
	67303B	Unit Price Estimating Methods, 4th Ed.	75.00	
	67354	Universal Design	21.95	
	67319A	Value Engineering: Practical Applications	90.00	

MA residents add 6.25% state sales tax ☐

Shipping & Handling** ☐

Total (U.S. Funds)* ☐

Prices are subject to change and are for U.S. delivery only. *Canadian customers may call for current prices. **Shipping & handling charges: Add 8% of total order for check and credit card payments. Add 8% of total order for invoiced orders.

Send order to: ADDV-1000

Name (please print) _____

Company _____

☐ Company

☐ Home Address _____

_____

City/State/Zip _____

Phone # _____ P.O. # _____

(Must accompany all orders being billed)

Mail to: RSMeans, 700 Longwater Drive, Norwell, MA 02061

RSMeans Project Cost Report

By filling out this report, your project data will contribute to the database that supports the RSMeans® Project Cost Square Foot Data. When you fill out this form, RSMeans will provide a $50 discount off one of the RSMeans products advertised in the preceding pages. Please complete the form including all items where you have cost data, and all the items marked (☑).

$50.00 Discount per product for each report you submit

Project Description (NEW construction only, please)

☑ Building Use (Office School . . .) _____

☑ Address (City, State)_____

_____

☑ Total Building Area (SF) _____

☑ Ground Floor (SF) _____

☑ Frame (Wood, Steel . . .) _____

☑ Exterior Wall (Brick, Tilt-up . . .) _____

☑ Basement: (checkone) ☐ Full ☐ Partial ☐ None

☑ Number of Stories _____

☑ Floor-to-Floor Height_____

☑ Volume (C.F.)_____

% Air Conditioned _____ Tons_____

Total Project Cost $ _____

Owner _____

Architect_____

General Contractor _____

☑ Bid Date _____

☑ Typical Bay Size _____

☑ Occupant Capacity_____

☑ Labor Force: _____ % Union _____ % Non-Union

☑ Project Description (Circle one number in each line.)

1. Economy 2. Average 3. Custom 4. Luxury

1. Square 2. Rectangular 3. Irregular 4. Very Irregular

Comments _____

_____

A	☑	General Conditions	$	
B	☑	Site Work	$	
C	☑	Concrete	$	
D	☑	Masonry	$	
E	☑	Metals	$	
F	☑	Wood & Plastics	$	
G	☑	Thermal & Moisture Protection	$	
GR		Roofing & Flashing	$	
H	☑	Doors and Windows	$	
J	☑	Finishes	$	
JP		Painting & Wall Covering	$	

K	☑	Specialties	$	
L	☑	Equipment	$	
M	☑	Furnishings	$	
N	☑	Special Construction	$	
P	☑	Conveying Systems	$	
Q	☑	Mechanical	$	
QP		Plumbing	$	
QB		HVAC	$	
R	☑	Electrical	$	
S	☑	Mech./Elec. Combined	$	

Please specify the RSMeans product you wish to receive. Complete the address information.

Product Name _____

Product Number _____

Your Name _____

Title _____

Company_____

☐ Company

☐ Home   Street Address_____

City, State, Zip _____

Email Address _____

Return by mail or fax 888-492-6770.

Method of Payment:

Credit Card # _____

Expiration Date _____

Check_____

Purchase Order _____

Phone Number _____
(if you would prefer a sales call)

RSMeans
Square Foot Costs Department
700 Longwater Drive
Norwell, MA 02061
www.RSMeans.com